| Element | Symbol | Atomic Number | Atomic Weight |
|---|---|---|---|
| Neon | Ne | 10 | 20.183 |
| Neptunium | Np | 93 | |
| Nickel | Ni | 28 | 58.71 |
| Niobium | Nb | 41 | 92.906 |
| Nitrogen | N | 7 | 14.0067 |
| Nobelium | No | 102 | |
| Osmium | Os | 76 | 190.2 |
| Oxygen | O | 8 | 15.9994 (±0.0001, nat.) |
| Palladium | Pd | 46 | 106.4 |
| Phosphorus | P | 15 | 30.9738 |
| Platinum | Pt | 78 | 195.09 |
| Plutonium | Pu | 94 | |
| Polonium | Po | 84 | |
| Potassium | K | 19 | 39.102 |
| Praseodymium | Pr | 59 | 140.907 |
| Promethium | Pm | 61 | |
| Protactinium | Pa | 91 | |
| Radium | Ra | 88 | |
| Radon | Rn | 86 | |
| Rhenium | Re | 75 | 186.2 |
| Rhodium | Rh | 45 | 102.905 |
| Rubidium | Rb | 37 | 85.47 |
| Ruthenium | Ru | 44 | 101.07 |
| Samarium | Sm | 62 | 150.35 |
| Scandium | Sc | 21 | 44.956 |
| Selenium | Sc | 34 | 78.96 |
| Silicon | Si | 14 | 28.086 (±0.001, nat.) |
| Silver | Ag | 47 | 107.870 (±0.003, exp.) |
| Sodium | Na | 11 | 22.9898 |
| Strontium | Sr | 38 | 87.62 |
| Sulfur | S | 16 | 32.064 (±0.003, nat.) |
| Tantalum | Ta | 73 | 180.948 |
| Technetium | Tc | 43 | |
| Tellurium | Te | 52 | 127.60 |
| Terbium | Tb | 65 | 158.924 |
| Thallium | Tl | 81 | 204.37 |
| Thorium | Th | 90 | 232.038 |
| Thulium | Tm | 69 | 168.934 |
| Tin | Sn | 50 | 118.69 |
| Titanium | Ti | 22 | 47.90 |
| Tungsten | W | 74 | 183.85 |
| Uranium | U | 92 | 238.03 |
| Vanadium | V | 23 | 50.942 |
| Xenon | Xe | 54 | 131.30 |
| Ytterbium | Yb | 70 | 173.04 |
| Yttrium | Y | 39 | 88.905 |
| Zinc | Zn | 30 | 65.37 |
| Zirconium | Zr | 40 | 91.22 |

nat. = Variation in atomic weight due to
natural variation in the isotopic composition.
exp. = Experimental uncertainty of magnitude given.

Adopted 1961 by the International Union of Pure and Applied Chemistry.

# STANDARD METHODS OF
# CHEMICAL ANALYSIS

The first four editions of STANDARD METHODS OF CHEMICAL ANALYSIS were prepared under the Editorship of Dr. Wilfred W. Scott, Professor of Chemistry at the University of Southern California. After his death, the Fifth Edition was edited by Dr. N. Howell Furman, then Professor of Chemistry at Princeton University. Professor Furman also edited Volume I of the Sixth Edition, and is Advisory Editor of Volume II, which is edited by Dr. Frank J. Welcher of the University of Indiana. Volume III is edited by Dr. Seymour Z. Lewin of New York University.

# STANDARD METHODS OF
# CHEMICAL ANALYSIS

## SIXTH EDITION

### Volume One—The Elements

### N. HOWELL FURMAN, Ph.D., *Editor*

*Professor of Chemistry, Emeritus, Princeton University*
*Visiting Professor of Chemistry, Wake Forest College, 1961–1962*

IN COLLABORATION WITH MANY CONTRIBUTORS
(SEE LIST ON PAGES FOLLOWING)

## D. VAN NOSTRAND COMPANY, INC.
### Princeton, New Jersey

Toronto                                        London

### New York

### D. VAN NOSTRAND COMPANY, INC.
120 Alexander St., Princeton, New Jersey (*Principal office*)
24 West 40 Street, New York 18, New York

### D. VAN NOSTRAND COMPANY, LTD.
358, Kensington High Street, London, W.14, England

### D. VAN NOSTRAND COMPANY (Canada), LTD.
25 Hollinger Road, Toronto 16, Canada

Published simultaneously in Canada by
D. VAN NOSTRAND COMPANY (Canada), LTD.

**Sixth Edition, March 1962**

PRINTED IN THE UNITED STATES OF AMERICA

# PREFACE

Throughout its various editions this work has been a source of analytical information of proven value for general use in the chemical laboratory. For more than fifty years it has been consulted by chemists as a reference for standard methods of analysis—those most widely accepted and readily applied. All of its characteristics—the plan of organization, the detail of presentation and even its selection of methods—have been determined by this function as a general, practical reference book.

Thus, it contains chapters of two kinds: (1) those dealing with a single element or a single class of substances, as exemplified by the chapters on aluminum or lead or uranium, and those on petroleum or plastics or water analysis; and (2) those chapters dealing with a single type of analytical method, as exemplified by the chapters on microanalysis or ion exchange or spectrographic analysis.

These characteristics of earlier editions have been maintained in the Sixth Edition. This has required, in view of the great advances of the intervening years, the addition of the third volume, devoted entirely to chapters on physical and instrumental methods and their applications. It has also necessitated the publication of the three volumes separately, at approximately annual intervals. However, the established policy has been followed by seeking as contributors men of wide specialized experience, either with individual elements and types of substances, or with particular methods of analysis. Furthermore, the basic organization of the chapters and within the chapters has been maintained, with certain minor changes made necessary by the extensive additions of new methods and new information.

In Volume I, the elements are taken up, chapter by chapter, in alphabetical order except for certain logical groupings of elements. Thus, tellurium is treated in the chapter with selenium, tantalum with niobium, technetium with rhenium, the rare earths with cerium, and the alkali metals in the first chapter of the book. An alphabetical listing of the elements, giving the page number of the chapter in which each element is treated, follows the comprehensive table of contents.

In Volume I on the elements the reader will note the omission of the analytical chemistry of the transuranium elements which is available in full detail only to those having access to classified information. The methods of determining the inert gases (helium family), are to be found under gas analysis, and under the mass spectrographic and spectral analysis in Volumes II and III, respectively.

Each chapter is arranged, for convenient reference, in accordance with a uniform sequence, that has been followed throughout the book. It is as follows:

*Physical Properties.* Atomic weight; specific gravity; melting-point; boiling-point; oxides.

*Detection.* Characteristic reactions leading to the recognition of the element.

*Estimation.* The subject is introduced with such information as is useful to the analyst.

*Preparation and Solution of the Samples.* Here directions are given for the preparation and decomposition of characteristic materials in which the element

v

occurs. Recommendations to the best procedures are included to assist the analyst in his choice.

*Separations.* This section is devoted to procedures for the removal of substances, commonly occurring with the element, that may interfere with its estimation. In the absence of such substances, or in case methods are to be followed by which a direct estimation of the element may be made in the presence of these substances, this section in separations may be omitted in the course of analysis. Here the discretion of the chemist is necessary, and some knowledge of the substance examined.

*Gravimetric Methods of Determination*
*Titrimetric Methods of Determination*
*Colorimetric/Photometric Methods of Determination*
*Other Methods of Determination*
*Determinations in Other Substances*

Under each of these headings are grouped those methods of determination which are most widely accepted, most certain to give consistent results and, in the case of analyses of other substances, most frequently to be needed by the chemist. Where a decision has been necessary as to where to include a method in Volume I, or one of the other two volumes of the book, the rule followed has been to place in Volume I those methods which, though used for special substances, are sufficiently general to be applicable to other materials, and to plan to include in the other volumes those methods used primarily for a single class of substances, as well as those requiring highly specialized equipment.

It is fortunate that the 1961 Table of Atomic Weights of the I.U.C. was published before the Sixth Edition of STANDARD METHODS OF CHEMICAL ANALYSIS, so that the values and factors throughout this volume have been recalculated accordingly.

In addition to the contributors listed in these pages, whose work has gone so far to make this book possible, acknowledgment is due to the American Society of Testing Materials for their generous permission to reproduce their methods; to Mr. W. R. Minrath, Vice President of D. Van Nostrand Company, without whose aid in the selection of contributors and in editing the progress of the work would have lagged immeasurably due to the critical illness of the editor at that time; and to Professor Morris B. Jacobs of Columbia University, for his help in evaluation and for his extensive contributions of material.

# INTRODUCTION

The fundamental importance of analytical chemistry is shown by the urgent demands on this branch of chemistry. Our present-day knowledge of elements has been made possible by analysis. The separations in metallurgy are dependent upon analytical principles. Startling discoveries in medicine have been dependent on accurate analysis and the same is true in regard to experimental research, where analytical methods are employed for ascertaining the composition of the products formed. The importance of analysis for control of chemical industrial processes has created a demand for rapid methods so that there is a constant effort on the part of the analytical chemist to simplify procedures of analysis. On the other hand our extended knowledge of the nature of substances and their chemical reactions has shown errors in former methods of procedure and the necessity for modifications which are being developed to take care of interferences. This accounts for the large number of specialized methods that appear in chemical literature and the vast amount of work that has been done for coupling accuracy with simplicity, wherever this is possible. Research demands accuracy in analytical procedures with sacrifice of simplicity and rapidity, should these be impossible; on the other hand rapid methods are essential to the economic control of chemical industrial processes.

A correct evaluation of materials for one or more of the substances desired, necessitates careful sampling, for obtaining representative portions for analysis. Ores and minerals of uniform composition are exceptions; even in the case of alloys, where a uniform composition would be expected, segregation of elements of the molten mixtures during the process of cooling is known to take place. Sampling of solutions is no exception to the necessity of careful procedure.

An early training in the chemical laboratory, generally starting in the high school and carried on in the college or university, has acquainted the chemist with the common apparatus employed in the analytical laboratory. He is familiar with the different forms of containers—beakers, casseroles, flasks, crucibles—closed or perforated forms, made of porcelain, silica or other refractory materials, or of metals—iron, nickel, platinum and certain resistant alloys. The chemist is familiar with different types of measuring apparatus—the balance, burette, measuring flasks, pipettes, etc. He has used different forms of heating or combustion apparatus—drying ovens, burners and furnaces. He has become familiar with laboratory operations and technique, details of which appear in elementary texts of analytical chemistry, used in his preparation for a professional career. It has been considered unnecessary to give such details here. Throughout the work attention is called to special apparatus and cautions in technique and operations where these are considered necessary. A chapter appears in the later portion of this volume on special apparatus and calibration methods that will be found useful.

In the preparation and decomposition of the material for analysis care must be exercised to avoid loss by volatilization or separation; for example the volatility of mercury compounds, silicon and fluorine in presence of each other during the acid attack, stannic chloride, boron in certain combinations; the precipitation of certain radicals with silica during the action of strong acids, and the co-precipitation of a number of substances with aluminum hydroxide (the ammonia precipitate). Throughout the text precautions are given to avoid such losses and attention is called to the steps where such losses are apt to occur. In the mechanical preparation of the material fine grinding of refractory substances is generally advisable. It must be remembered, however, that chemical changes may take place, for example oxidation of sulfide ores leading to low results. Then again contamination by abrasion of the grinding apparatus must be guarded against.

The amount of the sample required for analysis depends not only upon the percentage of the element or substance in the material, but also upon the delicacy of the method, that is to be used. In the determination of the more common elements in ores and minerals a 0.5 gram sample is generally sufficient. In micro-methods, a few milligrams are sufficient, while in the determination of the so-called "traces" of impurities much larger samples may be required.

In complete analysis of substances it may be advisable to take separate samples for individual estimations, as in case of carbon dioxide in carbonates, the estimation of carbon, fluorine, and chlorine. On the other hand combinations may be better, for example the determination of silica, titanium, manganese and nickel in the same sample; chromium and vanadium; barium and zirconium; iron, aluminum, titanium, vanadium, zirconium and the phosphate radical in the same sample. Procedures in the text indicate the best conditions for accuracy, and the operations necessary for removal of interfering substances.

# CONTRIBUTORS *Sixth Edition—Volume One*

Howard B. Bradley
Silicones Division
Union Carbide Corp.

W. J. Brown
National Lead Co.

O. P. Case
American Brass Co.

J. R. Churchill
Aluminum Co. of America

P. T. Cominskey
Freeport Sulphur Co.

W. Charles Cooper
Canadian Copper Refiners, Ltd.

Leon Curtis
National Bureau of Standards

C. Manning Davis
International Nickel Co.

R. G. Ernst
U. S. Smelting and Refining Co.

N. Howell Furman, Professor Emeritus
Princeton University

Arnold R. Gahler
Union Carbide Metals Co.

Morris B. Jacobs
Columbia University

Editha Karl-Kroupa
Monsanto Chemical Co.

H. E. Maddock
New Jersey Zinc Co.

Herbert Marshall
Canadian Copper Refiners, Ltd.

R. G. Mercer
New Jersey Zinc Co.

Edward G. Moorehead
Harvard University

G. H. Morrison
Cornell University

M. L. Moss
Aluminum Co. of America

J. J. Mulligan
U. S. Lead Refinery, Inc.

A. J. Nicklay
Eagle-Picher Lead Company

George Oplinger
Solvay Process Division
Allied Chemical and Dye Corp.

A. R. Powell
Johnson, Matthey and Company

C. J. Rodden
U. S. Atomic Energy Commission

S. N. Roeder
New Jersey Zinc Co.

Charles L. Rulfs
University of Michigan

Cecil H. Russell
Monsanto Chemical Co.

Edward R. Scheffer
National Lead Company

J. R. Sheppard
Eagle-Picher Lead Co.

Stanislaus Skowronski
International Smelting and Refining Co.

V. A. Stenger
Dow Chemical Co.

John R. Van Waser
Monsanto Chemical Co.

CONTRIBUTORS

Frank A. Vinci
Brush Beryllium Co.

G. B. Wengert
Dow Chemical Co.

James R. West
Texas Gulf Sulphur Co.

Roland S. Young
International Nickel Co. of
Canada, Ltd.

C. Zischkau
American Smelting and Refining Co.

# CONTENTS

xi

## BISMUTH

## BORON

## BROMINE

## CADMIUM

## CALCIUM

## CARBON

## CERIUM AND THE RARE EARTH METALS

## CHLORINE

## CHROMIUM

## COBALT

## COPPER

## FLUORINE

## GALLIUM

## GERMANIUM

## GOLD

## HYDROGEN

## INDIUM

## NITROGEN

## OXYGEN

## PHOSPHORUS

## THE PLATINUM METALS

## RADIUM

## RHENIUM AND TECHNETIUM

## SCANDIUM

# CONTENTS LISTED BY ELEMENTS

Alphabetical tabulation of initial pages or section numbers

xix

*Chapter* 1

# THE ALKALI METALS*†

The alkali metals, lithium, sodium, potassium, rubidium, and cesium, belong in Group IA of the Periodic System. All are extremely light in weight, compressible, and, relatively, very soft. Lithium, the hardest of the alkali metals, has a hardness of 0.6 on Mohs' scale. Freshly cut surfaces of the alkali metals show a silvery white luster which tarnishes quickly and becomes dull in air.

All the alkali elements are univalent, electropositive, and form strong bases. They react with and decompose water, the reaction increasing in vigor with atomic weight. Potassium, rubidium and cesium ignite when placed on water. The alkali salts and hydroxides are generally soluble in water and are essentially completely dissociated in aqueous solution. Lithium, the first member of the series, differs somewhat from the other alkalies, resembling the alkaline earth metals in respect to the low solubility of many of its salts—carbonate, fluoride, phosphate—and in the tendency to form double salts. Potassium is most typical of the alkali metals.

Sodium and potassium are the most abundant of the alkalies. From its position in the Periodic System, lithium would be expected to be more abundant. Its rarity is undoubtedly due to its disappearance through natural processes of nuclear bombardment. Francium occurs naturally only in minute amounts, having been only recently discovered and named by M. Perey.[1] Its four known isotopes are radioactive; the longest lived has a mass number of 223 and a half-life of 21 minutes. Both potassium and rubidium exhibit natural radioactivity. Of the three natural isotopes of potassium, the radioactive isotope with mass number 40 is present to an extent of about 0.012%. Mass number 87 isotope of rubidium exists to the extent of 27.2% along with the ordinary mass number 85 isotope. Lithium, sodium and cesium exhibit no radioactivity. Lithium has two isotopes of mass number 6 and 7; sodium and cesium are pure elements.

The alkali metals are the most closely allied group of elements in the Periodic System. Because of their similar properties, the analytical chemistry of the alkali metal ions poses some challenging problems. Many of the quantitative procedures involve elaborate separation techniques for the determination of particular alkali ions.

Since the alkali elements are associated in similar types of materials, methods for bringing them into solution and for separating interfering ions will be discussed first. Following this the individual alkali elements with the exception of francium will be treated in order of their natural abundance and commercial utilization.

* Chapter revised by George Oplinger, Research Supervisor, Solvay Process Division, Allied Chemical Corp.
 † Methods for the element, francium, are not included in this book.
 [1] Perey, J. chim. phys., **43**, 155, 1946.

## PREPARATION AND SOLUTION OF THE SAMPLE

Alkali metal-containing material for which analysis may be required can be grouped as follows.

### NATURAL AND MANUFACTURED MINERAL PRODUCTS

Included are hydrochloric acid and water insoluble materials such as silicate rocks, ores, soils, glass, refractories and other siliceous materials. Two generally applicable procedures are recommended for obtaining the alkali metals in the form of their chlorides, the only practical medium for making subsequent separations.

The first of these, devised by Berzelius,[2] involves the decomposition by means of hydrofluoric and sulfuric acids, subsequent removal of interfering ions, and conversion of the alkali sulfates to chlorides. A modification of this technique, using hydrofluoric, perchloric and nitric acid, is also described.

The second procedure was developed by J. Lawrence Smith.[3] This method is preferred for the reason that the alkali metals are converted directly to water soluble chlorides. Decomposition is effected by heating the sample with a mixture of ammonium chloride and calcium carbonate.

**Berzelius Procedure.**—Weigh accurately 0.5–1.0 g. of the ground sample in a platinum crucible or dish, wet with a few drops of water and add 2 ml. of 1:3 sulfuric acid. Mix the sample with a platinum wire and add 10 ml. of concentrated hydrofluoric acid. Evaporate in a radiator[4] until all the hydrofluoric acid is driven off. An iron dish fitted with a triangle to support the crucible or dish is satisfactory for the purpose. Stir the mixture with the platinum wire or spatula and if hard gritty particles are still present, add 5 ml. hydrofluoric acid and evaporate to dryness. Expel the excess sulfuric acid by continued heating. The removal of fluoride should be complete and it may be necessary to add more dilute sulfuric acid to effect its removal. By bringing the sulfates into complete solution before the final evaporation, the removal of fluoride is assured.[5] Sulfate is then precipitated as barium sulfate by the addition of a slight excess of barium chloride to a solution of the residue in dilute hydrochloric acid. Filter, wash, and then evaporate the filtrate to dryness in a platinum dish to remove the hydrochloric acid. Dissolve the residue in a little water, add saturated alkali-free calcium hydroxide solution to precipitate magnesium. Filter and wash the residue with dilute alkali-free calcium hydroxide solution. Proceed with the filtrate as directed for the removal of barium and calcium under "Separations," page 6. If potassium only is to be determined, the tetraphenylboron method, page 22, or the modified chloroplatinate method, page 22, may be used after expelling the hydrofluoric acid and filtering off any barium sulfate that may be present. If sodium only is to be determined, first proceed with the removal of sulfates as described before applying the zinc or magnesium uranyl acetate procedures, page 13 or 14.

**Alternate Berzelius Procedure: Hydrofluoric, Perchloric, Nitric Acid Decomposition.**—Weigh accurately 1.0 g. of the sample (silicate minerals and rocks, glass, ceramic material, etc.), ground to about 100 mesh in an agate mortar, into a platinum crucible and ignite to destroy any organic matter. Cool, then moisten

[2] Berzelius, Pogg. Ann., **1**, 169, 1824.
[3] Smith, Am. J. Sci., (2) **50**, 269, 1871; Annal. Chem. Pharm., **159**, 82, 1871.
[4] Hillebrand, Lundell, Bright and Hoffman, Applied Inorganic Analysis, Second Edition, p. 23, John Wiley & Sons, Inc., New York, 1953.
[5] Selch, Z. anal. Chem., **54**, 395, 1915.

with distilled water, add 1 ml. of concentrated nitric acid, 10 ml. of 70% perchloric acid and about 10 ml. of hydrofluoric acid. Evaporate in an air bath or radiator [4] to fumes of perchloric acid. Remove from the air bath, cool, add 5 ml. of perchloric acid and 10 ml. of hydrofluoric acid and evaporate as before, expelling excess hydrofluoric acid. Moisten the cool residue with 1 ml. of perchloric acid and again evaporate to dense fumes of perchloric acid.

Remove the crucible from the air bath, cool, moisten the residue with dilute hydrochloric acid and wash the contents into a small beaker, cleaning the crucible thoroughly by means of a rubber tipped glass rod. Add a few ml. of dilute HCl to the solution in the beaker and warm until all salts are in solution. If any gritty material remains, filter, wash, and return the filter paper to the platinum crucible. Dry and ignite the paper, then treat the residue with nitric, perchloric and hydrofluoric acid as above. Wash the residue into the beaker containing the main portion of the sample and heat to dissolve the salts. Transfer the solution to a 100-ml. volumetric flask, cool and dilute to the mark with distilled water.

Use suitable aliquots to determine potassium by the tetraphenylboron or the modified chloroplatinate method, and sodium by the magnesium uranyl acetate method. For each of the determinations, the aliquot is transferred to a small porcelain casserole or dish, evaporated to dryness on a steam bath, then heated gradually over a low flame to expel all free perchloric acid and finally heated to a dull red heat to convert the perchlorates to the chlorides. If lithium is present in excess of 2 mg. it must be removed, prior to the determination of sodium, by the absolute alcohol-ether method of Rammelsberg-Palkin, page 28.

For the lithium determination, nitric acid should be used in place of hydrochloric acid for solution of the salts after decomposition. The periodate method, page 29, is then applicable to an aliquot of the prepared solution or to the entire residue, depending on the lithium content.

*J. Lawrence Smith Procedure.*[6]—Weigh accurately 0.5 g. of the finely ground sample (200 mesh or finer, ground in an agate mortar) and transfer to an agate mortar. Add 0.5 g. of pure ammonium chloride and mix intimately by grinding with the agate pestle. Weigh 4 g. of precipitated calcium carbonate and add, in several portions, about 3 g. of the calcium carbonate, grinding intimately after each addition. Line the bottom of the J. Lawrence Smith crucible with a little of the calcium carbonate and transfer the ground mixture to the crucible. Rinse the mortar with the balance of the calcium carbonate by grinding with the pestle and transfer to the top of the contents of the crucible. Cover the crucible and place in the hole in the fire clay cylinder as shown in Fig. 1-1. This type of crucible permits the use of higher temperatures for the better decomposition of the sample. However, an ordinary 30-ml. platinum crucible with tight fitting cover may be used. In this case, the crucible should be set in a hole in an asbestos board, so that only one fourth of the crucible projects below.

Gradually heat the crucible with a low flame until no more ammonia is evolved. The heat should be low enough to avoid visible fuming of the ammonium chloride.

6 References for Modifications of J. Lawrence Smith Method: Lamar, M. O., Hazel, W. M., and O'Leary, W. J., Ind. Eng. Chem., Anal. Ed., **7**, 429, 1935; Scholes, S. R., and Wessels, J. E., Chemist-Analyst, **25**, 38, 1936; Pukall, W., Sprechsaal, **66**, 23, 1933; Makinen, E., Z. anorg. Chem., **74**, 74, 1912; Stevens, R. E., Ind. Eng. Chem., Anal. Ed., **12**, 413, 1940; Echdahl, W. P., Chemist-Analyst, **28**, 47, 1939; Tongeran, W. van., Z. anorg. allgem. Chem., **218**, 252, 1934; Chem. Weekblad, **32**, 224, 1935; Zentr. Mineral Geol., **1936A**, 243; and Athy, L. C., and Taylor, R. K., Chemist-Analyst, **29**, 76, 1940.

After the ammonia is evolved (15–20 minutes), gradually raise the temperature to 1000–1100°C. and maintain the heating for an hour and a half so that only the lower half of the crucible is at red heat. Allow the crucible to cool and remove the sintered cake by tapping the inverted crucible over a platinum dish.[7] If the cake cannot be removed by this process, digest the mass a few minutes with water and wash it into the platinum dish. Clean the crucible and cover thoroughly by rinsing with water into the dish. Disintegrate the cake in the dish by rubbing with a glass rod flattened on the end. Add distilled water to make about 50–60 ml. volume and digest on a steam bath for 0.5 hour, crushing any large particles with the stirring rod. Add 10 ml. of a saturated solution of pure calcium hydroxide to precipitate any magnesium. Filter by decantation four times through filter paper, catching the filtrate in a large dish, preferably of platinum. Finally wash the residue on the filter and wash several times with hot water, or better, with a hot saturated solution of pure calcium hydroxide. Remove the dish containing the filtrate and test the residue for complete decomposition by treating with hydrochloric acid. No trace of undecomposed mineral should remain. Lithium is partially retained in the residue and in the subsequent calcium removal operations. If lithium is to be determined, the Berzelius procedure for decomposition is preferred.

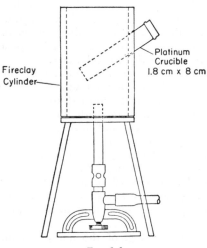

Fireclay Cylinder

Platinum Crucible 1.8 cm x 8 cm

FIG. 1-1.

The aqueous filtrate contains the alkali chlorides, calcium chloride, and possibly sulfate and borate. Remove calcium by treating the filtrate with ammonium carbonate and ammonium hydroxide. Cover the dish and heat to boiling. Filter and wash the precipitate with hot water, catching the filtrate in a platinum dish. Redissolve the precipitate with a slight excess of hydrochloric acid and repeat the precipitation and filtration. Evaporate the combined filtrates to dryness in a platinum dish and expel the ammonium salts by gentle ignition over a moving flame. Cool and dissolve the residue in a little water, add a few crystals of ammonium oxalate and a few drops of ammonium hydroxide to precipitate the last traces of calcium. Digest in a warm place for 0.5 to 1 hour, cool, filter off the precipitate and receive the filtrate in a weighed platinum dish. Evaporate the solution to dryness and ignite gently over a moving flame to remove the ammonium salts. Cool, moisten the residue with a few drops of hydrochloric acid to transform any carbonate to chloride, evaporate to dryness and ignite as before. In any of the ignitions, take care that the dish is not heated to more than a faint redness in any one spot and that incipient fusion of the salts is not exceeded. Cool the dish in a desiccator and weigh to determine the combined chlorides. Dissolve in water, and if an insoluble residue remains, filter it off, ignite and weigh the residue and deduct from the weight of the chlorides. Determine the potassium, sodium, or

[7] Platinum is preferable, but a Vycor or Pyrex dish will serve.

other alkalies by the methods described. If only two alkalies are present, determine one and obtain the value of the other by difference.

If sulfates are present, they are removed by treatment of the filtrate before the calcium removal step with a few drops of 10% barium chloride solution after making the solution slightly acid with hydrochloric acid. Borate, if present, may be removed as described on page 7.

A blank determination on reagents should be carried out in parallel with the procedure for the sample. The value obtained for the blank is deducted from the determined weight of chlorides in the sample.

## WATER AND ACID SOLUBLE MATERIAL

In this category are included soluble alkali salts, brines, saline residues, mineral waters, etc. Dissolve the sample in water, if soluble, or by the addition of a slight excess of hydrochloric acid and make up to a specified volume. In the case of alkali carbonates, the solution should be boiled after acidification to expel carbon dioxide before making up to volume. Mineral waters may be evaporated to provide a sufficient concentration of soluble salts for analysis.

Remove interfering ions by methods described under "Separations." The combined alkali chlorides may be weighed and then, if sodium and potassium only are present, potassium may be determined according to one of the chloroplatinate or tetraphenylboron procedures and sodium obtained by difference. If all the alkalies are to be determined, the procedure beginning on page 8 may be used.

## FERTILIZERS AND AGRICULTURAL MATERIALS [8]

Although the following dissolution procedures are approved by the Agricultural Chemists Association to apply in the determination of potassium, the other alkalies may be present and can be determined in the prepared sample solution.

*Procedure for Mixed Fertilizers.*—Place 2.5 g. of the sample in a 250-ml. volumetric flask, and add 125 ml. of water and 50 ml. of saturated ammonium oxalate solution. Add 1 ml. of diglycol stearate solution (20 g. diglycol stearate in 1 liter of 1:1 benzene-alcohol) when necessary to prevent foaming. Boil 30 minutes, add a slight excess of ammonium hydroxide and after cooling dilute to the mark and mix. Filter through a dry filter and use aliquots for analysis.

*Procedure for Ashes from Wood and Other Agricultural Material.*—Boil 10 g. of the sample with 300 ml. of water for 30 minutes. Add to the hot solution a slight excess of ammonium hydroxide and sufficient saturated ammonium oxalate solution to precipitate all the calcium present. Cool, dilute to 500 ml. in a volumetric flask, mix well, and filter through a dry filter. Use suitable aliquots for the analysis.

*Procedure for Organic Plant Material.*—Saturate a 10-g. sample with sulfuric acid in a platinum dish and ignite at dull red heat in a muffle furnace to destroy organic matter. Add a little hydrochloric acid, warm to loosen the mass from the dish. Transfer to a 500-ml. volumetric flask, add a slight excess of ammonium hydroxide and sufficient saturated ammonium oxalate solution to precipitate all the calcium present. Cool, dilute to 500 ml. and mix well. Filter through a dry filter and use suitable aliquots for the analysis.

For the determination of potassium, use the tetraphenylboron method, page 22,

8 Association of Official Agricultural Chemists, Methods of Analysis, 8th Ed., p. 16, Washington 4, D. C.

or the Lindo-Gladding method, page 24. To determine the other alkalies remove interfering ions, as described under "Separations," and continue with the desired procedures.

## SEPARATIONS

### SEPARATION OF THE ALKALIES AS A GROUP

In analytical procedures for their determination, the combined alkalies ideally are weighed initially as sulfates or chlorides after all other elements or radicals have been removed. Detailed procedures for making such separations are given below.

*Separation from Silica.*—Place the solution in a platinum dish, acidify with hydrochloric acid and evaporate to dryness on a steam bath. Heat the dish and contents in an oven at 110°C. for an hour. Cool, then moisten the residue with a few ml. of concentrated hydrochloric acid, break up the residue with a stirring rod, dissolve the salts in a small quantity of distilled water, filter and wash the residue free from chlorides with hot water. For accurate work the dehydration should be repeated. With the combined filtrate proceed with further separations if required, then with the determination of the alkalies.

*Separation from Heavy Metals.*—Hydrogen sulfide in strong hydrochloric acid solution will precipitate Cu, Ag, Hg, Pb, Bi, Cd, Ru, Rh, Pd, Os, As, Au, Pt, Sn, Sb, Ir, Ge, Se, Te, and Mo. In alkaline solution, hydrogen sulfide and ammonium sulfide will precipitate Mn, Ni, Co, Pb, Fe, Zn, Al, Be. The precipitate is removed by filtration. Sulfide is removed from the filtrate and washings by acidifying and boiling, followed by filtration.

*Separation from Fe, Al, Cr, Ti, U, Phosphoric Acid, etc.*—If phosphoric acid is present in amounts insufficient to combine with all the iron, aluminum, etc., or is absent, add an excess of hydrochloric acid, heat the solution to boiling, add a few drops of nitric acid to oxidize the iron, add dropwise a slight excess of ammonium hydroxide, continue boiling for a few minutes, allow the precipitate to settle and filter. Wash the precipitate free from chlorides with hot water.

If phosphoric acid is present in excess of that required to combine with the iron, aluminum, etc., heat the solution to boiling, oxidize with a few drops of nitric acid, add a slight excess of ferric chloride solution, and precipitate with ammonium hydroxide as described above. When the precipitate is considerable, it should be dissolved with hydrochloric acid and the precipitation repeated. Combine the filtrates and washings.

If chromates are present, convert them to the chromic salt by reduction with alcohol in acid solution on a steam bath or hot plate for a few minutes. Heat to boiling and precipitate with ammonium hydroxide as directed above. Sulfurous acid may be used for the reduction.

*Separation from Sulfates.*—Precipitate the sulfate as barium sulfate by the addition of a slight excess of barium chloride solution dropwise to a boiling solution of the alkalies in 75 ml. of water containing 1 ml. excess of hydrochloric acid. Let stand 15 minutes, filter, wash and then remove the excess of barium from the filtrate by the addition of ammonium hydroxide and ammonium carbonate as directed below.

*Separation from Barium, Calcium, and Strontium.*—To a solution of the sample, add a slight excess of ammonium hydroxide and ammonium carbonate solution, heat to boiling, allow the precipitate to settle and filter without washing. Dissolve the precipitate with a little dilute hydrochloric acid and repeat the precipitation with ammonium hydroxide and carbonate. Filter and wash the precipitate with water. Evaporate the combined filtrates and washings to a smaller volume, add a few crystals of ammonium oxalate and allow to stand for several hours to precipitate the last traces of the alkaline earths. Filter and wash the precipitate free from chlorides with a minimum of cold distilled water.

*Separation from Fe, Al, Cr, Ba, Sr, P, SO₄, etc., in One Operation.*—This procedure is time saving but a small portion of the alkalies is retained by the precipitate and lost.

To the hot slightly acid solution add a slight excess of barium chloride solution and boil for a few minutes. Then add a slight excess of ammonium hydroxide and ammonium carbonate solution, heat to boiling and allow the precipitate to settle. Filter and wash free from chloride with distilled water. Evaporate the filtrate to dryness in a platinum dish, remove the ammonium salts by careful ignition, dissolve the residue in a little distilled water and precipitate the last traces of calcium and other alkaline earths with a little ammonium hydroxide, ammonium carbonate and ammonium oxalate. Filter to remove the precipitate and wash with distilled water until free from chlorides. The filtrate contains the alkalies as chlorides.

*Separation from Boron.*—Evaporate the solution, acidified with hydrochloric acid, to dryness. Stir up and treat the residue with 25 ml. of methyl alcohol saturated with hydrochloric acid gas. Evaporate to dryness and repeat the treatment several times. This procedure may well be incorporated with the silica removal step.

*Separation from Magnesium.* **8-Hydroxyquinoline Method.**[9] Prepare a 5% solution of the reagent by dissolving 5 g. of 8-hydroxyquinoline ($C_9H_6NOH$, m.p. 73–74°C.) in 100 ml. of 2 N acetic acid. The sample solution should contain 0.05 g. or less of MgO per 100 ml., be slightly acid with hydrochloric acid, and contain sufficient ammonium salts to prevent the precipitation of magnesium hydroxide. Oxalates may be present. Heat the solution to 60–70°C. and make distinctly alkaline with ammonium hydroxide, sufficiently so as to remain slightly alkaline after the addition of the 8-hydroxyquinoline reagent. To the ammoniacal solution maintained at 60–70°C. add slowly, from a pipette with constant stirring, a slight excess of the reagent (25 ml. of the 5% 8-hydroxyquinoline reagent will precipitate 0.1 g. MgO). The color of the supernatant liquor will be yellow when an excess of the reagent is present. Allow the precipitate to settle, filter and wash with 1:40 ammonium hydroxide solution at 60–70°C. Evaporate the filtrate to dryness in a platinum dish, heat gently to expel the ammonium salts and excess reagent and determine the alkalies in the residue.

**Ammonium Phosphate Method.**—To the acid solution of the sample add an excess of ammonium chloride, an excess of freshly prepared 10% diammonium phosphate $((NH_4)_2HPO_4)$ solution, stir vigorously and add ammonium hydroxide slowly until the solution is alkaline. Add an excess of ammonium hydroxide (10 ml. for each 100 ml. of solution) and let the solution stand in a cool place. Filter and wash the precipitate with 1:20 ammonium hydroxide. If magnesium is high, dissolve the precipitate with dilute hydrochloric acid and reprecipitate the magnesium as before.

9 Berg, R., Z. anal. Chem., **71**, 23, 1927; Hahn, L., and Vierwig, K., *ibid.*, **126**; Moser, L., and Schutt, K., Monatsch., **51**, 23, 1929.

Expel most of the ammonia from the filtrate by evaporation, acidify slightly with hydrochloric acid and add an excess of ferric chloride solution to color the solution slightly yellow. Boil the solution and neutralize with ammonium carbonate, continue boiling for a few minutes and filter off the basic ferric phosphate and ferric hydroxide. Wash the residue with hot water. Evaporate the filtrate to dryness in a platinum dish, heat gently to expel ammonium salts and determine the alkalies in the residue. For accurate work the ferric phosphate precipitate should be dissolved in hydrochloric acid and the precipitation repeated.

*Separation from Ammonium Salts.*—The separation of ammonium salts from the alkali metals is effected by evaporating the acidified sample to dryness [10] in a platinum dish on the steam bath, drying in an oven at 110–130°C. followed by gentle ignition over a free flame held in the hand and moved back and forth under the dish until the ammonium salts have been expelled. Extreme care must be exercised to avoid losses of alkalies by decrepitation or volatilization.

Duval [11] gives the temperatures permissible for ignition of the alkali chlorides or sulfates without loss.

|  | Chloride | Sulfate |
|---|---|---|
| Lithium | 175–606°C. | 160–900°C. |
| Sodium | 407–878°C. | 90–878°C. |
| Potassium | 219–500°C. | 408–880°C. |
| Rubidium | 88–605°C. | 76–877°C. |
| Cesium | 110–877°C. | 105–876°C. |

## SEPARATION OF THE ALKALIES FROM ONE ANOTHER AND THEIR DETERMINATION [12]

This method is applicable in the presence of the chlorides of the alkali metals, as obtained according to methods under "Separation of the Alkalies as a Group," from the J. Lawrence Smith procedure, page 3, or the Berzelius method, page 2.

The alkali metals are first obtained as chlorides free from all other constituents and are then converted into perchlorates. Sodium and lithium are soluble in a mixture of n-butyl alcohol and ethyl acetate and are filtered from the insoluble potassium, rubidium and cesium perchlorates. The latter are weighed, the rubidium and cesium determined according to methods on pages 34 to 39 and the potassium determined by difference. Sodium is determined in the filtrate by precipitation as the chloride by the addition of a solution of hydrogen chloride gas in n-butyl alcohol. Lithium remains soluble in the filtrate and is determined as the sulfate after evaporation with sulfuric acid.

*Reagents.* 70% **Perchloric Acid.—Reagent Grade.**

**n-Butyl Alcohol.**—Reagent grade, having a boiling range of 116° to 117.7°C., prepared if required by fractional distillation of the reagent (sp. gr. 0.8065 at 25°/4°C.) preferably dried by refluxing over metallic calcium.

**Anhydrous Ethyl Acetate.**—Reagent grade free from ethyl alcohol and having a purity of 99.7 to 100%.

[10] Addition of 10 ml. of hydrochloric acid at the point where the salt begins to separate out will tend to prevent subsequent decrepitation.

[11] Duval, Clement, Inorganic Thermogravimetric Analysis, Elsevier Publishing Company, New York, 1953.

[12] Willard, H. H., and Smith, G. F., J. Am. Chem. Soc., **44,** 2816, 1922; **45,** 286, 1923; Smith, G. F., *ibid.,* **47,** 762, 1925; Smith, G. F., and Ross, J. F., *ibid.,* **47,** 774, 1020, 1925.

*n*-Butyl Alcohol Containing 20% HCl.—Prepared by passing dry HCl gas into the prepared *n*-butyl alcohol. Prepare a dilute solution containing 6–7% HCl by diluting 40 ml. of the 20% solution with 100 ml. of *n*-butyl alcohol.

*Procedure for Separation of Potassium, Rubidium and Cesium as Perchlorates.*— Dissolve the mixed chlorides, free from other constituents as described under "Preparation and Solution of the Sample" or under "Separations of the Alkalies as a Group," in a little water in a 150-ml. Pyrex beaker and add two or three times the equivalent quantity of 70% perchloric acid (not less than 1 ml. in any case). Carefully evaporate to dryness on a hot plate at not over 350°C. Expel any $HClO_4$ condensed on the side walls of the beaker by brushing with a free flame. Cool, dissolve the salts in 3 to 5 ml. of distilled water and repeat the evaporation on the hot plate.

Cool the beaker and contents to about 80°C., add 10 to 20 ml. of a mixture of equal parts by volume of *n*-butyl alcohol and ethyl acetate and digest near the boiling point for 2 or 3 minutes. Cool to room temperature and decant the supernatant liquid through a Selas filtering crucible which has previously been ignited and weighed. Wash the residue three times by decantation with 5-ml. portions of the *n*-butyl alcohol-ethyl acetate mixture. Reserve the filtrate and washings.

Dissolve the residue in the crucible in a minimum of hot distilled water, catch the solution in the original beaker and again evaporate to dryness as before. Cool, add 10 ml. of the *n*-butyl alcohol-ethyl acetate mixture, digest for 2 or 3 minutes near the boiling point, cool to 25°C. and filter through the original crucible, which has been dried in the meantime at 110°C. Transfer the precipitate to the crucible by means of a fine jet from a wash bottle containing the *n*-butyl alcohol-ethyl acetate mixture and finally wash 10 to 15 times with 1-ml. portions from the wash bottle. Combine and reserve the filtrates and washings, which should be less than 60 ml., for the determination of sodium and lithium.

Dry the original beaker on the hot plate and then brush any unremoved particles of perchlorate into the crucible containing the bulk of the precipitate. Dry the crucible and precipitate in an oven at 110°C. for a few minutes and finally for 15 minutes in a muffle at 350°C. Cool in a desiccator and weigh as $KClO_4$.

$$KClO_4 \times 0.2822 = K$$

$$\times 0.3399 = K_2O$$

$$\times 0.5381 = KCl$$

Notes.—The solubility of $KClO_4$ in the alcohol-acetate mixture at 25°C. is approximately 1.0 mg. in 100 ml. If the total volume of the filtrate and washings is less than 60 ml. no correction need be applied as a correspondingly small amount of sodium and lithium is retained in the $KClO_4$ precipitate.

The value for potassium thus found must be corrected for any rubidium or cesium present. The latter two elements may be determined as directed on pages 34 to 39.

*Procedure for Determination of Sodium.*—Evaporate the combined filtrates and washings from the above procedure in a 150-ml. beaker on a hot plate to 20 ml. to remove the ethyl acetate and then cool to room temperature. Add dropwise and with constant stirring 2 ml. of a 20% solution of HCl gas in *n*-butyl alcohol and then 6 ml. rapidly. Heat to 80° to 90°C. to coagulate the sodium chloride. Cool and filter through an ignited and weighed filtering crucible, transferring the precipitate to the crucible with a rubber tipped rod and washing 8 to 10 times with

1- to 2-ml. portions of the 6–7% HCl in *n*-butyl alcohol solution. Reserve the filtrate and washings for the determination of lithium.

Dry the crucible and contents in an oven at 250°C. for a few minutes, then ignite in a muffle at 600°C. for 5 minutes or at a very dull red heat over a free flame. Cool in a desiccator and weigh as impure NaCl. Wash the precipitate through the filter crucible with hot distilled water, dry and ignite the crucible, cool and weigh. The loss in weight represents pure NaCl.

To the weight of NaCl thus obtained there should be added 0.6 mg. for each 100 ml. of combined filtrate and washings from the HCl-*n*-butyl alcohol precipitation, because of the slight solubility of the NaCl in the wash liquid.

*Procedure for Determination of Lithium.*—To the combined filtrate and washings from the NaCl precipitation, add one-third their volume of distilled water, forming two layers. Cover with a cover glass supported on glass hooks and evaporate on a steam bath, avoiding any condensation on the upper part of the beaker which may cause loss by creeping. At the end, add 5 to 10 ml. of distilled water and continue the evaporation to make the removal of organic solvent more complete. At the appearance of a brown coloration remove the glass hooks and rest the cover glass on the beaker. Heat the covered beaker on a wire gauze with a free flame to fumes of perchloric acid. In case the perchloric acid is insufficient to oxidize the last traces of organic matter, a few more drops should be added. When the brown color has been completely removed, add 0.5 ml. of concentrated sulfuric acid, replace the cover glass and then fume off the acid on a hot plate or over a low flame on a wire gauze. Cool, add 5 to 10 ml. of distilled water and wash down the cover glass and inner walls of the beaker. Transfer to a platinum crucible which has been previously ignited and weighed with lid.

Evaporate the solution cautiously to dryness, cover the crucible and heat until every trace of acid is removed. Cool, add a little powdered ammonium carbonate to the residue and ignite at a dull red heat (700–800°C.) until no more fumes are given off. Cool in a desiccator and weigh as $Li_2SO_4 + Na_2SO_4$. Repeat the ignition to constant weight.

To correct for the $Na_2SO_4$, deduct 0.7 mg. for each 100 ml. of combined filtrate and washings from the HCl-*n*-butyl alcohol precipitation and obtain the corrected weight of $Li_2SO_4$.

$$\text{Corrected weight of } Li_2SO_4 \times 0.1262 = Li$$

$$\times 0.2718 = Li_2O$$

$$\times 0.7712 = LiCl$$

# SODIUM

Na, *at. wt.* 22.9898; *sp. gr.* 0.971; *m.p.* 97.5°C.; *b.p.* 880°C.; *oxides,* Na$_2$O, Na$_2$O$_2$, Na$_2$O$_3$

Sodium is the most abundant alkali element and is widely distributed in nature, constituting 3.12% of the earth's crust.[13] It occurs in soluble form in rock salt, brines, ocean water, salt and alkaline lakes, and is present in small quantities in nearly all natural waters. Large deposits of salt are located in Eastern and Southern United States, Stassfurt, Salzburg and Cheshire, England; natural soda deposits (mixtures of sodium carbonate, bicarbonate, chloride, sulfate, borate, etc.) occur in California, Nevada and Wyoming, in Mexico, East Africa and in various parts of Asia; sodium borate (borax) is found in California; sodium nitrate deposits are found in Chile and Peru; cryolite is found in Greenland. Sodium is associated in many rocks and minerals, being an important constituent of feldspar, of the nepheline group of silicates, of certain pyroxenes and of many other minerals.

## DETECTION [14]

Sodium may be identified by the color it imparts to a nonluminous flame or by means of the spectroscope. The solution is prepared as directed under "Preparation and Solution of Sample" and is freed from all constituents other than chlorides of magnesium and the alkalies according to the methods given under "Separations." With exceedingly small quantities of sodium, it may be necessary to remove magnesium also. After acidifying the solution with hydrochloric acid, a drop of the solution is brought into a nonluminous flame by means of a loop of platinum wire. In the presence of sodium the flame assumes an intense yellow color. The results may be confirmed by examining the flame through a spectroscope; the characteristic yellow double lines (at 5896 and 5890 Angstroms) will be prominent with the presence of sodium. Care must be exercised to avoid extraneous contamination; as a precaution, the platinum wire loop should be heated until no color is imparted to the flame before testing the solution. With soluble salts, a water solution may be used for the test. When testing waters, it may be necessary to concentrate by evaporation in a platinum dish before making the test.

Precipitation of sodium as zinc,[15] magnesium,[16] cobalt[17] or nickel[18] uranyl acetate may be used to identify the element.

The precipitation of sodium bismuth cesium nitrite may be used for identification of sodium.[19] The reagent is prepared by dissolving 30 g. of pure KNO$_2$ in

[13] Goldschmidt, V. M., J. Chem. Soc., **140**, 656, 1937.

[14] An excellent and precise method for the systematic qualitative separation and identification of the alkali metals is described in Qualitative Analysis for the Rarer Elements, A. A. Noyes and W. C. Bray, pages 245 to 267, The Macmillan Company, New York, 1927.

[15] Barber, H. H., and Kolthoff, J. M., J. Am. Chem. Soc., **50**, 1625, 1928; **51**, 3233, 1929.

[16] Caley, E. R., and Foulk, C. W., J. Am. Chem. Soc., **51**, 1664, 1929.

[17] Caley, E. R., J. Am. Chem. Soc., **51**, 1965, 1929.

[18] Feldstein, P., and Ward, A. M., Analyst, **56**, 245, 1931.

[19] Ball, W. C., J. Chem. Soc., **95**, 2126, 1909; **97**, 1408, 1910.

60 ml. of water, adding a solution of 3 g. of $Bi(NO_3)_3 \cdot 5H_2O$ in nitric acid and an aqueous solution of 1.6 g. $CsNO_2$ and diluting to 100 ml. Filter after standing overnight. Add 3 ml. of the cold reagent for each milligram of sodium to the concentrated test solution, mix and let stand in a cold place.

Potassium antimonate [20] produces a heavy white crystalline precipitate of $NaH_2SbO_4$ in neutral or weakly alkaline solutions. The alkalies only should be present.

## ESTIMATION

The estimation of sodium is required in the analysis of rocks, minerals, soils, waters, brines, saline residues, glass, refractories and many technical products.

General information on the preparation and solution of the sample and preparation for analysis is given on pages 2 to 6. Methods for separation from interfering elements and radicals are described on pages 6 to 8.

Precipitation of sodium with the various uranyl acetate reagents is the accepted standard procedure for its determination. Several of these are described below.

## METHODS FOR DETERMINATION OF SODIUM

### DETERMINATION AS SODIUM CHLORIDE

Sodium, in the absence of other alkalies, may be weighed as NaCl when it is already present as such, as in brines, or after conversion of other forms into the chloride. In the case of volatile acid salts, such as nitrate, the conversion is made by evaporating the solution to dryness with hydrochloric acid repeatedly, until only the chloride remains. When the sodium is present as a salt of a nonvolatile acid, the latter may be removed and the conversion effected according to procedures under "Separations."

*Procedure.*—If the solution containing the sodium chloride results from previous operations, some ammonium salts will be present. Proceed as described for the removal of ammonium salts under "Separations" (page 8), cool the residue in the dish, dissolve in a little water and filter to remove any carbonaceous matter, catching the filtrate and washings in an ignited and weighed platinum dish. Acidify the filtrate with hydrochloric acid and evaporate to dryness on a steam bath, dry in an oven at 110–130°C. and ignite cautiously over a free flame as described for the removal of ammonium salts under "Separations." Cool in a desiccator and weigh as NaCl.

$$NaCl \times 0.3934 = Na$$

$$\times 0.5302 = Na_2O$$

$$\times 1.2149 = Na_2SO_4$$

### DETERMINATION AS SODIUM SULFATE

When sodium alone is present as the salt of a volatile acid, it may be determined as sodium sulfate by repeated evaporation with sulfuric acid. Sodium salts of nonvolatile acids are treated as described under "Separations," using sulfuric acid for acidification. For sodium present as an organic salt, the substance is moistened with concentrated sulfuric acid and carefully heated over a free flame until the

[20] Behrens, H., Z. anal. Chem., **30**, 104, 1891.

organic matter is destroyed and fumes cease to come off. The residue is dissolved in distilled water and any carbonaceous matter is removed by filtration.

*Procedure.*—The solution, containing the sodium as the salt of a volatile acid or as the sulfate and a slight excess of sulfuric acid, is evaporated to dryness on a steam bath in an ignited and weighed platinum dish. Cautiously heat the dish over a free flame until fumes cease to come off. Cool, add a little powdered ammonium carbonate to the residue and ignite at a dull red heat (700–800°C.) until no more fumes are given off. Cool in a desiccator and weigh. Repeat the ignition with ammonium carbonate until a constant weight is obtained. The ammonium carbonate serves to convert any $Na_2S_2O_7$, formed during the ignition, to $Na_2SO_4$ according to the equation:

$$Na_2S_2O_7 + (NH_4)_2CO_3 \rightarrow Na_2SO_4 + (NH_4)_2SO_4 + CO_2$$

$$Na_2SO_4 \times 0.3237 = Na$$

$$\times 0.4363 = Na_2O$$

$$\times 0.8229 = NaCl$$

## DETERMINATION BY DIFFERENCE

If both sodium and potassium are present as chlorides or sulfates and the quantities are determined as described above for sodium, potassium may be determined by the tetraphenylboron procedure, page 22, or as the chloroplatinate or perchlorate (pages 22 to 25) and the value for sodium obtained by difference.

## DETERMINATION AS SODIUM ZINC URANYL ACETATE [15]

The method is applicable to the determination of small amounts of sodium in the presence of moderate amounts of potassium, ammonium, magnesium, calcium, barium and small amounts of lithium and strontium. Lithium forms a sparingly soluble triple acetate. When lithium is present in significant amounts the sodium may be determined as the sodium copper uranyl acetate without interference.[21] The salts should be present preferably as chlorides. Sulfates may be present if the solution contains no calcium, barium or strontium. Phosphates, silicates, oxalates and tartrates interfere. For removal of interfering ions, proceed first as described under "Separations."

Sodium is precipitated as sodium zinc uranyl acetate $(NaC_2H_3O_2 \cdot Zn(C_2H_3O_2)_2 \cdot 3UO_2(C_2H_3O_2)_2 \cdot 6H_2O)$ air dried and weighed.

*Reagents.* **Zinc Uranyl Acetate.**—Weigh 100 g. of crystallized uranyl acetate $(UO_2(C_2H_3O_2)_2 \cdot 2H_2O)$ in a 600-ml. beaker, add 15 ml. of glacial acetic acid, 500 ml. of distilled water, warm to about 70°C. and stir until dissolved (= Solution $A$). Weigh 27.8 g. of crystallized zinc acetate $(Zn(C_2H_3O_2)_2 \cdot 2H_2O)$ in a 600-ml. beaker, add 12 ml. of glacial acetic acid, 400 ml. of distilled water, warm to about 70°C. and stir until dissolved (= Solution $B$). Mix solutions $A$ and $B$ at about 70°C., add a few milligrams of sodium chloride and let stand for 24 hours. Filter at 20°C. and store in a glass-stoppered bottle. The reagent should be used at 20°C. At lower temperatures, high results will obtain; at higher temperatures, low results will be experienced.

**Wash Solution.**—To 100 ml. of 95% ethyl alcohol add 1 ml. of 30% acetic acid and an excess of sodium zinc uranyl acetate $(NaC_2H_3O_2 \cdot Zn(C_2H_3O_2)_2 \cdot 3UO_2$-

[21] Caley, E. R., and Rogers, L. B., Ind. Eng. Chem., Anal. Ed., **15**, 32, 1943.

$(C_2H_3O_2)_2 \cdot 6H_2O)$. Shake the solution to saturate it with the triple acetate and filter at 20°C.

*Procedure.*—Evaporate the neutral or feebly acid solution of the sample containing no more than 10 mg. of NaCl, free from the interfering substances mentioned above, to a volume of about 1 ml. in a small Pyrex beaker, avoiding separation of salts. Add 10 ml. of the zinc uranyl acetate solution (at 20°C.) and stir thoroughly. Allow to stand for at least 30 minutes, stirring occasionally, in a water bath at 20°C. Filter, by suction, through a dried (in a desiccator) and weighed porous porcelain or fritted glass crucible. Pass all the solution through the filter and suck it dry. Rinse the beaker with 2-ml. portions of the zinc uranyl acetate reagent and then wash the precipitate in the crucible 5 to 10 times with 2-ml. portions of the reagent, sucking the filter dry after each application. Then wash the precipitate 5 to 10 times with the wash solution (95% alcohol saturated with the triple acetate). Wash the precipitate once with ether to remove the alcohol, and pull dry air through the filter to remove the ether. Wipe the outside of the crucible with a moist and then a dry towel. Place the crucible in a desiccator for 10 to 15 minutes and weigh. Correct for reagents by a blank determination carried through the same steps as the sample.

$$\text{Grams of precipitate} \times 0.01495 = Na$$

$$\times 0.02015 = Na_2O$$

$$\times 0.0381 = NaCl$$

NOTE.—Duval [11] claims the air dried sodium zinc uranyl acetate precipitate contains 7.2 molecules of $H_2O$ rather than 6.

Various modifications of this method have been proposed.[22]

## DETERMINATION AS SODIUM MAGNESIUM URANYL ACETATE [16]

This method is applicable in the presence of potassium, ammonium, calcium, magnesium, barium, strontium, iron, aluminum, and chromium as chlorides. Lithium forms a sparingly soluble triple acetate. When lithium is present in significant amounts, sodium may be determined as the sodium copper uranyl acetate without interference.[19] Sulfate may be present when barium and strontium are absent and calcium and ammonium are low. Phosphates, silicates, oxalates and tartrates interfere.

Sodium is precipitated, dried and weighed as sodium magnesium uranyl acetate $(NaC_2H_3O_2 \cdot Mg(C_2H_3O_2)_2 \cdot 3UO_2(C_2H_3O_2)_2 \cdot 6.5H_2O)$.

*Reagents.* **Magnesium Uranyl Acetate.**—Dissolve 90 g. of uranyl acetate $(UO_2(C_2H_3O_2)_2 \cdot 2H_2O)$ in 60 ml. of glacial acetic acid and distilled water to make 1 liter by warming the solution to 70°C. and stirring (= Solution *A*). Dissolve 600 g. of magnesium acetate $(Mg(C_2H_3O_2)_2 \cdot 4H_2O)$ in 60 ml. of glacial acetic acid and

[22] For volumetric determination of uranium in the precipitate, see: Churchill, H. V., Bridges, R. W., and Miller, A. L., Ind. Eng. Chem., Anal. Ed., **8**, 348, 1936; Dobbins, J. T., and Byrd, R. M., J. Am. Chem. Soc., **53**, 3288, 1931.

For spectrophotometric modifications, see: Arnold, E., and Pray, A. R., Ind. Eng. Chem., Anal. Ed., **15**, 294, 1943; Darnell, M. C., and Walker, B. S., *ibid.*, **12**, 242, 1940; McCormick, D. R., and Carlson, W. E., Chemist-Analyst, **31**, 15, 1942.

For procedure modifications, see: Koenig, E. W., J. Am. Ceram. Soc., **22**, 24, 1939; Glaze, F. W., *ibid.*, **14**, 450, 1931; McCamley, W., Scott, T. E. L., and Smart, R., Analyst, **76**, 200, 1951; Harrison, M. F., Biochem. J., **48**, 283, 1951.

distilled water to make 1 liter by warming to 70°C. and stirring (= Solution *B*). Mix the two solutions, when completely dissolved, at 70°C., allow the solution to cool and stand at 20°C., preferably overnight. Filter through a dry paper at 20°C. and store in an amber glass stoppered bottle. Do not allow the reagent to cool below 20°C.

**Wash Solution.**—Saturate 95% alcohol at 20°C. with sodium magnesium uranyl acetate.

**Procedure.**—Evaporate the neutral solution of the sample containing 25 mg. or less of sodium, preferably as the chloride and free from the interfering ions mentioned, to a volume of 5 ml., or less if there is no separation of salts. Add rapidly 100 to 250 ml. of the magnesium uranyl acetate reagent, depending on the sodium content. For 10 mg. or less of sodium, 100 ml. is sufficient; for each additional milligram 10 ml. of reagent should be used. Partially immerse the beaker containing the mixture in a water bath at 20°C. and stir vigorously for 30–60 minutes. Filter by suction through a sintered glass filtering crucible of medium porosity, previously dried at 110°C. and weighed. Transfer the precipitate to the crucible by means of the magnesium uranyl acetate reagent, scrubbing the beaker with a rubber-tipped glass rod. Wash the beaker and the precipitate with four to six successive 5-ml. portions of the alcohol wash solution at 20°C., sucking the crucible dry after each washing. Wipe the outside of the crucible with a moist then a dry towel. Dry the crucible and contents in an oven at 85° to 90°C. for 30 minutes, cool in a desiccator and weigh. Correct for reagents by a blank determination carried through the same steps as the sample.

$$\text{Grams of precipitate} \times 0.0153 = Na$$

$$\times 0.0206 = Na_2O$$

$$\times 0.0389 = NaCl$$

Notes.—During the filtration the solution and precipitate should be continually agitated to prevent the crystalline precipitate from adhering to the sides of the beaker. The wash liquid should preferably be delivered from a graduated wash bottle having a fine tip. The end of the washing process is indicated by the wash liquid going through colorless. Usually 30 to 50 ml. of the wash liquid is sufficient. The alcoholic washings may cause salts to separate out in the filtrate.

Various modifications of this method have been proposed.[23]

## DETERMINATION OF SODIUM IN THE FILTRATE AFTER REMOVING POTASSIUM AS CHLOROPLATINATE

A determination of sodium may be made after removing the platinum from the filtrate obtained in the determination of potassium by the chloroplatinate method, page 22, and finally weighing the sodium as NaCl or $Na_2SO_4$ if no interfering ions are present.

[23] For volumetric determination of constituents of the triple acetate precipitate, see: Caley, E. R., J. Am. Chem. Soc., **52**, 1349, 1930; Nau, A., Bull. Soc. Phar. Bordeaux, **65**, 67, 1927; Kahane, E., Bull. Soc. Chim., **54**, 1344, 1932; Dobbins, J. T., and Byrd, R. M., J. Am. Chem. Soc., **53**, 3288, 1931; Furman, N. H., Caley, E. R., and Schoonover, I. C., *ibid.*, **54**, 1344, 1932; Kolthoff, I. M., and Lingane, J. J., *ibid.*, **55**, 1871, 1933; Trinder, P., Analyst, **76**, 56, 1951.

For a centrifuge method, see: Caley, E. R., Brown, C. T., and Price, H. P., Ind. Eng. Chem., Anal. Ed., **6**, 202, 1934.

For a nephelometric method, see: Lindsay, F. K., Braithwaite, D. G., and D'Amico, J. S., *ibid.*, **18**, 101, 1946.

*Procedure.*—Evaporate the alcoholic chloroplatinate filtrate in a small Erlen-meyer flask on a steam bath to remove most of the alcohol and add distilled water to make 100 or 200 ml. depending on the platinum content.   Insert in the flask a two-holed stopper fitted with inlet and outlet tubes.   Connect the inlet tube to a hydrogen generator, saturate the solution, expel air and fill the flask with hydro-gen.   Close the outlet tube and allow the flask to remain in a warm place under the slight hydrogen pressure of the hydrogen generator until all the platinum is precipitated and the liquid is clear and colorless.   Disconnect the flask, displace the hydrogen in the flask by an inert gas, filter the solution, wash with water and then evaporate the filtrate to dryness in a platinum dish on the steam bath.   The addition of 10 ml. of concentrated hydrochloric acid just as the first salts begin to separate will minimize decrepitation as the salts are dried.   Cover the crucible with a tight fitting lid when the residue is dry, transfer to a triangle and heat care-fully with a low flame kept in motion beneath the crucible.   Continue as described in the procedure under "Determination as Sodium Chloride."   The filtrate may also be heated with sulfuric acid and the sodium determined as the sulfate as described in the procedure on page 12.

Should any interfering elements (calcium, magnesium, strontium, etc.) be present they should first be removed as described under "Separations."   If lithium is present, separation is made according to the Rammelsberg-Palkin method, page 28.

The zinc or magnesium uranyl acetate procedure may also be used.

The procedure on page 34 may also be employed for the reduction of the chloroplatinate.

## DETERMINATION OF SODIUM IN THE PRESENCE OF LARGE QUANTITIES OF POTASSIUM [24]

This procedure is applicable to the determination of sodium (0.05–1% Na) in potassium salts such as potassium chloride, caustic potash, potassium carbonate.

The solution of the sample is treated with perchloric acid to convert the alkalies to perchlorates.   The sodium perchlorate is extracted with isopropyl alcohol.   The sodium in the extract is precipitated as sodium magnesium uranyl acetate, filtered and weighed.

*Reagents.*   **Magnesium Uranyl Acetate.**—Dissolve 160 g. of uranyl acetate $(UO_2(C_2H_3O_2)_2 \cdot 2H_2O)$, 180 g. of magnesium acetate $(Mg(C_2H_3O_2)_2 \cdot 4H_2O)$ and 45 ml. of glacial acetic acid in 750 ml. of distilled water at 70°C. with stirring.   Cool to 25°C., dilute to 1 liter and let stand for several hours at 25°C.   Filter and store in an amber bottle at 25°C.

**70–72% Perchloric Acid, Reagent Grade.**

**Isopropyl Alcohol, 99%, Reagent Grade.**

*Procedure.*—Prepare a solution of the potassium salt containing about 0.7 g. of potassium and 25 mg. or less of sodium and transfer to a 100-ml. Kjeldahl flask.   If the solution is caustic potash or potassium carbonate, add a drop of methyl red indicator, neutralize by adding 70% perchloric acid dropwise and then 1 ml. in excess.   If potassium chloride, add an equivalent amount of per-chloric acid and 1 ml. in excess.   Evaporate the water by placing the flask in a slanting position over a hole in an asbestos pad and heat carefully to fumes of perchloric acid with an Argand or equivalent burner.   Brush a Bunsen flame

[24] Williams, D., and Haines, G. S., Ind. Eng. Chem., Anal. Ed., **16,** 157, 1944.   For a rapid centrifuge method, see Haslam, J., and Beeley, J., Analyst, **71,** 223, 1946.

over the entire flask to insure complete removal of water. Cool the flask and contents to 20°C. by immersing the flask in cold water. *This cooling must be done in order to avoid hazards upon the addition of the alcohol.*

To the cool residue in the flask add 10 ml. of isopropyl alcohol and swirl the flask to dissolve the sodium perchlorate in the alcohol. Filter by suction through a medium-porosity fritted-glass crucible, collecting the filtrate in a 150-ml. beaker. This is accomplished easily by means of a Fisher Filtrator or similar apparatus. Wash the flask with two 5-ml. portions of isopropyl alcohol and transfer to the crucible. Rinse the sides of the flask and the crucible with isopropyl alcohol, using a fine-tipped wash bottle. The volume of the filtrate should be about 25 ml.

Gently swirl the contents of the beaker, add 10 ml. of the magnesium uranyl acetate reagent and continue swirling for about 20 seconds. Allow the mixture to stand for 20 minutes at 25°C. and filter through a medium-porosity fritted-glass crucible which has previously been dried in an oven at 110°C. and weighed. Transfer the precipitate completely to the crucible and wash with a total of 25 ml. of isopropyl alcohol. Dry the crucible and precipitate in an oven at 110°C. for 30 minutes, cool in a desiccator and weigh as $NaMg(UO_2)_3(C_2H_3O_2)_9 \cdot 7H_2O \cdot 0.3(CH_3)_2CHOH$ (molecular weight = 1534).

$$\text{Grams of precipitate} \times 0.0150 = Na$$

$$\times 0.0203 = Na_2O$$

$$\times 0.0381 = NaCl$$

**Colorimetric Modification.**[25]—After filtering and washing the sodium magnesium uranyl acetate precipitate in the final paragraph above, dissolve the precipitate by adding water to the filter crucible and stirring with a small stirring rod. Collect the aqueous solution in a 100-ml. volumetric flask placed in the Filtrator. When the precipitate in the crucible is completely dissolved and the crucible thoroughly rinsed, dilute the solution in the flask to the mark and mix. Determine the absorbancy at 430 m$\mu$ with a suitable spectrophotometer or with a colorimeter using a 400–450 m$\mu$ blue filter and read the milligrams of sodium from the prepared standard curve. Deduct the milligrams of sodium present in a blank determination on the reagent used.

$$\text{Milligrams Na} \times 0.00135 = \text{grams } Na_2O$$

$$\times 0.00254 = \text{grams } NaCl$$

*Preparation of Standard Curve.*—To a series of 100-ml. Kjeldahl flasks add, respectively, 0.0, 0.5, 1.0, 2.0, 4.0, 7.0 and 10.0 ml. of a standard sodium chloride solution (prepared by dissolving 1.2710 g. of dried reagent grade NaCl in distilled water and diluting to 1 liter in a volumetric flask so that 1.0 ml. = 0.5 milligrams Na). To each flask add 2.5 g. of reagent grade $KClO_4$ (equivalent to 0.7 g. potassium), 10 ml. of distilled water and 1 ml. of perchloric acid. Treat these standards as samples according to the procedure outlined, beginning with the evaporation using the Argand burner. Deduct the absorbancy value for the standard to which no sodium chloride had been added from the absorbancy of each of the other standards and plot the net values against milligrams of sodium.

[25] Unpublished work, 1948, Solvay Process Division, Allied Chemical Corporation, Syracuse 1, New York.

## DETERMINATION OF SODIUM IN CALCIUM CHLORIDE
## BY CENTRIFUGE METHOD [26]

This method is applicable to the determination of sodium in calcium chloride in the range 0.1–1.5 percent sodium. The precision is of the order of 5–10% and is suitable for routine control.

The method involves the precipitation of the sodium with magnesium uranyl acetate and the determination of sodium from the volume of the triple acetate after centrifuging.

*Reagents.* **Magnesium Uranyl Acetate.**—See page 16 for preparation.

**Glycerin, Reagent Grade.**

**Glacial Acetic Acid, Reagent Grade.**

*Apparatus.* **Clinical Centrifuge.**—Equipped with suitable head for special centrifuge tubes.

**Centrifuge Tubes.**—Pear shape, total graduated volume of 35 ml., with lower graduated capillary tube. The capillary dimensions are: length, 2.8 cm.; outside diameter, 0.9 cm.; inside diameter, 0.3 cm.; volume, 0.11 ml., graduated in 0.005 ml. divisions.

*Procedure.*—For samples containing 2% NaCl or less, weigh a 25-g. sample, transfer to a 500-ml. volumetric flask, dissolve in distilled water, add 25 ml. glacial acetic acid, cool and make up to the mark with distilled water. For samples containing 2–4% NaCl use half the quantity.

Prepare as used a well-mixed solution containing 55 ml. of the magnesium uranyl acetate reagent and 5 ml. of glycerin at 25°C. Transfer 30 ml. of the glycerin-magnesium uranyl acetate solution at 25°C. to each of two centrifuge tubes, filling the capillary with the reagent by the use of a platinum wire. Pipette a 2.00-ml. aliquot of the sample solution directly into the reagent without stirring during the addition. Then stir a few seconds with a thin glass rod to get complete mixing of the sample and reagent. Rinse the rod with a little of the reagent and place the tube in the centrifuge. Prepare a duplicate in a similar manner. Allow to stand 5 minutes and then centrifuge the balanced tubes at 1500 r.p.m. for 5.0 minutes. Let the centrifuge come to rest without braking so as not to disturb the precipitate. Read the volume of the precipitate by averaging the highest and lowest readings of the surface of the capillaries in the two tubes. From the standard curve read the milligrams of sodium chloride in the 2.00-ml. aliquot.

$$\text{Milligrams NaCl} \times 0.001 = \text{grams NaCl}$$

$$\times 0.000393 = \text{grams Na}$$

$$\times 0.00053 = \text{grams Na}_2\text{O}$$

**Preparation of Standard Curve.**—Prepare a calcium chloride solution containing 400 g. per liter calcium chloride by dissolving 36 g. of reagent grade calcium carbonate (containing less than 0.02% alkalies) in a minimum of hydrochloric acid. Evaporate to dryness on a steam bath to expel excess hydrochloric acid. Take up in distilled water, filter and make up to 100 ml. in a volumetric flask.

To each of six 100-ml. volumetric flasks add 10 ml. of the prepared calcium

[26] Unpublished work, 1950, Solvay Process Division, Allied Chemical Corporation, Syracuse 1, New York.

chloride solution and 5 ml. of glacial acetic acid. Then add, respectively, 0.0, 5.0, 10.0, 15.0, 20.0 and 25.0 ml. of a standard sodium chloride solution (1 ml. = 5 mg. NaCl), dilute to 100-ml. mark with distilled water and mix well. Continue as directed in the procedure, paragraph 2, using 2.00-ml. aliquots of the prepared standard solutions. Average duplicate standards, deduct the blank and plot the net volumes of precipitate against the known sodium chloride content for the standard curve.

## OTHER METHODS FOR THE DETERMINATION OF SODIUM

Direct determination of sodium as sodium cesium bismuth nitrite [27] is of interest. Determination of sodium by precipitating sodium manganese uranyl acetate followed by oxidation of the manganese by periodate in phosphoric acid solution and measuring the permanganate color was developed by Woelfel.[28] Sodium may be determined volumetrically after precipitation of pyroantimonate.[29] An excellent review of reagents and methods for the determination of sodium has been compiled by R. Belcher.[30]

Spectrographic, polarographic, and chromatographic methods have been used to some extent. Flame photometric methods are becoming increasingly important. Radiochemical determination of sodium in potassium nitrate has been described.[31]

## METHODS FOR SODIUM IN ANALYSES IN OTHER CHAPTERS

| | |
|---|---|
| Sodium in Aluminum Alloys | See Analysis Aluminum Alloys |
| Sodium in Bauxite | See Analysis of Bauxite (Aluminum Chapter) |
| Sodium in Hydrated Alumina | See Analysis of Hydrated Alumina |
| Sodium in Calcined Alumina | See Analysis of Calcined Alumina |
| Sodium in Magnesium Alloys | See Magnesium Chapter |
| Sodium in Phosphorus Ores | See Analysis of Phosphorus Ores |
| Sodium in Commercial Phosphates | See Analysis of Commercial Phosphates |

[27] Ball, W. C., J. Chem. Soc., **95**, 2126, 1909; **97**, 1408, 1910; Tschopp, E., Helv. Chim. Acta, **8**, 893, 1925.
[28] Woelfel, W. V., J. Biol. Chem., **125**, 219, 1938.
[29] Hurka, W., Z. physiol. Chem., **276**, 130, 1942; Herzka, A., Chemistry & Industry, p. 221, 1954.
[30] Belcher, R., Ind. Chemist, 731, 1946; **33**, 205, 1947.
[31] Pauly, J., C. R. Acad. Sci. Paris, **238**, 80, 1954.

# POTASSIUM

**K,** *at. wt.* 39.102; *sp. gr.* 0.87; *m.p.* 62.3°C.; *b.p.* 760°C.; *oxides,* $K_2O$, $K_2O_2$, $K_2O_4$

Potassium of the alkalies is next to sodium in abundance, constituting 2.86% of the earth's crust.[13] The most important mineral is sylvite (KCl). Potassium is also found in many rocks and minerals, in saline residues, in practically all natural waters, and in ashes of plants. Some of the minerals that may be mentioned are feldspar, carnallite, muscovite, kaliophilite, mica, leucite, among many others. Commercial sources of potassium include those in Stassfurt, Alsace, Searles Lake and Carlsbad.

## DETECTION [14]

Potassium may be identified by the color it imparts to a non-luminous flame or by means of the spectroscope.

For the detection of potassium in insoluble compounds, bring the sample into solution by one of the methods given under "Preparation and Solution of the Sample." In other cases, prepare a concentrated solution of the material to be tested. Where only small amounts of potassium are present, remove other constituents from solution except the chlorides of magnesium and the alkalies under "Separations." After acidifying with hydrochloric acid, bring a drop of the solution into a non-luminous flame by means of a platinum wire loop and observe through a cobalt blue glass. In the presence of potassium, a distinct reddish violet coloration will be apparent. This must not be confused with large amounts of sodium which appear bluish-violet through the glass. Cesium also gives a reddish violet coloration. Comparison with pure potassium salts is advisable. The presence of potassium may be determined or confirmed by examining the flame through a spectroscope. In the presence of potassium two bright red lines at 7699 and 7665 A will be readily seen. With larger amounts of potassium, a less distinct violet line will be visible at 4047 A.

Potassium may be identified by precipitation as potassium sodium cobaltinitrite ($K_2NaCo(NO_2)_6$). Place a small volume of the test solution in a test tube, acidify slightly with acetic acid, add an equal quantity of 30% $NaNO_2$ solution and half as much 10% $Co(NO_3)_2$ in 30% acetic acid. Mix and allow to stand until effervescence ceases and the cherry red solution is transparent. If an appreciable amount of potassium is present a yellow precipitate will settle to the bottom of the tube. Ammonium salts must be removed as they produce a similar precipitate.

Bismuth nitrate and sodium thiosulfate in alcohol will precipitate potassium as the yellow $K_3Bi(S_2O_3)_3$.[32] The sodium salt is soluble in alcohol. The presence of ammonium chloride will interfere.

Chloroplatinic acid in concentrated solutions of the chloride gives a yellow precipitate of potassium chloroplatinate. Rubidium, cesium and ammonium chlorides give similar precipitates.

[32] Carnot, A., *Z. anal. Chem.,* **512,** 1897.

Hexanitrodiphenylamine (*p*-dipicrylamine),[33] as a one per cent solution in 0.2 *N* sodium carbonate, gives an orange-red crystalline precipitate with potassium. The sodium salt is soluble, giving a yellow solution. Rubidium, cesium, and ammonium gives similar precipitates.

Potassium acid tartrate, perchlorate, picrate, silicofluoride, phosphomolybdate, phosphotungstate, chloronitrotoluene sulfonate[34] and naphthol yellow S[35] are all sparingly soluble in water or alcohol while the corresponding sodium salts are readily soluble.

## ESTIMATION

The estimation of potassium is required in the analysis of rocks, minerals, soils, ashes of plants, waters, brines, saline residues, fertilizers and many technical products. It is of particular importance in the analysis of fertilizers and soils.

General information on the preparation and solution of the sample and preparation for analysis is given on pages 2 to 8.

The determination of potassium, until recently, has been beset by problems due to variable composition and solubility of precipitates, non-selectivity of precipitants, and, in the case of chloroplatinic acid, the cost of the reagent. Until the discovery of the new reagent, sodium tetraphenylboron, by Wittig *et al.*,[36] the chloroplatinate procedures were considered the most accurate. The perchlorate method also has been used extensively. Although the tetraphenylboron procedures have only had the benefit of a decade of experimentation, the advantages in ease of use and the formation of a virtually insoluble precipitate of stoichiometric composition, have assured sodium tetraphenylboron a foremost place in the analytical chemistry of potassium.

## METHODS FOR THE DETERMINATION OF POTASSIUM

### DETERMINATION AS THE CHLORIDE OR SULFATE

Potassium may be weighed as the chloride or sulfate after separating all other constituents as described under "Separations." The procedures are the same as those described for sodium on page 12. The temperature of ignition for potassium chloride should not exceed 500°C.; for potassium sulfate 880°C.[11]

$$KCl \times 0.5244 = K$$

$$\times 0.6317 = K_2O$$

$$\times 1.1687 = K_2SO_4$$

$$K_2SO_4 \times 0.4487 = K$$

$$\times 0.5406 = K_2O$$

$$\times 0.8557 = KCl$$

[33] Poluektov, N. S., Mikrochemie, **14**, 265, 1934.

[34] 6-chloro-5-nitro-m-toluene sulfonate. Davies, H., and Davies., W., J. Chem. Soc., **123**, 2976, 1923. The cesium salt is also insoluble.

[35] The potassium salt of 3,4-dinitro-1-naphthol-7-sulfonic acid. Clark, A. W., and Willits, C. O., Ind. Eng. Chem., Anal. Ed., **8**, 209, 1936.

[36] Wittig, G., *et al.*, Annalen, **563**, 114, 118, 126, 1949.

## TETRAPHENYLBORON METHOD [37]

This method is applicable in the presence of chloride, sulfate, phosphate, alkaline earths, sodium and lithium, and most metals. Rubidium, cesium and ammonium salts interfere.

Potassium is precipitated as potassium tetraphenylboron from a dilute acid solution of the sample. The precipitate is washed, dried and weighed.

*Reagents.* **Sodium Tetraphenylboron, 1% Solution.**—Dissolve 2.5 g. of sodium tetraphenylboron in 250 ml. of distilled water, add 0.5–1 g. of reagent grade aluminum hydroxide, stir for 5 minutes and filter. Reject or refilter the first 20–30 ml. of filtrate.

**Wash Solution.**—Prepare a saturated solution of potassium tetraphenylboron by shaking 20–30 mg. of the precipitate with 250 ml. of distilled water for about 20 minutes. Add 0.5–1 g. of aluminum hydroxide, stir for a few minutes and filter, rejecting or refiltering the first 20–30 ml. of filtrate. Precipitate potassium tetraphenylboron from 50 ml. of 0.2 $N$ hydrochloric acid containing about 0.1 g. of potassium chloride by adding the reagent slowly with stirring from a pipette, until no further precipitation takes place. Filter through a glass filter crucible, wash with distilled water, and dry in a desiccator.

*Procedure.*—Adjust the sample solution, containing about 10 mg. of potassium and free of ammonium salts, to about 50 ml. and add 2 ml. of concentrated hydrochloric acid. Cool in an ice bath for 10 minutes. Add slowly with a pipette 25 ml. of the reagent solution previously cooled in an ice bath. Swirl the solution in the beaker during the addition of the reagent. Continue cooling the solution and precipitate in an ice bath for 10 minutes. Filter through a tared glass filter crucible. Wash with several small portions of the wash solution. Dry the precipitate for an hour at 110°C., cool in a desiccator and weigh.

$$\text{Weight of precipitate} \times 0.1091 = \text{K}$$

$$\times 0.1314 = \text{K}_2\text{O}$$

NOTES.—From 2 to 20 mg. of potassium can be determined conveniently by the procedure, the solution volume and reagent volume being adjusted accordingly. An excess of reagent is not detrimental. The final acidity should be about 0.2 $N$.

The precipitate will also contain rubidium and cesium as the tetraphenylboron salts if present. These elements may be determined as described on pages 34 to 39 and then potassium can be obtained by difference.

## THE CHLOROPLATINATE METHODS

### DETERMINATION AS POTASSIUM CHLOROPLATINATE

This method is applicable in the presence of chlorides of sodium, lithium, magnesium, calcium and strontium. Sulfates and ammonium salts must be absent.

The sample, in the form of the chlorides of the alkali metals, is treated with an excess of chloroplatinic acid, water is evaporated, the residue taken up in 80% alcohol. Potassium chloroplatinate is practically insoluble; the other chlorides are soluble. Rubidium and cesium chloroplatinates are insoluble also (see note below).

---

[37] The method is that of M. Kohler, Z. anal. Chem., **138**, 9, 1953, adapted by Sporek, K., and Williams, A. F., Analyst, **80**, 347, 1955. Survey articles by G. H. Gloss, Chemist-Analyst, **42**, 50, 1953, A. J. Nutten, Ind. Chemist, **30**, 29, 57, 1954, and A. Sykes, *ibid.*, **31**, 245, 305, 1955, **32**, 164, 223, 1956 review the use of the tetraphenylboron reagent and list references to titrimetric and other modifications of the method.

*Reagents.* **Chloroplatinic Acid Solution.**—Containing 1 gram of platinum in 10 ml.

**80% Ethyl Alcohol.**

*Procedure.*—To a small volume (10 ml.) of the sample, containing about 0.25 g. of the chlorides and free from ammonium salts, in a small porcelain dish add a slight excess of chloroplatinic acid (2 ml. for each 0.1 g. of the chloride is sufficient). Evaporate the solution on a steam bath to a syrupy consistency that will solidify on cooling. Do not evaporate to dryness as this will render the sodium salt insoluble. Flood the cooled residue with about 10 ml. of 80% alcohol, crush the crystals with a glass stirring rod flattened on the end, and allow the mixture to stand for 0.5 hour. Filter by decantation through a previously dried and weighed fritted-glass crucible. Add a small portion of alcohol to the residue, grind the residue in the dish and filter again by decantation. When the filtrate runs clear, transfer the precipitate to the crucible and wash two or three times with small portions of alcohol. Dry in an oven between 110° and 130°C. to a constant weight.

$$K_2PtCl_6 \times 0.1609 = K$$

$$\times 0.1938 = K_2O$$

$$\times 0.3068 = KCl$$

$$\times 0.3586 = K_2SO_4$$

Notes.—The platinum in the precipitate and filtrate may be recovered, reconverted to chloroplatinic acid and used repeatedly.[38] The potassium chloroplatinate solubility is negligible if the filtrate and washings are kept to about 50 ml. Ethyl alcohol stronger than 80% will decompose sodium chloroplatinate and precipitate sodium chloride.[39] The composition of the precipitate has been questioned by Fresenius;[40] for the smaller percentages of potassium occurring in rocks and minerals the theoretical factors are suitable. Smith and Shead[41] have described the use of lithium chloroplatinate as the precipitating reagent claiming the formation of potassium chloroplatinate of theoretical composition that can be safely dried at 260°C.

The chloroplatinate precipitate will also contain rubidium and cesium as chloroplatinates if present. They may be determined as outlined on pages 34 or 39 and the potassium then obtained by difference.

## MODIFIED CHLOROPLATINATE METHOD [42]

The method is applicable in the presence of chlorides, sulfates, phosphates, nitrates, carbonates, borates, silicates, alkaline earths, magnesium, sodium, iron and aluminum. Rubidium, cesium and ammonium salts interfere.

The chloroplatinate precipitate obtained in the usual way is reduced with magnesium metal to precipitate platinum which is then filtered, dried and weighed as metallic platinum.

*Procedure.*—Follow the same procedure as described above except add 5 ml. of hydrochloric acid to the solution before the addition of the chloroplatinic acid reagent.

Dissolve the alcohol washed precipitate of $K_2PtCl_6$ in the filter crucible, along with other soluble salts present, with hot distilled water. Wash the crucible thoroughly with hot water, catching the filtrate and washings in a small beaker. To

[38] Swisher, M. C., and Rummel, F. F., Ind. Eng. Chem., Anal. Ed., **11**, 162, 1939.
[39] Morozewicz, J., Bull. acad. sci. Cracovie, 796, 1906.
[40] Fresenius, H., and Brinton, H. M. P., Z. anal. Chem., **50**, 21, 1911.
[41] Smith, G. F., and Shead, A. C., J. Am. Chem. Soc., **53**, 947, 1931.
[42] Hicks, W. B., J. Ind. Eng. Chem., **5**, 650, 1913; Wells, R. C., Bailey, R. K., and Fairchild, J. G., *ibid.*, **16**, 935, 1924.

the hot solution add 5 ml. of concentrated hydrochloric acid and about 0.5 g. of pure magnesium rod or ribbon for each 0.2 g. of potassium present. Stir the solution and hold the magnesium ribbon at the bottom of the beaker with a glass rod. When the action has nearly ceased add a few milliliters of dilute hydrochloric acid and allow the platinum to settle. If reduction is complete the supernatant liquid will be clear and limpid like water. To make sure, add more magnesium in which case the solution will darken if reduction is incomplete. To the completely reduced solution add concentrated hydrochloric acid and boil to dissolve any basic salts, filter, and wash with hot water until the filtrate gives no test for chlorides. Ignite and weigh as platinum.

$$Pt \times 0.4009 = K$$

$$\times 0.4829 = K_2O$$

$$\times 0.7643 = KCl$$

NOTE.—Excessive amounts of silica, iron or alumina should be removed preferably before proceeding with the determination. Care should be taken to insure the complete removal of the soluble chloroplatinates.

### LINDO-GLADDING METHOD [43]

This method is applicable in the presence of chlorides, sulfates, phosphates, nitrates, sodium and magnesium.

The chloroplatinate precipitate is first washed with 80% alcohol, then with a special ammonium chloride wash solution, and finally with 80% alcohol.

*Reagents.* **Acid Alcohol.**—Mix 200 ml. of alcohol with 20 ml. of concentrated hydrochloric acid and cool to room temperature.

**Wash Solution.**—Dissolve 100 g. of pure ammonium chloride in 500 ml. of distilled water, add 5 to 10 g. of pulverized $K_2PtCl_6$ and shake at intervals for 6 to 8 hours. Allow the mixture to settle overnight and filter. The residue may be used for preparing additional wash solution.

*Procedure.*—To the solution containing the alkalies in a 100-ml. Vycor, silica, or platinum dish, add sufficient dilute sodium hydroxide (1–2 ml. of $N$ NaOH) to prevent formation of free $H_3PO_4$ and evaporate nearly to dryness on a steam bath. Add 1 ml. of 1:1 sulfuric acid and 6–8 granules of granulated sugar, evaporate to dryness and ignite to whiteness at dull red heat. Dissolve the residue in distilled water (at least 20 ml. for each 0.1 g. $K_2O$), add a few drops of hydrochloric acid and an excess of chloroplatinic acid. Evaporate on a steam bath to a thick paste, avoiding exposure to ammonia. Cool and treat the residue with about 6 ml. of the acid alcohol. After about 15 minutes filter through a tared fritted glass filter-ing crucible of medium porosity. Wash the precipitate first by decantation then in a crucible with the acid alcohol until the filtrate is colorless.

After washing the precipitate thoroughly with the acid alcohol, wash with 10 ml. of the special ammonium chloride wash solution. Repeat the washing with successive portions of the wash solution five or six times in order to remove the impurities from the precipitate. Wash again thoroughly with 80% alcohol, dry for 30 minutes at 100°C., cool in a desiccator and weigh as $K_2PtCl_6$. The precipitate should be completely soluble in water. If it is not, dissolve the $K_2PtCl_6$ in hot distilled water, wash the crucible with hot water, dry and reweigh. Make correction for the water insoluble residue.

[43] Chem. News, **53**, 202, 296, 1886; Association of Official Agricultural Chemists, Methods of Analysis, 8th Ed., p. 17, Washington, D. C.

$$K_2PtCl_6 \times 0.1609 = K$$

$$\times 0.1938 = K_2O$$

$$\times 0.3068 = KCl$$

$$\times 0.3586 = K_2SO_4$$

Various modifications of the chloroplatinate method have been proposed.[44]

## PERCHLORATE METHOD [45]

This method is applicable in the presence of chlorides and nitrates of the alkaline earths, phosphates, sodium and lithium. Sulfates and ammonium salts should be absent.

The alkalies and other salts are converted to the perchlorates, the insoluble potassium perchlorate is separated by filtration from an absolute alcohol solution.

*Reagents.* **Extraction Solution.**—Absolute ethyl alcohol containing 0.2% of 70% perchloric acid.

**Wash Solution.**—Just before use, saturate a portion of the extraction solution with crystals of potassium perchlorate at room temperature, decanting the clear liquor for use as the wash solution.

*Procedure.*—To the concentrated solution of the salts (less than 1 g.) add 2 ml. of 70% perchloric acid and evaporate on a steam bath, with stirring, to a syrupy consistency. Add a little hot water and continue the evaporation until all other acids are expelled and heavy fumes of perchloric acid are given off. Cool the residue to 20°C., add 20 ml. of the extraction solution and let stand for 20 minutes, triturating the mixture occasionally. Filter by decantation through a sintered glass filtering crucible using suction, and wash the residue in the beaker once or twice with the extraction solution. Suck dry and then dissolve the residue in the crucible with hot distilled water catching the filtrate in the original beaker. Add 1 ml. of perchloric acid, evaporate and extract as before. Filter with suction through an ignited and weighed Selas filtering crucible, transferring the precipitate by means of the prepared wash solution. Dry at 110° to 130°C., finally heat in a muffle at 350°C. for 15 minutes. Cool in a desiccator and weigh as $KClO_4$.

$$KClO_4 \times 0.2822 = K$$

$$\times 0.3399 = K_2O$$

$$\times 0.5381 = KCl$$

NOTE.—The potassium perchlorate weighed will also contain rubidium and cesium perchlorates if present. These latter elements can be determined as described on pages 34 to 39 and potassium then obtained by difference.

[44] Shahl, A. T., and Bennett, H. G., J. Biol. Chem., **78**, 643, 1928; Smith, G. F., and Shead, A. G., J. Am. Chem. Soc., **54**, 1722, 1932; O'Leary, W. J., and Papish, J., Ind. Eng. Chem., Anal. Ed., **6**, 107, 1934; Joy, A. B., Ind. Eng. Chem., Anal. Ed., **16**, 383, 1944; Adams, M. F., and St. John, J. L., Ind. Eng. Chem., Anal. Ed., **17**, 435, 1945; Perrin, C. H., Anal. Chem., **21**, 984, 1949.

[45] Wense, W., Z. angew. Chem., 691, 1891; 233, 1892; Caspari, R., *ibid.*, 68, 1893; Hillebrand, Lundell, Bright and Hoffman, Applied Inorganic Analysis, 2nd Ed., p. 664, John Wiley and Sons, Inc., New York, 1953. The perchlorate method, using *n*-butyl alcohol and ethyl acetate as the extraction and wash solution is described on page 8 of this present book. Smith, G. F., J. Am. Chem. Soc., **45**, 2072, 1923, uses *n*-butyl alcohol for the extraction.

# OTHER CHEMICAL METHODS FOR THE DETERMINATION OF POTASSIUM

## THE PERIODIC ACID METHOD [46]

Potassium is precipitated from a small volume of a nitrate solution by the addition of periodic acid and a 1:1 mixture of ethyl alcohol and ethyl acetate. The precipitate may be weighed or reduced with potassium iodide and the liberated iodine titrated. Chloride interferes, sulfate interferes with the gravimetric procedure, and other metals such as manganese, iron and chromium must be removed before precipitation.

## THE SODIUM COBALTINITRITE METHOD [47]

This method is one of the most sensitive for the determination of potassium but suffers from a number of uncertainties. The precipitate is of variable composition, depending on the potassium concentration, amount of reagent used and temperature. However, for routine analysis of similar materials, the procedure can be made to provide satisfactory results. Silver cobaltinitrite [48] will detect 1 part of potassium per million.

## PRECIPITATION AS THE 12-PHOSPHOMOLYBDATE [49]

Potassium may be precipitated as $K_3PO_4 \cdot 12MoO_3$, titrated alkalimetrically or converted to lead molybdate and determined gravimetrically.

## METHODS FOR POTASSIUM IN ANALYSES IN OTHER CHAPTERS

| | |
|---|---|
| Potassium in Bauxite | See Analysis of Bauxite (Aluminum Chapter) |
| Potassium in Magnesium Alloys | See Magnesium Chapter |
| Potassium in Phosphorus Ores | See Analysis of Phosphorus Ores |
| Potassium in Commercial Phosphates | See Analysis of Commercial Phosphates |

[46] Willard, H. H., and Boyle, A. J., Ind. Eng. Chem., Anal. Ed., **13**, 137, 1941; Jentoft, R. E., and Robinson, R. J., Anal. Chem., **28**, 2011, 1956.

[47] de Koninck, L. L., Z. anal. Chem., **38**, 396, 1881; Adie, R. H., and Wood, T. B., J. Chem. Soc., **77**, 1076, 1900; Drushel, W. A., Am. J. Science, **24**, 433, 1907; **26**, 329, 555, 1908; Van Rysselberge, P. J., Ind. Eng. Chem., Anal. Ed., **3**, 3, 1931; Piper, C. S., J. Soc. Chem. Ind., **53**, 392, 1934; Wilcox, L. V., Ind. Eng. Chem., Anal. Ed., **9**, 136, 1937; Koenig, E. W., J. Am. Ceramic Soc., **22**, 164, 1939; Kelly, O. J., Hunter, A. S., and Sterges, A. J., Ind. Eng. Chem., Anal. Ed., **18**, 319, 1946; Kaye, I. A., ibid., **12**, 310, 1940; Dupuis, T., Anal. Chim. Acta, **9**, 413, 1953.

[48] Burgess, L. L., and Kemm, O., J. Am. Chem. Soc., **34**, 652, 1912; Lutz, O., Z. anal. Chem., **59**, 145, 1920; Ismail, A. M., and Harwood, H. F., Analyst, **62**, 443, 1937; Robinson, R. J., and Putnam, G. L., Ind. Eng. Chem., Anal. Ed., **8**, 211, 1936; Breh, F., and Gaebler, O. H., J. Biol. Chem., **87**, 81, 1930; Kawe, A., Z. anal. Chem., **115**, 385, 1939.

[49] Belcher, R., and Robinson, J. W., Anal. Chim. Acta, **8**, 239, 1953.

# LITHIUM

**Li,** *at. wt.* **6.939;** *sp. gr.* **0.534;** *m.p.* **186°C.;** *b.p.* **1336°C.;** *oxides,* **Li$_2$O, Li$_2$O$_2$**

Lithium is a comparatively rare element although it is widely disseminated in nature, being found in nearly all igneous rocks and in many mineral springs. It is an important constituent of spodumene, lepidolite, petalite, amblygonite, triphyllite, and in certain tourmalines. It frequently occurs in feldspar, muscovite and beryl. Large deposits of lithium minerals, spodumene particularly, are found in the Black Hills, South Dakota and Kings Mountain, North Carolina.

## DETECTION [14]

Bring the sample into solution and convert the alkalies to their chlorides as described in "Preparation and Solution of the Sample" on pages 2 to 6 and in "Separations" on pages 6 to 8. Treat the dry alkali chlorides with amyl alcohol, a mixture of alcohol and ether, or *n*-butyl alcohol, filter and evaporate the filtrate to dryness. Moisten the residue with hydrochloric acid and test a drop in a non-luminous flame with a platinum wire loop. A carmine-red color indicates the presence of lithium. Sodium, if present, will mask the red color but if observed through a cobalt-blue glass the red color due to lithium becomes visible. Examined through a spectroscope the bright red line at 6708 and an orange line at 6104 Angstroms will appear if lithium is present.

Ammonium fluoride precipitates white, gelatinous Li$_2$F$_2$ in ammoniacal solution. Evaporate the test solution with hydrofluoric acid in a platinum dish and treat the residue with dilute ammonium hydroxide.

White lithium phosphate, Li$_3$PO$_4$, will be precipitated by Na$_2$HPO$_4$ in alkaline solution.

The addition of ammonium carbonate and ammonium hydroxide to a concentrated solution of the alkali chlorides will precipitate Li$_2$CO$_3$ if lithium is present.

In the presence of a saturated solution of the other alkali salts lithium will produce an extremely insoluble compound with trivalent iron and periodic acid.[50]

## ESTIMATION

The estimation of lithium may be required in the analysis of rocks and minerals, mineral waters, glass, ceramics, other technical products, medicinal products, lithia waters, etc.

Minerals and rocks insoluble in acid are brought into solution by the Berzelius procedure, page 2 or the J. Lawrence Smith procedure, page 3. Not all the lithium is leached out in the residue of the J. L. Smith procedure; in addition some lithium may be lost in the calcium removal operations. The Berzelius method, or a modification, therefore, is to be preferred for the decomposition. Usually lithium is present in extremely small amounts in igneous rocks, an average composition being 0.008% Li$_2$O.[51] In these small quantities lithium is best determined by the spectrograph or flame photometer.

[50] Procke, O., and Uzel, R., Mikrochim. Acta, **3,** 105, 1938.
[51] Clarke, F. W., Data of Geochemistry, Bull. U. S. Geol. Survey, No. 770, 29, 1924.

## SEPARATIONS

Lithium along with sodium is separated from potassium, rubidium and cesium by the chloroplatinate procedures, pages 22 to 25, and by the perchlorate procedure, page 25. The *n*-butyl alcohol-ethyl acetate procedure, page 8, also is applicable. Larger quantities of sodium and/or potassium can be separated from small quantities of lithium by treating a saturated solution of the chlorides in an ice bath with HCl gas, filtering off the sodium and/or potassium chlorides and washing with ice-cold hydrochloric acid. The filtrate and washings, containing the lithium and smaller quantities of sodium and/or potassium, are evaporated to dryness to remove HCl before proceeding with the selected procedure.

## METHODS FOR THE DETERMINATION OF LITHIUM

### DETERMINATION AS LITHIUM CHLORIDE

Lithium may be weighed as LiCl in the absence of other salts except ammonium. The procedure is practically the same as that described for sodium chloride, page 12, but since lithium chloride is very hygroscopic, this salt must be weighed out of contact with the air. For this purpose lithium chloride is ignited in a platinum crucible, cooled in a desiccator, and the crucible and contents weighed in a tared glass-stoppered weighing bottle. The ignition temperature should not exceed 600°C.

$$LiCl \times 0.1637 = Li$$

$$\times 0.3524 = Li_2O$$

$$\times 1.2966 = Li_2SO_4$$

### DETERMINATION AS LITHIUM SULFATE

Lithium is weighed preferably as $Li_2SO_4$ in the absence of any other salts except ammonium. The procedure is the same as that as described for sodium sulfate, page 12. Since lithium bisulfate is readily decomposed to $Li_2SO_4$ on heating, it is not necessary to ignite with ammonium carbonate.

$$Li_2SO_4 \times 0.1262 = Li$$

$$\times 0.2717 = Li_2O$$

$$\times 0.7712 = LiCl$$

### THE RAMMELSBERG-PALKIN METHOD [52]

This method is applicable to the alkali chlorides. The solution is prepared free from all constituents except the alkali chlorides as directed under "Separations," pages 6 to 8, finally obtaining the anhydrous mixed alkali chlorides by ignition to remove ammonium salts and organic matter.

Anhydrous lithium chloride is soluble in a mixture of alcohol and ether, while the other alkali chlorides are insoluble. Lithium chloride is converted to $Li_2SO_4$ and weighed.

*Procedure.*—Using about 0.5 g. of the dried mixed chlorides, dissolve the chlo-

[52] Rammelsberg, C., Pogg. Ann., **66**, 79, 1845; Palkin, C. S., J. Am. Chem. Soc., **38**, 2326, 1916.

rides in a minimum of distilled water (not over 1.5 ml. for 0.5 g. of the mixed chlorides) in a tall beaker. Add a drop of hydrochloric acid and introduce gradually, while rotating the beaker, 20 ml. of absolute ethyl alcohol in the center of the beaker, not on the sides. The sodium and potassium chlorides precipitate in a granular condition. Continue rotating the beaker, add 60 ml. of ether and allow the mixture to stand about 5 minutes, or until the precipitate is well agglomerated and the supernatant liquid is almost clear.

Filter through an ignited and weighed Selas filtering crucible using suction, catching the filtrate and subsequent washings in an Erlenmeyer flask. A Fisher Filtrator is convenient for this operation. Wash the beaker with a mixture of 1 part absolute alcohol and 4 to 5 parts of ether, using a rubber-tipped rod to scrub the beaker. Wash the residue in the crucible with the wash mixture and set the crucible aside. Wash the funnel to remove any lithium therefrom into the flask with the filtrate.

Evaporate the filtrate and washings in the flask to dryness on a steam bath, with a gentle current of filtered air directed into the flask. Take up the dried residue with 10 ml. absolute alcohol, warming slightly and rubbing any film on the sides and bottom of the flask with a rubber-tipped rod. While rotating the flask add 50 ml. of ether and 1 drop of concentrated HCl. Then let the mixture stand for 0.5 hour, with intermittent rotating of the flask. After the fine precipitate has agglomerated (only a very small amount is usually precipitated), filter through the same crucible as was used for the first precipitate. Wash thoroughly with the ether-alcohol mixture as before. Save the filtrate and washings which contain the LiCl. Dry the crucible and contents in an oven and ignite gently as described for the removal of ammonium salts under "Separations," page 8, cool in a desiccator and weigh as NaCl + KCl (also RbCl and CsCl, if present).

Evaporate the ether-alcohol solution of LiCl to dryness on a steam bath. Take up the residue in a little water and transfer to an ignited and weighed platinum dish. Add a slight excess of sulfuric acid and evaporate to dryness on a steam bath. Ignite gently over a low flame and finally at a dull red heat (700–800°C.). Cool in a desiccator and weigh as $Li_2SO_4$.

$$Li_2SO_4 \times 0.1262 = Li$$

$$\times 0.2717 = Li_2O$$

$$\times 0.7712 = LiCl$$

NOTE.—The original Rammelsberg method involved the extraction of lithium chloride with a mixture of alcohol and ether saturated with HCl gas. Palkin's modification is less cumbersome, provides comparable results with less manipulation and is preferred because it is a precipitation method.

## DETERMINATION OF LITHIUM AS PERIODATE [53]

This method is applicable to the determination of lithium in the presence of alkali chlorides, nitrates, perchlorates or sulfates. Other metals should be removed as described in "Separations," pages 6 to 8.

Lithium is precipitated as a complex periodate in strongly alkaline potassium periodate solution. The precipitate is titrated iodometrically, using either sodium thiosulfate or arsenite, standardized against known lithium values.

[53] Rogers, L. B., and Caley, E. R., Ind. Eng. Chem., Anal. Ed., 15, 209, 1943; Bacon, F. R., and Starks, D. T., ibid., 17, 230, 1945; Gottfried, J., Chem. Prumsyl, 5, 390, 1955.

*Reagent.* **Alkaline Potassium Periodate.**—Dissolve 24 g. of potassium hydroxide in 100 ml. of distilled water. When cool add 10 g. of potassium metaperiodate and dissolve. Store in a polyethylene bottle in the dark (discard after 1 month).

*Procedure.*—Evaporate the solution of the alkali chlorides, nitrates, perchlorates or sulfates, containing between 1 and 50 mg. of lithium, to 2 ml. in a 50-ml. beaker. Immerse the bottom half of the beaker in a water bath maintained at 60° to 70°C. and after a few minutes add the special periodate reagent dropwise, with constant swirling, at a rate not exceeding 1 drop every 5 seconds until 2 ml. have been added. If a heavy precipitate forms, add 3 ml. more of the reagent in the same manner. If the precipitate is very heavy, as shown by the formation of a mixture that does not flow freely, add another 3 to 5 ml. of the reagent. Allow the mixture to digest at 60° to 70°C. for 20 minutes and then filter through a Gooch crucible fitted with a moderately thick asbestos pad. Wash the precipitate with four successive 2-ml. portions of approximately 5 $N$ KOH added slowly from a pipette. If more than 20 mg. of sodium are present, carry out the entire procedure at room temperature.

Transfer the pad and precipitate to a 250-ml. beaker with distilled water and add 5 ml. of $N$ sulfuric acid in order to ensure complete solution of the precipitate.

Titrate the periodate in the solution with sodium thiosulfate or sodium arsenite, standardized by titration of a known quantity of lithium carried through the same procedure. For quantities of lithium up to 10 mg., thiosulfate is recommended. Add 2 g. of potassium iodide to the dilute acid solution and titrate the liberated iodine with 0.1 $N$ sodium thiosulfate, using starch as an indicator. For quantities of lithium in excess of 10 mg., add an excess of borax or sodium bicarbonate to the dilute acid solution and titrate the liberated iodine with 0.1 $N$ sodium arsenite, using starch as an indicator.

$$\text{Ml. of standard arsenite} \times \text{factor} = \text{mg. of Li}$$

$$\text{Ml. of standard thiosulfate} \times \text{factor} = \text{mg. of Li}$$

NOTES.—The precipitate formed is a complex periodate, a mixture of lithium periodates. The ratio of lithium to iodine is sufficiently constant, when the precipitation is carried out under fixed conditions, to permit the determination of lithium by titration of the liberated iodine associated with the precipitate. Under the conditions given in the procedure it was found that 1 ml. of 0.1 $N$ sodium thiosulfate is equivalent to 0.42 mg. Li; 1 ml. 0.1 $N$ sodium arsenite is equivalent to 1.61 mg. Li.

For the determination of lithium after decomposition of the sample by the hydrofluoric, perchloric, nitric acid procedure, page 2, neutralize an aliquot of the prepared nitric acid solution or a dilute nitric acid solution of the residue with 5 $N$ KOH. Reacidify with a drop of concentrated nitric acid. Heat to boiling, add 0.1–0.2 g. powdered $Ba(OH)_2 \cdot H_2O$ and continue boiling for 5 minutes. Then add 10 ml. of a solution containing 0.5 g. $K_2SO_4$ and 0.1 g. $K_2C_2O_4 \cdot H_2O$ and continue boiling for 3 minutes. Cool and transfer to a 100-ml. volumetric flask, make up to volume, mix thoroughly and allow the precipitate to settle. Filter through a dry filter paper and proceed with the method using an aliquot containing 1 to 10 mg. of lithium.

## EXTRACTION WITH ORGANIC SOLVENTS

### GOOCH METHOD [54]

Anhydrous amyl alcohol is used to extract anhydrous LiCl from a mixture of the alkali chlorides. Corrections must be made for the slight solubility of potassium and sodium chlorides.

### BROWN AND REEDY METHOD [55]

The anhydrous alkali chlorides, free from calcium, magnesium and ammonium chlorides, are treated with anhydrous acetone two or three times to extract the soluble lithium chloride. After volatilizing the acetone from the extract, the LiCl is converted to $Li_2SO_4$ with sulfuric acid, dried, ignited and weighed as $Li_2SO_4$.

### KAHLENBERG AND KRAUSKOPF METHOD [56]

Treat the anhydrous alkali chlorides with anhydrous pyridine at boiling temperature to extract lithium chloride. After filtration, dissolve the sodium and potassium chlorides with water, evaporate to dryness and then repeat the treatment with boiling pyridine. If the quantities of sodium and potassium chloride are large, repeat the treatment a third time. Evaporate the pyridine from the filtrate, convert the lithium chloride to the sulfate, dry, ignite and weigh as $Li_2SO_4$.

### n-BUTYL ALCOHOL METHOD

The Willard-Smith method [12] is described on page 8. Kallmann [57] has modified the procedure to separate lithium from sodium and potassium by extraction with n-butyl alcohol and a 20% solution of HCl in n-butyl alcohol, and then washing with a 6% solution of HCl in n-butyl alcohol. Also described by Kallmann is a combined J. Lawrence Smith-Berzelius procedure for the isolation of lithium and other alkali metals.

## OTHER METHODS FOR LITHIUM

Other methods described for the determination of lithium include the stearate method,[58] the iso-butyl alcohol method,[59] and a Volhard titration method following extraction with 2-ethyl hexanol.[60] Measurement of the fluorescence of the complex lithium forms with 8-hydroxyquinoline has been employed.[61] Extraction of lithium with n-propanol [62] and determination colorimetrically or gravimetrically as the LiK ferricyanide-hexamethylenetetramine complex [63] has been proposed. Two other colorimetric methods may be of interest. Thomason [64] measures the color complex that lithium forms with thoron in alkaline solution.

[54] Gooch, F. A., Proc. Am. Acad. Arts Sci., **22**, 177, 1886; Am. Chem. J., **9**, 33, 1887.
[55] Brown, M. H., and Reedy, J. H., Ind. Eng. Chem., Anal. Ed., **2**, 304, 1930.
[56] Kahlenberg, L., and Krauskopf, F. C., J. Am. Chem. Soc., **30**, 1104, 1908.
[57] Kallmann, S., Ind. Eng. Chem., Anal. Ed., **16**, 712, 1944.
[58] Caley, E. R., J. Am. Chem. Soc., **52**, 2754, 1930.
[59] Winkler, L. W., Z. anal. Chem., **52**, 628, 1913.
[60] White, J. C. and Goldberg, G., Anal. Chem., **27**, 1188, 1955.
[61] White, C. E., Fletcher, M. H., and Parks, J., Anal. Chem., **23**, 478, 1951.
[62] Plyuschev, V. E., and Skakno, I. V., J. Anal. Chem. USSR, **8**, 293, 1953.
[63] Forster, C. F., Analyst, **79**, 629, 1954.
[64] Thomason, P. F., Anal. Chem., **28**, 1527, 1956.

Specker et al.[65] titrates photometrically or conductimetrically a cyclohexanone or acetone solution of lithium with standard copper perchlorate. Precipitation as lithium phosphate has also been described.[66]

## METHODS FOR LITHIUM IN ANALYSES IN OTHER CHAPTERS

Lithium in Magnesium Alloys            See Magnesium Chapter

[65] Specker, H., Hartkamp, H., and Jackwerth, E., Z. anal. Chem., **163**, 111, 1958.

[66] Caley, E. R., and Simmons, G. A. Jr., Anal. Chem., **25**, 1386, 1953; Nozaki, T., J. Chem. Soc. Japan, Pure Chem. Sect., **76**, 445, 1955; Kindyakov, P. S. and Khokhlova, A. V., Trudy-Moskov. Inst. Tonkoi Khim. Tekhnol., **6**, 9, 1956.

# RUBIDIUM AND CESIUM

Rb, *at. wt.* 85.47; *sp. gr.* 1.53; *m.p.* 38.5°C.; *b.p.* 700°C.; *oxides,* $Rb_2O$, $Rb_2O_2$, $Rb_2O_4$

Cs, *at. wt.* 132.905; *sp. gr.* 1.873; *m.p.* 28.5°C.; *b.p.* 670°C.; *oxides,* $Cs_2O$, $Cs_2O_2$, $Cs_2O_4$

Excepting francium, rubidium and cesium are the rarest of the alkalies in abundance, and although they are widely distributed in nature they occur only in very small amounts.

Rubidium almost always is associated with cesium and is found in many mineral waters. It is found in carnallite, lepidolite, triphyllite and in spodumene in small quantities.

Cesium replaces potassium in some feldspars and micas and may be found in mineral waters. The rare cesium mineral pollucite has the composition $H_2Cs_4Al_4(SiO_3)_9$.

Rubidium and cesium were discovered by means of the spectroscope by Bunsen and Kirchhoff in 1860 in the mother liquor of Durkheimer brine.

## DETECTION [14]

Solution of the sample is effected by the procedures given on pages 2 to 6 and the alkali chlorides are isolated as described on pages 6 to 8.

Examination of the concentrated solution of the chlorides with the spectroscope is sufficient for the identification of rubidium and cesium. For rubidium, double lines in the violet at 4215 and 4202 A and in the red at 7948 and 7800 A will appear when a drop of the solution is tested in a non-luminous flame. For cesium, intense blue lines at 4593 and 4555 A will appear when a drop of the solution is tested in a non-luminous flame.

Several chemical methods for identification of rubidium and cesium as the chlorides may be used. By treating a concentrated solution of the alkali salts with antimony trichloride in 6 $N$ HCl, any cesium in excess of 5 mg. will be precipitated as white $Cs_3SbCl_6$. At least 100 mg. of rubidium will remain in solution. With the cesium removed from solution, rubidium can be precipitated with sodium acid tartrate or with chloronitrotoluene sulfate. However, sodium will precipitate as $NaH_2SbO_4$ and potassium as the acid tartrate if present. A solution of $SnCl_4$ in concentrated HCl produces a white, crystalline precipitate of $Cs_2SnCl_6$; ammonium salts interfere. Silicotungstic acid will precipitate white $Cs_8SiW_{12}O_{42}$. The rubidium salt is more soluble.

## ESTIMATION

The determination of these rare alkalies is seldom called for, but may be required in the analysis of rocks, minerals and mineral waters. They have found some commercial application in the manufacture of photoelectric cells and vacuum tubes and their estimation is of importance in this connection.

The sample is brought into solution as described for the other alkalies on pages 2 to 6.

Both rubidium and cesium will be associated with potassium in the common methods used for its determination. Therefore, in solutions where potassium is absent, rubidium and cesium may be determined as the chloroplatinates or perchlorates. In the presence of potassium, differences in the solubility of certain of their salts is resorted to for their separation and determination. The methods for their determination, therefore, involve a series of separations as described below.

The chlorides of potassium, rubidium and cesium, after their separation from lithium and sodium as the chloroplatinates, page 22, or as the perchlorates, page 25, are obtained as follows.

*Reduction of the Chloroplatinates.*—Dissolve the potassium, rubidium and cesium chloroplatinate precipitate with hot water. Dilute to about 100 to 150 ml., depending on the quantity of platinum, add 5 ml. of formic acid and boil until the solution turns brown and initial reduction to platinum is indicated. Add a slight excess of ammonium hydroxide and continue boiling to complete the reduction. Allow the mixture to settle on a hot plate. Filter hot and wash the residue free from chlorides with hot water. Add 1 ml. hydrochloric acid and evaporate the filtrate and washings to dryness on a steam bath and ignite gently to remove ammonium salts and organic matter. The reduction may be accomplished with hydrogen as described on pages 15 and 16.

*Conversion of Perchlorates.*—Transfer a solution of the perchlorates (potassium, rubidium and cesium) to a porcelain dish, evaporate to dryness on a steam bath and then ignite at a dull red heat (600–700°C.) to convert the perchlorates to chlorides.

## METHODS FOR SEPARATION AND DETERMINATION OF RUBIDIUM AND CESIUM

### DETERMINATION AFTER SEPARATION OF POTASSIUM BY 9-PHOSPHOMOLYBDIC ACID [67]

This method is applicable to the determination of rubidium and cesium in the presence of potassium, chlorides or nitrates.

Potassium is separated as the phosphomolybdate, rubidium is separated from cesium and determined as the silicotungstate, and cesium is determined as the chloroplatinate.

*Reagent. 9-Phosphomolybdic Acid (Luteo Acid).*—Heat dodecaphosphomolybdic acid, carefully with continual stirring, until the temperature reaches 300° to 350°C. and the color of the dry acid turns from orange to green. Continue heating until no orange particles remain. Cool and extract with distilled water. Filter if not clear and oxidize the green solution with a little bromine water. Evaporate the solution slowly to obtain short, stout yellow prisms of the luteo acid ($P_2O_5 \cdot 18MoO_3 \cdot 24$–$30H_2O$). Filter off the crystals and prepare a 20% solution of the crystals by dissolving in distilled water.

[67] O'Leary, W. J., and Papish, J., Ind. Eng. Chem., Anal. Ed., **6**, 107, 1934.

*Procedure.*—To the dried residue containing not more than 1.0 g. of potassium, 0.08 g. of rubidium and cesium as the chlorides or nitrates add 100 ml. of 1:3 nitric acid, transfer to a beaker, heat to boiling, and add with vigorous stirring an excess of the 20% solution of 9-phosphomolybdic acid. The quantity of reagent required will be about 50 ml. for each gram of mixed chlorides present. Allow the mixture to settle at 50° to 60°C. for an hour, stir, and allow to settle for an hour or longer at room temperature. Test a portion of the clear liquor with additional 9-phosphomolybdic acid reagent for complete precipitation. Filter through a fritted glass filtering crucible and wash with a 1% sodium nitrate solution.

The filtrate contains all the potassium, excess reagent, sodium nitrate and nitric acid. It may be discarded and the potassium obtained by difference; or it may be treated with hydrogen sulfide to remove molybdenum as described below and the potassium determined by one of the methods given on pages 22 to 25.

The precipitate contains all the rubidium and cesium as phosphomolybdates.

**Procedure for the Determination of Rubidium.**—To remove the molybdenum, dissolve the precipitate in a minimum of 5% sodium hydroxide solution, saturate the solution with hydrogen sulfide, heat to boiling and just acidify with dilute nitric acid. Boil to coagulate the precipitate, allow to settle, filter, wash with slightly acidified hydrogen sulfide water and discard the precipitate. If the precipitation was incomplete, boil the filtrate to remove $H_2S$, add a little bromine water and boil to oxidize any molybdenum which may have been reduced, and then repeat the precipitation with hydrogen sulfide.

Evaporate the filtrate to about 20 ml., add 60 ml. of 95% alcohol, add a slight excess of chloroplatinic acid and then 2–3 ml. of ether. Allow the precipitate to settle, filter through a filtering crucible and wash with 80% alcohol. The precipitate contains the chloroplatinates of rubidium and cesium along with a small quantity of sodium phosphate.

Dissolve the precipitate in the crucible in a little distilled water and wash through the crucible into a beaker. Add a few drops of hydrazine hydrate and allow the reaction to proceed until vigorous evolution of gas ceases. Filter off the platinum and wash with distilled water. Cautiously add a few drops of aqua regia to the filtrate and boil for short time to remove excess hydrazine.

Evaporate the filtrate to a small volume, add a little concentrated hydrochloric acid and continue the evaporation to dryness. Add more hydrochloric acid and evaporate to dryness to ensure complete removal of nitric acid. Take up the residue in 50 to 75 ml. of 6 N hydrochloric acid and to the cold solution add 0.5 to 1.0 g. of solid silicotungstic acid dissolved in a few ml. of distilled water to precipitate the cesium. Allow the mixture to stand for 12 hours, filter through a filtering crucible and wash with 6 N hydrochloric acid. Reserve the precipitate. To the filtrate, which contains all the rubidium, add a little nitric acid and precipitate and determine the rubidium as the chloroplatinate by one of the methods described on pages 22 to 25, or above, without removing the excess silicotungstic acid.

$$Rb_2PtCl_6 \times 0.2954 = Rb$$

$$\times 0.4178 = RbCl$$

$$Pt \times 0.8762 = Rb$$

$$\times 1.2400 = RbCl$$

**Procedure for the Determination of Cesium.**—Dissolve the cesium silicotungstate precipitate above in a minimum quantity of 5% sodium hydroxide, acidify faintly with nitric acid and dilute to 200 ml. To the cold solution add slowly with stirring a slight excess of 10% mercurous nitrate solution. The mercurous silicotungstate flocculates and settles rapidly. Filter, wash with 1% mercurous nitrate solution and discard the precipitate. Add a little aqua regia to the filtrate and boil to oxidize the mercury. Determine the cesium in this solution by precipitation as the chloroplatinate by one of the methods described on pages 22 to 25, or above.

$$Cs_2PtCl_6 \times 0.3946 = Cs$$

$$\times 0.4999 = CsCl$$

$$Pt \times 1.3624 = Cs$$

$$\times 1.7260 = CsCl$$

## SEPARATION FROM POTASSIUM BY SODIUM BISMUTH NITRITE [68]

This method is applicable to the alkalies as chlorides or nitrates, as obtained on page 2 or under "Separations," pages 6 to 8.

The alkalies, as nitrates, are treated with sodium bismuth nitrite to precipitate rubidium and/or cesium as triple nitrites. Bismuth is removed with $H_2S$ and rubidium and cesium determined by one of the methods below.

*Reagent.* **Sodium Bismuth Nitrite.**—Dissolve 50 g. of reagent grade sodium nitrite ($NaNO_2$) in 100 ml. of distilled water, neutralize with a few drops of nitric acid if necessary, add 15 g. of reagent grade bismuth nitrate, $Bi(NO_3)_3 \cdot 5H_2O$, and stir until solution is complete. Filter the solution and store in a well stoppered bottle to prevent absorption of oxygen from the air. Use fresh solution for the method.

*Procedure.*—Convert the alkali chlorides to nitrates by evaporation to dryness with an excess of nitric acid in a 50-ml. Erlenmeyer flask. Dissolve the residue in as little distilled water as possible, add 10 ml. of sodium bismuth nitrite reagent for each 1 ml. of sample, stir thoroughly and allow to stand for 24 hours, stoppering the flask to prevent exposure to the air. Break up the precipitate with a glass rod, filter with suction through a filtering crucible. Transfer the precipitate to the crucible, using the filtrate and a rubber tipped rod for this purpose. Wash the precipitate with a 1:1 mixture of acetone and distilled water and then with pure acetone.

Dry the precipitate at 100°C. then wash it through the filter into a small Pyrex beaker with hot distilled water. A little hydrochloric acid may be used if necessary. Also dissolve any residue remaining in the precipitation flask and add it to the main solution. Evaporate to dryness with an excess of hydrochloric acid to remove nitrites and nitrates. Dissolve the residue in a little hydrochloric acid and about 50 ml. of distilled water and precipitate the bismuth with $H_2S$. Filter off the precipitate, wash and discard. Boil the filtrate to expel $H_2S$ and evaporate to dryness. Separate rubidium and cesium with silicotungstic acid and then determine each as the chloroplatinate as described above.

[68] Ball, W. C., J. Chem. Soc., **95**, 2126, 1909; **97**, 1408, 1910; Ball, W. C., and Abram, H., *ibid.*, **103**, 2110 and 2130, 1913.

## WELLS-STEVENS METHOD [69]

This method is applicable to the alkali chlorides.

The alkali chlorides are first separated into two groups by the use of chloroplatinic acid: lithium and sodium are soluble; potassium, rubidium and cesium precipitate as chloroplatinates. Platinum is removed from both groups by reduction with formic acid (page 34) and filtration. The two resulting solutions, containing the respective groups are evaporated to dryness and the organic matter destroyed. Lithium is determined as $Li_2SO_4$ by the Rammelsberg-Palkin method, page 28, sodium is weighed as NaCl or converted to $Na_2SO_4$ and weighed. Rubidium and cesium are separated from potassium by extraction with hydrochloric acid-alcohol solvent. The potassium residue may contain some rubidium which is recovered later. The dried rubidium and cesium chlorides are treated with ammonium sulfate and alcohol solution. Cesium is soluble and is determined as the sulfate. Rubidium is determined in the residues.

*Reagents.* **Ammonium Sulfate Solution.**—Dissolve 5 g. of reagent grade ammonium sulfate in 100 ml. of distilled water.

**Alcoholic Ammonium Sulfate.**—Dissolve 1 g. of ammonium sulfate in 20 ml. of distilled water and add slowly, with stirring, 100 ml. of 95% alcohol. Remove, by filtering, the excess ammonium sulfate that precipitates and to the clear filtrate add a few crystals to keep the solution saturated.

**Wash Solution.**—Prepare as above except that 0.16 g. of ammonium chloride is added to the water solution of ammonium sulfate before the addition of the alcohol.

*Procedure.*—Treat the alkali chlorides with chloroplatinic acid as described for the determination of potassium on page 22. If sodium and lithium are to be determined, the chloroplatinates in the filtrate are converted to their chlorides by reduction with formic acid as described on page 34. Lithium is determined according to the Rammelsberg-Palkin method, page 28. Sodium is weighed as NaCl in this procedure.

The potassium, rubidium and cesium chloroplatinates are converted to the chlorides by reduction with formic acid as described on page 34. Dissolve the chlorides in distilled water, transfer to a 30-ml. glass-stoppered Erlenmeyer flask, evaporate to dryness and then heat at about 106°C. for a short time. Cool, add 0.4 ml. of distilled water, warm, cool again, saturate with dry HCl gas and add 10 ml. absolute alcohol previously saturated with HCl gas. Filter with suction through a fritted-glass crucible and wash with 2 ml. of a mixture of absolute alcohol and ether. Reserve the residue for recovery of residual rubidium. Evaporate the filtrate to dryness in a weighed small porcelain dish, ignite gently but not to redness, cool in a desiccator and weigh. If the weight is not more than 0.6 mg., and potassium was known to be present, rubidium and cesium are absent. The 0.6 mg. represents the solubility of potassium chloride in a single extraction.

If the weight of chlorides is more than 0.6 mg. rubidium or cesium or both may be present. Nearly all the cesium is found in the first extract; however, if appreciable amounts are present a second extraction should be made, carrying out the filtration through the same dish as before. Determine the total weight of extracted chlorides.

[69] Wells, R. C., and Stevens, R. E., Ind. Eng. Chem., Anal. Ed., **6**, 439, 1934; **9**, 236, 1937; Hillyer, J. C., *ibid.*, **9**, 236, 1937.

**Procedure for the Determination of Cesium.**—To the dry alkali chlorides obtained above in the small porcelain dish add 0.1 ml. of the 5% ammonium sulfate solution and stir to dissolve the chlorides. Add 5 ml. of the alcoholic ammonium sulfate dropwise, with stirring, from a burette, at a rate of about one drop per second for the first milliliter. Allow the solution to stand for 0.5 hour with occasional stirring and then filter with mild suction through an asbestos pad, catching the filtrate and subsequent washings in a tared platinum crucible. Rinse the precipitate, beaker and filter thoroughly with three 0.5-ml. portions of the wash solution. Add a small quantity of ammonium sulfate to the filtrate in the crucible to convert cesium chloride to sulfate during the subsequent evaporation and ignition. Evaporate on a steam bath until salts begin to crystallize and add a few drops of alcohol.

Evaporate to dryness, add a few drops of absolute alcohol and again evaporate. Cover the crucible with a watch glass and heat gently in a radiator[4] until ammonium chloride deposits on the glass. Remove the glass, increase the heat slowly to avoid loss through spattering and, after all ammonium salts are removed, apply the full flame and finally ignite at moderate redness (about 800°C.) over a burner keeping the crucible in constant motion. Cool in a desiccator, covered with a watch glass and weigh as $Cs_2SO_4$. Repeat until a constant weight is obtained.

$$Cs_2SO_4 \times 0.7345 = Cs$$

$$\times 0.9305 = CsCl$$

The presence of cesium may be confirmed with the spectroscope by examination of a drop of a concentrated solution of the residue on a platinum loop in a Bunsen flame.

If the weight of cesium calculated to cesium chloride, plus 0.6 mg. of potassium chloride for each extraction with alcohol and hydrochloric acid, accounts for all the chlorides extracted, rubidium is absent; otherwise, rubidium is present in the residue from the alcoholic ammonium sulfate treatment as well as in the residue from the alcohol-hydrochloric acid treatment.

**Procedure for the Determination of Rubidium.**—Dissolve the precipitate, from the alcoholic ammonium sulfate treatment, in distilled water and evaporate to dryness in a tared crucible, ignite at dull red heat (about 800°C.), cool in a desiccator and weigh as rubidium and potassium sulfate. Subtract from this weight, the weight of potassium sulfate calculated from the weight of potassium chloride expected in the extraction treatment ($(0.6$ mg. $\times K_2SO_4/2KCl) \times$ number of extractions). The residual sulfate is rubidium and is calculated to RbCl.

$$Rb_2SO_4 \times 0.9058 = RbCl$$

To determine the rubidium remaining in the residue from the alcohol-hydrochloric acid extraction, repeat the extraction of this residue with alcohol and hydrochloric acid as long as any more rubidium chloride is extracted, allowing 0.6 mg. of potassium chloride for each extract. Evaporate these combined extracts nearly to dryness with a slight excess of chloroplatinic acid. Add 5 ml. of 15% alcohol and stir to dissolve the potassium chloroplatinate, filter, wash with 95% alcohol, dry at 130°C., cool and weigh as $Rb_2PtCl_6$.

$$Rb_2PtCl_6 \times 0.4177 = RbCl$$

The sum of the weights of RbCl obtained above and in the preceding paragraph represents the total weight of RbCl.

$$RbCl \times 0.7068 = Rb$$

$$\times 1.1040 = Rb_2SO_4$$

## OTHER METHODS

Krochta and Mellon [70] describe a colorimetric finish to the silicotungstate procedure.[67] Colorimetric procedures for cesium have been studied by Duval.[71] Hexanitrohydrazobenzene has been used as a reagent for the colorimetric determination of rubidium and cesium.[72]

Cesium may be determined as $Cs_2SnBr_6$,[73] by precipitation from a solution of potassium and rubidium bromide with alcoholic stannic bromide solution.

Precipitation of rubidium and cesium as the chlorostannates [74] is satisfactory in the presence of little potassium. Cesium then is separated from rubidium as cesium antimony chloride ($Cs_3Sb_2Cl_9$). Rubidium is determined by difference.

Improvements in the cesium bismuth iodide procedure are described.[75]

Cesium may be separated from rubidium by precipitation with antimony chloride-ferric chloride reagent,[76] and finally determined as the chloroplatinate. Rubidium is determined by difference. However, the cesium precipitation may be incomplete.

Montgomery [77] reports separation of cesium from potassium by precipitation of the cesium salt of hexachlorotellurous acid.

Cesium is precipitated as $Cs_2NaLa(NO_2)_6$ in the presence of potassium and rubidium. Gravimetric or volumetric determinations are applied. One part of cesium is determined without interference in the presence of 100 parts of potassium or 25 parts rubidium.[78]

Rubidium and cesium have been determined in the presence of potassium on the basis of differences in stability of their tri-iodides.[79]

70 Krochta, W. G. and Mellon, M. G., Anal. Chem., 29, 1181, 1957.
71 Duval, C. and Doan, M., Mikrochim. Acta, 3, 200, 1953.
72 Cherkesov, A. I., Uch. Zap. Saratov. Univ., 42, 85, 1955.
73 Feldman, R. V., J. Applied Chem. (U.S.S.R.), 11, 1017, 1938.
74 Strecker, W., and Diaz, F. O., Z. anal. Chem., 67, 321, 1925.
75 Plyushchev, V. E. and Korshunov, B. G., Zh. Anal. Khim. S.S.S.R., 10, 119, 1955.
76 Moser, L., and Ritschel, E., Z. anal. Chem., 70, 184, 1927.
77 Montgomery, H. A. C., Analyst, 85, 687, 1960.
78 Dutt, N. K., J. Indian Chem. Soc., 22, 71, 1945.
79 Yamatera, H., J. Chem. Soc. Japan, 72, 559, 1951.

# Chapter 2

# ALUMINUM *

**Al, *at. wt.* 26.9815; *sp. gr.* 2.70; *m.p.* 660°C.; *b.p.* 2327°C.†; *oxide* Al$_2$O$_3$**

Aluminum is a silvery-white metal widely occurring in nature, but only in combination with other elements. Oxides or silicates of aluminum are present in feldspar, granite, mica, mica schist, clay, obsidian, porphyry, slate, and zeolite. Aluminum minerals include cryolite, alunite, and the precious stones ruby, garnet, sapphire, topaz, turquoise, and tourmalin. Bauxite, an impure hydrated alumina, is the main commercial source of aluminum oxide for smelting and for chemical products of aluminum.

The alchemists knew alum as a product obtainable from alum stone, and certain preliminary observations and predictions as to the presence of an unknown metal in alumina were made by Marggraf, Lavoisier, and Davy during the period 1754 to 1807. The metal was not discovered until 1825 when Hans Christian Oersted reduced aluminum chloride with potassium amalgam. In 1886, Charles Martin Hall discovered the electrolytic process for producing aluminum from the oxide in molten cryolite. At about the same time, Paul L. T. Héroult made the same discovery in Europe. This original process, with certain improvements, is still in use.

As a result of its outstanding characteristics, aluminum finds extensive use in the building, manufacturing, and process industries, both as a material of construction and as a chemical commodity, in its various compounds. Its strong alloys are highly important in the field of transportation, for aircraft, railway, automotive, and marine equipment. Aluminum is also valuable as an electrical conductor and as a material for handling, processing, and packaging foods, pharmaceuticals, chemicals, and a variety of other products. For decorative applications, aluminum can be obtained in virtually any color by means of dyes, pigments, enamels, or other surface treatments.

## DETECTION

Emission spectroscopy offers the most sensitive, reliable, and direct method for establishing the presence of aluminum in virtually any type of material. The *raies ultimes*, 3961.5, 3944.0, 3092.7, and 3082.2 A permit the detection of less than 1 part per million with the arc and spark discharges normally used in spectrochemical analysis. Specific methods will not be given here, since the techniques

---

* Chapter contributed by J. R. Churchill, M. L. Moss, and the Analytical Chemistry Staff of Aluminum Company of America.

† Value from American Institute of Physics Handbook. Widely different values are found in the literature.

of emission spectroscopy are determined more by the material analyzed than by the element sought. Suffice it to say that almost any spectrochemical method suitable for general qualitative analysis of a given material is suitable for testing for aluminum. Sensitivity of detection is impaired somewhat by the presence of volatile or easily excited elements such as the alkali metals. For best sensitivity with the carbon or graphite arc, it is often necessary to volatilize completely the sample because of the high boiling point, low conductivity, and chemical stability of the oxide. With sparks, sensitivity of detection is generally favored by high power and by increasing the arc-like character of the discharge through added self-inductance. Further enhancement may be obtained by restricting the observation to the more favorable portions of the time cycle of the discharge.

Flame spectroscopy presently has little practical application in the detection of aluminum because of the feeble excitation produced by the oxyacetylene and oxy-hydrogen flames. Aluminum can be detected by x-ray spectroscopy and mass spectrometry, but these techniques are presently restricted to applications beyond the scope of this chapter.

Chemical tests based on characteristic reactions, although less sensitive, are satisfactory for most purposes and do not require special equipment. Numerous synthetic and natural dyes will react with solutions of aluminum salts to form colored lakes, although interference by other metals which hydrolyze to insoluble products under the same conditions is common in tests of this kind. Under controlled conditions, quantitative results may be obtained in many cases by measuring the color produced. Among the reagents used are alizarin, aluminon, carminic acid, eriochrome cyanine, hematoxylin, and quinalizarin. Additional reagents and procedures for their use have been reviewed by Welcher.[1]

*Preparation of the Sample for Detection Tests.*—Dissolve the sample by appropriate means and separate silica and the hydrogen sulfide group by the usual methods, if present. Boil out excess $H_2S$, oxidize iron with nitric acid, precipitate iron and chromium with sodium hydroxide, and filter. Neutralize the filtrate with hydrochloric acid to precipitate aluminum hydroxide and filter.

*Aluminon Test.*—Dissolve a portion of the precipitate from the filter with 5 ml. of 1 $N$ hydrochloric acid and add 1 ml. of 0.1% aluminon solution and 5 ml. of 5% ammonium acetate. A red color or red precipitate forms in the presence of aluminum, depending on the concentration. Aluminon is not a specific reagent for aluminum but is useful for confirmatory purposes provided certain lake-forming metals, such as iron, beryllium, and gallium, are absent. A quantitative procedure using aluminon is included later in this chapter.

*Hematoxylin Test.*—Dissolve a portion to precipitate in dilute hydrochloric acid, dilute to 25 ml., and adjust to pH 7.5 with 2 $N$ ammonium carbonate. Add 5 ml. of glycerol and 5 ml. of 0.1% hematoxylin solution, mix, and allow to stand for 15 minutes. At this stage, the solution will be blue or purple if aluminum is present, depending on the concentration. Add 5 ml. of 10% boric acid solution, prepared in 1 $N$ $NH_4OH$ and allow to stand for 2 minutes. A blue color indicates presence of aluminum and the intensity is proportional to the concentration.

*Cobalt Nitrate Test.*—Dissolve a portion of precipitate in a few drops of $HNO_3$. Dip an asbestos thread looped in a platinum wire into 0.05 $N$ cobalt nitrate solution, ignite, and dip into the $HNO_3$ solution containing the dissolved precipitate.

[1] Welcher, F. J., Organic Analytical Reagents, D. Van Nostrand Co., Inc., Princeton, N. J., 1948.

Repeat the ignition. A blue color on the thread indicates the presence of aluminum and the test is sensitive to about 0.02 mg.

*Fluorescence Test.*—Dissolve a portion of the precipitate in 1 ml. of 0.5 N acetic acid, dilute to 10 ml. with water, and heat in a test tube to about 80°C. Add 0.5 ml. of a 0.1% alcoholic solution of Pontachrome Blue Black R (4-sulfo-2,2′ dihydroxyazonaphthalene). Presence of aluminum is indicated by a fluorescence under ultraviolet illumination. Chromium and iron interfere and require a separation before applying the test.[2]

*Blowpipe Tests.*—Although blowpipes are nonexistent in most laboratories, they can be highly useful when skillfully used, particularly in field tests. Aluminum can be readily detected by the following test using cobalt nitrate.

**For Ammonia Precipitate.**—Moisten a small amount of the precipitate on a plaster tablet with 5% cobalt nitrate solution, avoiding an excess, and heat strongly in the oxidizing flame. A blue color indicates the presence of aluminum.

**For Ground Minerals.**—Heat slowly in the oxidizing flame on a plaster or charcoal slab, allow to cool, and add a small amount of cobalt nitrate solution. Heat intensely in the oxidizing flame. A blue color indicates aluminum.[3]

## REAGENTS, SOLUTIONS, AND INDICATORS

Because of the large number of reagents and solutions required in aluminum analyses, and their repeated use in various methods and procedures, they have been grouped together in the early part of the chapter. Moreover, to avoid confusion, they are arranged under the four sub-headings below: Reagents and General Solutions, Standard Solutions, Wash Solutions and Indicators.

### REAGENTS AND GENERAL SOLUTIONS

Chemicals used in the analytical procedures given in this chapter should be reagent grade. Concentrated acids and ammonium hydroxide are to be used unless otherwise specified. Concentrations of dilute solutions are generally in terms of the volume ratio of concentrated solution to water added or in percentage of solute by weight.

**Acid Mixtures.** *No. 1 Acid.*—Mix with 350 ml. of water, in order, 250 ml. of 1:1 $H_2SO_4$, 200 ml. of $HNO_3$, and 200 ml. of HCl.

*No. 2 Acid.*—Add 400 ml. of $HNO_3$ to 600 ml. of 2:1 $H_2SO_4$.

*No. 3 Acid.*—Mix with 425 ml. of $H_2O$, in order, 200 ml. of 1:1 $H_2SO_4$, 125 ml. of $H_3PO_4$, and 250 ml. of $HNO_3$.

*Triacid.*—Prepare a mixture of 715 ml. of 1:2 $H_2SO_4$, 215 ml. HCl, and 70 ml. $HNO_3$.

**Acetone.**

**Alkaline methanol solution.**—Dissolve 0.4 g. NaOH in 1 liter of absolute $CH_3OH$. Store in a boron-free container.

**Aluminum Wire, Foil, or Sheet of 1100 alloy grade.**

**Ammonium Acetate Solution.**—150 g. per liter.

**Ammonium Acetate Buffer Solution.**—154 g. per liter.

[2] Wiessler, Alfred; White, Charles E., Fluorometric Determination of Aluminum in Steels, Bronzes, and Minerals, Industrial and Engineering Chemistry, Anal. Ed., **18**, 530, 1946.

[3] Smith, Orsino C., Identification and Qualitative Chemical Analysis of Minerals, 2nd ed., D. Van Nostrand Co., Inc., Princeton, N. J., 1953.

**Ammonium Mercuric Thiocyanate Solution.**—Dissolve 68 g. of ammonium thiocyanate and 54 g. of mercuric chloride in 500 ml. of water, add 5 ml. of 1:1 hydrochloric acid, and allow to stand overnight. Filter and dilute to 1 liter.

**Ammonium Molybdate Solution.**—100 g. of $(NH_4)_6Mo_7O_{24} \cdot 4H_2O$ per liter.

**Ammonium Persulfate Solution.**—300 g. per 100 ml. Prepare fresh as needed.

**Ammonium Sulfide Solution.**—Saturate 1:10 ammonium hydroxide with hydrogen sulfide. Prepare fresh daily.

**Bromine Water Saturated.**

**Calcium Hydroxide Suspension.**—Calcine low-boron calcium carbonate ($CaCO_3$) in a platinum crucible at 1100°C. to the oxide, and cool in a desiccator. Transfer 3 g. of the oxide to a polyethylene bottle, add 500 ml. of water, and mix. Shake frequently when using to insure that the suspension withdrawn is uniform.

**Denatured Alcohol, Formula 30.**

**Diammonium Phosphate Solution.**—100 g. per liter.

**Dilute Sulfurous Acid.**—Saturate water with sulfur dioxide and dilute to 1:50.

**Diphenylcarbazide Solution.**—Prepare fresh by dissolving 0.5 g. in 100 ml. of denatured alcohol, Formula 30.

**Ferrous Ammonium Sulfate Solution.**—To 40 g. of $FeSO_4 \cdot (NH_4)_2SO_4 \cdot 7H_2O$, add 1 ml. of 1:3 sulfuric acid and dissolve with 100 ml. of hot water. Allow to cool before use. Prepare daily.

**Formic Acid Solution.**—1:4 dilution of 90% acid.

**Gum Arabic Solution.**—10 g. per liter. Add a few drops of ammonium hydroxide to stabilize, and filter.

**Hydrogen Peroxide 6%.**—1 volume of 30% diluted with 4 volumes of water.

**Hydrogen Peroxide 30%.**

**Hydrogen Sulfide Gas.**

**Hydroxylamine, Solution.**—10 g. of $NH_2OH \cdot HCl$ per 100 ml.

**8-Hydroxyquinoline Solution.**—5 g. of 8-hydroxyquinoline in 10 ml. of acetic acid diluted to 100 ml. with water.

**8-Hydroxyquinoline-Carbon Tetrachloride Solution.**—1 g. per 100 ml.

**Isopropyl Alcohol, 95:5.**—Dilute 95 ml. of isopropyl alcohol, $(CH_3)_2CHOH$, with 5 ml. of water.

**Oxalic Acid Solution.**—Add 5 ml. of HCl to 20 ml. of warm oxalic acid stock solution. Prepare fresh as needed and keep warm to avoid crystallization.

**Oxalic Acid Stock Solution.**—Dissolve 20 g. of $H_2C_2O_4 \cdot 2H_2O$ in water and dilute to 100 ml. Store in a low-boron glass container. If crystals form on standing, they will dissolve when the solution is warmed.

**1,10-Phenanthroline.**—Dissolve 0.250 g. in 10 ml. of denatured alcohol and dilute to 100 ml. with water.

**Phosphoric Acid ($H_3PO_4$), 90%.**

**Potassium Iodide Solution.**—300 g. per liter.

**Potassium Permanganate Solution.**—2 g. per liter.

**Potassium Permanganate Solution.**—10 g. per liter.

**Powdered Antimony.**

**Silver Nitrate Solution.**—3 g. per liter.

**Sodium Acetate Buffer Solution.**—240 g. sodium acetate trihydrate and 10 ml. acetic acid in 1000 ml. of water.

**Sodium Bicarbonate.**—Saturated solution. Approximately 10 g. per 100 ml.

**Sodium Diethyldithiocarbamate Solution.**—1 g. per liter. Filter into an amber bottle and protect from strong light.

**Sodium Dimethylglyoximate Solution.**—Dissolve 2.6 g. of sodium dimethylglyoximate octahydrate in 100 ml. of water and filter.

**Sodium Hydroxide Solution, 30%.**—Dissolve 300 g. NaOH in 100 ml. of $H_2O$.

**Sodium Hydroxide Solution (for Si determination).**—Prepare in a nickel vessel by dissolving 450 g. of sodium hydroxide in 1 liter of water. This solution must not be prepared or stored in glass.

**Standard Potassium Permanganate Solution.**—Equivalent to about 1 mg. iron per ml.

**Tartaric Acid Solution.**—250 g. per liter.

**Turmeric Extract.**—Stir 1 g. of powdered turmeric with 100 ml. of isopropyl alcohol for 2 hours and filter. Prepare at least 2 hours before use. The solution is considered stable for several days. (Curcumin, $(2\text{-}CH_3OC_6H_3\text{-}1\text{-}OH\text{-}4\text{-}CH\text{:}CHCO)_2CH_2$, has been recommended in place of turmeric extract.)

**Zinc Uranyl Acetate Solution.**—To 100 g. of uranyl acetate, $UO_2(C_2H_3O_2)_2 \cdot 2H_2O$, add 25 ml. of acetic acid and 500 ml. of water. Warm to 95°C. and stir to dissolve. Weigh 300 g. of crystallized zinc acetate, $Zn(C_2H_3O_2)_2 \cdot 3H_2O$, into a 500-ml. beaker. Add 8.0 ml. of glacial acetic acid, 325 ml. of water, warm to 70°C., and stir until solution is complete. Mix the two solutions while still warm, and allow to stand for 24 hours. Usually, sodium zinc uranyl acetate will be formed by traces of sodium in the reagents. If no precipitate is formed, add a few milligrams of sodium chloride to saturate the precipitant with the triple salt. Filter portions of the reagent as needed.

## STANDARD SOLUTIONS

**Bismuth Sulfate Solution.**—Equivalent to 0.1 mg. bismuth per ml. Dissolve 0.100 g. of bismuth metal in nitric acid. Add 50 ml. of 1:1 sulfuric acid and evaporate to sulfur trioxide fumes. Cool and dilute to exactly 1 liter.

**Boron Stock Solution.**—1 ml. = 0.05 mg. B. Dissolve 0.1430 g. of boric acid $(H_3BO_3)$ in water and dilute to 500.0 ml. Store in a polyethylene bottle.

**Boron Standard Dilute Solution.**—1 ml. = 1 microgram B. Dilute 10 ml. of the boron stock solution to 500 ml. Store in a polyethylene bottle.

**Chromic Sulfate Solution.**—Equivalent to 0.01 mg. chromium per ml. Weigh 74.7 mg. of potassium chromate into a 2-liter volumetric flask, dissolve in water, add 10 ml. of 1:1 sulfuric acid, and 0.5% hydrogen peroxide drop by drop to reduce the chromium. Destroy the excess peroxide by adding potassium permanganate (10 g. per liter) to a faint pink color. Dilute to 2 liters. This procedure gives a chromic sulfate solution comparable to filtrate obtained after titrating iron.

**Copper Sulfate Solution.**—Equivalent to about 2 mg. copper per ml. Dissolve about 8 g. of copper sulfate pentahydrate in distilled water, add 10 ml. of 1:3 $H_2SO_4$ and dilute to 1 liter. Determine the copper value per milliliter by electrolyzing two separate 50-ml. aliquots.

**Copper Sulfate Solution.**—Equivalent to about 0.05 mg. copper per ml. Pipette 25 ml. of the standard copper solution as prepared above into a 1-liter volumetric flask, add 10 ml. of 1:3 sulfuric acid, and dilute to the mark.

**Ferrous Ammonium Sulfate Solution.**—Equivalent to about 1.24 mg. chromium per milliliter. Transfer 2.80 g. of ferrous ammonium sulfate hexahydrate to a 100-ml. volumetric flask, add 5 ml. of 1:3 sulfuric acid, dissolve with water and dilute to the mark. Determine the permanganate equivalent as follows: Dilute a measured aliquot to about 100 ml., adding 10 ml. of 1:1 sulfuric acid, and titrate with standard potassium permanganate equivalent to about 4 mg. iron per ml.

**Hydrochloric Acid, 0.2 N.**—Standardized against aluminum.

**Ferric Sulfate Solution.**—Equivalent to 0.1 mg. iron per ml. Dissolve 0.0250 g. of pure iron wire or 0.1755 g. $FeSO_4(NH_4)_2SO_4 \cdot 6H_2O$ in 25 ml. of 1:10 sulfuric acid, oxidize with potassium permanganate and dilute to exactly 250 ml.

**Nickel Sulfate Solution.**—Equivalent to 0.025 mg. nickel per ml. Dissolve 0.1683 g. of $NiSO_4(NH_4)_2SO_4 \cdot 6H_2O$ in water containing 10 ml. of hydrochloric acid and dilute to 1 liter.

**Potassium Fluoride Solution.**—Add 40 g. of KF to 300 ml. water, adjust pH to 10 with KOH solution, and add excess KOH solution until further addition does not change pH more than equivalent of 1 drop 0.2 N HCl.

**Potassium Iodate Solution.**—Equivalent to about 2 mg. tin per ml. Dissolve 1.20 g. of potassium iodate, 20 g. of potassium iodide, and 0.25 g. of potassium hydroxide in water and dilute to 1 liter. Standardize against the standard tin solution.

**Potassium Permanganate Solution.**—Equivalent to about 1 mg. iron per ml. Dissolve 0.58 g. of potassium permanganate per liter of solution. Store in a dark-colored, glass-stoppered bottle. Allow to stand for 2 weeks in the dark. Standardize as follows: accurately weigh about 50 mg. of sodium oxalate that has been previously dried for 1 hour at 105°C. Dissolve in a 400-ml. beaker in 100 ml. of 5:95 sulfuric acid that has been boiled for 15 minutes and then cooled to 27° ± 3°C. Add 36 to 37 ml. of the standard potassium permanganate solution from a burette at a rate of 25 to 30 ml. per minute while stirring slowly. Let stand until the pink color disappears (about 45 seconds). Heat to 55–60°C. and complete the titration by adding permanganate until a faint pink color persists for 30 seconds. Add the last 0.5 to 1 ml. drop by drop, with particular care to allow each drop to become decolorized before the next is introduced. Deduct the blank required to impart a pink color to the same amount of water and acid.

**Potassium Permanganate Solution.**—Equivalent to about 4 mg. iron or 1.24 mg. chromium per ml. Prepare and standardize as above, but quadruple the quantities of permanganate and oxalate.

**Sodium Silicate Solution.**—Equivalent to about 0.04 mg. silicon per ml. To prepare a stock solution, dissolve 0.6 g. of silicic acid with water and a few pellets of sodium hydroxide, warm, dilute to 500 ml., and filter into a plastic bottle. To standardize, dehydrate a suitable aliquot with sulfuric acid, ignite, and weigh the residue. Volatilize with hydrofluoric and sulfuric acids, ignite, and reweigh.

**Sodium Thiosulfate Solutions.**—Equivalent to about 1 mg. and 4 mg. copper per ml. Dissolve, respectively, 4 g. and 16 g. sodium thiosulfate pentahydrate in water containing 1 g. of sodium bicarbonate. Dilute each solution to 1 liter. Store in dark bottles. To standardize, transfer a measured quantity of standard copper sulfate solution into a 250-ml. Erlenmeyer flask, add 3 ml. of acetic acid and 5 ml. of potassium iodide solution. After mixing and allowing the solution to stand a few minutes, titrate with the sodium thiosulfate, adding a few drops of starch solution near the end of the titration. Calculate the equivalency in grams of copper per ml. of thiosulfate solution.

**Stannous Chloride Solution.**—Dissolve 50 mg. of National Bureau of Standards Sample No. 42 (melting point standard for tin) by warming gently with a small amount of hydrochloric acid. Add 100 ml. of water and 50 ml. of hydrochloric acid. Reduce the tin and titrate according to the procedure for tin in aluminum.

**Titanium Sulfate Solution.**—Equivalent to about 0.6 mg. titanium or 1 mg. titanium dioxide per ml. Weigh 4.44 g. of reagent grade titanium potassium oxalate, $K_2TiO(C_2O_4)_2 \cdot 2H_2O$, into a 500-ml. Kjeldahl flask. Add 4 g. of ammonium sulfate and 50 ml. of sulfuric acid. Heat carefully until foaming subsides and then boil 10 min. to decompose the oxalate. Cool and pour carefully into 500 ml. of water. To insure absence of oxalate add potassium permanganate solution until a permanent pink color is obtained. Dilute to 1 liter.

## WASH SOLUTIONS

**Hydrogen Sulfide Acid Wash Solution.**—1:100 sulfuric acid cooled and saturated with hydrogen sulfide.

**Ammonium Acetate Wash Solution.**—Make 50 ml. of the ammonium acetate reagent solution distinctly acid to methyl red with acetic acid and dilute to 1 liter.

**Ammonium Chloride Wash Solutions.**—Dilute 30 ml. of hydrochloric acid to 1 liter and neutralize with ammonium hydroxide, using methyl red indicator for alumina wash solution and rosolic acid for beryllium wash solution.

**Ammonium Mercuric Thiocyanate Wash Solution.**—Dilute 10 ml. of the ammonium mercuric thiocyanate reagent solution to 1 liter.

**Ammonium Sulfide Wash Solution.**—Neutralize to methyl red 10 ml. of 1:1 sulfuric acid with ammonium hydroxide, dilute to 1 liter, saturate with hydrogen sulfide, and add 1 ml. of ammonium hydroxide in excess. Prepare fresh as required.

**Formic Acid Wash Solution.**—Dilute 25 ml. of 1:4 formic acid to 1 liter and saturate with hydrogen sulfide.

**Sodium Carbonate Wash Solution.**—5 g. per liter.

## INDICATORS

**Barium Diphenylaminesulfonate Indicator.**—Dissolve 0.5 g. of reagent in 100 ml. of water and filter.

**Congo Red Paper.**

**Methyl Orange.**—1 g. per liter of water.

**Methyl Red.**—Dissolve 1 g. with a minimum amount of ammonium hydroxide and dilute to 1 liter with water.

**Phenolphthalein.**—Dissolve 0.1 g. in 75 ml. of denatured alcohol (Formula 30), and dilute to 100 ml. with water.

**Starch Indicator (1%).**—Make a paste of 1 g. of soluble starch in about 5 ml. of water, add 100 ml. of hot water, boil for about 3 minutes, and cool before using. Prepare fresh as required.

**Starch-Potassium Iodide Solution.**—Dissolve 1 g. of potassium iodide in 5 ml. of 1% starch solution. Prepare fresh as needed.

## ESTIMATION

### PREPARATION OF SAMPLE

The sampling procedure for aluminum should take into account the chemical, metallurgical, and commercial aspects of the metal and its alloys. The best obtainable sample is one taken from the metal in the molten state. The melt should be thoroughly mixed, if possible, and a portion taken which may be cast in a metal mold in the form of a circular disk, 2½ inches in diameter and ¼–⁵⁄₁₆ inch thick. This procedure reduces the possibility of segregation. Segregation is frequently encountered in certain die-casting alloys, strong alloys, and rich alloys. For analysis of metal by other than the producer, the sample must usually be taken from plate, sheet, extruded shapes, pipe or tubing, castings or forgings. In these cases, random samples are usually satisfactory, since the analysis is ordinarily made for identification of alloy or for compliance with specifications. In the case of castings, adequate chill minimizes segregational difficulties.

The representative, clean, uncontaminated sample is milled, drilled, or turned—not chiseled or sawed. Drillings through the disks are made with a ½-inch drill unlubricated, using special care to avoid the sprue area. Small uniform cuttings are desirable because they can be more readily mixed and dissolved.

The weight of the sample actually taken for analysis is a compromise between the large weight desirable from a sampling standpoint and the small weight usually convenient to handle. The sample weights suggested in these methods are sufficiently large to be representative, and not too bulky to be handled chemically.

## DECOMPOSITION REAGENTS

Aluminum and aluminum alloy samples are dissolved in various media. In general, these may be classed either as alkaline or acidic. When no separations are to be made, as in the case of determining manganese, the choice of decomposition reagent is based upon the ultimate environment in which the element is to be measured. When separations are to be made, and if the element being sought is insoluble in sodium hydroxide solution, the use of sodium hydroxide has the advantage of effecting immediate separation of the desired element from the large bulk of aluminum necessarily present. However, if the desired element is wholly or partially soluble in sodium hydroxide solution, the use of acid methods of decomposition is indicated, thus avoiding the presence of comparatively large amounts of sodium salts in the final solution. The determination of silicon presents a special case where the use of alkaline decomposition is desirable because, especially in the presence of hydrogen peroxide, the silicon is completely oxidized to silicate. When acid decomposition is used, the oxidation of silicon may be incomplete and some silicon may be lost as silicon hydride.

Another factor to be considered in the choice of a decomposition reagent is that, frequently, more than one element is to be determined in a single weighed portion of the sample. If the elements sought are insoluble in sodium hydroxide solution, that reagent is used because the subsequent separation of such insoluble elements from one another is usually greatly simplified by the prior separation of aluminum during dissolution. Acid methods of solution are most commonly used in aluminum analysis when single elements are being determined, and when the presence of aluminum is not objectionable in the final solution in which measurement of the desired constituent takes place. Acid solution of the sample is also used in cases in which the desired element is precipitable or separable from solutions containing aluminum salts.

## DISSOLUTION OF ALUMINUM

Hydrochloric acid, concentrated or moderately dilute, dissolves aluminum readily. The same is true of hydrofluoric and other binary halogen acids. Strong sulfuric acid, about 2:1, initially attacks aluminum, but the reaction quickly becomes sluggish. Weak sulfuric acid has little action, but the addition of a small amount of mercury salt is effective in promoting attack. Metallic mercury amalgamates with aluminum and thus permits the acid to be brought into contact with a very reactive form of the metal. Moderately strong nitric acid has slow action on the commercial metal, and more rapid action on the alloys, but the addition of a small amount of mercury salt causes solution to take place readily. The action of most other inorganic acids is slight unless mercury salts are added. Organic acids are, in general, not used as solvents of aluminum for analytical purposes because of their slow action. It is usual in dissolving the metal in acid to make use of mixed acids, such as the hydrochloric-nitric-sulfuric acid solution, which has been a standard reagent in the industry almost since its inception.

Bromine reacts with aluminum, but the reaction is difficult to control in aqueous solutions. The reaction with iodine is more conveniently controlled. Aluminum chloride is readily formed when the metal is heated in the presence of dry, oxygen-free chlorine or hydrogen chloride, subliming at a fairly low temperature. A method of attack based upon this reaction is used for the determination of certain nonmetallic constituents such as oxide.

Solutions of alkali hydroxides dissolve aluminum readily, accompanied by evolution of hydrogen and the formation of aluminate ions. The action of carbonate solutions is slow, and bicarbonates, for analytical purposes, do not react. The action of ammonium hydroxide is only superficial.

High-purity aluminum is resistant to attack by hydrochloric acid but dissolves readily in aqua regia or in sodium hydroxide.

## SEPARATIONS

In numerous cases, it is possible to determine a substance in the presence of aluminum, and these usually involve titrimetric or colorimetric procedures. With certain other methods, it is necessary to effect a separation of aluminum and the desired substance. It is rarely possible to make such separations by precipitation of the aluminum, because the large quantity of aluminum is difficult to handle and other ions are readily coprecipitated. This latter effect is especially serious because of the bulky, gelatinous nature of aluminum hydroxide. Even the various techniques for precipitation of aluminum hydroxide by slow hydrolysis or precipitation of such compounds as the basic acetate are not satisfactory when the quantity of aluminum greatly exceeds that of the element sought. A procedure frequently used takes advantage of the fact that aluminum chloride is almost completely insoluble in strong hydrochloric acid solution. Details for performing this separation are given in the procedure for determining beryllium in aluminum.

The precipitation of minor constituents from aluminum-containing solutions is usually made under one of the following conditions: (1) Acid solution of pH less than about 2.5, in which aluminum is soluble; (2) neutral solution with aluminum held soluble with tartrate, citrate, or other masking reagents; and (3) alkaline solution of pH greater than about 12 in which aluminum is soluble as aluminate. The first medium is used for precipitation of the members of the acid sulfide group, the second, for precipitation of the basic sulfide metals, and the latter for magnesium hydroxide.

Selective oxidation can be used for separation of elements such as copper, mercury, and tungsten in acid medium. A sample of the metal is treated with the minimum amount of cool, dilute hydrochloric acid necessary to dissolve the aluminum. In this case, metals with lower solution potentials will not dissolve. The method is most effective in preventing solution of metals in the extreme lower part of the electromotive series.

In separations based on treatment of the sample with alkali, aluminum dissolves, leaving other metals in the insoluble residue. Most, but often not all, of the zinc dissolves; titanium, manganese, cadmium, and iron either dissolve to a slight extent or are so finely divided that their removal by filtration is incomplete. Copper is not attacked by alkali but may be oxidized to copper hydroxide by atmospheric oxygen.

Sodium hydroxide may be used to precipitate iron, cobalt, chromium, titanium, and zirconium from aluminum which remains in solution, along with phosphate, silicate, gallium, zinc, vanadium, and tungsten. Partial precipitation of aluminum occurs if magnesium or nickel are present. If silicate interferes in subsequent operations, a separation should be made in resistant ware such as platinum. A mercury cathode separation is usually to be preferred.[4]

Extraction separations involving aluminum offer attractive possibilities, although they have not been employed in analysis of aluminum products to any great extent. Among the reagents that have been studied, 8-hydroxyquinaldine in chloroform is one of the most promising for separating various metal ions from aluminum.[5] Following this extraction to remove elements that would interfere with the subsequent determination of aluminum, a final extraction with 8-hydroxyquinoline in chloroform is performed and the aluminum complex measured colorimetrically. The theory of extraction of aluminum with 8-hydroxyquinoline has been studied in considerable detail.[6]

With acetylacetone in chloroform, aluminum can be extracted from aqueous solution at pH 4 to 6. This transfer is more than 90% complete, and higher recoveries can, of course, be achieved by several successive extractions. This and other separations based on solvent extraction are to be found in the current literature and in the recent book of Morrison and Freiser.[7] A new extraction method for separating aluminum using certain perfluorocarboxylic acids has been proposed recently by Whetsel and Mills.[8] This method has not been completely evaluated but shows promise as a replacement for the Gooch method of precipitation using HCl.

## DIRECT DETERMINATION OF ALUMINUM

Of all the common elements, aluminum is probably the most difficult to determine accurately because of interference by other elements normally accompanying it and because of incomplete separations used prior to measuring the aluminum. Gravimetric methods following separation by precipitation with ammonia, 8-hydroxyquinoline, phosphate, and various organic acids in alkaline medium are used —precipitation with ammonia being the most common. This requires careful control of conditions in order to achieve complete precipitation and an excess of ammonia must be avoided because freshly precipitated alumina is partially soluble in ammonia. Precipitation of other metal ions along with aluminum is a common source of error requiring correction or separation at appreciable concentrations such as are encountered in some mineral samples. Silicon, chromium, beryllium,

[4] Werz, W., and Neuberger, A., Arch. Eisenhüttenw., **26**, 205, 1955.
[5] Hynek, R. J., and Wrangell, L. J., Anal. Chem., **28**, 1520, 1956.
[6] Kambara, T., and Hashitani, H., Anal. Chem., **31**, 567, 1959.
[7] Morrison, G. H., and Freiser, H., Solvent Extraction in Analytical Chemistry, John Wiley and Sons, New York, 1957.
[8] Mills, G. F., and Whetsel, H. B., U. S. Patent 2,874,176, February 17, 1959.

iron, titanium, zirconium, and a number of the less common elements may be encountered in the ammonia precipitate. The alkaline earths precipitate in the presence of phosphate, arsenate, carbonate, or fluoride. Removal of these interferences is necessary in securing correct results for aluminum.

The determination of aluminum is usually indirect, although this term is frequently used in bauxite analysis to distinguish the calculation of alumina by difference from 100%, in contrast to calculating alumina by difference from the weight of the $R_2O_3$ residue and making the usual corrections for iron, phosphate, and titanium.

Titrimetric methods for aluminum are based on reaction of aluminum or aluminate salts with standard alkali or standard acid with or without addition of potassium fluoride. Fluoride methods are used when it is desired to titrate acidimetrically the hydroxide or hydrogen ion equivalent to the aluminum when interfering constituents are present and aluminum can be precipitated as an insoluble cryolite-type compound. An indirect titrimetric method used for aluminum is based on precipitation of aluminum with 8-hydroxyquinoline, followed by dissolving the precipitate, and titration with standard bromate solution.

## RAPID TITRIMETRIC METHOD

A method modified by M. B. Jacobs [9] from those of Viebock and Brecher [10] and of Snyder [11] is used widely for organic materials (after ashing). It is based upon the solution of the aluminum-containing ash in acid, the buffering of the mixture with a tartrate buffer, the neutralization of the test mixture with barium hydroxide sequestration of aluminum by the use of potassium fluoride with consequent liberation of three moles of alkali hydroxide for every mole of aluminum,

$$Al^{+3} + 3OH^- \rightarrow Al(OH)_3$$

$$Al(OH)_3 + 6KF \rightarrow AlF_3 \cdot 3KF + 3KOH$$

and finally estimation of the liberated alkali acidimetrically.

*Procedure.*—Prepare an acid solution of the ash as follows: The food or other organic material is ashed in the dry way and the silica dehydrated as usual. If no heavy metals are present, the residue is now taken up in 5 ml. of hydrochloric acid and 50 ml. of water, filtered and washed. The filtrate and washings are made up to about 200 ml. Take an appropriate aliquot. Add 3 drops of phenolphthalein indicator and 20 ml. of 30% potassium sodium tartrate solution. Mix gently and neutralize with saturated barium hydroxide solution to a definite pink end point. Add 20 ml. of 30% potassium fluoride solution and mix. Allow the test solution to stand 15 minutes. Titrate with standardized 0.03 $N$ hydrochloric acid until the pink coloration is discharged and remains discharged for 30 seconds.

## AMMONIA METHOD

The sample is dissolved by appropriate means and separations are made as required. Ammonium hydroxide is added to precipitate hydrated aluminum oxide which is filtered, ignited, and weighed. The ignited precipitate is commonly referred to as $R_2O_3$ if oxides other than $Al_2O_3$ are also present. These are determined separately and deducted. The ammonia method is applicable to samples containing 1 to 200 mg. of $R_2O_3$.

[9] Jacobs, J. Am. Pharm. Assoc., Sci. Section, **39**, 523, 1950.
[10] Viebock and Brecher, Arch. Pharm., **270**, 114, 1932.
[11] Snyder, Ind. Eng. Chem., Anal. Ed., **17**, 37, 1945.

***Preliminary Treatment.***—If organic matter is present, destroy by wet oxidation or by ignition of 600°C. in a furnace. Cool and dissolve the ash. If organic matter is absent, preliminary treatment, e.g., addition of acid, fusion, etc., if required, will depend on the nature of the sample.

***Separations.***—If silica is present, add sulfuric acid, evaporate to fumes, cool, dilute, boil, and filter. Ignite the insoluble residue, volatilize the silica with hydrofluoric acid, fuse the residue with potassium pyrosulfate, dissolve, and add to the filtrate.

If fluoride is present, add sulfuric acid and evaporate to dryness.

Heavy metals and certain other elements may be separated by electrolysis with a mercury cathode. Several instruments for carrying out mercury cathode separations using recommended procedures are available commercially. Most of these instruments provide for stirring and cooling in order to permit rapid separations at relatively high current densities. In a Melaven cell without stirring or cooling, ordinary separations require electrolysis for 2 to 4 hours at 1 ampere. Sulfuric acid 0.1 to 0.2 $N$ is the most generally satisfactory electrolyte.

***Procedure.***—Adjust the volume to about 200 ml., add 10 ml. of HCl, and heat just to boiling. Neutralize to methyl red with $NH_4OH$ added dropwise with stirring. Add dilute HCl dropwise to return the pink color and finally add $NH_4OH$ just sufficient to obtain the bright yellow indicator color. Remove from the source of heat, allow the precipitate to settle, filter hot on a medium paper, and wash with hot $NII_4Cl$ wash solution.

Return the paper and precipitate to the beaker, add 10 ml. of hydrochloric acid plus water, and heat to dissolve the precipitate. Dilute to 100 ml. with hot water, heat just to boiling, and reprecipitate as before. Filter, police the beaker, and wash well with hot ammonium chloride wash solution.

Weigh a porcelain crucible and cover, dry the paper and precipitate in the crucible, and ignite at 1100°C. for 1 hour. Cover the crucible, cool in a desiccator, and weigh. Deduct a determined blank to obtain g. $R_2O_3$.

$$\text{g. Al} = \text{g. Al}_2O_3 \times 0.5292$$

If the $R_2O_3$ contains impurities such as $Fe_2O_3$, $TiO_2$, $P_2O_5$, $Cr_2O_3$, $V_2O_5$, or $ZrO_2$, determine separately and deduct from the $R_2O_3$ weight.[12]

## POTENTIOMETRIC TITRATION

***Procedure.***—Transfer a portion of solution containing 0.005 to 0.1 g. $Al_2O_3$ to a 600-ml. beaker. Dilute to 200 ml. and adjust the pH to 12 with 25% NaOH using a glass electrode pH meter. Add 1:1 HCl dropwise until the pH is reduced to 11. Wash down the electrodes and beaker with water and dilute to 300–350 ml. Adjust the pH to 10.0 with 0.2 $N$ HCl. (If too much acid is added, repeat the procedure starting at pH 12.) Add 40 ml. of 30% KF solution and titrate to pH 10.0 with 0.2 $N$ HCl.

NOTES.—Separation of silica if present in amounts comparable to the alumina is recommended, although interference can be minimized by reducing the amount of sample used.

If calcium is present, add 10–15 ml. of 10% $K_2C_2O_4 \cdot H_2O$ solution before adjusting to pH 12.

[12] For a detailed discussion of the ammonia method see Hillebrand, Lundell, Bright, and Hoffman, Applied Inorganic Analysis, p. 500, John Wiley and Sons, Inc., New York, 1953.

## 8-HYDROXYQUINOLINE METHOD

The following gravimetric method is applicable to samples containing 0.2 to 50 mg. of aluminum. Preliminary treatment depends on the nature of the sample. Metals and minerals are usually dissolved by acid treatment or fusion. Organic materials and solutions generally require ashing at 500°C. Separation of silica, if present, is done by acid dehydration followed by volatilization with hydrofluoric acid. Iron and other heavy metals may be separated by means of cupferron or mercury cathode electrolysis prior to determining aluminum.

*Procedure.*—Acidify the sample solution (75 to 150 ml.) with 1:3 $H_2SO_4$, adding 4 drops in excess. Add sufficient 8-hydroxyquinoline solution (5% in 10% acetic acid) to precipitate the aluminum and heat to 80°C. Add 30% ammonium acetate solution dropwise until a precipitate forms and 15 ml. in excess. Cool and adjust the pH to 5.7 with $NH_4OH$. Allow to stand, preferably overnight.

Filter through a weighed, medium fritted-glass crucible and wash with 1:100 $NH_4OH$. Dry at 135°C. for 2 hours, cool in a desiccator, and weigh.

$$\text{g. Al} = \text{g. Al}(C_9H_6NO)_3 \times 0.0587$$

## ALUMINON METHOD

*Preliminary Treatment.*—Preparation of the sample will, of necessity, depend on the nature of the material to be analyzed. Solutions or water samples are first evaporated to dryness with sulfuric and nitric acids. The residue is then dissolved in boiling water with a little sulfuric acid, filtered to remove any insoluble material and, if necessary to remove heavy metals, electrolyzed in a mercury cathode cell. Oxides or other insoluble materials may be dissolved by acid treatment or fusion methods. Samples containing organic matter are usually first ashed at 500°C.

*Separations.*—Silica, if present, is removed by the usual dehydration and volatilization procedure, the residue being fused and combined with the sample. For example, for an ashed sample add 20 ml. of water and 5 ml. of 1:3 $H_2SO_4$. Evaporate just to fumes. Cool, add 30 ml. of $H_2O$, boil, and filter. Ignite the filter paper and contents in a platinum crucible at 500°C. Cool, add a few drops of 1:3 $H_2SO_4$ and several ml. of HF, evaporate to dryness, and ignite at 500°C. Fuse the residue with about 1 g. of a molecular mixture of sodium and potassium carbonates. Dissolve the melt in the original filtrate.

Iron must be separated since it gives a red lake with aluminon. To separate, electrolyze on a mercury cathode cell, or make a cupferron-chloroform extraction.

In the absence of complexing agents such as fluoride, tartrate, acetate, etc., aluminum can be separated from alkaline earths and magnesium by precipitation with ammonium hydroxide, or as aluminum phosphate. For the phosphate separation, the following is suggested: Add 1 ml. of iron solution and 1 ml. of $H_3PO_4$, and neutralize with 1:1 $NH_4OH$ to pH 4.2. Transfer to a centrifuge tube and centrifuge at 1800 r.p.m. for 5 minutes. Decant the supernatant liquid, and add 1 ml. of 1:3 $H_2SO_4$ and 25 ml. of hot water to the tube to dissolve the precipitate.

Chloride, if present, may be volatilized by acidifying with a few ml. of 1:3 $H_2SO_4$ and evaporating to fumes.

*Procedure.*—Acidify the sample solution to litmus with 1:3 $H_2SO_4$. Transfer a portion containing 0.01 to 0.3 mg. aluminum to a 100-ml. volumetric flask, dilute to the mark, and mix.

Carry a sample blank through the entire procedure.

For the standard, pipette into a 100-ml. volumetric flask a measured quantity of standard aluminum solution that approximates the aluminum expected in the sample, dilute to the mark, and mix.

Pipette 20 ml. each of the sample, sample blank, and standard into separate 125-ml. Erlenmeyer flasks. Also, carry a standard blank of 20 ml. of water. To each add 25 ml. of combined reagent. Heat in a boiling water bath for 10 minutes. Cool in running water, swirling the flasks to bring condensate into solution.

Measure or compare the colors in the usual way using a wavelength of 525 m$\mu$ for photometric measurement.

## EUDIOMETER METHOD

The sample reacts with sodium hydroxide to evolve hydrogen gas, the volume of which is proportional to metallic aluminum content. Corrections are provided for zinc and silicon. This method is used principally for assaying aluminum powder and is based on Joint Army-Navy Specification—Aluminum Powder, Flaked, Grained and Atomized, JAN-A-289.

$$2Al + 2NaOH + 2H_2O \rightarrow 2NaAlO_2 + 3H_2$$

$$Zn + 2NaOH \rightarrow Na_2ZnO_2 + H_2$$

$$Si + 2NaOH + H_2O \rightarrow Na_2SiO_3 + 2H_2$$

*Apparatus.* **Eudiometer Apparatus.**—The parts of this apparatus are as follows (see Fig. 2-1):

*A. Leveling bottle,* 500-ml. capacity.

*B. Water jacket* surrounding the gas burette—a glass tube of at least 7-cm diameter, 73-cm length, with a 2-hole rubber stopper at both ends provides openings for the gas burette and for circulation of water.

*C. Gas burette,* consisting from top to bottom of a 35/25 socket joint, a glass cylinder of about 450-ml. volume, a 50-ml. burette, and a 12/5 socket joint.

*D. Glass adapter,* 90°, 35/25 ball joint at each end, length of each arm about 8 cm.

*E. Reaction flask,* 500-ml. capacity, single neck with 35/25 socket joint, Pyrex, round bottom or flat bottom.

*F. Magnetic stirrer,* laboratory type.

*G. Pump,* circulating, laboratory type.

*H. Water bath,* glass beaker, 2000-ml. capacity.

*I. Water reservoir,* glass, 5-gal. capacity.

**Auxiliary equipment** required for this eudiometer apparatus:

*Rubber hose* (sufficient to circulate water as indicated by dotted arrow line in sketch).

*Magnetic stirring bar,* ¾- to 1⅛-in. length, Teflon covered.

*Thermometers,* 0 to 100°C. range, 1°C. graduations, one each for water jacket and water reservoir and one of short length for the reaction flask.

*Clamps* for ball and socket joints.

*Clamp* for hose between leveling bottle and gas burette.

*Magnet.*

*Barometer.*

*Masking tape,* 1-in. width.

*Vacuum grease,* for ground joints.

**Calibration and Assembly of Apparatus.**—Make a grease pencil mark or other suitable calibration mark near the top of the gas burette and determine the volume (about 500 ml.) between this mark and the lowest marking on the 50-ml. burette. This may be done by filling with a known volume of water or by filling and withdrawing a measured volume of water.

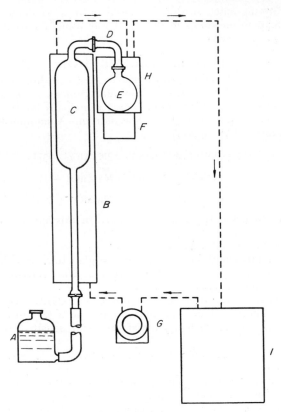

Fig. 2-1. Eudiometer Apparatus.

Assemble the apparatus as shown in Fig. 2-1, inserting a thermometer inside the water jacket and another in the water reservoir. Fill the water reservoir, start the pump, and add additional water. With the pump running and the water jacket and the water bath full, the reservoir should contain about 4 gallons of water. Fill the leveling bottle with 0.1% sulfuric acid containing several drops of methyl red indicator, raise the leveling bottle to fill the gas burette to the calibration mark, and clamp the hose between the leveling bottle and the gas burette.

*Procedure.*—Fold a 7-cm close-textured filter paper into quarters, and add 0.335 to 0.345 g. of sample in the center of the folds. Place a magnetic stirring bar upright in the center of the paper and fold the paper around the bar. Wrap one turn of 1-in. masking tape around the paper to secure the sample and the stirring bar in the paper. Insert the paper in the horizontal arm of the adapter with the closed end of the paper toward the flask and clamp the adapter to the gas burette.

Add 100 ml. of sodium hydroxide solution to the reaction flask, insert a thermometer in the flask, and clamp the flask to the adapter. Place the water bath around the flask, move the magnetic stirrer into position under the water bath, and start the pump.

When the thermometers in the water jacket, water reservoir, and reaction flask come to temperature equilibrium, release the leveling bottle hose clamp and lower the leveling bottle so the water level in the burette is about 3 cm above that in the leveling bottle. Observe the burette water level. If the level changes indicating a leak, it will be necessary to reseal the ground joint connections; if no leaks are indicated, record the equilibrium temperature.

Place a magnet over the horizontal arm of the adapter and draw the sample into the reaction flask. As the reaction proceeds, generating gas, lower the leveling bulb to maintain a negative pressure in the gas burette. When the reaction subsides, start the magnetic stirrer and continue stirring until the reaction is completed.

When temperature equilibrium is again established within $\pm 1°C$. of the initial equilibrium temperature, adjust the position of the leveling bottle so the liquid levels in the leveling bottle and in the gas burette are the same. Record the final temperature $(T)$ and the volume of hydrogen gas evolved.

**Calculation.—**

$$\% \text{ Metallic Al} = \frac{V(P_1 - P_2)(0.0288)}{(273 + T)(W)} - (\% \text{ Zn})(0.275) - (\% \text{ Si})(1.281)$$

where $V$ = volume of gas in burette, in ml.,

$P_1$ = barometric pressure, in mm. Hg,

$P_2$ = vapor pressure of water at equilibrium temperature $T$, in mm. Hg,

$T$ = equilibrium temperature, in deg. C.,

$W$ = weight of sample, in g.,

$\%$ Zn = zinc concentration, and

$\%$ Si = silicon concentration.

## OTHER METHODS

Numerous compleximetric methods using ethylenediaminetetraacetic acid (ethylenedinitrilotetraacetic acid) have been proposed for aluminum, as well as for most of the other metallic elements. These generally involve back titrations of excess EDTA with zinc, copper, or iron. Schwarzenbach's method uses Eriochrome Black T indicator with a zinc titrant.[13] Wänninen and Ringbom reviewed previous methods for titrating aluminum and recommended back titration of excess EDTA with zinc using dithizone indicator.[14] Their method is carried out in 40–50% alcohol with pH controlled at 4.0–4.5. These procedures, although not used extensively in the aluminum industry, appear to be highly promising in miscellaneous applications incidental to the use of aluminum.

An isotope dilution technique employing the long-lived $Al^{26}$, first discovered in 1954, was suggested by Rightmire et al.[15] Apparently no detailed procedure based on this principle has been reported.

[13] Schwarzenbach, G., Compleximetric Titrations, translation by H. Irving, Inter-Science Publishers, Inc., New York, 1957.

[14] Wänninen, E., and Ringbom, A., Anal. Chim. Acta, **12**, 308, 1955.

[15] Rightmire, Robert A., Kolman, T. P., Allen, A. J., Production of Carrier-Free Aluminum$^{26}$ and Sodium$^{22}$, Int. J. of Applied Radiation and Isotopes, **2**, 274–279, (Numbers 3/4), 1957.

## DETERMINATIONS IN SPECIFIC SUBSTANCES

The number of aluminum-containing materials is continually increasing, accompanied by a corresponding increase in the number of procedures required for their analysis and control. Only a few of the commercial aluminum-containing products can be covered in this chapter, although most of the procedures selected will be applicable in a variety of situations inasmuch as the analytical problems are similar for most materials once the samples are dissolved. Those elements which interfere require separation or other treatment whether the solution is prepared by dissolving a metal, mineral, or chemical product. Procedures for products such as activated alumina are not included in this chapter because they are essentially the same as those for hydrated alumina. The methods described, particularly those used in the analysis of metal, can be adapted for other applications where required.

## ANALYSIS OF ALUMINUM ALLOYS

### DETERMINATION OF BERYLLIUM

*Procedure.*—Dissolve a 3-g. sample (containing at least 0.4 mg. of beryllium) in 25 ml. of 1:1 HCl, adding a few drops of dilute hydrogen peroxide. If elemental silicon is present, filter on a medium paper and wash with hot water. Evaporate almost to dryness, add 90 ml. of HCl, and cool in an ice bath. Gas with hydrogen chloride for 30 to 60 minutes. Filter off the precipitated aluminum chloride on a coarse sintered-glass crucible and wash with cool HCl. Evaporate the filtrate to 50 ml. and add 50 ml. of saturated $H_2S$ water. Heat with filter paper pulp to coagulate the sulfides and filter on a medium paper, washing with hot water.

Boil to remove hydrogen sulfide, adding a few drops of nitric acid to oxidize iron and dilute to 200 ml. with water. Add ammonium hydroxide until alkaline to rosolic acid indicator. Filter on a medium paper and wash with 3% ammonium chloride adjusted to pH 7 with ammonia. Dissolve the precipitate from the filtrate with 1:1 HCl and wash with water. Boil and add ammonium hydroxide until alkaline to methyl red. Neutralize with HCl and add 5 drops in excess, warm, add 10 ml. of 5% 8-hydroxyquinoline and stir. Add 25 ml. of 15% ammonium acetate and additional 8-hydroxyquinoline until an excess is present. After 30 minutes, filter on a medium paper containing paper pulp, washing with ammonium acetate. Boil the filtrate and filter if a precipitate forms, washing with hot water. Evaporate to 25 ml., add 5 ml. of $HNO_3$ and evaporate to dryness. Repeat the nitric acid treatment to eliminate ammonium salts and organic matter. Add 5 ml. of HCl, 5 ml. of $HNO_3$, 10 ml. of 1:1 $H_2SO_4$, and evaporate to fumes. Add 10 ml. of 1:1 HCl and again evaporate to fumes.

Add 25 ml. of water, 5 ml. of 1:1 HCl, and heat to dissolve any salts. Add 25 ml. of $H_2S$ water, heat, filter on a medium paper with pulp, and wash with hot water. Boil to remove $H_2S$ and add ammonium hydroxide until alkaline to rosolic acid. Add paper pulp and heat to coagulate the precipitate. Filter on a medium paper containing paper pulp, and wash with ammonium chloride.

Transfer the paper and precipitate to a weighed platinum crucible, and ignite at a low temperature, and finally at 1100°C. for about 20 minutes after the paper is completely burned. Cool and weigh as BeO. Deduct a determined blank.

$$g. \; Be = g. \; BeO \times 0.3603$$

## BISMUTH (GRAVIMETRIC METHOD)

*Procedure.*—Dissolve a 2-g. sample in No. 1 acid and evaporate until fumes have been evolved for several minutes. Cool, add 10 ml. of 1:3 $H_2SO_4$, 100 ml. of hot water, and boil to dissolve salts. Filter on a medium paper with pulp, washing with hot water. To the filtrate add 50 ml. of $H_2S$ water, heat to boiling, and gas for 2 minutes with $H_2S$. Filter on a medium paper with pulp, washing with an acid $H_2S$ solution. Ignite in a porcelain crucible at 600°C., cool the ignited residue, and dissolve in 2 ml. of 1:1 nitric acid. Add 5 ml. of $HNO_3$, boil, and evaporate to 5 ml. Filter on a medium paper with pulp and wash with hot water. Add $NH_4OH$ until the solution becomes cloudy or neutralize to methyl red if a precipitate is not readily visible. Add 1 ml. of 1:1 HCl, 100 ml. of hot water, and boil vigorously. Continue boiling and gradually dilute to 300 ml. Boil gently for 30 minutes and filter on a weighed, fine porosity, sintered-glass crucible, washing with hot water containing a few drops of HCl. Dry at 125°C. and weigh as BiOCl.

$$\text{g. Bi} = \text{g. BiOCl} \times 0.8024$$

## BISMUTH (COLORIMETRIC METHOD)

*Procedure.*—Dissolve 1 g. of sample in 35 ml. of No. 1 acid and evaporate to fumes. Cool, add 10 ml. of 1:3 $H_2SO_4$ and 60 ml. of water and boil to dissolve salts. Filter on a medium paper, washing with hot water. To the filtrate add 50 ml. of $H_2S$ water, heat to boiling, and gas for 2 minutes with $H_2S$. Filter on medium paper and wash with acid $H_2S$ water. Ignite at 600°C. in a porcelain crucible and dissolve in a few ml. of $HNO_3$. Add 0.5 ml. of $H_2SO_4$ and evaporate to dryness. Add 3 ml. of 1:1 $H_2SO_4$ and 25 ml. of water and heat to dissolve the residue. Cool, add 1 ml. of hypophosphorous acid and dilute to 50 ml. Prepare a blank solution using 3 ml. of 1:1 $H_2SO_4$, 25 ml. of water, and 1 ml. of hypophosphorous acid, diluting to 50 ml. Add 2 ml. of 30% KI and 0.2 ml. of dilute $H_2SO_3$ with swirling (saturated solution diluted 1:50). Add dry filter pulp, mix, and allow to stand 5 minutes. Filter through a dry, dense paper and measure or compare the color with standards carried through the procedure. For photometric measurement, use a 420-m$\mu$ filter.

## BORON

**Apparatus. Decomposition Unit.**—Consisting of a sample flask (a 300-ml. round-bottom quartz flask) topped by a water-cooled vertical condenser, the tube of which is of low-boron glass.

**Boron Still.**—See Fig. 2-2.

*A. Loop trap,* made of low-boron glass.

*B. Methanol flask,* a 200- to 300-ml. round-bottom quartz or low-boron glass flask. Support the flask in a casserole water bath and add one or more boiling tubes to the flask.

*C. Glass tubing,* of low-boron glass.

*D. Sample flask.*—The 300-ml. round-bottom quartz flask, used to dissolve the sample initially, is supported in a casserole water bath.

*E. Condenser,* water-cooled, with tube of low-boron glass.

*F. Receiver,* a 250-ml. low-boron glass beaker with cover glass.

*G. Fisher burner,* to heat the water baths.

**Evaporating dishes,** porcelain, 3-in. diameter.

**Water bath,** constant temperature, between 55 and 60°C.

**Centrifuge,** equipped to handle colorimeter tubes.

**Photoelectric colorimeter,** equipped with a 540-m$\mu$ filter.

*Cleaning Instructions.*—Clean all the glass apparatus that is in contact with alkaline solutions with hot HCl and rinse with hot water prior to use. It is recommended that all glassware, including reagent containers and evaporating dishes, be rinsed with HCl and then with water.

*Preliminary Check.*—As a check on reagents and technique, it is recommended that the procedure be performed with 0.5 g. of boron-free aluminum plus known

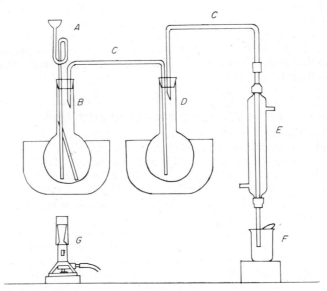

Fig. 2-2. Boron Still.

amounts of $H_3BO_3$ solution. If section (*B*) is used to dissolve the sample, reduce the water in the HCl to compensate for the water added with the $H_3BO_3$.

*Procedure.*—Start with section *A* or *B* as appropriate.

(*A*) **Solution of Silicon Alloys.**—Add 12 ml. of 90% $H_3PO_4$ acid and 5 ml. of water to a 0.5-g. sample, set the sample flask in a beaker, and heat moderately until the aluminum is dissolved. Increase the temperature and continue heating until the silicon is in solution. Remove the flask from the source of heat, allow to cool to about 60°C., add 2 ml. of water, and mix. Attach the flask to a vertical condenser, add 1 ml. of HCl, and reflux gently for 5 minutes. If copper remains undissolved, add a few drops of 6% $H_2O_2$ through the top of the condenser. Continue refluxing until $H_2O_2$ is decomposed. Proceed to section *C*.

(*B*) **Solution of Other Alloys.**—Place 0.5 g. of sample in the sample flask. Add 12 ml. of 90% $H_3PO_4$ and 2 ml. of 1:1 HCl. Attach the flask to a vertical condenser and heat gently to dissolve the sample. Dissolve copper with a few drops of 6% $H_2O_2$ added through the top of the condenser. Continue refluxing until the $H_2O_2$ is decomposed. Proceed to section *C*.

(*C*) **Distillation.**—Insert the sample flask in the boron still. Add to the methanol flask about 125 ml. of alkaline methanol solution and to the receiver 2 ml. of calcium hydroxide suspension plus water until the end of the tube from the condenser is just covered. Heat the casserole water bath around the methanol flask with a medium flame until about 50 ml. of $CH_3OH$ has distilled into the sample flask. Remove the burner.

Place a second casserole containing hot water around the sample flask, and cover the casserole with a shield (heavy aluminum foil). Heat the water bath surrounding the sample flask with the full heat of the burner for 15 minutes. Move the burner and again distill 50 ml. of $CH_3OH$ from the methanol flask into the sample flask. Reheat the water bath under the sample flask and continue heating for 15 minutes after the main portion of $CH_3OH$ was distilled.

Transfer the distillate to a 250-ml. volumetric flask, washing the beaker with 1 drop of HCl and water. Dilute to the mark and mix.

Carry a sample blank through the same procedure as for the sample.

(D) **Color Development.**—To each of four evaporating dishes add 2 ml. of calcium hydroxide suspension. To one, add an aliquot of sample, 50 ml. or a lesser volume containing not more than 2 micrograms of boron. To the second, add the same volume of sample blank. To the third, add 2 ml. of standard boron solution. The four solutions are designated, respectively, sample, sample blank, standard, and standard blank.

Evaporate each solution *just* to moist dryness on a water bath (100°C.). Remove from the bath and add 1.0 ml. of oxalic acid solution. Rotate to bring the liquid into contact with all solids, allow to stand 10 minutes, and then repeat the rotation. Add 2.0 ml. of turmeric extract and rotate again.

Set the dishes in a water bath held at 56°C. After evaporation to dryness, allow to stand in the bath for 45 minutes. Maximum color intensity is obtained in about 25 to 30 minutes, but the longer time of 45 minutes carries the test through the critical development period, and a time interval of 1 hour may be used.

Remove the dishes from the bath and immediately wash down with about 5 ml. of 95:5 isopropyl alcohol. Transfer each solution to a colorimeter tube, loosen any solids with a policeman, and wash into the tube with 95:5 isopropyl alcohol. Dilute to 25.0 ml. with additional 95:5 isopropyl alcohol, stir, and break up any lumps. Centrifuge the tubes until the solutions are clear (5 to 10 minutes at 1700 r.p.m.).

Measure the transmittances at 540 m$\mu$.

## CHROMIUM (TITRIMETRIC METHOD)

**Procedure.**—Dissolve 1 g. of sample in 30 ml. of No. 2 acid. If elemental silicon is present, add a few drops of HF. Boil to expel brown fumes. Dilute to 300 ml. with hot water, add 1 ml. of 3% $AgNO_3$ and 3 g. of ammonium persulfate and heat to boiling. If no manganese is present, boil for 20 minutes. If present, boil 10 minutes and add 3 drops of HCl to reduce manganese. Boil to remove chlorine. Cool, and add a measured volume of standard ferrous ammonium sulfate and back titrate the excess with standard $KMnO_4$.

NOTE.—Vanadium may be determined after chromium by reducing with ferrous ammonium sulfate and continuing as directed under vanadium.

## CHROMIUM (COLORIMETRIC METHOD)

**Procedure.**—Dissolve 1 g. of sample in 35 ml. of No. 1 acid and evaporate to $SO_3$ fumes. Add 15 ml. of 1:3 $H_2SO_4$ and 50 to 60 ml. of water. Boil to dissolve salts and add 50 ml. of $H_2S$ water.

Boil to coagulate the precipitate, filter on medium paper containing paper pulp, and wash with hot water. Boil to remove $H_2S$, evaporate to 75 ml., and titrate the iron with standard permanganate solution.

Dilute to 100 ml. and withdraw a 10-ml. aliquot containing up to 0.03 mg. Cr. Add 0.5 ml. of 1:1 $H_2SO_4$, 1 ml. of $KMnO_4$, and 0.1 ml. of $H_3PO_4$. Add 30 ml. of water and boil 3 minutes. Add 3 drops of HCl and continue boiling to discharge the permanganate color. Cool, transfer to a 50-ml. volumetric flask, add 1 ml. of diphenylcarbazide solution (0.5 g. in 100 ml. of alcohol), and mix. Measure or compare the color with suitable standards containing measured amounts of chromium, correcting for a blank on the reagents. For photometric measurement, a 540-m$\mu$ filter is recommended.

### COPPER (IODOMETRIC METHOD)

*Procedure.*—Dissolve 1 g. of sample in 35 ml. of No. 1 acid. Evaporate until fumes have been evolved for 15 minutes and add 10 ml. of 1:1 $H_2SO_4$ and 60 ml. of water. Boil and filter through a medium paper with pulp, washing with hot water.

Ignite the paper and residue in a platinum crucible at 600°C., add a few drops of $H_2SO_4$ and a few ml. of HF together with a few drops of $HNO_3$, and evaporate to dryness. Dissolve in 1:3 $H_2SO_4$ and add to the original filtrate. Add 50 ml. of $H_2S$ water and boil. Filter the copper sulfide on a medium paper with pulp, washing with hot water. Ignite at 600°C., dissolve in 5 ml. of $HNO_3$, and add 0.5 ml. of $H_2SO_4$. Evaporate until fumes are evolved. Cool and add 25 ml. of water and 3 ml. of acetic acid. Heat until the solution is clear, cool, and add 2 g. of KI. Allow to stand a few minutes and titrate the liberated iodine with standard thiosulfate. Add starch indicator as the end point is approached and titrate until the blue color is discharged.

### COPPER (ELECTROLYTIC METHOD)

*Procedure.*—Dissolve 1 g. of sample in 35 ml. of No. 1 acid and evaporate until fumes have been evolved for 15 minutes. Cool, add 10 ml. of 1:3 $H_2SO_4$ and 60 ml. of water. Boil and filter through a medium paper with paper pulp and wash with hot water. If silicon content is high, ignite the paper and residue at 600°C., volatilize the silica with HF, dissolve the residue in 1:3 $H_2SO_4$, and add to the original filtrate. To the filtrate add 50 ml. of $H_2S$ water, heat to boiling, and filter through a medium paper containing paper pulp, washing with hot water. Ignite the precipitate in a porcelain crucible at 600°C., and dissolve the residue in $HNO_3$. Evaporate to about 2 ml. and dilute to 150 ml. Electrolyze on a weighed platinum cathode at 0.6 amperes. Wash the electrode with water and alcohol and dry at 125°C. for 15 minutes. Cool and weigh.

### COPPER (COLORIMETRIC METHOD)

*Procedure.*—Proceed as in the electrolytic method, separating copper as the sulfide and igniting at 600°C. Dissolve the residue in 2 ml. of 1:1 $HNO_3$. Add 5 ml. of $HNO_3$ and 0.5 ml. of $H_2SO_4$ and evaporate to fumes. Cool, add 20 ml. of water and 0.25 g. of tartaric acid, and boil to dissolve. Dilute to about 75 ml. with water or if more than 0.3 mg. is present, use a suitable aliquot and adjust the pH to 9.1 with dilute $NH_4OH$. Add 5 ml. of 1% gum arabic solution and 10 ml. of 0.1% sodium diethyldithiocarbamate, dilute to 100 ml., and mix. Measure or compare the color against suitable standards with a 420-m$\mu$ filter or at a wavelength of 440 m$\mu$. Apply a blank correction for all reagents used, and also for any color derived from the sample, omitting the dithiocarbamate.

## IRON (TITRIMETRIC METHOD)

*Procedure.*—Dissolve 1 g. of sample in 35 ml. of No. 1 acid and evaporate to $SO_3$ fumes. Cool, add 10 ml. of 1:3 $H_2SO_4$, and 100 ml. of hot water. Boil and filter into a 250-ml. beaker, using pulp on a medium paper. Wash with hot water and reserve the filtrate. Ignite the paper and contents in a platinum crucible at 600°C. Moisten the residue with a few drops of 1:3 $H_2SO_4$ and add several ml. of HF. Add $HNO_3$ until the solution becomes clear. Evaporate to dryness. Dissolve the nonvolatile residue in 2 ml. of 1:3 $H_2SO_4$, heating just to fumes. Transfer the solution from the crucible to the beaker containing the original filter. Add 50 ml. of saturated $H_2S$ water and heat to boiling. Filter on a medium paper with pulp and wash with hot water.

To the filtrate add 25 ml. of 25% tartaric acid solution and neutralize to litmus with $NH_4OH$. Gas with $H_2S$ for 2 minutes and add a few drops of $NH_4OH$. Cool, filter on a medium paper with pulp, and wash with ammonium sulfide solution. Dissolve the precipitate with 40 ml. of warm 1:6 $H_2SO_4$, washing the paper with hot water. Boil out the $H_2S$ and add 1% $KMnO_4$ dropwise until a pink color persists. Gas with $H_2S$ for 5 minutes and filter on a medium paper into a 250-ml. flask. Wash with hot water. Boil vigorously for 30 minutes, cool, and titrate with standard $KMnO_4$. Deduct a determined blank.

NOTES.—In the absence of vanadium, volatilize the silica, recover the residue and precipitate the sulfides omitting tartaric acid. Boil the acid sulfide filtrate 30 minutes, cool, and titrate with permanganate.

To prepare ammonium sulfide wash solution, neutralize 10 ml. of 1:1 $H_2SO_4$ with $NH_4OH$, dilute to 1,000 ml., saturate with $H_2S$, and add 1 ml. of $NH_4OH$ in excess. Prepare fresh as required.

## IRON (COLORIMETRIC METHOD)

*Procedure.*—Dissolve approximately 0.5 g. of sample containing up to 0.3 mg. iron in 20 ml. of 1:1 HCl. Boil off most of the acid, cool, and dilute to about 50 ml. Add 1 ml. of 10% hydroxylamine hydrochloride, 10 ml. of 0.25% 1,10-phenanthroline, and 15 ml. of 15% ammonium acetate. Neutralize to Congo red paper with 1:1 $NH_4OH$. Shake to dissolve any precipitated alumina and dilute to 100 ml. Measure or compare the color by any of the usual means using appropriate standards and blanks. Maximum absorption occurs at 510 m$\mu$.

## LEAD

*Procedure.*—Dissolve 3 g. in 60 ml. of 1:1 HCl, adding the acid slowly. Add a few ml. of 6% $H_2O_2$, boiling to complete solution, and to remove excess $H_2O_2$. Add 10 ml. of 1:1 HCl, dilute to 50 ml. with hot water, and boil. Filter on a medium paper with pulp and wash with hot water. To the filtrate add 75 ml. of 25% tartaric acid, dilute to 300 ml. with hot water, and neutralize with $NH_4OH$ to methyl red. Add 25 ml. of 1:4 formic acid solution and gas with $H_2S$ for 15 minutes. Filter on a fine paper with pulp and wash with 0.5% formic acid solution saturated with $H_2S$. Ignite the precipitate in porcelain at 600°C. and transfer the residue to the original beaker with a few ml. of $HNO_3$.

Add 10 ml. of 1:1 $HNO_3$ and evaporate to about 5 ml. Add 20 ml. of water, filter through a dense paper, and wash with 1:100 $HNO_3$. In the absence of bismuth, dilute the solution and proceed with the electrolysis. If bismuth is present, neutralize the solution to methyl red with $NH_4OH$, add 1 ml. of 1:1 HCl, dilute to 100 ml. with hot water, and boil vigorously, gradually increasing the volume to 300 ml. Boil for another 30 minutes, filter on a dense paper, and wash with hot water (see Note). Add 5 ml. of 25% tartaric acid to the filtrate, and neutralize to methyl red with $NH_4OH$. Add 5 ml. of formic acid solution and gas with $H_2S$ for 15 minutes. Filter on a medium paper with pulp and wash with the formic acid-$H_2S$ wash solution. Ignite in porcelain at 600°C. Heat the residue with a few drops of $HNO_3$ and transfer to the original beaker.

Add 10 ml. of 1:1 $HNO_3$ and evaporate to about 5 ml. Dilute to 150 ml., transfer to a 200-ml. electrolytic beaker and heat to 90°C. Electrolyze on ignited platinum electrodes at about 0.4 amperes. After most of the lead is deposited, gradually increase the amperage and finish the electrolysis at not less than 2.3 volts. Lower the solution from electrodes with the current on while washing with a stream of water. Remove the anode and rinse in alcohol. Dry at 125°C. for 15 minutes, cool, and weigh as $PbO_2$.

Small amounts of lead may be determined iodometrically using a larger sample and stripping the lead deposit from the anode with acetic acid and sodium acetate.

$$\text{g. Pb} = \text{g. PbO}_2 \times 0.8662$$

NOTE.—Bismuth may be determined by filtering on a fine, fritted-glass crucible, washing with hot water, drying at 125°C., and weighing as BiOCl.

## MAGNESIUM

*Procedure.*—Dissolve a sample, containing not more than 50 mg. of magnesium, in NaOH using 3 g. of NaOH per gram of sample, adding water in small portions. After the initial reaction has subsided, heat the solution. When hydrogen evolution ceases, add a few drops of 6% $H_2O_2$ and dilute to 150 ml. with hot water. If calcium is present, add 1 g. of $Na_2CO_3$ dissolved in water. Allow the precipitate to settle, filter on a dense paper, and wash with hot 0.5% $Na_2CO_3$ solution. Dissolve the residue by adding 40 ml. of hot 1:1 HCl to the filter, and wash with hot water. Neutralize the filtrate to methyl red with $NH_4OH$ adding a few drops in excess. Precipitate the sulfides with 5 ml. of a fresh solution of 1:10 $NH_4OH$ saturated with $H_2S$. Filter with pulp on a medium paper and wash with hot water.

If more than 20 mg. of magnesium is present, dissolve in 1:1 HCl, reprecipitate, and filter. Boil the combined filtrates vigorously and filter if any additional sulfide precipitate forms. Evaporate to 75 ml., add 5 ml. of bromine water, and boil. Add an additional 10 ml. of bromine water and $NH_4OH$ with stirring until the bromine color is discharged. Add 15 drops of $NH_4OH$ in excess and allow to stand 10 minutes, stirring occasionally. Filter the $MnO_2$ on a medium paper, washing with hot water. Acidify the filtrate to methyl red with HCl and boil if any bromine is still present. Add 10 ml. of 10% $(NH_4)_2HPO_4$ and a few drops of $NH_4OH$. Stir vigorously until precipitation is initiated.

Add $NH_4OH$ dropwise with stirring until precipitation is complete followed by an excess of 5 ml. per 100 ml. of solution. Stir vigorously and allow to stand at least 1 hour and preferably overnight. Filter on a medium paper with pulp and wash with 5:95 $NH_4OH$.

Ignite the paper and precipitate in a weighed porcelain crucible at 600°C. and finally at 1100°C. for 30 minutes. Weigh as $Mg_2P_2O_7$ and deduct a determined blank.

$$\text{g. Mg} = \text{g. Mg}_2P_2O_7 \times 0.2185$$

NOTES.—If the magnesium precipitate is in excess of 20 mg., dissolve the first $MgNH_4PO_4$ precipitate from the filter with HCl and reprecipitate.

For alloys containing more than 4% silicon, dissolve the sample in 1:1 HCl added in small portions, using 20 ml. per gram of sample. Add a few ml. of 6% $H_2O_2$ to dissolve copper and boil to destroy the excess. Dilute with 50 ml. of hot water, filter through a dense paper with pulp, and wash with hot $H_2O$. Ignite in platinum at 600°C. Cool, add a few drops of 1:1 $H_2SO_4$ and a few ml. of HF, and carefully drop 1:1 $HNO_3$ into the crucible, allowing the $HNO_3$ to react before making further additions. When most of the silicon is dissolved, rinse down the wall of the crucible with additional $HNO_3$. Cool, wash down with $H_2O$, add 1 ml. of 1:1 $H_2SO_4$ and warm to dissolve the residue. Combine with the filtrate and washings. Add 50 ml. of $H_2S$ water and heat to boiling. Filter through a medium paper with pulp and wash with hot water. Boil out the $H_2S$ and add 20% NaOH to dissolve most of the alumina. Add a few drops of 6% $H_2O_2$, stir, and heat to dissolve the remaining alumina and coagulate the precipitate. Dilute to 150 ml. with hot water. Add $Na_2CO_3$ if calcium is present and continue as directed in the preceding alkaline-attack procedure.

A correction for calcium and manganese may be made by determining these elements in the pyrophosphate residue. Dissolve in sulfuric acid, add water, and evaporate to dense fumes. Cool, add 10 ml. of water, and heat to dissolve. Cool and add 100 ml. of absolute methanol, stir vigorously and allow to stand at least 12 hours. Filter and wash with 90% methanol acidified with sulfuric acid. Boil the filtrate to remove methanol and determine manganese colorimetrically. Dissolve the filtered calcium sulfate in a minimum amount of HCl, precipitate the oxalate, and titrate with standard permanganate.

## MANGANESE

**Procedure.**—Dissolve 0.5 g. of sample in 30 ml. of No. 3 acid with heating. If the manganese content exceeds 0.2%, reduce the sample size accordingly. Add hydrofluoric acid dropwise and boil to volatilize silicon. Dilute to about 30 ml. with hot water. Add 0.3 g. of potassium periodate and digest near the boiling temperature for 15 minutes, maintaining the volume at about 30 ml. If the permanganate color does not develop within a few minutes, add more $KIO_4$. Cool to room temperature, transfer to a 100-ml. volumetric flask, dilute to the mark, and mix. Measure or compare the color against appropriate standards at 550 m$\mu$.

NOTE.—If zirconium is present, dissolve in 20 ml. of No. 2 acid, using the same acid in the standards and blank.

## NICKEL (GRAVIMETRIC METHOD)

**Procedure.**—Weigh a 1-g. sample for alloys containing up to 5% nickel or a proportionally smaller weight if the nickel content is higher. Dissolve in 35 ml. of No. 1 acid, evaporate to fumes. Cool, add 10 ml. of 1:1 $H_2SO_4$, dilute to 100 ml., boil to dissolve salts, add 50 ml. of $H_2S$ water, and again heat to boiling. Filter on a medium paper containing pulp and wash with hot water. Boil the filtrate 10 minutes to remove $H_2S$, add 5 ml. of $HNO_3$, and boil to oxidize iron. Dilute to 200 ml. with hot water and add 25 ml. of 25% tartaric acid. Neutralize to methyl red with ammonium hydroxide, adding 5 ml. in excess. Heat to 90°C. and add 1% alcoholic dimethylglyoxime solution with stirring, using 20 ml. for 20 mg. of nickel and 5 ml. for each additional 10 mg. Allow to stand 30 minutes to 1 hour. Filter on a weighed, fritted-glass crucible, and wash with hot 1:200 $NH_4OH$. Dry at 125°C. for 1 hour, cool in a desiccator, and weigh as $(C_4H_7O_2N_2)_2Ni$.

$$\text{g. Ni} = \text{g. } (C_4H_7O_2N_2)_2Ni \times 0.2032$$

NOTE.—If cobalt is present, dissolve the precipitate in cold 1:3 HCl and reprecipitate with dimethylglyoxime.

### NICKEL (COLORIMETRIC METHOD)

*Procedure.*—Dissolve up to 1 g. of sample containing not more than 0.1 mg. of nickel in 15 ml. of 1:1 HCl. Add a few drops of 6% $H_2O_2$ and boil to remove free chlorine and destroy excess peroxide. Add 25 ml. of 25% tartaric acid solution per gram of sample and dilute to 100 ml. Neutralize to litmus with ammonium hydroxide, add 2 ml. of sodium dimethylglyoxime solution and extract three times with 3-ml. portions of chloroform. Extract the combined chloroform solutions with 10 ml. of 1:50 ammonium hydroxide. Withdraw the chloroform layer and wash the ammonium hydroxide layer with 2 ml. of fresh chloroform. Combine the two chloroform extracts and extract twice with 5 ml. of 1:25 HCl. Collect the acid solution in a 25-ml. flask. Add 0.5 ml. of bromine water, followed by sufficient ammonium hydroxide to destroy the bromine color plus four drops excess. Dilute to the mark and measure or compare the color with standards against a suitable blank at 520 m$\mu$.

### OXIDE

Metallic aluminum is volatilized as $AlCl_3$ in a stream of dry HCl. Aluminum is then determined in the ignited residue and calculated to $Al_2O_3$.

*Apparatus.*—**Oxide train** (see Fig. 2-3).

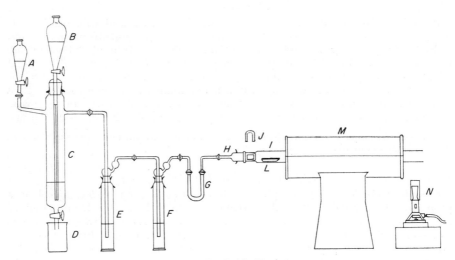

Fɪɢ. 2-3.  Oxide Train.

*C. HCl generator,* equipped with separate inlets for hydrochloric and sulfuric acids from burettes *A* and *B* (Note 1).

*E* and *F. Bubblers* containing $H_2SO_4$.

*G. U-tube* containing glass wool and $P_2O_5$.

*H. Combustion tube cap* with a 1⅖ ball joint and 2⅞₂ TS joint.

*I. Pyrex combustion tube* with 2⅞₂ TS inner joint on inlet end and ¼-in. outlet hole.

*J. Permanent magnet.*

*Steel pusher,* 1-in. length of steel tube or rod for positioning boat (shown in tube, below *J*).

*L. Combustion boats,* glazed silica.

*M. Combustion furnace,* hinge type, controlled at 450°C. Gas burner to burn exit gas and prevent condensation of $AlCl_3$.

*N. Burner* for heating outlet of combustion tube.

*Procedure.*—Add 0.5 g. of sample, preferably in one piece, to a combustion boat previously ignited at 1100°C. (Note 2). Place the boat in the inlet end of the combustion tube followed by the steel pusher (Note 3). Pass HCl gas through the train at about 5 bubbles per second. After 15 minutes, lift the top of the furnace and push the boat into the center of the combustion tube with the magnet. Close the furnace and allow one hour for volatilization of metallic aluminum, heating the outlet of the combustion tube with the burner.

Fuse the residue with 0.8 g. of $KHSO_4$ and dissolve in 40 ml. of $H_2O$. If the sample contains less than 0.2 mg. of $Al_2O_3$, transfer the solution to a 125-ml. separatory funnel. If greater than 0.2 mg. $Al_2O_3$, dilute and transfer an appropriate aliquot to the separatory funnel, adjusting the volume of the aliquot to 40 ml.

Add 40 ml. of $CHCl_3$, 10 ml. of NaOAc buffer solution, and 10 ml. of 1% sodium diethyldithiocarbamate solution. Extract on a mechanical shaker for 10 minutes. Discard the $CHCl_3$ layer. Add to the separatory funnel 50 ml. of 8-hydroxyquinoline-carbon tetrachloride solution and shake 20 minutes. Filter through a medium paper and measure or compare the color with suitable standards at 395 $m\mu$. A 400-$m\mu$ glass filter is satisfactory for photometric measurement.

NOTES.—1. Compressed HCl gas of a commercial grade is not recommended for this determination because traces of $CO_2$ and grease sometimes encountered tend to cause high results.

2. Use a clean combustion tube dried at 105°C. for each determination.

3. Boats are initially placed in the cold portion of the combustion tube while air is being displaced with HCl.

## SILICON (GRAVIMETRIC ALKALI ATTACK METHOD)

*Procedure.*—Dissolve 1 g. of sample containing up to 60 mg. of silicon in a covered nickel beaker using 3 g. of sodium hydroxide pellets with water added in small portions. After violent action ceases, wash down the cover and beaker with hot water and evaporate to a paste. To ensure complete oxidation of silicon, add several ml. of 6% hydrogen peroxide and repeat the evaporation. Add 15 ml. of water, heat to dissolve, and cool. Transfer to a beaker containing 10 ml. of nitric acid. Wash the nickel beaker with water, followed by 1:1 HCl, and add 40 ml. of 70% $HClO_4$. Cover, evaporate until crystallization begins, and then discontinue heating. Cool, dilute to 150 ml. with hot water, and stir until the soluble salts are dissolved. Add pulp and filter on a medium paper. Wash with hot water, followed by 15 ml. of 1:10 sulfuric acid, being careful to wet the paper completely and finally with hot water until the soluble salts are removed. Ignite the paper and contents in a platinum crucible at 600°C. until free from carbon and then at 1100°C. for 20 minutes. Cool in a desiccator and weigh. To the residue, add a few drops of 1:3 $H_2SO_4$, several ml. of HF, and a few drops of $HNO_3$. Evaporate to dryness, repeat the treatment with HF, and ignite at 1100°C., cool, and reweigh. Deduct a determined blank.

$$\text{g. Si} = \text{g. } SiO_2 \times 0.4674$$

NOTE.—For accurate work, it is essential to recover silica from the filtrate. Evaporate the solution to fumes, cool, dilute, and filter as usual. Combine the recovered and main residues before ignition.

## SILICON (GRAVIMETRIC ACID ATTACK METHOD)

*Procedure.*—Dissolve a 1-g. sample in 40 ml. of 1:2 $HNO_3$. Add 10 ml. of HCl and 9 ml. of 1:1 $H_2SO_4$ and evaporate until fumes of $SO_3$ have been evolved for 15 minutes. Cool, add 10 ml. of 1:1 $H_2SO_4$, 60 ml. of hot water, and 2 drops of 6% $H_2O_2$. Boil to dissolve salts and filter with pulp on a fine paper. Wash with hot water, ignite the paper and contents in a platinum crucible at 1100°C., cool in a desiccator, and weigh. Moisten with a few drops of 1:3 $H_2SO_4$ and add a few milliliters of HF and a few drops of $HNO_3$. Evaporate to dryness, ignite at 1100°C., cool, and weigh. Deduct a determined blank.

$$\text{g. Si} = \text{g. SiO}_2 \times 0.4674$$

Notes.—If elemental silicon is present in the silica precipitate, a carbonate fusion is necessary. Ignite the paper containing the dehydrated silica at 600°C., cool, add sodium carbonate, and fuse. Cool and dissolve in 25 to 80 ml. of 1:3 $H_2SO_4$, and proceed with the dehydration.

Samples containing magnesium give low results and must be analyzed by the alkali attack method.

## SILICON (COLORIMETRIC METHOD)

*Procedure.*—Place a 0.25-g. sample containing up to 0.2 mg. Si and 1 g. of NaOH pellets in a platinum dish. Add water in small portions and warm until the sample is dissolved. Evaporate to a paste, add a few drops of 6% $H_2O_2$ to oxidize copper, and boil to destroy the excess. Cool and dilute with cold water to approximately 65 ml. Stir the solution and adjust to pH 1.6 with 1:1 $H_2SO_4$. Transfer to a 250-ml. beaker, add 0.5 ml. of sulfurous acid, cover, and boil for 5 minutes. Add 2 drops of bromine water and boil to remove excess bromine. Cool to room temperature and dilute to approximately 75 ml. Stir the solution and adjust to pH 1.4 using 1:3 $H_2SO_4$. Cool in ice water and add 5 ml. of ammonium molybdate solution and mix. After 5 minutes, add 10 ml. of 1:1 $H_2SO_4$. Remove from the ice water and dilute to 100 ml. Add 5 ml. of ferrous ammonium sulfate solution, and mix. Measure the color against a blank and suitable standards using a 660-m$\mu$ filter or at 680–700 m$\mu$ with a spectrophotometer.

## SODIUM

*Procedure.*—Weigh 15 g. of medium-sized millings or turnings, containing about 2 mg. Na, into a 75-ml. nickel beaker and cover with a close-fitting lid. Heat for 1 hour at 650°C. in the case of silicon alloys and at 700°C. for pure metal. The final temperature should be high enough to melt the sample but the rate of heating should not be so rapid that the individual pieces fuse together. Allow to cool in the furnace. Transfer to a 400-ml. beaker containing 100 ml. of water and 1 ml. of 1:1 $H_2SO_4$. Rinse the cover and crucible with 1:500 $H_2SO_4$. Break any adherent turnings apart. Boil 10 minutes and decant through a medium filter paper. Cover the metal with another portion of water, add 0.1 ml. of $H_2SO_4$, and boil for 5 minutes.

Filter through the same paper and repeat the washing with hot water. Evaporate the combined filtrates to 25 ml., transfer to a 250-ml. beaker, and evaporate to 5 ml. Cool, and add 50 ml. of zinc uranyl acetate reagent. Stir occasionally and allow to stand for 2 hours. Filter on a medium, fritted-glass crucible, using additional reagent solution to transfer the precipitate. Wash twice with reagent solution, twice with denatured alcohol, and twice with acetone. Dry the precipitate for 15 minutes at 125°C., cool in a desiccator, and weigh. Dissolve the precipitate from the crucible by drawing hot water through it, and wash twice with acetone. Dry the crucible at 125°C. for 15 minutes, cool in a desiccator, and weigh. Deduct a determined blank.

g. Na = g. $NaC_2H_3O_2 \cdot Zn(C_2H_3O_2)_2 \cdot 3UO_2(C_2H_3O_2)_2 \cdot 6H_2O \times 0.01495$

NOTE.—For samples containing more than 0.1% sodium, dissolve 1 g. of drillings or turnings in 25 ml. of 1:1 HCl. Add a few drops of 6% $H_2O_2$ and boil to remove chlorine and destroy peroxide. Filter on a medium paper with pulp and wash with hot water. Evaporate just to crystallization. Add 70 ml. of zinc uranyl solution, stir, and allow to stand for at least 1 hour. Filter, wash, dry, and weigh the precipitate as directed in the foregoing procedure.

## TIN

*Apparatus.*—**Erlenmeyer flask**, 500 ml., fitted with 1-hole stopper and inverted U-shaped glass tube dipping into a 400-ml. beaker.

*Procedure.*—Start with section *A* or *B* as appropriate. Section *A* applies to samples that dissolve completely in hydrochloric acid and may be used when the accuracy desired does not warrant the extra work required in section *B*.

(*A*) Place up to 3 g. of sample containing not more than 50 mg. of Sn in the flask of the tin apparatus. Dilute to 100 ml. with water and add 0.1 g. of Sb powder. Proceed to *C*, or if the sample taken is less than 1 g., first carry out the following: Add 25 ml. of 1:1 HCl, cover, and warm to dissolve. Add a few ml. of 6% $H_2O_2$, and boil to decompose excess peroxide and to volatilize chlorine. Dilute to 100 ml., and add 0.1 g. of Sb powder and 1 g. of Al metal.

(*B*) Place up to 10 g. of sample in a beaker and add 35 ml. of No. 1 acid per gram of sample. Heat to dissolve and evaporate to heavy fumes of $SO_3$. Cool, and add 60 ml. of hot water per gram of sample and 10 ml. of 1:1 HCl. Stir and then boil until salts are dissolved. Filter through a fine paper containing paper pulp and wash with hot water.

If necessary, add Cu solution so that 5 mg. of Cu is present. Add 50 ml. of $H_2S$ water, boil, and then gas with $H_2S$ for 5 minutes. Filter on a medium paper and wash with $H_2S$ wash solution. Wet ash the precipitate and cool. Add 50 ml. of water and 10 ml. of HCl, and boil to dissolve salts. If Cu is less than 20 mg., proceed to section *C*; otherwise, separate the bulk of the Cu as in the following paragraph.

Add 10 mg. of Fe as a ferric salt, adjust the pH to the yellow color of methyl red with $NH_4OH$, and add a few drops of $NH_4OH$ in excess to complex Cu. Digest, filter through a medium paper, and wash with hot $NH_4Cl$ wash solution. Wet ash the precipitate and cool. Add 50 ml. of water and 10 ml. of HCl, and boil to dissolve salts. Transfer the solution to the flask of the tin apparatus. Dilute to 100 ml. with water, and add 0.1 g. of Sb powder and 1 g. of Al metal. Proceed to section *C*.

(*C*) Add 50 ml. of HCl and stopper the flask with the outer end of the U-tube dipping in the empty beaker. Warm until the Al is dissolved and then boil for about 5 minutes. Continue boiling and replace the empty beaker with one containing $NaHCO_3$ solution.

Transfer the flask to a pan of cold water with the U-tube still in the $NaHCO_3$ solution. Avoid excessive back pressure by having the level of the cooling bath near the liquid level in the flask.

When the solution is cool, open the flask, immediately add 5 ml. of starch-KI solution, and titrate with standard $KIO_3$ solution to a blue color. Deduct a determined blank (0.05 ml.).

## TITANIUM

**Procedure.**—Dissolve 1 g. of sample in 35 ml. of No. 1 acid and determine silica in the usual way. Fuse the silica residue with a few grams of $KHSO_4$. Dissolve in 5:95 $H_2SO_4$ and combine with the filtrate and washings from the silica separation. Gas with $H_2S$ for 5 minutes and heat to boiling to coagulate sulfide. Filter on a medium paper with pulp and wash with hot water. (Determine copper in the precipitate if desired.) Boil the filtrate 30 minutes and evaporate to about 5 ml. Add dilute permanganate to a faint pink color. Cool, dilute to 100 ml. and mix. To a 25-ml. portion of the solution, add 2 drops of 30% $H_2O_2$ and measure the color at approximately 400 $m\mu$ against a similar portion of the solution without the peroxide. Suitable standards for calibration may be prepared from titanium potassium oxalate $(K_2TiO(C_2O_4)_2 \cdot 2H_2O)$ converted to titanium sulfate. Titanium dioxide and titanium fluoride may also be used.

NOTE.—If vanadium is present, perform a cupferron separation on the filtrate from the sulfide precipitation. Ignite the residue at 600°C., fuse with sodium carbonate, dissolve in water, and filter. Dissolve the residue in hot 1:1 HCl adding several ml. of $HNO_3$ and 5 ml. of $H_2SO_4$. Evaporate to fumes, take up in water, and follow the peroxide method.

## ZINC

**Procedure.**—Dissolve 1 g. of sample in 35 ml. of No. 1 acid and evaporate to fumes. Cool and add 10 ml. of 1:3 $H_2SO_4$ and 60 ml. of hot water. Boil to dissolve salts and add 50 ml. of $H_2S$ water. Heat to boiling and filter with pulp on a medium paper, washing with hot water. Boil the filtrate for 30 minutes to remove $H_2S$ and dilute to 150 ml. Add a slight excess of 1% $KMnO_4$ solution. Stir vigorously while adding 5 ml. of ammonium mercuric thiocyanate solution. Continue stirring until precipitation starts and add an additional 20 ml. with stirring. Allow to stand at least 2 hours and filter on a weighed medium, fritted-glass crucible. Wash with diluted ammonium mercuric thiocyanate (1:100). Dry at 125°C. for 1 hour, cool, and weigh. Deduct a determined blank. The factor for calculating zinc mercuric thiocyanate to zinc is approximately 0.1289, varying somewhat with the chemicals used. An occasional determination of this factor, particularly when using new lots of reagents, is recommended.

# ANALYSIS OF BAUXITE

**Preparation of Sample.**—Obtain a representative sample of the material to be analyzed and for determinations other than moisture, pulverize to pass a 100-mesh sieve, recrushing and resieving the oversized material. Mix thoroughly and dry for at least 1 hour at 110°C. unless the results are to be reported on other than a dry basis.

## MOISTURE

**Procedure.**—Crush and coarsely grind a suitable amount of sample with minimum exposure to the air. Weigh, dry at 120°C., and reweigh.

## LOSS ON IGNITION

**Procedure.**—Place 1 g. of dry sample in a weighed crucible. Heat slowly at first and finally ignite at 1100°C. to constant weight. Cool in a desiccator and weigh.

## SILICA

*Procedure.*—Heat a 1-g. sample with 70 ml. of triacid in a covered beaker or casserole. Evaporate slowly until fumes have been evolved for 20–30 minutes. Cool, dilute to 100 ml. and boil to dissolve salts. Filter on a medium paper with pulp, washing well with hot water. Re-evaporate the filtrate to fumes, dilute, and filter again in order to recover additional silica. Filter into a 250-ml. volumetric flask and collect the washings in a 250-ml. beaker. Transfer the precipitates to a small platinum crucible, ignite at 1100°C. to constant weight, cool in a desiccator, and weigh. Moisten the residue with a few drops of 1:1 $H_2SO_4$, add a few ml. of HF, evaporate to dryness, and ignite at 1100°C. Repeat the volatilization of silica. Cool and weigh the residue. Deduct a determined blank.

For subsequent determinations, fuse the residue with 1 g. of $KHSO_4$, cool, and place the crucible in a beaker containing the silica washings. Add 10 ml. of 1:1 $H_2SO_4$, heat to dissolve, and remove the crucible. Boil and gas with $H_2S$ for 5 minutes to precipitate the platinum. Heat to boiling, filter with pulp, and wash with hot water. Boil the filtrate to expel $H_2S$. Cool and add to a volumetric flask containing the silica filtrate. Dilute to the mark.

## TOTAL IRON

*Procedure.*—To a 100-ml. aliquot of the silica filtrate, add a few drops of 1% $KMnO_4$. Heat to boiling and add 10 ml. of HCl. Evaporate to 500 ml. To the hot solution, add 5 ml. of chlorostannous acid dropwise until the yellow color of ferric chloride is discharged. Avoid more than 2 or 3 drops excess. Cool to room temperature and add 15 ml. of saturated mercuric chloride solution. Stir until a white precipitate of mercurous chloride forms, add 10 ml. $H_3PO_4$, dilute to 150 ml., add 5 drops of sodium diphenylamine sulfonate and titrate immediately with standard potassium dichromate solution. Deduct a determined blank based on titrating measured amounts of standard iron solution.

## ALUMINA

*Procedure.*—To 100 ml. of the silica filtrate, add 10 ml. of HCl, dilute to 200 ml. and neutralize to methyl red with ammonium hydroxide. Add a few drops in excess and boil for 2 to 3 minutes. Adjust to a faint pink with 1:1 HCl and then add 1:4 $NH_4OH$ dropwise until the end point is attained (see Note). Allow to settle 3 to 5 minutes and filter on medium paper washing with hot ammonium chloride wash solution. Return the paper and precipitate to the beaker and dissolve by heating with 10 ml. of HCl plus 50 ml. of water. Dilute to 150 ml., heat to boiling, and repeat the ammonia precipitation. Filter, wash with hot $NH_4Cl$ wash solution, and transfer the paper and precipitate to a weighed porcelain crucible. Dry carefully, ignite at 1100° for 1 hour, cover the crucible, cool in a desiccator, and weigh. Deduct a determined blank. For careful work, the weight of the residue must be corrected by determining and deducting the weights of the oxides of iron, titanium, phosphorus, chromium, vanadium, and zirconium, if present.

Note.—Particular care must be exercised in adjusting this end point. Precipitation is incomplete if either insufficient or excess ammonia is used. In the color change (pink to yellow), two shades of yellow are observed, the first a dull yellow and the second, a bright canary yellow. When the second is reached, four drops of 1:4 ammonia should be added in excess. Use of dilute HCl before final adjustment of the end point makes the color change in the presence of the precipitate easier to observe.

## TITANIUM

*Procedure.*—Transfer a 25-ml. aliquot of the silica filtrate to a 100-ml. volumetric flask. Add 10 ml. of 1:1 $H_2SO_4$, dilute to the mark, and mix. Add 2 drops of 30% $H_2O_2$, measure the color using the unoxidized solution as a reference, and compare with suitable standards. A blue filter or wavelength of 400 m$\mu$ is satisfactory for photometric measurement.

NOTES.—For calibration, use a standard solution prepared from titanium potassium oxalate standardized gravimetrically by the cupferron method.

Vanadium and molybdenum also give colors but are not normally present in sufficient concentration to interfere.

## CALCIUM

*Procedure.*—Mix 2 g. of sample with 8 g. of anhydrous $Na_2CO_3$ and 2 g. of anhydrous $Na_2B_4O_7$ in a platinum crucible. Heat gradually over a burner to drive off moisture and finally fuse under the full heat of the burner. Place the crucible in a beaker and add 150 ml. of hot water, stirring until the melt is well broken up. Filter on a medium paper and wash with hot 1% $Na_2CO_3$. Puncture the paper and wash the residue into the same beaker. Wash the paper with 20 ml. of 1:1 HCl followed by hot water. Boil, add a few drops of methyl red and sufficient $NH_4OH$ to change the color to a distinct yellow. Boil not more than 2 minutes and filter at once on a medium paper. Wash with hot $NH_4Cl$ solution. Return the paper and precipitate to the beaker, dissolve in 10 ml. of HCl and dilute with hot water. Heat to boiling and repeat the precipitation. Filter into the beaker used to collect the preceding filtrate and wash with hot $NH_4Cl$ solution.

Evaporate the combined filtrate to 75 ml. and add 10 ml. of bromine water. With stirring, add $NH_4OH$ to discharge the bromine color and then add 15 drops in excess. Allow to stand with occasional stirring. Filter the manganese dioxide on a medium paper with pulp, washing with hot water. Evaporate the filtrate to dryness and then heat to 500°C. to expel ammonium salts. Cool, dissolve the residue in 3 ml. of HCl plus a few ml. of water, filter on a medium paper, and wash with hot water. Dilute to about 100 ml., add 10 ml. of saturated $(NH_4)_2C_2O_4$ solution and heat to boiling. Add methyl red and stir vigorously while adding $NH_4OH$ dropwise until the color changes to a distinct yellow and then add a few drops in excess. Digest near the boiling temperature for 1 hour, keeping the solution ammoniacal.

For small amounts of calcium, overnight standing is recommended. Cool, filter through a small, medium paper, and wash with small portions of hot water to remove the excess sodium oxalate. Reserve the filtrate for the determination of magnesium. Wash the calcium oxalate precipitate from the paper with hot water to remove the excess sodium oxalate. Reserve the filtrate for the determination of magnesium. Wash the calcium oxalate precipitate from the paper with hot water into the original beaker, leaving the paper drawn up on the side of the beaker. Add 150 ml. of boiling $H_2O$ and 10 ml. of 1:1 $H_2SO_4$. Titrate with $KMnO_4$ standardized against calcium, adding the paper to the solution toward the end of the titration. Deduct a determined blank.

NOTE.—If decomposition of the sample is difficult, increase the proportion of sodium tetraborate.

## MAGNESIUM

**Procedure.**—Evaporate the calcium filtrate to dryness and heat to 500°C. to expel ammonium salts. Cool, add 2 ml. of HCl and a small amount of water, heat to boiling, and adjust to the alkaline color of methyl red with ammonium hydroxide. Filter on a medium paper and wash with hot ammonium chloride wash solution. Acidify with 1:1 HCl and add 10 ml. of 10% $(NH_4)_2PO_4$ solution. Add a few drops of $NH_4OH$ and stir vigorously to precipitate magnesium. Add additional ammonium hydroxide dropwise with stirring until no further precipitation occurs and then add excess of 5 ml. per 100 ml. of solution. Stir vigorously and allow to stand at least 1 hour or, preferably, overnight. Filter on a medium paper with pulp and wash with 5:95 ammonium hydroxide. Dry the paper and precipitate in a weighed porcelain crucible and finally ignite at 1100°C. Weigh the residue and deduct a determined blank.

$$\text{g. MgO} = \text{g. Mg}_2\text{P}_2\text{O}_7 \times 0.3622$$

NOTE.—This determination may also be done with the flame photometer at 285 m$\mu$ and by titration with EDTA.

## MANGANESE

**Procedure.**—To an aliquot of the silica filtrate containing approximately 1 mg. of MnO, add 10 ml. of No. 2 acid, boil to expel nitrogen oxides and adjust to 25–30 ml. Add 0.3 g. of $KIO_4$ and heat near the boiling point for 20 minutes adding hot water as needed to maintain the solution at 25–30 ml. Cool, transfer to a 100-ml. volumetric flask, and dilute to the mark. Measure or compare the color at 522 m$\mu$ against suitable standards carried through the oxidation procedures. Deduct a determined blank.

## PHOSPHATE

**Procedure.**—Add 70 ml. of triacid to a 1-g. sample and heat in a covered beaker so as to concentrate slowly and then evaporate to strong fumes of $SO_3$. Cool, add cold water, dilute to about 100 ml., and boil to dissolve salts. Filter with pulp through a medium paper, washing with hot water. To the filtrate, add 5 ml. of $HNO_3$ and a slight excess of 1% $KMnO_4$. Boil 10 minutes, add $KNO_2$ to discharge the pink color and boil again for 10 minutes. Cool and dilute to 250 ml. in a volumetric flask. Withdraw a 25-ml. aliquot and adjust until just alkaline to Congo red with $NH_4OH$. Add 25 ml. of mixed reagent solution and dilute to 100 ml. Measure or compare the color against suitable standards and apply any necessary blank on the reagents. A blue filter or wavelength at approximately 400 m$\mu$ is recommended for photometric measurement.

## ZIRCONIUM

**Procedure.**—To a 3-g. sample in a large platinum crucible add 10 ml. of $HNO_3$, 20 ml. of HF, and 20 ml. of $H_2SO_4$. Evaporate to fumes, cool, and add 50 ml. of water plus 20 ml. of HCl. Heat to dissolve salts. Filter off any insoluble residue and fuse with sodium carbonate-borate mixture. Dissolve in dilute sulfuric acid and add the solution to the filtrate. Adjust to 200 ml. Cool to 10°C. and add ice cold cupferron solution until the precipitate turns reddish brown indicating partial precipitation of iron. Allow to stand 15 minutes. Stir in paper pulp and filter with suction on a medium paper backed with a dense paper. Wash with ice cold cupferron wash solution. Transfer the paper and contents to a platinum crucible, char carefully, and burn off the carbon at 600°C. Fuse the residue with $KHSO_4$ and dissolve the cake in 50 ml. of water and 20 ml. of 1:1 $H_2SO_4$. Filter on a medium paper and wash with hot water. To the filtrate, add 3 ml. of 6% $H_2O_2$, 10 ml. of 10% $(NH_4)_2HPO_4$ and allow to stand overnight at 60–70°C. Filter on a medium paper and wash with cold ammonium nitrate wash solution. Ignite the paper and contents in a weighed porcelain crucible at 1100°C. Cool and weigh as $ZrP_2O_7$.

$$\text{g. } ZrO_2 = \text{g. } ZrP_2O_7 \times 0.4647$$

### FERROUS IRON

*Procedure.*—Place a 2-g. sample in a 250-ml. flask. Add 15 ml. of 1:1 $H_2SO_4$ in 45 ml. of water. Boil for 10 minutes, cool, add 5 drops of diphenylamine indicator, and titrate with standard $K_2Cr_2O_7$. If insoluble material obscures the end point, pour the solution into 200 ml. of water in a 400-ml. beaker and complete the titration.

NOTES.—This method determines iron present as siderite. Ferrous iron in other minerals such as ilmenite, marcasite, and pyrite, is insoluble under these conditions.

With some mineral samples, it is virtually impossible to detect a visual end point. In such cases, the titration can be performed potentiometrically using Pt-calomel electrodes. 1,10-Phenanthroline may also be used for colorimetric determination of the ferrous iron.

### VANADIUM

*Procedure.*—Place 3 g. of sample in a 400-ml. beaker, add 100 ml. of No. 1 acid, cover, and evaporate to heavy fumes of $SO_3$. Cool, dilute to about 100 ml., and boil to dissolve salts. Filter on a medium paper with pulp and wash with hot water. To the filtrate add 30 ml. of HCl, dilute to 300 ml., and cool to about 10°C. Add ice-cold cupferron solution with stirring until precipitation is complete, and allow to stand 15 minutes. Filter with suction using pulp on a medium paper backed by a dense paper. Wash with ice-cold cupferron wash solution. Dry the filter and precipitate in a platinum crucible and ignite at 600°C. Fuse the residue with sodium carbonate and dissolve in hot water. Filter on a medium paper, washing with hot water. Add 10 ml. of 1:1 $H_2SO_4$ and heat to boiling, adding dropwise an excess of $KMnO_4$. Cool, transfer to a 50-ml. volumetric flask, and dilute to the mark. To a 25-ml. aliquot, add four drops of 30% $H_2O_2$, mix, and allow to stand 5 minutes. Measure or compare color against a blank with suitable standards prepared from sodium metavanadate oxidized with $KMnO_4$ and carried through the foregoing treatment with $H_2O_2$. Deduct a determined blank on the reagents if necessary.

NOTE.—Molybdenum also gives a color with peroxide but may be removed by performing an acid sulfide separation on the silica filtrate.

### POTASSIUM

*Procedure.*—Pulverize 1 g. of sample to an impalpable powder in an agate or steel mortar. Add 1 g. $NH_4Cl$ and grind with the already pulverized sample. Weigh 8 g. of $CaCO_3$, transfer a small amount to a J. Lawrence Smith crucible and grind most of the remainder with the sample and $NH_4Cl$ (Note 1). Transfer the mixture to the crucible, grind the remaining $CaCO_3$ in the mortar, and add to the charge in the crucible. Cover the crucible and tamp by tapping lightly on a table. Incline the crucible in a hole in an asbestos board and heat with a Fisher burner at a sufficient rate to evolve ammonia but not $NH_4Cl$.

After the evolution of ammonia is completed, increase the temperature and continue heating for 1 hour (Note 2). Cool the crucible, add 5 ml. of water, heat to disintegrate the fused mass and transfer to a 250-ml. beaker. Wash the material adhering to the crucible with hot water and add to the beaker. Dilute with hot water to 100 ml. and boil gently for 15 minutes. Decant through a medium paper into a 400-ml. beaker. Add 40 ml. of hot water to the residue. Stir, allow to settle, and decant.

Repeat the hot water extractions 5 times. To the filtrate, add a few ml. of $NH_4OH$ and 25 ml. of saturated $(NH_4)_2CO_3$. Heat merely to boiling. Allow the $CaCO_3$ to settle. Filter on a medium paper into a 600-ml. beaker, washing twice with hot water. Wash the precipitate back into the 400-ml. beaker, dissolve in a little HCl, reprecipitate with $NH_4OH$ and $(NH_4)_2CO_3$, filter into a 600-ml. beaker, and wash with hot water. Evaporate the filtrate to dryness and heat in a furnace at 500°C. to volatilize $NH_4Cl$. Cool and take up the residue with a few ml. of $H_2O$ and 5 ml. of HCl. Add $H_2PtCl_6$ solution slightly in excess of that necessary to precipitate the potassium. Evaporate on a steam bath to a sirupy consistency until the liquid is sufficiently concentrated to solidify on cooling. Cool and add 25 ml. of alcohol.

Break up the $K_2PtCl_6$ with a stirring rod and allow to stand 30 minutes. Decant through a small medium filter paper. Repeat with small portions of alcohol until the filtrate is colorless. Transfer the residue to the paper and wash several times with alcohol. Dissolve the residue through the filter into a 100 ml. beaker by washing with hot water. Reduce the chloroplatinate by adding for every 0.2 g. potassium present 1 ml. of HCl and 0.5 g. of pure magnesium crystals. If the magnesium does not dissolve, add additional HCl and boil. Allow the platinum to settle, filter on a medium paper, and wash with hot water. Ignite in a weighed platinum or porcelain crucible at 1,000°C., cool, and weigh. Deduct a determined blank.

$$\text{g. } K_2O = \text{g. Pt} \times 0.4829$$

NOTES.—1. An ordinary platinum crucible with a well-fitting cover may also be used. For the fusion, it should be mounted in an asbestos board with a hole to fit the crucible about one-third from the bottom. A small beaker of water is placed on the cover to avoid excessive heating of the upper part of the crucible.

2. The temperature for decomposition of the sample should be sufficiently high that not more than 5% of the residue is insoluble in HCl.

3. The flame photometer may also be used for determining potassium, as well as sodium, and is probably the method of choice in those laboratories so equipped.

## SODIUM (ZINC URANYL ACETATE METHOD)

*Procedure.*—Weigh 1 g. of the ground sample and transfer to a platinum dish. Add 20 ml. of HF, 200 ml. of $H_2O$, and 50 ml. of 1:1 $NH_4OH$. Evaporate to fumes and heat under a Dutch oven or other overhead heater until dry. Add 10 ml. of HF, 10 ml. of $H_2O$, and 25 ml. of $NH_4OH$. Repeat the fuming without taking to dryness, and remove the dish from the Dutch oven while it is still moist and fuming.

Add 5 ml. of $H_2SO_4$ and heat until all fumes are driven off. Ignite at 500–550°C. Add 5 ml. of $H_2SO_4$ and heat again until all fumes are driven off. Add 2 ml. of $H_2SO_4$ and fume, leaving about 1 ml. of acid in the dish.

Add 50 ml. of $H_2O$ and evaporate to 7 ml. Cool, add 70 ml. of filtered zinc uranyl acetate solution (Note 2) and stir until a precipitate forms. Let stand for at least 0.5 hour. Filter with suction through a Gooch or medium fritted-glass crucible. Use a minimum quantity of solution to wash the precipitate into the filter. Wash several times with 2-ml. portions of denatured alcohol, then 5 times with 2-ml. portions of acetone. Draw air through the crucible for several minutes, dry in an oven at 105°C. for not more than 15 minutes, cool in a desiccator, and weigh.

Dissolve the precipitate through the crucible with hot $H_2O$ and wash five times with acetone. Apply suction for several minutes, dry at 105°C. for 15 minutes, cool in a desiccator, and weigh. The difference in weight represents sodium zinc uranyl acetate. Deduct a determined blank.

$$g. \ Na_2O = g. \ NaC_2H_3O_2 \cdot Zn(C_2H_3O_2)_2 \cdot 3UO_2(C_2H_3O_2)_2 \cdot 6H_2O \times 0.02015$$

NOTES.—1. If complete solution of the sample is not obtained, start a new sample and fume 3 times instead of twice with ammonium fluoride.

2. The solubility of sodium zinc uranyl acetate is appreciable and varies with temperature. The quantity of sodium soluble in the solution should be controlled by filtering the reagent and the test solutions at approximately the same temperature.

## ANALYSIS OF HYDRATED ALUMINA

### MOISTURE

*Procedure.*—Dry a 2-g. sample to a constant weight at 110°C. Report the loss as moisture.

### LOSS ON IGNITION

*Procedure.*—Dry a 1-g. sample in a weighed, covered platinum crucible at a gradually increasing temperature, ignite at 1100°C. to constant weight, cool in a desiccator, and weigh.

NOTE.—Gradual heating in a furnace starting below 500°C. is recommended in order to avoid loss of solid material.

### INSOLUBLE MATTER

*Procedure.*—To a 10-g. sample add 50 ml. of 1:1 $H_2SO_4$ and boil until the solution is clear. Do not fume. Dilute with 150 ml. of hot water and boil for several minutes. Filter on a medium paper and wash thoroughly with hot water. Transfer the paper and contents to a weighed 10-ml. platinum crucible. Burn off the paper and ignite 1 hour at 1000°C. Cool in a desiccator and weigh.

### SILICA

*Procedure.*—Mix together on a clean paper 4 g. of sample, 2.5 g. of $Na_2B_4O_7$, and 10 g. of $Na_2CO_3$. Transfer to a 150-ml. platinum dish and fuse at about 1000°C. Swirl the contents of the dish, fuse for an additional 15 minutes and allow to cool. Fill the dish with water, heat to dissolve the melt, and transfer the solution to a 400-ml. beaker containing 100 ml. of $H_2O$. Rinse the dish with 10–20 drops of 1:1 $H_2SO_4$. Adjust the pH to 1.6 by adding 1:1 $H_2SO_4$ dropwise. Cool to room temperature, transfer to a 250-ml. volumetric flask, dilute to the mark, and mix. Withdraw a 50-ml. aliquot and dilute to about 70 ml. Adjust the pH to 1.4 with dilute $H_2SO_4$ and transfer to a 100-ml. volumetric flask. Cool in ice water. Add 5 ml. of ammonium molybdate solution and mix. After 5 minutes, add 10 ml. of 1:1 $H_2SO_4$. Remove from the ice bath, add 5 ml. of ferrous ammonium sulfate, dilute to the mark, and mix. Measure or compare the color with suitable standards prepared by adding measured amounts of standard sodium silicate solution to carbonate-borate mixtures carried through the fusion procedure. For preparing a blank or reference solution, also use a fused carbonate-borate mixture. A 660-m$\mu$ filter, or wavelength of near 700 m$\mu$, is satisfactory for photometric measurement.

## IRON

*Procedure.*—Weigh a 10-g. sample and boil with 40 ml. of 1:1 $H_2SO_4$ in a 400-ml. beaker until dissolved. Do not evaporate to fumes. Cool, add cold water, filter, and wash with hot water. Cool the filtrate and washings, transfer to a 250-ml. volumetric flask, dilute to the mark, and mix. Transfer a 25-ml. aliquot to a 100-ml. volumetric flask. Add 1 ml. of hydroxylamine hydrochloride solution and mix. Add 10 ml. of 1,10-phenanthroline solution and 15 ml. of ammonium acetate buffer solution. Add a small piece of Congo red paper to a flask and neutralize with 1:1 $NH_4OH$ to the red color. Dilute to 100 ml. and mix. Measure or compare the color with suitable standards using a blank reference solution prepared with the same quantities of reagents used for the sample. For photometric measurement, use a wavelength of 510 m$\mu$.

NOTE.—Reserve the remainder of the 250-ml. sample solution for the determination of titanium.

## TITANIUM

*Procedure.*—Transfer a 100-ml. aliquot of the sample solution prepared for the iron determination to a 100-ml. Nessler tube. Add 10 ml. of 1:1 $H_2SO_4$ and 8 drops of 30% $H_2O_2$ and mix. To 100 ml. of a blank solution representing the same quantities of reagents, add standard titanium solution to match the color of the sample.

NOTE.—Photometric measurement with a blue filter or wavelength in the 400-m$\mu$ region may be used, provided cells of sufficient depth are available for the instrument used. Because of the low titanium content, visual comparison using Nessler tubes is usually more sensitive than photometric measurement in ordinary cells of 1 to 2 cm.

## SODIUM

*Procedure.*—Transfer 1 g. of sample to a 250-ml. beaker, moisten with water, and add 2.5 ml. of $H_2SO_4$. Continue heating until most of the acid is driven off. Add a little water and heat further to dissolve salts. Evaporate to 7 ml. without taking to dryness. Add 70 ml. of filtered zinc uranyl acetate solution and allow to stand for 1 hour at room temperature with occasional stirring. Filter on a medium porosity, fritted-glass crucible using zinc uranyl acetate solution to transfer the precipitate. Wash twice with this solution. Wash twice with denatured alcohol and twice with acetone. Dry 15 minutes at 105°C., cool in a desiccator, and weigh. Dissolve the precipitate by drawing hot water through the crucible and wash twice with acetone. Dry the crucible at 105°C. for 15 minutes, cool, and weigh. Deduct a determined blank.

$$g. Na_2O = g. NaC_2H_3O_2 \cdot Zn(C_2H_3O_2)_2 \cdot 3UO_2(C_2H_3O_2)_2 \cdot 6H_2O \times 0.02015$$

NOTE.—Filter the precipitate and reagent solution at approximately the same temperature in order to compensate for solubility of the triple acetate. Also, if a saturated alcohol wash solution is used, this should be filtered under the same conditions.

## ANALYSIS OF CALCINED ALUMINA

Alumina, although ordinarily soluble in acids, is very difficult to dissolve if calcined. It may be best dissolved, in this case, by fusion with sodium carbonate and sodium borate or with acid potassium sulfate, followed by an acid extraction. Calcined aluminas are also dissolved by hydrochloric acid on heating in sealed tubes.[16] This is an excellent method of decomposing samples preparatory to determining trace impurities, although special bombs for holding the tubes are required.

### LOSS ON IGNITION

*Procedure.*—Weigh 1 g. of sample in a weighed, covered crucible. Heat gradually at first, ignite at 1100°C. to constant weight, cool in a desiccator, and weigh.

### SILICA

*Procedure.*—Mix together on a clean paper 2.5 g. of sample, 2.5 g. of $Na_2B_4O_7$ and 10 g. of $Na_2CO_3$. Transfer to a platinum crucible with cover and fuse at about 1000°C. When fusion is complete, swirl the contents of the crucible, remove the lid, heat for an additional period of 15 minutes, and allow to cool.

Fill the crucible with $H_2O$ and heat until the entire melt has dissolved. Cool and transfer the solution to a 400-ml. beaker containing about 100 ml. of $H_2O$ (see Note). Rinse the dish with 1 to 2 ml. of 1:1 $H_2SO_4$. Adjust the pH to 1.6 with 1:1 $H_2SO_4$ and dilute to 250 ml. in a volumetric flask. Prepare a blank in the same way. These solutions may be used for determining iron and titanium, in addition to silica.

Pipette 50 ml. of the sample solution into a 250-ml. beaker. In addition, pipette 50-ml. aliquots of the blank solution for use as a reference solution and for preparation of a standard. Add to one portion of the blank a measured volume of standard silica solution approximating the silica of the sample aliquot. Dilute each to about 70 ml. and adjust to pH 1.4 using 1:3 $H_2SO_4$. Cool in an ice bath and add 5 ml. of ammonium molybdate solution to each beaker and mix. After 5 minutes add 10 ml. of 1:1 $H_2SO_4$. Remove from the ice bath, transfer to 100-ml. volumetric flasks, dilute to approximately 90 ml., add 5 ml. of $FeSO_4 \cdot (NH_4)_2SO_4$ solution, and mix. Dilute to the mark and again mix. Measure or compare the colors of the sample and standard solutions against the reference solution. For photometric measurement, a 660-m$\mu$ filter or wavelength of 670 to 700 m$\mu$ is satisfactory.

NOTE.—Contamination by silica from glass beakers can be avoided by neutralizing the solution immediately. Plastic beakers are preferable.

### IRON

*Procedure.*—From the sample and blank solution, prepared in the determination of silica, pipette 50-ml. aliquots into 250-ml. beakers for preparation of sample, blank, and standard solution. To prepare the standard, add a measured volume of standard iron solution approximating the iron content of the sample to one of the portions of the blank solution. To each solution, add 1 ml. of 10% hydroxylamine hydrochloride and mix. Add 10 ml. of 0.25% 1,10-phenanthroline

---

[16] Jackson, H., Analyst, **75**, 414, 1950; Gordon, C. L., Schlecht, W. G., and Wichers, E., J. Research Nat. Bur. Standards, **33**, 457, 1944.

solution and neutralize with ammonium acetate solution using Congo red paper. Dilute each to 100 ml. Measure or compare the color of the sample and standard solutions against the blank using a wavelength of 510 m$\mu$.

### TITANIUM

*Procedure.*—To 100-ml. aliquots of the sample and blank solutions prepared in the silica determination, add 10 ml. of 1:1 $H_2SO_4$ and 8 drops of 30% $H_2O_2$. Transfer to Nessler tubes and add standard titanium solution to the blank until the color matches that of the sample solution. Nessler tubes are commonly used for this determination because the concentration of titanium is too low for measurement in the absorption cells ordinarily used for photometers.

### SODIUM

*Procedure.*—Weigh 1 g. of finely ground sample into a platinum dish. Add 20 ml. of HF, 20 ml. of $H_2O$, and 50 ml. of $NH_4OH$. Evaporate to fumes and heat until almost dry, preferably with overhead heating. Do not bake. Add 10 ml. of HF, 10 ml. of $H_2O$, and 25 ml. of 1:1 $NH_4OH$ and repeat the fuming but do not take to dryness. While still moist, add 5 ml. of $H_2SO_4$ and heat until all fumes are evolved. Ignite at 500 to 550°C. Add 50 ml. of $H_2SO_4$ and heat again until fumes are driven off. Add 2 ml. of $H_2SO_4$ and fume again leaving about 1 ml. of acid. Add 50 ml. of $H_2O$ and digest until the solution clears. If complete solution of the sample is not achieved, start a new sample and fume 3 times instead of twice with the HF, $H_2O$ and $NH_4OH$. Evaporate to 7 ml., cool, and add 70 ml. of filtered zinc uranyl acetate solution (Note 2). Stir until a precipitate forms. Allow to stand for 30 minutes. Filter with suction through a medium-porosity, fritted-glass crucible. Wash the precipitate into the filter with a minimum quantity of zinc uranyl acetate. Wash twice with 2-ml. portions of denatured alcohol followed with 2-ml. portions of acetone. Draw air through the crucible at 105°C. for 15 minutes, cool, and weigh. Dissolve the precipitate through the crucible with hot water and wash with acetone. Apply suction for a few minutes, dry at 105°C. for 15 minutes, cool, and weigh. Deduct a determined blank.

$$\text{g. } Na_2O = \text{g. } NaC_2H_3O_2 \cdot Zn(C_2H_3O_2)_2 \cdot 3UO_2(C_2H_3O_2)_2 \cdot 6H_2O \times 0.02015$$

NOTES.—1. For samples containing less than 0.1% $Na_2O$ a measured amount of sodium may be added to the sample and carried through the procedure. In such cases, use the same quantity of sodium in establishing the blank.

2. In order to minimize solubility errors, the precipitation reagent solution should be filtered at the same temperature.

3. The foregoing procedure for dissolving the sample may be combined conveniently with flame photometric measurement of the sodium in the usual way.

## ANALYSIS OF FUSED ALUMINUM OXIDE [17]

*Preparation of Sample.*—Select a sample of appropriate size, and crush to approximately ⅛-in. mesh size, taking precautions to avoid contamination during crushing. If the crushed sample is of non-uniform composition, mix and quarter as needed to provide a representative sample. Pulverize the crushed sample to pass a 60-mesh sieve, preferably using equipment that will not introduce constituents to be

[17] Method used by the Norton Company; courtesy of M. O. Lamar and R. M. Rebert.

determined. To free the sample of magnetic material, stir the pulverized sample repeatedly with a magnet.

*Blank.*—Carry a reagent blank through the same procedure as for the sample, preferably using a pure solution of an aluminum salt known to be free from the elements sought.

*Fusion of Sample.*—Weigh 2 g. of pulverized sample in a 30-ml. platinum crucible, add 4 g. of sodium carbonate-borax mixture (1:1 ratio by weight of anhydrous salts), mix thoroughly, and cover. Heat over a Fisher burner, first using only enough heat to melt the mixture and then raising to full heat for about 5 minutes. Allow to cool, add 4 g. more of the sodium carbonate-borax mixture, and repeat the fusion, finally heating with full heat for 45 minutes. At 15-minute intervals, swirl the crucible to assure that unfused particles are carried into the melt. Pour the melt into a clean, dry aluminum plate and cover the resulting button with the platinum crucible.

## SILICA

*Procedure.*—Place the button, crucible, and cover in a beaker containing 80 ml. of 1:1 $H_2SO_4$, and boil to dissolve the button. Remove the crucible and cover and rinse with hot water. Cover the beaker and evaporate to strong fumes of $SO_3$, taking precautions to avoid bumping and spattering. Cool, add 125 ml. of water, and boil to dissolve salts. Filter while hot, police the beaker, and wash 10 to 12 times with hot water. For more accurate work, take the filtrate and repeat the evaporation, addition of water, and filtration as before. (Reserve the filtrate, *A*.)

For accurate work, char the paper and contents in a platinum dish, fuse the impure $SiO_2$ residue with 1 g. of $Na_2CO_3$, and make double evaporations with HCl (or $H_2SO_4$). (When silica is dehydrated from a borate solution, it carries a slight contamination of $B_2O_3$ which is volatilized as $BF_3$ and counted as $SiO_2$.) For ordinary work, char the paper and contents in a platinum crucible. In either case, ignite the platinum container at full heat of a burner for 15 minutes, cool in a desiccator, and weigh. Add 2 drops of 1:1 $H_2SO_4$ and 2 to 3 ml. of HF and evaporate to dryness. Re-ignite, cool, and weigh. Record the loss in weight and multiply by 50 (for 2-g. sample) to report the percentage of $SiO_2$.

Fuse the residue with 2 to 3 g. of $KHSO_4$, dissolve the melt in a minimum amount of 1:3 $H_2SO_4$, and add the solution to the silica filtrate, *A*.

## SEPARATION OF IRON, TITANIUM, ZIRCONIUM, CALCIUM, MAGNESIUM, AND MANGANESE FROM CHROMIUM, VANADIUM, ALUMINUM, AND PHOSPHORUS

*Procedure.*—Evaporate the silica filtrate, *A*, to about 150 ml. and cool. Neutralize by adding 50% NaOH until the precipitate formed just re-dissolves. Pour the neutralized solution into 150 ml. of cold 15% NaOH containing 1 g. each of $Na_2CO_3$ and $Na_2O_2$. Rinse the beaker twice with hot water, adding the rinsings to the solution. Heat the solution on a steam bath for 1 hour. (Iron, titanium, and zirconium are precipitated as hydroxides, calcium and magnesium as carbonates, and chromium is oxidized to chromate and goes into solution with aluminum, vanadium, and phosphorus.) Cool, filter on a paper previously washed with 15% NaOH, and wash the precipitate *B* with 1% $Na_2CO_3$ several times. (Reserve the filtrate, *C*, for determining chromium, vanadium, and phosphorus.)

Dissolve the precipitate, $B$, in 25 ml. of hot 1:2 HCl and wash the paper thoroughly with hot 1:100 HCl. Dilute to about 150 ml. and heat to boiling. Add a few drops of methyl red and neutralize with $NH_4OH$, adding a few drops in excess. Filter and wash with hot 2% $NH_4Cl$. Repeat the $NH_4OH$ separation as before. (The precipitate, $D$, resulting from the double $NH_4OH$ separation contains iron, titanium, and zirconium.) Combine the filtrates, $E$, from the $NH_4OH$ separations, evaporate to about 75 ml., and reserve for determining manganese, calcium, and magnesium.

### SEPARATION OF IRON FROM TITANIUM AND ZIRCONIUM

*Procedure.*—Dissolve the precipitate, $D$, in hot 1:1 HCl, add 4 g. of tartaric acid, dilute with water to 150 ml., and neutralize with $NH_4OH$. Add 2 ml. of HCl for each 100 ml. of volume, heat to boiling, and saturate with $H_2S$. Allow to stand (preferably overnight), filter off any platinum sulfide present, and wash with 1:100 $H_2SO_4$ saturated with $H_2S$. Make the filtrate alkaline with $NH_4OH$, pass in $H_2S$ for 5 minutes, and allow to stand 30 minutes. Filter and wash the iron precipitate, $F$, with a 5:95 HCl solution containing 2% $NH_4Cl$ and saturated with $H_2S$. Reserve the filtrate, $G$, for determining titanium and zirconium.

Return the paper and precipitate, $F$, to the beaker in which the iron was precipitated, add 20 to 30 ml. of $HNO_3$ and 5 ml. of $H_2SO_4$, and cover. Evaporate to strong fumes of $SO_3$, adding more $HNO_3$ as needed to destroy organic matter. Cool and reserve for the determination of iron.

### IRON (GRAVIMETRIC METHOD)

*Procedure.*—Dilute the solution obtained from $F$ to 100 to 200 ml. (depending on the amount of iron present), heat to boiling, and precipitate with a slight excess of $NH_4OH$. Add paper pulp, filter, and wash with hot 2% $NH_4Cl$. (Discard the filtrate.) Ignite the paper and contents and weigh as $Fe_2O_3$. For greater accuracy, correct for $SiO_2$ by treating with HF and a few drops of $H_2SO_4$, evaporating to dryness, and igniting at 950°C.

### IRON (COLORIMETRIC METHOD)

*Procedure.*—Dilute the solution obtained from $F$ to 250 ml., and pipette 10-ml. aliquots into a 50-ml. volumetric flask and a small beaker. Add 4 drops of bromphenol blue indicator and titrate with 2 $M$ sodium acetate to a blue-purple color, thus adjusting to about pH 3.5. Add to the flask 2 ml. of 10% hydroxylamine hydrochloride to reduce the iron, and 3 ml. of 0.2% 1,10-phenanthroline and the same volume of 2 $M$ sodium acetate required for the titration, with thorough swirling of the flask between additions. Dilute to the mark, mix, and allow to stand for 20 minutes. Determine $Fe_2O_3$ colorimetrically directly from a prepared calibration chart.

### TITANIUM AND ZIRCONIUM

*Procedure.*—Neutralize the filtrate, $G$, in a covered beaker with $H_2SO_4$ and dilute to 200 ml. Add 20 ml. of $H_2SO_4$, boil out $H_2S$, and cool to 5 to 10°C. Add cold 4% cupferron solution until a white milkiness is produced which disappears on stirring. Add paper pulp, filter with suction, and wash with 1:10 HCl 15 times.

Place the paper in a weighed crucible, char slowly, ignite to constant weight, and weigh as $TiO_2 + ZrO_2$.

Fuse the residue with $K_2S_2O_7$ and dissolve in cold 10% $H_2SO_4$, keeping the volume small. Add an excess of $H_2O_2$ and 0.5 g. of diammonium phosphate, and stir until the phosphate is dissolved. Allow to stand overnight at about 40°C. Filter, wash with 5% $NH_4NO_3$, ignite carefully to avoid decrepitation, and weigh as $ZrP_2O_7$. Calculate $ZrO_2$ equivalent and subtract from the weight of $TiO_2 + ZrO_2$.

## MANGANESE

*Procedure.*—Heat the filtrate, $E$, to 60°C., and add $NH_4OH$ until distinctly alkaline and bromine water in excess. Set on a steam bath until $MnO_2$ has flocculated. Filter on a dense paper and wash with water a few times. (Reserve the filtrate, $J$.) Dissolve the precipitate in 1:9 $HNO_3$ containing a few drops of $H_2O_2$, boil out excess $H_2O_2$, and determine Mn either colorimetrically or volumetrically.

For the colorimetric determination, add 5 ml. of $H_2SO_4$ and 0.3 g. of $KIO_4$, and heat to develop the color. Adjust the volume and compare with standards.

For the volumetric determination, add 15 ml. of $AgNO_3$ (6 g. per liter) and 10 ml. of 15% $(NH_4)_2S_2O_8$, and heat to 90°C. to develop the permanganate color. Cool in ice water, add 10 ml. of 10% $NaCl$, and titrate with sodium arsenite standardized against a standard steel or standard permanganate.

## CALCIUM

*Procedure.*—Evaporate the filtrate, $J$, from the manganese determination, if necessary, to 100 to 120 ml., heat to boiling, and add 10 ml. of 4% ammonium oxalate solution. Let stand overnight, filter, and wash with 0.5% ammonium oxalate. Dissolve the precipitate in dilute HCl and wash several times with water. Add 0.1 g. of $(NH_4)_2C_2O_4 \cdot 2H_2O$ and reprecipitate with $NH_4OH$. Let stand at least 4 hours, filter and wash as before, ignite, and weigh as CaO. Combine the filtrates, $K$, and reserve for the determination of magnesium.

## MAGNESIUM

*Procedure.*—If the magnesia content is small, destroy the ammonium salts in the filtrate, $K$, with nitric-hydrochloric acid, take up the residue in water and a few ml. of 1:1 HCl, and filter to remove silica. Otherwise, evaporate the filtrate, $K$, to 200 ml. In either case, add 1 g. of diammonium phosphate dissolved in a few ml. of water. Add 10% by volume of $NH_4OH$, set the beaker in ice water, and stir vigorously. Let stand overnight, filter, and wash with 5% $NH_4OH$. Dissolve the precipitate in hot dilute HCl and wash with warm water. Let the filtrate cool, add 0.1 g. of diammonium phosphate, and reprecipitate with $NH_4OH$. Let stand at least 4 hours, filter, and wash as before. Char the paper, ignite in a muffle or under good oxidizing conditions, and weigh as $Mg_2P_2O_7$. Calculate to MgO.

## CHROMIUM

*Procedure.*—Dilute the filtrate, $C$, to 500 ml. or 250 ml., depending on the color, and compare with a standard $K_2CrO_4$ solution containing approximately the same amount of sodium hydroxide. Calculate to $Cr_2O_3$. The amount found is usually less than 0.10%.

Platinum from the crucible, if present, interferes with the chromium color. To check, acidify with $HNO_3$ and reduce with $SO_2$. If the solution becomes colorless on stirring, no interference is indicated. If Pt is found, match the color with $K_2CrO_4$ and apply the proper correction. Reserve the chromium solution for the determination of vanadium.

## VANADIUM

*Procedure.*—Acidify the chromium solution and precipitate with a slight excess of $NH_4OH$ without use of an indicator. It will be necessary to precipitate in rather a large volume (about 1000 ml.) because of the alumina present. Filter on one or more large loose-textured papers and wash with hot 3% $NH_4NO_3$ a few times to remove the bulk of the sodium salts. Transfer most of the precipitate back to the beaker and dissolve that on the papers by repeatedly pouring through 100 ml. of hot 1:9 $HNO_3$. Add a few drops of $H_2O_2$ to the cold solution, and if any color develops, compare with a standard vanadium solution colorimetrically under the same conditions. Report as $V_2O_5$. Reserve the vanadium solution for the determination of phosphorus.

## PHOSPHORUS

*Procedure.*—Transfer the vanadium solution to a 300-ml. Erlenmeyer flask and boil out the $H_2O_2$. Add strong $KMnO_4$ to a pink color and a sulfite solution to decolorize. Add 15 ml. of $HNO_3$, cool, and adjust the volume to about 125 ml. Add 50 ml. of ammonium molybdate, shake for 10 minutes, and let settle for 1 hour. Filter on a dense paper, wash with 1% $KNO_3$ until free from acid, and place the paper in the flask. Add an excess of 0.1 $N$ NaOH, shake to disintegrate the paper, and dilute to 100 ml. with $CO_2$-free water. Add a few drops of phenolphthalein and discharge the pink color with standard $HNO_3$. Add 0.1 $N$ NaOH to return the pink color and from the ratio of the acid and alkali and their respective volumes used, calculate $P_2O_5$, using the ratio 1 $P_2O_5$ to 46 NaOH. Standardize the NaOH against a standard sample of steel or against reagent-grade potassium acid phthalate.

## TOTAL SULFUR AS $SO_3$

*Procedure.*—Fuse a 2-g. sample with $Na_2CO_3 \cdot Na_2B_4O_7$ just as for the silica determination, using an electric muffle furnace or other means to avoid contamination by sulfur. Dissolve the melt with hot water, filter, and wash with 1% $Na_2CO_3$. Acidify the filtrate with HCl using only enough excess to give about 1% by volume. Heat to boiling, precipitate with $BaCl_2$, and let stand overnight. Filter, ignite at 900°C., and weigh as $BaSO_4$.

## SODA AND POTASH

*Procedure.*—Grind a portion of sample to an impalpable powder in an agate mortar (preferably an old one because of the abrasive action). Determine soda and potash using a 0.5-g. sample by the J. Lawrence Smith method,[3] applying blanks for the reagents $CaCO_3$ and $NH_4Cl$. Use of the special crucible is almost compulsory because the full heat of the Fisher burner must be used for 1.5 hours in order to insure complete decomposition of the sample. After the mixed NaCl and KCl are weighed, determine potassium by weighing as the chloroplatinate.

## METHODS FOR ALUMINUM IN ANALYSES
## IN OTHER CHAPTERS

| | |
|---|---|
| Aluminum in Beryllium Metal | See Analysis of Beryllium Metal |
| Aluminum in Magnesite | See Analysis of Magnesite (Magnesium Chapter) |
| Aluminum in Magnesium Alloys | See Magnesium Chapter |
| Aluminum in Metallic Nickel | See Analysis of Metallic Nickel |
| Aluminum in Commercial Phosphates | See Analysis of Commercial Phosphates |
| Aluminum in Sodium Silicate | See Analysis of Sodium Silicate (Silicon Chapter) |
| Aluminum with Titanium | See Analysis of Titaniferous Ores |

## Chapter 3

# ANTIMONY

Sb, *at. wt.* 121.75; *sp. gr.* 6.691; *m.p.* 630.5°C.; *b.p.* 1380°C.; *oxides,* $Sb_2O_3$, $Sb_2O_4$, $Sb_2O_5$.

Antimony occurs chiefly as stibnite, a gray or black iridescent substance, $Sb_2S_3$. There are small occurrences of the free element as well as various antimonides and sulfantimonides. The chief uses of antimony are in alloys, paints, and rubber.

### DETECTION

*Hydrogen sulfide* precipitates orange-colored antimony sulfides from 0.2 to 0.5 $N$ solutions of hydrochloric or sulfuric acid. The following elements are also completely precipitated: $Ag+$; As(III); Au(III); Bi(III); $Cd++$ (at 0.2 $N$ [$H+$]); $Cu++$; $Hg++$; $Pd++$; Se(IV); $Sn++$; $Sn+4$; $Te+4$. The following are incompletely precipitated: $As+5$; $Re+7$; $Ge+4$; $Ir+4$; $Mo+6$; Os; $Pb+$ (at 0.5 $N$ acid); $Pt+4$; $Rh+4$; $Ru+4$; $Se+6$; $Tc+6$.

Upon treatment of the precipitate with NaOH, KOH, $Na_2S$, or $(NH_4)_2S_x$, antimony sulfide is dissolved and reprecipitated upon acidifying the filtrate. As, Sn, Mo, Ge, Ir, and Te form soluble sulfo-salts which behave in a manner similar to antimony. If arsenic, antimony, and tin are present, the precipitated mixture of sulfides is dissolved in hot concentrated hydrochloric acid with the addition of crystals of potassium chlorate, from time to time, until the sulfides are dissolved. The solution is placed in a Marsh apparatus, pure zinc is added, and the evolved gases are passed into a neutral solution of silver nitrate. The black precipitate of silver antimonide and silver is filtered off, washed free of arsenious acid, and the antimonide is dissolved in concentrated hydrochloric acid (silver remains insoluble). The orange-colored antimony sulfide may now be precipitated by diluting with water and passing in $H_2S$ gas to saturation.

*Minerals* that contain antimony, when heated alone or with 3 to 4 parts of a fusion mixture ($K_2CO_3$ and $Na_2CO_3$), on charcoal, yield dense white fumes, a portion of the antimony oxide remaining as a white incrustation on the charcoal. A drop of ammonium sulfide placed upon this sublimate gives a deep orange stain.

*Hydrolysis.*—Most of the inorganic salts of antimony are decomposed by water, forming insoluble basic salts or hydrous oxides or acids. Tartaric acid forms soluble complex compounds and an excess of this acid will prevent hydrolysis.

*Traces of Antimony.*—Traces of antimony may be detected by evolution of stibine that forms when the antimony solution is treated with zinc and hydrochloric or sulfuric acid in a Marsh test apparatus. Sensitive colorimetric methods will be described for micro amounts of antimony; these methods also serve for the detection.

*Antimonic salts* liberate iodine, whereas the formation of green chromic ion occurs when antimonous solutions are treated with potassium dichromate. These reactions serve to distinguish the states of oxidation.

## ESTIMATION

Provision must be made for decomposing various types of samples, such as ores, bearing and type metal alloys, hard lead, paints, vulcanized rubber, organic and biological products, etc. The volatility of the chlorides and bromides and the hydrolytic tendencies must be taken into account in planning a procedure.

## PREPARATION AND SOLUTION OF THE SAMPLE

Metallic antimony is practically insoluble in cold dilute hydrochloric acid, nitric acid, or sulfuric acid; $Sb_2O_3$ or $Sb_2O_5$ are precipitated as acids or hydrous oxides in concentrated nitric acid. The element is readily soluble in hydrochloric acid containing an oxidizing agent, such as nitric acid, potassium chlorate, chlorine, bromine, etc. The oxides of antimony are soluble in hydrochloric acid or in sodium or potassium hydroxide. The boiling points of the chlorides are $SbCl_3$ 223°C., $SbCl_5$ 140°C. Appreciable losses occur when one attempts to concentrate a dilute hydrochloric acid solution of antimony trichloride down to half its volume on a steam bath. Little loss of the pentavalent material occurs on mild concentration. If antimony in either state of oxidation in HCl solution is evaporated with sulfuric acid to displace the chloride, very serious losses occur. Moreover, because of the low boiling point of $SbCl_5$, antimony may be lost in acid digestions with oxidizing agents.

If siliceous material containing antimony is fused with sodium carbonate, antimony may hydrolyze and remain with the silica unless the latter is washed with sufficiently concentrated hydrochloric acid to prevent hydrolysis.

Concentrated sulfuric acid decomposes alloys, ores, etc., and a solution of the antimony may be obtained if a complexing agent, such as tartaric acid, is used after diluting the sulfuric acid solution.

Alloys and many other materials containing antimony dissolve upon moderate warming of the material with a solution containing 5 ml. of concentrated hydrofluoric and 5 ml. of concentrated nitric acid in 30 ml. The complexing action of the fluoride prevents hydrolysis.

### *SOLUTION OF SULFIDE ORES, LOW-GRADE OXIDES, ETC.*[1]

From 0.5 to 1 g. of the finely powdered ore, placed in a Kjeldahl flask, is mixed with 5 to 7 g. of granular or powdered potassium sulfate and 10 ml. of concentrated sulfuric acid. About 0.5 g. of tartaric acid, or a piece of filter paper, is added to reduce arsenic or antimonic compounds and the mixture is heated, gradually at first and then with the full Bunsen flame. The heating is continued until the carbon is completely oxidized and most of the free acid driven off, leaving a clean fusion mixture, but taking care not to expel all the $H_2SO_4$. The melt is allowed to cool over the bottom and sides of the flask by rotating gently during the cooling.

Then 50 ml. of hydrochloric acid $(1 + 1)$ are added and the melt is dissolved by gentle warming. The contents of the flask are transferred to an Erlenmeyer flask, rinsing the original flask with 25 ml. of concentrated hydrochloric acid.

[1] Method of A. H. Low, Modified.

Arsenic sulfide may now be precipitated by $H_2S$ from the strongly acid solution, while antimony, etc., remain in solution. The sulfide is filtered through a double filter supported by a platinum cone and moistened with hydrochloric acid $(2 + 1)$, or a glass or porcelain filter crucible may be used. The flask is rinsed out with $(2 + 1)$ hydrochloric acid, and the precipitate is washed at least six times with this acid. Antimony passes into the filtrate together with other elements in the ore.

The filtrate is diluted with double its volume of warm water and then is saturated with hydrogen sulfide. Antimony sulfide, together with other elements of the hydrogen sulfide group, will precipitate. These sulfides are washed with hydrogen sulfide water. Antimony sulfide is separated from sulfides of Cu, Pb, Cd, Bi, etc., by addition of sodium sulfide-sodium hydroxide solution (5–10 ml. of a mixture of 60 g. $Na_2S$ with 40 g. of NaOH diluted to 1000 ml.).

The solution and washings containing the antimony is treated with 2 g. of potassium sulfate and 10 ml. of concentrated sulfuric acid and heated finally until sulfur is destroyed and most of the free acid has been expelled. The melt is dissolved in hydrochloric acid and the antimony is titrated according to one of the methods under "Titrimetric Procedures."

NOTE.—If an insoluble residue remains from the acid extraction of the first melt, it may be dissolved by fusion with sodium hydroxide and extraction with hot water. If a white crystalline precipitate forms when this solution is acidified with hydrochloric acid, the presence of barium sulfate is indicated.

*Sulfides.*—Howard and Harrison [2] recommended the following procedure for fusion of sulfide ores with sodium carbonate: 0.5 gram of the powdered ore is fused with a mixture of 8 grams of sodium carbonate and sodium peroxide, 1:1, in a nickel crucible. The cooled melt is dissolved with sufficient hydrochloric acid to neutralize the alkali and about 15 ml. of concentrated acid added in excess. The solution is diluted to 250 ml., antimony being kept in solution by addition of potassium chlorate. An aliquot portion of the solution is taken, antimony is reduced by metabisulfite and titrated with iodine.

*Treatment of Speisses, Slags, Mattes, etc.*[3]—0.5 to 2 g. of the sample is treated with 10 to 15 ml. of concentrated nitric acid and the mixture evaporated to dryness. Fifteen ml. of concentrated hydrochloric acid are added and the sample transferred to a 350-ml. flask, additional hydrochloric acid being used to wash out the beaker. Arsenic is precipitated from the concentrated acid solution as the sulfide, and antimony determined in the filtrate.

## DECOMPOSITION OF THE ORES BY FUSION WITH SODIUM HYDROXIDE

*Oxides.*—0.5 to 1 g. of the powdered ore is mixed with about 10 g. of sodium hydroxide and placed in a thin-walled iron crucible of 60 ml. capacity. It is advisable to fuse a portion of the alkali hydroxide in the crucible with a pinch of potassium nitrate and then add the ore mixed with the remainder of the sodium hydroxide. The covered crucible is heated until the fusion becomes homogeneous. The melt is poured out on a large nickel crucible cover or shallow dish. On cooling, the cake is detached and placed in a casserole containing water, any adhering cake on the cover, or melt remaining in the iron crucible, being dis-

2 Pharm. Jour., **83,** 147, 1909.
3 H. E. Hooper's method.

solved with dilute hydrochloric acid and added to the sample in the casserole. About 30 to 40 ml. of concentrated hydrochloric acid are now added and the mixture heated (casserole covered) until the melt has dissolved. Two to 3 g. of tartaric acid having been added to keep antimony dissolved, the solution is diluted to about 300 ml., and antimony is then precipitated as the sulfide with hydrogen sulfide. The treatment of the precipitate at this stage has been given in the "Solution of Sulfide Ores."

## SOLUTION OF ALLOYS

Alloys are generally decomposed by treatment with mixtures of hydrochloric acid together with an oxidizing agent—nitric acid, potassium chlorate, bromine, etc.

Care must be exercised to prevent volatilization of the chlorides, as has been stated in the introductory paragraph.

*Alloys of Antimony, Lead, and Tin.*—0.5 to 1 g. of the finely divided alloy is warmed with 100 ml. of concentrated hydrochloric acid until the action subsides. Solid iodine is now added, small quantities at a time, until the alloy completely dissolves. The excess of iodine is now removed by boiling, and the small amount of free iodine remaining is neutralized with a few drops of a weak solution of sodium thiosulfate. Although tin is oxidized to the higher state, antimony is not oxidized by iodine in acid solution beyond the trivalent form. The solution may now be titrated with standard iodine in presence of an excess of sodium bicarbonate according to the procedure given under titrimetric methods.

*Tin-Base Alloys.*[4]—See "Tin-Base Alloys by the Potassium Bromate Method," page 101.

*Hard Lead.*—The method of dissolution and titration is as given under "Potassium Bromate Method" (page 92).

## ORGANIC COMPOUNDS AND BIOLOGICAL MATERIALS

The wet "ashing" of organic matter for samples of weight of about 1 g. and lower is to treat with diluted sulfuric acid (10 ml. of concentrated sulfuric acid added to 30 ml. of water) and 10 ml. concentrated nitric acid in a Kjeldahl flask. After vigorous action has subsided, the flask is heated, eventually to fumes of sulfuric acid. The solution is diluted after cooling and more nitric acid is added, if needed, and the solution is again heated to fumes of sulfur trioxide. After cooling and diluting, traces of resistant organic matter may be oxidized by adding a few drops of 70% perchloric acid and again evaporating to fumes. Finally the cooled solution is diluted to about 30 ml. and hydrochloric acid or other suitable addition is made to prevent the antimony from hydrolyzing. When blood or urine is to be analyzed, the amounts of reagents are kept at a minimum. Details are given under "Colorimetric Methods" (page 98).

The use of concentrated sulfuric or phosphoric acid plus oxidants, such as potassium permanganate, should be avoided. Even concentrated phosphoric acid plus potassium permanganate has been known to explode, apparently due to formation of $Mn_2O_7$, which is an extremely unstable substance. A concentrated sulfuric acid–peroxide procedure has been reported in which the acid is first allowed to attack the compound, followed by cautious addition of 30 per cent hydrogen peroxide, drop by drop.[5] The most desirable use of the more powerful

[4] Luke, C. L., Ind. Eng. Chem., **16,** 448, 1944.
[5] Tabern and Shelberg, Ind. Eng. Chem., Anal. Ed., **4,** 401, 1932.

and unstable oxidants appears to be the destruction of traces of organic matter after prior destruction of the bulk of the organic matter.

When arsenic and antimony in biological materials are to be retained in a dry ashing procedure, the sample is mixed with 6 g. of magnesium nitrate. After the burning of the organic matter, the residue is dissolved in hydrochloric acid, or other acid as called for in the method that is to be used.

## SEPARATIONS

*The Separation of Antimony (together with Members of the Hydrogen Sulfide Group) from Iron, Chromium, Aluminum, Cobalt, Nickel, Manganese, Zinc, the Alkalies, the Alkaline Earths, and the Rare Earths.*—The acid solution of the elements is saturated with hydrogen sulfide, the elements of the Hydrogen Sulfide Group are precipitated as sulfides, the other elements remaining in solution. Antimony sulfide may be precipitated from a solution containing 15 ml. of concentrated acid per 100 ml. of solution; lead and cadmium are incompletely precipitated.

Thioacetamide is frequently substituted for hydrogen sulfide particularly in semimicro qualitative analytical procedures.

*The Separation of Antimony (together with Arsenic and Tin) from Mercury, Copper, Bismuth, Cadmium, and Lead.*—The sulfides of antimony, arsenic and tin are soluble in a mixture of sodium hydroxide and sodium sulfide (60 g. $Na_2S$ and 40 g. NaOH per liter) with formation of sulfo-salts, whereas mercury, copper, bismuth, cadmium and lead remain as insoluble sulfides. The acid solution is treated with 3 to 5 g. of tartaric acid and diluted slightly, more tartaric acid being added if the solution becomes turbid, then poured into a mixture of 150 ml. of the sodium sulfide-sodium hydroxide mixture plus 150 ml. of water. The mixture is warmed and the insoluble sulfides are allowed to settle out and are filtered off. The filtrate and washings may be treated in either of the following ways:

(a) The sulfo-salts may be oxidized by addition of 30% hydrogen peroxide to the alkaline solution in small portions until the yellow solution is decolorized, then 1 to 2 ml. in excess, and the solution is then boiled to oxidize sulfides completely to sulfates and to expel the excess of hydrogen peroxide. The solution is then acidified.

(b) The sulfo-salt filtrate may be acidified, then heated with addition of potassium chlorate to oxidize the sulfur to sulfuric acid. Upon adding an excess of hydrochloric acid, the sulfides of the three elements are precipitated, but dissolve upon treatment with the potassium chlorate.

**Removal of Arsenic.**—If the determination of arsenic is not needed, this element may be removed by distillation from concentrated hydrochloric acid solution by the procedure described in the Chapter on Arsenic. The arsenic must first be reduced by sodium metabisulfite or potassium iodide and boiling. Antimony and tin remain in the concentrated acid solution. The temperature should be kept below 108°C.; otherwise antimony trichloride may volatilize.

An alternative procedure for separating trivalent arsenic from antimony and tin has been given under "Preparation and Solution of the Sample." The arsenic is precipitated by hydrogen sulfide in a concentrated hydrochloric acid solution, but antimony and tin remain in solution.

**Separation of Antimony from Tin.**—After arsenic has been separated from antimony and tin, the antimony may be determined directly in the presence of the tin by several of the titrimetric methods to be described later. If a gravimetric separation is desired, antimony may be precipitated as the trisulfide in the presence of tin by adding a suitable complexing agent for the latter, which must be in the stannic state.

**Clark's Method.**[6]—This method depends upon the fact that antimony is precipitated as the sulfide, whereas tin forms a soluble complex in a solution containing an excess of oxalic acid. If an acidic solution is at hand, it is made alkaline with about a twentyfold excess of KOH relative to the weights of Sb and Sn, e.g., 2 g. of KOH per 0.1 g. of the metals. Tartaric acid to about ten times the combined weights of the metals is then added, followed by 30% hydrogen peroxide to decolorize the solution plus about 1 ml. in excess. The tin is thus oxidized to the stannic state and the excess hydrogen peroxide is decomposed by boiling. Then 5 g. of oxalic acid, dissolved in hot water, is added to the somewhat cooled solution. After boiling for 10 minutes the solution is diluted to 100 ml. Hydrogen sulfide is passed into the boiling solution until the white turbidity changes to an orange color and antimony sulfide begins to precipitate. The passage of the gas is continued for 15 minutes, the solution is diluted to 250 ml., and the passage of the gas is continued 15 minutes longer. The flame is now removed and the gas is passed in 10 minutes longer. The precipitated antimony pentasulfide is collected on a filtering crucible. It may be determined gravimetrically as $Sb_2S_3$ after washing with 1% oxalic acid and acetic acid, the solutions being hot and saturated with hydrogen sulfide. The precipitate is heated in a current of $CO_2$ at 280–300°C. and weighed as $Sb_2S_3$.

Tin may be determined electrolytically in the filtrate after evaporating it to 150 ml., the oxalic acid being nearly neutralized with ammonia. See "Electrolytic Determination of Tin" in Chapter on Tin.

**Separation by Iron.**—Antimony and tin sulfides are dissolved by treatment with hydrochloric acid and potassium chlorate. Metallic iron displaces antimony from the hot solution that should contain 10% by volume of concentrated HCl. More of this acid is added as the iron dissolves, and the antimony metal is precipitated.

**Separations in Solutions Containing Fluoride.**—Trivalent antimony or arsenic, together with copper, lead, bismuth, and cadmium are separated from stannic tin by hydrogen sulfide in solutions that contain a moderate amount of hydrochloric or sulfuric acid together with 2 to 5 ml. of 48% hydrofluoric acid per 100 to 500 ml.[7] Vessels of platinum, paraffin, glass coated with paraffin, Bakelite and other plastic beakers, Vycor and even glass have been used successfully. If glass is used, the solutions must be transferred to more resistant ware for storage. After the removal of antimony as the sulfide, the filtrate may be heated with excess boric acid to complex the fluoride. Tin may then be precipitated by cupferron, by hydrogen sulfide, or by electrodeposition. A rather large amount, 4 g. of boric acid is necessary to complex the fluoride from 2 ml. of 48% hydrogen fluoride.[8] The electrolytic separation of the tin from the fluoborate solution, with oxalic acid added, is less satisfactory than its removal by cupferron.

[6] Chem. News, **21,** 124, 1870.

[7] McCay, J., Am. Chem. Soc., **31,** 373, 1908; Separation of Tin and Arsenic, J. Am. Chem. Soc., **45,** 1187, 1923; Separation of Arsenic and Antimony, J. Am. Chem. Soc., **50,** 368, 1928. Arsenic precipitated as silver arsenate: Analysis of Tin-Antimony Alloys, J. Am. Chem. Soc., **32,** 1241, 1910; H. Ravner, Ind. Eng. Chem., Anal. Ed., **17,** 41, 1945, uses Vycor ware, employing modifications of McCay's electrolytic procedures in fluoride solutions.

[8] Furman, N. H., Ind. Eng. Chem., Anal. Ed., **15,** 1071, 1923.

**The Separation of Arsenic, Antimony, and Tin by Distillation.**—An all-glass apparatus, such as that shown in Fig. 3-1, as recommended by Scherrer,[9] is very satisfactory for separations of the three elements. The solution is prepared by $HNO_3$-$H_2SO_4$ attack and all but 5 ml. of the latter is evaporated off; 30–40 ml. of sulfurous acid are added and the solution is evaporated to 10 ml. and transferred with 100 ml. of HCl to the distilling flask. The arsenic is distilled off at 111–112°C., until the residual volume is 50 ml. Then 25 ml. more of the acid is added and the solution is distilled down to 50 ml. again. The receiver contains the arsenic in a volume of solution of 50–100 ml.

The receiver is changed and the antimony chloride is distilled in a stream of $CO_2$, after 7 ml. of 55% phosphoric acid has been added, until 75 ml. of distillate, at the rate of 30–40 drops per minute, have distilled, adding HCl during the distillation to keep constant the volume in the distilling flask. The receiver is changed and 25 ml. more of the acid are added and distilled in the same manner. The temperature during the distillation is 155–165°C.

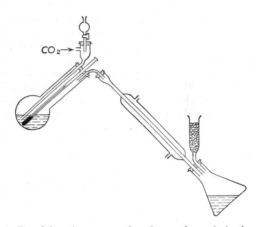

FIG. 3-1. Apparatus for Separation of Antimony and Tin.

The solution is cooled to 140°C., the receiver is changed, and a mixture of HCl (3 volumes) and HBr (1 volume) is added at the rate of 30–40 drops per minute. After 50 ml. of the mixed acid have distilled, the receiver is changed and 25 ml. more of the mixed acid are added and distilled over. The distillate contains the tin.

The arsenic, antimony, and tin are determined by conventional procedures.

**Separations by Solvent Extraction.**—Pentavalent antimony is extracted to ethyl acetate from a solution 1–2 $N$ in HCl, to which oxalic and citric acids have been added to prevent the extraction of various other elements.[10] Under these conditions Fe, Sn, Cu, Cd, Pb, Ge, and Te are not extracted. Trace amounts of As, Bi, and Mo extract. Gold is essentially completely extracted and mercury appreciably; hence these elements should be removed prior to the extraction. The method is applied chiefly for the separation of traces of antimony prior to its photometric estimation. The sample, e.g., 1 g. of an alloy, is dissolved in aqua regia, and evaporated to a small volume, then made up to 10 ml. with concentrated HCl, and transferred to a 100-ml. flask with 4 $N$ HCl. A suitable aliquot of the homogeneous solution (containing 30–40 micrograms of $Sb^{+5}$) is treated with a little 0.1 $N$ ceric sulfate solution and the excess ceric ion is reduced by a little 0.1% hydroxylamine hydrochloride solution. Then 10 mg. each of oxalic and citric acid is added. The aliquot is diluted to 25 ml. and extracted three times with

[9] Scherrer, J. A., J. Res. Nat'l Bureau of Standards. Earlier studies of the distillation method were published by Biltz, H., Z. anal. Chem., **81**, 82, 1930; **99**, 1, 1934. Also by Plato, Z. anorg. Chem., **68**, 26, 1911; Z. anal. Chem., **50**, 641, 1911; and by Hartmann, Z. anal. Chem., **58**, 148, 1919; and by Röhre, K., Z. anal. Chem., **65**, 109, 1924.

[10] White, C. E., and Rose, H. J., Anal. Chem., **25**, 351, 1953.

25-ml. portions of ethyl acetate. The combined extracts are evaporated after adding 5 ml. of concentrated hydrochloric acid. The determination is completed by a photometric method as described later in this chapter.

Trivalent antimony is extracted as the cupferrate to a chloroform layer.[11] This method has been used in connection with the determination of antimony in transistor materials. The antimony is reduced by heating the sulfuric acid solution, after removal of germanium by distillation below 200°C. About 30 mg. of sulfur serves as the reductant. After dilution to 20 ml., in a separatory funnel, 2 ml. of fresh 1% cupferron are added and the antimony is extracted to 10 ml. of redistilled chloroform. A second extraction with 4–5 ml. more of chloroform is made. If iron is present, and ferric cupferrate has also been extracted, the extracts after evaporation, with acid added, and oxidation, may be re-extracted with cupferron to separate the $Fe^{+3}$ from the $Sb^{+5}$. The latter does not extract. The determination of the antimony is completed by the rhodamine B photometric method.

Trivalent antimony is extracted as the diethyldithiocarbamate complex by carbon tetrachloride.[12] From a solution of pH 9.2–9.5 after complexing with disodium dihydrogen dinitrilotetraacetate (disodium salt of E.D.T.A.) and with sodium cyanide, small amounts of Sb, up to 0.2–0.3 mg. may be extracted by carbon tetrachloride. The complex has an absorption peak at approximately 350 m$\mu$. Large amounts of copper, mercury, selenium, and arsenic and small amounts of bismuth, tellurium and trivalent thallium interfere seriously.

## GRAVIMETRIC METHODS

In general, titrimetric methods are preferred for the estimation of macro quantities of antimony. Occasionally it may be desirable to use a gravimetric method. The following methods have been most frequently used.

### DETERMINATION OF ANTIMONY AS THE TRISULFIDE

Even though the antimony may have been present as $Sb^{+5}$, during the action of hydrogen sulfide some $Sb_2S_3$ is produced. If the mixture of well-washed sulfides is dried and eventually heated to 280–300°C. in a current of dry carbon dioxide or other inert gas, $Sb_2S_3$ is formed and the sulfur thus liberated is volatilized.[13]

*Procedure.*—The solution of antimony, free from arsenic and from other elements that are precipitated by $H_2S$ in acid solution, is treated in an Erlenmeyer flask with concentrated hydrochloric acid until about 20% by volume of the acid is present. The solution is heated to 90–100°C. and a slow current of hydrogen sulfide is passed into the hot solution until the precipitate passes from a yellow color through orange and finally becomes dark red to black in color. The flask is agitated gently to coagulate the precipitate, which settles in crystalline form. The solution is diluted with an equal volume of water, washing down the walls of the flask. A slight turbidity is generally seen, due to precipitation of small amounts of antimony that remain in the strongly acid solution. $H_2S$ is now passed into the diluted solution until it becomes clear; 35–40 minutes are usually sufficient to precipitate all the antimony. The precipitate is transferred to a

[11] Luke, C. L., and Campbell, M., Anal. Chem., **25**, 1588, 1953.
[12] Bode, H., Z. Anal. Chem., **144**, 165, 1955.
[13] Modified procedure of Vortman and Metzl, Z. Anal. Chem., **44**, 525, 1905.

weighed filter crucible, washed with small portions of water containing hydrogen sulfide, and finally with pure water.

It is common practice to wash the precipitate with carbon disulfide or carbon tetrachloride to remove precipitated sulfur. Alcohol, followed by ether, is used and the precipitate is sucked dry.

The filter crucible is placed in a large combustion tube and heated in a current of pure, dry $CO_2$ at 130°C. for an hour. The temperature is then raised to 280–300°C. and the heating is continued 2 hours to convert to the trisulfide and to remove sulfur. After cooling in the $CO_2$ stream, the precipitate is weighed as $Sb_2S_3$.

$$\text{Wt. of } Sb_2S_3 \times 0.7168 = Sb$$

$$\times 0.8581 = Sb_2O_3.$$

NOTES.—Antimony may be determined by oxidation of the sulfide precipitate by means of fuming nitric acid. The mixture, evaporated to dryness, is ignited and the residue weighed as $Sb_2O_4$. The temperature of the ignition should be 750–850°C. There is stated to be slight further loss of moisture up to 900°C.[14] The volatile trioxide is stated to form above 950°C. The procedure requires greater care than the sulfide method and possesses no advantages.

Properties of $Sb_2S_3$: mol. wt. 339.72; sp. gr. 4.65; fusible and volatile; solubility 0.000175 g. per 100 ml. of water; decomposed by hot water; soluble in alkalies, $NH_4SH$, $K_2S$, concentrated HCl.

## DETERMINATION OF ANTIMONY AS THE OXIDE, $Sb_2O_4$

The sulfide of antimony obtained as described in the sulfide procedure is treated with ammonia and hydrogen peroxide is added in excess and the solution evaporated in a weighed porcelain crucible to dryness, with necessary precautions, and, after being moistened with sulfuric acid, it is ignited to expel ammonium salts. The residue is weighed as $Sb_2O_4$. (See the preceding notes.)

## ELECTROLYTIC DETERMINATION OF ANTIMONY

An older procedure consisted in electrodeposition of antimony from sodium sulfide solution.[15] Polysulfide dissolves antimony: $2Sb + 3Na_2S_2 = 2Na_3SbS_3$. This solvent action is prevented by addition of potassium cyanide: $Na_2S_2 + KCN = Na_2S + KCNS$. The results of this method according to Henz[16] are invariably high by 1.5–2%. The sample for analysis should not contain over 0.2 g. of antimony.

*Procedure.*—Antimony, precipitated as the sulfide, is washed and then dissolved off the filter by pouring through small portions of pure sodium sulfide of sp. gr. 1.14, the solution being caught in a weighed platinum dish. The sodium sulfide is used until 80 ml. of filtrate is obtained. Sixty ml. of water followed by 2 to 3 g. of potassium cyanide is added and the cyanide is dissolved by rotating the anode. The solution is heated to 60–70°C. and electrolyzed with stirring by a current of 1–1.5 amperes at 2–3 volts. Two hours are generally needed. The solution is siphoned off without breaking the current, with addition of water until the current falls to zero. The light-gray deposit is finally washed with alcohol and

14 Duval, C., Thermogravimetric Analysis, p. 378. Elsevier, 1953.

15 Parrodi and Mascazzini, Z. anal. Chem., **18**, 587, 1879. Luckow, Z. anal. Chem., **19**, 13, 1880. Classen and Reiss, Ber., **14**, 1629, 1881; **17**, 2474, 1884; **18**, 408, 1885; **27**, 2074, 1894.

16 Henz, F., Z. anorg. Chem., **37**, 31, 1903.

ether, dried at about 80°C., cooled in a desiccator, and weighed. The antimony deposit may be dissolved in a solution of alkali polysulfide or by a mixture of equal parts of a saturated tartaric acid solution and nitric acid.

*Alternative Procedure.*—A better electrolytic procedure appears to be that described by Norwitz.[17] The antimony is deposited from a sulfuric-hydrochloric acid solution with hydroxylamine hydrochloride added.

The antimony compound, or solution, freed from copper, etc., as well as arsenic, is dissolved in 15 ml. of concentrated sulfuric acid. The cooled mixture is diluted to 125 ml., 10 ml. of 3% $H_2O_2$ is added, and the solution is boiled for 10 minutes. After diluting to 190 ml. and dissolving 5 g. of $NH_2OH \cdot HCl$ in it, the solution is electrolyzed with a platinum gauze cathode and a platinum anode at 2 amperes per 100 sq. cm. of cathode surface for 15 minutes, then at 1 ampere for 45 minutes longer. The deposit is washed, dried, and weighed in the usual manner. Good results were obtained for amounts of antimony in the range 0.1 to 0.4 g. of antimony.

## TITRIMETRIC METHODS

### THE POTASSIUM BROMATE METHOD [18]

This method has been found to be of special value for determining antimony in hard lead, alloys of antimony and tin, etc.[19] The method is also popular for the titration of antimony and arsenic in the analysis of micro samples of organic substances. It has been shown to be an accurate method on the micro, semimicro, and ultramicro scale. The process is based on the oxidation of antimony from the tri- to the pentavalent state:

$$BrO_3^- + 3Sb^{+3} + 6H^+ \rightarrow Br^- + 3Sb^{+5} + 3H_2O.$$

*Reagents.* **Antimony Chloride Standard Solution.**—Six grams of reagent-grade pulverized antimony are dissolved in 500 ml. of concentrated hydrochloric acid together with 100 ml. of saturated bromine solution. After expelling excess bromine by boiling, about 200 ml. of concentrated hydrochloric acid are added and the solution is made homogeneous at 1 liter. Fifty ml. = 0.3 g. of antimony.

**0.1 N Potassium Bromate Solution.**—2.7836 g. of analytical reagent salt, recrystallized and dried at 150°C., are dissolved in water and made uniform at 1.000 liter. The solution may be prepared in standard concentration by careful work, or, if desired, it may be standardized against pure antimony or arsenious oxide, the latter obtainable from the National Bureau of Standards as a primary standard substance. One ml. of the 0.1 N $KBrO_3$ = 0.006088 g. Sb.

**Methyl Orange.**—An aqueous solution containing 0.1 g. per 100 ml.

**Saturated Bromine Solution.**—500 ml. of concentrated hydrochloric acid saturated with 70 ml. of bromine.

*Procedure.* **Dissolution.**—One gram of the finely powdered alloy is brushed into a 500-ml. beaker, 100 ml. of concentrated hydrochloric acid and 20 ml. of saturated bromine solution are added. The beaker is covered and placed on the steam bath until the metal dissolves. It may be necessary to add more bromine and

[17] Norwitz, G., Anal. Chem., **23,** 386, 1951.

[18] Györy, S., Z. anal. Chem., **32,** 415, 1893.   Duncan, J. B., Chem. News, **95,** 49, 1907.

[19] Nissensohn, H., and Siedler, P., Chem. Ztg., **77,** 749, 1903; Rowell, H. W., J. Soc. Chem. Ind., **25,** 1181, 1907; Luke, C. L., Ind. Eng. Chem. Anal. Ed., **16,** 448, 1944.

acid to effect complete solution. In case oxides of antimony and tin separate out and do not redissolve it may be necessary to fuse the precipitate with sodium hydroxide. Bromine is now expelled by evaporating the solution down to about 40 ml.

**Reduction.**—One hundred ml. of concentrated hydrochloric acid and 10 ml. of a fresh saturated solution of $Na_2SO_3$ are added and the solution is boiled down to 40 ml. on a sand bath, to expel arsenic and the excess of sulfite. Samples high in arsenic may require a repetition of the reduction step.

**Titration.**—The cover and sides of the beaker are rinsed down with 20 ml. of concentrated hydrochloric acid, followed by a few ml. of hot water and the solution is heated to boiling on a sand bath. The standard bromate solution is now run into the hot solution of antimony to within 2 to 3 ml. of the end point, as determined by premature bleaching of a drop or two of methyl orange indicator, 4 drops of methyl orange solution are added and the titration completed slowly until the color of the indicator is destroyed. If iron or copper is present the final color will appear yellow. Since the end-reaction is slow the last portion of the reagent should be added drop by drop with constant stirring.

NOTES.—Antimonous chloride begins to volatilize at 110°C. and boils at 223°C. Hence, the evaporation must not be carried too far when the arsenic is being expelled.

Lead, zinc, tin, silver, chromium, and sulfuric acid have no effect on the determination, but large quantities of calcium, magnesium, and ammonium salts tend to make the results high. Low [20] found that copper produced high results, approximately 0.012% high for every 0.1% of copper present. The effect of the copper can be minimized by passing a stream of air or oxygen through the antimonous solution for five minutes to reoxidize the cuprous ion that is formed during the reduction of the antimony. If this is done the results are slightly low due to partial reoxidation of antimony. The alternative is prior separation of copper. Lead up to 95% of the antimony has caused no difficulty. Iron in the amounts commonly encountered in antimony alloys does not interfere.

Sources of Error. (a) Imperfect volatilization of arsenic. (b) Incomplete expulsion of $SO_2$. (c) Over-titration if insufficient hydrochloric acid is present. No loss of antimony occurs at temperatures below 108°C.

Sweetser and Bricker [21] found that upon titration of small amounts of antimony, e.g., 3 to 30 mg., with standard bromate-bromide solution, using spectrophotometric observation in the near ultraviolet (326 m$\mu$), there is little change in absorbance while $As^{+3}$ is being oxidized to $As^{+5}$. This oxidation precedes that of antimony ($Sb^{+3}$) and the absorbance falls until all the trivalent antimony has been oxidized, then rises sharply. Results good to ±0.2% were obtained for either arsenic or antimony, if present by itself. However, in mixtures of arsenic and antimony, errors as large as 1–1.7% of the amount of each might occur.

**Determination of Antimony and Arsenic.**—The sum of the arsenic and the antimony may be determined. In another aliquot of the mixture, or in the solution after the titration of both $As^{+3}$ and $Sb^{+3}$ with standard potassium bromate, the antimony may be reduced selectively by shaking the solution vigorously with metallic mercury, as was demonstrated by McCay.[22] The solution should be 3 to 4 $N$ in hydrochloric acid at the time of reduction. The solution is shaken vigorously for five minutes, in a narrow-neck glass-stoppered bottle, with 20–25 ml. of mercury. The air is displaced from the bottle by carbon dioxide gas. After reduction, the solution is filtered away from the slate gray mass of calomel and

[20] Low, A. H., Technical Methods of Ore Analysis.
[21] Sweetser, P. B., and Bricker, C. E., Anal. Chem., **24**, 1107, 1952.
[22] McCay, L. W., Ind. Eng. Chem. Anal. Ed., **5**, 1, 1933.

finely divided mercury. Most of the washing with 1–2 $N$ hydrochloric acid can be done by decantation, letting the washings flow through a filter. The filtrate of 200 ml. volume is titrated with standard potassium bromate. If copper is present, reoxidation of the cuprous ion prior to the titration is necessary.

## THE SODIUM HYPOCHLORITE METHOD

*Preparation of Standard Sodium Hypochlorite Solution.*[23]—Transfer 8.0 ml. of a commercial preparation of sodium hypochlorite solution containing 5% of available chlorine to a glass-stoppered brown-glass bottle, and dilute with water to about 2 liters. If necessary, add sufficient sodium hydroxide (1 g.) to raise the pH to about 12.5, the optimum pH for stability. To ascertain if the proper pH has been reached, the customary colorimetric methods for the determination of pH in the range 12 to 14 may be used. Obtain the titer of the solution by titration against a primary standard of sodium arsenite made as follows:

Weigh 0.2473 g. of arsenious oxide (National Bureau of Standards) and dissolve in 25 ml. of 10% sodium hydroxide solution. Transfer to a 1-liter volumetric flask, make slightly acid with sulfuric acid (1:6), and dilute with water to 1 liter. This solution is 0.005 $N$.

The solution of sodium hypochlorite made as directed above is generally somewhat stronger than 0.005 $N$. Its exact titer can be determined by titration against the standard arsenite solution. Its normality may be adjusted to exactly 0.005 $N$ by the usual procedure.

*Procedure.*—Transfer a known aliquot of standard arsenite solution to a 125-ml. Erlenmeyer flask or a 150-ml. beaker: a 4-ml. aliquot if a microburette is to be used for the standard hypochlorite solution and a 5-ml. aliquot if a semimicroburette is to be used. A standard solution of tartar emetic (potassium antimonyl tartrate, $2K(SbO)C_4H_4O_6 \cdot H_2O$) containing 1 mg. of antimony per 10 ml. of solution may also be used. Add 5 ml. of concentrated hydrochloric acid and adjust the volume of the solution to 35 to 40 ml. by adding distilled water. Fill a micro- or semimicroburette with the standard hypochlorite solution. Add 1 drop of 0.05% methyl orange indicator solution to the test solution and titrate directly with the sodium hypochlorite solution. Add another drop of methyl orange indicator solution near the end point and continue the titration until the color of the methyl orange is destroyed. Make a blank titration using exactly the same volume of hydrochloric acid, water and 2 drops of methyl orange indicator solution replacing the volume of arsenite or antimony test solution by additional distilled water. The blank should run about 0.12 to 0.14 ml.

Titrate aliquot portions of test solutions of antimony samples prepared so that the antimony is in the trivalent state as detailed above.

Several precautions must, however, be observed in using sodium hypochlorite solution as a titrimetric reagent. It must be preserved in brown, glass-stoppered bottles. It may be kept at room temperature without deterioration over considerable periods of time. Keeping the solution at lower temperatures is perhaps preferable.

The optimum conditions for the titrations are a volume of at least 35 to 40 ml. with an acid concentration equivalent to 5 ml. of concentrated hydrochloric acid.

[23] Goldstone and Jacobs, Ind. Eng. Chem., Anal. Ed., **16**, 206, 1944.

## THE PERMANGANATE METHOD

The titration is ordinarily carried out on a solution of trivalent antimony that contains both sulfuric and hydrochloric acid. In a volume of 200 ml. there should be progressively less hydrochloric acid added if the amount of sulfuric acid is larger. For example, if 10 ml. of $H_2SO_4$ is present, HCl should be 30–35 ml.; if 20 ml. of $H_2SO_4$, the volume of concentrated HCl should be only 15–20 ml.[24] The solution, at room temperature (20°C.), is titrated with 0.1 N permanganate solution until a faint purplish pink tint persists for 15–30 seconds. 1 ml. of 0.1000 N $KMnO_4$ = 0.006088 g. Sb.

*Procedure for Antimony in Brass.*—The following is a typical procedure, applicable to several kinds of non-ferrous alloys. An approximately 0.01 N potassium permanganate solution is standardized against pure antimony, or preferably against samples of arsenious oxide or sodium oxalate from the National Bureau of Standards.

A 5.000 g. sample of brass is dissolved in a 250-ml. beaker in 25 ml. of nitric acid (sp. gr. 1.42). After the action has ceased, the solution is boiled to expel oxides of nitrogen. Now 125 ml. of boiling water are added and the solution is allowed to stand for 1 hour or more, at a temperature just below boiling. The tin-antimony oxide precipitate is filtered on double 9-cm filter papers of fine texture, keeping the solution hot, and washing with boiling water. The filtrate is discarded.

The papers and precipitate, transferred to a 400-ml. beaker, are treated with 25 ml. of concentrated nitric acid (sp. gr. 1.42), 5 g. of ammonium persulfate and 15 ml. of concentrated sulfuric acid (sp. gr. 1.84) and boiled down to strong fumes. This process may also be carried out conveniently in a Pyrex Erlenmeyer flask. If the solution is brown, 5 ml. of concentrated nitric acid and about 1 g. more of potassium persulfate are added and the boiling to fumes of $SO_3$ is repeated.

When the solution is colorless, it is cooled and 20 ml. of water is added, together with 20 ml. of hydrochloric acid (sp. gr. 1.2), and, cautiously, 1 g. of sodium sulfite, and the $SO_2$ is completely expelled by gentle heating for 10 minutes or longer.

The solution is diluted with 200 ml. of water, and cooled to 10–12°C., then titrated with the standard permanganate solution until a decided pink color persists for 15 to 30 seconds.

NOTES.—Antimony is precipitated quantitatively with the metastannic acid in alloys containing a large amount of tin.

The filter paper is destroyed by ammonium persulfate and nitric acid, while tin and antimony go into solution in the sulfuric acid. Fuming nitric and sulfuric acids may be used in place of the persulfate and nitric acid, but are not as efficient.

The initial heating after dissolution is to render the metastannic acid insoluble.

Arsenic in an alloy necessitates a correction.

In case of alloys that contain considerable amounts of tin and antimony smaller samples should be used and the permanganate should be either 0.05 or 0.1 N depending on the range of the antimony.

If the oxides are not dissolved upon fuming with sulfuric acid, a piece of filter paper about ⅛th inch square will effect reduction and the solution of the oxides. The solution must be heated until the carbon of the filter is destroyed and the solution becomes clear and colorless.

The permissible acidity is 10–20% of concentrated hydrochloric acid by volume.

[24] Pugh, W., J. Chem. Soc., (Lon.), **136**, 1, 1933.

## CERIC SULFATE METHOD

A standard solution of ceric sulfate in 0.5 to 1 $N$ sulfuric acid oxidizes trivalent antimony to the pentavalent state in a solution that contains from one-sixth to one-third of concentrated hydrochloric acid by volume. Under these conditions an accurate determination of antimony may be made in the presence of minor amounts of trivalent arsenic. When the arsenic concentration is equal to or greater than that of the antimony, partial oxidation of the arsenic occurs.[25] If a catalyst such as iodine monochloride (10 ml. of 0.005 $M$ in 6 $M$ HCl) is added, the arsenic may be titrated with the ceric sulfate. If the iodine monochloride catalyst is added at the start, both antimony and arsenic will be oxidized. The end of the antimony oxidation is indicated either by the bleaching of methyl orange indicator, or by the potentiometric method.

*Iodine Monochloride Procedure.*—A sample of 0.25–0.35 g. antimony content is decomposed by heating with 5 ml. of concentrated sulfuric acid. After completion of the reaction and cooling, 20 ml. of water and 25 ml. of concentrated hydrochloric acid and 1 g. of sodium sulfite are added, and the mixture is warmed for 10 to 20 minutes while leading a stream of carbon dioxide through in order to remove the sulfur dioxide. After diluting to 90 ml. and cooling, 10 ml. of 0.005 $M$ iodine monochloride in 6 $N$ hydrochloric acid is added. One drop of 0.025 $M$ ferroin indicator is added and the titration is made with the solution at 50°C. Potentiometric indication is more satisfactory.[26]

## POTASSIUM IODIDE METHOD

*Procedure.*—A 1.000 g. sample of finely divided alloy is heated in a 500-ml. Erlenmeyer flask at water-bath temperature with 50 ml. of concentrated hydrochloric acid. When hydrogen is no longer evolved, the liquid is decanted and the residue of undissolved antimony is washed twice with concentrated hydrochloric acid, retaining the antimony in the flask. Now dissolve the antimony by adding 15 ml. of concentrated hydrochloric acid and solid potassium chlorate, a few crystals at a time, until the antimony is in solution, the liquid being kept hot. Expel chlorine by boiling, add 50 ml. of concentrated hydrochloric acid and again bring to boiling. Cool and add 20 ml. of 20% potassium iodide solution and 1 ml. of carbon tetrachloride or carbon bisulfide. Titrate the liberated iodine with 0.1 $N$ sodium thiosulfate. The brown color will gradually disappear from the solution and the last traces of iodine will be collected in the carbon tetrachloride or bisulfide, giving it a pink color. Titrate until on thorough stirring this pink color disappears, marking the end point.

One ml. of $Na_2S_2O_3$, 0.1 $N$ = 0.006088 g. of Sb.

Sodium thiosulfate may be standardized against pure antimony by the same procedure. The antimony must be free from copper or arsenic.

NOTES.—Due to the reversible nature of the reaction between the antimonic-antimonous system and the iodine-iodide system: $SbO_3^- + 3I^- + 2H^+ \rightarrow SbO_2^- + I_3^- + H_2O$, the reaction goes to the right when acid is present and to the left when a suitable base (bicarbonate ion) is present to neutralize the hydrogen ion that would otherwise tend to reverse this reaction.

The solution should not contain more than $\frac{1}{5}$ of its volume of hydrochloric acid (sp.

[25] Rathsburg, H., Ber., **61,** 1663, 1928; Furman, N. H., J. Am. Chem. Soc., **54,** 4235, 1932.

[26] Willard, H. H., and Young, P., J. Am. Chem. Soc., **50,** 1372, 1928.

gr. 1.16). Too little acid leads to the separation of basic salts of antimony. The solution is best boiled down to 20% in hydrochloric acid by volume.

Sannous chloride may be used in place of thiosulfate as a titrant for the iodine that is liberated.

## DETERMINATION BY OXIDATION WITH IODINE

This method, originated by Mohr and improved by Clark, depends upon the oxidation of trivalent antimony by a standard iodine-potassium iodide solution.

*Procedure.*—The sample is brought into solution by one of the procedures given under "Preparation and Solution of the Sample." Alloys of antimony, lead, and tin are treated according to directions given for this combination of elements.

**Titration.**—To the hydrochloric acid solution of antimony is added tartaric acid or Rochelle salts, and the excess of acid is neutralized with sodium carbonate. The solution is made barely acidic with hydrochloric acid and a saturated solution of sodium bicarbonate is added in the proportion of 10 ml. of bicarbonate for each 0.1 g. of $Sb_2O_3$. Starch is added as an indicator and the solution is titrated with 0.1 $N$ iodine.

One ml. of 0.1 $N$ iodine = 0.006088 g. of Sb.

Notes.—The titration should be made immediately upon addition of the sodium salts. Addition of starch as the end point is approached will result in a more intense blue color and a sharper end point.

If desired, trivalent antimony may be titrated in 1–2 $N$ acidic solution with iodine solution, provided mercuric chloride has been added to complex the iodide ion and thus force the oxidation of the $Sb+3$ completely to $Sb+5$. A potentiometric end point may be used or alternatively, some chloroform may be added to indicate the presence of the first slight excess of iodine.[27]

Procedure.—Add to the trivalent antimony solution 1–2 $N$ in HCl, 15–30 ml. of saturated mercuric chloride solution and 5 ml. of chloroform or carbon tetrachloride. Titrate with standard iodine solution to first permanent appearance of the pink color of iodine in the carbon tetrachloride layer.

## INDIRECT EVOLUTION METHOD
## HYDROGEN SULFIDE-IODINE METHOD

The process depends upon the evolution of $H_2S$ from the sulfide of antimony upon reaction with concentrated hydrochloric acid, the amount of hydrogen sulfide being the same for either sulfide:

1. $Sb_2S_3 + 6HCl \rightarrow 2SbCl_3 + 3H_2S$.

2. $Sb_2S_5 + 6HCl \rightarrow 2SbCl_3 + 2S + 3H_2S$.

Other sulfides must be absent.

The details of this method are practically the same as in the determination of sulfur in steel by the evolution method. See Chapter on Sulfur. The antimony sulfide precipitate is placed in the evolution flask, water and concentrated hydrochloric acid in equal volumes are added through the funnel and the hydrogen sulfide is absorbed in an ammoniacal solution of cadmium chloride. The precipitated cadmium sulfide is then titrated with iodine in acidic solution.

One ml. of 0.1 $N$ Iodine = 0.001603 g. S. Since 3 S are equivalent to one Sb, the equivalent weight of antimony for this process is one-third of its atomic weight. Hence 1 ml. of 0.1 $N$ Iodine = 0.004059 g. of Sb.

[27] Furman, N H., and Miller, C. O., J. Am. Chem. Soc., **59**, 152, 1937.

*Analysis of Stibnite.*—The method of McNabb and Wagner [28] makes use of the evolution method for the determination of sulfide sulfur, with additional provision for sulfate and free sulfur, which are apt to be present in the mineral. Antimony is determined in the hydrochloric acid solution after the hydrogen sulfide has been evolved and swept over by a current of carbon dioxide into the cadmium chloride-ammonia solution.

## COLORIMETRIC METHODS

Two methods have found much favor for the estimation of antimony in biological materials or when present in traces in inorganic materials such as lead. These are the rhodamine B method and the iodoantimonous acid method.

## THE RHODAMINE B METHOD

This method is based on the observation that pentavalent antimony reacts with rhodamine B to produce a red-violet compound that is extractable to benzene or to ether. One procedure applicable to biological material is that of Maren.[29] A sample of 15 g. for blood or 50 ml. for urine is treated with 5 ml. of concentrated sulfuric acid and 5 ml. of concentrated nitric acid. Alundum chips and 1 drop of capryl alcohol are added and after the preliminary action the vessel is placed on a hot-plate at low heat. After nitrous fumes cease to be evolved, medium heat is used for 1–2 hours. If charring occurs, remove, add 1–2 ml. of nitric acid and re-heat. When organic matter is practically completely destroyed, add 2 drops of 70% perchloric acid. After the solution is clear, cool and add 3 ml. of water and heat until fumes of $SO_3$ appear. Cool, add 5 ml. of 6 $N$ hydrochloric acid. A deep yellow color indicates 1 mg. or more of ferric iron. If the amount of iron is large and that of antimony small, use the ether procedure.

*Benzene Procedure.*—Add 8 ml. of 3 $N$ phosphoric acid and 5 ml. of 0.02% rhodamine B solution (aqueous). Shake and cool the solution and transfer it to a separatory funnel and add 10 ml. of benzene, and shake thoroughly. The benzene layer is transferred to the photometer cell and the absorbance is read at 565 m$\mu$. The color is stable for as long as 4 hours.

*Ether Procedure.*—After addition of the hydrochloric acid, add 13 ml. of water, using the latter to rinse out the vessel into a separatory funnel. Add 15 ml. of isopropyl ether and shake thoroughly (100 times). Add to the ether layer after its separation, 5 ml. of rhodamine B solution and shake. Discard the aqueous layers and collect the ether layer in a small test tube or centrifuge tube. Read the absorbance at 545 m$\mu$.

The standard curve is prepared by putting known samples through the procedure.

According to Ward and Lakin,[30] the procedure of extracting $Sb^{+5}$ with isopropyl ether from the aqueous medium 1–2 $M$ in HCl, and formation of the rhodamine B complex is applicable to soils and rocks and in the determination of 2 micrograms of Sb. There is no interference by 30,000 micrograms of Fe, 250 of As, 300 of Au, or 300 micrograms or less of Tl.

*Procedure for Determination of Antimony in Lead.*[31]—Most of the lead is re-

[28] McNabb, W. M., and Wagner, E. G., Ind. Eng. Chem. Anal. Ed., **1,** 32, 1929.
[29] Maren, T. H., Anal. Chem., **19,** 487, 1947.
[30] Ward, F. N., and Lakin, H. W., Anal. Chem., **26,** 1168, 1954.
[31] Luke, C. L., Anal. Chem., **25,** 674, 1953.

moved as lead sulfate, and under the procedural conditions so little antimony is retained by this precipitate that it may be ignored.

A 0.25 to 1.00 g. sample is treated in a 125-ml. conical flask with 5 g. of $KHSO_4$ and 6 ml. of concentrated sulfuric acid. After the dissolution, boil off all but 5 ml. of the solution; cool, add 25 ml. of water, mix, add 5 ml. of concentrated hydrochloric acid, boil to dissolve all black material, cool, filter off the lead sulfate and wash 1–2 times with dilute HCl (1 + 99).

Add carborundum chips, 10 ml. of concentrated HCl, and 5 ml. of 6% sulfur dioxide solution, dilute to 60 ml. Heat to boiling and boil down to 40 ml. Ignore elemental Se and Te. Cool. Add 1 ml. of ceric sulfate solution (0.5 g. of $Ce(HSO_4)_4$ in 100 ml. of diluted $H_2SO_4$ (3 + 97)). At once add 3 ml. of 0.2% aqueous solution of rhodamine B and mix in a Squibb separatory funnel. Add 15.00 ml. of benzene, shake for 1 minute, separate the layers, and draw off the aqueous layer. Filter some of the benzene extract through glass wool into a 2-cm. absorption cell. Measure the absorbance at 565 m$\mu$. The working curve is constructed by putting 0, 4, 8, 12, and 16 micrograms of Sb through the procedure.

*Procedure for Determination of Antimony in Germanium.*[32]—Metal samples are finely powdered in a forged tool steel Plattner mortar with pestle of the same material. A 150-mesh platinum screen mounted in plastic is used to sieve the powder. Pure distilled water, redistilled chloroform, and high-grade reagents must be used, and a careful reagent blank is run in connection with setting up the calibration curve. Germanium or germanium dioxide is treated as follows:

A 2.000 g. sample of germanium or the dioxide is treated in a 125-ml. Vycor conical flask with 2 ml. of 70% perchloric acid and 50 ml. of a mixture of 1 volume of redistilled nitric acid plus 5 volumes of redistilled hydrochloric acid, covered and heated on a low temperature hot-plate at not over 200°C. After the vigorous action has ceased the flask is swirled to wash down metallic particles and allowed to boil down. Cool, add 2 ml. of sulfuric acid and heat to copious fumes of $SO_3$. Cool somewhat, add 30 mg. of sulfur and follow the following procedure that is also used in constructing the calibration curve.

Calibrations are run on 0, 1.0, 2.0, and 3.0 ml. of standard antimony solution containing 1 microgram per ml. Each portion is fumed in Vycor with 2 ml. of sulfuric acid, 30 mg. of sulfur added, and boiled down to 1 ml. using a similar flask with 1 ml. of acid for comparison.

Cool, add 10 ml. of water, and heat to dissolve salts. Cool and transfer to a 60-ml. Squibb-type separatory funnel, having a cut-off stem with about 1 cm remaining below the stopcock. Dilute the sample to 20 ml., add 2 ml. of 1% fresh cupferron solution, and mix. Extract with 10 ml. of redistilled chloroform. The chloroform layer is drained through a plug of glass wool into a 25-ml. conical flask. Extract with 4–5 ml. more of chloroform, adding this to the flask.

Add 1 ml. of nitric acid and warm on the low temperature hot-plate to remove the chloroform. Add 2 ml. of sulfuric acid plus 0.25 ml. of perchloric acid and boil down to 1 ml. on a flame to destroy organic matter. Cool, add 10 ml. of water, heat to dissolve salts, transfer to the 60-ml. separatory funnel, dilute to 20 ml., repeat the cupferron-chloroform extraction, but discard the chloroform layers, since the antimony now in the $Sb^{+5}$ state is not extracted. The aqueous solution is transferred to a 125-ml. Vycor flask.

Add 1 ml. of nitric acid and boil down to $SO_3$ fumes. Cool, add 1 ml. of sulfuric and 0.25 ml. of perchloric acid and boil down to 1 ml. Cool to room temperature, add 1 ml. of selenium solution (0.5 g. per 100 ml.). The selenium is

[32] Luke, C. L., and Campbell, M. E., Anal. Chem., **25**, 1588, 1953.

dissolved in 5 ml. of nitric acid. After adding 10 ml. of sulfuric acid, evaporate until copious fumes of $SO_3$ come off, cool, add 10 ml. of water, again evaporate to expel nitric acid, cool, dilute to 100 ml. and mix. Add 5 ml. of sulfurous acid (6%) and heat to 95–100°C. Allow to stand 5 minutes then filter through a 9-cm No. 42 Whatman paper into a 125-ml. Vycor flask. Wash well with distilled water and discard the paper and precipitate. Boil down to 2.5 ml. on a Meker type flame. From this point complete the photometric determination without delay.

Cool quickly to room temperature, wash down the flask with 5 ml. of 6 $N$ HCl, swirl, and pour the contents into a 100-ml. calibrated flask. Repeat the washing out process with 8 ml. of phosphoric acid $(1 + 99)$ and pour into the same volumetric flask. Cool to room temperature. Add 1 ml. of ceric sulfate solution (0.2 g. of $Ce(HSO_4)_4$ in 10 ml. of diluted sulfuric acid $(1 + 4)$ warming, then cool and make up to 100 ml.). Stopper the flask and invert. Add 5 ml. of 0.1% aqueous rhodamine B solution, stopper, and invert. Add 1 ml. of butyl Cellosolve solution (1 volume $+ 2$ volumes of water) then 15.0 ml. of benzene from a burette. Stopper and shake vigorously for 30 seconds. Pour the mixture into a 150-ml. Squibb separatory funnel and allow the layers to separate. Drain off all the lower layer plus 0.5 ml. of the benzene layer. Pour the benzene layer through a 9-cm No. 41 Whatman filter paper into a 5-cm Corex cell. Without delay measure the absorbance at 565 m$\mu$ using benzene as the reference solution. Use the ultraviolet-sensitive phototube and a slit width of 0.02 mm. Determine the amount of antimony from the calibration curve.

## THE IODOANTIMONOUS ACID METHOD

The yellow color of iodoantimonous acid or its anion is a sensitive method for the photometric determination of antimony. It is usually applied to a solution containing 0.15 to 1.8 mg. of antimony in 100 ml. of a solution slightly acidic with sulfuric acid. A reducing reagent such as ascorbic acid is added to destroy the color that would be formed by the action of the oxygen of the air on the hydrogen iodide to liberate iodine. The method is applied chiefly to biological materials such as blood plasma or urine. The method may be applied to both antimony and bismuth.

*Procedure for Blood Plasma.*—A 10 ml. sample is treated in a Kjeldahl flask with 1.8 ml. of concentrated sulfuric acid. Then 5 ml. of a mixture of 3 volumes of 70% perchloric acid and one volume of concentrated nitric acid is added to complete the destruction of organic matter. The mixture is boiled down until nitric and perchloric acids are removed and fumes of sulfur trioxide come off strongly. Cool, add a little water, and again boil down to $SO_3$ fumes. The solution is diluted to 10 ml. An equal volume of the potassium iodide reagent containing per liter 112 g. of KI and 20 g. of ascorbic acid is added. Blanks and calibration curves are established in the same manner, and the absorbance is read at 420 m$\mu$.

*Procedure for Urine.*—A 25 ml. sample is heated with 4.2 ml. of sulfuric acid and 10 ml. of nitric acid in a Kjeldahl flask. A few drops of perchloric-nitric acid mixture $(3 + 1)$ are added to clear the organic matter after heating to fumes of $SO_3$ and cooling. After fuming again the solution is made up to 25 ml. and an equal volume of the potassium iodide-ascorbic acid reagent is added, and the absorbance is read at 420 m$\mu$.[33]

33 McChesney, E. V., Ind. Eng. Chem. Anal. Ed., **18**, 146, 1946.

If both Sb and Bi are to be determined, the concentrated reagent gives an absorbance proportional to the sum of both elements at 420 m$\mu$. The amount of bismuth alone is estimated by treating another aliquot with a dilute reagent containing per liter 16 g. of KI and 20 g. of ascorbic acid. The solutions are read against a blank containing equal volumes of 16% by volume of sulfuric acid and the appropriate potassium iodide reagent. A chief source of error is any yellow color due to remaining traces of organic matter. At the 100 microgram level, equal amounts of $As^{+3}$, $Hg^{++}$, $Cu^{++}$, or 200 micrograms of $Fe^{++}$, Pb, $W^{+6}$ cause no error. If 200 micrograms of $Tl^{+}$ are present, the results for antimony are about 18% low.

The method has been investigated by reading absorbances at 330 m$\mu$ for 0.3–3.5 p. p. m. of Sb, or at 425 m$\mu$ for 3 to 25 p. p. m. of Sb.[34] At this wavelength the maximum permissible amounts of other elements are, in p. p. m.: $As^{+3}$, 0.0; Bi, 0.0; $Pb^{++}$, 0.0; $Cu^{++}$, 20; $Hg^{++}$, 0; $Mo^{+6}$, 30; Ni, 100; $Sn^{++}$, 5; $W^{+6}$, 4. The final acidity should be 2.4 to 3.8 $N$ in sulfuric acid. The procedure was established on the basis of 10 ml. of the solution tested plus 25 ml. of reagent containing 140 g. of potassium iodide and 10 g. of ascorbic acid per liter.

## DETERMINATIONS IN SPECIFIC SUBSTANCES

### TIN-BASE ALLOYS BY THE POTASSIUM BROMATE METHOD [35]

*Procedure.*—A 1.0 g. sample of the finely divided alloy (free of metallic iron) is placed in a dry 500-ml. Erlenmeyer flask. Add 10 ml. of sulfuric acid and heat without a cover first on a hot plate and then on a Tirrill flame until complete dissolution of the sample is attained and copious white fumes are being evolved. During the initial treatment with acid, avoid heating the sample on a plate that is too hot; otherwise the sample may melt and complete dissolution will become very difficult. Cool, add 10 ml. of water, and 3 or 4 g. of 12-mesh silicon carbide to prevent bumping. Add 50 ml. of hydrochloric acid and warm to dissolve all salts. Adjust the temperature to approximately 50°C. Add 25 ml. of sulfurous acid (6%) and place the flask on a hot plate with a surface temperature of 275–300°C. Boil the solution without a cover until the volume is reduced to 60 ml. ± 5 ml., remove from the plate, and dilute to 350 ml. with boiling water. Pass a fairly rapid stream of air or oxygen through the solution for 5 minutes. Titrate in the usual manner with 0.1 $N$ potassium bromate, using methyl orange indicator.

$$\text{g. Sb} = (\text{ml. KBrO}_3 - \text{ml. blank}) \times \text{normality of KBrO}_3 \times \frac{\text{At. wt. Sb}}{2 \times 1000}$$

The equivalent weight of potassium bromate for this process is ⅙th of its molecular weight.

NOTE.—The procedure, as modified by Luke, is aimed at minimizing the interference of cuprous ion which is produced during the reduction of quinquivalent antimony. By proceeding in hydrochloric acid solution with sulfurous acid as reductant the reduction of the copper is less extensive than with many other reductants, and the co-oxidation of antimony during the reoxidation of the cuprous ion by oxygen or air is thus at a minimum.

34 Elkind, A., Gayer, K. H., and Boltz, D. F., Anal. Chem., **25**, 1744, 1953.
35 Luke, C. L., Ind. Eng. Chem., **16**, 448, 1944.

## DETERMINATION OF SMALL AMOUNTS OF ANTIMONY IN ALLOYS

The method is accurate and is of special value in determining traces of antimony in copper and in alloys. Since arsenic may also be determined a separation by distillation is necessary if the latter is present.

*Description of Generator.*—The generator consists of three separate parts (see Fig. 3-2):

1. Glass cap which is placed over funnel *A*, to hold the disc of test paper in place.

2. *F–G*, this part of the apparatus has two small parts: *F*, which is a tube of glass $1\frac{3}{16}''$ long, $\frac{1}{16}''$ wide, fitted into a rubber tube *G* $\frac{5}{16}''$ wide,

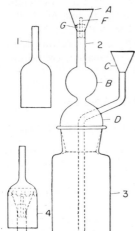

FIG. 3-2. Fitzpatrick Apparatus for Determining Traces of Antimony.

which in turn is fitted into the lower part of funnel *A*. The part *F* is a very important one and care should be taken to have exactly the same size glass tubing and that the distance from the top of *A* to top of *F* is $\frac{5}{16}''$.

The entire apparatus consists of parts *A*, *B*, *C*, *D*, *E*, *F*, *G*.

*A*. The funnel for test paper.

*B*. Bulb for holding cotton saturated with lead acetate to absorb any $H_2S$ gas should any be present when generator is operating. Use 0.5 gm. of cotton.

*C*. This part extends to *E*, which has two purposes: No. 1. For introducing acid, $H_2O$, the test, etc., without opening the apparatus. No. 2. As a safety valve, should the apparatus become clogged or stopped up the pressure will exert itself in this direction.

*D*. Upper part acts as condenser. The lower part is ground to fit the bottle No. 3.

*E*. This part is explained in *C*.

3. This part is the bottle which has 250-ml. capacity with a ground mouth to receive the No. 2 part of generator.

NOTE: All generators must be made and assembled as nearly uniformly as possible to assure concordant results.

4. This figure shows the manner in which the test is placed on funnel *A*, and how the cap fits over and holds the test paper in position. See Fig. 3-2.

*Reagents.*—All chemicals and solutions must be previously tested for arsenic and antimony before using.

**HCl–C.P. Concentrated Redistilled,** As and Sb free.

**HNO$_3$–C.P. Concentrated.**

**NH$_4$OH–C.P. Concentrated.**

**Fe(NO$_3$)$_3$**—250 g. per liter $H_2O$, about 3% solution.

**KClO$_3$**—Use dry crystals.

**FeCl$_2$**—450 g. per liter $H_2O$.

**ZnCl$_2$**—1000 g. per liter HCl (purified by dissolving 15 g. zinc in 500 ml. of the above stock solution).

**Zinc Shot**—Wash in dilute HCl before using.

**SnCl$_2$ Solution**—52.5 g. per liter.

**5% HgCl$_2$,** used for test paper.  5 g. to 100 ml. H$_2$O.  (Cut with die into circles of 1⅝" in diameter.)

**10% Pb (C$_2$H$_3$O$_2$)$_2$,** for cotton.  10 g. to 100 ml. H$_2$O.

**5% Ammonia Solution,** for developer of test paper, 200 ml. ammonia per liter.

**1% AuCl$_3$ Solution.**

*Preparation of Test Paper.*—The paper used must be selected, when purchased, for evenness of thickness and texture in sheets of 24" × 40".

The above sheets are cut in half and saturated with a 5% HgCl$_2$ solution—the wet sheet is then placed on a glass plate and the surplus solution is squeezed out with a 10" rubber roller, which is rolled over the paper twice.  Care must be exercised to roll the paper evenly and with good pressure using the same conditions for each sheet.  The sheet is now hung over a line to dry, in a warm place away from the sunlight or any influence of hydrogen sulfide.  Do not dry paper in oven.  When dry the paper is cut with die in pieces of 1⅝" in diameter.  Keep the discs of test paper in a dark-brown bottle and away from the light until used.

Enough test paper should be made at one time to last for about 3 months.

Each new lot made should be tested with known amounts of As and Sb and compared with standards, before using.  Should they not check closely it is advisable to make new set of standards from the test paper just made.

**Preparation of Lead Acetate Cotton.**—A roll of absorbent cotton is opened and saturated with a 10% solution of lead acetate and surplus drained off, then hung on a line to dry in a warm place away from the influence of hydrogen sulfide.  Do not dry in oven.  When dry, place in stoppered bottle until used.

*Precautions.* **Blank.**—A blank test should be run with each day's work, using all the reagents used in actual tests.

The stain obtained on test paper from blank is subtracted from the actual test.

**Limits.**—The limits of As or Sb that can be determined by this method must be within the following figures:

> As separately from .00002 g. to .00010 g.
> Sb separately from .00002 g. to .00015 g.

**Checks.**—A 10 g. sample of standard copper known to be free from As or Sb is weighed out and known amounts of As and Sb are introduced.

**Distillation.**—The distilling apparatus should *not* be used for any other tests when the As or Sb is known to be higher than the limits for this work.

**Zinc.**—The zinc shot must be cleaned with dilute HCl and washed with distilled water each day to insure proper action in generator, and to expel any sulfide present which would spoil the test.

**Generator.**—The presence of nitrates, chlorates, or compounds of copper interferes with generation of arsine and stibine, so care must be exercised to have these compounds eliminated.

Large quantities of ferrous and ferric compounds interfere also in the generation of stibine to some degree.  The small amount of Fe that gets into the test from the process of distillation is overcome by the addition of 2 ml. stannous chloride—at times more may be required.

**Uniformity.**—Uniformity must be strictly adhered to throughout the test.

In the determination of antimony in presence of arsenic the removal of the latter is necessary.  This is accomplished by distillation of AsCl$_3$ according to the procedure outlined in the Chapter on Arsenic.

*Standard Antimony Solution and Standard Stains.* **Antimony Solution.**—A stock solution is made up by weighing out 0.553 g. $KSbO_3C_4H_4O_6$, which is dissolved in distilled water and made up to 2000 ml., which represents 1 ml. = 0.0001 g. Sb.

From the above stock solution take 100 ml. and make up to 1000 ml. This solution now equals 1 ml. = 0.00001 g. Sb, which is used for making the standard stains and introducing into checks.

**Preparation of Standard Stains.**—Extreme care must be taken when preparing the standard stains.

Wash the generator thoroughly with distilled water, place freshly prepared lead acetate cotton in the bulb, *B*, No. 2, and see that the top of part *F*, No. 2, is exactly $\frac{5}{16}''$ from the top of part *A*, No. 2.

Now introduce into bottle of generator, No. 3, the required amount of As or Sb as desired and then add 50 ml. redistilled HCl, As free, 2 ml. stannous chloride solution and make up to 220 ml. with distilled water.

The disc of mercuric chloride test paper is now placed on top of funnel *A*, No. 2, and the glass cap, No. 1, is forced over the paper holding it in place.

Now introduce 15 g. metallic zinc shot and place the No. 2 section with No. 1 attached into the No. 3 or bottle of generator. The apparatus now being assembled, observe that the apparatus is fitted together tightly, because as soon as the zinc is introduced, arsine and stibine are generated immediately. Place the generator into the water bath to maintain constant temperature, which should be about 70°F. Allow the generator to operate for 1 hour.

The glass cap, No. 1, is now removed and the test paper is developed in a No. 2 beaker with 5% $NH_4OH$ solution for three minutes, then washed 5 times with distilled water. The test paper is now toned with a 1% $AuCl_3$ solution by allowing the test paper to remain in solution for five minutes. The test paper will now have a violet or purple stain, the intensity depending on the amount of As or Sb introduced. Wash the paper 5 times with distilled water and preserve in 50 ml. glass-stoppered bottles containing about 5 ml. water. Keep bottles in dark place, because the stains darken on exposure to light.

Duplicate tests are made, finally selecting of two the one which is the most uniform.

The stains are made to represent the following amounts:

|  | Sb |
|---|---|
| 1........ | .00002 |
| 2........ | .00004 |
| 3........ | .00006 |
| 4........ | .00008 |
| 5........ | .00010 |
| 6........ | .00012 |
| 7........ | .00014 |
| 8........ | .00016 |

*Procedure for Refined Copper.*—A blank is run with all tests.

Weigh 10 g. of the shot or drilled sample into a No. 3 beaker. Add 50 ml. concentrated $HNO_3$, C.P. As free, let stand covered with watch glass until the action has subsided. Now place beaker on wire gauze over Bunsen flame and heat until all the copper is dissolved.

Remove from flame, dilute to 150 ml. with distilled water (if too basic add a few drops of HCl to clear the solution).  Add 2 ml. ferric nitrate solution, stir, then make ammoniacal by adding C.P. concentrated ammonia solution (As free). Bring to boiling.  Remove from flame and filter through a 15-cm fluted Perfection filter paper.  Immediately wash the filter paper free from copper compounds with hot water, using dilute ammonia where necessary to wash out any copper salts that have crystallized.

The precipitate (which contains both As and Sb) is dissolved off the filter with hot dilute hydrochloric acid, by means of a wash bottle, into a No. 4 casserole. Wash the filter three times with hot water.

Add a pinch of KClO$_3$ to the casserole, cover with watch glass, place the casserole in an asbestos cut out over Bunsen burner and boil the contents down to 10 ml., taking care that it does not roast on the sides.

**Distillation.**—Transfer the contents of the casserole to the distilling apparatus. Add 20 ml. ferrous chloride and 20 ml. zinc chloride solution, and distill until the contents of flask begin to froth.  Now add, drop at a time, 35 ml. HCl, through the dropping funnel which is connected to flask.  Distill until all the HCl is out of the funnel and out of the flask.

The distillate is received in a No. 4 beaker having 40 ml. H$_2$O in which both the As and Sb are contained.

The above distillate is now transferred and washed from the beaker into the special designed generator.  Add 2 ml. stannous chloride, which insures a complete reduction of any ferric compounds present.  Dilute the contents of generator to 220 ml.  Place disc of HgCl$_2$ test paper on the funnel top, then put on cap to hold in place.  Add 15 g. metallic zinc.  Take care that the generating apparatus is properly closed, then place into water bath to maintain constant temperature, which should be about 70°F.  The apparatus is allowed to operate for one hour during which time the arsine and stibine generated react upon the HgCl$_2$ test paper, causing a yellow or orange colored spot which varies in color and size according to the amount of As and Sb present.  The paper is now removed from the apparatus and developed in a No. 2 beaker containing 5% NH$_4$OH solution for three minutes.  The color of the spot now changes to a brownish black.  Wash test paper five times with distilled water.  Now cover the test paper with 10 ml. of 1% gold chloride solution, which tones the color of the spot to a violet or purple hue that fixes it so comparison can be made with the standard stains or spots to determine the amount of arsenic or antimony in the sample.

## METHODS FOR ANTIMONY IN ANALYSES
## IN OTHER CHAPTERS

Antimony in Arsenious Oxide     See Analysis of Arsenious Oxide
Antimony in Refined Copper     See Analysis of Refined Copper

# Chapter 4

# ARSENIC

$As_4$, *at. wt.* 74.9216; *sp. gr.* (gray, hexagonal) 5.727; *m.p.* 814°C. (36 atm.); *subl.* 615°C.; *oxides,* $As_2O_3$, $As_2O_5$.

Ores of arsenic were known to the early Greeks and Romans, and the element was isolated during the alchemistic period. Native, or elemental arsenic is found in limited quantities. It occurs combined as arsenides and sulfarsenides; the trisulfide, the pentasulfide and white arsenic, $As_2O_3$, are familiar compounds. The commercial minerals are realgar, $As_2S_2$ (red), orpiment, $As_2S_3$ (yellow), smaltite, $CoAs_2$, arsenopyrites or mispickel, $FeAsS$, the most common. Numerous other arsenic minerals are known. The metal is used in alloys for hardening purposes, for example in making lead shot. Its compounds are used as insecticides and in certain pharmaceutical preparations.

A yellow cubic form of arsenic of density near 2.0 is obtained by condensing the vapor under carbon disulfide. Dark amorphous forms of densities intermediate between 2 and 5.7 are obtained. The gray form is the stable modification.

## DETECTION

*Hydrogen sulfide* precipitates the yellow sulfide, $As_2S_3$, from strongly acidified solutions (HCl). If the solution contains more than 25% of hydrochloric acid, sp. gr. 1.125, the other common members of the hydrogen sulfide group do not precipitate. Arsenic acid or strongly acidified solutions of arsenates, containing two volumes of 12 $N$ HCl to 1 volume of water, yield $As_2S_5$ when treated with hydrogen sulfide at 0–5°C. Solutions containing one-fifth of the volume of concentrated HCl, when treated with a slight excess of hydrogen sulfide in a pressure bottle, followed by stoppering and heating at 100°C., yield practically pure $As_2S_5$. At intermediate concentrations of acid, at room temperature, treatment with hydrogen sulfide yields mixtures containing $As_2S_5$, $As_2S_3$, and S.

Arsenic trisulfide is soluble in alkali carbonates whereas reddish-yellow antimony trisulfide is not. Both $As_2S_5$ and $As_2S_3$ dissolve in 1:1 sodium hydroxide, the former to yield thio and thiooxy salts.

*The volatility of $AsCl_3$* is an important means of separation and distinction of arsenic. Details of the procedure are given under "Separations." The distillate may be tested for arsenic as has been indicated.

*Traces of arsenic* may be detected either by the Gutzeit or the Marsh test. Details are given following the titrimetric procedures.

*Distinction between Arsenates and Arsenites.*—Magnesia mixture precipitates white magnesium ammonium arsenate, $MgNH_4AsO_4$, when added to ammoniacal solutions of arsenates, but it produces no precipitate with arsenites.

Red silver arsenate and yellow silver arsenite are precipitated from neutral solutions by silver nitrate. An arsenate forms a yellow precipitate with ammonium molybdate in nitric acid medium.

Either form of arsenic is reduced to the brown-black element by stannous chloride in concentrated hydrochloric acid solution (Bettendorf test). A more sensitive form of the test is by reduction of trivalent arsenic with mercurous chloride in a solution containing 27–28% of concentrated HCl by volume. 0.1 g. of mercurous chloride is added to 5 ml. of the solution. A brown down to pink or cream shade is given by 0.1 down to 0.0001 mg. of arsenic.[1]

## ESTIMATION

The determination of arsenic is required in the valuation of native arsenic, white arsenic, $As_2O_3$; ores of arsenic—orpiment, $As_2S_3$; realgar, $As_2S_2$; arsenopyrites, FeAsS; cobaltite or cobalt glance, CoAsS; smaltite, $CoAs_2$; niccolite, NiAs. Arsenic is also estimated in copper ores, speiss, regulus; in basic iron arsenates. It is determined in pigments, Scheele's green, etc. It is determined in germicides, disinfectants, and pesticides—Paris green, lead arsenate, zinc arsenite. Traces are tested for in food products and others where arsenic is harmful.

In the preparation of materials for analysis, the volatility of arsenious chloride, $AsCl_3$, necessitates care in dissolution and in other operations. Arsenious solutions should not be boiled unless provision is made to prevent loss by volatilization. There is less danger of loss of pentavalent arsenic. Treatment with aqua regia, with fuming nitric acid, or fusion with a mixture of sodium carbonate and nitrate, with later conversion to chloride by action of HCl in the presence of an oxidizing agent, are recommended procedures.

### PREPARATION AND SOLUTION OF THE SAMPLE

In dissolving arsenic compounds it should be remembered that the oxide, $As_2O_3$, is not readily acted upon by dilute hydrochloric or sulfuric acid. The oxide is soluble, however, in alkali carbonates or hydroxides. Nitric acid oxidizes $As^{+3}$ to $As^{+5}$; $As_2O_5$ is soluble in water or acids. The sulfides $As_2S_3$ and $As_2S_5$ are practically insoluble in hydrochloric acid or in dilute sulfuric acid. They are decomposed by concentrated sulfuric acid. They are dissolved by alkali hydroxides or carbonates. All arsenites, except alkali arsenites, require acids to effect solution.

*Pyrites Ore and Arsenopyrites.*—The amount of the sample may vary from 1 to 20 grams,[2] according to the arsenic content. The finely ground sample in a large casserole is oxidized by adding 10 to 50 ml. of bromine solution (75 g. KBr + 50 ml. liquid $Br_2$ + 450 ml. $H_2O$), covering and allowing to stand for fifteen minutes, then 20 to 50 ml. of concentrated nitric acid are added in three or four portions, allowing the action to subside upon each addition. The glass cover is raised by means of riders, and the sample evaporated to dryness on the steam bath; 10 to 25 ml. of hydrochloric acid are now added and the sample again taken to dryness. Again 10 to 25 ml. of hydrochloric acid are added and the sample taken to dryness. Finally 25 ml. of hydrochloric acid and 75 ml. of water are added, and the mixture digested over a low flame until all the gangue, except the silica, is dissolved. The solution is now examined for arsenic by distillation of the arsenic after reduction, the distillate being titrated with standard iodine solution according to directions given later.

[1] Pierson, G. G., Anal. Ed. Ind. Eng. Chem., **11**, 86, 1939.
[2] 0.1% arsenic determined on a 20-g. sample.

*Arsenious Oxide.*—The sample may be dissolved in sodium hydroxide, the solution neutralized with hydrochloric acid, and the resulting sample titrated with iodine.

*Fusion Method.*—One gram of the finely powdered mineral is fused in a nickel crucible with about 10 grams of a mixture of potassium carbonate and nitrate, 1:1, and the melt extracted with hot water. Two hundred ml. of a saturated solution of $SO_2$ is added to the filtrate to reduce the arsenic, the excess of $SO_2$ then expelled by boiling, the solution diluted with dilute sulfuric acid, and arsenic determined in the filtrate.

*Arsenic in Sulfuric Acid.*—Arsenious acid may be titrated directly with iodine in a 20- to 50-gram sample, which has been diluted to 200 to 300 ml. with water and nearly neutralized with ammonium hydroxide and then an excess of sodium bicarbonate added, followed by the iodine titration.[3]

*Arsenic Acid in Sulfuric Acid.*—Twenty-five ml. of the acid containing about 0.1% arsenic or a larger volume in case the percentage of arsenic is less than 0.1% $As_2O_3$ (the sp. gr. of the acid being known) are measured out into a short-necked Kjeldahl flask. About half a gram of tartaric acid and 2 g. of fused, arsenic-free potassium bisulfate are added and the acid heated over a low flame until the liberated carbon is completely oxidized and the acid again becomes clear, e.g., a pale straw color. It is not advisable to heat to violent fuming, as a loss of arsenic is then apt to occur. The cooled acid is poured into about 300 ml. of water, the excess acid nearly neutralized with ammonia, sodium bicarbonate added in excess and the arsenious acid titrated with standard iodine. Total arsenic as $As_2O_3$ minus arsenic(III) as $As_2O_3$ = arsenic(V) in terms of $As_2O_3$. This result multiplied by $1.1618 = As_2O_5$.

*Arsenic in Hydrochloric Acid.*—The arsenic in a 20- to 100-ml. sample is reduced by ferrous chloride, the arsenic distilled according to directions given later, and the distillate titrated with iodine.

*Arsenic in Organic Matter.*[4]—0.2 to 0.5 gram of the sample finely powdered is oxidized by mixing with 10 to 15 grams of sodium carbonate and sodium peroxide, 1:1, in a nickel crucible, a portion of the fusion mixture being spread over the charge. After heating gently for fifteen minutes, the fusion is completed by heating to dull redness for five minutes longer. The contents of the crucible are rinsed into an Erlenmeyer flask after extraction with water, and the solution made acid with dilute sulfuric acid, 1:1. The mixture is boiled down to 100 ml., 1 to 2 grams of potassium iodide added and the solution further concentrated to about 40 ml. Iodine is reduced with sulfurous acid or thiosulfate, the solution diluted with hot water and saturated with hydrogen sulfide. Arsenious sulfide is filtered off, washed, dissolved in 15 to 20 ml. of half-normal sodium hydroxide and 30 ml. of 30% hydrogen peroxide solution added, and the solution boiled. About 12 ml. of dilute sulfuric acid, 1:1, are added, together with 1 to 2 grams of potassium iodide, the solution concentrated to 40 ml. and free iodine reduced with thiosulfate as before. Arsenic is now titrated, with standard iodine, upon neutralization of the free acid with sodium hydroxide and sodium acid carbonate.

*Lead Arsenate.*—Ten grams of the thoroughly mixed paste or 5 g. of the powder are dissolved by treating with 25 ml. of 10% hot sodium hydroxide solution, and

---

[3] $SO_2$ should be expelled by heat or by a current of air before treating with the alkali.
[4] Organic matter may be destroyed by heating the substance on addition of 10% $H_2SO_4$ and solid $(NH_4)_2S_2O_8$.

diluted to 250 ml. An aliquot part, 50 ml. (= 2 g. paste and 1 g. powder), is placed in an Erlenmeyer flask and 20 ml. of dilute sulfuric acid, 1:1, added, and the solution diluted to 150 ml. About 3 g. of solid potassium iodide are added and the solution boiled down to about 50 ml. (but not to fumes). The liquor will be colored yellow by free iodine. Tenth normal sodium thiosulfate is added drop by drop until the free iodine is neutralized (solution loses its yellow color), it is now diluted to about 250 ml. and the free acid neutralized by ammonium hydroxide (methyl orange indicator), then made slightly acid with dilute sulfuric acid, and an excess of bicarbonate of soda added. The arsenic is titrated with standard iodine.

The arsenic may be reduced by placing the 50-ml. sample in a Kjeldahl flask, adding 25 ml. of concentrated sulfuric acid (sp. gr. 1.84), 0.5 g. tartaric acid and 2 g. acid potassium sulfate, $KHSO_4$, and digesting over a strong flame until the organic matter is destroyed and the solution is a pale yellow color. The cooled acid is diluted and neutralized, etc., as directed above.

*Water-soluble Arsenic in Insecticides.* **Rapid Works Test.**—Two grams of the paste is digested with 1000 ml. of water at 90°C. for five minutes, in a graduated 1000-ml. flask. An aliquot portion is filtered and the arsenic determined by the Gutzeit method.

Water-soluble arsenite may be titrated directly with iodine in presence of sodium bicarbonate.

*Zinc Arsenite.*—About 5 g. of powder or 10 g. of paste are taken and dissolved in a warm solution containing 300 ml. of water and 25 ml. of strong hydrochloric acid. The cooled solution is diluted to 500 ml. and 100 ml. portions taken for analysis. The acid is partly neutralized with ammonium hydroxide and 50 ml. of a saturated solution of ammonium oxalate added (to prevent precipitation of the zinc as $ZnCO_3$), and an excess of sodium bicarbonate, $NaHCO_3$. Arsenic is now titrated with iodine as directed later.

*Soluble Arsenic in Zinc Arsenite.*—A 1-gram sample is rubbed into an emulsion with several portions of water until the whole is in suspension. The cloudy liquor is diluted to 1000 ml. and a portion filtered through a filter crucible or ¼-in. asbestos mat on a perforated plate, the asbestos being covered with a layer of filter paper. The first 50 ml. are rejected. One hundred ml. of the clear filtrate (= 0.1 g.) is treated with 10 ml. of concentrated sulfuric acid, 0.05 g., $Fe_2O_3$ (use ferric ammonium sulfate) and 0.5 ml. of 80% stannous chloride solution and heated until colorless. Arsenic is now determined by the Gutzeit method, using the larger-sized apparatus.

*Arsenic Acid, Alkali Arsenates, etc.*—The sample is dissolved in 20 to 25 ml. of dilute sulfuric acid, 1:1, in an Erlenmeyer flask, and reduced by addition of 3 to 5 g. of potassium iodide, the action being hastened by placing the mixture on a steam bath. The iodine liberated is exactly titrated with thiosulfate and the arsenious acid titrated with iodine according to the procedure given later.

*Arsenic in Steel, Iron, Pig Iron, etc.*—One to 50 grams of steel, etc., may be treated according to the scheme for pyrites. If a large sample is taken, it is advisable to treat it in a 500-ml. flask, connected with a second flask containing bromine, to guard against loss of arsenic by volatilization. When the sample has dissolved it is taken to dryness (the bromine in the second flask being combined with it) and treated as directed in pyrites. Arsenic chloride, $AsCl_5$, is transferred to the distilling flask with strong hydrochloric acid, and arsenic separated from the iron by volatilization of reduced chloride according to the procedure given below.

*Arsenic in Copper.*—Arsenic is precipitated with iron by the basic acetate method, and thus freed from copper. Details of procedure are given under the determination of impurities in copper in the Chapter on Copper.

NOTES.—In the decomposition of the sample Low recommends the addition of a little sodium sulfide to ores containing oxides. To prevent loss of arsenic during the treatment with $H_2S$ he uses a flask with a two-hole rubber stopper through which passes an inlet tube reaching to the bottom of the flask and an exit tube, the latter a thistle tube containing a little absorbent cotton soaked with dilute NaOH to retain any arsenic escaping from the flask.

Iron sulfate dissolves slowly, so that if much is present in the ore time must be allowed for this to dissolve.

As arsenious chloride is volatile, great care must be exercised in heating solutions containing HCl and arsenious salts as a loss will occur. B.P. 130.2°C.

The ore may be brought into solution by fusion with a mixture of sodium carbonate, potassium nitrate and zinc oxide, 1:1:2, the fusion being made in a platinum dish. The potassium iodide procedure may be followed for reduction of arsenic. (See Lead Arsenate.)

*Organic Substances.*—The methods of decomposition which have been described in the Chapter on Antimony may also be used for organic compounds containing arsenic.

## SEPARATIONS

## SEPARATION AND ISOLATION OF ARSENIC BY DISTILLATION

Distillation of arsenic as arsenious chloride serves for its separation from antimony, tin, and other heavy metals. The method is especially valuable for the direct determination of arsenic in ores of copper or iron and similar substances; it is widely applicable. At a temperature not exceeding 110–111°C. arsenic is effectively separated from antimony and tin by distilling in a current of HCl gas, or by passing a stream of carbon dioxide through the mixture. If an oxidizing treatment is used to prepare the solution, the arsenic must be reduced to the trivalent state. Cuprous chloride, hydrazine sulfate, or sulfur are often used as reducing agents. In case of sulfur, the reducing action occurs in concentrated sulfuric acid solutions containing arsenic, antimony, and tin.

The apparatus and methods for separating arsenic, antimony, and tin by distillation have been described in the Chapter on Antimony. A brief description of the hydrazine method for materials containing arsenic is given below.

**Hydrazine Distillation Procedure.**—Weigh a suitable amount of sample into a 275-ml. Pyrex sulfur flask. Treat with a small amount of $HNO_3$ (5–10 ml.), and a pinch of potassium chlorate. Take to dryness. Add 3–5 ml. HCl and take again to dryness. Add 20 ml. 1:1 HCl and boil several minutes. Filter, if insoluble matter is appreciable, into another flask, and wash. Add 30 ml. HCl, 0.5 g. NaBr, and 0.5 g. hydrazine sulfate. Place the flask on a small electric plate, and at the same time, insert in the flask a two-hole stopper, in one hole of which is a separatory funnel, and in the other a glass tube leading to an 8-in. 250-ml. condenser, set vertically. The lower end of the condenser is immersed in cold water contained in a beaker, which rests on a block of wood. Have the stopcock of the funnel open. Have a good stream of cold water running through the jacket of the condenser.

Distill until the volume in the flask has been reduced to 20 ml. Close the cock of the funnel, add 20 ml. HCl, remove the block of wood from underneath the beaker and hold the beaker in one hand. Holding the beaker at such a height that no liquid may be sucked back into the flask, open the funnel cock and let the acid run into the flask. Now, place the block under the beaker, and distill until liquid in flask is again reduced to 20 ml.

Remove the flask from the plate, and disconnect it from the condenser. Wash the condenser, allowing washings to run into the distillate. Remove the beaker from under the condenser. Add 8–10 drops of methyl orange (1 g. of salt per liter of water). Make the solution alkaline with $NH_4OH$, then just acid with HCl. Cool. Add 10 g. $NaHCO_3$ and 10 ml. starch solution (10 g. soluble starch boiled in a liter of water; cooled).

Titrate with iodine solution, one ml. of which equals about 0.005 g. $As_2O_3$. Subtract a blank determination that amounts to 0.4 or 0.5 ml.

## SEPARATION OF ARSENIC FROM ANTIMONY AND TIN BY PRECIPITATION AS SULFIDE IN A CONCENTRATED HYDROCHLORIC ACID SOLUTION [5]

This procedure for isolation of arsenic depends upon the insolubility of the sulfide of arsenic in concentrated hydrochloric acid, whereas that of antimony dissolves. The sulfide of tin is also soluble.

**Procedure.**—The metals present in their lower conditions of oxidation are precipitated as sulfides in presence of dilute hydrochloric acid (5% solution) to free them from subsequent groups (Fe, Al, Ca, etc.). The soluble members of the hydrogen sulfide group are now dissolved and separated from copper, lead, etc., by potassium or sodium hydroxide as follows: The greater part of the washed precipitate is transferred to a small casserole, that remaining on the filter paper is dissolved off by adding to it a little hot dilute KOH solution, catching the filtrate in the casserole. About 5 g. weight of solid potassium hydroxide or sodium hydroxide is added to the precipitate. Arsenic, antimony, and tin sulfides dissolve. The solution is filtered if a residue remains, and the filter washed. This preliminary treatment is omitted if alkaline earths and alkalies are the only contaminating elements present.

The casserole containing the sample is covered and placed on a steam bath. Chlorine is now conducted into the warm solution for an hour, whereby the alkali is decomposed and antimony and arsenic oxidized to their higher states. Sufficient hydrochloric acid is added to decompose the chlorate formed, and the uncovered solution evaporated to half its volume. An equal volume of hydrochloric acid is added and the evaporation repeated, to expel the last trace of chlorine. The acid solution is washed into an Erlenmeyer flask, cooled by ice to 0°C. and two volumes of cooled, concentrated, hydrochloric acid added. $H_2S$ gas is rapidly passed into this solution for an hour and a half. The flask is now stoppered and placed in boiling water for an hour. The yellow arsenic sulfide, $As_2S_5$, is filtered through a weighed Gooch crucible, washed with hydrochloric acid, 2:1, until free from antimony, i.e., the washing upon dilution remains clear. The residue is now washed with water, followed by alcohol, and may be dried and weighed as $As_2S_5$, or determined titrimetrically. Antimony and tin are determined in the filtrate. McCay recommends washing $As_2S_5$ with alcohol, $CS_2$ and finally alcohol.[6]

The sulfide may be dissolved in concentrated sulfuric acid by heating to sulfuric acid fumes and until the solution becomes clear. No arsenic is lost, provided the

[5] Neher, Z. anal. Chem., **32,** 45, 1893.
[6] McCay, Le Roy W., Chem. News, **56,** 262, 1887.

heating is not unduly prolonged. Fifteen to twenty-five minutes is generally sufficient to dissolve the sulfide and expel $SO_2$, etc. The acid may be neutralized with ammonia or NaOH, made again barely acid and then alkaline with sodium bicarbonate, and arsenious acid titrated with iodine.[6]

The separation of arsenic from tin by precipitation as arsenious sulfide in dilute hydrofluoric acid solution has been described in the Chapter on Antimony.

## GRAVIMETRIC METHODS

As in the case of antimony, the accuracy and rapidity of the titrimetric methods for the determination of arsenic make these generally preferable to the more tedious gravimetric methods. The following methods, however, are of value in certain analytical procedures.

### DETERMINATION OF ARSENIC AS THE TRISULFIDE, $As_2S_3$

Arsenic acid and arsenates should be reduced to the arsenious form before precipitation as the sulfide. The procedure is especially adapted to the isolation of arsenic from other elements, when this substance is present in the solution in appreciable quantities, advantage being taken of the extreme difficulty with which arsenious sulfide, $As_2S_3$, dissolves in hydrochloric acid solution.

*Procedure.*—The solution containing arsenic in the arsenious form, strongly acid with hydrochloric acid (9 $N$ HCl), is saturated with $H_2S$ at room temperature. The hydrogen sulfide pressure generator is recommended for this treatment (Fig. 4-1). The precipitate is filtered into a weighed Gooch crucible (previously dried at

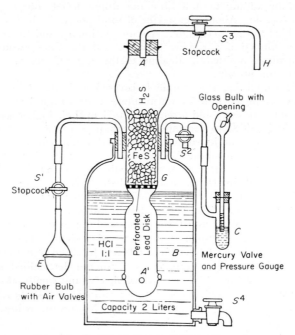

Fig. 4-1.  Scott's Hydrogen Sulfide Generator.

105°C.). The $As_2S_3$ is washed with HCl that has been saturated with $H_2S$, then with alcohol, followed by $CS_2$ to remove free S and finally again with alcohol. The compound dried at 105°C. to constant weight is weighed as $As_2S_3$.

Factors.

$$As_2S_3 \times 0.6090 = \text{grams As.}$$

$$As_2S_3 \times 0.8041 = \text{grams } As_2O_3.$$

$$As_2O_3 \times 1.1618 = \text{grams } As_2O_5.$$

$$As_2O_5 \times 1.3135 = \text{grams } H_3AsO_4 \cdot \tfrac{1}{2}H_2O.$$

$$As_2S_3 \times 1.2607 = \text{grams } As_2S_5.$$

If a preliminary separation of $AsCl_3$ by distillation was made the arsenic will be in form for this method.

NOTE.—Arsenic may also be determined as arsenic sulfide by passing a rapid stream of $H_2S$ into a cooled solution of arsenic acid containing at least two parts of concentrated hydrochloric acid for each part of water present in the solution.

## DETERMINATION OF ARSENIC AS MAGNESIUM PYROARSENATE

The method worked out by Levol depends upon the precipitation of arsenic as $MgNH_4AsO_4 \cdot 6H_2O$, when magnesia mixture is added to an ammoniacal solution of the arsenate. Although 600 parts of water dissolve 1 part of the salt, it is practically insoluble in a 2.5% ammonia solution, 1 part of the anhydrous salt requiring 24,558 parts of the ammonia water according to Virgili.[7] The compound loses 5½ molecules of water at 102°C. and all of the water when strongly ignited, forming in presence of oxygen the stable magnesium pyroarsenate, $Mg_2As_2O_7$, in which form arsenic is determined.

*Apparatus.*—Figure 4-1 shows a convenient form of a generator for obtaining hydrogen sulfide gas under pressure. The apparatus is the writer's modification of the Banks' generator sold by Fisher and is designed for large quantities of hydrogen sulfide gas. The cylinder $AA'$ is constricted, as shown, to support perforated lead disk $G$, upon which rests the iron sulfide. The lower end of the chamber is closed to catch small particles of FeS that may be carried through the perforations of the disk. Small openings admit the acid to $A'$. The level of the acid is below the disk $G$, so that the acid only comes in contact with the sulfide when pressure is applied by means of the rubber bulb $E$, the stopcock $S^1$ being open and $S^3$ closed. The mercury gauge $C$ is adjusted to blow out at a given pressure, to prevent accident, the bulb $D$ preventing the mercury from being blown out of the apparatus. A small opening in $D$ allows the escape of the gas. When the apparatus is in operation, $H$ is connected to an empty heavy-walled bottle, which in turn is attached with glass tube connection to the pressure flask in which the precipitation of the sulfide is made, the flask being closed to the outside air. By pressure on the rubber bulb $E$, acid is forced into the chamber $A'$ past the disk into the sulfide in $A$. The entire system will now be under the pressure indicated by the gauge $C$. The pressure is released by opening the stopcock $S^2$ and the flask containing the precipitate then disconnected. The reservoir is designed to hold

[7] Average of three results. Virgili, J. F., Z. anal. Chem., **44**, 504, 1905.

about two liters of acid, and the cylinder containing the sulfide is of sufficient capacity to hold over one pound of FeS, so that the apparatus will deliver a large quantity of hydrogen sulfide.

*Procedure.*—The solution containing the arsenic, in the form of arsenate, and having a volume not exceeding 100 ml. per 0.1 g. arsenic present, is treated with 5 ml. of concentrated hydrochloric acid, added, with constant stirring, drop by drop. Ten ml. of magnesia mixture are added (Reagent = 55 grams $MgCl_2 + 70$ g. $NH_4Cl + 650$ ml. $H_2O$ and made up to 1000 ml. with $NH_4OH$, sp. gr. 0.96), for each 0.1 g. of arsenic present. Ammonia solution (sp. gr. 0.96) is added from a burette, with stirring, until the mixture is neutralized (a red color imparted to the solution in presence of phenolphthalein indicator), and then ammonia added in excess equal to one-third the volume of the neutralized solution. The precipitate is allowed to settle at least twelve hours and is then filtered into a weighed porcelain filter crucible and washed with 2.5% ammonia until free from chloride. After draining as completely as possible by suction the precipitate is dried at 100°C. and then heated to a dull red heat (400 to 500°C.), preferably in an electric oven, until free of ammonia. The temperature is then raised to a bright red heat (800 to 900°C.) for about ten minutes, the crucible then cooled in a desiccator and the residue weighed as $Mg_2As_2O_7$.

$$\text{Factors, } Mg_2As_2O_7 \times 0.4826 = As$$
$$\times 0.6372 = As_2O_3$$
$$\times 0.7403 = As_2O_5$$
$$\times 0.7924 = As_2S_3.$$

Notes.—In place of an electric furnace the Gooch crucible may be placed in a larger non-perforated crucible, the bottom of the filter being 2–3 mm. above the bottom of the outer crucible. The product may now be heated in presence of a current of oxygen passed through a perforation in the covering lid of the crucible or in place of the oxygen, a thin layer of powdered $NH_4NO_3$ may be placed on the arsenate residue and the heat gradually applied until the outer crucible attains a light red glow.

## TITRIMETRIC METHODS

### OXIDATION OF THE ARSENITE WITH STANDARD IODINE ($KI_3$)

This procedure finds applications whenever other reductants than arsenite are absent and when no substances that might precipitate and occlude arsenite in bicarbonate medium are present. It is applicable to the determination of arsenic that has been distilled as $AsCl_3$. The method depends upon the reaction:

$$AsO_3^{-3} + I_3^- + H_2O \rightarrow AsO_4^{-3} + 2H^+ + 3I^-$$

which proceeds to completion only when the hydrogen ion is neutralized by bicarbonate ion. The end point is detected by the blue color with starch and a slight excess of iodine.

*Procedure.*—If the solution is acidic it is neutralized by sodium hydroxide or carbonate to phenolphthalein indicator, then made slightly acidic. Alkaline solutions are made slightly acidic. Then 2–4 g. of sodium bicarbonate and starch indicator are added and the solution is titrated with 0.1 $N$ iodine solution until a permanent blue color results.

A blank should be run on the reagents that are used and this blank should be deducted from the ml. noted in titrations.

One ml. of 0.1 $N$ iodine = 0.003746 g. As, or 0.004946 g. $As_2O_3$.

$As_2O_3 \times 1.1618 = As_2O_5$. As $\times$ 1.3204 = $As_2O_3$, or As $\times$ 1.534 = $As_2O_5$. $As_2O_3 \times$ 0.7574 = As.

*The Iodine Method in the Presence of Mercuric Salts.*—If mercuric chloride is present in a solution containing trivalent arsenic or antimony and hydrochloric acid from 1–3 $N$ it is possible to titrate the trivalent form of either element, using the color of iodine in a carbon tetrachloride layer, or the potentiometric method for indication.[8]

## THE POTASSIUM BROMATE METHOD [9]

Potassium bromate is readily purified by recrystallization followed by drying at 150°C. Solutions may then be prepared by dissolving the calculated amount of the pure $KBrO_3$ in the appropriate volume of pure water. For a liter of 0.1000 $N$ oxidimetric solution 2.7836 g. of $KBrO_3$ are weighed and dissolved. If desired, the normality of the solution can be checked against weighed samples of pure $As_2O_3$. This oxidant may be used for the titration of trivalent arsenic or antimony, ferrous ion, and many other reductants. It is a preferred reagent for the estimation of arsenic or antimony. The end point may be detected by the bleaching of irreversible indicators such as 0.1% methyl orange, 0.1% naphthol blue black, 0.2% brilliant ponceau R, etc.[10] A reversible organic indicator, alpha naphthoflavone, was found by Uzel[11] and by Schulek.[12] Potentiometric indication and amperometric titration as well as potentiometry at small current input,[13] and spectrophotometric titration[14] have been shown to be suitable for the titration of arsenic in the milligram range and at 0.001 $N$ or lower concentrations. Bricker and Sweetser demonstrated also that arsenic was oxidized preferentially in the presence of antimony by 0.1 $N$ bromate-bromide solution. The absorbancy at 326 $m\mu$ remains nearly constant during the oxidation of the arsenite, then falls during the oxidation of the antimonite and rises when excess bromine is present. The results for 10 mg. of each element were slightly high (0.1–1.0%) for each element.

*Procedure.*—The arsenic must be present in the trivalent form and the initial concentration of hydrochloric acid should be from 1.6–3.5 $N$ when methyl orange or naphthol blue black are used as indicators. Near the end of the titration the indicator that is first added will be appreciably bleached. The addition of 1–2 drops more of indicator is then made and the bromate is added dropwise, closing the flask or bottle, and shaking vigorously, until a sharp end point is reached.

It was shown by McCay[15] that the sum of arsenic and antimony in the trivalent forms could be titrated. The oxidized solution, after concentration to about 100 ml., is treated with mercury in a stoppered bottle, that can be shaken vigorously; only antimony is reduced to the trivalent state. The air is expelled by carbon dioxide before stoppering and the bottle is shaken for an hour. The settled

[8] Furman, N. H., and Miller, C. O., J. Am. Chem. Soc., **59**, 152, 1937.

[9] Györy, S., Z. anal. Chem., **32**, 415, 1893.

[10] Smith, G. F., and Bliss, H. H., J. Am. Chem. Soc., **53**, 2091, 1931; Smith, G. F., and May, R. L., Ind. Eng. Chem. Anal. Ed., **13**, 460, 1941.

[11] Uzel, R., Coll. Czech. Chem. Commun., **7**, 380, 1935.

[12] Schulek, E., Z. anal. Chem., **102**, 111, 1935.

[13] Adams, R. N., Anal. Chem., **26**, 1933, 1954.

[14] Sweetser, P. B., and Bricker, C. E., Anal. Chem., **24**, 1107, 1952.

[15] McCay, L. W., Ind. Eng. Chem. Anal. Ed., **5**, 1, 1933.

calomel and mercury is separated by decantation of the solution and washings through a filter. If copper is known to be present, air is bubbled through the solution for 5–10 minutes to reoxidize cuprous ion. Finally the solution is titrated with standard potassium bromate. The results for antimony tend to be slightly low, presumably due to its partial reoxidation during the destruction of cuprous ion by aeration.

If arsenic and antimony occur together as their sulfides, treatment with concentrated sulfuric acid yields a solution that contains both elements in their trivalent states. Details are given in the Chapter on Antimony.

## TITRATION BY POTASSIUM IODATE

The titration is rapid under conditions in which iodine monochloride is the product of reduction of the iodate. A solid sample of an arsenite is treated with 30 ml. of 12 $M$ hydrochloric acid; the acid concentration should be 6 $N$ at the beginning of the titration, and 6 ml. of chloroform to serve as an indicating layer. The stoichiometry may be represented by the equation:

$$IO_3^- + 2H_3AsO_3 + 2H^+ + Cl^- \rightarrow 2H_2AsO_4 + ICl + H_2O$$

The titration is carried out in a bottle that can be stoppered. Prior to the end point some free iodine is formed by interaction between iodine monochloride and arsenite. At the end point the iodine color disappears sharply from the chloroform layer upon vigorous shaking.

If potassium iodate has been made up to be 0.1 $N$ oxidimetric relative to liberation of iodine, the solution is 0.01667 $M$. Such a solution is equivalent to 0.002497 g. As per ml. Each ml. of an empirically prepared solution containing 3.245 g. of $KIO_3$ per liter will be equivalent to 0.003000 g. of $As_2O_3$.

## CERIC SULFATE METHOD

In the absence of a catalyst the oxidation of trivalent arsenic by ceric sulfate is sluggish. The reaction may be catalyzed by iodine monochloride in 6 $M$ hydrochloric acid, or by traces of osmium tetroxide as suggested by Gleu [16] in dilute sulfuric acid medium.

*Procedure of Gleu.*—For a 0.1 $N$ solution the amount of arsenic trioxide that can be handled per 50.0 ml. of titrant is 0.247 g. A weight of sample is taken that will give a 40–50 ml. titration. If the material contains arsenious oxide it is dissolved in sodium carbonate (1.0 g. in 15 ml. of water) by heating. After diluting to 80 ml. and adding 20 ml. of 6 $N$ sulfuric acid and 0.15 ml. (3 drops) of 0.01 $M$ osmium tetroxide solution (0.2555 g. of $OsO_4$ in 100 ml. of 0.1 $N$ sulfuric acid) the solution is titrated with the standard ceric sulfate solution, using 0.15 ml. of 0.01 $M$ 1,10-phenanthroline ferrous sulfate indicator. Hydrochloric acid up to 0.1 $N$ concentration does not interfere. The effect of larger amounts of chloride ion may be masked by adding mercuric sulfate.

## TITRATION BY PERMANGANATE

The interaction of permanganate and arsenite ions is very sluggish and irregular in sulfuric acid medium. The process is catalyzed by osmium tetroxide, by iodine monochloride in 6 $N$ hydrochloric acid, or by iodate in dilute hydrochloric acid

[16] Gleu, Z. analyt. Chem., **95,** 305, 1933.

medium. Lang's method, using iodate, appears to be one of the most effective procedures.[17]

*Procedure.*—The sample of trivalent arsenic compound or mixture should contain in a volume of 50–75 ml. enough free hydrochloric acid to make the solution 1.5 $N$. After diluting to 120 ml. add 0.05 ml. of $2.5 \times 10^{-3}$ $M$ $KIO_3$ and 1 g. of sodium chloride. Titrate to the first faint tint of potassium permanganate. If desired, the end point may be determined using 3 drops of 1,10-phenanthroline ferrous indicator, in which case the final change is from a pale red to a very pale blue color. This indicator should not be added until the reaction is obviously nearly complete as shown by the slow fading of the permanganate color prior to the end point.

## THE TITRIMETRIC DETERMINATION OF ARSENATE
## AFTER PRECIPITATION AS SILVER ARSENATE

An indirect determination is based upon the precipitation, filtration and washing of silver arsenate, followed by dissolving the precipitate in nitric acid and titrating the silver by Volhard's thiocyanate method.[18]

*Procedure.*—A sample of 0.5 g. or less of the finely powdered, accurately weighed sample is fused with 3–5 g. of a 1:1 mixture of sodium carbonate and potassium nitrate, about one-third of the flux being placed above the sample mixed with the remaining two-thirds. The cooled mass is extracted with boiling water, filtered, and washed. The filtrate, containing the alkali arsenate, is strongly acidified with acetic acid, boiled to expel the carbon dioxide, then cooled and made slightly alkaline to phenolphthalein indicator with sodium hydroxide. The excess sodium hydroxide is neutralized with acetic acid to the color change of phenolphthalein. A slight excess of neutral silver nitrate is added with vigorous stirring and the precipitate of silver arsenate is allowed to settle in the dark. The supernatant liquid is poured off through a filter and the precipitate is washed by decantation with cold distilled water and then filtered and washed free of silver nitrate solution. The funnel is filled with water and 20 ml. of concentrated nitric acid is added. The dissolved silver arsenate is received in the beaker in which the precipitation was made, the residue on the filter is washed with cold water thoroughly, and the filtrate is made up to 100 ml. The silver is now titrated with a standard solution of potassium or ammonium thiocyanate until a faint red-brown color is evident in the supernatant liquid, the indicator being ferric ammonium alum indicator, according to the procedure described for determination of silver (see Chlorine and Silver Chapters).

One ml. of 0.1 $N$ thiocyanate solution = 0.010787 g. Ag.

Factor Ag $\times$ 0.2315 = As.

NOTE.—The silver arsenate has a molecular weight nearly six times the atomic weight of arsenic, so that very small amounts of arsenic may be determined by the procedure, hence it is unnecessary to use more than 0.5 g. of sample. The Gutzeit method should be used for traces of arsenic.

Small amounts of Ge, Sb, Sn do not interfere. Chromates, molybdates, phosphates, tungstates, and vanadates should be absent since they yield precipitates with silver ion. Ammonium salts have a solvent action on silver arsenate.

[17] Lang, R., Z. anorg. Chem., **152,** 203, 1926.

[18] McCay, L. W., Chem. News, **48,** 7, 1883; Am. Chem. J., **8,** 77, 1886; Pearce and Low, Chem. News, **48,** 85, 1883.

## DETERMINATION OF ARSENIC IN PRESENCE OF ANTIMONY

McCay [19] developed a method of separation based upon the precipitation of silver arsenate with fluoride present to prevent hydrolytic precipitation of antimony.

*Procedure.*—If the two elements are present as sulfides they are treated with fuming nitric acid to dissolve them; after expelling most of this acid, 2 ml. of hydrofluoric acid is added followed by warming and diluting to 100 ml. The antimony is oxidized completely by adding potassium persulfate a little at a time until 3–5 g. have been added. After cooling, ammonia is added until methyl orange indicator turns yellow. Heat to boiling and add a slight excess of silver nitrate, with vigorous stirring. If necessary, add ammonia until litmus paper just turns blue. The precipitate, after cooling and standing, is washed with water containing 0.25 g. $AgNO_3$ and 4–5 g. of $NH_4NO_3$ per liter, and finally with alcohol. The precipitate is then dissolved in nitric acid and the silver, equivalent to the arsenic, is determined by titration with thiocyanate.

## ALTERNATE TITRATION METHOD FOR THE SILVER ARSENATE [20]

The silver arsenate precipitate is dissolved in nitric acid (60 ml. of $N$ acid) and then is made 1–2 $N$ in total acid at a volume of 150 ml. by adding sulfuric acid. Titration is made with 0.1 $N$ KI solution, using ceric ion—0.15 ml. of 0.1 $N$—and 3 ml. of 0.5% starch solution. At the end point the first trace of unprecipitated iodide is oxidized by ceric ion and the iodine thus formed colors the starch indicator.

# EVOLUTION METHODS FOR DETERMINATION OF SMALL AMOUNTS OF ARSENIC

## MODIFIED GUTZEIT METHOD

The following procedure furnishes a rapid and accurate method for determination of exceedingly small amounts of arsenic ranging from 0.001 milligram to 0.5 milligram $As_2O_5$. It is more sensitive and less tedious than the Marsh test. The details, given below with slight modifications, have been carefully worked out in the laboratories of the General Chemical Company and have proved exceedingly valuable in estimating small amounts of arsenic in acids, bases, salts; soluble arsenic in lead arsenate and zinc arsenite and other insecticides; and traces of arsenic in food products, baking powders, canned goods, etc.

The method depends upon the evolution of arsine by the action of hydrogen on arsenic compounds under the catalytic action of zinc, the reaction taking place either in alkaline or acid solutions. The evolved arsine reacts with mercuric chloride, forming a colored compound. From the length and intensity of the color stain the amount of arsenic is estimated by comparison with standard stains.

Although the acidity of the sample and the amount of zinc shot should be kept within certain limits, the results are not affected by slight variation as was formerly thought. The physical characteristics of the zinc used rather than the surface exposed to acid action appears to have an effect on the evolution of arsine. The best results are obtained with zinc having a fine crystalline structure.

[19] McCay, L. W., J. Am. Chem. Soc., **50,** 368, 1928.
[20] Bloom, A., and McNabb, W. M., Ind. Eng. Chem. Anal. Ed., **8,** 167, 1936.

Iron present in the solution tends to prevent evolution of stibine, but has no apparent effect on arsine generation.

Stannous chloride is essential to the complete evolution of arsine, hence this reagent is added to the solution in which arsenic is determined.

Antimony present in the solution in amounts less than 0.0001 gram, does not interfere with the determination of arsenic. If a greater amount of antimony is present a separation of arsenic should be made by distillation. The following modification of the method is recommended. In place of the generator for HCl

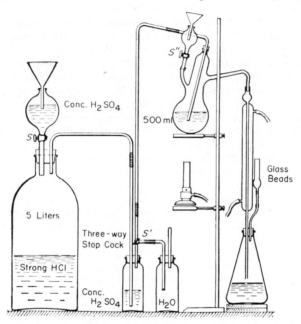

Conc. $H_2SO_4$

500 ml

Glass Beads

5 Liters

Strong HCl

Three-way Stop Cock

Conc. $H_2SO_4$

$H_2O$

Fig. 4-2. Apparatus for the Distillation of Arsenious Acid.

gas shown in Fig. 4-2, air saturated with HCl gas, by passing it through a gas wash bottle containing concentrated hydrochloric acid, is drawn through the boiling solution containing the sample in a saturated HCl solution, reduction of arsenic to arsenious chloride having been effected with cuprous chloride as prescribed. The air sweeps the arsine into the water in the receiving flasks (Fig. 4-2). It is advisable to have two flasks connected in series in place of one as shown. Gentle suction is applied at the receiving end of the train. The apparatus may be made in fairly compact form.

NOTES.—An accuracy of ±0.002 mg. to ±0.004 mg. can be obtained by this method.
Interferences.—$HNO_3$, Cl, Br, I, $H_2S$, $SO_2$, $PH_3$ must be absent. Hg, Pt, Ag, Pd, Ni, Co, $CuSO_4$ are undesirable. Sb should not exceed 0.1 mg.

**Reagents. Standard Arsenic Solution.**—One gram of resublimed arsenious acid, $As_2O_3$, is dissolved in 25 ml. of 20% sodium hydroxide solution (arsenic-free) and neutralized with dilute sulfuric acid. This is diluted with fresh distilled water, to which 10 ml. of 95% $H_2SO_4$ has been added, to a volume of 1000 ml. Ten ml. of this solution is again diluted to a liter with distilled water containing acid.

Finally 100 ml. of the latter solution is diluted to a liter with distilled water containing acid. One ml. of the final solution contains 0.001 milligram $As_2O_3$.

**Standard Stains.**—Two sets of stains are made, one for the small apparatus for determining amounts of $As_2O_3$ ranging from 0.001 to 0.02 milligram, and a second set for the larger-sized apparatus for determining 0.02 to 0.5 milligram $As_2O_3$. Stains made by $As_2O_3$ in the following amounts are convenient for the standard sets; e.g., small apparatus, 0.001, 0.002, 0.004, 0.006, 0.01, 0.015, 0.02 milligram $As_2O_3$. Large apparatus, 0.02, 0.05, 0.1, 0.2, 0.3, 0.4, 0.5 milligram $As_2O_3$.

In making the stain the requisite amount of standard reagent, $As_2O_3$ solution, is placed in the Gutzeit bottle with the amounts of reagents prescribed for the regular tests and the run made exactly as prescribed in the regular procedure.

**Preservation of the Stains.**—The strips of sensitized paper with the arsenic stain are dipped in molten paraffin (free from water), and mounted on a sheet of white paper, folded back to form a cylinder. The tube is placed in a glass test tube containing phosphorus pentoxide, which is then closed by a stopper. It is important to keep the stained strips dry, otherwise the stain soon fades, hence the paper on which the strips are mounted and the glass test tube, etc., must be perfectly dry. It is advisable to keep the standard in a hydrometer case, while not in use, as light will gradually fade the color.

**Sensitized Mercuric Chloride (or Bromide) Paper.**—20 x 20 in. Swedish Filter Paper No. 0 is cut into four equal squares. For use in the large Gutzeit apparatus the paper is dipped into a 3.25% solution of mercuric chloride (mercuric bromide may be used in place of the chloride) or if it to be used in the small Gutzeit apparatus it is dipped into a 0.35% mercuric chloride solution. (The weaker the solution, the longer and less intense will be the stain.) The paper should be of uniform thickness, otherwise there will be an irregularity in length of stain for the same amounts of arsenic. (The thicker the paper the shorter the stain.) The paper is hung up and dried in the air, free from gas fumes, $H_2S$ being particularly undesirable. When dry, half an inch of the outer edge is trimmed off (since this is apt to contain more of the reagent), and the paper cut into strips. The paper with more concentrated reagent is cut into strips 15 cm by 5 mm. and that with 0.35% mercuric chloride into strips 12 cm by 2.5 mm. The paper is preserved in bottles with tight-fitting stoppers. Standards should be made with each batch of paper. Paper with a white deposit of $HgCl_2$ should not be used. Prepared paper may be purchased from chemical dealers.

**Mercuric Bromide Paper.**—Kemmerer and Schrenk [21] recommend that the paper that is to be sensitized be dried at 105°C. for 1 hour and stored in a desiccator over $CaCl_2$. The paper is cut into 2.5 mm. strips and saturated with a 1.5% solution of mercuric bromide in 95% ethyl alcohol. After draining the strips are dried in a desiccator for 10 minutes and used. The treated strips should not be stored for longer than 2 hrs. before use.

In the *Marsh* test arsine is passed through a glass tube constricted to capillarity. By application of heat the arsine is decomposed and metallic arsenic deposited. The tube is heated just before the capillary constriction so that arsenic deposits in the drawn out tube. Comparison is made with standards, the length of the stain being governed by the amount of arsenic in the evolved gas. Slight variations in the size of the capillary tube and rate of evolution make a notable variation in length of stain.

[21] Kemmerer, G., Schrenk, H. H., Ind. Eng. Chem., **18,** 707, July, 1926.

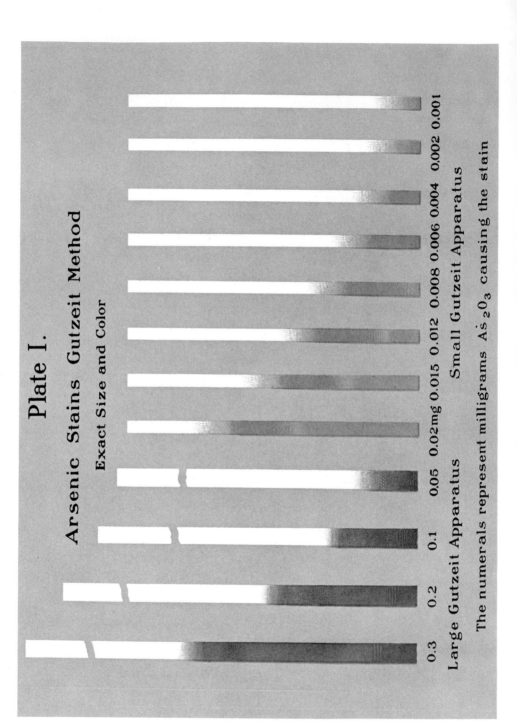

# Plate I.

## Arsenic Stains  Gutzeit Method

### Exact Size and Color

0.3   0.2   0.1   0.05   0.02mg 0.015 0.012 0.008 0.006 0.004 0.002 0.001

Large Gutzeit Apparatus    Small Gutzeit Apparatus

The numerals represent milligrams $As_2O_3$ causing the stain

**Ferric Ammonium Alum.**—Eighty-four grams of the alum with 10 ml. of mixed acid is dissolved and made up to a liter. Ten ml. of this solution contains approximately 0.5 g. $Fe_2O_3$.

**Lead Acetate.**—One per cent solution with sufficient acetic acid to clear the solution.

**Zinc.**—Arsenic-free zinc shot, 3- to 6-in. mesh. The zinc is treated with C. P. hydrochloric acid, until the surface of the zinc becomes clean and dull. It is then washed, and kept in a casserole, covered with distilled water, a clock-glass keeping out the dust.

**Mixed Acid.**—One volume of arsenic-free $H_2SO_4$ is diluted with four volumes of pure water and to this are added 10 g. of NaCl per each 100 ml. of solution.

**Stannous Chloride.**—Eighty grams of stannous chloride dissolved in 100 ml. of water containing 5 ml. arsenic-free hydrochloric acid (1.2 sp. gr.).

**Arsenic-free Hydrochloric Acid.**

**Lead Acetate Test Paper for Removal of $H_2S$.**—Large sheets of qualitative filter paper are soaked in a dilute solution of lead acetate and dried. The paper is cut into strips 7 x 5 cm.

Blanks should be run on all reagents used for this work. The reagents are arsenic-free if no stain is produced on mercuric chloride paper after forty-five minutes' test.

*Special Apparatus.*—The illustration, Fig. 4-3, shows the Gutzeit apparatus. Rubber stoppers connect the tubes to the bottle. The apparatus consists of a wide-mouth 2-oz. or 8-oz. bottle according to whether the small or large apparatus is desired, a glass tube (see Fig. 4-3) containing dry lead acetate paper and moist glass wool for removal of traces of hydrogen sulfide and a small-bore tube containing the strip of mercuric chloride paper.

*Preparation of the Sample.*—The initial treatment of the sample is of vital importance to the Gutzeit Method for determining traces of arsenic. The following procedures cover the more important materials or substances in which the chemist will be called upon to determine minute amounts of arsenic.

**Traces of Arsenic in Acids.**—The acid placed in the Gutzeit apparatus should be equivalent to 4.2 g. of sulfuric acid or 3.1 g. of hydrochloric acid and should contain 0.05 to 0.1 g. $Fe_2O_3$ equivalent. If large samples are required for obtaining the test it is necessary either to expel a portion of the acid in order to obtain the above acidity or to make standard stains under similar conditions of acidity. It must be remembered that arsenious chloride is readily volatile, whereas the arsenic chloride is not, hence it is necessary to oxidize arsenic before attempting to expel acids. If nitric acid or bromine or chlorine (chlorate) be added for this purpose, it must be expelled before attempting the Gutzeit test. Nitric acid may be expelled by adding sulfuric acid and taking to $SO_3$ fumes. Free chlorine, bromine, or iodine will volatilize on warming the solution. Chlorine in a chlorate is expelled by taking the sample to near dryness in presence of free acid. Sulfurous acid or hydrogen sulfide, if present, should be expelled by boiling the solution, then making faintly

FIG. 4-3. Gutzeit Generator.

pink with $KMnO_4$ and destroying the excess with a drop or so of oxalic acid. $SO_2$ is reduced by zinc and hydrogen to $H_2S$, which forms black HgS with mercuric chloride, hence removal of $SO_2$ and $H_2S$ are necessary before running the test.

**Sulfuric Acid.**—With amounts of arsenic exceeding 0.00005% $As_2O_3$, 5 to 10 grams of acid, according to its strength, are taken for analysis and diluted to 15 or 20 ml. If $H_2S$ or $SO_2$ are present, expel by boiling for fifteen or twenty minutes. Prolonged fuming of concentrated acid should be avoided by previously diluting the acid with sufficient water. In mixed acid containing nitric acid the sample is taken to $SO_3$ fumes to expel nitric acid. The procedure given later for the regular determination is now followed.

For estimating very minute amounts of arsenic, 0.000005 to 0.00005% $As_2O_3$, it is necessary to take a 25- to 50-g. sample for analysis. The acid is treated as directed above for removal of $H_2S$ or $SO_2$ or nitric acid and diluted in the Gutzeit apparatus to at least 130 ml., using the large apparatus. Add the iron and stannous chloride as directed in the procedure described on page 124 for large Gutzeit test. The stains are compared with standard stains produced by known amounts of arsenic added to 50-gram portions of arsenic-free sulfuric acid of strength equal to that of the sample. The stains are longer and less intense than those produced by less acid.

**Hydrochloric Acid.**—Twenty ml. is taken for analysis (sp. gr. being known); the sample should contain an acid equivalent of about 3.1 g. of hydrochloric acid. Chlorine is expelled by bubbling air through the acid before taking a sample. The procedure is given for further treatment of the sample following the section on preparation of the sample.

**Nitric Acid.**—One hundred ml. of the acid (sp. gr. being known) is evaporated with 5 ml. of concentrated sulfuric acid to $SO_3$ fumes, to expel nitric acid. Arsenic is determined in the residue by the standard procedure.

**Iron Ores, Pyrites, Burnt Pyrites, Cinders, etc.**—One gram of the finely ground ore is oxidized by treating with 5 ml. of a mixture of 2 parts liquid bromine and 3 parts of carbon tetrachloride. After fifteen minutes, 10 ml. of concentrated nitric acid are added and the mixture taken to dryness. Five ml. of concentrated sulfuric acid (95%) are added and the mixture taken to $SO_3$ fumes to expel the nitric acid. The cooled sample is taken up with 50 ml. of water and digested until all of the iron sulfate has dissolved; it is now washed into a 100-ml. flask, made to volume, and arsenic determined in an aliquot portion in the usual way, given later. Insoluble $Fe_2O_3$, briquettes, etc., are best dissolved by fusion with potassium bisulfate, $KHSO_4$. The fused mass is dissolved in warm dilute hydrochloric acid, and then washed into the Gutzeit bottle.

**Alumina Ores. Bauxite.**—One gram of bauxite is treated with one part of concentrated nitric acid and 6 parts of concentrated hydrochloric acid, and taken to dryness on the water bath. The residue is taken up with an equivalent of 4.7 g. of hydrochloric acid or 6.3 g. of sulfuric acid in a volume of 25 ml. and the mix heated until the material has dissolved. The sample is diluted to exactly 100 ml. and arsenic determined on an aliquot portion.

**Phosphates, Phosphoric Acid.**—Arsenic, in phosphoric acid, combined or free, cannot be determined in the usual way, as $P_2O_5$ has a retarding effect upon the evolution of arsine, so that the results are invariably low, small amounts of arsenic escaping detection. Arsenic, however, may be volatilized from phosphates and phosphoric acid, as arsenious chloride, $AsCl_3$, in a current of hydrogen chloride by heating to boiling. One gram or more of the phosphate is placed in a small distilling flask, connected directly to a 6-in. coil condenser dipping into the Gutzeit bottle, containing 20–30 ml. of cold distilled water. A second bottle connected in series may be attached for safeguarding loss (this seldom occurs). Fifty ml. of concentrated hydrochloric acid are added to the sample and 5 grams of cuprous chloride. Arsenic is distilled into the Gutzeit bottle by heating the solution to boiling and passing a current of air through strong hydrochloric acid into the distilling flask by applying suction at the receiving end of the system. All of the arsenic will be found in the first 10 or 15 ml. of the distillate. Arsenic may now be evolved after addition of iron, stannous chloride and zinc, as directed in the procedure.

**Salts, Sodium Chloride, Magnesium Sulfate, etc.**—One-gram samples are taken and dissolved in a little water and an equivalent of 6.3 g. of sulfuric acid added. The solution of iron and stannous chloride having been added, the run is made with 5 ml. of zinc shot, placed in the Gutzeit bottle.

**Baking Powder, Other than Phosphate Baking Powder.**—A 10-g. sample is heated with 10 ml. hydrochloric acid, 10 ml. of ferric ammonium alum and 30 ml. of distilled water, until the starch hydrolyzes. 0.5 ml. of stannous chloride is added to the hot solution and the mixture washed into the Gutzeit apparatus. The required amount of zinc is added and the arsenic determined as usual.

**Phosphate Baking Powders.**—Ten grams of the material mixed to a paste with about 50 ml. of hydrochloric acid are transferred to a small distilling flask with a few ml. of HCl. A tube, connected to a bottle of concentrated hydrochloric acid, passes into the mixture in the flask through a ground glass stopper. The flask is attached to a tube, which dips into water in a Gutzeit bottle. Two grams of cuprous chloride are added, the apparatus made tight and the flask immersed in boiling hot water. By aspirating air through the system into the Gutzeit bottle, which is water cooled, arsenic distills into the bottle and may be determined by the procedure outlined.

**Arsenic in Organic Matter, Canned Goods, Meat, etc.**—The finely chopped, well-mixed sample is placed in a large flask and enough water added to produce a fluid mass. An equal quantity of concentrated hydrochloric acid and 1 to 2 grams of potassium chlorate are added. The flask is shaken to mix the material and it is then placed on the steam bath. Upon becoming hot, nascent chlorine is evolved and vigorously attacks the organic matter. Half-gram portions of potassium chlorate are added at five-minute intervals, shaking the flask frequently. When the organic material has decomposed and the solution becomes a pale yellow color, the mass is diluted with water and filtered. Arsenic will be found in the filtrate. A white, amorphous substance generally remains on the filter, when cadaver is being examined. The filtrate is diluted to a given volume and an aliquot portion taken for analysis. This is evaporated to near dryness to expel excess of acid and decompose chlorates. An equivalent of 4.7 g. of hydrochloric acid is added (three times this amount for the large apparatus), the volume of the solution made to about 30 ml., 10 ml. of ferric ammonium alum and 0.5 ml. of stannous chloride added, and the solution poured into the Gutzeit apparatus for the test as follows.

*Procedure.*—For amounts of arsenic varying from 0.001 milligram to 0.02 milligram $As_2O_3$, the small apparatus is used. The volume of the solution should be 50 ml. It should contain an equivalent of 4.2 to 6.3 grams sulfuric acid and should have about 0.1 g. equivalent of $Fe_2O_3$ reduced by 0.5 ml. of stannous chloride solution. Arsine is generated by adding one 5-ml. crucible of arsenic-free zinc shot, ⅛ to ⅙-inch mesh. Temperature 75 to 80°F.

For amounts ranging from 0.02 to 0.5 milligram $As_2O_3$, (it is advisable to use smaller samples when the arsenic content is over 0.3 milligram $As_2O_3$, as the longer stains are unreliable) the large apparatus is used. The volume of the solution should be about 200 ml. and should contain an equivalent of 18.5 grams of sulfuric acid and should have 0.1 gram equivalent of $Fe_2O_3$, reduced by 0.5 ml. stannous chloride solution. Arsine is generated by adding one 12-ml. crucible of zinc shot (⅛ to ⅙-inch mesh). The temperature should be 105°F. The sample taken should be of such size that a stain is obtained equivalent to that given by 0.1 to 0.5 milligram $As_2O_3$.

Lead acetate paper is placed in the lower portion of tube $B$; the upper portion of $B$ contains glass wool moistened with lead acetate solution; the tube $A$ contains the test strip of mercuric chloride paper. See Fig. 4-3. Immediately upon adding the required amount of zinc to the solution in the bottles, the connected tubes are put in position, as shown in the illustration, and the bottle gently shaken and allowed to stand for one hour for the small apparatus, forty minutes for the large. The test paper is removed, dipped in molten paraffine and compared with the standard stains. See Plate I.

**Calculation.—**

$$\frac{\text{The milligram } As_2O_3 \text{ stain} \times 100}{\text{Weight of sample taken}} = \% \ As_2O_3.$$

NOTES.—A possible error in the Gutzeit procedure, due to the change in surface area of the zinc, has been pointed out by Goldstone.[22] To avoid this error, cylinders of zinc coated except at the ends by wax, are proposed. Molten zinc is poured into 15 x 125 mm. test tubes. Cylinders 15 x 375 mm. (1.5 in.) have the flat ends protected by $MgCO_3$-gum arabic paste while coating the cylindrical walls with a mixture of 1 part paraffin plus 3 parts of Aerowax C (Glyco Products, Brooklyn, N. Y.). The coating is about ⅟₁₆th inch thick. The ends are then stripped by treatment with $SnCl_2$-HCl, 1:7. The cylinders will serve during the course of about 15 Gutzeit determinations.

H. S. Satterlee and G. Blodgett[23] have proposed the use of suction to bring the arsine into contact with circular discs of the mercuric bromide paper, held in precisely machined methyl methacrylate tubes by silver washers plated with gold and an accurately machined and threaded methacrylate cap provided with a tube for connection with the suction line. The vacuum line is accurately controlled with the aid of proper gauging. The darkening of the analytical stains and the standards is compared photoelectrically. The technique is especially useful for amounts of arsenic ranging from 0.04 to 1 microgram.

## THE MARSH METHOD FOR ARSENIC

The Marsh test is based on the reduction of arsenic compounds to arsine by the action of zinc and acid. A flask containing arsenic-free zinc and dilute sulfuric acid is allowed to evolve hydrogen until air is displaced from a hard glass delivery tube clamped horizontally and constricted at two points. The compound or mixture to be tested for arsenic is added through a funnel tube inserted in the stopper of the apparatus. The arsine formed in the flask is heated as it passes

22 Goldstone, N. I., Ind. Eng. Chem. Anal. Ed., **18,** 797, 1946.
23 Satterlee, H. S., and Blodgett, G., Ind. Eng. Chem. Anal. Ed., **16,** 400, 1944.

through the delivery tube and the element is deposited as a shiny mirror. It is best to have the mirror form in a constriction. As little as a microgram of arsenic may be detected in this way, and the test has had an important role in forensic cases. The constrictions in the mirror tube are usually 1 mm. in diameter, and, by comparison with standard mirrors, rough quantitative estimates can be made.

## COLORIMETRIC METHODS

## THE MOLYBDENUM BLUE PHOTOMETRIC METHOD FOR ARSENIC (JACOBS-NAGLER HETEROPOLY BLUE METHOD) [24]

Molybdic acid forms heteropoly yellow acids with arsenic, phosphorus, silicon and germanium. The molybdenum combined in these heteropoly acids is more easily reducible than the uncombined molybdate, and a blue substance of undetermined composition is formed by various reductants, of which hydrazine sulfate is generally preferred, although stannous chloride and other reductants are frequently used. The regions of maximum absorbance vary slightly with the four elements and the details of reduction, but are generally in the range 820–840 m$\mu$, the last wavelength, 840, being used for arsenic. The conditions must be carefully standardized and careful blank determinations must be made in connection with the calibrations and analyses. A summary of the general conditions for the four elements is given by Boltz and Mellon,[25] together with references to earlier literature.

The basis of the method is treatment of the concentrated sample by metallic zinc and acid, liberating arsine, which is freed from hydrogen sulfide and other contaminating hydrides by passage through a column containing paper or cotton wet with lead acetate solution. The arsine is then absorbed in sodium hypobromite solution, the arsenic is oxidized to the pentavalent state, and converted to the heteropoly blue by treatment with an acid solution of ammonium molybdate, in the presence of hydrazine sulfate as a reducing agent. The arsenic is then estimated colorimetrically. Phosphorus and silicon interfere only if present in the absorption tube or the apparatus following it. Such apparatus should be washed with dilute nitric acid and distilled water.

*Apparatus.* **Arsine Generator (Gutzeit).**—(*A* in Fig. 4-4.)

**Scrubbing Tube.**—(*B* in Fig. 4-4.)

**Absorption Tube and Packing of 2 x 3 mm. Glass Beads.**—(*C* in Fig. 4-4.)

**Colorimeter Tubes 6 x ⅝ inch, for calibration at 25 ml.**

*Reagents.* **Sulfuric Acid Solution (50%).**

**Concentrated Nitric Acid.**

**Lead Acetate Solution.**—10 mg. of lead acetate trihydrate dissolved in 100 ml. water.

[24] Clarke, J. Assoc. Official Agr. Chem., **11**, 438, 1938; Deniges, Compt. rend., **171**, 802, 1920; Atkins and Wilson, Biochem. J., **20**, 1225, 1926; Maechling and Flinn, J. Lab. Clin. Med., **15**, 779, 1930; Deemer and Schricker, J. Assoc. Official Agr. Chem., **16**, 226, 1933; Zinzadze, Ind. Eng. Chem., Anal. Ed., **7**, 227, 230, 1935; Snell and Snell, Colorimetric Methods of Analysis. Van Nostrand, New York, 1936; Chaney and Magnuson, Ind. Eng. Chem., Anal. Ed., **12**, 691, 1940; Jacobs and Nagler, Ind. Eng. Chem., Anal. Ed., **14**, 442, 1942; Ruchhoft, Placak, and Schott, U. S. Pub. Health Service, Reprint, **2527**, 1943.

[25] Boltz, D. F., and Mellon, M. G., Anal. Chem., **19**, 873, 1947.

**Sodium Hypobromite Solution.**—Add 2 g. bromine to 470 ml. of distilled water in dark glass bottle. Add 30 ml. 6 $N$ sodium hydroxide solution and shake until bromine dissolves.

**Stannous Chloride Solution.**—Dissolve 40 g. stannous chloride dihydrate (arsenic free) in 25 ml. concentrated HCl and make volume up to 100 ml.

**Sulfuric Acid, 1 $N$.**—Prepare 1 liter.

**Zinc, 20–30 Mesh.**—(Arsenic free.)

**Ammonium Molybdate Solution.**—Add to 400 ml. water, 310 ml. concentrated sulfuric acid. To this cooled solution, add a solution of 50 g. $(NH_4)_6M_7O_{24} \cdot 4H_2O$ in 200 ml. water. Dilute to 1 liter.

**Hydrazine Sulfate Solution.**—One gram of hydrazine sulfate dissolved in 100 ml. water.

**Arsenic Solution 0.01%.**—Dissolve 0.132 g. arsenic trioxide in 10 ml. $N$ NaOH. Add 10 ml. $N$ $H_2SO_4$ and dilute with water to 1 liter.

**Arsenic Solution 0.001% (0.01 mg. As per ml.).**—Dilute 10 ml. of the 0.01% solution with water to 100 ml.

**Absorbent Cotton.**—One-inch lengths.

*Procedure.*—Use an amount of sample containing 0.002–0.040 mg. As. Add 7 ml. 50% sulfuric acid and 5 ml. concentrated nitric acid and evaporate to dense fumes ($CO_3$). Cool and add 25 ml. water and repeat evaporation. If any organic matter remains, repeat evaporations with nitric-sulfuric acids and with water. Dilute to 25 ml. Pour 3 ml. of the sodium hypobromite solution on to the beads in the absorption tube,

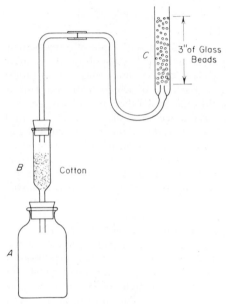

C, 3"of Glass Beads

B Cotton

A

Fig. 4-4. Apparatus for Heteropoly Blue Method for Arsenic.

$C$, and place a piece of the cotton moistened with the lead acetate solution in the scrubbing tube, $B$. Transfer the 25 ml. concentrated sample to the generator, $A$, add 7 ml. of the 50% sulfuric acid, cool, and add 5 ml. of the potassium iodide solution and 5 drops of the stannous chloride solution. Add 3–5 g. of zinc to the generator and promptly connect the apparatus. Keep the generator at a temperature of 20–25°C. for 60 to 90 minutes. Disconnect the apparatus and wash the contents of the absorption tube, $C$, into a colorimeter tube, using successive (5 or 6) 2 ml. amounts of distilled water. Add to the colorimeter tube with mixing 5 ml. of $N$ sulfuric acid, then exactly 1.00 ml. of the ammonium molybdate solution, then 1.0 ml. of the hydrazine sulfate solution. Dilute to 25 ml. with water, let stand for 1 hour, and read in the colorimeter against standards. The standards are prepared from 0.001% (0.01 mg. As per ml.) solution by adding various volumes of this solution to the reagents used above in the colorimeter tube, diluting to 25 ml., and letting stand for 1 hour. Comparison may be made visually or photometrically. In the latter case, a light path of at least 1 cm should be used with a red filter, or readings taken at 650 or 820 m$\mu$. As a check on losses, at least one standard should be carried through the entire procedure.

**Calculation.—**

$$\text{As (mg/l)} = \frac{(\text{mg. As found})(1{,}000)}{\text{Volume of sample (in ml.)}}$$

NOTE.—The molybdenum blue method may be applied after the evolution of arsenic as arsine from a Gutzeit bottle provided with a delivery tube to lead the arsine into a mixture of 1 ml. of mercuric chloride (1.5 g. per 100 ml.), 3 drops of KMnO$_4$ (0.1 g. per 100 ml.) and 4 drops of 6 N sulfuric acid, well mixed. The mixture, possibly containing some manganese dioxide, formed during the oxidation of the arsine, is treated with 5 ml. of molybdate-hydrazine reagent, heated for 15 minutes at 100°C. and made up to volume in a 25-ml. or a 10-ml. volumetric flask. Due to possible turbidity, a portion of the solution is discarded after filtering through glass (wool or filter) and some of the clear filtrate is read at 840 m$\mu$, relative to a blank. Standards are prepared in the same manner as the analytical samples.

The distillation method is more generally used prior to the molybdenum blue method for arsenic, and the arsine evolution method is usually concluded by the Gutzeit procedure.

## APPLICATION OF THE MOLYBDENUM BLUE METHOD TO BIOLOGICAL MATERIALS

The organic material is decomposed by a wet oxidizing attack, and the arsenic, after reduction, is collected by distillation.

Magnuson and Watson [26] used an all glass apparatus for the distillation, as shown in Fig. 4-5. Maren [27] proposed the modification of adding hydrochloric acid to the molybdic acid solution in order to ensure full color development. The apparatus is commercially available.

*Reagents.* **Potassium Bromide.**—30% in water.

**Ammonium Molybdate.**—1 g. added to a cooled mixture of 10 ml. of concentrated sulfuric acid in 40 ml. of water; dissolve and dilute to 100 ml. Maren recommends 2 vols. of this reagent plus 1 volume of N HCl, and to use 3 ml. of this reagent instead of 2 ml. of the reagent of Magnuson and Watson.

**Hydrazine Sulfate.**—0.05% solution in distilled water.

**Arsenic Solution.**—Dissolve 1.5 g. of arsenic pentoxide in 100 ml. of N NaOH, add 600 ml. of distilled water, neutralize with 100 ml. of N HCl and dilute to 1 liter. Standardize by the iodometric method, titrating the iodine liberated with 0.1 N sodium thiosulfate solution, after treating each 25.00 ml. of the arsenic solution with 25 ml. of concentrated HCl and 50 ml. of 10% potassium iodide, and allowing the stoppered flasks to stand in the dark for 2 hours. Portions of the stock solution are diluted to give solutions of 10 and 50 micrograms of As per ml.

*Procedure.*—The sample is decomposed by heating with 5 ml. of sulfuric acid plus excess nitric acid at all times. The final traces of organic matter are decomposed after adding 5 ml. of water to the cold mixture by a few drops of perchloric acid after practically all the organic matter has been destroyed. Finally the solution is heated until fumes of SO$_3$ appear.

Five ml. of water is added to the digest and 2 ml. of 30% KBr is placed in funnel, A, Fig. 4-5. The digest is contained in the round bottom flask of the apparatus. The distilling head is attached at the center neck of the flask and using a 350 watt hot-cone heater (Cenco), distillation is begun and after boiling

[26] Magnuson, H. J., and Watson, E. B., Ind. Eng. Chem. Anal. Ed., **16**, 339, 1944.
[27] Maren, T. H., Ind. Eng. Chem. Anal. Ed., **18**, 521, 1946.

has started, 3 ml. of water is added through the distilling head and the condenser is attached and water drips down the tube, *C*, with capillary section. The KBr is blown through the dropping funnel, *A*, followed by 2 ml. of water. The distillation is continued 4 minutes after blowing in the KBr. The still head is disconnected from the flask and the condenser, and the condensate is poured into the test tube in which the color is to be developed, followed by 2–3 rinsings with 2 ml. each of water

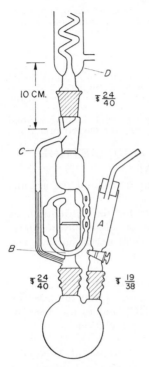

**Color Development.**—To the solution and rinsings of 15–20 ml. volume, add 3 ml. of the Maren solution and 2 ml. of hydrazine sulfate solution, and mix thoroughly. Heat for 10 minutes at 90–100°C., cool, dilute to 25.00 or 35.00 ml. and read in a photoelectric colorimeter, at 840 m$\mu$, or with a suitable filter.

Undistilled standards are prepared, being sure that each solution contains 3 ml. of $N$ HCl to compensate for the fact that acid distills over in the analytical process.

*Arsine Evolution Procedure.*[28]—The apparatus consists of a Pyrex digestion flask and sintered glass filter and dispersion barriers as shown in Fig. 4-6. Cotton, moistened with 3 drops of saturated lead acetate solution is placed above the disc to absorb hydrogen sulfide during the evolution.

For arsenic expected to be less than 15 micrograms, 5 ml. of serum or 25 ml. of urine or weighed portions of solid tissues, are emulsified with 4 parts of distilled water for 10 minutes in a Waring Blendor and are digested with hydrochloric acid. The distillation is made with the apparatus shown after letting potassium iodide and stannous chloride act on the digest. Zinc is then added, and the arsine is collected in 5 ml. of 0.001 $N$ iodine, or for samples expected to contain 15–40 micrograms of As, into 10 ml. of 0.001 $N$ iodine. The color is finally developed by the molybdate-hydrazine method.

Fig. 4-5. Apparatus for Magnuson and Watson.

The dry ashing of biological materials may be done as follows: [29] The sample is treated with 6.0 ml. of saturated magnesium nitrate, dried and ignited at 600°C. The cooled residue is moistened with water and 17 ml. of HCl (175 ml. concentrated acid plus 285 ml. water) are added. According to these authors, the hydrochloric acid procedure of Kingsley and Schaffert is not adequate to recover arsenic from eggs.

## DETERMINATIONS IN SPECIFIC SUBSTANCES

### DETERMINATION OF ARSENIC IN METALS AND ALLOYS

In general, the distillation method serves to separate arsenic from most of elements that would interfere with its determination by photometric or titration

[28] Kingsley, G. R., and Schaffert, R. R., Anal. Chem., **23,** 914, 1951.
[29] Evans, R. J., and Bandemer, S. L., Anal. Chem., **26,** 595, 1954.

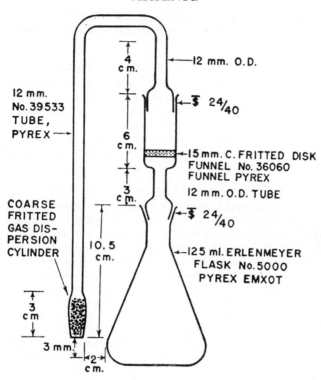

FIG. 4-6. Apparatus for Digestion of Samples and Evolution of Arsenic.

methods. Germanium and selenium interfere in the photometric method, and reductants generally interfere in the bromate titration method.

## A. DETERMINATION WHERE ARSENIC EXCEEDS 0.05 PER CENT AND IS NORMALLY 2 PER CENT OR LESS

*Procedure.*—A sample of 2–5 g., depending on the expected arsenic content, is decomposed by heating with 10–15 g. of potassium bisulfate and 15–20 ml. of sulfuric acid, starting with a low temperature for fusible alloys and gradually heating to dense fumes of $SO_3$. The final amount of free sulfuric acid should not exceed 15 ml. The dissolution can best be performed in a distillation flask that is either a 500- or a 300-ml. Erlenmeyer flask with a standard taper mouth (24/40) to hold a distilling head provided with an inlet tube, bulbed, to extend below the surface of the liquid, a thermometer supported in a standard taper support, and a tube fitted with a condenser jacket to lead the arsenic trichloride over into a receiving flask or a beaker. Alternatively, a Kjeldahl digestion flask, a head with spray trap, and a delivery tube leading through a condenser to the receiver may be used.

Add 15 ml. of water to the cooled mixture, and again cool. Then add 40 ml. of concentrated hydrochloric acid, about 1 g. of hydrated ferrous sulfate and 10 g. of sodium chloride. Distill until the arsenic is carried over, which usually requires 15–20 minutes. The temperature of the vapor should be 105°C. The arsenic may be determined by titration with standard 0.01 $N$ potassium bromate, iodine, or other suitable oxidant.

## B. ARSENIC LESS THAN 0.05 PER CENT

*Procedure.*—The sample size is gauged by the expected arsenic content. The dissolution of the sample is as has been described under (*A*). Since the arsenate-molybdenum blue method is to be used, the arsenic is received in a container containing 1 ml. of bromine water, or other oxidant, e.g., bromate, to convert $As^{+3}$ to $As^{+5}$ prior to the addition of the molybdate and hydrazine reagents. The details of the photometry and conditions are as have been described in this chapter.

## ARSENIC IN TRANSISTOR METALS

It was found by Luke and Campbell [30] that the distillation of germanium from oxidized solutions containing nitric acid gave low results for arsenic by the photometric method. The arsenic, in the trivalent state, was separated from the bulk of the germanium by extraction with diethylammonium diethyldithiocarbamate (Eastman Kodak Co.) to chloroform, from a solution complexed with oxalate. The arsenic is then separated by distillation from the small amount of entrained germanium and estimated by the molybdate-hydrazine sulfate photometric method.

Silicon is dissolved in sodium hydroxide and the solution is treated with hydrogen peroxide, made barely acid (congo red), reduced with potassium iodide and sodium metabisulfite, and the arsenite extracted with diethylammonium diethyldithiocarbamate. Finally, the molybdate-hydrazine technique is applied after the oxidation of the arsenite and the destruction of the organic matter.

The details of the original procedure must be followed with great care when determining trace additions to or impurities in transistor metals.

## THE VANADOMOLYBDATE METHOD FOR ARSENIC IN COPPER-BASE ALLOYS

This method has been studied as to fundamentals by Gullstrom and Mellon [31] and has been found to be less sensitive than the molybdenum blue method. Baghurst and Norman [32] have applied the method to the determination of arsenic and phosphorus in copper-base alloys, without prior separations. The phosphate complex develops in a more strongly acidic solution than does the arsenate complex.

*Reagents.* **Nitric Acid, Concentrated.**

**Nitric Acid, 4 $N$.**

**Nitric Acid, 2 $N$.**

**Mixed Color Reagent.**—Dissolve 3.60 g. of sodium vanadate in 800 ml. of cold water, then add 48 g. of sodium molybdate dihydrate. Filter, if necessary, and make homogeneous at 1 liter.

*Procedure: Phosphorus-free Alloys.*—A 1.500-g. sample is dissolved in 10 ml. of concentrated nitric acid, and after boiling off the nitrous fumes, most of the nitric acid is evaporated off. Dilute to 30 ml. and neutralize carefully with ammonia until a faint permanent precipitate appears. Add 2 $N$ nitric acid dropwise until

[30] Luke, C. L., and Campbell, M. E., Anal. Chem., **25**, 1588, 1953.
[31] Gullstrom, D. K., and Mellon, M. G., Anal. Chem., **25**, 1809, 1953.
[32] Baghurst, H. C., and Norman, V. J., Anal. Chem., **29**, 778, 1957.

the solution clears and make it homogeneous at 100 ml. Transfer a 50.00 ml. portion to another 100-ml. flask.

To one flask add 10.00 ml. of 2 $N$ nitric acid, followed by 25 ml. of the mixed color reagent. Let stand 10 minutes and dilute to 100 ml. To the second flask add 10.00 ml. of 2 $N$ nitric acid and dilute to 100 ml. In a third flask add 20.00 ml. of 2 $N$ nitric acid, 25 ml. of color reagent, let stand 10 minutes and dilute to 100 ml. Measure the absorbances at the same temperature. Subtract the absorbances of the two blank solutions from that of the analytical solution to find the net absorbance, all readings at 430 m$\mu$ or with a suitable filter. The calibration curve is prepared by adding known amounts of arsenate to the same amount of pure copper as is present in the samples. The calibrations are usually made from 0 to 0.75 per cent arsenic.

*Procedure: Arsenic and Phosphorus Both Present.*—The sample is dissolved as in the arsenic procedure. Then 20.00-ml. aliquots, representing 0.3000 g. of sample are transferred to three 100-ml. flasks. Add to one flask 40.0 ml. of 4 $N$ nitric acid and 25 ml. of mixed color reagent and water to 100 ml. After 15 minutes read the absorbance at 430 m$\mu$. (Absorbance of phosphorus at 1.6 $N$.) To the second flask is added 10.00 ml. of 2 $N$ nitric acid, 25 ml. of mixed color reagent and water to 100 ml. This flask and the reagent blank, prepared in the same way, but with no sample, are placed in a water bath at room temperature (between 17 and 30°C.). The sample blank is prepared by adding 10 ml. of 2 $N$ nitric acid to the third flask and diluting to the mark. Separate calibration curves must be made for phosphorus in 1.6 $N$ nitric acid; for phosphorus in 0.2 $N$ nitric acid; and for arsenic in 0.2 $N$ nitric acid.

The percentage of phosphorus is found by the absorbance in 1.6 $N$ acid minus the reagent blank.

The percentage of arsenic is found from absorbance due to sample at 0.2 $N$ acidity less (absorbance of reagent blank plus absorbance of reagent blank plus phosphorus correction). The phosphorus correction is the determined absorbance of the phosphate complex at 0.2 $N$ acidity. Graphs of the phosphorus calibration at 1.6 $N$ and that at 0.2 $N$ enable one to estimate the phosphate correction for any determined amount of phosphorus.

## DETERMINATION OF ARSENIC AND ANTIMONY IN A WHITE METAL ALLOY

This method is based in part on the procedure of Stief,[33] and it consists in distillation of the arsenic as the chloride after decomposing the alloy with sulfuric acid. The arsenic may be titrated in the distillate by the iodine method, the bromate method, etc. The antimony remaining after the distillation may be titrated with standard potassium permanganate or other standard oxidant.

*Apparatus.* **Flask.**—Provided with distilling head and condenser.

*Reagents.*—**Iodine Solution,** 0.1 $N$, or **Potassium Bromate Solution,** 0.1 $N$, or **Potassium Permanganate Solution,** 0.1 $N$.

**Starch Solution.**—1 g. of "soluble" starch made into a paste and poured slowly with stirring into 100 ml. of boiling water. The solution is stabilized by adding a small amount of solid mercuric iodide (not larger than the head of a common pin).

[33] Stief, J. Ind. Eng. Chem. Anal. Ed., **7**, 211, 1915.

*Procedure.* **Determination of Arsenic.**—Weigh 1.000 g. of sawings into a 300-ml. flask, add 15 ml. of concentrated sulfuric acid and heat on the hot-plate until the alloy is completely decomposed. Cool, cautiously add 15 ml. of water and some boiling chips, and boil gently for five minutes or until the odor of $SO_2$ can no longer be detected. Cool, add the distilling head provided with funnel and stopcock leading under solution, thermometer with bulb in vapor about 1 inch above the liquid, and side tube connected to the condenser. Place a 300-ml. beaker containing 75 ml. of water in contact with the exit end of the condenser tube. Cautiously add 25 ml. of concentrated hydrochloric acid, sp. gr. 1.18–1.19, and heat to gentle boiling for 10–15 minutes, being sure that the temperature of the vapor is 107°C., not higher, for at least 5 minutes. Wash the condenser tube letting the washings flow into the distillate. Adjust the conditions and titrate by one of the preferred methods below.

*Iodine Titration.*—Neutralize the solution with sodium bicarbonate and add 2 g. in excess. Dilute to 200 ml. with cold distilled water, add 2–4 ml. of starch and titrate with standardized iodine solution to the first permanent blue tinge.

*Potassium Bromate Titration.*—Add to the distillate 10 ml. of concentrated hydrochloric acid, dilute to 100 ml., and titrate with standard potassium bromate using the bleaching of methyl orange indicator as the end point. Ten drops of 0.1 g. methyl orange per 100 ml. are approximately equivalent to 1 drop of 0.1 *N* potassium bromate.

A blank correction should be found for either method. Ordinarily the blank is between 0.05 and 0.1 ml.

**Determination of Antimony.**—Wash the stopper, thermometer and funnel and inlet tube into the main solution in the flask. If 0.1 *N* permanganate solution is to be used, add 10 ml. of concentrated HCl, dilute to 200 ml., with cooling to room temperature. Titrate to a faint pink tinge that persists for 30 seconds or longer, with stirring. A blank correction of 0.1 ml. is made. Alternatively, the antimony may be titrated under the same conditions of acidity, using 0.1 *N* potassium bromate and methyl orange as irreversible indicator.

## ARSENIC IN IRON AND STEEL

*Procedure.*—Ten grams of the sample is placed in a distillation flask, dissolved in dilute nitric acid, and the solution is evaporated to dryness and heated to expel oxides of nitrogen. Then 100 ml. of HCl and 20 g. of cuprous chloride are added and the arsenious chloride is distilled and determined by titration, or if its amount is too small, by the molybdate-hydrazine photometric method.

## ARSENIC IN COPPER

*Procedure.*—One gram of the material is placed in a distillation flask with 10 ml. of ferric chloride solution (containing 3 g. $FeCl_3 \cdot 6H_2O$), 100 ml. of HCl, and 5 g. of KCl. After distillation of the arsenic the titration is made with 0.1 *N* iodine.

An alternative procedure that is applicable to copper and copper base alloys consists in dissolution in nitric acid, addition of 2 g. of ferric nitrate hydrate, $Fe(NO_3)_3 \cdot 9H_2O$, addition of a distinct excess of ammonia, and boiling for 5–7 minutes. The arsenate is coprecipitated with the hydrous ferric oxide. After partial washing, but not complete removal of the copper, the precipitate is dissolved into the original beaker with hot dilute sulfuric acid (about 9 *N*), and water, then transferred to a distilling flask, and the excess acid is evaporated in a stream of carbon dioxide or other inert gas. Finally the arsenic is distilled from a mixture of approximately 6 $N$ HCl after reduction with 0.5 g. of hypophosphorous acid, $H_3PO_2$ (1 ml. of concentrated solution).

## DETERMINATION OF ARSENIC IN ORGANIC SUBSTANCES [34]

The procedure depends upon the destructive oxidation of the organic matter and the conversion of arsenic to arsenate. The latter is allowed to liberate iodine in strong hydrochloric acid solution, and the iodine is titrated with 0.01 $N$ sodium thiosulfate.

The most general method consists in heating 7–12 mg. of the organic substance with 0.5–0.6 ml. of fuming nitric acid, sp. gr. 1.50, in a sealed Carius combustion tube at 250°C. for 6–8 hours. The nitric acid is then evaporated, and the residue is treated with 1 ml. of water and a total of 5 ml. of recently boiled and cooled concentrated hydrochloric acid. The solution is then transferred to the stoppered titration bottle, 2 ml. of fresh 4% potassium iodide is added, and the iodine is titrated after the flask has stood in the stoppered bottle in the dark 10–15 minutes, with 0.01 $N$ sodium thiosulfate.

An alternative procedure is to boil 7–12 mg. of the substance with 1 ml. of 30% sulfuric acid and a few drops of concentrated nitric acid, add more drops of nitric acid and continue the boiling, evaporate several times with a few drops of 30% hydrogen peroxide added after making sure that practically all of the organic matter has been decomposed. Repeat this process, add 1 ml. of water (boiled to expel air), add 5 ml. of recently boiled and cooled concentrated HCl and 2 ml. of 4% KI, free of iodate, let stand 10 minutes in the stoppered vessel, add 5 drops of 1% starch solution, and titrate the free iodine with 0.01 $N$ sodium thiosulfate. If the solution is only pale yellow, make it up to 20 ml., add 5 drops of 1% starch solution and titrate. When halogens are present in the organic substance, special precautionary measures are necessary to obtain correct results.

## METHOD FOR ANALYSIS OF COMMERCIAL "ARSENIC," ARSENIOUS OXIDE, $As_2O_3$

The following substances may be present commonly as impurities: moisture, $SiO_2$, and oxides of Sb, Fe, Ni, Co, Ca, Cu, Pb, Zn and S ($SO_3$).

### DETERMINATION OF MOISTURE

*Procedure.*—Two 10-g. samples are dried to constant weight in the oven at 100°C. Loss in weight = moisture.

### SULFURIC ACID, $H_2SO_4$

*Procedure.*—The samples from the moisture determination are dissolved in concentrated hydrochloric acid, heating to boiling if necessary, and the samples diluted to 300 to 400 ml. Barium chloride solution is added in slight excess to the hot solution, the precipitate, $BaSO_4$, allowed to settle and filtered and the sulfate dried and ignited as usual.

$$BaSO_4 \times 0.343 = SO_3$$

[34] For molybdenum blue method, see page 127.

## DETERMINATION OF ARSENIC AS As₂O₃

*Procedure.*—Duplicate 5-g. samples are dissolved in 20 g. potassium carbonate in 60 ml. of hot water, by boiling until solution is effected. The samples are made up to 1 liter and aliquots of 100 ml. (= 0.5 g.) taken for analysis. The solution is made faintly acid with hydrochloric acid, testing the solution with litmus paper or by adding methyl orange directly to the solution. An excess of bicarbonate is added and the arsenic titrated with 0.1 $N$ iodine according to the standard procedure for arsenic. One ml. 0.1 $N$ iodine = 0.004946 gram $As_2O_3$.

## RESIDUE UPON SUBLIMATION of As₂O₃. (SiO₂, PbO, CuO, Fe₂O₃, NiO, CoO, ZnO)

*Procedure.*—Two 5-g. samples are weighed into tared porcelain crucibles and heated gently on sand baths with the sand banked carefully around the crucible so as to heat the entire receptacle. After the greater part of the arsenious oxide has volatilized, the crucible is ignited directly in the flame to a dull red heat, until fumes are no longer given off. The residue is weighed as total non-sublimable residue.

### SILICA

*Procedure.*—The residues are transferred to beakers and treated with aqua regia, taken to dryness, and the silica dehydrated at 110°C. for an hour or more. The residue is taken up with hot dilute hydrochloric acid, boiled, and the silica filtered off, ignited, and weighed.

### LEAD AND COPPER

*Procedure.*—The filtrate from the silica is treated with $H_2S$ and the precipitate filtered off. The filtrate is put aside for determination of iron, etc. The precipitate is dissolved in hot dilute nitric acid, 2 to 3 ml. of concentrated sulfuric acid added, the solution taken to $SO_3$ fumes, the cooled concentrate diluted to 20 or 30 ml., and the lead sulfate filtered off, ignited, and weighed as $PbSO_4$.

The filtrate from the lead sulfate containing the copper is treated with aluminum powder and the copper thrown out of solution; the excess of aluminum is dissolved with a few ml. of hydrochloric acid. The filtrate should be tested for copper with $H_2S$ and the precipitate added to the copper thrown out by the aluminum. The copper on the filter is dissolved in hot dilute nitric acid, the extract evaporated to 2 or 3 ml., the acid neutralized with ammonia and then made acid with acetic acid, potassium iodide added and the liberated iodine titrated with standard thiosulfate solution according to the regular method for copper.

### IRON, NICKEL, COBALT, AND ZINC

*Procedure.*—The filtrate from the $H_2S$ Group is boiled to expel the $H_2S$ and the iron oxidized by addition of nitric acid and boiling. The iron (and alumina) is precipitated with ammonium hydroxide and the precipitate filtered off and washed several times with hot water. If alumina is suspected (light-colored precipitate) it may be determined by the difference method—ignition of the precipitate, weighing, and finally subtracting the iron found by titration with standard stannous chloride solution. The iron is dissolved in hydrochloric acid and titrated hot with stannous chloride solution.

The filtrate from the iron is boiled and a 1% alcoholic solution of dimethylglyoxime added to precipitate the nickel. The salt is filtered on a weighed filter crucible, the precipitate dried at 100°C., and weighed. The weight of the salt ×️ 0.2032 = Ni.

The filtrate from the nickel is boiled until all the alcohol has been driven off and the cobalt precipitated by addition of sodium hydroxide in excess, filtered, ignited, and weighed as $Co_3O_4$.

The filtrate is made acid with hydrochloric acid, and then alkaline with ammonium hydroxide and colorless sodium sulfide solution added to precipitate the zinc. The mixture is boiled five to ten minutes, the precipitated ZnS allowed to settle, filtered off, and washed once or twice and then dissolved in hydrochloric acid and the zinc determined by titration directly with potassium ferrocyanide; or it is converted to the carbonate by addition of potassium carbonate, filtered and washed free of alkali, the precipitate dissolved in a known amount of standard acid, and the excess acid titrated with standard sodium hydroxide (methyl orange indicator) according to the procedure given for zinc. $H_2SO_4 \times 0.6666 = Zn$.

## ANTIMONY AND CALCIUM OXIDES

*Procedure.*—Two 15-g. samples are treated with 300 ml. of concentrated hydrochloric acid, boiled down to 50 ml. to expel the arsenic as $AsCl_3$, an equal amount of concentrated hydrochloric acid is added, and the last traces of arsenic precipitated by $H_2S$ passed into the hot concentrated hydrochloric acid solution. The arsenious sulfide, $As_2S_3$, is filtered off. Antimony is precipitated by diluting the solution with an equal volume of water, the solution having been concentrated by boiling down to about 50 ml. The $Sb_2S_3$ is filtered off, washed several times with hot water, dissolved by washing through the filter with concentrated hydrochloric acid, and antimony determined in the strong hydrochloric acid solution by the potassium bromate method—addition of methyl orange indicator and titration with standard potassium bromate added to the hot solution to the disappearance of the pink color of the indicator.

The filtrate from the antimony is concentrated, made slightly alkaline with ammonium hydroxide, and gassed with hydrogen sulfide to remove iron, nickel, cobalt, zinc, chromium, and last traces of lead, etc. The filtrate is then concentrated and made acid with crystals of oxalic acid, boiled and methyl orange added and then ammonia drop by drop, slowly, until the indicator changes to an orange color. An excess of ammonium oxalate is now added and the beaker placed on the steam bath until the calcium oxalate has settled. The calcium is now determined by filtering off the precipitate and washing, drying and igniting to CaO, or by titration with standard permanganate, according to the regular procedure for calcium.

## DETERMINATION OF ARSENIC IN AIR [35]

This method was developed by Vasak and Sedivec [36] and may be applied to urine and to other organic materials.

Arsine reacts with a solution of silver diethyldithiocarbamate in pyridine, to give a red color proportional to the amount of arsine. In the method to be described, arsine is liberated from the sample and bubbled into a solution of

[35] Method of the American Conference of Governmental Industrial Hygienists.
[36] Vasak, V., and Sedivec, V., Chem. Listy, **46**, 341, 1952; Chem. Abstracts, **47**, 67, 1953.

silver diethyldithiocarbamate in pyridine. The absorbance of this solution is measured with a Beckman DU spectrophotometer, and the amount of arsenic in the sample is read directly from a calibration curve. The method is simpler than molybdenum methods, and more sensitive than the Gutzeit method.

When present as fume or dust, samples may be taken with the electrostatic precipitator at 3 cfm., or with the Greenburg-Smith impinger at 1 cfm., using water or decinormal sodium hydroxide solution as collecting medium.

The only substances likely to interfere with the test are hydrogen sulfide, which is normally removed by the lead acetate glass wool plug, and stibine. Stibine does not interfere in the amount likely to be present.

*Reagents.* **Silver Diethyldithiocarbamate.**—This reagent must be prepared at temperatures below 20°C., if decomposition is to be avoided. The decomposed material is pink to brown in color. The dry silver salt is apparently quite stable when properly prepared. A cooled solution of silver nitrate (1.7 g. in 100 ml. distilled water) is added to a cooled solution of sodium diethyldithiocarbamate (2.25 g. in 100 ml. distilled water). The lemon yellow precipitate is filtered off, washed thoroughly with distilled water and dried in a vacuum desiccator below 20°C.

**Pyridine.**—Reagent-grade pyridine is passed through an alumina column 1 inch in diameter and 6 inches in depth, at the rate of approximately 150 ml. per hour. This process may remove a considerable quantity of colored material.

**Arsine Absorbing Solution.**—One gram of silver diethyldithiocarbamate is dissolved in 200 ml. of the chromatographed pyridine and the solution is filtered. This reagent is stable.

**Hydrochloric Acid.**—Baker's analyzed; sp. gr. 1.19.

**Potassium Iodide Solution.**—Fifteen grams reagent grade potassium iodide dissolved in 100 ml. distilled water.

**Stannous Chloride Solution.**—Forty grams stannous chloride dihydrate are dissolved in 100 ml. hydrochloric acid, sp. gr. 1.19.

**Zinc.**—Baker's analyzed; granular 20 mesh.

**Lead Acetate.**—10 g. reagent grade lead acetate is dissolved in 100 ml. distilled water. The glass wool in the scrubber may be soaked in this solution, drained and dried, or a few drops may be placed on the glass wool before the evolution of arsine.

**Arsenic Standard Stock Solution.**—1.320 g. arsenic trioxide is dissolved in 10 ml. of 40% sodium hydroxide and diluted to 1 liter with distilled water. Various strengths of standard solutions are prepared by further diluting this stock solution with suitable volumes of water.

The water used to make up the reagents, and throughout the analysis is triple distilled in Pyrex. Naturally, all reagents used should be checked to ensure a low individual and a low total reagent blank.

**Nonaq.**—This stopcock grease, available from Fisher Scientific Company, Pittsburgh, provides gas tight joints during gas evolution, and being water soluble is easily removed during glass washing.

*Procedure.*—The inside surfaces of precipitator tubes are rinsed into a beaker with a stream of 1% sodium hydroxide solution from a polyethylene wash bottle, rubbing the walls meanwhile with a rubber policeman on a glass rod. This is immediately followed by a distilled water rinse. The volumes of both rinse liquids are kept to a minimum. The alkali is neutralized by dropwise addition of concentrated hydrochloric acid using phenolphthalein indicator. The cooled solution is transferred and made up to 50 ml. in a volumetric flask. Impinger samples are made up to a 50 or 100 ml. final volume as convenient. If water was used in the impinger no neutralization is required.

**Calibration Curve.**—Known microgram amounts of arsenic (1–15 micrograms) in the form of standard arsenic solution, are pipetted into 125-ml. Erlenmeyer flasks. Distilled water is added to make the total volume 35 ml. To the flasks are added 5 ml. hydrochloric acid, 2 ml. 15% potassium iodide solution, and 8 drops of stannous chloride solution. The flasks are swirled, and allowed to stand for 15 minutes to ensure reduction of all arsenic to the trivalent form.

Three ml. of the pyridine solution of silver diethyldithiocarbamate are placed in the absorbing tube, which is attached to the scrubber containing glass wool impregnated with lead acetate.

The ground joints are lubricated with "Nonaq" stopcock grease, 3 g. of granulated zinc are added to the solution in the flask, and the receiving tube is inserted immediately. Arsine evolution is completed in about 30 minutes.

At the end of this time the absorbing solution is transferred to a 1 cm square cell and the absorbance measured at 560 m$\mu$ in the Beckman spectrophotometer. Plotting measured absorbances against micrograms of arsenic taken produces the standard curve.

Air samples, after the previously described preparation treatment, are treated in the same manner as the standards. Depending upon the operator's knowledge of the sampling conditions, a 5–25 ml. aliquot may be taken for analysis. From previous experience with known amounts of arsenic the operator can decide from the color of the absorbing solution, whether the sample aliquot taken will be within the range of the calibration curve. If necessary, the prepared sample may be diluted, or the volume of the absorbing solution may be varied to adjust the color intensity to the scale of the standard curve.

**Calculations.**—If a 25-ml. aliquot of a 50-ml. prepared sample is taken for analysis, and using 3 ml. of absorbing solution, the arsenic concentration in milligrams per cubic meter is:

$$\frac{\text{Micrograms arsenic from curve} \times 2}{\text{Volume of air sampled in cubic meters} \times 1,000}$$

**Sensitivity.**—Considering an aliquot of one-half the prepared sample, the sensitivity is 0.1 microgram arsenic (As), corresponding to 0.24 microgram arsenic per cubic meter, in a 30 cubic foot air sample. Using the same units the Threshold Limit Value for arsenic is 500 micrograms per cubic meter.

## METHODS FOR ARSENIC ANALYSES IN OTHER CHAPTERS

Arsenic in Refined Copper      See Analysis of Refined Copper
Arsenic in Commercial Phosphates      See Analysis of Commercial Phosphates
                                         (Phosphorus Chapter)

# Chapter 5

# BARIUM

**Ba, *at. wt.* 137.34; *sp. gr.* 3.78; *m.p.* 850°C.; *volatile at* 950°C.; *oxides,* BaO, BaO$_2$**

Barium occurs combined in nature as sulfate, BaSO$_4$, barite or heavy spar; as carbonate, BaCO$_3$, witherite, and as baryto-calcite, BaCO$_3$·CaCO$_3$. It occurs in feldspatic rocks, commonly associated with strontium, and in minute quantities (less than 0.2%) in many of the silicate rocks. Barium is never found free in nature.

Barite was investigated by V. Casciorolus, a shoemaker of Bologna, in 1602, who found that the material became phosphorescent upon ignition with a combustible material (Bolognian phosphorus). Scheele found heavy spar in pyrites in 1774. The discovery of the metal was accomplished by Sir Humphry Davy, by electrolysis of the chloride in presence of mercury (1808).

Metallic barium is used as a lining in photoelectric cells and in amplification tubes. The oxide was formerly used in preparing oxygen, and the peroxide in making hydrogen peroxide. The sulfide is used in luminous paint and as a depilatory, the chromate is used as a paint pigment, the sulfate in medical X-ray work, and in lithopone. The oxide has been proposed for sugar refining and as a substitute for calcium in sulfur insecticides.

## DETECTION

Barium is precipitated as the carbonate together with strontium and calcium, by addition of ammonium hydroxide and ammonium carbonate to the filtrate of the ammonium sulfide group. It is separated from strontium and calcium by precipitation as yellow barium chromate, BaCrO$_4$, from a dilute acetic acid solution.

*Saturated solutions of calcium or strontium sulfate* precipitate white barium sulfate, BaSO$_4$, from a chloride or nitrate or acetate solution, barium sulfate being the least soluble of the alkaline earth sulfates.

*Soluble chromates* precipitate yellow barium chromate from a neutral or dilute acetic acid solution, insoluble in water, moderately soluble in chromic acid, soluble in hydrochloric or nitric acid.

*Fluosilicic acid, H$_2$SiF$_6$,* precipitates white, crystalline barium fluosilicate, BaSiF$_6$, sparingly soluble in acetic acid, insoluble in alcohol. (The fluosilicates of calcium and strontium are soluble.)

*Flame.*—Barium compounds color the flame yellowish green, which appears blue through green glass.

*Spectrum.*—Three characteristic green bands ($\alpha$, $\beta$, $\gamma$).

Barium sulfate is precipitated by addition of a soluble sulfate to a solution of a barium salt. The compound is extremely insoluble in water and in dilute acids (soluble in hot concentrated sulfuric acid). The sulfate is readily distinguished from lead sulfate by the fact that the latter is soluble in ammonium salts, whereas barium sulfate is practically insoluble.

*Microscopical Examination.*—G. Deniges (Compt rend., **170**, 996–9, 1920) gives a technic for testing for the alkaline earths with 10% solution of $HIO_3$. The salt is pulverized, a drop of water added and then a minute drop of the $HIO_3$ reagent. The microscope reveals pointed octahedra for Ca, shorter octahedra and rhombic prisms with high refraction for Sr, and needle prisms grouped in clusters for Ba.

## ESTIMATION

The determination of barium is required in the valuation of its ores, barite, heavy spar, $BaSO_4$; witherite, $BaCO_3$; baryto-calcite, $BaCO_3 \cdot CaCO_3$. It is determined in certain white mixed paints and colored pigments, Venetian, Hamburg or Dutch whites, chrome paints, etc., in analysis of Paris green, baryta insecticides, putty, asphalt, dressings and pavement surfacings. It may be found as an adulterant in foods, wood preservatives, filler in rubber, rope, fabrics. It is determined in salts of barium. The nitrate is used in pyrotechnics, in mixtures for green fire.

The formation of water soluble chlorides is desired in the decomposition of the material. This is accomplished by the action of HCl followed by $Na_2CO_3$ fusion of the acid insoluble material with subsequent water extraction and final solution of the water insoluble carbonate with HCl. In presence of phosphates, fluorides, or carbonates the alkaline earth group (Ba, Ca, Sr) will precipitate with iron and alumina.

### PREPARATION AND SOLUTION OF THE SAMPLE

Compounds of barium, with the exception of the sulfate, $BaSO_4$, are soluble in hydrochloric and nitric acids. The sulfate is soluble in hot concentrated sulfuric acid, but is reprecipitated upon dilution of the solution. The sulfate is best fused with sodium carbonate, which transposes the compound to barium carbonate; sodium sulfate may now be leached out with water and the residue, $BaCO_3$, then dissolved in hydrochloric acid.

*Solution of Ores.* **Sulfates.**—0.5 to 1 g. of the finely divided ore is fused with 3 to 5 grams of sodium and potassium carbonate mix, 2:1, or sodium carbonate alone, in a platinum dish. (Prolonged fusion is not necessary.) The melt is cooled and then extracted with hot water to dissolve out the alkali sulfates. Barium carbonate, together with the other insoluble carbonates, may now be dissolved by hot dilute hydrochloric acid. From this solution barium may be precipitated by addition of sulfuric acid. If it is desired to separate barium along with strontium, calcium, and magnesium, the members of the preceding groups are removed by $H_2S$ in acid and in ammoniacal solution, as directed under "Separations."

**Sulfides.**—The ore is oxidized, as directed for pyrites under the subject of sulfur. After the removal of the soluble sulfates, the residue, containing silica, barium, and small amounts of insoluble oxides, is fused and dissolved according to the procedure for sulfates.

**Carbonates.**—In absence of sulfates the material may be dissolved with hydrochloric acid, taken to dryness to dehydrate silica, and after heating for an hour in the steam oven (110°C.) the residue is extracted with dilute hydrochloric acid and filtered. The filtrate is examined for barium according to one of the procedures given later.

*Salts Soluble in Water.*—Nitrates, chlorides, acetates, etc., are dissolved with water slightly acidulated with hydrochloric acid.

*Material Containing Organic Matter.*—The substance is roasted to destroy organic matter before treatment with acids or by fusion with the alkali carbonates.

*The insoluble residue* remaining from the acid treatment of an ore may contain barium sulfate in addition to silica, etc. The filter containing this residue is burned and the ash weighed. Silica is now volatilized by addition of hydrofluoric acid with a few drops of sulfuric acid, and evaporation to dryness. If an insoluble substance still remains after taking up the remaining residue with dilute hydrochloric acid, barium sulfate is indicated. This is treated according to the method given for sulfates.

NOTE.—The insoluble substance remaining is frequently ignited and weighed as barium sulfate without fusion with the carbonate.

## SEPARATIONS

*Causes of Loss.*—In the determination of barium, calcium, and strontium, several causes may lead to loss of the elements sought.

The first is the fact that phosphoric acid, free or combined, has a decided influence upon the determination of the members of this group. Combined as phosphate it will cause the complete precipitation of barium, calcium, and strontium, along with iron, alumina, etc., upon making the solution alkaline for removal of the ammonium sulfide group. It is a common practice to hold up the iron + alumina by means of tartaric, citric, or other organic acids before making ammoniacal for precipitation of this group as oxalates, or again the basic acetate method is used for precipitation of iron and alumina; calcium, barium, and strontium going into solution. These procedures may be satisfactory for the analysis of phosphate rock and similar products, but do not cope with the difficulty when large amounts of phosphates are present. In samples containing free phosphoric acid, barium, calcium, and strontium, present in small amounts, may remain in solution in presence of sulfates or oxalates. Appreciable amounts of calcium, 1% or more, may escape detection by the usual method of precipitation by ammonium oxalate added to the alkaline solution, on account of this interference, so that the removal of phosphoric acid before precipitation of this group is frequently necessary. This may be accomplished by addition of potassium carbonate in sufficient excess to combine completely with the phosphoric acid and form carbonates with the bases. The material taken to dryness is fused with additional potassium carbonate in an iron crucible, and the fusion leached with hot water—sodium phosphate dissolves and the carbonates of the heavy metals remain insoluble.

Another source of loss is the presence of sulfates, either in the original material or by intentional or accidental addition, in the latter case due to the oxidation of hydrogen sulfide, which has been passed into the solution during the removal of elements of the hydrogen sulfide and ammonium sulfide groups, barium and strontium sulfate being precipitated along with these members. A potassium carbonate fusion will form $K_2SO_4$, which may be leached out with water.

Loss may be caused by occlusion of barium, calcium, strontium, and magnesium by the gelatinous precipitates $Fe(OH)_3$, $Al(OH)_3$, etc. A double precipitation of these compounds should be made if considerable amounts are present.

A large excess of ammonium salts, which accumulate during the preliminary separations, will prevent precipitation of the alkaline earths. This can be avoided by using the necessary care required for accurate work, the addition of reagents by means of burettes or according to definite measurements in graduates, etc. Careless addition of large amounts of ammonium hydroxide and hydrochloric acid should be guarded against. In case large amounts of ammonium chloride are present, time is frequently saved by a repetition of the separations. Ammonium chloride may be expelled by heating the material, taken to dryness in a large platinum dish, the ammonium salts being volatilized.

Carbon dioxide absorbed by ammonium hydroxide from the air will precipitate the alkaline earths with the ammonium sulfide group.

*Preliminary Tests.*—Much time may be saved by making a preliminary test for barium, strontium, and calcium by means of the spectroscope and avoiding unnecessary separations.

By means of the spectroscope with the use of the ordinary Bunsen flame exceedingly minute amounts of calcium, strontium and barium may be detected per ml. The test is very much more delicate by the arc spectral method.[1] The liquid containing the substance is connected to the positive pole and an iridium needle is connected by means of an adjustable resistance of 300 to 500 ohms to the negative pole. An E.M.F. of 100 to 200 volts and 1 ampere current are required. By the arc it is possible to detect 0.002 milligram of calcium, 0.003 milligram of strontium, 0.006 milligram of barium, 0.1 milligram of magnesium per ml. In these concentrations, calcium shows one brilliant line (423 m$\mu$), a bright line (616 m$\mu$), and a faint line between them; strontium two bright lines (422 and 461 m$\mu$) and two fairly bright lines; barium two brilliant lines (455 and 493 m$\mu$), two other bright lines, and a fairly bright one; and magnesium a brilliant band composed of three lines (516.8 to 518.4 m$\mu$), as well as a fairly bright line further towards the violet end of the spectrum.

The flame test may be of value in absence of sodium; barium giving a green flame, strontium a brilliant scarlet, and calcium an orange red.

*Direct Precipitation on Original Sample.*—For the determination of barium, calcium, and strontium, it is advisable to take a fresh sample, rather than one that has been previously employed for the estimation of the hydrogen sulfide and ammonium sulfide groups, as is evident from the statements made above. The alkaline earths are isolated by being converted to the insoluble sulfates and separations effected as given later under "Sulfate Method."

*Separation of the Alkaline Earths from Magnesium and the Alkalies.*—Two general procedures will cover conditions commonly met with in analytical work.

*Oxalate Procedure.*—Applicable in presence of comparatively large portions of calcium. The acid solution containing not over 1 g. of the mixed oxides is brought to a volume of 350 ml. and for every 0.1 g. of magnesium present about 1 g. of ammonium chloride is added, unless already present. Sufficient oxalic acid is added to completely precipitate the barium, calcium, and strontium.[2] ($H_2C_2O_4 \cdot 2H_2O = 126.07$, Ba = 137.36, Ca = 40.08, Sr = 87.63.) The solution is slowly neutralized by addition, drop by drop, of dilute ammonium hydroxide (1:10), methyl orange being used as indicator. About 0.5 g. of oxalic acid is now added in excess, the solution again made alkaline with ammonium hydroxide, and allowed to settle for at least two hours. The precipitate is filtered off and washed with water containing 1% ammonium oxalate, faintly alkaline with ammonia.

---

[1] Riesenfeld, E. H., and Pfützer, G., Ber., **46**, 3140–3144, 1913; Analyst, **38**, 584, 1913.

[2] Calcium and strontium will slowly precipitate in the oxalic acid solution. Barium oxalate will precipitate upon making the solution alkaline.

The precipitate contains all the calcium and practically all the barium and strontium. If Mg is present in amounts of 10 to 15 times that of the alkaline earths a double precipitation is necessary to remove it completely from this group. The oxalates are dissolved in hydrochloric acid and reprecipitated with ammonium oxalate in alkaline solution.

The filtrate contains magnesium and the alkalies. Traces of barium and strontium may be present. If the sample contains a comparatively large proportion of barium and strontium, the filtrate is evaporated to dryness, the ammonium salts expelled by gentle ignition of the residue, and the Ba and Sr recovered as sulfates according to the method described below. Magnesium is precipitated as magnesium ammonium phosphate from the filtrate.

The oxalates of barium, calcium, and strontium are ignited to oxides, in which form they may be readily converted to chlorides by dissolving in hydrochloric acid, or to nitrates by nitric acid.

**Sulfate Procedure.**—Applicable in presence of comparatively large proportions of barium, strontium, or magnesium. The solution containing the alkaline earths, magnesium, and the alkalies is evaporated to dryness and about 5 ml. concentrated sulfuric acid added, followed by 50 ml. of 95% alcohol. The sulfates [3] of barium, calcium, and strontium, are allowed to settle, and then filtered on to a fine grained ashless filter paper and washed with alcohol until free of magnesium sulfate. In presence of large amounts of magnesium (as in case of analyses of Epsom salts and other magnesium salts) it will be necessary to extract the precipitate by adding a small amount of water, then sufficient 95% alcohol to make the solution contain 50% alcohol and filter from the residue. Magnesium is determined in the filtrate.

The residue containing barium, calcium, and strontium as sulfate is fused with 10 parts of potassium carbonate or sodium acid carbonate until the fusion becomes a clear molten mass, a deep platinum crucible being used for the fusion. A platinum wire is inserted and the mass allowed to solidify. The fusion may be removed by again heating until it begins to melt around the surface next to the crucible, when it may be lifted out on the wire. The mass is extracted with hot water and filtered, $Na_2SO_4$ going into the solution and the carbonates of barium, strontium, and calcium remaining insoluble. The carbonates should dissolve completely in hydrochloric acid or nitric acid, otherwise the decomposition has not been complete, and a second fusion of this insoluble residue will be necessary.

*Separation of the Alkaline Earths from One Another.*—This separation may be effected by several procedures.

**Separation of Barium from Strontium (and from Calcium).**[4]—In presence of an excess of ammonium chromate, barium is precipitated from solutions, slightly acid with acetic acid, as barium chromate (appreciably soluble in free acetic acid), whereas strontium and calcium remain in solution.

The mixed oxides or carbonates are dissolved in the least amount of dilute hydrochloric acid and the excess of acid expelled by evaporation to near dryness. The residue is taken up in about 300 ml. of water and 5–6 drops of acetic acid (sp. gr. 1.065) together with sufficient ammonium acetate (30% solution) to neutralize any free mineral acid present. The solution is heated and an excess of

---

[3] Solubility of $BaSO_4$ = 0.17 milligram, $CaSO_4$ = 179 milligram, $SrSO_4$ = 11.4 milligrams per 100 ml.

[4] Method of Stromayer and Rose. Rose, H., Pogg. Ann., **110,** 292, 1860.

ammonium chromate (10% neutral solution)[5] added (10 ml. usually sufficient). The precipitate of barium chromate is allowed to settle for an hour and filtered off on a small filter and washed with water containing ammonium chromate until free of soluble strontium and calcium (test—addition of $NH_4OH$ and $(NH_4)_2CO_3$ produces no cloudiness), and then with water until practically free of ammonium chromate (e.g., only slight reddish brown color with silver nitrate solution).

To separate any occluded precipitate of strontium or calcium the filter paper is pierced and the precipitate rinsed into a beaker with warm dilute nitric acid (sp. gr. 1.20) (2 ml. usually are sufficient). The solution is diluted to about 200 ml. and boiled. About 5 ml. of ammonium acetate, or enough to neutralize the free $HNO_3$, are added to the hot solution and then sufficient ammonium chromate to neutralize the free acetic acid, 10 ml. usually being sufficient. The washing, as above indicated, is repeated. Barium is completely precipitated and may be determined either as a chromate or a sulfate or by a volumetric procedure. Strontium and calcium are in the filtrates and may be separated as follows:

**Separation of Strontium from Calcium.**—The method depends upon the insolubility of strontium nitrate and the solubility of calcium nitrate in a mixture of ether-alcohol, 1:1.

Solubility of $Sr(NO_3)_2 = 1$ part $Sr(NO_3)_2$ in 60,000 parts of the mixture. Ca easily soluble. According to Fresenius[6] 0.0023 g. $Sr(NO_3)_2$ per 250 ml. and 0.37 g. $Ca(NO_3)_2$ per 1 ml.

If the solution is a filtrate from barium, 1 ml. of nitric acid is added and the solution heated and made alkaline with ammonium hydroxide followed immediately with ammonium carbonate, the carbonates of strontium (together with some $SrCrO_4$) and calcium will precipitate. The precipitate is dissolved in hydrochloric acid and reprecipitated from a hot solution with ammonium hydroxide and ammonium carbonate. The precipitate, $SrCO_3$ and $CaCO_3$, is washed once with hot water and is then dissolved in the least amount of nitric acid, washed into a small casserole, evaporated to dryness and heated for an hour at 140 to 160°C. in an oven, or at 110°C. overnight. The dry mass is pulverized and mixed with 10 ml. of ether-alcohol (absolute alcohol, one part, ether-anhydrous, one part). Several extractions are thus made, the extracts being decanted off into a flask. The residue is again dried in an oven at 140 to 160°C., then pulverized and washed into the flask with the ether-alcohol mixture and digested for several hours with frequent shaking of the flask. The residue is washed on to a filter moistened with ether-alcohol mixture. Strontium nitrate, $Sr(NO_3)_2$, remains insoluble, and may be dissolved in water and determined gravimetrically as a sulfate, oxide, or carbonate or titrimetrically. Calcium is in the filtrate and may be determined gravimetrically as an oxide or titrimetrically.

Instead of using a mixture of ether-alcohol, amyl alcohol (b.p. = 130°C.) may be used (hood), the mixture being kept at boiling temperature to dehydrate the alcohol to prevent solution of strontium.

**Separation of Barium and Strontium from Calcium.**[7]—The procedure depends upon the insolubility of barium nitrate, $Ba(NO_3)_2$, and strontium nitrate, $Sr(NO_3)_2$,

---

[5] The solution is prepared by adding $NH_4OH$ to a solution of $(NH_4)_2Cr_2O_7$ until yellow. The solution should be left acid rather than alkaline.

[6] Z. anal. Chem., **32**, 189, 1893.

[7] Fresenius, Z. anal. Chem., **29**, 413–430, 1890.

in a mixture of anhydrous ether and absolute alcohol or anhydrous amyl alcohol, whereas $Ca(NO_3)_2$ dissolves.

The mixed oxides or carbonates are dissolved in nitric acid and taken to dryness in a beaker or Erlenmeyer flask, and heated for an hour or more in an oven at 140 to 160°C. Upon cooling, the mixture is treated with ten times its weight of ether-alcohol mixture and digested, cold, in a covered beaker or corked flask for about two hours with frequent stirring. An equal volume of ether is now added and the digestion continued for several hours longer. The residue is washed by decantation with ether and alcohol mixture until calcium is removed (test—no residue on platinum foil with drop of filtrate evaporated to dryness).

**Separation of Barium from Strontium.**—The dry mixed chlorides are dissolved in the least possible amount of water (0.2 ml., or more if necessary), the solution warmed, then cooled. More water is added if crystals appear. (The solution should be saturated.) A mixture of 4:1 of HCl (33%) and ether is added dropwise with stirring. Sufficient reagent is added to precipitate $BaCl_2$ and dissolve $SrCl_2$. The mixture is decanted on an asbestos filter and washed with the HCl-ether reagent. The $BaCl_2$ is dried at 150°C. and weighed. (Method of Gooch and Soderman.)

Barium and strontium may be separated by precipitation of barium as a chromate, the nitrate residue being dissolved in water and barium precipitated according to directions given under "Separation of Barium from Strontium."

Amyl alcohol may be used in place of ether-alcohol by digesting the nitrates in a boiling solution (130°C.), calcium going into solution and barium and strontium remaining insoluble as nitrates.

**Separation of Barium from Calcium.**[8]—Upon addition of 100% nitric acid to aqueous solutions containing barium and calcium, the precipitation of barium as the nitrate is complete when the concentration of nitric acid is 76% in the mixture. Other nitrates that precipitate under similar conditions are those of strontium and lead. The optimum concentration of free nitric acid is 76% for precipitation of barium nitrate, 80% for precipitation of strontium nitrate, and 84% for precipitation of lead nitrate. Willard and Goodspeed found that 56.6 mg. of Ba (107.7 mg. of $Ba(NO_3)_2$) could be separated quantitatively from 125 mg. of Ca, 500 mg. each of Bi, Cd, or Ni present as nitrates.

The aqueous solution of the nitrates is evaporated to dryness, and the dried residue is dissolved in 5 ml. of water. Upon addition of 3.0 ml. of 70% nitric acid with stirring, the barium nitrate is partially precipitated, then, while stirring, 11 ml. of 100% nitric acid is added from a burette to bring the nitric acid concentration up to 76%. After 30 minutes, the barium nitrate is collected on a weighed filter crucible and washed 10 times with small amounts of 76% nitric acid and dried for 2 hours at 130–140°C.

NOTES.—Fuming nitric acid may be made up to a known density with water to give 100% nitric acid, or alternately, the 100% acid may be made by distillation from a mixture of sodium nitrate and concentrated sulfuric acid, e.g., 500 g. of dry sodium nitrate and 500 ml. of the acid heated in the 2-liter flask of an all-glass distilling apparatus.

The following information on the effect of concentration of nitric acid upon the completeness of precipitation is given by Willard and Goodspeed:

8 Willard, H. H., and Goodspeed, E. W., Ind. Eng. Chem. Anal. Ed., **8**, 414, 1936.

*Errors, in mg., at various acidities*

| % Nitric Acid: | 66 | 69 | 74 | 78 | 80 | 83 | 85 | 87 |
|---|---|---|---|---|---|---|---|---|
| Sr (57.9 mg. taken) | — <br> — | −1.3 <br> −1.7 | −0.3 <br> −0.3 | 0.0 <br> −0.1 | 0.0 <br> 0.0 | 0.1 <br> 0.0 | 0.0 <br> 0.0 | — <br> — |
| Ba (56.6 mg. taken) | −0.8 <br> −0.9 | 0.0 <br> −0.1 | 0.0 <br> −0.1 | 0.0 <br> −0.1 | 0.0 <br> −0.1 | 0.0 <br> −0.1 | — <br> — | 0.0 <br> −0.1 |
| Pb (101.7 mg. taken) | −8.8 <br> −9.5 | — <br> — | −1.3 <br> −1.4 | −0.9 <br> −0.7 | −0.2 <br> −0.4 | −0.2 <br> −0.1 | — <br> — | −0.1 <br> −0.1 |

The solubility of calcium nitrate decreases with increasing percentage of $HNO_3$:

| Percentage Nitric Acid | 77 | 79 | 81 | 83 | 85 |
|---|---|---|---|---|---|
| Solubility, mg. Ca/ml. | 26.5 | 10.0 | 5.0 | 1.9 | 1.1 |

**Separation of Calcium, Strontium, and Barium by Ion Exchange.**—In early work on the separation of fission products it was demonstrated that the alkaline earths could be separated on ion exchange columns.[9] Lerner and Rieman [10] were able to separate the three elements, present in the form of chlorides, on a Dowex 50 cation exchange resin that had been previously charged with 1.20 $M$ ammonium lactate solution. The sample in a volume of 6 ml. or less, was eluted with 1.20 $M$ ammonium lactate at the rate of 0.56 cm. (1.4 ml.) per minute. All the calcium was in the first 74 ml., the strontium in the next 58 ml., and the barium was found in a diffuse elution pattern in the next 325 ml. The amounts separated ranged from about 1 millimole of each element down to about 0.01 millimole. Various concentration ratios were studied. The errors for each element were in general less than 0.005 millimole.

A general study of the paper chromatographic separation of alkali and alkaline earth ions and a table of separation factors ($R_f$ values) in the presence of various anions is given by Gordon and Hewel.[11]

**Separation of the Alkaline Earths from Molybdenum.**—The substance is fused with sodium carbonate and the fusion extracted with water and filtered. Molybdenum passes into the filtrate and the alkaline earths remain in the residue.

**Separation of Phosphoric Acid from the Alkaline Earths.**—Ammonium carbonate is added to the hydrochloric acid solution until a slight permanent turbidity is obtained, and the solution just cleared with a few drops of HCl. Ferric chloride is now added drop by drop until the solution above the yellowish white precipitate becomes brownish in color. The solution is diluted to about 400 ml. and brought to boiling and then filtered and the residue washed with water containing ammonium acetate. The filtrate contains the alkaline earths, free from phosphoric acid.

**Separation from Lead.**—If the ore has been treated with $H_2SO_4$, $BaSO_4$ and $PbSO_4$ will be found with $SiO_2$. In the acetate extraction of lead the presence of 1% ammonium sulfate eliminates the solubility of $BaSO_4$, but does not seriously

9 Tompkins, E. R., J. Am. Chem. Soc., **70**, 3520, 1948.
10 Lerner, M., and Rieman, W., III, Anal. Chem., **26**, 610, 1954.
11 Gordon, H. T., and Hewel, C. A., Anal. Chem., **27**, 1471, 1955.

interfere with the solubility of $PbSO_4$ in the ammonium acetate. $CaSO_4$ dissolves and accompanies lead. The investigation of Alldredge and Scott shows a complete extraction of $PbSO_4$ by means of ammonium acetate with no appreciable solution of $BaSO_4$. See Chapter on Lead.

## GRAVIMETRIC METHODS

For reasons given under "Separation," it is advisable to take a special sample for the determination of barium that has not undergone treatment with hydrogen sulfide or ammonium hydroxide, since these may cause the loss of barium as stated.

*Barium in Insoluble Residue.*—In the complete analysis of ores the residue remaining insoluble in acids is composed largely of silica, together with difficultly soluble substances, among which is barium sulfate. This residue is best fused in a platinum dish with sodium carbonate or a mixture of sodium and potassium carbonates (long fusion is not necessary). The cooled mass is digested with hot water to remove the soluble sodium compounds, silicate being included. Barium, together with the heavy metals, remains insoluble as carbonate and may be filtered off. The residue is now treated with dilute ammonia water to remove the adhering sulfates (testing the filtrate with hydrochloric acid and barium chloride solution; the washing being complete when no white precipitate of barium sulfate forms). The carbonates are washed off the filter into a 500-ml. beaker, the clinging carbonate being dissolved by pouring a few ml. of dilute, 1:1, hydrochloric acid on the paper placed in the funnel. This extract is added to the precipitate in the beaker and the latter covered to prevent loss by spattering. Additional hydrochloric acid is cautiously added so that the precipitate completely dissolves and the solution contains about 10 ml. of free hydrochloric acid (sp. gr. 1.2). Barium is precipitated from this solution best as a sulfate according to directions given later.

*Silicates.*—One gram of the finely pulverized sample is treated with 10 ml. of dilute sulfuric acid, 1:4, and 5 ml. of concentrated hydrofluoric acid. The mixture, evaporated to small bulk on the steam bath, is taken to $SO_3$ fumes on the hotplate. Additional sulfuric acid and hydrofluoric acid are used if required. By this treatment the silica is expelled and barium, together with other insoluble sulfates, will remain upon the filter when the residue is treated with water and filtered. Lead sulfate, if present, may be removed by washing the residue with a solution of ammonium acetate. Barium sulfate may be purified by fusion with potassium carbonate as above directed or by dissolving in hot concentrated sulfuric acid, and precipitating again as $BaSO_4$ by dilution.

*Ores* may be decomposed by either of the above methods or a combination of the two. Sulfide ores require roasting to oxidize the sulfide to sulfate.

*Barium Sulfate* is decomposed by fusion with sodium and potassium carbonates. The fusion is leached with water to remove the soluble sulfate and the residue, $BaCO_3$, is dissolved in HCl. Barium is determined in this solution.

## DETERMINATION OF BARIUM AS THE CHROMATE

A preliminary spectroscopic test has indicated whether a separation from calcium and strontium is necessary. If these are present, barium is separated along with strontium from calcium as the nitrate in presence of alcohol-ether mixture, according to directions given under "Separations." Barium is now precipitated as the chromate, $BaCrO_4$, from a neutral or slightly acetic acid solution, strontium remaining in solution.

*Procedure.* **Precipitation of Barium Chromate.**—If barium is present in the form of nitrate, together with strontium, the mixed nitrates are evaporated to dryness and then taken up with water, about 10 ml. ammonium acetate (300 g. $NH_4C_2H_3O_2$ neutralized with $NH_4OH + H_2O$ to make up to 1000 ml.) added and the solution heated to boiling. Five ml. of 20% ammonium bichromate are added drop by drop with constant stirring and the precipitate allowed to settle until cold. The solution is decanted off from the precipitate through a filter and washed by decantation with dilute (0.5%) solution of ammonium acetate until the excess chromate is removed, as indicated by the filtrate passing through uncolored. If much strontium was originally present, a double precipitation is necessary, otherwise the precipitate may be filtered directly into a Gooch crucible and dried (120°C.), to constant weight.

**Purification from Strontium.**—The precipitate is dissolved from the filter by running through dilute (1:5) warm nitric acid, poured upon the chromate, catching the solution in the beaker in which the precipitation was made; the least amount of acid necessary to accomplish this being used and the filter washed with a little warm water. Ammonium hydroxide is now added to the solution, cautiously, until a slight permanent precipitate forms and then 10 ml. of ammonium acetate solution added with constant stirring and the mixture heated to boiling. The precipitate is allowed to settle until the solution is cold and then filtered and washed by decantation as before, a Gooch crucible being used to catch the precipitate.

**Ignition.**—The precipitate is washed with dilute alcohol once, then dried at 110°C. The crucible containing the $BaCrO_4$ is gently heated in a larger crucible (allowing an encircling air space around the crucible) until the color of the chromate becomes uniform.

$$BaCrO_4 \times 0.6053 = BaO$$

$$\times 0.5421 = Ba$$

NOTES.—The use of sodium hydroxide or acetate in place of the ammonium hydroxide and acetate is sometimes recommended, owing to the slight solubility of $BaCrO_4$ in ammonium salts, as seen by the following table, approximate figures being given:

| | |
|---|---|
| 100,000 parts of cold water dissolves | 0.38 parts $BaCrO_4$ |
| 100,000 parts of hot water dissolves | 4.35 parts $BaCrO_4$ |
| 100,000 of 0.5% solution of $NH_4Cl$ dissolves | 4.35 parts $BaCrO_4$ |
| 100,000 of 0.5% solution of $NH_4NO_3$ dissolves | 2.22 parts $BaCrO_4$ |
| 100,000 of 0.75% solution of $NH_4C_2H_3O_2$ dissolves | 2.00 parts $BaCrO_4$ |
| 100,000 of 1.5% solution of $NH_4C_2H_3O_2$ dissolves | 4.12 parts $BaCrO_4$ |
| 100,000 of 1% acetic acid dissolves | 20.73 parts $BaCrO_4$ |

Although the solvent action of ammonium salts is practically negligible under conditions of analysis given above, the solvent action of free acetic acid is of importance, so that it is necessary to neutralize or eliminate free mineral acids before addition of the acetate salt.

The edges of the $BaCrO_4$ precipitate upon drying may appear green, owing to the action of alcohol; upon ignition, however, the yellow chromate is obtained. The color orange yellow, when hot, fades to a light canary yellow upon cooling.

$BaCrO_4$, *mol. wt.*, 253.37; *sp. gr.*, 4.498 (at 15°C.); 100 ml. $H_2O$ soln. cold will dissolve 0.00038 gram (at 18°C.), hot dissolves 0.0043 gram; soluble in HCl, $HNO_3$, yellow rhombic plates.

## DETERMINATION OF BARIUM AS THE CARBONATE

The solution free from previous groups and from calcium and strontium is made ammoniacal after addition of ammonium chloride if not already present for the purpose of preventing precipitation of magnesium. Ammonium carbonate is now added in slight excess and the precipitated $BaCO_3$ allowed to settle on the water bath or in a warm place for an hour or preferably longer. The precipitate is filtered and washed with dilute $NH_4OH$, dried, ignited, and weighed as $BaCO_3$. The method proposed by Fresenius, is considered by some to be more accurate than the sulfate method.

$$BaCO_3 \times 0.696 = Ba$$

## DETERMINATION OF BARIUM AS THE SULFATE

This method depends upon the insolubility of barium sulfate in water and in very dilute hydrochloric acid or sulfuric acid, one gram of the salt requiring about 344,000 ml. of hot water to effect solution.

**Reaction.**—$Ba^{++} + SO_4^{=} \rightarrow BaSO_4$.

$BaSO_4$, *mol. wt.*, 233.42; *sp. gr.*, 4.47 *and* 4.33; *m.p.*, 1580°C. (*amorphous decomposes*); $H_2O$ *dissolves* 0.000172 (at 0°C.) *and* 0.0003 (at 34°C.) g. *per* 100 *ml.* 3% HCl *dissolves* 0.0036 g. *Soluble in concentrated* $H_2SO_4$. *White, rhombic and amorphous forms.*

**Procedure.**—The slightly acid (hydrochloric) solution of barium chloride, prepared according to directions given, is heated to boiling (volume about 200–300 ml.) and a slight excess of hot dilute sulfuric acid added. The precipitate is settled on the water bath and the clear solution then decanted through a weighed Gooch crucible or through an ashless filter paper (S. and S. 590 quality). The precipitate is transferred to the Gooch crucible (or paper), and washed twice with very dilute sulfuric acid solution (0.5% $H_2SO_4$), and finally with hot water until free of acid. The precipitate is dried and ignited, at first gently and then over a good flame to a cherry red heat, for 30 minutes. The residue is weighed as barium sulfate, $BaSO_4$.

$$BaSO_4 \times 0.5885 = Ba$$

$$\times 0.6570 = BaO$$

$$\times 0.8456 = BaCO_3.$$

Notes.—The determination of barium is the reciprocal of the determination of sulfur or sulfuric acid. Precautions and directions given for the sulfur precipitation apply here also, with the exception that dilute sulfuric acid is used as the precipitating reagent in place of barium chloride.

The author found that precipitation of barium sulfate in a large volume of cold solution containing 10 ml. of concentrated hydrochloric acid per 1600 ml. of solution, by adding a slight excess of cold dilute sulfuric acid in a fine stream, exactly in the manner that barium chloride solution is added in the precipitation of sulfur, and allowing the precipitate to settle, at room temperature, for several hours (preferably overnight), gives a precipitate that is pure and does not pass through the Gooch asbestos mat. We refer to the chapter on Sulfur for directions for filtering, washing, and ignition of the residue.

The addition of hydrochloric acid causes rapid settling of the barium sulfate. F. A. Gooch has shown that the precipitation should be conducted at temperatures over 75°C., preferably at 90°C. Gooch, Methods in Chemical Analysis, p. 168, 1912.

Lead, strontium and calcium should be absent. Cl, Al, and Fe, if present in appreciable amounts, will contaminate the $BaSO_4$.

**Precipitation from Homogeneous Phase.**—The slow generation of sulfate ions by the hydrolysis of sulfamic acid [12] or of dimethyl sulfate [13] and similar reagents yields a better separation of barium from ferric iron, calcium, magnesium, phosphate, and nitrate than the conventional method. If 1–100 mg. of barium is precipitated in the presence of 1–10 mg. of strontium, from 10 to 20% of the strontium is precipitated along with the barium sulfate. Presumably lead and strontium should be absent during the precipitation of barium by this method.

**Sulfamic Acid Procedure.**—The barium solution containing 1–100 mg. of barium in 100 ml. is treated with 1 g. of sulfamic acid, heated at 100°C. for 30 minutes after the first turbidity due to barium sulfate appears, then filtered through a weighed Selas porcelain filter crucible (No. 3001). The precipitate is washed with distilled water and dried and heated to 900°C. in an electric muffle to constant weight.

**Dimethyl Sulfate Procedure.**—The solution containing 1–100 mg. of barium in 75 ml. is treated with 20 ml. of methanol and not less than 2 ml. of dimethyl sulfate and a total corresponding to 0.5 ml. per each 10 mg. of barium expected to be present. Dilute to 100 ml. and heat 1¼ hours on a steam bath. Filter through a porcelain filter crucible (Selas No. 3001), and wash with 20% methanol-water of which 50 ml. should be sufficient. Dry at 100–150°C. for 15 minutes and heat to 750°C. to constant weight in an electric muffle. From 0.5 to 1 hour should be sufficient for the heating.

## TITRIMETRIC METHODS

## TITRATION OF THE BARIUM SALT WITH DICHROMATE

This method is of value for an approximation of the amount of barium present in a solution that may also contain calcium, strontium, and magnesium or the alkalies. It depends upon the reaction,

$$2Ba^{++} + Cr_2O_7^{=} + H_2O \rightarrow 2BaCrO_4 + 2H^+$$

0.1 $N$ $K_2Cr_2O_7$ (precipitation purposes) contains 7.355 g. pure salt per liter.

**Procedure.**—The solution containing the barium is treated with ammonia until it just smells of it. (If an excess of ammonia is present the solution is made faintly acid with acetic acid.) It is then heated to about 70°C. and the standard dichromate added, with stirring, until all the barium is precipitated and the clear supernatant solution is a faint yellow color from the slight excess of the reagent. For accurate work it is advisable to titrate the precipitate formed by one of the methods given below. One ml. $K_2Cr_2O_7$ = 0.00687 g. Ba. (Note reaction given above.)

NOTE.—An excess of potassium dichromate may be added, the precipitate filtered off, washed, and the excess of dichromate determined as stated below.

[12] Wagner, W. F., and Wuellner, J. A., Anal. Chem., **24**, 1031, 1952.
[13] Elving, P. J., and Van Atta, R. E., Anal. Chem., **22**, 1375, 1950.

## REDUCTION OF THE CHROMATE WITH FERROUS SALT
## AND TITRATION WITH PERMANGANATE

Ferrous sulfate reacts with barium chromate as follows:

$$2BaCrO_4 + 2H^+ \rightarrow 2Ba^{++} + Cr_2O_7^{=} + H_2O$$

$$Cr_2O_7^{=} + 6Fe^{++} + 14H^+ \rightarrow 6Fe^{+3} + 2Cr^{+3} + 7H_2O$$

An excess of ferrous salt solution is added and the excess determined by titration with 0.1 $N$ KMnO$_4$ solution. Fe = ⅓ Ba.

*Reagents.* 0.1 $N$ solution of KMnO$_4$.

0.1 $N$ FeSO$_4$·7H$_2$O (27.80 grams per liter) or FeSO$_4$·(NH$_4$)$_2$SO$_4$·6H$_2$O (39.213 g. per liter).—One ml. = 0.004579 g. Ba.

*Procedure.*—The well-washed precipitate of barium chromate is dissolved in an excess of standard 0.1 $N$ ferrous ammonium sulfate solution containing free sulfuric acid. The excess ferrous salt is titrated with standard 0.1 $N$ potassium permanganate solution.

(The ml. 0.1 $N$ ferrous solution minus the ml. permanganate solution) multiplied by 0.004579 gives grams barium in the solution. Iron factor to barium is 0.8200.

## POTASSIUM IODIDE METHOD

The procedure depends upon the reactions:

1.
$$2BaCrO_4 + 2H^+ \rightarrow 2Ba^{++} + Cr_2O_7^{=} + H_2O$$
(Hydrochloric acid medium)

2.
$$Cr_2O_7^{=} + 6I^- + 14H^+ \rightarrow 2Cr^{+3} + 3I_2 + 7H_2O$$
$$3I^- + 3I_2 \rightarrow 3I_3^-$$

3.
$$3I_3^- + 6S_2O_3^{=} \rightarrow 3S_4O_6^{=} + 9I^-$$

*Procedure.*—The precipitate, BaCrO$_4$, is dissolved in 50 to 100 ml. of dilute hydrochloric acid and about 2 g. of solid potassium iodide salt added and allowed to react about ten minutes. The liberated iodine is now titrated with 0.1 $N$ thiosulfate. Near the end of the titration starch solution is added and followed by 0.1 $N$ thiosulfate until the color disappears.

One ml. 0.1 $N$ Na$_2$S$_2$O$_3$ = 0.004579 g. Ba.

## TITRATION OF BARIUM CARBONATE
## WITH STANDARD ACID

To the well-washed barium carbonate, BaCO$_3$, an excess of 0.1 $N$ H$_2$SO$_4$ is added and the excess acid determined.

One ml. 0.1 $N$ acid = 0.00687 g. Ba.

## TITRATION OF THE BARIUM SALT WITH STANDARD
## SULFATE SOLUTION

Sodium rhodizinate has been proposed as an indicator for this titration.[14] Tetrahydroxyquinone is a more satisfactory indicator and may be added to the solution

[14] Giblin, Analyst, **58**, 752, 1933; Friedrich and Rapoport, Mikrochemie, **14**, 41, 1933. The solution is spotted on paper.

to be titrated.[15] The barium solution should be below 0.05 $N$ with respect to hydrochloric acid and should be at room temperature. To each 50 ml. of solution should be added 15 ml. of alcohol. Chloride, carbonate, silicate, calcium, magnesium, and aluminum do not interfere unless they are present in high concentration.

*Indicator.*—One part of the disodium salt of tetrahydroxyquinone is ground with 400 parts of dried potassium chloride, and 0.2 g. of this mixture is used, measured by a small cup. The solution of the indicator is unstable.

The solution is titrated with standard potassium sulfate, 0.05 $M$, to the disappearance of the red color of the barium salt of the indicator.

## TITRATION OF BARIUM ION WITH E.D.T.A. SOLUTION

The compleximetric titration of barium is useful for the estimation of barium in simple solutions and for the indirect determination of sulfate.[16]

*Reagents.* **E.D.T.A.**—Disodium salt of ethylenediamine tetraacetic acid, $Na_2H_2Y \cdot 2H_2O$, where Y represents the ethylenediamine tetraacetate residue. Formula: $Na_2H_2C_{10}H_{12}O_8N_2 \cdot 2H_2O$, mol. wt. 372.25. Either 0.1 or 0.01 $M$ solutions are prepared and standardized against pure barium nitrate solution.

**Buffer, pH 11.**—A stock solution of 10 g. of ammonium chloride dissolved in a liter of concentrated ammonia is stored in polyethylene or other resistant containers. 10 ml. of this stock solution is diluted to 60 ml.

**Indicator.**—A metalphthalein indicator made by the interaction of o-cresolphthalein, iminodiacetic acid, and formaldehyde, has the characteristics both of a phthalein indicator and a complexone. The indicator is stable in triethanolamine. Sixty mg. are added to 60 ml. of the solvent and a clear solution is obtained after several days. Ten drops of this "Phthalein Purpur" solution are used per titration. The solution of the indicator in ammonia is only stable for a few days (less than a week) whereas the solution in the ethanolamine is stable for over three months. Indicator tablets containing 0.5 mg. of the sodium salt 3,3'-(bis-N,N'-di(carboxymethyl)-aminomethyl)-thymosulfonphthalein ($C_{37}H_{44}N_2S$) designed for use in the E.D.T.A. titration of barium are commercially available (Fisher Scientific Co.). The pH should be adjusted with a $NH_3$; NaOH buffer and the color change is from blue to gray.

*Procedure.*[17]—The solution is neutralized if necessary, and buffered to pH 11. If no screening dyes are used, the color of the metalphthalein is suppressed if 30 to 50% of ethanol is added. If a pure aqueous solution is used the mixed indicator consists of 0.1% metalphthalein and 0.05% each of methyl red and diamine green dissolved in about 0.5 ml. of concentrated ammonia then diluted to 100 ml. with water. The solution plus indicator is titrated to a sudden decrease in the color intensity.

The optimum concentration of barium is of the order of $1-5 \times 10^{-3}$ $M$.

Spectrophotometric titration gives excellent results for small amounts of barium. The maximum absorbance of the colored complex is at or near 575 m$\mu$, and this absorption peak falls regularly as the barium is complexed. Beyond the equivalence-point the absorbance falls more slowly.[17]

[15] Schroeder, Ind. Eng. Chem., Anal. Ed., **5**, 403, 1933. The reverse titration is described in the Chapter on Sulfur.

[16] Cohen, A. I., and Gordon, L., Anal. Chem., **28**, 1445, 1956.

[17] Anderegg, G., Flaschka, H., Sallman, R., and Schwarzenbach, G., Helv. Chim. Acta, **37**, 113, 1954.

## PHOTOMETRIC METHODS

### THE CHROMATE METHOD

In this procedure the barium is precipitated as the chromate, filtered, and washed. The amount of barium is estimated indirectly from the amount of light absorbed by the solution of the precipitate in acid. Conversely, the excess of chromate may be estimated after the precipitate has been removed.

*Procedure.*—The barium chromate is precipitated in a buffered ammonium acetate solution, after adding ammonia to neutralize free mineral acid, then 1 drop of glacial acetic acid and 1.0–1.25 g. of ammonium acetate dissolved in 5 ml. of water. The barium is precipitated by adding ammonium or potassium chromate (1 g. per 10 ml.).

After washing with cold water, the barium chromate is dissolved in 20 milliequivalents of hydrochloric acid and made homogeneous at a measured volume in a volumetric flask (10.00, 50.00, or 100.00). A calibration curve is established by treating known amounts of a standard solution of barium in similar fashion.

### THE BARIUM *o*-CRESOLPHTHALEIN COMPLEXONE (METALPHTHALEIN)

This method depends upon the ability of the indicator to form a highly colored complex with barium ion. Calcium and strontium also form colored complexes with the reagent which is recommended for the estimation of small amounts of the alkaline earth elements after separation by appropriate methods, e.g., paper chromatography.[18]

*Reagents.* **Standard Barium Solution.**—100 mg. of barium per liter, from pure barium chloride dihydrate.

**Ammonia Solution.**—5 ml. of concentrated $NH_4OH$ per 100 ml.

*o*-**Cresolphthalein Complexone Indicator.** 0.1 g. per 100 ml. of a mixture of 28 ml. of dilute $NH_4OH$ and 72 ml. of water. Prepared fresh each day.

*Procedure.*—The barium solution is placed in a 100-ml. calibrated flask and the solution is diluted to 50 ml., 10 ml. of the indicator solution and 25 ml. of the dilute ammonia are added, and the solution is rapidly diluted to the mark, made homogeneous, and measured. The calibrations are made under the same conditions. The calibration is linear from 0 to 5.0 mg. Ba per liter and the slope is 0.239 absorbance units per milligram of Ba per liter. The strontium complex has a slope of 0.373 absorbance units per mg. Sr per liter, under similar conditions.

## DETERMINATIONS IN SPECIFIC SUBSTANCES

### ANALYSIS OF BARITE AND WITHERITE. METHOD FOR COMMERCIAL VALUATION OF THE ORE [19]

Barite or heavy spar is a variety of native barium sulfate, and witherite a native barium carbonate. These minerals are typical examples of barium-bearing ores. The analysis may involve the determination of barium and calcium sulfates or carbonates, magnesia, iron and aluminum oxides and moisture. Traces of lead, copper, and zinc may be present, as well as sulfide, sulfur and fluorine in fluorspar.

[18] Pollard, F. H., and Martin, J. V., The Analyst, **81**, 348, 1956.
[19] Standard Method of the New Jersey Zinc Company.

*Reagents Required (For Barium and Strontium).* **Ammonium Acetate.**—Dissolve 300 g. $NH_4C_2H_3O_2$ in distilled water and dilute to 1000 ml.

**Ammonium Acetate, Dilute.**—20 ml. of above solution are diluted to 1000 ml.

**Ammonium Dichromate.**—Dissolve 100 g. $(NH_4)_2Cr_2O_7$ (free from $SO_3$) in distilled water and dilute to 1000 ml.

**Ammonia Solution (1:5).**—Mix 200 ml. of $NH_4OH$ (sp. gr. 0.90) with 1000 ml. of distilled water.

**Ammonium Sulfate.**—Dissolve 30 g. $(NH_4)_2SO_4$ (C.P.) in distilled water and dilute to 1000 ml.

**Ammonium Sulfate, Dilute.**—Dissolve 2 g. of $(NH_4)_2SO_4$ (C.P.) in distilled water and dilute to 1000 ml.

**Hydrochloric Acid (1:4).**—Mix 200 ml. of HCl (sp. gr. 1.20) with 800 ml. of distilled water.

**Nitric Acid (1:4).**—Mix 200 ml. of $HNO_3$ (sp. gr. 1.42) with 800 ml. of distilled water.

**Sodium Carbonate.**—Dissolve 2 g. $Na_2CO_3$ (C.P.) in distilled water and dilute to 1000 ml.

**Sulfuric Acid (1:1).**—Mix cautiously 500 ml. of $H_2SO_4$ (sp. gr. 1.84) with 500 ml. of distilled water.

**Ethyl Alcohol Solution.**—Mix 100 ml. of ethyl alcohol (95%) with 100 ml. distilled water and add 1 ml. of $H_2SO_4$ 1:1.

## DETERMINATION OF BARIUM SULFATE

*Procedure for Barite Essentially Free from Strontium.*—Weigh 1 g. of sample into a platinum crucible and add 8 g. of sodium carbonate (C.P.) (1).* Cover and fuse the mixture over a Meker burner for 40 minutes (2). Cool (3) and leach out the fusion with 200 ml. of hot water in a 400-ml. beaker. Filter (4), washing the paper and residue 12 times with the hot sodium carbonate solution. (Reserve this filtrate for the determination of $SO_3$.)

Dissolve (5) the carbonates from the paper and crucible with hot HCl (1:4), catching the solution in a 600-ml. beaker, and wash the paper with hot water until free of chlorides.

Neutralize (6) this solution with $NH_4OH$ (sp. gr. 0.90) and add 0.4–0.6 ml. of HCl (sp. gr. 1.20). Dilute to 400 ml. with hot distilled water, bring the solution to boiling, and add 25 ml. (±0.5 ml.) of hot ammonium sulfate solution dropwise with constant stirring. Transfer the beaker to a warm plate and allow to stand for at least four hours. Filter on an ignited weighed Gooch crucible (8), wash (9) thoroughly with hot water and ignite the crucible in a muffle for 35 minutes at 850°C. Cool in a desiccator and weigh. Make a blank determination in a similar manner on an equal amount of sodium carbonate and other reagents reserving the first filtrate for blank determination of $SO_3$.

Calculate the per cent of $BaSO_4$ as follows:

$$(A - B - C) \times 100 = \% \ BaSO_4,$$

where $A$ is the weight in grams of the Gooch crucible and the barium sulfate,

$B$ is the weight in grams of the ignited Gooch crucible, and

$C$ is the weight in grams of the blank determination.

* Numbers in parentheses refer to NOTES on pp. 155 and 156.

*Procedure for Barite Containing an Appreciable Percentage of Strontium.—*
Weigh 1 g. of sample into a platinum crucible and add 8 g. of sodium carbonate
(C.P.) (1). Cover and fuse the mixture over a Meker burner for 40 minutes (2).
Cool (3) and leach out the fusion with 200 ml. of hot water in a 400-ml. beaker.
Filter (4), washing the paper and residue 12 times with hot sodium carbonate
solution. (Reserve the filtrate for the determination of $SO_3$.)

Dissolve (5) the carbonates from the paper and crucible with hot $HNO_3$ (1:4),
catching the solution in a 600-ml. beaker, and wash the paper well with hot water.
Cool, neutralize with $NH_4OH$ (sp. gr. 0.90) and make the solution just acid with
$HNO_3$ (1:4). Dilute to 300 ml. with water and add 10 ml. of ammonium acetate
solution. Heat to boiling and add while stirring 20 ml. of ammonium dichromate
(10) solution. Let stand on a warm plate for 3 hours or more, filter the supernatant
liquid (11) and wash by decantation with dilute ammonium acetate solution (12).
Discard the filtrate.

Dissolve the precipitate on the paper with warm $HNO_3$ (1:4) into a 600-ml.
beaker and wash with hot water. Dilute to 300 ml. and add ammonium hydroxide
solution (1:5) slowly with stirring until the precipitate forming again no longer
dissolves. Add 10 ml. ammonium acetate solution and 5 ml. ammonium dichromate solution, and bring the liquid to boiling while swirling; let stand on a warm
plate 2 hours or more, filter and wash once with dilute ammonium acetate solution.
Discard the filtrate.

Dissolve the precipitate into a 600-ml. beaker with hot HCl (1:4) and wash paper
with hot water until free from chlorides.

Add 10 ml. $H_2O_2$ (3%) and 25 ml. ethyl alcohol (95%), boil for 5 minutes (13),
cool, neutralize (14) with $NH_4OH$ (sp. gr. 0.90) and add 0.4–0.6 ml. of HCl (sp. gr.
1.20). Dilute to 400 ml. with hot distilled water, heat to boiling, and add 40 ml.
of hot ammonium sulfate solution dropwise with stirring. Let stand on a warm
plate for four hours or more. Filter on an ignited weighed Gooch crucible (8),
wash (9) thoroughly with hot dilute $(NH_4)_2SO_4$ solution, and ignite the crucible
in a muffle furnace for 35 minutes at 850°C. Cool and weigh. Make a blank
determination on an equal amount of sodium carbonate and other reagents reserving the first filtrate for blank determination of $SO_3$.

Calculate the percentage of $BaSO_4$ as described at the end of "Procedure for
Barite Essentially Free from Strontium," above.

## DETERMINATION OF STRONTIUM SULFATE

*Gravimetric Procedure in Barite Concentrates.—*Weigh 2 g. of sample into a
platinum crucible and add 10 g. of C.P. sodium carbonate (1). Cover and fuse
the mixture over a Meker burner for 1 hour (2). Cool (3) and leach out the fusion
with 200 ml. of hot water in a 400-ml. beaker. Filter (4), washing the paper and
residue 12 times with hot sodium carbonate solution.

Dissolve (5) the carbonates from the paper and crucible with hot $HNO_3$ acid
(1:4), catching the solution in a 400-ml. beaker, and wash the paper well with hot
water. Evaporate to about 50 ml. and transfer to a 150-ml. beaker. Continue
evaporation to dryness at 125–135°C. (15).

Disintegrate the dried residue as thoroughly as possible with a glass rod, add
25 ml. of hot absolute amyl alcohol and leach thoroughly by agitation with the
rod (16). Let stand on a warm plate 3 or more hours, filter (17), and wash twice
with 5 ml. portions of hot absolute amyl alcohol.

Dissolve the nitrates from the paper and from the 150-ml. beaker with hot water into a 600-ml. beaker, dilute to 300 ml. with water and add 10 ml. ammonium acetate solution. Heat to boiling and add while stirring 30 ml. ammonium dichromate (10) solution. Let stand on a warm plate for 3 hours or more, filter the supernatant liquid (11) into a 1000-ml. beaker and wash by decantation with dilute ammonium acetate solution (12). Dissolve the precipitate on the paper with warm $HNO_3$ (1:4) into the 600-ml. beaker and wash with hot water. Dilute to 300 ml. and add ammonium hydroxide solution (1:5) slowly with stirring until the precipitate forming again no longer dissolves. Add 10 ml. ammonium acetate solution and 5 ml. ammonium dichromate solution, bring the liquid to boiling while swirling, let stand on a warm plate for 2 hours or more, filter (11) into the 1000-ml. beaker and wash once with dilute ammonium acetate solution.

Make the solution in the 1000-ml. beaker slightly acid with $HNO_3$ (sp. gr. 1.42) and evaporate to about 100 ml. volume (18). Transfer to a 250-ml. beaker, add 10 ml. $NH_4OH$ (sp. gr. 0.90) and 3 g. powdered C.P. $(NH_4)_2CO_3$ and heat to boiling (19). Let stand on a warm plate for 2 hours or more, filter (20), and wash once with hot water.

Dissolve the precipitate into the original beaker with HCl (1:4) and evaporate to about 10 ml. volume. Add 50 ml. $H_2SO_4$ (1:1) and 60 ml. 95% ethyl alcohol. Stir, allow to stand for 12 hours or more, filter and wash well with ethyl alcohol solution (1:1) and finally with 95% ethyl alcohol. Dry the paper and precipitate in a weighed platinum crucible, char paper at a low temperature and ignite at dull redness, cool, and weigh. Make a blank determination in similar manner on an equal amount of sodium carbonate and other reagents.

Calculate the per cent of $SrSO_4$ as follows:

$$\frac{(A - B - C) \times 100}{2} = \% \; SrSO_4,$$

where $A$ is the weight in grams of the crucible and strontium sulfate,

$B$ is the weight in grams of the platinum crucible initially, and

$C$ is the weight in grams of the blank determination.

NOTES ON THE DETERMINATION OF BARIUM SULFATE AND STRONTIUM SULFATE. (Numbers correspond to those in the procedures.)

1. The crucible is prepared as follows: A layer of sodium carbonate about ¼″ deep is placed in the bottom of the crucible, the sample placed on top of this, and both mixed with a glass rod. The rest of the $Na_2CO_3$ is then added to the crucible.

2. The fusion is started with a low flame which is gradually raised to full blast. This precaution is necessary to prevent loss by overflowing.

3. As the melt cools, rotate the crucible so that the fusion will solidify in a thin layer. This will shorten the time required for leaching.

4. Use a Whatman No. 40 15-cm. filter or similar paper. Wash several times by decantation, then remove the crucible from the beaker, transfer the insoluble carbonates to the filter, and wash with hot sodium carbonate solution, testing after the twelfth washing to be certain that sulfates have been removed completely.

5. Cover the funnel containing the carbonates with a watch glass and add the acid, carefully, in small portions at a time to prevent loss. Add hot dilute acid to the platinum crucible and cover in the beaker in which the leach was made and pour over the filter.

6. Use methyl orange as the indicator.

7. This procedure is necessary to prevent coprecipitation of calcium and strontium.

8. The Gooch crucible should be of platinum and ignited with asbestos pad to constant weight.

9. Wash with hot water several times by decantation. The beaker should be scrubbed thoroughly to remove any adhering barium sulfate. Continue the washing until free of chlorides.

10. The barium is precipitated as $BaCrO_4$.
11. Use a Whatman No. 40 15-cm. filter or similar paper.
12. Use several portions of dilute ammonium acetate solution totaling about 100 ml.
13. To reduce the chromium completely.
14. The precipitation of $Cr(OH)_3$ serves as an indicator. The solution should be made slightly acid with HCl (sp. gr. 1.20) before adding the excess.
15. The sample should be held at 125–135°C. until thoroughly dry and ready to proceed.
16. Calcium nitrate is dissolved. Boil the absolute amyl alcohol for a few minutes before using. Equal volumes of ethyl alcohol and absolute ether may be used in place of the absolute amyl alcohol. One extraction is sufficient for samples containing less than 3% CaO.
17. Use a Whatman No. 40 9-cm. filter or similar paper.
18. The concentration should be carried no further to prevent reduction of the chromates.
19. The strontium is precipitated as $SrCO_3$.
20. Use a Whatman No. 40 9-cm. filter or similar paper.

## TOTAL SULFUR AS $SO_3$

**Procedure.**—The filtrate containing the $SO_3$ and the washings from the barium carbonate is oxidized by warming with 10 ml. of $H_2O_2(3\%)$, neutralized with HCl (sp. gr. 1.20) and 1.0–1.5 ml. added in excess, concentrated to proper volume, and the sulfate is precipitated from the boiling solution by adding hot 10% $BaCl_2$ solution. The filtration, washing and final ignition are made in the usual fashion. The blank is determined in the same manner.

## SILICA

**Procedure.**—One gram of the sample is weighed into a platinum crucible and fused with sodium carbonate as under "Determination of Barium Sulfate." The fusion is leached out in a 150-ml. platinum dish with hot water. Leaching is carried on until disintegration of the fusion is complete. The residue, composed of mixed carbonates, silicates, etc., is filtered off, catching filtrate in a 400-ml. beaker, and washed thoroughly with hot water containing sodium carbonate. The residue on the paper and in the crucible is dissolved with hot dilute hydrochloric acid, catching in a separate 400-ml. beaker, and the paper thoroughly washed with hot water. This paper containing a portion of the silica is placed in a platinum crucible and retained.

The first filtrate, from the barium carbonate, is acidified with HCl and evaporated to dryness to dehydrate the silica. The second solution, containing the barium in solution as chloride is also evaporated to dryness. After dehydrating, the residues in both beakers are taken up with dilute HCl and filtered. They may be filtered through the same paper, washing the paper thoroughly before passing the second solution. The first filtrate, from the barium carbonate, is again evaporated to dryness, taken up and filtered as before on a new paper. After the papers are thoroughly washed with hot water, they are added to the original paper in the crucible, ignited, and weighed. The contents of the crucible are treated with hydrofluoric and sulfuric acids, evaporated to dryness, ignited, and weighed. The difference in weight is amount of silica present.

## IRON

**Procedure.**—Two grams of the sample are weighed into a 250-ml. beaker, moistened with water, 15 ml. concentrated hydrochloric acid and 10 ml. concentrated nitric acid added. After digesting a short time 10 ml. dilute sulfuric acid (1:1) are added and the solution evaporated to complete dryness. Ten ml. concentrated hydrochloric acid and 25 ml. water are added and heated to boiling. The iron is reduced with stannous chloride solution. The reduced solution and residue are washed into a 600-ml. beaker containing 15 ml. titrating solution and diluted to 400 ml. with cold water. After standing for 3 minutes, the iron is titrated with standard potassium permanganate solution. The titrating solution is prepared and the reduction and titration are conducted according to the details given in the chapter on Iron.

## IRON AND ALUMINA

*Procedure.*—The two filtrates from the silica determination are reduced in volume and nearly neutralized with $NH_4OH$ (acidity 1 ml. HCl), and combined. Ammonium sulfate solution is added to assure complete precipitation of all the barium, the beaker placed on a steam plate for two hours. The barium sulfate is then filtered off. The iron and alumina in the filtrate are precipitated with ammonium hydroxide, the precipitate filtered off, dissolved with dilute hydrochloric acid, re-precipitated and filtered, washed with 2% ammonium nitrate solution, ignited in a platinum crucible, and weighed.

## LIME

*Procedure.*—The filtrate from the precipitated iron and alumina is acidified slightly with hydrochloric acid, boiled down to a volume of less than 100 ml. and filtered if necessary. The solution is now made ammoniacal, heated to boiling, and 10 ml. of ammonium oxalate solution added. After standing for two hours in a warm place the precipitate of calcium oxalate is filtered off, washed with hot water, ignited, and weighed as calcium oxide.

## MAGNESIA

*Procedure.*—The filtrate from the lime determination is acidified with hydrochloric acid, evaporated to about 200 ml., cooled to room temperature, and 15 ml. microcosmic salt (saturated solution) added; $NH_4OH$ is added with 40 ml. in excess and the precipitate allowed to settle overnight. The precipitate is then filtered off, dissolved with hydrochloric acid (1 part concentrated acid to four parts of water), diluted to 100 ml., 10 ml. of microcosmic salt solution added, followed by $NH_4OH$ with 40 ml. excess and allowed to stand overnight. The precipitate is then filtered off, dissolved with hydrochloric acid (1 part concentrated acid to four parts of water), diluted to 100 ml., 10 ml. of microcosmic salt solution added, followed by $NH_4OH$ with 40 ml. excess and allowed to stand overnight. The precipitate of magnesium ammonium phosphate is filtered off, washed, carefully ignited and weighed.

## CARBON DIOXIDE

*Procedure.*—The carbon dioxide is determined according to the method given for carbonates under Chapter on Carbon. It is necessary to use a large sample, i.e., 5–10 grams, and for samples containing a small amount of carbonates a Geissler absorption bulb is preferable to the heavy Fleming type bulb.

## FLUORINE

*Procedure.*—One gram of sample is placed in a lead bomb with 12 ml. of sulfuric acid (sp. gr. 1.84), the bomb closed with glass plate in place and heated in an oil bath for 45 minutes at 165°C. The etching on the glass plate is compared with etching using known amounts of fluorine as $CaF_2$ and the same kind of glass.

The glass plate is kept cool by circulating cold water. The type of bomb and its connections are shown in Fig. 5-1.

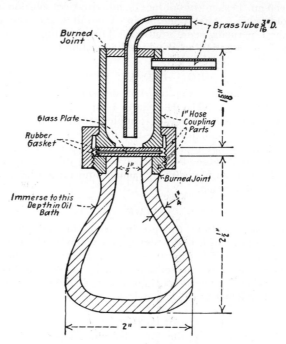

Fig. 5-1. Apparatus for Fluorine Determination.

### LOSS ON IGNITION

**Procedure.**—One gram of the sample is weighed out into a platinum crucible, dried at 110°C. for two hours, and weighed. This moisture is to be used for calculating all results to a dry basis. The crucible is heated gently at first and then placed in a muffle furnace or over a blast lamp and ignited until it ceases to lose weight on reheating. This loss is calculated to a basis of one gram of dry material.

## ANALYSIS OF BLANC FIXE

The sulfate of barium is generally marketed as paste and less commonly in the dry form. Both pulp and dry forms should contain not less than 97.5% $BaSO_4$ on the dry basis. The pulp (paste) should not contain over 30% $H_2O$. Blanc Fixe is used in photography, in coating paper, and in paint.

### QUALITATIVE TESTS

**Suitability for Photographic Purposes.**—Spread a sample on a glass plate and apply a drop of 10% $AgNO_3$ solution. Set aside in a dark closet. No dark brown or black stain should be evident in five minutes.

**Alumina and Iron.**—Heat a small portion with $HNO_3$, dilute and filter. Test the filtrate with $NH_4OH$. A gelatinous colorless precipitate = $Al(OH)_3$, a red precipitate = $Fe(OH)_3$ and possibly $Al(OH)_3$ with the iron.

*Lead.*—Extract a small portion with ammonium acetate and test the extract with $K_2Cr_2O_7$. A yellow precipitate indicates $PbCrO_4$, showing the presence of $PbSO_4$.

*Silica.*—Test about 0.5 g. with 10 ml. concentrated $H_2SO_4$, complete solution shows the absence of $SiO_2$.

*Organic Matter.*—Coloration of the acid in the silica test indicates the presence of organic matter.

*Carbonates.*—Addition of acid will cause effervescence in presence of carbonate.

*Phosphates.*—Extract a small portion with $HNO_3$ and test the extract with ammonium molybdate for phosphate.

## QUANTITATIVE ANALYSIS

The qualitative tests will indicate the presence of impurities. These can now be determined by the standard procedures. The following brief outline may be found useful as a guide for the method of examination.

*Moisture.*—Determine loss on 2-g. sample dried at 105°C. for two hours.

*Loss on Ignition.*—Ignite residue from above. Loss is due to escape of $CO_2$ and to organic matter and combined water.

*Iron and Alumina.*—Digest a 5-g. sample with 150 ml. HCl (1:3). Evaporate extract to dryness, take up with 100 ml. dilute HCl and filter to remove $SiO_2$. Precipitate iron and alumina in filtrate in usual manner and determine. If $P_2O_5$ is present it will be present with the precipitate. If present it will be necessary to add a known quantity of iron as $FeCl_3$ to carry down all the $P_2O_5$. This iron and the $P_2O_5$, determined on a separate sample, must be deducted, to obtain the iron and alumina in the sample.

*Phosphate.*—Extract a 2-g. sample with water by decantation. Digest the residue with a 10% solution of $HNO_3$ and filter. Precipitate $P_2O_5$ in the filtrate with ammonium molybdate in the usual manner. The yellow precipitate is dissolved in $NH_4OH$ and $P_2O_5$ precipitated with magnesia mixture and determined by the standard procedure.

$$Mg_2P_2O_7 \times 0.6379 = P_2O_5$$
$$\times 2.7040 = Ba_3(PO_4)_2.$$

*Lead Sulfate.*—This may be determined in the residue from the iron and alumina determination by extraction with ammonium acetate and precipitation with dichromate reagent by usual procedure.

$$PbCrO_4 \times 0.9383 = PbSO_4.$$

# Chapter 6

# BERYLLIUM *

**Be, at. wt. 9.0122; sp. gr. 1.845 (at 20°C.); m.p. 1285°C.; oxide, BeO**

Vauquelin [1] (1797) was the first to separate beryllium from aluminum by hydrolysis of a KOH solution derived from beryl. French chemists named the new element glucinium, Gl, because of the sweetish taste of its salts. Metallic Be was first produced in 1828 by Wöhler [2] (and also by Bussy) through reduction of $BeCl_2$ with potassium. By 1897 Lebeau [3] had produced beryllium copper which was to give beryllium its first industrial foothold. Today its extended use as a metal is limited by its high cost, its alleged toxicity,[4] and somewhat low ductility.

Beryllium is the only stable light metal of high melting point. It possesses fair strength, good electrical conductivity, and excellent sound transmission. It is extremely penetrable to X-rays (used for X-ray windows); has a low neutron capture and high neutron scatter cross-section; and provides a good source of neutrons (for possible use as a moderator or reflector in nuclear power reactors). Be-Cu alloys [5] are well known for their excellent formability before heat treatment followed by remarkable increase in physical properties after simple precipitation hardening, for their anti-sparking properties, and unusual resistance to fatigue. Beryllium oxide [5, 6] finds useful applications especially in refractory crucibles because of its high melting point (2570°C.), high thermal with low electrical conductivity (even at high temperatures), and good resistance to thermal shock.

Beryl ($3BeO \cdot Al_2O_3 \cdot 6SiO_2$) is the only one of the more than thirty recognized minerals of beryllium, including chrysoberyl ($BeO \cdot Al_2O_3$), phenacite ($2BeO \cdot SiO_2$), helvite ($3(Mn,Fe)BeSiO_4 \cdot MnS$), and bromellite (BeO), that is of any commercial

---

* Chapter contributed by Frank A. Vinci of The Brush Beryllium Company, Cleveland, Ohio.

[1] Vauquelin, L. N., Aquamarine or Beryl, and the Discovery of a New Earth in This Rock, Ann. Chem., **26,** 155, 1798.

[2] Wöhler, F., Pogg's Ann. d. Phys., **13,** 577, 1828.

[3] Lebeau, P., Researches on Beryllium and Its Compounds, Ann. Chem. Phys., **16,** 457, 1899.

[4] Margis, G. G., and Forbes, J. J., Review of Health Hazards of Beryllium and Its Compounds, Bureau of Mines Information Circular 7574, July, 1950; Sterner, J. H., M.D., and Eisenbud, Merril, Epidemiology of Beryllium Intoxication, A.M.A. Archives of Industrial Hygiene and Occupational Medicine, Vol. **4,** 123, 1951; Breslin, A. J., Am. Ceram. Soc. Bull., **30,** 11, 395, 1951; DeNardi, J., M.D., VanOrdstrand, H. S., M.D., and Carmody, M. G., M.D., Acute Dermatitis and Pneumonitis in Beryllium Workers, The Ohio State Medical Journal, June, 1949; Welford, George, and Harley, John, Fluorimetric Determination of Trace Amounts of Beryllium, Am. Ind. Hyg. Assn. Quart., **13,** 232, 1952; Bass, N. W., Bibliography on Beryllium Health Problems, Am. Ceram. Soc. Bull., Vol. **30,** 3, 79, 1951; Schwenzfeier, C., and Vinci, F. A., Procedure for the Determination of the Beryllium Concentration in the Atmosphere, The Brush Beryllium Co., Cleveland, Ohio.

[5] Sawyer, C. B., Yale Scientific Magazine, Spring, Summer, and Fall (1941) Issues.

[6] Norton, F. H., Journal Am. Ceram. Soc., Vol. **30,** 8, 1947.

importance. Theoretically, beryl contains 14% BeO, 19% $Al_2O_3$, and 67% $SiO_2$. Gem-beryl (emerald or aquamarine) approaches this composition; but the commercial ore is contaminated with quartz, feldspar, granite, and mica with which it is usually associated. Beryl occurs in irregular deposits of hexagonal crystals, as in pegmatite dykes, and is recovered most often as a by-product through hand sorting and cobbing. The present largest sources are South America (Brazil, Argentina) and Southern Africa. Utilization, through concentration processes, of plentiful but generally low grade domestic ore (South Dakota, North Carolina, Arizona, Utah, and New England states) is currently being developed.

## DETECTION

*General Procedure.*—The sample solution, previously freed of all organic matter, carbonates, fluorides, silica, and phosphates is treated in the presence of free acid with $H_2S$ to remove the members of this group. The filtrate is boiled to expel $H_2S$ and iron is oxidized by the addition of $HNO_3$. Ammonium hydroxide is added, in the presence of ammonium chloride, to a pH of 8.5. The hydroxides, including the beryllium, aluminum, iron, chromium, etc., are separated by filtration. The combined hydroxides are dissolved in HCl. The resulting solution, boiled down to low volume and then diluted with water, is treated by the 8-hydroxyquinoline separation method (see under Separations) to remove quinolates insoluble in acetic acid-acetate buffered solution at a pH of 5.7. The filtrate containing the beryllium is boiled vigorously to expel the bulk of excess 8-hydroxyquinoline, aqua regia is added, the solution is boiled down to small volume, diluted, and refiltered. Ammonium hydroxide is added to a pH of 8.5. The solution is boiled and filtered. A white gelatinous precipitate caught on the filter paper is beryllium hydroxide and should be confirmed by the following test.

*p-Nitrophenylazoorcinol Spot Test for Beryllium.*[7]—A portion (estimated to represent 3 to 30 milligrams of BeO content) of the hydroxide precipitate obtained by the preceding procedure is dissolved into 10 ml. of cold 2 $N$ NaOH solution to give the test solution. With a stirring rod put 2 drops of *p*-nitrophenylazoorcinol solution [8] on a double thickness of filter paper, forming a brownish-yellow spot. Transfer one drop of the caustic test solution to the center of the dye spot. A red to pink coloration confirms the presence of beryllium.

*A "Quick" Spot Test for the Detection of Beryllium in Ores.*—The following method, in essence the same as the confirmatory test outlined above, is based upon the selective action of the dye *p*-nitrophenylazoorcinol. A moderately alkaline solution of the reagent turns immediately from yellow to red in the presence of Be in alkaline solution due to a colored lake formation. Although the following procedure will not reliably detect small amounts of Be (less than 0.75% BeO content in an ore) it has the great advantage of being very rapid, almost specific, and so simple that it can be carried out in the field (to aid in prospecting activities) as well as in the laboratory.

Knock off a small piece of the mineral or of the composite ore to be tested,

[7] Komarovskii, A. S., and Poluektov, N. S., Mikrochemie, **14**, 315, 1934.

[8] To prepare the dye solution, dissolve 0.025 g. of *p*-nitrobenzeneazoorcinol powder (Eastman Kodak Co.) in 100 ml. of 0.1 $N$ sodium hydroxide solution and filter through a Gooch crucible with asbestos mat. Store in a dark bottle and renew no less frequently than once a month.

crush it to a coarse powder in a Plattner crushing mortar and then grind to a very fine powder by means of a mullite mortar and pestle. Melt 1.5 g. of sodium hydroxide (13 to 15 pellets) in a 20-ml. nickel crucible. Add an estimated 0.1 to 0.15 grams of the finely powdered ore sample to the crucible. Remelt and complete the fusion by heating the bottom of the nickel crucible to a dark cherry red for 5 minutes. Cool until the melt solidifies then thoroughly cool the crucible by immersing the bottom half in cold water. Add 10 ml. of cold water and stir until the melt is dissolved, continuing the cooling during dissolution. If a turbid solution results, allow the precipitate to settle and use the supernatant liquid for the test (or, if the procedure is being carried out in the laboratory, centrifuge or filter the solution). With a stirring rod, put two drops of the dye solution on a double thickness of filter paper. To the same spot add a drop of 25% potassium cyanide solution, then apply a drop of the clear test solution to the center of the large spot. A red to pink coloration indicates the presence of Be. Absence of a pink color means that the sample contains less than 0.75% BeO. The best light for observing the spot test is bright daylight. Do not attempt to use direct sunlight. To test the efficacy of the reagents it is advisable to carry a beryl-quartz mixture having a known 1% BeO content through the procedure.

*Quinalizarin (1,2,5,8-Tetrahydroxyanthraquinone) Test.*[9]—The Be(OH)$_2$ precipitate, obtained as in the General Procedure given above, is dissolved in acid and carefully neutralized with Mg-free NaOH solution. Five ml. of 2 N NaOH solution is then added to each 10 ml. of neutralized solution. Two to three drops of 0.05% solution of quinalizarin dye in 0.25 N NaOH (or 10 to 15 drops of a 0.01% solution of the dye in absolute alcohol) are added. Be colors the solution a cornflower blue. A blank run, made with water and the reagents used, should be colored violet-red. Aluminum does not interfere but phosphate, tartrates, iron, and magnesium must be absent. In addition, rare earths and Zr give a similar test and must be absent.

The following further tests have been recommended. All, however, suffer from considerable interference from other elements and require, therefore, prior isolation of the Be: Curcumin;[10] Alkannin or Naphthazarin;[11] Naphthachrome Green G[12] or Naphthachrome Azurine 2B;[12] Aluminon;[13] Quinizarin-2-sulfonic acid;[14] Morin (3,5,7,2′,4′, pentahydroxyflavone);[15] Quinizarin (1-4-dihydroxyanthraquinone);[16] 1-amino-4-hydroxyanthraquinone.[17] The last three depend upon fluorescence when an alkaline solution of Be is exposed to ultraviolet light.

## ESTIMATION

Beryllium accompanies aluminum in the general analytical procedures and, if not detected, would, in great part, be reported as aluminum. Whereas, however,

9 Fischer, Hellmut, Z. Anal. Chem., **73,** 54, 1928.
10 Kolthoff, I. M., J. Amer. Chem. Soc., **50,** 393, 1928.
11 Underwood, A. L., and Newman, W. F., Anal. Chem., **21,** 1348, 1949.
12 Aldridge, W. N., and Liddell, H. F., Ministry of Supply Chemical Defence Experimental Station, Porton Wilts.
13 Luke, C. L., and Campbell, Anal. Chem., **24,** 1056, 1952.
14 Cucci, M. W., Newman, W. F., and Mulryan, B. J., AECD-1990, 1948.
15 Sandell, E. B., Ind. Eng. Chem., Anal. Ed., **12,** 674 and 762, 1940.
16 Fletcher, M. H., and White, C. E., Am. Mineralogist, **31,** 82, Jan. and Feb., 1946.
17 White, C. E., and Lowe, C. S., Ind. Eng. Chem., Anal. Ed., **13,** 809, 1941.

precipitation of aluminum is complete at pH 7–7.5, beryllium hydroxide precipitation is not complete until the pH has been raised to 8.5.

Generally, the estimation of the beryllium content is best accomplished by the spectrophotometric method (following partial segregation of the beryllium to remove interfering quantities of other elements) if milligram or microgram quantities of beryllium content in reasonably sized samples are involved.  For macro quantities of beryllium, a titrimetric method is employed, usually when only beryllium is a major constituent of the sample, when aluminum content is known and small, and when interfering elements such as Zr, Hf, and rare earths are absent.  The gravimetric method involving precipitation of beryllium hydroxide and ignition to BeO, following removal of other $R_2O_3$ hydroxides, is widely used. Details of the procedures most commonly employed follow.

## PREPARATION AND SOLUTION OF THE SAMPLE

Since beryllium is chemically quite closely related to aluminum, methods of dissolution for both are quite similar.  It will suffice here, therefore, to merely note the following generalities and slight differences: Beryllium, for analytical purposes, is best dissolved in diluted sulfuric acid.  It is, however, readily attacked by all of the commonly used acids, strong or diluted; except nitric acid, which, if cold and concentrated, has little effect.  Alkalies react with beryllium with the evolution of hydrogen.  The hydroxide, $Be(OH)_2$, formed is amphoteric and, with excess alkali, forms beryllate which differs from the aluminate in that the former is fairly easily hydrolyzed by heating or diluting.  The freshly precipitated hydroxide of beryllium is easily soluble in dilute acids, in alkalies, and in alkali carbonates and bicarbonates.  Beryllium oxide is practically insoluble in dilute hydrochloric acid but can be put into solution by boiling with nitric, hydrofluoric, or sulfuric acids or by fusion with potassium bisulfate and dissolution of the fusion in acidified water.  When beryllium sulfate solutions are dehydrated, as by fuming strongly in sulfuric acid, it should be remembered that upon dilution with water, vigorous and prolonged ebullition is required to effect dissolution.  Powdered beryl ores respond best to fusion with sodium carbonate when the proportion, by weight, of sodium carbonate to ore is kept down to two parts to one.[18]  The temperature should approach 1000°C. and the time at full temperature should be 30–45 minutes.  Beryllium ores, like aluminum ores, are amenable to attack by hydrofluoric and sulfuric acids.  Alloys of beryllium and copper or nickel are usually attacked with nitric acid; those with iron, aluminum, or magnesium are attacked with hydrochloric acid.

## SEPARATIONS

In the usual course of analysis, the sample or its fusion is boiled with acid and taken to copious fumes of $SO_3$, treated with $HNO_3$ to destroy organic matter in the usual manner, and again taken to fumes of $SO_3$.  The residue is boiled strongly with water and filtered.  The insolubles are treated with HF and $H_2SO_4$ in the usual manner and the residue is fused with $KHSO_4$, dissolved and added to the main solution.  Perchloric acid can be substituted for the sulfuric; or initial treatment with hydrofluoric and sulfuric acids to volatilize off gaseous $SiF_4$ with subsequent strong fuming to remove all fluorine and fusion of any remaining in-

[18] Osborn, G. H., Analyst, **72**, 475, 1947.

solubles, of course, can be employed.  Fusion of beryl with NaF or KF followed by $H_2SO_4$ treatment is sometimes used.  At any rate, any of the above treatments simultaneously provide for removal of silica.

*Removal of Phosphoric Acid.*—In the gravimetric determination of beryllium by weighing as BeO, the presence of phosphoric acid would cause high results.  In addition, phosphates of other elements of the group and of the alkaline earths would precipitate upon making the solution ammoniacal, rendering their removal cumbersome.  Phosphoric acid is best removed, then, prior to the ammonia separation, with ammonium molybdate from the solution made acid with $HNO_3$. After expulsion of the $HNO_3$, excess Mo, along with other members of the hydrogen sulfide group, can be removed with $H_2S$ from acid solution.

*Separation of Beryllium from a Preponderance of Aluminum.*—Aluminum chloride is precipitated, by the method of Gooch and Havens, from a concentrated solution of hydrochloric acid and ether saturated with HCl gas.  The small amounts of aluminum remaining can then be removed (if required) by means of 8-hydroxyquinoline.

*Separation of Beryllium from a Preponderance of Iron.*—Ferric chloride can be extracted out of a cold hydrochloric acid solution having a specific gravity of 1.10 by ether.  Two or three extractions serve to remove the bulk of the iron.  The small amounts remaining can be removed by means of 8-hydroxyquinoline.  Alternatively, the acid solution treated with tartaric acid is rendered ammoniacal and saturated with $H_2S$ to precipitate quantitatively iron as sulfide.

*Separation of Beryllium from a Preponderance of Copper.*—If the determination of the copper is not required, it is usually most expedient to remove it as the soluble tetrammine copper complex.  Sufficient ammonium hydroxide is added to convert all of the copper to the blue complex, and the beryllium hydroxide formed is separated by filtration.  A double precipitation, with washing of the beryllium hydroxide with ammoniacal ammonium nitrate wash solution, is usually sufficient to effect complete elimination of the copper.  If determination of the copper is required, then electrodeposition on a platinum cathode from a solution made acid with nitric and sulfuric acids is most convenient, leaving a copper-free solution containing all the beryllium.

*Separation of Beryllium from a Preponderance of Nickel or Cobalt.*—Ammonium hydroxide added in excess permits complete precipitation of beryllium hydroxide, leaving the nickel and cobalt in solution in a manner analagous to removal of copper (see above).

*Complete Separation of Beryllium from Aluminum and Iron by the 8-Hydroxy-quinoline Method.*—Ammonium hydroxide is added to the solution acidified with HCl and oxidized with $HNO_3$ to the first permanent precipitate.  A minimum of acetic acid is added to the warmed solution to just completely dissolve the hydroxides (pH should be 4.8 to 5.0).  The solution temperature is adjusted to 55–60°C. and an excess of 8-hydroxyquinoline solution (in acetic acid) is added.  2 N ammonium acetate solution (adjusted to a pH of 7 with $NH_4OH$ or acetic acid) is added, slowly and with constant stirring, to a pH of 5.7.  Allow to stand for 2 or more hours, depending upon the size of the precipitate, filter, and wash.  Beryllium passes into the filtrate quantitatively.  The elements precipitated as insoluble quinolates include no beryllium but all of the ammonium hydroxide group members with the exception of some rare earths.  Discounting these, chromium is the only hydroxide group member not completely precipitated.  In addition to the above, the quinolate separation serves to remove Mo, W, U, Cu, Ni, Co, Zn, Cd, Hg, and Bi, as well as greater or lesser quantities of Mn and V.

*Separation of Be from Fe, Cr, Ni, Cu, Sn, Mo, Zn, and Pb.*—Electrolysis with a mercury cathode from a sulfate solution weakly acid with sulfuric acid serves to leave a solution containing all of the beryllium practically free from the above elements.

*Separation from Zr, Hf, Ti, and Pa.*—These can be precipitated as insoluble phosphates, if present, with diammonium phosphate from a solution containing 10% of free concentrated hydrochloric or sulfuric acid by volume, and removed by filtration.

*Separation of Be from Fe, Ti, Zr, V, Ta, Nb, and Tetravalent U.*—The above can be precipitated from an ice-cold acid solution containing free HCl or sulfuric (but no $HNO_3$ or other oxidizing agents) with a 6% solution of cupferron. After filtration and washing, the resulting filtrate, containing all the beryllium, is treated in the usual manner to remove organic matter, and the beryllium is precipitated with ammonium hydroxide.

*Separation of Be from the Rare Earths (Elements 58–71 inclusive and Y), Sc, Ac, and Th.*—The combined hydroxides are dissolved in HCl and the solution, in a platinum dish, is evaporated nearly to dryness. An excess of hydrofluoric acid is added and the solution is evaporated to dryness in a steam bath. The residue is wetted with 1 ml. of hydrofluoric acid and 0.5 ml. of concentrated hydrochloric acid; 25 ml. of water are added. The solution is stirred thoroughly with a platinum rod, digested for a few minutes, and filtered using a hard rubber funnel. The filtrate is caught in a second platinum dish. The rare earth fluorides on the paper are washed with 1% hydrofluoric acid solution. Sulfuric acid is added to the filtrate containing the beryllium and the solution is heated to copious fumes of $SO_3$.

## GRAVIMETRIC METHODS

### DETERMINATION BY PRECIPITATION OF BERYLLIUM HYDROXIDE AND IGNITION TO BERYLLIUM OXIDE

This method, although widely used, contains many pitfalls. With proper recognition of and careful precaution against these, however, the method is capable of highly accurate results.

The solution from which beryllium hydroxide is to be finally precipitated must be free from all other members of the ammonium hydroxide group. This is generally obtained by segregating the group members (Be, Al, Ga, In, Cr, Fe, Sc, Ac, Ti, Zr, Hf, Th, Nb, Ta, Pa, U plus the 16 rare earths, elements of at. no. 58–71 inclusive plus Y) and then removing all of these present but none of the beryllium (see under "Separations"). The method also, of course, precludes the presence of tartrates, citrates, fluorides, carbonates, etc., which would cause incomplete precipitation of beryllium and of phosphates which would cause inclusion of $P_2O_5$ in the final BeO to be weighed.

Precipitation of $Be(OH)_2$ is complete at 8.5 and slight excesses of $NH_4OH$ in the presence of ammonium salts, above this, cause no appreciable resolution of beryllium hydroxide.

*Procedure.*—The solution, in a 600-ml. beaker, containing from 4 to 40 milligrams of beryllium and 10 ml. of free hydrochloric acid, diluted to a volume of

300–400 ml., is heated to boiling and then partially cooled. Ammonium hydroxide solution (freshly prepared by bubbling tank ammonia through boiled and cooled distilled water and then stored in a polyethylene bottle) is added slowly and with constant stirring to a pH of 8.5. Cover the beaker with a watch glass. Digest below the boiling point for 30 minutes to coagulate the hydroxide. Filter through a Whatman No. 40 or equivalent filter paper. Wash the beaker and precipitate 3–4 times with hot 2% ammonium nitrate solution previously adjusted to a pH of 8.5 with $NH_4OH$. Discard the filtrate. Dissolve the precipitate back into the orginal beaker with hot 1:2 hydrochloric acid. Boil down to small volume, dilute to 200 ml. with boiled distilled water, and repeat the precipitation with $NH_4OH$. Carefully police the beaker and wash onto the filter with hot 2% ammoniacal ammonium nitrate solution. Finally wash 6–8 times. Fold the paper about the precipitate and transfer to a platinum crucible (with lid) that has been previously fired, cooled in a desiccator, and weighed. Dry in an oven. Transfer to a warm muffle furnace, carbonize the paper, and then slowly burn the carbon and decompose the hydroxide to oxide at temperatures gradually rising to a maximum of 600°C. (appreciable losses of BeO occur when it is heated at temperatures in excess of 700°C. in presence of moisture).[19] Raise the temperature to 1000°C. and ignite for 1 hour at 1000°C. once only. Cool the covered crucible and contents in a desiccator containing anhydrous magnesium perchlorate. Preset the balance (desiccant should be contained within the balance case) at the approximate weight expected then transfer the covered crucible to the balance pan and quickly but carefully weigh. The weight in excess of the tare represents the weight of "impure" BeO. This always contains slight amounts of silica picked up from glassware and may, in addition, contain greater or lesser quantities of $Al_2O_3$. Oxides of other metals of the ammonium hydroxide group may also be present due to incomplete prior removal. For accurate work, the "impure" BeO weight obtained must be corrected in the following manner.

Transfer the weighed "impure" BeO to a 100-ml. beaker, add 30 ml. of 1:1 $H_2SO_4$ and heat to copious fumes of $SO_3$. Cool, add 50 ml. of water, and boil vigorously until all soluble salts are dissolved. Add a small amount of filter paper pulp and filter through a small-diameter Whatman No. 42 paper. Police the beaker and wash onto the filter with hot water acidulated with a few drops of $H_2SO_4$ and wash the paper 8 times. Reserve the filtrate and washings. Determine the weight of $SiO_2$ on the filter by the usual procedure and deduct this weight from that of the "impure" BeO.

The filtrate from the above silica removal is treated by the 8-hydroxyquinoline method (see under "Separations") to precipitate the quinolates insoluble in acetic acid-acetate buffered solution. These are filtered off, ignited to oxides, and their weight deducted from the "impure" BeO weight. Mn, Cr, V, and rare earths are not completely removed by 8-hydroxyquinoline and, if present in the initial solution, may not now be completely corrected for. In such event, the filtrate from the above separation would need to be analyzed for these and further correction made.

$$\text{Corrected BeO wt.} \times 0.3603 = \text{Be wt.}$$

[19] Hutchison, C. A., Jr., and Malm, J. G., Argonne National Laboratory, AECD-2345, Oct., 1947.

## PHOSPHATE METHOD IN THE PRESENCE
## OF A CHELATING AGENT

Precipitation of beryllium as beryllium ammonium phosphate with subsequent ignition to $Be_2P_2O_7$ has the advantage of giving 3.838 times as much mass to weigh per equivalent beryllium content as compared to the BeO method. Prior removal of phosphates, if present, is not required. In addition, since the precipitate is somewhat granular, occlusion of impurities is less troublesome.

Ethylenediaminetetraacetic acid or its sodium salts are capable of combining in selective order with many metallic ions in solution to form soluble but nonionic chelates and in effect removing them from solution; 500 grams of the tetrasodium salt will complex one mole of most of the divalent and trivalent metals, but only about 0.002 mole of beryllium. As a consequence, providing that the amount of other metals in solution that can be thus sequestered is roughly known, a slight excess of the chelating agent can be added to remove their interference; and beryllium can then be precipitated with very little loss. The above scheme can be utilized, for example, in determining the Be content in Be-Cu alloys.

*Procedure.*—A beryllium content of 1 to 10 milligrams in the final solution from which the beryllium is to be precipitated is satisfactory. Thus, a 1-g. sample is chosen when the Be content is about 0.5%. For alloys richer in Be it is well not to decrease the size sample below 1 g. but rather to choose, after determination of the sample's $R_2O_3$ content, an appropriate aliquot portion. Be-Cu alloy sample, in the form of clean drillings, millings, or small pieces is brought into solution by treating with a large excess of $HNO_3$, boiling down to small volume, adding 10 ml. of HCl, diluting to 300–400 ml., and bringing to a boil.

Carbonate-free $NH_4OH$ solution is added to the above unfiltered solution until the deep blue color of the soluble tetrammine copper complex is obtained. The solution is brought to a boil and then allowed to settle for 30 minutes to coagulate the hydroxides. Filter through a Whatman No. 41H paper and wash the precipitate with hot 2% solution of ammonium nitrate that has been made slightly ammoniacal. (Only one ammonium hydroxide separation need be made.) The precipitate is dissolved off the paper into the original beaker with hot 1:2 HCl. Add sufficient $H_2SO_4$ and boil down to strong fumes of $SO_3$. Dilute, boil, and filter. Volatilize the silica in the usual manner with HF and $H_2SO_4$, fuse any residue with $KHSO_4$, dissolve, and add to the main solution of the combined hydroxides. Use all of this solution or an appropriate-sized aliquot for the precipitation of the beryllium ammonium phosphate.

Dilute the solution to 100 ml. and adjust to a pH of 2 with dilute $NH_4OH$ solution. Add 5 ml. of 15% monoammonium phosphate solution and 5 ml. of Versene solution,[20] stir well, and adjust the pH to 5.5 with 15% ammonium acetate solution. Heat to boiling and allow to simmer at near boiling for several minutes. Cool in a water bath for 2 hours and then filter through Whatman No. 42 paper. Wash beaker and paper several times with 0.5% ammonium acetate wash solution adjusted to a pH of 5.5. Dissolve the precipitate off the paper into the original beaker with warm 1:1 HCl. Evaporate off the bulk of the excess HCl, dilute to 100 ml., and repeat the precipitation as above but using only 1 ml. of monoammonium phosphate solution. Filter, scrubbing the walls of the beaker carefully and washing onto the filter, and wash with ammonium acetate

[20] Disodium salt of ethylenediaminetetraacetic acid, dry powder. Dissolve 30 g. in distilled $H_2O$, adjust the pH to 5.5 with $H_2SO_4$, and dilute to 200 ml.

wash solution until the filtrate is free of phosphates. Dry, carbonize, burn off, and finally ignite at 1000°C. in a tared crucible until white. Cool and weigh as $Be_2P_2O_7$.

$$Be_2P_2O_7 \times 0.0939 = Be.$$

## TITRIMETRIC METHODS

## DETERMINATION OF TOTAL BERYLLIUM CONTENT BY THE EMPIRICAL TITRIMETRIC METHOD

Beryllium can be completely precipitated as hydroxide from its sulfuric or hydrochloric acid solutions at a pH of 8.5. If an excess of NaF or KF is then added to the $Be(OH)_2$, the beryllium hydroxide is converted to very weakly ionized $BeF_2$, liberating the hydroxyl ions as NaOH or KOH. This released alkalinity can be taken as a measure of the amount of beryllium present. Aluminum reacts in similar manner, however, and must, therefore, be absent or corrected for, if present. Zirconium, hafnium, rare earths, uranium, and thorium must also be absent.

In practice the above reaction does not seem to take place stoichiometrically due, perhaps, to such complicating factors as beryllium's amphoteric character. However, if the conditions of the titration are closely duplicated, the method, although empirical, becomes very useful because of its reasonable accuracy and speed. The titration must be performed precisely and slowly, giving sufficient time for the reactions to come to equilibrium. Starting with a sample solution consisting of $BeSO_4$ plus free $H_2SO_4$, the following reactions occur (some of the NaOH serving in (1) and (4) to neutralize the initial $H_2SO_4$ and that formed from the $BeSO_4$).

(1) $$2NaOH + H_2SO_4 \rightarrow Na_2SO_4 + 2H_2O$$

(2) $$BeSO_4 + 2NaOH \xrightarrow{pH\ 8.5} Be(OH)_2 + Na_2SO_4$$

(3) $$Be(OH)_2 + 2NaF \rightarrow BeF_2 + 2NaOH$$

(4) $$2NaOH + H_2SO_4 \xrightarrow{pH\ 8.5} Na_2SO_4 + 2H_2O$$

*Reagents.* **50% ($Na_2CO_3$-free) NaOH Solution.**—Dissolve 2000 g. C.P. NaOH pellets in 2 liters of boiled and cooled distilled water. Cool thoroughly and filter with suction using a medium-porosity Buechner funnel. Store in stoppered 500-ml. polyethylene bottles.

**5 N NaOH Solution.**—Dilute 65.7 ml. of 50% NaOH to 250 ml. with boiled and cooled distilled water.

**Mixed Indicator.**—(a) Dissolve 4 g. phenolphthalein in 400 ml. of $C_2H_5OH$. (b) Dissolve 0.2 g. methyl orange in 200 ml. of distilled water. (c) Dissolve 0.4 g. thymolphthalein in 400 ml. of $C_2H_5OH$. Mix the three above solutions together thoroughly.

**1 N $H_2SO_4$ Solution.**—504 ml. of concentrated reagent $H_2SO_4$ (sp. gr. 1.845) is made up to 18 liters in a Pyrex bottle, cooled and then agitated by bubbling air through it for several hours. After 1–2 weeks' aging, elevate the bottle to a raised shelf and connect to a bottom fill, water-jacketed, standardized, automatic burette. Standardize by using this acid to titrate (in exact accordance to the following procedure) a beryllium sulfate solution containing an exactly predetermined amount of beryllium (approximately 0.2 grams). This standardization is to be repeated in duplicate with each group of samples to be titrated.

**Standard BeSO$_4$ Solution for Standardizing the 1 $N$ Sulfuric Acid.**—Using beryllium metal of known assay (99% Be or better, with low Al content) make up an ample quantity of stock solution such that each 50 ml. will contain 0.2 grams of Be. Use 20 ml. of 1:1 H$_2$SO$_4$ for each 1 g. of metal to be dissolved, boiling thoroughly, filtering, cooling, and making up to volume (at 20°C.) with boiled and cooled distilled water. The temperature of the solution in the flask should be adjusted to 20°C. prior to removal (by standardized 50-ml. pipette) of aliquot portions for titration. Using a 25-ml. aliquot portion, the Be content and the Al content of the standard BeSO$_4$ solution are predetermined, preferably in triplicate, by the gravimetric BeO and quinolate methods. The corrected Be content plus ½ the Al content of the solution gives the standard beryllium equivalent value of the 25-ml. aliquot portion taken. This sum doubled gives the beryllium equivalent per 50 ml. of standard BeSO$_4$ solution.

*Procedure.*—The BeSO$_4$ solution (containing about 0.2 g. Be and about 2.5 ml. of free 1:1 H$_2$SO$_4$) in a 600-ml. beaker is diluted to 300 ml. Add 50% NaOH solution to a permanent precipitate, then 5 drops of mixed indicator, and, dropwise, additional NaOH to a definite pink. Add 1:1 H$_2$SO$_4$ (dropwise with constant stirring) until the pink color is just discharged. Cover with a watch glass and cool in a water trough.

Add 20 drops of mixed indicator and then 5 $N$ NaOH dropwise to a definite pink plus 3 drops in excess. Stir, cover, and let stand for a timed 5 minutes. Add 10 more drops of mixed indicator, wash in the cover and sides of beaker. Titrate to the first end point adding 1 $N$ H$_2$SO$_4$ from the burette slowly and with constant stirring. This initial end point has been reached when the last drop of acid added after a 30 second wait produces no color change. Fill the burette and read the temperature of the water bath around the burette.

Add 20 g. of C.P. NaF powder and stir well. Add, with constant stirring, 1 $N$ H$_2$SO$_4$ from the burette at a rate of 15 ml. per minute until the red is reduced to a light pink and then make further additions dropwise. Wash down the sides of the beaker and obtain the second end point in exactly the same manner as the first. Record the number of ml. of 1 $N$ H$_2$SO$_4$ used to go from the first to the second end point.

**Calculation.**—The ml. of 1 $N$ H$_2$SO$_4$ consumed in restoring the end point (pH = 8.5) is a measure of the NaOH liberated in the reaction:

$$Be(OH)_2 + 2NaF \rightarrow 2NaOH + BeF_2$$

and is, therefore, also a measure of the beryllium present:

$$\text{Total Be} = \frac{\text{ml. of titrant} \times \text{Be Equiv.} \times 100}{\text{Wt. of sample}}$$

The grams of Be equivalent to 1 ml. of titrant is calculated from the titration required by a known weight of Be in the aliquot portion of standard BeSO$_4$ solution:

$$\text{Be equivalent} = \frac{\text{grams of Be}}{\text{ml. of titrant}}$$

PRECAUTIONS AND NOTES.—(1) Slight differences existing in separate batches of NaF exert an effect on the titration. Therefore NaF from the same bottle should be used for each group of titrations.

(2) In adding strong NaOH solutions to a sample solution, do not let the caustic touch the sides of the beaker as it may be difficult to wash down.

(3) Slightest contamination of a solution with NaF at any point prior to the 20 g. addition will result in an erroneously low titration.

(4) End points must be approached carefully and slowly. Continuous stirring throughout the titration is best done by means of a mechanical stirrer.

(5) Volumetric flasks and pipettes used should be standardized periodically.

(6) The method has a precision such that duplicate determinations should show a maximum deviation of ±0.25% of the Be content.

(7) Temperature corrections should be applied to correct the volume of titrant to a standard temperature unless variations in excess of 4–5°C. do not occur over a normal period of titrating a group of samples and standards.

**Potentiometric Titration Utilizing a Standard Calomel Reference Electrode and a Glass Electrode Improves the Accuracy Obtainable.**—The foregoing titration can be made more rapidly and conveniently with potentiometric equipment. Figure 6-1 shows an arrangement apparatus that has proved particularly effective for this

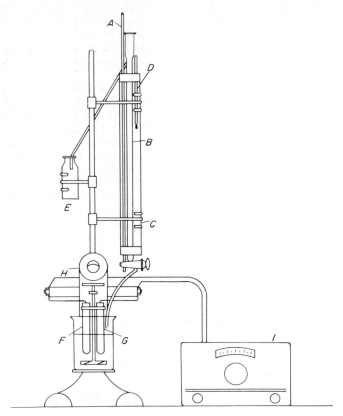

FIG. 6-1. Total Beryllium by Empirical Potentiometric Titration.

$A$ = 1 $N$ $H_2SO_4$ Titrant from raised reservoir; $B$ = Automatic, bottom fill, 50-ml. burette; $C$ = Waterjacket around burette; $D$ = Thermometer; $E$ = Bottle for burette overflow; $F$ = Reference calomel electrode; $G$ = Glass electrode; $H$ = "Magic Eye" end point indicator; $I$ = Fisher Titrimeter control unit.

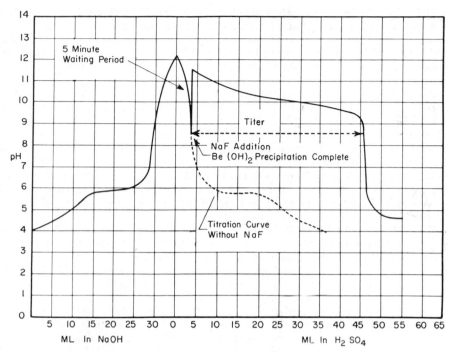

FIG. 6-2.  Potentiometric Titration Curve.  0.2 g. Be as BeSO₄ treated by the Empirical
Titrimetric Procedure.

purpose.  Figure 6-2 shows the titration curve obtained by this equipment for a
solution containing 0.2 g. Be as $BeSO_4$.

## COLORIMETRIC METHODS

### COLORIMETRIC 4-($p$-NITROPHENYLAZOORCINOL) METHOD [21]

The basis for this method is furnished by the fact that when an alkaline solution
of 4-($p$-nitrophenylazoorcinol) ("Zenia") is added to an alkaline solution containing
beryllium, a red-brown lake is formed.  The absorption of light by this colored
complex does not strictly follow Beer's law; but by careful control and duplication
of conditions, such as optimum alkalinity, amount of foreign ions, dye strength,
temperature, etc., the relationship of light absorption to beryllium content can
be accurately fixed.  Correct alkalinity, the range of which is quite small and critical, is maintained by means of a sodium borate-citrate or tartrate buffer.  The
buffer is simultaneously useful in keeping metal ions like iron, which would normally precipitate at the alkalinities involved, in solution.  Aluminum is without
effect on the dye and large amounts, limited only by the quantity that can be

21 Stross, W., and Osborn, G. H., The Photometric Determination of Beryllia in the
Presence of Alumina with $p$-Nitrobenzeneazoorcinol, J. Soc. Chem. Ind., 63, 249, 1944;
Osborn, G. H., and Stross, W., Rapid Photometric Determination of Beryllium in Be
Containing Minerals and Rocks, Metallurgia, 30, 175, 3, 1944.

held in the solution, cause only a small salt effect on light absorption. The dye is almost specific for beryllium, reacting only in an interfering manner with Mg, which, if present, consumes dye forming a brownish precipitate, and with Zn which reacts in similar manner to beryllium but with an entirely lower order of sensitivity. Metals like Cu that form highly colored ions or that will precipitate in the alkaline solution, of course, interfere. These may, in effect, be simply removed, if present, by rendering them inactive through formation of soluble non-ionic chelates. "Versene T" [22] is used to accomplish this. Unfortunately, a desensitizing effect on the "Zenia" dye-Be color, reaction results simultaneously (due to slight sequestering of Be by excess chelating agent); so that a suitable balance must be struck between this failing and the ability to remove interferences due to possible presence of Mg, Ca, Fe, Cu, Ni, Co, Zn, etc. Using 5 ml. of a 13.9% water solution of Versene-T per 100 ml. of final colored solution, up to 5 mg. of Mg, 20 mg. of Ca, or 10 mg. of Fe can be present singly without affecting the Be value obtained (in the range of 0.3 to 1 mg. of Be) by any more than 3% of the Be present.

*Reagents.* **Standard Be Solutions.**—(a) A stock solution is first made: Transfer a weight of beryllium metal powder (of known total Be content) to give 3.6000 grams of Be, to a 600-ml. beaker. Add 50 ml. of $H_2O$ to cover the metal completely. With a watch cover in place and pouring through the lip, gradually add 70 ml. of 1:1 $H_2SO_4$. When the reaction has ceased, wash the cover and sides of beaker and boil for 15 minutes. Filter through a Whatman No. 40 paper, into a 1000-ml. volumetric flask, washing beaker and paper thoroughly. Cool and make up to volume at specified temperature. Mix thoroughly. One ml. of this stock solution contains 3.6 mg. of Be or an equivalent of 10 mg. of BeO. (b) Transfer a 20-ml. aliquot portion to a 1000-ml. volumetric flask. Add 0.1 ml. of 1:1 $H_2SO_4$, dilute to the mark with distilled water, adjust to temperature and mix thoroughly. Five ml. of this standard Be solution contains 0.36 mg. of Be or an equivalent of 1 mg. of BeO.

**Buffer Solution.**—(a) To 2 liters of distilled water in a 4-liter beaker add 288 g. of boric acid and 512 g. of citric acid, fine cryst. monohydrate. Stir to dissolve as much of the two acids as possible. (b) Dissolve 960 g. NaOH, C.P. pellets in 1 liter of distilled water. Cool solutions (a) and (b) and then add (b) to (a) slowly, with constant stirring and cooling. Cool to room temperature, dilute to 4 liters, and filter.

**"Zenia" Dye Solution.**—Dissolve 0.3 g. of 4-(*p*-nitrophenylazoorcinol) powder (Eastman Kodak) in one liter of 0.1 N NaOH by stirring with a mechanical stirrer for 5 hours. Filter and store in a red (low actinic glass) bottle.

*Procedure.*—The cooled sample solution or suitable aliquot portion (containing from 0.06 to 1.1 milligrams of beryllium, 3 ml. of 1:1 equivalent $H_2SO_4$, and preferably no more than 35 mg. of Al) is transferred to a 100-ml. volumetric flask and the volume adjusted to about 35 ml. Add (burette) 5 ml. of "Versene T" 13.9% solution, mix, and let stand 5 minutes. Adjust the pH to 5.0–5.5 with 5 N NaOH or $H_2SO_4$ solution. Add 10 ml. of citrate-borate buffer solution, mix, and let stand 5 minutes. Add exactly 10 ml. of "Zenia" solution (burette). Dilute to the 100-ml. mark, mix thoroughly, and let stand 10 minutes. "Zero" the photoelectric colorimeter to a reagent blank carried through the above procedure, using

[22] A blend of tetrasodium salt of ethylenediaminetetraacetic acid and triethanolamine.

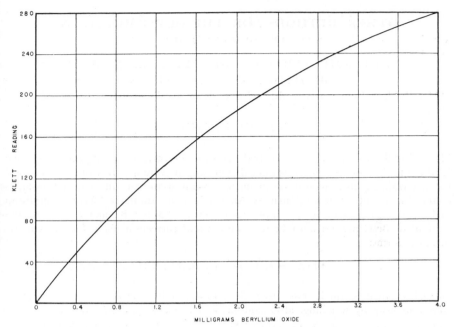

Fig. 6-3. Sample Calibration Curve. Photometric $p$-Nitrophenylazoorcinol Method for Determination of Beryllium.

a 20-mm. light path cuvette and a green (**No. 54**) filter. (Or, if a spectrophotometer is being used, set it to 100% transmittance with a 20-mm. light path cuvette filled with the reagent blank, containing like amounts of Versene T, buffer, and "Zenia" dye solution, using 515 m$\mu$ wavelength light source.) Remove the reagent blank solution from the cuvette, rinse the cuvette with a portion of the developed sample solution, and then fill it to ¾ its volume with this solution. Replace in the instrument and determine the optical density or transmittance.

With each set of colorimetric Be determinations, carry through the procedure, besides a blank of 0 mg. of Be, three solutions containing the equivalent of 1, 2, and 3 mg. of BeO respectively. The photometer or spectrophotometer readings for these are used to correct, each time, a previously constructed calibration curve.

**Preparation of Standard Calibration Curve.**—Transfer to 100-ml. volumetric flasks a series of aliquot portions of the standard Be solution (5 ml. = 1 mg. BeO) to contain 0 to 4 mg. of BeO in short increments. Add 3 ml. of 1:1 $H_2SO_4$ to each and continue as in procedure. Plot the instrument readings versus the corresponding milligrams of BeO or Be, as in Fig. 6-3.

**Calculation of Results.**—From the corrected calibration curve, determine the milligrams of Be equivalent to the instrument reading obtained for the sample:

$$\% \text{ Be} = \frac{\text{Milligrams of Be} \times 100}{\text{Wt. of Sample in Milligrams}}$$

## OTHER METHODS FOR THE DETERMINATION OF BERYLLIUM

## DETERMINATION OF METALLIC BERYLLIUM BY HYDROGEN EVOLUTION

Metallic beryllium reacts readily with acids or alkalis evolving hydrogen:

$$Be + 2KOH \rightarrow K_2BeO_2 + H_2.$$

Measuring the volume of liberated hydrogen (or the corresponding pressure change if the gas is confined to a standard unchanged volume) furnishes a method for determining the amount of metallic beryllium present in slags or residues containing no other metals, such as Al, which react similarly. When beryllium carbide is also present in a sample to be evaluated for Be metal content, the amount of $Be_2C$ present must be determined and correction made for the volume of gas it forms:

$$Be_2C + 4KOH \rightarrow 2K_2BeO_2 + CH_4$$

In such event it is usually more expedient to determine the $Be_2C$ and metallic Be simultaneously by weighing, after combustion, the $CO_2$ and the water: [23]

$$CH_4 + 2O_2 \rightarrow CO_2 + 2H_2O; \quad 2H_2 + O_2 \rightarrow 2H_2O$$

(See Determination of $Be_2C$ in Be metal.) Should appreciable beryllium nitride be present, in the sample being reacted with alkali, correction should also be made for its effect on the volume of gas evolved, since:

$$Be_3N_2 + 6KOH \rightarrow 3K_2BeO_2 + 2NH_3$$

*Procedure.*—Weigh a portion of sample to contain an estimated 0.03 to 0.2 grams of Be metal into the 250-ml. Erlenmeyer flask (see Edwards Analyzer, Fig. 6-4). Attach the flask to the analyzer. Evacuate the system through the 3-way stopcock until the differential manometer reading is between 600–700 mm. Read the manometer. Add 35–40 ml. of 50% (by weight) KOH solution to the dropping funnel. Run in, very slowly, exactly 25 ml. of the alkali. When reaction has ceased, turn on the hot plate and simmer the solution below boiling until all reaction has ceased. Cool the assembly to room temperature and read the manometer. Read the barometric pressure and room temperature.

*Calculations.*—$h_1$ = initial manometer reading. $h_2$ = final manometer reading. $P_1$ = barometric pressure, $P_2$ = total pressure after hydrogen evolution. $t$ = room temperature, °C., $V_1$ = volume of flask assembly; determined by closing stopcock $G$, and filling with water, parts $B$, $C$, $E$ (to stopcock $D$) and $F$ (to point $G$) and weighing before and after. $V_2$ = volume of 50% KOH solution added. $V_3$ =

[23] Bergholtz, Walter A., Journal of Research of the National Bureau of Standards, **48**, 3, 1952, Research Paper 2306.

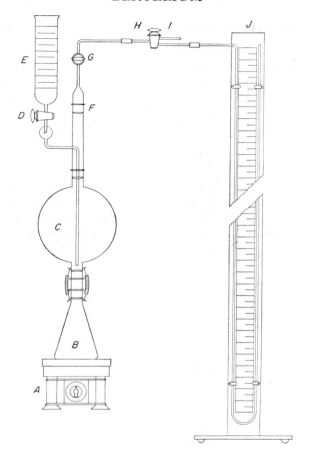

FIG. 6-4. Edwards Analyzer.

$A$ = Electric hot plate; $B$ = Sample decomposition flask, 250 ml., Pyrex, 24/40 standard taper joints; $C$ = Fixed capacity bulb, 1 l., 24/40 standard taper joints; $D$ = Stopcock, one way, 1-mm. bore; $E$ = Graduated addition funnel, 60 ml.; $F$ = Connecting tube; $G$ = Stopcock; $H$ = Two-way stopcock, 2-mm. bore; $I$ = Vacuum outlet; $J$ = Manometer.

volume of hydrogen evolved at standard conditions. $P_{mc}$ = vapor pressure of 50% KOH solution at temperature $t$.

(a)
$$P_2 = (h_1 - h_2) - P_{mc} - (P_1 - h_1) \frac{V_2}{V_1 - V_2}$$

(b)
$$V_3 = \frac{P_2}{760} \times (V_1 - V_2) \times \left( \frac{273}{273 + t} \right)$$

(c)
$$\text{Wt. of metallic Be} = 0.0004021 \, V_3$$

To correct the above computed weight of metallic Be for $Be_2C$ or $Be_3N_2$, deduct: $0.30016 \times$ wt. of $Be_2C$ in sample, and $0.3275 \times$ wt. of $Be_3N_2$ in sample.

## DETERMINATIONS IN SPECIFIC SUBSTANCES

## THE ANALYSIS OF BERYLLIUM METAL

*Preparation of Sample Solution.*—Five grams or more of metal sample (in the form of clean drillings, lathe chips, small solid pieces, flakes, or powder, properly chosen to represent the entire lot, vacuum cast ingot, sintered billet, or extrusion) are dissolved by covering with 100 ml. of distilled water and adding slowly 100 ml. or more (provide a 60–65% excess) of 1:1 $H_2SO_4$. After reaction has ceased, boil down to salts. If fluorides are present, increase the $H_2SO_4$ used and heat to strong fumes of $SO_3$, dilute with water, boil vigorously to dissolve all soluble salts and filter into a volumetric flask (500-ml. for a 5-g. sample). Any insoluble matter on the paper is burned off in a platinum crucible, treated with HF and $H_2SO_4$ in the usual manner, and any remaining residue fused with at least a tenfold weight of $KHSO_4$. The water solution of the fusion is filtered into the same volumetric flask containing the main solution. After cooling, diluting to the mark at specified temperature and thoroughly mixing, individual aliquot portions are removed for determination of: Total Be, Fe, Mn, Cr, Al, Ni, Cu, and Mg. Other determinations, including Si, BeO, $Be_2C$, $Be_3N_2$, and moisture, require individual portions of the metal sample.

### DETERMINATION OF TOTAL BERYLLIUM

*Procedure.*—An aliquot portion of the solution, chosen to contain approximately 0.2 g. of Be, is transferred, by means of a pre-standardized pipette, to a 600-ml. beaker containing 300 ml. of boiled and cooled distilled water. The total beryllium content is determined by the empirical titrimetric method. Since aluminum is simultaneously titrated, correct the calculated result:

$$\% \text{ Total Be} = \% \text{ calculated Be} - \frac{\%\text{Al}}{2}$$

### TOTAL IRON

*Procedure.*—An aliquot portion containing 0.1 to 0.5 mg. of Fe is transferred to a 100-ml. volumetric flask. Add 5 ml. of 1:1 $H_2SO_4$ and 0.05 $N$ $KMnO_4$ solution to a definite pink, plus 2 drops. Add exactly 10 ml. of 5% KCNS solution, dilute to the mark, and mix thoroughly. Transfer a portion to a cuvette and immediately determine the transmittance by means of a spectrophotometer (or a filter photometer) at a wavelength of 450 m$\mu$ vs. a reagent blank, using a 20-mm. light path. Read the milligrams of Fe from a plot of milligrams of Fe versus % transmittance or optical density using an appropriate standard curve corresponding to the Be content of the sample aliquot. Interpolate between two standard curves when necessary.

### ALUMINUM BY THE GRAVIMETRIC QUINOLATE METHOD

*Procedure.*—An aliquot portion of the total solution corresponding to a 1-g. sample for Al contents of 0.05% or greater and a 2-g. sample for Al contents as low as 0.01% is suitable. (For Al contents below 0.01% it is best to use the colorimetric procedure [24] or the fluorometric Pontochrome Blue Black R [25] method.)

[24] Richmond, M. S., and Rodden, C. J., National Bureau of Standards, June, 1947.

After oxidation with $HNO_3$, the pH of the solution is adjusted to 4.8–5.0 with ammonium hydroxide or acetic acid. Add 5–10 ml. of 8-hydroxyquinoline solution (10 mg. 8-hydroxyquinoline crystals dissolved in 20 ml. of glacial acetic acid and diluted to 200 ml. with distilled water) and stir well. Adjust pH to 5.7 with 2 $N$ ammonium acetate, warm to 60–70°C. and let stand for 2 hours. Filter through Whatman No. 40 paper and wash 2 times with warm wash solution (20 ml. of 4 $N$ ammonium acetate diluted to 1 liter and pH adjusted to 5.7 with acetic acid). Dissolve back into original beaker with hot 1:1 HCl. Add 5 ml. of 1:1 $H_2SO_4$ and heat to fumes of $SO_3$. Destroy organic matter with $HNO_3$, return to strong fumes of $SO_3$, and cool. Dilute with about 50 ml. of distilled water and boil vigorously to dissolve all soluble salts. Adjust to a pH of 1.5 with $NH_4OH$ and electrolyze in a mercury cathode cell. Filter the electrolyte and reprecipitate the Al with 8-hydroxyquinoline at a pH of 5.7 as above. Filter through a preweighed Selas Gooch crucible with asbestos mat, policing in the beaker. Wash 4 times with ammonium acetate wash solution and 2 times with small portions of cold water. Dry at 125–130°C. for 2 hours. Cool in a desiccator and weigh:

$$\% \text{ Al} = \frac{\text{Weight of Al quinolate} \times 5.87}{\text{Weight of sample}}$$

For accurate work, the aluminum quinolate should be brought into solution, the Mn and Cr contents determined, and correction made for the Mn and Cr quinolate wts. possibly included: Wt. of Mn $\times$ 6.24 = wt. of Mn quinolate, wt. of Cr $\times$ 9.32 = wt. of Cr quinolate. For control work, the mercury electrolysis is omitted, total quinolates are weighed and corrections made for the Fe, Ni, Mn, Cr, and Cu quinolates:

Wt. of Al quinolate

= Wt. of total quinolates − (Wt. of Fe, Ni, Cr, Mn, and Cu quinolates).

## TOTAL MAGNESIUM

**Procedure.**—An aliquot portion equivalent to a 1-g. sample for magnesium contents above 0.05% or to a 2-g. sample for magnesium contents down to 0.01% is used for the gravimetric determination of Mg by weighing as $Mg_2P_2O_7$. The solution, adjusted to about 250 ml. is treated with saturated NaOH solution until a heavy precipitate of $Be(OH)_2$ results. After cooling, 2 ml. of 3% $FeCl_3$ and 50 ml. of saturated NaOH solution are added to redissolve the $Be(OH)_2$ and to precipitate out the $Mg(OH)_2$ with $Fe(OH)_3$ as gathering agent. Filter through a hardened and retentive paper. The alkaline filtrate containing most of the Be is discarded and the hydroxides are dissolved back into the original beaker with hot 1:2 HCl solution. Boil off the bulk of the HCl, dilute, and add $NH_4OH$ to a pH of 8.5. Filter and save the filtrate. Dissolve the hydroxides off the paper into the original beaker and repeat the $NH_4OH$ separation, adding the second filtrate to the first. If the bulk of hydroxides is sizeable, make a third precipitation.

[25] White, C. E., and Lowe, C. S., Ind. Eng. Chem. Anal. Ed., **9**, 430, 1937; Weissler, Alfred, and White, C. E., Ind. Eng. Chem. Anal. Ed., **18**, 530, 1946; Eberle, A. R., and Petretic, G. J., NYO-2014, 1951, USAEC, New Brunswick Lab.

The combined Mg containing filtrates are boiled down to about 250 ml. Mn is removed in the usual manner with bromine water and ammonium hydroxide. If necessary, Ca is next removed as oxalate. Mg is precipitated by adding 20 ml. of 10% diammonium hydrogen phosphate solution and 30 ml. of $NH_4OH$, stirring vigorously, and letting stand in a cooling trough overnight. The precipitate is weighed as $Mg_2P_2O_7$:

$$\% \ Mg = \frac{(\text{Weight } M_2P_2O_7 - \text{Weight blank}) \times 21.84}{\text{Weight of sample}}$$

## COPPER

A $CCl_4$ solution of dithizone will react with Cu to form Cu dithizonate and then to extract this compound, the color of the reagent changing from green to red violet. When this extraction is carried out at a pH of 1, the only interfering elements are Ag, Au, Hg, and Pd. These, in the case of Be metal samples, can be neglected.

*Procedure.*—An aliquot portion chosen to contain about 25 mg. of copper is adjusted to 25 ml. volume and a pH of 1 and transferred to a separatory funnel. Exactly 15 ml. of a 0.005% $CCl_4$ solution of dithizone (previously adjusted to give a standardized optical density when diluted to 50 ml. with $CCl_4$ and read versus $CCl_4$) is added and the solution shaken vigorously for 2 minutes. The lower organic layer is transferred to a 50-ml. volumetric flask, the aqueous layer is washed several times with small portions of $CCl_4$, and these are added to the flask. The dithizone solution is made up to the 50-ml. mark with $CCl_4$ and mixed well. About ½ of the extract is filtered through a dry Whatman No. 40 paper into a small, dry, glass-stoppered Erlenmeyer flask. A tube cuvette of 12-mm. light path is rinsed with a portion of this solution and then filled to the 10-ml. mark and the optical density read vs. a blank carried through the procedure, using a green (No. 54) filter. Copper concentration is determined by reference to a previously prepared standard curve:

$$\text{Copper present in sample (in p. p. m.)} = \frac{\text{Cu found (in micrograms)}}{\text{Weight of sample (in grams)}}$$

## NICKEL

In an alkaline medium, Ni reacts with dimethylglyoxime to form nickel dimethylglyoxime. This is soluble in chloroform and can be separated and concentrated by chloroform extraction. It can then be extracted from the chloroform by dilute acid. By again reacting the Ni, so separated, with dimethylglyoxime in an alkaline medium, in the presence of an oxidizing agent, a wine-red complex suitable for colorimetric estimation is formed.

*Procedure.*—An aliquot of the original solution containing about 25 micrograms and not over 50 micrograms of Ni is freed of Cu by extracting at a pH of 1, with 10 ml. of 0.005% dithizone solution in $CCl_4$. The aqueous layer is washed with $CCl_4$ to remove all the dithizone and then warmed to remove all $CCl_4$. Add 5 ml. of $CHCl_3$ and 5 ml. of 20% ammonium citrate solution to the solution. Mix well, add 5–6 ml. of $NH_4OH$ and again mix. Add 3 ml. of 1% dimethylglyoxime solution in $C_2H_5OH$. Shake vigorously for 1 minute and draw off the chloroform layer into a 60-ml. separatory funnel containing 10 ml. of 0.5 $N$ HCl. Again extract the Be solution with 5 ml. of $CHCl_3$ and add to the first $CHCl_3$ extract. Shake the extracts with the acid for one minute. Transfer the acid layer to a 25-ml. volumetric flask, add bromine water dropwise until the solution is colored, and then $NH_4OH$ until the bromine color is discharged +4 drops excess. Add 0.5 ml. of 1% dimethylglyoxime, make the solution up to the 25-ml. mark and mix. Fill a 12-mm. light path tube cuvette to the 10-ml. mark and read the optical density, using a blue (No. 42) filter, versus a reagent blank. Read the Ni content from a previously prepared standard calibration curve:

$$\text{Nickel present in sample (in p. p. m.)} = \frac{\text{Ni found (in micrograms)}}{\text{Weight of sample (in grams)}}$$

## CHROMIUM

Chromium in a sulfuric acid medium can be oxidized to hexavalent form by persulfate in the presence of Ag ion. The resulting chromate reacts with s-diphenylcarbazide in a cold solution approximately 0.25 $N$ in sulfuric acid to form a reddish-purple colored complex. The color is stable and obeys Beer's law.

*Procedure.*—An aliquot containing about 20 micrograms but not more than 50 micrograms of Cr is treated with 5 $N$ NaOH, dropwise, until a permanent precipitate of $Be(OH)_2$ is formed. Add 20% $H_2SO_4$ dropwise to just clear, then 2 ml. in excess. Dilute the solution to 120 ml. Heat to boiling and add 10 ml. of 0.25% $AgNO_3$ solution and 10 ml. of freshly prepared 20% ammonium persulfate solution. Boil for a minimum of ½ hour until the pink color of permanganate develops. Add small portions of sodium azide until the pink color is discharged, boil for 1 minute, and filter. Cool the solution thoroughly with running tap water, add 5 ml. of a 0.25% solution of diphenylcarbazide in ethanol (containing 4% phthalic anhydride stabilizer). Dilute to 100 ml. with distilled water and mix. Determine the optical density by means of an electrophotometer, using a green (No. 54) filter and a 10-ml. tube cuvette of 12-mm. light path versus a reagent blank. Determine the Cr content from a previously prepared standard curve:

$$\text{Chromium found in sample (in p. p. m.)} = \frac{\text{Cr found (in micrograms)}}{\text{Weight of sample (in grams)}}$$

## MANGANESE

Mn, in sulfuric, nitric, or phosphoric acid solution, is readily oxidized by an excess of potassium periodate to permanganate. The purple to violet color produced shows conformity to Beer's law up to concentrations of 15 mg. of Mn per 100 ml. of solution. A bleached blank may be prepared by discharging the permanganate color with sodium azide and deducting the background color to correct for the effects of color due to ions of other metals that may be present.

*Procedure.*—An aliquot portion of solution, representing about 0.5-g. sample, is adjusted to 75 ml. Add 35 ml. of 1:1 $H_2SO_4$ and cool. Add 0.5 g. of $KIO_4$ powder and boil for at least 5 minutes. Cool, dilute to 100 ml. in a volumetric flask, and mix. To prepare a bleached blank, return a 50-ml. portion of the colored solution to the beaker, heat to boiling, add small portions of sodium azide powder to discharge the permanganate color, and boil for 1 minute. Cool and make up to 50 ml. in a volumetric flask. Determine the optical density of the permanganate colored solution (20-mm. light path cuvette) versus the bleached blank by means of a spectrophotometer (at 540 m$\mu$) or an electrophotometer using a green (No. 54) filter. Read the Mn content of the sample from a standard calibration curve:

$$\text{Manganese present in sample (in p. p. m.)} = \frac{\text{Mn found (in micrograms)}}{\text{Wt. of sample (in grams)}}$$

## SILICON

The molybdenum blue method, based on the preliminary formation of silicomolybdic acid followed by reduction to the heteropoly blue complex, is applied after HF treatment of the sample solution to ensure complete solution of the silicon. Phosphorus, germanium, and arsenic must be absent.

*Reagents.* **Standard Si Solution.**—0.214 gram of pure standard $SiO_2$ powder is thoroughly fused in a platinum crucible with about 2 g. of Si-free $Na_2CO_3$, dissolved in water, and made up to 1 liter in a volumetric flask. From this stock solution, stored in a polyethylene plastic bottle, prepare a standard solution containing 10 micrograms of Si per ml. by diluting 50 ml. to 500 ml. Store the standard solution in a polyethylene plastic bottle.

**10% Molybdic Acid Solution.**—Dissolve 25 g. of $(NH_4)_6Mo_7O_{24} \cdot 4H_2O$ C.P. crystals in water, acidify with 40 ml. of 1:1 $H_2SO_4$, cool and dilute to 250 ml.

**Freshly Produced Reducing Solution.**—Dissolve 11 g. of sodium bisulfite, 0.8 g. NaOH C.P. pellets and 0.2 g. of 1,2,4-aminonaphthol-sulfonic acid in distilled water and dilute to 100 ml.[26]

**Ammonium Hydroxide Solution (about 20% $NH_3$).**—Bubble tank $NH_3$ gas through distilled water in a plastic bottle surrounded by a cooling bath of ice water to a sp. gr. of about 0.925.

*Procedure.*—Weigh a portion of Be metal sample to contain an estimated 50 to 200 micrograms of Si into a fluorethene beaker and just cover with water. Add very slowly and with constant cooling 20 ml. of distilled water containing 3 drops 1:1 $H_2SO_4$ and 5 ml. of concentrated $HNO_3$. When reaction is complete, remove from the water cooler and add 3 ml. of 5% HF solution (by means of a plastic pipette). Cover with a fluorethene watch glass and warm in a shallow hot water bath at 60–70°C. for 1 hour. Cool and add 40 ml. of saturated boric acid solution. Adjust the pH to 2.5 ± 0.2 by addition of silica-free ammonium hydroxide, stirring by means of a plastic rod. Add 5 ml. of acidified 10% ammonium molybdate solution and adjust pH to 2.2–2.3 by means of Si-free ammonium hydroxide solution. Allow to stand 10 minutes, add 5 ml. of 20% tartaric acid solution and stir. Add 1 ml. of reducing solution, stir, and let stand 10 minutes. Transfer to a 100-ml. volumetric flask. Make up to volume, mix, and let stand for 15 minutes. Determine the optical density at 820 m$\mu$ or with a red (No. 66) light filter, using a 20-mm. light-path cuvette, versus distilled water. Carry a blank through the entire procedure and deduct its optical density from that of the sample. Determine the Si content from a standard calibration curve previously prepared by carrying through the procedure individual portions of 0.2 g. Be in the form of Si-free $BeSO_4$ solution to which have been added 10 to 200 $\mu$g. of Si (standard Si solution):

$$\text{Silicon in sample (in parts per million)} = \frac{\text{Si found (in micrograms)}}{\text{Weight of sample (in grams)}}$$

[26] Carlson, A. B., and Banks, C. V., AECU-1375, June, 1951.

## BeO IN BERYLLIUM METAL

The method is based upon the fact that at temperatures of 520–800°C. dry HCl gas will, when passed over beryllium metal, convert it to $BeCl_2$ which is volatilized:

$$Be + 2HCl \rightarrow BeCl_2 + H_2$$

Under the same conditions, the BeO content is unaffected and remains behind as a residue. During the above volatilization the beryllium contents of both $Be_2C$ and $Be_3N_2$ are also volatilized off as $BeCl_2$:

$$Be_2C + 4HCl \rightarrow 2BeCl_2 + CH_4; \quad Be_3N_2 + 8HCl \rightarrow 3BeCl_2 + 2NH_4Cl$$

The residue, after dissolution can be analyzed for Be by the colorimetric p-nitrophenylazoorcinol method and calculated to equivalent BeO content.

*Apparatus.* **Boat Train.**—See Fig. 6-5.

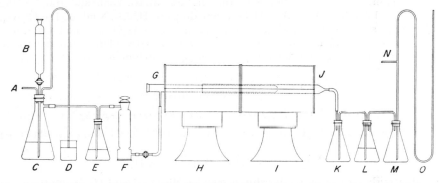

Fig. 6-5. Beryllium Oxide by Volatilization of Beryllium Metal with Dry Hydrogen Chloride.

$A$ = He gas inlet; $B$ = 250-ml. separatory funnel filled with HCl acid; $C$ = 2-liter filter flask ½ filled with concentrated $H_2SO_4$; $D$ = 30″ Hg Manometer and reservoir; $E$ = 500-ml. flask partially filled with concentrated $H_2SO_4$; $F$ = Drying tower filled with anhydrous Mg $(ClO_4)_2$; $G$ = ⅞″ o.d. × 22″ long clear quartz tube with side arm near open end and $\frac{3}{16}$″ diameter orifice at opposite end; $H$ = Hevi-duty tube furnace, temperature varied from 600°C. to 800°C.; $I$ = Hevi-duty tube furnace maintained at 900–1000°C.; $J$ = 1.25″ o.d., 1″ i.d. fused quartz tube 30″ long, reduced end; $K, L, M$ = 500-ml. flasks, $L$ contains concentrated $H_2SO_4$; $N$ = To water aspirator; $O$ = Water manometer.

**Boats.**—Of slip-cast, high-fired BeO.

**Be Metal Pellets.**—When Be metal powder is to be analyzed for BeO content, it is first cold compacted into a ¼″ to ½″ diameter pellet in a die and plunger by means of a 3-ton hydraulic press. Samples can also consist of solid Be metal slivers or pieces.

*Procedure.*—Heat the BeO combustion boat for 30 minutes in a muffle furnace at about 1000°C. and cool in a desiccator. Weigh the sample (solid piece, sliver, or thin pellet of Be metal) and place in the cooled boat. For Be containing greater than 1% BeO, use approximately 0.2 g. of sample. For lower BeO contents, use 0.25–0.50 grams of sample. Place the boat (or boats) with sample in the cold middle zone of the side arm quartz tube and close off with a neoprene rubber stopper. With only the orifice end of this tube in the furnace and with the sample boat cold, flush the entire train with He for 1 hour. Start the dry HCl gas flowing through the train, cut off the He flow, and adjust the HCl gas rate at about 5 bubbles per second. Continue for about ½ hour with a 2 to 3 inches of water negative pressure, maintained by means of the water aspirator, at the exit end of the outer quartz tube. Push the side arm quartz tube into the tube furnace so that the sample is brought into the middle of the hot zone of the first furnace (previously adjusted to 600°C.) and so that the orifice end of this quartz tube is at the middle of the hot zone of the second furnace (maintained at above 900°C.). After 30 minutes, increase the temperature of the first furnace gradually to 800°C. Continue the HCl flow for 15 to 20 minutes after $BeCl_2$ ceases coming off. (About 1.5 total hours in the hot zone is ample for 0.2 g. samples.) Discontinue the flow of HCl solution into the $H_2SO_4$ flask, close the stopcock leading into the side arm of the quartz tube, and shut off the water aspirator. Carefully remove the boat from the quartz tube (residue is very light and pulverant and is easily lost with the slightest draft), cool, and transfer the residue to a 150-ml. beaker. Add $H_2O$, a few drops of $HNO_3$, 3 ml. of 1:1 $H_2SO_4$, and heat to strong fumes of $SO_3$. Cool, add 25 ml. of $H_2O$, and boil vigorously for a minimum of 15 minutes to dissolve all soluble salts. Filter and determine the Be content by the colorimetric $p$-nitrophenylazoorcinol method:

$$\% \text{ BeO} = \frac{\text{Milligrams of Be} \times 2.774 \times 100}{\text{Milligrams of sample}}$$

### BERYLLIUM CARBIDE IN BERYLLIUM METAL

Beryllium carbide, $Be_2C$, is attacked by hot 60% KOH solution liberating methane:

$$Be_2C + 4KOH \rightarrow 2K_2BeO_2 + CH_4$$

Simultaneously, of course, the beryllium metal is dissolved and $H_2$ evolved:

$$Be + 2KOH \rightarrow K_2BeO_2 + H_2$$

The evolved $CH_4$ and $H_2$ can be oxidized to $CO_2$ and $H_2O$ by passing over copper oxide (packed in a quartz tube) heated to 600–800°C.:

$$H_2 + CuO \rightarrow Cu + H_2O; \quad CH_4 + 4CuO \rightarrow 4Cu + 2H_2O + CO_2$$

The water formed can be removed by absorption in anhydrous magnesium perchlorate.[23] The $CO_2$ can be absorbed by Ascarite and weighed in the usual manner.

*Apparatus.* **$Be_2C$ Train.**—See Fig. 6-6.

*Procedure.*—Prior to making a $Be_2C$ determination the apparatus must be blanked. With cold water flowing through the jacket of the condenser and with the furnace temperature adjusted to 850°C., 100 ml. of water in the reaction flask is maintained at boiling. Nitrogen gas is allowed to flush through the system at a rate of 4–5 bubbles per second in the final $H_2SO_4$ scrubber for one hour. The $CO_2$-absorbing ascarite bulb and the similarly packed counterpoise bulb are removed from the train, placed in the balance case to attain equilibrium, each momentarily opened to the atmosphere, and weighed, one against the other. Both are replaced in the train, the flow of $N_2$ resumed as before for an additional ½ hour and then weighed as above. Repeat flushings and weighings are made until

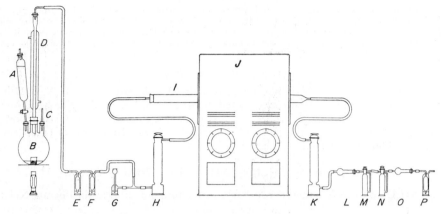

FIG. 6-6. Beryllium Carbide by Methane Evolution.

$A$ = 150-ml. Separatory funnel containing 100 ml. 60% KOH; $B$ = 500-ml. 3-neck Pyrex distillation flask; $C$ = Nitrogen inlet; $D$ = Water-cooled condenser; $E$ and $F$ = Bubblers containing concentrated $H_2SO_4$; $G$ = Mercury safety manometer; $H$ = Drying tower filled with Ascarite; $I$ = 1¼" o.d., 1" i.d. fused quartz tube, 30" long, reduced end; $J$ = Lindberg glo-bar combustion furnace; $K$ = Drying tower filled with anhydrous Mg $(ClO_4)_2$; $L$ = Drying tube filled with Drierite; $N$ = Nesbitt counterpoise bulb, packed the same as $M$; $O$ = Drying tube filled with anhydrous Mg $(ClO_4)_2$; $P$ = Bubbler containing concentrated $H_2SO_4$.

the weight of the $CO_2$ absorber, weighed against the counterpoise bulb, remains constant to 0.0002 grams. Discard the water in the reaction flask. The train is now ready to receive the sample.

Place 20 ml. of distilled water in the reaction flask and 100 ml. of 60% KOH in the reagent separatory funnel. The sample (usually about 1 g.) is weighed into a 5-ml. beaker, several glass beads are added, and, by means of forceps, the beaker is lowered through the condenser neck and placed on the bottom of the reaction flask so that the Be metal is not wetted. Connect the condenser tube to the flask and start the $N_2$ flow, adjusting the rate at 4–5 bubbles per second at the final $H_2SO_4$ scrubber. Bring the water to a boil by means of a micro burner and flush for 15 minutes. Weigh the $CO_2$ absorber versus the counterpoise bulb as in the blanking and ascertain its starting weight having remained constant. Replace the bulbs in the train (during their absence, the gap is bridged by a glass tube). With the water boiling and a minimum nitrogen stream flowing, upset the sample beaker, and allow the water to wash out the sample. Add, dropwise, 60% KOH solution (from the reagent funnel) slowly enough to avoid too rapid reaction. After all of the 100 ml. of KOH has been added and reaction has ceased, resume nitrogen flow at 4–5 bubbles per second. Continue boiling the solution for an additional 30 minutes and remove the two ascarite bulbs from the train. Weigh in the usual manner. The increase in weight of the $CO_2$ absorption bulb represents the weight of $CO_2$ equivalent to the $Be_2C$ present:

$$\% \ Be_2C = \frac{\text{Grams } CO_2 \times 68.24}{\text{Weight of sample (in grams)}}$$

NOTES.—(1) Each CuO-packed quartz tube should be regenerated with oxygen after it has been used to oxidize the hydrogen and methane evolved from 10 to 12 g. of Be metal.

Precautions should be taken to avoid water condensation at points leaving the copper oxide tube, bearing in mind the solubility of $CO_2$ in water. (2) By weighing the absorbed water resulting from the combustion of the gases evolved in the above procedure, it is possible to simultaneously determine metallic Be content of the sample, as well as the $Be_2C$ content.

### $Be_3N_2$ IN Be METAL

Combined nitrogen in beryllium metal is assumed to be present as $Be_3N_2$. This, then, can be determined by a conventional micro Kjeldahl method. The beryllium metal together with its $Be_3N_2$ content is first reacted with an excess of hydrochloric acid in such manner that the ammonia liberated is immediately converted to ammonium chloride and held in solution:

$$Be_3N_2 + 6HCl \rightarrow 3BeCl_2 + 2NH_3; 2NH_3 + 2HCl \rightarrow 2NH_4Cl$$

The $NH_4Cl$ so formed is then decomposed with strong alkali to again liberate $NH_3$:

$$NH_4Cl + NaOH \rightarrow NH_3 + H_2O + NaCl$$

This may be distilled into standard acid or into a saturated solution of boric acid (neutral to methyl orange) and titrated.

**Reagents. Standard Nitrogen Solution (1 ml. = 0.0001 g. N).**—Dissolve 0.3816 g. of dried $NH_4Cl$ (reagent grade, fine crystals, dried at 110°C.) in water and make up to 1 liter in a volumetric flask.

**Mixed Indicator.**—Dissolve 0.0166 g. methyl red and 0.0834 g. bromcresol green in 100 ml. ethanol.

**Standardized 0.01 N HCl Solution.**—Carry 5 ml. of standard $NH_4Cl$ solution through the distillation procedure and titrate the distillate with the approximate 0.01 N acid solution to be standardized.

**Apparatus. Distillation Apparatus.**—See Fig. 6-7.

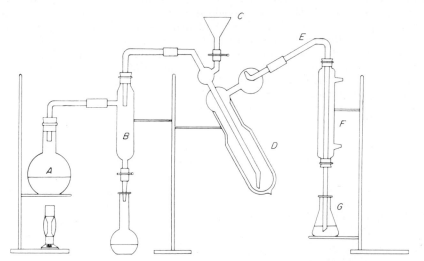

Fig. 6-7. Parnas-Wagner Micro Kjeldahl Distillation Apparatus.

$A$ = 1-Liter Flask; $B$ = Steam trap; $C$ = Funnel; $D$ = Parnas-Wagner micro-Kjeldahl flask; $E$ = Silver condenser tube; $F$ = Water condenser jacket; $G$ = Receiver.

*Procedure.*—Dissolve 1 g. of the Be metal sample in a flask (connected to a reflux condenser) by adding very slowly 20 ml. of concentrated HCl through the top of the condenser and finally boiling the solution for 5 minutes and then cooling. Steam out the Parnas-Wagner micro Kjeldahl distillation apparatus, then cool. Pour 35 ml. of 50% NaOH into the distillation flask through the funnel. Five ml. of 2% $H_3BO_3$ solution and 4 drops of indicator are added to the distillate-receiver flask and the tip of the condenser outlet is immersed under the surface of the liquid level. The sample solution is transferred to the distillation flask through the funnel, washing it several times with small portions of distilled water. Close all connections, apply a flame to the steam generator, and allow the distillation to proceed for 5 minutes from the first observation of condensation in the steam trap. Lower the receiver flask so that the condenser tip is above the liquid level and continue the distillation for an additional 2 minutes. Titrate the contents of the receiving flask with 0.01 $N$ HCl solution to a faint pink tint. Run a blank through the entire procedure:

$$\% \text{ N} = \frac{\text{titre} \times (\text{normality of HCl}) \times 1.4}{\text{Weight of sample (in grams)}} \qquad \% \text{ Be}_3\text{N}_2 = \% \text{ N} \times 1.96$$

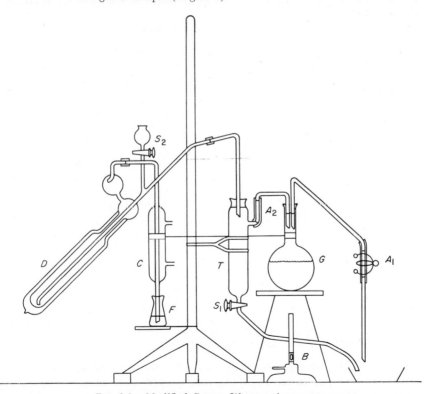

FIG. 6-8.  Modified Parnas-Wagner Apparatus.

$A_1$ = Position 1 of Pinch clamp; $A_2$ = Position 2 of pinch clamp; $B$ = Burner; $C$ = Condenser; $D$ = Distillation tube; $F$ = Receiving flask; $G$ = Steam generator; $S_1$ = Stopcock attached to steam trap; $S_2$ = Stopcock attaching funnel to distillation tube; $T$ = Steam trap.

The modified Parnas-Wagner apparatus [27] shown in Fig. 6-8 permits the water in the generator to boil continuously since the flame need not be removed in order to induce a vacuum. This speeds up the operations considerably. Placing the pinch clamp in position $A_2$ causes a vacuum while at the same time the steam being generated can escape through the vent. Placing the pinch clamp in position $A_1$ forces the steam through the apparatus for distillation. The distillation tube can be cleaned more rapidly following this procedure. Stopcocks may be used instead of pinch clamps.

## MOISTURE

Water in beryllium metal powder exists, presumably, combined with its beryllium oxide and, perhaps, adsorbed as a surface film. This water is held so tenaciously that it is very difficult to remove by ordinary means. By submitting the beryllium to elevated temperatures (850°–950°C.) the water that is not driven off as such is caused to react with the metal to form beryllium oxide and hydrogen:

$$Be + H_2O \rightarrow BeO + H_2$$

The hydrogen on passing over heated copper oxide, at 650°–750°C., is converted back to water:

$$H_2 + CuO \rightarrow Cu + H_2O$$

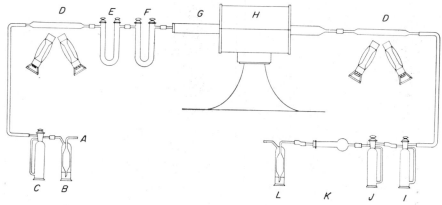

FIG. 6-9. Moisture Train for the Determination of Water in Beryllium Metal Powders.

$A$ = He inlet; $B$ = $H_2SO_4$ bubbler; $C$ = Anhydrous Mg $(ClO_4)_2$ dryer; $D$ = Quartz tube, ½″ o.d., 12″ long, filled with CuO wire; $E$ = U-Tube, upstream leg filled with Ascarite, downstream leg with anhydrous Mg $(ClO_4)_2$; $F$ = U-tube packed with anhydrous Mg $(ClO_4)_2$; $G$ = Fused quartz tube, 1.25″ o.d., 1″ i.d., 30″ long, reduced end; $H$ = Hevi-duty combustion tube furnace, maintained at 850–950°C.; $I$ = Nesbitt weighing bulb packed with anhydrous Mg $(ClO_4)_2$; $J$ = Nesbitt counterpoise bulb, same as $I$; $K$ = Drying tube filled with anhydrous Mg $(ClO_4)_2$; $L$ = $H_2SO_4$ bubbler.

An inert gas, such as helium, freed of discernible hydrogen and water, is used to carry the water vapor to an absorbing tube packed with anhydrous magnesium perchlorate. The water can then be weighed in the usual manner.

*Apparatus.* **Moisture Train.**—See Fig. 6-9.

[27] Jacobs, M. B., and Shepard, D. L., J. Am. Pharm. Assoc., Sci. Ed., **40**, 151, 154, 1951.

*Procedure.*—Prior to conducting a determination, a blank run is made to insure freedom of the entire system from leaks and sources of moisture. The two CuO tubes are brought to about 750°C. and the quartz combustion tube to 850°C. and maintained at their respective temperatures throughout. The empty porcelain boat (glazed inside and out and prefired in a muffle furnace at 1000°C. and cooled in a desiccator) is charged into the quartz tube during the blanking and the flow of helium is maintained for 1 hour (at a flow of 4 bubbles per second) before weighing the absorber versus its similarly packed downstream counterpoise bulb. Blanking is repeated until two consecutive weighings remain constant to ±0.0002 grams.

A 2-g. sample of the beryllium metal is charged into the prefired and desiccator-cooled boat and rapidly inserted into the hot zone of the quartz tube. The helium flow is started (4–5 bubbles per second) and maintained for 2 hours. The moisture absorber bulb is finally weighed versus its downstream counterpoise bulb in the usual manner:

$$\% \text{ Moisture content} = \frac{\text{Increase in wt.} \times 100}{\text{Wt. of sample}}$$

## REPRESENTATIVE ANALYTICAL RESULTS

The following table serves to summarize a typical chemical analysis of an average, hot-pressed from powder, beryllium metal sample and to indicate the method of determination:

| Determination | Average Analysis | Method of Determination |
|---|---|---|
| 1. Total Be | 99.1% | Volumetric, Empirical Titrimetric |
| 2. Fe | 1350 p. p. m. | Photometric, Thiocyanate or 1,10-phenanthroline |
| 3. Al | 300 p. p. m. | Fluorimetric, Pontochrome Blue Black R, Gravimetric, or Colorimetric Al-quinolate |
| 4. Mn | 150 p. p. m. | Photometric, Permanganate, Persulfate Oxidation |
| 5. Cr | 100 p. p. m. | Photometric, Diphenylcarbazide, Periodate Oxidation |
| 6. Ni | 200 p. p. m. | Photometric, Dimethylglyoxime |
| 7. Cu | 100 p. p. m. | Photometric, Dithizone |
| 8. Mg | 80 p. p. m. | Gravimetric, Pyrophosphate |
| 9. Si | 600 p. p. m. | Photometric, Molybdenum Blue |
| 10. B | 0.5 p. p. m. | Methyl Borate Distillation and Turmeric Colorimetric |
| 11. BeO | 0.80% | Dry HCl Gas Evolution, followed by *p*-nitrophenylazoorcinol Colorimetric |
| 12. Be$_2$C | 0.14% | Evolution of Methane and Ignition to CO$_2$ |
| 13. Be$_3$N$_2$ | 0.02% | Micro Kjeldahl |
| 14. H$_2$O | 0.15% | H$_2$ Evolution with Ignition to H$_2$O |
| 15. Ag | 3 p. p. m. | Polarigraphic or Spectrographic |
| 16. Co | 3 p. p. m. | Polarigraphic or Spectrographic |
| 17. Cd | 0.2 p. p. m. | Polarigraphic or Spectrographic |
| 18. Pb | 30 p. p. m. | Polarigraphic or Spectrographic |
| 19. Zn | 30 p. p. m. | Polarigraphic or Spectrographic |
| 20. Li | 0.3 p. p. m. | Spectrographic or by Flame Photometry |
| 21. Ca | 40 p. p. m. | Spectrographic |

Determinations 1–8 are performed on individual aliquot portions of a single sulfuric acid solution of the sample.

Determinations 9–14 are performed on individual portions of metal sample.

Determinations 2–9 and 15–21 can be performed spectrographically.

Determinations 1 and 10–14 are performed only by wet chemical methods.

## ANALYSIS OF ORES OF BERYLLIUM

"A Quick Spot Test for the Determination of Be in Ores" has already been given (see "Detection").

The quantitative estimation of the Be content is most often performed by the colorimetric 4-($p$-nitrophenylazoorcinol) method. Dissolution of the ore is first accomplished by HF and $H_2SO_4$ acid treatment followed by fusion of any remaining insolubles with $KHSO_4$; or alternatively, by $Na_2CO_3$ fusion, followed by dehydration and volatilization of $SiO_2$ with HF and $H_2SO_4$ acids in the usual manner and fusion of any residue with $KHSO_4$. The $NH_4OH$ group is next precipitated, dissolved in acid, and the colorimetric procedure applied after prior removal of any interfering quantities of the group elements. The method is fairly rapid, specific, reasonably accurate, and applicable to rich or low grade ores alike. However, in the case of low grade ores, excesses of Al must be removed. This is done by means of the Gooch and Havens method (see Methods of Separation). Excesses of Fe are removed by the ether extraction of the HCl acid solution. Alternatively, a very quick and convenient method for removal of interferences is precipitation of the hydroxides with excess $NH_4OH$ in the presence of ethylenediamenetetraacetic acid. The quantity of reagent present, however, must be carefully controlled, providing enough to chelate only the major portions of Fe, Al, etc., and leaving no appreciable excess to sequester Be.

The gravimetric determination of Be by weighing as BeO has already been given and its merits and limitations discussed. In the analysis of ores, this method is generally considered the most accurate when applied to high grade ores (10% BeO content or better). It is not recommended for use in the case of ores having less than 1% BeO content.

## ANALYSIS OF ALLOYS OF BERYLLIUM

Beryllium copper alloys, presently, are the most industrially important alloys of beryllium. These include master alloy (4.00–4.25% Be with Fe, Al, and Si as impurities) and the ternary alloys, employing Ni or Co hardener, made from master alloy. The most common of these contain 1.9–2.0% Be with 0.35% Ni or 0.25–0.50% Be with 1.5–2.5% Ni.

The Be in the above alloys can be determined gravimetrically, titrimetrically or photometrically after removal of the copper content. The sample, in the form of clean drillings, millings, or small pieces, dragged with a magnet, is weighed and dissolved in excess $HNO_3$. When the Be content, only, is sought, it is usually most expedient to determine this, after removal of copper as soluble tetramine copper complex, by the colorimetric procedure if an accuracy of about 10% (at a 95% confidence level) of the Be content present is satisfactory; or by the titrimetric method (see Empirical Titrimetric Method) when an accuracy of ±0.3% of the Be content is required. When using the colorimetric procedure, the size sample should be chosen to contain about 0.3 mg. of Be (never dissolving less than 1 g. of metal samples, but if necessary, choosing an appropriately sized aliquot portion of the solution of the $R_2O_3$ hydroxides). When using the titrimetric procedure, the size sample should be large enough to contain 0.1 to 0.2 grams of Be, and the Al content of the solution must be known and correction made or must be removed.

If, in addition to the Be analysis, determinations of Fe, Al, Cu, Ni, and Co are also required, then it is usually best to remove Cu by electrodeposition with subsequent analysis of individual aliquot portions of the remaining solution for each of the constituents sought. The methods used, generally, are those outlined for the analysis of beryllium metal.

## ZENIA METHOD FOR BERYLLIUM IN THE ATMOSPHERE

This method [28] is especially suitable for monitoring the air in plants processing beryllium compounds, which, because of their high toxicity and low density, constitute a health hazard. The method consists of pumping the air through a filter medium, treating the sample of dust to destroy the organic matter by ignition, complexing or removal of interfering elements and colorimetric evaluation of the lake formed by any beryllium present with 4-($p$-nitrophenylazoorcinol) (Zenia) described earlier in this Chapter. (Any ion that yields a color in alkaline solution will cause interference. These are, in general, rendered inactive through the formation of soluble complexes. Iron and other heavy metals are complexed with Dow's Versene T. Cyanide treatment complexes copper and zinc. Magnesium and chloride ions should be absent since they interfere.)

*Apparatus.*—The sampling equipment consists essentially of a filter medium, air pump and flow meter. Whatman No. 41 paper is recommended for the filter medium. A pump capable of drawing a relatively large volume of air in a short time is necessary in order to obtain enough beryllium on the sample pad for analytical work. For general area sampling, a large volume of air is not necessary since the sampler can be run long enough to obtain a large enough sample for analysis. However, for operational samples which are often of short duration, it is necessary to collect a sample in short time which is sufficiently large for analysis. To meet these sampling requirements, the Staplex Hi Volume sampler, which draws approximately 0.5 cubic meters of air per minute using a Whatman No. 41 filter paper, is satisfactory.

The colorimetric equipment may be a spectrophotometer, to be used at a wavelength of 515 m$\mu$, or a filter-type photometer, such as a Klett, using a No. 54 green filter (500–575 m$\mu$).

*Reagents.* **Standard Beryllium Solution.**—Dissolve sufficient beryllium powder of known assay in a small quantity of 1:1 $H_2SO_4$ so that when made up to 1 liter, the strength will be such that 1 ml. equals 100 micrograms. After the initial reaction between beryllium and the acid, it is usually necessary to boil the liquid to get all beryllium into solution. Standard solutions can be aliquoted as necessary for making up standards to plot the curve of Klett reading versus micrograms of beryllium.

**Buffer Solution.**—Dissolve in water 78 g. of sodium hydroxide, 31.5 g. of citric acid, and 18.5 g. of boric acid and make volume up to 1 liter in a volumetric flask.

**Zenia ($p$-Nitrophenylazoorcinol Solution).**—Dissolve 0.25 g. of dye in 1.0 l. of 0.1 $N$ NaOH. Stir in darkness for at least five hours, using a magnetic stirrer, or equivalent, then filter under vacuum. Allowing this solution to stand for 8 hours in darkness and refiltering tends to stabilize the resultant standardization curve.

[28] Hiser, Donaldson, and Schwenzfeier, paper presented at the April, 1961, Meeting of the American Ind. Hyg. Assn.

This reagent is not uniform; a new standardization curve must be plotted for each lot of dye made up. (The dye is available from Eastman Kodak Co., Catalog List No. 41, as No. P4414 which is 4-(*p*-nitrophenylazoorcinol.)

*Versene-T.*—Dilute one part of Dow's Versene-T (55.5% solids) with 1 part water.

*Procedure.*—In sampling, extreme care must be taken to insure that the filter paper does not become contaminated. In the laboratory, the sampler heads are washed in detergent, dried and are then loaded with 10.5 centimeter Whatman No. 41 filter paper. These loaded heads are sealed in Cellophane bags until ready to be placed on the sampler. After sampling, the head is carefully removed, the filter paper is removed with tweezers and placed in a new Cellophane bag. These bags are enclosed in a manila envelope for transport to the laboratory. It should be noted that sample heads are used only once between detergent washes.

Remove filter paper containing sample from Cellophane bag and place in platinum dish (bag and filter can be ignited, but experience has shown that all beryllium is impinged on filter paper and bag will not contain a significant quantity of beryllium). Wet with 1:1 $H_2SO_4$ from a dropping bottle. Evaporate on hot plate to fumes, then place on gas burner, increasing heat slowly until sample is thoroughly ashed. Cool platinum dish, wet with $HNO_3$ (dropping bottle), place on cool portion of hot plate to evaporate, then repeat firing. Again cool platinum dish, add about 10 drops HF and swirl dish to dissolve the ash, evaporate to dryness at low heat. (*Caution:* Do not allow hot plate surface to exceed 200°F.!) Dissolve residue in platinum with a few milliliters of cold water. Add 1 drop of Versene T reagent. (Solution should be alkaline to litmus at this point; if not, adjust with a few drops of 1 N NaOH.) If copper is present, as indicated by blue color, or zinc is suspected, add KCN solution until color disappears. Then add 1.0 ml. of buffer solution, transfer into cuvette tube, taking care to leave room in cuvette for 1.0 ml. of Zenia (dye). Add 1.0 ml. of dye, make up to 10 ml. with distilled water. Mix by stopping cuvette with finger and upending tube. Centrifuge for 10 minutes. Place cuvette in Klett and read, the instrument having been zeroed with a reagent blank containing exactly the same amount of Versene Reagent, buffer, and dye.

Read the amount of beryllium from a previously prepared curve of instrument reading versus micrograms of beryllium. Usually 20 or more samples are read at the same time. The zero reading should be checked before and after each set of samples. Along with samples, a known standard should be prepared and read to make certain that the prepared curve remains valid.

Samples in excess of 45.0 micrograms of beryllium must be aliquoted, since accuracy falls off at this point.

## METHODS FOR BERYLLIUM IN ANALYSES IN OTHER CHAPTERS

Beryllium in Aluminum Alloys         See Analysis of Aluminum Alloys

# Chapter 7

# BISMUTH

**Bi**, *at. wt.* 208.980; *sp. gr.* 9.7474; *m.p.* 271.3°C.; *b.p.* 1420°C.; \* *oxides,* $Bi_2O_3$, $Bi_2O_5$

Bismuth was known during the Middle Ages, although it was confused, frequently, with tin, lead, antimony, and zinc. Paracelsus named the element "wissmat" which later became latinized "bisemutum." The metal is used in the preparation of alloys of low melting point, which are characterized by their expansion on cooling. The compounds are used for medical purposes, the subnitrate being especially useful. The salts are generally not poisonous and may be taken internally without danger.

Bismuth is not an abundant element. It occurs free in nature and combined as oxides and sulfides (bismuthinite). It is found combined as arsenate, carbonate, molybdate, oxide, telluride, silicate, and vanadate. In small quantities it is found in conjunction with copper, cobalt, arsenic, lead, nickel, molybdenum, silver, tin, vanadium. The principal source in the United States is from the residues of lead refining.

## DETECTION

Bismuth is precipitated from its solution, containing free acid, by $H_2S$ gas, as a brown sulfide, $Bi_2S_3$. The compound is insoluble in ammonium sulfide (separation from arsenic, antimony, and tin), but dissolves in hot dilute nitric acid (separation from mercury). The nitrate, treated with sulfuric acid and taken to $SO_3$ fumes, is converted to the sulfate and dissolves upon dilution with water (lead remains insoluble as $PbSO_4$). Bismuth is precipitated from this solution by addition of ammonium hydroxide, white $Bi(OH)_3$ being formed (copper and cadmium dissolve). If this hydroxide is dissolved with hydrochloric acid and then diluted with a large volume of water, the white, basic salt of bismuth oxychloride, $BiOCl$, is precipitated. The compound dissolves if sufficient hydrochloric acid is present. It is insoluble in tartaric acid (distinction from antimony).

*Reducing Agents.*—Formaldehyde in alkaline solution, hypophosphorous acid, potassium, or sodium stannite, reduce bismuth compounds to the metallic state. For example, a hot solution of sodium stannite poured onto the white precipitate of $Bi(OH)_3$ on the filter will give a black stain. The test is very delicate and enables the detection of small amounts of the compound.

$$2Bi^{+3} + 3SnO_2^= + 6OH^- \rightarrow 2Bi + 3SnO_3^= + 6H_2O$$

*Blowpipe Test.*—A compound of bismuth heated on charcoal with a powdered mixture of carbon, potassium iodide, and sulfur, will give a scarlet incrustation on the charcoal.

\* American Institute of Physics Handbook.

191

## ESTIMATION

The determination of bismuth is required in complete analysis of ores of cobalt, nickel, copper, silver, lead, and tin, in which it is generally found in small quantities, and in the evaluation of bismuthite, bismuth ochre, etc. Bismuth is often determined in the analysis of such minerals as molybdenite and wolframite. It is determined in the residues from the refining of lead (the principal source of bismuth in the United States), in alloys—antifriction metals, electric fuses, solders, stereotype metals, certain amalgams used for silvering mirrors (with or without lead or tin), and in bismuth compounds.

In general methods of analysis of ores it must be kept in mind that bismuth is apt to be left with the silica residue as an oxycompound. Unless taken care of a portion may pass into the ammonium sulfide group where it is precipitated with aluminum causing an error in its determination. Bismuth deposits both on the anode and cathode in electrolysis and is apt to contaminate copper in its electrolytic determination.

For determination of bismuth the ore is decomposed by treatment with $HNO_3$, followed by HCl and finally $H_2SO_4$, taking to fumes. After extracting the greater part of bismuth with water, the residue is fused with $Na_2CO_3$, and S and the silicate is leached out with water and the bismuth recovered from the residue by dissolving in $HNO_3$ and converting to $BiOCl$.

Molten bismuth alloyed with uranium or enriched (U-235) uranium has been proposed as a liquid system for nuclear power. Bismuth with a small percentage of magnesium added has been proposed as a dispersing and circulating medium for thorium oxide. This activity has lead to a searching inquiry as to the methods of separating fission and corrosion products as well as the chief fuel or breeder elements. Volatility separations, extractions with fused salt media, low temperature solvent extractions, and conventional precipitations from aqueous solution by the homogeneous sulfide technique, or by other hydrolytic methods, have been found to be of service.

## PREPARATION AND SOLUTION OF THE SAMPLE

In dissolving the substance, the following facts must be kept in mind. Nitric acid is the best solvent of the metal. Although it is soluble in hot sulfuric acid, it is only very slightly soluble in the cold acid. The metal is practically insoluble in hydrochloric acid, but readily dissolves in mixed nitric and hydrochloric acids. The hydroxides, oxides, and most of the bismuth salts are readily soluble in hydrochloric, nitric, and sulfuric acids.

*Ores or Cinders.*—One gram of the finely pulverized ore or cinder (or larger amounts where the bismuth content is very low) is treated in a 400-ml. beaker with 5 ml. of bromine solution followed by the cautious addition of about 15 ml. of $HNO_3$ (sp. gr. 1.42). (The bromine solution is made by dissolving in water 75 g. of KBr, to which are added 50 grams of liquid bromine and the mixture diluted to 500 ml. with water.) When the violent action has ceased, which is apt to occur in sulfide ores, the mixture is taken to dryness on the steam bath, 10 ml. of concentrated HCl and 20 ml. of concentrated $H_2SO_4$ added and the covered sample heated until $SO_3$ fumes are freely evolved. The cooled solution is diluted with 50 ml. of water and gently heated until only a white or light gray residue remains. The solution is filtered and the residue washed with dilute $H_2SO_4$ (1:10), to remove any adhering bismuth. Silica, the greater part of the lead (also $BaSO_4$) remain in the residue, whereas the bismuth, together with iron, alumina, copper, antimony, etc., are in the solution. Details of further treatment of the solution to effect a separation of bismuth are given under "Separations" and in the procedures for the determination of bismuth.

*Alloys, Bearing Metal, etc.*—One gram of the borings, placed in a small beaker, is dissolved by adding 20 ml. of concentrated HCl and 5 ml. of concentrated $HNO_3$. The alloy will usually dissolve in the cold, unless considerable lead is present, in which case prolonged heating on the steam bath may be necessary. (A yellow or greenish-yellow color at this stage indicates the presence of copper.) Lead may now be removed either as a sulfate by taking to $SO_3$ fumes with $H_2SO_4$ or by precipitating as chloride, in the presence of alcohol, according to directions given under "Separations." The bismuth is determined in the filtrate from lead according to one of the procedures given later.

*Lead Bullion, Refined Lead.*—Ten to twenty-five grams of the lead, hammered or rolled out into thin sheets and cut into small pieces, are taken for analysis. The sample is dissolved by a mixture of 250 ml. of water and 40 ml. of concentrated nitric acid, in a large covered beaker, by warming gently, preferably on the steam bath. When the lead has dissolved, the beaker is removed from the heat and dilute ammonia (1:2) added to the warm solution, very cautiously and finally drop by drop until the free acid is neutralized and the liquid remains faintly opalescent, but with no visible precipitate. Now 1 ml. of dilute HCl (1:3) is added. The solution will clear for an instant and then a crystalline precipitate of bismuth oxychloride will form, if any considerable amount of bismuth is present. The beaker is now placed on the steam bath for an hour, during which time the bismuth oxychloride will separate out, together with a small amount of lead and with antimony if present in appreciable amounts. The further isolation and purification of bismuth is given under "Separations." In brief—antimony is removed by dissolving the precipitate in a small amount of hot dilute HCl (1:3), precipitating bismuth, traces of lead, and the antimony by $H_2S$, dissolving out the antimony sulfide with warm ammonium sulfide, dissolving the $Bi_2S_3$ and PbS in $HNO_3$ and reprecipitating the bismuth according to the procedure given above. Bismuth is now determined as the oxychloride. Further details of this method are given under "Gravimetric Procedures."

## SEPARATIONS

The following procedures are given in the order that would be followed in the complete analysis of an ore in which all the constituents are sought. This general scheme, however, is not required for the majority of bismuth-bearing samples commonly met with in the commercial laboratory, direct precipitations of bismuth frequently being possible.

*Separation of Bismuth from Members of Subsequent Groups, Fe, Cr, Al, Mn, Co, Ni, Zn, Mg, the Alkaline Earths and Alkalies, Together with Rare Elements of these Groups.*—The solution should contain 5 to 7 ml. of concentrated hydrochloric acid (sp. gr. 1.19) for every 100 ml. of the sample. The elements of the hydrogen sulfide group are precipitated by saturating the solution with $H_2S$ (Hg, Pb, Bi, Cu, Cd, As, Sb, Sn, Mo, Se, Te, Au, Pt). The members of subsequent groups remain in solution and pass into the filtrate.

*Separation of Bismuth from Uranium by Thioacetamide.*[1]—The homogeneous precipitation of bismuth sulfide by thioacetamide does not cause loss of uranium with the precipitate. The alloy is dissolved in concentrated nitric acid, and the solution is diluted so that there is approximately 0.1 g. Bi per ml. An aliquot containing 0.2 g. of Bi is diluted to 75 ml., and 5 ml. of 5% thioacetamide is added. The temperature is maintained at 50°–60°C. until the precipitation is complete. Filtration on a Whatman No. 42 paper and washing with water separates the bismuth completely from uranium; amounts of uranium ranging from 7 to 1400 micrograms are recovered quantitatively in the filtrate.

*Separation of Bismuth from Arsenic, Antimony, Tin, Molybdenum, Tellurium, Selenium.*—In presence of mercury, the soluble members of the hydrogen sulfide group are separated from the insoluble sulfides by digesting the precipitate above obtained with ammonium sulfide. Arsenic, antimony and tin sulfides dissolve. Bismuth sulfide remains insoluble (as do Hg, Pb, Cu, Cd).

*Separation of Bismuth from Mercury.*—The insoluble sulfides, remaining from the above treatment with ammonium sulfide after being washed free of the soluble members of this group, are placed in a porcelain dish and boiled with dilute nitric acid (sp. gr. 1.2 to 1.3). The solution thus obtained is filtered, upon dilution, from the insoluble sulfide of mercury. A little of the lead may remain as $PbSO_4$, and the solution may contain lead, bismuth, copper, and cadmium.

*Separation of Bismuth from Lead.*—This is the most important procedure in the determination of bismuth as the separation is almost invariably necessary, since these elements commonly occur together.

**Oxy-Bromide Procedure for Separating Bismuth.**—The usual procedure for a preliminary separation of lead as $PbSO_4$ does not effect a complete separation from bismuth as this will in part be carried down with the lead sulfate. The method recommended by L. Moser and W. Maxymowicz (Z. anal. Chem., **67**, 248, 1925–26) is the Oxy-Bromide Method, which also effects a separation of bismuth from copper, cadmium, zinc as well as the lead.

The nitric acid solution containing the elements in question (free from chlorides and ammonium salts) is carefully neutralized by addition of small portions at a time of sodium carbonate solution until the precipitate that forms dissolves tardily. The solution diluted to about 300 ml. is treated with 2–3 g. of potassium or sodium bromate ($KBrO_3$ or $NaBrO_3$) and heated to boiling. If the solution becomes cloudy it is cleared with a few drops of $HNO_3$. To the hot solution is now added a 10% solution of KBr or NaBr dropwise from a pipette until the solution becomes turbid, the solution being colored brown by free bromine. It is now boiled until a clear yellow color is obtained. More bromide is added and the solution is again boiled as before. This is repeated as long as a precipitation occurs with the addition of the bromide. Additional bromate at this stage will cause no further precipitation. The bromine is expelled by boiling and the precipitate filtered off. It is advisable to dissolve the precipitate in $HNO_3$ and repeat the precipitation to completely eliminate lead etc. The precipitate is BiOBr.

**Separation of Bismuth as the Oxy-Chloride.**—See under "Methods."

**Separation from Lead by Chloride-Cupferron-Phosphate Procedure.**[2]—The phosphate procedure for the determination of bismuth (see under "Gravimetric Methods") will not tolerate more than 0.01 g. of lead when 0.5 g. of bismuth is being

[1] Stoner, G. A., and Finston, H. L., Anal. Chem., **29**, 570, 1957.
[2] Silverman, L., and Shideler, M., Anal. Chem., **26**, 911, 1954.

precipitated as the phosphate under optimum conditions. The cupferron precipitation procedure will not tolerate more than 0.2 g. of lead during the separation of 0.5 g. of bismuth. A preliminary separation of the greater portion of the lead as the chloride, followed by a cupferron separation of the bismuth in the filtrate, permits an accurate determination of lead to be made in a 1:1 alloy of lead and bismuth.

A 1.000-g. sample of the alloy is placed in a 600-ml. beaker, dissolved in 10 ml. of nitric acid (1 acid plus 3 water). Then 8 ml. of 72% perchloric acid is added and the solution is evaporated nearly to dryness. Cool; wash down cover and sides of beaker with 30 ml. of water.

Add, drop by drop, with stirring, 70 ml. of hydrochloric acid (2 volumes concentrated acid plus 3 volumes of water) to precipitate the lead partially as lead chloride. Filter on a Whatman No. 40 15-cm. paper and wash with 100 ml. of 1:9 ($H_2O$) hydrochloric acid. The filtrate will contain not over 0.2 g. of lead from a 1 g. 1:1 alloy sample.

The bismuth is precipitated by adding 50 ml. of cold 6% aqueous cupferron solution. The bismuth is completely precipitated and contains at most a small fraction of a per cent of lead. The precipitate is filtered rapidly through a 15-cm. Whatman No. 40 paper and is washed six times with cold 2% hydrochloric acid mixed with 1% cupferron solution and then six times with cold water.

The paper and precipitate are decomposed in the original beaker by 25 ml. of nitric acid, sp. gr. 1.42, and 15 ml. of 72% perchloric acid by gentle heating, followed by evaporation to a concentrated solution, dilution with 50–100 ml. of water and boiling to remove chlorine and other decomposition products. The solution is now ready for the phosphate determination of the bismuth (*vide infra*).

NOTE.—Presumably the extraction of bismuth cupferrate by chloroform from an acidic solution would make possible the clean separation of bismuth from equal or larger weights of lead. According to Sandell,[3] a few micrograms of bismuth may be recovered quantitatively from as much as 10 grams of lead.

***Separation of Bismuth from Copper and Cadmium.***—This separation is accomplished by precipitating bismuth as the oxychloride by hydrolysis, or as the carbonate by adding a slight excess of ammonium carbonate to the solution nearly neutralized by ammonia, or as the hydroxide by adding an excess of ammonia. Details of these procedures are given under the gravimetric methods for determining bismuth.

## GRAVIMETRIC METHODS

### DETERMINING SMALL AMOUNTS OF BISMUTH BY PRECIPITATION AND WEIGHING AS THE BASIC CHLORIDE, BiOCl

The method is best suited to amounts of bismuth below 10 mg. The determination depends upon the formation of the insoluble oxychloride, BiOCl, when a hydrochloric acid solution of bismuth is sufficiently diluted with water, the following reaction taking place, $BiCl_3 + H_2O = BiOCl + 2HCl$.

The procedure is recommended for the determination of bismuth in refined

[3] Sandell, E. B., Colorimetric Determination of Traces of Metals, p. 342, 3rd Ed., Interscience Publishers, New York, 1959.

lead, bearing metal, and bismuth alloys. Copper, cadmium, and lead do not interfere; appreciable amounts of antimony and tin, however, should be removed by $H_2S$ precipitation and subsequent treatment with $(NH_4)_2S$ and the residual sulfides dissolved in hot dilute nitric acid, according to directions given under "Separations." Silver, mercurous mercury, thallium, and zirconium should be absent.

*Procedure.*—The solution of bismuth, freed from appreciable amounts of tin and antimony, is warmed gently and treated with sufficient ammonia to neutralize the greater part of the free acid. At this stage a precipitate is formed which dissolves with difficulty; the last portion of the dilute ammonia (1:2) is added drop by drop, the solution is diluted to about 300 ml., and the remainder of the free acid neutralized with dilute ammonia added cautiously until a faint opalescence appears, but not enough to form an appreciable precipitate. One to 3 ml. of dilute hydrochloric acid (1 part HCl, sp. gr. 1.19, to 3 parts $H_2O$) are now added, the mixture stirred and the bismuth oxychloride allowed to settle for an hour or so on the steam bath, then filtered hot by decanting off the clear solution through a weighed Gooch crucible. The precipitate is washed by decantation twice with hot water and finally washed into the crucible, then dried at 100°C., and weighed as BiOCl.

$$BiOCl \times 0.8024 = Bi$$

NOTE.—Three ml. of dilute hydrochloric acid (or 1 ml. concentrated HCl, sp. gr. 1.19) are sufficient to precipitate completely 1 g. of bismuth from solution.

## DETERMINATION OF LARGE AMOUNTS OF BISMUTH (OVER 10 Mg.) AS THE OXIDE, $Bi_2O_3$

The determination of bismuth as the oxide requires the absence of hydrochloric acid or sulfuric acid from the solution of the element, since either of these acids invariably contaminates the final product. In presence of these acids, which is frequently the case, determination of bismuth by precipitation as $Bi_2S_3$ or by reduction to the metal and so weighing is generally recommended; a brief outline of the methods is given later. A solution of bismuth free from hydrochloric acid and practically free of sulfuric acid may be obtained by precipitating $Bi_2S_3$, together with CuS, CdS, and PbS, and dissolving the sulfides in nitric acid, the amount of sulfuric acid formed by the reaction being negligible.

Two general conditions will be considered: 1. Solutions containing lead. Copper and cadmium may also be present. 2. Solutions free from lead. Copper and cadmium may be present.

*1. Separation from Lead, Copper, and Cadmium, by Precipitation as Basic Nitrate.*[4]—Either the sulfuric or hydrochloric acid methods may be employed for effecting the separation of lead by precipitation. Furthermore, advantage may be taken of the fact that bismuth nitrate is changed by the action of water into an insoluble basic salt, while lead, copper, and cadmium do not undergo such a transformation.

*Procedure.*—The bismuth nitrate solution is evaporated to syrupy consistency and hot water added with constant stirring with a glass rod. The solution is again evaporated to dryness, and the hot-water treatment repeated. Four such evaporations are generally sufficient to convert the bismuth nitrate completely into the basic salt; when this stage is reached the addition of water will fail to produce a

4 Löwe, J., J. prak. Chem. (1), **74**, 344, 1858.

turbidity. The solution is finally evaporated to dryness and, when free from nitric acid, is extracted with cold ammonium nitrate solution (1 $NH_4NO_3$:500 $H_2O$) to dissolve out the lead and other impurities. After allowing to stand some time with frequent stirring, the solution is filtered and the residue washed with ammonium nitrate solution, then dried.

**Ignition to Bismuth Oxide.**—As much of the precipitate as possible is transferred to a weighed porcelain crucible, the filter is burned and the ash added to the main precipitate. This is now gently ignited over a Bunsen burner. Too high heating will cause the oxide to fuse and attack the glaze of the crucible.

$$Bi_2O_3 \times 0.8970 = Bi$$

**2. Precipitation of Bismuth as the Subcarbonate or Hydroxide, Lead being Absent.**—Either of these procedures effects a separation of bismuth from copper and cadmium.

**A. Procedure. Precipitation of the Subcarbonate.**—The solution is diluted to about 300 ml. and dilute ammonia added cautiously until a faint turbidity is obtained and then an excess of ammonium carbonate. The solution is heated to boiling, the precipitate filtered off, washed with hot water, dried and ignited according to directions given in the bismuth subnitrate method. The residue is weighed as $Bi_2O_3$.

**B. Procedure. Isolation of Bismuth by Precipitation as the Hydroxide.**—The solution is taken to dryness and the residue treated with 5 ml. of nitric acid (1:4) and 25 ml. of water added. The resulting solution is poured, with constant stirring, into 25 ml. of concentrated ammonia and 50 ml. of 4% hydrogen peroxide. Upon settling of the bismuth hydroxide, the clear solution is filtered off and the residue is treated with more ammonia and peroxide. It is then filtered onto a filter paper, washed with hot, dilute ammonium hydroxide (1:8), followed by hot water and washed free of any adhering copper or cadmium (no residue when a drop is evaporated on platinum foil). Re-solution in hot dilute nitric acid and reprecipitation may sometimes be necessary to obtain the pure product. The hydroxide may be dried, ignited and weighed as $Bi_2O_3$ according to directions already given.

## DETERMINATION AS THE PHOSPHATE, $BiPO_4$

This method is applicable to relatively large amounts of bismuth, e.g., 0.25–0.5 g. It serves to separate bismuth from the alkalies, calcium, magnesium, copper, and zinc. Positive errors are caused by as little as 10 mg. of lead when 0.5 g. of bismuth is to be determined.[5]

**Reagents. Diammonium Phosphate.**—Dissolve 31 g. of the salt per liter of water, adjust the pH to 0.6 with nitric acid after boiling and cooling.

**Diammonium Phosphate Wash Solution.**—Dilute 50 ml. of the above reagent solution to 300 ml. with water. Adjust to pH 0.6 with nitric acid.

**Procedure.**—The bismuth solution, previously freed from lead by the chloride-cupferron separations, and after destruction of the filter paper and the cupferron, is diluted to 300 ml. in a 600-ml. beaker, and adjusted to pH 0.6 with concentrated nitric acid, sp. gr. 1.42. Heat the solution nearly to boiling and add, preferably with mechanical stirring, 50 ml. of hot diammonium phosphate solution. Keep the mixture at 90°C. for 30 minutes, filter through a 15-cm What-

5 Silverman, L., and Shideler, M., Anal. Chem., **26,** 911, 1954.

man No. 42 paper and wash with the special diammonium phosphate wash solution to remove lead, then ten times with hot water to remove the phosphate solution. Transfer the paper and precipitate to a weighed porcelain crucible, char the paper and finally heat in an electric furnace at 650°C. until the weight is constant. Weigh as $BiPO_4$, factor for Bi, 0.68755.

## DETERMINATION AS THE SULFIDE, $Bi_2S_3$

The procedure is applicable to the determination of bismuth in a hydrochloric or sulfuric acid solution, freed from other members of this group.

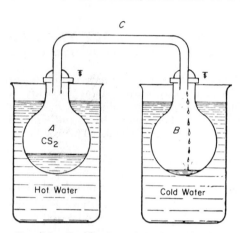

*Procedure.*—Bismuth sulfide is precipitated by passing $H_2S$ into the slightly acid solution, preferably under pressure. When the precipitation is complete, the bismuth sulfide, $Bi_2S_3$, is filtered off into a weighed Gooch crucible, the precipitate washed with $H_2S$ water, then with alcohol to remove the water, followed by carbon disulfide to dissolve out the precipitated sulfur, then alcohol to remove the disulfide, and finally with ether. After drying for fifteen to twenty minutes, the residue is weighed as $Bi_2S_3$, factor for Bi, 0.8130.

FIG. 7-1. Purification of Carbon Disulfide.

Note.—The carbon disulfide used should be freshly distilled. This may be accomplished by placing the carbon disulfide in a small flask (*A*, Fig. 7-1) connected by means of a glass tube (*C*) to a second flask (*B*), which are provided with ground-glass joints as shown. The vessels are immersed in beakers of water, the container with the reagent being placed in hot water (60–80°C.) and the empty flask in cold water. The reagent quickly distills into the empty flask in pure form.

## DETERMINATION AS THE METAL

*Procedure.*[6]—Bismuth precipitated as the carbonate and ignited to the oxide according to the procedure given, is fused in a weighed porcelain crucible with 5 times its weight of potassium cyanide over a low flame. The cooled melt is extracted with water, pouring the extracts through a filter that has been dried and weighed with the crucible. Bismuth is left undissolved as metallic bismuth. After washing with water, alcohol, and ether, the filter, with the metal and loosened pieces of porcelain glaze, is dried at 100°C. together with the crucible. These are then weighed and the increase in weight taken as the amount of bismuth present in the sample.

## ELECTROLYTIC DEPOSITION OF BISMUTH

With samples containing less than 0.03 g. bismuth, the metal may be satisfactorily deposited by electrolysis of its sulfuric acid solution, lead having been

[6] Method by Rose, H., Pogg. Ann., **110**, p. 425. Vanino and Treubert (Ber., **31**, 1303, 1898) reduce bismuth by adding formaldehyde to its slightly acid solution and then making strongly alkaline with 10% NaOH solution and warming.

removed previously by sulfuric acid by the standard procedure. The solution should contain about 6 ml. of concentrated sulfuric acid per 100 ml. It is electrolyzed with a current of 0.6 to 0.7 ampere and about 2.7 to 3 volts.

*Spontaneous Electrolysis (Internal Electrolysis).*—Bismuth plus copper may be recovered quantitatively on a platinum cathode using a soluble anode of pure lead wire enclosed in a porous thimble and connected to the platinum electrode. Bismuth is separated in this way from the solution of metallic lead, or from tin.[7]

Graded potential separation from an 0.5 $M$ tartrate solution at pH 4.5 is fairly successful (99.5%) in separating copper from bismuth if the mercury cathode is held at $-0.13$ to $-0.16$ v. versus a standard calomel electrode during the removal of the copper. The possibility of separating bismuth from lead is somewhat better than for separation of copper from bismuth.[8]

## OTHER METHODS

Bismuth may be precipitated quantitatively by adding a solution of $K_3Cr(CNS)_6$ (blue-violet) to a solution that is 0.3 to 1 $N$ in $HNO_3$. The precipitate is brick-red and has the formula $BiCr(CNS)_6$ after drying at 120–130°C.[9] The method is best applied with amounts of bismuth ranging from 50–125 mg. It serves to to separate bismuth from Cr, Mo, Al, Fe(II), Zn, Mn, Ni, Co, the alkaline earths, Mg, and the alkalies.

Bismuth may be converted into complex iodide or bromide ions like $BiI_4^-$, $BiBr_6^{-3}$, and the latter may be precipitated with suitable cobalt or chromium ammines, or with certain basic organic substances.[10]

Numerous organic precipitants and color tests for bismuth have been proposed.

## TITRIMETRIC METHODS

### THE TITRATION OF BISMUTH WITH STANDARD ETHYLENEDIAMINETETRAACETATE SOLUTION, E.D.T.A.[11]

Bismuth forms a 1:1 complex with E.D.T.A., and at pH 1.5–2.0 it may be titrated selectively with E.D.T.A. using thiourea as a complexer to hold the bismuth in solution, and as an indicator. As soon as the bismuth is complexed as the E.D.T.A. compound the yellow color of the bismuth-thiourea complex fades sharply, and provides an indication. This method is not interfered with by the presence ions of Ag, Al, Ba, Be (with fluoride added), Ca, Cd, Ce$^{+3}$, Co, Cr, Cu, Fe (with ascorbic acid added), Hg, La, Mg, Mn, Nb$^{+5}$ (with F added), $NH_4$, Ni, Pb, Sb$^{+3}$ with tartrate added, Sn$^{+4}$ with tartrate added, Sr, Ta$^{+5}$ with fluoride added, Th with sulfate added, uranyl ion, Zn, or Zr with sulfate and fluoride added. The common anions do not interfere, e.g., chloride, nitrate, perchlorate, sulfate, fluoride, tartrate; but oxalate and phosphate do interfere.

*Reagents.* **E.D.T.A. Standard Solution (0.05 M).**—Prepared from reagent grade disodium dihydrogen ethylenediaminetetraacetate dihydrate.

**Thiourea.**—Practical grade.

[7] Clarke, B. L., Wooten, L. A., and Luke, C. L., Ind. Eng. Chem. Anal. Ed., **8**, 411, 1936.
[8] Lingane, J. J., Ind. Eng. Chem. Anal. Ed., **16**, 147, 1944.
[9] Mahr, C., Z. anorg. allgem. Chem., **208**, 313, 1932; Montequi and Carrero, C. A., **27**, 2903, 1933.
[10] Berg and Wurm, Ber., **60**, 1664. 1927; Mahr, Z. anal. Chem., **93**, 433, 1933; Spacu et al. ibid., **79**, 196, 1930; **93**, 260, 1933.
[11] Fritz, J. S., Anal. Chem., **26**, 1978, 1954.

*Procedure.*—The solution containing 0.03–0.08 g. of Bi in a volume of 10–15 ml. plus 0.5 0.8 g. of thiourea is warmed until the thiourea is dissolved, then ammonia is added until the precipitate, which forms temporarily, dissolves rather slowly, i.e., in a few seconds. The solution is diluted to 40–50 ml. and the pH is adjusted to 1.5–2.0 by adding perchloric acid. The titration is made with the standard titrant until the yellow color of the bismuth-thiourea complex fades. The titrant is standardized against pure zinc metal using eriochrome black T indicator.

If iron is present, 0.3–0.4 g. of ascorbic acid is added after addition of the thiourea. Turbidity due to antimony is cleared by adding a tartrate after the solution is at pH 2.

There are many modifications of the compleximetric titration of bismuth. The fading of the color of bismuth iodide complex may be used for indication.[12] The process may be carried out as back titration, if desired. The processes are carried out at pH 1.5 to 2, and the indicator is 1–2 ml. of 0.5% potassium iodide solution. The color change is from yellow to colorless in the direct titration. The interferences are those already considered in the thiourea procedure plus specific interference due to reaction of various ions with iodide, e.g. Tl(I), cerous, ferric, titanium(III), zirconium, silver, mercuric mercury, molybdate, and vanadate. Cupric ion interferes, but may be reduced to cuprous ion with hydroxylamine hydrochloride. Lead can be tolerated up to the point where lead iodide begins to precipitate, i.e., somewhat less than 1 g. of lead per 50 ml.

**Photometric Titration.**—From 0.5 to 100 mg. of Bi per 100 ml. may be titrated photometrically. If copper is present or added, the absorbance at 745 m$\mu$ changes little until the bismuth has been complexed, then it increases linearly until the copper complex is formed, after which the absorbance remains practically constant. The pH should be approximately 2. Alternatively thiourea may be used. The absorbance then falls linearly to the end point and remains fairly constant beyond.[13]

## DETERMINATION BY PRECIPITATION AS OXALATE AND TITRATION BY POTASSIUM PERMANGANATE [14]

Normal bismuth oxalate, produced by addition of oxalic acid to a nitric acid solution of the element, boiled with successive portions of water, is transformed to the basic oxalate. This may be titrated with potassium permanagate in presence of sulfuric acid.

*Procedure.* **Preparation of the Sample.**—One gram of the finely ground sample is treated with 5 to 10 ml. of concentrated nitric acid and digested on the steam bath and finally evaporated to dryness, the residue is taken up with 5 ml. of nitric acid (sp. gr. 1.42) plus 25 ml. of water, and diluted to 100 ml.

**Precipitation of the Oxalate.**—About 5 g. of ammonium oxalate or oxalic acid are added and the liquid boiled for about 5 minutes, the precipitate allowed to settle and the supernatant solution filtered off. The precipitate is boiled twice with 50-ml. portions of water and the washings poured through the same filter. If the

12 See Cheng, K. L., Anal. Chem., **26,** 1977, 1954, for prior papers and detailed procedure.
13 Underwood, A. L., Anal. Chem., **26,** 1322, 1954; for the successive photometric titration of bismuth and lead see White, R. N., and Underwood, A. L., Anal. Chem., **27,** 1334, 1955. A wavelength of 240 m$\mu$ is used while titrating with standard E.D.T.A. solution.
14 The method is rapid and is sufficiently accurate for commercial work. Warwick and Kyle, Chem. News, **75,** 3; Muir and Robbs, J. Chem. Soc., **41,** 1.

filtrate still passes through acid, the washing is continued until the acid is removed and the washings passing through the filter are neutral. The bulk of the basic oxalate precipitate is placed in a beaker and that remaining on the filter paper is dissolved by adding 2 to 5 ml. of hydrochloric acid, 1:1, the solution being added to the bulk of the precipitate. This is now warmed until it goes into solution and the liquid is diluted to 250 ml. with hot water. Dilute ammonia is now added until the free acid is neutralized; the resulting precipitate is taken up with dilute sulfuric acid, 1:4, added in slight excess. The resulting solution, warmed to 70°C., is titrated with standard potassium permanganate.

$$\text{One ml. KMnO}_4 \ 0.1 \ N = 0.01045 \ \text{g. Bi}$$

NOTE.—Lead, copper, arsenic, iron, zinc, and tellurium do not interfere. Hydrochloric acid should not be used to dissolve the sample, as it interferes with the oxalate precipitation.

## PHOTOMETRIC METHODS

There are many sensitive procedures for the photometric determination of bismuth. The yellow or orange-yellow iodobismuthate complex, $BiI_4^-$, and its acid or salts serve as the basis for one of the most useful methods. The cations of certain organic bases, e.g., brucine, form salts with $BiI_4^-$ that may be extracted by organic solvents such as chloroform. The dithizone method is one of the most sensitive methods and it is frequently applied in biochemical work. A method based on the yellow complex between bismuth and thiourea is much used in the analysis of alloys. Another excellent method is based on the yellow complex of bismuth with diethyldithiocarbamate.

### THE IODIDE METHOD [15]

This method is usually applied to amounts of bismuth ranging from 0.01 to 0.5 mg. A linear calibration is obtained at 460 m$\mu$ in a spectrophotometer. Quite satisfactory results may be obtained using a filter photometer, a colorimeter, or Nessler tubes.

The solution is usually prepared to be 2 $N$ in nitric or sulfuric acid. Potassium iodide is added to a final concentration of 1 g. per 100 ml. Sulfurous acid, either alone or together with ascorbic acid, is added to prevent the liberation of iodine by ferric or cupric ions. If the amount of lead or thallium is too small to give a precipitate with the iodide there is no interference. If a large precipitate of lead iodide forms, bismuth is retained in the precipitate and erroneously low results are obtained. An extraction of bismuth cupferrate is necessary to separate bismuth from metallic lead and lead-base alloys. The chloroform of the extract is removed by evaporation and the cupferron is decomposed by sulfuric and nitric acid attack followed by perchloric acid.

**Reagents.** **Potassium Iodide.**—A fresh 10% aqueous solution is used.

**Reducing Agents.**—A 1% sulfur dioxide solution and 1% ascorbic acid are prepared daily.

**Extraction Solvent.**—One volume of ethyl acetate plus three volumes of amyl alcohol.

[15] This method goes back at least as far as 1880 based on work of Thresh. Papers that give references to early work are: Sproull, R. C., and Gettler, A. O., Ind. Chem. Anal. Ed., **13**, 462, 1941, and Wiegand, C. J. W., Lann, G. H., and Kalisch, F. V., Ind. Eng. Chem. Anal. Ed., **13**, 912, 1941.

*Procedure.*—The solutions should be about 10 ml. in volume and 2 $N$ in acid, preferably sulfuric. Chloride or fluoride decreases the absorbance. The possible effect of ferric iron or copper is eliminated by adding 1 ml. of the sulfur dioxide solution and 4–5 ml. of the ascorbic acid reagent. One ml. of the potassium iodide solution is added and the solution is made homogeneous at 25.00 ml. The photometric reading is made at 460 m$\mu$ relative to a reagent blank. The calibration points are found in the same manner.

If oxidants are known to be present the measurement is repeated after the solution has stood for various periods. If necessary, other aliquots are treated, using greater amounts of reducing agents.

If extraction is necessary, the 10 ml. portion of the original solution, after treatment with iodide, sulfite, and ascorbic acid, is shaken with successive 3-ml. portions of the ethyl acetate-amyl alcohol mixture. The combined extracts are made up to 10.00 ml. with the solvent, and a portion, filtered through cotton, after discarding the first ml. or so, is read at 460 m$\mu$. The calibration line is prepared in a similar manner.

The majority of the colorless ions—the alkalies, alkaline earths, magnesium, aluminum, and zinc, as well as the colored ions of cobalt, nickel, chromium(III), and uranium(VI)—do not interfere when the extraction procedure is used. Antimony is extractable, but its absorbing power is only about one-thousandth that of an equal weight of bismuth. Arsenic and tin would interfere, but these elements may be volatilized by adding hydrobromic acid during the preparation of the sample.

In the brucine extraction method, 5 ml. of a 1% solution of brucine citrate is added after the sulfite and potassium iodide have been added. The colored complex is extracted by chloroform and the absorbance, after dilution to a definite volume and filtration through cotton, is read at 425 m$\mu$.[16]

## THE THIOUREA METHOD [17]

The basis of this method is the foundation of the yellow bismuth-thiourea complex and its spectrophotometric measurement at 322 m$\mu$ or 470 m$\mu$. The choice between these two wave lengths depends upon the acid used in the solution. Nitric acid solutions are commonly used if the absorbance is to be read at 470 m$\mu$, whereas a perchloric acid medium must be used at 322 m$\mu$. At high concentrations various metallic ions interfere and the maximum concentrations that can be tolerated are given by Lisicki and Boltz [18] as follows:

| Element or Ion | Parts per million tolerated | Element or Ion | Parts per million tolerated |
|---|---|---|---|
| Sb | 0 | Ni | 500 |
| Pb | 1 | $VO_4^{-3}$ | 200 |
| $Hg^{++}$ | 3 | $WO_4^{-3}$ | 5 |
| $As^{+3}$ | 10 | $Cl^-$ | 100 |
| $Cu^{++}$ | 1 | $Br^-$ | 200 |
| $Fe^{+3}$ | 10 | $F^-$ | 200 |
| $Fe^{++}$ | 300 | | |

[16] Sandell, E. B., Colorimetric Determination of Traces of Metals, p. 336, 3rd Ed., Interscience Publishers, Inc., 1959.
[17] Mahr, C., Z. anal. Chem., **94**, 161, 1933.
[18] Lisicki, N. M., and Boltz, D. F., Anal. Chem., **27**, 1722, 1955.

The optimum acid concentration is 1 $N$ and a high concentration of thiourea is needed, e.g., 5–10%. A particular final concentration of thiourea must be used, e.g., 5% or 6%, etc. The acid concentration, thiourea concentration, and temperature $\pm 1°C$. must be constant during calibrations and analyses.

*Reagent.* **Thiourea.**—A 5% solution is made by dissolving the proper weight in about 80% of the necessary water, filtering, and diluting to the proper volume. The solution should be freshly prepared.

*Procedure.*—An aliquot of the prepared solution is acidified so that at its final volume it will be 1 $N$ in nitric acid. Ten ml. of the 5% thiourea solution is added (measured to 0.1 ml.), and the solution is diluted to 50.00 ml. at the temperature that was used in the calibration experiments. The absorbance is then read at 470 m$\mu$ against a reagent blank.

In the absence of interfering elements a 1 $N$ perchloric acid solution containing bismuth can be read at 322 m$\mu$ with about fourfold greater absorbance per unit weight of bismuth than at 470 m$\mu$. Lead and copper interfere at this wavelength.

## THE DIETHYLDITHIOCARBAMATE METHOD

Bismuth forms a yellow complex with this reagent in the alkaline region (pH 8–10), and the complex is extractable to carbon tetrachloride and its absorbance may be read in this medium. The method is highly selective if the other metals are complexed with cyanide and E.D.T.A., with tartrate added, if necessary, to prevent the precipitation of hydrous oxides.[19]

*Reagents.* **Standard Bismuth Solution.**—The stock solution contains 1.000 g. of bismuth dissolved in 10 ml. of concentrated nitric acid and diluted to 1 liter. A solution containing 20.00 mg. of bismuth per liter of 1% nitric acid is prepared from the stock solution.

**Sodium Diethyldithiocarbamate.**—Dissolve 0.2 g. in 100 ml. of water and store in a brown glass bottle.

**Complexing Mixture.**—50 g. of E.D.T.A. and 50 g. of sodium cyanide dissolved per liter in 1.5 $M$ ammonia (1 volume of concentrated ammonia plus 9 volumes of water).

*Standardization.*—Aliquots of the prepared solution are treated with 10 ml. of complexing mixture to give 0.0, 0.05, 0.10, . . . 0.3 mg. of bismuth and 1 ml. of diethyldithiocarbamate solution is added to each solution, which is then extracted with 10.00 ml. of carbon tetrachloride. The extract is filtered through a Whatman No. 1 filter paper. The absorbances are read at 370 m$\mu$ and 400 m$\mu$ within 30 minutes.

*Procedure.*—Aliquots of the prepared solution are treated with 10 ml. of complexing mixture or even 30 ml. if needed. The reagent is added and the rest of the process is as in the standardization.

1 mg. of mercury or 100 mg. of lead causes a large positive error if the reading is at 370 m$\mu$. As much as 1 mg. each of Cd, Ag, or Pb did not cause error in determining 0.115 mg. of Bi if the readings were made at 400 m$\mu$. The absorbances per 0.115 mg. of Bi are 0.537 at 370 m$\mu$ and 0.344 at 400 m$\mu$. In the absence of interfering elements the method is roughly 60% more sensitive at 370 than at 400 m$\mu$.

In the determination of bismuth in lead-base alloys, 3 g. of E.D.T.A., and 10 g. of tartaric acid are added per gram of alloy after its dissolution in nitric acid, prior

[19] Cheng, K. L., Bray, R. H., and Melsted, S. W., Anal. Chem., **27**, 24, 1955.

to the adjustment to pH 7–8 with ammonia. A suitable aliquot, e.g., 10.00 ml. or 25.00 ml., is taken for the rest of the analytical process.

## THE DITHIZONE METHOD

This very sensitive method is frequently used for the determination of bismuth in biological materials. The destruction of the organic material is often done by nitric-sulfuric acid digestion in a Kjeldahl flask, followed by perchloric acid.[20] Dry ashing of the samples was advocated by Lang[21] followed by Hubbard's[22] procedure for the separation of bismuth from lead and other metals by extraction in acetic acid medium to prevent the interference of chloride and phosphate ions. An alternative separation method is to extract both lead and bismuth from alkaline cyanide medium at pH 11–12. The lead is then extracted to an aqueous phthalate buffer of pH 3.4, the bismuth dithizonate remaining in the chloroform layer. The bismuth is then transferred to aqueous 1% nitric acid, the aqueous layer is washed with chloroform, the bismuth is transferred again to chloroform by extraction from ammoniacal cyanide medium, the extract is diluted to a standard volume with chloroform, and the absorbance is read at 505 m$\mu$.

Blanks and standardizations are run through the procedure.

*Decomposition of Samples.—*

| Nature of Sample | Amount | Reagents | Remarks |
|---|---|---|---|
| Urine | 100 ml. | (a) 7.5 ml. concentrated $H_2SO_4$ <br> (b) $HNO_3$-$HClO_4$ 1:2 vols. | Digest in Kjeldahl flask. Add nitric-perchloric mixture dropwise to clear when practically all organic matter is gone. |
| Blood serum | 10 ml. | 1.5 ml. concentrated $H_2SO_4$ <br> 5 ml. concentrated $HNO_3$ | Digest in Kjeldahl flask. |
| Liver, kidney, or muscle | 25 g. or less | 2 ml. concentrated $HNO_3$ per each g. of tissue Add 7.5 ml. concentrated $H_2SO_4$; heat until $SO_3$ fumes appear. | Heat until clear in an Erlenmeyer flask. The yellow solution is filtered through glass wool into a Kjeldahl flask. |
| Various samples | Appropriate weight | Dry ashed in muffle at 500°C. | The residue is dissolved in 2 ml. $HNO_3$; 10 ml. of glacial HOAc is added and pH is adjusted to 2.5 by adding 2 $N$ NaOH to yellow color of thymol blue indicator. |

*Reagents.—***Ordinary distilled water** stored and dispensed in a metallic system may need to be redistilled from a Pyrex glass still. Deionized water if kept in contact with resistant glass or polyethylene surfaces is suitable.

[20] Sproull, R. C., and Gettler, A. O., Ind. Eng. Chem. Anal. Ed., **13,** 462, 1941. The iodide photometric method was used in this investigation.
[21] Lang, E. P., Anal. Chem., **21,** 188, 1949.
[22] Hubbard, D. M., Ind. Eng. Chem. Anal. Ed., **11,** 343, 1939.

**Dithizone Solutions.**—(a) 7 mg. per liter of redistilled chloroform; (b) 100 mg. per liter of redistilled carbon tetrachloride; (c) 60 mg. per liter of redistilled chloroform.

Dithizone, redistilled carbon tetrachloride and chloroform, nitric and acetic acids, ammonia, potassium cyanide, and potassium bromide must all be of the best analytical reagent grade.

Separatory funnels and other glassware must be scrupulously clean and of resistant quality toward reagents.

*Procedures.* **Extraction from Acidic Medium.**—After the dry ashing of the sample, dissolution of the residue, and adjustment of the acetic acid medium to pH 2.5, extract in a separatory funnel with 10-ml. portions of dithizone in carbon tetrachloride [solution (b)], until the last portion is pure green in color. Shake the combined extracts vigorously in a separatory funnel with 50 ml. of 0.2% nitric acid. The carbon tetrachloride is washed with 50 ml. of 0.2% nitric acid plus 5 ml. of 40% KBr solution. The carbon tetrachloride is discarded and the aqueous solution is washed with 5 ml. of carbon tetrachloride.

The aqueous solution is adjusted to pH 9.5 with $NH_3$-cyanide solution. (5 ml. of a solution containing 40 ml. concentrated $NH_3$ and 25 g. KCN per liter.) Exactly 10.00 ml. of the chloroform solution [solution (a), 7 mg./liter] is added and the extract is filtered through cotton into a photometric cell, discarding the first ml. or so of the solution. The absorbance is read versus a blank at 490 m$\mu$.

**Extraction from Alkaline Solution.**[23]—The prepared acidic solution of bismuth is made alkaline, followed by the addition of 8–10 ml. of ammoniacal cyanide solution (40 ml. of concentrated ammonia and 25 g. of KCN per liter). Extraction is made with 10 ml. portions of dithizone in chloroform [solution (c) 60 mg./liter]. Three or four 10 ml. portions are usually needed. To separate the lead from the bismuth dithizonate in the chloroform extracts, the combined chloroform extracts are shaken with 50 ml. of a phthalate buffer of pH 3.4. (Buffer: 9.1 ml. of concentrated $HNO_3$ is neutralized with ammonia in about 500 ml. of solution to pH 3.4, then 50 ml. of pH 3.4 phthalate, made by mixing 50 ml. of 0.2 $M$ potassium acid phthalate and 9.95 ml. of 0.2 $M$ HCl, is added and the solution is diluted to a liter.) [24] Upon shaking the lead is extracted to the buffer.

The bismuth is then extracted to a nitric acid layer as in the above extraction from an acidic medium. Then, after addition of ammonia and cyanide to the nitric acid solution, the bismuth dithizonate is extracted to chloroform and the absorbance is read at 505 m$\mu$, according to Hubbard's recommendation.

## THE E.D.T.A. METHOD

The absorbance of the Bi-E.D.T.A. complex at 263 m$\mu$ at pH 1 is not altered by the presence of alkalis, alkaline earth metals, zinc, aluminum, nickel, or cobalt. In perchlorate medium 15 p. p. m. of lead only absorb as strongly as 0.1 p. p. m. of bismuth. The chief interferences are from ferric and cupric ions and from antimony(III), stannous and lead ions. Chromium(III) and manganous ions interfere only at concentrations higher than 20 p. p. m. Lead and bismuth may be determined in the same solution, a perchlorate medium buffered at pH 4.6. The lead absorption maximum is at 241.5 m$\mu$. The conditions must be controlled rigorously.[25]

[23] Hubbard, D. M., Anal. Chem., **20**, 363, 1948.
[24] Bambach, K., and Burkey, R. E., Ind. Eng. Chem. Anal. Ed., **14**, 904, 1942.
[25] West, P. W., and Coll, H., Anal. Chem., **27**, 1221, 1955.

## ABSORBANCE IN 6 *M* HYDROCHLORIC ACID

The absorbancy maxima of bismuth (327 mμ), thallium(I) (245 mμ) and lead (271 mμ) are more widely separated in chloride medium than in hydrobromic or hydriodic acids. Mercury overlaps the thallium peak and interferes in the region of the lead peak.[26] In the absence of mercury, the other three metals can be estimated with the aid of calibration data and readings at the three peaks. Ferric, cupric, antimonous, and vanadate ions interfere seriously, as do also iodide, nitrate and, to a lesser extent, bromide ions.

# DETERMINATIONS IN SPECIFIC SUBSTANCES

## BISMUTH DETERMINATION IN LEAD BULLION [27]

Ten to twenty-five grams of the lead, hammered or rolled out and cut into small pieces, are taken for analysis. The sample is dissolved in a mixture of 200 ml. water and 50 ml. nitric acid (sp. gr. 1.4) in a large covered beaker, and warmed gently on water or steam bath. When lead has dissolved, the beaker is removed and placed on cool surface and enough sulfuric acid (1:1) added to precipitate lead.

The lead sulfate is allowed to settle and the clear supernatant liquid is decanted into another beaker and held. To the residue of lead sulfate 10–20 ml. concentrated sulfuric acid is added and brought down to strong fumes on hot plate. After strong fuming, the portion containing lead sulfate is diluted with water. To the first clear decanted portion, 10 ml. sulfuric acid is added and this also evaporated down to fumes of sulfuric acid. Both portions are removed from hot plate and when cool add 50 ml. water and 3 to 5 g. of tartaric acid to each. Heat to dissolve tartaric acid and filter over asbestos pad, the clear portion first, and then follow with the one containing bulk of lead sulfate. The bulk of lead sulfate is washed by decantation three or four times with warm water before transferring to asbestos pad. When bismuth is higher than 0.30% in the bullion, the sulfate residue may be retreated with sulfuric acid, fumed, and washed. The clear solution is allowed to stand for one hour and refiltered to ensure removal of all lead sulfate. The filtrate is then warmed, treated with hydrogen sulfide gas, filtered on a paper, and washed with cold $H_2S$ water. The sulfides are washed from filter back to precipitating beaker. The sulfides of Sb, Sn, Te, etc., are leached out with a 10% $K_2S$ solution, which has been saturated with hydrogen sulfide, and allowed to stand in warm place and filtered over the original sulfide paper. After washing with warm water containing a few drops of $K_2S$ solution, the precipitate is dissolved in nitric acid and a few drops of bromine to ensure solution of all sulfur. It is all important to remove Sb, Sn, and Te from sulfide precipitate before going any further by repeating hydrogen sulfide precipitation.

The nitric acid solution of Bi, Cu, etc. is made faintly alkaline with ammonia, 1 g. ammonium carbonate is added, and the solution boiled for five to ten minutes so that the bismuth is precipitated as the basic salt. To ensure solution of the copper, a few drops of free ammonia are added with stirring before filtering. The bismuth precipitate is filtered on a tared Gooch crucible, washed with water, dried and ignited to $Bi_2O_3$ over a Bunsen flame.

$$Bi_2O_3 \times .8970 = Bi$$

[26] Merritt, C., Jr., Hershenson, H. M., and Rogers, L. B., Anal. Chem., **25,** 572. 1953.
[27] This portion of the chapter was contributed by J. J. Mulligan, Superintendent, U. S. Lead Refinery, Inc.

If the bismuth precipitate is dark after precipitation with ammonia and ammonium carbonate, the color may be due to tellurium. If so, the filtered precipitate is dried, ignited and fused with caustic potash and sulfur to put the tellurium in a soluble form and thus remove the tellurium from insoluble bismuth sulfide. Another procedure is redissolving in acid, reprecipitating as sulfides and washing the sulfides with $K_2S$ solution as mentioned above.

This method is applicable to refined lead when larger portions are taken.

## BISMUTH IN ALLOYS

The alloy is dissolved in nitric acid, with as little hydrochloric acid as possible, and 10 ml. sulfuric acid, and run down to strong $SO_3$ fumes. Then proceed as for ores.

Where bismuth is present with considerable tin, the cementation of the bismuth with pure iron wire to free it from tin and the treatment of the residue as for ores and mattes, is the best means for obtaining a bismuth preparation free of tin for control analyses.

In the presence of considerable copper, the bismuth can be precipitated as basic carbonate, filtered, the impure basic precipitate treated with nitric and sulfuric acids, and evaporated to fumes of $SO_3$, the procedure then being the same as for ores and mattes.

## DETERMINATION OF BISMUTH IN ORES AND MATTES

A qualitative test for lead and insoluble bismuth compounds on all products to be analyzed for bismuth is an important step, with the removal of lead as sulfate as soon as perfect solution of the sample is insured.

For products containing 0.5% to 25% bismuth, one gram portions are taken; for 50% or higher, 0.5 g. portions are weighed.

The weighed portion is transferred to a 250-ml. beaker and 25 ml. $H_2O$ and 10 ml. concentrated nitric acid added, and where sulfur is present a few drops of bromine are added cautiously after acid has been allowed to act for a sufficient time. After all sulfur is dissolved, the solution is boiled to dryness on water bath or hot plate, 2 ml. of nitric acid and 1 ml. hydrochloric acid are added, then 10 ml. of sulfuric acid cautiously added, and the covered sample taken down on hot plate to strong fumes of $SO_3$. The cooled solution is diluted with 50 ml. water and 2 to 3 g. tartaric acid are added and the mixture brought to a boil. The residue containing insoluble lead sulfate, silica, and other insolubles is filtered and washed with 2% solution of sulfuric acid to free residue of soluble bismuth.

The filtrate contains Bi, Cu, Sb, As, Te, and possibly a small amount of Pb. After standing for one-half hour or more, the solution is refiltered to remove any lead sulfate that may have gone through on first filtration.

The clear solution containing bismuth is saturated with hydrogen sulfide gas for one-half hour.

The sulfides are filtered on filter paper and washed with $H_2S$ water. If much iron is present the sulfides are redissolved in nitric and sulfuric acids, taken to fumes, and the sulfide precipitation repeated.

The sulfides are leached with a 10% solution of $K_2S$ saturated with $H_2S$ gas to remove As, Sb, Sn, Te and Se. The remaining sulfides containing Cu, Cd, Bi are dissolved in nitric acid and a little bromine water, bromine boiled off and solution made slightly alkaline with ammonia water and 1 g. of ammonium carbonate added. The solution is boiled for five to ten minutes and 1 ml. of ammonia is added and the basic carbonate filtered on a tared Gooch crucible, ignited and weighed as $Bi_2O_3$.

$$Bi_2O_3 \times .8970 = Bi$$

## METHODS FOR BISMUTH IN ANALYSES
## IN OTHER CHAPTERS

Bismuth in Aluminum Alloys      See Analysis in Aluminum Alloys
Bismuth in Refined Copper      See Analysis in Refined Copper

*Chapter 8*

# BORON

B, *at. wt.* 10.811 ($\pm$0.003); $\begin{cases} \textit{amorp. sp. gr. 2.37; m.p. 2150°C.;* b.p. sublimes.} \\ \textit{cryst. sp. gr. 2.34; m.p. 2500°C.; b.p. 3500°C.; oxide,} \\ \textbf{B}_2\textbf{O}_3 \end{cases}$

Boron occurs combined in nature as boric acid, and the combination of this acid with certain bases. It is frequently associated with calcium and aluminum in siliceous rocks in such minerals as datolite, a calcium borosilicate; axinite, a calcium aluminum borosilicate; tourmaline, a complex borosilicate. The commercial sources of boron are borax, $Na_2B_4O_7 \cdot 10H_2O$ (36.6% $B_2O_3$); tincalconite (tincal) ($Na_2O \cdot 2B_2O_3 \cdot 5H_2O$) found in great quantities in the Mojave desert in southern California; kernite, $Na_2B_4O_7 \cdot 4H_2O$; ulexite, $NaCaB_5O_9 \cdot 8H_2O$ (43% $B_2O_3$); colemanite, $Ca_2B_6O_{11} \cdot 5H_2O$ (50.9% $B_2O_3$); boracite, $Mg_7Cl_2B_{16}O_{30}$ (62.5% $B_2O_3$) and kramerite ($Na_2O \cdot 2CaO \cdot 5B_2O_3 \cdot 10H_2O$) (49.5% $B_2O_3$). The demand for boron in the past twenty years has increased greatly because of its use in special alloys, refractory compounds, and in high-energy fuels.

Boron was isolated by Gay-Lussac and L. Thenard (1808) by reduction of the trioxide with potassium. Sir Humphry Davy obtained it about the same time by reduction of boric acid.

Borax is an important constituent of enamels. It is employed in the glass that is used for making heat resisting glassware. It is used to protect the citrus fruit from "blue mold." Compounds of boron have a marked effect on plant growth.

Boron has a high cross section for neutron-capture. It is objectionable, therefore, in chain-reacting atomic energy piles, but its alloys are useful for control rods.

## DETECTION

*Flame Test.*—Boric acid is displaced from its salts by nearly all acids, including even carbonic acid. Upon ignition, however, it in turn drives out other acids which are volatile at lower temperatures. A powdered borate, mixed with potassium sulfate and calcium fluoride, placed on the loop of a platinum wire, is held in the colorless flame of a Bunsen burner, a green color will be imparted to the flame by boron. Copper salts should first be removed with $H_2S$ and barium as $BaSO_4$ if present, as these also color the flame green.

The flame test may be conveniently made by treating the powdered sample in a test tube with sulfuric acid and methanol. A cork carrying a glass tube is inserted and the test tube gently warmed. The escaping gas will burn with a green flame.

The test may be made by igniting the mixture of powder, alcohol, and sulfuric

* From the Merck Index, 7th Ed., 1960.

acid in an open porcelain dish. The green color will be seen in presence of a borate. The test is not as delicate as the one with the test tube.

**Borax Bead.**—$Na_2B_4O_7 \cdot 10H_2O$ fused in a platinum loop, swells to several times its original volume as the water of crystallization is being driven out, then contracts to a clear molten bead. If the bead is dipped into a weak solution of cobalt and plunged into the flame, until it again becomes molten, the bead upon cooling will be colored blue.

**Turmeric Test.**—A few drops of acetic acid are added together with 2 or 3 drops of an alcoholic turmeric solution to an alcoholic extract of the sample, placed in a porcelain dish. The solution is diluted with water and then evaporated to dryness on the water bath. 0.001 milligram of boric acid will produce a distinct color, 0.02 milligram will give a strong reddish-brown colored residue, which becomes bluish-black when treated with a drop of sodium hydroxide solution.[1]

## ESTIMATION

The determination of boron (generally reported as $B_2O_3$) may be required in a variety of substances, boron bearing ores, borax, alkaline brines, soils, commercial boric acid and borate concentrates, atomic energy materials, high-energy fuels, ceramic materials, paint pigments, food preservatives etc.

During an analysis boron may be left in part with the silica residue, causing high results for silica, as it volatilizes with silicon tetrafluoride during the treatment of $SiO_2$ with HF and $H_2SO_4$. A portion may be carried down with the ammonium hydroxide precipitate, giving high results for aluminum.

In the decomposition of the substance for the determination of boron care must be exercised to avoid the loss of boron, as boric acid is easily liberated from its combinations by acids and volatilizes with steam. Digestions carried out in covered beakers practically eliminate the loss, provided the heating is done cautiously, avoiding vigorous boiling. Loss occurs if the digestion is conducted in uncovered beakers.

The reagents used in the determination should be free from boron, as should the glass vessels in which the reactions are conducted.

## PREPARATION AND SOLUTION OF THE SAMPLE

Crystalline boron is scarcely attacked by acids or alkaline solutions; the amorphous form, however, is soluble in concentrated nitric and sulfuric acids. Both forms fused with potassium hydroxide are converted to potassium metaborate. Boric acid is more readily soluble in pure water than in hydrochloric, nitric, sulfuric, or acetic acids, but is more soluble in tartaric acid. Borax is insoluble in alcohol. The addition of an acid to borax liberates boric acid, forming at the same time the salt of the added acid.

**Boronatrocalcite, Ulexite, Colemanite, Water-Insoluble Borates.**—A 5- to 10-g. sample of the material is digested in a flask with reflux condenser with sufficient hydrochloric acid to combine with the bases with which boric acid is united. Following the digestion (0.5 hour is generally sufficient) the sample is filtered, and the filtrate and washings of the residue and apparatus transferred to a volumetric flask and diluted to definite volume. If preferred the material may be transferred to a volumetric flask, made to volume and allowed to settle, and aliquot portions

---

[1] Turmeric test—Bertrand, G., and Agulhon, H., Compt. rend., **157**, 1433, 1913.

filtered for analysis, using dry filters. Allowance is made for the residue in the flask.

**Borax, Borax Concentrates, Tincal, Rasorite, Water-Soluble Borates.**—Details for evaluation will be found in a later section of this chapter.

**Boric Acid in Mineral Water.**—For water containing more than 0.1 g. boric acid per liter, about 200 ml. are evaporated to small volume, the precipitated salts are filtered off and washed. Boric acid passes into the filtrate and may be determined by the distillation method of Gooch given on page 214.

With water containing traces of boric acid, 5 liters or more are evaporated to about one-tenth the original volume, the precipitate filtered off, and washed with hot water. The filtrate is evaporated down to a moist residue. If the residue is small, it is acidified with acetic acid and the boric acid determined by distillation, as stated on page 214. If considerable residue is present, hydrochloric acid is added to acid reaction, and then the mixture digested with absolute alcohol in a corked flask for ten to fifteen hours, with occasional shaking. The solution is filtered, the residue washed with 95% alcohol, the filtrate diluted with water, 10 ml. of 10% sodium hydroxide solution added and the alcohol distilled off. A second alcoholic extraction is generally recommended. The final alkaline solution is taken to dryness and gently ignited. The residue is extracted with water, made acid with acetic acid, and $B_2O_3$ determined by distillation.

**Carbonates.**—The material is treated with sufficient acid (methyl orange indicator) to liberate all the $CO_2$ and react with the combined alkali of boric and carbonic acids; it is boiled in a flask with reflux condenser to expel $CO_2$, ten to fifteen minutes, the solution exactly neutralized with sodium hydroxide (methyl orange), and the liberated boric acid titrated in presence of glycerol and phenolphthalein as usual.

If cautiously conducted the expulsion of $CO_2$ may be effected in a covered beaker without loss of boric acid.

**Boric Oxide in Silicates, Enamel, etc.**—About 0.5 g. of the finely ground material is fused with five times its weight of sodium carbonate, the melt extracted with water and the extracts, containing the sodium salt of boric acid, evaporated to small volume. The greater part of the excess sodium carbonate is neutralized with hydrochloric acid and finally made acid with acetic acid (litmus paper test = red). Boric oxide is now determined by the distillation process according to the procedure given later in the chapter.

**Acid Insoluble Boron Minerals.**—Minerals in which boron is not completely liberated by acid treatment must be fused with sodium carbonate in a platinum crucible, the flux being weighed. The fusion is dissolved by adding the necessary amount of standard acid to neutralize the base and then a slight excess. During the neutralization heating is avoided. Should the volumetric titration method be followed in the subsequent analysis it is necessary to expel the carbon dioxide in solution, but considerable care should be exercised to avoid loss of boric acid, which is volatile with steam. A reflux condenser will prevent loss, if boiling the solution is necessary to effect expulsion of $CO_2$, or the expulsion may be accomplished in a covered beaker, heating at "simmering" temperature for 10–15 minutes.

## SEPARATIONS

Boron may be separated from other interfering elements by distillation in presence of acid and methyl alcohol according to the procedure given under the methods that follow. (See "Distillation Method as Modified by Chapin.") Methods for the separation of boron from aluminum alloys are given in the Chapter on Aluminum.

Uranium oxides and many other substances that are of interest in atomic energy materials are dissolved by phosphoric acid in a silica distillation apparatus. The boron is distilled as methyl borate. A receiver containing lime water is used during the dissolution and the distillation as described later in this chapter.

*Separation by Distillation as the Trimethyl Ester of Boric Acid.*—The form of apparatus shown in Fig. 8-1 has been widely used in connection with the separa-

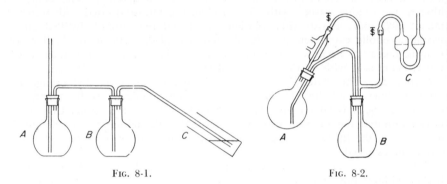

FIG. 8-1.                    FIG. 8-2.

tion of boron from many types of materials. Dissolution of the sample is performed in the silica flask, B, by phosphoric acid, with the stopper, condenser, and receiver, C, in place. The silica flask, A, is used to distil the methanol after adding a pellet or two of sodium hydroxide. The methanol passes through the solution of the sample and into the silica receiver, C, containing 5 ml. of lime water.

Similar functions are performed by the apparatus shown in Fig. 8-2. In this apparatus only flasks A and B are of silica. The connecting tubes are of Corning 7280 low-boron glass.

**Reagents.**—*Sodium hydroxide,* U.S.P. pellets.

*Methanol,* C.P. grade.

*Phosphoric Acid, 85%.*—Analytical reagent grade.

*Calcium Hydroxide.*—Calcium carbonate, boron-free or of known low-boron content, is heated in platinum to form lime. A 0.1 N solution is prepared by dissolving 0.56 g. in 100 ml. of water. A 5-ml. portion of this solution is used in the receiver, C. The stock solution is kept in a boron-free vessel (silica, plastic, or metal).

**Procedure.**—Illustrated for materials that are soluble in 85% phosphoric acid, in the apparatus shown in Fig. 8-1.

A 1.000-g. sample of the substance to be analyzed is placed in the clean, dry silica flask, B, and the receiver C is provided with 5 ml. of the lime solution.

Ten ml. of 85% phosphoric acid is added to flask $B$. Flask $A$ is provided with 50 ml. of methanol and one or two pellets of sodium hydroxide.

The contents of flask $B$ are heated with a small flame until dissolved. Flask $B$ is then surrounded with water at 55°C., and the methanol flask, $A$, is surrounded with a beaker of hot water. As the volume of methanol condensed in flask, $A$, nears 25 ml., heat is applied to the beaker surrounding this vessel and the methanol is distilled into receiver $C$ for 30 minutes. Then 50 ml. of methanol is added to flask $A$ through its safety tube and the distillation is continued. Boil the water surrounding flask $B$ for 10 minutes after the distillation is complete. The flames are extinguished and the distillate and washings are transferred to a 75-mm. Coors porcelain evaporating dish, and the solution is evaporated to dryness on the water bath. See "Turmeric Method" for the development of the color.

*Separation by Ion Exchange.*—Ions of various metals interfere with most of the methods for the photometric estimation of boron. An ion-exchange separation is an alternative to the tedious distillation method. Martin and Hayes[2] found that Dowex-50 and Amberlite IR-100 A.G. were suitable for the separation of metals prior to the titrimetric estimation of boron. The procedure separated boric acid from 60 times its weight of iron or ten times its weight of Al, Be, Zn, Cd, Co, Cu, Hg, Ni, Th, Sn(IV), Ti, U, and Zr. Arsenate, molybdate, phosphate, and silicate are not separated from borate in the procedure and large relative amounts interfere during titration. A fresh 1.9 x 30 cm column is used in the acid form. It is regenerated by 10% HCl. In micro work, boron-free tubes are used.

Calkins and Stenger[3] found that titanium could be separated as the peroxy complex on a Dowex 50, X-8 column of 20- to 30-mesh material. Vanadium does not interfere if the alloy contains less than 0.3% V.

**Procedure.**—A 1.000-g. sample is dissolved in 10 ml. of 1:4 sulfuric acid under a reflux with dry ice in the funnel after displacing the air by small pieces of dry ice. Dissolution requires several hours. Finally 5 ml. of 30% $H_2O_2$ and 5 ml. of water are added through the condenser. The solution is washed out with small portions of $H_2O_2$ and water alternately and the volume is made up to 50.00 ml. A 10.00-ml. aliquot plus 2 ml. of $H_2O_2$ and 18 ml. of water are passed slowly through the column in a 1 cm x 50 cm tube. This column is washed before and after use with a solution containing 2 ml. of 30% $H_2O_2$ and 1 ml. of 1:4 sulfuric acid per 100 ml. The eluate and washings are made to 100 ml. in a flask containing a few drops of $H_2O_2$ to detect any titanium that might come through the column. Aliquots of the solution are evaporated in platinum or nickel crucibles after adding 2 or 3 drops of 5 $N$ NaOH, after first decomposing the $H_2O_2$ with the crucible covered at 100°C. The cover is rinsed into the crucible and after evaporation and heating at 120°C., the crucible is rinsed with 2 ml. of concentrated sulfuric acid, and further rinsings with sulfuric acid are collected in a cylinder until the volume is 12 ml. The determination is then made by the Carminic Acid Method.

## GRAVIMETRIC METHODS

The solubility of boron compounds prevents complete precipitation by any of the known reagents, hence most of the gravimetric methods are indirect.

[2] Martin, J. R., and Hayes, J. R., Anal. Chem., **24**, 182, 1952.
[3] Calkins, R. C., and Stenger, V. A., Anal. Chem., **28**, 399, 1956.

## DISTILLATION AS TRIMETHYL BORATE AND FIXATION BY LIME [4]

This excellent method, originally worked out by F. A. Gooch, and later modified by Gooch and Jones, depends upon the fact that the borates of alkaline earths and alkalies give up their boron in the form of the volatile trimethyl borate (*b.p.*, 65°C.), when they are distilled with absolute methyl alcohol (acetone-free). The trimethyl borate passed over lime in presence of water is completely saponified, the liberated boric acid combining with the lime to form calcium metaborate, which may be dried, ignited, and weighed. The increase of the weight of the lime represents the $B_2O_3$ in the sample.

$$2B(OCH_3)_3 + CaO + 3H_2O \rightarrow 6CH_3OH + Ca(BO_2)_2$$

*Procedure.*—About 1 g. of pure calcium oxide is ignited to constant weight over a blast lamp and then transferred to the dry, Erlenmeyer receiving flask (Fig. 8-3).

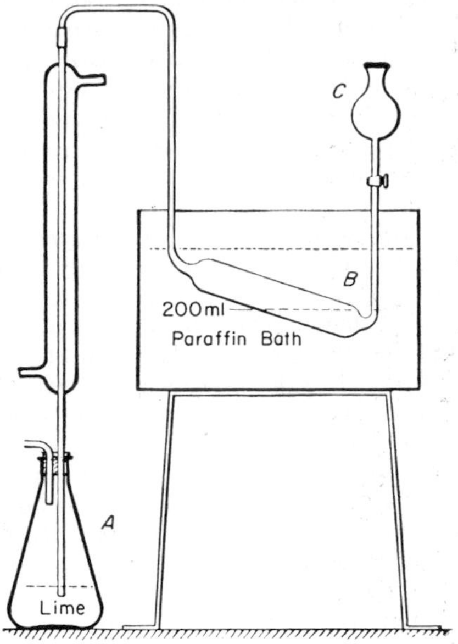

FIG. 8-3.    Distillation of Methyl Borate.

The crucible in which the lime was heated and weighed is set aside in a desiccator for later use.

0.2 g. or less of the alkali borates, obtained in solution by a procedure given under "Preparation and Solution of the Sample," is treated with a few drops of litmus (or lacmoid) solution and the free alkali neutralized with dilute HCl solution added drop by drop. A drop of dilute sodium hydroxide solution is added and then a few drops of acetic acid. The slightly acid solution is transferred to the pipette-shaped retort *B*, Fig. 8-3, by means of the attached funnel, *C*, washing out the beaker and funnel with three 2- to 3-ml. portions of water. The stopcock of the funnel is closed, the apparatus is connected up as shown in the illustration, the paraffin bath, heated to not over 140°C., placed in position [5] and the liquid in the retort distilled into the receiver containing the known amount of lime. When all the liquid has distilled over, the paraffin bath is lowered, the retort allowed to cool for a few minutes, 10 ml. of methanol (acetone-free) added to the residue in *B*, and the contents again distilled by replacing the paraffin bath. The process is repeated three times with methanol. The contents of the retort (which are now alkaline), are made distinctly acid by addition of acetic acid, and three more distillations made with 100-ml. portions of methanol, as before. The paraffin bath is now removed, the receiving flask is stoppered, the contents thoroughly mixed by shaking, and set aside for an hour or more for complete saponification of the methyl borate. The contents are now poured into a large platinum dish

[4] Proc. Am. Acad. of Arts and Sciences, **22,** 167–176, 1886.  Anal. Chem., Treadwell-Hall, Vol. 2.

[5] Submerge the retort in the paraffin bath gradually to prevent too violent a reaction.

and evaporated on the water bath at a temperature below the boiling point of the alcohol. (Loss of boric acid will occur if the alcohol boils.) The adhering lime in the receiving flask is dissolved by wetting its entire surface with a few drops of dilute nitric acid (the flask being inclined and revolved to flow the acid over its sides). The contents are transferred to the dish with a little water and the evaporation repeated. No loss of boric acid will take place at this stage, the alcohol having been removed during the first evaporation. The residue is gently heated to destroy any calcium acetate that may have formed, the cooled borate and lime are taken up with a little water, and transferred to the crucible in which the lime was heated and weighed. The material clinging to the dish is dissolved with a little nitric acid (or acetic acid), and washed into the crucible. The contents of the crucible are evaporated to dryness on the water bath, then heated very gently over a flame (the crucible being covered) and finally more strongly. The heating is continued until a constant weight is obtained. The increase of weight of the lime represents the amount of $B_2O_3$ in the sample.

Notes.—Gooch and Jones worked out a procedure which utilizes sodium tungstate as a retainer of the trimethyl borate, in place of the lime. This substance is definite in weight, not hygroscopic, soluble in water, and recoverable in its original weight after evaporation and ignition. Methods in Chem. Anal., p. 204, 1st Ed. By F. A. Gooch, John Wiley & Sons, Publishers.
The receiving flask has a cork stopper with a hole to accommodate the tube of the condenser and a slit to permit the escape of air from the flask.
Gooch recommends cooling of the receiving flask.

## TITRIMETRIC METHODS

*Introductory.*—The boron bearing material is brought into solution by an appropriate method and the solution freed from carbon dioxide, aluminum, iron, and any substance other than boric acid which reacts with sodium hydroxide. If the solution is alkaline it is made slightly acid and heated to expel carbon dioxide (covered beaker). Boric acid is liberated by the acid treatment. The free mineral acid is very carefully neutralized in presence of a suitable indicator, which is unaffected by free boric acid, such as methyl orange, methyl red, or Sofnol Red No. 1. With the indicators mentioned the end point is the first definite yellow color. A polyhydric alcohol is added (mannitol or glycerol are generally used, glucose has been found to be satisfactory) and the titration of boric acid by means of standard alkali, is conducted in presence of a suitable indicator, such as phenolphthalein. In the presence of glycerol the following reaction has been suggested:

$$C_3H_5OH \cdot HBO_3 + NaOH \rightarrow C_3H_5OH \cdot NaBO_3 + H_2O$$

1 ml. of 1 $N$ NaOH is equivalent to 0.03481 g. $B_2O_3$

*Removal of Carbon Dioxide.*—This is accomplished by slightly acidifying the solution and heating gently for ten to fifteen minutes in a covered beaker. Vigorous boiling must be avoided as loss will occur with the resulting steam. Loss also occurs if the beaker is uncovered during the expulsion of the $CO_2$. If carbon dioxide is not completely expelled the results will be too high for boric acid.
*Removal of Iron and Aluminum.*—The precipitation of the hydroxides of these elements by addition of an alkali hydroxide to the ferric or aluminum salts would lead to high results for boric acid, hence iron and aluminum should be removed from the solution titrated. Various methods have been suggested for the removal

of iron and aluminum, by precipitation with magnesium oxide or by addition of barium or sodium carbonates, or sodium hydroxide in presence of boric acid with a suitable indicator which would avoid an excess of the alkali (aluminate will form with an excess).  Since the hydroxides occlude boric acid, provision is made for determining the occluded acid.  Ammonium hydroxide should not be used for precipitation of iron and aluminum as it leads to high results for boric acid, the ammonium chloride formed reacting with the alkali hydroxide.  Details of analysis for the commercial evaluation of borates follow.

Iron, aluminum, and many other metals may be separated from borates by precipitation by 8-hydroxyquinoline ("oxine") at pH 4–5.

## COLORIMETRIC AND RELATED METHODS

The emission spectrographic method is widely used in the routine estimation of boron in steels, uranium and its compounds, and related atomic energy materials such as graphite, refractories, etc.  The direct estimation of traces of boron in transistor materials is possible if excitation is made in an argon atmosphere.

Various absorption photometric methods are used either directly or after separation of boron as the volatile trimethyl ester of boric acid, or after separation from metals by ion-exchange procedures.  (See "Separations.")

Special precautions to avoid loss of boron or its introduction from reagents or apparatus are critical in the determination of amounts of boron ranging from less than a microgram up to 10 to 20 micrograms.  Acid dissolution steps are carried out in silica vessels provided with silica condenser tubes.  Alkaline fusions are made in platinum or in other metallic vessels.

### TURMERIC METHOD

This procedure is based on a refinement by Rodden and Scherrer [6] of a procedure devised by Robinson.[7]

*Reagents.*  **Hydrochloric Acid-Oxalic Acid Mixture.**—This contains 16 g. of crystallized oxalic acid and 20 ml. of concentrated hydrochloric acid per 100 ml.  It is made immediately before use by mixing four volumes of hot 20% oxalic acid and one volume of concentrated hydrochloric acid.

**Turmeric Extract.**—Prepared by stirring 1 g. of turmeric for 2 hours with 100 ml. of 95% alcohol.  After filtering the solution is ready for use.

*Procedure.*—The evaporated residue from the distillation method, or the sample treated with 5 ml. of lime water and evaporated, is treated in the 75 mm. porcelain dish with 1 ml. of the hydrochloric-oxalic acid solution and 2 ml. of turmeric extract.  The dish is rotated so that the reagents come into contact with all parts of the surface.  Evaporate to dryness at 55°C.  Continue the heating for 30 minutes at this temperature.  Cool and extract the residue with 95% alcohol and centrifuge.  The clear liquid is made up to 25 ml. with alcohol.  The solution is compared with a blank run through the whole distillation and color development at 540 m$\mu$ in a 1-cm. cell.

The procedure requires adequate reagents and strict attention to detail.  The calibration is made by the same procedure.  Normally the absorbance measurement is applied to solutions that contain 0–2 micrograms of boron over blank in the

[6] Rodden, C. J., and Scherrer, J. A., Report A-123, National Bureau of Standards.

[7] Robinson, K. L., Analyst, **64,** 324, 1939; a critical study of the variables of the procedure was made by Mundy, R. J., and Furman, N. H., MDDC-1624, revised May, 1947.

final 25 ml. alcoholic solution. With quantities of boron from 2 to 16 micrograms a curved calibration line is found for absorbance versus micrograms of B per 25 ml.

## THE CARMINIC ACID METHOD

Many investigators have used the change caused by boron of carminic acid from a red to a bluish tint in concentrated sulfuric acid for the estimation of boron.[8] The method is suitable for waters, soil extracts, and plant materials, and is not interfered with by the amounts calcium, magnesium, sodium, and potassium or soluble silicates, phosphates, etc. that are likely to be present.

*Reagents.* **Sodium Hydroxide.**—Dilute solution boron-free.

**Carmine Solution.**—0.05% Carmine No. 40 N.F. shaken until dissolved in sulfuric acid of sp. gr. 1.84.

**Boric Acid.**—0.5716 g. per liter of water. One ml. contains 0.1 mg. of B diluted to give appropriate amounts of boron from 1 to 10 micrograms.

*Procedure.* **Solution Samples.**—Add 2 ml. of the sample and one or two drops of concentrated HCl. Add 10 ml. of concentrated $H_2SO_4$, cool and add 10 ml. of carmine reagent, mix, and allow to stand 45 minutes. Read the absorbance at 585 mμ vs. 2 ml. of water carried through the rest of the procedure.

**Plant Material.**—The material is dried and an appropriate weight of material is treated with 0.1 g. of pure calcium oxide by mechanical mixing. The carbonaceous material is destroyed by heating in a muffle at 500°–550°C. The residue is heated 30 minutes with 6 N hydrochloric acid, 15 ml. per 5 g. sample, at steam bath temperature. Filter, wash, and make up to a convenient volume in a calibrated flask. Use 2 ml. aliquots for color development but add two drops of water instead of acid.

## DETERMINATIONS IN SPECIFIC SUBSTANCES

### THE DETERMINATION OF BORON IN ALUMINUM AND SILICON-ALUMINIUM ALLOYS BY DIANTHRIMIDE METHOD [9]

Aluminum alloys containing 0.5–1.0% of boron are finding increasing use in the semiconductor industry. In this procedure the use of glassware has been largely avoided, the exception being the use of calibrated flasks for a short time with acid solutions; pick-up of boron under these conditions is extremely slight.

*Reagents.* **Sulfuric Acid, sp. gr. 1.84.**

**Sulfuric Acid, Diluted (4 + 1).**

**Sulfuric Acid, 2 N.**

**Sodium Carbonate Solution, 10%.**—Store in a polyethylene bottle.

**Sodium Peroxide.**

*Cation-Exchange Resin.*—Zeo-Karb 225 (less than 60 to greater than 100 mesh) in the hydrogen form (or Rohm and Haas equivalent).

**Dianthrimide Reagent Solution.**—Dissolve 0.4 g. of 1,1'-dianthrimide in 100 ml. of concentrated sulfuric acid. Store this solution in a lightly stoppered bottle in a desiccator. For use, transfer 5 ml. of the solution to a dry 100 ml. calibrated flask and dilute to the mark with concentrated sulfuric acid.

---

[8] Hatcher, J. T., and Wilcox, L. V., Anal. Chem., **22**, 567 (1950) have reviewed former methods and devised the procedure here given.
[9] Towndrow and Webb, The Analyst, **85**, 850, 1960.

**Standard Boron Solution.**—Dissolve 0.228 g. of boric acid in 1 liter of water, and dilute 10 ml. of this solution to 100 ml. with water.

$$1 \text{ ml.} = 4 \text{ micrograms of boron}$$

*Procedure.*—From the sample in the form of filings or fine sawings, weigh 0.1 g. into a nickel crucible, and mix with 2 g. of sodium peroxide. Allow the mixture to sinter for 30 minutes on an asbestos mat over a Bunsen burner, and then fuse over the free flame. After solidification, leach the melt with water in a polyethylene beaker, cool, transfer to a 250 ml. acrylic-resin measuring cylinder, make up to 250 ml., and return to the beaker. Allow the precipitated hydrated nickel oxide to settle, and then transfer a 10-ml. aliquot of the solution, by means of a pipette, to a small polyethylene beaker or platinum vessel. Treat the solution with 2 N sulfuric acid, dropwise, until its pH is approximately 2, as judged by the use of universal indicator, and then transfer to a 7″ x 1″ column of cation-exchange resin contained in a polyethylene tube. Elute with 250 ml. of water, and collect the effluent in a polyethylene beaker. Make the effluent faintly alkaline by adding 15 ml. of 10% sodium carbonate solution, check that the pH is between 8 and 9, and evaporate to dryness in a platinum dish.

Allow the residue to cool, dissolve it in 7.5 ml. of water, and add 7.5 ml. of diluted sulfuric acid (4:1) rapidly to avoid overheating. Transfer the solution to a 20-ml. calibrated flask, and use diluted sulfuric acid (4:1) for rinsing the dish and diluting the contents of the flask to volume. At this stage, the flask should contain the assay solution in diluted sulfuric acid (1:1). Transfer a 5-ml. aliquot to a 50-ml. calibrated flask, add 5 ml. of dianthrimide reagent solution, dilute to the mark with concentrated sulfuric acid, transfer to a silica boiling tube, and cover with a loosely fitting silica cover. Heat the solution at $95° \pm 1°C$. for 16 hours, cool to room temperature, and measure the optical density in a 4-cm. cell at 640 m$\mu$ with a Unicam SP500 spectrophotometer or similar instrument. Determine boron by reference to a standard graph prepared as described below.

**Preparation of Standard Graph.**—Place 0.1-, 1.5-, and 2-ml. portions of standard boron solution in separate polyethylene beakers, dilute each to 2.5 ml., and add 10 ml. of concentrated sulfuric acid. Cool, transfer each solution to a 50-ml. calibrated flask, add 5 ml. of dianthrimide reagent solution to each, and dilute to the mark with concentrated sulfuric acid. Treat these solutions as described above, measure the optical densities at 640 m$\mu$, and plot a graph of optical density against boron content.

## EVALUATION OF CRUDE BORATES

The procedures below are applicable for the determination of water-soluble and total borates in borax, kernite, tincalconite, ulexite, colemanite, boracite etc. Should borosilicates be present, conversion to the soluble sodium salt may be effected by fusion with sodium carbonate. It is very necessary that the analysis be conducted on representative samples. Borate concentrates rapidly pick up moisture so that the samples must be kept sealed from the air to obtain concordant results.

Crude borates generally contain shale, which must be separated from the water-soluble borates. This is accomplished by extraction with sufficient water to dissolve the soluble borates; which, in crude borax, tincalconite, kernite, and other sodium borates, constitute practically all of the available borates. In presence of iron and aluminum, which is left entirely with the residue from the water extraction, some boric acid invariably is occluded in the residue and must be recovered, should total boric acid be desired. Details for the estimation of borate in the residue are given.

*Reagents.* **N or 0.5 N Hydrochloric Acid.**

**N or 0.5 N Sodium Hydroxide (CO$_2$ free).**

**Approximately 0.167 N Hydrochloric Acid.**

**Mannitol or Glycerol (neutral).**

**Indicators.**

**Water (carbonate free).**

*Procedure.* **Preparation and Extraction of the Sample.**—A 5-gram sample is taken from the representative, finely ground material and is placed in a 250-ml.–300-ml. beaker, 200 ml. of pure water are added, the beaker covered and placed on a hot plate and brought to gentle simmering. After 15–20 minutes of heating, with occasional stirring, 2–3 ml. of sodium chloride crystals are added and the residue allowed to settle clear (10–15 minutes of settling is generally sufficient). The clear solution is carefully decanted through a rapid filter into a 500-ml. flask, taking care to avoid transferring any residue to the filter as this would seriously retard filtration. The extraction of the residue is repeated three times more with 75 ml. portions of pure water, settling each time with addition of 1 ml. of solid sodium chloride crystals, and cautiously decanting the solution through the filter into the flask. The extractions are best made by gently heating, and stirring, for a few minutes with each 75-ml. portion. Practically all of the soluble borates are extracted with the first two portions. Finally the residue is transferred to the filter by a 1% solution of NaCl and the filter allowed to drain. If much shale is present with iron and aluminum hydroxides this last step is slow. (If the residue is not to be examined for occluded and insoluble borates, the procedure may be greatly hastened by transferring the extracts and the final residue directly to the flask without filtration. An allowance of 0.5 ml. for the residue is generally more than sufficient for the space occupied by this.) The 500-ml. flask is now filled to the mark with distilled water and thoroughly mixed. Aliquot portions are taken for analysis, usually 100 ml. (1 g.) when 0.5 N reagents are to be used, or 200 ml. (2 g.) when N reagents are used.

**Titration of Boric Acid.**—To the solution in a 250-ml. beaker are added 2–3 drops of Sofnol Red No. 1, methyl red, or methyl orange indicator and just sufficient 6 N HCl to give a red color and about 0.3–0.5 ml. excess. The beaker is covered and the solution gently heated to simmering temperature, avoiding vigorous boiling. Ten minutes is sufficient to expel carbon dioxide. (CO$_2$ if present would cause high results.) The solution is cooled by placing the beaker in a container of cold water. The solution and cover rinsings are carefully neutralized by addition of just sufficient standard alkali to give a yellow color. (A drop of the reagent will give this color at the end point.) The free boric acid is now titrated, after the addition of 25–50 ml. of glycerol (or 4–8 g. of mannitol) and 1 ml. of phenolphthalein indicator. The standard alkali is added until a faint pink color is obtained, and then a drop or more additional, until the color is a definite reddish pink, the true end point.

1 ml. 1 N NaOH is equivalent to 0.03481 g. B$_2$O$_3$

1 ml. 0.5 N NaOH is equivalent to 0.01741 g. B$_2$O$_3$

**Determination of Boric Acid in the Water-Insoluble Residue.**—The residue on the filter from the water extraction is washed into a tall 250-ml. beaker, 10 ml. of 6 $N$ HCl added, the beaker covered and the mixture heated gently on a hot plate, just below boiling, for 15–20 minutes. (No loss of boric acid results under these conditions. With vigorous boiling a loss will occur.) The solution is cooled, filtered, and powdered sodium carbonate added to the filtrate until the free HCl is neutralized (avoiding an appreciable excess), the solution reacting blue to litmus paper. The iron, aluminum, and silica are filtered off. Boric acid is determined in the filtrate and washings of the residue, according to the procedure for titration of boric acid, as described:—acidification with acid, expulsion of $CO_2$, neutralization to Sofnol Red or methyl orange as indicator, and titration of boric acid in presence of glycerol and phenolphthalein.

NOTES.—If much residue is present a second treatment may be necessary. If silicoborates are present the residue should be fused with sodium carbonate and the borate determined in the fusion.

A 5-g. sample is ample, larger amounts are difficult to handle and are unnecessary.

The finely divided clay remains in suspension for hours and would be difficult to filter. The addition of sodium chloride flocculates this suspended matter, causing it to settle rapidly. The added salt does not affect results.

It is important to wash by decantation, otherwise the finely divided clay will clog the filter and greatly lengthen the time of filtration and washing.

Carbonates must be expelled from the solution that is titrated for boric acid, as $CO_2$ leads to high results. In covered beakers no loss of boric acid occurs during this expulsion of $CO_2$. By experiment it was found that at simmering temperature no loss occurred during 45 minutes of heating in a covered beaker, while there was a loss of 8.7 milligrams from a total of 491 milligrams during the same period of time in an uncovered beaker.

Glycerol is apt to contain free fatty acids. Should these be present, prepare the glycerol as follows:—To a liter of glycerol add 100 ml. of distilled water and 10 ml. of phenolphthalein indicator. Now cautiously add standard sodium hydroxide until a faint pink color is obtained.

Where doubt exists regarding the end point in the boric acid titration, add 6 $N$ HCl until the red color of methyl orange or methyl red is obtained. Neutralize with NaOH and repeat the titration of boric acid with NaOH.

The reagents should be carbonate free.

All analysis should be conducted on the sample that is representative. The calcined borate concentrate rapidly picks up moisture so that the sample should be kept in an air tight container.

Iron and aluminum carry out boric acid in direct proportion to the amount of these hydroxides present. Recovery of the occluded or adsorbed boric acid must be accomplished if total boric acid is desired. A double precipitation is seldom necessary of the iron and aluminum from which a recovery is made, since the amount generally present in the reprecipitation is inappreciable, unless the precipitate is large.

Precipitation of iron and aluminum by addition of ammonium hydroxide has been suggested. This is highly undesirable as the presence of ammonium salts lead to a serious error in the titration of boric acid and the end point is uncertain. Ammonium salts are difficult to expel from the solution.

# EVALUATION OF BORON BEARING ORES—
## ACID EXTRACTION METHOD

The method is applicable for the determination of total boric acid in borates of sodium, calcium, and magnesium in materials such as crude borax, tincalconite, kernite, boracite, ulexite, colemanite, etc. Silicoborates require a preliminary fusion with sodium carbonate. The acid residue should be examined for these. Iron and aluminum, ammonium salts, and substances other than boric acid, should be absent from the solution if they react with sodium hydroxide.

*Reagents.* **$N$ or 0.5 $N$ HCl and NaOH (carbonate free).**

**6 N HCl.**—Acid of constant boiling point is satisfactory.

**Sodium Hydroxide.**—Saturated solution, carbonate free.

**Water.**—Carbon dioxide free.

**Sofnol Red No. 1.**

**Water Solution.**—$p$-Nitrophenol saturated.

**Phenolphthalein 1%.**—In a 50% alcohol solution.

**Mannitol or Glycerol.**

*Procedure Acid Extraction.*—A 5-gram sample, finely ground, is placed in a 250-ml. volumetric flask, 15–20 ml. of 6 N HCl are added, together with an equal volume of water and the flask connected to a reflex condenser. The mixture is heated to boiling and boiled for 20–25 minutes. After allowing to cool slightly, 75 ml. of water are poured into the flask through the condenser tube, the solution mixed, and then the heating and boiling repeated for 10–15 minutes. The flask is again allowed to cool slightly and about 50 ml. of water poured through the condenser tube into the flask. The condenser is disconnected, the flask placed in a cold water bath and cooled. Water is now added to the 250-ml. mark, and if necessary an additional amount to allow for the volume occupied by the residue. One gram of the residue occupies a volume slightly less than 0.5 ml. Generally the amount is so small that this additional water is unnecessary. After the residue has settled, the clear solution, in the quantity desired, is decanted through a dry filter into a dry, clean beaker, and portions of this filtrate taken for analysis. Fifty ml. are equivalent to 1 g. of the original sample.

### TITRIMETRIC DETERMINATION OF BORIC ACID

Fifty ml. of the filtrate or 100 ml. are taken, according to the strength of the reagents used. The work is conveniently carried out in 400-ml. beakers.

*Removal of Iron and Aluminum.*—Salts of iron and aluminum react quantitatively with sodium hydroxide when the solutions of the compounds are combined. Iron is completely precipitated as hydroxide when its combined acid is neutralized by the NaOH, and an excess of the alkali has no further action except to make it more flocculent. Aluminum is precipitated at a pH of 6.0 to 7.5, but an excess of the alkali forms the soluble sodium aluminate, causing the aluminum compound to redissolve. Aluminum may be quantitatively precipitated by sodium hydroxide in boric acid solutions, in the absence of polyhydric alcohols, when using $p$-nitrophenol indicator which gives a yellow color at the proper pH for the precipitation of the aluminum. The indicator shows the end point when all of the combined acid of iron and aluminum are neutralized. Advantage is taken of this action in the removal of iron and aluminum from boric acid solutions. This avoids the introduction of an ammonium salt, which would interfere in the boric acid determination if ammonium hydroxide were used to precipitate aluminum and iron. It avoids introduction of a carbonate. When sodium carbonate is employed in this precipitation, the carbonate interferes with the boric acid titration, and must be removed by boiling the solution, slightly acidified, keeping the beaker covered, otherwise loss of boric acid occurs.

**Procedure.**—To the boric acid solution in a beaker are added 3–4 drops of Sofnol Red, or $p$-nitrophenol indicator. Standard sodium hydroxide is added cautiously until the yellow color of the indicator remains. All the iron and the aluminum will be precipitated at this point. The solution is heated gently, then allowed to stand for several minutes. The iron and aluminum hydroxide is filtered off and washed with hot water, and the filtrate and washings titrated for boric acid according to the procedure given under titration of boric acid.

**Recovery of Occluded Boric Acid.**—The iron and aluminum hydroxide carry out very appreciable quantities of boric acid, when precipitated in the presence of a large excess of this acid. If the amount of these hydroxides is appreciable, the recovery of boric acid is essential for accurate results. The hydroxides are dissolved in the filter by addition of 6 N HCl, added in sufficient excess. The acid solution is caught in a beaker together with hot washings of the filter. Three to four drops of Sofnol Red or p-nitrophenol are added to the solution, and sodium hydroxide (50% solution) is now added dropwise until about neutral, then 0.5 N NaOH until the yellow color of the indicator remains. The solution is gently heated and allowed to stand for several minutes and the iron and aluminum hydroxides filtered off. The filter is washed with warm water. The filtrate is now acidified with 0.5 N HCl. The solution is neutralized to Sofnol Red or p-nitrophenol by addition of NaOH dropwise, and the boric acid determined by titration with NaOH in the presence of mannitol or glycerol (about 5 ml.) and phenolphthalein indicator. Time is saved by carrying this titration separately from the main solution.

*Titration of Boric Acid.*—The solution from the precipitation of iron and aluminum is acidified again with HCl and then just neutralized cautiously with NaOH to yellow color of Sofnol Red or p-nitrophenol. Now about 10 drops of phenolphthalein indicator are added and 25–50 ml. of neutral glycerol, or solid mannitol (according to the amount of boric acid titrated) and then the standard alkali until a distinct reddish pink color appears, the true end point for boric acid (pH 11).

NOTE.—The boric acid in the solution recovered from the iron and aluminum precipitate is determined also as directed above, and the amount added for total percentage of $B_2O_3$.

One ml. 1 N NaOH is equivalent to 0.03482 g. $B_2O_3$; or 0.09536 g. $Na_2B_4O_7 \cdot 10H_2O$; or 0.06184 g. $H_3BO_3$.

One ml. 0.5 N NaOH is equivalent to half the above amounts.

NOTES ON THE ACID EXTRACTION METHOD FOR TOTAL ACID. The acid extraction generally effects complete solution of the borates that are available in crude borate minerals. Should silicoborates be present a fusion of the acid residue should be made with sodium carbonate flux, and the fusion examined for borates.

The reflux condenser is used to avoid loss of the boric acid by volatilization. (The 6 N HCl is approximately acid of constant boiling point.)

The removal of iron and aluminum is necessary from the extract, as these, especially the aluminum salt, lead to high results for boric acid by the action of their combined acid with the standard base.

Definite amounts of borate are invariably carried out by the iron and aluminum hydroxides, so that a recovery must be effected if the precipitates are present in appreciable amounts.

The isoelectric point of aluminum is between pH 6.0–7.5, and it is at this point where the aluminum compounds are least soluble. Some aluminum hydroxide will go into solution if too much NaOH is added to precipitate the aluminum.

The end point is a combination of the two colors, yellow and pink, and is a distinct reddish pink color. The Sofnol Red or p-nitrophenol gives a *distinct* yellow color in alkaline solutions. Both indicators are colorless in acid solutions.

A concentrated solution of NaOH is used to neutralize the 6 N HCl so as to not increase the volume for filtering.

Neutral glycerol is prepared as follows—To 1000 ml. of glycerol add 4–5 ml. of phenolphthalein and neutralize with regular NaOH reagent. The color will fade due to the formation of acid, so add more NaOH reagent as needed to keep it colored pink. A sharper end point is obtained with mannitol.

In cases where less than 0.1 g. of $B_2O_3$ is found, greater accuracy may be obtained by use of 0.1 $N$ NaOH.

If end points are run over, back titrations are possible with either indicator.

Precipitation of iron and aluminum with NaOH in place of $Na_2CO_3$, avoids the necessity of expulsion of $CO_2$, which would cause high results for boric acid. If the latter is used, the solution should be acidified, the beaker covered and $CO_2$ expelled by heating gently at simmering temperature for 10–15 minutes.

It has been found that in place of attempting to recover the boric acid in the iron and aluminum precipitate, a close result may be obtained by taking the average boric acid titrations of two equal solutions, one from which the iron and aluminum have been removed and the other in which they remain. This procedure is more rapid and will check the 3 lower methods within 0.2–0.3%. By an actual test on a borate, the long method gave 44.04% $B_2O_3$, and the short method, 43.87%.

*Settlement Basis.*—Since the borate concentrates will pick up moisture on shipment,[10] especially overseas, it is necessary that the analysis be conducted by shipper and purchaser on the same basis of moisture content. (The material as shipped is spoken of as "dry" and that as received as "wet.") This can be accomplished by sampling the material at the dock of shipment, and enclosing a sealed sample to the customer. Should separate samples "dry" and "wet" be examined, the settlement should be made on the average of analysis on "dry" and "wet" basis and the average of weights. For example, if 100 tons of concentrate is shipped and there is a gain of 5 tons of moisture, making a total of 105 tons received, and the analysis of the sample on the "dry" basis is 47.25% $B_2O_3$ and on the "wet" basis 45% $B_2O_3$; settlement should be made for 102.5 tons of concentrate with the average analysis of 46.12% $B_2O_3$.

## DETERMINATION OF BORIC ACID IN CRUDE BORATES
## METHOD OF THE PACIFIC COAST BORAX COMPANY [11]

In the determination of $B_2O_3$ in crude borates such as rasorite, colemanite, or ulexite, many elements may interfere with the direct titration. Iron, alumina, soluble silica, and manganese are common interfering substances.

To remove these substances a procedure called the "Barium Carbonate Method" is used.

The determination is based upon the fact that barium borate, formed by the addition of barium carbonate to boric acid, is quite soluble. It acts as a buffer solution of such hydrogen-ion concentration as to cause the precipitation of the hydroxides of the heavy metals. Insoluble barium compounds of the acidic compounds present, such as silica, are also formed.

*Procedure.*—One gram of the finely ground borate is stirred with 50 ml. of water in a 250-ml. beaker and enough concentrated hydrochloric acid then added to decompose all the borate present. About 15 drops (1.5 ml.) are usually required. This is boiled until the borate is decomposed and dissolved, and if long boiling is found necessary it should be done under a reflux condenser. If a large excess

---

[10] By actual test on a dry concentrate a gain of over 1%, due to moisture absorbed from the air, took place during a 2½ hour exposure of the sample to the air.

[11] Developed by G. A. Connell and K. Jacoby. Submitted by W. F. Dingley, Technical Department, Pacific Coast Borax Company.

The method in general follows the standard procedures for the determination of boric acid. Certain modifications are of interest.

of acid is present after the reaction is complete, it should be nearly neutralized with sodium hydroxide or sodium carbonate. Care should be taken, however, that the solution is slightly acid to methyl red before the next step is taken. A few drops of bromine water are added, enough to oxidize all the ferrous iron, and the excess of bromine boiled off. To this slightly acid solution of borate about 2 g. of finely powdered barium carbonate are added, and the solution boiled for at least 2 minutes. At this point the volume of the solution should be at least 100 ml. for each 0.5 gram $B_2O_3$ present, in order to avoid precipitation of $B_2O_3$ as barium borate. There should be a little undissolved barium carbonate left in the beaker after boiling, otherwise an insufficient quantity of barium carbonate has been used. More barium carbonate can be added at this point, if needed.

Completion of the reaction is indicated by no further evolution of carbon dioxide, and care should be taken that a sufficient application of heat has been given. After boiling, the contents of the beaker are allowed to stand for at least an hour or, if convenient, for several hours. The solution is filtered and residue washed with water. The filtrate is acidified with hydrochloric acid, boiled to remove carbon dioxide, and neutralized with 0.5 $N$ sodium hydroxide solution, using methyl red as an indicator, and titrated in the same manner as given for the determination of $B_2O_3$ in sodium borate. When analyzing borates which have a tendency to lose moisture during preparation of the sample, or borate samples that contain associated materials which yield a precipitate difficult to filter, it is desirable to use a larger sample, say 5–10 g., conducting the preliminary treatment in a larger volumetric flask, and using an aliquot proportion for the final titration.

NOTES.—Practically all heavy metals with the exception of ferrous iron are precipitated by barium carbonate. Ferrous iron is oxidized to the ferric state and bromine water is used for this purpose, since the excess of bromine is easily removed by boiling. If excess of bromine is not removed it will decolorize the methyl red used as an indicator.

Methyl red is used as an indicator for several reasons: Its color change occurs at a hydrogen-ion concentration very close to that of boric acid solution of the strength used in the determination. Its color changes are suitable since the yellow tint does not interfere with the pink color of the phenolphthalein. Its color change is not greatly affected by temperature and fairly hot solutions may be titrated if haste is necessary. The end points in both titrations can be sharpened by addition of 1 drop of 0.5% water solution of methylene blue at the time of addition of the methyl red.

When glycerol or mannitol is added to boric acid and methyl red is present, the solution will turn pink or red in color. This color should not be confused with the pink of phenolphthalein. During titration with sodium hydroxide the pink or red of methyl red will turn to yellow and remain this shade until the pink end point of phenolphthalein is reached.

## EVALUATION OF BORIC ACID

One hundred ml. of the solution, prepared as directed under "Preparation of the Sample," equivalent to 2 g. of the original material, is treated with 50 ml. of glycerol or 1 g. of mannitol, and the acid titrated with standard caustic, in presence of phenolphthalein indicator according to the procedure given under "Evaluation of Borax."

One ml. normal acid contains 0.062 gram $H_3BO_3$, hence the ml. of caustic required multiplied by 0.062 = grams boric acid.

*Example.*—Two grams $H_3BO_3$ by actual test required 32.1 ml. $N$ NaOH = 32.1 × .062 = 1.99 grams $H_3BO_3$.

## MODIFIED CHAPIN'S DISTILLATION METHOD [12]

The method takes advantage of the volatility of methyl borate, $B(OCH_3)_3$, when alkaline earth or alkali borates are acidified, methyl alcohol added and the solution boiled. The method serves for the separation of boron from other substances and may be used as a check determination where doubt may exist regarding the accuracy of the more rapid methods described, occasioned by disagreements in evaluations of commercial boron bearing materials.

**Reagents.**[13] **Sofnol Red No. 1 Indicator.**—0.4% in 95% ethanol, or methyl red indicator, 1% in 50% ethanol, is recommended in place of the p-nitrophenol indicator originally used in the Chapin method.

**Phenolphthalein.**—One gram dissolved in 100 ml. of ethyl alcohol and made up to 200 ml. with water.

**Hydrochloric Acid, 0.1 N.**—The water should be boiled to remove carbonic acid.

**Hydrochloric Acid, 1:1 Strength.**—A dropping bulb should be filled with this acid when it is needed in accurate small amounts.

**Sodium Hydroxide Solutions, 0.046, 0.5, and 0.1 N.**—These should be standardized as follows: Fuse pure boric acid in a platinum dish. While still warm break the melt up and place the fragments quickly in a weighing tube. Dissolve 1.75 grams in 250 ml. of hot, recently boiled water, cool, and dilute the solution to 500 ml. This solution is 0.1 N—that is, in presence of mannite or glycerol 1 ml.[14] is neutralized to the phenolphthalein end point by 1 ml. of 0.1 N sodium hydroxide.

In standardizing the sodium hydroxide against this solution both indicators should be used, so that the end point may be the same as that seen in actual titration. Follow exactly the directions given under "Titration of Boric Acid," below, for the final titration, only assuming that the boric acid solution is exactly neutral to the Sofnol Red (or methyl red) indicator, that is, free from mineral acid. When sodium hydroxide is standardized in this way the small amount of carbonate present does no harm.

**Mannitol.**—This is preferable to glycerol, for it requires no special preparation, does not materially increase the bulk of the solution to be titrated, and gives an equally sharp end point. Glucose may be substituted for mannitol. See p. 228.

**Methanol.**—This should be distilled over lime after it has been heated for some hours in contact with the lime under a reflux condenser. The more nearly anhydrous, the methanol is the better.

**Calcium Chloride.**—This should be granular, anhydrous, and free from boron.

**Preparation of the Sample.** **For Minerals.**—Chapin used not more than 0.5 g. of mineral powder for even very small amounts of boron, and not less unless the percentage exceeded 10. When the percentage is high it is best to limit the weight of the sample so that the $B_2O_3$ shall not exceed 0.1 g. If a flux is used it should be weighed to within a milligram or two; then the amount of acid required to take up the melt can be measured out at once and there is no danger of using too great an excess.

If the mineral is soluble in hydrochloric acid, transfer 1 g. of it to a 250-ml. flask, without letting any adhere to the neck, and treat with not more than 5 ml. of 1:1 hydrochloric acid. Heat gently on a water bath until solution is complete.

If the mineral is not soluble, add to it exactly six times its weight of sodium

[12] Wilcox, L. V., Ind. Eng. Chem., Anal. Ed., **2**, 358, 1930.
[13] Bulletin 700, The Analysis of Silicate and Carbonate Rocks, by W. F. Hillebrand. Department of the Interior, U. S. Geological Survey.
[14] Am. Jour. Sci., 4th Ser., Vol. **14**, 195, 1903.

carbonate or of an equimolecular mixture of sodium and potassium carbonates, mix, and fuse in the usual manner. Without removing from the crucible, decompose the melt with 1:1 hydrochloric acid in calculated amount added by degrees. While this is being done the crucible should rest in a casserole, and the lid should be kept in place as much as possible. Toward the end it may be necessary to heat a little, but care should be taken not to boil, for boric acid would be lost with the steam. Pour the solution into a 250-ml. flask and rinse the crucible with a very little water.

Then add pure anhydrous calcium chloride, using about 1 g. for each milliliter of solution and running it through a paper funnel to keep the neck of the flask clean. Twirl the flask a little to allow the chloride to take up the water, connect it with the rest of the apparatus shown in Fig. 8-4, placing a casserole partly filled

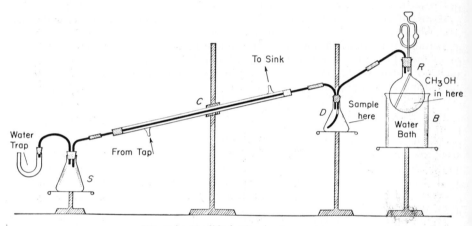

Fig. 8-4. Modified Chapin Apparatus.

with water beneath the 250-ml. flask (marked $D$ in the figure, in which the casserole is not shown). Raise the casserole beneath it until the flask rests in the water but does not touch the bottom, and then begin the distillation of the alcohol from the flask $R$, taking care that the open end of the capillary "boiling tube" is free from alcohol and that the U-tube attached to the receiver is trapped with water.

**For Water.**—Evaporate 2500 ml. to a moist residue in a 1-liter copper beaker, keeping it alkaline to phenolphthalein with saturated sodium hydroxide. Transfer to a 250-ml. low-boron glass flask, washing the copper beaker finally with 0.1 $N$ hydrochloric acid. This acid may acidify the solution in the flask; if so, make alkaline as before and evaporate to a solid residue. It is not necessary to dehydrate completely. Acidify with concentrated hydrochloric acid; 5 ml. are usually sufficient. Heat to boiling, but avoid evaporation as boron will be lost. Test with indicator to make sure that the contents of the flask are acid. Add one ml. in excess. Add 10 g. of $CaCl_2$ and 50 ml. of methanol (synthetic) and distill as described under "Distillation."

**For Plant Materials.**—Dry at 70–80 degrees C., grind to a fine powder, and composite. Weigh 10 g. of the material and transfer to a decomposition flask (low-boron glass). Add 80 ml. of methanol, 5–8 ml. of HCl and 10 g. of $CaCl_2$ (free from boron). Distill as described below. The operations following the distillation are the same for plant material as for waters and will be described in the following paragraphs.

*Procedure.* **Distillation.**—Connect flask $D$ containing the sample as shown in Fig. 8-4. Flask $S$ should contain 10 ml. of 0.5 $N$ NaOH to prevent escape of methyl borate. Start methanol distilling from reservoir $R$. When the contents of $D$ are hot, light a small flame under the flask. Try to regulate the heat so that the volume in the flask $D$ does not change. Distillation is carried along until 150 to 200 ml. are collected in the receiver $S$. Rinse the contents of the trap tube into $S$ and treat the distillate as detailed below.

**Treatment of Distillate.**—Make the solution alkaline to phenolphthalein, then add 10 ml. of 0.5 $N$ NaOH in excess. Transfer the liquid to a 1-liter copper Kjeldahl flask, not shown in diagram of apparatus, and distill off the methanol. This methanol can be fractionated and used again. Transfer the liquid left in the Kjeldahl flask to a 250-ml. copper beaker, evaporate to dryness, and ignite at a red heat. Add about 10 ml. of water, heat to boiling and, with the aid of a stirring rod having a rubber tip, transfer to a volumetric flask. Then add 7 drops of Sofnol indicator. Make distinctly acid with 2 $N$ HCl. Shake to expel $CO_2$ and then make distinctly alkaline to phenolphthalein with 0.5 $N$ NaOH. Make up to 110 ml. and filter into another of the 100-ml. flasks. Take an aliquot of 100 ml. of the filtrate, transfer to a 250-ml. low-boron flask, and proceed with titration as described below.

**Titration of Boric Acid.**—Make the alkaline filtrate acid to Sofnol with 2 $N$ HCl and then add 5 drops in excess. Boil 3 minutes, shaking the flask occasionally to aid in the expulsion of $CO_2$. Cool. Titrate as follows: Add $CO_2$-free 0.5 $N$ NaOH until a slight yellow color of Sofnol shows. Add 1 or 2 drops of 0.1 $N$ HCl. The solution should become pink. Add the standard 0.046 $N$ sodium hydroxide drop by drop until the pink just disappears. The color will be an orange not unlike that of neutral methyl orange. (If methyl red is used, the neutral color is also orange.) This is the neutral point for Sofnol and the initial point for titration. Read the burette. Add 1 drop of standard alkali. The indicator should change to a clear lemon yellow. If it does not, one would suspect that carbon dioxide was not completely removed. Continue adding the standard alkali until a reddish color appears, showing phenolphthalein alkalinity. Add about 1 g. of mannitol. The red color will be discharged if boric acid is present. If the red color is discharged, continue adding standard alkali until the red of phenolphthalein reappears. Add another gram of mannitol. The color will remain but, if it does not, add more alkali and another gram of mannitol until a permanent end point is obtained. This first red color that is permanent in the presence of mannitol is the end point of the titration.

The blank is determined exactly as described above, all of the reagents being used. The author's blanks ranged from 0.45 to 0.60 ml. standard $N$ NaOH.

**Calculations.**—Milliliters of standard 0.046 $N$ NaOH used between the initial point and the end point less a blank equals the net titration, which multiplied by 0.5 gives the weight in milligrams of boron in the aliquot. In this titration boric acid acts as a monobasic acid.

**Discussion on the Above Method.**—This method for the determination of boron differs from the Chapin method chiefly in the employment of copper flasks and beakers and of low-boron glass flasks for the hot alkaline solutions. Copper beakers are used for the first concentration of the water sample, which must be kept alkaline to prevent the loss of boron by volatilization. Copper Kjeldahl flasks are used when separating the methanol from the alkaline distillate, and finally copper beakers are used in drying and igniting the alkaline residues from the Kjeldahls.

**Regarding the Accuracy of the Method.**—(a) The method is practically quantitative when dealing with pure compounds of boron in amounts not exceeding 5 mg.

(b) Where boron is added to a natural water, it is possible to recover from 90–95% of the total boron present.

NOTES.—Allen and Ziez [15] tested the Chapin method very fully in its application to the determination of boron in glasses and regard it as far superior to other methods, even though it is subject to a slight but very uniform correction of 1 mg. or less, to be determined by a blank run. The correction seems to be due always in part to a boron content of the reagents used and in part to a titration error. The fact that such correction is unavoidable makes the method of uncertain value for determining the very small amounts of boron that rocks may be presumed to carry, but the constancy of results is so great that a consistent excess found over what the blank affords is strong evidence that boron is actually present.

Allen and Ziez found the method to be affected appreciably by relatively large amounts of arsenious acid but not by arsenic acid. The effect of the former can be eliminated by converting it to arsenic acid by oxidizing with hydrogen peroxide after making the solution distinctly alkaline with sodium hydroxide.

Allen and Ziez also found that relatively large amounts of fluorides affect the accuracy of the method but do not seriously impair its usefulness for ordinary work.

Glucose may be used in place of mannitol in titrations of borax as shown by LeRoy S. Weatherby and H. H. Chesney (Ind. Eng. Chem., **18**, 820, Aug., 1926). Though a larger quantity of glucose (about 10 times) is required than of mannitol, this is of no disadvantage, as a large background of white material is helpful in distinguishing the end point.

The distillation is usually complete when the vapor reaches a temperature of 95°C.

## ANALYSIS OF BORON CARBIDE [16]

### DETERMINATION OF BORON

**Preparation of Standard Solutions.**—0.2 N and 0.10 N solutions of NaOH are needed. They must be carbonate free. To prepare them proceed as follows:

Dissolve 75 g. of C.P. NaOH in 75 ml. of water. Pour into a large test tube or similar tall vessel and allow to stand several days or until all solid matter settles. Of the clear solution use 12 ml. per liter for the 0.2 N NaOH and 6 ml. per liter for the 0.10 N NaOH. Dilute with water that has been boiled and cooled to rid it of $CO_2$.

Titrate a 25-ml. portion of each solution with a standard acid and methyl red indicator, calculate and make the necessary dilutions with $CO_2$-free water to bring the solutions to their respectively desired normalities, and standardize them accurately against pure, anhydrous $B_2O_3$ glass.

**Standardization of the Solutions.**—Fuse C.P. boric acid thoroughly and store the resulting $B_2O_3$ glass in a well-stopppered bottle. If the boric acid at hand is not considered sufficiently pure, recrystallize it twice from hot water before fusing.

[15] Analysis of Silicate and Carbonate Rocks, W. F. Hillebrand, Bull. 700, U. S. Geol. Survey, 1919.

[16] Method used by the Norton Company, Worcester, Mass., supplied by the courtesy of M. O. Lamar.

For standardizing the 0.2 $N$ solution use approximately 0.3000 g. of the glass. For the 0.10 $N$ solution use 0.1500 g.

Weigh the sample roughly into a clean, ignited, and weighed platinum crucible. Cover the crucible tightly, ignite for five minutes at a good red heat, cool and weigh again to get the weight of the sample. Dissolve the sample from the crucible with 50 ml. of $CO_2$-free water, add 4 drops of $p$-nitrophenol, 1 ml. phenolphthalein and titrate with the alkali being standardized, using mannite to obtain the end point. One g. of mannitol is added at the start of the titration and further one g. additions are made as needed while approaching the end point.

Four samples should be treated in the above manner for each solution. Divide the weight of each sample by the number of ml. used for its titration and if the four results show satisfactory agreement, average them and take the result as the $B_2O_3$ value per ml. of the solution. The $B_2O_3$ value multiplied by 0.31074 gives the B value per ml. of the solution.

**Indicators.** *p*-**Nitrophenol.**—Dissolve 1 g. in 100 ml. denatured alcohol.

**Phenolphthalein.**—Dissolve 1 g. in 200 ml. denatured alcohol.

**Blanks.**—Weigh and treat four $B_2O_3$ glass samples as in standardizing up to the point where they are dissolved in water. Wash off the crucibles thoroughly, keeping the volumes of the solutions at approximately 100 ml. Acidify the solutions distinctly with 1:1 HCl and treat them as in the method next to be described, up to and through the main titration with 0.2 $N$ NaOH.

The main titrations with the 0.2 $N$ NaOH will show amounts of $B_2O_3$ slightly larger than the weights of the samples. Average these slight excesses, calculate their value in terms of ml. of the standard solution, and subtract this value from all main titrations when analyzing samples.

This blank might be taken care of by taking the original samples through the method, but the above procedure gives such very satisfactory results that it is followed as a routine step.

For the blank on the small recovery titration with the 0.10 $N$ NaOH a new solution is made up and titrated exactly as in the recovery part of the method. This blank is large when compared with the small amounts of $B_2O_3$ obtained in the recoveries but it is very consistent.

**Procedure.**—Weigh 0.12 gram of the sample into a platinum crucible. Mix thoroughly with $Na_2CO_3$ and cover with a layer of the carbonate, using 1 g. in all. Cover the crucible tightly and fuse slowly with gradually increasing temperature, finishing with a temperature as low as is consistent with complete fusion. Remember that during fusion there is always danger of volatilizing boric acid, and care must be used in performing the operation. When fusion is complete spread the melt on the inside of the crucible walls, allow to cool and place the crucible and cover in a 250-ml. beaker. Add 50 ml. of water and allow the melt to dissolve. Heat may be used to hasten solution but it should be used sparingly with the beaker well covered. Do not boil.

When solution is complete wash off the crucible and cover keeping the solution in the beaker down to 100 ml. Acidify with 7–8 ml. of 1:1 HCl and add four drops of $p$-nitrophenol. Dilute one volume of the strong NaOH stock solution used in making the standard solutions with one volume of water and by means of it and a medicine dropper bring the solution in the beaker nearly to the neutral point. Complete the neutralization to the $p$-nitrophenol end point with the 0.2 $N$ NaOH.

When the iron in the solution amounts to about 2 mg. or over, its color appears and deepens as neutralization is approached and may be mistaken for the indicator end point. This must be guarded against as under-neutralization ruins the analysis. Several drops over the end point do no harm, so make sure that neutralization is complete.

Cover the beaker and heat, *do not boil,* just until the precipitate coagulates. Stir in one quarter of a 7-cm. Whatman No. 41 filter paper macerated to pulp. Filter through a 7-cm. Whatman No. 41 filter paper, wash the beaker three times and give the precipitate six thorough washings on the paper. Catch the filtrate in a suitable pressure flask. If the precipitate is small hot water is satisfactory for washing, but if it amounts to 4 or 5 mg. or more a hot 1% solution of sodium chloride must be used to prevent hydrolysis. Set this main filtrate aside for titration.

Place the original beaker under the funnel and dissolve the precipitate through the paper by dropping hot 1:1 HCl on it. It does not take much of the acid to do this but make sure no undissolved precipitate remains mixed with the pulp. Wash the filter and pulp six times with hot water or 1% NaCl solution, add four drops of *p*-nitrophenol, and repeat exactly the first precipitation and filtration, this time catching the filtrate in a 500-ml. Erlenmeyer flask. This filtrate contains the recovery titration. Before starting the filtration the small wad of pulp in the filter is carefully removed and stirred into the precipitate in the beaker.

Acidify the main filtrate in the pressure flask with 1:1 HCl adding about three drops in excess. Warm the flask on a pan of sand until the solution is about 40°C., transfer the flask still on the sand bath to a suction pump, and boil under reduced pressure until bubbles cease to come from the solution. Perform this operation carefully to avoid loss by splashing. Disconnect the flask, cool it in running water, and thoroughly wash down the stopper and inside of the flask with $CO_2$-free water. Nearly neutralize the solution with strong carbonate-free NaOH and finish the neutralization with the 0.10 $N$ NaOH standard solution. In the solution as here prepared this end point is very sharp and one drop of the 0.10 $N$ solution will give it distinctly, especially if the flask is examined at eye level toward a window between the additions of the last few drops.

When the solution has been adjusted to the neutral point add 1 ml. of phenolphthalein indicator and 1 g. of mannitol. Begin the titration with the 0.2 $N$ NaOH and continue until the pink color of the phenolphthalein indicator develops. Add another gram of mannitol and again develop the pink color. Continue these additions of mannitol until the last one has no effect on the fully developed pink color. As this end point is properly obtained only through familiarity with it, an attempt is made to describe its approach. As the end of the titration nears, the pink color persists more and more when mannitol is added. First a pink tinge will persist even though the yellow is greatly restored. After the next addition the pink will remain decidedly, mixed with the yellow color. Finally a stage will be reached where the pink color only lightens upon the addition of mannitol, no yellow being discernible. When this stage is reached one or two drops of the 0.2 $N$ solution will give a sudden, definite, fully developed pink color that will remain for hours after the addition of another gram of mannitol. This is the end point.

Now make the recovery titration on the solution in the Erlenmeyer flask in the same manner, except that the 0.10 $N$ NaOH solution is used, and as no $CO_2$ is present the solution is not boiled under reduced pressure. This end point is not difficult to obtain.

Subtract the respective blanks from each titration. Multiply each titration by the B value per ml. of the solution used. Add the B values together, divide by the weight of the sample and multiply by 100 to obtain the percentage of B in the sample.

## SILICA

*Procedure.*—Weigh 0.5 g. of the sample and 8 g. of $Na_2CO_3$. Mix the sample thoroughly in a platinum crucible with most of the carbonate and cover the mixture with the remainder. Fuse with gradually increasing temperature. Use the highest heat of the burner only if the last bits of the sample do not fuse at a moderate heat.

Run the melt up on the walls of the crucible and cool. Place the crucible and cover in a casserole and leach the melt with water. Acidify the solution with 25 ml. strong HCl, wash off the crucible and cover, add 25 ml. methyl alcohol and evaporate slowly to dryness with the casserole uncovered. Evaporate twice more with 5 ml. of HCl and 25 ml. of methyl alcohol. If boric acid remains condensed on the sides of the casserole, evaporate a third time.

When boric acid is no longer evident, cool the casserole, moisten the residue with 10 ml. 1:1 HCl, add 50 ml. hot water and warm until all soluble salts are in solution. Filter, wash the precipitate with hot 2% HCl five times, then five times with hot water. Return the filtrate to the casserole and repeat the dehydration and filtration.

Burn off both papers in a platinum crucible, ignite intensely for 20 minutes, cool, and weigh. Add a few drops of water, two drops of strong $H_2SO_4$, and 5–10 ml. of HF. Evaporate until both acids are gone, ignite the crucible, and residue for five minutes, cool, and weigh. The loss in weight represents the silica. This weight divided by the weight of the sample and multiplied by 100 gives the percentage of silica in the sample.

High silica in boron carbide samples is seldom found but if silica should be encountered much over 5% there is danger of it being contaminated with boric acid in spite of the evaporations with alcohol. In such a case, after the first ignition of the silica, fuse it with 1–2 g. of sodium carbonate, make two dehydrations with intervening filtration as above, then ignite, weigh, and finish as directed. No alcohol is necessary in these dehydrations.

## OTHER CONSTITUENTS

Iron, aluminum, calcium, and magnesium are determined in the filtrate from the silica determination. Carbon is determined by combustion with a red lead flux. Refer to the analysis of silicon carbide, where instructions for making these determinations are given in great detail.

NOTES.—This is a very exacting analysis; especially the determination of boron. In this determination the analyst is placed in a disadvantageous position. The sample operated upon is small and the percentage determined is large. This multiplies any errors greatly, so that errors must be held to an absolute minimum.

The $B_2O_3$ used for standardizing must be pure, completely anhydrous, and properly weighed. The operations of standardizing solutions and obtaining blanks must be performed with the utmost care. All titration end points must be obtained with precision, and last, but far from least, absolutely clean glassware must be used, especially burettes. "Ordinarily" clean glassware will not do.

# BORIC ACID IN MILK, BUTTER, MEAT, AND OTHER FOODS

## MILK [17]

*Procedure.*—One hundred ml. of milk is treated with 1 to 2 g. of sodium hydroxide, and evaporated to dryness in a platinum dish. The residue is thoroughly charred [18] by gently heating; at this stage care must be exercised or loss of boric acid will result; 20 ml. of water are added, the sample heated and hydrochloric acid added drop by drop until all but the carbon has dissolved. The mixture is washed into a 100-ml. flask with as little water as possible, 0.5 gram calcium chloride added, then a few drops of phenolphthalein indicator, then a 10% sodium hydroxide solution until a slight permanent pink color is obtained and finally 25 ml. of lime water. (All $P_2O_5$ is precipitated as calcium phosphate.) The liquid is made to 100 ml., mixed thoroughly, and then filtered through a dry filter. To 50 ml. of the filtrate, equivalent to 50 ml. of the milk taken, $N$ sulfuric acid is added until the pink color disappears, then methyl orange indicator is added, followed by more of the standard acid until the yellow color changes to a faint pink. Carbon dioxide is expelled and the liberated boric acid titrated in presence of glycerol, according to the procedure given for evaluation of borax and boric acid, under "Titrimetric Determination of Boron."

## BUTTER [19]

*Procedure.*—Twenty-five grams of butter are weighed out in a beaker and 25 ml. of a sugar-sulfuric acid mixture added. (Mix 6 g. lactose and 4 ml. $N$ sulfuric acid per 100 ml. of solution.) The beaker is placed in the oven (100°C.) until the fat is melted and the mixture is thoroughly stirred. When the aqueous solution has settled, 20 ml. are pipetted out, phenolphthalein added, the solution brought to boiling and 0.5 $N$ sodium hydroxide added until a faint pink color is obtained. Ten ml. of neutral glycerol are added and the titration carried on until a permanent pink color appears. The difference between the two titrations multiplied by the factor for equivalent boric acid gives the weight of boric acid in the portion taken.

The determination is not affected by the phosphoric or butyric acid or by the lactose in the butter.

## MEAT [20]

*Procedure.*—Ten grams of the chopped meat are mixed in a mortar with 40–80 g. of anhydrous sodium sulfate, and dried in the water oven. The mass is powdered, then placed in a flask and 100 ml. of methanol added and allowed to stand for about twelve hours. The alcohol is distilled into a flask and saved. Fifty ml. more of alcohol are added to the residue and this again distilled into the first distillate. The distillates are made up to 150 ml., a 50-ml. portion diluted with 50 ml. of water and 50 ml. of neutral glycerol added with phenolphthalein indicator, and the boric acid titrated with 0.05 $N$ sodium hydroxide.

One ml. 0.05 $N$ NaOH = 0.003092 g. boric acid, $H_3BO_3$

---

[17] Thomson, R. T., Glasgow City Anal. Soc. Repts., 1895, p. 3.
[18] The milk residue thoroughly charred will give a colorless solution upon extraction.
[19] Richmond, Droop H., and Harrison, J. B. P., Analyst, **27**, 197.
[20] Fresenius, C., and Popp, G., Chem. Centr., **2**, 69, 1897.

Boric acid in canned goods, sauces, cereals, etc., may be determined by evaporation of the substance with sodium hydroxide and incineration as in case of milk. The sodium hydroxide is neutralized and boric acid titrated as usual.

## DETERMINATION OF BORON IN TISSUES

This method [21] is based on the spectrophotometric determination at 625 m$\mu$ of a carmine-boron complex formed in acid solution. (See "Carminic Acid Method.") The details are concerned primarily with the effective extraction and distillation of the boron, without material losses.

*Apparatus.* **Polyethylene Stirring Rods. Round-bottom Pyrex Distilling Flasks, 50 ml., standard taper 19/38.**
**Side Arm.**—As per Fig. 8-5.
**Dropping Funnel.**—As per Fig. 8-5.
**Coil Condenser.**—Water cooled as per Fig. 8-5.
**Boron-free Beakers, 250 and 400 ml. Electric Hot Plates.**
**Glass-stoppered Tubes.**—Spectrophotometrically matched.
**pH Paper.**
**Automatic Burettes for H$_2$SO$_4$ and Carmine Solutions.**
**Spectrophotometer (Coleman Junior).**
*Reagents.* **Methanol.**—Redistilled in laboratory.
**Ethanol.**—Redistilled in laboratory.
**Potassium Hydroxide Solution.**—Reagent-grade.
**Hydrogen Peroxide.**—30% Baker's analyzed.
**Saturated Sodium Hydroxide Solution, 50%.**
**Concentrated Hydrochloric Acid, C.P. Concentrated Sulfuric Acid, C.P.**
**Methanol, Acid.**—1 ml. concentrated hydrochloric acid added to 450 ml. of methanol.
**Carmine Reagent.**—0.5 g. carmine added to 1 liter of concentrated H$_2$SO$_4$.
**Carmine No. 40 NF.**

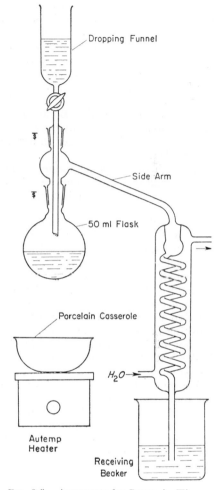

FIG. 8-5. Apparatus for Boron in Tissues.

*Procedure.* **Tissue Preparation.**—Tissue to be analyzed is removed from the refrigerator freezing compartment and thawed at room temperature. After thawing, it is transferred to a watch glass for removal of fat and any adherent foreign

[21] Hill, Merrill, Nontiegel, Palm, Schmitt and Schulte, A.M.A. Archives of Industrial Health, **17**, 210, 1958.

tissue that may be present. As tissue is being trimmed, the cleaned pieces are placed on a watch glass where the mincing and mixing are done.

Mincing the tissue can be done in two ways: first, using scissors; second, using a sharp knife. A combination of the two is much faster. The tissue should be cut into such small pieces that the mixture looks somewhat like a paste. Before the tissue is weighed for analysis, the minced paste should be thoroughly mixed, in order to get a truly representative sample.

**Weighing Tissue.**—The minced and mixed tissue is weighed into 50-ml. round-bottom Pyrex distilling flasks, care being taken that no tissue hangs up on the ground-glass surface of the standard taper top. Small beakers are used to hold the flask during weighing. An analytical balance is used for weighing out tissue samples (1–3 g.).

**Preparation for Methyl Borate Distillation.**—The flask containing the tissue is attached to a side arm, containing a dropping funnel, leading to a coil condenser, the tip of which is submerged in 5 ml. 0.6 $N$ NaOH contained in a 250-ml. boron-free beaker.

Through the dropping funnel 15 ml. of methanol and 0.2 ml. of concentrated HCl are added (solution must be slightly acid). Before stewing, the acid methanol and tissue mixture are shaken, in a closed set-up, for better contact of liquid and tissue.

The stewing step requires 6 hours. For stewing, the flask is surrounded by water contained in a casserole and kept warm (about 50–60°C.) with an electric hot plate.

**Methyl Borate Distillation.**—After the stewing period, the methyl borate formed in the flask during stewing is distilled off (for distilling, the temperature of the water bath is kept at about 75–80°C.). During distillation 30 ml. of acid methanol are added slowly through the dropping funnel. The contents of the flask are distilled down as far as possible without fuming (fuming causes browning of the solution when the $H_2SO_4$ is added in the carmine tests, giving darker color and resulting in lower readings on the spectrophotometer).

After distillation, the residue in the flask is washed into a 400-ml. boron-free beaker with the aid of ethanol and subject to alkaline digestion. The side arm and condenser are rinsed with methanol into the 250-ml. receiving beaker. This is known as the distillate, and, after evaporation on the steam bath, it is ready for the carmine test.

**Alkaline Digestion.**—The residue (above), washed into a 400-ml. boron-free beaker with 15 ml. of ethanol, is made basic by adding KOH. The amount of KOH needed at this point is variable with the amount and type of tissue, about 5 pellets per gram of tissue being a normal amount for good digestion. To the basic solution, 10 ml. of 30% $H_2O_2$ is added, using additional ethanol if foaming becomes excessive. The contents of the beaker should be allowed to react at room temperature for at least 10 minutes before being placed on a steam bath for further digestion and evaporation.

After evaporation, the sides of the beaker should be washed down with distilled water and the digested tissue brought into solution. The beaker is then replaced on the steam bath for re-evaporation. After this first washing, the solution may appear to have some feathery tissue flakes, but these usually disappear during the second evaporation.

The beaker contents are dissolved with water a second time and evaporated to dryness on the steam bath a third time. Now the tissue is digested and ready to be transferred to a 50-ml. round-bottom flask for methyl borate distillation.

**Tissue Transfer and Final Distillation.**—With the aid of 2 ml. of water, the digested tissue is transferred to a 50-ml. round-bottom flask. The beaker is carefully washed with 15 ml. of methanol, using a polyethylene stirring rod to get as much as possible of the salt into the flask.

The flask is then attached to the methyl borate distillation set-up (in the same manner as described under "Preparation for Methyl Borate Distillation"). The contents of the flask are made acid with concentrated HCl. Distillation is the same as described under "Methyl Borate Distillation."

After this distillation, the side arm and condenser are washed down with methanol as described before. The receiving beaker is placed on the steam bath for evaporation. This is known as the residue sample, and is now ready for the carmine test. The residue in the flask is tested for acidity with pH paper, and, if it is acid, it is discarded. If the residue is alkaline, the distillation is repeated.

**Blanks for Carmine Tests.**—A blank is prepared, using the same amount of KOH and $H_2O_2$, and the same number of washings as were used in the sample. These blanks are also evaporated to dryness, methanol-distilled, etc., in the same manner as the samples. These are used as the 100% transmittance blanks against which the samples are read.

**Carmine Test.**—A standard curve is prepared each time the boron content of samples is determined by the carmine method. Into boron-free beakers 5 ml. of 0.6 $N$ NaOH and 1 ml. of each boron standard (1, 2, 4, 6, 8, 10 micrograms of boron per ml.) are pipetted and allowed to evaporate to dryness on the steam bath. A blank is prepared in the following manner: 5 ml. of 0.6 $N$ NaOH and 1 ml. of water in a boron-free beaker evaporated to dryness.

After the contents of the beakers have dried, 1 ml. of water is added to each, dissolving as much of the salt as possible; then they are placed into a bath cooled with ice water. To each beaker is added 2 drops of concentrated HCl, to rid the contents of oxides of nitrogen.

From an automatic burette 5 ml. of concentrated $H_2SO_4$ is added to the beaker (which is placed in a small vessel of cold ice water). The acid is swirled around in the beaker to get all of the salt that may be on the beaker sides into the solution. The acid solution is allowed to cool thoroughly before the 5 ml. of carmine reagent is added (no cold bath needed at this point).

The carmine-sulfuric acid solution is swirled around in the beaker to get thorough mixing, then poured into a matched glass-stoppered tube. The tube is then shaken to ensure thorough mixing for proper color development.

The carmine-boron solutions are read 60 minutes after mixing on the spectrophotometer at a wavelength of 625 m$\mu$. The samples are read against the chemical blank, which is set at 100% transmittance.

The curve is then plotted in micrograms of boron versus per cent transmittance.

**Samples.**—In cases where dilutions are needed, samples are diluted and proper aliquots taken and evaporated to dryness before carmine tests can be done. The samples, with their respective blanks, are treated in the very same manner as the standard curve (1 ml. of water, 2 drops of concentrated HCl, 5 ml. of $H_2SO_4$, 5 ml. of carmine, etc.). Dilutions cannot be carried out after the unknowns have been mixed with the carmine reagents.

## DETERMINATION OF BORON IN BLOOD [22]

This method is similar in spectrophotometric procedure, and apparatus and reagents required, to the preceding method for "Determination of Boron in Tissues."

*Procedure.* **Distillate Boron.**—The blood is measured in graduated 15-ml. centrifuge tubes, which drain more completely than does a graduated cylinder. The sample is transferred to a 100-ml. Pyrex distilling flask that is then connected to a vertical Pyrex condenser. The connecting side arm also carries a dropping funnel through which 30 ml. of methanol and 0.3 ml. of concentrated HCl are added to the distilling flask. The tip of the condenser dips into a boron-free beaker which contains 5 ml. of 0.6 $N$ NaOH. The sample is heated in the flask for 6 hours, just short of active distillation (using a water bath and small hot-plate). This step has been referred to as the "stewing" or the "simmering" step and is intended to give boranes a chance to hydrolyze. The sample is then distilled, and during the distillation 30 ml. of acid methanol is gradually added through the dropping funnel. The distillate is evaporated on the steam bath, and its boron content is determined by the carmine method. The boron value thus obtained is referred to as "distillate boron." The residue left in the distilling flask is washed into a 400-ml. boron-free beaker, ethanol being used for the transfer.

**Distillate Blank.**—Since water is of importance in methyl borate distillation, and since the sodium hydroxide of the receiver may contain some boron, a blank run is made substantially as outlined above. Blood contains approximately 80% water, and therefore 8 ml. of water and 0.3 of concentrated HCl are distilled with 45 ml. of acid methanol to imitate the water introduced with the normal blood sample of 10 ml. The smaller quantity of methanol is used, because in the blank substantially all of it distills over, while in the blood procedure a large amount is held back by the flask residue. The distillate is caught in 5 ml. of 0.6 $N$ NaOH; it is evaporated on the steam bath, and the residue is subject to the carmine test. The solution thus obtained is used as the 100% transmittance "blank" against which the "distillate boron" is read. Transmittance is determined at 625 m$\mu$.

**Residue Boron.**—The residue obtained in the above "distillate boron" step is broken up with a stirring rod so that no larger blood clots are left. Ten pellets of KOH and 10 ml. of 30% hydrogen peroxide are added to hydrolyze the protein materials. Considerable foaming occurs in this step. As soon as it has subsided, another 10 pellets of KOH and 10 ml. of hydrogen peroxide are added and enough ethanol to keep the foaming at a minimum. The beaker is placed on the steam bath, and as soon as the sample is dry it is washed down with water. This is evaporated again, and the walls of the beaker are washed down with water a second time. The solution is evaporated a third time, and the residue in the beaker is then transferred to a 100-ml. distilling flask with the aid of 2 ml. of water and 20 ml. of methanol for rinsing. The flask is attached to the distilling apparatus, and 3 ml. of concentrated HCl is added through the dropping funnel. After gas evolution has ceased, the contents are distilled into the receiver, which contains the customary 5 ml. of 0.6 $N$ NaOH. Toward the end of the distillation, another 30 ml. of acid methanol is added gradually and distillation is completed. Before discarding the residue in the flask, check to see that the sample is still acid. The distillate is evaporated on the steam bath, and its boron content is

[22] Hill, Merrill, Montiegel, Palm, Schmitt, and Schulte, A.M.A. Archives of Industrial Health, **17,** 210, 1958.

determined by the carmine method. The boron value thus obtained is referred to as "residue boron."

**Residue Blank.**—A blank for the above carmine color determination of the "residue boron" is obtained by carrying the residue of the distillate blank, ethanol, 20 ml. of 30% hydrogen peroxide, and 20 pellets of KOH through the same procedure as for "residue boron," with the same amount of NaOH being used in the distillate receiver. The distillate is evaporated on the steam bath, and the residue is used in making up the "blank."

## BORANES BY THE CARMINIC ACID METHOD

This spectrophotometric method [23] is useful for determining micro quantities of boranes. A solution of the borane, in suitable concentration, is introduced into concentrated sulfuric acid, the carmine-sulfuric acid solution is added, and the absorbance readings taken. Some of the boranes, such as dimethylamineborane, dissolve well in water, and no difficulty is encountered in preparing solutions from them. In other cases it is necessary to bring the compound into solution with the aid of solvents or alkali. In the case of pyridine-borane, for instance, 0.4258 g. of the compound is dissolved in 10 ml. of propylene glycol, and the solution is diluted with water to the desired concentrations. Decaborane is best dissolved in a mixture of 10 ml. ethanol and 10 ml. of 0.6 $N$ NaOH and then diluted to the desired volume. Other solvents or alkaline materials can be used if they do not produce a discoloration on addition to concentrated sulfuric acid.

*Apparatus.* **Spectrophotometer.**—Method developed on Coleman Junior Spectrophotometer 6B, with constant voltage transformer.

**Glass-stoppered Tubes.**—Matched ($\pm 0.5\%$), with standard taper 14/20 stoppers, made of Pyrex culture tubes, Corning Catalog No. 9820, without rim, size 18 x 150 mm. Boron-free tubes would be preferable but cannot be fitted with glass stoppers.

*Reagent.* **Carmine No. 40 N.F. Solution.**—0.5 gram per liter of concentrated sulfuric acid.

*Procedure.*—The borane in question is dissolved in water, with or without the aid of a solubilizing agent, so that the stock solution contains somewhere between 50 and 200 micrograms of boron per milliliter. Dilutions are then prepared to represent 1, 2, 5, 8, and 10 micrograms of boron per ml. From each dilution 1 ml. is pipetted into the carmine tubes, whereupon 5 ml. of concentrated sulfuric acid is added and then 5 ml. of carmine reagent. If nitrates are suspected to be present, a few drops of concentrated hydrochloric acid are added. After one hour the colors thus produced are compared at a wavelength of 625 m$\mu$ with a standard curve obtained in a similar manner, but using boric acid standard solutions. Blanks are prepared in exactly the same manner as the standards and the unknowns. They compensate in a large measure for the insignificant amounts of boron extracted from the Pyrex glass tubes by the reagents employed. For "unknown" boranes or their solutions it is generally necessary to prepare several dilutions in order to get into the proper range of concentration in which the method is applicable, namely about 1–10 micrograms of boron per ml. of solution tested.

**Limitations.**—The method cannot be used for boranes that give colored solutions with concentrated sulfuric acid, which could conceivably be the case if the borane carries a heavy organic "tail." In the work here reported no such discolorations

[23] Hill, Merrill, and Palm, Jour. of Amer. Ind. Hygiene Assn., **19,** 461, 1958.

have been observed, neither with the boranes nor with the amine portions of the compounds when the latter were tested by themselves. Gaseous and low boiling boranes can be handled only if they can be absorbed in concentrated sulfuric acid, an alkali, an amine, or other suitable solvent. For instance, it has not been possible so far to apply the method to pentaborane ($B_5H_9$) because this compound does not dissolve easily in the ordinary solvents. Attempts to remove it from the exit air of animal exposure chambers by means of alkali, triethanolamine, xylene, and even concentrated sulfuric acid were unsuccessful because of incomplete absorption. The method is non-specific since it is based on a measurement of the boron content and not the borane itself. For this reason, it cannot differentiate between several boranes in a mixture, nor between boranes and boric acid or boric oxide contained in the samples as impurities.

## METHODS FOR BORON IN ANALYSES IN OTHER CHAPTERS

Boron in Aluminum Alloys        See Analysis in Aluminum Alloys
Boron in Commercial Phosphates      See Analysis of Commercial Phosphates

## Chapter 9

# BROMINE *

Br, *at. wt.* 79.909 ($\pm 0.002$); *sp. gr.* ($20°/4°$) 3.123; *m.p.* $-7.2°$C.; *b.p.* $58.78°$C.; *acids*, HBr, HBrO, $HBrO_3$

Bromine occurs in nature only in the form of bromides, generally as those of the alkali or alkaline earth elements. The most abundant source is ocean water (65 p. p. m. Br), but richer concentrations occur in salt deposits and particularly in mineral brines. Traces occur in plants, coal, and rocks, and in association with silver chloride or iodide.

Bromine was first isolated from the salts of the waters of the Mediterranean by Balard in 1826. The element is a valuable laboratory reagent used for oxidation purposes. Its silver salt is used in photography. The bromides find application in medicine. The major use of bromine is in the form of ethylene bromide, an ingredient of antiknock gasoline fluid. Methyl bromide is a commercial fumigant.

## DETECTION

*Silver Nitrate* solution precipitates silver bromide, AgBr, light yellow, from solutions containing the bromide anion. The precipitate, which darkens on exposure to light, is insoluble in dilute nitric acid but dissolves with difficulty in ammonium hydroxide and is practically insoluble in ammonium carbonate solution (distinction from AgCl).

*Carbon Disulfide or Carbon Tetrachloride* shaken with free bromine solution, or with a bromide to which a little chlorine water has been added (a large excess of chlorine must be avoided, as this forms BrCl compound), will extract the bromine and become a reddish-yellow color, or if much bromine is present, a brown to brownish-black. In the latter case a smaller sample should be taken to distinguish it from iodine.

Bromates are first reduced by a suitable reducing agent such as cold oxalic acid, sodium nitrite, hydrochloric acid, etc., and the liberated bromine is tested as directed above. Silver nitrate added to a sufficient quantity of bromate in solution precipitates $AgBrO_3$, which is decomposed by hydrochloric acid to bromine vapor.

*Magenta Test for Bromine.*[1]—A stock solution is prepared by adding 10 ml. of 0.1% solution of magenta to 100 ml. of 5% solution of sulfurous acid and allowing to stand until colorless. Mix 25 ml. of the stock solution with 25 ml. of glacial acetic acid and 1 ml. of sulfuric acid to obtain the test reagent.

Five ml. of the magenta test reagent is mixed with 1 ml. of the solution tested. Chlorine produces a yellow color. Bromine gives a reddish-violet coloration. The

---

* Chapter contributed by V. A. Stenger, The Dow Chemical Co., Midland, Michigan.
[1] Denigès, G., and Chelle, L., Ann. chim. anal., **18**, 11, 1913; Analyst, **38**, 119, 1913.

colored compound in each case may be taken up with chloroform or carbon tetra-chloride and compared colorimetrically with a standard.

In halogen mixtures, iodine is first eliminated by heating with a ferric salt. Bromine is now liberated by adding sulfuric acid and potassium chromate. A glass rod with a pendant drop of sodium hydroxide solution is held in the vapor to absorb bromine, and the drop is then tested with the magenta reagent. After iodine and bromine are eliminated, chloride may be tested for by heating the solution with potassium permanganate, which liberates free chlorine.

## ESTIMATION

In the preparation of a sample for analysis it should be kept in mind that bromides are easily lost by ashing above 600°C., or even at lower temperatures if an excess of alkali hydroxide or carbonate is lacking. Oxidants are likely to cause losses of bromine from acid solutions. In the course of a classical silicate analysis, bromide will remain with the silica residue as silver bromide if silver is also present. Mercuric salts may prevent the detection of bromide by form-ing the slightly dissociated mercuric bromide. Oxidation in the presence of organic matter may result in the formation of brominated compounds.

### PREPARATION AND SOLUTION OF THE SAMPLE

The following facts regarding solubility should be remembered: The element bromine is very soluble in alcohol, ether, chloroform, carbon disulfide, carbon tetrachloride, concentrated hydrochloric acid, and in alkali bromide solutions. One hundred ml. of water at 0°C. is saturated with 2.31 g. of bromine, and at 50°C. with 3.49 g. The aqueous solubility of bromine is increased in the presence of various chloride salts.

*The element* is a dark, brownish-red, volatile liquid, giving off a dark reddish vapor with suffocating odor, irritating to the mucous membrane (antidote: dilute $NH_4OH$), and very corrosive. It acts violently on hydrogen, sulfur, phosphorus, arsenic, antimony, tin, aluminum, mercury, and potassium, but has practically no action on sodium, magnesium, nickel, or lead if these are dry. Bromine is a strong oxidizing agent and it bleaches indigo, indicators, and most organic coloring mat-ter. Bromine displaces iodine from its salts, but is displaced from its own combina-tions by chlorine.

*Bromides,* with the exception of silver, lead, mercurous, thallous, and cuprous bromides, are quite soluble in water.

*Bromates* are soluble in water, with the exception of barium and silver bro-mates and some basic bromates. However, the solubilities of lead, cesium, and rubidium bromates are somewhat limited.

*Decomposition of Organic Matter for Determination of Bromine.*—The sub-stance is decomposed with nitric acid in presence of silver nitrate in a bomb combustion tube by the Carius method described in the chapter on Chlorine, un-der "Preparation and Solution of the Sample." The residue, containing the halides, is dissolved in warm ammonia water and filtered, as stated. The filtrate and washings are acidified with nitric acid, heated to boiling and the silver bromide is settled in the dark, then filtered through a weighed Gooch crucible, the washed precipitate dried at 130°C. and weighed as AgBr.

In the presence of two or three halogens the lime method is recommended, as given in the Chapter on Chlorine.

*Salts of Bromine.*—The ready solubility of bromides and bromates has been mentioned. A water extract is generally sufficient. Insoluble salts are decomposed by acidifying with dilute sulfuric acid and adding metallic zinc. The filtrate contains the halogens.

## SEPARATIONS

*Separation of Bromine from the Heavy Metals.*—Bromides of the heavy metals are transposed by boiling with sodium carbonate, the metals being precipitated as carbonates and sodium bromide remaining in solution.

*Separation of Bromine from Silver (AgBr) and from Cyanides (AgCN).*—The silver salts are heated to fusion. The mass is now treated with an excess of zinc and sulfuric acid, the metallic silver and the paracyanogen are filtered off, and bromine is determined in the filtrate.

*Separation of Bromine from Chlorine or from Iodine.*—Details of the procedure for determining the halogens in presence of one another are given in the Chapter on Chlorine, page 339. Free bromine is liberated when the solution of a bromide is treated with chlorine.

*Separation of Bromine from Iodine.*[2]—The neutral solution containing the bromide and iodide is diluted to about 700 ml. and 2–3 ml. of dilute sulfuric acid (1:1) is added, together with about 10 ml. of 10% sodium nitrite, $NaNO_2$, solution. (Nitrous acid gas may be passed through the solution in place of adding sodium nitrite, if desired.[3]) The solution containing the halides is boiled until colorless and about twenty minutes longer, keeping the volume of solution above 600 ml. 0.5 gram KI may be decomposed and the iodine expelled in half an hour. The bromide is precipitated from the residue remaining in the flask by addition of an excess of silver nitrate and is determined as silver bromide.

The procedure for determining iodine is given in the chapter on this subject.

## GRAVIMETRIC METHODS

### PRECIPITATION AS SILVER BROMIDE

The general directions for determination of hydrochloric acid and chlorides apply for determining hydrobromic acid and bromides.

#### HYDROBROMIC ACID AND BROMIDES OF THE ALKALIES AND ALKALINE EARTHS

*Procedure.*—The bromide in cold solution is made slightly acid with nitric acid and then silver nitrate is added slowly with constant stirring until a slight excess is present. The mixture is now heated to boiling and allowed to stand for a short time in the dark, then filtered through a weighed filter crucible and washed, first with water containing a little nitric acid and finally with pure water to remove the acid. After drying at 150°C. the silver bromide is cooled and weighed as AgBr.

$$AgBr \times 0.4256 = Br \qquad \text{or} \qquad AgBr \times 0.6338 = KBr$$

[2] Gooch, F. A., and Ensign, J. R., Am. Jour. Sci., 3, **40**, 145, 1890.
[3] Nitrous acid gas is generated by dropping dilute $H_2SO_4$ from a separatory funnel onto sodium nitrite in a flask.

### HEAVY METALS PRESENT

If heavy metals are present it is not always possible to precipitate silver bromide directly. The heavy metals may be removed by precipitation with ammonia, sodium hydroxide, or carbonate and the bromide then determined in the acidified filtrate as usual.

## TITRIMETRIC METHODS

Free hydrobromic acid may be titrated with standard alkali exactly as is described for the determination of hydrochloric acid in the chapter on Acids. One ml. of normal caustic solution is equivalent to 0.08092 g. HBr.

## DETERMINATION OF FREE BROMINE.
## POTASSIUM IODIDE METHOD

The method depends upon the reaction $KI + Br \rightarrow KBr + I$.

*Procedure.*—A measured amount of the sample is added to an excess of potassium iodide, in a glass-stoppered bottle, holding the point of the delivering burette just above the potassium iodide solution. The stoppered bottle is then well shaken, and the liberated iodine is titrated with standard thiosulfate solution.

One ml. of 0.1 $N$ thiosulfate, $Na_2S_2O_3 = 0.007992$ g. Br.

## DETERMINATION OF TOTAL HALIDE IN SOLUBLE INORGANIC BROMIDES. SILVER THIOCYANATE-FERRIC ALUM METHOD (VOLHARD)

The procedure is the same as that used for the determination of chloride. The bromide solution is treated with an excess of 0.1 $N$ silver nitrate solution, and the excess of this reagent is determined by titration with ammonium thiocyanate, using ferric alum indicator. One ml. of the thiocyanate should be equivalent to 1 ml. of silver nitrate solution. The formation of amber-pink ferric thiocyanate indicates the completed reaction. (Consult the procedure in the Chapter on Chlorine, page 329.)

One ml. of 0.1 $N$ $AgNO_3 = 0.007991$ g. Br.

NOTES.—1. Eosin Adsorption Indicator in Halide Titrations.—Titration of bromide with silver nitrate in presence of the adsorption indicator, eosin, is of interest. The dyestuff is adsorbed by the silver bromide with formation of a dark-red colored substance. The titration may be made in feebly acid solution, as 0.1 $N$ acetic acid, using 2–5 drops of a 0.5% sodium eosinate in water per 10 ml. of 0.1 $N$ bromide solution. More dilute solutions may be titrated using 1–2 drops of the indicator per 25 ml. of 0.01 $N$ halide. The color of the indicator changes to a bluish hue and the silver bromide separates out with an intense rose-red color. In 0.001 $N$ solutions the color changes from rose to a purplish red.

2. The Volhard method may be improved by eliminating the filtration. One method [4] is by the use of nitrobenzene. This immiscible liquid draws the silver bromide to the interface and thus removes it from the aqueous solution, the nitrobenzene forming an insoluble layer over the precipitate. Other immiscible liquids may also be used.

[4] Caldwell and Moyer, Ind. Eng. Chem., Anal. Ed., **7**, 38, 1935.

# DETERMINATION OF TRACES OF BROMINE

## BROMINATION OF MAGENTA [5]

By means of the magenta reagent, described under "Detection," small amounts of bromine may be determined colorimetrically.

*Procedure.*—To 5 ml. of the solution are added 0.2 ml. of concentrated hydrochloric acid, 1 ml. of concentrated sulfuric acid, 1 ml. of the stock magenta reagent, and 0.2 ml. of a 10% solution of potassium chromate. The mixture is shaken with addition of each reagent, then, without cooling, 1 ml. of chloroform is added. Comparison is made with a standard sample containing a known amount of bromide. A solution containing 0.001 g. bromine per liter produces a violet to reddish-violet color.

NOTE.—By means of the magenta reagent it is possible to detect bromine in the ash of plants, beet root, spinach, etc. The organic matter may be decomposed by heating in a combustion tube. Filter paper moistened with the reagent and held in the fumes of the organic substances gives the characteristic test if bromine is present.

## BROMINATION OF PHENOL RED [6]

*Procedure for 0–4 Microgram Range.*—To 1 ml. of neutral sample add 0.05 ml. of phenol red (1 mg. per 10 ml.), 0.1 ml. of a dilute manganous sulfate solution (20 mg. Mn per liter), and 0.2 ml. of saturated borax solution. Add 0.2 ml. of 0.01 $N$ calcium hypochlorite (H.T.H.; solution filtered), and let stand exactly four minutes with occasional shaking; then add 0.05 ml. of 0.1 $N$ sodium arsenite, followed by 0.20 ml. of acetate buffer (30 ml. glacial acetic acid and 68 g. of sodium acetate per liter). The color will be yellow with less than 1 $\mu$g. Br, reddish with 1.5–2 and blue-violet above 2.5 micrograms.

*Procedure for 3–18 Micrograms Range.*—The same procedure as above is used with the following quantities: 10 ml. sample; 0.2 ml. phenol red, 0.5 ml. manganous solution, 2 ml. borax, 0.2 ml. 0.1 $N$ hypochlorite, 0.5 ml. arsenite and 1.5 ml. of acetate buffer. Compare with fresh standards prepared in the same manner. Larger quantities of bromide cause the color to fade.

NOTES.—Ammonium salts and other reducing agents interfere with the action of the hypochlorite and are to be removed or oxidized. Iodide is removed by oxidation with nitrous acid: Treat 10–15 ml. of solution containing 60 mg. of iodide or less with 2 ml. of 1 $N$ H$_2$SO$_4$ and 1 ml. of 0.5 $M$ NaNO$_2$. Boil to expel iodine and replace the water lost by evaporation.

Chlorides may cause fading if present in a ratio to bromine exceeding 10,000 to 1.

# DETERMINATION OF BROMATES

## BY REDUCTION WITH ARSENIOUS ACID

Bromic acid may be reduced by arsenious acid in accordance with the reaction $3AsO_3^{-3} + BrO_3^= \rightarrow 3AsO_4^{-3} + Br^-$. In the process a considerable excess of arsenious acid is added, the excess is titrated with iodine, and the bromate is calculated.

[5] Denigès, G., and Chelle, L., Ann. chim. anal., **18**, 11, 1913; Analyst, **38**, 119, 1913.

[6] Stenger, V. A., and Kolthoff, I. M., J. Am. Chem. Soc., **57**, 831, 1935. See also Hahn, F. L., Compt. rend., **197**, 245, 1933; Turner, W. J., Ind. Eng. Chem., Anal. Ed., **14**, 599, 1942.

*Procedure.*[7]—The sample of bromate, dissolved in water, is treated with a considerable excess of 0.1 $N$ arsenious oxide (dissolved in alkali hydrogen carbonate) reagent and the solution, acidified with 3–7 ml. of dilute sulfuric acid (1:1), is diluted to a volume not exceeding 200 ml. After boiling for ten minutes, the free acid is neutralized with alkali hydrogen carbonate ($NaHCO_3$ or $KHCO_3$) and the excess of arsenite is titrated with 0.1 $N$ iodine.

Let $x$ ml. equal the difference between the two titrations with 0.1 $N$ iodine (i.e., of total arsenite minus excess arsenite). Then:

$$\% \ RBrO_3 = \frac{x \ ml. \times mol. \ wt. \ RBrO_3 \times 100}{6 \times 10 \times 1000}$$

### BY THIOSULFATE TITRATION

*Procedure.*—About 1 g. of potassium iodide and a few drops of 1% sodium molybdate[8] are added to the bromate solution, followed by 10 ml. of 1:4 sulfuric acid per 50 ml. The liberated iodine is titrated with standard thiosulfate solution.

## DETERMINATIONS IN SPECIFIC SUBSTANCES

### ANALYSIS OF CRUDE POTASSIUM BROMIDE AND COMMERCIAL BROMINE

#### CHLORINE IN CRUDE POTASSIUM BROMIDE

Chlorides in the presence of bromides may be determined by Andrews' modification of Bugarszky's method, as given below.

*Procedure.*[9]—The following amounts of sample and reagents should be taken:

| Approx. Per cent Impurity as KCl | Amount Substance to be Taken (in grams) | Iodate Solution 0.2 N Required (in ml.) | 2 N HNO₃ Required (in ml.) |
|---|---|---|---|
| Over 5 | 0.6 | 36 | 20 |
| 1.5–5.0 | 1.8 | 96 | 26 |
| 0.2–1.5 | 3.6 | 186 | 35 |

The mixture is gently heated to boiling in a long-necked Kjeldahl flask inclined at an angle of 30°; potassium iodate solution is added, then nitric acid and sufficient water to make the volume about 250 ml. The boiling is continued until bromine is expelled (test steam with moistened starch-iodide paper). The mixture is boiled down to not below 90 ml. Now 1.0–1.5 ml. of 25% phosphorous acid are added and the mixture is boiled for five minutes after all the iodine has been expelled. The colorless liquid is cooled and mixed with a slight excess of 0.05 or 0.02 $N$ silver nitrate solution (according to the proportion of chloride). The excess of silver nitrate is determined by titration with standard thiocyanate with ferric nitrate as indicator. [See "Procedure for Silver Thiocyanate-Ferric Alum Method (Volhard)" for determination of chlorine.]

[7] Gooch, F. A., and Blake, J. C., Am. Jour. Sci., **14**, 285, 1902.
[8] Kolthoff, I. M., Z. anal. Chem., **60**, 348, 1921.
[9] Andrews, L. W., J. Am. Chem. Soc., **29**, 275–283, 1907; Bugarszky, S., Z. anorg. Chem., **10**, 387, 1895.

## CHLORINE IN CRUDE BROMINE

*Procedure.*—Three grams of bromine (or more if less than 0.5% chlorine is present) in 50 ml. of 4% potassium iodide solution in a glass-stoppered flask (cooled in ice during hot weather) are shaken and then transferred to a Kjeldahl flask. Sixty ml. of 0.2 $N$ $KIO_3$ solution and 24 ml. of 2 $N$ $HNO_3$ are introduced, the solution is diluted to 250 ml., and chlorine is determined as directed above.

Commercial bromine is available with less than 0.2% chlorine. Larger quantities may be detected through their effects on the specific gravity or upon the heat of reaction with potassium bromide.

## DETERMINATION OF BROMINE IN BRINES

Bromine in the form of bromide occurs in natural brines, ocean water, and "bitterns" produced by evaporation of the latter. For industrial and geochemical purposes the bromine content is frequently determined by a modification of the Doering-van der Meulen method,[10] in which bromide is oxidized to bromate by hypochlorite in a buffered solution. The excess hypochlorite is decomposed by reaction with formate and the bromate is titrated iodometrically. A correction is necessary for any iodide that may be present.

*Reagents.* **1 $N$ Potassium Hypochlorite in 0.1 $N$ Potassium Hydroxide.**—Prepare 2 liters of 1.1 $M$ potassium hydroxide. Pass in about 70 g. of chlorine, while cooling under water and mixing, until the solution is 0.98–1.02 $N$ in oxidizing value. This is tested by treating 5 ml. with water, potassium iodide, and dilute sulfuric acid, then titrating the liberated iodine with 0.1 $N$ thiosulfate. Keep the solution in a bottle painted black on the outside.

**Sodium Formate Solution, 2 $M$.**—Dissolve 80 g. of sodium hydroxide in 500 ml. of water and add a solution containing 100 g. of C.P. formic acid per 500 ml., until the mixture becomes neutral to litmus. Make up to one liter.

**Standard 0.05 $N$ Sodium Thiosulfate Solution.**

**Calcium Carbonate (U.S.P. Precipitated).**

**Potassium Fluoride.**

**Potassium Iodide.**

**Starch Indicator.**

**1:2 Hydrochloric Acid.**

**1:4 Sulfuric Acid.**

**Methyl Red Indicator (0.01% solution in water).**

**Sodium Molybdate Solution (1% in water).**

*Procedure.*—Brines containing more than 0.05% bromine should be diluted to approximately this concentration. If iron, manganese, or organic matter is present, about 100 ml. of the diluted brine should be treated with 1 g. of calcium hydroxide, mixed well, and filtered through a dry fluted paper. Pipette into a 125-ml. Erlenmeyer flask an aliquot of the filtrate, containing from 1 to 20 mg. of bromine in a volume of not more than 50 ml. Add enough water to make the total volume 50 ml. and add one drop of 0.01% methyl red indicator solution. Barely acidify with 1:2 hydrochloric acid and introduce 8 ml. of hypochlorite solution, followed by 0.5 ml. of 1:2 hydrochloric acid and enough calcium carbonate to give an excess of about 0.1 g. Introduce a few silicon carbide chips, heat the mixture to boiling and keep hot for 8 minutes, then cautiously add 5 ml.

[10] Doering, H., Z. anal. Chem., **108**, 255, 1937; van der Meulen, J. H., Chem. Weekblad, **28**, 82, 1931.

of the sodium formate solution and keep hot for 8 minutes more. Cool, add several drops of the sodium molybdate solution, and also about 1 g. of potassium fluoride if any iron is present. When ready to titrate, put in about 0.5 g. of potassium iodide and 10 ml. of 1:4 sulfuric acid. Titrate at once with 0.05 N thiosulfate, adding starch just before the end point and disregarding any return of blue color at the end.

$$\text{Total Br} + \text{I as mg. Br per liter} = \frac{\text{ml. } 0.05 \ N \text{ sodium thiosulfate} \times 666}{\text{ml. sample}}$$

Correct for any iodine present on the basis that 1.0 mg. I is equivalent to 0.63 mg. Br.

$$\text{Br (in p. p. m.)} = \frac{\text{corrected mg. Br per liter}}{\text{specific gravity}}$$

NOTES.—1. Iodine may be determined by a similar method in which bromine water is used in place of hypochlorite, at room temperature (see Chapter on Iodine). The iodine content of ocean water is too low to require a correction.

2. A diluted "Clorox" solution may be used in place of the 1 N potassium hypochlorite, but is likely to give an appreciable blank.

3. If more than 20 mg. of bromine are present, the results are likely to be low and erratic.

## METHYL BROMIDE IN AIR BY ETHANOLAMINE METHOD

The van der Meulen method [11] depends on the hydrolysis of methyl bromide by ethanolamine. The resulting bromide ion may be determined either by Volhard method, which has already been described, or by the Kolthoff-Yutzy modification,[12] in which the methyl bromide is absorbed in ethanolamine and, after addition of NaCl and NaHCO$_3$ solutions, the ethanolamine is evaporated, and the bromide oxidized to bromate with sodium hypochlorite solution. After destroying the excess of the latter with sodium formate solution, iodide is added and the resulting iodine titrated with sodium thiosulfate solution.

*Procedure.*—Air samples are taken in large 1 or 2 liter bottles, which should be previously evacuated or, if not, very well flushed in sampling. Insert into the bottle 2 ml. of ethanolamine that is within a soft glass container, and immediately replace the bottle stopper. Invert or shake the bottle to break container and allow 0.25 hour for the reaction to go to completion. Wash the sample into a 250-ml. flask, add 0.5 g. of sodium bicarbonate and 0.5 ml. of saturated sodium chloride solution, and evaporate to fumes of ethanolamine, but not below 10 ml. Connect a steam supply to pass steam through the flask, and continue evaporation to dryness. After cooling, resume passage of steam until residue is dissolved in condensate. Dilute with water to 50 ml. Add 2.5 ml. of saturated sodium chloride solution, 1 g. of sodium dihydrogen phosphate monohydrate, and 2 ml. N sodium hypochlorite solution that is 0.1 N in sodium hydroxide. Heat to boiling, discontinue heating, and add a solution of 1 g. sodium formate in 2 ml. of water. Boil for 2 minutes. Cool, dilute to 75 ml., add 1 drop of 1% sodium molybdate solution and dilute to 100 ml. Add 0.5 g. of potassium iodide and 10 ml. of 6 N sulfuric acid. Titrate at once with 0.01 N sodium thiosulfate solution, adding a few drops of 1% starch solution near the end of the titration. A blank run on the ethanolamine is necessary.

[11] van der Meulen, Chem. Weekblad, **28**, 82, 1931.
[12] Kolthoff, I. M., and Yutzy, H. C., Ind. Eng. Chem., Anal. Ed., **9**, 75, 1937.

# BROMINATED (HALOGENATED) HYDROCARBONS IN AIR

## *SULFUR LAMP METHOD*

The basis of this method [13] is the absorption of the vapor in a combustible solvent, its decomposition by combustion of the latter, and determination of the released halogen.

**Apparatus. Standard Absorption Apparatus (Bubbling Type).**[14]

**A.S.T.M. Sulfur Lamp.**—Shown in Fig. 9-1.

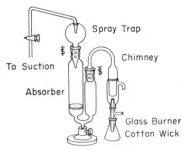

**Procedure.**—Pass a sufficient sample, usually about 50 l. through 60–80 ml. of amyl acetate in a bubbling absorber, at a rate not exceeding 1 l. per minute. Transfer to a 100 ml. graduated cylinder. Rinse absorber with three 5-ml. portions of amyl acetate and add to cylinder. Mix and transfer weighed aliquot to burner flask in Fig. 9-1. Charge absorber with 25 ml. 0.01 $N$ sodium hydroxide **solution.** Burn for two hours and reweigh to determine solvent consumed. Transfer contents of absorber to 200-ml. casserole, neutralize with

Fig. 9-1. Sulfur Lamp for Brominated (or other Halogenated) Hydrocarbons.

0.03 $N$ nitric acid solution using methyl red indicator. Evaporate to 4 ml., add a few drops of saturated potassium dichromate solution, cool, and titrate with 0.01 $N$ silver nitrate solution to a permanent red color.

## METHODS FOR BROMINE IN ANALYSES IN OTHER CHAPTERS

Carius Method for Organic Compounds          See Chlorine Chapter

[13] Wirth and Stross, Ind. Eng. Chem., Anal. Ed., **5,** 85, 1933; Malisoff, Ind. Eng. Chem., Anal. Ed., **7,** 428, 1935.

[14] Elkins, Hobby and Fuller, J. Ind. Hyg. Toxical., **19,** 474, 1937.

*Chapter* 10

# CADMIUM *

**Cd, *at. wt.* 112.40; *sp. gr.* 8.65 (at 20°C.); *m.p.* 320.9°C.; *b.p.* 767°C.; *oxide* CdO**

Cadmium occurs in small quantities in practically all zinc ores. It is found in most slab zinc and zinc materials, sheet zinc, zinc oxide, etc. In ores it occurs usually as sulfide, the rare mineral greenockite being CdS. The metal cadmium is largely obtained as a by-product from zinc smelting.

Cadmium is used in alloys. Its alloy with gold is green colored, a popular metal in jewelry; its alloy with silver resists tarnishing. The metal coating is used for rust proofing articles. Added to copper it increases the tensile strength of this metal. It is used in certain alloys as trial plates for silver coinage, and more recently as substitutes for tin base bearing metals. It is used as a paint pigment as the yellow sulfide. It is contained in some dental amalgams.

Cadmium was discovered in zinc carbonate by Stromeyer and simultaneously it was discovered by Hermann in zinc oxide (1817).

## DETECTION

The sample is dissolved in aqua regia followed by sulfuric acid, heating until the fumes of $H_2SO_4$ are strongly evident. The cooled residue is extracted with water and tests made on the extract.

*Hydrogen Sulfide Test.*—Cadmium is detected in the *wet way* by precipitation as the yellow sulfide by hydrogen sulfide from an acid solution. It is distinguished from arsenic, antimony, and tin (stannic) by the insolubility of its sulfide in ammonium hydroxide or colorless ammonium sulfide; from tin (stannous) by its insolubility in yellow ammonium sulfide; and from mercury by its solubility in warm dilute nitric acid. The separation of cadmium may be made from lead since cadmium sulfate is soluble in dilute sulfuric acid while lead sulfate is not; from bismuth since ammonium hydroxide precipitates bismuth hydroxide but holds cadmium in solution, and from copper by passing hydrogen sulfide into the solution containing potassium cyanide which prevents the precipitation of copper sulfide but not cadmium sulfide.

*Blowpipe Tests, Dry Methods.*—The detection of cadmium may be made in the *dry way* through the tube test. This test is carried out in the following manner. A piece of hard glass tubing of about 5 mm. bore is sealed at one end. From 200 to 400 milligrams of the fine dried ore is mixed with a reducing agent as dry powdered charcoal and introduced into the tube.[1] The tube is heated just above

---

* Original Chapter by L. S. Holstein and L. A. Wilson. Revised for the 5th Edition by L. A. Wilson, and for the 6th Edition by R. G. Mercer with the assistance of H. E. Maddock and S. N. Roeder, all of The New Jersey Zinc Co.

[1] All metals present in the ore must be in the oxidized state. Sulfide ores must be carefully roasted before using in this test. In the case of metallic substances, however, no reducing agent is necessary.

the mixture of ore and reducing agent and drawn out to a capillary of about 1 mm. diameter. The end of the tube containing the mixture is now heated in the blast lamp and the cadmium together with zinc, arsenic, antimony, etc., is volatilized and condensed in the capillary in the form of separated rings. The cadmium ring is detected from the others by introducing a little powdered sulfur into the tube and heating so that the sulfur vapor passes over the rings. The cadmium

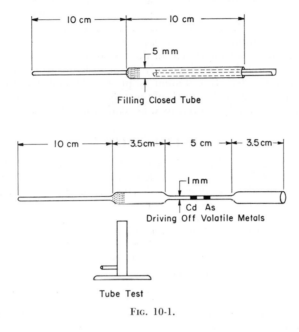

Fig. 10-1.

is converted to sulfide and appears red while hot and yellow while cold. Very small amounts of cadmium may be detected in this way and it is possible with experience to estimate, from the appearance of the ring, the amount of cadmium present. See Fig. 10-1.

Heated on charcoal in the reducing flame, cadmium gives a brown incrustation which is volatile.

*Spectrum.*—The characteristic lines of cadmium are a red line (6438.49 A), a green line (5085.92 A) and a blue line (4799.96 A) in the visible portion of the spectral range.

*Detection of Cadmium in Plated Ware.*—Goldstone [2] devised a method for the detection of cadmium on plated ware which is performed easily in the field. This method is a refinement and adaptation of the laboratory method proposed by Coleman. It depends on the precipitation of yellow cadmium sulfide in the presence of excess cyanide.

**Reagents.** *Ammonia-Sodium Nitrate Solution.*—Dissolve 200 ml. of 28% ammonia and 100 g. of sodium nitrate in water and dilute with water to 1 liter.

[2] Jacobs, M. B., Chemical Analysis of Food and Food Products, Van Nostrand, Princeton, 1958.

*Sodium Sulfide Solution.*—Dissolve 100 g. of sodium sulfide in water and dilute with water to 1 liter.

*Potassium Cyanide Solution.*—Dissolve 100 g. of potassium cyanide in water and dilute with water to 1 liter.

**Procedure.**—To a small pinch of the metal scrapings in a test tube, add 3 ml. of the ammonia-sodium nitrate reagent; bring the mixture to a boil over a flame and allow to stand for a minute or two. Pour the clear supernatant liquid into another test tube, add 1 ml. of the cyanide reagent and, after shaking, add 1 drop of sodium sulfide reagent. This produces a canary yellow precipitate if cadmium is present. The metals, iron, tin, antimony, arsenic, silver, copper, nickel, chromium, zinc, and aluminum do not interfere. In the case of zinc and aluminum, a whitish gray precipitate is formed which is readily distinguishable from the canary yellow color of cadmium sulfide. If cadmium is present in addition to any of these metals, it is instantly detected. The only metals which do interfere are lead and mercury, but these are rarely, if ever, used as plating metals under these conditions.

## ESTIMATION

The determination of cadmium is required in slab zinc sold under specified rejection limits, and in ores to be smelted for slab zinc. It is determined in zinciferous materials where cadmium is deleterious to the finished product.

It is determined in ores, especially zinc bearing in which it commonly occurs, in alloys, paint pigments, and amalgams.

Cadmium may be determined after separation from other elements by weighing the CdS (the accuracy of this method has been questioned); [3] by converting the sulfide to sulfate and weighing; as the metal following electrolysis or by titration with iodine of the $H_2S$ liberated from CdS.

### PREPARATION AND SOLUTION OF THE SAMPLE

Samples of metals, as slab zinc, cadmium metal, brass, etc., should be in the form of drillings, sawings, or pourings, taken in a proper manner to be representative of the lot and of sufficient fineness to preclude a nonrepresentative sample being weighed for analysis. The samples of ore or fine material should be ground to pass a 100-mesh screen. Metallics, if also present, are kept separate from the fine material which passes through the screen, and in weighing out the sample, proportional amounts of each are taken.

*Metallic cadmium* is slowly soluble in hot, moderately dilute hydrochloric acid and in hot dilute sulfuric acid. It is readily soluble in nitric acid. The oxide of cadmium is soluble in mineral acids.

*Ores.*—Decomposition is best effected by the action of hydrochloric acid, followed later by nitric acid, or by the immediate treatment with aqua regia. When the action has subsided sulfuric acid is added and the solution taken to fumes. The cooled solution is now extracted with water and filtered from the silica and lead sulfate residue.

*Carbonates* are best decomposed with hydrochloric acid.

*Alloys, Slab Zinc, Amalgams.*—These are decomposed by action of hydrochloric acid, aqua regia, followed by sulfuric acid and expulsion of $HNO_3$ (and HCl) by taking to strong white fumes of $H_2SO_4$.

[3] See method following "Separation of Cadmium as Cadmium Sulfide."

## SEPARATIONS

*Removal of Silica and Lead.*—Evaporate to fumes with sulfuric acid, cool, take up with water, warm until all soluble salts are dissolved. Allow to stand until the lead has settled and filter. Any lead remaining in solution may be removed later as covered under separation of cadmium as cadmium sulfide.

*Separation from Ammonium Sulfide Group (Except Zn), Alkaline Earths, and Alkalies.*—The solution from lead and silica separation containing 12 ml. sulfuric acid (1:1) per 100 ml. of solution is saturated cold with hydrogen sulfide, passing a steady stream for twenty to thirty minutes, and after the first five minutes adding a drop of ammonium hydroxide and continuing until zinc sulfide precipitates in quantity. It is necessary to add ammonium hydroxide to bring down zinc in order to assure the complete precipitation of cadmium. The precipitate of sulfides is filtered off and washed with cold water.

*Removal of Arsenic, Antimony, and Tin.*—The precipitate on the filter is washed with ammonium hydroxide or colorless ammonium sulfide, dissolving out the arsenic, antimony, and tin (stannic). If tin in the stannous condition is found to be present, yellow ammonium sulfide must be used. This treatment is not always necessary since arsenious sulfide is practically insoluble in the hydrochloric acid of the concentration (1:2) used in dissolving the cadmium sulfide. Antimonious sulfide is also only slightly soluble, so that these sulfides remain behind in carrying out the analysis.

Tin may be removed with the bismuth by precipitation with ammonium hydroxide as described in the following.

*Removal of Bismuth, Copper, and Mercury.*—Bismuth is not removed in the course of analysis as its sulfide is soluble in hydrochloric acid and hence it must be removed by precipitating with ammonium hydroxide before the final precipitation of cadmium is made. Copper sulfide is, however, practically insoluble in the hydrochloric acid used and remains behind when dissolving the first precipitates of cadmium sulfide. Mercuric sulfide is practically insoluble in cold hydrochloric acid (1:2) and is left behind in carrying out the analysis.

*Separation from Zinc.*—Cadmium is separated from the accompanying zinc by successive precipitations with hydrogen sulfide, each time bringing down less zinc, until finally only cadmium is precipitated. In the presence of a large quantity of zinc it is not possible to precipitate all cadmium with the acidity required to prevent the precipitation of any zinc sulfide.

See further details for the separation of cadmium under "Gravimetric Methods."

## GRAVIMETRIC METHODS

### SEPARATION OF CADMIUM AS CADMIUM SULFIDE

*Procedure.*—A 10-g. sample of the finely pulverized ore is weighed out into a 400-ml. beaker, moistened with water, and 50 ml. of aqua regia carefully added.[4]

---

[4] This procedure is also applicable for slab zinc, alloys, etc. A 10-g. sample is suitable for materials containing about 0.1% to 1.0% Cd. It is necessary when other amounts of samples are taken to vary the quantity of sulfuric acid so that approximately 7% of free acid is present before precipitating.

When violent action has stopped, the beaker is placed on a warm plate to complete decomposition. The cover glass and sides of beaker are washed down with water, 25 ml. of sulfuric acid (1:1) added, and evaporation carried to fumes. Water (100 ml.) is added, boiled until all soluble salts are dissolved, and the residue filtered off, and washed, using suction.

A steady stream of hydrogen sulfide is passed through the filtrate, which should have a volume of approximately 300 ml., for 30 to 40 minutes. After all iron in solution has been reduced, ammonium hydroxide is added 1 ml. at a time until a heavy precipitation of zinc sulfide has taken place.[5] The precipitate is allowed to settle, the clear solution decanted, and finally the bulk of the precipitate transferred to a 15-cm. paper, and washed with cold water. The sulfides on the paper are dissolved with hydrochloric acid (1:2) catching the solution in a clean beaker. Any precipitate adhering to the sides of the original beaker is also dissolved off and poured into the filter. After all zinc sulfide has been dissolved, the paper is washed three more times with the hydrochloric acid.[6] To the solution 15 ml. of sulfuric acid (1:1) is added and evaporation carried just to fumes. Water is added (200 ml.) and hydrogen sulfide passed through as before. Ammonium hydroxide should be added one drop at a time, only to start the precipitation of cadmium sulfide. This precipitate is filtered off, redissolved as previously, and a third precipitation made.[7] Before making the final precipitation, the solution should be allowed to stand, and any lead sulfate filtered off. The final precipitate of cadmium sulfide is filtered on a weighed Gooch crucible. After drying at 110°C. for one hour, the crucible is cooled, reweighed, and the cadmium calculated from the difference in weights.[8]

$$CdS \times 0.778 = Cd$$

The cadmium sulfide need only be washed once or twice, as it usually receives sufficient washing in the transfer to the filter, and in the scrubbing and washing out of the beaker.

NOTES.—It is seldom that bismuth and tin will be encountered in making a determination for cadmium so that the procedure for removing these elements need rarely be used. Cadmium sulfide precipitated from sulfuric acid is bright yellow to orange. If the precipitate is brown in color, bismuth and tin should be looked for and removed.

## DETERMINATION OF CADMIUM AS CADMIUM SULFATE

Cadmium separated from other elements as CdS may now be converted to $CdSO_4$ and so determined.

*Procedure.*—The final precipitate of cadmium sulfide is dissolved with hydrochloric acid, and evaporated to dryness in a weighed platinum crucible or dish. A slight excess of dilute sulfuric acid is poured over the residue and evaporated

[5] The solution should always be sufficiently acid so that no iron, etc., precipitates.

[6] This strength of acid will leave on the paper as an insoluble residue all the As, Cu, and Hg, most of the Sb, and some of the Bi and Sn. The second precipitation of CdS should free the Cd of the rest of the Sb, but not the Bi or Sn.

[7] It is necessary to make three or even four precipitations of cadmium sulfide in order to free it completely of zinc. The filtrates may be readily tested for zinc by adding a few drops of a 10% solution of potassium ferrocyanide. Not more than a slight turbidity should be present in the filtrate from the final precipitation.

[8] Results will be slightly high—approximately 3%—because the composition of the precipitate is not exactly CdS. Where greater accuracy is desired, weighing the cadmium as cadmium sulfate or an electrolytic determination of the cadmium is recommended.

over a steam bath or warm plate. The excess of sulfuric acid is driven off by heating in an air bath, or in a muffle heated below a dull red heat. For an air bath, the crucible or dish may be placed in a larger vessel, and this outer vessel heated to redness.

$$CdSO_4 \times 0.5392 = Cd$$

## ELECTROLYTIC DETERMINATION OF CADMIUM

The final precipitate of CdS is dissolved and the cadmium determined electrolytically as given under cadmium in slab zinc, Chapter on Zinc, or if the amount of cadmium is large the electrolytic determination is best carried out with a potassium cyanide electrolyte.

*Procedure.*—The hydrochloric acid solution of cadmium, after separation of interfering elements, is taken to fumes with sulfuric acid, a drop of phenolphthalein added for indicator, and a pure solution of sodium hydroxide added until a permanent red color is obtained. A strong solution of potassium cyanide is added drop by drop until the cadmium hydroxide just dissolves, avoiding any excess. The solution is diluted to 100 ml. with water, electrolyzed cold using a gauze electrode with a current of 0.5–0.7 ampere and voltage of 4.8–5.0. At the end of five to six hours the current is increased to 1–1.2 amperes and electrolysis continued for an hour more. The electrode is removed from the solution the instant the current is broken and immediately washed with water, followed by alcohol and ether. After drying at 100°C., the electrode is cooled and weighed. Prolonged heating of the deposit should be avoided.

**Rapid deposition** can be effected by means of the rotating anode (600 revolutions per minute). The solution of cadmium sulfate containing 3 ml. of $H_2SO_4$ (1:10) per 150 ml., heated to boiling, is electrolyzed with a current of $N.D._{100} = 5$ amperes, E.M.F. = 8–9 volts. Fifteen minutes is sufficient for the deposition of 0.5 g. of cadmium.[9]

NOTES.—Before washing and discontinuing the current, it is advisable to add a little water to raise the level of the liquid and continue the electrolysis to ascertain whether the deposition is complete.

Traces of cadmium may be estimated in the above solution by saturating this with $H_2S$ and comparing the yellow-colored colloidal cadmium sulfide solution with a known quantity of cadmium and the same amounts of potassium hydroxide and cyanide as in the solution tested.

## TITRIMETRIC METHODS

### TITRATION OF CADMIUM SULFIDE WITH IODINE [10]

The method is applicable to the determination of from 10 mg. to 200 mg. or more, and depends upon the following reaction:

$$CdS + 2HCl + I_2 \rightarrow CdCl_2 + 2HI + S$$

Low results are apt to be obtained—as much as 8% for 0.2 g. Cd and 4% for

9 Smith, E. F., Electro Analysis, P. Blakiston's Son & Co., Phila., Pa.

10 P. von Berg (Z. anal. Chem., **26**, 23, 1887) transfers the precipitate and filter to a stoppered flask, expels the air with $CO_2$ and by boiling and then titrates in an hydrochloric acid solution. Experiments by the author have shown this caution to be unnecessary.

0.05 g.—because the precipitate is not pure CdS but contains some of the cadmium in the form of the sulfate.

*Procedure.*—The amount of the sample taken should be such that the cadmium content is between 10 mg. to 200 mg. and the material is treated as outlined in the gravimetric method.

The precipitate of CdS is washed and allowed to drain on the filter. The filter, together with the sulfide, is placed in a beaker or an Erlenmeyer flask, water added, and the whole shaken to break up the precipitate. A moderate quantity of hydrochloric acid is added and the solution titrated with standard 0.2 $N$ or 0.1 $N$ iodine solution. Towards the end a little starch solution is added and the titration continued until the excess of iodine colors the solution blue. If preferred, an excess of iodine solution may be added and the excess determined by a back-titration with standard thiosulfate solution.

One ml. 0.1 $N$ iodine = 0.00562 g. cadmium.

## OTHER TITRIMETRIC METHODS

Cadmium is precipitated quantitatively by sodium anthranilate from a neutral solution. Zinc, nickel, copper, and cobalt form similar precipitates under the same conditions, but the alkali and alkaline earth ions are not precipitated.[11] The precipitate may be weighed, or it may be dissolved and titrated by the bromate-bromide excess method.[12]

Cadmium pyridine thiocyanate may be precipitated, filtered and the excess of thiocyanate titrated with standard silver nitrate.[13]

## PHOTOMETRIC METHOD

### DITHIZONE METHOD

This method has been extended to solutions containing other cations.[14] Copper and iron are removed by extraction of the cupferrates with $CHCl_3$. Cadmium is separated from the remaining cations, including zinc, by extraction into $CHCl_3$ as the brucine-cadmium iodide complex. Cadmium is removed from the $CHCl_3$ by a dilute solution of HCl, the solution made basic with NaOH, and the cadmium extracted as the colored dithizonate with $CCl_4$.

*Apparatus.* **Spectrophotometer or Filter Photometer.**—Equipped with a filter having maximum transmittance near 510 m$\mu$.

**Separatory Funnels, 125-ml. Squibb Type.**—Amber ware is best, but not essential.

**Electrodeposition Apparatus.**—For standardizing the cadmium stock solution.

**Amber Volumetric Flasks with Ground-glass Stoppers.**—These are desirable, but not essential.

*Reagents.*—**Acetic Acid, Glacial.**

**Bromine Water.**—Distilled water saturated with bromine.

**Brucine Sulfate Solution.**—Dissolve 2 g. of brucine sulfate in 100 ml. of a 5% solution of acetic acid. Warm to 60° to 70°C. if necessary to dissolve the crystals.

**Cadmium Chloride Standard Solution.**—Prepare a stock solution so that the cadmium concentration is approximately 1,000 p. p. m. Pipette 25.00 ml. of the stock solution into an electrolytic beaker and make alkaline to phenolphthalein

[11] Funk and Ditt, Z. anal. Chem., **91,** 332, 1933.
[12] Shennan, Smith and Ward, Analyst, **61,** 395, 1936.
[13] Spacu and Kuras, Z. anal. Chem., **99,** 26, 1934.
[14] Butts, Gahler and Mellon, Sewage and Industrial Wastes, **22,** 12, 1950.

indicator with NaOH. Add 10% sodium or potassium cyanide dropwise until the precipitate of $Cd(OH)_2$ just dissolves. Dilute the solution to 100 ml. with water, and electrolyze for 30 minutes at a current density of 0.6 amp. per sq. dm., then for 30 minutes more at 1.2 amp. per sq. dm. Test for complete deposition by passing $H_2S$ through a small sample of the electrolyte. If a yellow precipitate or color forms, continue the electrolysis until no cadmium remains in solution. Wash the plated platinum cathode in ethanol, dry at 110°C. for 3–5 minutes, cool, and weigh. Dissolve the cadmium in $H_2SO_4$ (1:1), wash the electrode, dry, and weigh as before. The difference in weight is the amount of cadmium present in the aliquot taken. If $Cd(NO_3)_2$ is used instead of $CdCl_2$, the sample taken for electrolysis must be fumed with $H_2SO_4$ to remove the nitrate.

**Carbon Tetrachloride, C.P.**—If the $CCl_4$ is not C.P., it must be redistilled. Pure $CCl_4$ may be obtained by refluxing the impure material with 5% NaOH for 2 hours, separating the $CCl_4$ from the NaOH, washing the $CCl_4$ with water, drying over $CaCl_2$, and then distilling over CaO.

**Chloroform, C.P.**

**Cotton.**—Metal-free absorbent cotton is prepared by digesting the cotton for several hours with warm 0.2 $N$ HCl. The cotton is filtered on a Buechner funnel, washed with large volumes of distilled water to remove the acid completely, and dried.

**Cupferron Reagent, Aqueous 1% (Ammonium Salt of Nitrosophenylhydroxylamine).**—Store in refrigerator or make up fresh for each determination.

**Dithizone Solution, 20 mg. Dithizone per 100 ml. of $CCl_4$.**—Dissolve 0.100 g. of diphenylthiocarbazone in 500 ml. of pure $CCl_4$. Store in a dark bottle in a cool place, preferably in a refrigerator.

**Dithizone Solution, 10 mg. Dithizone per 100 ml. of $CCl_4$.**—Purify the solution containing 20 mg. dithizone in 100 ml. of $CCl_4$ just before use as follows: Measure 75 ml. of the dithizone solution into a 250-ml. separatory funnel, add 75 ml. of distilled water, and then 8 ml. of 6 $M$ $NH_4OH$. Shake well, discard the $CCl_4$ layer, and shake with portions of fresh $CCl_4$ until the $CCl_4$ layer becomes colorless. Add 75 ml. of pure $CCl_4$, make acidic with 6 $M$ HCl and shake. Draw off the $CCl_4$ layer, wash with a 100 ml. portion of distilled water, and dilute the $CCl_4$ to 150 ml. The solution should be repurified if allowed to stand more than one-half day.

**Hydrochloric Acid, C.P., 0.5 $M$.**

**Hydroxylamine Hydrochloride Solution.**—Dissolve 10 g. of $NH_2OH \cdot HCl$ in 90 ml. of distilled water.

**Methyl Red Indicator.**—A 0.1% solution in 95% ethanol.

**Potassium Iodide, C.P.**—Dissolve 10 g. of KI in 90 ml. of water.

**Sodium Citrate, C.P.**—Dissolve 10 g. of $Na_3C_6H_5O_7 \cdot 2H_2O$ in 90 ml. of water.

**Sodium Hydroxide, C.P.**—Dissolve 20 g. of NaOH in 80 ml. of water.

**Water.**—Redistilled water free from all metals is essential for preparation of reagent solutions.

*Preparation of Calibration Curve.*—Prepare a dilute cadmium solution from the stock solution so that the cadmium concentration is about 2.5 p. p. m. Pipette suitable volumes of this solution into 125-ml. separatory funnels so that from 3 to 17.5 micrograms of cadmium are present in the samples. Carry through the operations as described under "Procedure." The absorbancy-concentration calibration curve should be a straight line for this range of concentration.

*Procedure.* **Separation of Copper and Iron.**—Take an aliquot containing from 3 to 17.5 micrograms of cadmium, place in a separatory funnel, add 10 ml. of sodium citrate, one drop of methyl red indicator, and enough dilute NaOH to make the solution just basic to the indicator. Add 2–3 ml. of glacial acetic acid to adjust the pH to 3.0 to 3.8. Cool the solution by running cold tap water over the separatory funnel. Add 4 ml. of cold, fresh cupferron reagent and shake the solution with 10 ml. of $CHCl_3$. Allow the layers to separate, and add more cupferron until a white silky precipitate forms, which indicates that an excess of cupferron is present. Shake the mixture, allow the layers to separate, and discard the $CHCl_3$ layer. Repeat with a fresh 10-ml. portion of $CHCl_3$. Add 1 ml. of bromine water, mix, let stand 1 minute, extract excess bromine water with 5 ml. of $CHCl_3$, and then add 1 ml. of $NH_2OH \cdot HCl$ solution.

**Separation of Cadmium from Chromium, Lead, Nickel, Manganese, and Zinc.**— Five ml. of KI solution and 5 ml. of brucine sulfate reagent are added to the solution from the previous separation. Extract three times with 15 ml. portions of $CHCl_3$ and collect the $CHCl_3$ layers in another 125-ml. separatory funnel. (This separatory funnel should have been cleaned thoroughly to remove metal ions by shaking in the funnel about 10 ml. of dithizone solution with some pure water to which a few drops of dilute NaOH have been added, and finally rinsing with redistilled water.) Re-extract the cadmium into the aqueous phase with 20 ml. of HCl. Allow the phases to separate. Transfer the $CHCl_3$ layer to another clean separatory funnel and wash with 10 ml. of HCl. Discard the $CHCl_3$ layer. Add the wash solution to the other solution containing cadmium. Rinse the stopper and funnel with about 10 ml. of distilled water, and add it to the cadmium solution. After the addition of 30 ml. of NaOH to the cadmium solution, cool the solution to room temperature. Extract the cadmium with one 10-ml. portion of recently purified dithizone in $CCl_4$ (10 mg. dithizone in 100 ml. of $CCl_4$). Allow the layer to stand at least 1 minute before drawing off the $CCl_4$. Pass the $CCl_4$ through a small pledget of cotton in a short-stem funnel placed in a dry 25-ml. volumetric flask. Repeat the extraction with two 5-ml. portions of dithizone and one 4-ml. portion of fresh $CCl_4$. Dilute to volume with fresh $CCl_4$, mix, and measure the absorbancy of the solution at 510 m$\mu$ in a 1-cm. cell using $CCl_4$ in the reference cell.

During the extraction of the cadmium with dithizone it is advisable to darken the room, if amber glassware is not used. A towel may be wrapped around the volumetric flasks to prevent sunlight from affecting the light-sensitive solution. A blank is not necessary if the dithizone solution has been recently purified.

## DETERMINATIONS IN SPECIFIC SUBSTANCES

### DETERMINATION OF CADMIUM IN METALLIC CADMIUM

*Procedure.*—One gram of the metal is dissolved in a 400-ml. beaker, after addition of a few ml. of water, by 10 to 15 ml. of $HNO_3$ and warming gently. Ten ml. of $H_2SO_4$ are now added and the solution evaporated to strong fumes, using care to prevent splattering. After cooling, 100 ml. of water are added and the solution heated to boiling, then cooled and filtered if a precipitate ($PbSO_4$) is present.

The filtrate is carefully neutralized by addition of dilute $NH_4OH$ (litmus indicator) and diluted to 250 ml. Five ml. of concentrated $H_2SO_4$ are added and the solution saturated with $H_2S$ (30 minutes). The sulfide is filtered off and the filtrate tested for zinc by addition of $NH_4OH$. If much zinc is evident by the cloudy precipitate forming (ZnS) it is advisable to repeat the precipitation of CdS to eliminate the ZnS occluded. The precipitate on the filter is dissolved in warm HCl (1:1) and the precipitation of CdS repeated according to the directions above.

The purified sulfide is dissolved in hot HCl (1:1) in the original beaker in which the precipitation was made. Twenty to 25 ml. of concentrated $H_2SO_4$ are added and the solution evaporated to small bulk on the steam bath, then on a hot plate to near dryness. After cooling 20 ml. of water are added, the sulfate brought into solution by warming and the solution transferred to a weighed porcelain crucible. The rinsings of the beaker are placed in a second weighed crucible. The solutions in both crucibles are evaporated to dryness on a steam plate.

The residues are heated to expel free sulfuric acid and then ignited in a muffle below a red heat and the sulfates weighed. The results are excellent, a high degree of accuracy being obtained.

## DETERMINATION OF CADMIUM IN ORES, SLAGS, METALS, ETC.

*Polarographic Determination.*—This determination is made using the method given under "Polarographic Determination of Zinc, Cadmium and Copper in Ores, Slags and Metals" in the Chapter on Zinc.

## METHODS FOR CADMIUM IN ANALYSES IN OTHER CHAPTERS

Cadmium in Slab Zinc       See Analyses of Slab Zinc

# Chapter 11

# CALCIUM

Ca, *at. wt.* 40.08; *sp. gr.* 1.5446 (at 29°C.); *m.p.* 842°–848°C.; *b.p.* 1240°C.; * *oxide,* CaO

This exceedingly important and widely distributed element occurs in nature only in combined state. It is estimated that calcium forms 3.5 per cent of the earth's crust. It occurs combined as carbonate, sulfate, phosphate, fluoride, silicate, and in a large number of complex compounds associated with a number of elements, among which are silicon, iron, aluminum, boron, titanium, sodium, and potassium. Among the better known minerals are calcite, limestone, iceland spar, dolomite, anhydrite, gypsum, fluorite or fluor spar, and apatite. Calcium is found in nearly all mineral springs, artesian and river water, principally as bicarbonate. As oxalate it occurs in plants; as phosphate in bones of animals. It is an essential constituent of many rock forming minerals.

Calcium oxide or lime has been known for many centuries. It was for a long period considered to be an elementary substance. Davy believed the substance to be made up of an oxide and a metal, but was not successful in his attempt to obtain the pure element, although he paved the way to its isolation by electrolysis of the chloride.

Lime is an important constituent of cement, lime stucco, and plaster. Its numerous uses in the industries, in building materials, in pharmaceutical preparations, in insecticides, in the beet sugar industry, in tanning, in the dairy in butter-making, in the paper industry, etc., are well known.

Metallic calcium and calcium hydride, $CaH_2$, are powerful reductants and are sometimes used to produce metals by reduction of their oxides. Calcium hydride produces two moles of hydrogen per mole of $CaH_2$ when it reacts with water and has been used for the inflation of balloons.

## DETECTION

In the usual course of qualitative and quantitative analysis calcium passes into the filtrates from the elements precipitated by hydrogen sulfide in acid and alkaline solutions (Ag, Hg(I), Hg(II), Pb, Cu, Cd, As, Sb, Sn, Fe, Cr, Al, Mn, Ni, Co, Zn, etc.), and is precipitated from an ammoniacal solution by ammonium carbonate as calcium carbonate along with the carbonates of barium and strontium. The separation of calcium from barium and strontium is considered under Separations. The oxalate of calcium is the least soluble of the alkaline-earth group. All, however, are soluble in mineral acids. Calcium oxalate may be precipitated from weak

* Handbook of Chemistry and Physics, 42nd Edition, 1960–61.

acetic acid solution by ammonium oxalate, or from neutral solutions by oxalic acid, as a colorless crystalline compound, $CaC_2O_4 \cdot H_2O$.

*Flame Test.*—The flame of a Bunsen burner is colored yellowish red when a platinum wire containing calcium salt moistened with concentrated hydrochloric acid is held in the flame.

*Spectrum.*—An intense orange and green line with a less distinct violet line.

See also the Chapter on Barium under Separations—Preliminary Tests.

## ESTIMATION

In practically all complete analyses of rocks, minerals, soils, water the determination of calcium is necessary. Its estimation is required in the analysis of mortar, cement, bleaching powder, plaster of Paris, certain paint pigments, fluorescent paint (CaS), plant ash, certain fertilizers, etc.

In analytical procedures and separations it should be kept in mind that the sulfates of the alkaline earths are difficultly soluble, so that in presence of sulfates, combined barium, calcium, and strontium are apt to remain, wholly or in part with the silica residue, and must be recovered there. If fluorine has not been expelled in the preliminary treatment, calcium will precipitate with iron and aluminum when ammonia is added, $CaF_2$ being insoluble in ammoniacal solutions. If phosphates are present and iron is not present in sufficient amount of take care of $PO_4$, calcium will precipitate with the ammonium sulfide group when the solution is made ammoniacal, causing an error in the aluminum determination as well as that of calcium.

The alkaline earths are best converted to chlorides by the action of HCl on their ores. The silica residue remaining from the acid extraction is fused with $Na_2CO_3$, extracted with water to remove sodium silicate and the carbonate residue dissolved in HCl. Calcium will be found in the hydrochloric acid solutions.

## PREPARATION AND SOLUTION OF THE SAMPLE

The oxide, hydroxide, carbonate, phosphate, and fluoride of calcium are soluble in hydrochloric or nitric acids. The sulfates (gypsum, anhydrite, etc.), certain silicates and complex compounds require fusion with $Na_2CO_3$ followed by solution in water and hydrochloric acid. Characteristic substances will be considered. Special products will receive attention later.

*Decomposition of Material.*—Though carbonates are easily dissolved in hydrochloric acid, sulfates and fluorides of calcium require fusion with sodium or potassium carbonate to effect decomposition. In case calcium fluoride is being decomposed, the addition of an equal weight or more of silica is necessary, and sodium or potassium hydroxide may be substituted for potassium carbonate. The fusion is leached with water to remove the mineral acids, and the residue, containing all of the calcium, is dissolved in hydrochloric acid. Calcium is now determined in the hydrochloric acid solution. If phosphate is present in the sample, it is not completely removed by the water leaching as sodium phosphate, as this reacts in the solution with calcium carbonate causing a partial conversion to calcium phosphate, which remains in the residue. In this case it is advisable to precipitate calcium oxalate by addition of ammonium oxalate from a slightly acid solution, in which calcium phosphate will not precipitate, as it would if the solution was made ammoniacal.

*Solution of Limestones, Dolomites, Magnesites, Cements, Lime, etc.*—One gram of the powdered material is digested in a 250-ml. beaker with 20 ml. of water, 5 ml. of concentrated hydrochloric acid, and 2 or 3 drops of nitric acid (sp. gr. 1.42). The beaker is covered to prevent loss by effervescence. When the violent action has subsided, the sample is placed on a hot plate and boiled for a few minutes. The watch glass is rinsed into the beaker and the solution filtered. The residue is washed, dried and ignited in a platinum crucible, and then fused with a little sodium carbonate or bicarbonate. The cooled fusion is dissolved in hot dilute hydrochloric acid, the liquid added to the main solution and calcium determined by precipitation as calcium oxalate, after removal of silica, iron, alumina, etc.

In presence of sulfates it may be advisable to leach out the silica before dissolving the water insoluble carbonates containing the alkaline earths.

*Silicates.*—Solution of silicates is best obtained by direct fusion of 1 g. of the powdered material with 4–5 g. of sodium carbonate, in a platinum crucible. The cooled melt is now covered with water and dissolved with hydrochloric acid according to the standard procedure for carbonate fusions. The hydrochloric acid solutions are taken to dryness and the silica dehydrated in an oven at 110°C. for an hour and then the residue is extracted with dilute hydrochloric acid and filtered. The filtrate contains iron, alumina, magnesium, lime, etc.

In presence of sulfates and the alkaline earths it will be necessary to remove sodium silicate by extraction with water, before treating the water insoluble carbonates of this group with acid. This must be borne in mind in all separations of silica from this group.

*Solution of Gypsum, Plaster of Paris, and Sulfates of Lime, etc.*—The treatment of the sample is similar to the one given above with the exception that it is advisable to add a larger amount of concentrated hydrochloric acid, e.g., about 20–25 ml. If barium sulfate is present it is indicated by the clouding of the solution upon acidifying the water extract of the carbonate fusion.

*Chlorides, Nitrates, and Other Water-soluble Salts.*—These are dissolved in water slightly acidified with hydrochloric acid.

*Sulfides, Pyrites Ore, etc.*—The ore should be oxidized with bromine or by roasting, previous to the acid treatment.

## SEPARATIONS

The solution for calcium determination should be free from silica, sulfur, phosphates, fluorides and carbonates and from the hydrogen sulfide and ammonium sulfide group elements.

*Removal of Silica.*—The acid solution obtained by the decomposition of the ore is evaporated to dryness and baked at 110°C. to dehydrate $SiO_2$. The residue is moistened with HCl and water added. After heating to near boiling the solution is filtered from the impure $SiO_2$. The residue is washed with water containing HCl (1:100). The filtrate is set aside for the calcium determination.[1]

In presence of sulfate, calcium is apt to be left in part with the silica. It may be recovered by fusion of the residue with $Na_2CO_3$ leaching out the sodium silicate (and sulfate), dissolving the water-insoluble carbonate with HCl and again evaporating to separate any occluded silica. The residue is again extracted with HCl

---

[1] The perchloric acid procedure is excellent for the separation of the silica. See Chapter on Silicon.

and water and filtered. The combined filtrates and washings containing calcium are further treated to remove substances interfering with the calcium determination.

*Removal of Copper, Nickel, Cobalt, Manganese, Zinc and Other Elements Precipitated by $H_2S$ in Acid and Alkaline Solutions.*—This separation is seldom required in lime-bearing ores. In the analysis of pyrites, and ores commonly containing the above elements this separation should be made.

The solution obtained after separation of silica is made slightly ammoniacal (see Notes below) and saturated with $H_2S$, and filtered. If arsenic, antimony, and tin are present, precipitation is first carried out in acid solution and filtered and the filtrate made alkaline and again saturated with $H_2S$ and filtered. The details are carried out according to the well known standard procedures used in removing the $H_2S$ and $(NH_4)_2S$ groups. Calcium is in the filtrate.

NOTES.—Should phosphates be present in excess of the amount that would be removed by iron and alumina, calcium will precipitate as phosphate when the solution is made ammoniacal. Provision should be made for its recovery, if this is the case.

Fluoride should be absent for in their presence $CaF_2$ precipitates here also.

The ammonia should be free from carbonate, whose presence would cause the precipitation of $CaCO_3$.

*Removal of Fluoride.*—The presence of the fluoride ion will cause the precipitation of $CaF_2$ during the procedure for removal of iron and aluminum, since $CaF_2$ is insoluble in ammoniacal solution. Fluorine is removed in the initial decomposition of the ore. Sufficient silica should be present to form silicon fluoride which is expelled by taking to fumes with $H_2SO_4$. It may be necessary to add a few milligrams of fine, pure silica.

*Removal of Phosphate.*—If phosphate ion is present in excess of that which the iron in the solution will precipitate, it may be removed by adding an excess of iron,[2] or by precipitation with ammonium molybdate (free from calcium). Molybdenum does not interfere in the precipitation of calcium as oxalate. Consult the Chapter on Phosphorus.

*Removal of Iron and Aluminum.*—The removal of iron and aluminum is generally necessary in the analysis of natural substances carrying calcium. In absence of fluoride, phosphate and carbonate ions the iron and aluminum may be precipitated with ammonia added in amount sufficient to turn methyl orange indicator yellow, avoiding an excess that would dissolve aluminum hydroxide. (Consult the Chapter on Aluminum.) The precipitate is filtered off, saving the filtrate for calcium. The hydroxides are dissolved in HCl and the filtrate, diluted with the washings of the filter, again treated with ammonia, added drop by drop to complete precipitation of iron and aluminum. The precipitate is again filtered and the two filtrates combined for the determination of calcium.

NOTE.—Good results have been obtained by precipitation of calcium oxalate from an acid solution in presence of iron and aluminum. Separation may be effected from iron, aluminum, titanium, zirconium, phosphate ion, barium, and magnesium. The outline of the procedure is below.

*Precipitation of Calcium Oxalate in Presence of Iron and Aluminum, etc.*—The solution containing the phosphates freed from silica is oxidized by boiling with nitric acid as usual. Ammonia water is added to the cooled solution until a slight precipitate forms, and then citric acid is added in sufficient quantity to just dis-

---

[2] For example, in presence of 0.005 g. $P_2O_5$ and 0.05 g. CaO, a tenfold excess of iron or aluminum, i.e., 0.03 g. Fe or Al, is used.

solve the precipitate. If this does not readily occur, additional ammonia is added, followed by citric acid until the solution clears, then about 15 ml. of citric acid in excess. The solution is diluted to 200 ml. and heated to boiling. Calcium oxalate is now precipitated by addition of ammonium oxalate. Iron and alumina remain in solution.

**Citric Acid Solution** is made by dissolving 70 g. of the acid, $H_3C_6H_5O_7 \cdot H_2O$, in a liter of water.

**Wagner's Solution.**—In place of citric acid, the following solution may be used. Twenty-five grams of citric acid and 1 g. of salicylic acid are dissolved in water and made to 1000 ml. Twenty-five to 50 ml. of this reagent is effective in preventing precipitation of iron and alumina.

An excellent separation of calcium from iron, aluminum, titanium, zirconium and large amounts of phosphorus may be made by precipitation of calcium oxalate from neutral solution by means of oxalic acid followed by ammonium oxalate. In a double precipitation, barium and magnesium do not interfere. Details are given under the gravimetric methods for determining calcium.

*Separation of Calcium from the Alkaline Earths, Barium and Strontium and from Magnesium.*—The separations have been discussed in the Chapter on Barium. A brief outline follows:

**Separation of Calcium from Barium and from Strontium.**—The alkaline earths are converted to nitrates, all moisture expelled by heat, and calcium nitrate extracted from the insoluble nitrates of barium and strontium by a mixture of anhydrous ether and absolute alcohol, in equal parts, or by boiling the dry nitrates in amyl alcohol (*b.p.*, 137.8°C.). Details of the procedure are given under "Separations of the Alkaline Earths" in the Chapter on Barium.[3]

**Separation of Calcium from Magnesium and the Alkalies.**—In the presence of considerable amounts of calcium and comparatively small quantities of magnesium the oxalate method of precipitating calcium, in presence of ammonium chloride, is generally sufficient for precipitating calcium free from magnesium and the alkalies. In analysis of dolomite, $MgCO_3 \cdot CaCO_3$, and of samples containing comparatively large amounts of magnesium, a double precipitation of calcium is generally necessary for removal of occluded magnesium.

If the homogeneous precipitation method is used, a single precipitation of the calcium is adequate (p. 263).

## GRAVIMETRIC METHODS

### PRECIPITATION OF CALCIUM OXALATE AND IGNITION TO CALCIUM CARBONATE OR TO CALCIUM OXIDE

The solution of calcium free from interfering elements is treated as follows:—Calcium oxalate is precipitated from feebly ammoniacal solutions or from solutions acidified with acetic, oxalic, citric, salicylic, or o-phthalic acids, by means of ammonium oxalate. The presence of ammonium chloride hinders precipitation of magnesium and does not interfere with that of calcium. If, however, much magnesium (or sodium) is present it will contaminate the calcium precipitate so that a second precipitation is necessary to obtain a pure product. The compound formed from hot solutions is crystalline or granular and filters readily, whereas the flocculent precipitate formed in cold solutions does not. Calcium oxalate $CaC_2O_4 \cdot$

---

[3] 100 ml. dissolves 37 g. of $Ca(NO_3)_2$ and only 0.001 g. $Sr(NO_3)_2$.

$H_2O$ [4] decomposes at 475–525°C. to yield calcium carbonate, or at 840–1025°C. to yield calcium oxide. Either form may be used, but weighing $CaCO_3$ is more convenient.

*Procedure.*—If the calcium to be determined is in the filtrate from previous groups, hydrogen sulfide is expelled by boiling and the precipitated sulfur filtered off, the solution having been concentrated to about 100 ml. The filtrate should contain sufficient ammonium chloride to hold magnesium in solution in presence of ammonium oxalate (i.e., about 10 g. $NH_4Cl$ per 0.0015 g. MgO per 100 ml. of solution). If not already present, the chloride is added in sufficient amount, and the solution diluted to about 150 ml. Generally, sufficient $NH_4Cl$ is obtained by adding 10 ml. HCl (sp. gr. 1.2) and neutralizing with $NH_4OH$. The solution is now acidified with a weak organic acid, oxalic acid preferred, and 10 ml. added in excess (10% solution) to the hot solution, stirring vigorously. Now about 150 ml. of a saturated solution of ammonium oxalate (4% solution) are added in a fine stream with vigorous stirring. The precipitate is settled on a steam bath for an hour or more and is filtered. The calcium oxalate is washed with water containing oxalic acid and ammonium oxalate (1 g. oxalic acid or 2 g. ammonium oxalate per liter).[5]

If considerable magnesium is present a double precipitation should be made. The washed precipitate is dissolved in about 50 ml. of dilute HCl (1:4) and calcium oxalate reprecipitated as in the first procedure, by neutralizing HCl with $NH_4OH$ and adding a small amount of oxalic acid and ammonium oxalate and again filtering and washing.

As stated on page 262, the double precipitation may be avoided by use of the homogeneous precipitation method. Heat the solution of calcium and magnesium ions containing the ammonium oxalate or oxalic acid to boiling, and add, with stirring, 15 g. of urea. Keep the solution boiling gently until it first shows an alkaline reaction to methyl orange indicator. This neutralization requires from 30 to 60 minutes. Cool the solution and allow it to stand from 3 to 5 hours— no longer. On longer standing the calcium oxalate becomes contaminated with magnesium. Filter the precipitate through a previously ignited and weighed filtering crucible. Wash the precipitate with cold 1% ammonium oxalate solution and then ignite it as directed below.

**Ignition.** *Weighing as Calcium Carbonate.*—The calcium oxalate is dried at 100–110°C. for one hour, then heated in a muffle at 500°C. for one hour, cooled in a desiccator and weighed, repeating the heatings to constant weight.

*Weighing as Calcium Oxide.*—The calcium oxalate precipitate and filter paper is placed in a weighed crucible and gently heated, the crucible being covered, until the water is expelled and the paper charred. The heat is increased to the full temperature of the burner (1200°C.) and the heating continued for 5 to 10 minutes. It is well to remove the cover for an instant to assist escape of the $CO_2$ during the blasting. The covered crucible and its contents are cooled in a desiccator containing concentrated sulfuric acid. The cooled CaO is weighed and the ignition

---

[4] According to C. Duval, Inorganic Thermogravimetric Analysis, Elsevier Publishing Company, 1953, the monohydrate is stable up to 100°C., the anhydrous calcium oxalate from 226 to 398°C. and the calcium carbonate is stable between 420 and 660°C. Transition to yield lime is complete at 840–850°C.

[5] Acidity should not exceed pH 4, according to A. T. School (J. Biol. Chem., **50**, 527–36, 1922).

H. D. Chapman (Soil Sci., **26**, 479–86, 1928) recommends a pH of 4 for Ca in soils. Fe, Al, Ti, Mn, Mg, $P_2O_5$ do not interfere. $CaC_2O_4$ precipitates at this acidity.

repeated until the weight is constant. If a platinum crucible is used constant weight is rapidly attained. A longer period is required when porcelain is used. The Tirrill, Meker, or Teclu burners give satisfactory results.

Weighing should be done quickly as CaO absorbs moisture from the air.

Factors. $CaO \times 0.7147 = Ca$

$\times 1.7847 = CaCO_3$

$\times 2.8908 = Ca(HCO_3)_2$

$\times 2.4276 = CaSO_4$

## OTHER GRAVIMETRIC METHODS

Calcium may be converted to carbonate, sulfate, fluoride, tungstate and so weighed. The oxide, obtained by ignition of the oxalate may be converted to sulfate by moistening with a few drops of $H_2SO_4$, then adding an excess of $NH_4OH$ and igniting to expel excess of sulfate and $NH_3$.

Calcium sulfate may be precipitated by adding an excess of $H_2SO_4$ and then 95% alcohol (two to four times the total volume of the solution). The precipitate is washed with alcohol and then ignited to constant weight. (Fresenius.)

Calcium tungstate by Saint Sernin's method is precipitated by adding ammonia until the solution is alkaline and then an excess of 20% solution of sodium tungstate. The precipitate is best filtered into a weighed Gooch crucible and washed with ammonia (1:10 solution) then dried at 100°C. and weighed as $CaWO_4$.

## TITRIMETRIC METHODS

### TITRATION OF THE OXALATE WITH PERMANGANATE

This procedure may be applied successfully in a great variety of instances on account of the readiness with which calcium oxalate may be separated. In the presence of iron, alumina, manganese, magnesia, etc., it is advisable to make a reprecipitation of calcium oxalate to free it from adhering contaminations.

The following reaction takes place when potassium permanganate is added to calcium oxalate in acid solution:

$$5C_2O_4^= + 2MnO_4^- + 16H^+ \rightarrow 10CO_2 + 2Mn^{++} + 8H_2O$$

*Procedure.*—Calcium oxalate, obtained pure, by precipitation and washing [6] according to directions given under the gravimetric determination of calcium, is washed into a flask through a perforation made in the filter paper, the filter is treated with a little warm, dilute sulfuric acid and the adhering oxalate dissolved and washed into the flask. About 25 ml. of dilute sulfuric acid, 1:1, is added and the solution diluted to 250 to 300 ml.

When the precipitate has dissolved, the solution is titrated with standard potassium permanganate as described for the standardization of permanganate solution in the section on standard solutions that concludes this book.

One ml. 0.1 $N$ $KMnO_4$ = 0.002004 gram Ca, or $\times$ 0.002804 = CaO.

Factors. $Ca \times 1.3992 = CaO$

$\times 2.4970 = CaCO_3$

$\times 3.3967 = CaSO_4$

$\times 2.5805 = Ca_3(PO_4)_2$

NOTES.—**Precipitation from Acetic Acid Solution.**—This is recommended if the material contained phosphates. The solution should contain about 1 ml. free glacial acetic acid

[6] Finish the washing with distilled water, since the precipitate is first washed with an oxalate solution.

per 200 ml. of solution. In presence of phosphate, iron and aluminum cannot be removed by addition of ammonia as calcium would also precipitate as phosphate. Citric or oxalic acid may also be used to prevent precipitation of iron.

**Procedure.**—To a volume of about 75 ml. of solution containing 0.1 to 0.15 g. Ca add 10 ml. acetic acid (glacial), heat to boiling and add slowly 10 ml. of a saturated solution of ammonium oxalate. Now add a slight excess of ammonia and make slightly acid with acetic acid (about 0.5 ml. per 100 ml. solution). If phosphate is present this last acidification is necessary, likewise in presence of aluminum.

"Photomicrographs indicate that better crystals are formed by precipitation from acetic acid solutions than from $NH_4OH$ solutions. The following procedure is recommended. To a water solution of 0.1–1.5 g. Ca in 75 ml. add 10 ml. concentrated acetic acid, heat to boiling and add slowly from a burette 7–10 ml. of a cold saturated solution of $(NH_4)_2C_2O_4$ at the rate of 1 drop in 5 seconds. Finally add a slight excess of $NH_4OH$." Erdenbrecher, A. H., Mikrocosmos, **16**, 201–2, 1923 (C. A., **17**, 3462).

Phosphate ion should be absent or taken care of in the precipitation of calcium. Manganese may be removed by treating the solution with $NH_4OH$, bromine chlorides being absent. See Chapter on Manganese.

## ETHYLENEDINITRILOTETRAACETATE TITRIMETRIC METHOD [7]

This method is applicable to the determination of calcium in concentrations greater than 5% with a relative error of 1%. For alloys having calcium contents under 5%, the flame spectrophotometric procedure is usually employed. Calcium is separated from the bulk of the magnesium as the tungstate. The calcium tungstate is then dissolved in sodium hydroxide and an excess of standard ethylenedinitrilotetraacetate (ethylenediaminetetraacetate) solution. The excess ethylenedinitrilotetraacetate is back titrated with a standard calcium solution using Cal-Red indicator.

*Interferences.*—Aluminum and iron would interfere, if present, but can be removed by precipitation as benzoates. Barium and strontium would be included with the calcium if they are present, but since these are not usually present in magnesium alloys, no interference would be expected from this source.

*Apparatus.* Crucible, Filtering, Selas, #3001 or #4001.

**Magnetic Stirrer.**—Equipped with a Teflon-covered magnetic stirring bar.

*Reagents.* **Ammoniacal Wash Solution.**—Add 20 ml. of the buffer solution to water and dilute to 1 liter.

**Ammonium Benzoate Solution (100 g. per liter).**—Dissolve 100 g. of pure ammonium benzoate ($NH_4C_7H_5O_2$) in 1 liter of warm water and add 1 mg. of thymol as preservative.

**Ammonium Benzoate Wash Solution.**—To 100 ml. of the ammonium benzoate solution, add 900 ml. of water and 20 ml. of glacial acetic acid.

**Buffer Solution.**—Dissolve 67.5 g. of reagent grade $NH_4Cl$ in 300 ml. of water. Add 570 ml. of $NH_4OH$ and dilute to 1 liter with water.

**Calcium Standard Solution, 0.05 $M$ (1 ml. = 2.004 mg. Ca).**—Weigh 5.0050 g. of primary standard calcium carbonate and transfer it to a 400-ml. beaker. Add 50 ml. of water and dissolve in 10.6 ml. of HCl, added in small increments. When the dissolution is complete, boil the solution to remove carbon dioxide. Cool the solution to room temperature, transfer to a 1-liter volumetric flask, and dilute to volume with water.

**Cal-Red Indicator.**—Available from Scientific Service Laboratory, Inc., Dallas, Texas.

[7] This method is a development of the West Analytical Laboratory, 3-143 Bldg., Dow Chemical Company, Midland, Mich., for analysis of magnesium and magnesium base alloys.

**EDTA Solution, 0.05 $M$.**—Dissolve 18.61 g. of disodium dihydrogen ethylenedinitrilotetraacetate (ethylenediaminetetraacetate) in water and dilute with water to 1 liter in a volumetric flask. Standardize this solution against known amounts of calcium standard carried through the entire procedure. From this standardization can be obtained the volume ratio of the EDTA to calcium solution and the gram calcium equivalent of the EDTA solution.

**Sodium Hydroxide Solution (500 g. per liter).**—Dissolve 500 g. of reagent grade sodium hydroxide (NaOH) in 400 ml. of water. Cool to room temperature and dilute to 1 liter with water. Store in a polyethylene bottle.

**Sodium Tungstate Solution (100 g. per liter).**—Dissolve 10 g. of reagent grade sodium tungstate ($Na_2WO_4 \cdot H_2O$) in water and dilute to 100 ml. with water. Prepare fresh as needed.

**Procedure.**—($A$) Weigh, to the nearest milligram, 1 g. of sample and transfer it to a 400-ml. beaker. Add 50 ml. of water and dissolve the sample with 10 ml. of HCl added in small increments. When dissolution is complete, cool the solution to room temperature. Transfer the solution to a 250-ml. volumetric flask and dilute to volume with water. Pipette an aliquot which will contain from 10 to 100 mg. of calcium, but not more than 125 mg. of aluminum, if aluminum is present, into a 400-ml. beaker. If aluminum is not present, proceed in accordance with step ($C$) below.

($B$) To the aliquoted solution which contains 10–100 mg. of calcium and not more than 125 mg. of aluminum, add $NH_4OH$ (1:1) dropwise, with stirring, until the precipitate that forms as each drop strikes redissolves only very slowly; that is, until nearly all the free acid is neutralized without permanent precipitation of aluminum hydroxide. Add 1 ml. of glacial acetic acid, about 1 g. of $NH_4Cl$ and 25 ml. of the ammonium benzoate solution. Heat the mixture to boiling while stirring, keep at a gentle boil for 5 minutes and then filter on a medium-porosity paper (Whatman No. 40). Wash the beaker several times with the hot benzoate wash solution, and the precipitate from eight to ten times as well. Make no effort to transfer all of the precipitate to the paper. Discard the precipitate and paper.

($C$) To the filtrate from step ($B$), or the aliquot from step ($A$), add 25 ml. of the buffer solution and 15 ml. of the $Na_2WO_4$ solution. Heat mixture to boiling and then digest, just under boiling, for five minutes. Cool the mixture to room temperature and filter the solutions on a #3001 or #4001 Selas filtering crucible, making no effort to transfer all of the precipitate to the crucible. Wash the beaker three to four times and the precipitate three to four times with the ammoniacal wash solution. Transfer the crucible containing the calcium tungstate to the original beaker. Add 100 ml. of water, 10 ml. of the NaOH solution, and a measured amount of standard 0.05 $M$ EDTA solution until there is a 10–15 ml. excess over the amount needed to sequesterize the calcium. Heat the mixture to boiling and digest just below boiling until all of the calcium tungstate is solubilized. (There is usually a small amount of magnesium which is co-precipitated with the calcium tungstate. The magnesium tungstate co-precipitated does not dissolve in the strongly alkaline solution, even in the presence of EDTA, and causes no interference.) Remove the crucible from the solution and wash it well with water. Cool the solution to room temperature.

($D$) Dilute the solution to about 200 ml. with water, insert a magnetic stirring bar and add about 0.2 g. of Cal-Red indicator. Titrate with the standard 0.05 $M$ calcium solution from a color change of pure blue to wine red. (The back titration with the 0.05 $M$ calcium solution can be done spectrophotometrically on the

Sargent-Malmstadt Automatic Titrator, Model SE. The additional conditions necessary are a flow rate of 5–6 ml. per minute for the first 10 ml., a polarity of one and a wavelength of 650 m$\mu$. The advantages of using the instrument are that the end points are more consistent and the accuracy better.)

**Calculation.**—Calculate the per cent calcium as follows:

$$\text{Calcium, } \% = \frac{(A - BC) \times D \times 100}{E}$$

where $A$ = total milliliters of 0.05 $M$ EDTA solution added; $B$ = milliliters of 0.05 $M$ calcium solution used in the back titration; $C$ = EDTA equivalent of the 0.05 $M$ calcium solution expressed in milliliters of 0.05 $M$ EDTA solution per milliliter of 0.05 $M$ calcium solution; $D$ = calcium equivalent of the 0.05 $M$ EDTA solution expressed in grams of calcium per milliliter of 0.05 $M$ EDTA solution; and $E$ = grams of sample represented in the aliquot.

## COLORIMETRIC/PHOTOMETRIC METHODS

### CHLORANILIC ACID METHOD

A rapid method of analysis for calcium consists of measuring the reduction of the color of chloranilic acid by formation of calcium chloranilate. The color is not unlike that of permanganate ion and has a minimum light absorption at 550 m$\mu$. Because of its high coloration this minimum is used. The reduction in absorption on precipitation by calcium ion conforms to Beer's law over the range up to 30 mg. of chloranilic acid per 100 ml. of solution. Hydrogen-ion concentration must be carefully controlled. Time must be allowed for full precipitation of calcium chloranilate. Therefore a reagent control must be run with every group of samples.

Ferric ion and aluminum ion interfere by forming soluble complexes which may completely prevent precipitation of calcium chloranilate. As little as 0.02 mg. of ferric ion in the developed sample, shifting the absorption maximum but 0.01 mg., can be tolerated. Aluminum to 0.05 mg. is allowable. Copper, manganese, barium, and strontium interfere by forming precipitates with the reagent. Up to 0.05 mg. of copper or 0.01 mg. of manganese is tolerated. Barium and strontium do not interfere. The presence of iron increases the absorption, magnesium decreases it.

**Procedure.**—Select a sample containing 0.01–0.5 mg. of calcium and dilute to about 20 ml. Add 10 ml. of 0.1% aqueous solution of chloranilic acid and mix. Let stand for 3 hours or overnight. At temperatures over 30°C., refrigerate. When precipitation is complete, dilute to 50 ml. and filter. Read against a water blank at 550 m$\mu$.

### INDIRECT PHOSPHATE METHOD [8]

This method depends on precipitation of tricalcium phosphate, washing the precipitate, dissolution in acid and photometric determination of the equivalent phosphoric acid by the molybdenum blue method.

**Reagents.** **Methyl Orange Indicator.**—Dissolve 0.1 g. of methyl orange in 100 ml. of 90% ethyl alcohol.

---

[8] Briggs, J. Biol. Chem., **59**, 255, 1924; Kuttner and Cohen, *ibid.*, **75**, 517, 1927; Roe and Kahn, *ibid.*, **81**, 1, 1929.

**Ammonium Oxalate Solution 4%.**—Dissolve 4 g. of ammonium oxalate monohydrate in 100 ml. of water.

**Ammonium Oxalate Solution, Weak.**—Dilute 3 ml. of the 4% solution to 100 ml.

**Ammonia Solution, 1:1.**—Add 100 ml. concentrated ammonium hydroxide to 100 ml. of water.

**Hydrochloric Acid, 1:1.**—Add 25 ml. of concentrated hydrochloric acid to 25 ml. of water.

**Hydrogen Peroxide, 30%.**

**Sodium Hydroxide, 6 N.**—Dissolve 120 g. of NaOH in 300 ml. of water and dilute to 500 ml.

**Trisodium Phosphate Solution.**—Dissolve 1 g. $Na_3PO_4$ in 100 ml. of water.

**Precipitate Wash Solution.**—Add 10 ml. amyl alcohol to 58 ml. ethyl alcohol. Add 1 drop of the 6 N NaOH solution and dilute with water to 100 ml.

**Ammonium Molybdate Solution.**—Dissolve 2.5 g. of ammonium molybdate in 100 ml. of 6 N sulfuric acid.

**ANSA Solution.**—In 100 ml. of water, dissolve 15 g. of sodium bisulfite and 0.5 g. of sodium sulfite. Then add 0.25 g. of 1-amino-2-naphthol-4-sulfonic acid and let stand, shaking periodically. If not clear after several hours, filter. Store in dark-glass bottle.

**Standard Phosphate Solution.**—Concentration depends on concentration of sample. Basis of calculation is 4.39 g. of potassium dihydrogen phosphate per liter giving 1 mg. P per ml.

*Procedure.*—Use a sample having an estimated calcium content of 0.2–0.5 mg. and a volume of about 10 ml. Acidify to methyl orange with the 1:1 hydrochloric acid and add several drops in excess. Heat nearly to boiling and add 1 ml. of the ammonium oxalate solution, and add the 1:1 ammonia solution until just alkaline to the methyl orange. Cool, let stand for about 2 hours, and filter. Wash the precipitate with the weak ammonium oxalate solution, and dissolve it in 0.5 ml. of hot 1:1 hydrochloric acid, washing the filter with water, and evaporate filtrate and wash water to a volume of about 0.5 ml. Add 0.5 ml. of 30% hydrogen peroxide and heat on the steam bath for 30–40 minutes. Dilute to 5 ml. and add 0.5 ml. of the 6 N sodium hydroxide, and after 10 minutes, 0.5 ml. of the trisodium phosphate solution. Let stand for 1 hour, and filter through a filtering crucible. Wash with no more than 5 ml. of the precipitate wash solution, divided into portions. Let the precipitate stand for 10 minutes, and dissolve it in 0.5 ml. of the ammonium molybdate solution, washing the crucible with a little water into the filtrate. Add 1 ml. of the ANSA solution, and dilute to 10 ml. Let stand (preferably in the dark) for 10 minutes and read at 700 m$\mu$ against a standard phosphate solution prepared in the same way.

## PHOTOMETRIC TITRATION OF CALCIUM IN THE PRESENCE OF MAGNESIUM [9]

The principle of this method is the large absorbancy exhibited by the EDTA ($Y^{-4}$ and $HY^{-3}$ anions) at 222 m$\mu$, and the little absorbancy at that wavelength (and higher) of the cations of calcium and magnesium and their EDTA complexes. Thus spectrophotometric measurements show a sharp increase in absorbancy when the EDTA anions are present in excess.

[9] Sweetser and Bricker, Anal. Chem., **26(I)**, 195, 1954.

*Reagents.* **Standard Disodium EDTA Solution, 0.01338** *M.*—Dissolve approximately 5.0 g. of disodium dihydrogen ethylenediaminetetraacetate dihydrate in water and dilute to 1 liter. Standardize this solution against the standard calcium solution using the spectrophotometric end point.

**Standard Calcium Solution, 0.01** *M.*—Dissolve exactly 1.0 g. of reagent grade calcium carbonate in hydrochloric acid and dilute the resulting solution to 1 liter.

**Buffer Solution, pH 10.**—Dissolve 6 g. of ammonium chloride in water; add 570 ml. of concentrated ammonia solution and dilute the solution to 1 liter with water.

**Citric Acid Solution.**—Dissolve 65.0 g. of citric acid in 1 liter of water.

**6 *N* Sodium Hydroxide Solution.**—Dissolve 240 g. NaOH in 800 ml. of water and dilute to 1 liter.

*Procedure.* **Standardization of Disodium EDTA Solution.**—Pipette a 5- to 10-ml. aliquot of the standard calcium solution into the titration cell, add 2 ml. of the pH 10 buffer, and dilute with water up to 90–100 ml. The wavelength used for titrations with the 0.01338 *M* Disodium EDTA should be 228 m$\mu$, reserving the lower 222 m$\mu$ value for titrations with more dilute (e.g., 0.001 *M*) Disodium EDTA solutions. Titrate to spectrophotometric end point. A blank on the buffer and distilled water is desirable for titrations with 0.01338 *M* Disodium EDTA solutions; for titrations with more dilute solutions, it is essential.

**Determination.**—Place in the titration cell 5 ml. of the citric acid solution and 10 ml. of the 6 *N* NaOH solution, and dilute with water to a total volume of 90 ml. Set the wavelength of the spectrophotometer at 228 m$\mu$ and titrate with the standard Disodium EDTA solution. The end point gives the amount of blank correction for the impurities present in the reagents.

After the end point has been passed and recorded, as indicated by the absorbancy of the solution, the calcium and magnesium solution is added to the titration cell and the titration is continued until the second end point is reached. The amount of calcium is equivalent of the difference between these two end points. When several determinations of calcium are going to be made it is not necessary to determine the blank correction for every titration, provided the sodium hydroxide and citric acid are carefully measured so that the blank correction may be measured once and will remain the same. The blank should, in any case, be checked periodically.

## DETERMINATIONS IN SPECIFIC SUBSTANCES

### TITRIMETRIC PERMANGANATE METHOD APPLIED TO DETERMINATION OF CALCIUM IN WATER

The hardness of water is due largely to the presence of calcium and magnesium carbonates or bicarbonates. Calcium may be determined titrimetrically by precipitation as oxalate and titration in an acid solution by standard potassium permanganate, according to the reaction given on page 264.

In the gravimetric method it is necessary to remove $SiO_2$, $Fe_2O_3$, and $Al_2O_3$ before precipitating $CaC_2O_4$. Ferrous iron alone titrates so that it is necessary only to make provision for iron in case it is present in appreciable amount.

*Procedure.*—Measure a 250-ml. portion of the water to be examined by means of a 250-ml. graduated flask into a 400-ml. beaker. Add 1 ml. of HCl (sp. gr. 1.2) and evaporate to half its volume if the water is considerably hard or to about one-fifth its volume if it is moderately hard. By means of a dropper add 4–5 drops of methyl red and then ammonium hydroxide drop by drop until a reddish-yellow color appears. If a precipitate appears just dissolve in a drop or so of HCl. If iron is indicated add 2–3 small crystals of citric acid. (This should be ample. A large excess is not desired.) The solution will now be faintly acid. Heat to boiling and add slowly about 25–30 ml. of a saturated solution of oxalic acid. Boil for a few minutes, make alkaline with $NH_4OH$, and allow to settle.

Filter and wash the filter free of the oxalate reagent. (Twenty ml. of the wash water should not decolorize 1 drop of 0.1 $N$ $KMnO_4$ reagent.) Open out the filter on a beaker cover, and hold slanting over a beaker. By means of a stream of 10% $H_2SO_4$ dissolve off the precipitate into the beaker, using about 50 ml. of the dilute acid. Now rinse off into the beaker by means of about 50 ml. of water, the acid clinging to the filter.

Heat the solution in the beaker to boiling and titrate with 0.1 $N$ $KMnO_4$ until a faint pink color appears.

One ml. 0.1 $N$ $KMnO_4$ is equivalent to 0.002 g. Ca. Report results in parts per million, first as Ca and also as $CaCO_3$.

NOTE.—In water containing considerable magnesium it may be necessary to dissolve the precipitate in HCl and reprecipitate as $CaC_2O_4$ to purify the precipitate from occluded magnesium as in the gravimetric method.

Conversion factors. Ca × 2.5 = $CaCO_3$; 1 liter = 0.264 gallon. 1 gram = 15.43 grains. Convert above results to grains per gallon.

## CALCIUM (AND MAGNESIUM) IN WATER BY THE DISODIUM EDTA TITRIMETRIC METHOD

The total hardness of water, that is, both calcium and magnesium hardness, may be determined by titration of a suitably buffered sample by EDTA solution in the presence of various Eriochrome Black T solutions. The calcium forms a less stable complex with the dye than does the magnesium, so the overall titration may be represented by the reactions:

$$H_2Y^= + Ca^{++} \rightarrow CaY^= + 2H^+$$

$$H_2Y^= + MgIn^- \rightarrow MgY^= + HIn^= + H^+$$

where Y represents the ethylenediaminetetraacetate radical.

The color change of the indicator is from wine red to blue.

*Reagents.* **EDTA Solution.**—Dissolve 4.0 g. of disodium EDTA in 800 ml. of distilled water and add 0.86 g. of sodium hydroxide. Adjust against a standard calcium chloride solution (1 ml. = 1 mg. calcium carbonate) so that 1 ml. of the reagent solution corresponds to 1 mg. of calcium carbonate.

**Indicator Solution.**—Dissolve 1.0 g. of Eriochrome Black T and 1.0 ml. of 1 $N$ sodium carbonate solution in 30 ml. of distilled water, and dilute to 100 ml. with isopropyl alcohol.

**Buffer Solution.**—Dissolve 40 g. of sodium borate, $Na_2B_4O_7 \cdot 10H_2O$, 10 g. of sodium hydroxide, and 5 g. of sodium sulfide in distilled water and dilute to 1 liter.

*Procedure.*—Transfer a 50-ml. sample to an Erlenmeyer flask, and add 0.5 ml. of buffer solution and 5 drops of indicator. Titrate slowly with the reagent solution until the last trace of red disappears and the solution is pale blue in color.

Total hardness, in p. p. m. as calcium carbonate, is determined by multiplying the titer (ml.) by 1000 and dividing by the volume of sample used in milliliters. Betz and Noll [10] have studied the effect of interfering ions upon this method and

[10] Betz, J. D., and Noll, C. A., J. Am. Water Works Assoc., **42**, 49, 1950.

have indicated the maximum concentration of the various ions which may be present when the sulfide buffer is used. This is shown in the following table:

Maximum Concentration of Foreign Ions

| Ion | Concentration (in p. p. m.) | Ion | Concentration (in p. p. m.) |
|-----|-----|-----|-----|
| Copper(II) | 10 | Sulfate | 10,000 |
| Iron(II) | 20 | Sulfite | 500 |
| Iron(III) | 20 | Chromate | 500 |
| Zinc | 10 | Phosphate | 100 |
| Lead(II) | 10 | Nitrate | 500 |
| Tin(II) | 10 | Nitrate | 500 |
| Tin(IV) | 10 | Carbonate | 1,000 |
| Aluminum | 10 | Silicate | 200 |
| Chloride | 10,000 | | |

## DETERMINATION OF CALCIUM HARDNESS IN WATER BY EDTA TITRATION

The determination of calcium hardness in the presence of magnesium hardness is preferably made gravimetrically by precipitation of the calcium as the oxalate (see p. 262). However, the calcium may be titrated in alkaline solution using Murexide indicator, provided that the concentration of foreign ions does not exceed limiting values (see table above).

*Reagents.* **EDTA Solution.**—Dissolve 4.0 g. of disodium EDTA in 800 ml. of distilled water, and add 0.86 g. of sodium hydroxide. Adjust against a standard calcium chloride solution (1 ml. = 1 mg. calcium carbonate) so that 1 ml. of the reagent solution corresponds to 1 mg. of calcium carbonate.

**Indicator.**—Mix 0.20 g. of Murexide and 100 g. of sodium chloride, and grind intimately to a fine powder.

*Procedure.*—Transfer 50 ml. of the water to be analyzed to an Erlenmeyer flask, and add 2 ml. of 1 $N$ sodium hydroxide solution and 0.2 g. of the indicator. Titrate slowly with the reagent solution until the pink color changes to purple, and an additional drop of reagent causes no further color change. Calcium hardness, in p. p. m. of calcium carbonate, is obtained by multiplying the titer in milliliters by 1000 and dividing by the number of milliliters of sample used.

The end point in the above titration is fairly sharp, and consistent results are obtained after some experience.

## TITRIMETRIC METHOD FOR AVAILABLE LIME

This is the usual method followed in cyanide mills for determining the percentage which will dissolve the lime added to the mill solution, and therefore the amount to add to maintain the desired protective alkalinity.

*Reagent.* **Standard 0.1 $N$ Oxalic Acid Solution.**—Dissolve 6.303 g. $H_2C_2O_4 \cdot 2H_2O$ in distilled water and dilute to 1000 ml. The solution ordinarily need not be standardized as the weight of the oxalic acid is constant.

To standardize, take 30 ml. of the solution, add 100 ml. of water and 5 ml. of concentrated $H_2SO_4$, heat to 70°C. and titrate to a permanent pink with 0.1 $N$ $KMnO_4$.

*Procedure.*—One gram of the finely ground sample is placed in a glass-stoppered bottle which has been previously marked to hold 500 ml. Thirty grams of sugar and about 300 ml. of water are added and the bottle shaken vigorously. The solution is diluted to 500 ml. and shaken at ten minute intervals for 1½ to 2 hours. Then the insoluble material is allowed to settle, part of the solution filtered through a coarse filter paper, 50 ml. of the filtrate drawn out with a pipette into an Erlenmeyer flask, two drops of phenolphthalein indicator added, and the solution titrated with 0.1 N oxalic acid solution till the pink color disappears. The lime is reported as per cent available **CaO**.

$$1 \text{ ml. } 0.1 \ N \text{ oxalic acid} = 0.0028 \text{ g. CaO}$$

# RAPID IODINE METHOD FOR CALCIUM OXIDE IN PRESENCE OF CALCIUM CARBONATE

The method worked out by John C. Bailar, Great Western Sugar Company, is based on the fact that a solution of iodine reacts with calcium hydroxide, but does not react with calcium carbonate. The method is used in the evaluation of lime.

*Reagents.* **Iodine Solution.**—A standard solution is made by dissolving 90 g. of potassium iodide and 45.27 g. of iodine in the least quantity of water necessary to effect solution, and diluting with water to 1 liter. 1 ml. is equivalent to 0.01 g. CaO.

**Thiosulfate Solution.**—The reagent is made by dissolving 44.27 g. of sodium thiosulfate in water and diluting to 1 liter. 2 ml. of this solution is equivalent to 1 ml. of the iodine solution.

**Standardization.**—A definite weight of 0.5 to 1.0 g. of pure arsenious oxide $(As_2O_3)$ is dissolved in 10% sodium hydroxide solution and the resulting product acidified with hydrochloric or sulfuric acid. This solution is now neutralized with sodium bicarbonate and 4 to 5 g. added in excess. Starch indicator is now added and the arsenite titrated with the standard iodine solution. Since 1 g. of $As_2O_3$ is equivalent to 0.5670 g. of CaO, the weight of the arsenic taken multiplied by 0.5670, divided by the ml. of iodine required, gives the equivalent lime per ml. of the standard iodine reagent. Use this factor in the iodine titrations of lime.

The thiosulfate may be standardized against a definite volume of the iodine reagent and its equivalent value established in terms of the standard iodine solution. See Notes below.

*Procedure.*—The sample of lime (1 g. is recommended) is slacked by adding boiling water (5 to 10 minutes is ample to accomplish this). An excess of iodine is added (see Notes) and the mixture stirred occasionally until the lime is all in solution. Insoluble silica is generally present but can easily be distinguished from the milky appearing lime. When the solution of the lime is complete (1 to 10 minutes will accomplish this), the excess of iodine is titrated with the standard thiosulfate. The excess thus determined is subtracted from the total iodine added and the equivalent CaO, to the combined iodine, calculated from the CaO factor of iodine $(I_2 \times 0.4419 = \textbf{CaO})$.

NOTES.—Any substance which liberates iodine quantitatively from a solution of potassium iodide can be used for the standardization of sodium thiosulfate. Among such substances are potassium permanganate, potassium dichromate, potassium iodate, potassium bi-iodate, metallic copper oxidized to a cupric salt, etc. In using any of the above reagents first acidify the solution of an excess of potassium iodide with hydrochloric acid (strongly acid if dichromate is used, end point in this case is green in place of colorless) and then add the permanganate or dichromate or other reagent desired and titrate the liberated iodine in presence of starch indicator.

An excess of 5 ml. of iodine is recommended in the lime determination. To the same amount of water used in the analysis add 5 ml. of the iodine and use this as a standard for color comparison in running in the necessary excess of iodine in the sample.

# STANDARD METHODS OF TESTING GYPSUM AND GYPSUM PRODUCTS [11]

## DETERMINATION OF FREE WATER

*Procedure.*—Weigh a sample of not less than 1 lb. of the material as received and spread it out in a thin layer in a suitable vessel. Place in an oven and dry at 113°F. (45°C.) for 2 hours, then cool in an atmosphere free from moisture, and weigh again. The loss of weight corresponds to the free water, and shall be calculated as a percentage of the sample as received.

Retain the dried sample in an air-tight container until used.

## PREPARATION OF SAMPLE

*Procedure.*—Weigh a sample of not less than 1 lb. of the material as received and spread it out in a thin layer in a suitable vessel. Place in an oven and dry at 113°F. (45°C.) for 2 hours, then cool in an atmosphere free from moisture. Reduce the sample to pass a No. 60 (250-micron) sieve, taking extreme care not to expose unduly the material to moisture or to overheating. Thoroughly remix the ground sample, and store in an air-tight container until used.

## COMBINED WATER

*Procedure.*—Place 1 g. of the sample in a covered crucible and dry to constant weight at 420–445°F. (215–230°C.). Calculate the loss of weight to percentage of sample as received, and report as combined water.

## CARBON DIOXIDE

*Procedure.*—Place the residue, obtained after drying as described in preceding section, in a suitable flask and dissolve it in dilute HCl (not stronger than 1:4) in such a way that the gas evolved, after being freed from water vapor by calcium chloride or sulfuric acid, can be collected in either soda-lime or caustic potash and weighed. Boil the solution for 1 minute, and pass a current of $CO_2$-free air through the apparatus for 30 minutes. The increase of weight of the soda-lime or caustic potash corresponds to the weight of carbon dioxide. Then calculate the $CO_2$ to percentage of sample as received.

## SILICA AND INSOLUBLE MATTER

*Procedure.*—Place 0.5 g. of the sample in a porcelain casserole. Add about 25 ml. of HCl (1:5), and evaporate to apparent dryness on a hot-plate. Cool, and add enough HCl (sp. gr. 1.18) to wet thoroughly. Add about 10 ml. of water, boil, filter, and wash. Put the filtrate back in the same casserole. Evaporate it to dryness and heat to about 250°F. (120°C.) for 1 hour and then cool. Add enough HCl (sp. gr. 1.18) to wet thoroughly. Add about 25 ml. of water, boil, filter, and

[11] Adopted by A.S.T.M., 1923; Revised, 1927, 1930, 1933, 1939, 1940, 1942, 1950, 1952, 1954, 1956, 1959.

wash. Transfer the two papers containing the two precipitates to the same crucible, ignite, and weigh. Calculate the $SiO_2$ and insoluble matter to percentage of sample as received.

## IRON AND ALUMINUM OXIDES

*Procedure.*—To the filtrate obtained as described add a few drops of $HNO_3$, and boil to insure oxidation of the iron. Add 2 g. of $NH_4Cl$ previously dissolved in water. Make alkaline with $NH_4OH$. Digest hot for a few minutes until the precipitate coagulates. Filter, wash, ignite the precipitate, and weigh as $Fe_2O_3 + Al_2O_3$. Calculate the iron and aluminum oxides to percentage of sample as received. This precipitate may be further treated to separate the two oxides, but this is generally unnecessary.

## LIME

*Procedure.*—To the filtrate obtained as described in preceding paragraph, add 5 g. of $(NH_4)_2C_2O_4$ dissolved in water. Digest hot for 30 minutes, making sure that the solution is always alkaline with $NH_4OH$. Filter, wash, and ignite to constant weight in a platinum crucible over a strong blast. Calculate the CaO to percentage of sample as received.

*Alternative Procedure.*—To the filtrate obtained from the iron and aluminum precipitates, add 5 g. of $(NH_4)_2C_2O_4$ dissolved in water. Digest hot for 30 minutes, making sure that the solution is always alkaline with $NH_4OH$. Filter and wash. Transfer the precipitate to a beaker, and wash the filter paper with hot diluted $H_2SO_4$, catching the washings in the same beaker. Heat gently to complete solution, adding more $H_2SO_4$ if necessary. While still warm, titrate with a solution of $KMnO_4$ containing 5.6339 g. per liter, until the pink color is permanent. The number of milliliters of $KMnO_4$ used gives directly the percentage of lime in the dried sample. Recalculate the CaO to percentage of sample as received.

## MAGNESIA

*Procedure.*—To the filtrate obtained from the calcium precipitate, add enough water to give a total volume of about 600 ml. Cool, and add 10 ml. of $NH_4OH$ and 5 g. $NaNH_4HPO_4$ dissolved in water. Stir until precipitate begins to form. Let stand overnight. Filter, wash with 2.5% $NH_4NO_3$. Ignite and weigh. Multiply this weight by 0.36027 to find the weight of MgO. Calculate the MgO to percentage of sample as received.

## SULFUR TRIOXIDE

*Procedure.*—Dissolve 0.5 g. of the sample (prepared as described in Section on "Combined Water") in 50 ml. of HCl (1:5). Boil. Add 100 ml. of boiling water, and continue boiling for 5 minutes. Filter immediately and wash thoroughly with hot water. Boil, and while boiling, add slowly 20 ml. of a boiling solution of 10% $BaCl_2$. Digest hot for 1 hour, or until the precipitate settles. Filter and wash. Dry carefully. Ignite over a Bunsen burner at the lowest heat possible until the filter paper is burned off. Ignite at bright red heat for 15 minutes, and weigh. Multiply this weight by 0.34297 to determine the weight of $SO_3$. Calculate the $SO_3$ to percentage of sample as received.

## SODIUM CHLORIDE

**Procedure.**—Dissolve in boiling water a 1 g. sample (prepared as described in Section on "Combined Water"), filter and wash with 250 ml. of boiling water. Add two or three drops of $K_2CrO_4$ to the filtrate and titrate with 0.05 $N$ $AgNO_3$. One milliliter of $AgNO_3$ is equivalent to 0.002923 g. of sodium chloride. Calculate the NaCl to percentage of sample as received.

## REPORT OF RESULTS

Report the results obtained in the analysis as follows:

|  | Per cent |
|---|---|
| Free water........................................ | ........ |
| Combined water.................................... | ........ |
| Carbon dioxide, $CO_2$............................. | ........ |
| Silicon dioxide ($SiO_2$) and insoluble matter......... | ........ |
| Iron and aluminum oxides, $Fe_2O_3 + Al_2O_3$......... | ........ |
| Lime, CaO....................................... | ........ |
| Magnesium oxide, MgO............................ | ........ |
| Sulfur trioxide, $SO_3$ ............................ | ........ |
| Sodium chloride, NaCl............................. | ........ |
| Total...................................... | 100.00± |

Since it is frequently advisable to recalculate the results obtained in the chemical analysis in order that they may be more enlightening, the following is submitted for consideration:

(a) Multiply percentage of MgO by 2.0912 to find the percentage of $MgCO_3$.

(b) Multiply the percentage of MgO by 1.0914 to find the percentage of $CO_2$ as $MgCO_3$.

(c) Deduct $CO_2$ as $MgCO_3$ from the $CO_2$ determined.

(d) Multiply the $CO_2$ remaining by 2.2742 to find percentage of $CaCO_3$.

(e) Add the percentages of $SiO_2$, $Fe_2O_3 + Al_2O_3$, $MgCO_3$, and $CaCO_3$ and report in the aggregate.

(f) Multiply the percentage of $CaCO_3$ by 0.56031 to find the percentage of CaO as $CaCO_3$.

(g) From the total percentage of CaO, deduct the percentage of CaO as $CaCO_3$. The remainder may be called "available CaO."

(h) The "available CaO" should bear to the $SO_3$ a ratio of 0.6991 to 1. Determine which (if either) is in excess.

(i) If the CaO is in excess, multiply the $SO_3$ by 0.6991, and subtract the result from the "available CaO." The remainder is reported as "excess CaO."

(j) If the $SO_3$ is in excess, multiply the "available CaO" by 1.4304 and subtract the result from the $SO_3$. The remainder is reported as "excess $SO_3$."

(k) Add the "available CaO," and the $SO_3$, and subtract the "excess CaO" or "excess $SO_3$." The remainder is $CaSO_4$.

(l) If the $CaSO_4$ is present as $CaSO_4 \cdot \frac{1}{2}H_2O$, the percentage of $CaSO_4$ should bear to the percentage of combined water a ratio of 15.12:1. Determine which (if either) is in excess.

(m) If the $CaSO_4$ is in excess, some of it is present in the anhydrous form. Multiply the percentage of combined water by 15.12 to find the percentage of $CaSO_4$ as $CaSO_4 \cdot \frac{1}{2}H_2O$. The difference between the total $CaSO_4$ and the percentage of $CaSO_4$ as $CaSO_4 \cdot \frac{1}{2}H_2O$, is the $CaSO_4$ in the anhydrous form.

(n) If the water is in excess, some of the $CaSO_4$ is present as gypsum. Let $x$ = percentage of $CaSO_4 \cdot \frac{1}{2}H_2O$, and $y$ = percentage of $CaSO_4 \cdot 2H_2O$. Then:

$$x + y = \text{percentage of } CaSO_4 \text{ [as found in } (k)\text{]} + \text{percentage of water}$$

$$0.06206x + 0.2093y = \text{percentage of combined water}$$

Solve these equations for $x$ and $y$. Report $x$ as percentage of "calcined gypsum," $CaSO_4 \cdot \frac{1}{2}H_2O$. Report $y$ as percentage of gypsum, $CaSO_4 \cdot 2H_2O$.
Having made these calculations, the results may be reported as follows:

*Per cent*

Gypsum, $CaSO_4 \cdot 2H_2O$.....................  ........  
Calcined gypsum, $CaSO_4 \cdot 1/2H_2O$ ........  ........  
Anhydrite, $CaSO_4$..........................  ........  
Excess CaO  
   or  
Excess $SO_3$..............................  ........  
Sodium chloride, NaCl....................  ........  
Other ingredients.........................  ........  

Total............................. 100.00±

The presence of the different forms of $CaSO_4$ may be corroborated by a microscopic examination.

## ALTERNATIVE PROCEDURE FOR CALCIUM SULFATE BY AMMONIUM ACETATE METHOD

This procedure is intended for determining calcium sulfate in gypsum and gypsum products by extraction with ammonium acetate solution, and may be used as an alternative method to the complete procedure described above.

*Reagents.* **Ammonium Acetate Solution.**—Dissolve 454 g. of ammonium acetate in 2 liters of water. Add sufficient $NH_4OH$ to make the solution distinctly ammoniacal, using phenolphthalein as the indicator.

**Ammonium Hydroxide Wash Solution.**—Dilute 100 ml. of $NH_4OH$ (sp. gr. 0.90) to 1 liter.

**Filter Aid.**—Analytical-grade diatomaceous silica.

*Procedure Using Gooch Crucible.*—Weigh rapidly approximately 4 g. of the well-mixed sample and transfer to a 600-ml. beaker. (All weighings should be made to 0.001 g. except that weights of crucibles and of their contents should be determined to 0.0001 g.)

Without delay, weigh 1 g. of the well-mixed sample in a tared weighing bottle having a ground-glass stopper. Dry the sample and weighing bottle to constant weight at 45°C., and calculate the percentage loss in weight at 45°C. (largely uncombined water) as follows:

$$\text{Loss in weight at 45°C., } \% = \frac{A - B}{C} \times 100,$$

where $A$ = original weight of sample and weighing bottle,

$B$ = weight of sample and weighing bottle dried to constant weight at 45°C., and

$C$ = original weight of sample.

Calculate the weight of the 4-g. sample above, corrected for loss on heating to constant weight at 45°C.

If the percentage by weight of combined water held by the calcium sulfate is desired, heat the sample and weighing bottle to constant weight at 220°C. (stopper weighing bottles immediately upon removal from the oven in order to prevent absorption of moisture from the air upon cooling), and calculate the percentage of combined water as follows:

$$\text{Combined water, } \% = \frac{B - D}{B - E} \times 100,$$

where $B$ = weight of sample and weighing bottle dried to constant weight at 45°C.,

$D$ = weight of sample and weighing bottle dried to constant weight at 220°C., and

$E$ = weight of weighing bottle.

To the contents of the 600-ml. beaker, add 350 ml. of the ammonium acetate solution, and stir the mixture thoroughly so as to loosen all of the solid matter from the bottom of the beaker. Add 0.2000 g. of redried diatomaceous silica to the mixture, heat the beaker and contents to 70°C. on a steam bath, and maintain at that temperature for 30 minutes, while stirring frequently. During the heating, keep the solvents ammoniacal by additions of $NH_4OH$ and phenolphthalein, if indicated. (Meanwhile heat a supply of the ammonium acetate solution to 70°C., keeping it also distinctly ammoniacal.) Filter the mixture, with suction, through a tared Gooch crucible, stirring frequently during filtration to keep the diatomaceous earth suspended in the liquid. Wash the Gooch crucible containing the residue with 10-ml. portions of the warm acetate solution, draining thoroughly after each washing. Wash in the same manner with eight 10-ml. portions of the $NH_4OH$ wash solution. Care should be exercised to wash the upper walls of the Gooch crucible. Drain the crucible dry with suction, place in an oven at 70°C., and dry to constant weight (avoid overheating in all oven drying of ammonium acetate residues; that is, place crucibles well away from the heating elements. This is of particular importance for samples high in impurities, as these impurities often have water of hydration that is lost on local overheating). Allow the crucible to cool in a desiccator before weighing.

**Calculation of Results.**—Calculate the percentage of $CaSO_4 \cdot xH_2O$ on the basis of the sample dried to constant weight at 45°C. as follows:

$$CaSO_4 \cdot xH_2O, \% = \frac{F - (G - H)}{F} \times 100$$

where $F$ = weight of sample, corrected for loss on heating to constant weight at 45°;

$G$ = weight of dried crucible and contents; and

$H$ = weight of crucible plus diatomaceous silica used as filter aid.

*Procedure Using Tared Filter Papers.*—Dry a quarter-folded, 11-cm, quantitative filter paper overnight at 70°C. in a wide-form, glass-stoppered, 30 x 60-mm.

weighing bottle. After drying, cool the weighing bottle and paper in a desiccator and weigh.

Treat the sample exactly as described on page 276 prior to the filtration. Filter the mixture by gravity through an ordinary 7-cm glass funnel, stirring frequently during filtration to keep the diatomaceous silica suspended in the liquid. Wash the filter paper and residue with five 10-ml. portions of warm acetate solution, draining thoroughly after each washing. Wash in the same manner with eight 10-ml. portions of the $NH_4OH$ wash solution. After final draining replace the paper and residue in the weighing bottle, and dry at 70°C. to constant weight. Cool the weighing bottle, paper, and residue in a freshly prepared desiccator before weighing; this is essential, due to the hygroscopic character of paper.

Calculate the percentage of $CaSO_4 \cdot xH_2O$ as described on page 277, substituting the weight of the weighing bottle and filter paper for the weight of the crucible.

## METHODS FOR CALCIUM IN ANALYSES IN OTHER CHAPTER

| | |
|---|---|
| Calcium in Bauxite | See Analysis of Bauxite (Aluminum Chapter) |
| Calcium in Fused Alumina | See Analysis of Fused Alumina |
| Calcium in Arsenious Oxide | See Analysis of Arsenious Oxide |
| Calcium in Barite | See Analysis of Barite (Barium Chapter) |
| Calcium Carbonate in Fluorspar | See Analysis of Fluorspar (Fluorine Chapter) |
| Calcium in Magnesite | See Analysis of Magnesite (Magnesium Chapter) |
| Calcium in Magnesium Alloys | See Analysis of Magnesium Alloys |
| Calcium in Phosphorus Salts | See Analysis of Phosphorus Salts |
| Calcium in Commercial Phosphates | See Analysis of Commercial Phosphates |
| Calcium in Sodium Silicate | See Analysis of Sodium Silicate (Silicon Chapter) |
| Calcium in Sand | See Analysis of Sand (Silicon Chapter) |
| Calcium in Titanium Pigments | See Analysis of Titanox-C Pigments (Titanium Chapter) |

# Chapter 12

# CARBON

C, *at. wt.* 12.01115 (±0.00005); *sp. gr. amorp.* 188; *cryst.: graphite,* 2.25; *diamond,* 3.51; *m.p. sublime at* 3500°C.; *oxides,* CO *and* CO₂

Carbon occurs free in nature in the forms—diamond, graphite, and amorphous carbon. It occurs combined widely distributed in organic compounds in the animal and vegetable kingdoms in combination with hydrogen, oxygen, nitrogen, and other elements. As hydrocarbons it occurs in natural gas, petroleum, and bitumen. As carbon dioxide it is found in the air and confined under pressure in pockets in the earth. It occurs as carbonate in rocks combined principally with calcium, magnesium, and iron.

## DETECTION

*Element.*—Carbon is recognized by its appearance and by its inertness towards general reagents. It is seen in the charring of organic matter when heated or when acted upon by hot concentrated sulfuric acid.

Upon combustion with oxygen or by oxidation with chromic and sulfuric acids, carbon dioxide is formed. The gas passed into lime water forms a white precipitate, $CaCO_3$. Penfield fuses the substance with precipitated and washed $PbCrO_4$ in a hard glass tube closed at one end. The $CO_2$ is tested at the mouth of the tube.

*Carbon Dioxide.*—A white precipitate is formed with lime water, baryta water, ammoniacal solutions of calcium, or barium chlorides, or lead acetate (basic).

*Carbonates.*—Action of mineral acids causes effervescence, $CO_2$ being evolved. The gas is odorless (distinction from $SO_2$, $H_2S$, and $NO_2$) and is colorless (distinction from $NO_2$). See test for $CO_2$ above.

*Distinction between Soluble Carbonates and Bicarbonates.*—The solution of the former is alkaline to phenolphthalein indicator (pink). Bicarbonate solutions remain colorless with this indicator. Normal carbonates precipitate magnesium carbonate when added to magnesium sulfate solution; bicarbonates cause no precipitation.

*Free Carbonic Acid in Water in Presence of Bicarbonates.*—0.5 ml. of rosolic acid (1 part acid in 500 parts of 80% alcohol), produces a red color with bicarbonates in absence of free $CO_2$, and a colorless or faintly yellow solution when free $CO_2$ is present.

*Carbon Monoxide.*—The gas burns with a pale blue flame and is not absorbed by potassium hydroxide or lime water (distinction from $CO_2$). It is oxidized to $CO_2$ and so detected. With hot, concentrated potassium hydroxide, potassium formate is produced.

The gas is detected in the blood by gasometric methods with the Van Slyke

279

apparatus, by the pyrotannic acid method, and by means of the absorption spectrum.

The gas colors a mixture of $I_2O_5$ and fuming sulfuric acid (on a support of pumice) a transient green (Hoover and Lamb, "Hoolamite detector").

## ESTIMATION

Among the substances in which the determination of carbon is commonly made are the following:—organic compounds, carbonate rocks and minerals—such as calcite, marble, limestone, dolomite, magnesite, witherite, spathic iron ore; commercial products such as cement, soda and baking soda; alloys including carbon in steel; carbon dioxide in gases including air.

## PREPARATION AND SOLUTION OF THE SAMPLE

*Iron, Steel, and Alloys.*—The subject is discussed below in this chapter.

*Organic Matter.*—It is advisable to fuse this in a nickel or iron crucible with sodium peroxide. The carbonate thus formed may be determined as usual. The organic substance may be oxidized directly in the combustion furnace.

*Carbonates. Limestone, Dolomite, Cement, Alkali Carbonates and Bicarbonates.*—The powdered material is decomposed by addition of an acid as directed in the methods given later.

## SEPARATIONS

The element is generally determined as carbon dioxide, in which form it is liberated from most of the combinations in which it occurs, free from other substances by ignition in a current of oxygen, or by oxidation with chromic acid as directed later.

*Separation of Carbon in Iron and Steel.* **Cupric Potassium Chloride Procedure.**—0.5 to 2 g. of the drillings are treated with 100 to 200 ml. of cupric potassium chloride solution and 10 ml. of hydrochloric acid (sp. gr. 1.19). This mixture dissolves the iron according to the reaction,

$$CuCl_2 \cdot KCl + Fe \rightarrow FeCl_2 + Cu + KCl$$

$$CuCl_2 \cdot KCl + Cu \rightarrow Cu_2Cl_2 + KCl$$

Carbon is left as a residue.

The solution should be stirred frequently to hasten the solution of the iron. It is advisable to keep the temperature of the solution at about 50°C. When the iron and copper have dissolved the carbon is filtered off into a perforated platinum boat or crucible, as directed under the methods. It is now oxidized to $CO_2$ and so determined.

NOTE.—The cupric potassium chloride solution is prepared by dissolving 150 parts of potassium chloride and 170 parts of crystallized cupric chloride in water and crystallizing out the double salt. Three hundred grams of this salt are dissolved in 1000 ml. The solution may be used several times by chlorinating the dirty brown filtrate from the carbonaceous residue. The cuprous chloride formed during the solution of the steel is converted again to cupric chloride, and the chlorinated double salt is even more energetic in its solvent action than the freshly made reagent. (Blair.)

*In Presence of Sulfur.*—$SO_2$ is oxidized to $SO_3$ by passing the hot gases from the carbon combustion through ignited lead chromate with the resulting formation of the nonvolatile lead sulfate. The $SO_2$ may also be removed by passing the gases ($CO_2$ and $SO_2$) through a concentrated solution of chromic and sulfuric acids; $SO_2$ oxidized to $SO_3$ remains in the solution, while $CO_2$ is not absorbed and passes through.

## GRAVIMETRIC METHODS

The determination of carbon gravimetrically depends on conversion to carbon dioxide and weighing the gas. This is accomplished by absorption of the $CO_2$ in a suitable reagent. Carbon is converted to the dioxide by oxidation either by means of a fluid oxidizing reagent or by combustion in presence of air or oxygen. Details for carbon in steel and alloys and in organic matter follow. Carbon combined in carbonates is generally determined by decomposition with an acid and determining the $CO_2$ by absorption—direct method—or by the loss of weight in the substance due to evolved $CO_2$—indirect method or loss of weight method—details follow later.

## DETERMINATION OF CARBON BY COMBUSTION

### COMBUSTION APPARATUS

A simple electric furnace may be made by wrapping a silica tube with a thin covering of asbestos paper, which has been moistened with water. On drying the paper will cling to the tube. A spiral coil of Nichrome wire is wound around this core. On a 2-foot length of tube two 45-foot lengths of No. 18 wire, connected in parallel, will heat the tube to bright redness, if 110 volts A.C. are applied. The coils should be covered with 1/4-in. coating of alundum cement. For appearance' sake as well as for protection, the tube is placed in a large cylinder of sheet iron, packed around with asbestos, and is held in position by circular asbestos boards placed at the ends of the large cylinder. The cylinder is mounted on a stand.

### ABSORPTION APPARATUS

A large number of forms of absorption apparatus may be obtained. The Geissler and Liebig bulbs have been popular (Figs. 12-1 and 12-2), but are now being dis-

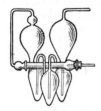

FIG. 12-1. Geissler Bulb.                    FIG. 12-2. Liebig Bulb.

placed by forms that have less surface exposed, that are more easily cleaned and less fragile, such as Gerhardt's, Vanier's, using solutions of NaOH or KOH, or Fleming's and Stetser's type of apparatus, using solids. (Figs. 12-3 and 12-4.)

**Details of the Absorption Apparatus.**—Figure 12-5 is Fleming's modification of Martin's apparatus. When properly filled this tube will serve for at least 70 combustions when operating on 1.5 g. of sample containing 1.03% carbon.

The anhydride in the upper chamber serves for at least 300 combustions. Soda lime, placed in the lower tube in alternate layers (⅛ in.) of the different meshes, has proved a very convenient and desirable reagent. The 12-mesh soda lime for

Fig. 12-3. Gerhardt Bulb.

Fig. 12-4. Vanier Bottle.

nitrogen can also be used with excellent results. If this is employed, part of it should be ground to about 60-mesh and alternate layers of fine and coarse used.

**Purification and Absorption Trains.**—Details of these are given in the portion of this chapter under the "Determination of Carbon in Steel."

### PROCEDURE FOR ORGANIC SUBSTANCES—I. ORGANIC SUBSTANCES FREE OF NITROGEN, HALOGENS, SULFUR, AND THE METALS

Carbon is determined by combustion to $CO_2$, the gas absorbed in a suitable reagent, such as caustic soda, soda lime, soda asbestos (Ascarite), contained in a convenient form of apparatus. The combustion is made in a tube (a form is shown below) heated to redness, by passing pure oxygen or air (free from moisture and $CO_2$) over the material. A description of the purification and absorption train is given under the section devoted to carbon determination in steel, in the following portion of this chapter. Usually hydrogen is determined at the same time as carbon, as it is necessary under any circumstance to take care of the moisture formed and prevent it from entering the absorption chamber. The same moisture absorbent for drying the gas entering the combustion chamber is used as for absorbing the moisture formed by combustion. This drying agent should not absorb $CO_2$. The following agents are satisfactory: concentrated sulfuric acid, magnesium perchlorate trihydrate, phosphorus pentoxide. It is advisable to have the moisture absorbent preceded by an empty tube in which most of the water can be condensed to prolong the effectiveness of the reagent.

*Apparatus.* **Combustion Tube for Determining Carbon and Hydrogen in Organic Matter.**—The combustion tube (Fig. 12-6) is about 95 cm in length with an internal diameter of about 12–15 mm. Three platinum gauze rolls and copper oxide appear in the figure above. Substances that contain halogens, nitrogen or sulfur require special reagents (not shown) in the combustion tube. For example lead chromate is substituted for copper oxide, when halogens and sulfur are present; a reduced copper roll is used at the exit end of the tube when nitrogenous compounds are present. The exit end of the tube is cooled by wrapping a strip of absorbent material about the tube and dipping the free ends in a beaker of water.

The apparatus is first swept out with pure oxygen to remove any moisture or $CO_2$. The water absorption bulbs and the $CO_2$ absorption bulbs are weighed. To take care of the error caused by air buoyancy similar apparatus is placed on the opposite pan as a counterbalance, this apparatus being slightly lighter than the absorption apparatus. For example if a Fleming's apparatus is used for absorption of $CO_2$, a slightly lighter Fleming's apparatus is used as a counterbalance.

It is often advisable to mix intimately the material that is being examined with about ten times its weight of powdered lead chromate and an equal amount of potassium chromate when the material contains much inert substance,[1] for example in determining organic matter in rocks and minerals. This is generally not required by pure organic substances.

Solids are placed directly in the combustion boat, weighing being conducted, if desired, in the previously weighed boat. Liquids are weighed in glass bulbs. The glass bulb may be blown, a capillary end drawn out and the weighing conducted during the sweeping out of the furnace. It is filled by heating the bulb, placing the capillary tip in the liquid and then cooling. The tip is wiped off and sealed in the flame and the bulb and contents again weighed. Just before placing in the boat and inserting in the combustion tube the tip of the capillary is filed off. Substances burning with difficulty can be burned by mixing with powdered CuO, which has been previously ignited.

The combustion tube, swept free of $CO_2$ and moisture, is prepared for the combustion run by heating the section of the tube containing the copper oxide to redness, at the same time keeping the portion zoned for the combustion boat cool, the last gauze plug (Fig. 12-6) being removed. The sample, placed in the boat, is now inserted in the combustion tube, the capillary tip pointing towards the open end of the tube, the 12 cm copper gauze plug replaced and the tube quickly closed. The current of oxygen is immediately

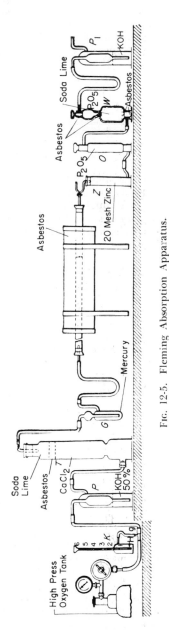

Fig. 12-5. Fleming Absorption Apparatus.

---

[1] *Caution.*—PbCrO$_4$ melts and decomposes at 600°C., K$_2$CrO$_4$ fuses at 971°C.

turned on and the run started, all the apparatus being connected and free of leaks. (See "Determination of Carbon in Steel.") After a few minutes the portion of the tube containing the sample is gradually heated to redness (600–800°C.) and the run continued until the combustion is complete. Some experience and skill is necessary for correct results. The combustion of solids should be conducted slowly, liquids

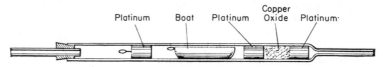

FIG. 12-6. Combustion Tube.

require a slightly more rapid flow of gas to furnish sufficient oxygen before any vapor escapes from the oxidizing zone. The tube is allowed to cool with the oxygen flowing through the apparatus. If hydrogen is also being determined, it may be necessary to sweep forward any condensed moisture in the apparatus previous to the moisture absorption tubes by heating with a naked flame, starting near the exit end of the combustion tube and carrying the heat cautiously towards the absorption tubes.

The absorption bulbs are weighed with the tare weights as recommended. Increase of weight is due to $H_2O$ and $CO_2$ in the respective apparatus.

$$H_2O \times 0.1119 = H$$

$$CO_2 \times 0.2729 = C$$

NOTE.—The oxygen gas should be free from hydrogen. A preheater, placed before the purifying tubes of the train, causes the combustion of the hydrogen and the absorption of the water formed before the gas enters the combustion tube.

### PROCEDURE FOR ORGANIC SUBSTANCES:
### II. NITROGEN-CONTAINING SUBSTANCES

A modification of the first procedure described for determinations of carbon and hydrogen in organic substances must be made, since from substances containing nitrogen, nitroso and nitro compounds, oxides of nitrogen are formed which would be absorbed in the calcium chloride and potash bulbs, giving high results for hydrogen and carbon. To overcome this difficulty, a copper spiral, that has been reduced (see Note below) is placed in the front end of the combustion tube (to the right in Fig. 12-6) to reduce the oxides of nitrogen to nitrogen.

NOTE.—Reduction of copper spiral may be accomplished as follows: The copper spiral is prepared by rolling together a piece of copper gauze about 10 centimeters wide, making it as large as will conveniently pass into the combustion tube. The spiral is heated till it glows by holding it in a large gas flame, and while still hot it is dropped into a test tube containing 1 or 2 ml. of methyl alcohol or ether. This quickly boils away, igniting at the end of the tube. The copper is completely reduced to bright metallic copper. The spiral is taken out with a pair of crucible tongs and dried by quickly passing it through a flame a few times, and while it is still warm it is introduced into the front of the combustion tube.

The substance is introduced into the tube and the connections made. The copper oxide spiral, that was pushed after the boat, is heated, and then the reduced spiral (right end of tube). The oxide near the boat, and finally the entire tube is heated to a red heat. When the bubbles cease to show in the potash bulb, the stopcock is opened to the oxygen-purifying train and a slow flow of oxygen turned on, the gas allowed to pass through the tube until it can be detected with a glowing splinter at the exit of the absorption end of the apparatus.

If the substance is difficult to burn, it is mixed with freshly ignited (cold) copper oxide, which assists combustion.

The remainder of the operation is the same as has been described.

### PROCEDURE FOR ORGANIC SUBSTANCES:
### III. HALOGEN-CONTAINING SUBSTANCES

The procedure is the same as that described for nitrogenous substances with the exception that a silver spiral is used in place of the reduced copper spiral. The heating of this spiral should be between 180 and 200°C. (not over 200°).

### PROCEDURE FOR ORGANIC SUBSTANCES:
### IV. SULFUR-CONTAINING SUBSTANCES

These are best ignited with sodium peroxide and the carbonate formed is determined by the procedure given for carbon dioxide in carbonates.

To oxidize the $SO_2$ that forms, lead chromate is used in place of copper oxide in the combustion tube, a lower temperature being necessary to prevent fusion of the chromate. The $SO_2$ is oxidized to $SO_3$, which reacts with the lead forming the nonvolatile $PbSO_4$, while $CO_2$ is not acted upon and passes on. See also separations under Estimation.

### SEMI-MICRO PROCEDURE FOR CARBON AND HYDROGEN

A systematic development of methods for the ultimate analysis of 20–50 mg. samples has been given by H. Ter Meulen, J. Hesslinga and other investigators.[2] This field of work has been noteworthy because of the application of active catalysts for oxidation or hydrogenation. The whole apparatus is very small and compact; suitable dimensions are indicated below, Fig. 12-7. The catalytic $MnO_2$ is prepared by mixing $MnSO_4$ and $KMnO_4$ in nitric acid solution in the ratio 2 mols:3 mols. The $MnO_2$ is washed by decantation, with distilled water, collected, compressed and cut into pellets about 0.2–0.5 cm. in diameter, dried in an air bath at 100°C. and finally heated for 30 minutes at 300°C. The fine material

[2] Meulen, H. Ter, Estimation of Oxygen in Organic Compounds, Rec. Trav. Chim., 41, 509, 1922; Meulen, H. Ter, and Hesslinga, J., Halogens, *ibid.*, 42, 1093, 1923; 43, 181, 1924; Hesslinga, J., Estimation of C, H and N, *ibid.*, 43, 551, 1924; Meulen, H. Ter, Estimation of N by Hydrogenation, *ibid.*, 43, 643, 1924; Estimation of O by Hydrogenation, *ibid.*, 43, 899, 1924. See also, *ibid.*, 44, 271, 1925; 45, 365, 1923; 45, 368, 1926; for Determination of N, As and Hg respectively. Maes, P., Determination of Nitrogen, Chem. Abs., 29, 2474, 1935; Wilson and Sun, C. H., J. Chinese Chem. Soc., 2, 129, 1934; Chem. Abs., 29, 76, 1935; Clark, E. P., Semi-Micro Technique, J. Assoc. Off. Agr. Chem., 16, 255, 1933; Meulen, H. Ter, Analysis by Hydrogenation and Some Oxidation Methods, Rec. Trav. Chim., 53, 118, 1934; Roger, R., and MacKay, W., J. Soc. Chem. Ind., 54, 46T, 1935; Russell, W. W., and Fulton, J. W., Determination of Oxygen, Ind. Eng. Chem., Anal. Ed., 5, 384, 1933; Also Russell and Marks, M. E., *ibid.*, 6, 381, 1934; 8, 453, 1936; Marks, M. E., *ibid.*, 7, 102, 1935; Griffing, E. P., and Alsberg, C. L., Nitrogen, J. Am. Chem. Soc., 53, 1037, 1931; Meulen, H. Ter, and Hesslinga, J., Neue Methoden der Organisch-Chemischen Analyse, Akademische Verlagsgesellschaft, Leipzig, 1927; Nouvelles Methodes d'Analyse Organique, Dunod, Paris, 1932.

is screened out. If oxygen rather than air is used for the combustion of the organic compound, an active catalyst may be used for many successive determinations; if air is used then a catalyst filling lasts for about five determinations. In

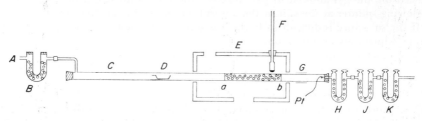

FIG. 12-7. Ter Meulen-Hesslinga Apparatus for Carbon-Hydrogen Determination.

$A$ = Inlet for purified air or oxygen; $B$ = U-tube for drying the gas; $C$ = Quartz combustion tube 32 cm. long and 0.8 cm. inner diameter; $D$ = Platinum boat; $E$ = Oven (electric or gas) 12 cm. long by 6 cm. diameter. The oven may be moved along nearly to the end of the tube, 3; $F$ = Nitrogen-filled thermometer or thermocouple; $G$ = Metal sleeve to aid in keeping material heated to 150–180°C. $Pt$ indicates platinum wire placed in side arm of U-tube $H$, to aid in driving condensed water into $H$; $a$-$b$ Catalyst. The oven $E$ and sleeve $G$ may be moved so that 2 cm. or so of the catalyst is at the right of the oven (see text); $H$ = U-tube filled with the same drying agent as was used in tube $B$. Calcium chloride or more effective desiccants may be used; $J$ = U-tube with left $\frac{2}{3}$ filled with ascarite and right $\frac{1}{3}$ filled with the same desiccant used in tube $H$; $K$ = Guard tube filled with the same desiccant as is used in tube $H$.

any event the filling should be renewed when $\frac{2}{3}$ of it has turned yellowish brown indicating loss of available oxygen.

Details of Fillings for the Combustion Tube

| The Compound Contains: | Catalyst for Oxidation: | Temp. of Catalyst | Notes |
|---|---|---|---|
| (1) C, H, O. | MnO$_2$ 6 cm long | 400°C. | Must not be heated above 450°C. |
| (2) C, H, O, Halogen | MnO$_2$ + PbO$_2$ 1:1 6 cm length | 400°C. | Active life longer than for (1). |
| (3) C, H, O, S | MnO$_2$ 8 cm long (PbO$_2$ is added if halogen is present) | 6 cm. at 400°C. 2 cm. at 150–180°C. | Part of the catalyst projects beyond the furnace to cool it. |
| (4) C, H, O, N | MnO$_2$ 6 cm; PbO$_2$ 2 cm. (PbO$_2$ is mixed with the MnO$_2$ if the compound contains halogen.) | MnO$_2$ at 400°C. | The PbO$_2$ layer is outside of the heated zone and its temperature is below that at which it loses oxygen. |

After the apparatus has been assembled and tested for blank correction, which should be practically negligible, with a 4 bubble per second stream of oxygen, the weighed substance is introduced in a platinum boat, and very slowly distilled to the catalyst by gentle heating with a micro burner. The combustion requires 15–25 minutes for 0.05 g. of material. The heating unit is moved to the left and any unburned carbon near the catalyst is heated by a suitable burner, and finally care is taken to drive any condensed moisture into the first U-tube.

## THE WET COMBUSTION PROCESS FOR DETERMINATION OF CARBON

The method depends upon the oxidation of carbon to carbon dioxide when the powdered material is digested with a mixture of concentrated sulfuric acid and chromic acid, or potassium dichromate, or permanganate. The procedure is applicable to oxidation of free carbon, carbon combined in organic substances and in certain instances to carbon combined with metals, where the substance may be decomposed by the action of the acids.[3] It is of value in determination of carbonates in presence of sulfides, sulfites, thiosulfates and nitrites, which would vitiate results were they not oxidized to more stable forms, before passing into the potash bulb with the carbon dioxide.

*Apparatus.*—The apparatus is identical with that used for determining carbon dioxide in carbonates, Fig. 12-14, with the exception that in place of the acid bulb nearest the decomposition flask two bulbs are placed. The first of these contains a strong solution of chromic and sulfuric acids, the second is filled with glass beads moistened with chromic acid solution. Following this is the drying bulb containing concentrated sulfuric acid and finally the absorption apparatus, as shown in the illustration.

*Procedure.*—0.2 to 1 g. of the powdered material, fine drillings, free carbon, or organic substance is placed in the decomposition flask. If the material is apt to pack it is advisable to mix with it pure ignited sea sand to prevent this. Five to 10 g. of granular potassium dichromate are added and the apparatus swept free of carbon dioxide by passing purified air through it before attaching the absorption apparatus. The potash bulb is now weighed, using a counterbalance bulb and following the precautions given in the dry-combustion method. The bulb is attached to the train.

**Oxidation.**—Concentrated sulfuric acid placed in the acid funnel, attached to the decomposition flask, is allowed to flow down on the sample until the funnel is almost empty; the stopcock is then closed. A flame is placed under the flask, when the vigorous action has ceased, and the material gently heated until the reaction is complete and the organic matter or carbon completely oxidized.

The apparatus is now swept free of residual $CO_2$ by applying suction, the gas being completely absorbed by the potash, or the soda lime reagent.

The increase of weight of the absorption bulb is due to carbon dioxide.

$$CO_2 \times 0.2729 = C$$

NOTE.—The following additional purifiers are frequently advisable: (*a*) an absorption bulb containing silver sulfate to absorb chlorine and vapors from sulfur compounds; (*b*) a capillary tube of silica or platinum heated to a dull redness to oxidize any hydrocarbons, carbon monoxide, etc., that may be evolved and imperfectly oxidized by the chromic acid.

[3] Not applicable for determining carbon in ferrosilicon, ferrochrome or tungsten.

## DETERMINATION OF CARBON IN STEEL AND OTHER FERROUS ALLOYS *

*TOTAL CARBON BY THE DIRECT-COMBUSTION METHOD*

**Apparatus for Determination of Metal Carbon by Direct Combustion.**—The apparatus should be suitable for the direct combustion of the metal in oxygen, with the $CO_2$ obtained being collected in a suitable adsorbent consisting of an inert base impregnated with NaOH [4] and with suitable purifying and protecting trains following the furnace. Figures 12-8 and 12-9 show two typical arrangements of the apparatus. The apparatus and arrangement may be modified, provided satisfactory results for the carbon determination are obtained.

**Combustion Apparatus.**—Any combustion apparatus (preferably heated by electricity) that will heat the sample to a temperature of 1000 to 1100°C. may be used for carbon steels and most low-alloy steels. Electric furnaces heated by silicon carbide rods, giving temperatures up to 1400°C., are very useful for determining carbon in refractory alloys. Combustion tubes may be of porcelain, sillimanite, clay, quartz, or platinum and must be gastight. Quartz is liable to devitrification when used intermittently at temperatures above 1000°C., and may then become porous. Tubes 30 in. in length and 1¼ in. in inside diameter, and drawn out at one end, may be used conveniently for the small Gooch crucibles of fused silica that are used in the determination of graphite in cast iron.

**Catalyzers.**—Though materials such as ironized asbestos, copper oxide, platinized quartz or asbestos, or platinum gauze are often put in the exit end of the combustion tube for the purpose of insuring complete combustion of carbon to $CO_2$, it is questionable whether they are of any value, except to serve as baffles for holding back finely divided solid metallic oxides and sulfur trioxide, since they soon become fouled. When such baffles are used, the fixed sulfur is burned out every 200 determinations or oftener by drawing the exit end of the combustion tube into the hot zone while a current of air or oxygen is passed through it. When carbon determinations are being made on materials with high sulfur contents, baffles should not be used in the exit end of the tube, but a special $SO_2$ absorber or purifier should be placed between the tube and the $CO_2$ absorber.

**Boats and Covers.**—The boats and covers may be of alundum, clay, zirkite, nickel, or platinum, and should preferably receive a lining of granular alundum or other material found to be suitable for the purpose. Nickel boats should be made of sheet nickel containing under 0.10% of carbon. Before use, new boats and covers should always be preheated in oxygen until no more $CO_2$ is given off or until a constant blank is obtained. In order to prevent injury to the tube from spattering, a platinum or nickel cover open at both ends and allowing free access of oxygen should be used.

*Material for Lining Boats.*—Granular alundum,[5] alkali-free, specially prepared for carbon determinations, and 60-mesh or finer, is entirely satisfactory for the lining of boats. Ignited low-silica chrome ore, or zirkite (natural oxide of zirconium), properly sized and freed from materials causing a blank may be employed. Ferric oxide is recommended as permitting combustion of carbon steels at low temperatures (800 to 900°C.) but is not recommended for high temperatures.

---

* Based upon A.S.T.M. Methods of Chemical Analysis of Metals, 1960.
[4] Ascarite and Caroxite have been found satisfactory for this purpose.
[5] R. R. Alundum has been found satisfactory for this purpose.

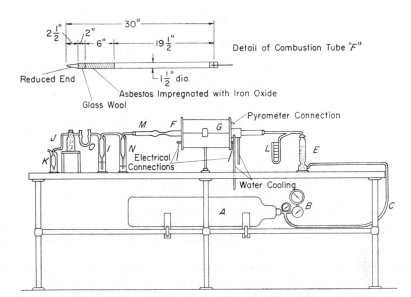

FIG. 12-8. Typical Arrangement for Determination of Carbon by the Direct Combustion Method.

$A$ = A 100-cubic-foot cylinder of oxygen; $B$ = Reducing valve; $C$ = Rubber tubing; $E$ = Tower containing soda lime for removing any $CO_2$ in the oxygen. A layer of about $\frac{1}{2}$ inch of anhydrous $Mg(ClO_4)_2$ is placed on top for removing traces of moisture; $F$ = Combustion tube. The asbestos impregnated with iron oxide is prepared by treating some asbestos with a saturated solution of $Fe(NO_3)_3$, drying and heating to $1000°C$. The treated asbestos is placed lightly in the combustion tube, and not packed; $G$ = Electric furnace; $L$ = Manometer gage; $M$ = Glass tube lightly packed with absorbent cotton to remove solid particles; $N$ = Bottle containing 25 ml. of $H_2SO_4$ (1:4) saturated with chromic acid to remove sulfur gases from the gas stream; $I$ = Bottle contains 50 ml. of $H_2SO_4$ (sp. gr. 1.84) for removing the bulk of the moisture that passes over from bottle $N$. Where a large number of carbon determinations are being made the acid in this bottle should be changed daily; $O$ = U-tube containing anhydrous $Mg(ClO_4)_2$; this tube is filled lightly and evenly, so as not to cause packing; $I$ = Absorbing bulb containing a 20–30-mesh inert base impregnated with NaOH, for absorbing the $CO_2$. A layer of glass wool is placed in the bottom and top of the bulb, and the soda-impregnated $CO_2$ absorbent is covered with a layer of anhydrous Mg $(ClO_4)_2$ approximately $\frac{1}{2}$ inch thickness; $K$ = Bottle containing $H_2SO_4$ (sp. gr. 1.84); may be omitted if the stopcock in $J$ is so manipulated during combustion that no air is drawn through the exit tube.

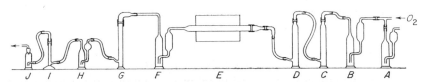

FIG. 12-9. Alternative Arrangement for Determination of Carbon by the Direct Combustion Method.

$A$ = Mercury valve; $B$ = Bottle containing concentrated $H_2SO_4$; $C$ = Tower, with gooseneck top, containing $CaCl_2$; $D$ = Tower containing stick NaOH; $E$ = Electric furnace with combustion tube and adapters; $F$ = Bottle containing $KMnO_4$ (50 g. per l.), inserted only for steels with over 0.05% sulfur; $G$ = Tower containing granulated zinc; $H$ = Bottle containing concentrated $H_2SO_4$; $I$ = Tower containing $P_2O_5$; $J$ = Weighed tower containing a 20–30-mesh inert base impregnated with NaOH, for absorbing the $CO_2$.

289

Quartz sand is objectionable, owing to its liability to fuse or to slag with oxides of iron, causing bubbles of gas to be enclosed.

**Absorbing Bulbs.**—No special types of absorbing bulbs are recommended, although the Fleming, Miller, Turner, and the Midvale (sometimes called Stetzer and Norton) bulbs have proved satisfactory. When filled, the tubes should not weigh over 200 g., and they should always be weighed filled with oxygen and against a like counterpoise. Open bulbs, such as the Midvale, lose oxygen by diffusion. They should be filled with oxygen before weighing when not in continuous use, and the same time interval should be held between weighings.

**Oxygen Purifiers.**—The purity of the oxygen should be not less than 99.5%. Organic matter of any kind is an undesirable impurity. It is usually absent, and it suffices to pass the oxygen through an absorbent such as a 20- to 30-mesh inert base impregnated with NaOH, followed by anhydrous $Mg(ClO_4)_2$. If carbonaceous matter is suspected, the oxygen should be passed through a tube that is loosely packed with copper oxide and heated to about 450°C. before it is passed through the NaOH-impregnated material.

**Carbon Dioxide Purifiers.**—The purifiers that follow the combustion tube must remove finely divided solid metallic oxides and oxides of sulfur or selenium, dry the gases before they enter the weighed $CO_2$ absorber, and protect the absorber from outside effects. Finely divided solid metallic oxides are removed from the gases during their passage through the liquids or columns of solids that precede the weighed absorber. The small amounts of $SO_2$ that are given off from materials low in sulfur may be satisfactorily removed by $H_2SO_4$ that has been saturated with chromic acid. Materials with high sulfur contents need other absorbents such as chromic acid (500 g. per l.) or $KMnO_4$ (50 g. per l.) followed by suitable desiccants, or heated platinized silica gel, that will convert the $SO_2$ to $SO_3$. The $SO_3$ that is so formed is not removed by any one absorbent, but is condensed and absorbed during its passage through the liquids or columns of solids in the train. An asbestos or glass-wool filter should be used after such absorbents as the chromic acid solution to prevent the spray from coming in contact with rubber connections, thus causing high values to be obtained. A tube containing a mixture of ironized asbestos and anhydrous $Mg(ClO_4)_2$ should be used after the platinized silica gel. The ironized asbestos should be prepared as follows: Saturate 20 g. of long-fiber asbestos with a saturated solution of $Fe(NO_3)_3$, dry, and ignite at 1000°C.

**Carbon Dioxide Absorbents.**—The most desirable absorbent for $CO_2$ is 20- to 30-mesh inert base impregnated with NaOH, followed by anhydrous $Mg(ClO_4)_2$ at the exit end. The latter is needed to absorb the water that is formed during the reaction and is not held by the unused $CO_2$ absorbent.

### PROCEDURE FOR CARBON AND HIGH-SILICON STEELS CONTAINING UNDER 0.1% SULFUR

(a) After having properly set up and tested the apparatus, spread 1 to 5 g. of the sample on the bed material in the boat so that the particles are in intimate contact. Cover the sample with a suitable cover and introduce the boat into the hot combustion tube. Close the tube and allow the sample to heat for 1 to 2 minutes,[6]

---

[6] If the sample is allowed to come to the temperature of the furnace before the oxygen is admitted, it usually bursts into a bright flame and burns completely. A period of 1 to 2 min. of preheating suffices.

depending upon the size of the particles.[7] Then admit oxygen [8] at a rate of 800 to 1000 ml. per minute while combustion is going on.[9] Use a furnace temperature of 1100°C. or above. When combustion is complete (1.5 to 2 minutes), reduce the rate of flow of oxygen to 400 to 500 ml. per minute and continue for 6 to 8 minutes in order to sweep out the $CO_2$.

(b) Withdraw the absorption tube filled with oxygen, place it in the balance case for 10 minutes,[10] open momentarily, and weigh against a similar tube used as a counterpoise. The increase in weight represents $CO_2$.

(c) Remove the boat from the tube and examine the fusion for evidences of incomplete combustion. If the drillings are not thoroughly fused in a solid pig, the determination should be rejected.

**Blank.**—Make a blank determination, following the same procedure and using the same amounts of all materials except the sample.

**Calculation.**—Calculate the percentage of carbon as follows:

$$\text{Carbon, } \% = \frac{(A - B) \times 0.2729}{C} \times 100$$

where $A$ = grams of $CO_2$,
$\quad B$ = correction for blank, in grams, and
$\quad C$ = grams of sample used.

## PROCEDURE FOR HIGH-SULFUR STEELS

Determine carbon in accordance with the procedure described above, but insert a special $SO_2$ oxidant in the train consisting of a tube of platinized silica gel heated to 440°C., followed by a tube containing ironized asbestos (see Fig. 12-8) and anhydrous $Mg(ClO_4)_2$.

## PROCEDURE FOR ALLOY STEELS

(a) Determine carbon in accordance with the procedure described above. Although most of the low-alloy steels burn perfectly at 1100°C. without the addition of an accelerator, many alloy steels require an accelerator to obtain complete combustion at this temperature. If a steel burns with difficulty, either place a small ⅛-in.) pellet of tin on each end of the sample (or spread 1 g. of tin millings over the sample) or mix with 1 to 2 g. of 40-mesh millings of open-hearth iron, and proceed as usual.[11]

---

[7] The finer the chips (excluding dust, which causes low values on a hot boat) the better, except with alloys that burn too vigorously. Drillings or millings sized between 14 and 60 mesh are satisfactory.

[8] "Hospital grade" oxygen is preferred for this purpose.

[9] The rate at which oxygen is admitted is also a factor in the velocity of combustion. Assuming the combustion apparatus has been heated to the temperature range above that recommended, it is possible, if the material is closely packed and if oxygen is admitted at too rapid a rate, that the combustion may be so violent as to cause excessive spattering of fused oxides and such fluidity of the molten slag that the boat or other container may be injured or destroyed. Sufficient oxygen, however, shall be run in to insure a current of gas through the absorber at all stages of the combustion. When tin is employed as an accelerator, combustion is very rapid and it is therefore necessary to increase the flow of oxygen during combustion.

[10] The tube will warm up when $CO_2$ is absorbed. It is not necessary to wait until it reaches room temperature if it is in continuous use, provided the same time interval is maintained, and approximately the same amount of $CO_2$ is absorbed.

[11] Red lead, copper oxide, lead, and powdered copper are also used as accelerators. Red lead to be used for this purpose should first be heated in an atmosphere of oxygen

(*b*) With high-chromium, high-nickel steels (18% chromium, 8% nickel; 20% chromium, 20% nickel; etc.), the principal sources of error in carbon determinations are (*1*) combustion at too low temperatures and (*2*) omission of, or faulty corrections for, blank determinations.    More certain combustion of all carbon is obtained if a temperature of 1250°C. or higher is employed and tin or open-hearth iron is used as an accelerator.    Preheating is necessary, and burning at higher pressures of oxygen seems advantageous; that is, a sufficiently rapid stream of oxygen should be maintained during the burning so that it is bubbling freely at the exit end of the train.    After the burning is completed, continue the flow of oxygen for 6 to 8 minutes in order to sweep out the $CO_2$.    If sulfur exceeds 0.06%, special precautions should be taken to eliminate oxides of sulfur.    Steels containing boron require a higher temperature than 1100 to 1150°C. if tin is used as the accelerator. This temperature is satisfactory if pure iron is used as the flux.

### PROCEDURE FOR SELENIUM STEELS

Determine carbon as described for high-sulfur steels.

### PROCEDURE FOR PIG IRON, CAST IRON, AND MALLEABLE IRON

Determine carbon in accordance with the procedure described above, using 1 g. of the sample.    Special care should be used in obtaining a representative sample. Precautions for sulfur are of no particular moment for cast iron, except, of course, for continuous combustions of iron containing more than 0.10% of sulfur.

### PROCEDURE FOR ALLOY CAST IRON

Determine carbon in accordance with the procedure described in "Procedure for Carbon and High Silicon Steels."    High-silicon and most alloy cast iron require a temperature of at least 1100°C. for complete combustion.    Accelerators are desirable for high-chromium, high-nickel iron.

### PROCEDURE FOR OPEN-HEARTH IRON AND WROUGHT IRON

Determine carbon in accordance with the procedure described above, using 3 to 4 g. of the sample, and pay special attention to proper blank corrections. With very low-carbon material, as open-hearth iron, the use of small absorption tubes [12] tends to reduce errors caused by variations in temperature and humidity.

### GRAPHITE IN CAST IRON

**Apparatus.    Gooch Crucible.**—A fused-silica Gooch crucible.

**Apparatus for Determination of Total Carbon by Direct Combustion.**—See Fig. 12-8.

in an open porcelain dish, with frequent stirring, at 500 to 550°C. for 15 to 24 hours; then cooled in a desiccator and transferred to a tightly stoppered bottle, preferably one with a ground-glass stopper.    When red lead is employed, the determination should be completed promptly in order not to expose the red lead to the atmosphere any longer than necessary, as it readily absorbs $CO_2$ from the air.    With high-silicon alloys known to contain silicon carbide, it is necessary to use red lead only when the temperature of the furnace is approximately 1100°C.    When a furnace temperature of 1350°C. or higher is used, all of the carbon can be obtained by mixing the sample with an equal weight of CuO and burning with the weight of ingot iron millings or drillings specified.

[12] Schwartz glass-stoppered, 10-cm, U-shape absorption tubes containing a $CO_2$ absorbent such as inert base impregnated with NaOH, and anhydrous $Mg(ClO_4)_2$, are satisfactory for this purpose.

*Procedure.*—(*a*) Transfer 1 to 3 g. of the sample to a 250-ml. beaker. Add 50 ml. of $HNO_3$ (3:5), cover, and heat on a steam bath for about 30 minutes, while stirring occasionally. Add 1 to 2 ml. of HF and boil gently for 4 to 5 minutes.

(*b*) Collect the residue, conveniently by suction on ignited asbestos contained in a fused-silica Gooch crucible of such diameter as will fit in the combustion tube. Wash thoroughly with hot water, hot KOH (120 g. per l.), hot water, HCl (1:20), and hot water, in the order given.

(*c*) Dry the residue at a temperature not exceeding 150°C., and determine the graphite by direct combustion at 1000°C. in the apparatus used for the determination of total carbon.

## TITRIMETRIC METHOD

## TOTAL CARBON BY ABSORPTION OF CARBON DIOXIDE IN BARIUM HYDROXIDE

The carbon dioxide evolved by oxidation of the material by dry combustion with oxygen or by oxidation with chromic sulfuric acid mixture is absorbed in barium hydroxide, free from carbonate, and the precipitated barium carbonate titrated with standard hydrochloric acid.

*Procedure.*—The essential difference in this method from those already described under the gravimetric methods is in the fact that a perfectly clear saturated solution of barium hydroxide is used for absorption of the carbon dioxide in place of caustic potash. Considerable care must be exercised to prevent contaminating the reagent with carbonate. The solution is drawn by suction through a siphon, dipping below the surface of the reagent, into the absorption tube, which should be of such construction that the material may readily be poured out. The precipitate, barium carbonate, is filtered off and washed, and then titrated with standard hydrochloric acid.

$$1 \text{ ml. } 0.1 \text{ } N \text{ HCl} = 0.0006 \text{ g. carbon}$$

## COLORIMETRIC METHODS

The colorimetric methods are used instead of the so-called "indirect methods," whereby the excess of carbon remaining when the graphitic carbon is subtracted from the total carbon (in iron and steel), is calculated as combined carbon.

## DIRECT COLORIMETRIC METHOD FOR DETERMINATION OF COMBINED CARBON

The procedure is of value to the steel laboratory where a large number of daily determinations of combined carbon are required. By this method over a hundred determinations a day may be made by an experienced manipulator. The method depends upon the color produced by combined carbon dissolved in nitric acid, the depth of color increasing with the combined carbon content of the material. Comparison is made with a standard sample of iron or steel, which is of the same kind and in the same physical condition as the material tested.[13] That is to say, a Bessemer steel should be compared with a Bessemer standard, open hearth with open hearth, crucible steel with crucible steel, the standards containing approxi-

[13] Blair, A. A., The Chemical Analysis of Iron, J. B. Lippincott, Philadelphia, 1917.

mately the same amounts of carbon, and as nearly as possible the same chemical composition. The samples should be taken from the original bar which has not been reheated, hammered, or rolled. Copper, cobalt, and chromium will interfere with the test; the other elements have very little effect.

*Procedure.*—One standard sample of 0.2 to 1 g., depending on the carbon content of the steel, and the same amount of sample drillings are taken for analysis. The weighings are conveniently made in brass or aluminum pans, boat-shaped to enable the drillings to be dumped into test tubes. A counterpoise, weighing the same as the boat, is placed on the opposite pan, together with the 0.2 g. weight. A magnetized knife will assist in removing the excess of material. The weighed sample is brushed into a test tube 6 in. long (150 mm.) $\frac{5}{8}$ in. (16 mm.) in diameter. (Each test tube has a label near the open end to distinguish the sample.) A rack or a 600-ml. beaker may be employed for holding the test tubes during the weighing. After the batch is ready the tubes are transferred to a perforated rack and this is then placed in the water bath filled with cold water.

The proper amount of nitric acid (sp. gr. 1.2; e.g., 1 concentrated $HNO_3$:1 $H_2O$), from a burette, is now added to each test tube.

| | |
|---|---|
| 3 ml. $HNO_3$ for 0.3% C. | 6 ml. $HNO_3$ for 0.8 to 1% C. |
| 4 ml. $HNO_3$ for 0.3 to 0.5% C. | 7 ml. $HNO_3$ for over 1% C. steel. |
| 5 ml. $HNO_3$ for 0.5 to 0.8% C. | |

The depth of color produced by the acid will give an idea of the amount required. One ml. of acid is added at a time until the depth of color is correct. This requires experience gained from observation of the color produced by standard samples. The acid is added slowly to the coarse drillings. Insufficient acid gives a solution that is darker than it properly should be. The nitric acid should be free from chlorine and hydrochloric acid, since these produce a yellow color. (Cl and $FeCl_3$ are yellow.)

A glass bulb or a small funnel is placed in each test tube and the water in the bath then heated to boiling and boiled until all the carbonaceous matter has dissolved, the tubes being shaken from time to time to prevent formation of a film of oxide. Low-carbon steels require about twenty minutes, whereas steels of over 1% carbon require about forty-five minutes. As soon as the bubbles cease and the brownish flocculent matter disappears, the rack is removed from the bath and placed in a casserole of cold water. (Prolonged heating and strong light each causes fading of the color due to combined carbon.)

**Color Comparison.**—This is made in graduated, clear, colorless, glass cylinders called carbon tubes. The form shown in Fig. 12-10 was found by W. W. Scott to be the most satisfactory type for a steel-works laboratory where rapidity of manipulation was essential. The bend at the upper portion of the tube facilitates mixing of the solution upon dilution with water, the tube being tilted back and forth until the solution is homogeneous, the bend preventing the liquid from spilling. The dilution should be at least twice that of the amount of nitric acid used, as this amount of water is necessary to destroy the color due to ferric nitrate.

The standard is poured into the carbon tube and the rinsings from the test tube added. The solution is diluted to a convenient multiple in ml. of the carbon content. For example, 0.45% carbon sample may be diluted to 9 ml., then each ml. will represent 0.05% carbon. The sample is placed in a second tube of exactly the same diameter, wall thickness, and form. If the solution of the sample is darker than the standard, water is added little by little, followed by mixing, until the shade matches the standard. If the standard, on the other hand, is darker than the sample, a greater dilution of the standard is necessary, the volume in ml. again representing a multiple of the carbon content. For example dilution of the 0.45% carbon sample to 15 ml. makes each ml. represent 0.03 carbon. (It is frequently advisable to take a standard of lower carbon content in place of greater dilution of the standard.)

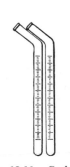

FIG. 12-10. Carbon Tubes.

FIG. 12-11. Color Comparator or Camera.

**Example.**—Suppose in the first case the dilution of the sample was 15 ml. in order to match the standard, then $15 \times 0.05 = 0.75\%$ carbon. Six ml. dilution case $2 = 6 \times 0.03 = 0.18\%$ carbon.

The color comparison can be best made in a "camera," a long box with one end closed by a ground-glass screen, Fig. 12-11. Parallel to the screen and near it, two holes through the top of the box admit the test tubes. The inner walls of the camera are blackened to prevent reflection of light. If a camera is not available, the tubes may be held side by side and compared against a sheet of white paper held as a background.

## SPECTROPHOTOMETRIC METHOD FOR COMBINED CARBON

This method [14] is a modification of the preceding colorimetric one. The samples should be taken from the original bar which has not been reheated, hammered, or rolled. Copper, cobalt, and chromium will interfere with the test; the other elements have very little effect.

*Procedure.*—To 500 ml. distilled water add 100 ml. concentrated sulfuric acid. Cool, and add 50 ml. concentrated orthophosphoric acid (88% $H_3PO_4$) followed by 350 ml. nitric acid.

Transfer 0.8 g. of the sample to a 125-ml. Erlenmeyer flask and add 25 ml. of the mixed acid. Place flask in a 600-ml. beaker half full of boiling water and keep boiling until all action has ceased. When only a small trace of action is left, remove the flask frequently, swirl the contents and replace in beaker if action is not yet complete. As soon as the sample has been completely dissolved, remove the flask and cool rapidly in a water bath. Filter through Whatman No. 41H

14 Jamieson, Foundry, **83,** 10, 132–4, 1955.

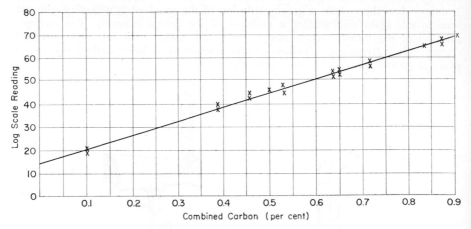

Fig. 12-12.

### Carbon Values Obtained

|  | | *Combined Carbon %* | | |
|--------|-----------|-----------|-----------|---------|
| *Sample* | *Log Scale Reading* | *by Difference* | *From Equation* | *Error %* |
| 107a | 67.0 | 0.88 | 0.88 | Nil |
| 122c | 58.0 | 0.72 | 0.73 | +0.01 |
| 99 | 44.5 | 0.50 | 0.51 | +0.01 |
| 4h | 54.0 | 0.65 | 0.66 | +0.01 |
| 62 | 53.5 | 0.64 | 0.66 | +0.02 |
| 67 | 65.0 | 0.84 | 0.85 | +0.01 |
| 127 | 20.0 | 0.10 | 0.10 | Nil |
| 130 | 69.0 | 0.93 | 0.91 | −0.02 |
| 139 | 52.0 | 0.64 | 0.63 | −0.01 |
| 82a | 46.0 | 0.53 | 0.53 | Nil |
| 4h | 52.2 | 0.65 | 0.63 | −0.02 |
| 107a | 66.0 | 0.88 | 0.86 | −0.02 |
| 122c | 57.0 | 0.72 | 0.71 | −0.01 |
| 127 | 19.0 | 0.10 | 0.09 | −0.01 |
| 82a | 45.0 | 0.53 | 0.53 | Nil |
| 5J | 43.0 | 0.46 | 0.48 | +0.02 |
| 7E | 37.8 | 0.39 | 0.40 | +0.01 |
| 5J | 43.5 | 0.46 | 0.49 | +0.03 |
| 7E | 38.6 | 0.39 | 0.41 | +0.02 |

Mean error ± 0.01%.  Maximum spread 0.05%.

paper into a 100-ml. volumetric flask and wash Erlenmeyer and filter paper with cold distilled water, care being taken to use a large number of very small washes. Dilute to the mark and mix thoroughly.

Transfer approximately 20 ml. to the cylindrical absorption cell of a Fisher Electrophotometer and measure the light transmitted, using distilled water in the reference cell, blue filter No. 425, and light intensity setting "B." Using the reading obtained, the combined carbon content of the sample is taken then from the graph or calculated from the calibration equation.

**Calibration.**—The calibration graph obtained by Jamieson is shown in Fig. 12-12 and the data is given in the table "Carbon Values Obtained."

**Slow Solution.**—An average batch of five determinations can be completed in 1 hour, but this time is dependent mainly on the rate of solution and can vary more or less. Occasionally samples are found which take a particularly long time to dissolve; in the case of Bureau of Standards Iron No. 82a this amounted to 40 minutes. In extreme cases such as this, the graphite may agglomerate due to the formation of silicic acid. If this happens, add 0.25 to 0.5 ml. (6 to 12 drops) of hydrofluoric acid and continue heating until all action stops; otherwise the solution will not filter.

On no account should hydrofluoric acid be added before the graphite is seen to coagulate. During calibration, the Bureau of Standards Iron No. 82a was the only sample which required the hydrofluoric acid treatment, and extremely few others were found during a period of two years.

The calibration covers the complete range normally associated with gray cast iron, namely 0.1 to 0.9% CC.

The equation of the best line passing through the points shown in the table and Fig. 12-12 was found to be:

$$\text{Combined Carbon, } \% = \frac{\text{Log Scale Reading} - 13.7}{60.7}$$

$$= (\text{Log Scale Reading} - 13.7) \times 0.0165$$

For greatest freedom of error due to deterioration of color it is preferable to carry out this determination under artificial lighting conditions or shielded from direct sunlight.

## DETERMINATION OF CARBON IN GRAPHITE

The procedure for determining carbon in graphite is the same as that described for determination of carbon in difficultly combustible organic substances.

The material is broken down in a steel mortar and powdered in an agate mortar. About 0.2 g. is taken for the determination and mixed with copper oxide to assist the combustion, then placed in the boat and the combustion of the carbon carried on according to the standard method in the combustion tube.

$$CO_2 \times 0.2729 = C$$

# DETERMINATION OF CARBON DIOXIDE IN CARBONATES

## ABSORPTION METHOD

### *TOTAL CARBON DIOXIDE*

The method is applicable for determination of carbon dioxide in limestone, dolomite, magnesite, strontianite, witherite, spathic iron ore, carbonates of sodium

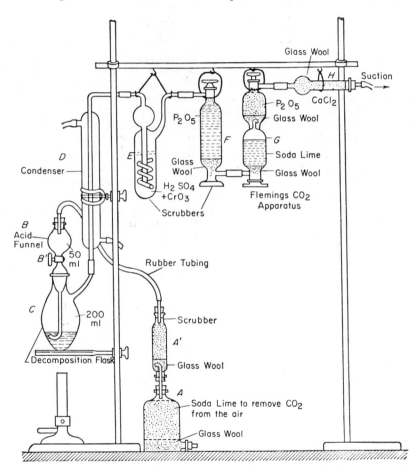

Fig. 12-13. Apparatus for Determining Carbon Dioxide.

and potassium, bicarbonates in baking powder, carbon in materials readily oxidized to $CO_2$ by chromic sulfuric acid mixture. The procedure depends upon the evolution of carbon dioxide by a less volatile acid, or the oxidation of carbon. The $CO_2$ is absorbed in caustic and weighed.

*Apparatus.*—The illustration (Fig. 12-13) shows the apparatus found suitable for this determination. It is Knorr's apparatus slightly modified. The absorption bulb or bottle should be one that will effectively absorb carbon dioxide entering at a rapid rate. The Vanier or the Fleming forms are satisfactory for this purpose. Magnesium perchlorate trihydrate may be used in place of $P_2O_5$ and $CaCl_2$ for drying agent, and soda asbestos in place of soda lime for absorbing $CO_2$.

*Procedure.*—A sample weighing 0.5 to 2 g., according to the carbon dioxide content, is placed in the dry decomposition flask (C). The flask is closed by inserting the funnel tube (B) fitted with the soda lime tube (A), and connected by means of a condenser to the train for removing impurities from carbon dioxide, leading to the absorption bulb, as shown in Fig. 12-13.

The apparatus is swept out with a current of dry, purified air before attaching the weighed absorption bottle. This is accomplished by applying gentle suction at the end of the purifying train. The absorption apparatus is now attached (Fleming absorption apparatus is shown in the illustration). The tube (B) is nearly filled with dilute sulfuric acid (1:3), the stopcock (B') being closed. The soda lime tube is now inserted into place as shown in the cut. The acid in (B) is now allowed to run slowly down on the sample at a rate that evolves gas not too rapidly to be absorbed; 1 to 2 ml. of acid being retained in (B) to act as a seal, the stopcock (B') being then closed.

When the violent action has ceased, the solution in (C) is heated to boiling and boiled for about three minutes. If the sample is baking powder, or contains organic matter, the decomposition flask is protected from excessive heat by placing a casserole of hot water under it. This prevents charring of the starch or organic matter, which would be apt to occur if the direct flame was used. Gentle suction is now applied to the absorption end of the apparatus and the stopcock (B') opened, allowing the remainder of the acid to flow into the flask (C) and admitting a current of air, purified by passing through the soda lime in (A). The suction should be gentle at first, and then the speed of the flow increased to the full capacity of the absorption bottle. A fairly rapid current is preferred to the old-time procedure of bubbling the gas through the apparatus at a snail-like pace, but discretion should be used in avoiding a too rapid flow.

In the analysis of baking powders, where foaming is apt to occur, the decomposition flask should be of sufficient capacity to prevent foaming over. A small flask is generally to be preferred for obvious reasons. By gently heating to boiling during the passage of the air, steam assists in expelling any residual $CO_2$ in the flask. When the passage of air is rapid, this boiling should be discontinued.

The increase of weight of the absorption bottle is due to the carbon dioxide of the sample. This procedure gives total $CO_2$.

## DETERMINATION OF RESIDUAL CARBON DIOXIDE

This is the $CO_2$ remaining after baking powder has been treated with water and the evolved $CO_2$ expelled by warming.

The procedure recommended by the U. S. Department of Agriculture is as follows: [15]

*Procedure.*—Weigh 2 g. of baking powder into a flask suitable for the subsequent determination of carbonic acid, add 20 ml. of cold water, and allow to stand 20 minutes. Place the flask in a metal drying cell surrounded by boiling water and heat, with occasional shaking, for 20 minutes.

To complete the reaction and drive off the last traces of gas from the semi-solid mass, heat quickly to boiling and boil for one minute. Aspirate until the air in the flask is thoroughly changed, and determine the residual carbon dioxide by absorption, as described above for "Total Carbon Dioxide."

[15] Bureau of Chem. Bulletin No. 107.

The process described, based on the methods of McGill and Catlin, imitate, as far as practicable, the conditions encountered in baking, but in such a manner that concordant results may be readily obtained on the same sample, and comparable results on different samples.

### AVAILABLE CARBON DIOXIDE

The residual is subtracted from the total, and the difference taken as available $CO_2$.

## LOSS OF WEIGHT METHODS

### GRAVIMETRIC METHOD I

An approximate estimation of the carbon dioxide in carbonates—baking powders, bicarbonate of soda, limestone, etc., may be obtained by the loss of weight of the material when treated with a known weight of acid.

Various forms of apparatus are used for this determination. The Schroetter and Mohr types are shown, Figs. 12-14 and 12-15.

Fig. 12-14. Schroetter Alkalimeter.

Fig. 12-15. Mohr's Alkalimeter.

**Procedure.**—About 0.5 to 1.0 g. of sample is taken and placed in the bottom of the flask, dilute hydrochloric and concentrated sulfuric acids then placed in the bulbs as indicated in the illustrations. The apparatus is weighed as it is thus charged. The hydrochloric acid is now allowed to flow down on the carbonate and the stopper closed. The evolved gas passes through the concentrated sulfuric acid, which absorbs the moisture. After the vigorous action has subsided the apparatus is placed over a low flame and the solution heated to boiling and boiled very gently for about three minutes. $CO_2$-free air is aspirated through the solution to expel the last traces of $CO_2$, by applying gentle suction at *a* and opening *b*, the air being purified by passing through soda lime. The apparatus is again weighed and the loss of weight taken as the $CO_2$ of the material.

Available $CO_2$ in baking powder may be determined by substituting water in place of hydrochloric acid.

### GRAVIMETRIC METHOD II [16]

**Apparatus.**—An Erlenmeyer flask of 50-ml. capacity, Fig. 12-16, is fitted with a two-hole rubber stopper bearing a short calcium chloride tube, filled with calcium

[16] Scott, Wilfred W., and Jewell, Paul W., Ind. Eng. Chem., Anal. Ed., **2**, 76, 1930.

chloride of about 16 mesh granules. The tube is best prepared by cutting down a regular sized tube so that its length over all will be not over 3″. The upper end of the calcium chloride tube is fitted with a one-hole rubber stopper through which passes a short glass tube, bent at right angles as shown in the drawing. This tube is closed with a rubber tip of a policeman rod. The other hole of the two-hole stopper is fitted with a glass tube passing through the stopper to the bottom of the flask, the lower end drawn to a capillary point. The upper end is bent as shown in the drawing. The upper end is also closed with a rubber policeman tip.

The purification train consists of a fairly large U tube, the arm next to the apparatus is filled with calcium chloride, and the other is filled with soda lime. The air as it enters the apparatus is drawn through this train and is thus freed from moisture and carbon dioxide.

*Procedure.*—When the apparatus is assembled, a volume of about 15 ml. of dilute hydrochloric acid, 1:1, is placed in the flask and the apparatus weighed. About 0.5-g. sample is placed in a weighed glass thimble, consisting of a two dram medicine vial, the upper part cut off so that one inch remains, the edge being fire dressed. The sample is now weighed. (Weight of vial and sample minus weight of vial.) The thimble and sample are carefully introduced in the flask by means of tweezers, being careful not to upset the vial. The weight of the entire apparatus, thimble and sample are now known. The apparatus is closed by replacing the stopper. The rubber policeman tip from the exit calcium chloride tube is removed. The

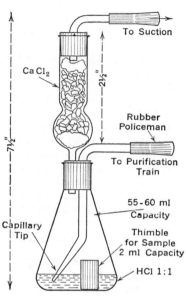

FIG. 12-16. Apparatus for Determining Carbon Dioxide by Loss in Weight.

thimble is overturned by agitating the apparatus. When the action has subsided the apparatus is attached to the purification train (the inlet policeman tip having been removed). Suction is applied so that the bubbles pass through the apparatus at the rate of about two per second. At this rate the aspiration is continued for fifteen minutes. The purification train is now detached, the policeman tips replaced on the apparatus, and the entire apparatus weighed.

The loss of weight is due to the escape of carbon dioxide.

$$\% \, CO_2 = \frac{\text{Loss of Weight} \times 100}{\text{Weight of Sample}}.$$

NOTES.—The method is accurate to 0.1%.

The calcium chloride should be replaced after about ten determinations. Dehydrite will last longer (about 25 determinations) but should this be used in place of calcium chloride, it must also be used in the purification train.

It is well to start with a sample of pure $CaCO_3$ to become familiar with the procedure. $CO_2$ in $CaCO_3$ is 44%. Run an "unknown" following the "known."

In cutting the vial or the calcium chloride tube make a short sharp scratch on the tube where the cut is to be made using a file. Now heat the edge of the file to redness and hold against the scratch. The tube will generally break off squarely at the cut.

## DETERMINATION OF CARBON DIOXIDE BY GAS
## MEASUREMENT AND ABSORPTION [17]

This method is applicable for the determination of small amounts of carbon dioxide in alkalies and related products with a high degree of accuracy. It may also be used to determine approximate values for larger amounts of carbon dioxide in limestone and miscellaneous materials.

The sample is acidified in a closed system, the evolved gas is collected in a burette, measured, passed through caustic potash solution to absorb $CO_2$; the residual unabsorbed gas is measured. The difference in volume is calculated to carbon dioxide.

*Apparatus.* **Apparatus for $CO_2$ Determination, Fig. 12-17.**—This consists of the following special parts:

*B. Gas burette, 100-ml.,* Fig. 12-18.

*C. Compensator tube,* Fig. 12-19, with mercury filled manometer shown as *A* in Fig. 12-18.

*D. Tubing assembly,* Fig. 12-20. Parts *B*, *C*, and *D* fabricated by Macalaster Bicknell Co., Syracuse, New York.

*E. Filling funnel,* 60-ml. cylindrical separatory funnel.

*F. Connectors,* heavy rubber or Tygon.

*G. Rubber tubing* about 3' long.

*J. Aspirator bottle* (250 ml.) used for leveling, connected by tubing *G*.

*K. Gas absorption pipette,* preferably of the bubbler type, Fisher Scientific Cat. No. 10-642 or equivalent, filled with a 300 grams per liter solution of potassium hydroxide. A rubber gas expansion bag $K_1$ protects the potassium hydroxide from contact with the air.

*L. Glass condenser* with jacket 12" long and 1¼" outside diameter and condenser tube of 8 mm. outside diameter. Usually the jacket needs only to be filled with water. Under extended continuous use, a condenser with a slow flow of cooling water through it is recommended.

*M. Rubber stoppers.*

*N. Sample receptacle,* 100-ml. Erlenmeyer flask or a 1" x 4" test tube as required. It is desirable that the flask and test tube fit the same rubber stopper.

*O. Glass water jacket* 2½" OD x 24" long, enclosing burette *B* and compensator tube *C*.

**Assembly of Apparatus.**—Assemble the apparatus, as shown in Fig. 12-17, after preparing the various parts as follows:

Compensator tube, *C*. Warm the bulb slightly and place two or three drops of distilled water in the tube. Then add sufficient mercury so that when the tube is at room temperature and normal atmospheric pressure the mercury columns are approximately level and are about 1½–2 inches in length. This is a trial and error operation. Manipulation by alternately warming and cooling the bulb is helpful in making this adjustment. Drawing mercury in the bulb after evacuation and adjusting the level by gently forcing air in the open end is also convenient.

Absorption pipette, *K*. Fill this pipette with sufficient caustic potash solution to fill the left bulb completely and to have about one-inch depth in the right bulb. Protect the solution from the atmosphere with a gas expansion bag $K_1$.

Glass water jacket, *O*. Bore suitable holes in two No. 12 rubber stoppers, as

[17] Contribution from Mr. George Oplinger, Research Supervisor, Solvay Process Division, Allied Chemical Corp.

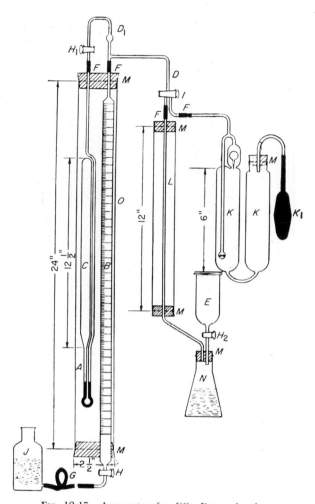

FIG. 12-17.  Apparatus for $CO_2$ Determination.

$A$ = Water above mercury column of manometer; $B$ = Gas burette; $C$ = Compensator tube; $D$ = Capillary glass tubing, with small bubble at $D_1$; $E$ = Filling funnel; $F$ = Heavy rubber or Tygon connectors; $G$ = Rubber tubing about 3 feet long; $H$, $H_1$, $H_2$ = Two-way glass stopcock; $I$ = Three-way Teflon stopcock; $J$ = Aspirator bottle; $K$ = Absorption pipette for KOH solution, with gas expansion bag, $K_1$; $L$ = Glass condenser; $M$ = Rubber stoppers; $N$ = Sample receptacle; $O$ = Glass water jacket.

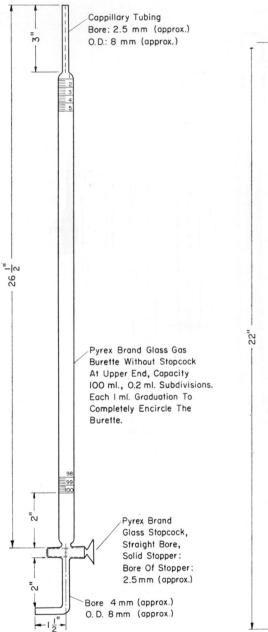

Capillary Tubing
Bore: 2.5 mm (approx.)
O.D.: 8 mm (approx.)

3"

26 $\frac{1}{2}$"

Pyrex Brand Glass Gas
Burette Without Stopcock
At Upper End, Capacity
100 ml., 0.2 ml. Subdivisions.
Each 1 ml. Graduation To
Completely Encircle The
Burette.

2"

2"

Pyrex Brand
Glass Stopcock,
Straight Bore,
Solid Stopper:
Bore Of Stopper:
2.5 mm (approx.)

Bore 4 mm (approx.)
O.D. 8 mm (approx.)

1 $\frac{1}{2}$"

FIG. 12-18.   Gas Burette.

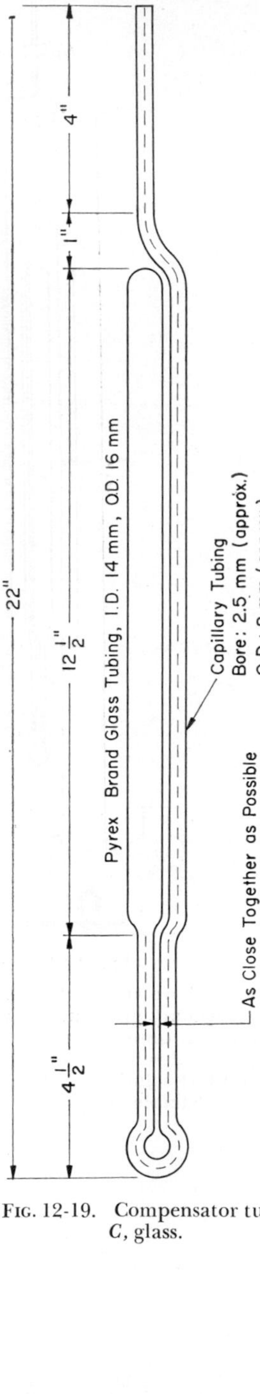

4"

1"

22"

12 $\frac{1}{2}$"

Pyrex Brand Glass Tubing, I.D. 14 mm, O.D. 16 mm

Capillary Tubing
Bore: 2.5 mm (approx.)
O.D.: 8 mm (approx.)

As Close Together as Possible

4 $\frac{1}{2}$"

FIG. 12-19.   Compensator tube
C, glass.

shown in Figure 12-17, to support the burette and compensator tube. An additional hole in the top stopper will permit easy filling with distilled water.

Use a ring stand about 30″ high with a heavy base to mount the various parts of the apparatus with suitable clamps. Arrange the parts so that glass tube connections are as close as possible and held with the rubber or Tygon connectors, $F$.

Aspirator bottle, $J$. Fill with a strong solution of NaCl or $CaCl_2$, acidify slightly

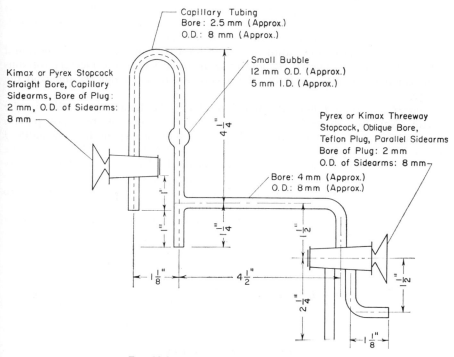

FIG. 12-20. Tubing Assembly $D$, glass.

and add a few drops of methyl red indicator to color the solution. Distilled water may be used in place of the salt solution.

**Reagents.** **Methyl Orange Indicator.**
**Potassium Hydroxide Solution, 300 grams per liter.**
**Sodium Carbonate, acidimetric standard.**
**Hydrochloric Acid, concentrated.**

**Procedure.**—Place an accurately weighed or measured volume of the sample in the sample receptacle $N$. The quantity taken should be such that the equivalent sodium carbonate content is less than 0.2 g. Add a piece of iron wire about the size of a pin head, a drop of methyl orange and distilled water until $N$ is about three-quarters full. See "Note" for samples containing sulfide.

Before connecting $N$ to the apparatus, be sure the absorbing solution in absorption pipette $K$ fills the entrance tube up to stopcock $I$; then close $I$. Open stopcock $I$ to connect the burette to the condenser tube, fill the burette and condenser tube with liquid from the leveling bottle, and close stopcock $H$. Open stopcock $H_2$ and rinse the funnel $E$ and the rubber stopper with distilled water. Now connect $N$ to the apparatus and close stopcock $H_2$.

Open stopcock $H$ and pour an excess of concentrated hydrochloric acid into $E$. Now open stopcock $H_2$ sufficiently to let the acid drop slowly into $N$ until very slightly in excess. Close stopcock $H_2$, fill $E$ nearly full with distilled water, heat the contents of $N$ to boiling and continue boiling gently for at least 2 minutes. Remove the burner, open stopcock $H_2$ and lower the leveling bottle $J$ (if necessary) until the water from $E$ fills $N$ and the condenser tube just up to the stopcock $I$. Turn stopcock $I$ one-quarter turn to close all its openings.

Raise the leveling bottle $J$ until the liquid level is about the same as the liquid in the burette, open stopcock $H_1$, and raise or lower $J$ until the mercury columns in the compensator tube are level. Then close stopcocks $H$ and $H_1$ and read the burette, $A$.

Open $H$ and raise $J$ until the liquid level in $J$ is slightly above that in the burette. Next turn stopcock $I$ to connect the burette to the gas absorption pipette $K$. Conduct the gas in the burette into pipette $K$ by raising the leveling bottle $J$ until the leveling liquid reaches stopcock $I$. Return the unabsorbed gas to the burette by lowering $J$. Repeat this operation until all the carbon dioxide is absorbed (three times should suffice). After returning the inert gas to the burette for the last time, allow the absorbing solution in pipette $K$ to fill the tube up to stopcock $I$; then close $I$ to cut off all its openings.

Now level the mercury columns in the compensator tube in the same manner as before and read the burette $= B$.

$$\frac{(A - B) \times \text{Apparatus Factor} \times 100}{\text{Grams of Sample}} = \% \ CO_2$$

$$\frac{(A - B) \times \text{Apparatus Factor} \times 1000}{\text{Ml. of Sample}} = \text{gpl } CO_2$$

$$CO_2 \times 2.4083 = Na_2CO_3$$

$$CO_2 \times 3.1405 = K_2CO_3$$

**Determination of Apparatus Factor.**—The apparatus factor is determined conveniently by a series of actual tests using a sample of known carbon dioxide content.

Weigh 2.0000 g. of sodium carbonate for acidimetric standard, dissolve in $CO_2$-free distilled water, dilute to 100 ml. in a calibrated volumetric flask at 20°C. and mix thoroughly. Use 10.0 ml. of this solution, measured with a standard pipette, and follow the procedure given above. At least five determinations should be made and the results averaged.

$$\text{Apparatus Factor} = \frac{C \times 0.2000 \times 0.41523}{(A - B)}$$

where $C = Na_2CO_3$ equivalent in standard sample ($= 1$ if $Na_2CO_3 = 100\%$); $0.2000 =$ wt. of sample in aliquot taken; $0.41523 =$ chemical factor $Na_2CO_3$ to $CO_2$; and $(A - B) =$ volume of $CO_2$ measured.

NOTE.—For samples containing sulfide add sufficient copper sulfate solution (200 grams per liter $CuSO_4 \cdot 5H_2O$) to the sample receptacle to combine with the sulfide present. A ratio of 8 parts $CuSO_4$ to 1 part $H_2S$ will suffice.

# DETERMINATION OF $CO_2$ IN CARBONATES—HYDROMETER METHOD OF BARKER [18]

No mechanical balance or scale is required by the following procedure.

The method depends upon the principle of the hydrometer, Fig. 12-21, following the law that when an object is immersed in a liquid it is buoyed up by a force equal to the weight of the liquid displaced by the object. The carbon dioxide set free from the sample decreases the weight; and the rise of the graduation scale tube above the water records the percentage of carbonates from which the gas was released. The procedure is suitable for determining the comparative strengths of baking powders, for rapid tests of the quality of limestone and for estimation of carbon dioxide of carbonates in general.

*Procedure.*—To analyze a sample for carbonates measure out 40 ml. of hydrochloric acid (sp. gr. 1.15), using a small graduate; pour this into the acid reservoir through the opening $A$. With graduated stem disconnected hang a 10 gram weight at $B$. The hydrometer should then float in a cylinder of water and be immersed to some point at $C$. Remove the 10 gram weight and introduce pulverized limestone, or other substance that is being tested, until the instrument is immersed to exactly the same point that it occupied with the suspended weight. The reservoir will now contain 10 grams of sample. Connect up the graduated stem and add water, a drop at a time, through the funnel-shaped top, until immersed to the zero point. Raise the hydrometer out of the water and open the stopcock $D$ until the acid drops slowly into the reaction chamber, decomposing the carbonate. As the reaction proceeds the instrument rises slowly and at the conclusion the point on stem at the surface of the water gives the percentage of calcium carbonate equivalent to the carbon dioxide in the sample. This figure is the calcium carbonate equivalent so often mentioned in connection with limestone analyses.

A Fahrenheit thermometer accompanies each instrument and is hung inside the floating cylinder. Its reading is taken before and after each determination to allow for any error due to change in temperature. To the figure for calcium carbonate equivalent add 0.5 for each degree rise, or subtract 0.5 for each degree fall in temperature between the two readings. This temperature change need seldom amount to more than a fraction of a degree.

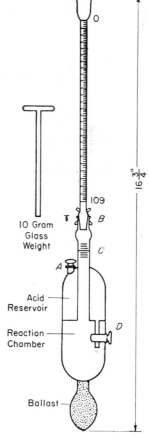

Fig. 12-21. Barker's Hydrometer.

NOTES.—The limestone may be weighed to an accuracy of 0.2 gram. The weight of $CO_2$ remaining in the apparatus tends to offset the loss due to moisture escaping with the gas, but the difference, together with any other sources of error has been accounted for in the graduation of the reading stem.

[18] Barker, J. F., J. Ind. Eng. Chem., **9**, 786–787, 1917.

# DETERMINATION OF PERCARBONATES

Percarbonates are decomposed by dilute sulfuric acid according to the reaction

$$K_2C_2O_6 + 2H_2SO_4 \rightarrow 2KHSO_4 + 2CO_2 + H_2O_2$$

*Procedure.*—Two-tenths of a gram of the salt is added to about 300 ml. of cold dilute sulfuric acid (1:30). The liberated hydrogen peroxide is titrated with potassium permanganate.

$$1 \text{ ml. } 0.1 \ N \text{ KMnO}_4 = 0.00991 \text{ g. K}_2C_2O_6$$

# METHODS FOR CARBON IN ANALYSES
# IN OTHER CHAPTERS

| | |
|---|---|
| Carbon in Metallic Nickel | See Analysis of Metallic Nickel |
| Carbon Phosphorus Ores | See Analysis of Phosphorus Ores |
| Carbon in Silicon Carbide | See Analysis of Silicon Carbide (Silicon Chapter) |
| Carbon in Ferrovanadium | See Analysis of Ferrovanadium (Vanadium Chapter) |

## Chapter 13

# CERIUM AND THE RARE EARTH METALS*

The rare earth elements to the chemist are commonly taken to mean the elements of atomic number 57 to 71 inclusive, as well as the element yttrium of atomic number 39. From the physicist's viewpoint the rare earth elements are those from atomic number 58 to 71 inclusive.

Chemically they are very much alike with a common valence of three. Cerium has a higher valence of four while europium, ytterbium, and samarium can have a valence of two.

In discussing the rare earths it is convenient to divide them into two groups, the cerium group and the yttrium group. The cerium group includes the elements lanthanum, cerium, praseodymium, neodymium, samarium, and europium; the yttrium group includes yttrium, gadolinium, terbium, dysprosium, holmium, erbium, thulium, ytterbium, and lutecium. The division is by no means sharp and is chiefly based on the solubility of the double alkali sulfates. The cerium group elements are difficultly soluble while the yttrium group elements are soluble. Europium, gadolinium, and terbium are slightly soluble and are sometimes termed the terbium group. Many analyses on minerals have been reported on this arbitrary designation. However, this difference in solubility should be considered as a variation from element to element rather than as a definite variation from group to group. The order of increasing atomic numbers is often spoken of as the "Serial Order" of the rare earth elements, for the basic strengths of these elements become progressively weaker in this order, and the solubilities of most salts vary in the same order, either directly or inversely. These variations in solubility, very slight as they are, are of tremendous importance in separations, for the chemical reactions of all the rare earth elements are so strikingly similar that with the exception of cerium, europium, and ytterbium, no rare earth element can be separated from the others by the use of any specific precipitant so far discovered.

The name "rare" earth is somewhat of a misnomer since the rare earths are widely distributed in nature. They are often found in small amounts in pegmatite veins. The most common minerals are considered below.

*Silicates.*—Gadolinite contains iron, beryllium, and members of the yttrium group, with small amounts of the cerium and terbium groups. Cerite consists mainly of the silicates of the cerium group. Allanite, of which there are several varieties carrying special names, contains principally calcium, iron, aluminum, and the cerium earths.

*Phosphates.*—Monazite sand, the most important commercial source of cerium is essentially an orthophosphate of the cerium earths, but carries small amounts of

---

* Revised for the Sixth Edition by C. J. Rodden, U. S. Atomic Energy Commission, New Brunswick, N. J. Previous Edition revised by P. H. M. P. Brinton.

the other earths, and is likewise the source of most of the thorium that comes into the market.  Monazite occurs largely in Brazil, India, Idaho, and South Carolina.  Xenotime is an orthophosphate of the yttrium earths.

*Tantalates and Niobates.*—Fergusonite is a tantalate and niobate of the yttrium earths, with varying amounts (often reasonably large) of cerium and terbium group members.  Euxenite is a niobium titanate of the yttrium group, with small amounts of the cerium group, and considerable uranium.  Samarskite, a niobium tantalate of yttrium, iron, and calcium, is also rich in uranium, and forms one of the best sources of the terbium group.

The industrial application of the rare earths has been expanding somewhat in the past few years with their use in the steel industry.  Lanthanum oxide is used in some optical glasses.  Cerium is used in the manufacture of "flints" for lighters and for cored arc lamps.  "Mischmetall," a mixture of the cerium group elements, is used in metallurgy.  Some use of the rare earths has been in the manufacture of sun glasses, while the colors imparted by the oxides has resulted in their use in ceramic ware manufacture.  The colors obtainable run through practically the whole spectrum.  Cerium sulfate is used to a considerable extent as an oxidizing agent in analytical chemistry.

Many of the metals have been prepared by electrolysis of the fused chloride.  They are readily oxidized and have no commercial use as such.  The melting points of a few of the elements are: Lanthanum 917°C., cerium 801°C., praseodymium 930°C., neodymium 1020°C., and dysprosium 1500°C.

## DETECTION

The most satisfactory method for chemically detecting the rare earth elements as a group is by means of an oxalate precipitation of the elements found in the ammonium hydroxide group.  While thorium and scandium are also precipitated, they can be separated by methods given under these elements.  In general, an acid solution (pH 2) is treated with a saturated oxalic acid solution and the precipitate is allowed to stand overnight before filtration.

The combined rare earth oxides are best tested for the individual elements by spectrographic means.  The lines which are most useable are given in the following table.

Lines for Qualitative Spectrographic Detection

| | | | |
|---|---|---|---|
| Yttrium | 3242.28A | Europium | 3971.99A |
| | 3200.27 | Gadolinium | 3422.47 |
| | 3664.61 | | 3100.51 |
| Lanthanum | 3988.52 | Terbium | 3324.40 |
| | 3265.67 | Dysprosium | 3405.66 |
| | 3303.11 | | 4000.45 |
| | 3949.11 | Holmium | 3416.46 |
| Cerium | 4012.39 | | 3398.98 |
| | 4040.76 | Erbium | 3264.78 |
| Praseodymium | 3908.43 | Thulium | 3131.26 |
| | 4008.71 | Ytterbium | 3289.37 |
| Neodymium | 3951.15 | | 2891.38 |
| | 3963.11 | Lutecium | 2911.39 |
| Samarium | 3634.27 | | 2900.30 |

The absorption spectra of certain rare earths are so characteristic that they can be used for detection. Solutions of compounds of praseodymium, neodymium, samarium, europium, dysprosium, holmium, erbium, thulium and ytterbium give absorption spectra in the visible region which can be readily seen with an ordinary glass prism spectroscope of reasonably good grade. Fig. 13-1 shows these spectra of the chlorides. A small direct vision spectroscope will serve an experienced observer. The material to be examined is brought into solution in nitric acid, and this solution in a glass vessel (an ordinary beaker serves for qualitative observation) is placed closely up in front of the slit of the spectroscope. A bright electric light bulb is set directly behind the solution. (A fluorescent light bulb should not be used.) The absorption bands can then be seen as dark vertical lines of varying breadth against the bright background of the colored continuous spectrum given by the light. The sun, a bright cloudy sky, or a sheet of white paper in sunlight may also serve as sources of illumination. The breadth and intensity of the bands naturally increase with increasing concentration of the solution and with increasing thickness of the layer of the solution. Moreover, the nature of the solvent and the degree of acidity affect somewhat the intensity and the exact position of the bands, but for rough qualitative examination these variations have no great significance. If the solution is too rich in neodymium, the whole field may be obscured to the point where observation of the bands of other earths is practically impossible, since neodymium has bands of great width and intensity. In such cases, the solution must be diluted, but it will be understood that if very much neodymium and comparatively little of the other colored earths are in the solution, the dilution might have to be carried to a point where the minor constituents are no longer detectable.

By using a spectrophotometer, such as the Beckman instrument, the absorption bands are readily detected. The method used is described under determination on page 109. Scandium, yttrium, lanthanum, lutecium, thorium, terbium, and gadolinium show no absorption in the region listed. There are some interferences and it is generally necessary on mixtures of both the cerium and yttrium group to make an alkali sulfate separation of the two groups.

Of all the elements in the rare earth group, cerium is the only one which gives a simple chemical test. Cerium is qualitatively detected in a mixture of earths by adding ammonium hydroxide to an acid solution until there is the faintest suggestion of a permanent precipitate. Upon the addition of a few drops of hydrogen peroxide the solution becomes reddish-orange if only a little cerium is present, while in the presence of much cerium a precipitate of the same color separates.

## ESTIMATIONS

The elements of the rare earth group form oxalates which are insoluble in oxalic acid solutions. The past practice of precipitating in mineral acid solution is not desirable since several of the rare earths are appreciably soluble. The solution should have a pH of about 2. The oxalates, filtered after allowing the solution to stand overnight, are then ignited to the oxides at 1000°C. It is well to remember that praseodymium forms a higher oxide (sometimes listed as $Pr_6O_{11}$) as does terbium (sometimes listed as $Tb_4O_7$). For accurate work where these elements may predominate, it is necessary to reduce the oxides by heating and then cooling in hydrogen. In this case it is well to remove the cerium prior to

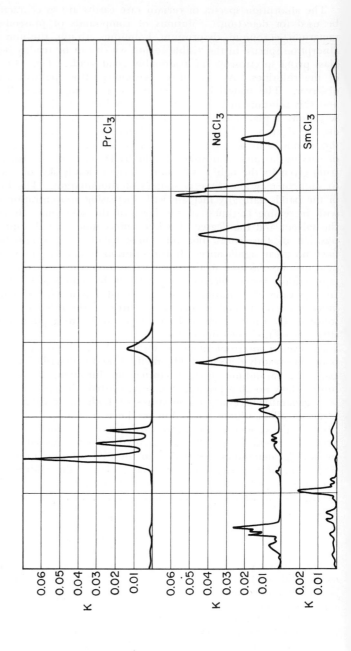

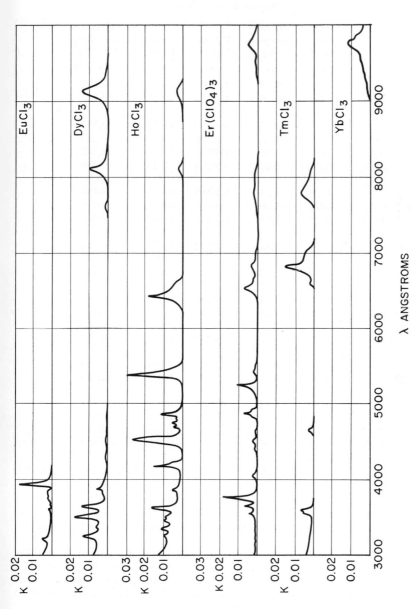

λ ANGSTROMS

FIG. 13-1.   Absorption Spectra of Rare Earth Solutions.*

* PrCl₃, NdCl₃, SmCl₃, EuCl₃, Er(ClO₄), TmCl₃ and YbCl₃ from Moeller, T., and Brantley, J. C., Anal. Chem., 22, 433, 1950. DyCl₃ and HoCl₃ by Sheehy, T., New Brunswick Laboratory, U. S. Atomic Energy Commission. See, also, Stewart and Kato, Anal. Chem., 30, 164–172, 1958.

Spectrophotometric Data

| Salt Used | Wave-length, A | Molecular Absorption Coefficient, E | Absorption Coefficient, k | Slit Width, mm. | Minimum Sensitivity, 1-cm Cell, g. metal/100 ml. |
|---|---|---|---|---|---|
| $PrCl_3$ | 4445 | 9.85 | 0.0700 | 0.025 | 0.143 |
| $Pr(NO_3)_3$ | 4445 | 9.20 | 0.0654 | 0.025 | 0.156 |
| | | | | | |
| $NdCl_3$ | 5218 | 4.33 | 0.0300 | 0.013 | 0.333 |
| $Nd(ClO_4)_3$ | 5218 | 4.30 | 0.0298 | 0.013 | 0.336 |
| $Nd(NO_3)_3$ | 5218 | 3.88 | 0.0269 | 0.013 | 0.372 |
| $Nd(C_2H_3O_2)_3$ | 5230 | 3.80 | 0.0263 | 0.013 | 0.380 |
| | | | | | |
| $SmCl_3$ | 4020 | 3.14 | 0.0210 | 0.044 | 0.480 |
| $Sm(NO_3)_3$ | 4020 | 3.28 | 0.0218 | 0.044 | 0.458 |
| $Sm(C_2H_3O_2)_3$ | 4025 | 3.68 | 0.0244 | 0.044 | 0.410 |
| | | | | | |
| $EuCl_3$ | 3939 | 2.92 | 0.0192 | 0.029 | 0.520 |
| $Eu(NO_3)_3$ | 3945 | 2.05 | 0.0135 | 0.053 | 0.743 |
| $Eu(C_2H_3O_2)_3$ | 3947 | 1.92 | 0.0126 | 0.053 | 0.793 |
| | | | | | |
| $GdCl_3$ | 2728 | 2.34 | 0.0149 | 0.205 | 0.670 |
| $Gd(C_2H_3O_2)_3$ | 2729 | 3.28 | 0.0209 | 0.205 | 0.479 |
| | | | | | |
| $Er(ClO_4)_3$ | 3792 | 4.00 | 0.0239 | 0.030 | 0.419 |
| | | | | | |
| $TmCl_3$ | 6825 | 2.58 | 0.0152 | 0.018 | 0.659 |
| $Tm(ClO_4)_3$ | 6825 | 2.49 | 0.0147 | 0.018 | 0.680 |
| | | | | | |
| $YbCl_3$ | 9750 | 1.94 | 0.0111 | 0.026 | 0.901 |
| $Yb(NO_3)_3$ | 9750 | 1.91 | 0.0110 | 0.026 | 0.912 |
| $Yb(ClO_4)_3$ | 9750 | 1.96 | 0.0113 | 0.026 | 0.885 |
| $Yb(C_2H_3O_2)_2$ | 9720 | 1.99 | 0.0116 | 0.026 | 0.864 |

precipitation of the other rare earths since $CeO_2$ is very difficult to reduce with hydrogen.

All the earths are precipitated with ammonium hydroxide but in the case of lanthanum it is necessary to have at least a 5% excess of ammonium hydroxide. Excess ammonium salts are also undesirable since they exert a solvent effect on lanthanum hydroxide.

Many of the oxides have a distinctive color, and when the analyst is working with minerals which may contain the rare earths, he should be on his guard when the ammonium hydroxide group is ignited. A chocolate brown color may well indicate the presence of praseodymium or terbium oxides. The oxides should be dissolved and the absorption spectrum examined as given above.

The rare earth fluorides are insoluble in hydrofluoric acid and this property can be used to separate the rare earths from many other elements.

## PREPARATION AND SOLUTION OF THE SAMPLE

If the rare earth is in the form of a recognized mineral, it is possible in some instances to use simple methods for decomposition, such as solution of a silicate in hydrochloric acid. In many cases, however, the material may be an ore containing several minerals. In general, a potassium bifluoride fusion has been found applicable for ores. The method is given in the Chapter on Thorium on page 1066.[1]

The use of sodium peroxide for decomposing ores may be applicable in certain instances.[2]  It is especially good for the decomposition of gadolinite. The method is given in the Chapter on Thorium on page 1059. For solution of monazite sand refer to the Chapter on Thorium.

The separation of the rare earths will depend to some extent on the other elements that are present. After solution of the sample, the silica, if present, is removed by dehydrating in the usual manner. After an ammonium hydroxide precipitation, which should be repeated if much calcium is present, the hydroxides are dissolved in hydrochloric acid. After evaporating to dryness to remove the excess acid, the rare earth oxalates, with thorium and scandium, are precipitated in a nearly neutral solution. If ferric ion or uranyl ions are present, it is necessary to add sufficient oxalic acid to complex all of the iron or uranium, otherwise an incomplete precipitation of the rare earth oxalates is made. If niobium and tantalum are present, it is generally preferable to precipitate the rare earths as fluoride. The rare earth fluorides are fused with sodium pyrosulfate and dissolved in water. After precipitating with ammonium hydroxide, the conversion to oxalate is made as above. For the separation of thorium and scandium from the oxalate precipitation, consult the chapters dealing with these elements.

In the presence of much iron, such as in steel, it is advisable to remove the bulk of the iron by an ether extraction of the chloride. During the course of solution with hydrochloric acid, chromium can be volatilized as the chloride. The rare earths are then precipitated as fluorides and converted to oxides as above.[3]

Cerium may be separated from the other rare earth elements by oxidizing it to the tetravalent state and then precipitating with potassium iodate as given below.

Europium and ytterbium may be separated from accompanying rare earth elements by the use of sodium amalgam.[4]  Ion exchange methods have been used for bulk separation of rare earths.[5]  Recently solvent extraction methods using tributylphosphate extraction of nitrate solution has shown promise.[6]  None of these can be classed as analytical methods at the present time.

## DETERMINATION OF RARE EARTH ELEMENTS

Quantitative methods for the determination of rare earth elements in mixtures of one another are rather meager. Cerium can be determined as well as europium

---

[1] The solution of rare earth fluorides by KF does not appear to be serious. E. Julian of the New Brunswick Laboratory found less than 0.2 mg. loss after carrying 250 mg. of $Y_2O_3$ as well as 70 mg. of $Nd_2O_3$ through the above procedure.

[2] Rafter, Analyst, **75**, 485, 1950.

[3] Lundell, G. E. F., Hoffman, J. I., and Bright, H. A., Chemical Analysis of Iron and Steel, John Wiley and Sons, New York, 1931.

[4] Marsh, J. Chem. Soc., **8**, 1943.

[5] J. Amer. Chem. Soc., **69**, 2769–2881, 1947.

[6] Weaver, Kappelman and Topp, J. Amer. Chem. Soc., **75**, 3943, 1953.

if present in sufficient amount. Spectrographic and spectrophotometric methods can be used for certain elements. The procedure for the determination of the total rare earth oxides and thorium is given on page 1064 under Thorium.

## THE APPROXIMATE DETERMINATION OF THE CERIUM AND YTTRIUM GROUPS

Having obtained the total rare earth oxides, it is possible to get an approximate determination of the percentage of the total cerium group oxides and of the total yttrium group oxides, based on the difference in the solubilities of the double alkali sulfates of the two groups in saturated solutions of the respective alkali sulfate. The sodium salt in solid form is widely recommended, but with a saturated solution of potassium sulfate, there is less tendency to precipitate the yttrium group.

It is well to have as large a sample as possible for this separation, and with less than 0.5 g. of oxides the results are not very trustworthy.[7] Only a small quantity of acid should be present, so if in the form of a chloride or nitrate the solution should be evaporated to approximate dryness, moistened with a drop or two of the respective acid, and taken into solution with as little water as possible. If a sulfuric acid solution be present, it is more convenient to precipitate with ammonium hydroxide and redissolve in hydrochloric acid than to carry out the tedious expulsion of the excess sulfuric acid at an elevated temperature.

*Procedure.*—To the cold, concentrated chloride or nitrate solution about 200 ml. of a saturated solution of potassium sulfate are added, and then a few grams of finely powdered potassium sulfate are sifted in, the mixture being vigorously stirred in the meantime, and for some minutes afterwards. After not less than 12 hours the precipitate is filtered and washed twice with saturated potassium sulfate solution, no attempt being made to thoroughly clean the beaker. The filter with the double sulfates is dropped back into the original beaker. The liquid adhering to the funnel is rinsed into the filtrate, and this solution, containing the bulk of the yttrium earths, is temporarily set aside. The first precipitate and paper are boiled with about 100 ml. of 10% sodium hydroxide solution, diluted to about 250 ml., again boiled, filtered and washed. The hydroxides are dissolved in hydrochloric acid, freed from filter paper by filtration, evaporated to approximate dryness, moistened with a drop or two of hydrochloric acid, taken up with a little water, and the sulfate precipitation is repeated just as before. This second precipitate is again treated with sodium hydroxide and hydrochloric acid just as described before. In the resulting chloride solution the cerium earths are precipitated as oxalates and weighed as mixed oxides just as outlined in the method for total rare earth oxides. The combined filtrates from the double sulfate precipitations are treated with ammonium hydroxide, the resulting yttrium earth

---

[7] Rather than take the total oxides obtained from an analysis as the starting point for the potassium sulfate precipitation, it is often better, if the amount of the original material is sufficient, to take a larger sample and make the separation on the oxides obtained from the oxalate precipitation. This preparation is made just before the separation from thorium and scandium. Both thorium and scandium will go practically quantitatively into the precipitate. (This is not true of scandium if sodium sulfate is used.) The percentage of thorium oxide will usually have been separately determined by one of the methods given in the chapter on that element, so the weight of $ThO_2$ can be deducted from the weight of the cerium group oxides. The amount of scandium in any mineral likely to be met is so small that its effect could hardly be significant in a separation no more exact than the one under consideration.

hydroxides are dissolved in hydrochloric acid, precipitated as oxalates, ignited to oxides, and weighed. In the case of the yttrium earths, the use of hydrogen for the ignition would never be necessary in the analysis of any naturally occurring group of earths, for praseodymium is absent, and not more than traces of terbium could be present, owing to the scarcity of this element. It is evident that if no further investigation is to be carried out, the weighing of either the cerium group or the yttrium group would suffice, since the other group could be determined by difference from the percentage of the total oxides already determined.

On the whole, a fair idea can be had from this separation as to the relative proportions of the two main groups present, and as long as working conditions are maintained reasonably constant, and the amounts worked upon are not too small, fair checks can be obtained in duplicate analyses.

## DETERMINATION OF CERIUM

The individual determination of cerium is one of the few processes in the chemistry of the rare earths which is reasonably exact. It can be separated from all other rare earths by gravimetric methods, and it can also be accurately determined by titrimetric procedures without having to separate it from its neighbors.

### GRAVIMETRIC DETERMINATION

Potassium iodate [8] is the only specific precipitant which has been proposed that is not dependent upon hydrolysis, and it offers a ready means of separating cerium quantitatively from even large amounts of other rare earths. Thorium, if not previously removed, would be quantitatively precipitated along with the cerium. However, it is entirely justifiable to make a separate determination of the thorium by one of the specific methods given for that element in the Chapter on Thorium, and then deduct the weight of $ThO_2$ from the combined weight of the cerium and thorium oxides found.

*Procedure.*—To the solution containing the rare earth nitrates (thorium having been previously removed) is added enough concentrated nitric acid so that the latter will make up ⅓ of the volume of the solution. The volume of the solution at this point should not greatly exceed 75 ml. It is also better that the amount of ceria present should not exceed about 0.15 g., since the precipitate is bulky, and the washing is rendered more difficult by the very large precipitate. About 0.5 g. of solid potassium bromate is added, and when it has dissolved, an amount of potassium iodate which is not less than 50 times the weight of the estimated cerium dioxide present is added in form of a solution containing 100 g. of potassium iodate and 333 ml. of concentrated nitric acid per liter. The reagent is slowly added with constant stirring. The precipitate of ceric iodate is allowed to settle in the cold until the supernatant liquid is practically clear, and it is then filtered on paper of close texture, such as Whatman No. 42. In filtering, the precipitate is brought as completely as possible onto the paper with the mother liquor, and the beaker is rinsed just once with a small amount of a solution of 8 g. of potassium iodate and 50 ml. of concentrated nitric acid per liter. After draining, but not standing longer than is necessary, the precipitate is rinsed from the paper back into the beaker with more of the washing solution. Any clots should be broken up with a rod and the mixture well churned. The precipitate is again brought

[8] Brinton, P. H. M. P., and James, C., J. Am. Chem. Soc., **41**, 1080, 1919.

on the filter paper in the same way, and allowed to drain. It is then rinsed back into the beaker with hot water, heated to boiling with constant stirring, and concentrated nitric acid is dropped in until the precipitate is completely dissolved. Any unnecessary excess of nitric acid is to be avoided. To the solution 0.25 g. of potassium bromate and about the same amount of potassium iodate solution originally used are added. If the use of the iodate solution would unduly increase the volume, the correct amount of the salt can be dissolved by heating in a small volume of 1:2 nitric acid and added in that form. The precipitate is allowed to settle as before, and the perfectly cold mixture is filtered through the original paper, given one very small washing with the nitric acid-potassium iodate washing solution, rinsed back into the beaker with the same solution, well churned, and finally brought onto the paper and washed with 3 small portions of the washing solution. Every trace of ceric iodate need not be removed from the beaker. The paper and precipitate are dropped into the original beaker, any trace of precipitate removed from the funnel with a fragment of "ashless" paper. About 5–8 g. of oxalic acid crystals are now added, and then 50 ml. of water. The covered beaker is heated gently, and the contents are finally boiled until iodine vapors are no longer given off, and all sublimed iodine is vaporized from the cover glass and upper edges of the beaker. After standing several hours the cerous oxalate and filter pulp are filtered, washed with cold water, and ignited to constant weight at 1000°C.

The sum of the other rare earths can be determined in the combined filtrates from the ceric iodate by precipitation with sodium hydroxide, dissolving in hydrochloric acid, precipitating as oxalates and igniting to oxide, finishing in hydrogen if the weight of the sesquioxides is desired.

## TITRIMETRIC DETERMINATION

Two titrimetric methods for the determination of cerium in the presence of other rare earths give accurate results if attention is paid to certain details. The methods are alike in principle.

### THE PERSULFATE METHOD OF VON KNORRE-WILLARD AND YOUNG [9]

*Procedure.*—The sample, usually mixed oxides obtained from the ignition of oxalates, is moistened with water and then digested with concentrated hydrochloric acid until solution is complete. Ten ml. of concentrated sulfuric acid are added and the mixture is evaporated to copious fumes to expel all hydrochloric acid.[10] After cooling, the sulfates are dissolved in cold water and diluted to about 200 ml. Five ml. of a solution of 2.5 g. of silver nitrate per liter are added as catalyst, and then 5 g. of solid ammonium persulfate. The solution is boiled 10 minutes, cooled to room temperature, and titrated electrometrically with ferrous sulfate solution (about 0.05 N) which has been standardized against a ceric sulfate solution of known strength.[11]

[9] von Knorre, Z. f. angew. Chem., **10,** 685, 717, 1897; Ber., **33,** 1924, 1900; Willard and Young, J. Am. Chem. Soc., **50,** 1397, 1928.

[10] While the sample may be dissolved directly in sulfuric acid by long digestion, and must be so dissolved if the ceria in the sample amounts to more than about 50%,—since such mixtures are very difficultly soluble in hydrochloric acid,—yet for most samples the method here given is more rapid. It has the advantage of allowing one to see when the solution is complete (which cannot readily be done in the syrup of sulfates in sulfuric acid) and the resulting sulfates seem more readily soluble in water than when the sample has been treated with sulfuric acid from the start.

[11] Willard and Young, J. Am. Chem. Soc., **51,** 149, 1929.

## THE SODIUM BISMUTHATE METHOD OF METZGER [12]

Fully as accurate, and more convenient for an occasional determination, is the bismuthate method.

*Procedure.*—The sample is brought into solution, just as described for the persulfate method, except that 20 ml. of concentrated sulfuric acid are to be used instead of 10 ml. The sulfate mass is cooled, about 2 g. of ammonium sulfate crystals are added, and then carefully, 80 ml. of cold water. About 1 g. of sodium bismuthate is introduced and the solution is heated slowly to the boiling point. After cooling somewhat, 50 ml. of 2% sulfuric acid are added and the solution is filtered from the excess bismuth salt by gentle suction through asbestos. After passing the ceric sulfate solution through the filter, the latter is washed with 100–150 ml. of 2% sulfuric acid. The ceric solution is treated with a measured excess of ferrous ammonium sulfate solution (10 g. of the crystallized salt and 50 ml. of concentrated sulfuric acid per liter) as shown by the disappearance of the yellow ceric color, and the excess of ferrous solution is then back titrated with 0.025 $N$ potassium permanganate to a pink end point that will persist for half a minute.

The permanganate is standardized against sodium oxalate in the approved manner. To establish the relationship between the permanganate and the ferrous solution, which should be checked daily, a mixture of 80 ml. of water, 20 ml. of concentrated sulfuric acid, 2 g. of ammonium sulfate, and 1 g. of sodium bismuthate are heated to boiling, filtered through asbestos, and washed with 100 ml. of 2% sulfuric acid. To this solution 25 ml. of the ferrous solution are added from a pipette and titrated with the permanganate.

## DETERMINATION OF EUROPIUM

Trivalent salts of europium can be reduced to the divalent stage in a number of ways.[13] On the basis of reduction by zinc, McCoy has developed an iodometric method for the determination of europium in the presence of other rare earths.

*Procedure.*—The mixture of oxides, free from phosphate, sulfate, and iron, is dissolved in hydrochloric acid, and diluted to give an acidity of 0.1–0.2 $N$. The solution is poured through a Jones reductor (charged with 20- to 30-mesh amalgamated zinc in the conventional way), the tip of which dips into an excess of approximately 0.04 $N$ iodine solution. The excess of iodine is titrated with standard sodium thiosulfate solution.

## QUANTITATIVE SPECTROGRAPHIC ANALYSIS

The determination of individual rare earths is difficult using spectrographic methods. The matrix in many instances affects the values obtained.[14] A porous cup procedure, however, has been used which has a precision of $\pm 10\%$.[15] Strontium is used as an internal standard. Care must be taken that the original sam-

[12] J. Am. Chem. Soc., **31**, 523, 1909. Cf. Furman, *ibid.*, **50**, 755, 1928.

[13] Yntema, L. F., J. Am. Chem. Soc., **52**, 2782, 1930; Selwood, P. W., *ibid.*, **57**, 1145, 1935; McCoy, H. N., *ibid.*, **57**, 1756, 1935; **58**, 1577, 2279, 1936; Marsh, J. K., J. Chem. Soc., **8**, 1943.

[14] When gadolinium was determined in a cerium matrix by a direct burn method, the results were different than when a yttrium matrix was used.

[15] Norris, J. A., and Pepper, C. E., Anal. Chem., **24**, 1399, 1952.

ples are free from strontium, otherwise this contamination biases the line intensity ratios of rare earth to strontium. The possibility of contamination always exists, as strontium may precipitate along with rare earth oxalates and most rare earth concentration processes contain this step. When strontium is suspected, the sample is put into solution at twice the regular concentration, 20 mg. per ml., and the sample is run both with and without the addition of the strontium internal standard. From the resulting spectra it can be determined if the strontium is present in sufficient concentration to interfere with the analysis. Precision analysis requires that any strontium contamination be removed; however, if other impurities are known to be absent, it can be assumed that a low total rare earth percentage is due to bias from the additional strontium present and the determined values can be adjusted until their sum totals 100%.

The following table gives the lines used for analysis.

*Procedure.*—100-mg. samples of the rare earth oxides are weighed into 10-ml. volumetric flasks and from 2 to 4 ml. of concentrated hydrochloric acid are added. Distilled water is added and the samples are placed on a hot plate to dissolve the oxide completely. The solutions are cooled and made up to volume with distilled water, and 100 microliters of a 0.05% strontium metal solution are added, giving a final concentration of 5 p. p. m. of strontium.

The following conditions are used in the exposure of the samples:

Electrode, porous cup electrode with $\frac{1}{8}$ inch graphite counterelectrode.

The excitation is obtained by a relatively high power spark discharge (5 to 7 radio-frequency amperes at 12,000 volts as compared to 3 radio-frequency amperes at the same voltage for normal porous cup work). The discharge circuit gives 4 sparks per half cycle. The electrodes are held in special tantalum water cooled holders. A water flow rate of 300 ml. per minute is necessary to prevent boiling of the sample solution.

The spectrum from 3450 to 4600 A is photographed on SA No. 2 plates using the second order of a large stigmatic grating spectrograph with a dispersion of approximately 2.5 A per mm.

The transmittancies of the indicated spectral lines are measured using a comparator-densitometer and the analytical curves are drawn from standards run on each plate.

## SPECTROPHOTOMETRIC ESTIMATION

The spectrophotometric estimation of rare earths in mixtures is, at the present time, the most satisfactory. The method has its drawbacks since certain of the rare earths do not have characteristic absorption spectra. The method is relatively simple and the time for analysis is not great. The greatest drawback is the procurement of pure individual rare earths and the time involved in setting up working curves with these elements. The nitrate [16] or chloride [17] can be used. The papers to which reference is made contain data on certain elements which can be used directly within limits. The determinations can be made by using the absorption coefficient $k$.

$$\text{where } k = \frac{\log I_0/I}{cl}$$

[16] Rodden, J. Research Natl. Bureau of Standards, **26**, 557, 1941, and **28**, 265, 1942.
[17] Moeller and Brantley, Anal. Chem., **22**, 433, 1950.

Lines for Quantitative Spectrographic Analysis

| Element | Wavelength A | Interference |
|---------|-------------|--------------|
| Y | 4309.63 | High Lu |
| La | 4429.90 | |
| | 4238.38 | |
| | 4196.55 | |
| Pr | 4222.98 | High Gd |
| | 4298.92 | |
| Nd | 4247.37 | High Sm |
| | 4303.57 | High Pr |
| Sm | 4424.34 | High Pr |
| | 4256.40 | |
| Eu | 4435.60 | |
| | 3971.99 | |
| Gd | 4251.74 | High Sm |
| | 4342.19 | High Yb |
| Tb | 3702.85 | |
| | 3703.92 | |
| | 3874.18 | |
| Dy | 3944.69 | |
| Ho | 3891.02 | |
| | 4103.84 | |
| Er | 3906.32 | |
| Tm | 3761.33 | |
| | 3761.92 | |
| | 3848.02 | |
| Yb | 3694.20 | |
| | 3987.99 | |
| Lu | 3554.43 | |
| Sr | 4215.52 | |

In this expression, $c$ is concentration in grams of metal per liter, $l$ is the light path (in cm) and $I_0$ and $I$ are the intensities of the incident and transmitted light, respectively. Expression of $c$ in moles per liter would give corresponding molecular absorption coefficients $E$.

From the analytical point of view, selection of bands free from interference by other rare earth metal ions would be desirable. It is also important that the bands chosen be the strongest in the given spectrum, in order that maximum sensitivity be obtained. Examination of the spectra, shows that many of the strongest bands are subject to greater or lesser interference by other rare earth metal ions. In most cases, however, the interfering ions may be determined with accuracy and corrections applied. A double alkali sulfate separation should be made where both cerium and yttrium groups are present. Such corrections become important only when the interfering ion is present in larger concentration than the ion being determined.

The wavelengths summarized in the Table on page 314 are those that are most useful for analytical determinations. Because cerium is most accurately determined by oxidimetric means, a value for it is not given.

The following procedure is recommended for the spectrophotometric estimation of rare earth metal ions that show characteristic absorption bands.[17]

*Procedure.*—The freshly ignited, weighed (1–3 g.) oxide sample is slurried with water and dissolved in a slight excess of hydrochloric or perchloric acid. Excess acid is removed by evaporating to dryness, taking up the residue in water, and re-evaporating. The final residue is taken up in water and the resulting solution is diluted to a suitable volume (say 100 ml.). The log $I_0/I$ values are then determined, using a Beckman spectrophotometer, at wavelengths and slit widths summarized in the Table on page 314 if a mixture is being studied or at an individual recommended wavelength if but a single element is to be estimated. (These values apply *rigidly* only to the specific instrument. Anyone using another instrument should obtain his own set of calibration data.) The sharp nature of the bands may make peak settings difficult with some instruments. It is recommended that no less than five readings be made in the vicinity of each peak at slightly differing wavelength settings and that the maximum log $I_0/I$ value so obtained be used in subsequent calculations.

The quantity of rare earth ion present is then calculated from the measured log $I_0/I$ value and the characteristic $k$ value as summarized in the table on page 314, using the expression

$$\text{Grams of } R^{+3} \text{ per liter} = \frac{\log I_0/I}{k}$$

use of 1-cm cells being assumed.

In the cases where other ions interfere, necessary corrections may be made by calculating log $I_0/I$ due to the interfering ion and subtracting this value from the measured log $I_0/I$. This correction factor is obtained by multiplying the concentration of the interfering ion by the absorption coefficient of this ion at the wavelength in question. Thus, to determine the amount of rare earth, $A$, present when another one, $B$, interferes, one uses the expression

$$\text{Grams of } A \text{ per liter} = \frac{\log I_0/I - (\text{grams of } B \text{ per liter} \times k_B)}{k_A}$$

Values of $k$ listed in the following Table are for such calculations.

Interferences with Bands Chosen for Analytical Purposes

| Salt Used | Wave-length A | k | Interfering Ion | k of Inter-fering Ion |
|---|---|---|---|---|
| PrCl₃ | 4445 | 0.0700 | Sm⁺³ | 0.0012 |
| NdCl₃ | 5218 | 0.0300 | Er⁺³ | 0.00998 |
| SmCl₃ | 4020 | 0.0210 | Eu⁺⁺ | 0.0006 |
| EuCl₃ | 3939 | 0.0192 | Sm⁺³ | 0.00101 |
| Tm(ClO₄)₃ | 6825 | 0.0147 | Nd⁺³ | 0.00240 |
| Yb(ClO₄)₃ | 9750 | 0.0111 | Er⁺³ | 0.00529 |

The mutual interference between the 3939 A band for europium and the 4020 A band for samarium, the only strong bands available for these ions, presents a more difficult problem.  Two alternatives are suggested.  The first involves chemical estimation of europium by oxidimetric means and corresponding correction of the samarium determination.  The second, which is simpler and of equal accuracy, involves a preliminary calculation of the quantity of material present in the larger amount.  This quantity is then used to correct the measured concentration of the other ion in the fashion outlined above.  The resulting concentration of the second ion is then used in arriving at a more accurate value for the first.

## METHODS FOR CERIUM IN ANALYSES IN OTHER CHAPTERS

Cerium (and Rare Earths) in Magnesium Alloys          See Magnesium Chapter
Cerium, Neodymium, Praseodymium and Lanthanum     See Magnesium Chapter

# Chapter 14

# CHLORINE

$Cl_2$, *at. wt.* 35.453; *d.* 3.214 g./l. (15°C.); *m.p.* −101.6°C.; *b.p.* −34.6°C.; *oxides,* $Cl_2O$, $ClO_2$, $Cl_2O_7$

Chlorine occurs combined in nature generally with sodium, potassium, and magnesium. It is a component of rock forming minerals such as sodalite. It occurs in the minerals rock salt, halite, NaCl; sylvine, KCl; carnallite, $KCl \cdot MgCl_2 \cdot 6H_2O$; and combined in minerals of copper, lead, silver, etc. It occurs more commonly in rocks high in sodium and low in silica, but is also found in quartz-bearing ores. It occurs in sea water, mineral springs and ground waters. It is widely distributed in nature.

The element, first obtained by Scheele by the action of pyrolusite, $MnO_2$, on hydrochloric acid ("marine acid") in 1774, finds extended uses, bleaching, germicide, extraction of gold from its ores, chemical industries, etc. Among the compounds—table salt, NaCl, chlorides, chlorates, perchlorates, hypochlorites are well known.

## DETECTION

*Free Chlorine.*—The yellow gas is recognized by its characteristic odor. It liberates iodine from iodides; it bleaches litmus, indigo, and many organic coloring substances.

*Chlorides. Silver Nitrate Test.*—In absence of bromides and iodides, which also form insoluble silver salts, silver nitrate precipitates from solutions containing chlorides white, curdy, silver chloride, AgCl (opalescent with traces), soluble in $NH_4OH$ (AgBr slowly soluble, AgI difficultly soluble), also soluble in concentrated ammonium carbonate (AgBr is very slightly soluble; AgI is insoluble). Silver chloride turns dark upon exposure to light.

*Free Hydrochloric Acid. Manganese Dioxide, Potassium Permanganate,* and certain oxidizing agents liberate free chlorine gas when added to solutions containing free hydrochloric acid. The gas passed into potassium iodide liberates free iodine, which produces a blue solution with starch.

*Concentrated Sulfuric Acid* added to chlorides and heated liberates HCl gas, which produces a white fume in presence of ammonium hydroxide.

*Detection in Presence of Cyanate, Cyanide, Thiocyanate.*—An excess of silver nitrate is added to the solution, the precipitate filtered off and boiled with concentrated nitric acid to oxidize the cyanogen compounds and the white precipitate, silver chloride, subjected to the tests under chlorides to confirm the compound.

*If Chlorates are Present.*—The halogens are precipitated with silver nitrate, the precipitate dissolved with zinc and sulfuric acid and the solution treated as directed in the preceding paragraph.

*Test for Hypochlorite.*—Potassium hypochlorite, KClO, shaken with mercury forms the yellowish-red compound $Hg_2OCl_2$, which does not form with the other potassium salts of chlorine, i.e., KCl, $KClO_2$, $KClO_3$, $KClO_4$.

Hypochlorites decolorize indigo, but do not decolorize potassium permanganate solutions. If arsenious acid is present, indigo is not decolorized until all of the arsenious acid has been oxidized to the arsenic form.

*Tests for Chlorite.*—Potassium permanganate solution is decolorized by chlorites. (The solution should be dilute.)

A solution of indigo is decolorized, even in presence of arsenious acid (distinction from hypochlorites).

*Detection of Chlorate.*—The dry salt heated with concentrated sulfuric acid detonates and evolves yellow fumes.

Chlorates liberate chlorine from hydrochloric acid.

*Perchlorate.*—The solution is boiled with hydrochloric acid to decompose hypochlorites, chlorites, and chlorates. Chlorides are removed by precipitation with silver nitrate, the filtrate evaporated to dryness, the residue fused with sodium carbonate to decompose the perchlorate to form the chloride, which may now be tested as usual.

*Detection in Presence of Bromide and Iodide.*—About 10 ml. of the solution is neutralized in a casserole with acetic acid, adding about 1 to 2 ml. in excess, and then diluting to about 6 volumes with water. About half a gram of potassium persulfate, $K_2S_2O_8$, is added and the solution heated. Iodine is liberated and may be detected by shaking the solution with carbon disulfide, which is colored violet by this element. Iodine is expelled by boiling, the potassium persulfate being repeatedly added until the solution is colorless. Bromine is liberated by adding 2 or 3 ml. of dilute sulfuric acid and additional persulfate. A yellowish-red color is produced by this element. Carbon disulfide absorbs bromine, becoming colored yellowish red. Bromine is expelled with additional persulfate and by boiling. The volume of the solution should be kept to about 60 ml., distilled water being added to replace that which is expelled by boiling. When bromine is driven out of the solution, the silver nitrate test for chlorides is made. A white, curdy precipitate, soluble in ammonium hydroxide and reprecipitated upon acidifying with nitric acid, is produced if chlorides are present.

## ESTIMATION

The determination of chlorine is required in a large number of substances. It occurs combined as a chloride mainly with sodium, potassium, and magnesium. Rock salt, NaCl; sylvine, KCl; carnallite, $KCl \cdot MgCl_2 \cdot 6H_2O$; matlockite, $PbCl_2 \cdot PbO$; horn silver, AgCl; atacamite, $CuCl_2 \cdot 3Cu(OH)_2$, are forms in which it is found in nature. Chlorine is determined in the evaluation of bleaching powder. It is estimated in the analysis of water.

Many of the chlorides are easily soluble in water. Chlorides of insoluble compounds such as lead and silver may be readily decomposed by fusion with sodium or potassium carbonate; the mercurous chloride by digestion with sodium or potassium hydroxide.

## PREPARATION AND SOLUTION OF THE SAMPLE

In dissolving the sample the following facts should be borne in mind: Although chlorides are nearly all soluble in water, silver chloride is practically insoluble

(100 ml. dissolve 0.000152 g. at 20°C.); mercurous chloride is nearly as insoluble as silver chloride (0.00031 gram); lead chloride requires heat to bring it into solution (in cold water only 0.673 g. soluble per 100 ml. of water). Chlorides of antimony, tin, and bismuth require free acid to keep them in solution. Hydrochloric acid increases the solubility of silver, mercury, lead, antimony, bismuth, copper (Cu(I)), gold, and platinum, but decreases the solubility of cadmium, copper (Cu(II)), nickel, cobalt, manganese, barium, calcium, strontium, magnesium, thorium, sodium, potassium, and ammonium chlorides.

Chlorine gas is most readily dissolved in water at 10°C. (1 vol. $H_2O$ dissolves 3.095 vols. Cl). Boiling completely removes chlorine from water.

Hypochlorites, chlorites, chlorates, and perchlorates are soluble in water.

The chlorine may be present either combined or free. In the combined state it may be present as free hydrochloric acid or as a water-soluble or insoluble salt.

*Water-soluble Chlorides.*—Chlorides of the alkali or alkaline earth groups may be treated directly with silver nitrate upon making slightly acid with nitric acid, the chlorine being determined either gravimetrically or volumetrically according to one of the procedures given later. It is convenient to work with samples containing 0.01 g. to 1 g. of Cl. The sample is dissolved in about 150 ml. of water, made acid with nitric acid with about 5 to 10 ml. in excess of the point of neutralization, should the sample be alkaline. Then the chlorine combined as chloride is determined as directed later.

If the water solution contains a chloride of a heavy metal which forms basic salts (e.g., stannic, ferric, etc., solutions), or which may tend to reduce the silver solution, it is necessary to remove these by precipitation with ammonium hydroxide, or by sodium hydroxide, or potassium carbonate solution. The salt is dissolved in water and acidified with $HNO_3$, adding about 10 ml. in excess, for about 150 ml. of solution. (This excess $HNO_3$ should be sufficient to oxidize substances which would tend to reduce the silver reagent; e.g., $FeSO_4$, etc.) Ammonia solution (free from chloride) is added in sufficient quantity to precipitate the heavy metals iron, manganese, aluminum, etc. The mixture is filtered and the residue washed several times with distilled water. Chlorine is determined in the filtrate by acidifying with $HNO_3$ as directed above.

*Water-insoluble Chlorides.*—The chloride may frequently be decomposed by boiling with sodium carbonate solution. Many of the minerals, however, require fusion with sodium carbonate to prepare them for solution; e.g., apatite, sodalite, etc. Silver chloride may also be decomposed by fusion.

*Silver Chloride.*—The sample is mixed with about three times its weight of $Na_2CO_3$ and fused in a porcelain crucible until the mass has sintered together. The soluble chloride, NaCl, is leached out with water, leaving the water-insoluble carbonate of silver, which may be filtered off. The filtrate is acidified with $HNO_3$ and chlorine determined as usual.

*Chlorine in Rocks.*—The finely ground material is fused with about five times its weight of potassium carbonate. The melt is extracted with hot water, cooled and the solution acidified with nitric acid (methyl orange indicator), and the solution allowed to stand several hours (preferably overnight). If silicic acid precipitates, the solution is treated with ammonia and boiled, filtered and the filter washed with hot water. The cooled filtrate is acidified with nitric acid and chlorine determined as usual. If silicic acid does not separate, the addition of ammonia may be omitted and chlorine determined in the solution.

*Free Chlorine.*—Free chlorine may be determined titrimetrically according to the procedure given under this section. If it is desired to determine this gravimetrically, a definite amount of the chlorine water is transferred by means of a pipette to a flask containing $NH_4OH$ solution and the mixture heated to boiling. The cooled solution is acidified with nitric acid and the chloride precipitated with silver nitrate according to the standard procedure given on page 328.

NOTE.—Free chlorine cannot be precipitated directly, as the following reaction takes place: $3Cl_2 + 6AgNO_3 + 3H_2O \rightarrow 5AgCl + AgClO_3 + 6HNO_3$.

Reaction of chlorine with ammonia: $Cl_2 + 2NH_4OH \rightarrow NH_4Cl + NH_4OCl + H_2O$. When the solution is boiled, $NH_4OCl$ breaks down, e.g., $3NH_4OCl + 2NH_3 \rightarrow 3NH_4Cl + N_2 + 3H_2O$.

*Chlorine in Ores and Cinders.*—One hundred grams of the finely ground ore or cinder are placed in a 500-ml. flask, containing 300 ml. of concentrated sulfuric acid (Cl-free). The flask is shaken to mix the sample with the acid and then connected with an absorption apparatus, containing distilled water or dilute caustic solution. The sample is gradually heated, the distillation flask resting upon a sand bath. After two hours, which is sufficient to expel all the chlorine as hydrochloric acid, the contents of the absorption tubes are filtered, if free sulfur is present (sulfide ores), nitric acid added, and the filtrate brought to boiling to oxidize any $SO_2$ that may be present. Chlorine is precipitated according to the standard procedure on page 328.

During the run the distilling flask should be shaken occasionally to prevent caking. Suction applied at the absorption end of the apparatus and a current of air swept through the system aids in carrying over the HCl into the water or NaOH.

*Chlorine and Chlorides in Gas.*—The gas is bubbled through dilute sodium hydroxide contained in one or more cylinders, gas wash bottle type, measuring the gas by means of a dry meter, placed after the cylinders. The meters are protected from moist gas by passing this through sulfuric acid and an asbestos filter, loosely packed. Aliquot portions of the sodium hydroxide are now examined for chlorine by acidifying with nitric acid and adding silver nitrate. If only traces are present the turbidity of the solution is compared with standards made up with known amounts of sodium chloride dissolved in water. The comparisons may be made conveniently in Nessler tubes. To different quantities of the standard made up to a convenient volume, silver nitrate reagent is added and the solution diluted to 50 or 100 ml. The unknown, placed in a Nessler tube, is treated with nitric acid and silver nitrate and matched with the standards, after dilution to the same volume adopted for the standards.

## SEPARATIONS

The following separations may be necessary in presence of substances interfering with the chlorine determination. The hydrolysis of antimony and bismuth in solutions not sufficiently acid makes the removal of these elements advisable. The removal of cyanide and the halogens, bromine and iodine, on account of their co-precipitation with chlorine necessitates a preliminary procedure for each as outlined below. These steps are not required in absence of the interfering substances.

*Removal of the Heavy Metals from the Halogens.*—The solution is boiled with sodium carbonate. The heavy metals precipitate as carbonates while the halogens remain in solution as sodium salts.

*Separation of the Halogens from Silver Cyanide and Silver Ion.*—The solution is treated with an excess of zinc and sulfuric acid. The metallic silver and the paracyanogen are filtered off and the halogens determined in the filtrate.

*Separation of the Halogens.* **Separation of Iodine from Chlorine.**—Iodine may be expelled from the solution by addition of sodium nitrite and sulfuric acid and boiling. The solution diluted to about 700 ml. with water and containing not over 0.25 g. of each halide is treated with about 3 g. of sodium nitrite, 3 ml. of dilute $H_2SO_4$ (1:1) and boiled, the solution being kept to a volume of over 500 ml. The iodine will be completely expelled in about 45 minutes. Chlorine and bromine will remain in the flask. If the determination of iodine is desired its vapor is caught in a 5% solution of NaOH containing 3% of hydrogen peroxide.

**Separation of Bromine from Chlorine.**—If bromine is present the solution from which the iodine has been expelled as outlined above is neutralized with NaOH and the solution evaporated to about 50 ml. Dilute acetic acid is added to the cooled solution with about 65 ml. excess (glacial acetic 1 water 2). About 1.5 g. of $KMnO_4$ crystals are added and bromine expelled by steam distillation. If the determination of bromine is desired it is absorbed in NaOH.

## GRAVIMETRIC METHOD

### SILVER CHLORIDE METHOD

The procedure is based on the insolubility of silver chloride in dilute nitric acid, the following reaction taking place:

$$Ag^+ + Cl^- \rightarrow AgCl$$

*Reagents.* **0.5 N Silver Nitrate Solution.**—Make up a solution containing 84.95 g. $AgNO_3$ per liter of distilled water.

**Very Dilute Nitric Acid.**—Add 0.5 ml. of concentrated $HNO_3$ to 200 ml. distilled water.

*Procedure.*—Weigh 0.5 g. of the substance on a watch glass or in a weighing bottle and transfer to a 250 ml. beaker. Dissolve in a little water, dilute the solution to about 150 ml., and add 10 drops of concentrated nitric acid.

Calculate the volume of silver nitrate solution to be added to precipitate the chloride in the sample, assuming that it is all sodium chloride. Example: for 0.5000 g., there are required 0.5000/0.05845 = 8.56 milliequivalents or 17.12 ml. of 0.5 N $AgNO_3$ solution. Without heating the solution of the sample, add the $AgNO_3$ solution slowly, with constant stirring. When 10 ml. have been added, allow the precipitate to settle and test the supernatant liquid for complete precipitation by the addition of a few drops of $AgNO_3$ solution. Test the liquid in this way after the addition of each 2 or 3 ml. of the precipitating agent until no further precipitate appears. Then heat the solution nearly to boiling and hold it at this temperature, with frequent vigorous stirring, until the precipitate coagulates and the supernatant liquid is clear.

As soon as the solution clears, test it again with a few drops of $AgNO_3$ solution to make sure precipitation is complete, then decant it through a weighed filtering crucible. Add about 25 ml. of the (cold) very dilute nitric acid to the precipitate in the beaker, stir it thoroughly, let it settle, and again decant the supernatant liquid through the crucible. Wash the precipitate 4 or 5 times in this way, then transfer it to the filtering crucible, and wash it with the very dilute nitric acid until the filtrate gives no test for silver ion.

Dry the precipitate by heating the crucible gradually to 110–120°C., and holding it there until fairly well dried, then increasing the temperature to 145–150°C. until fully dried. If the AgCl appears dark, moisten with HCl and heat to expel the excess acid.

Cool in a desiccator.

Weigh as silver chloride: (Wt. crucible + AgCl) − (Wt. crucible) = (Wt. AgCl).

$$\% \text{ Cl in sample} = \frac{(\text{Wt. Ag Cl}) \times 0.2474}{(\text{Wt. of sample})} \times 100$$

PRECAUTION.—This precipitate decomposes on continued exposure to light, so avoid strong light in the working area. If AgCl darkens, moisten with HCl and heat to expel excess acid.

NOTE.—The silver chloride may be removed from the crucible by adding a piece of zinc and dilute sulfuric acid to the residue. AgCl is soluble in ammonium hydroxide solution. Concentrated hydriodic acid (sp. gr. 1.70) is an excellent agent for the removal of AgCl, AgBr, or AgI from filter crucibles (Caley and Burford, Ind. Eng. Chem., Anal. Ed. **8,** 67, 1936).

## TITRIMETRIC METHODS

### DETERMINATION OF CHLORINE IN ACID SOLUTION, SILVER THIOCYANATE-FERRIC ALUM METHOD

The method, devised by Volhard,[1] is applicable to titration of chlorine in acid solutions, a condition frequently occurring in analysis, where the Silver Chromate Method of Mohr cannot be used. The method is based on the fact that when solutions of silver and an alkali thiocyanate are mixed in presence of a ferric salt, the thiocyanate has a selective action towards silver, combining with this to form thiocyanate of silver, any excess of that required by the silver reacting with the ferric salt to form the reddish-brown ferric thiocyanate, which color serves as an indication of the completion of the reaction. An excess of silver nitrate is added to the nitric acid solution containing the chloride, AgCl filtered off, and the excess of silver titrated with the thiocyanate in presence of the ferric salt.

Copper (up to 70%), arsenic, antimony, cadmium, bismuth, lead, iron, zinc, manganese, cobalt, and nickel do not interfere, unless the proportion of the latter metals is such as to interfere by intensity of the color of their ions.

*Reagents.* **0.1 N Ammonium or Potassium Thiocyanate Solution.**—About 8 g. of ammonium or 10 g. of potassium salt are dissolved in water and diluted to one liter. The solution is adjusted by titration against the 0.1 N silver nitrate solution. It is advisable to have 1 ml. of the thiocyanate equivalent to 1 ml. of the silver nitrate solution. Owing to the deliquescence of the thiocyanates the exact amount for an 0.1 N solution cannot be weighed.

**0.1 N Silver Nitrate.**—This solution contains 10.787 g. Ag or 16.988 g. AgNO$_3$ per liter. The silver nitrate salt, dried at 120°C., or pure metallic silver may be taken, the required weight of the latter being dissolved in nitric acid and made to volume, or 17.1 g. of the salt dissolved in distilled water and made to 1000 ml.

[1] Liebig's Ann. d. Chem., **190,** 1; Sutton, Volumetric Analysis; Z. anorg. Chem., **63,** 330, 1909.

The solution is adjusted to exact decinormal strength by standardizing against an 0.1 $N$ sodium chloride solution, containing 5.846 g. of pure NaCl per liter.

**Ferric Indicator.**—Saturated solution of ferric ammonium alum. Should this not be available, $FeSO_4$ may be oxidized with nitric acid, and the solution evaporated with an excess of $H_2SO_4$ to expel the nitrous fumes. A 10% solution is desired. Five ml. of either of these reagents are taken for each titration.

**Pure Nitric Acid.**—This should be free from the lower oxides of nitrogen. Pure nitric acid is diluted to contain about 50% $HNO_3$, and boiled until perfectly color-less. The reagent should be kept in the dark. Dilute nitric acid does not inter-fere with the method.

*Procedure.*—To the solution, containing 0.003 to 0.35 g. chlorine, in combination as a chloride, is added sufficient of the pure $HNO_3$ to make the solution acid and about 5 ml. in excess. To the solution, diluted to about 150 ml., is added an excess of standard silver nitrate reagent. The precipitated AgCl is filtered off and washed free of silver nitrate. The filtrate and washings are combined and titrated with standard thiocyanate.[2]

The filtrate from the precipitated chloride is treated with 5 ml. of the ferric solution,[3] and the excess silver determined by addition of the thiocyanate until a permanent reddish-brown color is produced. Each addition of the reagent will produce a temporary reddish-brown color, which immediately fades as long as silver uncombined as thiocyanate remains. The trace of excess produces ferric thiocyanate, the reddish-brown color of this compound being best seen against a white background. From this titration the amount of silver nitrate used by the chloride is ascertained.

$$\text{One ml. } 0.1 \ N \ AgNO_3 = 0.003545 \text{ g. Cl or } 0.005844 \text{ g. NaCl}$$

**Titration without Filtering off the Silver Chloride.**—If 1 ml. of nitrobenzene is added for each 50 mg. of chloride, the solution may be titrated by thiocyanate without filtering off the silver chloride.[4] The solution containing 48 to 260 mg. of chloride in a volume of 25–50 ml. acidified with 8–10 drops of concentrated $HNO_3$ is treated with excess of silver nitrate and the amount of nitrobenzene above stated, shaken in a glass-stoppered bottle until spongy flakes of AgCl are obtained, and then titrated with thiocyanate after adding ferric alum indicator.

## SCHÖNIGER COMBUSTION METHOD *

By this method chlorine is determined in a wide variety of materials by burning them in a closed flask filled with oxygen. It has the advantage of speed and ready adaptability to a micro or semi-micro scale. The method is useful for the determination of bromine, iodine and sulfur as well. (See Chapter on Sulfur.) The sample is wrapped in filter paper attached to a platinum wire sealed in the

---

[2] Time is saved by filtering, through a dry filter paper, only a portion of the mixture made to a definite volume, and titrating an aliquot portion. The first 10–15 ml. of the filtrate are rejected.

[3] Upon addition of the ferric solution no color should develop. If a reddish or yel-lowish color results, more nitric acid is required to destroy this. The amount of nitric acid does not affect results when within reasonable limits.

[4] Method of Caldwell, J. R., and Moyer, H. V., Ind. Eng. Chem., Anal. Ed., **7**, 38, 1935.

* Schöniger, Microchim., Acta, 1956, 859.

stopper of a flask, and the paper is ignited immediately before placing the stopper; the products of combustion being dissolved in a solution placed in the flask.

*Apparatus:* **Conical Flask,** 250–1,000 ml., with a ground-glass stopper fitted with a platinum wire coming to about the middle of the flask. The sample is attached to the end of the wire by twisting it or clamping it to the wire by platinum gauze.

*Reagents.* **Oxygen Supply.**—Tank oxygen is preferred, although its purification by passage through solid NaOH is desirable.

**Hydrogen Peroxide (30%).**

**Mercuric Oxycyanide Solution, Standard.** Shake 20 g. of mercuric oxycyanide with 1 liter of distilled water until saturated. Filter, and store in a brown bottle.

**Methyl Red-Methylene Blue Indicator.** Shake 0.125 g. of methyl red with 50 ml. of 90% alcohol until dissolved. Also dissolve 0.083 g. of methylene blue in 50 ml. of 90% alcohol. Mix equal parts of these solutions before use.

**Sulfuric Acid Solution, 2 N.**

**Sulfuric Acid Solution, 0.01 N.**

**Sodium Hydroxide Solution, 2 N.**

**Sodium Hydroxide Solution, 0.01 N.**

**Sodium Chloride Solution, Standard 0.01 N.**

*Procedure.*—Weigh on a small piece of Whatman No. 44 filter paper (3 x 3 cm) 10–100 micrograms of sample, depending upon the expected chlorine content. Fold and cut the paper so as to leave hanging a short end. Attach the folded paper to the wire. Place in the flask 10 ml. of water, 2 ml. of 2 N NaOH and 3–5 drops of hydrogen peroxide. Pass a rapid current of oxygen into the flask until all air has been displaced. Ignite the short end of the paper immediately, place the stopper in the flask. It is well to tilt the flask so that the solution wets the edge of the stopper to make sure that it is completely sealed. After combustion has ended, shake the flask frequently for 10 minutes. Remove the stopper and rinse it into the flask with water. Boil the solution for 5 minutes to remove the peroxide, cool, add 5–8 drops of indicator, neutralize with 2 N sulfuric acid, and determine the chlorine by the following method.†

The color of the solution should match that of a standard prepared by adding the same amount of indicator (5–8 drops) to a volume of distilled water equal to that of the solution under analysis. If it does not, adjust the acidity of the latter with 0.01 N sodium hydroxide or 0.01 N sulfuric acid, or adjust its color with additional indicator, whichever is necessary. Add to the solution under analysis 10.00 ml. of the mercuric oxycyanide solution, and titrate with 0.01 N sulfuric acid until the color of the solution again matches that of the standard. Now add to the standard solution 10.00 ml. of the mercuric oxycyanide solution and the same amount of 0.01 N sulfuric acid as used in the foregoing titration. Titrate the standard solution with 0.01 N sodium chloride until it again matches the color of solution under analysis. This titer is the amount of chloride contained in the original sample.

## COMPLEXIMETRIC TITRATION OF CHLORIDE

Mercuric nitrate is used as a reagent to complex chloride. The first excess of free mercuric ion is indicated by the transformation of the color of the mixed indicator diphenylcarbazone-bromophenol blue from yellow to violet. Other halogen ions, thiocyanate ion, etc., interfere. Ferric and chromate ions react with

† Viebock, Ber., **65,** 496, 1932.

diphenylcarbazone and should be removed prior to the titration. Many common ions do not interfere; these include nitrate, sulfate, phosphate, magnesium, calcium, or aluminum, even in concentrations as great as that of the chloride.

**Reagents. 0.025 N Mercuric Nitrate Solution.**—Dissolve 4.17 g. $Hg(NO_3)_2 \cdot \frac{1}{2}H_2O$ in water and dilute to 1 liter. Standardize this solution against 5.00-ml. aliquots of an accurately prepared 0.1 N sodium chloride solution.

**Mixed Indicator Solution.**—Dissolve 0.5 g. C.P. crystalline diphenylcarbazone and 0.05 g. crystalline bromophenol blue in 100 ml. 95% ethanol.

**Procedure.**—Pipette an aliquot of an aqueous solution of the sample, containing not over 20 mg. of chloride, into a 250-ml. beaker or porcelain casserole and dilute with distilled water to about 100 ml. Add 5 drops of the mixed indicator and adjust the acidity of the solution by the dropwise addition of 0.05 N nitric acid until the color changes to yellow. Then add 1 ml. of this acid in excess. If, on the addition of the indicator to the solution, a yellow color forms, dilute sodium hydroxide (chloride free) should be added until the color is blue-violet. The solution can now be acidified to the proper pH by the addition of 0.05 N nitric acid. Add the mercuric nitrate solution slowly to the yellow, acidified solution until a blue-violet color persists throughout the solution. Record the volume of titrant used and calculate the milligrams of chloride in the aliquot taken,

$$\text{Mg. of chloride} = \text{ml. of } Hg(NO_3)_2 \times N \times 35.45.$$

## DETERMINATION OF CHLORINE IN A NEUTRAL SOLUTION, SILVER CHROMATE METHOD

The method, worked out by Fr. Mohr, is applicable for determination of chlorine in water or in neutral solutions containing small amounts of chlorine; the element should be present combined as a soluble chloride. Advantage is taken of the fact that silver combines with chlorine in presence of a chromate, $Ag_2CrO_4$ being decomposed as follows: $Ag_2CrO_4 + 2NaCl \rightarrow 2AgCl + Na_2CrO_4$. When all the chlorine has gone into combination as AgCl, an excess of $K_2CrO_4$ immediately forms the red $Ag_2CrO_4$,[5] which shows the reaction of $AgNO_3$ with the chloride to be complete.

**Reagents. 0.1 N Silver Nitrate Solution.**—Theoretically 16.988 g. $AgNO_3$ per liter are required. In practice 17.1 g. of the salt are dissolved per 1000 ml. and the solution adjusted against an 0.1 N NaCl solution containing 5.846 g. NaCl per liter.

**Potassium Chromate.**—Saturated solution.

**Procedure.**—To the neutral solution are added 2 or 3 drops of the potassium chromate solution. A glass cell[6] (or a 50-ml. beaker) is filled to about 1 cm. in depth with water tinted to the same color as the solution being titrated. The cell is placed on a clear glass plate half covering the casserole containing the sample. The standard silver solution is now added to the chloride solution from a burette until a faint blood-red tinge is produced, the red change being easily detected by looking through the blank, colored cell.

$$\text{One ml. 0.1 } N \text{ } AgNO_3 = 0.003545 \text{ g. Cl.}$$

[5] Six parts $Ag_2CrO_4$ dissolved in 100,000 parts $H_2O$ at 15.5°C.—W. G. Young, Analyst, **18**, 125.

[6] Depré, Analyst, **5**, 123.

NOTES.—Chlorides having an acid reaction ($AlCl_3$) are treated with an excess of neutral solution of sodium acetate and then titrated with silver nitrate.

Elements whose ions form colored solutions with chlorine are precipitated from the solution by sodium hydroxide or potassium carbonate, and the filtrate, faintly acidified with acetic acid, is titrated as usual.

Free hydrochloric acid is neutralized with ammonium hydroxide and titrated.

It is advisable to titrate the sample under the same conditions as those observed during standardization. The solution should be kept to small bulk and low temperature for accuracy on account of the solubility of the silver chromate.

Free chlorine should be converted to a chloride before titration. This may be accomplished, as stated under preparation of the sample, by boiling with ammonium hydroxide. Free chlorine may be determined by sweeping the gas, by means of a current of air, into a solution containing potassium iodide, the liberated iodine titrated by 0.1 $N$ thiosulfate, $Na_2S_2O_3$, and the equivalent chlorine estimated.

## ADSORPTION INDICATOR METHOD (FAJANS)

A 0.2% alcoholic solution of fluorescein, or a 0.2% aqueous solution of sodium fluoresceinate (Uranin) is used as indicator.[7] 1.5–6 drops of the indicator are added per 10 ml. of the neutral halide solution. Titration is made with standard silver nitrate until the precipitate suddenly appears reddish. In more dilute solutions the color change and the coagulation coincide. This indicator is not satisfactory for solutions of chloride content less than 0.005 $N$, as for example, drinking water. With *dichlorfluorescein* as indicator, solutions 0.025 $N$ in chloride may be titrated satisfactorily down to pH 4, or 0.0005 $N$ solutions at pH 7.[8] Not more than 2–4 drops of a 0.1% aqueous solution of the sodium salt of dichlorfluorescein need be used per 50 ml. of a very dilute chloride solution; in other cases 2 drops of indicator are added per 10 ml. of halide solution. In the very dilute solutions the end point is given by a distinct change to an orange shade. The rose or reddish tints appear beyond the end point.[9]

## DETERMINATION OF FREE CHLORINE

The determination depends upon the reaction $Cl_2 + 2I^- \rightarrow I_2 + 2Cl^-$. The iodine liberated by the chlorine is titrated with $Na_2S_2O_3$ and the equivalent Cl calculated.

*Procedure.*—A measured amount of the chlorine water is added to a solution of potassium iodide in a glass-stoppered bottle by means of a pipette, the delivery tip of which is just above the surface of the iodide solution. The bottle is then closed and the contents vigorously shaken. The liberated iodine is titrated with tenth-normal sodium thiosulfate ($2S_2O_3^- + I_2 \rightarrow S_4O_6^- + 2I^-$). When the yellow color of the iodine has become faint, a little starch solution is added and the titration completed to the fading out of the blue color.

One ml. 0.1 $N$ $Na_2S_2O_3$ = 0.003546 g. Cl

## NEPHELOMETRIC ESTIMATION OF CHLORIDE

Tubes containing turbid suspensions of silver chloride are viewed at right angles to the direction of the incident light in a suitable instrument. The intensity of the light transmitted to the eye or a photocell is compared with that from a stand-

[7] Fajans, K., and Wolf, H., Z. anorg. allgem. Chem., **137**, 221, 1924.

[8] Kolthoff, I. M., Lauer, W. M., and Sunde, C. J., J. Am. Chem. Soc., **51**, 3273, 1929.

[9] Fajans, Neuere Massanalytische Methoden, Vol. XXXIII, Die Chemische Analyse, Margosches-Böttger, F. Enke, Stuttgart, 4th Edition, 1956.

ard.[10] The following procedure is based on a critical study of the process by Kolthoff and Yutzy.[11] The method agrees well with electrometric procedures.[12]

**Reagents.** **Silver Nitrate Solution (0.5 N).**—Dissolve 8.5 g. of $AgNO_3$ in 100 ml. of distilled water. Keep in dark-brown bottle.

**Nitric Acid Solution (0.5 N).**—Add one volume concentrated $HNO_3$ to 31 volumes distilled $H_2O$.

**Standard Chloride Solution (0.01 mg. chloride per ml.).**—Dissolve 0.1648 g. of NaCl in distilled water and dilute to 1 liter. This solution contains 0.1 mg. Cl per ml. and a 10 ml. aliquot of it is diluted to 100 ml. to produce the standard solution containing 0.01 mg. Cl per ml.

**Procedure.**—Tubes are prepared with 25 ml. of alcohol, 1 ml. of 0.5 N silver nitrate and 5 ml. of 0.5 N nitric acid. Then ten (10.00) ml. of unknown and standard chloride solutions are added to separate tubes with shaking. After standing 1 hour in the dark, the unknown and standard solutions are compared in a suitable instrument. For ratios of standard and unknown between 1.5 and 0.7 the concentration of chloride in the unknown may be calculated from the inverse proportion between depths of standard and unknown that match in intensity of light diffracted or reflected at right angles to the incident light.

The preparation of the suspensions is more critical than other points in the procedure. If the unknown contains sulfate, it is recommended that sulfate be added to the standard at 0.01 N concentration. If the sulfate concentration is greater than 0.3 N the suspension of silver chloride coagulates. Potassium or barium nitrate up to 1 N does not seriously affect the procedure.

**Alternate Procedure (Approximate).**—If less accuracy is required proceed as follows: Transfer the sample to a 50-ml. cylinder, add an equal volume of water containing the same impurities to another cylinder. Dilute both with distilled water to 20–30 ml. and add 5 ml. concentrated nitric acid and 2 ml. 0.1 gelatin solution. Dilute the sample to 49 ml., add 1 ml. of 1.7% $AgNO_3$ solution and mix. Dilute the standard to 45 ml., add 1 ml. of 1.7% $AgNO_3$ solution, mix, and add the standard NaCl solution (0.01 mg. chloride per ml.) to this standard until it matches the sample in the nephelometer. Then chloride content of sample = volume of standard NaCl × 0.01 mg.

## DETERMINATIONS IN SPECIFIC SUBSTANCES

### COLORIMETRIC ESTIMATION OF CHLORINE IN WATER

#### o-TOLIDINE METHOD FOR TOTAL FREE AND COMBINED AVAILABLE CHLORINE

The method makes use of the fact that when water containing free chlorine is treated with o-tolidine reagent, a definite color is obtained. Small amounts of free chlorine give a yellow, and larger amounts an orange color. The quantitative estimation is carried out by comparing this color with color standards representing definite amounts of free chlorine.

This method is most useful for chlorine concentrations below 0.01 g. per liter.

[10] Richards, T. W., and Wells, P. V., Am. Chem. J., **31**, 235, 1904; Wells, P. V., Chem. Reviews, **3**, 331, 1927.

[11] Lamb, A. B., et al., J. Am. Chem. Soc., **42**, 251, 1920; Kolthoff, I. M., and Yutzy, H., J. Am. Chem. Soc., **55**, 1915, 1933.

[12] Furman, N. H., and Low, G. W., Jr., J. Am. Chem. Soc., **57**, 1588, 1935.

It requires pH values of 1.3 or lower when the readings are taken and is sensitive to interference from organic substances, nitrites (over 0.0001 g. per liter) and certain metal ions, of which $Fe^{+3}$ (over 0.0003 g. per liter) $MnO_4^=$ (over 0.00001 g. per liter) are most likely to occur.

*Apparatus.* **Light Source.**—This should be north daylight, or if a more dependable source is required, fluorescent daylight lamp.

**Filter Photometer.**—An instrument with a light path of at least 1 cm, equipped with a blue filter (maximum transmittance about 490 m$\mu$, and a violet filter (maximum transmittance about 400–450 m$\mu$). A spectrophotometer may be used instead. Modifications of this method for direct visual comparison with standards are also in use.

**Nessler tubes, 100 ml.**

*Preparation of Standards.*—Chlorine-demand-free water is required for this purpose. It may be prepared by passing chlorine through the water to a concentration of at least 0.001 g. per liter, allowing it to stand for 12 hours or longer, and exposing it to ultraviolet light or sunlight until this chlorine has been eliminated. A similar preliminary treatment should be applied to the glassware by keeping in it water having a chlorine concentration of at least 0.01 g. per liter for at least three hours, and washing with chlorine-free water.

*Reagents.* *o*-**Tolidine Reagent.**—Prepared by dissolving 1.35 g. *o*-tolidine dihydrochloride in 500 ml. of distilled water, and add it to a mixture of 150 ml. concentrated HCl and 350 ml. of distilled water. Store in the dark.

A strong chlorine solution is prepared from chlorine water or household hypochlorite solution by diluting to a strength in the range from 0.1 to 1.0 g. per liter depending upon the required analysis.

*Preparation of Calibration Curve.*—The calibration curve is prepared by taking readings on a series of standards at various dilutions throughout the range of concentrations of the sample. Using the photometer and filters, readings are taken with the violet filter (400 m$\mu$–450 m$\mu$) for chlorine concentrations below 0.0015 g. per liter, while the blue filter (490 m$\mu$) is preferred for concentrations of chlorine running from 0.0005 to 0.007 mg. per liter. If a spectrophotometer is used, the wavelengths of 435 m$\mu$ and 490 m$\mu$ are recommended for the low and high concentrations respectively.

Readings on the photometer should be taken at the time of maximum color development, which is relatively shorter in standards prepared from chlorine water than in those from hypochlorite solutions. Take readings within five minutes after full color development.

*Procedure.*—The analytical procedure is the same as that used in standardization. It consists of placing 5 ml. of the *o*-tolidine reagent in a 100-ml. Nessler tube, adding the sample to the mark, and mixing. The photometer readings are taken, as in standardization, at the time of maximum color development.

## *o*-TOLIDINE-ARSENITE METHOD FOR FREE CHLORINE AND COMBINED AVAILABLE CHLORINE

This method is a modification of the preceding *o*-tolidine method. By this method, determination can be made of the relative amounts of free available chlorine, combined available chlorine and color products by interfering substances.

*Apparatus.*—Same as in the preceding method.

*Reagents.* *o*-**Tolidine Reagent.**—Same as in preceding method.

**Sodium Arsenite Reagent.**—Dissolve 5 g. of sodium arsenite in distilled water and dilute to 1 liter.

*Procedure.*—To a 100-ml. Nessler tube add 5 ml. of the *o*-tolidine reagent, followed by 90 ml. of the water sample. Mix, add quickly 5 ml. of the sodium arsenite reagent and mix rapidly, and take photometer reading at once. Designate this reading as *x*.

To a second 100-ml. Nessler tube add 5 ml. of the sodium arsenite reagent and 90 ml. of the water sample. Mix and add at once 5 ml. of the *o*-tolidine reagent. Take the photometer reading at once and then again after 5 minutes. Designate the readings as $y_1$ and $y_2$.

To a third Nessler tube add 5 ml. of *o*-tolidine reagent and 95 ml. of water sample, mix quickly, and take photometer reading in 5 minutes. Designate this reading as *z*.

Convert these four readings into equivalent chlorine concentrations by use of the calibration curve. Designate these values, now expressed in g. per liter, as $X$, $Y_1$, $Y_2$ and $Z$.

**Calculations.**—Free Available Chlorine (in g. per l.) = $X - Y_1$.

Total Residual Chlorine (in g. per l.) = $Z - Y_2$.

Combined Available Chlorine (in g. per l.) = (Total Residual Chlorine) − (Free Available Chlorine).

## DETERMINATION OF HYPOCHLOROUS ACID IN THE PRESENCE OF CHLORINE

The determination depends upon the reactions:

$$2I^- + ClO^- + H^+ \rightarrow I_2 + Cl^- + OH^-$$

$$2I^- + Cl_2 \rightarrow 2Cl^- + I_2$$

The alkali liberated by hypochlorous acid and the total iodine are determined and the calculations made for each of the constituents.

*Procedure.*—A measured volume of 0.1 $N$ HCl is added to a potassium iodide solution. To this the sample containing the hypochlorous acid and chlorine are added. The liberated iodine is titrated with 0.1 $N$ $Na_2S_2O_3$. (The addition of starch is omitted.) The colorless solution is treated with methyl orange indicator and the excess of hydrochloric acid is titrated with 0.1 $N$ NaOH. The potassium hydroxide, produced by the action of the hypochlorous acid upon the iodide, requires half as much acid for neutralization as the volume of thiosulfate required by the iodine set free by the hypochlorous acid.

**Calculation.**—The ml. back titration with NaOH are subtracted from the total ml. of HCl taken = ml. HCl required by NaOH liberated by HOCl = $A$. Then $2A$ ml. = ml. $Na_2S_2O_3$ required by the I liberated by HOCl. Ml. $A \times 0.005247$ = gram HOCl. The total $Na_2S_2O_3$ titration minus $2A$ ml. (due to the iodine liberated by HOCl) = ml. $Na_2S_2O_3$ that are required by the iodine liberated by chlorine. The ml. thus required multiplied by 0.003546 = grams chlorine in the sample taken.

## GRAVIMETRIC DETERMINATION OF CHLORIC ACID, HClO₃, OR CHLORATES, BY REDUCTION TO CHLORIDE AND PRECIPITATION AS SILVER CHLORIDE

*Reduction of the Chlorate.*—Among the reductants used in analysis of chlorates the following deserve special mention: 1. Sulfurous Acid.[13]  2. Ferrous sulfate. 3. Zinc.

1. About 0.2 to 0.5 g. of the salt is dissolved in 100 ml. of distilled water and either $SO_2$ gas passed into the solution or sulfurous acid in solution added in excess. The solution is now boiled to expel $SO_2$ and the chloride precipitated as AgCl in presence of free nitric acid.

2. The sample in 100 ml. of distilled water is treated with 50 ml. of crystallized ferrous sulfate (10% solution), heated to boiling, with constant stirring, and then boiled for fifteen minutes. Nitric acid is added to the cooled solution, until the deposited basic ferric salt is dissolved. The chloride is now precipitated as AgCl, as usual.

3. The dilute chlorate solution is treated with acetic acid until it reacts distinctly acid. An excess of powdered zinc is now added and the solution boiled for an hour. Nitric acid is added to the cooled solution in sufficient quantity to dissolve the zinc remaining. The solution is filtered, if necessary, and the chloride precipitated as usual.

Factors.  $AgCl \times 0.855 = KClO_3$
$\times 0.2474 = Cl$

NOTE.— In absence of cyanides, carbonates and acids decomposed and volatilized by hydrochloric acid, or oxides, hydroxides and substances other than chlorates that may be decomposed or acted upon by this acid, evaporation of the salt with HCl and ignition of the residue, or addition of an excess of ammonium chloride, and subsequent heating will give a residue of chloride, which may be determined as usual and the equivalent chlorate calculated. Method by L. Blangey.

The methods may be used in determining chlorates in presence of perchlorates,[14] only the former being reduced to chlorides. Outline of the procedure is given later.

## GRAVIMETRIC DETERMINATION OF PERCHLORIC ACID BY REDUCTION TO CHLORIDE

A perchlorate ignited with about four times its weight of ammonium chloride in a platinum dish may be decomposed to chloride. A second treatment is usually necessary to change the salt completely. Platinum appears to act as a catalyser, so must be added in solution if a porcelain crucible is used.

*Procedure.*—About 0.2 to 0.5 g. of potassium perchlorate is intimately mixed with about 2 g. of ammonium chloride in a platinum crucible, the latter then covered with a watch glass and the charge ignited gently for one and a half to two hours, the temperature being below the fusing-point of the residual chloride (otherwise the platinum would be attacked). A second addition of ammonium chloride is made and the mix again heated as before. The resulting chloride may now be determined as usual.

Factors.  $AgCl \times 0.9666 = KClO_4$;  $AgCl \times 0.2474 = Cl$.

[13] Blattner and Brassuer, Chem. Zeit. Rep., **24**, 793, 1900.
[14] Perchlorates are decomposed by ignition with $NH_4Cl$ in presence of platinum.

## DETERMINATION OF CHLORATES AND PERCHLORATES IN PRESENCE OF ONE ANOTHER

*Procedure.*—1. A portion of the sample is treated with about twelve times its weight of ammonium chloride in a platinum dish (or in a porcelain dish with the addition of 1 ml. of hydroplatinic acid), and the mixture heated according to the procedure given for perchloric acid. The resulting chloride is determined as usual. This is the total chlorine in the sample.

2. In a second portion the chlorate is reduced by means of $SO_2$ or $FeSO_4$, according to directions given for determination of chloric acid, and chlorine determined. The chlorine of this portion is subtracted from the total chlorine, the difference multiplied by 3.9076 = $KClO_4$. The chlorine of the second portion multiplied by 3.4563 = $KClO_3$, or AgCl in (2) subtracted from AgCl of (1) and the difference multiplied by 0.9666 = $KClO_4$. AgCl of (2) multiplied by 0.855 = $KClO_3$.

## DETERMINATION OF CHLORIDES, CHLORATES, AND PERCHLORATES IN THE PRESENCE OF ONE ANOTHER

(1) *Total Chlorine.*—If the determination is made in the valuation of niter a 5-gram sample is fused with about three times its weight of alkali carbonate [15] or calcium hydroxide,[16] in a platinum dish, whereby all the chlorine compounds are converted to chlorides. If the compounds are present as alkali salts, fusion with ammonium chloride in a platinum dish may be made and the total chlorides determined after dissolving the residue in nitric acid.

(2) *Chloride and Chlorate.*—If the estimation is being made in niter, 5 grams of the salt are treated with 10 grams of zinc dust (Cl-free) in presence of 150 ml. of 1% acetic acid. The solution is boiled for half an hour, filtered, and the chloride determined. In a mixture of alkali salts of hydrochloric, chloric, and perchloric acids, reduction may be accomplished by passing in $SO_2$ gas or by adding ferrous sulfate and boiling according to directions given for the determination of chlorate. The chloride now present in the residue is due to the reduced chlorate and to the original chloride of the sample.

(3) The chloride of the sample is determined by acidifying the salt with nitric acid (cold) and precipitating as AgCl.

*Perchlorate.*—The chloride and chlorate in terms of chlorine are subtracted from total chlorine of (1) and multiplied by the factor for the salt desired.

*Chlorate.*—The chlorine of (3) is subtracted from chlorine of (2) and multiplied by the factor for the compound desired.

*Chloride.*—The AgCl of (3) is multiplied by the appropriate factor.

Factors.  AgCl $\times$ 0.2474 = Cl      Cl $\times$ 3.4568 = $KClO_3$
$\times$ 0.2544 = HCl      $\times$ 3.9081 = $KClO_4$
$\times$ 0.4078 = NaCl      $\times$ 2.1029 = KCl
$\times$ 0.5202 = KCl      $\times$ 3.0023 = $NaClO_3$
$\times$ 0.8551 = $KClO_3$      $\times$ 3.4536 = $NaClO_4$
$\times$ 0.9667 = $KClO_4$      $\times$ 1.6485 = NaCl

[15] Mennick, Chem. Zeit. Rep., **22**, 117, 1898.
[16] Blattner and Brasseur, Chem. Zeit. Rep., **24**, 793, 1900.

## DETERMINATION OF CHLORIDE, BROMIDE, AND IODIDE IN THE PRESENCE OF EACH OTHER

The procedure in Bekk's modification of Baubigny's method.[17]

*Procedure.*—The halogens are precipitated with an excess of silver nitrate, filtered onto asbestos or glass wool, washed, dried, and weighed as total halogens as silver salts. A second portion is precipitated and the moist, washed silver salts (0.3–0.4 gram) are treated with a solution of 2 g. of potassium dichromate in 30 ml. of concentrated sulfuric acid at 95°C., and digested for thirty minutes. By this procedure the iodine is oxidized to iodic acid ($HIO_3$) and chlorine together with bromine is liberated in form of the free halogen. Toward the end of the reaction a stream of air is led through the solution to remove any chlorine and bromine. This is now diluted to 300 to 400 ml., filtered, and the iodic acid reduced by adding, drop by drop, with constant stirring, a concentrated solution of sodium sulfite, $Na_2SO_3$, until a faint odor of $SO_2$ remains after standing ten minutes. (Under certain conditions an excess may result in a partial reduction of the silver iodide.) The precipitated silver salt is filtered, washed with hot, dilute nitric acid, dried, and weighed as AgI. The filtrate containing the silver, formerly with the chlorine and bromine, is treated with potassium iodide in sufficient amount to completely precipitate the silver as AgI. This is filtered, washed, and weighed. From the three weights the chlorine, bromine, and iodine can be easily calculated.

NOTE.—Bekk claims an accuracy within less than 0.15%.

## DETERMINATION OF FREE HYDROCHLORIC ACID

In absence of other free acids, hydrochloric acid may be accurately determined by titration with standard alkali.

One ml. 1 $N$ NaOH = 0.03647 g. HCl

## DETERMINATION OF CHLORIDE AND CYANIDE IN PRESENCE OF ONE ANOTHER

The cyanide is determined by Liebig's method described on page 761.

*Procedure.*—To the neutral solution is added sufficient 0.1 $N$ silver nitrate to combine with all of the cyanide and chloride present and an excess. The solution is acidified with nitric acid and diluted to a definite volume and a portion filtered through a dry filter. A portion of the filtrate, an aliquot of the whole, is titrated with standard thiocyanate solution (page 329) using ferric alum indicator and the excess of the $AgNO_3$ added thus ascertained. From this the amount combined with the CN and Cl is known. The equivalent required by the cyanide is deducted, the difference being due to the chloride present in the solution.

1 ml. 0.1 $N$ AgNO₃ = 0.005204 g. CN, or 0.013023 g. KCN, or 0.003545 g. Cl

or 0.005844 g. NaCl, or 0.007456 g. KCl

[17] Bekk, Julius, Chem. Ztg., **39**, 405–6, 1915. C. A., **9**, 2042, 1915.

## DETERMINATION OF CHLORIDE, CYANIDE AND THIOCYANATE IN PRESENCE OF ONE ANOTHER

The cyanide is determined by the method of Liebig described on page 761, and the equivalent $AgNO_3$ required recorded $= A$.

*Procedure.*—An excess of 0.1 $N$ $AgNO_3$ over that required by CN, CNS, and Cl is added and the solution acidified with nitric acid. After making to a definite volume, the solution is filtered through a dry filter, the residue being saved. A portion of the filtrate, an aliquot of the whole solution, is titrated with standard thiocyanate solution using ferric alum indicator (see page 330), the excess of $AgNO_3$ is calculated. The amount combining with CN, CNS, and Cl is now known $= B$.

The silver salts on the filter paper are washed with water and transferred by means of concentrated nitric acid to a flask and boiled for an hour. The cyanide and thiocyanate are decomposed and dissolved, while the silver chloride remains unchanged. The sulfuric acid formed by oxidation of the thiocyanate is precipitated by barium nitrate (as $BaSO_4$). Without removing the precipitates AgCl and $BaSO_4$ the silver nitrate in this solution is determined by Volhard's method (page 329) and the $AgNO_3$ required by thiocyanic acid and cyanide thus ascertained $= C$.

By deducting the $AgNO_3$ of $A$ from $C$ the silver nitrate required by thiocyanic acid is determined.

Deducting the $AgNO_3$ required by CN and CNS ($C$) from the total $AgNO_3$ required by CN, CNS and Cl ($B$), the amount required by chlorine is obtained.

## EVALUATION OF BLEACHING POWDER, CHLORIDE OF LIME, FOR AVAILABLE CHLORINE

When chloride of lime is treated with water, it gives a solution of calcium hypochlorite, $Ca(OCl)_2$, and calcium chloride, $CaCl_2$. The calcium hypochlorite constitutes the bleaching agent. The technical analysis is confined to the determination of available chlorine, which is expressed as percentage by weight of the bleaching powder.

*Procedure.*—Ten grams of the sample are washed into a mortar and ground with water, the residue allowed to settle and the supernatant liquor poured into a liter flask. The residue is repeatedly ground and extracted with water until the whole of the chloride is transferred to the flask. The combined extracts are made up to 1000 ml.

To 50-ml. portions (0.5 g.) of the solution, 3–4 g. of solid potassium iodide and 100 ml. of water are added and the solution acidified with acetic acid. Iodine equivalent to the available chlorine is liberated. This is titrated with 0.1 $N$ arsenious acid.

One ml. 0.1 $N$ arsenious acid $= 0.003545$ g. Cl. Weight of Cl (in g.) multiplied by $200 = \%Cl$.

NOTE.—In the analysis of compounds containing hypochlorites and chlorides, the conversion of hypochlorites to chlorides by heating with hydrogen peroxides is a great convenience.

For instance in the analysis of bleach liquors, washes, etc., the (OCl) and Cl may be very easily and quickly determined by titrating an aliquot with $As_2O_3$ and then a similar aliquot with $AgNO_3$ after converting all the OCl to Cl by warming with $H_2O_2$.

## THE ANALYSES OF BLEACH LIQUORS

*Preparation of Samples.*—Pipette a 25-ml. sample of strong (15%) bleach liquor or 75 ml. of weak (5%) bleach liquor into a suitable-size, tared weighing bottle and weigh to 0.1 mg. Transfer the sample to a 250-ml. volumetric flask and dilute to 250 ml. with distilled water. Mix thoroughly and use aliquot portions of this sample solution for analyses.

### DETERMINATION OF AVAILABLE CHLORINE AND HYPOCHLORITE

This method involves the determination of available chlorine present by adding the sample to an acid solution of potassium iodide whereby an equivalent amount of iodine is liberated. This free iodine is determined by titration with standard sodium thiosulfate solution.

**Reagents.** **Concentrated Hydrochloric Acid (C.P.).**

**Potassium Iodide Crystals (A.R.).**

**Standard 0.1 *N* Sodium Thiosulfate.**—Corrected to 20°C.

**Starch Indicator Solution.**

*Procedure.*—Pipette a 10-ml. aliquot portion of the sample solution into a 250 ml. flask or beaker containing 50 ml. of distilled water, approximately 2 g. of potassium iodide crystals, and 2 ml. of concentrated hydrochloric acid. Mix the solution thoroughly. Titrate the liberated iodine with standard 0.1 *N* sodium thiosulfate solution until the mixture is straw-yellow in color. Add 5 ml. of starch indicator solution and continue titrating until the dark blue color of the iodine-starch complex disappears. Observe the temperature of the standard sodium thiosulfate solution and correct the volume consumed for the titration to 20°C. (See Temperature Correction Table.)

**Calculation.**—

$$\text{Available Chlorine (grams/liter)} = \frac{A \times N \times 0.03546 \times 1000}{\frac{\text{ml. Aliquot}}{250} \times \text{ml. Bleach Liquor Sample}}$$

$$\text{Available Chlorine (Trade \%)} = \frac{\text{Available Chlorine (g./liter)}}{10}$$

$$\text{\% NaOCl (by weight)} = \frac{A \times N \times 0.03723 \times 100}{\frac{\text{ml. Aliquot}}{250} \times \text{Sample Wt.}}$$

$$\text{\% Ca(OCl)}_2 \text{ (by weight)} = \frac{A \times N \times 0.03575 \times 100}{\frac{\text{ml. Aliquot}}{250} \times \text{Sample Wt.}}$$

$A$ = ml. of standard sodium thiosulfate consumed.

$N$ = normality of standard sodium thiosulfate.

Temperature Correction Table

| Temperature °C. | Water and 0.1 N Solutions (ml./liter) |
|---|---|
| 15 | +0.77 |
| 16 | +0.64 |
| 17 | +0.49 |
| 18 | +0.34 |
| 19 | +0.17 |
| 20 | 0 |
| 21 | −0.19 |
| 22 | −0.39 |
| 23 | −0.60 |
| 24 | −0.81 |
| 25 | −1.04 |
| 26 | −1.28 |
| 27 | −1.53 |
| 28 | −1.80 |
| 29 | −2.05 |
| 30 | −2.33 |

The above gives the correction to be added per liter to the observed volume of water or standard 0.1 $N$ solution, to give the volume at the standard temperature 20°C. Conversely, by subtracting the corrections from the volume desired at 20°C., the volume that must be measured out at the designated temperature in order to give the desired volume at 20°C. will be obtained. The volumes are measured in glass apparatus having a coefficient of cubical expansion of 0.000025 per degree C.

## CHLORIDE

This method involves the reduction of the hypochlorite present to chloride. This mixture is titrated for chloride by the Volhard method and correction made for the chloride produced in the reduction reaction.

*Reagents.* **Dilute Nitric Acid 1:1 (C.P.).**

**Standard 0.1 $N$ Silver Nitrate Solution.**—Corrected to 20°C.

**3% Hydrogen Peroxide Solution (U.S.P.).**

**Standard 0.1 $N$ Potassium Thiocyanate.**—Corrected to 20°C.

**10% Ferric Nitrate Indicator Solution.**

*Procedure.*—Pipette a 10-ml. aliquot portion of the sample solution into a 250-ml. beaker and add 35 ml. of 3% hydrogen peroxide solution. Add a strip of litmus paper and acidify the mixture with dilute nitric acid. Cool to room temperature and add 2 ml. of 10% ferric nitrate indicator solution. Add 0.2 ml. of standard 0.1 $N$ potassium thiocyanate solution. Titrate slowly with standard 0.1 $N$ silver nitrate solution until the red color disappears, then add an excess of at least 2 ml. Stir vigorously until the silver chloride coagulates and allow to stand until the supernatant liquid clears. Titrate the excess silver nitrate with standard 0.1 $N$ potassium thiocyanate until a faint rust-red color persists. Correct the volumes of the standard solutions used for titration to 20°C. (See Temperature Correction Table.)

**Calculation.—**

$$\% \text{ NaCl} = \frac{[B - (\frac{1}{2}A \times N)] \times 0.05846 \times 100}{\dfrac{\text{ml. Aliquot}}{250} \times \text{Sample Wt.}}$$

$$\% \text{ CaCl}_2 = \frac{[B - (\frac{1}{2}A \times N)] \times 0.0555 \times 100}{\dfrac{\text{ml. Aliquot}}{250} \times \text{Sample Wt.}}$$

$A$ = ml. of standard sodium thiosulfate consumed in determination of available chlorine.
$N$ = Normality of sodium thiosulfate used in determination of available chlorine.
$B$ = (ml. AgNO$_3$ × normality) − (ml. KCNS × normality).

## CHLORATE

This method involves the reduction of the chlorate and hypochlorite present by an excess of standard sodium arsenite solution and the back titration of the excess with a standard potassium bromate solution. The amount of standard sodium arsenite solution consumed is equivalent to both the chlorate and hypochlorite present in the sample. The chlorate is calculated by correcting this titration for the amount of hypochlorite present.

**Reagent. Concentrated Hydrochloric Acid (C.P.).**
**Standard 0.1 N Sodium Arsenite.—**Corrected to 20°C.
**Standard 0.1 N Potassium Bromate Solution.—**Corrected to 20°C.
**Methyl Orange Indicator Solution.**

**Procedure.—**Measure carefully (2$A$ + 10) ml. of standard 0.1 $N$ sodium arsenite solution from a burette into a 250-ml. wide-mouth Erlenmeyer flask or beaker. ($A$ = ml. of 0.1 $N$ sodium thiosulfate consumed in the determination of available chlorine.) Pipette a 10-ml. aliquot portion of the sample solution into the same flask and add 2 drops of methyl orange indicator solution. Dilute the mixture to 100 ml. with distilled water and add 15 ml. of concentrated hydrochloric acid. Add 4 to 6 glass beads and boil for 2 minutes. Add 7 additional drops of methyl orange indicator solution and, while hot, titrate the mixture slowly with standard 0.1 $N$ potassium bromate solution. One or two drops of methyl orange indicator solution may be added to the mixture, if necessary, just before a colorless end point is reached. Correct the volumes of the standard solutions used for titration to 20°C. (See Temperature Correction Table.)

**Calculation.—**

$$\% \text{ NaClO}_3 = \frac{[C - (A \times N)] \times 0.01774 \times 100}{\dfrac{\text{ml. Aliquot}}{250} \times \text{Sample Wt.}}$$

$$\% \text{ Ca(ClO}_3)_2 = \frac{[C - (A \times N)] \times 0.01725 \times 100}{\dfrac{\text{ml. Aliquot}}{250} \times \text{Sample Wt.}}$$

$A$ = ml. of standard sodium thiosulfate consumed in determination of available chlorine.
$N$ = Normality of sodium thiosulfate used in determination of available chlorine.
$C$ = (ml. NaAsO$_2$ × normality) − (ml. KBrO$_3$ × normality).

*ALKALI*

This method involves the elimination of the hypochlorite present by reduction with hydrogen peroxide and the subsequent titration of the alkali hydroxide and carbonate with standard acid, first to a phenolphthalein end point and then to a methyl orange-xylene cyanol end point.

**Reagent. Standard 0.1 N Hydrochloric Acid.**—Corrected to 20°C.

**Phenolphthalein Indicator Solution.**

**3% Hydrogen Peroxide Solution (U.S.P.).**

**Methyl Orange-Xylene Cyanol Indicator Solution.**—Dissolve 3.00 g. of Xylene Cyanol FF (Eastman Kodak Co.) and 1.33 g. of methyl orange in water and dilute to 1 liter.

**Procedure. Soda Bleach.**—Pipette a 50-ml. aliquot portion of the sample solution into a 250-ml. beaker. Add 20 ml. of 3% hydrogen peroxide solution, mix thoroughly, and titrate immediately with standard 0.1 N hydrochloric acid to the phenolphthalein end point. Note the volume of standard acid required. Add 2 drops of methyl orange-xylene cyanol indicator solution and continue the titration with the standard acid to the end point.

**Calculation.**—

$$\% \text{ NaOH (by weight)} = \frac{[E - 2(E - D)] \times N_2 \times 0.040 \times 100}{\dfrac{\text{ml. Aliquot}}{250} \times \text{Sample Wt.}}$$

$$\text{NaOH (grams/liter)} = \frac{[E - 2(E - D)] \times N_2 \times 0.040 \times 1000}{\dfrac{\text{ml. Aliquot}}{250} \times \text{ml. Bleach Liquor Sample}}$$

$$\% \text{ Na}_2\text{CO}_3 \text{ (by weight)} = \frac{2(E - D) \times N_2 \times 0.053 \times 100}{\dfrac{\text{ml. Aliquot}}{250} \times \text{Sample Wt.}}$$

$$\text{Na}_2\text{CO}_3 \text{ (grams/liter)} = \frac{2(E - D) \times N_2 \times 0.053 \times 1000}{\dfrac{\text{ml. Aliquot}}{250} \times \text{ml. Bleach Liquor Sample}}$$

$D$ = ml. of standard acid consumed for the phenolphthalein end point.
$E$ = ml. of standard acid consumed by the methyl orange-xylene cyanol end point.
$N_2$ = Normality of standard acid.

**Procedure. Calcium Bleach.**—Pipette a 50-ml. aliquot portion of the sample solution into a 250-ml. beaker. Add 20 ml. of 3% hydrogen peroxide solution, mix thoroughly, and titrate immediately with standard 0.1 N hydrochloric acid to the phenolphthalein end point.

**Calculation.**—

$$\% \text{ Ca(OH)}_2 \text{ (by weight)} = \frac{F \times N_2 \times 0.037 \times 100}{\dfrac{\text{ml. Aliquot}}{250} \times \text{Sample Wt.}}$$

$$Ca(OH)_2 \text{ (grams/liter)} = \frac{F \times N_2 \times 0.037 \times 1000}{\dfrac{\text{ml. Aliquot}}{250} \times \text{ml. Bleach Liquor Sample}}$$

$F$ = ml. of standard acid consumed.
$N_2$ = Normality of standard acid.

## CHLORINATED HYDROCARBONS IN AIR

Detection of chlorinated hydrocarbons in air can usually be effected by the Beilstein test.[18] It consists simply of placing a clean copper strip in a gas flame in the air. A *persistent* green color indicates the presence of chlorinated hydrocarbons.

The amount of chlorinated hydrocarbons may be estimated by mixing the air with natural gas, burning it in a microburner in the presence of ammonium carbonate cubes, absorbing the products of combustion and reaction in water, and determining the chloride by the silver thiocyanate-ferric alum method.

*Apparatus.*—The apparatus consists of a microburner so connected that the air to be tested constitutes both the primary and secondary air supply. Natural gas is used as fuel. The burner contains a glass T-tube on which ammonium carbonate cubes may be placed, and it is covered by a trumpet tube which conducts the products of combustion to an absorption column filled with glass beads, and discharging to a beaker. A water connection supplies a small stream of water to the top of the column.

*Procedure.*—Connect the air sample, which is contained in a microburette, to the air supply of the microburner. Place the ammonium carbonate cubes on the T-tube in the microburner, start the stream of water running through the absorption tower. Light the burner, at the same time opening the stopcock at the top of the microburette to displace the air by mercury. When the air is used up, turn off the flame, and wash the absorption tower and trumpet tube until they test negative for chlorides. Determine the total chloride in the combined effluent from the tower and the washings by means of the silver thiocyanate-ferric alum method given earlier in this chapter.

## DETERMINATION OF HALOGENS IN ORGANIC COMPOUNDS

### *METHOD OF CARIUS* [19]

Organic compounds may be decomposed by heating with concentrated nitric acid at high temperatures under pressure. If this heating is conducted in the presence of silver nitrate, the halogen hydride, formed by the action of nitric acid on the organic compound, is converted to the silver halide. This is weighed, or the excess $AgNO_3$ titrated (p. 330). Arsenic, phosphorus, and sulfur are oxidized to arsenic, phosphoric, and sulfuric acids, the metals present being converted to nitrates.

*Procedure.*—About 0.5 to 1 g. of powdered silver nitrate is introduced, by means of a glazed paper funnel, into a heavy-walled, bomb-glass tube, which is sealed at one end and is 50 cm. long, 2 cm. in diameter and about 2 mm. thickness of wall. About 3 ml. of fuming nitric acid (96%), free from chlorine, are introduced by means of a long-stemmed funnel, to avoid wetting the upper portion of the tubing.

[18] Ruigh, Ind. Eng. Chem., Anal. Ed., **11**, 250, 1939.
[19] Ann. d. Chem. u. Pharm., **136**, 129, 1865.

About 0.1 g. of the organic substance, contained in a small-bore, thin-wall, glass tube closed at one end (4–5 cm. long), is introduced into the bomb tube, inclined to one side. The small tube should float in the nitric acid, as it is important that the material should not come in contact with nitric acid until the bomb has been sealed, as loss of halogen is apt to occur with open tubes. The upper end of the bomb is softened in the blast-lamp flame, drawn out to a thick-walled capillary tube and fused.

When cold, the bomb is wrapped in asbestos paper, placed into an iron tube of a bomb furnace and the heat turned on. The heating is so regulated that the temperature is raised to 200°C. in three hours. If a higher temperature is necessary, the heating should be such as to cause a rise of 50°C. in three hours. Substances of the aromatic series require eight to ten hours heating at 250 to 300°C., while aliphatic substances may be decomposed at 200°C. in about four hours.[20] Occasionally it is necessary to relieve the pressure in a tube after heating to 200°C., before taking to a higher temperature, by softening the tip of the cooled bomb in a flame, allowing the accumulated gas to blow out, resealing and again heating to the desired temperature. Evidence of crystals or drops of oil in the glass tube indicates incomplete decomposition. When the bomb is cooled, it is removed by taking out the iron sheath from the furnace and inclining it so that the glass capillary tip slides partly out of the tube. (The eyes should be protected by goggles.) The point of the capillary is held in the flame until the tip softens and the gas pressure is released by blowing through a passage in the softened glass. When the gas has escaped, a scratch with a file is made below the capillary and the tip broken off by touching the scratch with a hot glass rod. The contents of the bomb are poured out into a beaker, the tube washed out with water and the combined solution made to about 300 ml. This is heated to boiling and then allowed to cool. The halide precipitate is filtered through a Gooch crucible, then dried and weighed, or by titrating the excess $AgNO_3$ by Volhard's method, the halide may be estimated.

NOTE.—The amount of $HNO_3$ should not exceed 4 g. per 50-ml. tube, as larger amounts may cause an explosion.

If pieces of glass should be present, the precipitates, AgCl or AgBr, are dissolved in the ammonium hydroxide, filtered and reprecipitated by acidifying with nitric acid. AgI may be dissolved by means of dilute sulfuric acid and zinc. The excess zinc is removed, the glass washed free of iodine, dried and weighed, and its weight subtracted from the original impure AgI, giving the weight of the pure silver iodide.

## SODIUM AND ALCOHOL METHOD (STEPANOV)[21]

A solution of the organic substance in 98% alcohol is treated with a large excess of sodium added in small portions over a period of 30 minutes.

*Procedure.*—Place the substance in a small Erlenmeyer flask, add 20–40 ml. of 98% alcohol, connect the flask to a vertical condenser and warm on a water bath. Add small pieces of sodium (25-fold excess) through the condenser, after the sodium has dissolved, add 20–40 ml. of water and distill off the alcohol. Finish the determination by any standard titrimetric or gravimetric procedure. If *a* represents the

20 Tomicek, O., Chem. Ztg., **49**, 281, 1925. Kingscott, P. C. R., and Knight, R. S. G., Methods of Quant. Org. Anal., Longmans, Green & Co., 1914. Clowes and Coleman, Quant. Chem. Anal., P. Blakiston's Son & Co., 1900.
21 Stepanov, Ber., **31**, 4056, 1906; Tseng, Hu, and Chiang, J. Chinese Chem. Soc., **3**, 223, 1935.

weight of the sample in grams, then the relative amounts of alcohol and sodium should be as follows:

| | Ml. of 98% Alcohol | Sodium to be used, gram |
|---|---|---|
| If chloride is present | $156 \times a$ | $19.5 \times a$ |
| If bromide is present | $68 \times a$ | $8.5 \times a$ |
| If iodide is present | $44 \times a$ | $5.5 \times a$ |

### THE SODIUM BIPHENYL METHOD [22]

Sodium biphenyl or the analogous reagent, sodium naphthalene, offer advantages over the direct treatment of organic compounds with metallic sodium.

*Reagents.* **Sodium Biphenyl Reagent.**—Disperse 58 g. sodium in 300 ml. dry toluene under an atmosphere of nitrogen, with vigorous stirring, in a flask provided with a reflux condenser, and means for warming to melt the sodium. When the dispersion is complete, cool to 10°C. Remove the reflux condenser and add 1250 ml. anhydrous ethylene glycol dimethyl ether. Continue passing the stream of nitrogen slowly through the apparatus. Add with moderate stirring 390 g. biphenyl. During this operation, the reaction vessel must be immersed in a cooling bath, composed of a medium that is not reactive with sodium, e.g., an oil bath. The reaction should be complete in one hour. The reagent will keep for one or two months if protected from moisture and air. It should be stored in small bottles, filled to the top, and tightly closed by foil-lined caps, the bottles being stored in a refrigerator at 5°C. Under these conditions the reagent will keep for as long as a year.

*Procedure.*—Dissolve the weighed sample in 10–15 ml. of water-free toluene, or in halogen-free benzene or ether. In a clean, dry separatory funnel add 20 ml. of the biphenyl reagent, stopper, and shake for 30 seconds. Then invert the separatory funnel and, after a few seconds, open its stopcock to release the pressure resulting from the heat of the reaction. The color should be dark green; if it is brown, add more reagent. After five minutes extract with 20 ml. of water and agitate gently until the excess reagent is destroyed as indicated by disappearance of the dark green color. The lower aqueous layer is drawn off and then two extractions are made with 50-ml. portions of 3 $N$ nitric acid. The chloride in the combined aqueous extracts is determined by adding excess of standard silver nitrate and titrating the excess silver with standard thiocyanate by the Volhard procedure. Filtration of the silver chloride is avoided by protecting it with 2 ml. of nitrobenzene before the back titration with thiocyanate is begun. Five ml. of ferric indicator is used. This indicator is a saturated solution of ferric alum in $N$ nitric acid.

### SODIUM AND LIQUID AMMONIA METHOD (DAINS) [23]

*Procedure.*—A 0.1–0.2 g. sample, accurately weighed, of the substance is dissolved in 30–50 ml. of liquid ammonia in a small open Dewar vessel. Small clean pieces of sodium are added until the blue color persists for 0.5 hour. The ammonia is then allowed to evaporate, the process being hastened with an air draft. A little alcohol is added to react with any sodium that remains, then water is added and the determination is completed by any convenient method.

[22] Liggett, L. M., Anal. Chem., **26**, 748, 1954.
[23] Dains, J. Am. Chem. Soc., **40**, 936, 1918; Dains and Brewster *ibid.*, **42**, 1574, 1920; Clifford, *ibid.*, **41**, 1051, 1919.

In a few cases cyanide is formed or remains after the sodium treatment, namely in the cases of chloroform, bromoform, carbon tetrachloride, chloral hydrate, bromal hydrate, 1,1-dichloroethane (ethylidene chloride), tetrachloroethylene, 1,1,2,2-tetra-chloroethane (acetylene tetrachloride), methyl cyanide, benzyl cyanide, and ethyl cyanoacetate. If cyanide is present, or in any doubtful case, transfer the solution to a 250-ml. beaker, dilute to 200 ml., and neutralize (Hood) with acetic acid to phenolphthalein, and add 1 ml. of 6 $N$ acetic acid in excess. Boil the solution for 1 hour, keeping the volume between 150 and 200 ml. by adding distilled water as may be necessary. After the HCN has been expelled, complete the determination of the halide by a standard method.

### LIME METHOD FOR DETERMINATION OF HALOGENS IN ORGANIC MATTER

*Procedure.*—A layer of lime (free from chloride), about 6 cm. long, is introduced into a difficultly fusible glass tube, closed at one end (35 cm. long and with 1 cm. bore), followed by 0.5 g. of the substance, and 6 cm. more of the lime. The substance is thoroughly mixed by means of a copper wire with a spiral end. The tube is nearly filled with lime and, in a horizontal position, gently tapped to cause the lime to settle and form a channel above the layer. The tube is placed in a small carbon combustion furnace. The heat is turned on, so that the front end of the tube is heated to dull redness and then the end containing the substance. When the organic matter has been decomposed, the tube is cooled and the contents transferred to a beaker and the lime dissolved in dilute nitric acid (Cl-free). The carbon is filtered off and the halogen determined as usual in the filtrate.

Should a sulfate be present in the mixture, organic matter will reduce it to a sulfide, so that $Ag_2S$ will be precipitated along with the halides. To prevent this, hydrogen peroxide is added to the solution, which should be slightly alkaline. The mixture is boiled to remove the excess of $H_2O_2$, and is then acidified with nitric acid, the solution filtered and the halide determined in the filtrate.

With substances rich in nitrogen, some soluble cyanide is apt to form. The silver precipitate containing the halides and the cyanide is heated to fusion. The residue is now treated with zinc and sulfuric acid, the metallic silver and the paracyanogen filtered off and the halides determined in the filtrate.

### SODIUM PEROXIDE METHOD

Organic compounds may be decomposed by sodium peroxide in an open crucible without recourse to a sealed tube, as is required by the Carius method. The following is the procedure outlined by Pringsheim.[24]

*Procedure.*—About 0.2 gram of substance in a small steel crucible is treated with a calculated quantity of sodium peroxide.[25] The crucible should be only two-thirds

[24] C. N., **91**, 2372, 215, 1905.
[25] Charge of sodium peroxide is judged as follows:

| Per cent C and O in material | Amount of sugar to add | Amount of $Na_2O_2$ required |
|---|---|---|
| Over 75 | 0 | 18 times wt. of sub. |
| 30 to 75 | 0 | 16 times wt. of sub. |
| 25 to 50 | $\frac{1}{2}$ the wt. of sub. | 16 times wt. of sub. |
| Below 25 | An equal weight | 16 times wt. of sub. |

of its height full; this is put in a large porcelain crucible, in which a little cold water is carefully placed, so that the steel crucible stands out 1 to 2 cm. This latter crucible is covered with its own cover, in which is a hole through which an iron wire heated to redness can be introduced with the object of starting the combustion. As soon as the combustion is completed the whole is plunged into the water in the larger crucible. The porcelain crucible is covered with a watch-glass and heated gently until the whole mass is dissolved. This point is recognized when no more bubbles are given off and when there are no more particles of carbon which have escaped combustion. The steel crucible is then removed and washed carefully; the solution is filtered and treated with an excess of sulfurous acid (to neutralize the alkaline liquid, and to reduce the oxidized products: bromic, iodic acids, etc.). The solution is acidulated with nitric acid, then made to a volume of about 500 ml., and the halogens precipitated with silver nitrate and the precipitate washed, dried and weighed as usual.

## METHOD FOR CHLORINE IN ANALYSES IN OTHER CHAPTERS

Chlorine in Crude Potassium Bromide and Bromine — See Analysis of Crude Potassium Bromide and Bromine (Bromine Chapter)

Chlorine in Commercial Phosphates — See Analysis of Commercial Phosphates

# Chapter 15

# CHROMIUM *

**Cr, at. wt. 51.996; sp. gr. 7.14; m.p. 1890°C.; b.p. 2482°C.; oxides, $CrO_2$; $Cr_2O_3$, $CrO_3$**

Chromium occurs in nature in combined state, more generally in rocks of high magnesia and low silica content. It is found associated with iron, aluminum, calcium, copper, magnesium. The minerals chromite, chrome iron, $FeO \cdot Cr_2O_3$, and crocoisite, $PbCrO_4$, are of commercial importance.

Chromium is used in alloys, in steel, in stainless steel, in paint pigments, in chrome plating and has accordingly received much attention regarding its properties, chemical reactions and methods of determination.

## DETECTION

Chromium(III) is precipitated by ammonium hydroxide as bluish-green, $Cr(OH)_3$, along with the hydroxides of iron and aluminum (members of previous groups having been removed). The chromic compound is oxidized to chromate by action of chlorine, bromine, sodium peroxide, or hydrogen peroxide added to the substance containing an excess of caustic alkali. The chromate dissolves and is thus separated from iron, which remains insoluble as $Fe(OH)_3$. The alkali chromates color the solution yellow.

*Barium acetate or chloride* added to a neutral or slightly acetic acid solution of a chromate precipitates yellow barium chromate, $BaCrO_4$. Addition of ammonium acetate to neutralize any free inorganic acid aids the reaction.

*Lead acetate* produces a yellow precipitate with chromates, in neutral or acetic acid solutions.

*Mercurous nitrate or silver nitrate* gives red precipitates with chromates.

*Hydrogen peroxide* added to a chromate and heated with an acid, such as sulfuric, nitric, or hydrochloric, will form a greenish-blue-colored solution. Chromates are reduced by hydrogen peroxide in acid solution, the action being reversed in alkaline solution.

*Reducing agents, hydrogen sulfide, sulfurous acid, ferrous salts, alcohol* form green chromic salts when added to chromates in acid solution.

*Ether* shaken with a chromate to which nitric acid and hydrogen peroxide are added is colored a transient blue by the unstable perchromic acid, which soon decomposes into chromic salt with evolution of oxygen and fading of the blue color.

*Diphenylcarbazide Test.*—To 5 ml. of the solution containing chromium as chromate, 2 drops of hydrochloric or acetic acid are added, and 1 drop of an acetic acid solution of diphenylcarbazide (0.2 g. $CO(NH \cdot NH \cdot C_6H_5)_2$ is dissolved in 5 ml.

---

* Based on a chapter in the Fifth Edition, revised and largely rewritten by Arnold R. Gahler, Research and Development Analytical Laboratory, Union Carbide Metals Co., Niagara Falls, N. Y.

glacial acetic acid and diluted to 20 ml. with ethyl alcohol). A violet pink color is produced in presence of a chromate. Less than 0.0000001 g. chromium may be detected.

Chromic salts are bluish green; chromic acid is red; chromates, yellow; dichromates, red; chrome alum, violet.

The powdered mineral, containing chromium, when fused with sodium carbonate and nitrate, produces a yellow colored mass.

## ESTIMATION

Among the substances in which chromium is determined are the following: Chromite, $FeO \cdot Cr_2O_3$, crocoisite, $PbCrO_4$; slags; chromic oxide, chrome green, in pigments; chromates and dichromates; stainless steel and ferro-chrome.

In analytical procedures chromium precipitates with iron and aluminum and causes difficulty in the determination of these two elements. In the iron determination by titration with $KMnO_4$, chromium, if present, is also reduced by zinc from a valence of three to a valence of two and is again oxidized to the trivalent form by $KMnO_4$, similar to the action with iron. (At room temperature Cr(III) is not reduced to Cr(II) at 10° or below by Zn(Hg). At 100° $KMnO_4$ oxidizes Cr(III) to Cr(VI).) No reduction of trivalent chromium occurs with use of $H_2S$, $SO_2$ or $SnCl_2$, while iron is reduced.

Details of getting chromium products into solution follow. The attack with sodium peroxide is generally satisfactory. Methods for the determination of chromium seldom require preliminary separations.

## PREPARATION AND SOLUTION OF THE SAMPLE

Although powdered metallic chromium is soluble in dilute hydrochloric or sulfuric acid, it is only slightly soluble in dilute or concentrated nitric acid. It is practically insoluble in aqua regia and in concentrated sulfuric acid. Chrome ore is difficult to dissolve. It is important to have the material in finely powdered form to effect a rapid and complete solution of the sample. An agate mortar may be used to advantage in the final pulverizing of the substance.

### GENERAL PROCEDURES FOR DECOMPOSITION OF REFRACTORY MATERIALS CONTAINING CHROMIUM

The following fluxes may be used:

A. Fusion with $KHSO_4$ and extraction with hot dilute HCl. The residue fused with $Na_2CO_3$ and $KClO_3$, 3:1, or with soda lime and $KClO_3$, 3:1.

B. Fusion with $NaHSO_4$ and NaF, 2:1.

C. Fusion with magnesia or lime and sodium or potassium carbonates, 4:1.

D. Fusion with $Na_2O_2$, or NaOH and $KNO_3$, or NaOH and $Na_2O_2$. Nickel, iron, copper, or silver crucibles should be used for D. Platinum may be used for A, B, or C.

### SPECIAL PROCEDURES

**Materials High in Silica.**—The finely ground sample, 1 to 5 g., is placed in a platinum dish and mixed with 2 to 5 ml. concentrated sulfuric acid (1.84), and 10 to 50 ml. of concentrated hydrofluoric acid added. The solution is evaporated to small volume on the steam bath and to $SO_3$ fumes on the hot plate. Sodium carbonate is added in sufficient amount to react with the free acid, and then an excess of 5 to 10 g. added and the mixture heated to fusion and kept in molten condition for half an hour. From time to time a crystal of potassium nitrate is added to the center of the molten mass until 1 to 2 g. are added. (*Caution:* Platinum is attacked by $KNO_3$, hence avoid adding a large amount at any one time.) Chromium and aluminum go into solution in the flux, but iron is thrown out as $Fe(OH)_3$. The cooled fusion is extracted with hot water and filtered from the iron residue. Chromium is in solution together with aluminum. If much iron is present it should be dissolved in a little hydrochloric acid and the solution poured into boiling 10% solution of potassium hydroxide, the cooled solution + $Fe(OH)_3$ precipitate is treated with hydrogen peroxide or sodium peroxide to oxidize any chromium that may have been occluded by the iron in the first precipitate. The mixture is again filtered and the combined filtrates examined for chromium.

**Sodium Peroxide Fusion. Chrome Iron Ores.**—One gram of finely pulverized ore is mixed with 8 g. of yellow sodium peroxide. (Fresh peroxide is best and fused in a nickel or iron crucible of 30 ml. capacity.) See p. 361 for detailed procedure. The cooled fusion is dissolved in a casserole with 100 ml. to 150 ml. of water, more peroxide being added to this solution if it appears purple. The excess of peroxide is decomposed by boiling the solution, and to the caustic solution free from peroxide is added 10 to 15 g. of ammonium carbonate or a sufficient quantity of the salt to neutralize four-fifths of the sodium hydroxide present in the solution, as the strong caustic would otherwise dissolve the filter. The solution is now filtered. The insoluble matter is treated on the filter with dilute sulfuric acid, 1:4. If a portion remains insoluble, it is an indication of incomplete decomposition of the ore, and this residue is again fused with peroxide and treated as above. The combined filtrates contain the chromium.

Since chromates are reduced in presence of free acid and peroxide, the latter should be expelled before making the solution acid.[1]

**Oxidations of Chromium.**—Small amounts of chromium may be oxidized by fusion with $Na_2CO_3$ and $KNO_3$, large amounts by fusion with $Na_2O_2$.

In acid solution oxidation is effected by $PbO_2$ or $KClO_3$ or $K_2S_2O_8$ or $(NH_4)_2S_2O_8$ (in presence of $AgNO_3$). Perchloric acid is useful in oxidation.[2] Potassium bromate may be used.[3]

**Method for Solution of Iron and Steel.**—See methods at close of chapter.

# SEPARATIONS

**Chromium, Iron, and Aluminum.**—If chromium has been fused with sodium peroxide or carbonate containing a little potassium nitrate, and the fusion extracted with boiling water, most of the chromium goes into solution as a chromate, together with alumina, but some of the chromium is occluded by $Fe(OH)_3$. If the amount of the iron precipitate is appreciable, and warrants the recovery of occluded chromium, it is dissolved in hydrochloric acid and the iron reprecipitated by pouring into a solution of strong sodium hydroxide. Before filtering off the iron hydroxide, a little $H_2O_2$ is added to oxidize the $Cr_2O_3$, if accidentally present,

[1] See Separations.

[2] Smith, G. F., Mixed Perchloric, Sulfuric, and Phosphoric Acids and Their Applications in Analysis, 2nd Ed., The G. Frederic Smith Chemical Co., Columbus, Ohio, 1942, p. 4.

[3] Kolthoff and Sandell, Ind. Eng. Chem., Anal. Ed., **2**, 140, 1930.

and the solution boiled and filtered. The combined filtrates will contain all of the chromium and aluminum.

If chromium is present as a chromic salt, instead of a chromate, it is oxidized to the higher form by adding peroxide ($H_2O_2$ or $Na_2O_2$) to the alkaline solution. Bromine added to this solution or chlorine gas passed in will accomplish complete oxidation.[4] It must be remembered that in acid solutions hydrogen peroxide, sodium peroxide, or nitrites will cause reduction of chromates to chromic salts (exception, see method for solution of steel), so that these should be boiled out of the alkaline solution before making decidedly acid with hydrochloric or sulfuric acid. Since these are difficult, if not impossible, to expel completely from an alkaline solution, after boiling the strongly alkaline solution, dilute sulfuric acid is added until the solution acquires a permanent brown color (nearly acid), acid potassium sulfate, $KHSO_4$, is added, and the boiling continued.[5] This will decompose the bromates and expel bromine, etc., but will not cause the reduction of the chromate, as would a strong acid solution.

**Separation of Chromium from Aluminum.**—This separation is necessary if chromium is to be precipitated as $Cr(OH)_3$. The sodium chromate and aluminate solutions are made slightly acid with nitric acid and then faintly alkaline with ammonium hydroxide, $Al(OH)_3$ is precipitated and chromium remains in solution as a chromate.

If chromium is present as a chromium salt, the solution can be evaporated to fumes with $HClO_4$ to oxidize the chromium(III) to chromium(VI). Large amounts of HCl should be absent to prevent loss of chromium as the volatile $CrO_2Cl_2$.

## GRAVIMETRIC METHODS

### DETERMINATION OF CHROMIUM AS BARIUM CHROMATE

Chromium, present as a chromate, is precipitated from a neutral or faintly acetic acid solution of an alkali chromate by addition of barium acetate or chloride. The $BaCrO_4$ is gently ignited and weighed. The solution should be free from sulfuric acid or sulfates.

**Procedure.**—The alkali chromate solution is neutralized with nitric acid or ammonia as the case may require, precautions for avoiding reduction having been observed as indicated under Preparation and Solution of the Sample. Ten ml. of 0.5 N $BaCl_2$ or $Ba(C_2H_3O_2)_2$ (approx. 10% solution) are added to the boiling solution for each 0.1 g. of chromium present. The reagent should be added in a fine stream or drop by drop to prevent occlusion of the reagent by the precipitate. The precipitated chromate is allowed to settle on the steam bath for two or three hours and then filtered into a weighed Gooch crucible and washed with 10% alcohol solution.[6] The precipitate is dried for an hour in the oven, then

---

[4] Br may be added and then NaOH to oxidize Cr and precipitate $Fe(OH)_3$.
Chromic oxide and most of its compounds, except chrome iron stone, may be decomposed by concentrated $HNO_3 + KClO_3$ (added in small portions). Gröger, M., Z. anorg. Chem., **81**, 233–242, 1913.

[5] $KHSO_4$ will not cause reduction of chromates. Kurtenacker, A., Z. anal. Chem., **52**, 401–407, 1913; Analyst, **38**, 449, 387.

[6] If the filtrate appears yellow, chromate is indicated, the solution should be reduced and the chromium precipitated as $Cr(OH)_3$. If the filtrate is pink, it should be boiled until it appears green and $Cr(OH)_3$ precipitates. These precipitates should be included in the above calculation for chromium.

placed in an asbestos ring suspended in a large crucible with cover and thus heated over a low flame, gradually increasing the heat until the outer crucible becomes a dull red. The cover is removed and the heating continued for five minutes, or until the precipitate appears a uniform yellow throughout. High heating should be avoided. The cooled residue is weighed as $BaCrO_4$.

$$BaCrO_4 \times 0.2053 = Cr$$

$$\times 0.3000 = Cr_2O_3$$

$$\times 0.7665 = K_2CrO_4$$

$$\times 0.5806 = K_2Cr_2O_7$$

NOTES.—If the precipitate on the sides of the crucible appears green, it is ignited until the green color disappears.

If sulfates are present. $BaSO_4$ will be precipitated; hence this method could not be used. In this case either reduction to the chromic salt and precipitation of chromium as $Cr(OH)_3$ or a titrimetric procedure should be followed.

## MERCUROUS NITRATE METHOD

*Procedure.*—To the chromate solution (containing 0.2–0.5 g. Cr) heated to boiling is added 2 g. of $Na_2CO_3$ and then a saturated solution of pure mercurous nitrate in $\frac{1}{10}$ solution concentrated $HNO_3$ (free from nitrous oxides), added in slight excess. The mixture is boiled until the brown precipitate changes to the orange crystalline form. The precipitate is filtered and washed with hot water, then ignited three hours over a Meeker burner until the weight is constant.

## TITRIMETRIC METHODS

## CHROMIUM BY REDUCTION OF THE CHROMATE WITH FERROUS SALTS

The procedure may be used for the determination of chromium in presence of ferric iron and alumina. Hydrochloric or sulfuric acid does not interfere. If hydrochloric acid is present in solution, the $K_2Cr_2O_7$ back titration should be made. In presence of $H_2SO_4$ either $KMnO_4$ or $K_2Cr_2O_7$ titrations may be made. The method depends upon the reduction of soluble chromates by ferrous salts.

Reaction.

$$Cr_2O_7^= + 6Fe^{++} + 14H^+ \rightarrow 2Cr^{+3} + 6Fe^{+3} + 7H_2O$$

*Procedure.* **Reduction.**—The sample, containing not over 0.17 g. chromium present as a chromate, is boiled to expel oxidizing reagents according to the method described under the potassium iodide procedure for chromium. The solution is made acid, if not already so, and about 5 ml. of 1:1 $H_2SO_4$ per 100 ml. of solution added in excess. Tenth normal ferrous ammonium sulfate solution containing free sulfuric acid is added until the solution changes from yellow through olive-green to deep grass-green. For every 0.1 g. of chromium about 65 to 70 ml. of 0.1 N ferrous salt solution should be added. The end point is usually determined potentiometrically. However, excess reducing reagent may be added and titrated either with permanganate or with dichromate as directed below.

**Potassium Permanganate Titration.**—To be used in presence of free sulfuric acid, free hydrochloric acid being absent.

Tenth normal potassium permanganate solution is run into the reduced chromate until the green color gives place to a violet tinge. At the end point the solution appears to darken slightly. A little practice enables one to get this with accuracy. A slight excess of permanganate gives the solution a pinkish color, readily distinguishable in the green. Addition of 3 to 4 ml. syrupy phosphoric acid gives a sharper end point. The color should hold one minute. o-Phenanthroline ferrous sulfate solution (Ferrion) may be used as the indicator. With one or two drops of this indicator (0.025 $M$) the end point is indicated by a change in color from pink to clear green.

**Potassium Dichromate Titration.**—The excess ferrous ammonium sulfate is titrated with 0.1 $N$ $K_2Cr_2O_7$. The end point is detected potentiometrically or visually to a violet color with sodium diphenylaminesulfonate as indicator. The accuracy and precision of the method can be improved by detecting the end point amperometrically.[7]

**Calculation.**—From the total ferrous ammonium sulfate added, subtract the ml. of back titration (the reagents being exactly 0.1 $N$); the difference gives the ml. of ferrous salt required for chromium reduction. If reagents are not 0.1 $N$, multiply ml. titrations by factors converting to 0.1 $N$.

$$\text{Ml. ferrous ammonium sulfate} \times 0.001733 = Cr$$

# CHROMIUM BY REDUCTION OF THE CHROMATE WITH HYDRIODIC ACID

Chromium present as a chromate is reduced in acid solution by addition of potassium iodide and the liberated iodine titrated by standard sodium thiosulfate. The method depends upon the following reactions:

(a) $$Cr_2O_7^= + 6I^- + 14H^+ \rightarrow 2Cr^{3+} + 3I_2 + 7H_2O$$

(b) $$I_2 + 2S_2O_3^= \rightarrow 2I^- + S_4O_6^=$$

The presence of large quantities of Ca, Ba, Sr, Mg, Zn, Cd, Al, Ni, Co, $H_2SO_4$, HCl, does not interfere.[8] However, elements such as arsenic, copper, iron, molybdenum, and vanadium in their higher valence states, which liberate iodine in an acidified solution of potassium iodide, must be absent.

*Procedure.*—The alkali chromate solution containing not over 0.17 g. Cr [9] and free from $Fe_2O_3$ is made nearly acid with $H_2SO_4$, boiled with 20 ml. of 30% potassium acid sulfate to decompose bromates or expel Br, Cl, or $H_2O_2$ as the case may require, more $KHSO_4$ being added if necessary. If the solution is not acid it is made so with sulfuric acid and 5 ml. of the acid per 100 ml. of solution is added in excess.[10] About 2 g. of solid potassium iodide are added and, after five minutes, the liberated iodine is titrated with 0.1 $N$ $Na_2S_2O_3$ solution. When the

[7] Keily, A. J., Eldridge, A., and Hibbits, J. O., Anal. Chim. Acta., **21**, 135, 1959.

[8] Sodium peroxide is generally used for oxidation of chromium. The solution is now neutralized with acid, the iodide added and 10 ml. of concentrated HCl. The liberated iodine is immediately titrated.

[9] If desired, stronger solutions of titration reagents may be used, and consequently a larger sample taken. A normal solution of $Na_2S_2O_3$ may be used to advantage with 1 g. samples of chromium salts or hydrates, where Cr exceeds 10%.

[10] Sutton recommends for every 0.5 g. $K_2Cr_2O_7$ present to add 0.5 g. KI and 1.8 g. $H_2SO_4$ per 100 ml. of solution. If more $K_2Cr_2O_7$ is present, increase the KI and $H_2SO_4$, but not the water.

green, color of the reduced chromate begins to predominate over the free iodine color (brownish-red) a little starch solution is added and the titration with the thiosulfate continued until the blue color of the starch compound is just destroyed, care being taken not to confuse the green color of the reduced chromium with the blue of the starch.

$$\text{One ml. of } 0.1 \ N \ Na_2S_2O_3{}^{11} = 0.001733 \text{ g. Cr}$$

## COLORIMETRIC METHODS [12]

Chromium may be determined colorimetrically by measuring the absorbance of an alkaline or acidic solution containing chromium(VI) ions. A more sensitive colorimetric system results from reaction of chromium(VI) in a weakly acid solution with diphenylcarbazide.

## CHROMIUM(VI)–ALKALINE SOLUTION METHOD [13]

The absorbance of the colored solution can be measured with a colorimeter near 366 m$\mu$. The concentration of chromium is obtained by reference to a calibration graph obtained by plotting the absorbance of standard chromium(VI) solutions over the concentration range of 5 to 100 p. p. m. The alkalinity of both the standard solutions prepared for the calibration graph and the sample solution must be identical. The standard solutions can be conveniently prepared from high purity potassium dichromate.

*Procedure.*—The solution containing the sample is nearly neutralized with sodium carbonate, the reagent being added until a slight cloudiness results. The solution is now cleared with a few drops of sulfuric acid, and then sufficient excess of a strong solution of sodium thiosulfate added to precipitate aluminum, chromium, manganese, etc. The precipitate is filtered off, dissolved in the least amount of dilute nitric acid, then filtered from the precipitated sulfur and diluted to 300 to 400 ml. Chromium is now oxidized by adding 10 ml. of 0.2% silver nitrate solution, about 10 g. each of ammonium nitrate and persulfate. After boiling for about twenty minutes, sufficient hydrochloric acid is added to decompose any permanganate present and to precipitate the silver, and a few ml. added in excess. The solution is again boiled for about ten minutes and then filtered through a fritted glass crucible. The filtrate is treated with a little sodium phosphate to repress the color of traces of iron that may be present and made to a definite volume.

The solution may now be compared with a standard solution containing the same amounts of acids, manganese, alumina, etc., as are present in the sample, tenth normal potassium dichromate being run into this standard solution until its color matches that of the sample. The burette reading is taken and the chromium calculated.

$$\text{One ml. of } 0.1 \ N \ K_2Cr_2O_7 = 0.001733 \text{ g. Cr}$$

[11] If desired, a normal solution of thiosulfate may be used with a 1 g. sample of chromium salts or hydroxides, when the chromium present exceeds 10%.

[12] Sandell, E. B., Colorimetric Determination of Traces of Metals, p. 388–408, Interscience Publishers, New York, 3rd Ed., 1959.

[13] Luke, C. L., Anal. Chem., **30**, 359, 1958.

NOTES.—Prolonged boiling after addition of hydrochloric acid to the solution of the chromate will cause its reduction. A green tint usually indicates that the chromate has been reduced.

The test may be carried on in the presence of sulfuric, hydrochloric, phosphoric, hydrofluoric, and nitric acids. Alumina, manganese, and small amounts of iron do not interfere.

Organic matter should be destroyed by either calcining the sample or by oxidation by taking to fumes with sulfuric acid. The presence of this prevents precipitation of chromium.

## CHROMIUM(VI)—ACID SOLUTION METHOD

Occasionally it is convenient to measure the absorbance of chromium(VI) in an acid solution. The system is less sensitive than chromium(VI) in an alkaline solution. The maximum absorbance for the solution is near 350 m$\mu$. The chromium may be oxidized either with the silver-persulfate procedure or by careful oxidation with perchloric acid. The perchloric acid method has been used in the analysis of chromium in steels. An example of a differential spectrophotometric method for the determination of chromium in stainless steel using the acid system is described later in this chapter.

## CHROMIUM(VI) IN ACID SOLUTION WITH DIPHENYLCARBAZIDE METHOD

In acid solution s-diphenylcarbazide forms a sensitive red-violet colored system with chromium(VI) which exhibits maximum absorbance near 540 m$\mu$. The reagent is nearly specific for chromium(VI) under the conditions of color formation. Molybdenum(VI) interferes by forming a color. Iron(III) and vanadium(V) react with the reagent to form yellow products. These elements, along with others such as copper, may be removed by reaction with cupferron and a preliminary extraction of the cupferrates with an organic solvent such as chloroform. For large concentrations of iron, a preliminary extraction with ether or butyl acetate from a hydrochloric acid solution (sp. gr. 1.13) is suggested. Separation of trace amounts of chromium(VI) from iron or other elements precipitated as hydrous oxides with ammonium hydroxide is avoided because of the danger of loss of part of the chromium. Large concentrations of nickel may be removed by precipitation as nickel ammonium perchlorate.[14]

Chromium is usually oxidized with ammonium peroxydisulfate, $(NH_4)_2S_2O_8$, in the presence of silver ions. Permanganate may be added if manganese is not present to visually insure when oxidation is complete. The permanganate is reduced with dilute hydrochloric acid, nitrite, or ethanol.

The acidity for best color development is about 0.2 $N$ in sulfuric acid or a combination of sulfuric and phosphoric acids.

The colored system follows Beer's law at 540 m$\mu$ over a concentration range of 0.01 to 0.10 mg. of chromium(VI) in a volume of 100 ml. using 1-cm cells.

The diphenylcarbazide method has been applied to the determination of chromium in electronic nickel,[14] in uranium metal and oxides,[15] and in titanium alloys.[16]

[14] Methods for Chemical Analysis of Metals, American Society for Testing Materials, Philadelphia, 1960.

[15] Analytical Chemistry of the Manhattan Project, C. J. Rodden, Editor-in-Chief, p. 449, McGraw-Hill Book Co., Inc., 1950.

[16] Singer, L., and Chambers, W. A., Jr., Ind. Eng. Chem., Anal. Ed., **16**, 507, 1944.

## DETERMINATIONS IN SPECIFIC SUBSTANCES

## COLORIMETRIC DETERMINATION OF CHROMIUM
### IN EFFLUENTS

These recommended procedures are designed to be used for the determination of 5 to 50 p. p. m. of chromium in a 10 ml. sample of effluent.

**Reagents. Nitric Acid, Concentrated, 16 N.**—Reagent grade.

**Sulfuric Acid, 36 N.**—Reagent grade.

**Hydrochloric Acid, Concentrated, 12 N.**—Reagent grade.

**Phosphoric Acid, 85% Syrup.**—Reagent grade.

**Cupferron Solution.**—5% w/v. in water; freshly prepared.

**Chloroform.**—Reagent grade.

**Silver Nitrate Solution.**—Approximately 0.1 N.

**Ammonium Persulfate.**—Reagent grade.

**Potassium Permanganate Solution.**—Approximately 0.1 N.

**Ferrous Sulfate.**—Reagent grade.

**s-Diphenylcarbazide Solution.**—Dissolve 0.5 g. of the compound in 100 ml. of 1:1 acetone and water. Prepare fresh as needed.

**Sulfuric Acid Solution, 1:3.**

**Standard Chromium Solution.**—Dissolve 0.141 g. of reagent grade potassium dichromate in distilled water and dilute to one liter.

1 ml. = 50 micrograms of chromium

For establishing a calibration curve, 1 ml. of this solution taken as a sample corresponds to 5 p. p. m. of chromium for a 10 ml. sample of effluent taken for analysis in step one of procedure.

**Procedure for the Determination of Total Chromium.**—Pipette a 10-ml. sample of the effluent into a 150-ml. beaker. In running a blank, use 10 ml. of water. In establishing a calibration curve, use 10 ml. of water and add 1 ml. of the standard chromium solution for each 5 p. p. m. of chromium. Add 5 ml. of concentrated nitric acid and evaporate the solution to dryness, but do not bake. Cool and add 5 ml. of concentrated nitric acid followed by 2 ml. of concentrated sulfuric acid. Evaporate to strong fumes of sulfur trioxide. Gently fume for 5 minutes. If the residue after fuming is discolored by organic carbon, cautiously add 2 ml. of concentrated nitric acid and fume again. Repeat as many times as is necessary. It may be necessary to add more concentrated sulfuric acid to prevent the mixture from going to dryness. Cool the solution to room temperature. Add about 50 ml. of water and add 8 ml. of concentrated sulfuric acid.

A total of about 10 ml. of concentrated sulfuric acid should be present in the solution at this point of the procedure. If necessary, heat to aid solution. Filter the solution, if necessary, through a Whatman No. 42 paper, saving the filtrate. If possible, use a centrifuge. Wash the filter at least three times with 5-ml. portions of water. Combine the washings and filtrate. Transfer the filtrate and washings to a 100-ml. volumetric flask and dilute to the mark with water. Shake well. Pipette 5 ml. of this solution into a separatory funnel. Chill the solution by immersing the funnel in an ice bath. Add 5 ml. of 5% cupferron solution and shake very well.

Let stand in the ice bath for one minute with an occasional swirling. Extract the solution in the separatory funnel with three separate 5-ml. portions of chloroform. Wash the combined chloroform extracts in another separatory funnel with one 5 ml. portion of water. Combine this wash water with the extracted solution in the first separatory funnel. Reject the chloroform layer. Transfer the solution from the separatory funnel to a 250-ml. beaker and wash the funnel with a small amount of water. Add this washing to the main solution. Adjust the volume of the solution in the beaker to about 100 ml. Add 5 ml. of silver nitrate solution and 0.5 g. of ammonium persulfate and cautiously bring the solution to a boil. If, on boiling, the solution turns dark in color due to small amounts of cupferron which have been carried over, *cool* the solution and add 0.5 g. of ammonium persulfate and slowly bring to a boil. Repeat the cooling and addition of persulfate until no dark color develops on heating for one or two minutes. To the warm solution, add 0.1 $N$ potassium permanganate dropwise until the solution is pink in color. Boil the solution for at least 5 minutes. If the solution is not pink at this point, add permanganate as before and repeat until the pink color persists on boiling for 5 minutes. Add 5 drops of hydrochloric acid to the gently boiling pink solution and continue heating for 3 minutes. If the pink color has not been destroyed, add 2 more drops of HCl and boil for two minutes. Repeat the HCl treatment until the hot solution is not pink. Do not allow the volume of the boiling solution to drop below about 75 ml. Cool the solution to room temperature.

The volume at this point should be about 75 ml. Filter the solution through sintered glass, or centrifuge. Asbestos mats may be used in the filtration, but paper or organic matter should not be permitted to come into contact with the solution. Wash the filter with two 5-ml. portions of water and combine the washings and filtrate. Transfer the filtrate and washings to a 100-ml. volumetric flask. Add 1 ml. of s-diphenylcarbazide solution. Bring to the mark with distilled water and shake well. Set the colorimeter to zero with water. Use a green (No. 54) filter. With a spectrophotometer, set the instrument to read full scale at 540 millimicrons. Transfer the solution to the sample cuvette and read the colorimeter. If necessary, convert the scale readings of the photometer to absorbance. Subtract the blank reading from the sample readings. If a calibration curve is being established, plot these corrected readings versus p. p. m. of chromium. If a sample is being run, read the amount of chromium from the calibration curve.

## SPECTROPHOTOMETRIC DETERMINATION OF TRACES OF CHROMIUM IN ELECTROLYTIC IRON AND STEELS

This method is suitable for the determination of chromium in electrolytic iron and steels within the range of 0.0005 to 0.1%.

*Reagents.* **Standard Chromium Solution.**—Dissolve 2.829 g. of high purity $K_2Cr_2O_7$ in water, add 10 ml. of $H_2SO_4$ (1:1), and dilute to 1 liter. One ml. = 1.00 mg. of chromium. Dilute 10.00 ml. of the stock solution to one liter after adding 20 ml. of $H_2SO_4$ (1:1). One ml. = 0.01 mg. of chromium.

**Diphenylcarbazide, 0.2%.**—Prepare fresh daily. Dissolve 0.20 g. of the salt in 100 ml. of 95% ethanol, acidify with 3 drops of $H_2SO_4$ (1:1). Store in a refrigerator.

**Sulfuric Acid, 6 $N$.**—To a liter beaker containing 800 ml. of water, add 163 ml. of $H_2SO_4$, sp. gr. 1.84. Add 3 drops of 0.05 $N$ $KMnO_4$ and boil for 5 minutes, adding more $KMnO_4$ as required to maintain a faint pink color. Cool, dilute to one liter, mix, and store in a Pyrex glass-stoppered bottle.

*Procedure.*—Place about 5 g. of small chips or grains of sample on the balance pan and weigh accurately. Transfer to a 400-ml. beaker and add 40 to 50 ml. of HCl. Digest at a low heat until the vigorous action ceases. Add 10 ml. of $HNO_3$ and evaporate to near dryness. Take up with 50 ml. of HCl (sp. gr. 1.13), stir, and warm to dissolve salts, and chill to 15°C. or less. Transfer to a 250-ml. separatory funnel using a small amount of HCl (sp. gr. 1.13) as wash. Add 60 to 75 ml. of butyl acetate, shake vigorously for one minute, and allow the phases to separate. Withdraw the lower acid layer into the original beaker. To the funnel add 10 ml. of HCl (sp. gr. 1.13), shake for ½ minute, separate, and withdraw the lower layer into the original beaker. It is not necessary to separate completely the iron at this point.

Evaporate the acid layer to 20 ml. or less, cool, and transfer to a 250-ml. volumetric flask. Dilute to the mark and mix. Transfer an aliquot (containing between 0.01 to 0.1 mg. of chromium) from the 250-ml. volumetric sample flask to a 250-ml. beaker. Add 15 ml. of $H_2SO_4$ (1:1), dilute to 50 ml., and chill to 10°C. or less. Transfer to a 250-ml. separatory funnel, add about 20 ml. of a saturated solution of cupferron, and 50 ml. of chloroform. Shake vigorously for one minute, allow the phases to separate, withdraw and discard the lower layer. Repeat the extraction with 5 ml. of cupferron and 25 ml. of chloroform. Avoid an excess of cupferron that would make its subsequent removal difficult.

When the separation of iron appears complete, remove the excess cupferron with two extractions of 10 ml. of chloroform. Finish the clean-up by shaking with 20 ml. of isopropyl ether. Withdraw the aqueous (lower) phase into the original 250-ml. beaker. Evaporate to about 30 ml. volume, add 10 ml. of $HNO_3$, and fume down to 2 or 3 ml. of $H_2SO_4$. If the solution becomes dark upon fuming, add additional $HNO_3$ and evaporate to fumes. Cool.

Add 15 ml. of water and boil to dissolve salts. Cool somewhat and make just basic to litmus with 10% NaOH solution. Add 3.0 ml. of 6 $N$ $H_2SO_4$ and transfer to a 100-ml. Pyrex volumetric flask. Add 5 drops of 0.1 $N$ $AgNO_3$, 1 drop of 0.05 $N$ $KMnO_4$, 10 ml. of freshly prepared 2% ammonium persulfate solution, and an $Al_2O_3$ boiling chip (Hengar). Dilute to 50 ml., mix, and boil for 30 minutes or longer. The permanganate color should persist. Cool to 20°C. Add 10.0 ml. of 0.2% diphenylcarbazide and immediately dilute to the mark and mix. Measure the absorbance after 5 minutes but before 15 minutes in 1-cm cells at 540 m$\mu$ using water as a null. Run a reagent blank through the color development procedure. Determine the mg. of chromium present from a previously established absorbance-concentration curve prepared as follows:

Using pipettes, transfer 1, 2, 5, 7, and 10 ml. aliquots of the diluted chromium standard solution (1 ml. = 0.01 mg. of chromium) to small beakers. Continue according to the chromium procedure above starting with ". . . make just basic to litmus with NaOH . . ." Plot absorbance versus weight of chromium in milligrams.

## DETERMINATION OF CHROMIUM IN A SOLUBLE CHROMATE

To a concentrated solution of potassium iodide is added a known amount of the soluble chromate dissolved in a little water. The liberated iodine is now titrated with standard thiosulfate reagent. Acidify mixture with hydrochloric acid.

One ml. of 0.1 $N$ $Na_2S_2O_3$ = 0.001733 g. Cr

## ANALYSIS OF CHROME ORES

The exact analysis of chrome ore is a matter of some difficulty, involving the separation and determination of large amounts of chromium, iron, aluminum, and magnesium. Although chromite is one of the most stable of the common minerals, complete decomposition may be obtained by heating the ore with perchloric and sulfuric acids or by fusion with sodium peroxide or a mixture of sodium carbonate and borax. For a review of methods of chrome ore analysis refer to Hartford, W. W., Anal. Chem., 25, 290, 1953. Methods are described for the determination of chromium, iron, alumina, lime, and magnesia.

### DETERMINATION OF CHROMIUM IN CHROME ORES
### (TITRIMETRIC METHOD)

This procedure is applicable to all grades of chrome ore. Results in two laboratories on the same sample should not differ by more than 0.15% chromium.

The sample is fused with $Na_2O_2$, the fusion dissolved in water, acidified with $H_2SO_4$ and $HNO_3$, and any reduced chromium oxidized with $(NH_4)_2S_2O_8$ and $AgNO_3$. $HMnO_4$ is reduced with HCl and the chromium(VI) titrated potentiometrically with iron(II).

Vanadium is also titrated with the chromium. Ordinarily, the small amount of vanadium in chrome ores is counted as chromium since 0.10% vanadium is equivalent to only 0.0339% chromium.

*Reagents.* **Ferrous Ammonium Sulfate Solution, Approximately 0.11 N.**—Dissolve 44 g. of $FeSO_4 \cdot (NH_4)_2SO_4 \cdot 6H_2O$ in one liter of water containing 20 ml. of $H_2SO_4$ (1:1), and mix thoroughly by passing in a brisk stream of $CO_2$ for 20 minutes. Store in a bottle containing a piece of pure aluminum sheet. Standardize just before using as the value changes from day to day. (One ml. of 0.11 N solution is equivalent to 0.0019074 g. of chromium.)

**Standard $K_2Cr_2O_7$.**—Fuse the best reagent grade of $K_2Cr_2O_7$ in a covered platinum or Pyrex dish at 415°C. in a muffle, cool, grind to approximately 80 mesh, and transfer to a well stoppered bottle. Determine the oxidizing value of this working standard by comparing through a ferrous sulfate solution with National Bureau of Standards standard dichromate.

*Apparatus.* **Potentiometric Apparatus.**—Potentiometric apparatus is the most satisfactory means for obtaining the end point in the highly colored chromium solutions. Either the platinum-calomel or bimetallic electrode systems are satisfactory. Suitable equipment includes the Kelley, Larrabee, Fisher, Sargent-Malmstadt, and similar instruments.

*Procedure.*—Transfer 1.000 g. of the 100-mesh sample dried for one hour at 105–110°C. to a 30-ml. iron crucible containing approximately 8 g. of dry $Na_2O_2$, and mix thoroughly with a platinum or iron rod. Carefully clean the rod by scraping with a small spatula. Place the crucible on a hot plate to keep the contents dry. Put on goggles, grip the crucible with a pair of tongs, and rotate it around the outer edge of the flame of a Fisher burner so that heat is applied to the sides of the crucible rather than the bottom.

When the charge blackens, increase the heat and rotate the crucible vigorously as the mixture fuses to stir up any particles adhering to the bottom or sides. Heat at a bright red heat for 3 or 4 minutes, cover, and then cool almost to room temperature.

Tap the tightly covered crucible on a solid object to loosen the fused mass as a cake. Transfer the cold cake to a dry 600-ml. beaker, cover, and add 150 ml. of cold water. When the reaction subsides, rinse the crucible thoroughly with warm water, adding the rinsings to the beaker. Add a boiling rod (made by sealing a 1-cm length of 2-mm. glass tubing on the end of a piece of 4-mm. glass rod) and boil for 5 minutes.

Cool somewhat and carefully add 60 ml. of $H_2SO_4$ (1:1) and 5 ml. of $HNO_3$. Boil until all the iron scale from the crucible has dissolved. Dilute to 300 ml. with hot water, add 10 ml. of $AgNO_3$ solution (25 g./liter), 10 drops of $KMnO_4$ solution (25 g./liter), and 3 to 5 g. of ammonium peroxydisulfate [$(NH_4)_2S_2O_8$]. Heat to boiling and boil at least 10 minutes. If the purple color of $HMnO_4$ fades on boiling, cool somewhat and add more $(NH_4)_2S_2O_8$ until the purple color persists after at least a 7-minute additional boiling.

Then add 10 ml. of HCl (1:3) and continue boiling for at least 5 minutes. If the purple color is not then discharged or precipitated $MnO_2$ remains, add more of the reducing agent and continue the boiling until the manganese is dissolved and reduced. Finally boil for 10 minutes after the last addition of reducing agent, then cool to 20°C. in cold water. Remove and rinse the cover and boiling tube.

Add 175.00 ml. of the 0.11 N ferrous ammonium sulfate solution and complete the titration potentiometrically with the ferrous ammonium sulfate solution. On the Kelley machine, add the ferrous sulfate solution until the galvanometer needle swings to +10 on the scale (Notes 1 and 2).

Standardize the ferrous ammonium sulfate solution by titrating 1.000 g. of the dried $K_2Cr_2O_7$ (0.3535 g. of chromium) in the same volume and acidity as were used for the determination. If the ferrous ammonium sulfate solution is exactly 0.11 N, 185.33 ml. will be required, and each milliliter is equivalent to 0.0019074 g. of chromium. Calculate the per cent chromium as follows (Note 3):

$$\% \text{ Cr} = \frac{(A)(B)(100)}{C}$$

where $A$ = ml. of ferrous ammonium sulfate solution required
$B$ = chromium equivalent of ammonium sulfate solution in grams
$C$ = weight of sample in grams.

Multiply the percentage of chromium found by 1.4615 to obtain the percentage of $Cr_2O_3$.

NOTES.—1. Similar end points are obtained on the other machines. If too much ferrous ammonium sulfate solution is added, either at first or through over-running the end point, add a measured excess of 0.1 N $K_2Cr_2O_7$ solution, and then titrate with the ferrous ammonium sulfate solution to the end point.

2. If a potentiometric apparatus is not available, add 5 ml. of $H_3PO_4$ and an excess of at least 5 ml. of the ferrous ammonium sulfate solution. An excess of the ferrous sulfate is indicated by the clear green color developed. Add several drops of o-phenanthroline indicator, and titrate with 0.1 N $KMnO_4$ to a clear green. The change is from pink to clear green.

3. If desired, vanadium can be determined on a suitable sample, and the percentage found multiplied by 0.339 to convert to equivalent chromium and subtracted.

## DETERMINATION OF FeO, $Al_2O_3$, MgO, AND CaO IN CHROME ORES

This method is designed for standard chrome ores.

After solution in $H_2SO_4$ and $HClO_4$, chromium is removed by volatilization as $CrO_2Cl_2$, $SiO_2$ is separated and any insoluble oxides are recovered from it. After a double $R_2O_3$ separation, iron is separated with cupferron and aluminum with $NH_4OH$. Calcium and magnesium are precipitated as phosphates, and then calcium as $CaSO_4$.

*Procedure.* **Solution of Sample.**—Transfer 1.0000 g. of the 100-mesh sample, which has been dried for one hour at 105 to 110°C., to a 250-ml. Philips beaker, add 50 ml. of $H_2SO_4$ (1:4), 5 g. of $(NH_4)_2SO_4$, and 20 ml. of $HClO_4$. Cover the beaker with a small watch glass and heat gently until fumes of $HClO_4$ are freely evolved and the chromium is oxidized to chromic acid. Remove the cover glass and continue the heating while the chromium is volatilized as $CrO_2Cl_2$ by the introduction of a stream of dry HCl gas, or by the addition of small portions of NaCl. Should chromic acid deposit on the sides or bottom of the beaker, cool the solution and add 5 to 10 ml. of water. Then continue the heating as described, and when fumes of $HClO_4$ begin to be evolved, introduce HCl gas at a moderate rate until all the chromium has been volatilized.

Cool somewhat, add about 75 ml. of water and boil the solution for several minutes. Filter on a 9-cm paper containing a little paper pulp catching the filtrate in a 400-ml. beaker. Wash thoroughly with hot water. Ignite the paper and silica in platinum at a dull red heat until the carbon has burned off completely. Cool and add several ml. of HF, 1–2 ml. of $HNO_3$, and 0.5 ml. of $H_2SO_4$ (1:1). Evaporate the solution to dryness to volatilize the silica. Fuse the residue with 1 g. (or a sufficient amount) of $Na_2S_2O_7$, dissolve in 25 ml. of hot HCl (1:9), and add to the filtrate from the silica.

**$R_2O_3$ Separation.**—Add 5 g. of $NH_4Cl$ and heat the solution just to boiling. Next add a very faint excess of diluted $NH_4OH$ (1:2) and heat to boiling for 1–2 minutes (no longer). Allow the precipitate to settle, filter on an 11-cm. paper containing a little paper pulp, and wash about 10 times with hot $NH_4Cl$ solution (20 g./liter neutralized with $NH_4OH$). Return the paper and precipitate to the original beaker and treat with 50 ml. of HCl (1:4). Heat the solution to boiling, dilute to 100 ml. with hot water, and precipitate with $NH_4OH$, filter, and wash as previously described. Combine the two filtrates and reserve for the determination of calcium and magnesium.

**FeO and $TiO_2$.**—Return the $NH_4OH$ precipitate and paper to the original beaker and add 10 ml. of $H_2SO_4$ and 20 ml. of $HNO_3$, and heat until the paper is destroyed, finally evaporate to dense fumes. Cool to $<20°C$. and precipitate the iron and titanium by the addition (dropwise and with constant stirring) of a freshly prepared, cold water solution of cupferron (60 g./liter) in slight excess. An excess is present when a drop of the precipitant forms a transient white precipitate.

Filter on an 11-cm paper containing a little paper pulp, catching the filtrate in a 600-ml. beaker, wash thoroughly with cold HCl (1:9) containing 10 ml. of the cupferron reagent per liter. Ignite at a low temperature in a porcelain or silica crucible until the carbon is oxidized (Note 1). Cool and add 10 ml. of HCl and a few drops of $SnCl_2$ (50 g./liter of HCl) (1:1), and heat until the iron oxide has dissolved. Transfer the contents of the crucible to a 400-ml. beaker. Heat to boiling, then reduce the iron with $SnCl_2$ solution, adding from 1 to 2 drops in excess. Cool to $<20°C$., add 10 ml. of saturated $HgCl_2$ solution, stir well, and allow to stand for 2 minutes. Dilute to 200 ml. with cold water, add 5 ml. of $H_3PO_4$, 10 ml. of $H_2SO_4$ (1:1), a few drops of sodium diphenylamine sulfonate indicator (Note 2), and titrate with 0.1 N $K_2Cr_2O_7$ to a purple end point. Calculate the FeO as follows:

$$\% \text{ FeO} = \frac{A \times 0.007185}{B} \times 100$$

where $A$ = ml. of 0.1 $N$ $K_2Cr_2O_7$
　　　$B$ = weight of sample in grams.

**$Al_2O_3$.**—Boil the filtrate from the cupferron precipitate down to a volume of 40 to 50 ml., add 25 ml. of $HNO_3$, and continue the evaporation until the volume has been reduced to 40 to 50 ml. Add 10 ml. of $HNO_3$ and 15 ml. of $HClO_4$, and continue the evaporation until dense fumes of $HClO_4$ are freely evolved and all organic matter has been oxidized. Add more nitric acid if the solution becomes dark upon fuming with $HClO_4$. Cool, dilute with 100 ml. of warm water, filter on a 9-cm. paper to remove any $SiO_2$, and wash the paper thoroughly with hot water.

Add approximately 5 g. of $NH_4Cl$ and some paper pulp, precipitate the aluminum by the addition of $NH_4OH$ (1:2) in very faint excess. Boil for 1–2 minutes (no longer) and allow to settle, and filter and wash about 10 times with hot $NH_4Cl$ solution (20 g./liter). Return the paper and precipitate to the original beaker, treat with 100 ml. of HCl (1:4) and heat to boiling. Repeat the precipitation, filtration, and washing as previously described. Transfer the paper and precipitate to a weighed platinum crucible and ignite first at a low heat and finally to constant weight at 1150–1200°C., cool, and weigh as $Al_2O_3 + P_2O_5 +$ any $Cr_2O_3$ not separated.

To correct for any contamination by chromium, fuse the oxides with 8–10 g. of $Na_2CO_3$, dissolve the fusion in water, and filter. Add 0.5 g. of $Na_2O_2$ and determine the chromium colorimetrically by comparison with a standard solution of $K_2CrO_4$, prepared by dissolving 1.867 g. of anhydrous $K_2CrO_4$ in 1 liter of water (one ml. = 0.0005 g. of chromium). Calculate any chromium found to $Cr_2O_3$ and deduct from the weight of impure alumina. Phosphorus is usually low in chrome ores but if required, it may be determined in the solution after the determination of chromium, calculated to $P_2O_5$, and deducted from the alumina.

**MgO.**—Acidify the combined ammoniacal filtrates from the $R_2O_3$ separation with HCl, evaporate to a volume of approximately 250 ml., and cool to 15°C. Add 50 ml. of a diammonium phosphate solution (100 g./liter) and then $NH_4OH$ slowly with vigorous stirring until the solution is ammoniacal and a crystalline precipitate appears. Add an excess of 25 ml. of $NH_4OH$, stir the liquid thoroughly, and finally cool to about 15°C. Allow to stand for several hours with frequent stirring, or preferably overnight. Filter on a tight 9-cm paper containing a little paper pulp, and wash 3 or 4 times by decantation with cold $NH_4OH$ (2:98).

Pour 25 ml. of hot HCl (1:1) through the filter, and collect in the original beaker containing the bulk of the precipitate. Wash the filter thoroughly with hot HCl (5:9). Dilute with cold water to a volume of 150 ml. and cool to room temperature. Add. 3 ml. of the diammonium phosphate solution and repeat at a temperature of about 15°C., filter, wash first about 15 times with cold $NH_4OH$ (2:98), and then twice with a cold $NH_4NO_3$ solution (50 g./liter). Ignite in a weighed platinum crucible at a dull red heat until the carbon has been burned, and finally to constant weight at 1000 to 1050°C. Weigh as $Mg_2P_2O_7 + Ca_3(PO_4)_2 + Mn_2P_2O_7$.

Dissolve in 20 ml. of hot diluted HCl (1:4). Filter on a 9-cm. paper into a 150-ml. beaker to remove any $SiO_2$ and wash the filter well with hot water. Ignite the paper and $SiO_2$ and complete the $SiO_2$ determination in the usual manner. Deduct any $SiO_2$ found from the weight of the magnesium pyrophosphate.

**CaO.**—Add 10 ml. of $H_2SO_4$ to the filtrate from the $SiO_2$, and evaporate to fumes of sulfur trioxide. Add 5 ml. of water and 100 ml. of 95% ethyl alcohol, and stir the solution vigorously for several minutes. Allow the calcium sulfate precipitate to settle for 2 or 3 hours, or preferably overnight, filter on a tight 9-cm paper containing a little paper pulp, and wash at least 20 times with 80% alcohol containing 2 ml. of $H_2SO_4$ per liter to ensure the complete removal of all phosphoric acid. Transfer the paper and precipitate to a crucible, ignite at a dull redness to constant weight. Cool and weigh as $CaSO_4$.

*Calculations.*—Calculate the percentage of CaO as follows:

$$\% \text{ CaO} = \frac{A \times 0.41196}{B} \times 100$$

where $A$ = weight of $CaSO_4$ in grams
$B$ = weight of sample.

Multiply the CaO $\times$ 1.8437 to convert to $Ca_3(PO_4)_2$ to deduct from the impure $Mg_2P_2O_7$.

Evaporate the alcoholic filtrate from the calcium sulfate until strong fumes of sulfur trioxide are evolved and all organic matter has been destroyed. Add a few drops of $HNO_3$ if necessary. Add 15 ml. of $H_3PO_4$, 100 ml. of water, and 0.5 g. of $KIO_4$. Heat to boiling and boil for 3–5 minutes to oxidize the manganese. Cool and dilute to 200 ml. in a volumetric flask, and measure the absorbance of the solution at 575 m$\mu$. Set up a calibration curve for the photometer to cover the range from 0 to 10 mg. of manganese. Multiply any manganese found by 2.5831 to convert to $Mn_2P_2O_7$.

Calculate the percentage of MgO as follows:

$$\% \text{ MgO} = \frac{A - (B + C + D) \times 0.3622}{E} \times 100$$

where $A$ = weight of crude $Mg_2P_2O_7$
$B$ = weight of $SiO_2$ in $Mg_2P_2O_7$
$C$ = weight of $Ca_3(PO_4)_2$
$D$ = weight of $Mn_2P_2O_7$
$E$ = weight of sample.

NOTES.—1. If the determination of titanium is required, proceed as follows:
Fuse the oxides with from 2 to 3 g. of $K_2S_2O_7$, dissolve the cold melt in 50 ml. of hot $H_2SO_4$ (1:9), and cool to <20°C. Transfer to a 100-ml. volumetric flask and dilute to volume with $H_2SO_4$ (1:9). Mix thoroughly and then fill the dry reference cell of the photometer with the solution. Do not rinse the cell as all the solution must be saved for the iron determination. Add 0.1 ml. of 30% $H_2O_2$ to the flask, mix thoroughly, and fill the sample cell of the photometer. Measure the difference in absorbance between the two solutions at 440 m$\mu$ and read the percentage of titanium from a graph prepared from standard titanium solutions containing the approximate amounts of iron, vanadium, and $K_2S_2O_7$ present.
Transfer the contents of both cells and the 100-ml. flask to a 400-ml. beaker. Boil the solution for at least 10 minutes, add 5 ml. of HCl, then reduce the iron with $SnCl_2$ solution, adding from 1 to 2 drops in excess. Cool to <20°C., add 10 ml. of saturated $HgCl_2$ solution, stir well, and allow to stand for 2 minutes. Dilute to 300 ml. with cold water, add 5 ml. of $H_3PO_4$, a few drops of sodium diphenylamine sulfonate indicator solution, and titrate with $K_2Cr_2O_7$.
2. Sodium diphenylamine sulfonate indicator (2 g./liter of water).

3. During the cooling in the desiccator and while on the balance pan, the crucible should be covered with a tight-fitting cover, since ignited alumina is very hygroscopic and absorbs within the first 10-minute exposure to the atmosphere a large proportion of the total water that it will take up in 24 hours.

## ALTERNATE METHOD FOR DETERMINATION OF ALUMINUM AND MAGNESIUM IN CHROME ORES [17]

*Procedure.*—Dissolve 0.5 g. of ore in perchloric acid by digesting at the boiling point. About 6 hours are generally required. Dilute and filter into a 500-ml. volumetric flask. Wash, dilute the filtrate to the mark, and draw off 100 ml. for the analysis. Add 1 ml. of sulfuric acid (1:1) and electrolyze with a mercury cathode, keeping the cell covered until the solution is clear. Test for removal of iron by a spot test with potassium ferricyanide, because iron interferes seriously with the 8-quinolinol precipitation.

When removal of iron is complete, without interrupting the current, lower the anode as close to the cathode as possible, and withdraw as much of the solution as possible into a beaker. Dilute and continue withdrawal until the cell has been washed four or five times, then transfer the remainder of the solution from the cell.

Heat the solution to 60°C., add 20 ml. of a 5% solution of 8-quinolinol in 2 $N$ acetic acid, and then slowly add 50 ml. of saturated ammonium acetate. Stir vigorously for a few minutes and allow the precipitate to settle for 3 hours. Filter on a tared Selas, Gooch, or sintered-glass crucible, wash with cold water, dry 1 hour at 130°–140°C., and weigh as anhydrous aluminum 8-quinolinolate containing 11.10% $Al_2O_3$.

Magnesium may be determined on the filtrate from the aluminum, or on a separate sample. If a separate sample is used, it is dissolved and electrolyzed as described above. The alumina is then preferably removed by a conventional ammonia precipitation, and the filtrate heated to 70°C. to prevent precipitation of 8-quinolinol and adjusted to pH with sodium hydroxide. If the filtrate from the alumina is used, excess 8-quinolinol is destroyed by heating with nitric and sulfuric acid to fumes, and the pH and temperature are then adjusted as before. The magnesium is precipitated by slow addition of 10 ml. of 2% alcoholic 8-quinolinol. The use of an alcoholic solution ensures correct composition of the precipitate. The solution is stirred and allowed to stand for 0.5 hour before filtering. The precipitate is filtered onto a tared weighing crucible, washed with hot 1 to 100 ammonium hydroxide, dried 1 hour at 160°C. to volatilize any excess precipitant, and weighed as anhydrous magnesium 8-quinolinolate containing 12.91% MgO.

## DICHROMATE METHOD FOR DETERMINING CHROMIUM IN IRON ORES AND ALLOYS

The method takes advantage of Knop's reaction with diphenylamine in titration of iron with potassium dichromate; here chromate is titrated with a solution of iron. The procedure is applicable to the determination of chromium in ores, ferrochrome, chrome steels and soluble chromates.

*Reagents.* **Potassium Dichromate.**—0.1 $N$ solution.

**Ferrous Ammonium Sulfate or Ferrous Sulfate.**—0.1 $N$ solution.

**Phosphoric-Sulfuric Acid.**—150 ml. sulfuric acid (sp. gr. 1.84) and 150 ml. phosphoric acid (sp. gr. 1.70) diluted to 1000 ml. with water.

[17] Hartford, Winslow H., Anal. Chem., **25**, 293–4, 1953.

**Sodium Diphenylamine Sulfonate Indicator.**—One gram of the reagent dissolved in 100 ml. of water. Use 4 drops (0.2 ml.). Deduct blank.

**Sodium Peroxide.**—Fresh powder.

*Procedure.*—The amount of the sample should be such as contains between 0.002 to 0.08 g. chromium. The finely powdered material is fused with ten times its weight of sodium peroxide in a nickel or iron crucible. (It appears unnecessary to heat to molten condition, provided the mass sinters.) After heating at dull red heat for ten minutes, the crucible is cooled and then upset in a 400-ml. beaker containing about 100 ml. of water. (The beaker should be immediately covered as the reaction is violent.) The crucible is washed out and removed, and the solution boiled to expel the peroxide. The solution is cooled and dilute sulfuric acid added until the alkali is neutralized and the solution is slightly acid. (Iron hydroxide dissolves, but manganese dioxide remains in suspension.)[18] If manganese is present, it is removed by filtration through asbestos. To the filtrate 15 ml. of phosphoric-sulfuric acid mixture is now added and, from a burette, a measured excess of standard ferrous ammonium sulfate. (With an excess of ferrous salt the solution turns green.) Four drops (0.2 ml.) of sodium diphenylamine sulfonate indicator are now added and the excess of ferrous salt titrated with standard potassium dichromate. The green color changes to a blue green and then to an intense blue or violet color. (If the end point is overrun, titrate back with ferrous sulfate to a green color and repeat the dichromate titration. Convert the reagents to exact equivalents, i.e., terms of 0.1 $N$ solution.) The difference between the ml. of ferrous solution and the dichromate reagent multiplied by the chromium equivalent represents the chromium in the sample. One ml. 0.1 $N$ solution is equivalent to 0.001733 g. chromium.

NOTES.—1. If it is desired to filter off the iron and manganese precipitates, it will be necessary to filter through asbestos.

2. If the iron precipitate has been dissolved and much manganese is present, the precipitate may be filtered off. Manganese dioxide does not occlude an appreciable amount of chromium.

3. Chrome steels may be dissolved with sulfuric acid followed by treatment with nitric acid to oxidize the iron.

4. It is evident that neither ferric salt nor dichromate alone produces the blue color, but an excess of dichromate in presence of ferric iron. If much chromium is present, the end point may be overrun owing to the depth of color, the excess of dichromate causing a greenish-blue color to reappear. Back titration with ferrous sulfate will restore the blue or violet color, and an excess will change the color to blue green.

## ANALYSIS OF CHROMIUM STEELS AND STAINLESS STEELS

### DETERMINATION OF CHROMIUM BY PERSULFATE OXIDATION METHOD

*Procedure.*  **Solution of Sample.**—Choose a sample weight according to the expected chromium content by referring to the tabulation in Note 1 below. Transfer this sample to a 600-ml. beaker.

For 0.5000- and 1.000-g. samples, add 20 ml. of $HClO_4$, 20 ml. of $H_3PO_4$, and heat until the sample is dissolved. Continue the heating until the chromium is oxidized. Cool, add 100 ml. of water, and boil for 3 minutes.

For 3.000- to 5.000-g. samples, add 60 ml. of $H_2SO_4$ (1 + 4) and 150 ml. of water. Heat until dissolution is complete and then add $HNO_3$ dropwise to the hot solu-

---

[18] The ferric hydroxide occludes chromium; hence solution of the iron with acid and reprecipitation is necessary to recover chromium.

tion until oxidation of the iron is complete as shown by a clear yellow solution (Note 2). Boil for 3 minutes.

**Oxidation of the Chromium.**—Dilute to 300 ml. Add 15 ml. of $AgNO_3$ solution (5 g. per l.), 3 g. of $(NH_4)_2S_2O_8$ and a few drops of $KMnO_4$ solution (25 g. per l.) to the warm solution and boil for at least 10 minutes. If the deep red color of permanganic acid fades from the solution on boiling, cool somewhat and add additional $(NH_4)_2S_2O_8$ until the purple color persists after at least 5 minutes' boiling. Add 5 ml. (or a sufficient amount to discharge the purple color due to the permanganic acid) of HCl $(1 + 3)$, and continue the boiling for from 5 to 10 minutes longer to ensure the complete removal of all chlorine; then cool to 15–20°C.

**Titration of the Chromate.** *Potentiometric Method.*—Dilute to 300 ml. with cold water, add 30 ml. of $H_2SO_4$ $(1 + 1)$, place on the potentiometric machine (Kelley, Pitschner, Larrabee, or other device), start the motor, and adjust the potentiometer so that the needle is on the left-hand side of the scale. Add standard 0.05 or 0.1 N ferrous ammonium sulfate solution from a burette until one drop causes a large permanent swing of the galvanometer needle, which usually forces it off scale to the right. (Should the end point be accidentally overrun, add a measured amount of 0.1 N $K_2Cr_2O_7$ and proceed slowly with the potentiometric titration.) Correct the volume of ferrous ammonium sulfate taken by the amount of 0.1 N $K_2Cr_2O_7$ added, and calculate the percentage of chromium. Standardize the ferrous ammonium sulfate solution by titrating 0.5000 g. of the pure $K_2Cr_2O_7$ in the same volume and acidity as were used for the determination. The calculations involved are shown in the following equations:

$$\frac{\text{Weight of } K_2Cr_2O_7 \text{ taken} \times 0.3535}{\text{Volume of FeSO}_4 \text{ required}} = \text{Titer of FeSO}_4 \text{ Solution}$$

$$\frac{\left(\begin{array}{c}\text{Titer of FeSO}_4 \text{ solution} \times \text{volume} \\ \text{of FeSO}_4 \text{ used in the titration} \times 100\end{array}\right)}{\text{Weight of sample taken}} = \% \text{ Chromium } (+ \text{ vanadium})$$

*Visual Method.*—Dilute with cold water to 400 ml. and add a 5- to 10-ml. excess of 0.05 or 0.1 N ferrous ammonium sulfate solution from a burette. Add a few drops of *o*-phenanthroline indicator solution (Note 3), and back-titrate the excess ferrous ammonium sulfate with 0.1 N $KMnO_4$ to a clear green color that remains permanent for at least 30 seconds. Standardize a 30-ml. portion of the ferrous ammonium sulfate solution by titrating with 0.1 N $KMnO_4$ to the same end point color in the presence of a few drops of the *o*-phenanthroline indicator solution in the same volume and acidity as were used in the determination. One ml. of 0.1 N ferrous ammonium sulfate = 0.001733 g. of chromium.

Any vanadium present will be titrated by either method. In ordinary alloys, however, the vanadium content is usually below 0.05% and may be ignored. If vanadium is known to be present, or for unknown alloys, the interference due to vanadium may be eliminated in the visual method by adding sodium acetate (about 25 g.), just before the solution is titrated, until more would cause a permanent precipitate. In the potentiometric method, the vanadium will be titrated and must be determined on a separate sample and deducted from the chromium content as shown in the following equation:

$$\% \text{ Cr found} - (\% \text{ V} \times 0.339) = \% \text{ Cr present}$$

NOTES.—1. Select the sample weight as follows:

>30% Chromium—0.5000 g.
5–30% Chromium —1.000 g.
1–5% Chromium —3.000 g.
<1% Chromium —5.000 g.

2. With most steels this is sufficient to dissolve any chromium carbides present. In case of doubt regarding insoluble matter, this can be filtered off, the paper destroyed with $HNO_3$, and the residue fumed in 5 ml. of $HClO_4$ plus 5 ml. of $H_3PO_4$. Add back to the main solution.

3. 0.01 $M$ Solution of $o$-phenanthroline.—Dissolve 1.49 g. of $o$-phenanthroline monohydrate in 100 ml. of cold water containing 0.7 g. of $FeSO_4 \cdot 7H_2O$. The reagent is available commercially.

## DIFFERENTIAL SPECTROPHOTOMETRIC METHOD [19]

This method is designed for Types 304, 316, 347, and similar 18-8 steels and requires solution of the sample in $HClO_4$, $H_3PO_4$, and HF, oxidation of the chromium with $HClO_4$ in the presence of $H_2SO_4$, quick cooling of the oxidized chromium by adding diluted $H_3PO_4$, and finally boiling with very dilute HCl to reduce oxidized manganese. Chromium is then determined colorimetrically.

*Caution.*—Goggles must be worn when making additions to hot or fuming acids. Strict adherence to the given procedures for additions to hot or fuming acids is necessary; otherwise, the analyst may be burned by splashing acid, or the determination spoiled by loss due to the spattering of the hot solutions.

*Reagents.* $H_2SO_4$-$HClO_4$ Mixture.—Add 250 ml. of 70% $HClO_4$ to 500 ml. of $H_2SO_4$ (1:1).

*Solution of Sample.*—Transfer 1 g. of the sample to a 750-ml. Erlenmeyer flask containing 3 or 4 glass beads and add 30 ml. of 70% $HClO_4$, 10 ml. of $H_3PO_4$, and 0.5 ml. (10 drops) of HF. Heat to boiling and boil or fume gently until the sample is in solution. When solution appears to be complete and before chromium oxidation begins, add 20 ml. of the $H_2SO_4$-$HClO_4$ mixture and continue heating strongly over a free flame until the chromium is oxidized. About 30 seconds after the solution turns orange-red is usually sufficient to oxidize the chromium completely. Immediately grasp the flask with a pair of metal tongs, swirl the contents vigorously for about 10 seconds in such a way that centrifugal force causes the liquid to wash much of the sides of the flask, and pour into the thickest layer of the swirling solution 30 ml. of $H_3PO_4$ (1:1) (see Note below). Continue the vigorous swirling and cautiously direct a stream of water against the inside of the neck of the flask, adding about 5 ml. in this way. Swirl until the violent bubbling ceases, then with continued swirling, slowly add 100 ml. of water containing about 0.35 ml. of HCl, and swirl over a free flame until boiling begins. Boil for 5 minutes or longer, if necessary, to completely reduce any oxidized manganese. Cool to room temperature, dilute to 500 ml., and mix thoroughly.

*Procedure.*—Determine the absorbance on a portion of the solution in the Beckman Spectrophotometer with the following settings:

| | |
|---|---|
| Wavelength | 450 m$\mu$ |
| Photocell | Blue sensitive |
| Cell | 1 cm |
| Slit width | Approx. 0.13 mm. |

[19] Culbertson, J. B., and Fowler, R. M., *Steel*, **122**, 108, 1948.

Set the null on 15.00% chromium obtained by processing a sufficient weight of N.B.S. Steel No. 101c or similar standard by this method. Convert the absorbance into chromium content from a calibration curve made by processing different weights of standard 101c to cover the range up to 22.50% chromium. This curve may be used in the form of a graph, an equation of the curve, an alignment chart, or a set of tabulated data columns.

NOTE.—If oxidation of the chromium is complete, some of the manganese will oxidize to give a permanganate color in the flask after the phosphoric acid addition.

## ANALYSIS OF FERROCHROMIUM AND CHROMIUM METAL

### DETERMINATION OF CHROMIUM

This procedure is applicable to all grades of ferrochromium, chromium metal, and ferrochromium-silicon and is a modification of the titrimetric method given under the "Determination of Chromium in Chrome Ores," above. Vanadium is also titrated. Ordinarily, the small amount of vanadium in these materials is counted as chromium since 0.10% vanadium is equivalent to only 0.034% chromium. Results of interlaboratory comparisons indicate that two laboratories should not differ by more than 0.15% chromium on a sample of ferrochromium.

The sample is fused with $Na_2O_2$, the fusion dissolved in water, acidified with $H_2SO_4$ and $HNO_3$, and any reduced chromium oxidized with $(NH_4)_2S_2O_8$ and $AgNO_3$. $HMnO_4$ is reduced with NaCl and the chromium(VI) titrated potentiometrically with $FeSO_4$.

*Reagents.* **Ferrous Ammonium Sulfate Solution, Approximately 0.11 *N*.**—Dissolve 44 g. of $FeSO_4 \cdot (NH_4)_2SO_4 \cdot 6H_2O$ in one liter of distilled water containing 20 ml. of $H_2SO_4$ (1 + 1), and mix thoroughly by passing in a brisk stream of $CO_2$ for 20 minutes. Store in a bottle containing a piece of pure aluminum sheet. Standardize just before using as the value changes from day to day. (1 ml. of 0.11 *N* solution is equivalent to 0.0019074 g. of chromium.)

**Standard $K_2Cr_2O_7$.**—Fuse the best reagent grade of $K_2Cr_2O_7$ in a covered platinum or Pyrex dish at 415°C. in a muffle furnace, cool, grind to approximately 80 mesh, and transfer to a well-stoppered bottle. Determine the oxidizing value of this working standard by comparing through a ferrous sulfate solution with N.B.S. standard dichromate No. 136.

*Apparatus.* **Potentiometric Apparatus.**—A potentiometric apparatus is the most satisfactory means for obtaining the end point in the highly colored chromium solutions. Either the platinum-calomel or bimetallic electrode system is satisfactory. Suitable equipment includes the Kelley, Larrabee, Fisher, and similar machines.

*Procedure.*—Weigh 0.5000 g. of the 40-mesh sample of low-carbon ferrochromium or the 100-mesh sample of high-carbon ferrochromium and ferrochromium-silicon, or 0.4000 g. of the 100-mesh sample of chromium metal.

Transfer the weighed sample to a 30-ml. iron crucible containing approximately 8 g. of dry $Na_2O_2$ (use 10 g. of $Na_2O_2$ for ferrochromium-silicon), and mix thoroughly with a platinum or iron rod. Carefully clean the rod by scraping with a small spatula. Place the crucible on a hot plate to keep the contents dry. Put on goggles, grip the crucible with a pair of tongs, and rotate it around the outer edge of the flame of a Fisher burner so that heat is applied to the sides of the crucible rather than the bottom.

When the charge blackens, increase the heat, and rotate the crucible vigorously as the mixture fuses to stir up any particles adhering to the bottom or sides. Heat at a bright red heat for 3 or 4 minutes, cover, and then cool almost to room temperature.

Tap the tightly covered crucible on a solid object to loosen the fused mass as a cake. Transfer the cold cake to a dry 600-ml. beaker, cover, and add 150 ml. of cold water. When the reaction subsides, rinse the crucible thoroughly with warm water adding the rinsings to the beaker. Add a boiling rod (made by sealing a 1-cm. length of 2-mm. glass tubing on the end of a piece of 4-mm. glass rod) and boil for 5 minutes.

Cool somewhat and carefully add 60 ml. of $H_2SO_4$ (1:1), 3 ml. of $H_3PO_4$, and 5 ml. of $HNO_3$. Boil until all the iron scale from the crucible has dissolved. Dilute to 300 ml. with hot water, add 10 ml. of 2.5% $AgNO_3$ solution, 10 drops of 2.5% $KMnO_4$ solution, and 3 to 5 g. of $(NH_4)_2S_2O_8$. Heat to boiling and boil at least 10 minutes. If the deep red color of $HMnO_4$ fades on boiling, cool somewhat and add more $(NH_4)_2S_2O_8$ until the red color persists after at least 7 minutes' additional boiling.

Then add 10 ml. of NaCl (100 g./l.) and continue boiling for at least 5 minutes. If the red color is not then discharged or there is still precipitated $MnO_2$, add more of the reducing agent and continue the boiling until the manganese is dissolved and reduced. Finally boil for 10 minutes after the last addition of reducing agent, then cool to 20°C. in cold water. Remove and rinse the cover and boiling tube.

Add 175.00 ml. of the 0.11 N ferrous ammonium sulfate solution (80.00 ml. for samples of ferrochromium-silicon), place the beaker on the potentiometric machine, and finish the titration with the ferrous ammonium sulfate solution (Notes 1 and 2).

Standardize the ferrous ammonium sulfate solution by titrating 1.000 g. of the dried $K_2Cr_2O_7$ (0.3535 g. of chromium) in the same volume and acidity as were used for the determination. If the ferrous ammonium sulfate solution is exactly 0.11 N, 185.33 ml. will be required, and each milliliter is equivalent to 0.0019074 g. of chromium (Note 3).

NOTES.—1. Similar end points are obtained on the other machines. If too much ferrous ammonium sulfate solution is added, either at first or through overrunning the end point, add a measured excess of 0.1 N $K_2Cr_2O_7$ solution, and then titrate with the ferrous ammonium sulfate solution to the end point.

2. If a potentiometric apparatus is not available, add 2 ml. of $H_3PO_4$ and an excess of at least 5 ml. of the ferrous ammonium sulfate solution. An excess of the ferrous sulfate is indicated by the clear green color developed. For a 70% chromium alloy approximately 190 ml. of 0.11 N ferrous ammonium sulfate will be required when working on 0.5000 g. of sample. Add several drops of o-phenanthroline indicator, and titrate with 0.1 N $KMnO_4$ to a clear green. The change is from pink to clear green.

3. If desired, vanadium can be determined on a suitable sample and the percentage found multiplied by 0.339 to convert to equivalent chromium and subtracted.

# THE SEPARATION AND DETERMINATION OF NICKEL, CHROMIUM, COBALT, IRON, TITANIUM, TUNGSTEN, MOLYBDENUM, NIOBIUM AND TANTALUM IN A HIGH TEMPERATURE ALLOY BY ANION-EXCHANGE [20]

*Procedure.* **Column Preparation.**—The ion-exchange column consists of 16-inch lengths of one-inch ID polystyrene tubing with a one-quarter inch wall. The

[20] Reprinted with permission from Wilkins, The Separation and Determination of Nickel, Chromium, Cobalt, Iron, Titanium, Tungsten, Molybdenum, Niobium and Tantalum in a High Temperature Alloy by Anion-Exchange, Talanta, **2**, 355–360, 1959. Pergamon Press, Limited.

lower end of the column is closed off with a section of Lucite rod with a three-sixteenths inch hole drilled through its axis. A section one inch long on the end of the Lucite rod is machined down to a three-eighths inch diameter so as to permit the connection of a short length of polyethylene tubing to the column. The other end of the Lucite rod, which is glued to the bottom of the column, is machined so as to have a 45° taper from the one-inch ID of the column to the three-sixteenths inch diameter hole through the rod. This taper eliminates the hold-up of the eluted species in the "corner" at the bottom of the column. A short length of quarter inch polystyrene tubing is inserted into the wall of the column about two inches from the top. This piece of tubing allows the connection of the column to an overhead gravity feed by means of polyethylene tubing. The top of the column is sealed with a rubber stopper when the overhead gravity feed is in use. The top of the column should also be threaded and capped with a threaded Lucite cap. This prevents the inadvertent removal of the rubber stopper during the elution. The resin bed * is supported by means of a layer of Teflon shavings.

The column is filled with 80 g. of a strongly basic anion-exchange resin, 200–400 mesh, chloride form, after the fine particles are removed from the resin by means of several decantations with water. This quantity of resin will give a column bed 8 in. long which is adequate for the separations in the procedure given below. A ⅞-in. polyethylene sphere inserted in the column serves to maintain a level surface in the resin bed. Without the sphere the introduction of the sample solution and the eluents to the column disturbs the surface of the resin in such a manner as to cause the sample constituents to be eluted in diagonal instead of horizontal bands. The polyethylene sphere breaks the fall of the solutions sufficiently so as to keep the surface level and give horizontal bands during the elution. Polyethylene is an ideal material for this purpose since it rests on the resin bed when the column is empty, serves as a shield when the solutions are being added to the column, and floats to the surface during the elution so as to give the eluents free access to the entire cross section of the column. In addition polyethylene is not wet by the solution and as a result the last quantities of the sample solution are easily rinsed on to the resin bed. The freshly prepared ion-exchange column should be washed several times alternately with 50-ml. portions of 9 $M$ HCl and 0.5 $M$ HCl followed by 100 ml. of 2.5% HF. A column which has been in use previously may be prepared for separations merely by washing with 50 ml. of 2.5% HF.

**Column Separations.**—Dissolve a 1-g. sample in an appropriate mixture of hydrofluoric, hydrochloric, and nitric acids and evaporate to dryness on the steam bath. Take up the sample residue in 5 ml. of concentrated HF plus 25 ml. of water. Warm on the steam bath for about 10 minutes and then add an additional 75 ml. of water. Transfer the sample solution to the anion-exchange column with 2.5% HF and after the sample solution is rinsed on to the resin bed, elute with 250 ml. of 2.5% HF. This eluate will contain elements such as iron, cobalt, nickel, chromium, manganese, aluminium, and copper. Further treatment of this eluate will be discussed below.

The column retains elements such as titanium, tungsten, molybdenum, niobium, and tantalum. Elute the titanium with 250 ml. of 8 $M$ HCl. Elute the tungsten with 300 ml. of a solution that is 10% HF–60% HCl. Elute the molybdenum with 300 ml. of a solution which is 20% HF–25% HCl. Elute the niobium with

* For one recommended resin, see "Notes" at end of this method.

300 ml. of a solution which is 14% $NH_4Cl$–4% HF. Elute the tantalum with 300 ml. of a solution which is 14% $NH_4Cl$–4% $NH_4F$.

To the 2.5% HF eluate which should contain the nickel, chromium, cobalt and iron, add ten ml. of concentrated HCl to this fraction and evaporate to dryness on the steam bath. Take up the residue with 9 $M$ HCl and transfer the solution to a strongly basic anion-exchange column with 9 $M$ HCl. Elute the nickel and chromium together with 9 $M$ HCl. Elute the cobalt with 4 $M$ HCl and finally elute the iron with 0.5 $M$ HCl.

## TITANIUM

*Procedure.*—Add 6 ml. of 1:1 sulfuric acid to the titanium fraction and evaporate to fumes of sulfuric acid. Cool to room temperature, add several grams of ice from distilled water and 0.5 ml. of 30 vol. per cent hydrogen peroxide and dilute to 100 ml. in the volumetric flask. Transfer an appropriate aliquot to a 250-ml. beaker, add 150 ml. of water and a measured excess of EDTA. Add 10 ml. of a sodium acetate-acetic acid buffer and if necessary adjust the pH to approximately 4.8 with a concentrated sodium hydroxide solution. Add two to three drops of a metalfluorechromic indicator * and back-titrate the excess of EDTA with a standard copper solution using ultraviolet light as the sole source of illumination.

## TUNGSTEN

*Procedure.*—To the tungsten fraction add 6 ml. of 1:1 sulfuric acid and evaporate the solution to fumes of sulfuric in order to remove the fluoride. Cool to room temperature and add several grams of ice followed by 25 ml. of water, and 1:1 ammonium hydroxide until the tungstic acid precipitate just redissolves. Add 20 ml. of the sodium acetate-acetic acid buffer and if necessary adjust the pH to approximately 4.8 with dilute acid. Add a small excess of 8-hydroxyquinoline in dilute acetic acid. Bring the solution to the boil on the hot-plate and then digest for about 5 minutes at about 80–90°C. Cool the solution to room temperature and filter the tungsten 8-hydroxyquinolate on a weighed Gooch crucible. Wash the precipitate several times with water, dry at 110°C. for 1 hour and weigh the crucible plus precipitate. The factor for tungsten is 0.365.

## MOLYBDENUM

*Procedure.*—Treat the fraction containing the molybdenum in an identical manner as that described above for tungsten. The factor for molybdenum is 0.2305.

## NIOBIUM

*Procedure.*—Add 9 g. of boric acid to the niobium fraction. After the boric acid is dissolved, transfer the solution to a glass beaker, add 60 ml. of 1:1 sulfuric acid and cool to 10°C. in ice. Add a slight excess of cupferron and filter the niobium cupferrate. Wash the precipitate thoroughly with a 5% sulfuric acid solution that is saturated with cupferron in order to remove the ammonium salts from the precipitate. Cautiously ignite the niobium cupferrate to the oxide and weigh as $Nb_2O_5$.

## TANTALUM

*Procedure.*—Treat the tantalum fraction in the same manner as is described above for niobium.

* See "Notes" at end of this method.

## NICKEL AND CHROMIUM

*Procedure.*—Evaporate the nickel and chromium fraction to dryness to remove the excess of hydrochloric acid. Dissolve the residue with water plus a small amount of dilute HCl and transfer to a 100-ml. volumetric flask. Transfer an appropriate aliquot to a 250-ml. beaker. Add 150 ml. of water, 10 ml. of sodium acetate-acetic acid buffer and a measured excess of EDTA over that which would be necessary for the nickel which is present in the sample. Add 2 to 3 drops of a metalfluorechromic indicator and back-titrate the excess of EDTA with a standard copper solution. This titration should be carried out at room temperature in order to avoid interference from the chromium present in this aliquot. Calculate the per cent nickel in the sample from the excess of EDTA and the copper used in the back-titration. To the solution in which the nickel was just determined add a measured excess of EDTA over that which would be required for the chromium present in the solution. Place the beaker on a hot-plate and boil the solution for 15 minutes in order to form the chromium-EDTA complex. Back-titrate the excess of EDTA with the standard copper solution using ultraviolet light. Calculate the percentage of chromium from the amount of EDTA added and the copper used in the back-titration.

## COBALT FRACTION

*Procedure.*—Transfer the cobalt fraction to a 100-ml. volumetric flask and take an appropriate aliquot in a 250-ml. beaker. Add 150 ml. of water, a measured excess of EDTA, and 10 ml. of ammonium chloride ammonium hydroxide buffer (pH approximately 9.5). If necessary adjust the pH to approximately 9.5 with ammonium hydroxide, add 2 to 3 drops of a metalfluorechromic indicator, and back-titrate the excess of EDTA with a standard copper solution. Calculate the percentage of cobalt from the amount of EDTA added and the volume of standard copper solution used for the back-titration.

## IRON FRACTION

*Procedure.*—Transfer a suitable aliquot of the iron fraction to a 250-ml. beaker. Add a measured excess of EDTA, dilute to approximately 150 ml., and adjust the pH to approximately 4.8. Add 2 to 3 drops of a metalfluorechromic indicator and back-titrate the excess of EDTA with a standard copper solution to the quenching of the fluorescence of the free indicator.

## NOTES

The volumes of eluents used during the elutions from the polystyrene column are suitable for the column dimensions and the resin particle size given under "Column Preparation." If a smaller amount of eluent is used there is a possibility of obtaining incomplete separations of the refractory metals. The use of larger volumes of eluent does not alter subsequent separations. The elution scheme shown in Fig. 15-1 is quite versatile and may be used for many combinations of refractory elements. In the event that some of the elements are absent in a sample one merely skips the elution step for those elements and proceeds with the elution of the next element on the flow sheet. If one or more elements are missing the volumes of eluents for the elements present are unchanged. In addition any eluent on the flow sheet will elute (in 300 ml.) all the elements that precede the eluent on the flow sheet. For example, the 20% HF–25% HCl eluent elutes titanium and tungsten as well as molybdenum. This is advantageous on occasions where one desires to determine one or two of the elements at the end of the flow sheet and does not need to conduct all the elutions preceding it. The procedure may be applied to the determination of one or all of the above mentioned elements in stainless steels as well as in high temperature alloys.

The 2.5% HF fraction which is first converted to a chloride solution is usually separated in small glass columns. For example with the alloy shown in the Table the glass columns contained 10 g. of Dowex 1-X8, 200–400 mesh, chloride form,

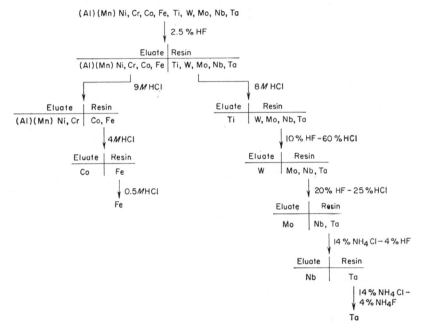

FIG. 15-1. Flow Sheet for the Analysis of a High Temperature Alloy.

in a resin bed 1 cm. ID x 12 cm. long. The use of a smaller column permits more rapid separations with smaller volumes of eluents.

Additional elements may be accommodated in this portion of the procedure. For example aluminum and manganese will be found in the 9 $M$ HCl eluent along with nickel and chromium. With all four elements the most suitable procedure is to take an aliquot for an aluminum, manganese, and nickel determination and remove the chromium by volatilization of chromyl chloride from a perchloric acid solution. The diluted solution is then passed through a cation-exchange resin. Aluminum may then be eluted with a dilute HF solution and then nickel and manganese with 4 $M$ HCl. Chromium is determined in a separate aliquot.

If copper is present in the original sample it will be found in the 2.5% HF eluate. In this case the separation of the elements in the 2.5% eluate must be done on a larger column in order to separate copper from cobalt.[21]

21 Hibbs, L. E., and Wilkins, D. H., Talanta, 2, 16, 1959.

COMPOSITE SAMPLE TO SIMULATE A HIGH TEMPERATURE ALLOY

| Ni found, mg. | Cr found, mg. | Co found, mg. | Fe found, mg. | Ti found, mg. | W found, mg. | Mo found, mg. | Nb found, mg. | Ta found, mg. |
|---|---|---|---|---|---|---|---|---|
| 19.2 | 17.6 | 43.0 | 22.0 | 70.6 | 45.9 | 38.5 | | |
| 19.2 | 17.6 | 43.0 | 22.0 | 70.6 | 45.9 | 38.5 | 31.6 | 22.3 |
| 19.2 | 17.6 | 43.0 | 22.0 | 70.1 | 46.1 | 39.1 | 31.5 | 22.3 |
| 19.3 | 17.6 | 43.0 | 22.1 | 70.7 | 46.6 | 39.4 | 32.6 | 22.6 |
| 19.1 | 17.7 | 43.0 | 22.0 | 69.7 | 46.3 | 39.6 | 32.8 | 22.4 |
| 19.2 | 17.7 | 43.0 | 21.9 | 69.4 | 46.4 | 39.4 | 33.4 | 22.7 |

Nominal values—Ni, 19.2 mg.; Cr, 17.5 mg.; Co, 42.9 mg.; Fe, 22.0 mg.; Ti, 70.5 mg.; W, 46.2 mg.; Mo, 39.8 mg.; Nb, 32.1 mg.; Ta, 22.0 mg.

Calcein W (0.1% in water) was used as a metalfluorechromic indicator for all the chelometric titrations in order to avoid any interference in the detection of the end point by highly coloured EDTA complexes.[22] An apparatus for these titrations has been previously described.[23]

## METHODS FOR CHROMIUM IN ANALYSES IN OTHER CHAPTERS

Chromium in Aluminum Alloys    See Analysis of Aluminum Alloys
Chromium in Fused Alumina    See Analysis of Fused Alumina
Chromium in Beryllium Metal    See Analysis of Beryllium Metal
Chromium in Cobalt Alloys    See Analysis of Stellite, etc. (Cobalt Chapter)

Chromium in Phosphorus Ores    See Analysis of Phosphorus Ores
Chromium in Commercial Phosphates    See Analysis of Commercial Phosphates

[22] *Idem,* Talanta, **2,** 12, 1959. *Idem,* Analyt. Chim. Acta., **20,** 324, 1959.
[23] Wilkins, D. H., Talanta, **2,** 88, 1959.

# Chapter 16

# COBALT*

Co, *at. wt.* 58.9332; *sp. gr.* 8.9; *m.p.* 1495°C.; *b.p.* 2900°C.; *oxides* $Co_3O_4$, $Co_2O_3$, CoO, $CoO_2$.

The term cobalt, which comes from the German *Kobald,* meaning goblin, was applied during the Middle Ages to substances resembling metallic ores that failed to give metals on smelting.   Later it was applied to a mineral that produced a blue color in glass.   Impure cobalt was prepared by Brandt in 1742.

Cobalt is an important constituent of many high speed steels, magnets, cemented carbides, and high temperature alloys.   It is also used as a catalyst, for electroplating, to impart color in the glass and ceramic industries, in enamelware to promote adhesion of the coating to steel, and as a drier in paints and varnishes.   Cobalt is also a minor but essential element in ruminant nutrition, and is now widely added to livestock feedstuffs and pasture fertilizers.

In minerals and ores, cobalt is usually associated with one or more of the following: copper, nickel, arsenic, iron, and sulfur.   The more commonly known minerals are linnaeite, $Co_3S_4$; carrollite, $CuCo_2S_4$; smaltite, $CoAs_2$; cobaltite, CoAsS; asbolite, $CoO_2 \cdot MnO_2 \cdot 4H_2O$; heterogenite, $CoO \cdot 2CoO_2 \cdot 6H_2O$.

## DETECTION

The ore or other substance to be examined is taken into solution by one of the methods outlined under "Preparation and Solution of the Sample."   The elements of the second group are removed by passing in hydrogen sulfide gas and filtering. The hydrogen sulfide is boiled out of the filtrate and the iron oxidized with nitric acid.   As ammonium salts are necessary to hold cobalt in solution, a few grams of either the chloride or the sulfate should be added, unless there is enough free acid in the solution to insure their presence after neutralization.   Ammonium hydroxide in slight excess is added to precipitate iron, aluminum and chromium, and the precipitate, after boiling, is removed by filtration.   If it is at all bulky it should be redissolved in acid and reprecipitated, as the hydroxides have a tendency to occlude cobalt.   Unless this is done, cobalt may be overlooked in a sample containing only a trace.   If cobalt is present in any considerable quantity, the filtrate will be pink, but this color may be masked by the presence of nickel.

The following confirmatory tests may now be made on the solution.

*Phenylthiohydantoic Acid.*—A few milliliters of the solution are slowly evaporated with a pinch of the salt, in a porcelain crucible lid.   A pink or reddish coloration shows cobalt.   The test is very sensitive.

*Ammonium Sulfide.*—A large portion of the ammoniacal solution is treated with

* Based on the chapter in the 5th edition; revised and largely rewritten by Roland S. Young, International Nickel Company of Canada, Ltd., 67 Wall Street, New York 5.

hydrogen sulfide gas. This precipitates cobalt, nickel, manganese, and zinc. The precipitation is seldom complete, owing to the formation of polysulfides, caused by the presence of oxidizing agents; a little ammonium sulfite helps to correct this. After collecting the precipitate, it is washed thoroughly with cold hydrochloric acid (sp. gr. 1.035), to remove manganese and zinc. A small quantity is then fused with borax in a loop of platinum wire. A blue color in the cold bead indicates cobalt.

The test is masked by large quantities of nickel, in which case the nitroso-beta-naphthol test may be made.

*Alpha-nitroso-beta-naphthol.*[1]—This reagent precipitates brick red cobaltinitroso-beta-naphthol which is insoluble in dilute hydrochloric acid. The solution of the salt must be freshly prepared each day and is made by dissolving 10 g. in 100 ml. of hot 50% acetic acid. To apply the test, the sulfides from the ammonium sulfide test are ignited to oxides in a porcelain crucible and dissolved in hydrochloric acid. After expelling most of the acid, the chlorides are diluted and the hot nitroso-beta-naphthol solution added till no further precipitation takes place. The precipitate may be filtered and, after igniting to oxide, used for other confirmatory tests. It is claimed that the nitroso-beta-naphthol test will precipitate 0.01 mg. of cobalt.

This test may also be applied to the ammoniacal filtrate after acidifying with hydrochloric acid.

*Potassium Nitrite.*—This salt added to a solution which is slightly acid with acetic acid, precipitates cobalt as a yellow complex nitrite having the formula $2K_3Co(NO_2)_6 \cdot 3H_2O$.

The test may be conveniently applied to a hydrochloric acid solution of the oxides, obtained by igniting either the nitroso-beta-naphthol precipitate or the precipitate from the ammonium sulfide test. The free acid is neutralized with potassium hydroxide and the solution reacidified with acetic acid. The addition of a hot concentrated solution of potassium nitrite, which has been slightly acidified with acetic acid, will precipitate the yellow potassium cobaltinitrite, on standing.

The test is not applicable in the presence of ammonium salts.

*Ammonium Thiocyanate.*—Cobalt forms a complex with ammonium thiocyanate which can be extracted with a mixture of amyl alcohol and ether, giving a blue solution which serves as a sensitive test for cobalt. To 5 ml. of the unknown in a solution faintly acid with HCl, $HNO_3$, or $H_2SO_4$, add the following solutions: 3 ml. of 10% sodium phosphate, 5 ml. of 20% sodium thiosulfate, 2 ml. of 70% ammonium acetate, a few drops of 5% tartaric acid, and 10 ml. of 60% ammonium thiocyanate. Add 10 ml. of a mixture of 3 parts amyl alcohol to 1 part ethyl ether and shake vigorously in a separatory funnel. The presence of even traces of cobalt is indicated by a blue color in the upper layer, and under the above conditions no interference will be encountered from any common element.

*Nitroso-R-Salt.*—The colored complexes formed by most of the common elements with nitroso-R-salt in the presence of sodium acetate, except cobalt, are destroyed by boiling with nitric acid. To the acidified unknown solution from which all group 2 elements have been removed by hydrogen sulfide, and from which the latter has been removed by boiling, add sodium hydroxide carefully to neutrality. Add 2 ml. of a solution containing 15% phosphoric and 15% sulfuric acid, 10 ml. 0.2% aqueous solution of nitroso-R-salt, and 10 ml. of a 50% sodium acetate solution. Bring to boiling, add 5 ml. $HNO_3$, and boil for at least 1 minute and not

[1] Ilinski and Von Knorre, Ber., **18**, 699, 1885.

more than 2 minutes. Cool and dilute with water. A red color indicates cobalt. Large quantities of Mn, Ni, and Cr interfere.

## ESTIMATION

Cobalt may be determined in a variety of ways, depending on the presence of interfering elements, the quantity of cobalt in the sample, and the precision required in the analysis. Cobalt may be determined gravimetrically as the oxide $Co_3O_4$, as the metal by electrolysis in ammoniacal solution, potentiometrically by its oxidation in ammoniacal solution with potassium ferricyanide, titrimetrically by titration with potassium cyanide, and colorimetrically by ammonium thiocyanate or nitroso-R-salt. In certain cases cobalt may be advantageously determined polarographically or spectrographically.[2]

The principal separations of cobalt are from members of previous groups by removal of these with hydrogen sulfide in acid solution, from iron by a zinc oxide or phosphate separation or ether extraction, and from nickel by precipitation of cobalt with alpha-nitroso-beta-naphthol or separation of nickel with dimethylglyoxime.

## PREPARATION AND SOLUTION OF THE SAMPLE

*General Procedures for Ores.*—The ores containing cobalt vary so widely in their chemical nature that it is difficult to lay down a method for treating all types. In all cases it is necessary to prepare the sample for treatment by grinding finely. Usually cobalt may be brought into solution by heating with concentrated nitric acid or a mixture of nitric and hydrochloric acids, except silver-bearing ores, which may usually be dissolved in a mixture of nitric and sulfuric acids.

In the case of refractory ores which fail to decompose on attacking with nitric, hydrochloric, or sulfuric acids, the insoluble matter is filtered off, washed, and treated with ammonium acetate to remove any lead sulfate that may be present. If the refractory character of the ore is known beforehand, the attack may begin with a preliminary nitric acid treatment to remove substances which are likely to attack platinum, and after filtering off the insoluble, washing it with ammonium acetate solution to remove lead, in case any galena has been oxidized to sulfate by the nitric acid. The ignited insoluble, from whichever method used, is then fused with either potassium bisulfate or a mixture of sodium and potassium carbonates, in a platinum crucible. The crucible is washed out with hot water and hydrochloric acid, and the washings are added to the main nitric acid filtrate. Cobalt is then determined by one of the procedures outlined below.

When large quantities of ore have been taken for assay, the insoluble may be too large for the fusion procedure, in which case it may be treated in a platinum dish with hydrofluoric acid and a little sulfuric acid till the silica has been eliminated, after which it is fumed, diluted, and added to the main acid solution.

*Cobalt Oxides.*—As a general rule both grey and black cobalt oxides are readily soluble in hot concentrated hydrochloric acid unless they are very impure; in this case, boil with concentrated sulfuric acid or fuse with potassium bisulfate in a Pyrex "copper" flask.

*Metallic Cobalt, Nickel and Cobalt Alloys.*—Metallic cobalt dissolves readily in nitric acid, as do nickel and the ordinary cobalt alloys. There are, however,

[2] Young, R. S., Cobalt, Reinhold Publ. Corp., New York, 1948.

certain alloys of cobalt that require a fusion with sodium peroxide before they become amenable to treatment; others may be decomposed by the use of perchloric acid. Among the latter are cobalt-chromium-tungsten alloys, such as Stellite, the method of analysis for which is given on page 392.

## SEPARATIONS

*Separation of the Ammonium Sulfide Group Containing Cobalt from the Hydrogen Sulfide Group—Mercury, Lead, Bismuth, Copper, Cadmium, Arsenic, Antimony, Tin, Gold, Molybdenum, Etc.*—Hydrogen sulfide passed through an acid solution containing 5 to 7 ml. concentrated hydrochloric acid or 3 to 5 ml. concentrated sulfuric acid per 100 ml. precipitates only members of the second group and silver. The separation is by no means clean cut with all the elements of this group, but with those metals commonly met with in industrial laboratory work, it is effective. When hydrochloric acid is used, the acidity of the solution should be no higher than stated, or the lead and cadmium may not be completely precipitated. In those cobalt analyses where the electrolytic method is preferable, sulfuric acid should be used. This offers the advantage that the lead may be almost completely eliminated with the insoluble material, and lead is an element sometimes associated with cobalt ores.

*Separation of the Ammonium Sulfide Group from the Alkaline Earths and Alkalies.*—Colorless ammonium sulfide, free from carbonates, added to a neutral solution, from which oxidizing agents are absent, and with sufficient ammonium salts to hold the magnesium in solution, will precipitate the members of the ammonium sulfide group from the alkaline earths and alkalies. The precipitation is seldom complete unless the formation of polysulfides is prevented by the addition of ammonium sulfite. This addition is advisable unless the partial precipitation of the alkaline earths as sulfites is undesirable. A second precipitation should be made if large quantities of the alkaline earths are present.

A convenient point at which to apply this method is after the hydrogen sulfide precipitate has been removed by filtration. To the filtrate, still saturated with hydrogen sulfide gas, ammonium hydroxide is added in excess and the gassing continued. The iron, being in the ferrous state, precipitates as flocculent ferrous sulfide which is easy to filter; and since no sulfur is formed by the reduction of ferric iron, no polysulfides are produced from that source. In filtering the sulfide precipitate, care should be taken to avoid unnecessary exposure to the air by covering the funnel with a watch glass whenever possible.

*Separation of Cobalt and Nickel from Manganese.* **Hydrogen Sulfide in Acetic Acid.**—A chloride or sulfate solution, free from second group elements, is treated with an excess of sodium carbonate and then made strongly acid with acetic. About 5 g. of sodium acetate for each gram of cobalt and nickel present are now added, the solution diluted to 200 ml., and heated to about 80°C. It is then saturated with hydrogen sulfide gas. Cobalt and nickel are precipitated as sulfides and the manganese remains in solution. The sulfides are filtered off and the filtrate concentrated. Colorless ammonium sulfide is added and the solution rendered acid with acetic. It is then warmed and filtered. This concentration and reprecipitation must be repeated if necessary.

**Electrolytic.**—Cobalt and nickel may be separated from manganese by electrolysis, the cobalt and nickel being plated out and the manganese remaining in solution or deposited at the anode.

**Sodium Chlorate.**—Manganese may be removed from a nitric acid solution of cobalt or nickel by boiling with sodium or potassium chlorate, preferably the former. An excess of chlorate at the end of the operation is essential. The manganese dioxide precipitated may be removed by filtration through an asbestos mat. For further details see Ford-Williams method in Chapter on Manganese.

**Potassium Bromate.**—Hampe [3] states that potassium bromate is an excellent precipitant for manganese in acid solution.

**Persulfates.**—Von Knorre [4] bases a separation for manganese on the action of potassium or ammonium persulfates in boiling acid solutions. Kolthoff and Sandell [5] found that with an acid concentration of 0.4 $N$ to 2 $N$ sulfuric acid, precipitation on boiling was complete, using potassium persulfate. Iron interferes, but not seriously until the ratio of iron to manganese exceeds 100 to 1. They recommend the potassium salt in preference to the ammonium. They also confirm the use of potassium bromate in acid solutions.

*Separation of Cobalt from Nickel.* **Dimethylglyoxime.**—Nickel is removed from the solution by precipitation with dimethylglyoxime. The details of the procedure may be found in the "Gravimetric Methods" in the Chapter on Nickel. Cobalt remains in solution.

**Alpha-nitroso-beta-naphthol.**—Cobalt is precipitated by alpha-nitroso-beta-naphthol, leaving nickel in solution. Details of the procedure are given under "Gravimetric Methods" in this chapter.

**Potassium Nitrite.**—Cobalt is precipitated as potassium cobaltinitrite, nickel remaining in solution. Details of the procedure are given under "Gravimetric Methods" in this chapter.

*Separation of Cobalt and Nickel from Zinc.* **As the Sulfide.**—Zinc sulfide is precipitated from dilute acetic and formic solutions by hydrogen sulfide. It is also precipitated by the same gas from hydrochloric and sulfuric acid solutions, if the acidity is properly adjusted. Full details are given under "Standard Methods for Zinc."

*Separation of Cobalt and Nickel from Chromium.*—Cobaltous and nickelous hydroxides precipitated from a sodium hydroxide solution are oxidized to the black cobaltic and nickelic hydroxides by chlorine, bromine, sodium hypochlorite, or sodium hypobromite, leaving the chromium in solution as chromate, from which they may be separated by filtration. Ammonium salts must be absent.

*Separation of Cobalt and Nickel from Iron.* **Electrolysis in the Presence of the Iron Hydroxide.**

**Repeated Precipitations with Ammonium Hydroxide and Hydrogen Peroxide.**

**Basic Acetate Separation.**—Full details of the procedure to be followed are given in the Chapter on Manganese.

**Ether Separation.**—Details are given under separations in the Chapter on Iron.

**Precipitation by Zinc Oxide.**[6]—An emulsion of zinc oxide, added to an oxidized solution of either chlorides or sulfates, from which the second group has been removed, precipitates iron, aluminum, and chromium, leaving cobalt, nickel, and manganese in solution. The solution is first rendered neutral to methyl orange with sodium carbonate, and the emulsion added in small lots at a time with agitation, till in decided excess. For routine work the precipitation may be carried

---

[3] Hampe, Chem. Ztg., **7**, 1106, 1883; **9**, 1083, 1885.
[4] Von Knorre, Z. angew. Chem., **14**, 1149, 1901; **16**, 905, 1903; Chem. Ztg., **27**, 53, 1903.
[5] Kolthoff and Sandell, Ind. Eng. Chem., Anal. Ed. **1**, 181, 1929.
[6] See Hoffman, Bur. Stds. J. Res., **7**, 883, 1931.

out in a 1000-ml. volumetric flask and as soon as the reaction is complete this is diluted up to the mark. It is allowed to settle for half an hour, then an aliquot portion filtered off. Generally this separation is used in conjunction with the alpha-nitroso-beta-naphthol method, which procedure is described under "Gravimetric Methods" in this chapter.

## GRAVIMETRIC METHODS

### PRECIPITATION OF COBALT BY $\alpha$-NITROSO-$\beta$-NAPHTHOL

When $\alpha$-nitroso-$\beta$-naphthol is added to a hydrochloric acid solution of cobalt, a brick red precipitate of cobaltinitroso-beta-naphthol, $Co[C_{10}H_6O(NO)]_3$, is formed. Copper, silver, bismuth, tin, chromium, iron, zirconium, titanium, vanadium, and nitric acid interfere, but mercury, lead, cadmium, arsenic, antimony, aluminum, manganese, nickel, calcium, magnesium, beryllium, zinc, and phosphate do not.

This is an excellent procedure for cobalt, especially for the determination of small to medium quantities in complex materials containing considerable nickel. The cobalt precipitate is voluminous, so the sample taken should preferably not contain over 0.1 gram of cobalt. Copper and other Group 2 metals are removed with $H_2S$, and iron, together with other remaining interfering elements, is separated with zinc oxide, sodium phosphate, or ether. The cobalt precipitate is ignited and weighed as $Co_3O_4$, or the latter may be dissolved and the cobalt determined by electrolysis.

#### SEPARATION OF IRON BY ZINC OXIDE

*Procedure.*—Weigh out 0.5–10 g. depending on the cobalt content of the sample, and take into solution with 10–25 ml. $HNO_3$, 10–25 ml. HCl, 10 ml. 1:1 $H_2SO_4$, and a few drops of HF if necessary. For high sulfide products initial treatment with a little bromine or potassium chlorate is advisable to avoid the inclusion of undissolved particles in a bead of sulfur. Certain high-cobalt alloys, such as Stellites, are best decomposed by prolonged treatment with perchloric acid. Evaporate to strong fumes of $SO_3$, cool, dilute with water, and boil. Adjust the acidity to 5–10% $H_2SO_4$ and gas out all Group 2 metals with $H_2S$. Filter off the precipitated sulfides and silica, and wash thoroughly with acidulated $H_2S$ water.

Boil the filtrate for 15 minutes to remove all $H_2S$, oxidize the iron with $H_2O_2$, and boil to remove the excess of peroxide. Nearly neutralize with $Na_2CO_3$ solution and boil to remove all $CO_2$. Add a suspension of zinc oxide until the precipitate assumes the color of coffee containing cream. Boil and filter, washing 3–4 times with hot water. Transfer the precipitate back to the original beaker, just dissolve with HCl and reprecipitate with zinc oxide emulsion. Filter through the original filter paper and wash thoroughly 7–8 times with hot water. The filtrate will contain only Co, Ni, Mn and a few other elements not affecting the alpha-nitroso-beta-naphthol precipitation. A turbidity in the filtrate caused by colloidal zinc oxide may be disregarded, as subsequent acid treatment dissolves this. For very accurate work on small quantities of cobalt in the presence of large amounts of iron, aluminum, etc., a third precipitation with zinc oxide may be necessary.

Add 20 ml. HCl in a volume of 500 ml. of the filtrate to dissolve the colloidal zinc oxide and hold nickel in solution, heat to boiling and cautiously add sufficient alpha-nitroso-beta-naphthol in 1:1 acetic acid to precipitate all the cobalt. Use 0.5 g. alpha-nitroso-beta-naphthol for each 0.01 g. cobalt. Allow the red precipitate of cobaltinitroso-beta-naphthol to boil several minutes, remove from the hot plate, and allow to stand in a warm place several hours.

Filter on a Whatman No. 42 paper, using pulp, wash several times with hot water, ten times with hot 5% HCl, and finally with hot water until free of chlorides. Place paper and precipitate in a weighed porcelain crucible, dry, ignite carefully in a muffle at a temperature not exceeding 850°C. Cool in a desiccator and weigh as $Co_3O_4$.

$$Co_3O_4 \times 0.7342 = Co$$

For routine work the precipitate may be ignited in a fireclay crucible or annealing cup and brushed onto the balance pan.

If the final residue of $Co_3O_4$ is contaminated with nickel, or if it is very bulky, it may be dissolved in HCl and cobalt reprecipitated with alpha-nitroso-beta-naphthol. If iron contamination is suspected, dissolve the cobalt oxide residue in acids, evaporate to strong fumes of $SO_3$, cool, make ammoniacal, and electrolyze as described later.

## SEPARATION OF IRON BY SODIUM PHOSPHATE

When iron is precipitated as ferric phosphate from a solution containing cobalt there is remarkably little occlusion of the latter. For all routine work one precipitation, even in the presence of large quantities of iron, is sufficient.[7] A filtrate is obtained upon which cobalt may be determined by alpha-nitroso-beta-naphthol precipitation, or directly by electrolysis. Aluminum, titanium, zirconium, and uranium are removed by the phosphate separation. Chromium and vanadium divide and therefore interfere, unless removed previously with sodium hydroxide.

*Reagents.* **Trisodium Phosphate Solution.**—Dissolve 34.05 g. $Na_3PO_4 \cdot 12H_2O$ in 1 liter of water.

**Acetic Acid Wash Solution.**—25 ml. glacial acetic acid in 1 liter of water.

*Procedure.*—Carry out the decomposition and initial treatment of the sample as given in the Separation above, to the point where excess $H_2O_2$ is removed by boiling. Add sufficient trisodium phosphate solution to precipitate all the iron, etc., plus 5 ml. excess. Ten ml. of the phosphate solution will precipitate 0.05 g. Fe. Then add $NH_4OH$ carefully from a burette with vigorous agitation until purple cobaltous phosphate is formed. If the sample is low in cobalt it may be difficult to see the cobaltous phosphate, and a piece of red litmus should be used as indicator. When the litmus turns blue a pH has been reached that is sufficiently low to ensure that cobaltous phosphate has been precipitated.

Dissolve the cobaltous phosphate by the addition of exactly 10 ml. glacial acetic acid, with vigorous stirring. This will give a pH of 3.0–3.5. Oxidize the solution by adding 5–20 ml. $H_2O_2$ and stir thoroughly. The iron is now precipitated as a creamy white precipitate of ferric phosphate. Bring the sample to the boil on the hot plate, stirring occasionally to prevent bumping if a heavy iron precipitate is present. Filter through a Whatman No. 531 or 541 paper on a fluted funnel, using paper pulp. If a heavy precipitate of ferric phosphate is present, filter through a Buechner funnel. Wash the precipitate 8–10 times with hot acetic acid

[7] Young, R. S., and Hall, A. J., Ind. Eng. Chem., Anal. Ed., **18**, 262–4, 1946.

wash solution. Proceed directly with the determination of cobalt by precipitation with alpha-nitroso-beta-naphthol, or add 10 ml. 1:1 $H_2SO_4$, 40 ml. $NH_4OH$, and electrolyze.

## SEPARATION OF IRON BY ETHER

Separation of iron by an ether extraction is particularly suitable for low-cobalt steels or slags, since several 5- or 10-g. portions may be combined after the ether separation.

*Procedure.*—Carry out the initial decomposition and treatment as outlined under "Separation of Iron by Zinc Oxide" above, up to the point where the excess hydrogen peroxide is boiled out. Evaporate to dryness with $H_2SO_4$, add a little HCl to bring salts into solution, and evaporate carefully to a syrupy consistency. Transfer the contents of the beaker to a 250- or 500-ml. separatory funnel, rinsing the beaker thoroughly with HCl of sp. gr. 1.10 and finally several times with ether. Add more ether to bring the concentration up to 30 ml. per gram of iron in 20 ml. HCl of sp. gr. 1.10. Hydrochloric acid of sp. gr. 1.10 is made by mixing 526 ml. concentrated HCl with 474 ml. water.

Shake the funnel vigorously under the cold water tap, allow to settle, and draw off the lower layer into a 400-ml. beaker. This contains the cobalt together with Ni, Mn, etc., while the upper layer contains nearly all the iron. Extract the upper and lower layers again with ether and HCl of sp. gr. 1.10 to make a complete separation.

Place the beaker containing cobalt on the edge of the hot plate on asbestos to drive off all ether, add 5 ml. 1:1 $H_2SO_4$, and evaporate to dryness. Add a few milliliters of HCl and water to bring salts into solution, adjust acidity to 4 ml. HCl per 100 ml. solution and proceed with the alpha-nitroso-beta-naphthol precipitation. If chromium or vanadium are present they must be removed with a sodium hydroxide-peroxide separation, or with zinc oxide, prior to the nitroso-beta-naphthol precipitation.

## PRECIPITATION OF COBALT BY POTASSIUM NITRITE

Cobalt is precipitated as potassium cobaltinitrite, $2K_3Co(NO_2)_6 \cdot 3H_2O$, from a solution made slightly acid with an excess of acetic acid, by adding a hot solution of potassium nitrite and allowing to stand for at least six hours in a warm place. So many substances interfere, such as oxidizing agents, free mineral acids, Group 2 metals, aluminum, iron, chromium, alkaline earths, and ammonium salts, that about the only place where the procedure is applicable is after a combined plating of cobalt and nickel from ammoniacal solution. Consequently, it is little used.

*Procedure.*—Dissolve the combined deposit of cobalt and nickel off the platinum cathode with hot nitric acid, after electrolysis as described under the "Electrolytic Method" below. Evaporate the solution to a low volume, dilute to 30 ml. with water, and neutralize with potassium carbonate. Add 2–3 ml. acetic acid and boil. Dissolve 15–20 g. potassium nitrite in 25 ml. water and acidify with 2 ml. acetic acid. Bring this solution to boiling and add to the cobalt solution with brisk stirring. Boil for 30 minutes and set aside in a warm place for at least 6 hours. Filter through a fritted-glass crucible, and wash six times with 5% potassium nitrite solution acidified with acetic acid. Transfer the crucible to the original beaker, dissolve the potassium cobaltinitrite with 35 ml. warm 1:6 sulfuric acid, remove the crucible and wash by passing water through it several times. Evaporate the solution to dryness. Add 10 ml. 1:1 $H_2SO_4$, 50 ml. of water, neutralize with ammonium hydroxide, and add 50 ml. excess ammonium hydroxide.   Electrolyze for cobalt in the usual manner.

## ELECTROLYTIC METHOD

For medium or large quantities of cobalt the electrolytic determination is the most satisfactory procedure.  Cobalt is electrolyzed in a strongly ammoniacal solution in the presence of ammonium sulfate.  Copper and other Group 2 metals are removed with $H_2S$, and iron removed with zinc oxide or ether and cobalt precipitated by alpha-nitroso-beta-naphthol, or iron eliminated by means of phosphate. Where only small quantities of iron are present, several precipitations with ammonium hydroxide will liberate virtually all the cobalt.  Cobalt may even be electrolyzed, for routine work, in the presence of iron.  Where cobalt has not been isolated by means of alpha-nitroso-beta-naphthol prior to electrolysis, any nickel of course will be deposited with cobalt and must be determined by dimethylglyoxime on the dissolved plating.

*Procedure.*—Weigh out 0.5–5.0 g. of finely ground sample and decompose with 10–25 ml. of $HNO_3$, 10–25 ml. of HCl and 10 ml. of 1:1 $H_2SO_4$.  For high sulfide products initial treatment with a little bromine or potassium chlorate is advisable, and for silicate materials a few drops of HF should be added during acid digestion. For certain cobalt alloys which are difficultly soluble in the above acids, prolonged treatment with perchloric acid, followed by filtration of any precipitated tungstic acid, is recommended.  If cobalt arsenides are present it may assist the subsequent hydrogen sulfide treatment if most of the arsenic is eliminated by reducing it to the arsenious state, after an initial decomposition to fumes of sulfuric acid, with a gram or two of sodium thiosulfate, adding 50 ml. HCl and evaporating to dryness.

After evaporating to strong fumes of sulfuric acid, cool the sample and adjust the acidity to 5–10% $H_2SO_4$.  Gas out all Group 2 metals with $H_2S$, filter, wash, and boil the filtrate to expel all $H_2S$, oxidize with $H_2O_2$, and boil out any excess of the latter.

If only small quantities of iron or aluminum are present, make strongly ammoniacal, boil, filter, redissolve the precipitate in sulfuric acid, and repeat the precipitation several times to pass almost all the occluded cobalt into the filtrate. When larger quantities of iron are present, separate by zinc oxide or ether followed by alpha-nitroso-beta-naphthol, or by sodium phosphate, as given in the section on "Gravimetric Methods."  Where chromium is present, the zinc oxide separation must be used, or chromium separated by a sodium hydroxide-sodium peroxide treatment.  If cobalt is precipitated with alpha-nitroso-beta-naphthol and ignited to oxide, transfer to a beaker, add a little HCl, $HNO_3$, and 5 ml. 1:1 $H_2SO_4$.  Evaporate to fumes of the latter, cool, neutralize with $NH_4OH$ and add 40 ml. excess.  If the sample has been fumed to dryness, add more 1:1 $H_2SO_4$ or ammonium sulfate to ensure the presence of the latter after making ammoniacal. Electrolyze overnight on a stationary cabinet at 0.5 ampere, or on a rotating electrolytic apparatus at 2 amperes for 1 hour.  Test the solution for complete deposition by withdrawing a few drops with a pipette onto a spot plate and testing with potassium thiocarbonate, phenylthiohydantoic acid, nitroso-R-salt, or ammonium sulfide, by the usual spot tests for these reagents.

Wash the cathode, rinse in alcohol, dry on a hot plate or in a blast of warm air from a hair dryer, and weigh the previously tared cathode.

If nickel was suspected in the original sample and the cobalt was not separated by alpha-nitroso-beta-naphthol, place the cathode in a tall-form 300-ml. beaker, add 50 ml. $HNO_3$ and dissolve the plating by placing on the edge of a hot plate for 10 minutes, making sure that all parts of the cathode come in contact with the hot acid. Remove the cathode, washing thoroughly into the beaker, and test the solution for nickel in the usual manner with dimethylglyoxime. Subtract the nickel content, if any, from the weight of the cobalt deposit obtained on the cathode.

For routine work, cobalt may be electrolyzed in the presence of iron. Electrolyze the ammoniacal cobalt solution containing suspended ferric hydroxide in a tall 600-ml. beaker for 45 minutes on a rotating apparatus at 2 amperes. Lower the beaker from the cathode, washing the latter, dissolve the ferric hydroxide with $H_2SO_4$, and reprecipitate with $NH_4OH$, adding 30 ml. excess. Continue the electrolysis for 30 minutes longer, lower the beaker, dissolve the ferric hydroxide and reprecipitate as before to set free any occluded cobalt. Continue the electrolysis a further 30 minutes. This should result in complete deposition of cobalt, indicated by a negative test for this element when a small portion of the solution is withdrawn with a pipette, filtered and tested on the spot plate with ammonium sulfide, phenylthiohydantoic acid, or nitroso-R-salt.

With the above procedure, a little iron is occluded with the deposited cobalt on the cathode. For accurate work it is necessary to dissolve the plating in hot $HNO_3$, take to fumes of $H_2SO_4$, make ammoniacal and reelectrolyze. This second electrolysis at 2 amperes on a rotating machine only requires 1 hour or less.

## TITRIMETRIC METHODS

### CYANIDE METHOD

In the absence of nickel, cobalt may be determined by cyanide titration in a manner similar to this familiar procedure for nickel.

Potassium cyanide reacts with cobaltic sulfate to give a complex cobalt cyanide. The end point of the reaction is determined by an indirect indicator, silver iodide, which gives a turbidity to the solution until a slight excess of potassium cyanide is present. Silver iodide is formed *in situ* by the action of $AgNO_3$ on KI. The end point of the reaction is indicated by the disappearance of the cloudy precipitate of silver iodide. Since it is generally easier to detect the appearance of a turbidity than its disappearance, a slight excess of KCN is added and a back titration with $AgNO_3$ carried out until a faint opalescence is again formed.

*Procedure.*—Decompose the sample with 10 ml. $HNO_3$, 10 ml. HCl, and a few drops of HF if necessary. Add 10 ml. 1:1 $H_2SO_4$ and fume strongly to dehydrate silica. Dissolve in water, gas out copper and other Group 2 elements with $H_2S$, and filter off precipitated sulfides, silica, etc. Boil out all $H_2S$ and oxidize thoroughly by adding 10 ml. $HNO_3$, 1–2 g. potassium chlorate and boil gently for 15 minutes. Cool in a water bath, add $NH_4OH$ just to the neutral point, and add 10–20 ml. of ammonium citrate-sulfate buffer solution for each 0.1 g. iron present. Place a piece of litmus paper against the side of the beaker and carefully add $NH_4OH$ until the litmus turns blue. Add exactly 2 ml. more $NH_4OH$ and boil gently for 2–5 minutes.

Cool in a water bath, add 5 ml. of 10% KI and 2–3 ml. of standard $AgNO_3$ from a burette. Add standard KCN solution from a burette with constant stirring until the cloudiness produced by silver iodide disappears. Finally, add standard $AgNO_3$ solution drop by drop with constant stirring, over a black background, until a persistent cloudiness is again produced. The total number of milliliters of standard $AgNO_3$ solution used is then subtracted from the number of milliliters of standard KCN to give the percentage of cobalt.

Standardize the cyanide solution against the silver nitrate and, in addition, titrate the cyanide against a solution containing a known amount of cobalt. One gram of $CoSO_4 \cdot 7H_2O$ contains 0.2097 g. cobalt, and a 25-ml. aliquot from a liter of solution containing 1 g. of this salt gives a convenient quantity for titration against dilute KCN. Check the solution of $CoSO_4 \cdot 7H_2O$ electrolytically. It is useful to have two standard KCN solutions, one for low cobalts with a value approximating 1 ml. = 0.001 g. Co, and another for high cobalts possessing a titer of 1 ml. = 0.005 g. Co.

The solutions are made up to contain 5.6 g. KCN + 1 g. KOH per liter, and 28 g. KCN + 5 g. KOH per liter, respectively. They are standardized against silver nitrate solutions containing 7.2060 g. $AgNO_3$ and 36.0300 g. $AgNO_3$ per liter, respectively. Standardization should be carried out at least once a week.

After the addition of silver nitrate to the samples, keep them out of direct sunlight, as the latter has a tendency to reduce AgI to metallic silver and to give erratic results.

The ammonium citrate-sulfate solution has the following composititon:

| | |
|---|---|
| Citric Acid | 200 g. |
| Ammonium Sulfate | 270 g. |
| Ammonium Hydroxide | 200 ml. |
| Water to make | 1000 ml. |

With the exception of copper, which is removed with $H_2S$, and of course nickel, very few elements interfere with the cyanide titration of cobalt.[8]

## POTENTIOMETRIC FERRICYANIDE METHOD

A very satisfactory procedure for cobalt on a wide range of products is a potentiometric one, based on the oxidation of cobalt in ammoniacal solution by potassium ferricyanide. In the cold, and in the presence of ammonium citrate, practically the only common element which interferes is manganese, and this can be removed by a nitro-chlorate separation. The potentiometric procedure is applicable in the presence of large quantities of copper, nickel, and iron, the three most common interfering elements in other methods for cobalt.

*Reagents.* **Ammonium Citrate Solution.**—Dissolve 200 g. citric acid in water and add slowly 270 ml. ammonium hydroxide. Cool and make up to 1 liter.

**Cobalt Nitrate Solution.**—Weigh out 5.00 g. cobalt nitrate, dissolve in water, and make up to 1 liter. Standardize the solution by determining the cobalt electrolytically. One ml. of this solution should contain approximately 1 mg. Co.

**Potassium Ferricyanide Solution.**—Weigh out 11 g. of potassium ferricyanide, dissolve in water, and make up to 1 liter. Keep this solution in a brown bottle.

*Standardization of the Potassium Ferricyanide Solution.*—Measure carefully 10 ml. of potassium ferricyanide solution from a standard burette or pipette into a 600-ml. beaker. Add 20 ml. ammonium citrate, 80 ml. ammonium hydroxide, and make up to 400–500 ml. with water. Place the beaker in position on a potentio-

8 Hall, A. J., and Young, R. S., Chemistry and Industry, 44, 394–395, 1946.

metric titration apparatus and switch on the current and stirrer. Run in standard cobalt nitrate solution from a burette until a large and permanent deflection is given on the galvanometer scale. Ten ml. of potassium ferricyanide should be equivalent to 20 ml. of cobalt nitrate, or 1 ml. of potassium ferricyanide equals 2 mg. Co.

*Procedure.*—Decompose the sample with $HNO_3$, HCl, and bromine or hydrofluoric acid where necessary. When all the sample is in solution, boil thoroughly to drive off nitrous fumes, but it is not necessary to evaporate to low volume. If the samples cannot be decomposed without the addition of $H_2SO_4$, add 10–25 ml. 1:1 $H_2SO_4$ and evaporate to fumes.

If manganese is present, evaporate the mixed acid solution nearly to dryness. Add 40–50 ml. $HNO_3$ and carefully add several small portions of sodium chlorate, boiling gently after each addition. Dilute slightly and filter off the $MnO_2$ through a Whatman No. 42 paper or through asbestos on a Gooch crucible.

The insoluble matter, other than $MnO_2$, need not be filtered off, but if large quantities are present it is good practice to do so. Cool the samples and titrate carefully with ammonium hydroxide until the iron just begins to precipitate. Redissolve the iron by the addition of a drop or two of 1:1 $HNO_3$. Cool the samples again thoroughly.

Measure out carefully from a standard burette or pipette into a 600-ml. beaker sufficient excess potassium ferricyanide solution to give a back titration of 10–15 ml. of cobalt nitrate solution. Add 10–20 ml. ammonium citrate for every 0.1 g. of iron present in the sample, followed by 80 ml. ammonium hydroxide. Pour the sample very slowly with constant stirring into the beaker containing potassium ferricyanide, etc. There must be no heating effect produced at this point, and if the sample has been almost neutralized and cooled beforehand, no heat will be developed.

Place the beaker containing the sample on the potentiometric apparatus and back-titrate the excess potassium ferricyanide with standard cobalt nitrate solution until the end point is shown by a large and permanent deflection of the galvanometer beam.

If chromium and vanadium are present, the sample should be decomposed with $HNO_3$ and HCl, and then taken to strong fumes of a low volume of perchloric acid. The sample is then poured directly into the beaker containing excess ferricyanide, ammonium citrate, and 80 ml. ammonium hydroxide, without preliminary neutralization. Vanadium is in the vanadate state and does not interfere with the titration.

Quantities of cobalt up to 150 mg. in complex materials can be accurately and rapidly determined in this manner. The following do not interfere: Hg(ic), Pb, Fe, Ni, Cu, Bi, Cd, As(ic), Sb, Sn(ic), Se, Te, Mo, Cr (ate), Be, Al, Zn, Ti, W, U, V (ate), Zr.

## COLORIMETRIC METHODS

### NITROSO-R-SALT METHOD

This determination is based on the fact that the colored complexes formed by most of the common elements with nitroso-R-salt, except cobalt, are destroyed by nitric acid. The full development of the color with cobalt is attained in the presence of sodium acetate, and such variables as quantity of nitric acid and of nitroso-R-salt, time of boiling etc. have an influence on the development of color.[9]

*Reagents.* **Cobalt Sulfate.**—Dissolve 0.2385 g. $CoSO_4 \cdot 7H_2O$ in water and make up to 1 liter. 1 ml. = 0.05 mg. Co.

**Nitroso-R-Salt.**—Dissolve 1 g. $C_{10}H_4OH \cdot NO(SO_3 \cdot Na)_2$ in water and make up to 500 ml.

**Spekker Acid.**—Mix 150 ml. $H_3PO_4$ and 150 ml. $H_2SO_4$, and make up to 1 liter.

**Sodium Acetate.**—Dissolve 500 g. $NaC_2H_3O_2 \cdot 3H_2O$ in water and make up to 1 liter.

*Procedure.*—For samples containing 0.01–0.20% cobalt, use a 0.25-g. sample. With higher grade materials take a 0.5-g. sample and, after decomposition, dilute to volume and take a suitable aliquot containing 0.01–0.5 mg. cobalt for analysis. For very low concentrations of cobalt, larger samples, 1–20 g. may be taken. The maximum quantity of cobalt permissible in a sample is 0.5 mg., as above this concentration the solution no longer appears to follow Beer's Law exactly.

Decompose with $HNO_3$, HCl, add 5.0–7.5 ml. 1:1 $H_2SO_4$, and take to strong fumes. Some products will require bromine or hydrofluoric acid to assist decomposition. Care should be taken in the addition of reagents, as an excessive concentration of salts in the final solution will increase the absorption.

Cool, dilute to about 30 ml., add 2 ml. HCl, and boil to solution of soluble salts. Pass a brisk current of $H_2S$ through the solution for 10 minutes and filter through a Whatman No. 40 paper, washing well with acidulated $H_2S$ water. Boil off $H_2S$, add 5 ml. $HNO_3$, and take to fumes of $SO_3$.

Cool, dilute to about 25 ml. with water, and boil to solution of salts. Cool, carefully neutralize with 20% NaOH to the first pink appearance with a few drops of phenolphthalein. Immediately add 2 ml. Spekker acid, followed by 10 ml. nitroso-R-salt solution, and 10 ml. sodium acetate solution. Bring to a vigorous boil, add 5 ml. $HNO_3$, and then boil for at least 1 minute and not more than 2 minutes. Cool and dilute with water to 100 ml.

Compare the absorption of the samples on a photoelectric colorimeter or similar instrument with that of a series of standards containing known quantities of cobalt carried through the same procedure.

Manganese over 10%, nickel over 3%, and chromium above 5%, must be removed prior to the color comparison. The following are without effect, even in quantities over 100 times that of the cobalt: Fe, Al, Zn, Ti, Th, U, Zr, W, Ba, Sr, Ca, and Mg. By increasing the sodium acetate and nitric acid additions, and paying strict attention to times of boiling, it has been shown that small quantities of copper need not be removed for this procedure.

## AMMONIUM THIOCYANATE METHOD

Cobalt forms a complex with ammonium thiocyanate which can be extracted with amyl alcohol and ether, and the blue cobaltothiocyanate color measured in a colorimeter.

*Reagents.* **Ammonium Thiocyanate.**—Dissolve 600 g. of $NH_4CNS$ in 1 liter of water.

[9] Young, R. S., Pinkney, E. T., and Dick, R., Ind. Eng. Chem., Anal. Ed., **18**, 474–6, 1946; Hall, A. J., and Young, R. S., Anal. Chem., **22**, 497, 1950.

**Sodium Phosphate.**—Dissolve 83.3 g. of $Na_3PO_4 \cdot 12H_2O$ in 1 liter of water.

**Sodium Thiosulfate.**—Dissolve 200 g. of $Na_2S_2O_3 \cdot 5H_2O$ in 1 liter of water.

**Ammonium Acetate.**—Dissolve 700 g. of $NH_4C_2H_3O_2$ in 1 liter of water.

**Tartaric Acid.**—Dissolve 50 g. of $C_4H_6O_6$ in 1 liter of water.

**Amyl Alcohol-Ether.**—Mix 3 parts by volume of amyl alcohol with 1 part of ethyl ether.

*Procedure.*—Decompose the sample with 10 ml. $HNO_3$ and 10 ml. HCl, adding a few drops of bromine initially for sulfide ores, or HF for silicate materials. For high iron material use $HNO_3$ and $KClO_3$. Evaporate the sample to dryness but do not bake.

Dissolve the samples in approximately 25 ml. of water, and add exactly 1 ml. HCl for every 50 ml. of subsequent dilution of the sample. Boil, cool, and dilute the sample so that 50 ml. will contain not more than 0.004 g. cobalt. Measure out 5 ml. sodium thiosulfate solution, 3 ml. sodium phosphate solution, 10 ml. ammonium thiocyanate solution, and 2 ml. ammonium acetate solution. Add with vigorous agitation a 5-ml. aliquot of the sample. If vanadium is present, add a few drops of tartaric acid.

Add 10 ml. of the amyl alcohol-ether mixture and shake the whole thoroughly again. Transfer to a separatory funnel, run off and discard the lower aqueous layer. Transfer the blue solution of the cobalt complex to a colorimeter and compare with a series of standards prepared similarly. Under the above conditions, the following do not interfere: Cu, Fe, Cr, Mn, Ni, Ti, Mo, U, Al, Si, Mg, Ca, P, Bi, As, Pb, and the alkalies.[10]

## DETERMINATIONS IN SPECIFIC SUBSTANCES

### BLACK AND GREY COBALT OXIDES

*Procedure.*—Decompose 1-g. sample with 15 ml. HCl and 15 ml. $HNO_3$, add 10 ml. 1:1 $H_2SO_4$ and take to strong fumes of the latter. If the insoluble is not pure white, or is large in quantity, filter it off, ignite, transfer to a platinum dish, decompose with HF and take to fumes of $H_2SO_4$, and add to the main filtrate. Gas out Group 2 metals with $H_2S$, filter, expel $H_2S$ by boiling, add $H_2O_2$, boil, and cool. Make strongly ammoniacal and determine cobalt by electrolysis, following the procedure given in the section entitled "Electrolytic Method."

### COBALT IN METALLIC COBALT

*Procedure.*—Determine cobalt by electrolysis after decomposition with nitric, hydrochloric, and sulfuric acids, similar to the procedure above for oxides.

### COBALT IN FERROCOBALT

*Procedure.*—Dissolve a 0.5-g. sample in 10 ml. $HNO_3$, 10 ml. HCl, and take to strong fumes with 10 ml. 1:1 $H_2SO_4$. Gas out Group 2 metals with $H_2S$, filter, expel $H_2S$ by boiling, add $H_2O_2$, boil, and cool. Remove iron by the procedures outlined for the zinc oxide, ether, or sodium phosphate separations, and determine cobalt electrolytically.

### COBALT IN METALLIC NICKEL

*Procedure.*—Dissolve a 5-g. sample in $HNO_3$ and HCl, add 10 ml. 1:1 $H_2SO_4$ and evaporate to strong fumes. Gas out Group 2 metals with $H_2S$, filter, boil the

[10] Young, R. S., and Hall, A. J., Ind. Eng. Chem., Anal. Ed., **18**, 264–6, 1946.

filtrate, and oxidize with $H_2O_2$. Remove iron with zinc oxide or ether, precipitate cobalt with alpha-nitroso-beta-naphthol, ignite to oxide, dissolve in HCl, add $H_2SO_4$ and evaporate to fumes, and electrolyze the cobalt in ammoniacal solution as directed in preceding sections. Check the dissolved plating for nickel with dimethylglyoxime and subtract if necessary.

For a very low concentration of cobalt in metallic nickel, copper may be removed by electrolysis or $H_2S$, and the cobalt determined colorimetrically by nitroso-R-salt.

A good routine method for cobalt in metallic nickel is the potentiometric procedure described previously, since copper, iron, and nickel do not require to be separated from the solution.

## COBALT IN CEMENTED CARBIDE

*Procedure.*—Decomposition of tungsten and other carbides is usually effected in a platinum dish with $HNO_3$ and HF, or by fusion with sodium peroxide in a nickel crucible. Cobalt may be determined by one of the standard methods, such as potentiometric titration.[11]

## OXIDE COBALT

It is often necessary in the mining and metallurgical industries to differentiate oxidized cobalt from sulfide cobalt. The following procedure is applicable to ores and concentrator products.[12] It is based on the selective solvent action of dilute $H_2SO_4$ or HCl, in the presence of HF and the reducing agent sulfurous acid, on oxidized cobalt minerals.

*Procedure.*—Depending upon the quantity of oxide cobalt present in the material and on the analytical method used for cobalt, select a weight of 200-mesh sample that will enable an accurate determination of cobalt to be made on the leached portion. For instance, in a mill feed or tail running 0.02% oxide cobalt, at least 25 g. must be taken for the initial sample if cobalt is to be precipitated by alpha-nitroso-beta-naphthol and weighed as oxide or determined electrolytically. If the colorimetric nitroso-R-salt procedure is employed on the same sample a weight of 0.25 g. will suffice.

The ratio of leach solution to sample may vary quite widely, depending on the quantity of oxide cobalt present and on the other constituents of the ore. In general, add 15–25 ml. of 10% by volume HCl saturated with $SO_2$, or of 5% by volume $H_2SO_4$ saturated with $SO_2$, to each gram of material in a stoppered Erlenmeyer flask or covered beaker. When the initial effervescence and attack has subsided, add 0.1–0.3 ml. HF per g. of sample. For large samples these quantities of HF can be reduced proportionally.

Shake the flask or beaker for 10–15 seconds every 10 minutes for 1 hour, allow to stand 1 hour, and again agitate briefly at intervals of 10 minutes during the third hour. A useful timer for controlling such intermittent mechanical shaking has been described.[13] Filter the sample through a Whatman No. 40 paper, using pulp, and wash thoroughly with hot water. To the filtrate add 10 ml. 1:1 $H_2SO_4$, if necessary, boil out $SO_2$, and evaporate to fumes of $SO_3$. Cool, dilute, boil to solution of salts, and remove copper and other Group 2 metals with $H_2S$.

[11] Furey, J. J., and Cunningham, T. R., Anal. Chem., **20**, 563–70, 1948; Touhey, W. O., and Redmond, J. C., Anal. Chem., **20**, 202–6, 1948.

[12] Young, R. S., Hall, A. J., and Talbot, H. L., Am. Inst. Min. Met. Eng. Tech. Publ. 2050, 1946.

[13] Young, R. S., Snaddon, R., and Tullett, V. A., J. Scientific Instruments, **29**, 266–7, 1952.

Filter off copper and other sulfides and wash well with acidulated $H_2S$ water. Boil out $H_2S$ from the filtrate and proceed with the determination of cobalt by any standard method.

## METALLIC COBALT IN SMELTER PRODUCTS

The following procedure, based on the report of Smirnov and Mishin,[14] has given good results on various smelter products.

*Procedure.*—To 2 g. of 200-mesh slag add 50 ml. of 7% mercuric chloride solution. Boil 1 minute, filter through Whatman No. 42 paper and wash thoroughly with hot water. The following reaction occurs:

$$Hg^{++} + Co \rightarrow Hg + Co^{++}$$

Metallic cobalt passes into the filtrate as the chloride and can be determined by any suitable procedure.

The following, if present in metallic form, will be extracted along with the cobalt: Mn, Cr, Fe, Ni, Bi, and Cu. Cobaltosic oxide, $Co_3O_4$, is insoluble in the mercuric chloride solution, and cobaltic oxide $Co_2O_3$ is only soluble to the extent of 0.1–0.3%. Cobaltous oxide, however, appears to be slightly soluble. The extent of its solubility is difficult to determine as it is invariably mixed with $Co_3O_4$ and $Co_2O_3$. Cobalt sulfide and cobalt silicate are apparently insoluble in the mercuric chloride solution.

NOTES.—When determining cobalt on the filtrate it is necessary to keep in mind the following facts. The $\alpha$-nitroso-$\beta$-naphthol and ammonium thiocyanate procedures can be applied directly, while electrolytic or nitroso-R-salt methods must be preceded by elimination of mercury with $H_2S$. By using an excess of $NH_4Cl$ the potentiometric procedure is directly applicable.

## DIFFERENTIATION OF COBALT OXIDES

*Procedure.*—Place 1 g. of the finely ground sample in a 250-ml. Erlenmeyer flask with 20 ml. water and shake well until all particles are thoroughly wetted. Add 30 ml. glacial acetic acid and attach to the flask a reflux condenser. Boil gently for 1 hour. Pour the contents of the flask onto a tared sintered-glass crucible and wash well with hot water. Dry to constant weight in the oven at 105°C.

Cobaltous oxide, CoO, is soluble in acetic acid under these conditions, whereas the higher oxides $Co_2O_3$ and $Co_3O_4$ are insoluble. Cobalt sulfide is virtually insoluble in dilute acetic acid under these conditions, and consequently cobaltous oxide can be separated from cobalt sulfide by this procedure.[15]

## ANALYSIS OF STELLITE AND OTHER COBALT BASE ALLOYS

The recent demand for high-temperature alloys has greatly enlarged the field of application for high cobalt alloys. In addition to maintaining their strength at elevated temperatures, many cobalt base materials, such as the Stellites, possess exceptional resistance to wear and corrosion. The analysis of a typical Stellite is given here as representative of this class of alloys, but may be modified as desired to suit the material under examination.

*Preparation of Sample.*—Reduce the material as finely as possible, without introducing significant contamination from abrasion of the mortar. Weigh out a 0.5–1.0-g. sample into a 300-ml. beaker, add several milliliters water, and 10–20

[14] Smirnov, V. I., and Mishin, V. D., Zavodskaya Lab., **11,** 1, 35–8, 1945.
[15] Young, R. S., and Simpson, H. R., Metallurgia, **45,** 51, 1952.

ml. perchloric acid. Take to strong fumes of perchloric acid. Cool, add 75 ml. hot water, and allow to digest on the side of the hot plate for an hour. Filter through Whatman No. 40 paper, with paper pulp, wash thoroughly with hot 5% HCl, and finally with hot water.

Wash the precipitated tungsten and the undissolved material back into the original beaker, add 5–10 ml. $NH_4OH$, and boil the solution until the tungsten is dissolved and the iron coagulated. Filter through the same paper and catch the filtrate in a tared platinum dish. Wash the residue on the filter paper with hot water and evaporate the filtrate in the platinum dish by placing on the hot plate. Spread the filter paper on the inside of the beaker, wash down the residue with a jet from a wash bottle containing hot 25% HCl, and finally wash with water. Fold the paper and put into a platinum crucible that is placed on the hot plate. Repeat the perchloric acid treatment on the residue, with the acid solution going to the main filtrate, the ammonia extract to the platinum dish, and the filter paper to the platinum crucible.

## DETERMINATION OF SILICON AND TUNGSTEN

*Procedure.*—Ignite the two filter papers in the platinum dish, which meanwhile should have evaporated to a few ml. Add 10 ml. HCl and continue evaporation to dryness. Ignite at a high temperature, cool, weigh, and record the increase in weight as $SiO_2 + WO_3$. Treat with 7 ml. HF and a few drops of 1:1 $H_2SO_4$, fume, ignite, cool, and weigh. The loss in weight is $SiO_2$, and by deducting this figure from the combined weight, the quantity of $WO_3$ is obtained.

## COPPER, COBALT, NICKEL, MANGANESE, IRON, AND CHROMIUM

*Procedure.*—Combine the filtrates from the perchloric acid treatments. Separate copper by evaporating to dryness, adjusting the acid concentration with HCl or $H_2SO_4$ to 5–10% and gassing with $H_2S$. Determine copper by the iodide method or other suitable procedure. Cobalt can be determined by the potentiometric method, after separating manganese by means of nitro-chlorate. Cobalt may also be determined by alpha-nitroso-beta-naphthol after removal of iron with zinc oxide, or by any other convenient procedure outlined above.

For high cobalt alloys where the great accuracy of the electrolytic procedure is required, remove the iron by zinc oxide and precipitate the cobalt with alpha-nitroso-beta-naphthol. Filter off the voluminous precipitate on a 15-cm Whatman No. 42 paper, washing thoroughly as described previously, and ignite the residue carefully in a large platinum dish. Dissolve the cobalt oxide in HCl, add $H_2SO_4$, and evaporate to fumes. Cool, make ammoniacal, add the usual excess, and electrolyze according to the directions given in the section on electrolysis of cobalt.

Nickel can be separated by dimethylglyoxime and weighed as such or determined electrolytically.

Manganese can be separated by filtration after oxidation of the iron with potassium persulfate, following the removal of copper with $H_2S$, and may be determined by the bismuthate procedure.

Iron can be determined titrimetrically with dichromate after precipitation with ammonium hydroxide, following removal of the copper with $H_2S$ and subsequent boiling and oxidation of the iron.

Chromium can be determined on a separate sample by fusing a 0.5-g. sample in a 50-ml. Armco iron crucible with 12–15 g. sodium peroxide. Dissolve in water and boil. Filter through a Buechner funnel and wash the residue thoroughly with hot 2% NaOH solution. Dilute the filtrate to 500 ml., acidify with 1:1 $H_2SO_4$, and add 50 ml. excess. Cool, add 5–7 g. KI, and titrate with 0.5 $N$ $Na_2S_2O_3$ solution, using starch as an indicator towards the end of the titration. If vanadium is present the iodide procedure cannot be used, and the ferrous sulfate-potassium permanganate method must be employed.

## METHODS FOR COBALT IN ANALYSES IN OTHER CHAPTERS

| | |
|---|---|
| Cobalt in Arsenious Oxide | See Analysis of Arsenious Oxide |
| Cobalt in Alloys by Ion Exchange | See Method in Chromium Chapter |
| Cobalt in Magnesium Alloys | See Analysis of Magnesium Alloys |
| Cobalt in Metallic Nickel | See Analysis of Metallic Nickel |

# Chapter 17

# COPPER *

Cu, *at. wt.* 63.54; *sp. gr.* 8.92 (at 20°C.); *m.p.* 1083°C. (in air 1065°C.); *b.p.* 2582°C.†; *oxides,* $Cu_2O$ *and* $CuO$

Copper is found in nature as the free metal and combined, principally as sulfide, oxide, and carbonate; less commonly in antimonides, arsenates, phosphates, silicates, and sulfates. Among the more common minerals are chalcopyrite, $CuFeS_2$; chalcocite, $Cu_2S$; bornite, $Cu_5FeS_4$; tetrahedrite, $Cu_8Sb_2S_7$; cuprite, $Cu_2O$; malachite, $CuCO_3 \cdot Cu(OH)_2$; and azurite, $2CuCO_3 \cdot Cu(OH)_2$.

Copper ores are widely distributed throughout the world and copper and its compounds occur in the sun, in meteorites, numerous rocks, soil, sea water, mineral water, plants, and many animal organisms. It is present either as a desired constituent or as an impurity in nearly all metallurgical products.

Copper was one of the earliest metals to be recognized and used by man. Its earliest use antedates all historical records. The earliest copper objects that have been preserved are dated at 4400 B.C. and bronze (copper-tin alloy) has been known nearly as long as the free metal, since objects dating to 3700 B.C. have been found. The early wide-spread use of this alloy gave the name to the civilization it did so much to develop—"The Bronze Age."

Pure copper is a salmon-pink, ductile metal. The reddish cast usually associated with the metal is due to a surface film of $Cu_2O$ which may be stripped with a dilute cyanide solution. Metallic copper is readily soluble in $HNO_3$. Other acids require the addition of an oxidizing agent (e.g. $H_2O_2$) before dissolution can be readily effected. Copper forms two oxides; red cuprous oxide, $Cu_2O$ and black cupric oxide, $CuO$. Both are basic anhydrides forming cuprous (univalent) and cupric (divalent) salts respectively. Cuprous salts except for the halides are rare. They are colorless, insoluble in water, but soluble in halogen acids forming colorless solutions which gradually darken due to air oxidation. Cupric salts are blue or green in aqueous solution; white or yellow when anhydrous. The chloride, nitrate, sulfate, and acetate are soluble in water; most of the other salts are insoluble in water, but readily soluble in dilute acids. Cupric salts in halogen acid solutions may be reduced to colorless cuprous compounds by metallic copper, $SnCl_2$, $H_3PO_2$, or $H_2SO_3$. When treated with caustic alkali cupric salts form a bluish gelatinous precipitate of $Cu(OH)_2$ which changes to black $CuO$ upon boiling. In strong caustic solutions the $Cu(OH)_2$ is slightly soluble. $Cu(OH)_2$ is not precipitated from caustic alkali solutions containing tartrate or citrate. However,

* Chapter contributed by O. P. Case, The American Brass Company, Waterbury, Conn.; with assistance from S. Skowronski, International Smelting and Refining Co.; C. Zischkau, American Smelting and Refining Co., and R. G. Ernst, U. S. Smelting and Refining Co.
† American Institute of Physics Handbook.

by heating these solutions with sugars, $As_2O_3$, hydrazine salts, or other reducing agents red $Cu_2O$ is precipitated. $NH_4OH$ precipitates a greenish basic salt from cupric solutions which dissolves readily in excess of $NH_4OH$ to form an intense blue complex. Addition of KCN to an ammoniacal cupric solution decolorizes it, forming the very stable cuprocyanide complex.

## DETECTION

*NH₄OH* in excess forms intensely blue cuprammonium ion. This test is sensitive to about 10 p. p. m. Cu. Ni also forms a blue complex with $NH_4OH$ which may be confused with the copper one. The two metals may be distinguished by the $K_4Fe(CN)_6$ test.

*Tetraethylenepentamine* in excess Cu also forms a blue complex which is about 3.5 times as intense as the one with $NH_4OH$. A complex is likewise formed with Ni, but the intensity is only about 1/70th that of the Cu complex.

*K₄Fe(CN)₆* in neutral or dilute acid solution with Cu forms a fine reddish precipitate that dissolves in $NH_4OH$ to form a blue solution (which distinguishes it from U and Mo ferrocyanides that dissolve to form yellow solutions). Ni in sufficient quantity may give a greenish precipitate under the same conditions. Directions are as follows: to 10 ml. of the neutral or slightly acid (acetic) sample solution add 0.5 ml. of 20% $K_4Fe(CN)_6$ and mix. A reddish precipitate indicates Cu. This test is sensitive to about 8 p. p. m. Cu.

*Alpha-Benzoinoxime (Cupron)* in weak $NH_4OH$ solution Cu forms a flocculent green precipitate. The addition of sodium potassium tartrate prevents interference from other metals. Large amounts of $NH_4^+$ salts reduce the sensitivity of the test. Directions are as follows: A drop of the weakly acid test solution is treated on filter paper with a drop of reagent (5% alcoholic solution) and held over $NH_4OH$. A green coloration indicates Cu. In the presence of large amounts of other metals precipitated by $NH_4OH$, a drop of 10% sodium potassium tartrate is placed on the filter paper before addition of the reagent. This test is sensitive to about 2 p. p. m. Cu. It has been applied to the detection of Cu in steel,[1] aluminum- and magnesium-base alloys,[2] zinc-base alloys,[3] and tin-base alloys.[4] These tests are applied to the surface of the metal and will detect about 0.10% Cu.

*Rubeanic Acid (Dithiooxamide)* in dilute acid solution with Cu forms a green precipitate. However, many other metals interfere by forming similar precipitates. Malonic acid and ethylenediamine form complexes with interfering metals leaving the test specific for Cu. Directions are as follows:[5] Place a drop of 20% malonic acid on a piece of spot test paper, then add a drop of solution to be tested. Next add a drop of 10% ethylenediamine followed by a drop of rubeanic acid (1% in ethanol). If Cu is present a green stain is obtained. This test is sensitive to about 1 p. p. m. of copper. It has been applied to the detection of copper in industrial waste water.[6]

*Sodium Diethyldithiocarbamate (Carbamate)* in $NH_4OH$ solution with Cu forms a yellow-brown precipitate which may be extracted with organic solvents. Many

[1] Evans, B. S., and Higgs, D. G., Analyst, **70**, 75, 1945.
[2] *Ibid.*, **71**, 464, 1946.
[3] *Ibid.*, **72**, 101, 1947.
[4] *Ibid.*, **72**, 439, 1947.
[5] West, P. W., Ind. Eng. Chem., Anal. Ed., **17**, 740, 1945.
[6] Butts, P. G., *et al.*, Sewage and Industrial Wastes, **22**, 1543, 1950.

other metals interfere by giving similarly colored precipitates which are also extracted. However, in the presence of ethylenediaminetetraacetic acid (Complexone or Versene) only Ag and Bi interfere.[7] Directions are as follows: To a sample solution of not more than 50 ml. add 10 ml. of 25% citric acid. Neutralize to litmus with $NH_4OH$ and add 3–5 ml. in excess. Add 15 ml. 4% disodium ethylenediaminetetraacetate and transfer to a separatory funnel. Add 10 ml. of 0.1% sodium diethyldithiocarbamate and 20 ml. of butyl acetate. Shake for 1 minute and allow layers to separate. A yellow-brown color in the butyl acetate layer indicates Cu. This test is sensitive to less than 1 p. p. m. Cu. It has been applied to the analysis of iron and steel.[8]

*2,9-Dimethyl-1,10-phenanthroline (Neo-Cuproine)* with cuprous Cu forms a yellow-amber color which is specific and extremely sensitive, especially when extracted with an organic solvent.[9] Directions are as follows: [10] Prepare a sample solution of not over 100 ml. in volume with the pH adjusted to 4–6, adding sodium citrate if necessary to prevent precipitation of Fe, etc. Transfer to a separatory funnel, add 5 ml. 10% hydroxylamine hydrochloride and shake to mix. Add 10 ml. of reagent (0.1% in absolute ethanol) and 10 ml. of chloroform. Shake for about 30 seconds and allow the layers to separate. A yellow-amber color in the chloroform layer indicates Cu. This test is sensitive to less than 0.05 p. p. m. Cu. It has been applied to the analysis of steels, water, manganese and tungsten ores, ferro-alloys, titanium alloys, and toxicological samples.

*Spectrographically* Cu in very small quantities may be readily detected in a variety of materials by means of its lines at 3247 and 3274 A.

## ESTIMATION

Materials commonly requiring the determination of copper are: ores, intermediate products in the production of refined copper (concentrates, tailings, mattes, furnace slags, blister copper, and tank-house electrolytes), electrolytic copper, fire-refined copper, copper-base alloys (brasses, bronzes, nickel silvers), other non-ferrous alloys (aluminum-, magnesium-, zinc-, nickel-, lead-, and tin-base alloys, Monel metal, silver solder, and precious metal alloys), steels, cast iron, plating baths, pesticides, water, sewage, industrial wastes, lubricants, and anti-fouling marine paints and pigments.

By far the greatest number of copper determinations are made by electrodeposition which can often be applied without any prior separations. Also widely used are the titrimetric iodide method and several photometric methods which can also often be directly applied.

## PREPARATION AND SOLUTION OF THE SAMPLE

It is assumed that the sample that has reached the laboratory is representative of the material being sampled.

Ores, concentrates, tailing, mattes, furnace slags, and similar materials should ordinarily be ground to pass a 100-mesh screen. Some exceptionally refractory materials may have to be ground to 200 mesh.

[7] Sedivec, V., and Vasak, V., Collection Czechoslov. Chem. Communs, **15**, 260, 1950 (in English).

[8] Hague, J. L., *et al.*, J. Research N.B.S., **47**, 380, 1951, R.P. 2265.

[9] Smith, G. F., and McCurdy, W. H., Anal. Chem., **24**, 371, 1952.

[10] Gahler, A. R., Paper presented at the Pittsburgh Conference on Analytical Chemistry and Applied Spectroscopy, Mar. 3, 1953.

Metallic materials may be brought into a form suitable for analysis by drilling, milling, or clipping in such a way as to obtain a representative sample. Sample chips containing grease or oil should be cleaned with ether. Oxide stains may be removed from the surface of copper or copper alloy chips by treatment with a solution of NaCN. After treatment the chips should be thoroughly washed, rinsed successively with alcohol and ether, and dried.

Liquid samples will ordinarily be measured by volume rather than by weight.

*Dissolution of the Sample.*—The dissolution of metallic copper requires an oxidizing acid. $HNO_3$ is usually employed, often in combination with $H_2SO_4$ or HCl. Hot $HClO_4$ is also quite effective. Either HCl or $H_2SO_4$ may be used in combination with 30% $H_2O_2$ as the oxidizing agent. HBr plus bromine is especially effective for alloys containing large amounts of Sn, Sb, or As that may be readily volatilized as bromides.

Aluminum alloys are usually treated with a strong solution of NaOH to dissolve the aluminum and finally with an excess of $HNO_3$ to dissolve Cu, Fe, Ni, etc.

Silicides or refractory materials may be decomposed by heating with HF and $HNO_3$ followed by $H_2SO_4$ or by a sodium carbonate or sodium peroxide fusion.

Bromine or potassium chlorate are often used in combination with $HNO_3$ for the decomposition of sulfide ores.

Samples containing organic material may be heated with a combination of $HNO_3$, $H_2SO_4$, and $HClO_4$ to destroy the organic matter.

## SEPARATIONS

*With $H_2S$.*—Copper may be separated as CuS from elements other than those in Group II [(a) $Hg^{++}$, Pb, Bi, Cd, etc.; (b) As, Sb, Sn, Se, Te, Mo, etc.] by precipitation with $H_2S$ in solutions up to 4 $N$ in HCl, assuming the prior separation of Ag and $Hg^+$ as chlorides. For separating amounts of Cu less than 0.1 mg. a little Pb may be added as a collector and the acidity adjusted to pH 2.0. This separation is widely used in the analysis of steels, aluminum and magnesium alloys, and nickel and its salts. In the absence of appreciable quantities of lead an $H_2SO_4$ solution may be used. $HNO_3$ solution may also be used, but considerable quantities of sulfur contaminate the precipitate.

*With Sodium Thiosulfate or Hydrosulfite (Dithionite).*—Copper may be separated from elements other than those of Group II as $Cu_2S$ by boiling a dilute $H_2SO_4$ solution with $Na_2S_2O_3 \cdot 5H_2O$ or $Na_2S_2O_4 \cdot 2H_2O$. Considerable sulfur also separates making a precipitate that is easily filtered and washed. This separation is much used in the analysis of copper ores. Directions are as follows: Prepare a sulfate solution containing approximately 5 ml. excess $H_2SO_4$, dilute to 250 ml., and heat nearly to boiling. Add approximately 20 ml. of 10% $Na_2S_2O_3$ and boil gently for about 15 minutes. Filter on a medium-textured paper and wash with cold water. It is usual to transfer the precipitate to a porcelain crucible and ignite to CuO which is then dissolved in $HNO_3$ before further treatment.

*With $Na_2S$ and $(NH_4)_2S$.*—Copper may be separated from the Group II (b) elements as CuS by precipitation with colorless $(NH_4)_2S$ (CuS is somewhat soluble in ammonium polysulfide) or $Na_2S$. The $H_2S$ separation is usually made first. The precipitated sulfides may be digested with a warm solution of $Na_2S$ or $(NH_4)_2S$ for a short time and the copper (and other Group II (a)) sulfides filtered off; or better, the sulfides from the $H_2S$ precipitation may be dissolved by heating the paper containing the sulfides with $H_2SO_4$ and $HNO_3$ until a clear solution is obtained which then may be made alkaline with NaOH or $NH_4OH$ and treated with $Na_2S$ or $(NH_4)_2S$. The $Na_2S$ separation is often used for recovering Cu (and other elements) from the metastannic acid precipitate obtained in the analysis of tin bronzes.

**Separation of Copper from Other Elements of Group II** (a). Mercury.—By gentle ignition of the mixed sulfides which volatilizes the Hg or by digestion of the mixed sulfides in boiling 2 N $HNO_3$ in which HgS is insoluble.

**Lead.**—By precipitating the Pb as $PbSO_4$ or by depositing the Cu electrolytically from an $HNO_3$ solution. Both methods are widely applied to the analysis of leaded brasses and bronzes.

**Bismuth.**—By precipitating the Bi with $NH_4OH$ or $(NH_4)_2CO_3$ in a dilute $NH_4OH$ solution. If the amount of Bi is very small a little Fe may be added as a collector. This method is often used to separate Bi (also Se, Te, As, and Sb) from low-grade casting copper before electrolytic determination of the copper.

**Cadmium.**—By precipitating the Cd as CdS with $H_2S$ from an alkaline cyanide solution or by electrolytic separation of the copper.

**By Electrodeposition.**—Copper, when present in amounts greater than 1 or 2%, may be separated under suitable conditions from almost all other elements by electrodeposition. Since the Cu is usually obtained in a form suitable for direct weighing these separations are discussed under "Methods."

**By Displacement from a Dilute Acid Solution by a More Positive Metal.**—Al, Zn, or Cd metal will quantitatively displace Cu from hot solutions containing approximately 10% $H_2SO_4$. This is primarily a separation from Fe. Sn and elements less positive will accompany the Cu. Granulated Pb will displace copper from hot dilute HCl or $HClO_4$ solution. This separation is often applied to aluminum, lead, tin, or antimony alloys prior to determining the Cu by the HBr photometric method.

**With Hot Caustic Alkali.**—Copper may be separated from Mo, V, W, Sn, As, Al, Sb, etc., as CuO by precipitation from a boiling solution of NaOH. Organic compounds must be absent and the final concentrations of NaOH must not be greater than 5%. This separation is often applied to the mixed sulfides of Cu and Mo that are obtained in the analysis of iron and steel.

**With $NH_4CNS$.**—Copper may be separated from metals other than Ag, Hg, Se, Te, and the precious metals by precipitation as CuCNS with $NH_4CNS$ from a dilute $H_2SO_4$ or HCl solution containing a reducing agent. This separation is of quite general application but is especially useful in the analysis of copper ores, iron, and steels. The precipitate may be carefully ignited and weighed as CuO or a titrimetric method may be applied. Directions for the separation are as follows: Prepare a solution free of oxidizing agents and containing approximately 1 ml. of $H_2SO_4$ or HCl in excess. Add 10 ml. of 10% $Na_2SO_3$ and dilute to 200 ml. The solution should smell strongly of $SO_2$. Heat nearly to boiling and add 10 ml. of 5% $NH_4CNS$. Boil for a few minutes, stirring to prevent lumping. Let the precipitate settle and add 1 or 2 drops of $NH_4CNS$ to test whether precipitation is complete (avoid a large excess of $NH_4CNS$). Let stand until cool, filter, and wash with a solution containing 2 g. $Na_2SO_3$ and 1 g. $NH_4CNS$ per liter. The precipitate may be dissolved in $HNO_3$ for further treatment. If the precipitate is to be weighed, $NH_4HSO_3$ must be used instead of $Na_2SO_3$.

**With alpha-Benzoinoxime (Cupron)** (see p. 409).—Separation of Cu as $CuC_{14}H_{11}O_2N$ from all metals which form soluble complexes in ammonical tartrate solution is possible; however, separation from large quantities of Fe is not satisfactory. This separation is applied principally to the mixed sulfides obtained in the analysis of molybdenum steels. Directions are as follows: [11] Dissolve the ignited sulfide precipitate in 10 ml. HCl. Transfer the solution to a 400-ml. beaker, add 2–3 drops $HNO_3$, and treat with excess $NH_4OH$. Heat to boiling and filter into a 600-ml. beaker. Wash with hot $NH_4OH$ water and discard the paper. Dilute the filtrate to 250 ml. and heat to boiling. Add 10–15 ml. of a 2% alcoholic solution of alpha-benzoinoxime slowly with constant stirring and boil for 1 minute. Add some ashless pulp and filter on a rapid paper. Wash 5–6 times with hot 3% $NH_4OH$ water, ignite the paper in a silica crucible, and weigh as CuO or dissolve in $HNO_3$ for further treatment.

*With Salicylaldoxime.*—Separation of Cu from all of the common metals in a dilute acetic acid solution as $Cu(C_7H_6O_2N)_2$ is possible, although large amounts of Fe interfere. Precipitation of the Cu salt is complete from pH 2.6, but above pH 3.3 other metals begin to interfere seriously. This separation has been applied to brass and to zinc-base die casting alloy.[12] Directions are as follows: Dilute the solution of the sample to about 100 ml. in a 250-ml. beaker. Add 2 N NaOH dropwise and with constant stirring until a permanent precipitate of the basic copper salt forms, then add 0.5 ml. excess. Dissolve the precipitate in the least possible amount of glacial acetic acid. Add salicylaldoxime reagent (1 g. of salicylaldoxime dissolved in 5 ml. of 95% ethanol added to 95 ml. of water heated to 80°C.) slowly with stirring until fresh additions no longer cause a precipitate to form, then add about 5 ml. in excess. Let stand until the precipitate settles. Filter through a filtering crucible and wash with cold water. The precipitate may be dried at 100°C. and weighed as $Cu(C_7H_6O_2N)_2$ or titrated [13] by a bromate-arsenite procedure.

*With Quinaldic Acid.*—Separation of Cu as $Cu(C_{10}H_6NO_2)_2 \cdot H_2O$ from nearly all metals except Zn may be carried out in a dilute $H_2SO_4$ solution. The separation of copper from cadmium has been found especially useful.[14] The method has also been applied to the analysis of cast iron and steels.[15] Directions are as follows: Dissolve sample in 15–20 ml. of aqua regia. Add 10 ml. dilute $H_2SO_4$ (1:1) and evaporate to fumes. Take up salts in 50 ml. of water and as much dilute $H_2SO_4$ (1:4) as necessary. Filter off insoluble material, wash paper with water, then with 25 ml. of solution containing 10 g. of ammonium tartrate and finally once with water again. To the filtrate add $NH_4OH$ until it is a deep cherry-red in color. Adjust the pH to 3.0 ± 0.2 with dilute $H_2SO_4$ (1:4) and heat the solution to 70–80°C. Add 5 ml. of quinaldic acid reagent (1% solution neutralized to pH 7.0 with NaOH) per mg. of copper. Digest on steam bath for 0.5 hour and then allow to cool to room temperature. Filter through a filtering crucible and wash with water. The precipitate is usually contaminated with other elements and must be dissolved in hot HCl (1:1) and reprecipitated before being dried at 115–120°C. and weighed as $Cu(C_{10}H_6NO_2)_2 \cdot H_2O$.

*By Extraction Methods.*—Nearly all of the many complexes formed between Cu and organic reagents may be extracted with organic solvents. This technique is a valuable method of concentration as well as a selective separation. In many cases the dissolved complex is immediately suitable for photometric measurement. When the technique is used merely as a separation, the organic solvent containing

[11] Kar, H. A., Ind. Eng. Chem., Anal. Ed., **7**, 193, 1935.
[12] Biefeld, L. P., and Howe, D. E., *ibid.*, **11**, 251, 1939.
[13] Furman, N. H., and Flagg, J. F., *ibid.*, **12**, 738, 1940.
[14] Majumdar, A. K., Analyst, **68**, 242, 1943.
[15] Flagg, J. F., and Vanas, D. W., Ind. Eng. Chem., Anal. Ed., **18**, 436, 1946.

the complex may be evaporated to small volume treated with a little $HNO_3$ and $H_2SO_4$ plus a few drops of $HClO_4$ and heated to destroy the organic material. The reagents below are especially useful.

**Dithizone.**—From a dilute mineral acid solution ($<1.0$ $N$) using a carbon tetrachloride solution of dithizone only Pd, Au, Ag, Hg, and Bi are extracted with the Cu. The interference of Ag, Hg, and Bi can be controlled by the addition of a little KI with which these metals form stable complexes. This separation has been applied to the analysis of silicate rocks, soils, steel, and biological materials.[16] Directions are as follows: Neutralize the sample solution to methyl orange using dilute $NH_4OH$ and add sufficient HCl to make its concentration 0.05 $N$. Transfer the cool solution (not over 50 ml. in volume) to a separatory funnel. Add 5 ml. of dithizone (0.01% in carbon tetrachloride) and shake vigorously for 2 minutes. Draw off the extract into another separation funnel and repeat the extraction with a fresh 5-ml. portion of dithizone combining the extract with the first one. Continue the extraction until the green color of the dithizone remains unchanged after shaking. Shake the combined extracts with 5 or 10 ml. of 0.01 $N$ HCl and transfer the carbon tetrachloride solution to a small Erlenmeyer flask. Evaporate to near dryness and treat to destroy organic matter. If traces of Hg or Ag or considerable Bi are suspected, shake the combined extracts with 10 ml. of 2% KI in 0.01 $N$ HCl, adding a little sulfite to destroy any free iodine and finally washing the separated carbon tetrachloride solution with 5 ml. of 0.01 $N$ HCl.

**Cupferron.**—From a hydrochloric acid solution (1:9) Cu may be quantitatively extracted as the cupferrate in chloroform. Fe(III), Sn(IV), Ti, U(IV), V and Mo(VI) accompany the copper.[17]

**Hydroxyquinoline (Oxine).**—Copper may be quantitatively extracted as the oxine in chloroform over a pH range of 2.7 to 14.0. Many other metals also extract, but some separations are possible. Of interest is the separation from Zn and Cd at pH 4.0 [18] and from Mo at pH 9.0.[19] When a clean separation may be accomplished the copper may be determined directly by photometric measurement at 510 m$\mu$.

**By Chromatographic Methods.**—Many interesting separations of Cu are possible by chromatographic techniques. An excellent review of methods using cellulose absorbents is available.[20] Applications to the analysis of alloy steel and iron pyrites [21] and nickel-plating baths [22] have been described.

**By Ion-Exchange Resins.**—An excellent method of concentrating traces of Cu from liquid samples and of separating Cu from anions is the use of ion-exchange resins. Dowex-50 and Amberlite 1R-100 resins have been used. The slightly acid sample solution is passed through a conventional exchange tube containing the resin previously treated with dilute HCl. Cu (and other cations) is quantitatively adsorbed on the resin and may be recovered by passing dilute HCl through the column. This separation has been applied to the analysis of powdered and fluid milk [23] and chromate-treated cooling waters.[24]

[16] Sandell, E. B., Colorimetric Determination of Traces of Metals, 2nd Ed., p. 312, New York, Interscience Publishers, Inc., 1950.

[17] Furman, N. H., et al., Anal. Chem., **21**, 1325, 1949.

[18] Moeller, T., Ind. Eng. Chem., Anal. Ed., **15**, 346, 1943.

[19] Gentry, C. H. R., and Sherrington, L. G., Analyst, **75**, 17, 1950.

[20] Burstall, F. H., and Kember, N. F., Industr. Chem. Mfr., **26**, 400, 1950.

[21] Lewis, J. A., and Griffiths, J. M., Analyst, **76**, 388, 1951.

[22] Burstall, F. H., Kember, N. F., and Wells, R. A., J. Electrodepositors Tech. Soc., **27**, Advance Copy No. 11, 1951.

[23] Cranston, H. A., and Thompson, J. B., Ind. Eng. Chem., Anal. Ed., **18**, 323, 1946.

[24] Sussman, S., and Partnoy, I. L., Anal. Chem., **24**, 1644, 1952.

## GRAVIMETRIC METHODS

## ELECTROLYTIC METHODS

Electrodeposition is the most widely used and most generally satisfactory method for the determination of Cu. In many instances other elements may be directly determined in the spent electrolyte after the removal of the Cu. With suitable modification it may be applied to a variety of materials without the necessity of prior separation. However, for many materials other methods of determination are more practical and often a prior separation of the copper is simpler than circumventing the separation. Without special treatment many of the Group II metals (Ag, Hg, Bi, As, Sn, Sb, Mo, Se, Te) interfere by depositing to some extent with the Cu. Large amounts of Fe prevent complete deposition of the Cu unless treated with a complexing agent. $HNO_2$ will prevent deposition of Cu and will also dissolve Cu that has been deposited. Thorough boiling of samples prior to electrolysis will remove $HNO_2$, as will the addition of a little sulfamic acid (5 ml. of a 5% solution). Urea should not be used for this purpose as it will deposit a carbon compound on the cathode, as will other organic compounds containing carbon. Cylindrical cathodes of platinum mesh or perforated platinum sheet and anodes of coiled platinum wire or small cylinders of platinum mesh are ordinarily used as electrodes. Deposition may be carried out at a low current density (about 0.4 amps. per sq. dm. for the deposition of 1 g. of Cu) for a period of about 15 hours or at high current density (over 2 amperes per sq. dm. for the deposition of 1 g. of Cu) for a period of about 1 hour. The more rapid deposition requires efficient circulation of the electrolyte by a mechanical stirrer, a solenoid, or agitation with compressed air. It is advantageous to add 5 ml. of 5% sulfamic acid about 15 minutes before the termination of electrolysis to assist in plating out the last traces of Cu. Two methods are used to remove the cathode containing the Cu from the electrolyte without loss of Cu. The electrolyte may be slowly siphoned off from the bottom of the electrolysis beaker (without breaking the circuit) while adding water to the top to maintain the solution level above the Cu plate until the current falls to zero, or the electrolysis beaker (previously mounted on a block) may be slowly lowered (without breaking the circuit) while directing a gentle, continuous stream of water from a wash bottle over the exposed Cu plate. The cathode may be dipped in 2 or 3 successive baths of acetone and dried in a current of warm air (hair drier) or for a few minutes in an oven at 100°C.

*With $HNO_3 \cdot H_2SO_4$ Electrolyte.*—When the sample is free from Ag, Hg, and Bi, contains less than 0.5 mg. of As, Sb, Se, and Te combined, less than 10 mg. of Sn, less than 50 mg. of Fe, and less than 1 mg. of Pb, this is the preferred method. The electrolyte solution should be free of chlorides and should contain about 3.5 ml. of $H_2SO_4$ and 2 ml. of $HNO_3$ per 100 ml. of solution. Simple brasses (Sn up to 1%), nickel silvers, and similar alloys are readily analyzed by this method.

*With $HNO_3$ Electrolyte.*—When the sample is free of Sn (and appreciable amounts of other interfering elements listed above), electrolysis in an $HNO_3$ solution containing a trace of chloride offers a convenient method for the simultaneous determination of Cu and Pb (Pb is deposited on the anode as $PbO_2$) [25] and for preventing the interference of small amounts of Mo. The electrolyte solution should contain about 3% $HNO_3$ and 1–2 drops of 0.1 $N$ HCl. A mesh anode somewhat larger than ordinary must be used if much Pb is to be deposited. This

[25] Scherrer, J. A., *et al.*, J. Research, N.B.S., **22**, 697, 1939, R.P. 1213.

s an excellent method for the analysis of leaded brasses. If Sn is present it may
be precipitated as metastannic acid and filtered off before electrolysis.

**With Electrolytes Containing Complexing Agents.**—Many addition agents have
been used to obviate interferences in the electrolytic determination of Cu. One of
the most useful is HF. About 0.5 ml. of HF will hold in solution, and prevent
the deposition of, about 100 mg. of Sn. The same amount will hold in solution
about 40 mg. of Si which otherwise would have to be dehydrated and filtered off
before electrolysis. Polyethylene beakers are useful for handling solutions containing HF, although they should not be heated much above 65°C. and sulfamic
acid must be used for destroying $HNO_2$. The attack on ordinary Pyrex beakers
is not too serious in most cases. The anode should be given a fairly heavy coating
of $PbO_2$ (unless the sample contains considerable Pb) before being used to prevent
attack by HF which would otherwise dissolve small amounts of Pt and deposit
it on the cathode with the Cu. For the analysis of Sn-bronzes (free of Pb) the
$HNO_3$-$H_2SO_4$ electrolyte may be used with the addition of about 5–10 drops of
HF. For the analysis of Sn-bronzes containing Pb and Si-bronzes, the $HNO_3$ electrolyte containing a trace of chloride plus 5–10 drops of HF should be used (the
HF does not take the place of the HCl). HF (and $H_2SiF_6$) may be expelled from
the spent electrolyte by heating to fumes with $H_2SO_4$ and the Sn determined by
titration. HF is also useful for complexing Fe in the direct electrolytic determination of Cu in steel.[26] $H_3PO_4$ has been used for the same purpose.[26, 27]

**With Electrolytes Containing Special Oxidants.**—The interference of moderate
amounts of As, Sb, Te, and Se may be prevented by keeping these metals in their
highest state of oxidation.[28] $NH_4NO_3$ (5 g. per sample) is often used to prevent
deposition of As and Sb, but $Mn(NO_3)_2$ (2 ml. of a solution containing 1 g. Mn
per 100 ml.) is more effective and also prevents deposition of Te, but is not effective for Se. To oxidize Se the solution must be made ammoniacal and boiled with
g. of $(NH_4)_2S_2O_8$. The solution is then acidified and electrolyzed as usual. For
samples containing large amounts of Fe the amount of $HNO_3$ present should be
limited to 1 ml.

**By Controlled Cathode Potential Methods.**—Usually the electrodeposition of Cu
is carried out by using an approximately constant current with no attempt to
control the potential at the cathode. By using a special electronic apparatus it
is possible to maintain a controlled potential on the cathode and to perform several interesting and valuable separations.[29] Of especial interest are the separations
from large amounts of Ag, Sb, Bi, Pb, and Sn.[29, 30]

**By Internal Electrolysis Methods.**—By using a soluble anode (usually of the same
metal as the base metal in solution) and connecting the anode directly to the
cathode, under certain conditions it is possible to deposit Cu quantitatively on the
cathode without any external source of current. Of especial interest is the separation of Cu (also Bi and Ag) from pig lead,[31] and from steels.[32] Usually the
anode is separated from the sample solution by an alundum shell or other means,

26 Frediani, H. A., and Hale, C. H., Ind. Eng. Chem., Anal. Ed., **12**, 736, 1940.
27 Silverman, L., et al., ibid., **14**, 236, 1942.
28 Skowronski, S., A.S.T.M. Bull. No. 174, 60, 1951.
29 Diehl, H., Electrochemical Analysis with Graded Cathode Potential Control, Columbus, Ohio, The G. Frederick Smith Chemical Co., 1948.
30 Lingane, J. J., and Jones, S. L., Anal. Chem., **23**, 1798, 1951.
31 Clarke, B. L., et al., Ind. Eng. Chem., Anal. Ed., **8**, 411, 1936.
32 Carpenter, D. L., and Hopkins, A. D., Analyst, **77**, 86, 1952.

but methods have been worked out for the separation of Cu (and Bi) from Pb-Zn
ores [33] and other ores [34] without the use of any type of anode envelope.

## OTHER GRAVIMETRIC METHODS OF DETERMINATION

While Cu is usually weighed as the metal, a few of its compounds are suitable
for direct weighing. The following are the usual forms.

*As CuO.*—A precipitate of CuS containing not more than 10 mg. Cu obtained
free from other metals may be cautiously ignited to CuO in an open porcelain
crucible by heating to almost 1100°C. Factor: 0.7988. The CuO is somewhat
hydroscopic and must be protected from moisture. Likewise a precipitate of
CuCNS or of the Cu salt of alpha-benzoinoxime may be ignited to CuO.

*As Cu Salicylaldoxime.*—The pure salt dried at 110°C. may be weighed as Cu
$(C_7H_6O_2N)_2$. Factor: 0.1894.

*As Cu Quinaldinate.*—The pure salt dried at 125°C. may be weighed as
$Cu(C_{10}H_6NO_2)_2 \cdot H_2O$. Factor: 0.1496.

## TITRIMETRIC METHODS

### THE IODIDE METHOD

The most widely used of the titrimetric methods is the estimation of free I
liberated from KI by $Cu^{++}$ in slightly acid solution:

$$2CuSO_4 + 4KI \rightarrow Cu_2I_2 + I_2 + 2K_2SO$$

$$2Cu^{++} + 2I^- \rightarrow 2Cu^+ + I_2$$

The usual titrating agent is $Na_2S_2O_3$:

$$2S_2O_3^= + I_2 \rightarrow S_4O_6^= + 2I^-$$

The reaction must be carried out at a pH of 5.5 or less since the reaction with
$Cu^{++}$ is slow at higher pH values. Oxidizing agents which liberate $I_2$ from K
must be absent or inactivated. At a pH of 3.5 or more $As^{+5}$ and $Sb^{+5}$ do no
interfere. Fluoride ion may be used to complex $Fe^{+3}$. The precipitate of $Cu_2I$
has a tendency to adsorb $I_2$ giving an indistinct end point. A little KCNS added
near the end of the titration helps give a sharper end point.

*Procedure.*—For samples free of Fe (or after a preliminary separation) prepare
an $HNO_3$ solution containing about 0.25 g. of Cu and evaporate carefully at a low
temperature until the excess acid is removed and the salts solidify on cooling
Add 25 ml. of water to dissolve salts and 1 N NaOH cautiously until a slight per
manent precipitate of $Cu(OH)_2$ forms. Dissolve this by adding 4 ml. of glacial
acetic acid and dilute to 70 ml. Cool and add 3 g. of KI dissolved in a little
water. Allow to stand for 0.5 minutes and titrate with 0.1 N $Na_2S_2O_3$. As the
end point is approached add 2 ml. of 1% starch indicator solution and 2 g. of
KCNS (tested for freedom from substances consuming $I_2$) dissolved in a little water
Continue the titration to the disappearance of the blue starch–iodide color. This
procedure is suitable for standardizing $Na_2S_2O_3$ solutions against pure Cu.

For samples containing up to 0.3 g. of Fe, especially ores and sulfide precipitate
(free from Mo and V) obtained in iron and steel analysis, prepare an $HNO_3$ (or
$H_2SO_4$) solution and evaporate to small volume. Add 30 ml. of water and 2 g. of

[33] Lurie, J. J., and Ginsberg, L. B., Ind. Eng. Chem., Anal. Ed., **9**, 424, 1937.
[34] *Ibid.*, **10**, 201, 1938.

$NH_4HF_2$. Add $NH_4OH$ until the solution just reacts alkaline to litmus. Acidify with acetic acid and add 1 ml. in excess. Cool, add 3 g. of KI and titrate as described above. A modification is available in which the $Cu_2I_2$ is dissolved in an excess of KI and the titration made in a clear solution.[35]

## TITRATION OF CuCNS WITH $KIO_3$

CuCNS is oxidized with $KIO_3$ in strong HCl solution according to the following equations:

$$2CuCNS + 3KIO_3 + 4HCl \rightarrow 2CuSO_4 + 3KCl + 2HCN + ICl + I_2 + H_2O$$

$$2I_2 + KIO_3 + 6HCl \rightarrow KCl + 5ICl + 3H_2O$$

The end point is the disappearance of the purple iodine color imparted to a few milliliters of chloroform added as indicator. The addition of a little ICl at the beginning of the titration prevents over-titration when the amount of Cu is small. Because vigorous shaking of the solution is required, the titration vessel should be a glass-stoppered flask or a separatory funnel. Since $KIO_3$ is a primary standard the solution may be made up by weight and need not be standardized. 1 ml. $KIO_3$ (214.01 g. per liter) = 0.03631 g. Cu. This method has been applied to the determination of Cu in ores, alloys, insecticides [36] and to a rapid determination of Cu in steel.[37]

*Procedure.*—Separate Cu as CuCNS (see p. 399) filter on a filter pad and wash well with cool, oxygen free water. Remove filter pad and insert it into a separatory funnel containing 25 ml. of chloroform, 60 ml. of HCl, 40 ml. of cool, oxygen-free water and 3 drops of ICl solution. Shake the solution and pad vigorously and add $KIO_3$ (1.1784 g. per l.; 1 ml. = 0.0002 g. Cu) gradually, shaking the solution after each addition, until the end point is reached.

## TITRATION OF $Cu(NH_3)_4{}^{++}$ WITH KCN

In ammoniacal solution Cu forms deep blue cuprammonium-ion:

$$Cu(NO_3)_2 + 4NH_4OH \rightarrow Cu(NH_3)_4(NO_3)_2 + 4H_2O$$

The complex may be titrated with KCN to the disappearance of the blue color:

$$2Cu(NH_3)_4(NO_3)_2 + 7KCN + H_2O \rightarrow K_4Cu_2(CN)_6 + NH_4CNO +$$

$$6NH_3 + 3 KNO_3 + NH_4NO_3$$

The method is highly empirical, but because of its simplicity is often used as a rapid method where approximate values are sufficient. Ag, Ni, Co, Cd, and Zn interfere. The method has been applied to mattes, calcines, and concentrates.[38]

## TITRATION OF $Cu^+$ WITH $Ce^{+4}$ SALTS

Cuprous compounds may be titrated with cerate solutions according to the following equation:

$$Cu^+ + Ce^{+4} \rightarrow Cu^{++} + Ce^{+3}$$

[35] Meites, L., Anal. Chem., **24**, 1618, 1952.

[36] Jamieson, G. S., Volumetric Iodate Methods, p. 27, New York, Chemical Catalog Co., Inc., 1926.

[37] Clardy, F. B., et al., Ind. Eng. Chem., Anal. Ed., **17**, 791, 1945.

[38] Keffer, R., Methods in Non-Ferrous Metallurgical Analysis, p. 107, New York, McGraw-Hill Book Co., Inc., 1928.

However, it is more common to reduce a ferric compound with $Cu^+$ and titrate the $Fe^{++}$ with the cerate solution:

$$Cu_2O + Fe_2(SO_4)_3 + H_2SO_4 \rightarrow 2CuSO_4 + 2FeSO_4 + H_2O$$

$$2FeSO_4 + 2Ce(SO_4)_2 \rightarrow Fe_2(SO_4)_3 + Ce_2(SO_4)_3$$

In either case ferroin (ferrous phenanthroline complex) is used as an indicator. These reactions have been made the basis for the determination of CuCl,[39] for the determination of Cu in Paris Green and Cu ores [40] and for the determination of metallic Cu and $Cu_2O$ in pigments.[41] $Cu^{++}$ in 2 $M$ HCl may be reduced by passing through a Ag reductor, caught in a ferric alum solution, and the $Fe^{++}$ titrated with a cerate solution.[42]

*Procedure.*—50 ml. of solution, containing from 0.1–0.4 g. Cu and 2 $M$ in HCl are passed through a Ag reductor at the rate of 25 ml. per minute. The reduced solution is collected under 20 ml. of 0.5 $M$ ferric alum solution with stirring and the reductor column washed with 150 ml. of 2 $M$ HCl. One drop of ferroin indicator (0.025 $M$) is added and the solution titrated with $H_2Ce(SO_4)_3$. Moderate amounts of $HNO_3$ do not interfere, nor do Zn, Sn, As, Bi, and Cd, Fe, Mo, U, and V must be absent. The method has been applied to the analysis of brass.

## AMPEROMETRIC TITRATIONS

Amperometric techniques are often useful for the titration of small amounts of Cu. This technique has been applied to the analysis of lubricating oils [43] and should be easily applicable to other organic residues.

*Procedure.*—Prepare a sample solution from 0.5–2 $N$ in HCl containing from 1 to 10 mg. of Cu (a similar amount of Fe may be present). Pass duplicate 5-ml. portions of the solution through a Ag reductor and wash with four 5-ml. portions of 0.5 $N$ HCl. Receive one of the portions and its washings under a solution of 0.5 $N$ ferric alum and the other in open air; purge the latter with a stream of air for 2 minutes (all of the $Cu^+$ will be oxidized in this portion). Titrate the solutions obtained amperometrically with a solution of 0.01 $N$ $K_2Cr_2O_7$ in a cell which has a rotating Pt anode at a potential of +1.0 volt in respect to a saturated calomel reference electrode. Measure the current produced at the anode and record a current reading for each increment of $K_2Cr_2O_7$ added. Plot the volume of $K_2Cr_2O_7$ added against the current readings obtained and draw straight lines through the two intersecting series of points. From the end point thus obtained, calculate the amount of Fe in the sample received in air and the amount of Cu and Fe in the sample received under ferric alum. Calculate the Cu by difference.

## COLORIMETRIC/PHOTOMETRIC METHODS

Very many methods have been proposed for the photometric determination of Cu, but only a few of these have been used widely. Most of the materials to which photometric methods have been applied contain Cu as a minor constituent (1% or less) but some workers have used photometric methods for Cu as a major

[39] Hatch, L. F., and Estes, R. R., Ind. Eng. Chem., Anal. Ed., **18,** 136, 1946.
[40] Mehlig, J. P., and Marsh, T. P., *ibid.,* **11,** 213, 1939.
[41] Baker, I., and Gibbs, R. S., *ibid.,* **15,** 505, 1943; **18,** 124, 1946.
[42] Birnbaum, N., and Edmonds, S. M., *ibid.,* **12,** 155, 1940.
[43] Parks, T. D., and Lykken L., Anal. Chem., **22,** 1503, 1950.

constituent (50% or more).[44]  The following methods are those most generally useful.

In each case a calibration curve must be prepared by carrying aliquots of a standard Cu solution through all stages of the process.  Preferably the increments of Cu should be added to Cu-free portions of the material being analyzed, but this is often not absolutely necessary.  Likewise, it is most desirable to use a Cu-free portion of the material being analyzed carried through all stages of the process as a reference solution or blank.  However, when this is not possible a simple reagent blank may suffice.  A standard Cu stock solution may be made by dissolving 0.100 g. of electrolytic cathode Cu or O.F.H.C. Cu in a few ml. of $HNO_3$ (1:1), heating to fumes with 5 ml. of $H_2SO_4$ and diluting to 1 liter in a volumetric flask. 1 ml. = 0.1 mg. Cu.  More dilute solutions should be prepared freshly from the stock solution.

## SODIUM DIETHYLDITHIOCARBAMATE
## (CARBAMATE) METHOD

With sodium diethyldithiocarbamate (carbamate) in ammoniacal or slightly acid solution $Cu^{++}$ forms a golden-brown precipitate which may be stabilized in colloidal solution with gum arabic or extracted with organic solvents such as carbon tetrachloride or butyl acetate.  Maximum absorption is at approximately 440 m$\mu$, but measurement is often made at higher wavelengths (i.e., 560–600 m$\mu$) to minimize interferences.  The concentration range which can be covered using a cell depth of 1 cm. is approximately 0.005 to 0.15 mg. Cu per 25 ml. at 440 m$\mu$.  In ammoniacal citrate solution above pH 9.0 the chief interfering metals are Ni, Co, and Bi.  The addition of disodium ethylenediaminetetraacetate (Complexone, Versenate, etc.) prevents interference from all metals except Ag and Bi and these do not interfere seriously in small amounts at 600 m$\mu$.  Modifications of the carbamate method are widely used for the analysis of water,[45] aluminum alloys,[46] and iron and steel.

*Procedure.*—Prepare an $H_2SO_4$ sample solution.  Add 10 ml. of citric acid (250 g./l.) and neutralize to litmus with $NH_4OH$, adding 3–5 ml. in excess.  Cool and transfer to a 125-ml. separatory funnel.  Add 15 ml. of disodium Versenate (40 g./l.) and 10 ml. of carbamate (1 g./l.) mixing between additions.  Add exactly 20 ml. of butyl acetate to the funnel and shake for 1 minute.  Cool the funnel if necessary and again shake for 1 minute.  Allow the layers to separate.  Drain off the aqueous layer and discard it.  Add 25 ml. of dilute $H_2SO_4$ (5 + 95) and shake for 15 seconds.  Cool and shake again.  Allow the layers to separate, then drain off the aqueous layer and discard it.  Transfer a portion of the butyl acetate extract to an absorption cell, cover and measure photometrically at approximately 560–600 m$\mu$.  Bis(2-hydroxyethyl)dithiocarbamate (Cuprethol) has been proposed as a superior substitute for diethyldithiocarbamate since the Cu salt is soluble. (Geiger, E. and Müller, H. G., Helv. Chim. Acta, **26**, 996, 1943.)  Interferences are approximately the same.  The interference of up to 20 p. p. m. of $Fe^{+3}$ may be prevented by the addition of a small amount of pyrophosphate and adjusting to a pH of 5.  The reagent is prepared as follows: (A) Dissolve 4.0 g. of diethanolamine in 200 ml. of methanol. (B) Dissolve 1.0 ml. of carbon disulfide in 200 ml. of methanol.  Mix equal parts of A and B just prior to use.

44 Bastion, R., Anal. Chem., **21**, 972, 1949.
45 Noll, C. A., and Betz, L. D., Anal. Chem., **24**, 1894, 1952.
46 Mills, E. C., and Herman, S. E., Analyst, **76**, 317, 1951.

The general procedure for samples containing less than 10 mg. $Fe^{+3}$ and 0.2 mg. Cu is as follows: Dilute the slightly acid solution to 50 ml., add 1.0 ml. of 3% sodium pyrophosphate for each 2.0 mg. of $Fe^{+3}$ and adjust to pH 5–6 with 20% sodium acetate. If no turbidity develops in 5 minutes, add 1.0 ml. reagent, dilute to 100 ml. and measure photometrically at approximately 440 m$\mu$. If the sample contains metals which are precipitated by pyrophosphate, Fe must be removed. This technique has been applied to the analysis of lubricating oils.[47]

## AMMONIA (OR AMINE) METHOD

With ammonium hydroxide (or tetraethylenepentamine, as well as other amines) Cu++ forms complexes of an intense blue color having a maximum absorption in the region of 620–650 m$\mu$. The complex formed with $NH_4OH$ has been long used for colorimetric estimation since it is easy to form under conditions which are not critical and is extremely stable. It suffers, however, from a lack of sensitivity and from interference from Ni and Co.[48] Tetraethylenepentamine gives a reaction with Cu which is about 3.5 times as sensitive as the reaction with $NH_4OH$,[49] and Ni and Co do not interfere.[50] Maximum absorption is at approximately 650 m$\mu$. The concentration range which can be covered using a cell depth of 1 cm. is approximately 0.5 to 20 mg. Cu per 100 ml. at 650 m$\mu$.

*Procedure.*—Prepare a sample solution using any convenient acid and dilute to about 50 ml. Add dilute NaOH solution drop by drop until the pH is 3.5–4.0 (indicator paper). Add 10 ml. of amine (2% aqueous solution). Stir well and let stand 2 or 3 minutes. Dilute to 100 ml. in a volumetric flask. Transfer a suitable portion of solution to an absorption cell and measure photometrically. The method has been applied to the analysis of Al alloys using tartaric acid to complex Al, Fe, etc.[50] The moderate sensitivity of this reaction combined with the high stability of the complex should make the method useful for determining the relatively high percentages of Cu in brass and other Cu alloys, tank house electrolytes copper plating solutions, etc.

## HYDROBROMIC ACID METHOD

Cu forms $CuBr_2$ which has a strong red-violet color in concentrated HBr showing a maximum absorption at about 510 m$\mu$. Since Fe interferes at this wavelength measurement is usually made at about 600 m$\mu$. The concentration range which can be covered using a cell depth of 1 cm. is approximately 0.1 to 5 mg. Cu per 50 ml. at 600 m$\mu$. A little free $Br_2$ must be present to insure that all of the Cu is in the oxidized form. The addition of $H_3PO_4$ helps to prevent interference from Fe. Large amounts of Mo, Ni, V, Cr, Co, Au, or Pt may interfere. The method is especially valuable for the analysis of white metal (Pb, Sn) alloys.[51]

*Procedure.*—Dissolve 0.100 g. of sample in 5 ml. of HBr containing 10% $Br_2$ and evaporate to dryness. Cool and dilute to 50 ml. with $HBr$-$H_3PO_4$ mixture (1 ml. $Br_2$ + 1 liter HBr + 1 liter $H_3PO_4$) in a glass-stoppered volumetric flask. Shake until all salts are in solution, transfer a suitable portion of solution to an absorption cell, and measure photometrically at about 600 m$\mu$.

[47] Woelfel, W. C., Anal. Chem., **20**, 722, 1948.
[48] Mehlig, J. P., Ind. Eng. Chem., Anal. Ed., **13**, 533, 1941.
[49] Crumpler, T. B., Anal. Chem., **19**, 325, 1947.
[50] Williams, L. H., Analyst, **75**, 425, 1950.
[51] Coppins, W. C., and Price, J. W., Metal Ind., **78 (II)**, 203, 1951.

## RUBEANIC ACID METHOD

With rubeanic acid (dithiooxamide) in a dilute acid solution (about pH 4.0) Cu reacts to form an olive-green precipitate which may be stabilized in colloidal solutions with gum arabic. Measurement is usually made at about 600 m$\mu$ to minimize interferences, although the point of maximum absorption is somewhat lower. The concentration range which may be covered by a cell depth of 1 cm. is from about 0.001 to 0.75 mg. Cu per 50 ml. at 620 m$\mu$. The addition of malonic acid prevents interference from Fe, Mn, Co, and Ni.

*Procedure for Cu in Water.*[52]—To 50 ml. of sample add 2 ml. of malonic acid (100 g. + 14 g. NaOH diluted to 500 ml.; pH 2.5 ± 0.1), 5 ml. of gum arabic (0.1% solution prepared freshly each day) and 5 ml. of reagent (saturated solution of rubeanic acid in ethanol; about 1 g. per 100 ml.). Mix thoroughly between additions. Transfer a suitable portion to an absorption cell and measure photometrically. Methods have also been worked out for the analysis of Mg and Mg alloys [53] and for steel.[54]

## ALPHA-BENZOINOXIME (CUPRON) METHOD

With alpha-benzoinoxime (Cupron) in alkaline solution Cu forms a green precipitate which may be extracted with chloroform. Maximum absorption occurs at about 440 m$\mu$. The concentration range which may be covered using a 1-cm. cell is from about 0.025–0.85 mg. Cu per 50 ml. at 440 m$\mu$. Rochelle salt prevents interference from Fe and other metals. However, large amounts of Ni and Co interfere.

*Procedure for the Determination of Cu in Steel:* [55]—Dissolve a 0.5-g. sample in 20 ml. of HNO$_3$ (1:2), adding 1–2 drops H$_2$O$_2$ (30%) if necessary, and boil off oxides of nitrogen. Add 25 ml. Rochelle salt solution (300 g. in 500 ml. of water) and 30 ml. of NaOH (10%). Adjust the pH to 11.3–12.3 and add exactly 2 ml. of reagent (0.5% solution of alpha-benzoinoxime in 0.25 $N$ NaOH). Transfer to a 250-ml. separatory funnel, add 40 ml. of chloroform, and shake vigorously for three 30-second periods. Filter the chloroform extract through a small dry paper into a dry 50-ml. volumetric flask. Add 5 ml. of chloroform to the solution in the separatory funnel, shake and run through the filter paper into the volumetric flask. Dilute the chloroform extract to the mark with chloroform and mix. Transfer a suitable portion to an absorption cell and measure photometrically.

## NEO-CUPROINE METHOD

With 2,9-dimethyl-1,10-phenanthroline (Neo-Cuproine) in buffered acetic acid solution Cu+ reacts to produce a bright orange colored complex which may be extracted with isoamyl alcohol, n-hexyl alcohol and other organic solvents. Maximum absorption occurs at 454 m$\mu$ to 460 m$\mu$ depending upon the solvent. The concentration range which may be covered with a 1-cm. cell is approximately from 0.005–0.6 mg. Cu per 50 ml. at 454 m$\mu$. Cu++ is conveniently reduced with hydroxylamine salts, the excess of which need not be removed. Citric acid may

52 West, P. W., and Campere, M., Anal. Chem., **21**, 628, 1949.
53 Willard, H. H., *et al.,* Anal. Chem., **21**, 598, 1949.
54 Miller, W. L., *et al.,* Anal. Chem., **22**, 1572, 1950.
55 Dunleavy, R. A., *et al.,* Anal. Chem., **22**, 170, 1950.

be used to complex Fe. This is an extremely sensitive method and is apparently specific for Cu+.

*Procedure for Ferrous Alloys.*—Dissolve sample by any appropriate means and add sufficient $HNO_3$ to oxidize Fe. Evaporate to small volume to remove excess acid. Transfer the solution (or a suitable aliquot) to a separatory funnel, add 5 ml of hydroxylamine hydrochloride (100 g./l.), and 10 ml. of sodium citrate (300 g./l.). Add $NH_4OH$ until the pH is 4–6 (pH paper). Add 10 ml. of the reagent (0.1% solution in absolute ethanol) and 10 ml. of chloroform. Shake about 30 seconds, allow the layers to separate, and draw off the chloroform layer into a dry, 25-ml. volumetric flask. Add 2–3 ml. of absolute ethanol to the chloroform extract. Repeat the extraction of the aqueous phase with 5 ml. of chloroform.

Transfer the extract to the volumetric flask, dilute to volume with absolute ethanol, and mix. Transfer a suitable portion of the extract to an absorption cell and measure photometrically at 457 m$\mu$. This method has been applied to water, Mn and W ores, steels, ferro-alloys, titanium alloys, and toxicological samples. A slightly different procedure using ethylene dichloride as extractant has been developed for the determination of Cu in water.[56]

## POLAROGRAPHIC METHODS

Polarographic measurement offers a rapid and simple method of determining Cu in a variety of materials. Often no preliminary separations are required and other metals in the sample may be likewise determined with a slight variation of conditions. Either noncomplex-forming supporting electrolytes (i.e. $HNO_3$) which give only a single wave, $Cu^{++} \rightarrow Cu(Hg)$ or complex-forming supporting electrolytes (i.e. $NH_4OH$, KCNS, pyridine, etc.) which give two waves, $Cu^{++} \rightarrow Cu^+$ and $Cu^+ \rightarrow Cu(Hg)$ may be used.[57] Detailed methods have been worked out for the analysis of Al alloys using an $HNO_3$ electrolyte;[58] brass plate using an $NH_4OH$ electrolyte;[59] brass, Al- and Zn-base alloys, Be, and Mg-base alloys using a pyrophosphate electrolyte;[60] and soils and plants using an $NH_4OH$ electrolyte.[61]

## SPECTROGRAPHIC METHODS

Spectrographic techniques are of great value for rapid, routine, large-volume estimations of Cu in Al and Mg-base alloys, Zn-base alloys, Pb- and Sn-base alloys, Ni-base alloys, ferrous alloys and similar materials. The spectral lines of greatest sensitivity are at 3247 A and 3274 A.

## DETERMINATIONS IN SPECIFIC SUBSTANCES

### DETERMINATION OF COPPER IN COPPER ORES

The usual Cu ores are sulfides, basic carbonates, or oxides and are likely to contain considerable Fe and silicious material as well as varying amounts of As, Sb,

[56] Brown, J. K., and Connell, J., Paper presented at the Pittsburgh Conference on Analytical Chemistry and Applied Spectroscopy, Mar. 3, 1953.

[57] Kolthoff, I. M., and Lingane, J. J., Polarography, p. 279 and p. 328, New York, Interscience Publishers, Inc., 1941.

[58] Kolthoff, I. M., and Matsuyama, G., Ind. Eng. Chem., Anal. Ed., **17**, 615, 1945.

[59] Tyler, W. P., and Brown, W. E., *ibid.*, **15**, 520, 1943.

[60] Reynolds, C. A., and Rogers, L. B., Anal. Chem., **21**, 176, 1949.

[61] Menzel, R. G., and Jackson, M. L., Anal. Chem., **23**, 1861, 1951; **24**, 732, 1952.

Ag, Ni, Pb, Bi, Se, and Te. The sulfide ores require strong oxidizing conditions to oxidize the S. Heating with $HCl + HNO_3$ or concentrated $HClO_4$ is usually effective. The addition of a little NaBr and subsequent heating to fumes with $H_2SO_4$ or $HClO_4$ volatilizes As, Sb, and Se.

Separation methods most commonly used for ores are the precipitation of $Cu_2S$ with $Na_2S_2O_3$ and the displacement of Cu with metallic Al. None of the methods listed below ordinarily require a preliminary separation.

## IODIDE METHOD [62]

**Procedure.**—Place the sample in a dry, small-mouthed 500-ml. Erlenmeyer flask and add 1 or 2 boiling chips. Wash down the side of the flask with 15 ml. of 70% $HClO_4$, cover with a small watch glass (or better with a refluxing still head obtainable from the G. Frederick Smith Co.) and heat rapidly to boiling. Adjust the heat so that the $HClO_4$ refluxes on the walls of the flask but does not escape into the room. Boil gently for about 5 minutes. Then allow to cool for about 2 minutes and add 50 ml. of water. Boil gently for about 5 minutes to remove chlorine. Cool and neutralize with $NH_4OH$ (1:1) until the $Fe(OH)_3$ precipitates and the first faint blue of the Cu ammonia complex is noted (giving an over-all greenish color to the solution). Avoid any excess of $NH_4OH$. Cool the solution and add 2 g. of $NH_4HF_2$, dilute to 150 ml. and mix thoroughly. Add 2 g. of KI and titrate immediately with 0.1 $N$ $Na_2S_2O_3$ until the solution has only a faint color of $I_2$, then add 2 ml. of 2% starch solution and continue the titration until the return of the starch-iodide color is slow. Add 2 g. of KCNS and titrate carefully to the disappearance of all blue color.

## ELECTROLYTIC METHOD [63]

**Procedure.**—Transfer a 1-g. portion of sample to a lipless 250-ml. electrolysis beaker. Add 0.5 ml. $H_2SO_4$, 8–10 ml. $HNO_3$, and place on the steam plate. When nitrous fumes are expelled add 2–3 ml. HCl and evaporate to dryness on the steam plate. Add a little hot water, 6 ml. of $HNO_3$, and about 100 ml. of hot water. Stir until all soluble material is dissolved, then dilute to about 200 ml., and allow to settle for 2–3 hours. Finally electrolyze at about 0.4 ampere until deposition of Cu is complete as indicated by failure of Cu to plate on fresh cathode surface when the sample is diluted with a little water.

## PHOTOMETRIC (TRIETHANOLAMINE) METHOD [64]

**Procedure.**—Transfer a 1-g. portion of sample to a casserole. Add 10 ml. HCl and 5 ml. $HNO_3$ and warm until dissolution is effected and only a white siliceous residue remains. Add 5 ml. $H_2SO_4$ and evaporate to dryness on a steam plate or by use of an infrared heat lamp. Add 15 ml. of water to the residue and heat until salts are in solution. If the amount of Fe present is slight, add triethanolamine (25% aqueous solution) to the boiling solution until a deep blue color appears, then 50 ml. in excess. Cool, filter, wash with 1% triethanolamine, dilute to 250 ml. in a volumetric flask, mix, and measure photometrically at approximately 650 m$\mu$. If Fe is present, add the reagent slowly to the boiling solution until $Fe(OH)_3$ appears, then add 0.25 g. ZnO and continue adding the reagent until

[62] Goetz, C. A., *et al.*, Anal. Chem., **21**, 1520, 1949.
[63] Keffer, R., Methods in Non-Ferrous Metallurgical Analysis, p. 104, New York, McGraw-Hill Book Co., Inc., 1928.
[64] Mehlig, J. P., and Durst, D., Chemist-Analyst, **37**, 52, 1948.

the blue color forms. Then add 25 ml. excess. Filter, catching the filtrate in a 250-ml. volumetric flask, and wash with 1% triethanolamine. Dissolve the precipitate in a little warm $H_2SO_4$ (1:4) and reprecipitate. Filter, adding the second filtrate to the first, dilute to 250 ml., mix and measure. The above technique covers a range of Cu of approximately 1–15%. The use of tetraethylenepentamine instead of triethanolamine would increase the sensitivity.

## POLAROGRAPHIC METHOD [65]

The following method was devised especially for the determination of Cu (and Ni and Zn) in iron pyrites, but should also be useful for the analysis of Cu ores high in Fe.

*Procedure.*—Dissolve a 0.5-g. portion of sample by cautious additions of small portions of $HNO_3$ and HCl finally evaporating to dryness on a steam plate. Dissolve the residue in 2 ml. of HCl and transfer the solution to a 100-ml. volumetric flask with distilled water. Dilute to about 75 ml. and add 2.9 ml. of pyridine and 2 ml. of the sodium salt of carboxymethylcellulose. Dilute to the mark and mix. Allow the precipitate of hydrous $Fe_2O_3$ to settle and decant the supernatant liquid through a filter. Transfer 40 ml. of the filtrate to a polarographic cell and add 0.8 ml. of pyridine to raise the pH of the solution from about 3.6 to 5.2. Deaerate and polarograph the solution from 0 to −1.3 volts. Correct the measured wave heights for the dilution caused by the further addition of pyridine by multiplying by 1.02. When this method is used for the analysis of Cu ores some variation in sample size and dilution will be necessary.

## DETERMINATION OF COPPER IN BRASS

Elementary brasses are essentially combinations of Cu and Zn. They often contain a small amount of Pb or Sn or both. Occasionally small quantities of Ni are present and always at least a trace of Fe. They may be analyzed by almost all of the methods previously described, but the two methods given below are as simple as any.

### ELECTROLYTIC METHOD ($HNO_3$ ELECTROLYTE)

*Procedure.*—Transfer a 1-g. portion of sample to a 200-ml. electrolysis beaker and add 15 ml. of $HNO_3$ (1:1). When dissolution is complete, boil gently until oxides of nitrogen are expelled. If the solution is clear indicating that no Sn is present, cool, dilute to about 150 ml., add 1–2 drops of 1 $N$ HCl, stir thoroughly and electrolyze at about 0.4 ampere overnight or at 2 amperes for about 1 hour using agitation. Pb if present will deposit on the anode as $PbO_2$ and may be weighed as such. Fe, Ni, Zn, etc., will be in the spent electrolyte. If the $HNO_3$ solution of the sample is turbid indicating the presence of Sn, add 50 ml. of hot water and a little paper pulp. Let the sample stand on the steam plate for an hour, or until the supernatant liquid is clear, then filter off the metastannic acid on a small close-textured paper, catching the filtrate in a 200-ml. electrolysis beaker. Wash the precipitate thoroughly with hot 1% $HNO_3$, combining the washings with the filtrate. The metastannic acid precipitate will retain a trace of Cu, but in routine work when the amount of Sn is small this may be disregarded. The metastannic acid may be ignited to $SnO_2$ and weighed as such. The filtrate is electrolyzed as described above.

[65] Cooper, W. C., and Mattern, P. J., Anal. Chem., **24**, 572, 1952.

## PHOTOMETRIC (NH₄OH) METHOD [66]

*Procedure.*—Dissolve a 0.2-g. portion of sample in 5 ml. $HNO_3$ (1:1) and boil gently to expel oxides of nitrogen. Cool, add about 25 ml. of water, 5 ml. of ammonium citrate (500 g. of citric acid dissolved in 500 ml. of $NH_4OH$ and diluted to 1 l. with water) and 10 ml. of $NH_4OH$. Transfer to a 100-ml. volumetric flask, dilute to the mark, and mix. Transfer a portion of solution to an absorption cell and measure photometrically at approximately 620 m$\mu$. If the solution is turbid filter sufficient for measurement through a dry filter. This method is not suitable for samples containing more than traces of Ni. Tetra-ethylenepentamine is a more sensitive reagent, pleasanter to use, and may be used in the presence of moderate amounts of Ni.

## DETERMINATION OF COPPER IN ALUMINUM-BASE ALLOYS

Cu is a common constituent of Al-base alloys. It may be determined by a variety of methods. A method used by the Aluminum Company of America is given in the Chapter on Aluminum, while given below are two methods much used in England.

### IODIDE METHOD [67]

*Procedure.*—Dissolve 2 g. of alloy in a 400-ml. beaker with 4 g. of NaOH and 20 ml. of water. After the reaction subsides wash down the sides of the beaker and warm until dissolution is complete. Add 100 ml. of 1% $Na_2CO_3$ and boil for a few minutes. Filter through a medium-textured paper and wash the residue with hot 1% $Na_2CO_3$. Discard the filtrate and dissolve the residue into the original beaker with $HNO_3$ (1:1). Evaporate almost to dryness. Cool, dilute to 25 ml. with water, neutralize with $NH_4OH$, make slightly acid with acetic acid, add 1 g. of $NaF_2$, and heat to boiling. Cool, add 2 g. of KI and titrate with 0.1 N $Na_2S_2O_3$ as described on page 404.

### PHOTOMETRIC (CARBAMATE) METHOD [68]

*Procedure.*—Transfer a 0.20-g. portion of sample to a 250-ml. beaker and continuously add 20 ml. of 15% NaOH. When the violent reaction is over allow the sample to digest for 20 minutes at 80–90°C., wash down sides of beaker and boil gently for 5 minutes. Dilute with 50 ml. of water and add from a dip pipette 20 ml. of $HNO_3$ (1:1) swirling the sample solution vigorously. Boil gently to expel oxides of nitrogen. Cool, transfer to a 200-ml. volumetric flask and dilute to the mark. Transfer an aliquot containing from 0.05 to 0.20 mg. of Cu to a 100-ml. volumetric flask and add 50 ml. of a gum arabic-citrate-$NH_4OH$ mixture (560 ml. 50% citric acid + 390 ml. water + 850 ml. $NH_4OH$ + 200 ml. 2% gum arabic) while swirling the flask. Dilute to the mark, add 1 ml. of 1% carbamate reagent and mix. Transfer a portion of solution to an absorption cell and measure photometrically at approximately 600 m$\mu$.

[66] Haywood, F. W., and Wood, A. A. R., Metallurgical Analysis by Means of the Spekker Photo-Electric Absorptiometer, p. 76, London, Adam Hilger Ltd., 1944.
[67] Association of Light Alloy Refiners, Modern Methods for the Analysis of Aluminum Alloys, p. 15, London, Chapman and Hall Ltd., 1949.
[68] *Ibid.*, p. 70.

## DETERMINATION OF COPPER IN MAGNESIUM-BASE ALLOYS

*(See also Magnesium Chapter)*

### PHOTOMETRIC (RUBEANIC ACID) METHOD [53]

**Procedure.**—Transfer a 2.00-g. portion of sample to a 400-ml. beaker, add 50 ml. of water and just enough $HNO_3$ to dissolve the metal. Boil to expel oxides of nitrogen, cool, transfer to a 250-ml. volumetric flask and dilute to the mark. Transfer a 25-ml. aliquot to a 100-ml. beaker and a similar aliquot to a 100-ml. volumetric flask. Add 3 drops of methyl orange to the beaker and just neutralize with $NH_4OH$. Add exactly the same amount of $NH_4OH$ to the solution in the 100-ml. volumetric flask. Add 5 ml. of 20% malonic acid followed by 25 ml. of reagent (300 g. sodium acetate + 300 ml. water + 280 ml. glacial acetic acid + 20 ml. 1% gum arabic + 20 ml. 0.5% rubeanic acid in ethanol + water sufficient for 1 liter) mixing between additions. Dilute to the mark, mix, and let stand for 30 minutes. Transfer a portion of solution to an absorption cell and measure photometrically at approximately 470 m$\mu$.

## DETERMINATION OF COPPER IN LEAD- AND TIN-BASE ALLOYS

Photometric (HBr) Method, see p. 408.

## DETERMINATION OF COPPER IN FERROUS ALLOYS

Gravimetric (Quinaldic Acid) Method, see p. 400; Photometric ($\alpha$-Benzoinoxime) Method, see p. 409; Titrimetric (CuCNS-KIO$_3$) Method, see p. 405.

## DETERMINATION OF COPPER IN SEWAGE AND INDUSTRIAL WASTES

### PHOTOMETRIC (NEO-CUPROINE) METHOD

**Procedure.**—Transfer 1 liter of well-mixed sample to a 1500-ml. beaker. Add 5 ml. of $HNO_3$ and evaporate to about 50 ml. at a temperature below boiling. Add 15 ml. $HNO_3$ and 10 ml. $HClO_4$ and heat until fumes of $HClO_4$ appear and organic material is completely oxidized. Cool slightly, rinse down sides of beaker (scrubbing with a policeman if necessary) and again heat to fumes. Add about 50 ml. of water, cover the beaker, and boil for about 5 minutes. Cool, filter through a small medium-textured filter, catching the filtrate in a 100-ml. volumetric flask. Wash the residue with hot water and discard. Dilute the sample in the volumetric flask to the mark and transfer an aliquot containing from 0.01 to 0.20 mg. of Cu to a 125-ml. separatory funnel. Complete the determination as described on p. 410. For other methods see the excellent monograph of Butts, *et al.*[7]

## THE DETERMINATION OF COPPER IN SOILS, FERTILIZERS, PLANTS, AND FOODS

These materials are all similar in that the Cu content is very low and the organic content high. Four separate steps are required to complete a determination: (1) Preparation of an air-dried sample ground to 100 mesh (unless the sample is a liquid, i.e. milk); (2) destruction of organic matter; (3) separation of Cu from the residue; (4) establishing a system of high sensitivity and specificity for measurement of the Cu.

Each type of material will require somewhat different conditions for decomposition and destruction of organic matter, but in general digestion at moderate temperature with a combination of $HNO_3$ and $HClO_4$ is effective. Soils and other materials high in $SiO_2$ should be treated in a platinum dish with HF after a preliminary digestion with $HNO_3$ and $HClO_4$. The dithizone extraction described on page 401 is an effective separation from other elements likely to be found in these materials and the neo-cuproine photometric method described on p. 410 is of sufficient sensitivity to determine at least 0.01 mg. Cu per 25 ml. of solution. A polarographic method for plants and soils [61] is available and a direct dithizone method for foods.[69]

## DETERMINATION OF COPPER IN LUBRICANTS

Amperometric Titration Method, see p. 406.

## THE DETERMINATION OF METALLIC COPPER IN CUPROUS OXIDE- CUPRIC OXIDE MIXTURES (ANTI-FOULING MARINE PAINT PIGMENTS)

It is often of importance to know the proportions of $Cu_2O \cdot CuO$ and Cu in an anti-fouling marine paint pigment or insecticide. The *total* Cu in the mixture may be readily determined by the electrolytic method described on p. 402. The $Cu_2O$ + metallic Cu may be determined by treating with $FeCl_3$ and titrating the $FeCl_2$ with $Ce^{+4}$ as described below.

*Procedure for Metallic Cu.*—Add about 20 ml. of 4-mm. glass beads to a 250-ml. Phillips conical beaker with lip, a carefully weighed portion of sample containing approximately 0.1 g. metallic Cu and 25 ml. of denatured alcohol (1 liter 95% ethanol + 5 ml. benzene). Swirl the beaker vigorously for 1 minute to break up lumps of pigment. Add slowly 100 ml. of extraction solution (40 ml. HCl + 1 liter denatured alcohol + 40 g. $SnCl_2 \cdot 2H_2O$) swirling during the addition. Continue swirling the flask vigorously for 5 minutes adding lumps of dry ice continuously to lower the temperature to 0°C. Break up any remaining lumps of pigment with a glass rod and filter off the Cu-CuO residue on a closely packed asbestos pad using suction. Continue to add dry ice to the extraction flask. Finally wash the flask and residue with 150–200 ml. of denatured alcohol solution. Transfer the filter pad and residue to the extraction flask and dissolve in 25 ml. of $FeCl_3$-HCl (75 g. $FeCl_3 \cdot 6H_2O$ + 150 ml. HCl + 400 ml. water + 5 ml. 30% $H_2O_2$ boiled to remove excess $H_2O_2$) by heating on a steam bath until the Cu is dissolved, meanwhile maintaining an atmosphere of $CO_2$ above the solution by the addition of dry ice. Add 50 ml. of water and 3 drops of o-phenanthroline indicator. Titrate with 0.1 N $Ce^{+4}$ solution standardized against pure Cu foil. From the values of total Cu, metallic Cu, and $Cu_2O$ + metallic Cu the percentages of the constituents of the mixture may be calculated. See [70] for complete details.

## THE DETERMINATION OF COPPER IN COPPER PLATING SOLUTIONS

Two types of baths are in common use: acid and alkali cyanide. Zn is often added to the alkali cyanide bath to produce a brass or "bronze" plate. Cu may be rapidly determined by an iodide titration (see p. 404), or by a photometric (tetraethylenepentamine) method (see p. 408). An aliquot from an acid bath may be treated directly, but in the case of an alkali cyanide bath an aliquot must be acidified with $H_2SO_4$ and heated to fumes *under a hood with a good draft* to

[69] Morrison, S. L., and Paige, H. L., Ind. Eng. Chem., Anal. Ed., **18**, 211, 1946.
[70] American Society for Testing Materials Method.

destroy cyanide. If organic material is present (brown color in concentrated $H_2SO_4$) a little $HNO_3$ must be added and the solution again heated to fumes.

## THE DETERMINATION OF COPPER IN NICKEL PLATING SOLUTIONS

The usual type of Ni plating bath is a solution of $NiSO_4$, $NiCl_2$, and $H_3BO_3$ having a pH of about 3.0. Cu is an objectionable impurity as it may darken the plate.

*Procedure.*[71]—Pipette a 10-ml. sample of bath into a 100-ml. volumetric flask and dilute to the mark with 0.1 $N$ HCl. Transfer a suitable aliquot from 1–10 ml. into a 125-ml. separatory funnel. Adjust the volume to 25 ml. with 0.1 $N$ HCl and add 10 ml. of dithizone solution (1–1.2 mg. per 100 ml. carbon tetrachloride). Shake vigorously 3–5 minutes. Allow the layers to separate and filter a portion of the $CCl_4$ layer through a pledget of cotton into an absorption cell. Measure photometrically at 510 m$\mu$. The original method prescribes measurement at two wavelengths, 525 and 650 m$\mu$, and determination of Cu concentration by reference to a nomograph. This technique is no doubt more accurate, but considerable time must be spent in the construction of the nomograph. An alternate procedure is to oxidize the dithizone extract by heating with $HNO_3$ and $H_2SO_4$ and complete the determination by the carbamate (p. 407) or neo-cuproine (p. 409) method. In such a case a stronger solution of dithizone should be used.

## THE DETERMINATION OF COPPER IN TEXTILES

The presence of traces of Cu in fabrics to be rubber coated is objectionable.

*Procedure.*[72]—Transfer 10 g. of the sample cut in small pieces and dried at 110°C. to a 90-ml. low-form porcelain crucible. Heat gently until the material is charred, but do not allow to flame. When only a carbonaceous skeleton is left add 1 ml. $H_2SO_4$ and heat until fumes cease to be evolved and only a gray ash remains. Digest the ash with 20 ml. of water and 5 ml. $H_2SO_4$ just below boiling for about 5 minutes. Transfer to a 150-ml. beaker and dilute to about 50 ml. Warm the solution and pass in $H_2S$ for about 15 minutes. Allow to stand for at least 1 hour and filter through a close-textured paper washing with $H_2S$ water. Dissolve the precipitate by treating with 30 ml. of warm $HNO_3$ (1:2). Cool, and make just alkaline to litmus with $NH_4OH$. Cool, transfer to a 50-ml. volumetric flask, add 10 ml. of $NH_4OH$, and dilute to the mark. Transfer a 25-ml. aliquot to a 50-ml. volumetric flask, add 1 ml. of 5% gum arabic, 10 ml. of 0.1% carbamate, dilute to the mark and mix. Transfer a suitable portion to an absorption cell and measure photometrically at approximately 440 m$\mu$.

## THE DETERMINATION OF COPPER IN GLASS

Small amounts of CuO impart a color to glass which may or may not be desirable.

*Procedure.*[73]—Transfer a 1-g. portion of sample to a platinum dish and treat with 7 ml. HF and 4 ml. $HClO_4$, finally evaporating to dryness. Dissolve the residue in 10 ml. of hot water and a few drops of HCl. Cool and transfer to a 60-ml. separatory funnel. Add 1 ml. of 10% hydroxylamine hydrochloride, 5 drops of thymol blue indicator, and adjust to a pH of about 2 (orange color) with $NH_4OH$

---

[71] Brown, E. A., Ind. Eng. Chem., Anal. Ed., **18,** 493, 1946.
[72] American Society for Testing Materials Method.
[73] Close, P., *et al.,* J. Am. Ceram. Soc., **33,** 345, 1950.

(1:6).  Add 5 ml. sodium acetate-acetic acid buffer (5 ml. acetic acid + 1.5 ml. 10% sodium acetate + 45 ml. water, pH 2.3), 5 ml. dithizone (0.01% in $CCl_4$) and shake 2 minutes.  Allow the layers to separate and transfer the $CCl_4$ layer to a 50-ml. Erlenmeyer flask.  Repeat the extraction with 5-ml. portions of dithizone (0.001% in $CCl_4$) until the green color of the reagent remains unchanged after shaking, combining all of the extracts.  Evaporate the combined extracts to dryness, add 0.5 ml. $H_2SO_4$ and 0.5 ml. $HClO_4$ and heat until the solution is clear. Add 2 ml. of water and transfer to a 60-ml. separatory funnel, make just alkaline with $NH_4OH$ and add 10 ml. borax buffer (0.61 g. $Na_2B_4O_7 \cdot 5H_2O$ in 50 ml. of water).  Add 10 ml. 0.1% carbamate, 10 ml. $CCl_4$, and shake for 3 minutes.  Allow to separate for 10 minutes, draw off a portion of the $CCl_4$ layer into an absorption tube, and measure photometrically at approximately 440 m$\mu$.

## THE DETERMINATION OF COPPER IN REFINED COPPER

The assay of refined copper is always made by electrolytic deposition, Ag counting as Cu.  The method is capable of great accuracy and precision (duplicate samples are expected to agree within ±0.01%) but only if a great deal of care is given to details.  The prepared sample should be cleaned with a 10% NaCN solution, washed with water, rinsed with alcohol followed by ether, dried below 110°C. and finally combed with a strong magnet to remove Fe particles.  A large part of the accuracy depends upon precise weighing techniques.  Specially calibrated weights should be used and the identical weights should be used for weighing the cathode + Cu as were used in weighing the clean cathode and sample. The weight of the clean cathode is taken prior to electrolysis by weighing the cathode together with the 5-g. weight used for weighing the sample and deducting 5 g. from the combined weight.  The cathode is preferably dried with a warm blast of air (from a hair dryer) then with a cool blast just prior to weighing.  Precaution should be taken against spray loss during dissolution of the sample.  A tall-form, lipless beaker with close fitting cover should be used and the rate of reaction should be controlled by cooling the sample if necessary.  The solution should not be boiled.  A little Cu always remains in the electrolyte after electrolysis which is largely compensated for by minute inclusions in the Cu plate and a slight oxidation of the deposited Cu so that no correction is necessary.

*Procedure.*[74]—Transfer 5.0050–5.0070 g. of sample to a tall-form 300-ml. lipless beaker.  Add 42 ml. of $H_2SO_4$-$HNO_3$ mixture (300 ml. $H_2SO_4$ + 750 ml. water + 210 ml. $HNO_3$) and quickly cover the beaker.  Let stand at room temperature (or cool in running water if the reaction is especially violent) until the reaction has nearly ceased.  Heat at 80–90°C. until dissolution is complete and brown fumes have been expelled.  Carefully wash down cover glass and sides of beaker and dilute the solution to about 200 ml.  Stir the solution gently, but thoroughly, with a platinum anode, insert a previously weighed cathode, secure the electrodes to the proper terminals, cover the sample with a pair of close-fitting split watch glasses and electrolyze at about 0.6 ampere for about 16 hours.  When the solution becomes colorless reduce the current to 0.3 ampere and wash down the cover glass, sides of the beaker, and electrode stems.  If no Cu plates on the new surface of the cathode stem in contact with the electrolyte within 30 minutes electrolysis may be judged complete.  Remove the cathode by one of the methods given on p. 402, dip in two successive baths of acetone, dry at 100°C. for 3–5 minutes, cool, and weigh.  This procedure is suitable only for Cu of about 99.90%

[74] American Society for Testing Materials Method.

purity. For low grade Cu containing appreciable impurities of As, Sb, Bi, Se, and Te modifications are required.[74] If the Cu plate obtained is of a dark color it is an indication that impurities are present at an abnormal level.

## THE DETERMINATION OF IMPURITIES IN REFINED COPPER

Refined Cu may be broadly classified into two types; electrolytically-refined and fire-refined. Electrolytically-refined Cu is an extremely pure substance with individual impurities, except O, usually not greater than 0.001%. Consequently, the accurate determination of these impurities by ordinary methods is an analytical process requiring considerable experience and skill as well as very large samples. In practice these impurities are usually determined by spectrographic means. The impurities in fire-refined Cu run somewhat higher and are consequently easier to determine.

The methods given below are suitable for determining adherence to this particular specification. All of the methods described involve photometric measurement. Sample size, aliquot fractions, final volume, etc., are specified for an absorption cell depth of 2 cm. and should be suitably modified for other cell depths. In each case a calibration curve should be prepared, preferably by adding increments of a standard solution of the element being determined to portions of the highest purity Cu and subjecting these synthetic samples to all stages of the procedure. If high purity Cu is not available a calibration curve prepared from increments of standard solution alone will usually provide sufficient accuracy. A reagent blank must always be carried along simultaneously with the sample being analysed. For a comprehensive list of gravimetric and titrimetric methods for the analysis of fire-refined copper see reference below.[75]

### ARSENIC BY THE HETEROPOLY BLUE METHOD [76]

*Procedure.*—Transfer a 5.00-g. portion of sample to a 400-ml. beaker and dissolve in 35 ml. of $HNO_3$ (1:1). Add 8 ml. of $H_2SO_4$ and evaporate to near-dryness (salts gray in color and barely moist with $H_2SO_4$). Dissolve salts in 60 ml. of water, add 75 ml. of HCl, and 15 ml. of 50% hypophosphorous acid with constant stirring. Digest the solution at 80°–90°C. for about 1 hour to precipitate metallic As (also Se and Te). Boil gently for 5 minutes and allow to digest on a steam plate at about 65°C. for an hour or longer. Filter the hot solution through a fritted-glass funnel of fine porosity using moderate suction. Wash beaker and precipitate thoroughly with hot freshly boiled water. Place a 200-ml. volumetric flask inside a filtering jar and insert the funnel containing the metallic arsenic in the top of the jar so that the funnel stem reaches into the volumetric flask. Rinse the precipitation beaker with 10 ml. of 0.02 N iodine to which has been added a drop of 10% aerosol and pour the iodine into the funnel containing the As. Stir the solution with a thin glass rod tipped with a rubber policeman and scrub the sides of the funnel lightly until any floating particles of As have been dissolved. Apply gentle suction to draw the iodine through the filter at the rate of about 1 drop per second, stirring occasionally. Wash beaker funnel and policeman well with hot water. Disregard any insoluble material left on the filter. Remove the 200-ml. volumetric flask from the filtering jar, dilute to the mark, and mix. Transfer a

[75] British Standards Institution, British Standard Methods for the Analysis of Raw Copper, London, 1951.
[76] Case, O. P., Anal. Chem., **20**, 902, 1948.

20-ml. aliquot to a 25-ml. volumetric flask and add 2.5 ml. of ammonium molybdate (1% in 5 N $H_2SO_4$) and 1 ml. of 0.15% hydrazine sulfate, mixing between additions. Heat the flask in a water bath at 90°–100°C. for 10 minutes. Cool, dilute to the mark, and mix. Measure photometrically at approximately 720 m$\mu$ (max. absorbance 840 m$\mu$). A standard As solution (1 ml. = 0.10 mg. As) may be prepared as follows: dissolve 0.1320 g. of $As_2O_3$ in 5 ml. of 5% NaOH using gentle heat. Dilute to about 100 ml., acidify to litmus with $H_2SO_4$ (1:1), and dilute to 1 liter. To prepare a calibration curve use increments up to 8 ml.

For a similar method in which As is separated by distillation as $AsCl_3$ see reference.[77]

## ANTIMONY BY THE IODIDE METHOD

*Procedure.*—Transfer a 15-g. portion of sample to an 800-ml. beaker and dissolve in 155 ml. of $HNO_3$ (1:2). When dissolution is complete, boil gently to remove oxides of nitrogen. Dilute to 500 ml., heat to boiling, add 5 ml. 10% $Mn(NO_3)_2$, 5 ml. 3% $KMnO_4$ and boil 5 minutes. Add an additional 3 ml. of 3% $KMnO_4$ and boil for 5 minutes more. Allow to settle on a steam plate until the supernatant liquid is clear, then filter through a medium-textured paper and wash with hot water. Transfer the paper and precipitate to the precipitation beaker, add 3 ml. $H_2SO_4$ and 15 ml. $HNO_3$ and heat to fumes. Cool, transfer to a 200-ml. tall-form lipless beaker and again heat to fumes. Cool, add 45 ml. of water, 50 ml. HCl and 5 ml. of 50% hypophosphorous acid, stirring between additions. Add 1 or 2 boiling chips and a flat spiral of Cu metal (formed from a 2.5 x 20 cm piece of pure thinsheet Cu) previously cleaned in dilute $HNO_3$ and well washed with water. Cover the beaker with a close-fitting cover glass and boil gently for 2 hours. Metallic Sb is plated on the surface of the Cu coil (Reinsch reaction). Remove the coil from the solution and transfer to a 180-ml. tall-form lipless beaker full of water. Pour off the water and refill the beaker 2 or 3 times to wash the coil thoroughly. Finally add just sufficient water to cover the coil and approximately 1 g. of fresh $Na_2O_2$, quickly covering the beaker to avoid spray loss. All of the operations of washing the coil and dissolving the Sb must be performed as rapidly as possible to prevent the Sb from becoming insoluble. Allow the solution to stand 5 or 10 minutes and then warm gently until the surface of the Cu darkens. Pour off the liquid into a 200-ml. tall-form beaker and rinse the coil and beaker several times with water. Pass a rapid stream of $H_2S$ into the solution for 15 seconds and allow the precipitated sulfides to coagulate on a steam plate for about 1 hour. Filter on a small close-textured paper catching the filtrate in a 150-ml. beaker and wash with 1% $NH_4NO_3$. Discard the precipitate. Make the filtrate acid to litmus with $H_2SO_4$ (1:1) and add 5 ml. in excess. Evaporate to about 15 ml., add 5 ml. $HNO_3$ and evaporate to fumes. Cool, rinse sides of beaker, and again heat to fumes. Cool, add 5–10 ml. of water, and warm until salts are in solution. Transfer to a 25-ml. volumetric flask, cool, add 5 ml. ascorbic acid-KI solution (30 g. KI + 5 g. ascorbic acid per 100 ml.) dilute to the mark, and mix. Measure photometrically at approximately 400 m$\mu$. A standard Sb solution (1 ml. = 0.05 mg. Sb) may be prepared as follows: heat 0.0500 g. of C.P. Sb metal with 10 ml. $H_2SO_4$ until dissolved, cool, carefully add 90 ml. of water, and dilute to 1 liter with 10% $H_2SO_4$. To prepare a calibration curve use increments up to 10 ml.

[77] American Society for Testing Materials Method.

Other related methods that have been found some use are the $MnO_2$ separation of antimony; [78] the Reinsch separation; [79] and the iodoantimonite reaction.[80]

## SELENIUM PLUS TELLURIUM BY THE HYPOPHOSPHITE REDUCTION METHOD [81]

*Procedure.*—Transfer a 5.00-g. portion of sample to a 250-ml. beaker and dissolve in 30 ml. of acid mixture (equal parts of water, $HNO_3$, and HCl). Boil gently to drive off oxides of nitrogen and excess chlorine. Avoid hard boiling and excessive acid loss. Cool and transfer to a 200-ml. volumetric flask containing 50 ml. HCl and 25 ml. of water. Cool, dilute to the mark and mix. Transfer a 50-ml. aliquot to the original beaker, add 12.5 ml. HCl, and cool. Add 7 g. $NaH_2PO_2$ and stir until the salt is dissolved. Transfer at once to a 100-ml. volumetric flask containing 2 drops of 5% gum acacia solution, dilute to the mark, mix by inverting 10 times, and transfer a portion of solution to an absorption tube. Allow to stand 10 minutes and measure photometrically at approximately 420 m$\mu$. In order to secure uniform results by this technique a standard pattern of reagent concentration, manipulation, and timing must be rigidly followed. The assumption is made that the Te will be considerably less than the Se, which is usually the case. If the Te is greater than about one-fifth of the Se the error may be significant. In doubtful cases a separation must be made. See reference below [82] for methods of separation and titrimetric determination. A standard Se solution (1 ml. = 0.10 mg. Se) may be prepared as follows: dissolve 0.100 g. of C.P. Se metal in 10 ml. $HNO_3$ (1:1) and 3 ml. HCl with gentle heating and dilute to 1 liter. To prepare a calibration curve use increments up to 15 ml.

## NICKEL BY THE OXIDIZED GLYOXIME METHOD

*Procedure.*—Transfer a 5.00-g. portion of sample to a 300-ml. electrolysis beaker, dissolve, and electrolyze to remove Cu as described on p. 417. Neutralize the spent electrolyte to litmus with $NH_4OH$ and add 5 ml. $H_2SO_4$ (1:1). Cool and transfer to a 250-ml. volumetric flask, dilute to the mark, and mix. Transfer a 50-ml. aliquot to a 100-ml. volumetric flask. Add 5 ml. of saturated $Br_2$ water and 20 ml. of composite nickel reagent (50 g. citric acid + 1.5 g. dimethylglyoxime + 250 ml. $NH_4OH$ per liter) mixing between additions. Let stand 10 minutes, dilute to the mark, add 1 drop of 10% Aerosol, and mix. Measure photometrically immediately at approximately 520 m$\mu$. A standard Ni solution (1 ml. = 0.25 mg. Ni) may be prepared as follows: dissolve 0.25 g. of C.P. Ni metal by heating gently with 25 ml. of $HNO_3$ (1:4). Cool and dilute to 1 liter. To prepare a calibration curve use increments up to 10 ml.

## BISMUTH BY THE IODIDE METHOD

*Procedure.*—Transfer a 15-g. portion of sample to a 600-ml. beaker and add 100 ml. $HNO_3$ (1:1). When dissolution is complete boil gently to expel oxides of nitrogen and dilute to about 200 ml. Add $NH_4OH$ (1:1) slowly with constant stirring until a permanent precipitate forms. Add $HNO_3$ (1:3) drop by drop with

78 Luke, C. L., Ind. Eng. Chem., Anal. Ed., **15**, 626, 1943.
79 Clarke, S. G., and Evans, B. S., Analyst, **54**, 23, 1929.
80 McChesney, E. W., Ind. Eng. Chem., Anal. Ed., **18**, 146, 1946.
81 Method of the Chase Brass and Copper Co., Waterbury, Conn., worked out by E. L. Smith and H. J. Smith.
82 Noakes, F. D. L., Analyst, **76**, 542, 1951.

constant stirring until the precipitate just dissolves then add 2.0 ml. in excess. Dilute to 400 ml. and heat to boiling. Add 5 ml. of 20% KBr and 3 ml. of 3% KMnO$_4$ and boil for about 10 minutes. Allow the solution to remain on a steam plate until the supernatant liquid is clear, then filter on a medium-textured paper and wash the precipitate once or twice with hot water. Transfer the filtrate to the original beaker and repeat the precipitation. Collect the second precipitate on the same paper as the first and wash several times with hot water. Transfer the combined precipitates to the original beaker, add 5 ml. of H$_2$SO$_4$ and 25 ml. of HNO$_3$ and heat to fumes. Cool, wash down sides of beaker, and again heat to fumes. Cool, add about 15 ml. of water, 4 ml. of 50% citric acid, about 0.2 g. hydroxylamine HCl and make alkaline to litmus with NH$_4$OH (1:1). Cool, add 5 ml. 20% KCN and transfer to a 125-ml. separatory funnel. Add 5 ml. of dithizone (5 mg. per 100 ml. chloroform) and shake vigorously for 1 minute. Allow the layers to separate and carefully draw off the chloroform layer into a 150-ml. beaker. Extract in the same manner with successive 5-ml. portions of dithizone until the original green color of the dithizone remains unchanged after shaking. Finally extract with 1 or more 5-ml. portions of chloroform. Evaporate the combined extracts on a steam bath to about 5 ml. Add 1 ml. H$_2$SO$_4$ and 5 ml. of HNO$_3$ and heat to fumes. Cool, wash down sides of beaker, and again heat to fumes. Cool, add a little water, and transfer to a 25-ml. volumetric flask. Add 5 drops of SO$_2$ water (saturated solution diluted 1:1) and 3 ml. of 10% KI mixing between additions. Dilute to the mark and mix. Measure photometrically at approximately 420 m$\mu$. To prepare a standard Bi solution (1 ml. = 0.05 mg. Bi) dissolve 0.05 g. of C.P. Bi metal in 20 ml. HNO$_3$ (1:1) by gentle heating. Cool and dilute to 1 liter. To prepare a calibration curve use increments up to 8 ml.

For a variation of the above procedure see reference.[83]

For a discussion of the MnO$_2$ separation of Sb see reference.[84]

## LEAD BY THE DITHIZONE METHOD [85]

*Procedure.*—Transfer a 1.00-g. portion of sample to a 200-ml. beaker and add 8 ml. of HNO$_3$ (1:1). When dissolution is complete boil gently to expel oxides of nitrogen. Add about 10 ml. of water, cool and cautiously add NH$_4$OH (1:1) until the basic salts first formed just redissolve. Cool and add 10 ml. citrate-acetate buffer (100 g. ammonium acetate + 100 g. sodium citrate per 500 ml.) and about 0.5 g. hydroxylamine HCl. Add 20% KCN until the blue color of cuprammonium ion is discharged and then 3 ml. in excess. Cool and transfer to a 125-ml. separatory funnel (the pH at this point should be 9.0-9.5). Add 5 ml. of dithizone (5 mg. per 100 ml. of chloroform) and shake vigorously for 1 minute. Allow the layers to separate and carefully draw off the chloroform layer into a 125-ml. separatory funnel. Extract in the same manner with successive 5-ml. portions of dithizone until the original green color of the dithizone remains unchanged after shaking. Finally, extract with 1 or more 5-ml. portions of chloroform. To the combined extracts in the separatory funnel add 10 ml. of HNO$_3$ (1:100) and shake for 1 minute. Allow the layers to separate and draw off the chloroform layer and discard.

[83] Yu-lin Yao, Ind. Eng. Chem., Anal. Ed., **17,** 114, 1945.

[84] Park, B., Ind. Eng. Chem., Anal. Ed., **6,** 189, 1934.

[85] Adapted from a method for the determination of Pb in zinc and zinc-die cast alloys worked out by C. Zischkau and K. C. Braun of the American Smelting and Refining Co. Research Laboratories, South Plainfield, N. J.

To the aqueous solution in the separatory funnel add 2–3 drops of thymol blue indicator and $NH_4OH$ (1:10) drop by drop until the solution is a clear yellow (pH 3.0). (This pH control is quite critical, since at a pH much below 3.0 Bi will be incompletely extracted and at pH values much above 3.0 Pb will be partially extracted. Indicator added to 10 ml. of water in a separatory funnel provides a useful standard of reference.) Add 3 ml. of dithizone (5 mg. per 100 ml. of chloroform) and shake vigorously for 2 minutes. Allow the layers to separate and drain off the chloroform layer (containing the Bi) and discard. Repeat the extraction with 2-ml. portions of dithizone until the original green color remains unchanged after shaking. To the aqueous solution in the separatory funnel add 2.5 ml. citrate-acetate buffer, about 10 mg. of hydroxylamine HCl, 2 ml. $NH_4OH$ (1:1) and 1 ml. 20% KCN mixing between additions (pH 9.0–9.5). Add exactly 25 ml. of dithizone (1 mg. per 100 ml. of chloroform) and shake vigorously for 1 minute. Allow the layers to separate and carefully draw off the chloroform layer into a 125-ml. separatory funnel containing 50 ml. of 11.5 pH buffer solution (1 g. $Na_2SO_3$ + 450 ml. $NH_4OH$ (1:1) + 20 ml. 20% KCN diluted to 1 liter). Shake vigorously for 1 minute and allow the layers to separate. Dry the funnel stem with a roll of filter paper, insert a pledget of cotton and draw off a suitable quantity of the chloroform solution of Pb dithizonate into an absorption cell. Stopper the cell to prevent evaporation and measure photometrically at approximately 520 m$\mu$.

This is an extremely sensitive method and extraordinary care should be taken to insure against Pb contamination. Glassware should be cleaned with hot $HNO_3$, only the highest-purity reagents should be used, all solutions should be stored in Pyrex glassware, and the determination carried out away from the vicinity of lead-lined sinks, etc. To prepare a standard Pb solution (1 ml. = 0.10 mg. Pb) dissolve 0.100 g. of high-purity Pb metal in 20 ml. of $HNO_3$ (1:1) by gentle heating and dilute to 1 liter. To prepare a calibration curve pipette 10 ml. of the above solution into a 200-ml. volumetric flask, dilute to the mark and mix (1 ml. = 0.005 mg. Pb). Use increments up to 10 ml.

For a discussion of the dithizone determination of Pb at pH 11.5 see reference.[86]
For a slightly different method of separating Bi see reference.[87]

## THE DETERMINATION OF PHOSPHORUS IN PHOSPHORIZED COPPER

It is common practice to deoxidize refined copper by the addition of a controlled amount of phosphorus. The residual phosphorus varies from 0.004% to 0.040% and may be conveniently determined by the following photometric method.

*Procedure.*—Transfer a 1.00-g. portion of sample to a 150-ml. beaker and dissolve in 10 ml. of $HNO_3$ (2:3). When dissolution is complete, heat gently until oxides of nitrogen are expelled, then add 5 ml. of 7.5% ammonium persulfate, and boil gently for 5 minutes. Add 2 ml. of ammonium vanadate and boil for about 1 minute, or until the solution is a clear blue color. Cool to room temperature and transfer to a 50-ml. volumetric flask. Add 5 ml. of 5% ammonium molybdate, dilute to the mark, mix, and let stand 5 minutes. Transfer a suitable

[86] Snyder, L. J., Anal. Chem., **19,** 684, 1947.
[87] Bamback, K., and Burkey, R. E., Ind. Eng. Chem., Anal. Ed., **14,** 904, 1942.

ortion to an absorption tube and measure photometrically at about 420 m$\mu$.  Use
a portion of phosphorus-free Cu similarly treated as a reference solution.

## METHODS FOR COPPER IN ANALYSES IN OTHER CHAPTERS

| | |
|---|---|
| Copper in Aluminum Alloys | See Analysis of Aluminum Alloys |
| Copper in Arsenious Oxide | See Analysis of Arsenious Oxide |
| Copper in Cobalt Alloys | See Analysis of Stellite, etc. (Cobalt Chapter) |
| Copper in Bullion | See Fire Assay in Gold Chapter |
| Copper in Magnesium Alloys | See Magnesium Chapter |
| Copper in Metallic Nickel | See Analysis of Metallic Nickel |
| Copper in Commercial Phosphates | See Analysis of Commercial Phosphates |
| Copper in Selenium | See Trace Analysis for Impurities in Selenium |
| Copper in Tellurium | See Determination of Selenium, Lead, Iron and Copper in Selenium |
| Copper in Zinc | See Zinc Chapter |

# Chapter 18

# FLUORINE

F', *at. wt.* 18.9984; **D.** 1.69 g./l. (15°C.); *m.p.* −223°C.; *b.p.* −188°C.; *acids,* HF, $H_2SiF_6$

Fluorine is not found free in nature. It occurs combined with calcium in the mineral fluorspar, $CaF_2$; in cryolite, $Na_3AlF_6$; in apatite, $Ca_5(Cl, F)(PO_4)_3$. It is found more frequently in silicic than in ferric rocks, the amounts being usually less than 0.1%. It occurs together with phosphorus in all animal and vegetable tissues.

Although fluorspar has been known for hundreds of years (named fluorspar during the period of Agricola, 1529) the element was not isolated until comparatively recent times (Moissan, 1886).

Hydrofluoric acid and other fluorine compounds have been used for many years as metal cleaning agents, in the electrodeposition of certain metals, in etching of glass, and in insecticides. More recent developments include extension of its use in pesticides to fluorine-containing organic compounds, and a wide range of fluorocarbons (analogous to the hydrocarbons). Their uses extend from Aerosol propellants and refrigerants to temperature-resistant, heat-resistant, and corrosion-resistant fluids and components. They are particularly useful as components of systems handling elemental fluorine, which is now used in industry and as a missile propellant.

## DETECTION

Fluorine is the most active element known, and is by far the most active of the halogens, displacing chlorine, bromine, and iodine from their combinations.

*Etching Test.*—The procedure depends upon the corrosive action of hydrofluoric acid on glass, the acid being liberated from fluorides by means of hot concentrated sulfuric acid. This test is applicable to fluorides that are decomposed by sulfuric acid. The reactions taking place may be represented as follows:

$$CaF_2 + H_2SO_4 \rightarrow CaSO_4 + 2HF.$$

$$SiO_2 + 4HF \rightarrow 2H_2O + SiF_4.$$

The test may be carried out in the apparatus shown in the illustration, Fig. 18-1. A clear, polished glass plate 2 in. sq., free from scratches, is warmed and molten wax allowed to flow over one side of the plate, the excess of wax being drained off. A small mark is made through the wax, exposing the surface of the plate, care being exercised not to scratch the glass. If the test is to be quantitative the marks should be of uniform length and width. The powdered material is placed in a large platinum crucible (*B*) (a lead crucible will do); sufficient concentrated sulfuric acid is added to cover the sample. The plate (*D*) with the wax side down is placed over the crucible and pressed firmly down. To prevent the wax from melting, a condenser (*C*), with flowing water, cools the plate. An Erlenmeyer flask (*C*) is an effective and simple form of condenser, though a metallic cylinder is a better conductor of heat. A little water placed on the plate makes better contact with the condenser. As a further protection a wide collar of asbestos board (*E*) may be placed as shown in the figure. In quantitative work, where a careful regulation of heat is necessary, the crucible is placed in a casserole with

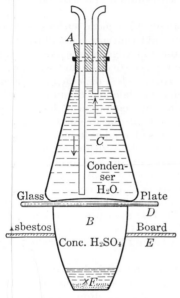

FIG. 18-1. Etching Test for Fluorine.

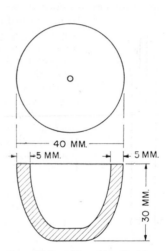

FIG. 18-2. Fluoride Etching Crucible and Cover.

concentrated sulfuric acid or in a sand bath, containing a thermometer to register the temperature. The run is best conducted at a temperature of 200°C. (not over 210°—$H_2SO_4$ fumes). After an hour the wax is removed with hot water and the plate wiped clean, and examined by reflected light for etching. A test is positive when the mark can be seen from both sides of the glass. Breathing over the etched surface intensifies the mark.

**Treatment of Fluosilicates not Attacked by Sulfuric Acid.**—The powdered material is mixed with about eight times its weight of sodium carbonate and fused in a platinum crucible. The cooled melt is extracted with water. Calcium fluoride is thrown out from the filtrate, according to directions under "Preparation and Solution of the Sample." The fluoride may now be tested as directed in the etching test or by the hanging drop test.

**Modified Etching Test.**[1]—An improved version of this test has the further advantage that it does not require a platinum crucible, but may be performed with a

[1] Jacobs, M. B., Chemical Analysis of Food and Food Products, 3rd Ed., pages 250–251, D. Van Nostrand Co., Inc., Princeton, N. J., 1958; Jacobs, M. B., and Goldstone, N. I., Anal. Chem., **21**, 781, 1949; Gettler and Ellerbrook, Am. J. Med. Sci., **197**, 625, 1939.

crucible which, while not commercially available, may be made as follows: Place a 30-ml., tall-form, porcelain crucible on a wire gauze over a Bunsen burner and melt sufficient printer's linotype metal to almost fill the crucible. Clamp the mold in a turning lathe and bore out to shape and approximate dimensions shown in Fig. 18-2. Place the top edge against a piece of sandpaper set on a flat surface and rub until smooth. For the cover, hammer a slug of lead on a flat metal surface to a thickness of 1 mm. and cut to size with a pair of shears. Smooth with sandpaper and punch a hole in center.

Clean after each test by soaking in hot alkali solution and scrubbing with a wad of steel wool.

**Procedure.**—Transfer a portion of the sample to a metal etching test crucible, moisten with a drop of water, and cautiously add concentrated sulfuric acid, drop by drop, until effervescence ceases. Wet the top edge of the crucible with sulfuric acid to form a seal, place cover on and set a glass microscope slide over hole in cover. Heat the crucible on a hot plate for 1 hour, wash and dry the slide and examine its surface for any etching produced by the generation of hydrofluoric acid. When the etching is very light due to small concentration of fluorine, breathing on it will render it more distinct, or its roughness may be felt by gently scratching with the fingernail.

H₂SO₄
Ca F₂

FIG. 18-3. Hanging Drop Test for Fluorine.

Hydrofluoric acid reacts with silica to form the volatile fluosilicic acid, and this, too, lacks the ability to etch a glass surface. However, it is unnecessary to make a separation, for the formation of fluosilicic acid serves as the basis of an even more sensitive test for a soluble fluoride than the etching test, for which it may be substituted or used as a confirmatory test, in the manner adapted by Gettler and Ellerbrook for the detection of fluorine in tissues.

**Confirmatory Test.**—Transfer a pinch of the dry ash to a 5 ml. porcelain crucible, mix with an equal amount of powdered glass or silica, cautiously add a few drops of concentrated sulfuric acid, and immediately cover with a microscope slide from the undersurface of which is suspended a small drop of sodium chloride solution. Place the crucible on a hot plate maintained at a temperature of 150°C. and put a drop of cold water on the upper surface of the slide directly over the suspended drop, to retard evaporation. After 5 minutes heating remove the slide, allow the suspended drop to dry in the air, and examine under a microscope (450 magnifications) for six-pointed stars or hexagonal crystals of sodium fluosilicate. Ten micrograms of fluorine under this treatment should be detected without difficulty. This is a sensitive modification of the conventional Hanging Drop Test, which follows.

**The Hanging Drop Test.**—The test depends upon the reaction $3SiF_4 + 3H_2O = 2H_2SiF_6 + H_2SiO_3$.

**Procedure.**—If the material contains carbonates, it is calcined to expel carbon dioxide. Half a gram of the powdered dry material is mixed with 0.1 g. dried precipitated silica and placed in a test tube, Fig. 18-3, about 5 cm long by 1 cm in diameter. A one-hole rubber stopper fits in the tube. A short glass tube, closed at the upper end, passes through the stopper, extending about 3 mm. below. Two or three drops of water are placed in this small tube by means of pipette, nearly filling it. Two ml. of concentrated sulfuric acid are added to the sample in the test tube and this immediately closed by inserting the stopper carrying the hanging drop tube, exercising care to avoid dislodging the drop of water. The test tube is placed in a beaker of boiling water and kept there for 30 minutes. If an appreciable quantity of fluorine is present a heavy gelatinous ring of silicic acid will be found at the end of the hanging drop tube in the stopper.

It is important to have material, test tube, and rubber stopper dry, so that the deposition may occur as stated.[2]

NOTE.—Olsen [3] made the test by heating the sample in a small Erlenmeyer flask, with concentrated sulfuric acid. A watch-crystal with a drop of water suspended on its curved surface is placed over the mouth of the flask. A spot etch is obtained in presence of fluorine.

**Sodium Fluosilicate Crystal Test.**[4]—Goldstone modified the composition of the hanging drop solution in the sodium fluosilicate crystal test for the microchemical detection of fluorides in order to render the test considerably more sensitive. The test can be applied to distinguish between inorganic fluorides and monofluoroacetic acid. It is possible to obtain a positive test with as little as 0.2 micrograms of fluoride. With increasing concentrations of fluoride larger numbers of crystals can be observed, thus with 1.0 micrograms of fluoride several thousand crystals of assorted size appear in the field.

Along with the increased sensitivity the modified test has the additional advantage of enabling the sodium fluosilicate crystals, which appear in characteristic hexagonal form or as six-pointed stars, to stand out individually and more distinctly from the larger sodium chloride crystals. Furthermore, they are tinted a deeper shade of pink and therefore are more easily recognized.

**Apparatus.** *Heating Block.*—A metal block approximately 2.5 cm thick and large enough to hold four 10 ml. porcelain crucibles is suitable. A well to hold the bulb of a thermometer is drilled into the block. A few drops of mineral oil are placed in the well to cover the bulb. The block is set on a tripod and preferably heated with multiple-jet gas burner. A satisfactory block may be constructed by melting sufficient printer's type metal in an aluminum pie plate. A small test tube 1 cm in diameter is set and held in the molten metal by a clamp on a ring stand, then the metal is allowed to cool slowly and to solidify.

*Glass Slides.*—Microscope-slide glass is cut into pieces 4 x 4 cm.

*Standardized Micropipette.*—For convenient delivery of uniform drops of standard fluoride solutions a satisfactory pipette may readily be constructed. A length of thin-walled glass tubing of 5 mm. diameter is drawn out into a fine capillary, which is broken off at a point where its diameter is less than 1 mm. It is standardized by allowing water to flow from it, drop by drop, at a uniform rate into a microburette filled with water exactly to the 1.00 ml. mark. If the zero mark is not reached by the addition of 50 drops, the individual drops are too small, and a short length of capillary is cut off and the trial repeated. The procedure is repeated until a uniform drop of exactly 0.02 ml. is delivered. The pipette is dried and inserted through a rubber stopper fitted to a test tube or small reagent bottle

[2] Howard C. D., J. Am. Chem. Soc., **28**, 1238, 1906.
[3] Communication from J. C. Olsen.
[4] Jacobs, M. B., Chemical Analysis of Food and Food Products, 3rd Ed., pages 907–910, D. Van Nostrand Co., Inc., Princeton, N. J., 1958; Goldstone, N. I., Anal. Chem., **27**, 964, 1955.

containing standard fluoride solution, from which definite quantities of fluoride may be accurately delivered when required.

*Crucibles.*—A number of high-form glazed porcelain crucibles of 10 ml. capacity.

**Reagents.** *Standard Sodium Fluoride Solution.*—Dissolve 0.0221 g. of pure sodium fluoride in water and dilute to 200 ml. Each milliliter of solution contains 50.0 micrograms of fluorine.

*Standard Sodium Monofluoroacetate Solution.*—Dissolve 0.05 g. of sodium monofluoroacetate in water and dilute to 250 ml. Each milliliter of solution contains 0.2 mg. of the salt; 0.05 ml. of solution contains 1.9 micrograms of fluorine.

*Standard Sodium Fluosilicate Solution.*—Dissolve 0.0165 g. of pure sodium fluosilicate in water and dilute to 200 ml. Each milliliter of solution contains 50 micrograms of fluorine.

*Sodium Chloride Hanging Drop Solution.*—Dissolve 1.0 g. of pure sodium chloride and 3.0 g. of pure glycerol in water, add 2 drops of 40% formaldehyde to preserve the reagent, dilute to 100 ml., and filter through paper into a glass reagent bottle. Insert a 3-mm. diameter glass rod, of suitable length, with fire-polished ends through a rubber stopper and keep the bottle well stoppered. This apparatus serves very conveniently for the transfer of a small drop of solution to the surface of the glass slide in the crystal test.

*Silver Sulfate.*—Pure crystalline silver sulfate stored in a brown bottle.

*Saturated Silver Sulfate Solution.*—An excess of silver sulfate suspended in water and stored in a brown dropping bottle.

*Silica.*—Fluorine-free powdered silicon dioxide.

**Procedure.**—Make a few grams of the material to be tested alkaline with a slight excess of sodium carbonate solution, dry in an oven at 100°C., cautiously burn off the organic matter over a Bunsen flame, then continue heating in a muffle furnace held below 500°C. until a gray or white ash is obtained. Transfer about 20 mg. of the ash to a 15-ml. test tube, add 10 ml. of water, shake until all soluble matter is dissolved, and then transfer half of the solution to another 15-ml. test tube. To the second tube, which serves as a control, add 2.0 micrograms of fluoride and heat both tubes in a beaker of boiling water. Add a pinch of silver sulfate powder to each and shake occasionally until the silver precipitate formed coagulates. Test the clear supernatant liquid by adding a drop of saturated silver sulfate solution, and if additional precipitation occurs, add more powdered silver sulfate; continue to heat, shake, and test until precipitation is complete. Cool the tubes in an ice bath and filter through small paper filters into 10-ml. porcelain crucibles, washing with 2 successive small portions of water. To each crucible add about 0.5 mg. of calcium carbonate powder and about 2 mg. of powdered silica; then evaporate gently (to avoid spattering) to dryness on a hot plate, allowing the crucibles to bake for a few minutes. Cool to room temperature. To the residue add 2 small drops of sulfuric acid (sp. gr., 1.84) and place the crucible on a metal block, maintained at 170°C. Cover immediately with a glass slide, on the undersurface of which has been placed a small drop (diameter, 0.4 cm) of modified hanging drop solution. Set a 50 ml. beaker containing an ice cube firmly on top of the slide and allow the distillation to proceed for 20 minutes, after which dry with filter paper and put in a warm place for a few minutes until the hanging drop is dry. If fluoride is present in the sample tested, it is indicated by the presence of the characteristic fluosilicate crystals, the control being, of course, positive.

Microscopic examination (440×) reveals the presence of several thousand decidedly pink crystals of various sizes, either in hexagonal form or as six-pointed stars. These crystals are not uniformly distributed throughout the field but are mainly concentrated along the periphery of the drop. Viewed very slightly out of exact focus, they appear opaquely black. The limit of sensitivity is reached when 0.2 microgram of fluorine is subjected to the test, producing a few tiny crystals, the number increasing to over 100 when 0.3 microgram is used. To perform the test on quantities less than 1.0 microgram the standard solution is diluted to one-tenth its fluoride content and the appropriate number of drops taken. When standard sodium fluoride solution is used instead of the fluosilicate, the procedure is not changed except for the addition of about 2 mg. of silica powder in the microdistillation; this converts the hydrofluoride into fluosilicic acid. Tests indicated that the recovery in the form of sodium fluosilicate crystals is not quantitative, only part of the fluoride being trapped in the hanging drop.

NOTE.—A number of common negative ions such as chlorides, nitrates, borates, carbonates, and sulfates influence in varying degrees the formation of sodium fluosilicate crystals in the hanging drop test. The presence of these ions tends to inhibit the quantity of fluoride recovered, and in general, the more negative ions present, the fewer crystals appear in the microscopic field. The ions mentioned above are listed in the descending order of their capacity to interfere. When the test is performed on 1.0 microgram of fluoride, to which has been added 1 mg. of sodium chloride or nitrate, interference is complete and no crystals can be observed in the field. Some of these ions influence the shape of the crystals, tending to round off the corners of the hexagon, so that they are more nearly circular. In the distillation the negative ions are volatilized along with the fluosilicic acid and are absorbed in the hanging drop, where they influence the formation of the crystals.

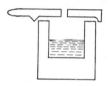

FIG. 18-4. Black Filter Paper Test for Fluorine.

*Black Filter Paper Test.*—According to Browning,[5] small amounts of fluorine may be detected by the converse method for detection of silicates and fluosilicates (see Chapter on Silicon). The fluoride is placed with a suitable amount of silica, in a small lead cup, 1 cm in diameter and depth (Fig. 18-4); a few drops of concentrated sulfuric acid are added; the cup is covered by a flat piece of lead with a small hole in the center; upon the cover is placed a piece of moistened black filter paper and upon this a small pad of moistened filter paper. The cup is heated on the steam bath for ten or fifteen minutes.

A white deposit will be found on the underside of the black filter paper, over the opening in the cover, if fluorine is present in an appreciable amount. (0.001 g. $CaF_2$ or above, and 0.005 g. $Na_3AlF_6$ will give the test.)

## ESTIMATION

The determination of fluorine in the evaluation of minerals used for the production of hydrofluoric acid is of technical importance. Because of its use in the fluoridation of water, sensitive methods for its determination are required.

Fluorine occurs only combined. It is found abundantly combined with lime in the mineral fluorspar, $CaF_2$. It occurs as cryolite, $Na_3AlF_6$; apatite, $Ca_4 \cdot CaF(PO_4)_3$. It is found in mineral springs, ashes of plants, in bones, and in the

[5] Browning, P. E., Am. Jour. Sci. (4), **32**, 249, 1910. Methods in Chemical Analysis, by F. A. Gooch.

teeth (CaF$_2$). It occurs sparingly, with aluminum and silicon, in topaz, and with cerium and yttrium in fluocerite, yttrocerite, also in wavellite, wagnerite, etc.

In the preparation of the material for analysis the volatility of silicon tetrafluoride should be borne in mind and loss of HF in evaporations to fumes with sulfuric acid. In presence of calcium a loss of fluorine will occur by precipitation as CaF$_2$ with iron and aluminum when the solution is made ammoniacal. Accurate determinations of the element require considerable experience and much care to avoid loss and effect separations. The qualitative tests are simple.

## PREPARATION AND SOLUTION OF THE SAMPLE

Fluorides of the alkalies, and of silver and mercury, are readily soluble; copper, lead, zinc, and iron fluorides are sparingly soluble; the alkaline earth fluorides dissolve in 100 ml. H$_2$O as follows: BaF$_2$ = 0.163 g., SrF$_2$ = 0.012 g., CaF$_2$ = 0.0016 g.

Fluosilicates of potassium, sodium, and barium are slightly soluble in water and practically insoluble if sufficient alcohol is added.

*Organic Substances.*[6]—These are best decomposed by the lime method, the details of which are given in the Chapter on Chlorine in the section for the "Preparation and Solution of the Sample," p. 325. For fluorides in organic matter it is advisable to decompose the substance in a seamless nickel tube, 40 mm. long by 4–5 mm. bore. The end of the tube is sealed with silver solder. The lime used should be soluble in acetic acid. The tube is heated to yellow heat for two hours. The lime is then extracted with acetic acid and fluorine determined as calcium fluoride. The Schoniger method, p. 330, is widely used today, especially for micro work.

*Silicious Ores and Slags.*—0.5 to 1.0 g. of material is fused in a crucible with ten times its weight of sodium and potassium carbonates (1:1) and poured into an iron mold. If a porcelain crucible has been used, this is broken up and added to the cooled fusion. The mass is digested with about 200 ml. of hot water for an hour, the mass having been broken up into small lumps (Kneeland recommends using an agate-ware casserole as diminishing the liability of subsequent bumping),[7] then boiled briskly for ten minutes longer and filtered, the solution being caught in a large beaker. The residue is washed with hot water, followed by a hot solution of ammonium carbonate, and the insoluble material rejected. The silica is removed with ammonium carbonate, followed by the zinc oxide treatment of the second filtrate, as described under the section on Separations. In presence of appreciable amounts of fluorides, the gravimetric precipitation of fluorine as calcium fluoride is recommended.

*Calcium Fluoride.*—The product is best decomposed by fusion with sodium and potassium carbonates, after mixing the fluoride with 2.5 times as much silicic acid, followed by ten times its weight of carbonates. Most of the silicic acid and all the fluorine will be changed to soluble alkali salts, while the calcium will be left as insoluble calcium carbonate. The mixture must be heated gradually to prevent the contents of the crucible from running over by the rapid evolution of carbon dioxide. The thin liquid fusion soon thickens to a pasty mass. The reaction is complete when there is no further evolution of carbon dioxide. The fused mass is now extracted with hot water as indicated above, and the soluble fluoride filtered from the calcium carbonate residue. Silicic acid is removed from the filtrate by addition of ammonium carbonate. Traces of silicic acid are removed

[6] Meyer, H., and Hub, A., Monatsh. Chem., **31,** 933, 1910.

[7] E. Kneeland, Eng. and Mining J., **80,** 1212, 1906. A. H. Low, Technical Methods of Ore Analysis.

from the filtrate taken to near dryness, after neutralizing the alkali with dilute hydrochloric acid (phenolphthalein indicator), by the zinc oxide emulsion method given under "Separations." Fluorine is precipitated as calcium fluoride, according to the procedure given later.

**Valuation of Fluorspar. Perchloric Acid Method.**—One gram of fluorspar is treated with 15 ml. perchloric acid and 15 ml. of water in a suitable distillation flask and heated in an oil bath until the residue is almost dry. The distillation is continued with 10-ml. and finally 5-ml. portions of perchloric acid and equal amounts of water. Hydrofluoric acid may be determined as lead chlorofluoride in the distillate and water soluble residue analyzed for metals. If a residue analysis is desired treat first with HF, evaporate, and follow with perchloric acid. The residue is soluble in water or dilute HCl.

## SEPARATIONS

**Removal of Silicic Acid from Fluorides.**—This separation is frequently required, especially in samples where the sodium and potassium carbonate fusion has been required for decomposition of fluosilicates, or calcium fluoride mixed with silicic acid. (See "Preparation and Solution of the Sample.")

**Procedure.**—To the alkaline solution about 5 to 10 g. of ammonium carbonate are added, the solution boiled for five minutes and allowed to stand in the cold for two or three hours. (An alternate method is heating to 40°C., and allowing to stand overnight.) The precipitate is filtered off and washed with ammonium carbonate solution. The fluoride passes into the filtrate, while practically all of the silicic acid remains on the filter.

Small amounts of silica in the filtrate are removed by evaporating the solution to near dryness on the water bath, then neutralizing the carbonate with dilute hydrochloric acid (phenolphthalein indicator) added to the residue taken up with a little water. Upon boiling the pink color is restored, the solution then cooled and acid again added to discharge the color; this is repeated until finally the addition of 1–2 ml. of 2 $N$ HCl is sufficient to discharge the color. Four to 5 ml. of ammoniacal zinc oxide solution (moist ZnO dissolved in $NH_4OH$—Low recommends 20 ml. of an emulsion of ZnO in $NH_4OH$) is added and the mixture boiled until ammonia has been completely expelled. The precipitate of zinc silicate and oxide is filtered and washed with water. The fluoride is determined in the filtrate by precipitation with calcium chloride as directed later.

**Separation of Hydrofluoric and Phosphoric Acids.**—The method of Rose, modified by Treadwell and Koch,[8] takes advantage of the fact that silver phosphate is insoluble in water, whereas silver fluoride is soluble.

**Procedure.**—The alkaline solution of the salts of the acids (solution of the sodium carbonate fusions) is carefully neutralized with nitric acid and transferred to a 300-ml. calibrated flask. A slight excess of silver nitrate solution is added, and the mixture made to volume and thoroughly shaken. After settling, the solution is filtered through a dry filter, the first 10 to 15 ml. being rejected; 225 ml. of this filtrate is again transferred to a 300-ml. volumetric flask, the excess of silver precipitated by adding sodium chloride solution, and after diluting to the mark and shaking, the precipitate is again allowed to settle; 200 ml. of this solution is taken for analysis, after filtering as previously directed. This sample represents 50% of the original sample taken. Fluorine is now determined by one of the procedures outlined.

[8] Z. anal. Chem., **43**, 469, 1904.

*Separation of Hydrofluoric and Hydrochloric Acids.* **Procedure.**—The solution containing hydrofluoric and hydrochloric acids, in a platinum dish, is treated with nitric acid and silver nitrate. The chloride is precipitated as the silver salt, whereas the fluorine remains in solution and may be filtered off through a glass funnel coated with paraffin or wax, or a hard rubber funnel. In presence of phosphoric acid, silver nitrate added to the solution will precipitate the phosphate as well as

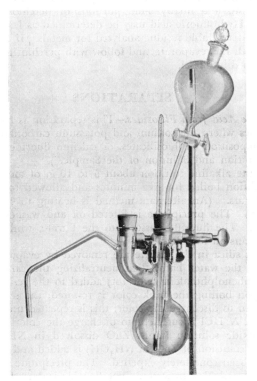

Fig. 18-5. Fluoride Distillation Apparatus.

the chloride, whereas the fluoride remains in solution. The phosphate may be dissolved out from the chloride by means of dilute nitric acid.

*Separation of Hydrofluoric and Boric Acids.* **Procedure.**—An excess of calcium chloride is added to the boiling alkali salt solutions of the two acids. The precipitate is filtered off and washed with hot water. The residue, consisting of calcium fluoride, borate and carbonate, is gently ignited and then treated with dilute acetic acid, taken to dryness, and the residue taken up with acetic acid and water. Calcium acetate and borate are dissolved, whereas the fluoride remains insoluble and may be filtered off and determined.

*Separation by Distillation Method.*—The determination of fluorine as developed by Willard and Winter [9] is based on the isolation of fluorine accurately and expeditiously from interfering materials by distillation as hydrofluosilicic acid

[9] Willard and Winter, Ind. Eng. Chem., Anal. Ed., **5,** 7, 1933.

which may subsequently be estimated colorimetrically by the bleaching of a zirconium-alizarin lake (see page 453) or by titration with thorium or cerous nitrate (see page 442).

The estimation of small amounts of fluorine is difficult because, unless the proper fixative is used, the fluorine will be lost in the ashing or will not be completely volatilized when the ash is distilled with perchloric acid. Winter[10] recommends magnesium acetate as the most satisfactory fixative in the following method.

**Preparation of Sample.**—Place 5–25 g. of material, according to the fluorine content, in a crucible or porcelain dish, add sufficient 5% magnesium acetate solution to moisten completely and no more. Dry in an oven for at least 24 hours, and ash in a muffle at dull redness. Brush the ash into the distillation flask.

**Apparatus.**—The distillation apparatus, Fig. 18-5, consists of a Claissen flask with neck 10 cm long instead of the usual length. The side arm that connects the flask with the condenser is bent upward for about 4 cm and then downward at two points in order to fit a vertical condenser. The straight neck of the distilling flask carries a rubber stopper fitted with a thermometer and a dropping funnel whose stem has been drawn to a capillary. Both the thermometer and the dropping funnel extend to within 5 mm. of the flask bottom. Preferably the side arm should fit the condenser by a ground glass joint as shown in the apparatus of Fig. 18-6 (which is used in a modified method whereby steam is added instead of water). More elaborate trapping devices are inadvisable, because the possible adsorption causes fluorine deficiencies.

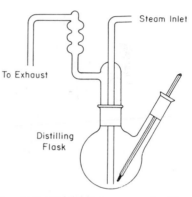

FIG. 18-6. Modified Apparatus for Fluoride Distillation.

**Procedure.**—Wash the crucible or dish several times with water and a small amount of sulfuric acid, adding the wash solution to the flask. Connect the apparatus as directed above. Remove the stopper, add sulfuric acid slowly from a pipette until the effervescence ceases, and then add approximately 12 ml. more of sulfuric acid. Replace the stopper, boil at 135–140°C., and collect the distillate in a 100-ml. volumetric flask. When the liquid temperature reaches 135°C. sufficient water is slowly dropped from the funnel to compensate for the water distilling out and to maintain the temperature at 135°C. The distillation requires constant supervision. After the 100 ml. flask is filled (distillate 1) collect another 50 ml. (distillate 2) to be certain that all the fluorine has been volatilized.

Churchill, Bridges, and Rowley[11] point out that phosphates may interfere in this determination, for in some products (especially food products) the phosphates are possibly reduced to a form which is readily carried over in the distillate. They recommend a double Willard-Winter distillation of the fluorine from the ash of the material. The first should be made with sulfuric acid to eliminate hazard, as some carbonaceous material may be present, and the second distillation should be made with perchloric acid at 135°C. This procedure yields a distillate free from sulfate and phosphate. Great care should be exercised in all distillations and operations in which perchloric acid is employed because of danger from explosion.

[10] Winter, J. Assoc. Official Agr. Chem., **19**, 362, 1936.
[11] Churchill, Bridges, and Rowley, Ind. Eng. Chem., Anal. Ed., **9**, 222, 1937.

For methods of determination of fluoride in the distillate, see titrimetric "Cerous Nitrate Method" or colorimetric "Zirconium-Alizarin Method."

***Separation of Fluoride by Volatilization of $H_2SiF_6$.***—This method serves to remove fluorine from solutions that contain various cations. It is described by Powell and Menis.[12]

The samples are heated in a stream of moist oxygen. For the more difficultly decomposed fluorides, e.g., alkali and alkaline earth fluorides, a reactive oxide is added to the sample to accelerate release of the fluoride. The maximum temperature of the heating depends upon the oxide used: with uranium oxide, this temperature may be 1000°C.; if tungstic oxide is used, or if no reactant is added,

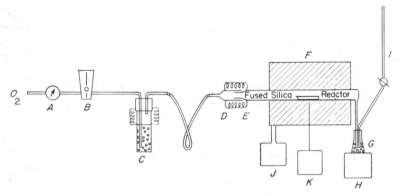

FIG. 18-7. Micro and Macro Pyrolytic Apparatus.

$A$ = Regulator; $B$ = Flow indicator; $C$ = Water tower; $D$ = Joint, T/S 29/42, fused silica; $E$ = Pyrolytic reactor tube, fused silica; $F$ = Split type furnace, 12″ 1¼″ bore; $G$ = Receiving flask; $H$ = Magnetic stirrer; $I$ = Burette, goose-neck; $J$ = Variable transformer; $K$ = Thermocouple and pyrometer.

this temperature should not exceed 825°C. The volatilized fluoride is absorbed in a small volume of dilute NaOH and determined either by acidimetric or spectrophotometric titration. Milligram quantities of fluoride can be separated in 20 minutes or less and subsequently determined with a coefficient of variation of 0.1%. For trace amounts of fluoride (~10 micrograms) the coefficient of variation is of the order of 5%.

**Apparatus.** *Gas Cylinder with Flowmeter, B, and Regulator A.*—Oxygen is supplied from the cylinder, while the flow of the gas is measured by means of a calibrated flowmeter. See Fig. 18-7.

*Water Tower, C.*—Oxygen is passed through the scrubbing water tower, containing water at room temperature, to saturate the gas with moisture.

*Reactor Tube, E.*—Fused silica, 24 inches in length and 1½ inches in outer diameter. The reactor tube is connected to the gas supply by a ²⁹/₄₂ standard taper joint, $D$, lubricated with powdered graphite.

*Delivery Tube.*—Fused silica, 10 inches in length and ⅜ inch in outer diameter. This tube is fused at right angles to the exit end of the reactor tube.

*Hevi-Duty, Split Combustion Furnace F.*—This furnace is used to heat the re-

12 Powell, R. H., and Menis, Oscar, Analytical Chemistry, **30**, 1546–1549, 1958.

actor tube; the power supply is controlled by a variable transformer, $J$ (Variac, Model V-20).

*A calibrated pyrometer* with a Chromel-Alumel thermocouple is used to measure the temperature of the furnace; the thermocouple is at the external wall of the reactor tube mid-point between the ends of the tube furnace.

*Combustion boats,* Alundum, $3\frac{1}{2}''$ long x $\frac{1}{2}''$ wide x $\frac{5}{16}''$ high, or platinum, $3\frac{1}{2}''$ long x $\frac{1}{2}''$ wide x $\frac{3}{8}''$ high.

**Reagents.** *Solid Sodium Fluoride.*—This reagent should be dried at 110°C. for 1 hour.

*Tungstic Oxide, $WO_3$.*—The purified, anhydrous oxide should be used.

*Uranium Oxide, $U_3O_8$.*—The oxide is prepared by igniting precipitated ammonium diuranate at 900°C. for 1 hour.

*Standard Mixture of Sodium Fluoride and Uranium Oxide, 100 Micrograms of Fluoride per Gram.*—A 12.7-mg. portion of sodium fluoride is mixed with 57.6 g. of uranium oxide by grinding the mixture in a mortar, after which the mixture is further blended by rotating it for 16 hours in a bottle attached to a V-shaped tumbler. During this period, portions of the mixture are removed, again ground in a mortar, and returned to the bottle for further blending.

*Standard 0.0020 N Sodium Hydroxide.*—Dilute with water 20 ml. of 0.1 $N$ NaOH solution (containing 4 g. per liter of NaOH) to 1 liter. Standardize against potassium hydrogen phthalate.

**Procedure.** *Preparation of Sample.* Solid Samples.—Transfer 3 g. of finely powdered tungstic oxide to a 4-inch diameter, octagonal Mullite mortar. Add a known weight of a solid sample (0.1–2.0 g.), depending on the fluoride concentration, to the mortar and mix by grinding. Transfer the dry mixture quantitatively to a platinum or Alundum boat of suitable size ($3\frac{1}{2}$ to 6 inches, depending on the volume of the dry mixture).

Liquid Samples or Slurry.—Transfer a 2-ml. test portion of a liquid sample or a suitable weight of slurry, to a $3\frac{1}{2}''$ platinum boat and place on a clean $7'' \times 9''$ porcelain tray. Add 3 drops of phenolphthalein solution to the boat. Add sufficient 1 $N$ sodium hydroxide to the boat to make the solution alkaline to phenolphthalein (avoid a large excess of sodium hydroxide). Evaporate to dryness under an infrared lamp. Keep the solution alkaline during the evaporation by addition of 1 $N$ sodium hydroxide as required. Add 3 g. of finely powdered tungstic oxide to the residue in the boat; pack with a microspatula.

*Pyrolytic Separation.*—Assemble the pyrolysis apparatus as shown in Fig. 18-7. Start the flow of oxygen, saturated with water vapor at room temperature, and regulate the flow rate at 4 to 6 cubic feet (120 to 180 liters) per hour. Turn on the variable voltage transformer which controls the temperature of the pyrolysis apparatus. Heat the fused silica reactor tube to a specified temperature according to the material being pyrolyzed and the reactant that is present: tungstic oxide 825°C.; and uranium oxide 1000°C. Adjust the setting of the variable voltage transformer to maintain the selected temperature. Add a suitable volume of standard sodium hydroxide solution to an Erlenmeyer or volumetric flask; place the flask under the delivery tube from the pyrolysis apparatus so that the tip of the tube is immersed in the solution to a depth of approximately 0.5 inch. Add 4 drops of phenolphthalein solution to the receiving vessel. Remove the plug from the fused silica reactor tube, and insert the platinum (or alundum) boat containing the prepared sample in the center of the furnace. Quickly replace the plug and continue the pyrolysis for 15 minutes, maintaining the selected temperature.

*Determination.*—Remove the flask containing the sodium hydroxide solution. Wash down the tip of the delivery tube; add the washings to the flask. Determine the fluoride content of the solution by alkalimetric or spectrophotometric titration, whichever is applicable. (See later sections of this chapter.)

## ION EXCHANGE TECHNIQUE FOR CONCENTRATING TRACE AMOUNTS OF FLUORIDE [13]

The determination of trace amounts of fluoride (e.g., in some water samples or in the quantities found in some animal tissues) is difficult, especially when the sample size must be restricted. By employing an ion exchange technique for concentrating the fluoride and freeing the solution from interfering ions, 1.0 to 10.0 microgram quantities can be estimated with a precision within 5% of the fluoride present. Moreover in the isolation of fluoride by the distillation procedure (described earlier in this Chapter) rather large amounts of distillate must be collected to ensure quantitative recovery; the concentration may thus be too low for satisfactory estimation when certain substances are analyzed. The method reported here employs an ion exchange resin for concentrating the fluoride. Estimation may then be carried out by various of the titrimetric on colorimetric methods described later in this Chapter. The Zirconium Eriochrome Cyanine R Colorimetric Method is recommended.

*Apparatus.* **Ion Exchange Columns.**—Straight borosilicate glass tubes, 9-mm. inside diameter and approximately 12″ long.

**A 00, One-Hole Rubber Stopper.**—This should contain a piece of 5- or 6-mm. glass tubing 4 or 5 cm long and is covered with a circular piece of thin nylon cloth, slightly larger than the smaller diameter of the stopper. This is inserted into the tube to contain the resin. No portion of the cloth should extend beyond the end of the tube.

A portion of resin in the chloride form is suspended in distilled water and allowed to settle, and the fines are decanted. The resin slurry is added to the tube to make a column when settled 2 cm in height. After the water has drained off and the surface is firm and smooth, a small plug of glass wool is inserted to prevent distortion of the surface when liquid is added to the tube.

The resin is converted to the acetate form by dripping into the column (4 to 12 drops per minute) 25 ml. of 1 $M$ sodium acetate. A small amount of chloride remaining in the resin does no harm. The resin swells to a height of about 2.5 cm when converted to the acetate form.

The acetate solutions and samples are conveniently added to the columns by means of pipettes. The suction end of each pipette is equipped with a short length of gum rubber tubing and a screw clamp. The pipette is supported above the column and the solution is allowed to drip onto the resin. A small wire (26-gauge Nichrome) inserted in the tubing aids greatly in controlling the rate of flow.

*Reagents.*—**Anion exchange resin Dowex 1-X8, 200 to 400 mesh.**

**Sodium Acetate Solution, 1 $M$.**

**Sodium Acetate Solutions.**—0.1 $M$, 0.2 $M$, and 0.3 $M$, made by dilution of the 1 $M$ solution.

[13] Neilson, Anal. Chem., **30**, 1009, 1958.

*Procedure.*—Excess acetate is removed from the resin by filling the tube with distilled water and allowing it to run through at an unrestricted rate.

The samples are added to the columns from pipettes at a flow rate of 6 to 12 drops per minute. The aliquot preferably should contain not more than 6 to 8 micrograms.

The fluoride is removed from the resin by stepwise elution with increasing concentrations of sodium acetate, beginning at 0.1 $M$ solution. Ten milliliters of this solution are run into the column at a rate of about 6 to 8 drops per minute, followed by 10 ml. of 0.2 $M$, and then 10 ml. of 0.3 $M$ solution. The effluent from each treatment is collected in a separate tube. If the sample contains less than 6 to 8 micrograms of fluoride, usually all will appear in the second fraction. If very small amounts of fluoride are expected, collecting the 0.2 $M$ effluent in two 5-ml. fractions may enable greater precision of estimation, as with proper adjustment of resin height and rate of flow, the total fluoride may be obtained in 5 ml. of effluent. Each fraction, however, should be checked for fluoride.

The 0.3 $M$ solution regenerates the resin sufficiently when distillates are analyzed. If the sample contains phosphate, chloride, or sulfate, the resin should be cleaned with 25 ml. of 1 $M$ acetate, followed with distilled water to remove excess acetate.

**Determination.**—Various colorimetric or titrimetric methods may be used. The Zirconium Eriochrome Cyanine B Method (*q.v.*) is recommended.

## FLUORINE IN SOLID (NONVOLATILE) HALOCARBONS [14]

This method of fluorine separation is based upon steam pyrohydrolysis. The apparatus is shown in Fig. 18-8.

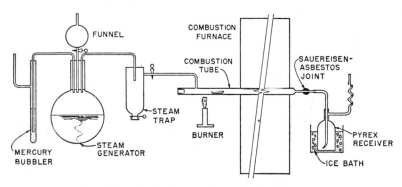

Fig. 18-8. Pyrohydrolysis Assembly for Fluorine.

*Procedure.*—Connect the steam supply (consisting of a 1-liter flask as a steam generator, a 500-ml. inverted wash bottle as a steam trap, and a mercury bubbler) to the combustion tube. The material of the latter must withstand a temperature of 1100°C., for which quartz, platinized quartz, or platinum are suitable. The portion of it within the combustion furnace is packed with platinum stars. The overall dimensions of the tube are 10 mm. I.D., and 60 cm long. The receiver and the tubing joining it to the combustion tube should be borosilicate. Put a

[14] Rickard, R. R., Bull, Frances L., and Harris, W. W., Anal. Chem., **23,** 919–921, 1951.

5-mg. sample in a platinum microcombustion boat, which is then set about 7.5 cm from the entrance to the furnace. Cool the receiver with ice as shown in the figure. Adjust the steam flow through the system to a rate of 1 g. per minute. Commence heating slowly by applying a flame about 5 cm from the sample, and as hydrolysis progresses, move it toward the furnace entrance. The furnace temperature should finally reach 1100°C. The foregoing cycle should be repeated to make certain it is complete. Remove receiver and dilute condensate with 1:1500 HCl to 100 ml.

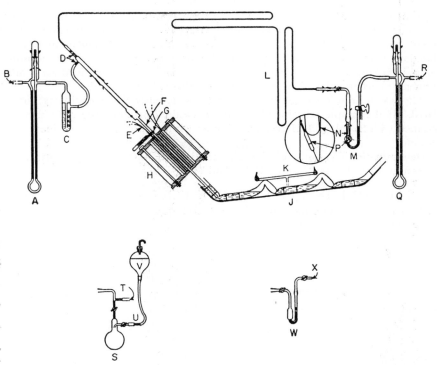

FIG. 18-9. Apparatus for Determination of Fluorine in Volatile Organic Substances.

$A$ = Oxygen capillary flowmeter; $B$ = Oxygen at constant pressure; $C$ = Water bubbler; $D$ = Capillaries; $E$ = Thermocouple leads; $F$ = Nickel tube silver-soldered to housekeeper seal and platinum tube; $G$ = Wet cloth wick; $H$ = Electric furnace at 1100°C.; $J$ = Saran tubing absorber wired to bent iron strip; $K$ = Small cool gas flames; $L$ = Flexible small-diameter glass tube; $M$ = Semimicro sample holder; $N$ = Glass-encased lead hammer; $P$ = Semimicro sample; $Q$ = Nitrogen capillary flowmeter; $R$ = Nitrogen at constant pressure; $S$ = Macro gas sample weighing bulb; $T$ = Nitrogen flow; $U$ = Fine capillary; $V$ = Mercury; $W$ = Macro liquid sample weighing tube; $X$ = Regulated nitrogen flow.

## FLUORINE IN VOLATILE HYDROCARBONS [15]

This is a micromethod, in which the sample is introduced into the apparatus (shown in Fig. 18-9) in a sealed tube, which is broken when conditions for its oxidation have been established. They consist of heating to 1100°C., in the

[15] Schumb, Walter C., and Radimer, Kenneth J., Anal. Chem., 20, 871–4, 1948.

presence of oxygen, and a flow of nitrogen that is adjusted according to the volatility of the sample. The water bubbler ($C$ in the figure) serves to wet the oxygen, which is necessary for samples requiring hydrolysis or additional hydrogen to form the HF. For such compounds as $CF_3CF_2CF_3$, $CF_3CF_3$ and $CF_4$ the oxygen must be saturated with $NH_3$ to provide the necessary hydrogen. The basis of the method is the formation of HF, which is dissolved in the water in the receiver.

*Procedure.*—Fill the absorber, $J$, with distilled water. Place a sample containing 15 mg. or less of fluorine in a borosilicate microsample tube drawn to a diameter of 2 mm., and seal the tube. Place it in the sample-tube holder, $M$, with its stopcocks closed and before connecting it to the apparatus. Break the sample tube with the glass-encased lead hammer, $N$, and then attach the sample-tube holder to the system. Adjust the nitrogen rate as required by the volatility of the sample, the oxygen rate to 3 ml. per second, and the furnace temperature to 1100°C. Adjust the flames, $K$, above the absorber, to about 1 inch in length. Open the stopcocks on the sample-tube holder. (Note that any stopcock grease used must be nonaqueous.) After 30 minutes apply a low flame to the sample-tube holder, $M$, to complete the volatilization and reaction of the sample. After 50 minutes transfer the reaction products from the absorber to a plastic beaker by washing with 1% NaOH solution. Neutralize to phenolphthalein.

## FLUORINE IN MONOFLUORINATED ORGANIC COMPOUNDS [16]

*Procedure.*—Place a 10- to 20-mg. sample in a round-bottomed flask of 50 or 100-ml. capacity with a tight (ground-glass) connection. Add 0.2 g. of metallic sodium and 15 ml. of hexyl alcohol, and reflux for 15 minutes. Extract with two 10-ml. portions of water.

## GRAVIMETRIC METHODS

### PRECIPITATION AS CALCIUM FLUORIDE

The method utilizes the insolubility of calcium fluoride in dilute acetic acid for its separation from calcium carbonate, the presence of which facilitates filtration of the slimy fluoride. The reaction for precipitation is as follows:

$$2NaF + CaCl_2 \rightarrow CaF_2 + 2NaCl$$

*Procedure.*—Solution of the sample and the removal of silica having been accomplished according to procedures given under "Preparation and Solution of the Sample," and "Separations," the solution is neutralized, if acid, by the addition of sodium carbonate in slight excess; if basic, by addition of hydrochloric acid in excess, followed by sodium carbonate. To this solution, faintly basic, 1 ml. of 2 $N$ sodium carbonate reagent is added, followed by sufficient calcium chloride solution to precipitate completely the fluoride and the excess of carbonate, i.e., until no more precipitate forms, and then 2–3 ml. in excess. After the precipitate has settled, it is filtered and washed with hot water. (The filtrate should be tested for fluoride and carbonate with additional calcium chloride.) The precipitate of calcium fluoride and carbonate is dried and transferred to a platinum dish, the ash of the filter, burned separately, is added and the material ignited. After cooling, an excess of dilute acetic acid is added, and the mixture evaporated to dry-

16 Salsbury, Jason M., Cole, James W., Jr., Overhalser, Lyle G., Armstrong, Alfred R., and Goe, John H., Anal. Chem., **23**, 603–8, 1952.

ness on the water bath. The lime is converted to calcium acetate, while the fluoride remains unaffected. The residue is taken up with a little water, filtered and washed with small portions of hot water, by which procedure calcium acetate is removed, while calcium fluoride remains on the filter.[17] The residue is dried, separated from the filter and ignited. This, together with the ash of the filter, is weighed as calcium fluoride, $CaF_2$.

To confirm the result, the residue is treated with a slight excess of sulfuric acid and taken to fumes in a platinum dish. The adhering acid is removed as usual by heating with ammonium carbonate, and the ignited residue weighed as calcium sulfate. One gram of calcium fluoride should yield 1.7437 g. of calcium sulfate.[18]

$$\text{Factors: } CaO \times 1.3923 = CaF_2$$
$$\times 0.6776 = F.$$
$$CaF_2 \times 0.4867 = F$$
$$\times 0.5125 = HF$$
$$\times 1.0758 = NaF$$
$$CaSO_4 \times 0.5739 = CaF_2$$

## PRECIPITATION OF FLUORINE AS LEAD CHLOROFLUORIDE [19]

This method [20] is applicable to rather simple,[21] soluble and neutral fluorides. It precipitates granular and easily filtered PbFCl using hydrochloric acid and lead acetate. The precipitate is ideal, being about fourteen times heavier than the fluorine which it contains, but since it is relatively soluble in water [22] a solution of PbFCl must be used for washing. The method is rapid and convenient. Its accuracy varies with the amount of fluorine present.[23] It has been used, with modification, in the analysis of simple fluorides, electrolytic solutions,[24] enamels, paints, glasses,[25] and simple minerals.

**Reagents. Lead Acetate.—**Ten per cent lead acetate solution containing 1% of glacial acetic acid.

**Wash Solution.—**Saturated PbFCl solution for washing precipitate.

NOTES.—Preparation of Wash Solution. (1) Ten grams $Pb(NO_3)_2$ dissolved in 20 ml. $H_2O$; (2) one gram NaF dissolved in 100 ml. $H_2O$, containing 2 ml. of concentrated HCl acid.

The two parts are combined and the precipitate of PbFCl is washed several times by decantation. One liter of cold $H_2O$ is added to the residue and allowed to stand one hour with stirring. The solution is filtered and the clear filtrate used.

[17] The results are slightly low, owing to the solubility of calcium fluoride: 100 ml. $H_2O$ dissolves 0.0016 g. $CaF_2$; 100 ml. 1.5 $N$ $HC_2H_3O_2$ dissolves 0.011 g.

[18] Low recommends disintegration of the fluoride with sulfuric acid, diluting the mixture with water, boiling with ammonium chloride, and then with ammonium hydroxide and hydrogen peroxide. Calcium oxalate is now precipitated from the filtrate and CaO determined by titration with standard permanganate according to the usual procedure for determination of lime.

[19] Compiled by Ernest P. Herner.

[20] Originated by Starck, Z. anorg. allgem. Chem., **70,** 173, 1911. C. A., **5,** 2049, 1911.

[21] Phosphates, sulfates, chromates, and arsenates of lead are precipitated, at least in part. Large quantities of alkali salts, boric acid, aluminum and iron prevent complete precipitation of PbFCl. Aluminum causes the greatest trouble. A preliminary acetic acid (1:10) extraction will remove most of these radicals. The effect of boric acid and alkali salts is lessened if the solution is allowed to stand longer.

[22] Solubility of PbFCl in 100 g. $H_2O$: at 18°C. 0.0325 g., at 100°C. 0.1081.

[23] Best results when 0.01–0.1 gram of fluorine is present.

[24] Hammond, L. D., J. Ind. Eng. Chem., **16,** 938, 1924.

[25] Lundell and Hoffman, J. Research Natl. Bur. Standards, **3,** 581, 1929.

*Procedure.*[26]—0.5 gram of the sample dried at 110°C. for one hour is dissolved [27] in about 200 ml. of water and heated to 40°C. The solution is made neutral to methyl orange indicator and then 3 drops of dilute nitric acid are added. To this solution (or extract from fusion) sixteen drops of concentrated hydrochloric acid are added (possibly 22–24 drops with high grade substance but great excess must be avoided). Ten drops of glacial acetic acid and 25 ml. of the lead acetate solution are added. The heavy white granular precipitate of PbFCl is allowed to stand for one hour, the temperature being kept above 15°C.[28]

The residue is filtered through a weighed Gooch crucible. After washing 3–4 times with the PbFCl solution and finally 1–2 times with cold water the residue is dried one hour at 110–120°C. and weighed as PbFCl.[29]

Factors: PbFCl $\times$ 0.16048 = NaF, or

$\times$ 0.07261 = F

## PRECIPITATION AS TRIPHENYLTIN FLUORIDE [30]

*Reagents.* **Triphenyltin Chloride.**—Dissolve in 95% methanol sufficient $(C_6H_5)_3$-SnCl to give 0.02 g. per ml.

**Wash Solution.**—Saturate 95% methanol with $(C_6H_5)_3$SnF at room temperature.

*Procedure.*—The aqueous solution of the fluoride is made up to 60–70% alcoholic by adding the proper volume of 95% alcohol. About twice the calculated quantity of triphenyltin chloride solution, diluted with an equal volume of 95% alcohol is heated to boiling and added slowly into the hot fluoride solution with rapid stirring, and the whole is again heated to boiling and the stirring is continued during part of the cooling. The vessel is allowed to stand overnight since the precipitation is a slow one. The vessel is then cooled in ice for 1 hour, if the amount of fluoride is small. The precipitate is collected on a weighed filtering crucible, washed with the saturated alcoholic wash solution, of which not more than 50 ml. should be required. Dry for 30 minutes at 100–110°C., cool and weigh. Weight of $(C_6H_5)_3$SnF $\times$ 0.05153 = weight of fluorine.

The solution should be between pH 7 and 9. The substances which interfere are carbonate, silicic acid and phosphate. Sulfates tend to be precipitated by the alcohol, but moderate amounts of the latter as well as nitrate, chloride, bromide or iodide do not interfere. The method is well adapted for the precise determination of amounts of fluorine ranging from 0.1 to 50 mg. in the absence of the interfering substances that have been mentioned.

[26] Procedure of F. G. Hawley is given above. In the original method of Starck the neutral solution is treated with a large excess of $PbCl_2$ solution. The precipitate is allowed to settle overnight, filtered off in a weighed Gooch and washed as directed above. The residue is dried 2–3 hours at 140–150°C. and weighed as PbFCl.

[27] If the fluoride is not soluble in $H_2O$ it must be fused according to the method of Berzelius and Rose. The $H_2O$ extract of the fusion, after the last trace of silica and ammonia has been removed, is neutralized, made to about 200 ml. and used to precipitate PbFCl.

[28] $PbCl_2$ will crystallize below this temperature.

[29] Because of the limited range and the number of interfering substances it is probably better, when applying this method to complex substances, to precipitate PbFCl as directed, but, instead of weighing, to determine chlorine in the residue according to the titrimetric method of Hawley described later in this Chapter, under "Other Titrimetric Methods."

[30] Allen and Furman, J. Am. Chem. Soc., **54**, 4625, 1932.

## TITRIMETRIC METHODS

### CEROUS NITRATE METHOD [31]

Add several drops of 0.04% phenol red solution to the solution of the fluoride or to the distillate obtained by the distillation method on page 432, and neutralize the liquid with dilute sodium hydroxide, avoiding a large excess. Boil the alkaline solution and bring back repeatedly to the apparent neutral point with 0.02 $N$ or 0.01 $N$ perchloric acid. During this neutralization reduce the volume to 5–10 ml. When the faint pink color is no longer restored by boiling (carbonate free), cool the solution, transfer quantitatively to a 50-ml. beaker and boil from about 25 ml. down to 2 to 3 ml. Add 2 drops of a saturated alcoholic solution of methyl red and 10 drops of 0.04% bromocresol green solution. (The bromocresol green is weighed out exactly and neutralized with standard sodium hydroxide to yield the monosodium salt. This prevents alteration of the neutrality of the solution when the indicator is added.) Titrate the liquid at 80°C. to the maximum red color with cerous nitrate solution 1 ml. of which is equivalent to 0.5 mg. of fluorine. When the amount of fluorine is less than 0.2 mg., thorium nitrate solution, 1 ml. of which is equivalent to 0.1 mg. of fluorine, may be substituted for the cerous nitrate, using the same mixed indicator.

*Thorium Nitrate Modification.*—The thorium nitrate solution may be standardized by titration against known volumes of 0.02 $N$ fluoride solution.

**Procedure.**—Transfer a known aliquot of standard 0.02 $N$ fluoride solution to a flask, add water to bring the volume to 20 ml. and then add an equal volume of ethyl alcohol. Add 6 drops of alizarin red indicator (prepared by dissolving 1 g. of sodium alizarin sulfonate in 100 ml. of ethyl alcohol, filtering off the residue, and making up the filtrate to 250 ml. with alcohol) and then only enough dilute hydrochloric acid to destroy the color. Avoid excess acid. Titrate with the thorium nitrate solution, over a white surface in a good light to a faint permanent reappearance of color. Titrate slowly near the end point. Run a blank titration on the indicator by determining the volume of standard 0.02 $N$ fluoride solution necessary to cause disappearance of color in a slightly acid water-alcohol solution of 6 drops of the indicator and compare this with the volume of standard thorium nitrate necessary to discharge the color. Calculate the strength of the thorium nitrate solution by use of the following equation:

$$1.0 \text{ ml. Th(NO}_3)_4 = \frac{\text{ml. of } 0.02 \ N \ F^- \text{ solution}}{\text{ml. of Th(NO}_3)_4 \text{ solution}} \times 0.38 = \text{mg. of } F^-$$

## MODIFIED THORIUM NITRATE METHOD

The thorium nitrate titration of fluorides has been simplified by Williams [32] by using a single titration against a permanent color standard.

*Reagents.* **Acidified Standard Thorium Nitrate Stock Solution.**—Dissolve 1.27 g. of thorium nitrate, $Th(NO_3)_4 \cdot 4H_2O$, and 72 ml. of $N$ hydrochloric acid in water and make up to 100 ml.

[31] Scott and Henne, Ind. Eng. Chem., Anal. Ed., **7**, 299, 1935; Jacobs, M. B., Chemical Analysis of Food and Food Products, 3rd Ed., pages 745–746, D. Van Nostrand Co., Inc., Princeton, N. J., 1958.

[32] Williams, Analyst, **71**, 175, 1947; Jacobs, M. B., Chemical Analysis of Food and Food Products, 3rd Ed., pages 747–748, D. Van Nostrand Co., Inc., Princeton, N. J., 1958.

*Dilute Solution.*—Dilute 5 ml. of the stock solution to 500 ml. with fluorine-free water. One ml. of the dilute solution is equivalent to 5 micrograms of fluoride.

**Acid-Indicator Solution.**—Dissolve 0.020 g. of sodium alizarinmonosulfonate (Alizarin-S) in water, add 100 ml. of the dilute acidified thorium nitrate solution, and 14.3 ml. of $N$ hydrochloric acid and make up to 200 ml. Two ml. of this solution added to 50 ml. of fluorine-free water and 10 ml. of 2 $N$ sodium chloride solution in a Nessler tube should give the correct end point color; if not, impurities in the salt or other chemicals may be responsible and the proportion of the dilute standard thorium nitrate solution used should be modified accordingly. The color should be judged when making the acid-indicator solution for it is likely to alter on standing.

**2,5-Dinitrophenol Indicator Solution.**—Dissolve 0.25 g. *p*-dinitrophenol in 100 ml. of water.

**Color Standards. Temporary.**—Dilute an aliquot of a standard fluoride solution made from sodium fluoride prepared from the purest sodium carbonate and hydrofluoric acid, containing 100 micrograms of fluorine to 50 ml. with water. Add 10 ml. of 2 $N$ sodium chloride solution, 2 ml. of the acid indicator solution, 20 ml. of the dilute standard thorium nitrate solution, and mix. This color is stable for several hours.

**Permanent.**—Mix 3 ml. of 10% hydrochloric acid with 50 ml. of a solution containing 1% of cobalt chloride, $CoCl_2$, add 30 ml. of 0.1% potassium chromate solution, and dilute to 100 ml. Dilute 3 ml. of this stock mixture with water to a volume approximately equal to the anticipated volume of the test solution when titrated. The color should be identical with that of the temporary standard. If it is not, possibly because of differences in the thorium nitrate used, the proportions of ingredients should be adjusted until a match is obtained. Alternatively, alizarin-S may be used as a color standard in a buffered solution of suitable pH.

**Procedure.**—Add 3 drops of 2,5-dinitrophenol indicator solution to an appropriate aliquot of the distillate of fluoride solution in a Nessler tube and add 0.05 $N$ sodium hydroxide solution until the solution, when mixed, assumes a faint yellow color. Then add a drop or sufficient 0.01 $N$ hydrochloric acid solution just to discharge the color. It is useful to have a Nessler tube containing water for comparison, because the color becomes very pale near the end point. If the presence of free halogen is suspected, add 1 ml. of 1% hydroxylamine hydrochloride solution just before the neutralization.

Transfer accurately 50 ml. of the neutralized solution, containing between 0.5 and about 150 micrograms of fluorine to another Nessler tube, add 10 ml. of 2 $N$ sodium chloride solution, 2 ml. of the acid-indicator solution, and mix. Titrate with the dilute standard thorium nitrate solution until the color exactly matches that of the standard color solutions. For a 5 g. sample, 1 ml. of dilute thorium nitrate solution is equivalent to 1 p. p. m., subject to correction blanks.

## ZIRCONIUM-ALIZARIN METHOD

(For Colorimetric Zirconium-Alizarin Method, see Page 453.)

### *INTERFERING ELEMENTS ABSENT* [32a]

**Reagents. Zirconium Nitrate.**—1 g. $Zr(NO_3)_4 \cdot 5H_2O$ in 250 ml. water.

**Alizarin red.**—1 g. of sodium alizarinsulfonate in 100 ml. of ethyl alcohol. Filter

---

[32a] Any ion which forms a precipitate or a nondissociated salt with fluorine or with thorium interferes with the titration—e.g. Ca++, Ba++, Fe+3, Al+3, PO4−3, etc.

off the undissolved residue and add 150 ml. of ethyl alcohol to the filtrate. The two solutions are kept in stock and mixed, 3 parts of the zirconium nitrate solution and 2 of the alizarin red solution as needed.

**Thorium Nitrate Solution.**—0.01 $N$, standardized against a known fluoride solution.

**Standard Fluoride.**—0.01 $N$ lithium fluoride or specially purified sodium fluoride.

**Hydrochloric Acid.**—Approximately 1 to 50.

**Procedure.**—Dissolve a weighed quantity of the fluoride in water and make up to a given volume. Transfer an aliquot of the solution to be analyzed to a small tall-form beaker, add water to make a volume of approximately 20 ml. and 3 drops of the zirconium-alizarin mixture.[33] If necessary, add just enough dilute hydrochloric acid to destroy the color. Add an equal volume of neutral ethyl alcohol, and titrate over a white surface in good light with the standard thorium nitrate to a faint permanent reappearance of color. The reaction is slow near the end point. When titrating with 0.01 $N$ thorium nitrate, make a correction for the fluorine which combines with the indicator. Determine this by titrating the number of drops of indicator used in the titration with 0.01 $N$ fluoride solution to the disappearance of the color.

## INTERFERING ELEMENTS PRESENT

When interfering elements are present in the soluble fluoride solutions, the fluorine must be separated from the other elements before the titrations can be made. This may be done by the Distillation Method described earlier in this Chapter. It is used chiefly where a large amount of silica is not present.

When a large amount of silica is present, the following procedure [34] is followed:

**Procedure.**—Fuse 0.5 g. of the sample with 2.5 g. of sodium carbonate, leach the mass with hot water, filter, and wash. Transfer the insoluble residue back to the dish in which it was leached by means of a fine jet with about 50 ml. of hot water, add sodium carbonate to make approximately a 2% solution, boil a few minutes, filter, and wash thoroughly with hot water. To the combined filtrates which should have a volume of 300 ml., add 0.5 g. of zinc oxide dissolved in perchloric acid, boil the alkaline solution for one minute, filter and wash with hot water. Concentrate the filtrate to 200 ml., add a drop of methyl red, neutralize to a very faint pink with dilute perchloric acid, add a solution of 0.25 g. of zinc oxide and 0.5 g. of ammonium carbonate dissolved in 0.5 ml. of ammonium hydroxide and 10 ml. of water. Place on steam bath until a clear solution is obtained. Boil the solution until the odor of ammonia has entirely disappeared, concentrate to about 100 ml., filter, and wash with cold water. Concentrate the filtrate to 25 ml., and either transfer to the distillation flask for the determination of fluorine, or to a 50-ml. volumetric flask, make up to volume, and take an aliquot for the determination.

[33] If the volume of the solution to be titrated is sufficiently small (4 to 8 ml.) so that the color can be distinguished, the accuracy of the titration is increased by using only one drop of the indicator. If the volume is large, it may be necessary to add more than 3 drops (50 to 75 ml. require 6 drops). For very accurate results it is necessary to standardize the thorium nitrate in approximately the same volume and with the same number of drops of indicator as the unknown, and titrate the two to the same color. The end point is not sharp in the presence of a large amount of thorium fluoride; not more than 10 ml. of 0.01 $N$ thorium nitrate should be used for the titration.

[34] Lundell and Hoffman, J. Research Natl. Bur. Standards, **3**, 581, 1929.

## DETERMINATION BY FORMATION OF SILICON TETRA-FLUORIDE AND ABSORPTION OF THE EVOLVED GAS IN WATER. OFFERMAN'S METHOD [35]

Silicon tetrafluoride is formed by the action of sulfuric acid upon a fluoride in presence of silica, the evolved gas is received in water and the resulting compound titrated with standard potassium hydroxide. The following reactions take place:

A. $3SiF_4 + 2H_2O \rightarrow 2H_2SiF_6 + SiO_2$

B. $H_2SiF_6 + 6KOH \rightarrow 6KF + SiO_2 + 4H_2O$

The method is suitable for determining fluorine in fluorspar in evaluation of this mineral.

*Procedure.*—The powdered sample, containing the equivalent of 0.1–0.2 g. calcium fluoride, is mixed with about ten times its weight of pulverized quartz (previously ignited and kept in a desiccator), placed in the decomposition flask $F$, shown in Fig. 18-10, and about 1 g. of anhydrous copper sulfate added, followed by 25 ml.

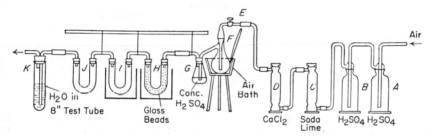

FIG. 18-10. Adolph's Apparatus for Determining Fluorine.

of concentrated sulfuric acid. The stopcock $E$ is closed and the air bath heated gradually till in 0.5 hour the temperature has risen to 220°C. The stopcock $E$ is now opened and air slowly forced through the apparatus (by means of a water pump) at the rate of about three bubbles per second, the temperature being kept at 220°C., and the flask containing the sample occasionally shaken. When the bubbles of silicon tetrafluoride have disappeared from $F$, the flame is removed, but the air current continued for half an hour longer. The solution in the receiving flask is now titrated with 0.1 $N$ KOH.

NOTES.—The apparatus shown in the cut is the form recommended by Adolph, and the details of procedure are essentially his. This method is preferred to that of Penfield,[36] in which an alcoholic solution of potassium chloride is used to absorb the tetrafluoride, and the liberated hydrochloric acid titrated with the standard alkali in presence of cochineal indicator.

The results obtained by this method are generally low, but the procedure is useful for rapid valuation of fluorspar.

The run having been made as directed, the solution in tube $K$ is poured into a beaker, an excess of standard potassium hydroxide added and the excess alkali

[35] Z. angew. Chem., **3**, 615, 1890. Wm. H. Adolph, J. Am. Chem. Soc., **37**, 11, 2500, 1915.

[36] Am. Chem. J., **1**, 27, 1879.

titrated with standard sulfuric acid in boiling solution. Norris prefers the use of litmus indicator to phenolphthalein, claiming that the end point is sharper.

It is found advisable to use mercury in the tube $K$ as a trap, thus preventing the stoppage of the delivery tube by crystallization. The gas readily passes up through the mercury and is absorbed in the supernatant solution.

In place of using 0.1 $N$ solutions the potassium hydroxide may be made of such strength that 1 ml. will equal 1% fluorine with 0.5-g. sample taken and the acid made to a corresponding strength.

Notes.—The following suggestions for the method are made by W. V. Norris, Colorado School of Mines.

It is especially necessary that all apparatus be dry, as the least amount of moisture will make the results run low. For this reason it is better to use phosphoric anhydride in washing bottle $B$ instead of sulfuric acid.

The sulfuric acid used should be previously treated as follows: Heat 500 ml. of acid to white fumes, cool, warm gently but not to fumes, then again cool in a desiccator until ready for use. This will produce an acid that will be an efficient dehydrator and will give off no free sulfur trioxide.

It is advisable to use a large excess of silica in the generator apparatus, preferably ten times the weight of the sample taken.

The copper sulfate must be anhydrous, and can best be obtained by heating very thin layers of the pure blue crystals in an oven for about five hours at 215°C.

Adhere strictly to the directions of keeping the temperature in the flask at 220°C., as that temperature will give the maximum recovery.

The bottles $A$, $B$, $C$ and $D$ are for the purpose of thoroughly drying the air. $G$ contains concentrated sulfuric acid, prepared as suggested above. $H$ is filled with glass beads, to remove sulfuric acid spray; $I$ and $J$ are empty tubes which should be thoroughly dry. The gas is completely absorbed in tube $K$.

## CALCIUM ACETATE METHOD [37]

The procedure involves two major operations—the first depending upon the estimation of fluorine from the percentage of calcium present with fluorine, the calcium combined with commonly occurring substances being extracted by glacial acetic acid; and the second depends upon separation of fluorine from its combination by converting it to soluble alkali salt and reprecipitating it from solution by addition of a known amount of calcium salt, the excess of the calcium being converted to oxalate and so determined, the amount combined with fluorine being thus estimated and the equivalent fluorine calculated.

*Reagents.* **Calcium Acetate** (0.25 $N$ solution).—12.51 grams of pure calcium carbonate are dissolved in 500 ml. of water and 75 ml. glacial acetic acid (large beaker necessary) and the acetate formed is placed in a liter volumetric flask and diluted to 1000 ml. The solution is standardized by precipitation of the calcium oxalate in an aliquot portion (40 ml.) and titration with standard potassium permanganate. Exact normality is recorded.

$$1 \text{ ml. } 0.25 \text{ } N \text{ solution} = 0.005 \text{ g. calcium}$$

**Potassium Permanganate** (0.25 $N$ solution).—7.91 g. of pure crystals ($KMnO_4$) per liter are standardized against 0.67 g. of pure sodium oxalate equivalent to 40 ml. 0.25 $N$ solution. Exact normality is recorded.

**Sodium Oxalate** (0.25 $N$ solution containing 16.75 g. of the salt per liter).—Solution is best prepared in hot water. (Solubility, 3.22 g. per 100 ml. at 15°C.)

*Preliminary Procedure.* **Minerals Containing Phosphates or Sulfates.**—One gram

[37] By Wilfred W. Scott. Reprinted from J. Ind. Eng. Chem., **16**, 703, 1924.

of the finely powdered mineral, ore, or calcium fluoride salt is extracted with 50 ml. of dilute acetic acid (1 part glacial acetic acid, 10 parts water) by gently warming for 15 to 20 minutes with stirring. The residue, transferred to a small, ashless filter, is washed with about 50 ml. of water, making the total extract 100 ml. (Save for calcium determination, if desired.) The filter and residue are dried rapidly by spreading out on a watch glass. The fluoride is carefully transferred onto a sheet of glazed paper, the filter ignited, and the ash added to the fluoride. The residue is fused as directed under "Fusion."

NOTE.—For exact work an allowance has to be made for the solubility of the calcium fluoride. The following solubilities were found, 0.5-g. samples of material being taken and treated with 100 ml. of acetic acid of the strength stated:

| Acid | $H_2O$ | $CaF_2$ | $CaCO_3$ | $Ca_3PO_4$ | $CaSO_4$ |
|------|--------|---------|----------|-----------|----------|
| 1 part | 2 parts | 0.0103 | Very soluble | 0.240 | 0.084 |
| 1 part | 10 parts | 0.0144 | Very soluble | 0.276 | 0.170 |

**Phosphates and Sulfates Absent.**—No acetic acid extraction is necessary.

**Sulfides Present.**—Sulfur as sulfide occurs generally combined with iron, copper, cobalt, etc. No special procedure is necessary here, as the sulfide is oxidized later.

**Fusion.**—Five grams of sodium carbonate and 10 g. of potassium hydroxide, placed in a 50- to 60-ml. silver or iron crucible, are brought to quiet fusion, and allowed to cool until a crust forms over the melt. Half a gram of the fluoride sample is intimately mixed with 0.5 to 1 g. of powdered silica prepared as outlined above (powdered sand free of fluorine will do), and placed in the crucible over the fusion. The crucible is covered and heat applied to bring the contents of the crucible to molten temperature. (High heat is not necessary.) Complete decomposition is effected in half to three-quarters of an hour. The crucible should be agitated frequently during fusion to mix the contents.

NOTE.—Calcium fluoride is not so easily decomposed as many existing methods indicate. Hydrochloric acid apparently dissolves the mineral, but on dilution calcium fluoride precipitates. Sulfuric acid and potassium acid sulfate fusion is far from satisfactory; platinum is required and a loss due to bumping is liable to occur. Complete decomposition by acid treatment is frequently doubtful. The alkali fusion appears to be the best method for decomposing the fluoride.

If the mass is in molten condition, it may be poured in the lid of the crucible; if too viscous to pour, it is spread over the inner surface of the crucible by rotating the crucible over the flame. The material is now disintegrated and removed from the crucible and lid by action of about 200 ml. of hot water in a 500-ml. beaker. Ten milliliters of hydrogen peroxide are added and the solution is boiled for about 5 minutes.

NOTE.—Fusions made in silver disintegrate more readily than those made in iron. Calcium carbonate tends to adhere to the walls of the crucible.

Boiling the solution expels the excess of peroxide, which interferes in the oxalate precipitation of calcium, if left in solution. Sulfides, iron, and other oxidizable materials are oxidized by the peroxide.

The solution containing the excess of sodium carbonate, potassium hydroxide, alkali fluoride, and the greater portion of the silica is filtered off; the residue, containing calcium carbonate (or phosphate if present in the fused material), silver, iron, some silica (10 to 15% of total), etc., is washed with hot water (10 times) and the washings are combined with the first filtrate. The residue is used for Procedure A, the filtrate for Procedure B.

Note.—Should phosphates be present in the material, the greater portion will remain in the residue, and a small amount will pass into the filtrate as sodium salt.

$$Ca_3(PO_4)_2 + 3Na_2CO_3 \rightarrow 3CaCO_3 + 2Na_3PO_4$$

***Procedure (A) Determination of Calcium and Equivalent Fluorine.***—The residue washed into a beaker is dissolved in hydrochloric acid (200 ml. of water, 20 ml. HCl). If any gritty material remains, it is advisable to filter it off, designating the filtrate as *Solution A*, and fusing the gritty material with about 2 g. of sodium carbonate and 3 to 5 g. of potassium hydroxide, repeating the extraction with water; the residue is dissolved in hydrochloric acid and added to *A* and the water extract to *B* (for Procedure *B*). The free acid is neutralized with ammonia, the solution heated and filtered, and the residue washed. Calcium passes into solution, iron (and silver) remains on the filter. (The crucible should be rinsed out with dilute hydrochloric acid, as calcium carbonate may adhere to the walls of the vessel.)

Note.—A small amount of calcium is liable to be occluded by the hydroxide of iron. If this is present in appreciable amount, it is necessary to dissolve this in hydrochloric acid, reprecipitate with ammonia, and filter, adding the filtrate to the main portion containing calcium.

Calcium is now precipitated from the filtrate by adding 0.25 *N* sodium oxalate. About 60 ml. are necessary for 0.5 g. of calcium fluoride (fluorspar). After heating to crystallize the oxalate, the calcium is filtered off, washed with water (6 times), dissolved in water containing sulfuric acid (200 ml. $H_2O$ + 10 ml. $H_2SO_4$), and titrated hot with 0.25 *N* potassium permanganate.

1 ml. 0.25 *N* KMnO$_4$ = 0.005 g. Ca and 0.00474 g. F

Note.—If the mineral was extracted with dilute acetic acid (1:10) to remove calcium phosphate, carbonate, or sulfate, an allowance should be made for the solubility of calcium fluoride of approximately 0.014 g. CaF$_2$ per 100 ml. extract at 18°C.

If total calcium is desired, the calcium in the extract should be determined and added to the calcium of the fluoride.

***Procedure (B) Determination of Fluorine.*** **Calcium Acetate Method.**—The alkaline filtrate (water extract of the fusion) contains the fluorine, sodium and potassium salts, and silicic acid.

The filtrate is heated to near boiling and sufficient 0.25 *N* calcium acetate reagent is added to precipitate all the fluorine and about 5 to 10 ml. excess (60 ml. per 0.5 g. CaF$_2$). Glacial acetic acid is now added until faintly acid (if the solution is alkaline, litmus paper test) and then an excess of 1 ml. per 100 ml. of solution. The heating is continued for about 5 minutes.

Note.—Upon addition of the calcium acetate, calcium carbonate also precipitates with calcium fluoride. When the solution becomes acid, the carbonate dissolves. If the acidity is correct, the precipitate settles readily and is easily filtered. Should it be finely divided and remain in suspension, the addition of sufficient potassium or sodium hydroxide to give an alkaline reaction will coagulate and settle the precipitate.

The solution and precipitate are transferred to a 500-ml. (or larger) graduated volumetric flask and, after cooling (18°C.), made to volume, then transferred to a large beaker and the precipitate allowed to settle for a few minutes. An aliquot portion of the clear solution is decanted through a filter, the first 5 to 10 ml. being rejected (several filters may be used to hasten filtration, if slow). A measured volume of the filtrate is now taken for the determination of excess calcium.

**Precipitation and Titration of Calcium.**—Sufficient 0.25 $N$ sodium oxalate solution is added to precipitate the calcium. It is safe to use as much oxalate as the aliquot requires in case no calcium was removed by fluorine—i.e., if one-half the total solution represents the aliquot, then 30 ml. of oxalate are added. The author prefers to precipitate the calcium from a weak acetic acid solution (about 0.5 ml. free glacial acetic acid per 100 ml.). This is the acidity of the solution obtained on adding calcium acetate and acetic acid, as directed, no alkali being added, as suggested, for settling stubborn calcium fluoride precipitates.

The calcium oxalate is coagulated by heating, then filtered, washed, and titrated with 0.25 $N$ potassium permanganate in a hot solution containing sulfuric acid. The oxalate is best dissolved from the filter by hot water containing sulfuric acid.

$$1 \text{ ml. } 0.25 \ N \text{ potassium permanganate} = 0.005 \text{ g. calcium}$$

**Calculation.**

If $A$ = ml. 0.25 $N$ calcium acetate,

$B$ = ml. 0.25 $N$ potassium permanganate,

$X$ = factor for converting the aliquot portion of solution taken in the calcium determination to total solution.

Then $A$ ml. $- XB$ ml. = ml. 0.25 $N$ calcium acetate required by fluorine.

The difference multiplied by 0.005 = calcium combined with fluorine, or multiplied by 0.006 = equivalent fluorine (Ca $\times$ 1.2 = F).

CORRECTION. Owing to the slight solubility of calcium fluoride and possibly to the formation of a complex compound, calcium fluoride with a fluosilicate, a corrective factor seems to be necessary, the ratio of calcium to fluorine being 40:48, rather than the ratio represented in the formula $CaF_2$.

## DETERMINATION IN ALKALI FLUORIDES

**Procedure. Decomposition.**—0.5 to 1 g. of the alkali fluoride is dissolved in about 100 ml. of hot water.

**Precipitation.**—The fluorine is precipitated by adding, from a burette, a known amount of 0.25 $N$ calcium acetate in sufficient amount to precipitate all the fluorine, and then 5 to 10 ml. in excess. If the solution has not become acid by addition of the reagent, make it so by adding acetic acid. The solution and precipitate are transferred to a 250-ml. graduated flask, and after cooling are made to volume and well mixed. An aliquot portion is now filtered through a fine-mesh filter (rejecting the first 5 to 6 ml.). A measured portion (half the original total is recommended) is heated to boiling, and calcium is precipitated by adding an excess of sodium oxalate. The solution is neutralized with ammonia and the calcium oxalate filtered off, washed, and titrated with 0.25 $N$ potassium permanganate, according to the standard procedure. (See "Precipitation and Titration of Calcium.")

**Calculations of Fluorine.**

If $A$ = total ml. of 0.25 $N$ calcium acetate,

$B$ = ml. of 0.25 $N$ potassium permanganate required by the calcium in half the total volume.

Then $A - 2B$ = % fluorine per 0.5 g. sample or $(A - 2B) \times 0.005 \times 0.948$ = g. fluorine.

Notes.—It appears that the compound formed by addition of calcium acetate to the soluble fluoride is $CaF_2$; it is thus possible to use the conversion factor 0.948 for converting the calcium, combined with fluorine, to its equivalent fluoride.

The method does not distinguish fluorine combined as a fluosilicate from fluorine combined as a fluoride.

The best method for decomposing fluorspar or calcium fluoride was found to be by fusion with sodium and potassium carbonates, sodium carbonate and potassium hydroxide, or sodium or potassium carbonate and sodium hydroxide. The presence of silica is necessary.

$CaF_2$ is precipitated by adding the calcium acetate reagent to the alkaline solution of the fluoride. The calcium carbonate, which also forms, redissolves as soon as the solution becomes acid. A large amount of acid is to be avoided, as this liberates silicic acid, which prevents the settling of the fluoride. When the solution is first acidified and the calcium fluoride is then precipitated, the compound settles badly and is difficult to filter. Should the fluoride be difficult to settle, it is preferable to make the solution alkaline by addition of sodium or potassium hydroxide, rather than to add an insoluble substance to carry down the flocculent material. The alkali treatment coagulates the fluoride (probably dissolving silicic acid) and causes rapid settling.

## OTHER TITRIMETRIC METHODS [38]

### THE METHOD OF HAWLEY

Fluorine is precipitated as PbFCl, using hydrochloric acid and lead acetate. The chlorine contained is determined by standard titrimetric method for chlorine and fluorine is calculated from the results. This procedure is applicable in the presence of fairly large amounts of the radicals that interfere in the gravimetric procedure. It can be used nearly equally as well with simple fluorides as with complexes such as topaz, mica, insecticides and other artificial mixtures. The method is especially well adapted to ores and mineral substances. Insoluble substances must be rendered soluble by fusion. The accuracy on low-grade materials is somewhat better than that of the Berzelius $CaF_2$ method.

*Reagents.* **Lead Acetate.**—10% lead acetate solution containing 1% glacial acetic acid.

**Wash Solution.**—Saturated PbFCl solution for washing. (For preparation see the gravimetric method on page 440.)

*Procedure.* **Preparation of Material.**—One-half gram of the dried sample is fused [39] with 7–8 grams of sodium-potassium carbonate mixture (1:1) in a platinum [40] crucible. About 4 times as much silica as fluorine should be present (a great excess should be avoided). Sulfur, if present, should be oxidized here with $H_2O_2$ or $Na_2O_2$ (an excess should be avoided; this treatment lowers the accuracy).

When well fused the mass is placed on a smooth metal plate and allowed to cool. The dish [40] and melt are heated with water in a casserole until completely disintegrated and then filtered. Any lumps remaining are heated with 1 g. of $Na_2CO_3$ [41] and thoroughly washed with hot $H_2O$. The washings are added to the above filtrate.

The beaker containing the filtrate (150–250 ml.) is covered and 16 drops of

[38] Compiled by Ernest P. Herner.

[39] If the fluoride is soluble the fusion may be omitted, but this seldom is the case in ores.

[40] A porcelain crucible may be used; if so it should be broken and boiled with the melt in extracting.

[41] The second boiling usually recovers all the fluorine, but with high fluorine content refusion increases the accuracy.

concentrated HCl are added (high-grade substance may require 22–24 drops but much more will precipitate $PbCl_2$).[42]

The solution is warmed to 40°C. and enough $HNO_3$ is added to make neutral to methyl-orange and to leave 3 drops in excess.

**Precipitation of PbFCl.**—Ten drops of glacial acetic acid and 25 ml. of the clear lead acetate are added. The precipitate of PbFCl, dense and granular, forms usually at once but the precipitation may not be complete for 30–60 minutes. The solution is stirred and cooled. The temperature must not fall below 15°C. or $PbCl_2$ [42] will crystallize; other Pb salts may precipitate here but they will not make a great deal of difference. The precipitate is filtered off (on fine paper), washed, first with a small amount of cold $H_2O$,[43] then with PbFCl wash solution 3–4 times and finally 1–2 with cold $H_2O$.

**Determination of Chlorine.**—Dissolve the PbFCl precipitate by pouring 20–30 ml. of hot 25% nitric acid through the filter. The mixture should be heated on a steam bath.[44]

The chlorine can now be determined by any standard method. The silver nitrate method of Volhard may be used, the silver may be deposited by electrolysis or silver chloride may be cupelled.

## COLORIMETRIC METHODS

### ZIRCONIUM-ERIOCHROME CYANINE R METHOD

The Zirconium Eriochrome Cyanine R Method is a much-modified version of the procedure of Megregian.[45] In acid solution, zirconium reacts with Eriochrome Cyanine R to form a red complex ion. Fluoride forms a more stable complex with zirconium ($ZrF_6{}^{-2}$) and withdraws zirconium from the organic complex to produce a bleaching effect. Eriochrome Cyanine R shows a decided specificity to zirconium. Under the experimental conditions the dye does not give a color with titanium or beryllium, two metals which react with many other zirconium agents. Aluminum reacts to give a positive interference that is easily eliminated. This is accomplished by allowing the solution to stand for at least 2 hours before making color comparison. Up to 10 parts per million can be tolerated.

Analytical conditions are not overly critical. The pH is controlled at a highly acid level by the addition of 1.7 ml. of concentrated hydrochloric acid to each sample. This assures that high concentrations of bicarbonate or other ions will not affect the pH significantly. Sulfate interferes but is removed in the procedure by precipitation as barium sulfate. Overnight standing is usually required to assure complete settling of barium sulfate before making color comparison. The clarification of the sample can be accelerated by centrifuging if the fluoride result is desired immediately. Filtration should not be used.

[42] $PbCl_2$ crystals can be recognized by their needle-like structure, transparency and high luster. They are also more soluble in $H_2O$ than PbFCl.

[43] Accuracy is much decreased if pure water is used for washing. Instead, a saturated solution of PbFCl should be used, as recommended earlier in this chapter.

[44] Much heat must not be used for there is danger of dispelling some chlorine. If there is a great deal of PbFCl it may not dissolve readily, but this does not matter unless much $PbSO_4$ is present. This will interfere later if not removed here; but since PbFCl is very soluble in nitric acid and $PbSO_4$ is not, a separation can be effected by filtering.

[45] Megregian, Steven, Anal. Chem., **26**, 1161–6, 1954; Methods for Collection and Analysis of Water Samples, U. S. Geological Survey, Water-Supply Paper 1454.

Residual chlorine, chromate, and probably other strong oxidants attack the indicator. The susceptibility of attack varies with batches of indicator. Stannous chloride is used to eliminate chromate and chlorine interference. Chromium, cadmium and nickel, in concentrations of less than 5 parts per million, do not interfere in the lower fluoride range. When the fluoride concentration exceeds 1.0 parts per million, larger quantities of these metals can be tolerated. Ten parts per million iron, zinc, lead, cyanide and phosphate, cause no appreciable interference if the sample is allowed to stand overnight.

The determination shows "salt effect"; the sensitivity is depressed by 5–10% at a dissolved-solids concentration of 10,000 parts per million. The effect of the usual type of color is not serious. A color of 70 on the Hellige scale is equivalent to an absorbancy error of only 0.005 in the spectrophotometric measurement. Therefore color correction is not often necessary.

The quality of batches of Eriochrome Cyanine R from different sources differs very significantly, and it is necessary to test the reagent each time it is prepared. The individual absorbancy curves show corresponding differences, and the sensitivity of fluoride between reagents may differ by 20%.

The method has rather good tolerance for temperature differences. For most purposes, operating at room temperature without other precautions is satisfactory.

With list apparatus, results are accurate and reproducible to ±0.0005 mg. in the lower ranges and approximately 0.001 mg. in the higher fluoride range.

*Apparatus.* **Spectrophotometer.**—Wavelength: 540 m$\mu$; cells: 40-mm. optical depth; phototube: blue-sensitive; blank: dilution water plus reagents; initial sensitivity setting: 3; slit width: 0.3 mm. (approximately).

*Reagents.* **Sodium Fluoride Solution (1.00 ml. = 0.010 mg. F$^-$).**—Dissolve 0.2210 g. NaF in water and dilute to 1 l. in metal-free water. Dilute 100.0 ml. of this stock solution to 1 l.

**Stannous Chloride Reagent, 2%.**—Dissolve 1 g. $SnCl_2 \cdot 2H_2O$ in 10 ml. concentrated HCl and dilute to approximately 50 ml.

**Eriochrome Cyanine R, 0.9%.**—Dissolve 1.80 g. Eriochrome Cyanine R in water and dilute to 200 ml. The National Aniline product labeled "Alizarol Cyanone RC" has been used successfully. With other products, a precipitate sometimes forms when the indicator solution is prepared.

**Zirconyl Nitrate, 0.2% in Acid.**—Dissolve 0.40 g. $ZrO(NO_3)_2 \cdot 2H_2O$ in 200 ml. (1:1) HCl.

**Indicator Solution.**—To about 300 ml. metal-free water add 20.0 ml. 0.9% Eriochrome Cyanine R and 10.0 ml. 0.2% $ZrO(NO_3)_2 \cdot 2H_2O$ in acid. Add 70 ml. concentrated HCl and 4 g. $BaCl_2$. Dissolve and dilute to 1 l. The solution is consumed rapidly and a large volume is normally prepared.

*Procedure.*—If the sample contains an excessive amount of interfering materials, the fluoride should be isolated by distillation (see "Separation by Distillation Method"). Pipette a volume of sample containing less than 0.03 mg. F$^-$ (10.00 ml. max.) into a 50 ml. centrifuge tube or test tube. Prepare a blank and sufficient standards, and adjust the volumes to 10.0 ml. If chromate, residual chlorine, or other strong oxidizing agents are present in the sample, add 0.1 ml. of 2% $SnCl_2$ and let the solution stand for 10 minutes. Add 25.0 ml. of indicator. Allow the solution to stand overnight for barium sulfate to settle. Decant approximately 25 ml. pure supernatant solution, taking care not to disturb the precipitate. Determine the absorbancy at 540 m$\mu$ of the test sample and standards against the blank, and when necessary make correction for water color.

**Calculations.**—Determine the weight in mg. $F^-$ in test sample from a plot of the absorbancies of standards containing known amounts of constituent.

$$F^- \text{ (in parts per million)} = \frac{1}{\text{density}} \times \frac{1000}{\text{ml. sample}} \times \text{mg. } F^- \text{ in sample}$$

## MODIFICATION OF FOREGOING METHOD FOR ION-EXCHANGE RESIN CONCENTRATES [46]

*Reagents.* **Eriochrome Cyanine R Solution.**—Dissolve 1.000 g. of the ECR in 1 l. of distilled water.

**Zirconyl Nitrate Solution.**—Dissolve 0.175 g. of zirconyl nitrate dihydrate in 500 ml. of distilled water and add 500 ml. of reagent-grade hydrochloric acid.

**Standard-Fluoride Solution.**—Prepare a solution containing 10.0 mg. of fluoride per liter.

**Reference Solution.**—Add 10.0 ml. of the Eriochrome Cyanine R solution and 5 ml. of the zirconyl nitrate solution to 1.05 ml. of distilled water.

**Sodium Acetate Solution, 0.2 *M*.**

*Procedure.*—To a 5-ml. aliquot of the sample solution add 0.5 ml. each of the Eriochrome Cyanine R solution and the zirconyl nitrate solution. The sample is thoroughly mixed and allowed to stand for 10 minutes or more. The absorbance of the sample is read in a spectrophotometer at 527.5 m$\mu$. The fluoride values are determined from a curve prepared by plotting the absorbance readings of standard fluoride solutions made to volume with 0.2 *M* sodium acetate solution against the concentration of fluoride. One to 5 micrograms per 5 ml. at intervals of 1 microgram are convenient standards to use in preparing the curve.

## ZIRCONIUM-ALIZARIN METHOD [47]

In acid solution, zirconium reacts with alizarin red S to form a reddish-violet lake. Upon addition of fluoride ion to the zirconium red lake, the more stable fluorozirconate complex ion, $ZrF_6^{-2}$, is formed. If the amount of zirconium and alizarin is carefully controlled, the amount of zirconium removed by fluoride subtracts from the reddish-complex color. The reaction simultaneously liberates free alizarinsulfonic acid which is yellow in acid solution. With increasing fluoride, the color change is from reddish-violet to yellow-green. The bleaching effect of the fluoride in the sample is compared visually with that in standard solutions. As the color approaches yellow green, the test is less sensitive; the method is most useful when the sample volume contains less than 0.10 mg. of fluoride, but the range can be extended a little higher. The reaction requires several hours to reach equilibrium, and the rate is somewhat dependent on temperature. Color comparison can be made at the end of 1 hour if the reagent was added to the sample and standards within 2 minutes and uniform temperature is maintained.

The interference of 20 mg. of calcium, 20 mg. of magnesium, 100 mg. of sodium, 20 mg. of potassium, and 30 mg. of nitrate is negligible, and even higher concentrations would cause very little trouble. Up to 1.5 mg. of iron does not interfere seriously, but larger amounts cannot be tolerated; 2.5 mg. of manganese does not interfere. Free residual chlorine interferes but can be removed by adding sodium

[46] Nielson, Anal. Chem., **30**, 1009–1012, 1958. See ion-exchange separation technique earlier in this chapter.

[47] Methods for Collection and Analysis of Water Samples, U. S. Geological Survey, Water-Supply Paper 1454.

arsenite. Several other ions common to water interfere; some give high results and others low. Aluminum gives a negative error because of the formation of aluminum-fluoride complex, which withdraws fluoride from the reaction of zirconium. The magnitude of the interference is dependent on the quantity of both aluminum and fluoride, but the percentage of fluoride complexed is approximately constant for a given concentration of aluminum. The ratio taken from the graph shown below (Fig. 18-11) and multiplied by the apparent fluoride concentration

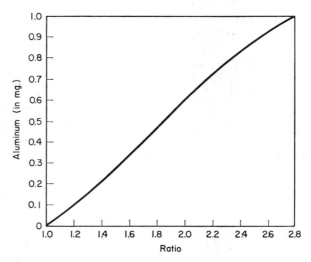

Fɪɢ. 18-11. Variation of the Ratio of Actual to Apparent Fluoride Content with Aluminum Content.

will give the actual fluoride content. For fluoride concentrations not exceeding 0.10 mg. and aluminum concentrations not exceeding 0.05 mg. the maximum variable errors will not exceed ±0.01 mg. of fluoride.

In the presence of 1.0 mg. of aluminum, the ratio of actual to apparent fluoride concentration is 2.8. The interference of 0.05 mg. of aluminum does not exceed the equivalent of 0.01 mg. of fluoride. Hexavalent chromium causes a positive error, but 0.05 mg. can be tolerated if the color comparison is made 1 hour after addition of the reagent, but only 0.01 mg. of chromium can be tolerated when readings are taken between 7 and 18 hours. The interference of orthophosphate and hexametaphosphate is lessened if the reaction is allowed to go 7–18 hours; 0.20 mg. can be tolerated. Below pH 4.5, hydrogen ion gives positive errors but the effect can be eliminated by raising the pH of the sample to 4.5–6.0 with sodium hydroxide.

Sulfate increases the fluoride reading, while chloride and alkalinity decreases it. These effects are substantially additive, and corrections taken from the following table can be applied to the apparent fluoride concentration. Alkalinity in excess of 10 mg. of calcium carbonate can be neutralized with an equivalent quantity of nitric acid.

Corrections for Fluoride Determination
(mg. Actual F = mg. apparent F + value indicated)

| Concentration of foreign ion, mg. per 100 ml. | Sulfate | Chloride | Alkalinity as CaCO₃ |
|---|---|---|---|
| 10 | −0.002 | | 0.005 |
| 20 | −0.002 | 0.002 | 0.011 |
| 30 | −0.003 | 0.003 | 0.017 |
| 40 | −0.006 | 0.004 | 0.023 |
| 50 | −0.009 | 0.006 | 0.028 |
| 60 | −0.011 | 0.007 | |
| 100 | −0.018 | 0.012 | |
| 200 | | 0.018 | |

Turbidity interferes with color precipitation, as does the natural color of the water to a lesser extent. Turbid water should be filtered through a Millipore filter membrane. Most quantitative filter papers are washed with hydrofluoric acid and can add fluoride to the sample. The effect of color can be partly compensated for by placing a tube of distilled water below the sample and an equal volume of water treated with acid below the standard and by making a color comparison through both tubes.

When color and turbidity do not interfere with color comparison results are generally accurate and reproducible to ±0.01 mg.

When interfering substances are present in significant amounts, distillation of the fluoride from the sample as hydrofluosilicic acid followed by reaction with zirconium-alizarin reagent is preferable to corrections of apparent fluoride concentrations.

*Apparatus.* **Color Comparator.**—3-hole, that permits longitudinal viewing of the contents of the tube.

**Nessler tubes,** low form, matched.

*Reagents.* **Acid Indicator Reagent.**—Add 25.0 ml. $ZrO(NO_3)_2$ solution to approximately 100 ml. water. With constant stirring, slowly add 25.0 ml. alizarin solution and dilute to approximately 450 ml. with water and mix well. Add 500 ml. 2.1 N $H_2SO_4$ and dilute to 1 l. with water. Allow the indicator to stand approximately 1 hour before use. Storage in a lightproof bottle increases the stability of the indicator. If the indicator precipitates on standing, shake it thoroughly before use.

*Zirconyl Nitrate (or Zirconyl Chloride).*—Dissolve 1.84 g. $ZrO(NO_3)_2 \cdot 2H_2O$ or 2.22 g. $ZrOCl_2 \cdot 8H_2O$ in water and dilute to 250 ml. Turbid solutions should not be filtered.

*Alizarin Red S.*—Dissolve 0.37 g. monosodium alizarinsulfonate in water and dilute to 250 ml.

**Sodium Arsenite (1.0 ml. = 1.0 mg. Cl₂).**—Dissolve 0.916 g. $NaAsO_2$ in water and dilute to 500.0 ml.

**Sodium Fluoride (1.00 ml. = 0.010 mg. F⁻).**—Dissolve 0.2210 g. NaF in water and dilute to 1,000 ml. Dilute 100.0 ml. of this stock solution to 1,000 ml.

*Procedure.*—If the sample contains an excessive quantity of interfering materials, the fluoride should be isolated by the Distillation Procedure (see page 432). Measure a volume of sample containing less than 0.12 mg. F⁻ (100.0 ml. max.) into Nessler tubes and adjust the volume to 100 ml. Neutralize residual chlorine with $NaAsO_2$ (1.0 ml. = 1.0 mg. $Cl_2$), adding 0.1 ml. in excess. Prepare a blank and sufficient standards, and adjust the volumes to 100 ml. Add 10.0 ml. acid indicator reagent and mix. Allow the solutions to stand 7–18 hours and visually compare the color of the sample with that of standards in the comparator.

**Calculations.**—Correct the apparent F⁻ concentration of sulfate, chloride, and alkalinity as required for Fig. 18-11 and the table of corrections.

$$F^-(\text{in parts per millon}) = \frac{1}{\text{density (in g. per ml.)}} \times \frac{1000}{\text{ml. sample}}$$
$$\times \left(\begin{array}{c}\text{corrected mg. F}^-\\ \text{in sample}\end{array}\right)\left(\begin{array}{c}\text{aluminum}\\ \text{correction ratio}\end{array}\right)$$

## CHLOROANILATE METHOD

This method [48] is based upon the reaction of certain chloroanilates (e.g. those of lanthanum or thorium) with fluoride ion to yield the acid chloroanilate ion, which is estimated colorimetrically. A reference curve, from various concentrations of fluoride, is required.

*Procedure.*—The determination is made upon aqueous solutions of fluoride ion resulting from the distillation, combustion or resin concentration procedures described earlier in this Chapter. An aliquot of the solution is placed in a 100-ml. flask, is buffered by addition of 10 ml. of an acetate buffer (pH 4.63), and is diluted to volume with a 50% aqueous solution of methyl Cellosolve. Then 0.3 g. of thorium chloroanilate is added, and the flask is shaken and allowed to stand for 0.5 hour. Filter with Whatman No. 50 filter paper. Determine the absorbance at 330 mμ or 530 mμ in a spectrophotometer, using a curve constructed from known samples for evaluation.

## DECOLORIZATION OF OXIDIZED TITANIUM SOLUTION

The method of Steiger and Merwin [49] was once used quite widely. It is based on the bleaching action of fluorine upon the yellow color produced by oxidizing a titanium solution by hydrogen peroxide. This method has been superseded by other colorimetric methods.

## DETERMINATION OF FLUORIDE AS MOLYBDENUM BLUE [50]

The method is based upon removal of the fluoride as silicon tetrafluoride, which is distilled into a buffer solution and hydrolyzed to silicate, which is then estimated. This method is well suited to trace amounts, such as those present in fluorinated water. The method gives only about 80% of the theoretical silicon,

---

[48] Bertolacine and Barney, Anal. Chem., **30**, 202, 1958; Fine and Wynne, Fisher Scientific Co.

[49] Stiger, J. Am. Chem. Soc., **30**, 219, 1908; Merwin, Am. Jour. Sci., (4), **28**, 119, 1909.

[50] Curry and Mellon, Anal. Chem., **28**, 1567–70, 1956; Peregud and Boikina, Zavodskaya Lab., **22**, 287–8, 1956.

and therefore the use of a calibration curve, obtained by distillation of known amounts of fluoride, is essential.

*Apparatus.*—The apparatus shown in Fig. 18-12 consists of a 250-ml. Erlenmeyer flask, *A*, a heating mantle, *B*, a three-way distilling head connected to the flask by a standard 29/42 joint, *C*, which is connected to the inlet for carrier gas, *D*, and a vacuum-tube connection *E*. *F* is a 125-ml. dropping funnel and *G* is a washing-bottle.

*Reagents.* **4% Sodium Hydroxide Solution.**—Dissolve 8 g. of NaOH in 160 ml. of water, and dilute to 200 ml.

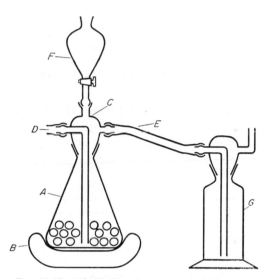

Fig. 18-12. Distillation Apparatus for Fluorine.

**40% Sodium Hydroxide Solution.**—Dissolve 40 g. of NaOH in 70 ml. of water (cooling) and dilute to 100 ml.

**2% Sodium Borate Solution.**—Dissolve 10 g. sodium borate decahydrate in 500 ml. of water.

**Hydrochloric Acid Solution (1:1).**—Add 50 ml. concentrated hydrochloric acid to 50 ml. water.

**Reducing Solution.**—Dissolve in 90 ml. of water 0.25 g. of 1-amino-2-naphthol 4-sulfonic acid, 0.50 g. of disodium sulfite, and 15.0 g. of sodium hydrogen sulfite.

**Ammonium Molybdate Solution (10%).**—Dissolve 10 g. ammonium molybdate in 90 ml. of water and dilute to 100 ml.

**Concentrated Sulfuric Acid.**

**Nitrogen.**—Conveniently obtained from cylinder or tank.

**Etched Soft Glass Beads.**

*Procedure.*—Adjust the pH of 80 ml. of the sodium borate solution to 8.5 by dropwise addition of the 1:1 hydrochloric acid. Transfer this solution to the wash bottle, *G*, but do not assemble its inlet tube at this time.

To a volume of sample in aqueous solution estimated to contain 1–2 mg. of fluoride, add sufficient 4% sodium hydroxide solution to adjust the pH to 9. (If necessary, concentrate to a volume less than 50 ml.). Transfer to Erlenmeyer flask, *A*, which is used for this operation without the glass beads. Evaporate to under 5 ml., and then add the glass beads. Pass nitrogen through the Erlenmeyer flask, connected to the inlet tube to the wash bottle, before putting the inlet tube of the wash bottle in place, to avoid formation of hydrolysis products on the inside of the tube. Add 50–60 ml. of concentrated sulfuric acid through the dropping funnel over a period of 2–3 minutes. Heat the flask to a temperature at which marked dissociation of the sulfuric acid occurs, using a rate of heating that requires about 30 minutes to reach this temperature, and continue heating for at least 15 minutes.

Dilute the contents of the wash bottle to 100 ml., and adjust its pH to 6.0–8.0 with the 40% sodium hydroxide solution. Add 2 ml. of the ammonium molybdate solution, and allow it to react for about 1 minute. Then add 1 ml. of the 1:1 hydrochloric acid, or as much more as necessary to adjust pH to 1.5. After 3 minutes add 2 ml. of the reducing solution. After 10 minutes, read against water at 700 m$\mu$.

## FLUOROMETRIC DETERMINATION OF SMALL AMOUNTS OF FLUORIDE

This method [51] is used for the determination of microgram quantities of fluoride. It depends upon the fact that the intensity of fluorescence of the compounds formed on reaction of aluminum chloride with the dihydroxyazo dyes, Eriochrome Red B and Superchrome Garnet Y, is decreased on addition of fluoride. The precision obtained is good and ions which are often present after distillation (see Distillation Method earlier in this Chapter), such as sulfate and phosphate, do not interfere seriously.

*Apparatus.* **Fluorometer (Scale readings given apply to Lumetron).**—Equipped with Corning 5860 primary filter and Corning 3389 secondary filter, and 25 ml. rectangular cells.

*Reagents.*—**Sodium Hydroxide Solution, 0.05 *N*.**

**Eriochrome Red B Standard Solution.**—Mix 60 ml. of 2 *M* acetic acid, 40 ml. of 2 *M* sodium acetate, 40 ml. of aluminum chloride solution (50 micrograms of aluminum per ml.), and 440 ml. of 95% ethyl alcohol in a 1 liter volumetric flask. Add 60 ml. of 0.1% solution of dye in 95% ethyl alcohol (prepared from Geigy dye as received, and filtered), and make up to 1 liter with distilled water.

**Superchrome Garnet Y Standard Solution.**—Mix 50 ml. each of 2 *M* acetic acid and 2 *M* sodium acetate, 40 ml. of aluminum chloride solution (50 micrograms of aluminum per ml.), 48 ml. of 0.1% aqueous solution of the National Aniline dye or 33.2 ml. of 0.1% aqueous solution of the Du Pont dye, and water to make 1 liter.

*Procedure.*—After interfering ions have been removed by distillation (see Distillation Method earlier in this Chapter), adjust the pH to between 4 and 5 with 0.05 *N* sodium hydroxide using a pH meter, make up exactly to volume, and mix well. Take an aliquot of 35 ml. or less, containing an amount of fluoride in the range of the standards and place in a 50-ml. volumetric flask. Prepare four or five standards in the range 0 to 50 micrograms of fluoride. Add 12.5 ml. of standard solution at about the same time to the standards and sample, make up to volume, and mix. At about the same time dilute 12.5 ml. of the blank solution,

[51] Powell and Saylor, Anal. Chem., **25**, 960–4, 1953; Jacobs, M. B., Chemical Analysis of Air Pollutants, Interscience Publishers, Inc., 1960.

which contains all reagents except aluminum chloride and fluoride ion, to 50 ml., and mix.

Let all solutions stand for 1 hour at room temperature if Superchrome Garnet Y is used and 3 hours if Eriochrome Red B is used. Rinse the 25 ml. fluorometer cell with the solution containing no fluoride, fill the cell, wipe with tissue paper, and set the instrument so that this solution reads 100. In a similar manner use the blank solution to set the instrument on zero. Read the intensity of fluorescence for the sample and standards, plot a calibration curve, and determine the fluoride content of the sample from the curve.

# DETERMINATIONS IN SPECIFIC SUBSTANCES

## ANALYSIS OF FLUORSPAR

The following procedure, worked out by Bidtel,[52] meets the commercial requirements for the analysis of fluorspar. The determinations usually required are calcium fluoride, silica, and calcium carbonate; in some particular cases lead, iron, zinc, and sulfur.

### DETERMINATION OF CALCIUM CARBONATE

*Procedure.*—One gram of the finely powdered sample is placed in a small Erlenmeyer flask, 10 ml. of 10% acetic acid are added, a short-stemmed funnel is inserted in the neck of the flask as a splash trap, and the mixture heated for an hour on a water bath, agitating from time to time. The calcium carbonate is decomposed and may be dissolved out as the soluble acetate, whereas the fluoride and silica are practically unaffected. The solution is filtered through a 7-cm. ashless filter, the residue washed with warm water four times, and the filter burned off in a weighed platinum crucible at as low a temperature as possible. The loss of weight minus 0.0015 g. (the amount of calcium fluoride soluble in acetic acid under the conditions named) is reported as *calcium carbonate*.

### SILICA

*Procedure.*—The residue in the platinum crucible is mixed with about 1 g. of yellow mercuric oxide, in form of emulsion in water (to oxidize any sulfide that may be present); any hard lumps that may have formed are broken up, the mixture evaporated to dryness and heated to dull redness, then cooled and weighed. About 2 ml. of hydrofluoric acid are added and the mixture evaporated to dryness. This is repeated twice to ensure complete expulsion of silica (as $SiF_4$). A few drops of hydrofluoric acid are then added, together with some macerated filter paper, and a few drops of ammonia to precipitate the iron. The solution is evaporated to dryness, heated to dull redness, cooled and weighed. The loss of weight is reported as *silica*.

### CALCIUM FLUORIDE

*Procedure.*—The residue is treated with 2 ml. of hydrofluoric acid and 10 drops of nitric acid (to decompose the oxides), the crucible covered and placed on a moderately warm water bath for thirty minutes, the lid then removed and the sample taken to dryness. The evaporation with hydrofluoric acid is repeated to ensure the transposition of the nitrates to fluorides, and if the residue is still colored,

[52] Bidtel, E., J. Ind. Eng. Chem., **4**, 201, 1912.

hydrofluoric acid again added and the mixture taken to dryness a third time; then a few drops of hydrofluoric acid are added and 10 ml. of ammonium acetate solution (the acetate solution is made by neutralizing 400 ml. of 80% acetic acid with concentrated ammonia, adding 20 g. of citric acid and making the mixture up to 1000 ml. with concentrated ammonia). The mixture is digested for thirty minutes on a boiling water bath, then filtered and washed with hot water containing a small amount of ammonium acetate, and finally with pure hot water. (Several washings by decantation are advisable.) The residue is ignited in the same crucible and weighed as *calcium fluoride*. An addition of 0.0022 g. should be made to compensate for loss of $CaF_2$.

Pure calcium fluoride is white. To test the purity of the residue, 2 ml. of sulfuric acid are added and the material taken to fumes to decompose the fluoride; 1 ml. of additional sulfuric acid is added and the excess of acid expelled by heating. The residue is weighed as calcium sulfate. This is now fused with sodium carbonate, and the fusion treated with hydrochloric acid in excess. If barium is present the solution will be cloudy ($BaSO_4$).

## ANALYSIS OF SODIUM FLUORIDE

*Preparation of the Sample and Insoluble Residue.*—Ten grams of the sample are dissolved in 250 ml. of water in a beaker, and boiled for five minutes, then filtered into a liter flask through an ashless filter; the residue is washed with several portions of water and ignited. This is weighed as insoluble residue. The filtrate and washings are made to 1000 ml. with distilled water.

### DETERMINATION OF SODIUM FLUORIDE

*Procedure.*—Fifty ml. of the solution equivalent to 0.5 g. of sample are diluted to 200 ml. in a beaker, 0.5 g. sodium carbonate is added and the mixture boiled. An excess of calcium chloride solution is now added slowly and boiled for about five minutes. A small amount of paper pulp is added to prevent the precipitate from running through the filter, the precipitate allowed to settle and then filtered, using a 9-cm S. & S. 590, or B. & A. grade A, filter paper. The fluoride is washed twice by decantation, and four or five times on the filter with small portions of hot water. The final washings should be practically free of chlorine.

The residue is ignited in a platinum dish, then treated with 25 ml. of acetic acid, and taken to dryness. This treatment is repeated and the residue taken up with a little hot water and filtered. The calcium fluoride is washed free of calcium acetate with small portions of water, because $CaF_2$ is slightly soluble in water. The ignited residue is weighed as $CaF_2$.

$$CaF_2 \times 1.0756 = NaF$$

### SODIUM SULFATE

*Procedure.*—To the filtrate from calcium fluoride is added 10 ml. hydrochloric acid and then a hot solution of barium chloride. The $BaSO_4$ is allowed to settle, filtered, washed, dried, ignited, and weighed as usual.

$$BaSO_4 \times 0.6086 = Na_2SO_4$$

### SODIUM CARBONATE

*Procedure.*—Sodium carbonate is determined on a 5-g. sample by the usual method for carbon dioxide as described in the chapter on Carbon.

Approximate results may be obtained by adding a small excess of normal sulfuric acid to 5 g. of the fluoride in a platinum dish, boiling off the carbon dioxide, and titrating the excess of acid with normal caustic, using phenolphthalein indicator.

$$\text{One ml. } N \text{ H}_2\text{SO}_4 = 0.053 \text{ g. Na}_2\text{CO}_3$$

$$\text{H}_2\text{SO}_4 \times 1.0807 = \text{Na}_2\text{CO}_3$$

### SODIUM CHLORIDE

*Procedure.*—Fifty ml. of the sample is titrated with 0.1 $N$ AgNO$_3$ solution.

### SILICA

*Procedure.*—This is probably present as sodium fluosilicate and silicate. One gram of the sample is dissolved in the least amount of water and a small excess of hydrofluoric acid added to convert the silicate to silicofluoride, then an equal volume of alcohol. After allowing to stand for an hour, the precipitate is filtered, washed with 50% alcohol until free of acid and the filter and fluoride are placed in a beaker with 100 ml. of water, boiled and titrated with 0.1 $N$ NaOH.

$$\text{One ml. } 0.1 \text{ } N \text{ NaOH} = 0.0015 \text{ gram SiO}_2 \text{ or } 0.0047 \text{ gram Na}_2\text{SiF}_6$$

### VOLATILE MATTER AND MOISTURE

*Procedure.*—One-gram sample is heated to dull redness to constant weight. Loss of weight is due to moisture and volatile products.

## METHODS FOR FLUORINE IN ANALYSIS IN OTHER CHAPTERS

Fluorine in Barite                                  See Analysis of Barite (Barium Chapter)
Fluorine in Phosphorus Ores                         See Analysis of Phosphorus Ores
Fluorine in Commercial Phosphates                   See Analysis of Commercial Phosphates

*Chapter 19*

# GALLIUM *

**Ga, *at. wt.* 69.72; *sp. gr.* 5.91 (at 20°C.); *m.p.* 29.75°C.; *b.p.* 1983°C.; *oxide,* Ga₂O₃**

Although gallium is very widely distributed in the earth's crust no mineral is yet known in which gallium is an essential constituent, but germanite, which occurs in the copper ores of South-West Africa, contains up to 0.7% of gallium. The metal occurs in trace amounts in most aluminum minerals, in many iron and zinc ores, and in the ash of most coals. It is recovered from various by-products obtained in the treatment of zinc ores and from the caustic liquors resulting from the treatment of bauxite by the Bayer process. In Great Britain relatively high concentrations of gallium are found in the flue dust resulting from the burning of producer gas; as much as 2% of gallium has been found in dust produced in some British gasworks. Gallium is the only element other than bromine and mercury which is a liquid at 30°C.

Gallium closely resembles aluminum in its chemical reactions. Ammonia or ammonium sulfide precipitates the white hydroxide, which is a weaker base than alumina, and therefore dissolves more readily in caustic soda. The hydroxide is markedly soluble in ammonia, the solubility being increased by the presence of ammonium salts. Gallium differs in two important respects from aluminum; it is precipitated by cupferron from sulfate solutions containing 6% of free acid, and its chloride can be extracted by ether from solutions in 6.5 N hydrochloric acid.

## DETECTION

The minute quantities in which gallium occurs in minerals (with the single exception of germanite) call for a spectroscopic method as the surest means of detection, the arc spectrum of the element showing an intense line in the violet at 4170 A and a less intense one at 4031 A. Twenty mg. of the thiosulfate precipitate obtained as described below is completely burned in the crater of the positive graphite electrode and the spectrum examined for the above two lines.

## ESTIMATION

### PREPARATION AND SOLUTION OF THE SAMPLE

Since gallium occurs in only minute quantities in the common ores it is necessary to take at least 100 g. for the determination. Zinc blende is boiled with strong hydrochloric acid and any insoluble sulfides are oxidized by the cautious addition of nitric acid, excess of which is expelled by evaporation with hydro-

* Chapter contributed by A. R. Powell, Research Manager, Johnson, Malthey and Company, Wembley, England.

chloric acid. Iron and manganese ores are dissolved in strong hydrochloric acid, bauxite in caustic soda, followed by fusion of the insoluble residue with pyrosulfate, and kaolin by fusion with sodium carbonate, followed by the usual evaporation with hydrochloric acid to remove the silica. Flue dust is sintered with sodium peroxide and the aqueous extract evaporated to dryness with an excess of hydrochloric acid to volatilize the germanium and remove the silica. Germanite is dissolved in aqua regia and the solution repeatedly evaporated with hydrochloric acid and a little ammonium bromide to volatilize arsenic and germanium.

## SEPARATIONS [1]

Gallium can be separated from most metals by extraction with ether from a solution of the chloride in 6.5 $N$ hydrochloric acid; of the elements which are co-extracted with the gallium, molybdenum, tin, arsenic, and antimony may be eliminated by precipitation with hydrogen sulfide in 10% hydrochloric acid, and iron either by boiling the extract with caustic soda after removal of the ether, or by reducing the ferric chloride to ferrous prior to the extraction. These separations are carried out as follows:—

The cold solution (containing 10 ml. of hydrochloric acid per 100 ml.) is saturated with hydrogen sulfide and left overnight in a stoppered flask before filtering the sulfides. The filtrate is boiled to expel hydrogen sulfide, cooled, treated with an equal volume of strong hydrochloric acid, and then with 1 ml. of 10% titanous chloride solution, and shaken three times with half its volume of ether which has previously been well shaken with 1:1 hydrochloric acid. The ethereal extract is diluted with a little water, the ether distilled off, and most of the acid evaporated. The residual solution is diluted and poured into an excess of 0.5 $N$ caustic soda. After boiling for a short time any precipitate is filtered off, the filtrate made 1.5 $N$ with sulfuric acid, cooled to 15°C., and treated with a 6% solution of cupferron until no further flocculent precipitate forms.

The precipitate is mixed with filter pulp, collected and washed with very dilute sulfuric acid containing a little cupferron.

Gallium can be separated from large amounts of iron by reducing the latter to the ferrous state with hydrogen sulfide, neutralizing the solution with sodium carbonate, boiling with 10 g. of sodium thiosulfate for an hour and then adding 1 ml. of 2% hydrazine carbonate solution. The precipitate is collected, washed with hot water, and ignited. The residual crude oxide is fused with potassium pyrosulfate, the melt leached with hot dilute sulfuric acid and the solution, after partial neutralization, poured into an excess of hot $N$ caustic soda sufficient to give an alkalinity of 0.3 $N$. This removes the last traces of iron together with any titanium or zirconium. Any aluminum present can be eliminated by acidifying the solution with sulfuric acid and precipitating the gallium with cupferron as described above.

To recover gallium from a solution containing only bivalent metals, ammonium nitrate (2 g. per 100 ml.) and 5 g. of ammonium acetate are added to the nearly neutral solution which is then boiled and treated with tannin equal to at least 10 times the weight of gallia present (minimum 0.5 g.). The voluminous white

[1] Moser and Brukl, Monatsch. Chem., **50**, 181, 1928; **51**, 325, 1929; Brukl, *ibid.*, **52**, 253, 1929; Swift, Jour. Amer. Chem. Soc., **46**, 2375, 1924.

precipitate is mixed with filter pulp, collected under gentle suction and washed with hot 2% ammonium nitrate solution. If at all substantial, it is dissolved in dilute hydrochloric acid and reprecipitated by addition of ammonium acetate and nitrate, together with a little more tannin.

## GRAVIMETRIC METHODS

Gallium is always weighed as the oxide, obtained by ignition of the tannin complex or the cupferron precipitate. The washed precipitate and paper are transferred to a tared porcelain crucible which is heated on an asbestos mat until the paper is completely charred, then more strongly to burn off the carbon, and finally over a blast burner. The oxide is hygroscopic, and should be weighed without delay. As gallium chloride is volatile, the precipitate must be washed free from chloride ion if this is present in the solution. Gallium precipitates should be ignited in porcelain; if a platinum crucible is used, some gallia may be reduced by diffusing burner gases and all metal readily alloys with the crucible.

### ESTIMATION IN BASE-METAL ORES

*Procedure.*—The cold acid solution of a large quantity of the ore, obtained as explained before, is treated with zinc to eliminate most of the heavy metals. The filtrate is boiled with a large excess of ammonium sulfate and nearly neutralized with dilute ammonia avoiding a permanent precipitate. A 2% solution of hydrazine carbonate is then added dropwise until the precipitate coagulates. The solution is filtered immediately and the precipitate washed with hot 5% ammonium sulfate solution. It is dissolved in 6 $N$ hydrochloric acid, 2 ml. of 2% titanous chloride solution are added, and the gallium is extracted by shaking the solution with several portions of ether. The extract is diluted with water, the ether distilled off, and the acid evaporated on the water bath. The residue is boiled with 0.5 $N$ caustic soda, any precipitate filtered off, the filtrate made 2 $N$ with sulfuric acid, and the gallium precipitated with cupferron.

### ESTIMATION IN FLUE DUST

*Procedure.*—Two to 5 g. of dust are intimately mixed with 5 to 10 g. of sodium peroxide and the mixture is sintered in a nickel crucible (fusion is unnecessary). The sintered mass is leached with hot water, the extract made strongly acid with hydrochloric acid, and the mixture evaporated to dryness on the water bath with a little hydrazine hydrochloride to volatilize the arsenic and germanium and render the silica insoluble. The dry mass is heated for a short time at 105°C., cooled and extracted with 10% hydrochloric acid. After saturation with hydrogen sulfide and standing overnight the liquid is filtered and the filtrate treated by the ether-cupferron method as explained above.

# Chapter 20

# GERMANIUM*

Ge, *at. wt.* 72.59; *sp. gr.* 5.36 (at 20°C.); *m.p.* 958°C.; *oxides,* GeO, GeO$_2$

The element was discovered by C. Winkler in 1866 in the mineral argyrodite, GeS$_2$·4Ag$_2$S. Germanium, when it is found as a major constituent of a mineral, is usually present as a sulfide. When it occurs as a trace element in nature, it is usually associated with sulfide minerals. A germanium ore of economic value is germanite, a complex sulfide ore, 7CuS·FeS·GeS$_2$, containing about 5% germanium with varying amounts of As, Zn, Pb, and Ga. In North America, germanium is found in very low concentrations in some isolated coal beds and in mid-continent zinc deposits. The zinc industry is the chief source of germanium in the United States. In Great Britain, germanium dioxide is commercially recovered from the flue dusts of some coal-burning power plants.

The valences of germanium are 2 and 4, the latter being more common. Germanium dioxide is a white powder of acid properties. GeO is a grayish powder. The tetrachloride is a liquid that boils at 86°C. The sulfide, GeS$_2$, is a white precipitate formed by the action of H$_2$S on germanium solutions. The precipitate is soluble in ammonium sulfide, polysulfide, and in ammonium hydroxide. Prior to World War II this element was of little economic importance; however, it now enjoys a great deal of prominence. The peculiar properties of Ge as a semiconductor and the vast growth of the electronics industry in the past few years has made this element very valuable in the ultrapure state.

## ESTIMATION

### PREPARATION OF THE SOLUTION

The metal and its alloys are best dissolved by a nitric-sulfuric acid mixture. Halogen acids, especially hydrochloric, with added H$_2$O$_2$ or HNO$_3$ are used to dissolve zinc concentrates, provision being made to trap the volatile halides. This attack is useful when followed by distillation of the tetrachloride. Direct chlorination followed by fractional distillation of the chloride is employed to obtain germanium from germanite.[1] Germanium itself is dissolved or rapidly attacked by molten alkalies, sodium carbonate, molten potassium nitrate and potassium chlorate.[2] Minerals are attacked by fusion with a sixfold quantity of a mixture of sulfur and sodium carbonate (1:1); the germanium forms a soluble sulfo salt that may be extracted by water.[3] Germanium and certain alloys attack platinum crucibles.

---

* Revised for the Sixth Edition by G. H. Morrison, Department of Chemistry, Cornell University, Ithaca, N. Y.

[1] Patrode, W. I., and Wock, R. W., Ind. Eng. Chem., **23**, 204, 1931.

[2] Dennis, L. M., Tressler, K. M., and Hance, J. E., J. Am. Chem. Soc., **45**, 2033, 1923.

[3] Winkler, C., Chem. Ber., **19**, 210, 1886.

The best method for separating germanium from complex mixtures is by distillation of the tetrachloride (b.p. 86°C.) from a hydrochloric acid solution (1:1). Using a suitable distillation column, germanium can be easily separated from elements that do not form volatile chlorides, as well as Sn, Sb, Se, and Te that do. Passing chlorine through the distilling flask or the addition of other oxidizing agents to oxidize arsenic to the pentavalent state results in the separation of germanium in the pure form.[4]

Germanium is a member of the polysulfide group and can be precipitated from solutions containing 5 $N$ $H_2SO_4$ by saturation with $H_2S$ and settling for 10–12 hours to coagulate the almost colloidal precipitate. The sulfides are filtered off and washed with 5 $N$ $H_2SO_4$ solution saturated with $H_2S$.[5] The sulfide of germanium obtained may be separated from Cu, Hg, Pb, Bi, and Cd by dissolving with alkaline sulfide or polysulfide and filtering as in the case with the separation of As, Sb, and Sn.

Separation of trace impurities from liquid germanium tetrachloride is accomplished by extracting with concentrated HCl.[6,7] Most elements are completely extracted into the acid phase, with the exception of arsenic. The addition of a few drops of $H_2O_2$ oxidizes the As to the pentavalent state and permits complete removal. The trace impurities thus separated can be then analyzed.

Germanium is complexed by fluoride or oxalate in acid solution and hence may be separated from As and Sb and many other metals of the $H_2S$ group by a preliminary precipitation of these elements with $H_2S$.

## GRAVIMETRIC METHODS

### DETERMINATION AS OXIDE

$GeO_2$ is the most common weighing form, but there are a number of variations in the methods used to obtain it. Two common methods are precipitation as the sulfide from highly acidic solutions, and precipitation in a 5% tannin solution, followed by ignition to the oxide in both methods.

*Sulfide Procedure.*[5]—The sulfide obtained by precipitation of $GeS_2$ from a 5 $N$ $H_2SO_4$ solution and washing with a 5 $N$ $H_2SO_4$ solution (saturated with $H_2S$) is dissolved in $NH_4OH$ and filtered into a weighed crucible or dish of platinum. The residue is washed until the washings pass through uncolored. To the filtrate and washings about 25 ml. of 3% $H_2O_2$ are added and the solution evaporated and the residue heated to 105°C. This is now moistened with $H_2SO_4$ and heated to expel ammonium sulfate and free acid, and then ignited to constant weight at 900–1000°C. and weighed as $GeO_2$.

*Tannin Procedure.*[8]—To the distillate from the chloride distillation of samples containing about 50 mg. of Ge are added 2 g. of hydroxylamine hydrochloride to reduce oxidizing substances. Thirty ml. of freshly prepared 5% tannin solution are added slowly with stirring. $NH_4OH$ is added to the methyl red point; then 10 drops of $H_2SO_4$ are added. The contents of the beaker are heated to incipient

4 Dennis, L. M., and Johnson, E. B., J. Am. Chem. Soc., **45**, 1380, 1923.

5 Johnson, E. B., and Dennis, L. M., J. Am. Chem. Soc., **47**, 790, 1925.

6 Allison, E. R., and Müller, J. H., J. Am. Chem. Soc., **54**, 2833, 1932.

7 Morrison, G. H., Dorfman, E. G., and Cosgrove, J. F., J. Am. Chem. Soc., **76**, 4236, 1954.

8 Rodden, C. J., Analytical Chemistry of the Manhattan Project, p. 374, McGraw-Hill Book Co., Inc., 1950.

boiling and the precipitate then allowed to settle. It is then filtered and washed free of chloride with a wash solution of 50 g. of $NH_4NO_3$, 5 g. of tannin, and 5 ml. of $HNO_3$ per liter of solution. The precipitate is dried and ignited in a weighed platinum crucible at 600°C. for 1 hour. The crucible is cooled, 5 drops of $H_2SO_4$ and 3 ml. of $HNO_3$ added, and acids expelled carefully, and the carbon burned off completely. The crucible is heated to 900–1000°C. for 10 minutes. After cooling the Ge is weighed as $GeO_2$.

## DETERMINATION AS MAGNESIUM ORTHOGERMANATE [9]

Magnesium orthogermanate, $Mg_2GeO_4$, is precipitated from aqueous solutions of germanium(IV) ions by a mixture of magnesium sulfate, ammonium sulfate, and concentrated ammonia. The precipitation does not occur in the presence of ammonium tartrate. Phosphate and arsenate are precipitated under these conditions.

*Procedure.*—Germanium is precipitated as sulfide as described in a previous paragraph. The precipitate is dissolved in $NH_4OH$ and $H_2O_2$. The excess peroxide is expelled by boiling the solution. The solution of germanium is made faintly acid with $H_2SO_4$ and about 15 ml. of 4 $N$ $(NH_4)_2SO_4$ solution added and 30 ml. of $N$ magnesium sulfate solution. Now $NH_4OH$ is added until the free acid is neutralized and 20 ml. in excess. The solution is heated to boiling and then allowed to cool for 10–12 hours. The precipitate is filtered and washed with dilute $NH_4OH$ (1:10), using as little of the wash reagent as possible, 40–50 ml. The residue is ignited according to the procedure recommended for magnesium estimation and then ignited to constant weight and weighed as $Mg_2GeO_4$.

## TITRIMETRIC METHODS

### MANNITOL METHOD

Germanium(IV) ions form a monobasic acid complex with mannitol which can be titrated with alkali to phenolphthalein.[10] This method is especially suitable when a preliminary separation of germanium as sulfide has been employed, and has been applied to the determination of from 1–50 mg. of Ge (as sodium germanate) in 10 ml. of solution.[11] For amounts of from 50 mg. down to 5 mg. of Ge the results are accurate to within 0.5–1.0%. With smaller amounts the accuracy is lower. Boron interferes. (See Chapter on Boron.)

*Procedure.*[11]—The solution is weakly acidified with $H_2SO_4$, boiled 5–10 minutes to expel $CO_2$, cooled under protection of a soda-lime tube, and neutralized with 0.1 $N$ alkali to a yellow color with $p$-nitrophenol (methyl red can be used). After the addition of 0.5–0.7 g. of mannitol, the solution is titrated to the color change of phenolphthalein. More mannitol is then added and the titration continued further if necessary.

Treatment of the mannitol-germanium complex with a mixture of potassium iodide and potassium iodate in the presence of strong electrolytes liberates iodine quantitatively, permitting titration with sodium thiosulfate.[10]

[9] Müller, J. H., J. Am. Chem. Soc., **44**, 2493, 1922.
[10] Tchakirian, A., Compt. rend., **187**, 229, 1928.
[11] Poluektoff, N. S., Z. Anal. Chem., **105**, 23, 1936.

## THIOGERMANATE METHOD [12]

$GeO_2$, in acetate buffered media, is quantitatively converted to potassium thiogermanate, $K_2Ge_2S_5$, by treatment with $H_2S$ or $K_2S$. The excess $H_2S$ is removed by passing a rapid stream of $CO_2$ through the solution, after which the sulfide ion is determined by treatment with an excess of standard iodine solution and back-titrated with sodium thiosulfate solution. High concentrations of NaCl cause appreciable error, therefore this method should not be used directly after a distillation separation of $GeCl_4$. Metals that form insoluble sulfides at a pH of 4.6 must be absent.

*Procedure.*–The solution containing germanium as $GeO_2$ is transferred to a 10-inch test tube and diluted to 25 ml., and 20 ml. of $K_2S$ solution (8 g. of KOH dissolved in 100 ml. of water, cooled to 0°C. and saturated with $H_2S$) added. Fifteen ml. of 2.5 $M$ acetic acid are added by allowing it to run down the side of the test tube. The solution is then allowed to stand for 5 minutes. $CO_2$ is bubbled through the solution rapidly for 20 minutes by means of a delivery tube extending to the bottom of the test tube. A mechanical stirrer is used to break up the bubbles of $CO_2$ to help in removal of excess $H_2S$.

The solution is transferred to a large beaker and diluted to 1 liter. A measured excess of standard 0.1 $N$ iodine solution is added, allowed to stand for 15 minutes, and back-titrated with standard 0.1 $N$ $Na_2S_2O_3$ solution using starch solution as indicator.

# COLORIMETRIC METHODS

## MOLYBDIGERMANIC ACID METHOD

The yellow color of molybdigermanic acid developed in 5 $N$ acetic acid solution follows Beer's Law in concentrations up to 40 mg. of Ge per liter, and comparison with known color standards permits estimation of as little as 1 p. p. m. of Ge. Arsenic, silicon, phosphorus, titanium, and vanadium interfere.

*Procedure.*[13]–After previous separation from other elements by distillation and sulfide precipitation and washing, the $GeS_2$ precipitate is dissolved in the smallest possible amount of distilled aqueous $NH_3$. The yellow solution is transferred to a platinum dish, decolorized with 30% $H_2O_2$, and 1 to 2 ml. added in excess. Excess peroxide is destroyed by gently boiling the solution. It is then cooled, neutralized with dilute $H_2SO_4$, and diluted to a definite volume. An aliquot of this solution containing 1–3 mg. of Ge is transferred to a 100-ml. volumetric flask and 30 ml. of glacial acetic acid are added. The solution is diluted to 80 ml. with water, and 10 ml. of a freshly prepared 2.5% solution of ammonium molybdate added. After diluting to the mark, the solution is mixed well and the color measured by any of the usual means. Using a spectrophotometer, transmittancy measurements are made in 5-cm. cells at 440 m$\mu$ within 15 minutes of the addition of the molybdate. Standards for comparison are prepared similarly.

## MOLYBDENUM BLUE METHOD [14, 15]

Reduction of the molybdigermanic acid to molybdenum blue increases the sensi-

12 Willard, H. H., and Zuehlke, C. W., Ind. Eng. Chem., Anal. Ed., **16,** 322, 1944.
13 Kitson, R. E., and Mellon, M. G., Ind. Eng. Chem., Anal. Ed., **16,** 128, 1944.
14 Boltz, D. F., and Mellon, M. G., Anal. Chem., **19,** 873, 1947.
15 Hybbinette, A., and Sandell, E. B., Ind. Eng. Chem., Anal. Ed., **14,** 715, 1942.

tivity of the determination. Beer's Law is valid up to 4 p. p. m. germanium. Arsenic, silicon, and phosphorus interfere.

*Procedure.*[14]—A quantity of sample containing not more than 2.0 mg. of Ge for every 100 ml. of solution is taken after completion of the separation step. The solution is made neutral to litmus using either $H_2SO_4$ or NaOH, and diluted to 100 ml. Twenty ml. of the Ge solution are transferred to a 50-ml. volumetric flask, and 0.75 ml. of 4 $N$ $H_2SO_4$ solution added. Next, 1 ml. of 10% ammonium molybdate is added, followed immediately by 25 ml. of reductant solution (20 ml. 4 $N$ $H_2SO_4$ and 5 ml. of a 2% ferrous ammonium sulfate solution made by dissolving 10 g. of Mohr's salt in 500 ml. of water containing 1.5 ml. of 4 $N$ $H_2SO_4$). The solution is diluted to the mark with water, mixed thoroughly and the transmittancy measured at 830 m$\mu$ in 1-cm. cells.

*Chapter* **21**

# GOLD

Au, *at. wt.* 197.967; *sp. gr.* 19.32 (at 17.5°C.); *m.p.* 1063°C.; *b.p.* 2600°C.; *oxides,* $Au_2O$, $Au_2O_3$.

Gold is usually found as the metal alloyed with varying quantities of silver. It is found in many types of rocks in quantities too small for commercial recovery, and it occurs in many tellurium minerals. Most gold ores are those in which the matrix is of high silica content. It is also found in sea water to the extent of 0.005 p. p. m. Metallic gold of no definite crystallinity is found associated with pyrites. It may be found alloyed with bismuth, copper, and lead. Alluvial deposits of gold, the result of weathering of igneous formations and the settling of the metal due to its high specific gravity, are very important sources of gold.

Gold is one of the few metals of distinctive color. It is the most malleable of metals and its hardness varies from 2.5 to 3.0 on Mohr's scale.

## DETECTION

Because of the limited application and the tediousness of wet methods, and because of the comparatively limited use of gold for purposes other than money or decoration, the detection and estimation of gold has been generally restricted to fire assay separations and concentration. (See page 475.)

However, wet methods can be applied to the determination of gold. In most cases advantage is taken of the insolubility of gold in one of the mineral acids.

### DETECTION IN ALLOYS

In alloys that are soluble in one of the mineral acids, gold, in the absence of any insoluble matter, may be detected as a heavy brownish residue by filtering the cooled and diluted solution. In the absence of all metals or other insoluble matter, this residue becomes yellow on ignition.

In the presence of insoluble matter the ignited gold residue is digested with aqua regia. The solution is carefully evaporated with hydrochloric acid to remove excess nitric acid and the solution is diluted to at least 100 ml. After standing the solution is filtered through close-grained filter paper with added paper pulp, and the most suitable of the tests mentioned under "Estimation" is applied for the determination of gold in the filtrate.

### DETECTION IN MINERALS

For the determination and estimation of gold in minerals the great precision of the fire assay technique (page 475) make it first choice. However, when wet procedures are necessary, the gold present in the thoroughly oxidized or roasted mineral may be dissolved in sodium cyanide or in hypochlorous acid solution with continued agitation in a closed container. If excessive amounts of easily oxidized elements are present a prior treatment with nitric acid is suggested.

As an alternate method, the gold may be extracted by a solution of iodine in 10% potassium iodide or by bromine or chlorine water. In any case the rate of the reaction is dependent upon the fineness of the material. Agitation in a closed container is recommended regardless of solvent.

Gold may also be detected spectrographically. Generally its concentration is below its limit of detection, which is about 0.001%.[1] Therefore, in most minerals and ores, the gold must first be concentrated. Fire assay procedures are suggested. In solutions free of oxidizing agents, gold may be co-precipitated with excess tellurium [2] and the resulting precipitate is examined spectrographically. Likewise, finely divided gold which has been precipitated, may be adsorbed in a hydrous oxide precipitate, such as those of aluminum, titanium, iron, or manganese, and the resulting precipitate filtered and examined spectrographically. The spectral lines of 2413 A and 2676 A are most frequently used.

## ESTIMATION

### PREPARATION AND SOLUTION OF THE SAMPLE

Gold is practically insoluble in any one of the mineral acids, but in the presence of an oxidizing agent is easily dissolved by hydrochloric acid. Under similar circumstances it is attacked by sulfuric acid.

Gold is sometimes found in the nitric acid solution of its alloys. The extent of such solution depends upon the alloying elements; when alloyed with selenium considerable gold may dissolve.

Gold is easily dissolved in aqua regia, in the usual ratio of four parts hydrochloric acid to one part of nitric acid. It is also dissolved by solutions of bromine and chlorine, by alkaline thiosulfates, and by cyanides.

It is attacked by molten oxidizing alkaline salts and, when in a finely divided condition, by the alkali hydroxides.

Gold dissolves easily in molten lead and bismuth and forms amalgams.

## SEPARATIONS

Gold may be readily separated from most base metals by reducing it with a more electropositive metal. Copper, zinc, aluminum, and magnesium may be used in acid solutions; zinc is frequently used in cyanide solutions.

Gold is easily reduced from solutions free of oxidizing agents by many reducing agents, among which the more common ones are ferrous sulfate, oxalic acid, hypophosphorous acid, sulfites, sulfurous acid, hydrogen peroxide or titanium trichloride.

The ready reducibility of the metal from solutions forms the basis for much of its quantitative chemistry.

Extractive methods have been proposed for the metal. Myleus [3] suggested the use of ether to extract gold from chloride solutions; Noyes and Bray [4] suggested

[1] Ahrens, Spectrochemical Analysis, p. 197, Addison-Wesley Press, Inc., 1950.
[2] Sandell, Colorimetric Determination of Traces of Metals, p. 341, Interscience Publishers, Inc., 1950.
[3] Myleus, F., Z. anorg. Chem., **70,** 203, 1911.
[4] Noyes and Bray, Qualitative Analysis for the Rare Elements, Macmillan Co., 1925.

ethyl acetate as a means of separating gold from the platinum metals. Reference has been made to fire assay procedures.

Many organic precipitants have been proposed. Pollard [5] suggested *o*-tolidine, Moltesta and Nola [4] proposed benzidine sulfate, Beamish suggested hydroquinone, and Santel suggested *p*-diethylaminobenzylidinerhodanine.[6] This latter reference is especially suggested for additional colorimetric procedures.

## GRAVIMETRIC METHODS

### PRECIPITATION WITH SULFUROUS ACID

Precipitation with sulfurous acid affords a good separation of gold from small quantities of palladium and platinum, and from large quantities of the base metals usually present in the gold alloys of commerce. When large amounts, on the order of 25–100 mg. of platinum are present, some platinum will contaminate the gold precipitate. Larger amounts of palladium can be tolerated but for most precise results the gold precipitate should be redissolved and reprecipitated.

*Procedure.*—After solution of the alloy or residue in aqua regia (4 parts HCl, 1 part $HNO_3$, 8 parts $H_2O$), any insoluble matter is filtered from the solution and the solution is carefully evaporated on a steam bath with hydrochloric acid to remove all free nitric acid. Two additions, each of 5 ml. of hydrochloric acid, may be necessary to decompose and volatilize the nitrates.

The solution is diluted to contain not more than 100 mg. of gold per 100 ml. and is allowed to stand for several hours. Any insoluble matter is removed by filtration. The clear solution is heated to 80–90°C., and 20 ml. of a saturated solution of sulfurous acid are added slowly. The solution is gently heated until the gold precipitate coagulates, then an additional 5 ml. of the sulfurous acid solution are added and the heating is continued for 10 minutes to insure complete precipitation of gold.

The cooled solution is filtered on a close-grained doubled filter paper, the paper is washed thoroughly with warm 1% hydrochloric acid and then to neutrality with water. The paper is dried, ignited, and, after cooling, the precipitate of gold is weighed.

Care must be taken in filtering gold chloride not to expose the solution in contact with the filter paper to sunlight since gold is photosensitive and under such conditions will be reduced in the filter paper. The same precautions should be observed with all platinum group elements (*q.v.*).

### PRECIPITATION WITH OXALIC ACID

A more complete separation of gold from the platinum group metals can be made by using oxalic acid instead of sulfurous acid. A close control of the acidity is necessary for complete precipitation of gold.

*Procedure.*—After solution of the alloy or residue in aqua regia (4 parts HCl, 1 part $HNO_3$, 8 parts $H_2O$) and after any insoluble matter has been filtered from the solution, the solution is carefully evaporated twice to moist salts with the addition each time of 5 ml. of hydrochloric acid. The final residue is diluted so as to contain about 100 mg. of gold per 100 ml. Any insoluble matter which separates after standing for several hours is removed by filtering the solution.

[5] Pollard, W. B., Analyst, **44,** 94, 1919.
[6] Beamish, Russell, and Seath, Ind. and Eng. Chem., Anal. Ed., **9,** 174, 1937.

To each equivalent of 100 mg. of gold, 25 ml. of a saturated solution of oxalic acid is added and the solution is heated to 80–90°C. for 20 minutes. Another 25 ml. of the oxalic acid solution is added and the heating is repeated for 20 minutes.

The solution is cooled to room temperature and filtered through close-grained doubled filter paper. The filter is washed thoroughly with warm 1% hydrochloric acid and then to neutrality with hot water. The filter is then dried and ignited, and the cooled precipitate is weighed as gold.

If excessive amounts of platinum are present the precipitation must be repeated.

## PRECIPITATION WITH SODIUM NITRITE

Gilchrist [7] described a procedure for the complete analysis of dental gold alloys that is also suitable for most gold alloys used in commerce. In this procedure the gold is first precipitated with sodium nitrite at pH 1.5 and by further adjustment to pH 8, copper, zinc, nickel, and indium are precipitated as hydroxides. After filtration the hydroxides are dissolved from the paper with hydrochloric acid, leaving the gold.

*Procedure.*—After the nitrates have been removed by two successive evaporations with 5 ml. each of hydrochloric acid, the solution is diluted to 150 ml. and the insoluble material filtered. The pH is adjusted to 1.5 with 10% sodium hydroxide, the solution is heated to boiling, and 10 ml. of a filtered 10% solution of sodium nitrite are added. The solution is boiled for 2 to 3 minutes to coagulate the gold, and the acidity is again adjusted to pH 1.5.

Twenty ml. of the nitrite solution is added and the warm solution is adjusted to pH 8 with 2% sodium hydroxide. The solution is boiled for 5 minutes and the pH again adjusted to 8. The precipitate includes gold, copper, lead, nickel, and indium.

The mixed precipitate is filtered on a close-grained filter paper and washed thoroughly to remove residual nitrite solution. The base metal hydroxides are dissolved from the filter with warm 5% hydrochloric acid. It is advisable, if possible, to retain the heavier gold precipitate in the beaker while transferring the hydroxides to the filter. The gold precipitate is transferred to the filter with warm hydrochloric acid and the filter washed to neutrality with hot water.

The dissolved metals should be reprecipitated by a repetition of this procedure in order to recover the small amount of gold that may dissolve with them.

Gilchrist recommends this procedure also as a means of separating gold from the platinum group metals.

## COLORIMETRIC METHODS

Colorimetric determinations of gold must be made in solutions free of colored ions and reducible metals. The usual association of gold with the metals of the platinum group limits the usefulness of many procedures suggested for its determination.

### THE STANNOUS CHLORIDE COLORIMETRIC PROCEDURE

One of the oldest of all colorimetric tests and yet one capable of great accuracy and precision is the stannous chloride test (purple of Cassius).

[7] Gilchrist, New Procedure for the Analysis of Dental Gold Alloys, National Bureau of Standards, Research Paper RP 1103.

*Procedure.*—The gold solution, free of all reducible metals such as mercury, selenium, platinum, palladium, ruthenium, and metals that form insoluble chlorides or colored reduction products, is diluted to contain not more than 0.5 mg. of gold; the acidity, measured as HCl, should be less than 0.1 $N$, and then 5 ml. of a solution containing 10% $SnCl_2$ and about 2 $N$ HCl is added.

The reaction is immediate and the gold content may be easily estimated by comparison to similarly prepared standards, or by reference to a previously prepared curve.

# THE FIRE ASSAY FOR
# GOLD AND SILVER[8]

*Definitions.*—**Fire assaying** is a branch of quantitative chemical analysis in which metals are determined in ores and metallurgical products by extracting and weighing them in the metallic state. The methods employed involve slag-melting temperatures and the use of reducing, oxidizing, and fluxing reagents, and are in principle the same as those used in metallurgy.

The metals ordinarily determined by fire assaying are gold, silver, and platinum. This method can not be recommended for the baser metals except as a means of concentration, for example of bismuth by means of lead, or of isolation of tin or white metals in preparing a sample of dross for wet analyses.

**Ores** are mineral aggregates from which one or more metals can be extracted at a profit.

**Metallurgical products** include a large number of metal-bearing mixtures and compounds, ranging from high grade gold and silver bullion to very weak cyanide and sulfate solutions.

The constituents of an ore are usually divided into two general classes, the valuable minerals containing the *metals,* and the nonvaluable minerals or *gangue.* A similar classification can be made in the case of many metallurgical products. In gold and silver bullion and other alloys most of the components are metallic, and the assaying problems involve mainly the separation of metals. Selenium (and at times tellurium) is found in certain types of Doré Bullion.

## GENERAL METHOD

With ores and metallurgical products containing nonmetallic elements the process consists, briefly, in the production of two liquids, liquid lead containing the valuable metals, and liquid slag containing the waste matter or gangue. The two liquids separate from each other by reason of the great difference in specific gravity and insolubility in each other. The valuable metals are separated from the lead and from each other by taking advantage of differences in chemical properties. The slag may frequently be discarded, but it is often necessary to run corrections to recover the silver and gold invariably lost in slags and cupels; hence some slags must be saved for this purpose.

In the operation of the process the gold and silver, and platinum metals, if present, are collected from the metal-bearing portion of the ore or metallurgical product by means of molten lead reduced from litharge or lead oxide. The descending "rain" of tiny droplets of lead reduced from the litharge acts as a collector of the gold, silver and platinum metals. Therefore the litharge and all other additions should be substantially free of silver, bismuth, antimony, and thallium, or else having a silver increment known to be negligible or exactly deter-

[8] Original material by the late Irving A. Palmer, Professor of Metallurgy, Colorado School of Mines. Revised in accordance with suggestions made by T. A. Wright, Technical Director, Lucius Pitkin, Inc.

minable on occasion, which is often necessary. The gangue is converted into a fusible slag by means of reagents known as fluxes.

The effectiveness of the fire assay in separating gold, silver, and platinum from ores and metallurgical products depends upon two properties of these metals: first, their weak affinity for nonmetallic elements, especially at high temperatures, and second, their very great affinity for molten lead. The collection of the precious metals in the lead, therefore, is the simplest part of the process. The fluxing of the gangue is much more difficult and requires considerable knowledge and skill. If the fluxing is properly performed, the collection of the valuable metals usually takes care of itself. It is often necessary to add silver to assist in the recovery of the gold (the silver acting as a collector), to reduce the loss of gold in the cupel, and to permit the subsequent parting operation to be effective.

*Reagents.*—A flux is a substance which when heated in contact with some difficultly fusible compound either combines with it or takes it into solution, in each case producing a compound or mixture which is easily fusible at ordinary furnace temperatures. The principal fluxes and other reagents used in fire assaying are described in the following paragraphs.

**Litharge** or oxide of lead, $PbO$, melting point 883°C., has several important uses. It furnishes the lead which collects the previous metals; it readily combines with silica, producing easily fusible silicates; and it acts as an oxidizing and desulfurizing agent. It is a very strong basic flux.

**Sodium carbonate**, $Na_2CO_3$, melting point 852°C., is a powerful basic flux. It combines with silica and alumina, producing fusible silicates and aluminates. When molten it has the property of dissolving or holding in suspension a number of refractory gangue materials. To some extent, also, it acts as an oxidizing and desulfurizing agent. The use of anhydrous sodium carbonate is in general preferable, but the bicarbonate, $NaHCO_3$, is employed where greater gassing action is desirable, since the latter gives off twice as much carbon dioxide as the former per unit of silica fluxed. Potassium carbonate, $K_2CO_3$, melting point 894°C., is rarely used in fire assaying because of its greater cost.

**Borax glass,** $Na_2B_4O_7$, melting point 742°C., is an acid flux used for combining with or dissolving the basic and some of the acid constituents of the gangue, producing easily fusible complex borates and mixtures of borates and other compounds. Even silica dissolves to some extent in molten borax glass. An excessive amount of borax glass should be avoided where silver values are important because of the tendency toward low results due to loss of silver in the slag under these conditions.

**Silica,** $SiO_2$, melting point 1755°C., is a strong acid flux. It combines with metallic oxides and produces silicates which in many cases are considerably more fusible than silica itself.

**Granulated lead** or **test lead,** melting point 327°C., is used in the scorification assay, which is conducted under oxidizing conditions, and in which, therefore, litharge could not be employed as a source of lead.

**Lead foil** or **sheet lead** is used in the assay of gold and silver bullion. For many purposes sheet lead may contain more silver or bismuth than test lead, although this is of course to be avoided if possible; the amount of sheet lead rarely exceeds 20 g. in good umpire practice as in Doré assays, or 10 g. in the combination fire and wet blister assays.

**Flour** is known as a reducing agent. It contains carbon, which reduces lead from litharge. Charcoal was formerly used for this purpose, but is not so convenient.

**Starch** is a convenient reducing agent and its use is common practice.

**Argol** or **crude cream of tartar,** $KHC_4H_4O_6$, is both a basic flux and a reducing agent. On being heated it decomposes as follows:

$$2KHC_4H_4O_6 + heat \rightarrow K_2O + 5H_2O + 6CO + 2C.$$

It is effective in assays requiring strong reducing action and low temperatures.

**Iron** is sometimes used as a desulfurizing and reducing agent. It decomposes most of the heavy sulfides, yielding the metals and iron sulfide.

**Potassium nitrate,** $KNO_3$, melting point 339°C., is a powerful oxidizing agent. It is used to neutralize the effect of an excess of reducing substances in the material to be assayed. High sulfur ores, if assayed without previous roasting, require the addition of nitre to the charge. In contact with a reducing agent two molecules of potassium nitrate give up five atoms of oxygen, as shown in the following equation:

$$4KNO_3 + 5C \rightarrow 2K_2CO_3 + 3CO_2 + 2N_2.$$

The potassium oxide coming from the decomposition of the nitre acts as a basic flux.

**Common salt,** NaCl, melting point 819°C., is a neutral substance sometimes used as a cover for crucible fusions to exclude the air. When molten it rests on top of the charge and does not enter into it.

All of the reagents used must be pure and in a finely divided condition. Sodium carbonate shows a tendency to form lumps. These should be broken up and the entire mass put through a moderately fine screen.

*Apparatus.* **Furnaces and Equipment.**—The major operations of fire assaying are usually conducted in muffle furnaces. The muffle is a box-like receptacle; formerly fire clay was used but the silicon carbide muffle is rapidly displacing other types. The muffle is so placed in the furnace that all sides except the front are heated. There is a generous vent of rectangular shape in the back of the muffle. The refractory vessels containing the material to be assayed are placed in the muffle, and there is no direct contact with the fuel or its products of combustion. The fuel may be coal, oil, gasoline or gas.

**Cupels.**—The separation of the precious metals from the lead alloys produced in fire assaying is effected in small shallow vessels of bone ash, known as *cupels.* The material consists mainly of calcium phosphate, small percentages of magnesium phosphate, calcium and magnesium fluoride and carbonate. It is a product of the burning of animal bones, preferably those of the sheep. It should be ground fine enough to pass a 40-mesh screen, in which case about 50% of it will pass a 150-mesh screen. The cupels are made by moistening the bone ash with a small amount of water and then compressing it in the cupel mould, which consists essentially of a ring and die. The bone ash is forced into the shape desired at a considerable pressure, so as to insure sufficient rigidity in the cupel. The amount of water needed varies, but should be as low as possible. By using high pressures good cupels can be made from perfectly dry bone ash.

The requirements of a good cupel are that it should be infusible at ordinary furnace temperatures, that it should not be attacked by metallic oxides, that it should be porous, and that it should be sufficiently rigid to permit of considerable handling.

The question of cupel losses, other than those due to the purity and silver-gold ratio of the bead, is governed by a number of factors. Among these are cupel material, batch moisture, pressure, diameter and depth of cup, and contour of cup depression. All of these factors have been the basis of an extended study by J. T. King [9] which is commended to all assayers interested in silver losses. The study did not, however, include determination of lead retention, an item not to be disregarded but which may in part offset silver absorption losses, nor did it include various gold-silver ratios. If, however, silver and gold are in the ratio of at least 5–1, gold absorption by good cupels (copper not being present in unusual amount) is, for weights most often encountered, usually negligible. Silver losses, in any event, for a cupellation to feathers will vary from about 1% for a bead 300 mg. or more up to about 4% for a bead of say 10 mg. weight. The loss is not a straight line relationship, however, for at 100 mg. the normal loss should be 1.90% ± 0.15. For all the experimental losses determined by King, however, less than 0.50% of the total loss could be attributed to volatilization. Reference should be made again to the original paper for the details.

Bone-ash cupels have been considered superior when made of a good grade bone-ash of properly proportioned particle size. In general, the grade known as XXX is preferable and King's recommendation of a water addition of 10 to 12% with a pressure of at least 800 lbs. per sq. in. at the die confirms good plant practice. Cupels should be dried slowly to avoid cracking but aging over a week is not necessary. A uniform height of about 1″ is indicated. Width varies with weight of lead button. Sizes 1⅛″ and 1½″ are most common.

If cupels must be purchased or transported, or for some kinds of interplant control, a less fragile composite cupel of 70% bone-ash and 30% cement may be used, but temperature control must be adjusted. Composite cupels are not favored for umpire assays or those of similar importance, though King found that silver losses at least were no higher than those made from bone-ash.

*The Assay-Ton System.*—As the precious metals are bought and sold by the troy system of weights, and ores by the avoirdupois system, considerable time would be lost in calculating assay results, were there no way of avoiding it. To simplify the calculation, the assay-ton system of weights is used. The assay-ton is equal to 29,166⅔ milligrams. As there are 29,166⅔ troy ounces in an avoirdupois ton of 2000 pounds, the number of milligrams and fractions of a milligram of precious metals found in an assay-ton of ore corresponds to the number of troy ounces in an avoirdupois ton.

*Sampling.*[10]—It goes without saying that good results in assaying presuppose accurate sampling. Silver is reported in assay certificates to the nearest tenth of an ounce; gold usually to the nearest one hundredth of an ounce. One tenth of an ounce means one part in 291,667; one hundredth of an ounce, one part in 2,916,-667. In the preparation of the sample, therefore, the ratio between the weight of any fractional portion and the weight of the largest particle in it must be very large, so that the accidental inclusion of a number of rich pieces in any portion shall not affect the results beyond the limits of error in assaying. Grinding to too fine a mesh should be avoided. From 80 to 120 mesh is probably the best range. The density of gold is so much greater than that of the country rock that segregation may occur on certain types of ore, if the grinding is too fine. The heat gener-

[9] King, J. T., The Influence of Cupels on Silver Loss, Bulletin 147, 1934; 70 pp.; Univ. of Toronto.
[10] Brunton, D., Am. Inst. Mining Engrs., **40,** 567–596, 1911; Dewey, F. P., Orig. Commun., 8th Internat. Cong. Appl. Chem., **1,** 155.

ated may volatilize sulfur as $SO_2$ or cause oxidation of other constituents to occur; this is of importance in rich material.

The division of the sample can often be done most precisely with Jones Samplers, the size of which is in relationship to the volume of the material to be divided.

**Balances and Weights.**—The balances used in fire assaying are somewhat different from those found in chemical laboratories. They are known as flux, pulp, and assay balances. The assay balances are for weighing the gold and silver, often exceedingly small in amount, and are the most delicate type of commercial balances made. They should be quick in action and not liable to changes in adjustment. The beam should be short, light and rigid. The balance should be sensitive to 0.005 milligram at least. It need not have a capacity of more than 1.0 gram but should be accurate with that load.

In large laboratories separate balances are furnished for weighing the gold. These balances should be adjusted before each weighing and should be handled with the greatest of care. In the assay of gold ores, when using a half assay-ton portion, every error of 0.01 mg. in weighing the gold means a variation in the value of the ore of forty cents per ton.

It is desirable that a set of Bureau of Standards certified weights (1 g. to 1 mg.) be secured, and used for checking the weights used in routine work, at regular intervals; the standards should be sent back occasionally for restandardization. Weights should be handled only with bone tweezers, and with every precaution to avoid change in their mass.

## THE CRUCIBLE ASSAY

This method of fire assaying is adapted to the great majority of gold and silver ores and to many metallurgical products. The process consists in treating a weighed portion of the sample, carefully mixed with the necessary reagents, in a fire-clay crucible. In order to do this effectively the character of the material to be assayed must be known. Thus, ores may be oxides or sulfides. They may be basic, acid, or neutral. They may be strongly oxidizing or strongly reducing. Each case requires a particular method of treatment.

The amount of sample of ores usually taken is one-half assay-ton, run in duplicate. Twenty-gram fire-clay crucibles are used, that is, crucibles capable of holding twenty grams of ore and the necessary reagents. In most cases the total charge will fill the crucible to within one inch of the top. For jewelers' sweeps the sample is no larger than one-quarter assay ton, and for some types of slimes and precipitates which can be subjected to crucible assays, no more than one-tenth or even in certain instances one-twentieth of an assay ton should be used.

**Lead Reduction with Oxidized Ores.**—Experience has shown that the best results are obtained when the lead reduced from the charge amounts to from 25 to 35 grams. If the ore is oxidized, a reducing agent must be added to precipitate the necessary lead. Flour is the reagent ordinarily used although charcoal or argol can be substituted for it. The lead is reduced according to the following equation:

$$2PbO + C \rightarrow 2Pb + CO_2$$

That is, 12 parts of carbon theoretically will reduce 414 parts of lead from litharge. Hence, the theoretical reducing power of carbon is 414/12 or 34.5. In practice, the reducing power of charcoal is found to range between 25 and 30, and that of flour from 10 to 12. Argol has a reducing power of about 8 or 9. In most oxidized ores, therefore, from 2.5 to 3.5 g. of flour will be required to reduce from 25 to 35 g. of lead from the litharge.

If the ore contains ferric oxide, manganese dioxide, or some other easily reducible oxide, more flour must be added. Some iron-manganese ores require as much as 5 grams of flour to throw down the necessary lead. With unknown ores the right amount can be determined only by trial.

For jewelers' sweeps a minimum lead button of 80–90 g. is indicated, to be then scorified to 20–25 g. Sweeps are oxidizing in character since they consist of well burnt material and of iron and chromium oxides or other similar polishing agents.

**Lead Reduction with Sulfide Ores.**—In the case of ores containing sulfides, arsenides or other reducing substances, there will be a reduction of lead without the addition of carbon. In fact it is usually necessary to add an oxidizing agent to prevent the precipitation of too much lead. The following reactions show the effect of a number of sulfide minerals when heated in contact with litharge and sodium carbonate.

(1)    $PbS + 3PbO + Na_2CO_3 \rightarrow 4Pb + Na_2SO_4 + CO_2$

(2)    $ZnS + 4PbO + Na_2CO_3 \rightarrow 4Pb + ZnO + Na_2SO_4 + CO_2$

(3)    $2FeS_2 + 15PbO + 4Na_2CO_3 \rightarrow 15Pb + Fe_2O_3 + 4Na_2SO_4 + 4CO_2$

The sodium carbonate induces the complete oxidation of the sulfur to $SO_3$, with the formation of the very stable compound sodium sulfate. In the absence of an alkaline carbonate most of the sulfur is oxidized to $SO_2$ only, and the amount of lead precipitated is correspondingly decreased.

Reaction (3) shows that pyrite has a greater reducing power than flour itself. If, therefore, a half-assay-ton of ore consisting mainly of pyrite were to be subjected to a crucible fusion, without the addition of some oxidizing agent, but with a large amount of litharge, anywhere from 100 to 150 g. of lead would be reduced. This would be entirely too much for the subsequent process of cupellation. In order to prevent the reduction of an excessive amount of lead, potassium nitrate is added to the charge. The following reactions show the oxidizing power of this reagent:

(4)        $2KNO_3 + 5Pb \rightarrow 5PbO + K_2O + N_2$

(5)        $2FeS_2 + 6KNO_3 \rightarrow Fe_2O_3 + 4SO_3 + 3K_2O + 3N_2$

Reaction (4) shows that 202 parts of nitre will oxidize 1035 parts of lead to litharge. The theoretical oxidizing power of nitre, as measured against lead, is, therefore, 5.12. Reaction (5) when compared with reaction (3), given above, shows that 606 parts of nitre will oxidize the pyrite needed to reduce 3105 g. of lead from litharge. Here again the oxidizing power of nitre is shown to be 5.12. In practice, it is found to be somewhat less, more nearly 4.5.

The fire assay of sulfide ores, therefore, involves either a preliminary assay, or a calculation from the chemical analysis, in order to determine the amount of nitre to be added. With unknown ores it is better to make a preliminary fusion, using 5 g. of the ore, 75 g. of litharge, 20 g. of sodium carbonate and 10 g. of borax glass. The button of reduced lead is weighed and its weight divided by 5. This gives the reducing power of the ore. From this can be calculated the reducing power of one half assay-ton of the ore, and the amount of nitre necessary to add in order to cut down the weight of the reduced lead to about 30 g. An excess of silica or borax glass decreases somewhat the amount of lead by causing the formation of difficultly reducible lead silicates or borates.

*Amount of Litharge.*—The amount of litharge for a half assay-ton charge usually ranges from 60 to 75 g. Only about half of this is needed to produce the 25 to 35 g. of metallic lead used as the collector. The excess litharge serves to prevent the reduction of other base metals, such as antimony, bismuth, iron, copper and zinc, to help flux the silica, to act as a solvent for some of the refractory gangue materials, and to make sure that every particle of the ore in the crucible is in close proximity to one or more particles of litharge. In special cases it may be advisable to use a very large excess of litharge, as in the assay of rich gold telluride ores, zinc precipitates and saturated cupels.

*Amount of Sodium Carbonate.*—The amount of sodium carbonate to be used depends somewhat upon the character of the ore, although the modern practice is to use about the same quantity in assaying a great variety of ores and metallurgical products. The principal function of the sodium carbonate is to flux the silica and alumina, which are nearly always present in greater or less degree. The reactions are as follows:

(6) $$Na_2CO_3 + SiO_2 \rightarrow Na_2SiO_3 + CO_2,$$

(7) $$2Na_2CO_3 + SiO_2 \rightarrow Na_4SiO_4 + 2CO_2,$$

(8) $$Na_2CO_3 + Al_2O_3 \rightarrow Na_2Al_2O_4 + CO_2.$$

The two silicates and the aluminate are both quite fusible at ordinary furnace temperatures.

The silicates used in assaying and in metallurgy are usually classified according to the ratio between the oxygen in the acid radical and that in the base. Only four of these type silicates are of any practical importance. They are shown in the following table:

| | |
|---|---|
| Subsilicate................... | $4RO \cdot SiO_2$ |
| Mono- or singulosilicate....... | $2RO \cdot SiO_2$ |
| Sesquisilicate................ | $4RO \cdot 3SiO_2$ |
| Bisilicate.................... | $RO \cdot SiO_2$ |

In the above silicates, the ratios are ½ to 1, 1 to 1, 1½ to 1, and 2 to 1, respectively.

Reactions (6) and (7) show that to flux one part of silica to bisilicate and monosilicate requires about 1¾ parts and 3½ parts, respectively, of sodium carbonate. If the half assay-ton of ore, therefore, consisted of almost pure quartz, it would take 25 g. of sodium carbonate to flux it to sodium bisilicate, and 50 grams to flux it to the monosilicate. As a matter of fact, the bisilicate slag is satisfactory in this case. In general, the acid silicates have lower melting points but greater viscosity than the basic silicates. The excess litharge in the charge also combines with silica, and may thus produce more basic silicates. Moreover, a mixture of silicates usually has a lower melting point than that calculated from the melting points of its components.

Reaction (8) shows that 1 part of sodium carbonate is required to flux 1 part of alumina.

In practice, from 30 to 35 g. of sodium carbonate are used in a half-assay-ton charge. In many cases this may seem to be a large excess. It must be remembered, however, that this reagent serves also to assist in the oxidation of the sulfides through the formation of sodium sulfate, that it has a solvent effect upon refractory oxides and other substances, and that it increases the bulk of the charge, thus protecting the ore from the action of the air and from the escape of the more volatile metals and their compounds. Being very fusible itself, an excess also serves to increase the fusibility of very refractory charges.

*Amount of Borax Glass.*—The rational formula of borax glass, $Na_2O \cdot 2B_2O_3$, shows that it is an unsaturated compound and can take up more of the base. This base may be sodium oxide or one or more of the heavier oxides. The result of the addition is a fusible complex borate. This is shown in the following reaction:

$$(9) \qquad\qquad Na_2O \cdot 2B_2O_3 + 2CaO = Na_2O \cdot 2CaO \cdot 2B_2O_3$$

The compound produced is a sodium-calcium borate and shows the fluxing of 0.5 part of lime by one part of borax. The solvent power of borax glass for various substances has been referred to above. In practice it does not matter whether there is chemical combination or solution. What is desired is perfect liquidity at furnace temperatures.

The amount of borax glass ordinarily used in a half-assay-ton charge varies from 10 to 15 g. If the ore is very basic and refractory, more borax should be used. It should be kept in mind that excess of borax tends to give low silver results.

Some assayers use silica in the assay of very basic ores. It is a good flux for iron and manganese oxides, producing fusible silicates. It is also very cheap. It cannot be used in excess, because of its very high melting point.

*Assay of Slags.*—The slags produced in crucible fusions in fire assaying are often very complex mixtures of silicates, borates, oxides, and other compounds. In the molten state there can be chemical combination, solution and suspension, all at the same time. Ordinarily it is quite useless to attempt the formation of a definite silicate or borate. If a sufficient amount of the proper fluxes is used, and a high temperature at the finish, there is usually no trouble in getting a good fusion. As a general rule, the greater the complexity of the slag the lower its melting point.

For certain types of material of an intermediate metallurgical nature, such as slimes, precipitates, etc. commercial practice often calls for a corrected assay. This means that the slag from a set of fusions and scorifications must be saved and assayed separately with a new charge or as combined with the pulverized bone ash from the cupel. Beads from these slag and cupel correction assays at times run considerably lower in fineness than does a normal assay bead.

*Procedure.* **Weighing and Mixing the Charge.**—It is usually most convenient to mix the charge within the crucible. The fluxes should be put in first, the most bulky one at the bottom. They should be measured rather than weighed, in order to save time. Only the flour and nitre need to be measured accurately. The ore is carefully weighed on a pulp balance and placed on top of the fluxes. The mixing is best done by means of a steel spatula, and should be very thorough. Good mixing is shown by the uniform appearance of the charge. The fluxes should be free from lumps. The practice of using a salt or borax cover on the charge is not so common as it was, and ordinarily it is not necessary. When a salt cover is used in assaying rich ores, there is some danger of the production of volatile silver and gold chlorides. Borax glass as a cover is expensive.

**Fusing the Charge.**—The fusion of the charge is best conducted in a muffle furnace, although it can be made in a coke furnace, or even in a blacksmith's forge. The crucibles should be placed in the muffle when the latter is at a bright red heat. The temperature is then gradually raised until at the end of 45 minutes it reaches a light yellow heat, say 1050°C. Sulfide ores should be run rather more quickly than oxide ores, so as to oxidize the sulfides before they have a chance to melt down into a matte. If the heat is raised too rapidly, there is danger of boiling over, due to the large volume of gases liberated.

The crucible fusion may be divided roughly into three stages. There is first the preliminary heating stage, accompanied by some reduction of lead from lith-arge, the partial fusion and decomposition of nitre if present, the partial reduc-tion of higher oxides, and some fluxing of silica by sodium carbonate and litharge. During the second stage most of the chemical reactions take place and the entire charge seems to be in a state of violent agitation. Lead is reduced from the litharge by flour, sulfur, or other reducing agent, and the multitude of small shots pick up the adjacent particles of gold and silver. Gold tellurides and silver sul-fides are decomposed by litharge, setting the metals free. Sodium carbonate and borax react upon the acid and basic constituents, respectively, of the charge, and produce slags. Alumina and other oxides either combine with these reagents or dissolve in the slag mixture. There is a copious evolution of gases, such as carbon dioxide, carbon monoxide, sulfur dioxide, and nitrogen. The third stage is known as the period of quiet fusion. It is for the purpose of completing the slag-forming reactions and of rendering the slag as liquid as possible. This enables all of the small particles of lead to fall down through the slag, collecting the re-maining traces of gold and silver. The latter are washed out of the slag much as a shower of rain sweeps the dust particles out of the air. The slag must be thoroughly liquid in order to insure a perfect separation from the lead.

A high temperature at the beginning of the fusion should be avoided, as it not only increases the chances of boiling over, but may cause some volatilization of compounds of the precious metals. After these metals are reduced and alloyed with lead, the temperature can be raised with less danger of loss. A row of empty crucibles or a prism of coke should be placed in front of the crucibles containing the fusions, and the muffle door should be kept closed.

The time required ranges from 40 to 55 minutes, according to conditions. A long-continued fusion at a low temperature usually means a small lead button and an imperfect collection of the gold and silver.

The period of quiet fusion should last about 10 to 15 minutes. The crucibles are then taken out of the muffle, tapped gently with a whirling motion, to collect stray shots of lead, and the contents poured into conical iron moulds. The greater part of the slag should be poured off first, so as to avoid splashing of the lead against the sides of the mould. When cold the lead buttons are taken out and hammered into rough cubes, so as to remove the adhering slag. If substantially free of copper the lead buttons are now ready for cupellation. It is not always advisable to pour the contents of a crucible charge. If iridium, for example, is present or any of the other platinum group it is better practice as a rule to cool the charge in the crucible after tapping while still hot but slightly, however, to help assist settling. The crucible is then broken. Examine the slag for shot.

**Crucible Charges.**—It is impossible to give a crucible charge that would be satisfactory in every case. Modifications in the amount and kind of reagents must be made to suit the character of the material to be assayed. However, the varia-tions are not so great as is generally supposed, and many assayers use stock fluxes for a great variety of ores and metallurgical products. Changes are made only when the conditions seem to require them.

The following table gives the approximate amount of the different reagents used in an ordinary crucible fusion:

| Ore | $\frac{1}{2}$ assay-ton |
|---|---|
| Sodium carbonate | 25 to 35 grams |
| Borax glass | 10 to 15 grams |
| Flour or Nitre | As required.  (See "Fusing the Charge") |
| Litharge | 60 to 75 grams. |

## THE SCORIFICATION ASSAY

The scorification assay is used principally in those cases in which an undue amount of interfering base metals would be reduced along with the lead if crucible fusions were made.  Thus, if a crucible fusion be made upon an ore containing copper or antimony, either of these two metals will be reduced along with the lead and produce a button which is difficult to cupel.  Even with sulfide ores there is a considerable reduction of the copper or antimony, as is shown in the following reactions:

(10)        $Cu_2S + 3PbO + Na_2CO_3 \rightarrow 2Cu + 3Pb + Na_2SO_4 + CO_2$

(11)        $Sb_2S_3 + 9PbO + 3Na_2CO_3 \rightarrow 2Sb + 9Pb + 3Na_2SO_4 + 3CO_2$

Nickel and cobalt are reduced in the same way.

In many instances scorification is a natural sequence operation after the crucible fusion, in order to remove Cu, Sb, etc.  Very high weights of lead—as much as 90–100 g.—are necessary per gram of high-nickel optical or jewelry alloys.  The combination of high lead and the maximum heat of the muffle is required to obtain a sufficiently fluid nickel-lead melt and slag, and thus minimize slag losses.

In the scorification assay the operations are carried out under oxidizing conditions so as to prevent the reduction of the interfering metals.  Metallic lead is used as the collector and is added as such.  The flux is mainly litharge, coming from the oxidation of the lead, with a small amount of borax.

The operation is conducted in shallow fire-clay dishes known as scorifiers, 3 inches in diameter.  A $2\frac{1}{2}''$ dish is used on the combination wet and fire assay.  The amount of ore taken is usually 1/10 assay-ton, sometimes 1/5 or 1/20 assay-ton.  About 25 g. of granulated lead are spread over the bottom of the scorifier and the ore then added and thoroughly mixed with the lead.  The mixture is then covered with about 25 g. more of granulated lead and one gram of a 1:1 mixture of silica and borax glass.  Usually from 5 to 20 portions of the ore are weighed up so as to lessen the chances of error.  The scorifiers are placed in a muffle heated to redness and the door closed.  As soon as the lead melts the door is opened, in order to admit air and increase the rapidity of the oxidation.  The ore is seen to be floating on the lead.  The latter begins to oxidize and the litharge produced in turn oxidizes the sulfides in the ore, assisted by the oxygen of the air.  The temperature at this point must be low in order to prevent volatilization of gold and silver.  The ore is not protected by a large bulk of fluxes as it is in the crucible assay.  As the oxidation proceeds a ring of slag, mainly litharge, begins to form around the bath of lead.  The ore gradually disappears, the gold and silver going into the molten lead and the gangue combining with or dissolving in the litharge.  Owing to the strong oxidizing conditions, most of the copper and practically all of the antimony present go into the slag.  As the ring of slag increases, the temperature is raised. Finally, the lead becomes completely covered, and the muffle door is closed in order that the slag may become thoroughly liquid. The contents of the scorifiers are then poured into conical moulds, as in the case of the crucible fusions. The lead buttons should weigh from 15 to 20 g. Very small buttons usually mean low results. With high copper material it is sometimes necessary to scorify two or three times and to use a large amount of lead. The buttons are cleaned and cupelled in the usual way.

The scorification assay is not adapted to ores containing volatile constituents, such as tellurides, arsenides, and metallic zinc. Carbonates and highly oxidized ores are also unsuited to this method. If the ore contains much basic gangue it should not be scorified, as there is not enough acid flux to take care of it. Low-grade gold ores are not usually assayed by scorification because of the small amount of ore taken. In practice the method is limited to the higher silver-bearing ores and metallurgical products containing considerable quantities of antimony, copper, nickel and cobalt. It is a standard method for the assay of copper matte. Scorification is also sometimes used to reduce the size of and to purify lead buttons produced in the crucible method.

Sometimes silver determinations in ores, especially those running 150 ounces or above, may best be handled by scorification rather than crucible fusion. One half assay ton is divided between three scorifiers and combined on the second heat to one. The test lead used must be checked for freedom from Ag, Bi, Sb, and Tl. Thallium in particular would go into the bead with the silver and give erroneous high results.

Some slimes and precipitates and silver sulfides are best assayed by initial scorification attack.

## CUPELLATION

Cupellation is the process by which the gold and silver are separated from the lead and other base metals with which they are alloyed. Design and make of cupel having been discussed under cupels, it remains to consider time, temperature and oxygen supply.

The lead buttons having been charged, the door should be closed to reduce the oxygen while melting and then immediately reopened. Even when opened it is not desirable to have such a strong draft that the "feathers" or litharge crystals formed are carried away. "Feathers" are the assayers' temperature control. Time varies from 20 to 25 minutes and losses for a finishing temperature of 875 ± 5°C. will vary about ±0.10 mg. for a 100 mg. silver bead.

In the cupellation process the lead is oxidized to litharge which is taken into the pores of the cupel by capillary attraction. This takes place because litharge is molten at the temperature of the operation. Most of the other base metal oxides are infusible at this temperature. When in moderate amounts, however, they dissolve in the liquid litharge and are carried into the cupel. If the lead contains much copper and antimony, the oxides of these latter metals accumulate on the cupel and may ruin the assay. Hence the need for scorification in these cases.

The cupels should be heated in the muffle for at least 20 minutes before putting in the lead buttons. Cupellations are best started at a bright red heat, say about 900°C. As soon as the buttons are put into the cupels, the muffle door should be closed. If the temperature is too low, an infusible oxide will form on the lead as soon as the latter is melted and refuse to go into the cupel. The disappearance of this film of oxide on further heating is referred to as the *"opening"* or *"un-*

*covering"* of the lead. Sometimes it is necessary to hasten the opening by means of a burning stick of wood placed immediately over the cupel. This reduces the oxide and at the same time raises the temperature. When all of the cupellations are uncovered, the muffle door is opened and the temperature lowered rapidly to the lowest possible point at which the operation can proceed. This must be done because a temperature higher than necessary increases the loss of gold and silver. This loss occurs by absorption into the cupel and by volatilization. If the temperature falls too low, the buttons "freeze"; that is, the litharge, which melts at 883°C., solidifies on top of the liquid lead, which melts at 327°C., and the operation stops. The melting point varies with the ratio Pb:Au:Ag.

At first thought it would seem that a temperature slightly above 883°C. would be the proper one for cupellation. As a matter of fact the temperature of the muffle need not be above 750°C. This is due to the fact that the oxidation of the lead generates a considerable amount of heat, and the buttons are thus hotter than either the muffle or the cupels. A good indication of the right cupellation temperature is the formation of solid flakes of litharge, known as "feathers," upon the inner edge of the cupels. The volatilized litharge strikes the comparatively cool bone ash and sublimes as flake crystals. If the beads contain platinum metals, it is not ordinarily desirable to cupel to feathers, but rather to raise the temperature slightly above that normally necessary through the 21 to 23 minutes operation. Otherwise unusually large amounts of lead are retained. When change is made from the clay muffle to the silicon carbide muffle, the operator must learn to associate temperatures with a different series of colors.

The presence of impurities usually increases the loss of gold and silver, and adds to the difficulties of the operation. Copper or nickel in quantity may cause the buttons to freeze even at moderately high temperatures. Antimony causes the formation of a hard, infusible crust of lead antimonate which retains silver and which often splits the top of the cupel.

The surface of the lead in the cupel is convex, owing to the high surface tension of the metal. During cupellation the drops of molten litharge can be seen rolling off of the lead and disappearing into the cupel. The surface tension of the melted litharge is less than the attractive force of the bone ash. In scorification, where the vessel is not porous, the litharge forms a concave surface and climbs up the sides of the scorifier. This explains in part the high gold losses in the cupellation of lead containing gold and tellurium. Some of the gold telluride passes into the cupel just as in the case of litharge. Gold telluride is also more volatile than metallic gold.

As the operation proceeds, the lead and other base metals gradually oxidize and disappear. Copper and bismuth are less readily oxidized than lead, and hence tend to remain until most of the lead has gone. The presence of bismuth can be seen by the so-called bismuth ring, and even when this is not noticeable, the bead may still retain bismuth sufficient to reduce the fineness to a point requiring correction when large tonnages are involved. The temperature should be raised slightly at this point in order to prevent the buttons from solidifying before the base metals are completely oxidized. Small amounts of these metals usually remain, even in a well-conducted cupellation. The melting point of gold and silver being considerably higher than the temperature of the muffle, the buttons solidify soon after the base metals are gone. At the moment of solidification the buttons flash or "blick," owing to the release of the latent heat of fusion. If the buttons are large and consist mainly of silver, they may *"sprout"* or *"spit"* on being withdrawn quickly. This is due to dissolved oxygen which escapes when the button solidifies. The sprouting may be prevented by covering the silver button with a hot inverted cupel as soon as the cupellation is finished, and allowing the covered cupel to remain in the muffle for several minutes. This insures a slow cooling of the silver bead. After cooling the buttons are removed from the cupel by means of forceps and the adhering bone ash brushed off. The buttons are then weighed on an assay balance to the nearest one-tenth of a milligram. If a half-assay-ton of ore was used, the results multiplied by two equal the ounces per ton of combined gold and silver.

In cleaning buttons which are sometimes large enough to require squaring with a hammer on an anvil before cleansing with a stiff brush, rather than by compressing with pliers, the bottom of the button should be examined for roots, which are evidence of faulty cupel material or manufacture. Such buttons should be discarded.

## PARTING

Parting is the separation of gold from silver in an alloy containing these metals, and is effected in fire assaying by means of nitric acid. This acid converts the silver into soluble silver nitrate, but is almost without action upon the gold. In order to part readily the alloy must contain at least twice as much silver as gold. Even at this ratio it is difficult to dissolve all of the silver. In practice, it is better to have a much larger proportion of silver, except in the assay of gold and silver bullion. If the buttons produced in the assay of an ore are known to contain enough gold to render parting difficult or impossible, they are subjected to the process known as *inquartation*. The buttons after weighing are wrapped with about 10 times their weight of pure silver foil in 3 to 5 g. of sheet lead and then cupelled. The resulting buttons are flattened and parted in the usual manner. It is preferable to add the necessary silver before cupelling as inquarted golds tend to be low.

An important point in parting is the strength of the acid. If a concentrated acid is used at first, the gold in the button is liable to break up into a fine powder which is difficult to manage without loss. By using a rather weak acid, containing 1 vol. concentrated $HNO_3$ + 5 vol. $H_2O$, the gold has a tendency to coalesce into a coherent mass which can be washed and weighed as one piece. If the bead (e.g. from some slimes) contains selenium, the use of a 1:9 first acid assists in minimizing flouring of the gold. The treatment with weak acid is always followed by one with a stronger acid, in order to remove the last traces of silver. The second acid should be about 1.26 sp. gr., made by diluting the concentrated acid with its own volume of water. In the case of buttons containing a small proportion of gold, the first acid should be very weak, not more than 10% $HNO_3$ by volume. With more gold a stronger acid can be used, although the weak acid is usually effective, except when the buttons are very large.

The parting may be done in porcelain capsules preferably or in small glass flasks, known as parting flasks. Only a few milliliters of acid are necessary. This should be heated to boiling and the flattened beads then dropped into it. Solution of the silver begins immediately. At the end of about 20 minutes, or when all visible action has ceased, the weak acid solution is decanted into a white casserole, carefully avoiding the loss of any gold. About 3 ml. of the stronger acid is now added to each flask or capsule and then heated almost to the boiling point. The heating is continued for at least 10 minutes, when most of the silver should be in solution. The acid is then poured off and the gold washed three times by decantation with chlorine-free water. If capsules are used, the water is drained out as completely as possible and the capsules then placed on a hot plate or in front of the muffle for drying. If parting flasks are used, a fire-clay annealing cup is inverted over the top of each completely filled flask and the flask then quickly reversed, allowing the gold to fall quietly into the annealing cup. After removing the flask by a quick side motion, the water is poured off of the gold and the cup placed on the hot plate. The final process is known as annealing. The capsules or annealing cups are placed in the muffle and heated to low redness for about 5 minutes. The heating causes the brownish-black spongy or fibrous gold to coalesce into a dense flake or bead having the characteristic yellow color of the metal. The annealing also serves to drive off any volatile impurities which may be present, and to render it easier to separate any specks of dust or dirt from the gold. After cooling the gold is weighed on a delicate balance to the nearest 0.01 mg.—with a little care to the nearest 0.005 mg. The weight of the gold is deducted from the weight of the button before parting and the difference represents the silver in the portion taken for assay.

In parting it is preferable to use for all ores and material low grade in character a weak acid, one of $HNO_3$ to six $H_2O$, for the first parting and a one to one acid for the second with no intermediate washing in between. It is advisable to add the hot "first" acid to the bead. This reduces flouring of the gold. It is also advisable to part in small casseroles as this gives a white background throughout the entire operation and the gold remains throughout until transferred to the pan. Washing should be by hot chlorine-free distilled water.

In Doré, precipitates, slimes, and rich gold-silver beads weighing up to as high as 990 mg. to the gram sample the first parting should be in a stronger acid, one of acid to four of water. This should be followed by an intermediate washing with hot water by filling the casserole and decanting. The second acid treatment consists of a 20 minute simmer at incipient boiling with a still stronger acid, two of acid to one of $H_2O$. This is followed by at least two complete washings with hot water. This particular practice has been followed for many years with many thousands of proofs run as a control.

If the platinum metals are present, there should preferably be five or six times as much gold as platinum and twelve times as much silver as there is gold + platinum if the maximum amount of platinum is to be dissolved out in nitric acid on the first parting.

If the gold contains rhodium or iridium, it is advisable after weighing to dissolve in dilute one aqua regia to ten $H_2O$. The gold may either then be recovered by precipitation and weighed or it will often suffice, if the residue is not too floury, to decant, dry carefully and transfer it to a pan, weigh and deduct from the gold + platinum group metals to obtain a "true gold."

Parting along the lines indicated for the ordinary gold ore type of beads with the one to six followed by one to one acid should give a gold purity, if hot water is used, of 997.5 to 998.0, whereas cold water and weaker acid may give as low as 996.0. The finenesses given are on the assumption that no platinum group metals are present.

## THE ASSAY OF BULLION

Bullion is an alloy of gold and silver with variable amounts of one or more of the base metals, and is the semi-final product of most nonferrous metallurgical plants. In lead smelting this product is usually known as base bullion, in copper smelting as blister copper, and in amalgamation and cyanide processes as retort bullion or Doré silver. The base metals may include antimony, arsenic, bismuth, cobalt, copper, lead, mercury, nickel, and zinc. Small amounts of selenium and tellurium are usually present, as well as traces of the platinum group of metals. In all cases the assay of bullion resolves itself into a problem of the separation of metals from each other, there being practically no non-metallic elements present.

*Bullion Sampling.*—The sampling of bullion involves some difficulties not encountered in the sampling of ores. Most alloys on solidifying segregate to some extent, so that the cooled metal is never uniform in composition. Whenever possible the samples should be taken from the thoroughly stirred molten alloy and then chilled quickly, either by pouring into water or by pouring into small moulds with thick metal sides and bottoms. When there is danger of oxidation, this method of course is not entirely satisfactory. In impure bullion there is often a very uneven distribution of the gold and silver, and it is necessary to drill or saw entirely through the bar in order to obtain accurate results. In copper anode plates and other forms of blister copper the plates or bars are drilled in series, so that the combined sample represents a proper percentage of drillings from all parts of each piece. Lead bullion is sometimes sampled in a similar manner, although in this case the bars are usually punched instead of being drilled. The modern tendency is to take melted samples of all metallic products, even in the case of blister copper.

## THE ASSAY OF GOLD AND SILVER BULLION

In the fire assay of gold and silver bullion a correction must always be made for the metal losses, because of the great value of the bullion and because the refining losses on a commercial scale are considerably less than the losses in assaying. The assays are, therefore, always run with a check or "proof center." The check is an artificial sample made up so as to have as nearly as possible the exact composition of the bullion to be assayed. Two checks and three portions of the bullion, all five of the same weight, are cupelled and parted under exactly the same conditions. The weights of gold and silver found in the bullion samples are then corrected by adding or subtracting the loss or gain experienced by the gold and silver in the checks. In the assay of gold bullion there is sometimes a gain in the weight of the gold, due to the imperfect elimination of the copper and silver. This, however, should be the same in both checks and bullion samples. Results are reported in "fineness" or parts per 1000.

*Silver Bullion or Doré Bullion Assay.*—Standard practice in umpiring doré bullion calls for running quadruplicates, the number of checks depending upon the number of lots of similar material being run. If only isolated samples are being assayed, then two proofs should be run. If a long series is being carried through, it will often suffice to have each position in each row of the furnace represented consecutively by a proof. Under this system a seven cupel row would call for proof units of seven. The standard umpire practice normally calls for one-gram portions, which in the case of drilled (and more unhomogeneous) samples is little enough. Shot samples are ordinarily more uniform but even there one gram seems to be standard practice. The sample is wrapped in 10 grams of gold-silver-free sheet lead, placed in the hot cupel and melted. As soon as they have opened up 10 grams more, folded in a little "T" shaped strip, is carefully inserted to wash down the sides. Ordinarily 1½ to 1¾" cupels are used rather than the 1⅛" or 1¼" more common in ore work. In bullion carrying about 5 parts per thousand of gold, with silver from 800 to 900, the silver retention in the gold bead offsets the cupel gold absorption as has been verified by innumerable checks for many years.

Up to about 20 parts per thousand the proof will show a loss, thus necessitating a plus correction. In beads carrying 50 parts per thousand of gold or over there is usually a surcharge, which of course results in a deduction or minus correction. Much depends on the gold:silver:copper ratio.

When proofs are made up it should be on the basis of a preliminary cupel on a 200-mg. portion of the sample. Doré cupellations should not be conducted to as low a temperature as evidenced by feathers. This tends to given uneven retention of lead and erratic results. The higher temperature, which results in a greater silver loss due to greater volatilization of the silver, causes no harm as it is compensated for by the similar loss in the proof.

The beads are cleaned, weighed, flattened, and parted. The first parting acid used should contain about 20% $HNO_3$ by volume, the second 50–66%. The amount of gold and silver loss in the checks is determined and the proper correction applied to the weights of gold and silver found in the bullion samples.

If the bullion contains antimony, the process must include scorification, which is applied to checks and samples as well. When bismuth, selenium, or tellurium is present in quantity, the silver must be separated by means of solution in nitric acid and subsequent precipitation as chloride.

**Gold Bullion Assay.**—The assay of gold bullion is in principle the same as that of silver bullion. As the gold is usually in excess of the silver, however, the process involves inquartation, with the use of a stronger first acid than when parting ordinary silver buttons.

**U. S. Mint Method.**—Sample portions of 500 mg. are taken for assay. A preliminary cupellation is made as in the case of doré bullion. The amount of silver to be added for the final assay is determined by the touchstone method. The cupelled gold and silver button is rubbed on a piece of black jasper and the streak made compared with those made by alloys of known composition. This gives the fineness within 2%, which is close enough. A ratio of silver to gold of 2½ to 1 is used in making up the checks. If no copper is present, about 3 or 4% is added as it facilitates the removal of the last traces of lead in cupellation. The cupelled buttons are flattened by hammering, annealed at a red heat, and then passed through a pair of jeweller's rolls, until they are converted into fillets about 2½ inches long and ½ inch wide. The fillets are again annealed and rolled up into "cornets" or spirals. Sufficient space should be left between the turns to permit of easy contact with the acid. The parting is done by boiling for 10 minutes in nitric acid of 1.28 sp. gr., and then transferring to another vessel containing acid of the same strength and boiling for 10 minutes longer. The cornets are then washed three times with distilled water, dried, annealed and weighed.

The proofs usually show a slight gain in the weight of the gold, so that the correction is made by subtracting the gain from the average weight of the gold found in the sample portions.

The gold after parting should be in one piece and have smooth edges, as otherwise there is danger of loss.

## THE ASSAY OF LEAD BULLION

The sampling of lead wherever possible should be by the "gum-drop method." These drops representing each stage of the casting process, and sampling process too, should be weighed as they come and not cut to a definite weight. The assay of lead bullion ordinarily involves only cupellation and parting. The bullion is often impure, however, and it may then be advisable to scorify the weighed portions before cupelling. If the sample contains much copper or antimony, it should always be scorified. The precious metal loss in scorification is less than it is in cupellation, especially in the case of an impure bullion requiring a high temperature in order to cupel it.

Lead bullion is usually run in four portions of one half assay-ton each or, at times, of approximately 1 assay ton each. The four silver buttons are weighed separately and if there is a satisfactory agreement in the weights, the average is taken and the result multiplied by two. The buttons are parted in pairs, thus saving time in washing and weighing. Great care should be exercised in the cupellation of lead bullion and in the subsequent parting, as the bullion is a high-grade product, and ordinarily no correction is made for losses in the cupel or otherwise.

If for silver, high bismuth-bearing lead bullion is best dissolved immediately in dilute nitric acid with some hydrofluoric acid present and the silver precipitated as the bromide. Scorification then follows as usual in a combination method.

## THE ASSAY OF COPPER BULLION

**Scorification Method.**[11]—This method of assay of copper bullion follows closely the scorification method already given (see page 484). The difference is that there is another step to recover most of the silver which has been lost in the scorification slag and original cupel.

The scorification slag is the waste product after treating the silver chloride precipitate with metallic test lead in a scorifier and heating to obtain a lead silver button.

The original cupel, in which the scorified lead button was oxidized and absorbed, is broken in a die and ring, with the aid of a hammer, then ground on a bucking board.

Scorification slag and pulverized cupel are placed in a 30-gram crucible, fluxed with 40 g. of calcined sodium carbonate, 15 g. of borax glass, 4 g. of flour and fused. The resulting lead button is cupeled, the silver bead weighed, and the recorded weight added to the weight of the original silver bead. The correction bead amounts to about 3 or 4 per cent of the weight of the original silver bead.

The sample is in pellet form, averaging, after screening off the undersize and oversize, from one thirty-second to one eighth inch in diameter. This is the end product of the smelter, obtained by splashing a portion of the casting stream into water. The cupels are made on a compressed air machine which puts 800 pounds pressure per square inch on the cupel material when the primary line pressure is held at 45 pounds.

Other differences are the use of XX bone ash (Denber Fire Clay Co.), and the use of calcined calcium carbonate instead of uncalcined, and granulated silica instead of pulverized.

**Combination Method.**—In the combination methods, the copper is first removed by solution in acid. Formerly nitric acid was used for this purpose, but it was found that the results were low in gold. There was a tendency for some of the gold to go into solution. The nitric acid method is a convenient way of determining the silver, as the copper dissolves very rapidly in nitric acid, and the precipi-

11 Contribution from Anaconda Copper Company.

tation of silver as chloride is very complete. With the increase of secondary metals certain types of silver-gold bearing blister or anodes may contain appreciable quantities of tin. If appreciable tin is present, it may be necessary to add hydrofluoric acid to a nitric acid determination of the silver and a bromide rather than a chloride precipitation may be advisable.

For the assay of both gold and silver the sulfuric acid-mercuric nitrate method is recommended. One assay-ton of the finely ground, well-mixed copper borings is treated in a large beaker with 10 ml. of water and 10 ml. of a solution of mercuric nitrate containing 25 grams of mercury per liter. The beaker is well shaken so as to amalgamate the copper, and 80 or 100 ml. of concentrated sulfuric acid then added. The beaker is covered, placed on a hot plate and heated until all of the copper is dissolved. This will require from one to two hours, according to the temperature and fineness of the sample. The beaker is now removed and the solution is allowed to cool. One hundred ml. of cold water are added, the mixture stirred, and then 400 ml. of boiling water added, with further stirring until all copper sulfate has dissolved. A solution of common salt is now added, just sufficient to precipitate all of the silver and mercury. Only a slight excess must be used, as silver chloride is soluble in strong sodium chloride solution. The beaker is replaced on the hot plate and the contents boiled so as to coagulate the silver chloride. The beaker is then removed, the solution diluted to 600 ml. with cold water and allowed to settle. The solution is then filtered through double filter papers, and the beaker and filter washed with hot water. The beaker should be wiped out with a filter paper and this added to the material in the filter. The filter and its contents are now transferred to a 2½-inch glazed scorifier and the filter paper burned off at a low temperature, so as to avoid loss of silver. After the paper is burned off, 30 grams of test lead are added and the material scorified until 12 to 15 grams of lead remain. The scorifier is poured and the lead button cupelled at as low a temperature as possible. The gold and silver are parted in the usual way. The results are very precise.

The object of the mercuric nitrate is to hasten the solution of the copper by forming a galvanic couple. It prevents also the formation of copper sulfide which is insoluble in dilute sulfuric acid.

Assays should be made in duplicate or triplicate.

NOTES.—If the sulfuric acid-mercuric nitrate (sulfate) method is used, as is recommended and as is common practice, not only should the copper borings be finely ground but they should only be ground in a mill which will give sharp facets to the grindings. A dull mill rounds, compacts the copper, and results in an undue amount of undissolved bullion causing innumerable inter-laboratory and accounting differences. Some laboratories do not add any water to the copper borings in the 800 ml. beaker and they employ only 80 or 90 ml. of concentrated sulfuric rather than 100 ml. Care should be taken that sufficient heat be given on the particular hot plate used. If the burners are poor, it may be necessary to finish for a few moments over a free flame. The salt cake should be a dull grey and the supernatant sulfuric acid practically colorless unless the material is very foul, in which event it may be of the same general greenish tint found when the heating has not been complete. If the temperature is sufficiently high and the drillings are properly ground, 40 minutes to an hour heating may suffice for a one assay ton portion. If silver is low, it is often advisable to add 10 or 15 milligrams to each charge at the start.

Many laboratories do not use glazed scorifiers, but rather fit a small sheet of about 10 to 15 grams of lead foil which serves to protect the bottom of the crucible from wetting by the filter paper and subsequent spitting. Fourteen to 18 gram lead buttons are preferred by many to the 12 to 15 range. *Avoid drafts* during charring of the filter and contents.

## THE ASSAY OF CYANIDE SOLUTIONS

A number of methods have been devised for the determination of gold and silver in cyanide solutions. Two of these methods will be described here.

### EVAPORATION IN LEAD TRAY

This method is adapted to cyanide solutions containing only small amounts of base metals or other impurities. A small tray or boat is made of lead foil, capable of holding the amount of solution to be assayed. A wooden block or form is used to make the trays if many assays are required. The solution has about the same specific gravity as water, so that 29.2 ml. are assumed to be equal to an assay-ton. An amount of solution varying with its richness is put into the lead tray and slowly evaporated to dryness on the hot plate. The lead tray is then folded up and cupelled in the usual manner.

### THE CHIDDEY METHOD

This method, first described by Alfred Chiddey, is adapted to almost every grade and character of cyanide solutions.

From 1 to 20 assay-tons of solution are heated in a beaker or evaporating dish. To the solution is added from 10 to 20 ml. of a 10% solution of lead acetate containing 40 ml. of acetic acid per liter. From ½ to 2 grams of zinc dust or zinc shavings is then added. The gold, silver, and lead immediately begin to precipitate on the zinc. The solution is heated for about 20 to 25 minutes, but not to boiling. The lead should coalesce into a spongy mass. Boiling the solution is liable to break up the sponge. The excess zinc is now dissolved by adding slowly 20 ml. of hydrochloric acid of 1.12 sp. gr. The heating is continued until effervescence ceases. It may be necessary to stir slightly in order to make sure that all zinc is dissolved. The solution is now decanted off and the lead sponge washed two or three times with water. The excess water is squeezed out of the sponge with the fingers, the sponge further dried by pressing between filter paper and then rolled into a ball with lead foil and the necessary silver for parting. A hole should be left in the lead foil for the escape of steam. The ball is then dried and cupelled.

As the lead sponge begins to break up and go into solution as soon as all of the zinc is dissolved, no time should be lost in decanting the solution after the zinc has disappeared.

## DETERMINATION OF PLATINUM, PALLADIUM, GOLD, AND SILVER [12]

*Procedure.*[13]—Scorify the lead buttons from two or more 0.5 assay-ton crucible fusions together, adding at least six times as much silver as the combined weight of the Pt, Pd, and Au present, and cupel *hot*. In rich materials such as slimes or concentrates, two 0.5 assay-ton fusions suffice, but low-grade ores may require 10 or more 0.5 assay-ton fusions combined for each determination.

Part the silver beads with $HNO_3$ (1:6), followed by stronger parting acid (1:1) and wash with water as usual. All Pd goes into solution, together with considerable Pt. The residue consists of Au plus some Pt. Dissolve residue in strong *aqua regia* and reserve the solution (solution *A*). Precipitate the silver in the

12 Smoot, A. M., Eng. Mining J., 99, 701, 1915.
13 See also the chapter on the Platinum Metals.

nitric-acid solution—containing Ag, Pd, and some Pt—with HCl. Practically all the Pt will remain in solution; but the precipitated AgCl is pink in color and contains considerable Pd. Filter off the AgCl, scorify and cupel it and part again with $HNO_3$ (1:6); all should dissolve. Reprecipitate the Ag with HCl. The liquid now contains most of the remaining Pd, but some is co-precipitated with AgCl. Filter off the AgCl and add the filtrate to the first filtrate from AgCl. Again scorify and cupel the silver chloride, dissolving the silver in nitric acid as before and reprecipitating the silver as chloride. In most cases the filtrate from this silver chloride contains all the remaining Pd. If, however, the AgCl is distinctly pink, another separation must be made.

Unite all filtrates from AgCl precipitations and evaporate to small bulk, adding the *aqua regia* solution of the Au and Pt (solution $A$). The liquid now contains all the Au, Pt and Pd present in the original ore, together with traces of Ag due to solubility of AgCl in excess of HCl, and also traces of Pb gathered from the lead retained in the silver buttons from several recupellations.

Evaporate the liquid to dryness on the steam bath; take up with dilute HCl (1:3) and evaporate again to dryness; take up with five drops of HCl and 40 ml. $H_2O$. Pay no attention to any insoluble residue of AgCl or $PbCl_2$.[14] Precipitate the gold by adding, say, 3 g. of oxalic acid to the solution and boiling it. Let stand overnight and filter off the Au. If Pt and Pd are high, it is necessary to redissolve the Au in *aqua regia,* evaporating with HCl to dryness and repeating the oxalic-acid precipitation, uniting the filtrate with that from the first gold precipitation. Burn the filter containing the gold and scorify it with six times its weight of silver and a little test lead; cupel, part and weigh the gold as usual.

To the oxalic-acid filtrates from Au add 5 ml. of HCl and make volume up to 150 ml.; heat to boiling and precipitate Pt and Pd with a rapid current of $H_2S$ in *hot* solution, passing the current of gas for some time and keeping the solution hot during precipitation. Filter and wash the Pt and Pd sulfides with $H_2S$ water containing a little HCl. Wash the precipitate from the filter with a fine water jet into the original beaker; spread the filter paper (which will contain a small amount of precipitate impossible to wash off) with the precipitate side down over the lower side of a watch-glass cover. Add *aqua regia* to the precipitate in the beaker and place the cover on the beaker; warm gently to dissolve the Pt and Pd sulfides. The fumes arising from the acid dissolve the traces of Pt and Pd adhering to the filter paper. When solution is complete and filter paper is white, remove the watch-glass cover, and wash the paper with hot dilute HCl thrown against it in a fine stream.

Evaporate the *aqua regia* solution to dryness, take up the residue with HCl and evaporate again to dryness to remove all $HNO_3$. Take up the residue with two or three drops of HCl and about 2 ml. of $H_2O$. The solution is usually perfectly clear but it may be slightly cloudy owing to the presence of a little AgCl in it. No attention need be paid to this, however. Add 5 to 10 ml. of a saturated solution of $NH_4Cl$, stir well, and allow to stand overnight. Platinum is precipitated

---

14 In materials rich in palladium the small amount of $AgCl + PbCl_2$ may be distinctly pink in color and retain weighable quantities of Pd. If this is the case, the Pd may be recovered in the solution from the nitric acid parting of the gold. To do this, precipitate the silver in this liquid by adding HCl, filter off the silver chloride and evaporate the filtrate to dryness. Take up with a drop of HCl and a little water, let stand overnight and filter through a very small filter. This liquid may be added to solution $B$ before precipitating palladium with glyoxime.

as ammonium platinum chloride—$(NH_4)_2PtCl_6$. Filter and wash the precipitate with 20% $NH_4Cl$ solution. All Pd passes into the filtrate which is reserved (solution *B*). Dissolve the Pt precipitate in boiling hot 5% $H_2SO_4$; heat the liquid to actual boiling and precipitate with $H_2S$ as before, filtering and washing with $H_2S$ water. Burn the filter and precipitate at a low temperature in a scorifier; add six times as much Ag as Pt, scorifying with lead, cupel and part the silver bead containing the platinum with $H_2SO_4$; decant off the silver solution and wash once with concentrated $H_2SO_4$, followed by 50% $H_2SO_4$ until practically all the silver is washed away; finally wash with water, anneal and weigh. A minute quantity of Ag is retained with the platinum, but it can usually be neglected. In very important work where the amount of platinum is large dissolve in *aqua regia*, evaporate the solution to dryness, take up with a drop of HCl, dilute largely with water and let the AgCl settle overnight; filter on a small paper, cupel it with a little sheet lead and deduct the weight from the weight of platinum. This refinement need not be considered in materials running less than 15 or 20 oz. to the ton.

It may seem an unnecessary step to precipitate the platinum as sulfide, scorify it with silver and part it as described in the foregoing. General practice has been to ignite the ammonium platinum chloride precipitate and weigh the metallic residue. When this is done, however, there is danger of losing considerable platinum, which is carried away mechanically during the decomposition of the compound; furthermore, it is extremely difficult (if not impossible) to collect the finely divided residue for weighing, and the precipitate invariably contains lead and silver. Precipitation as sulfide, scorification and cupellation with excess silver and parting with sulfuric acid overcome the difficulties inherent in handling the ammonium precipitate.

The palladium is all contained in the filtrate and washings from the platinum ammonium chloride precipitates (solution *B*). Add to this solution at least seven times as much dimethylglyoxime as there is Pd present (in any case, at least 0.1 g. glyoxime). The precipitant should be dissolved in a mixture of two-thirds concentrated HCl and one-third water. Dilute the liquid to 250–300 ml., heat on a steam bath for half an hour, and let stand overnight. Pd is precipitated as a voluminous yellow, easily filtered glyoxime compound $C_8H_{14}N_4O_4Pd$, containing, when dried at 110°C., 31.689% of Pd. Filter the Pd precipitate on a weighed Gooch crucible and wash it, first, with dilute HCl, half and half, then with warm water and finally with alcohol; dry it at 110 to 115°C. and weigh. The disadvantage of weighing palladium on a Gooch crucible is overcome—at least to some extent—by the fact that the Pd compound contains a relatively small amount of Pd—less than one-third of its weight. This compound may also be weighed on carefully counterpoised papers; but it is better to use Gooch crucibles, if they are available, because of the relatively strong acid which is required for washing. The object in using half-and-half hydrochloric acid as a wash liquid is to dissolve out any excess of the glyoxime precipitant. This is easily soluble in moderately concentrated HCl, but is substantially insoluble in water.

## DETERMINATION OF SILVER IN ORES AND CONCENTRATES CONTAINING PLATINUM AND PALLADIUM

*Procedure.*—Make the usual crucible fusion on a one-quarter, one-half or full assay-ton, according to the amount of silver present. Instead of cupelling the lead button, hammer it free from slag and dissolve it in dilute nitric acid. Most of the silver passes into solution together with palladium, and perhaps a trace of platinum; but gold and most of the platinum remain insoluble. The gold and platinum retain an appreciable proportion of silver which cannot be washed out. Filter out the insoluble residue and wash it thoroughly with hot dilute nitric acid, followed by hot water. Scorify the residue once more with a little lead and dissolve the lead button as before, filtering into the beaker containing the first filtrate. In this liquid precipitate the silver as AgCl by adding standard NaCl in sufficient quantity; stir well, and if the amount of silver is small, add about ½ ml. of concentrated $H_2SO_4$ to form a precipitate of lead sulfate. Let the silver chloride, or the silver chloride plus lead sulfate, settle overnight or until the supernatant liquid is clear; filter through double filter papers; ignite and scorify the residue of silver chloride with test lead.

If the amount of the palladium contained in the sample is small, the silver bead obtained by cupelling the lead button obtained by scorifying the silver chloride may be considered as sufficiently pure for ordinary purposes. It contains, of course, some palladium, and in accurate silver determinations the lead button from the first silver chloride precipitation should be redissolved and the silver reprecipitated, filtered and scorified as before. The amount of palladium retained after the second precipitation and scorification is so small as to be negligible.

*Chapter 22*

# HYDROGEN

**H**, *at. wt.* 1.00797 ($\pm$0.00001); *sp. gr.* 0.08988 g./l. (at 20°C.); *b.p.* −253°C.; *m.p.* −259.14°C.

Hydrogen occurs free in small quantities in gases of volcanoes, and certain petroleum and gas wells. It occurs as a decomposition product in the decay of organic matter. It is found in traces in the atmosphere. It occurs in combined form in all living organisms, and their products. It is an incidental component of ferrous and other alloys, where it occurs in an occluded or loosely combined form.

Although various types of combustible gases were known to the alchemists, hydrogen was not definitely proved to be a distinct element until 1766 when Cavendish established its identity. The element was further studied by Lavoisier, from whom it obtained the name hydrogen, water producer.

The value of hydrogen in fuel and illuminating gas is generally known. In form of atomic hydrogen its efficiency for producing a welding gas is greatly increased. Its lightness led to its use in balloons and dirigibles (1000 cubic feet of hydrogen will lift 700 pounds). It is used for the hydrogenation of fats (more than 350,000,000 pounds of solid fat produced from liquid fats per year); it is used in the conversion of coal into petroleum products by its removal of oxygen and building up of the hydrogen content; it is used in the production of ammonia (Haber-Bosch method). It is valuable in the commercial laboratory as a reducing agent.

*Isotopes of Hydrogen.*—Subsequent to the announcement of the spectral evidence for the existence of heavy hydrogen, or deuterium, D, the isotope of mass 2, in 1932,[1] a vast amount of work has been done on the properties of deuterium and its compounds. A third isotope, tritium,[2] exists in very minute concentrations in water and other sources of hydrogen.

The analytical chemistry of hydrogen, deuterium, hydrogen deuteride and other deuterium compounds is in part based on physico-chemical methods—spectrography; refractometry; mass spectrography; thermal conductance; specific gravity either of the oxide or of the element. Organic compounds are burned to form water and deuterium oxide, and the density of the mixture enables one to estimate the relative numbers of atoms of hydrogen and deuterium in the compound.

## DETECTION

The lightness of the gas, its combustibility with oxygen with formation of water and its union with chlorine to form hydrogen chloride are methods for its detection

[1] Urey, Brickwedde and Murphy, Phys. Rev., **39**, 164, 864, 1932.
[2] Eidenoff, M. L., J. Chem. Phys., **15**, 416, 1947.

in gas, by methods given in Volume II. Its detection and estimation in solid materials by oxidation to water necessitates the removal of free and combined water previous to the tests for hydrogen, or a separation of water from the gas before oxidation of the gas. For the determination of hydrogen in organic substances, see pp. 282 and 285.

## HYDROGEN, NITROGEN, AND OXYGEN IN METALS BY THE VACUUM FUSION METHOD [3]

This method is based on the fusion of the metal in the presence of carbon in a vacuum. Under these conditions, all oxides present are reduced to carbon monoxide, and nitrogen and hydrogen are liberated. The evolved gases are collected and analyzed by low-pressure techniques. The hydrogen is oxidized to water and absorbed in anhydrous magnesium perchlorate. The carbon monoxide is converted to carbon dioxide and frozen out in liquid nitrogen. The residual gas is nitrogen.

*Apparatus.* **Vacuum Fusion Apparatus.**—A suitable apparatus for the vacuum fusion determination of hydrogen, oxygen, and nitrogen is shown diagrammatically in Fig. 22-1. Such equipment is available commercially [4] or may be constructed in accordance with the following description. If it is constructed, the following components are required:

*Vacuum Pump,* used to evacuate the system prior to test, consisting of a suitable mechanical pump [5] in series with an oil-diffusion pump,[6] $DP_3$, Fig. 22-1.

*Manifold Exhaust Pump.*—A suitable mechanical pump [7] to evacuate the manifold to the mercury cutoff bulbs $C_1$, $C_2$, etc.

*Transfer Diffusion Pump, $DP_1$.*—A suitable diffusion pump,[8] mercury-in-glass, two-stage, having a pumping speed of 25 to 30 liters per second.

*Vacuum Furnace, F,* air-cooled and constructed of borosilicate glass, and conforming to the details illustrated in Fig. 22-2.

*Blower, B* (Figs. 22-1 and 22-2), to cool the furnace, capable of delivering 140 cu. ft. of air per minute.

*Graphite Crucibles* (Fig. 22-3) machined from high-grade graphite.[9]

*Graphite Funnels* (Fig. 22-3) from same material as the crucibles. Some users prefer to machine the funnels as an integral part of the crucibles.

*Graphite Powder,* which may be prepared from the same grade of carbon as the crucibles. The powder should pass a No. 200 (74-micron) sieve and should be passed over a magnet to remove any particles of iron or other magnetic material.

*Quartz Tube* (Fig. 22-4) clear, 2 in. OD by 6.5 in. long, having an approximately

---

[3] A.S.T.M. Methods for Chemical Analysis of Metals, 1960.

[4] The apparatus described and referred to in this discussion is a commercially available unit manufactured and sold by the National Research Corp., Cambridge, Mass.

[5] A National Research Corp. No. 2D or Welch No. 1405 mechanical pump, or other suitable mechanical pump of equivalent capacity, has been found satisfactory for this purpose.

[6] A National Research Corp. Model H-2-P oil-diffusion pump has been found satisfactory for this purpose.

[7] A National Research Corp. No. 2S or Welch No. 1400 mechanical pump, or equivalent, has been found satisfactory for this purpose.

[8] A National Research Corp. Model No. G-2-M diffusion pump, or equivalent, has been found satisfactory for this purpose.

[9] National Carbon Co. spectrographic pure grade and United Carbon Co. halogen-treated spectrographic grade graphite have been found satisfactory for this purpose.

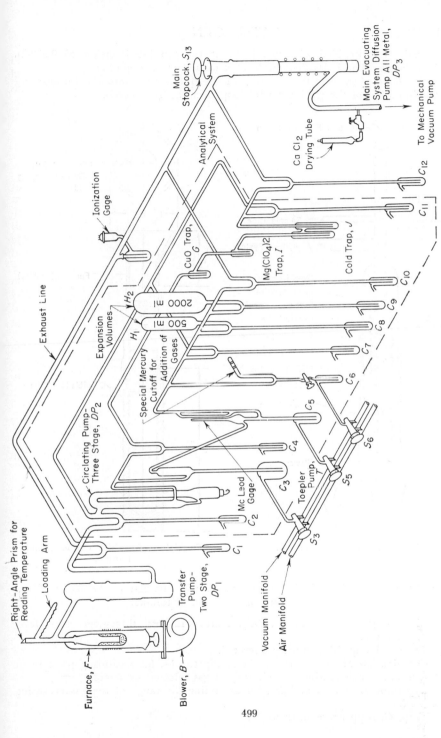

Right-Angle Prism for
Reading Temperature

Furnace, F

Blower, B

Loading Arm

Transfer Pump—
Two Stage, DP₁

Exhaust Line

Circlating Pump—
Three Stage, DP₂

Ionization
Gage

Special Mercury
Cutoff for
Addition of
Gases

Expansion
Volumes

H₁    H₂

2000 ml

500 ml

McLeod
Gage

Analytical
System

CuO Trap,
G

Mg(ClO₄)₂
Trap, I

Cold Trap, J

Main
Stopcock, S₁₃

Main Evacuating
System Diffusion
Pump All Metal,
DP₃

Ca Cl₂
Drying Tube

To Mechanical
Vacuum Pump

C₁

C₂

C₃

C₄

C₅

C₆

C₇

C₈    C₉

C₁₀

C₁₁

C₁₂

Toepler
Pump, T

S₃

S₅

S₆

Vacuum Manifold

Air Manifold

499

Fig. 22-1.  Diagram of Complete Vacuum Fusion Apparatus for Determining Hydrogen, Nitrogen, and Oxygen.

⅛-in. wall, and provided with two holes at the top for insertion of 0.050-in. platinum wire. The holes shall be located diametrically opposite.

*Special Tools* (Fig. 22-5) for insertion of the quartz tube into the furnace and for manipulation of the platinum wire loop over the glass hooks.

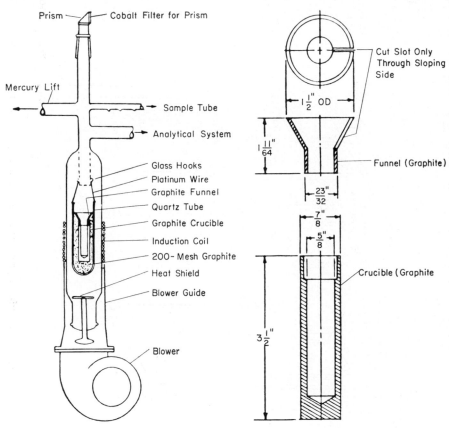

FIG. 22-2. Furnace Assembly.          FIG. 22-3.   Graphite Crucible and Funnel.

*Low-Pressure Gas Analysis Apparatus* as shown in Fig. 22-1 in the area enclosed by the dotted line. Special components are listed as follows:

(1) Circulating Diffusion Pump, $DP_2$, mercury-in-glass, three-stage, high fore-pressure tolerance.

(2) Toepler Pump, T, manually operated.

(3) Combination McLeod Gage and Gas Pipette, M, for measuring pressure in the system and for measuring the quantity of gas released by sample.

(4) Expansion Bulbs, $H_1$ and $H_2$, for extending the range of the gas-measuring pipette, M.

(5) Trap, G, copper-rare earth oxide.

(6) Bulb, *I*, filled with $Mg(ClO_4)_2$.

(7) Trap, *J*, cooled by liquid nitrogen.

*Induction Heater and Coil,* adequate to heat the crucible to at least 2400°C., having the general characteristics of approximately 500 kc. and 2 to 5-kw. output.

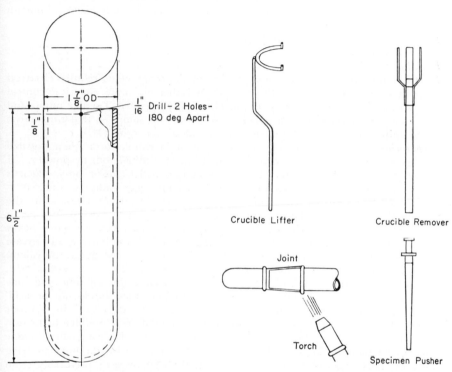

FIG. 22-4. Quartz Tube.  FIG. 22-5. Special Tools.

*Optical Pyrometer* to measure the range 1000 to 2500°C.

*Heaters,* glass mantle type, for copper oxide and $Mg(ClO_4)_2$ bulbs.

*Mercury Cutoff Valves,* $C_1$ to $C_{12}$.

*Dewar Flask* for containing liquid nitrogen.[10]

*Mercury,* high-purity, for pumps, gages, and cutoffs.

*Copper-Rare Earth Oxide Mixture.*[11]—Dissolve 150 g. of pure copper and 23.5 g. of rare earth oxides (cerium content not less than 35%) separately in concentrated nitric acid. Mix the two solutions and evaporate to dryness. Heat slowly to drive off the acid fumes, and then raise temperature to 800°C., and maintain it there

---

[10] If liquid nitrogen is not conveniently available, the procedure described by W. G. Guldner, Application of Vacuum Techniques to Analytical Chemistry, *Vacuum Symposium Transactions,* 1955, in which the carbon dioxide is removed by Ascarite, may be used.

[11] Walter, D. I., Determination of Oxygen in Titanium, Analytical Chemistry, **22,** pp. 297–303, 1950.

for 24 hours. Cool, crush to pass through an 80-mesh screen, mix with 36 g. of pure kaolin, moisten with water to form a plastic mass, dry and bake at 800°C. for 4 hours. Break into small lumps, reduce with $H_2$ at 300–400°C., and reoxidize at same temperature with air. Repeat reduction and oxidation, crush to pass through 10-mesh screen, retaining material that remains on 20-mesh screen.

*Magnesium Perchlorate* ($Mg(ClO_4)_2$), reagent grade, screened to remove fines, material passing a No. 20 (840-micron) sieve and retained on a No. 200 (74-micron sieve) being acceptable for use.

*Liquid Nitrogen,* for cooling trap *J*.

*Stopcock Grease.*[12]

*High-Vacuum Wax.*[13]

*Electrical Control Circuit.*—Since a number of the components require electrical heating at various times during the analysis, a rather elaborate electrical control circuit is desirable. Most analysts use an electrically operated Toepler pump and various types of interlocks with a panel board containing lamps so that the analyst can determine, at a glance, if the proper circuits are energized.

**Preparation of Sample.**—(a) The sample is used in chunk form when possible or in the form submitted for test such as wire, sheet, tubing, rod, or powder. If the sample is in the form of powder, compress into pellets, using only sufficient pressure to make the powder adhere. Do not mill ingot samples, since it is important to minimize the effect of surface and possible oxide films. Cut the sample in the form of a cube or similar shape and to proper size for loading in the furnace and to avoid sticking in the graphite funnel. Remove outer heavy scale with abrasive cloth or by slowly turning on a lathe. Remove any grease or oil present in a vapor degreaser using clean, dry trichloroethylene or equivalent.

(b) Remove light scale by immersion in a mixture of 750 ml. of acetic acid, 250 ml. of $HNO_3$, and 15 ml. of HCl at 50 to 60°C. for a limited time, the time being dependent on the thickness of the scale. Samples that should not be acid-cleaned or abraded, such as finished cathodes, should be degreased in a vapor degreaser using trichloroethylene or equivalent, followed by a Soxhlet extraction with acetone until no residue can be detected on a watch glass when the acetone extract is evaporated to dryness. Do not touch the samples with the fingers during or after the final stages of cleaning. Use clean rubber gloves, or preferably clean tweezers, for handling the specimens.

**Procedure.**—(a) Place about 1½ in. of graphite powder in the bottom of the quartz tube. Be very careful not to compact the graphite. Place the graphite crucible with funnel on top of this lightly and coaxially to the quartz tube. Place a close-fitting metal cap on top of the funnel and pour graphite powder into the quartz tube until the top of the funnel is reached. Remove the cap and blow out any fine graphite that may have fallen into the graphite crucible with a glass tube connected to a low-pressure air line. The removal of this graphite is important because any powder left inside the crucible will outgas incompletely and will intro-duct error into the initial samples. Now hook the special lifting rod (Fig. 22-5) into the two loops in the platinum wire and carefully lift the crucible assembly into place through the ground joint in the bottom of the furnace. Make sure the hooks are secure before removing the lifter. If the crucible does not hang straight, remove it by lifting out with the other holder shown in Fig. 22-5, and

---

[12] Apiezon L or N, or its equivalent, has been found satisfactory for this purpose.
[13] Apiezon W, or its equivalent, has been found satisfactory for this purpose.

bend the platinum hooks to correct the misalignment. Coat the glass plug for the bottom closure with high-vacuum wax by warming in a soft flame. Also warm the outer joint with a soft flame, and slip the wax-coated plug into place and rotate until well seated.

(b) Weigh 2 g. of the sample and insert into the sample loading arm on the furnace, F, Fig. 22-1. At any one time at least ten 2-g. samples may be loaded into the sidearm. Close the sidearm by sealing the cap at the end with high-vacuum wax.

(c) Set the blower and blower guide in place. Check the blower to make sure the air flow around the furnace is uniform. Make sure that all the three-way stopcocks are in a position such that the mercury bulbs are isolated both from the atmosphere and from the vacuum manifold. Close the large right-angle stopcock above the main evacuating pumping system and close the air release valve on the foreline of the oil-diffusion pump, $DP_3$. Stopcock $S_2$ on cutoff $C_2$ may be opened to the air.

Now, turn on the manifold pump. Next, turn on the forepump. Allow this pump to run until it is operating quietly (about 2 minutes).

Next, with extreme caution, *very slowly* open the large right-angle stopcock, $S_{13}$, located above the metal diffusion pump, until the mercury begins to rise *slowly* in the various tubes. *Leave* the stopcock in this position. In no case shall the system be pumped down in less than 5 minutes; 6 to 10 minutes is preferable. If the pump-down is too rapid, the fine graphite in the crucible will fluff and may be blown into the system, thus rendering the apparatus useless until *all* the graphite has been removed.

The mercury will rise slowly and uniformly in all the tubes. When a height of about 3 to 4 in. has been reached, lower the mercury column carefully by turning the stopcocks momentarily to connect the mercury-reservoir bulbs with the vacuum manifold. Leave stopcock $S_2$ open to the atmosphere at all times. It will be found that U-tubes $C_1$, $C_2$, $C_4$, $C_7$, $C_8$, $C_9$, $C_{10}$, $C_{11}$, and $C_{12}$ will need no further attention, since the mercury will not now reach the cutoff.

Cutoffs $C_3$, $C_5$, and $C_6$ will require attention during pump-down to keep mercury from rising into the bulbs of the Toepler pump, $T$, McLeod gage, $M$, and into the sidearm of the gas addition tube, $C_6$.

The cutoff, $C_5$, on the McLeod gage is the lowest and will require the most attention. Keep manipulating stopcocks $S_3$, $S_5$, and $S_6$ in such a fashion that the mercury does not reach the cutoff in any case. When no further upward movement is visible in the U-tube $C_2$, the main stopcock may be fully opened. Do this slowly. Next turn on the main diffusion pump and the transfer and circulating mercury diffusion pumps.

At this point it is good practice to adjust the height of all the mercury columns (with the exception of $C_2$, which is left all the way up) to a point just below the cutoff. The special cutoff, $C_6$, may be permanently closed and the mercury sealed off by closing the stopcock in the stem.

After 30 to 45 minutes, the pressure in the system as checked by the McLeod gage should be so low that the McLeod gage shows no differential in the heights of the mercury in the two capillary columns. Pumping for a minimum of 1 hour is necessary before applying heat to the furnace. Fine graphite outgasses very rapidly when first heated and may fluff out and into the system if caution is not used.

(d) Outgas the furnace assembly by heating the graphite crucible to a temperature of 2400°C. for at least 2 hours by means of the high-frequency induction heater. Turn on the air blower at the same time as the induction heater. Raise the temperature slowly to permit evacuation of the gases evolved and, also, to avoid displacement of the carbon powder. Measure the temperature of the crucible with an optical pyrometer directed through the right-angle prism and optical flat (Fig. 22-2).

(e) Make a blank determination by lowering the temperature of the crucible to 1650°C. and collecting the gas evolved during a period of 20 to 30 minutes. This blank heating period should correspond to the time the sample is to be heated.

Close all mercury cutoffs. Set the timer for the desired time interval and open cutoff $C_2$. Lower the mercury in the Toepler pump below the bulb. Maintain the mercury in the McLeod gage above the sidearm to the expansion bulbs but below the inlet from the Toepler pump. Gas evolved from the furnace is pumped through pumps $DP_1$ and $DP_2$ into the Toepler pump. At the end of the collection period, close cutoff $C_2$ and open $C_1$. Transfer the gas collected in the Toepler pump to the McLeod gage measuring system by manual operation of the Toepler pump, until the amount of gas measured in the McLeod capillary shows no further increase. Measure the amount of gas collected by reading the mercury level in the McLeod capillary from which the pressure-volume $(PV)$ product is calculated. Analyze the gas for CO, hydrogen, and nitrogen as described in paragraph (g). It is possible to obtain a blank level that will amount to approximately 0.0001 to 0.0002% oxygen for a 2-g. sample.

(f) The fusion of the sample is carried out at the same temperature and length of time as the blank. Turn off the power to the furnace and allow the furnace to cool 200 to 300°C. Introduce the sample by moving it by means of a magnet until it drops down the vertical tube into the crucible. Again turn on the induction heater and continue the fusion for 20 to 30 minutes at 1650°C. Completeness of removal of gas from the sample is readily confirmed by successive readings of the $PV$ product during the collection period. Should an abnormally long time period be required, a blank correction for a corresponding time must be made. Collect the gas as in the case of the blank.

After the gas is collected from the sample, raise cutoff $C_2$, lower cutoff $C_1$, and allow the furnace to exhaust to the main evacuation line until the next sample is dropped.

Transfer the gas collected in the Toepler pump to the McLeod gage, compress into the capillary pipette, and measure the $PV$ product. If more gas is collected than can be measured in the capillary pipette, allow it to expand into expansion bulb $H_1$ or $H_2$, or both, by lowering the mercury in the McLeod gage below the sidearm level. Since the total volume of the system including expansion bulbs, McLeod gage, and connecting tubing has been previously calibrated, the $PV$ product of the gas may be determined. A body of gas such that the product of its volume (in ml.) and pressure (in mm. of Hgu) is 3000 can be measured in the system shown.

The gas is now ready for analysis.

(g) Condition the reagents prior to an analysis as follows: First adjust the mercury cutoffs to open all reagents to vacuum. Use electric furnaces or heating mantles to bake out the reagents under vacuum, each adjusted by variable auto-transformers to the proper temperature—copper oxide at 325°C., and $Mg(ClO_4)_2$

at 240°C. Place a Dewar flask containing liquid nitrogen to cover trap $J$ before the analysis is begun.

(*h*) After transferring the gas by means of the Toepler pump to the McLeod gage and determining the $PV$ product of the combined CO, hydrogen, and nitrogen, lower the mercury in the McLeod gage below the cutoff. Open cutoffs $C_7$ and $C_4$ to permit the gas to be pumped into the analytical system. Check the McLeod gage reading after a few minutes to be sure all gas has been pumped out; then raise the mercury level in the McLeod gage to just above the cutoff level. Then close cutoff $C_7$. Open cutoff $C_{11}$ to permit the gas to circulate through the copper oxide tube, the $Mg(ClO_4)_2$ trap, and the trap cooled with liquid nitrogen. Circulate the gas for not less than 10 minutes. Close cutoff $C_4$ and lower the mercury in the Toepler pump, $C_3$, to just below the cutoff point. With the cutoffs in these positions, pump the residual nitrogen into the Toepler bulb. After ten minutes, transfer this nitrogen into the McLeod gage in the usual manner and measure the $PV$ product of the nitrogen. Allow the nitrogen to remain in the McLeod gage. Lower the mercury level in the Toepler pump below the side-arm, then remove the liquid nitrogen-filled flask from the trap, $J$, releasing $CO_2$ from the trap. Allow 5 to 10 minutes for the $CO_2$ to collect in the Toepler pump. Transfer the gas into the McLeod gage as before, and measure the $PV$ product of the combined $CO_2$ and nitrogen. The operation is now completed. The analytical system is exhausted by opening cutoffs $C_{10}$, $C_{11}$, and $C_{12}$ to prepare to run the next sample.

The $Mg(ClO_4)_2$ can be kept in a baked-out condition by maintaining at 250°C. during overnight periods with the system under vacuum. Activation or replacement of the copper oxide is required at intervals. Activation is accomplished by repeated reductions with hydrogen followed by an oxidation and vacuum bake.

**Calculations.**—The difference between the sum of the $PV$ products for $CO_2$ and nitrogen and the original $PV$ product of the combined CO, nitrogen, and hydrogen represents the $PV$ product of water vapor, which is also equivalent to the $PV$ product of hydrogen.

Measure the gas $PV$ evolved as a result of the fusion in units of milliliters and millimeters. In each case correct the amount of gas collected from the sample for the blank determination on the apparatus.

Calculate the percentages of nitrogen, oxygen, and hydrogen as follows:

*Nitrogen (measured as $N_2$):*

$$\text{Nitrogen, \%} = \frac{A \times 1.51}{B} \times 100.$$

*Oxygen (converted to CO and measured as $CO_2$):*

$$\text{Oxygen, \%} = \frac{A \times 0.86}{B} \times 100.$$

*Hydrogen:*

$$\text{Hydrogen, \%} = \frac{A \times 0.1084}{B} \times 100$$

where $A$ = pressure-volume ($PV$) product for the gas in question, in milliliters and millimeters at 25°C., and
$B$ = micrograms of sample used. For the 2-g. sample taken, $B$ is $2 \times 10^6$.

## DETERMINATION OF HYDROGEN IN STEEL

The method is based upon the oxidation of hydrogen liberated from steel by heat in presence of a current of oxygen. The water formed is absorbed and weighed.

*Procedure.* **Preliminary Test.**—The apparatus is set up as shown in detail in Fig. 22-6. The heat is turned on and the oxygen gas passed through the silica tube *I*, heated to redness (850°C.) at the rate of 100 ml. per minute, this rate having been established by a preliminary test noting the rate of bubbling through the acid in *G* and the pressure in *C* with the desired volume per minute. The

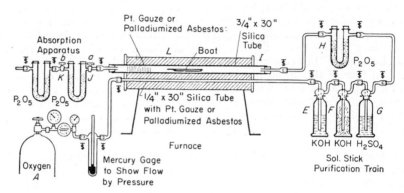

Fɪɢ. 22-6. Apparatus for Determining Hydrogen.

gas is purified by passing through *D, E, F, G,* and *H,* any hydrogen present being decomposed in the preheated tube *D.* Proceed now as follows:

Allow the gas to pass through the system for 5 to 10 minutes, disconnect the tube *J* after turning off the cocks *a* and *b* in the order named. Place in the balance case for 5 minutes, then open and close *b* rapidly. The oxygen in *J* will be at atmospheric pressure and at the temperature in the balance. Now weigh. Replace the tube again in the train, open the cocks *a* and *b* and continue the flow of oxygen for another 10 minutes. If there is an increase in weight repeat the test a third time, noting the increase of weight during a 30-minute run. This is the blank that must be deducted from the regular run. It should not exceed 1 mg.

**Determination.**—Place in a clay boat previously ignited in a current of oxygen, or in a platinum boat containing ignited alundum powder, 10 to 30 g. of steel in as large pieces as possible (hydrogen is liberated by drilling so that it is best to use the metal in strips or in a single piece). Insert the boat in the tube and quickly connect up the apparatus.

Turn on the oxygen at the rate of 100 ml. per minute and continue the flow for 30 minutes. Disconnect (after turning off cocks *a* and *b*) the absorption tube *J.* Place in balance case as before and equalize the pressure by opening the cock *b* for an instant. Weigh. The increase of weight, minus the blank, is due to the water formed. This weight multiplied by 0.111 gives the hydrogen of the sample.

Notes.—The blank should be determined and deducted from the regular run.

It is not necessary to burn all the metal to oxide to eliminate the hydrogen. A 30-minute run is sufficient.

The $P_2O_5$ is placed in the tubes interspersed with glass wool; otherwise the tubes would pack, preventing the passage of the gas.

*Testing Gas Apparatus for Leaks.*—Connections between the parts of the gas apparatus, stopcocks, etc., should be tight to avoid intake or loss of gas, thus causing an error. The following simple method for testing for leaks is applicable to apparatus for the volumetric determination of gas as well as testing the tightness of combustion trains.

**Procedure.**—Close one end of the train. To the other attach a Hempel gas burette with two-way stopcock and connected to a reservoir of water. Open the two-way cock to the air and raise the reservoir until half of the gas in the tube is expelled. Now turn the cock to open a passage to the combustion train (or gas apparatus). Have the level of the water in the reservoir and the burette the same and note the exact reading. Now raise the reservoir about 10 inches; the gas will be under pressure. Lower the reservoir to its former position, leveling the water. If the level in the Hempel tube has risen an outward leak is indicated. See Fig. 22-6.

Now lower the reservoir to the table and after a few minutes raise to the first position. After leveling the water as before note whether the level has dropped in the Hempel. If so, the apparatus leaks under reduced pressure.

# Chapter 23

# INDIUM*

In, *at. wt.* 114.82; *sp. gr.* 7.28 (at 20°C.); *m.p.* 156.4°C; *oxide,* $In_2O_3$.

Indium is a rare element found in minute quantities in many deposits of zinc blende, in some tungsten and most tin ores, and sometimes in pyrites, siderite, and galena. It is sometimes found concentrated as an indium-gallium alloy of low melting-point in residues from zinc retorts.

Indium, like gallium, resembles aluminum in its behavior. The pale yellow sesquioxide is obtained by ignition of the hydroxide, precipitated by ammonia from indium solutions: ammonium salts need not be added, and an excess of ammonia is immaterial as it has no solvent effect upon the precipitate. Indium is quantitatively precipitated as the yellow sulfide by hydrogen sulfide from solutions containing acetic acid and ammonium acetate and also from 0.03 to 0.05 $N$ hydrochloric acid solution.

## DETECTION

For the detection of indium in an ore, e.g., zinc blende, the mineral is dissolved in hydrochloric acid with the addition, if necessary, of a little nitric acid, the excess of which is expelled by boiling with hydrochloric acid. Digestion of the filtered solution with metallic zinc precipitates all the indium together with lead, copper, cadmium, etc. The precipitate is dissolved in nitric acid and the solution evaporated with sulfuric acid to fumes. The cold mass is diluted with water and the lead sulfate filtered off. The filtrate is treated with ammonia, boiled, and filtered. The precipitate is dissolved in the minimum of hydrochloric acid, the solution neutralized with ammonia, an excess of sodium bisulfite added, and boiling continued for some time. A white microcrystalline precipitate indicates indium. As a confirmatory test the precipitate is dissolved in a few drops of hydrochloric acid, and a platinum wire is dipped into the solution and held in the Bunsen flame. A bright blue color, showing two characteristic bright blue lines (4511.55 and 4101.95 A) when viewed through the spectroscope, confirms the presence of indium.

## ESTIMATION

### PREPARATION AND SOLUTION OF THE SAMPLE

As indium only occurs in minute amounts in ores of other elements, it is necessary to employ the procedure indicated by the nature of the material under examination.

* Chapter contributed by A. R. Powell, Research Manager, Johnson, Matthey & Co., Ltd., Wembley, England.

## SEPARATIONS

*From Iron.*[1]—The solution is treated with ammonia drop by drop until a precipitate begins to appear; this is dissolved in a minimum quantity of 0.1 N hydrochloric acid. The resulting acidity should be less than 0.05 N. Hydrogen sulfide is passed for 2 hours at 70°C., and the precipitate washed with hydrogen sulfide water barely acidified with hydrochloric acid. Large amounts of ferric salt are first reduced with hydrogen sulfide in acid solution; this is boiled under carbon dioxide for the removal of the gas, and neutralized after cooling.

*From Aluminum.*[1]—Indium is precipitated as sulfide from acetate solution treated with sulfosalicylic acid (which converts aluminum into a stable soluble complex), then neutralized with ammonium carbonate against methyl orange, and acidified with a little acetic acid. If the solution is too dilute, the indium sulfide does not flocculate readily.

*From Manganese.*[1]—In this case, indium is precipitated as sulfide from an acetate solution prepared as follows: mineral acid is first neutralized with ammonia; the solution is then treated with 30 ml. of 2 N acetic acid and 10 ml. of 2 N ammonia per 100 ml., heated to boiling, and subjected to a stream of hydrogen sulfide till cold.

*From Zinc, Copper, Cadmium, Nickel, Cobalt, and Manganese.*—The weakly acid solution is treated with six times as much ammonium sulfate as the zinc present. After addition of methyl red the solution is treated with 5% hexamethylenetetramine solution until the indicator turns yellow, and gradually heated to boiling. The dense precipitate of indium hydroxide is collected and washed. If zinc largely predominates, the precipitate is dissolved in dilute hydrochloric acid, the solution neutralized with ammonia, and the precipitation repeated.

*From Antimony, Bismuth, and Tin.*—This is effected by precipitating these three metals with tannin from a neutralized oxalate solution (see below).

*From Gallium.*—See Chapter on Gallium.

## GRAVIMETRIC METHODS

### DETERMINATION AS OXIDE

Precipitates of indium hydroxide, if formed in chloride solution, should be washed very thoroughly as indium chloride is volatile. The filter containing the hydroxide precipitate is dried in a tared porcelain or silica crucible and ignited gradually, finally over a blast burner for 15 minutes. The oxide is not volatile at the temperature reached, and is not hygroscopic after strong ignition. Factor: $In_2O_3 \times 0.8270 = In$.

### DETERMINATION IN ZINC BLENDE, RETORT RESIDUES, ETC.

It is advisable to take as much as 100 g. The procedure follows the lines of that described above under "Detection" with the usual precautions to render the separations quantitative. The accuracy of the estimation by precipitation with excess of sodium bisulfite is at least questionable. The following alternative procedure is therefore recommended.

*Procedure.*—The solution of the blende in hydrochloric acid, with the addition of a little nitric acid if necessary, is filtered and boiled with metallic zinc till

[1] Moser and Siegmann, Monatsh. Chem., **55,** 14, 1930.

nearly neutral. The precipitate is collected and dissolved in hydrochloric acid and a little bromine, the excess of bromine is boiled off, and the solution nearly neutralized with ammonium hydroxide. After addition of 5 g. of ammonium chloride a 2% solution of hexamethylenetetramine is added slowly with stirring to the hot solution until the precipitate coagulates and settles readily. The precipitate is collected, washed with hot 2% ammonium chloride solution, redissolved in hydrochloric acid, and reprecipitated as before. The second precipitate is dissolved in hydrochloric acid, the solution treated with 5 g. of ammonium oxalate, neutralized with ammonia (methyl red), and reacidified with two drops of hydrochloric acid. The antimony, bismuth, and tin are then precipitated by addition of tannin, the precipitate collected and washed with dilute ammonium chloride solution, and the filtrate made slightly ammoniacal and again treated with tannin to precipitate the indium. This precipitate is washed with hot 2% ammonium nitrate solution until the washings cease to give a chloride reaction, dried, ignited gently at first and then more strongly to obtain $In_2O_3$ for weighing.

## METHODS FOR INDIUM IN ANALYSES IN OTHER CHAPTERS

Indium in Magnesium Alloys                See Magnesium Chapter

# Chapter 24

# IODINE *

I, *at. wt.* 126.90441; *sp. gr.* 4.93 (at 20°C.); *m.p.* 113.5°C.; *b.p.* 184.35°C.; *acids,* HI, HIO, $HIO_3$, $HIO_4$.

Iodine is less common than the other members of the halogen group, occurring naturally as 1 part to 15 million of the earth's crust. It is found in a few rare minerals such as the iodides of copper, lead, and silver; calcium iodate, or "lautarite" is contained in Chile saltpeter which also contains potassium salts of iodate and periodate but in smaller quantities. The element occurs in sea deposits and is frequently found in mineral waters and brine. The observation of Courtois (1811) of the effect of ashes of sea weeds in corroding copper kettles and the liberation of a violet-colored gas by the action of sulfuric acid on the ash led to Gay-Lussac's work in isolating the element (1813). Drift kelp, *Laminaria digitata* and *Laminaria stenophylla,* incorporate iodine from the sea in which it occurs combined as iodides and iodates and, hence, are an important source of the element. It is produced on an industrial scale by treatment of iodides with colloidal silver. Iodine may be produced in the laboratory by treatment of iodides with strong sulfuric acid plus an oxidizing agent, e.g., $MnO_2$, followed by heating to drive off the free element. No stable isotopes of the element exist, but 19, ranging in mass number from $I^{121}$ to $I^{139}$, exist as unstable forms; $I^{131}$, half-life 8.04 days, is now the most commonly used radioisotope ($\beta$-0.60–0.3 Mev.; $\gamma$-0.364, 0.636, 0.284, 0.080 Mev.). $I^{131}$ is frequently employed in biological investigations.[1]

Iodine is used in the treatment of goiter; iodide and thyroxin may be used internally, but for open wounds an alcoholic solution of the element (tincture) is commonly used. Free iodine, iodides, and iodoform are important commercial products.

## DETECTION

*The element* may be recognized by its physical properties. It is a bluish-black crystalline solid, with a metallic luster, brownish-red in thin layers. It exhibits a vapor pressure of 1 mm. at 38.7°C.; the vapor has a characteristic odor and the solid element a sharp, acrid taste. Upon gently heating the solid element the vapor is evident, appearing a deep blue when unmixed with other gases and violet when mixed with air. The violet or blue color of the vapor arises from the excitation of one or more outer electrons to higher energy levels and is character-

---

* This chapter revised by Dr. Edward G. Moorehead of Harvard University.

[1] See, for example, Siri, W. E., Isotopic Tracers and Nuclear Radiations, p. 525, McGraw-Hill Book Company, Inc., New York, 1949, for a review of applications of iodine isotopes.

ized by absorption in the yellow and green bands of the visible spectrum. Chemically, iodine behaves in a manner similar to chlorine and bromine but is less reactive than these halogens.

*Free iodine* in solution exhibits either a violet or "brown" color.[2] In solvents of low dielectric constant, or low basicity, the element exists as the diatomic molecule coloring the solutions violet. With solvents of high dielectric constant the color is brown to reddish-brown; this color is attributed to interaction of the basic solvent with the polarizable iodine molecule. The violet color characterizes solutions of iodine, in solvents such as $CCl_4$, $CS_2$, $CHCl_3$, $PCl_3$ and fluorinated amines, whereas the brown color occurs with solutions of the element in ether, pyridine, water, alcohols, etc. Iodine colors benzene red; it is somewhat more reactive in the more basic solvents. Violet solutions absorb at 520–540 m$\mu$; brown solutions in the range 460–480 m$\mu$.

Iodine colors cold starch solutions blue;[3] this color formation constitutes a very sensitive test for the presence of iodine. The blue color fades upon heating.

Tannin interferes with the usual tests for iodine unless ferric chloride is present.

*Iodide.*—The dry powder, heated with concentrated sulfuric acid, evolves violet fumes of iodine. Iodine is liberated from iodides by solutions of As(V), Sb(V), Bi(V), Cu(II), Fe(III), Cr(VI), $H_3Fe(CN)_6$, $HNO_2$, Cl, Br, $H_2O_2$, ozone.

Insoluble iodides may be transposed by treatment with $H_2S$, the filtered solution being tested for the halogen.

*Iodate.*—The acidified solution is reduced by cold solutions of $SO_2$, or $K_4Fe(CN)_6$ (acidified with dilute $H_2SO_4$), or by $Cu_2Cl_2$, $H_3AsO_3$, $FeSO_4$, etc. An iodate in nitric acid may be detected by diluting the acid with water, adding starch solution, then hydrogen sulfide water, drop by drop, a blue zone forming in presence of the substance.

## ESTIMATION

In the determination of iodine it should be recalled that the element is volatile, so that care must be exercised in its determination in concentrated solutions in which it occurs free. Methods of decomposition of the sample are given in the following section.

### PREPARATION AND SOLUTION OF THE SAMPLE

In dissolving the substance, it will be helpful to remember that free iodine is soluble in many solvents of both high and low dielectric constant. One gram of iodine, e.g., dissolves in 2950 ml. $H_2O$, 12.5 ml. ethanol, 4 ml. carbon disulfide, 10 ml. benzene, 53 ml. carbon tetrachloride and 80 ml. glycerol. Aqueous solutions of HI or KI enhance the water solubility of free iodine by formation of the triiodide ion according to the following equilibrium:

$$I_2 + I^- \rightarrow I_3^-; K = 710$$

In the presence of water alone, elemental iodine is soluble to the extent of $1.33 \times 10^{-3}$ molar at 25°C.; in the presence of 1.0 molar free iodide, it is soluble to the extent of 0.94 molar.

---

[2] Kleinberg, J., and Davidson, A. D., Chem. Rev., **42**, 601, 1948.

[3] For a discussion of the properties of the iodo-starch complex see, e.g., Simerl, L. E., and Browning, B. L., Ind. Eng. Chem., Anal. Ed., **11**, 125, 1939; Rundle, R. E., and French, D., J. Am. Chem. Soc., **65**, 558, 1943; Swanson, M. A., J. Biol. Chem., **172**, 825, 1948.

Iodides of Ag(I), Cu(I), Hg(I), Tl(I), Pb(II), and Pd(II) are insoluble. Iodides of other metals are soluble, but those of Bi, Sn, and Sb require acid to hold them in solution.

Iodates of Ag, Ba, Pb, Bi, Hg, Sn, Fe, and Cr are relatively insoluble (less than 2 g. per l. $H_2O$ at 15°C.). The iodates of Cu, Al, Co, Ni, Mn, Zn, Ca, Sr, Mg, Na, and K are more soluble than this figure.

*Free Iodine.*—Iodine is best brought into aqueous solution by dissolving the commercial crystals in a concentrated solution of KI according to the procedure described for the standardization of potassium thiosulfate under Titrimetric Methods. Iodine is usually determined titrimetrically with standard thiosulfate in weakly acidic solution or with arsenic(III) at a pH of 4–9 controlled with bicarbonate.

*Iodine or Iodides in Water.*—The sample of water is evaporated to about one-fourth its volume and then made strongly alkaline with sodium carbonate. The precipitated calcium and magnesium carbonates are filtered off and washed. The filtrate containing the halogens is evaporated until the salts begin to crystallize out. The hot concentrated solution is poured into three volumes of absolute alcohol and the resulting solution again filtered. The residue is washed four or five times with 95% alcohol. All of the bromine and iodine pass into the solution, whereas a large part of the chlorine as sodium chloride remains insoluble and is filtered off. About 0.5 ml. of 50% potassium hydroxide is added and a greater part of the alcohol distilled off with a current of air. The residue is concentrated to crystallization and again poured into three times its volume of absolute alcohol and filtered as above directed. This time only one or two drops of the KOH solution is added and the procedure is repeated several times. The final filtrate is freed from alcohol by evaporation, the solution taken to dryness and gently ignited, then taken up with a little water and filtered. Iodine is determined in the filtrate, preferably by the titrimetric procedure, decomposition with nitrous acid, described under "Titrimetric Methods."

*Organic Substances.*—Difficultly soluble organic substances may be brought into solution with the Carius Method if iodine only is present, or with the "Lime Method" if the substance also contains chlorine and bromine. Alcoholic solutions of organic halides may be decomposed by the method of Stepanov, using metallic sodium, by the method of Dains, using liquid $NH_3$ and sodium, or by the method ascribed to Pringsheim which utilizes sodium peroxide. Details of these methods are to be found in the Chapter on Chlorine under "Preparation and Solution of the Sample."

In addition [4] to the above methods, organic iodides may be decomposed by simple treatment with large amounts of acid oxidizing agents, e.g., chromic-sulfuric acid or permanganate-sulfuric acid. After rigorous heating followed by reduction of the iodine to HI or $I_2$, the element is distilled into an alkaline absorbent and determined by conventional procedures. Acid washing with chloric or chloric-chromic mixtures may also be used. The iodate is reduced with As(III), then treated with Ce(IV) to a spectrophotometric end point.

[4] Willard, H. H., and Thompson, J. J., J. Am. Chem. Soc., **52**, 1895, 1930; Thomas, J. W., Anal. Chem., **22**, 726, 1950; Sobel, H., and Sapsin, S., *ibid.*, **24**, 1829, 1952; Moran, K. K., *ibid.*, **24**, 378, 1952; see also Bolz, D. F., "Colorimetric Determination of Non-metals," Interscience Publishers, Inc., N. Y., 1958, p. 197, *et seq.* for a recent survey of methods to effect solution of iodine containing substances.

Thompson and Oakdale [5] determined halogen in organic compounds by treating the sample with fuming sulfuric acid, and Beamish [6] states that halogen substituted diphenyl and diphenylbenzene compounds can be decomposed, with conversion of the halogen to NaX, by utilizing the $Na_2O_2$–sugar explosion method.

According to Schwenk *et al.*,[7] many aliphatic, aromatic, alicyclic, and heterocyclic compounds can be dehalogenized by treatment with Ni-Al alloy in strong hydroxide.

Winter [8] devised a method, tested on 36 organic halogen compounds, in which the sample is vaporized into a stream of combustible gas, then burned in a jet.

Radiometric studies [9] have shown that alkaline fusion of organic iodine compounds does not lead to appreciable loss of the halogen.

## SEPARATIONS

*Separation of Iodine from the Heavy Metals.*—The heavy metals are usually precipitated as the carbonates by boiling with solutions of alkali carbonates. The resulting alkali iodides are separated by filtration then determined by conventional procedures, or, if desired, the free element is released by treatment [10] with a suitable oxidizing agent, e.g., nitrous acid or ferric alum, then freed from solution by vigorous heating.

Silver iodide may be decomposed by warming with metallic zinc and sulfuric acid; alternatively, the iodide may be released by treating the insoluble AgI with a soluble cyanide.

*Separation of Iodine from Bromine or from Chlorine.*[11]—Details of separation and estimation of the halides in presence of one another are given in the Chapter on Chlorine. Advantage is taken of the action of nitrous acid on dilute solutions, free iodine being liberated, while bromides and chlorides are not acted upon.

The solution containing the halogens is placed in a large, round-bottom flask and diluted to about 700 ml. Through a two-holed stopper a glass tube passes to the bottom of the flask; through this tube steam is conducted to assist the volatilization of iodine. A second short tube connected to the absorption apparatus conducts the evolved vapor from the flask into a 5% caustic soda solution containing an equal volume of hydrogen peroxide (about 50 ml. of each). The absorption system may be made by connecting two Erlenmeyer flasks in series, the inlet tubes dipping below the solutions in the flasks. It is advisable to cool the receivers with ice.

Two to three ml. of dilute sulfuric acid (1:1) and 25 ml. of 10% sodium nitrite solution are added to the liquid containing the halogens, the apparatus is immediately connected, and the contents of the large flask heated to boiling, conducting steam into it at the same time. The iodine vapor is gradually driven over into the cooled receiving flasks.

When the solution in the large flask has become colorless, it is boiled for half an hour longer. The steam is now shut off, the flask disconnected from the

5 Thompson, J. J., and Oakdale, U. O., J. Am. Chem. Soc., **52**, 1195, 1930.
6 Beamish, F. E., Ind. Eng. Chem., Anal. Ed., **6**, 352, 1934.
7 Schwenk, E., Papa, D., and Ginsberg, H., *ibid.*, **15**, 576, 1943.
8 Winter, P. K., *ibid.*, **15**, 571, 1943.
9 Decker, J. W., and Hayden, H. S., Anal. Chem., **23**, 198, 1951.
10 Goodrich, F. A., and Mar, F. W., Am. J. Sci., **39**, 293, 1890.
11 Gooch, F. A., and Ensign, J. R., Am. J. Sci., (3), **40**, 145, 1890; Jannash, P., and Aschoff, K., Z. anorg. Chem., **1**, 144, 245, 1892.

receiving flasks and the heat turned off. The contents of the receiving flasks are combined with the washing from the connecting tubes and the solution heated to boiling to expel, completely, hydrogen peroxide. The cooled liquid is acidified with a little sulfuric acid and the solution decolorized with a few drops of sulfurous acid. Iodine is now precipitated as silver iodide by adding an excess of silver nitrate and a little nitric acid and boiling the mixture to coagulate the precipitate, which is then dried and weighed.

Chlorine and bromine remain in the large flask in combined form and may be determined in this solution if desired.

The mixed halides can be precipitated with a solution of silver nitrate followed by liberation of the free iodine from the silver salt by oxidation, with a mixture of sulfuric and chromic acids, or the solution containing the mixed halides may be divided, treated with $AgNO_3$ solution and Bekk's modification [12] of Baubigny's Method followed.

Turner [13] has shown that the separation and determination of small amounts of iodine may be enhanced by boiling the solution with excess bromine water to convert the iodides to iodates; after expelling the excess bromine water, KI is added in excess. The iodate and iodide react to produce 6 times the amount of iodine originally present. The liberated iodine is then determined with thiosulfate as described under "Titrimetric Methods."

*The Separation of Iodine by Solvent Extraction.*—The ability of iodine to dissolve in varying degree in both polar and nonpolar solvents is often utilized when separating the element from accompanying impurities; its preferred solubility in $CHCl_3$, $CCl_4$, or $CS_2$ affords a quick separation of iodine from aqueous solutions. The solubility of iodine in organic solvents is used frequently to shift chemical equilibria in water solutions involving the element, and its vivid red to violet color is used in end point detection in titrimetric methods of determination.

*The Separation of Iodine Using Chromatography and Ion Exchange.*—Paper chromatographic separation and identification of $IO_4^-$, $IO_3^-$, $BrO_3^-$ and $ClO_4^-$ can be achieved with an ethanol-water-ammonium hydroxide (30:10:5) elutant; $Cl^-$, $Br^-$ and $I^-$ can also be separated. The $R_f$ values for the periodate, iodate, bromate, and perchlorate are 0.0, 0.31–0.37, 0.68 and 0.80–0.85, respectively. [14]

Long *et al.*,[15] recommend an ethanol-water-ammonium hydroxide (80:16:4) elutant with Whatman paper No. 54 for the separation of the halogens; $R_f$ values: $F^-$ (0.27); $Cl^-$ (0.43); $Br^-$ (0.48); $I^-$ (0.53).

Iodide may be separated from a mixture of the halides [16] by using an anion exchange resin initially in the nitrate form, eluting at a flow rate of 1.3 ml. per minute with 0.1 $M$ $NaNO_3$ adjusted to a pH of 10.4 with NaOH. Fluoride, chloride, and bromide are eluted first and are removed sufficiently from the iodide band to effect separation.

12 Bekk, J., Chem. Ztg., **39**, 405, 1915; Baubigny, H., Compt. rend., **127**, 1219, 1898; *ibid.*, **128**, 51, 1899.

13 Turner, R. G., J. Am. Chem. Soc., **52**, 2768, 1930; J. Biol. Chem., **88**, 497, 1930.

14 Lederer, E., and Lederer, M., Chromatography, 2nd Ed., Elsevier Publishing Company, New York, 1957.

15 Long, A. G., Quayle, J. R., and Stedman, R. J., J. Chem. Soc., 2197, 1951. See also Yamaguchi, K., J. pharm. Soc. Japan, **73**, 1285, 1953, for the separation of halides and oxygenated halogen anions using an acetone-$M$ $NH_3$ (4:1) elutant; Servigine, Y., Compt. rend., **239**, 272, 1954.

16 Atteberry, R. W., and Boyd, G. E., J. Am. Chem. Soc., **72**, 4805, 1950.

DeGeiso et al.,[17] employ a column 7.0 cm. long of resin equilibrated with 0.5 $M$ $NaNO_3$ for this separation; a flow rate of 0.5 $M$ $NaNO_3$ at 1.0 cm. per minute was used. After elution of the chloride band, 2.0 $M$ $NaNO_3$ is passed through the column, and the halides then determined with silver nitrate with an average error of 0.80%. Smith and Willeford[18] report a procedure for the separation of periodate by ion exchange.

*Separation of Iodine from Chlorine and Bromine by Precipitation as Palladous Iodide.*—The solution containing the halogens is acidified with dilute hydrochloric acid, and palladous chloride solution added to complete precipitation of the iodide. See "Gravimetric Methods."

NOTE.—For the separation and determination of iodine in natural waters see: Brubaker, H. W., Van Blarcom, H. S., and Walker, N. H., J. Am. Chem. Soc., **48**, 1502, 1926; Meerburg, P. A., Z. physik. Chem., **130**, 105, 1927; for the determination of traces of iodine in organic matter, see McClendon, J. F., J. Am. Chem. Soc., **50**, 1093, 1928.

## GRAVIMETRIC METHODS

### PRECIPITATION AS SILVER IODIDE

This procedure is essentially the same as that used for the precipitation of silver chloride. However, silver iodide is the least soluble of the silver halides and has a strong tendency to occlude impurities which are much more difficult to remove than with silver chloride. The precipitation of the salt should, therefore, be made slowly by adding 0.05 $M$ $AgNO_3$ with stirring, to an equally dilute ammoniacal solution of the iodide until precipitation is complete, then adding $HNO_3$ to 1% by volume. The precipitate is filtered and washed with dilute $HNO_3$, and then with water. Prolonged contact of AgI with $HNO_3$ must be avoided, as the iodide will be attacked through oxidation. Water must be used sparingly in the final wash, as AgI has a strong tendency to peptize. The precipitated salt, in a Gooch crucible, is dried, gently ignited, and weighed as silver iodide.

**Factors.**—AgI $\times$ 0.5405 = I
$\times$ 0.7071 = KI.

NOTE.—If filter paper is used in place of a Gooch crucible, the precipitate is removed and the filter ignited separately. A few drops of nitric and hydrochloric acid are added, the acids expelled by heat, and the residue weighed as AgCl. This multiplied by 1.638 = AgI. The result is added to the weight of the silver iodide, which is ignited and weighed separately.

### DETERMINATION OF IODINE AS PALLADOUS IODIDE [18]

Iodine may be determined as the iodide in the presence of the other halogens by precipitation as palladous iodide which is insoluble in water and dilute HCl (1:100); its solubility increases, however, in the presence of excess salts. Organic reducing agents, e.g., ethanol, reduce the palladium to the metal and must be absent from solution; sulfides and cyanides must also be absent.

Pd(IV) must be avoided in solutions containing a mixture of the halogens as the element in this oxidation state forms an insoluble precipitate with chloride in the presence of potassium or ammonium ions.

*Procedure.*—The solution containing the iodide, after acidification to 1% HCl

[17] DeGeiso, R. C., Rieman III, W., and Lindebaum, S., Anal. Chem., **26**, 1840, 1954.
[18] Lassaigne, J. L., J. Chem. Med., **1**, 57, 1835; Strebinger, R., and Pollak, I., Mikrochemic, **3**, 38, 1925.

by volume, and containing no ethanol or other organic substances, is treated with Pd(II) until no further precipitation of $PdI_2$ occurs. After precipitation, the solution containing the precipitate is allowed to stand 24–48 hours at room temperature (20–30°C.). The precipitate is then filtered on a weighed Gooch crucible, washed with warm water and finally a *small* quantity of ethanol, dried at 90–95°C. for about 1 hour and then weighed as $PdI_2$.

A preferred treatment involves heating the $PdI_2$ to 1000°C. in a stream of hydrogen to reduce the palladium to the metal. In this case, the hydrogen flow is stopped as soon as the flame is removed; the crucible is then cooled and moistened with ethanol. The latter is burned off, and the precipitate, after cooling, is weighed as palladium metal.

**Factors.**—$PdI_2 \times 0.705 = I$, or $Pd \times 2.385 = I$.

## TITRIMETRIC METHODS

### DETERMINATION OF HYDRIODIC ACID-SOLUBLE IODIDES

Free hydriodic acid is not determined by the usual alkalimetric methods for acids. The procedure for its estimation, free or combined as a soluble salt, depends upon the liberation of iodine and its titration with standard sodium thiosulfate, in neutral or slightly acid solution; or by means of standard arsenious acid, in presence of an excess of sodium bicarbonate in a neutral solution. The following equations represent the reactions that take place:

**Thiosulfate:**

$$2S_2O_3^- + I_2 \rightarrow 2I^- + S_4O_6^=$$

**Arsenite:**

$$H_3AsO_3 + I_2 + H_2O \rightarrow HAsO_4^= + 4H^+ + 2I^-$$

The free acid formed in the second reaction is neutralized and the reversible reaction thus prevented:

$$HI + HCO_3^- \rightarrow I^- + H_2O + CO_2$$

The presence of free alkali is not permissible, as the hydroxyl ion would react with iodine to form iodide, hypoiodite, and finally iodate; hence sodium or potassium carbonates cannot be used. Alkali bicarbonates, however, do not react with iodine and provide proper acidity for the reaction.

*Reagents.* **0.1 N Sodium Thiosulfate.**—From the reaction above it is evident that 1 gram-molecule of thiosulfate is equivalent to 1 gram-atom iodine; hence a 0.1 $N$ solution is equal to one-tenth the molecular weight of the salt per liter, e.g., 24.82 g. for $Na_2S_2O_3 \cdot 5H_2O$; generally a slight excess is taken—25 g. of the crystallized salt. It is advisable to make up 5 to 10 liters of the solution by dissolving 125 to 250 g. sodium thiosulfate crystals in hot distilled water, boiled free of carbon dioxide. 0.1 g. of $Na_2CO_3$ is added per liter of solution. The solution is allowed to stand a week to ten days and then standardized.

The aged thiosulfate solution may be standardized against iodine liberated *in situ* from potassium iodide in the presence of hydrochloric acid by a known amount of potassium bi-iodate, $KIO_3 \cdot HIO_3$, a salt which may be obtained exceedingly pure; thus,

$$IO_3^- + 5I^- + 6H^+ \rightarrow 3H_2O + 3I_2$$

A 0.1 $N$ solution of the bi-iodate contains 3.2499 g. of the pure salt per liter; one ml. of this will liberate 0.01269 g. of iodine from potassium iodide. The purity of the salt can be established by standardizing against thiosulfate, which has been recently tested against pure, resublimed iodine—see Note. However, the purity of commercially available iodate or bi-iodate is usually sufficient for most purposes.

About 5.0 g. of potassium iodide free from iodate are dissolved in the least amount of water that is necessary to effect solution, and 10 ml. of dilute hydrochloric acid (1:2) are added, and then 50 ml. of the standard bi-iodate solution. The solution is diluted to about 250 ml. and the liberated iodine titrated with the thiosulfate reagent; 50 ml. will be required if the reagents are exactly 0.1 $N$.

NOTE.—Alternatively, the thiosulfate solution may be accurately standardized against pure, resublimed iodine crystals: about 0.5 g. of the purified iodine is placed in a weighing bottle containing a known weight of saturated potassium iodide solution (2–3 g. of KI free from $KIO_3$ dissolved in about 0.5 ml. of $H_2O$), the increased weight of the bottle, due to the iodine, being noted. The bottle and iodine are placed in a beaker containing about 200 ml. of $1\%$ KI solution (2 grams KI per 200 ml. $H_2O$), the stopper removed with a glass fork, and the iodine titrated with the thiosulfate to be standardized.

The weight of the iodine taken, divided by the volume in ml. of thiosulfate required, gives the iodine equivalent for 1 ml. of the reagent; this result divided by 0.01269 gives the normality factor.

**0.1 $N$ Arsenite.**—From the second reaction above, it is evident that $As_2O_3$ is equivalent to $2I_2$, e.g., to 4H; hence ¼ the gram-molecular weight of arsenious oxide (49.460 g.) per liter will give a normal solution.

Since $As_2O_3$ is not readily soluble in neutral or acid solutions, 4.95 g. of pure arsenious oxide are dissolved in a little $20\%$ sodium hydroxide solution, the excess of the alkali is neutralized with dilute sulfuric acid, using phenolphthalein indicator, the solution being just decolorized. Five hundred ml. of distilled water containing about 25 grams of sodium bicarbonate are added. If a pink color develops, this is destroyed with a few drops of weak sulfuric acid. The solution is now made up to a volume of 1000 ml. The reagent is standardized against $KI$-$KIO_3$ or against a measured amount of pure iodine. The oxide may be dissolved directly in sodium bicarbonate solution.

**Starch Solution.**—Five grams of soluble starch are dissolved in cold water, the solution poured into 2 liters of hot water and boiled for a few minutes. The reagent is kept in a glass-stoppered bottle.

The addition of a few mg. of $HgI_2$, then heating to boiling and filtering will preserve the starch.

NOTE.—A number of alternative procedures for the preparation and preservation of starch solutions to be used with the determination of iodine are reviewed by Hillebrand, W. F., Lundell, G. E. F., Bright, H. A., and Hoffman, J. I., Applied Inorganic Analysis, p. 191, John Wiley and Sons, New York, 1953; Houston, F. G., Anal. Chem., **22**, 493, 1950; Swanson, M. A., J. Biol. Chem., **172**, 825, 1948.

## OXIDATION OF IODIDE BY FERRIC SALTS

The method takes advantage of the following reaction:

$$2Fe^{+3} + 2I^- \rightarrow I_2 + 2Fe^{+2}$$

The procedure permits a separation from bromides, as these are not oxidized by ferric salts.

*Procedure.*—To the iodide in a distillation flask is added an excess of ferric ammonium alum, the solution is acidified with sulfuric acid, then heated to boiling, and the iodine distilled into a solution of potassium iodide. The free iodine in the distillate is titrated with standard thiosulfate, or by arsenious acid in presence of an excess of sodium bicarbonate.

The reagent is added from a burette until the titrated solution becomes a pale yellow color. About 5 ml. of starch solution is now added and the titration continued until the blue color of the starch fades and the solution becomes colorless.

One ml. of 0.1 $N$ reagent equals 0.012690 g. iodine, equivalent to 0.012791 g. HI, or 0.016601 g. KI.

## OXIDATION WITH POTASSIUM IODATE [19]

The reaction with potassium iodate is as follows:

$$5I^- + IO_3^- + 6H^+ \rightarrow 3H_2O + 3I_2$$

It is evident that $\frac{5}{6}$ of the titration for iodine would be equal to the iodine of the iodide; hence, 1 ml. of 0.1 $N$ thiosulfate is equivalent to $0.012690 \times \frac{5}{6} = 0.01058$ g. iodine due to the iodide.

*Procedure.*—A known amount of 0.1 $N$ potassium iodate is added to the iodide solution, in sufficient amount to liberate all of the iodine, combined as iodide, and several ml. in excess. Hydrochloric acid and a piece of calcite are added. The mixture is boiled until all of the liberated iodine has been expelled. To the cooled solution 2 or 3 g. of potassium iodide are added and the liberated iodine, corresponding to the excess of iodate in the solution, is titrated with standard thiosulfate. If 1 ml. of thiosulfate is equal to 1 ml. of the iodate, then the total milliliters of the iodate used, minus the milliliter thiosulfate required in the titration, gives a difference due to the volume of iodate required to react with the iodide of the sample.

One ml. of 0.1 $N$ KIO$_3$ = 0.01058 g. I in KI

Note.—Tenth normal potassium iodate contains 3.567 g. KIO$_3$ per 1000 ml.

## OXIDATION OF THE IODIDE WITH NITROUS ACID (FRESENIUS)

Nitrous acid reacts with an iodide as follows:

$$2HNO_2 + 2HI \rightarrow 2NO + 2H_2O + I_2$$

Since neither hydrochloric nor hydrobromic acid are attacked by nitrous acid, the method is applicable to determining iodide in presence of chloride and bromide; hence is useful for determining small amounts of iodine in mineral waters containing comparatively large amounts of the other halogens.

*Reagent.* **Nitrous Acid.**—This is prepared by passing the gas into concentrated sulfuric acid until saturated.

*Procedure.*—The neutral or slightly alkaline solution of the iodide is placed in a glass-stoppered separatory funnel, and slightly acidified with dilute sulfuric acid. A little freshly distilled colorless carbon disulfide (or chloroform) is added, then 10 drops of nitrous acid reagent. The mixture is well shaken, the disulfide allowed

---

[19] Dietz, H., and Margosches, B. M., Chem. Ztg., **2**, 1191, 1904; Treadwell and Hall, Analytical Chemistry, Vol. 2.

to settle, drawn off from the supernatant solution, and saved for analysis. The liquor in the funnel is again extracted with a fresh portion of disulfide and, if it becomes discolored, it is drawn off and added to the first extract. If the extracted aqueous solution appears yellow, it must be again treated with additional carbon disulfide until all the iodine has been removed (e.g., until additional $CS_2$ is no longer colored when shaken with the solution). The combined extracts are washed with 3 or 4 portions of water, then transferred to a filter and again washed until free from acid. A hole is made in the filter and the disulfide allowed to run into a small beaker and the filter washed down with about 5 ml. of water. Three ml. of 5% sodium bicarbonate are added and the iodine titrated with 0.05 $N$ or 0.02 $N$ standard thiosulfate, the reagent being added until the reddish-violet carbon disulfide becomes colorless.

The sodium thiosulfate used is standardized against a known amount of pure potassium iodide treated in the manner described above.

One ml. 0.05 $N$ $Na_2S_2O_3$ = 0.00635 g. I; 1 ml. 0.02 $N$ $Na_2S_2O_3$ = 0.002538 g. I

## OXIDATION OF IODIDE TO IODINE MONOCHLORIDE [20]

**Reaction.**—$IO_3^- + 2I^- + 6HCl \rightarrow 3ICl + 3Cl^- + 3H_2O$.

*Procedure.*—The titration is carried on in a glass-stoppered vessel. The solution of the iodide is treated with an equal amount of concentrated HCl and 5 ml. of chloroform are added as an indicating layer. During the titration the chloroform layer is colored with iodine but the color fades sharply with a single drop of 0.1 $N$ (0.01667 $M$) $KIO_3$ at the end point. The method is selective for iodide in the presence of chloride. A standard solution of potassium permanganate or of ceric sulfate may be used instead of the standard iodate. There are other somewhat similar procedures such as oxidation of iodide to iodine cyanide (Lang's Method), and oxidation to iodoacetone (Berg's Method).[21]

In the Mohr modification [22] of the Dupre Method, use is made of the fact that aqueous chlorine will oxidize iodide to iodine chloride (ICl); in the presence of a large excess of chlorine, the iodine is oxidized to the I(V) state, i.e., $ICl_5$, which undergoes spontaneous hydrolysis to iodic acid, $HIO_3$.

In this procedure, chlorine water, standardized by titrating the iodine released from KI with thiosulfate, is added from a burette to a glass-stoppered bottle containing the iodide until the resulting yellow just disappears. The solution is made slightly alkaline with bicarbonate; potassium iodide is added in excess followed by 4–5 ml. cold starch solution and the excess chlorine water determined by titrating the iodine released with standard thiosulfate solution. The iodine in the sample may be calculated from the difference.

## OXIDATION OF IODIDE TO IODATE

In addition to these methods, iodides acidified with phosphoric acid may be determined by the Kolthoff modification [23] of the Winkler Method which utilizes the oxidation of iodide to iodate with a 5% solution of bleaching powder, i.e.,

[20] Andrews, L. W., Z. anorg. allgem. Chem., **36**, 76, 1903; J. Am. Chem. Soc., **25**, 756, 1903; Jamieson, G. S., Volumetric Iodate Methods, Chem. Catalogue Company, New York, 1926; Swift, E. H., and Gregory, C. H., J. Am. Chem. Soc., **52**, 894, 1930.

[21] Lang, R., Neuere massanalytische Methoden, Chap. 3, F. Enke, Stuttgart, 1937.

[22] Sutton, Volumetric Analysis, 10th Edition.

[23] Kolthoff and Furman, Volume. Anal., **II**, J. Wiley & Sons, Inc., New York, 1929.

hypochlorite, followed by addition of 5 ml. of 10% phenol, then 5 ml. of 1 $N$ potassium iodide with subsequent titration of the liberated iodine by thiosulfate.

If bromides are mixed with the iodides, 3% boric acid is first added followed by the hypochlorite. Phosphoric acid is then added and the procedure, as described above, is followed. The method is said to be very good for the analysis of dilute iodide solutions.

Another method [24] liberates iodine from iodide solutions acidified with phosphoric acid by addition of hydrogen peroxide followed by distillation of the iodine into KI. The resulting triiodide is titrated with thiosulfate in the usual manner.

NOTE.—Iodine in urine may be determined by evaporating to $\frac{1}{10}$ its volume. After adding an excess of sodium hydroxide, the mixture is taken to dryness and gently ignited. The ash may be used for the iodine determination.

## VOLHARD'S METHOD FOR DETERMINING IODIDES

This procedure is very similar to those for determining chloride or bromide, with the exception that silver iodide formed will occlude both the iodide solution and the silver nitrate unless the additions of the silver salt are made in small portions with vigorous shaking.

*Procedure.*—Standard silver nitrate is added to the solution in a glass-stoppered flask, shaking vigorously with each addition. As long as the solution appears milky the precipitation is incomplete. When the silver iodide is coagulated and the supernatant liquid appears colorless, ferric alum is added, and the excess of silver nitrate titrated with potassium thiocyanate until the characteristic reddish end point is obtained.

The iodine is calculated from the amount of silver nitrate required. E.g., total $AgNO_3$ added, minus excess determined by KCNS = $AgNO_3$ required by the iodine.

NOTE.—The ferric salt oxidizes hydriodic acid with separation of iodine, whereas the silver iodide is not acted upon; hence, the indicator is added after all the iodide has combined with silver.

## ADSORPTION INDICATOR METHOD (FAJANS)

Iodide ion may be titrated with silver nitrate in a solution that is neutral or slightly acidified with acetic acid, using eosin (sodium salt of tetrabromofluoresceinate) indicator. The range of application is from 0.1 $N$ down to 0.0005 $N$ halide to be titrated.[25]

*Procedure.* **Iodide Alone.** From 1–3 drops of 0.5% solution of sodium eosinate in water are added per 10 ml. of 0.1 $N$ halide, or 1–2 drops of indicator per 25 ml. of the more dilute solutions. Titrate with standard silver solution until there is a sharp transition to rose red.

**Iodide in Presence of Chloride.**—Add 5 ml. of 0.5 $N$ ammonium carbonate per 100–200 ml. of solution, 1–3 drops of eosin indicator, and titrate with standard silver nitrate. In the absence of ammonium carbonate the end point appears when more silver has been added than is equivalent to the iodide.

[24] Winterstein, E., and Herzfeld, E., Z. Physiol. Chem., **63**, 49–51, 1909; Chem. Zentralbl., **1**, 473–474, 1910.
[25] Fajans and Wolff, Z. anorg. allgem. Chem., **137**, 221, 245, 1924; Kolthoff and van Berk, Z. anal. Chem., **70**, 369, 395, 1927.

## DETERMINATION OF IODATES AND PERIODATES

*Procedure.*—The procedure for the determination of iodates is the reverse of that outlined above for the determination of iodides by means of iodate. The solution containing the iodate is added to one containing an excess of potassium iodide acidified with hydrochloric acid; the liberated iodine is then titrated with standard thiosulfate. One ml. 0.1 $N$ $Na_2S_2O_3$ = 0.002934 g. $HIO_3$ or 0.003567 g. $KIO_3$.

The procedure for the determination of periodate is the same as that for the determination of iodate described above, except in this case the reaction is as follows:

$$IO_4^- + 7I^- + 8H^+ \rightarrow 4H_2O + 4I_2.$$

From this equation it is evident that the equivalent weight of periodate is ⅛ the molecular weight. Hence, one ml. of 0.1 $N$ solution would contain 0.002399 g. $HIO_4$. One ml. 0.1 $N$ $Na_2S_2O_3$ = 0.002399 g. $HIO_4$ or 0.002849 g. $HIO_4 \cdot 2H_2O$ or 0.002875 g. $KIO_4$.

## DETERMINATION OF IODATES AND PERIODATES IN A MIXTURE OF THE TWO

The procedure depends upon the fact that an iodate does not react with potassium iodide in neutral or slightly alkaline solutions, whereas a periodate undergoes the following reaction:

$$IO_4^- + 2I^- + H_2O \rightarrow 2OH^- + IO_3^- + I_2$$

*Procedure.*—The sample, dissolved in water, is divided into two equal portions.

*A.* To one portion a drop of phenolphthalein indicator is added and the solution made just faintly alkaline by addition of alkali to acid solution or hydrochloric acid to alkaline solution, as the case may require. Ten ml. of cold saturated solution of sodium bicarbonate are added and an excess of potassium iodide. The liberated iodine is titrated with 0.1 $N$ arsenious acid ($Na_2S_2O_3$ will not do in this case, as the solution is alkaline).

$$\text{One ml. 0.1 } N \text{ As}_2O_3 = 0.0115 \text{ g. } KIO_4$$

*B.* To the other portion potassium iodide is added in excess and the solution made distinctly acid. The liberated iodine is titrated with standard sodium thiosulfate. ($As_2O_3$ will not do.)

**Calculation.**—In the acid solution, *B*, both iodates and periodates are titrated, whereas in the alkaline solution, *A*, only the periodates are affected. From the reactions for periodates, it is evident that 1 ml. $Na_2S_2O_3 = 4$ ml. $As_2O_3$ for the periodate titration; hence

$$\text{Ml. 0.1 } N \text{ Na}_2S_2O_3 - \text{ml. 0.1 } N \text{ As}_2O_3 \times 4 = 0.1 \text{ } N \text{ ml. thiosulfate due to } KIO_3.$$

The difference multiplied by 0.003580 = g. $KIO_3$, in the sample.

## COLORIMETRIC METHODS

## DETERMINATION OF IODINE BY MEASUREMENT OF ITS CATALYTIC EFFECT ON THE CERIC OXIDATION OF As(III) [26]

Notwithstanding a very high favorable potential, the reaction,

$$As(III) + 2Ce(IV) \rightarrow As(V) + 2Ce(III),$$

does not proceed at an appreciable rate without the application of heat or the use of a catalyst. The presence of iodide causes the reaction to increase in rate in proportion to the amount of iodide in solution, thus providing an effective method for its determination in the range 0.005 to 0.20 micrograms per sample with a high degree of accuracy. As As(III), As(V) and Ce(III) ions are colorless, the variation of the intensity of the orange color exhibited by the Ce(IV) ion provides a means for spectrophotometrically estimating the amount of iodine in solution. Because the oxidation of arsenic by cerium progresses continuously in the presence of iodine, rapid measurement is necessary.

The concentration of Ce(IV), As(III), and Cl$^-$—which is added to enhance the reaction time—must be closely controlled; temperature, acidity, and the oxidation state of the iodine must also be rigidly regulated.

Absorbance of the solution versus the concentration of Ce(IV) does not follow Beer's Law. However, in the region, log $(Ce^+)$ = 0.4 to 0.8, the variation is a linear one at 420 m$\mu$; peak absorbance of the solution is at 315 m$\mu$, but this is not used. Cyanide, mercury, chloride, bromide, osmium, silver, thiocyanate, and citrate interfere and should be excluded from the solution. Important also is the necessity of excluding iodine as an impurity from all reagents used. It has been found [27] that a ratio of As(III):Ce(IV) of 20:1 is optimum for increased sensitivity of the reaction.

The empirical calibration curve of iodide versus absorbance of Ce(IV), for a fixed reaction-time, has been found to be nonlinear, but this is circumvented by the addition of chloride ion.

*Empirical Curve Method.*[28]—Meyer *et al.*, have developed the technique of determining iodide utilizing the empirical calibration curve.

*Reagents.* **Ceric Ammonium Sulfate Solution, 0.02 N,** containing 40 ml. concentrated $H_2SO_4$ per liter of reagent.

**Sodium Carbonate Solution, 4 N.**

**Sulfuric Acid Solution, 7 N.**

**Sodium Arsenite (Na$_3$AsO$_3$) Solution, 0.2 N,** containing 20 g. NaCl per liter.

*Procedure.*—Add 1 ml. Na$_2$CO$_3$ plus 3 ml. $H_2SO_4$ to 3.0 ml. of the aqueous solution containing the iodide in the range 0.02 to 0.06 microgram. (*Caution: avoid loss due to effervescence.*) Add 2.0 ml. of 0.2 N Na$_3$AsO$_3$ to a 3.0-ml. aliquot

[26] Sandell, E. B., and Kolthoff, I. M., J. Am. Chem. Soc., **56**, 1426, 1934; Mickrochem Acta, **1**, 9, 1951; Chaney, A. L., Ind. Eng. Chem., Anal. Ed., **12**, 179, 1940; Brode, W. K., J. Am. Chem. Soc., **48**, 1877, 1926; Lambert, J. L., Arthur, P., and Moore, T. E., Anal. Chem., **23**, 1101, 1951; Moran, K. K., *ibid.*, **24**, 378, 1952; Zak, B., Willard, H. H., Meyers, G. B., and Boyle, A. J., *ibid.*, **24**, 1345, 1952.

[27] Lein, A., and Schwartz, N., Anal. Chem., **23**, 1507, 1951.

[28] Meyer, K. R., Dickenman, R. C., White, E. G., and Zak, B., Am. J. Clin. Pathol., **25**, 1160, 1955; see also Barker, S. B., Humphrey, M. J., and Soley, M. H., J. Clin. Invest., **30**, 55, 1951 for a description of a kinetic curve technique.

of the solution in a cuvette, mix, and equilibrate the solution in a water bath at 35°C.

Pipette 1 ml. of 0.02 N ceric ammonium sulfate solution into each tube at exactly 1 minute intervals and place the tubes in the water bath. At the end of exactly 20 minutes for each tube, measure the absorbance of 420 mμ with a spectrophotometer using a water blank. Determine the concentration of iodide from a calibration curve prepared from analyses carried out in exactly the same manner.

Addition of 1 ml. of 17% mercuric acetate (in a 1% solution of acetic acid) to the solution after an arbitrary, fixed time arrests the reaction rate and enables the absorbance to be read more conveniently.

NOTE.—Iodide is known to affect catalytically the rates of several reactions, among which are the permanganate oxidation of As(III) [29] and the reaction of sulfite with methylene blue; [30] the fading red color of the Fe(III)-SCN complexes is accelerated in the presence of iodide.[31]

## THE SPECTROPHOTOMETRIC DETERMINATION OF IODINE AS THE TRIIODIDE ION [32, 33]

This procedure provides a sensitive method for the determination of iodine. The reaction for the formation of the triiodide ion from iodine and iodide has been given under "Preparation and Solution of the Sample." The procedure which follows is that of Custer and Natelson.[33]

*Reagents.* Potassium Permanganate Solution, 1%.

Sodium Hydroxide Solution, 1%.

Hydrogen Peroxide Solution, 6%.

Sulfuric Acid Solution, 5%.

Toluene.

Potassium Iodide Solutions, 1% and 5%.

*Procedure.*—Pipette 0.2 ml. of the iodide into a graduated centrifuge tube (5.0 ml. capacity) and treat with 0.1 ml. of the NaOH solution and 0.1 ml. of the $KMnO_4$ solution. Place the centrifuge tube containing the permanganate in a boiling water bath for ½ hour and cool in a refrigerator, then in an ice bath and add the cold $H_2O_2$ solution dropwise to decolorize the permanganate. Next heat the solution for one hour at 37°C. and allow to stand at room temperature overnight to decompose the excess $H_2O_2$; dilute to 2 ml. and centrifuge for 15 minutes. Remove an aliquot of 1.5 ml. to a 12-ml. glass-stoppered centrifuge tube and add 1 ml. of 1% KI solution and 0.2 ml. 5% $H_2SO_4$ solution. Add 1.8 toluene and shake for 10 minutes. Centrifuge the solution and transfer the toluene layer to a 1 cm quartz cuvette and read the absorbance on a spectrophotometer at 311 mμ.

Among other procedures that lend themselves to the colorimetric determination of iodine may be mentioned the reaction of iodine with alphanaphtholflavone which yields a blue-colored compound suitable for spectrophotometric measurement; the reaction with o-tolidine to produce a blue-green compound (chlorine

[29] Feigl, F., Chemistry of Specific, Selective and Sensitive Reactions, pp. 561–2, Academic Press, Inc., New York, 1949.

[30] Lundgren, H. P., J. Am. Chem. Soc., 59, 413, 1937.

[31] Iwasaki, I., Utsumi, S., and Ozowa, T., Bull. Chem. Soc. Japan, 26, 108, 1953.

[32] Brode, W. R., J. Am. Chem. Soc., 48, 1877, 1926.

[33] Custer, J. J., and Natelson, S., Anal. Chem., 21, 1005, 1949; Shahrokh, B. K., and Chesebro, R. M., ibid., 21, 1003, 1959.

also reacts with this reagent to form a colored substance, hence should be absent from solution when iodine is to be determined). Pyrogallol in the presence of iodate yields purpurgallin which exhibits a reddish-brown color. Iodine reacts also with dioxane.

A. F. Scott and F. H. Hurley [34] have developed a procedure for the turbidimetric measurement of iodine as AgI.

## ELECTROMETRIC METHODS

The intermediate oxidizing strength of iodine plus the excellent electrochemical reversibility of the iodine-iodide couple, combined with the fact that the oxidation-reduction behavior of the element can be directly related to acid-base chemistry through the hydrolysis of iodine, provide a very large number of excellent electrometric methods for the determination of this element. These methods, along with experimental procedures, have been reviewed extensively in the recent literature.[35]

It suffices at this point to mention but briefly a few interesting and frequently encountered methods of determination. Iodide may best be determined potentiometrically by titration of the unknown with a standard solution of $AgNO_3$, using a silver wire indicating electrode to reflect the large change in potential at the end point. The clarity of the end point in the titration of strong iodide (0.1 $M$) is somewhat lessened by the pronounced tendency of the AgI precipitate to absorb iodide prior to the equivalence point; low concentrations, however, can be determined with great accuracy.

MacNevin et al., developed a coulogravimetric technique which may be applied to the simultaneous determination of $Br^-$ and $I^-$ in aqueous solution; Lingane developed a procedure for the determination of iodide by coulometric generation of Ag(I), and Przybylowicz and Rogers, and DeFord and Hume determined $I^-$ by coulometric generation of Hg(I). Lingane and Small have determined $I^-$ by controlled potential coulometry, and Delahay has described the chronopotentiometric reduction of iodate.

Iodine may be determined polarographically at the dropping mercury electrode by measuring the anodic wave due to the depolarization of the mercury by the iodide.

Laitinen, Jennings and Parks have successfully employed the two-electrode amperometric technique for the simultaneous determination of $Cl^-$, $Br^-$ and $I^-$.

## MICRODIFFUSION METHOD

### THE DETERMINATION OF IODINE BY MICRODIFFUSION [36]

Iodine may be determined by the method of microdiffusion, or "isothermal distillation" which makes use of the Conway diffusion cell shown in Fig. 24-1.

*Procedure.*—The solution containing the iodide is placed in the annular space separating the two concentric tubes, the inner one of which is shorter than the

[34] Scott, A. F., and Hurley, F. H., J. Am. Chem. Soc., **56,** 333, 1934.

[35] See, for example, J. J. Lingane, Electroanalytical Chemistry, 2nd Edition, Interscience Publishers, Inc., New York, 1958, for a comprehensive review of electroanalytic methods.

[36] Conway, Edward J., Microdiffusion Analysis and Volumetric Error, p. 187, Crosby Lockwood & Sons, Ltd., London, 1947.

outer tube. A 20% solution of KI or a solution of starch is placed in the inner well to absorb the iodine; $K_2Cr_2O_7$ and $H_2SO_4$ are next placed in the outer, annular compartment, and a cover glass temporarily sealed on top of the appara-

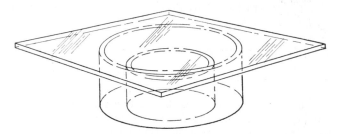

Fig. 24-1. Conway Microdiffusion Cell with Glass Cover.

tus with petroleum jelly plus paraffin. The cell is then rotated gently to allow the iodine to pass over into the KI; the resulting solution in the center well may then be titrated in the usual way with a standard solution of thiosulfate, and iodine determined.

## DETERMINATIONS IN SPECIFIC SUBSTANCES

### IODINE, ITS DETERMINATION IN TRACES AS EXISTING IN FEEDSTUFF, WATER, PLANTS, SOILS, TISSUES AND ALLIED MATERIALS [37]

The principal points to be emphasized in the determination of iodine are: (a) thorough destruction of the organic portion, without loss of iodine; (b) its extraction and measurement; (c) the use throughout of reagents that are iodine-free.[38]

Apparatus [39] for the destruction of the carbonaceous material are of the open and closed form, either in acid or alkali media. The modified closed type suggested by McClendon and Remington [40] because of its simplicity will, no doubt, be welcomed for certain types of work in iodine determinations. In the estimation of very small quantities ranging from 0.0004 to 0.001 mg. extreme care must be exercised; [41] in such cases, one should consult the original papers of von Fellenbergs,[42] R. L. Andrew [43] and Leitch and Henderson.[44]

*Preparation of the Sample.*—For the determination of iodine in 10.0 ml. of blood see Turner.[41]    For the determination of iodine in soils see Andrew.[43]    In general, for samples with estimated amounts of 0.05 mg. or more the following

[37] Contributed by W. D. Leech.
[38] Reith, J. F., Biochem. Z., **216**, 249, 1929.
[39] von Schwaibold, J., Z. anal. Chem., **78**, 161, 1929.
[40] Remington *et alii*, J. Am. Chem. Soc., **52**, 3, 1930; McClendon, Remington *et alii*, J. Am. Chem. Soc., **52**, 2, 1930.
[41] Turner, R. G., J. Biol. Chem., **88**, 2, 1930.
[42] von Fellenbergs, T., Biochem. Z., **139**, 371, 1923, and **152**, 116, 1924; von Fellenbergs, Ergeb. Physiol., **25**, 176, 1926.
[43] Andrew, R. L., Analyst, **55**, 649, 1930.
[44] Leitch and Henderson, Biochem. J., **20**, 1003, 1926.

method will suffice. Samples of high water content are dried in an oven at 110°C. from 4–5 hours; in rare cases of high fat content, the sample is extracted with ether, though this usually is not advisable. After dehydration the sample is pulverized. It is now ready to be weighed and treated as follows, which is essentially the modified method of Kendall[45] as suggested by Kelly and Husband.[46]

*Procedure.*—Place the dried sample of 0.5 to 2.0 g. in a 100-ml. nickel crucible; cover with 40.0% NaOH solution, and heat in an oven for one-half hour. Place the nickel crucible inside another crucible having sand in the bottom and heat gently over a low flame. When frothing has ceased, add about 5 g. of powdered or flaked NaOH. A few milligrams of $KNO_3$ are added at a time until all carbon is completely oxidized. Cool the melt and extract with boiling water (iodine free). The temperature must be carefully regulated at this stage to insure complete oxidation, yet not be high enough to volatilize any of the iodine. Transfer the extract to a 700-ml. conical flask (filtering if necessary). The cooled solution is then neutralized with concentrated $H_3PO_4$, using methyl orange as indicator; add 2 to 3 ml. in excess. The solution is then boiled for 15–20 minutes to expel any nitrous acid. Add 2 ml. of 20% sodium acid sulfite solution and boil for 10 minutes to drive off any $SO_2$. Usually pieces of broken porcelain are added at this point to prevent bumping.

On cooling, add 5 to 10 drops of bromine, at least to a distinctly brown color. (Various workers prefer to saturate the solution with chlorine in order to oxidize the iodide to iodate; however, care must be used in the amount added and the duration of boiling to remove the excess. Chlorine is added until a drop of methyl orange is decolorized instantly, followed by two minutes of boiling. Chlorine generated from NaCl, $MnO_2$ and $H_2SO_4$ seems to be safe for the above use, but not chlorine from calcium hypochlorite.) Boil at least 5 minutes after the color of bromine has disappeared to remove the last trace of bromine. Add a few crystals of salicylic acid to liberate any trace of bromine. When the solution is cooled, the unglazed porcelain is removed. The KI solution (0.25 g. of recrystallized KI in 20.0 ml. of iodine-free water) is added with 2 ml. of starch solution.[47] The liberated iodine is titrated with 0.005 N thiosulfate (thiosulfate prepared daily from 0.1 N solution; it may be preserved by adding a crystal of thymol to the 0.1 N solution). The 0.005 N thiosulfate solution should be standardized each day by titrating the released iodine from a standard iodate solution. In this method six times the amount of iodine is titrated as occurs in the unknown sample thus:

$$IO_3^- + 5I^- + 6H^+ \rightarrow 3I_2 + 3H_2O, \text{ and}$$

$$I_2 + 2S_2O_3^= \rightarrow 2I^- + S_4O_6^=$$

In this procedure, the starch solution is prepared by making a paste of 0.5 g. of potato starch, adding to 200 ml. of hot water, boiling for 15 minutes, stirring continually. Cool, add 0.2 g. of salicyclic acid and stir until the crystals dissolve. Iodine-free water is obtained by redistilling distilled water from KOH; KI is purified from traces of iodate by recrystallizing the salt from alcohol and finally from iodine-free water, the alcohol being previously distilled over potassium hydroxide.

[45] Kendall, J. Biol. Chem., **40**, 216, 1920.
[46] Kelly and Husband. Biochem. J., **18**, 951, 1924.
[47] Nichols, Ind. Eng. Chem., Anal. Ed., **1**, 4, 1929.

A control on the reagents should be run, as well as a sample of known iodine content if possible.

## METHODS FOR IODINE IN ANALYSIS IN OTHER CHAPTERS

Carius Method for Organic Compounds      See Chlorine Chapter

# Chapter 25

# IRON *

*Fe, at. wt.* 55.847; *sp. gr.* 7.87–7.88; *m.p. pure* 1537°C., *wrought* 1500°C., *white pig* 1075°C., *gray pig* 1275°C., *steel* 1300°C.; *b.p.* 3000°C.; *ore oxides,* FeO, $Fe_2O_3$, $Fe_3O_4$.

Iron was used during the early history of man in making weapons and tools. It was known to the Assyrians and Egyptians. The production of iron is mentioned in the Pentateuch. High grade steel was manufactured in Arabia and Spain during the Middle Ages. Pure iron finds little commercial use, but with small amounts of other elements it is one of the most important materials used in the industries. The determination of the constituents in ferrous alloys, in pig iron, wrought iron, and steel has received a vast amount of attention by chemists and the published analyses predominate with methods dealing with this subject.

Next to aluminum, iron is the most abundant of the metals. The free element occurs sparingly as small grains in certain rocks, as masses in basalt, and alloyed in meteorites. It occurs as both the divalent and trivalent oxidation states combined as ferrous and ferric compounds, and is found in a very large number of widely distributed minerals; the yellow to red color of soils is often due to the presence of iron compounds. Among the more common natural compounds and minerals are: ferrous oxide, FeO; ferric oxide (hematite), $Fe_2O_3$; magnetite, $Fe_3O_4$; limonite, $Fe(OH)_6 \cdot Fe_2O_3$; siderite, $FeCO_3$; pyrrhotite, $Fe_nS_n$; pyrite (fool's gold), and marcasite, $FeS_2$; chalcopyrite, $CuFeS_2$; chromite, $FeO \cdot Cr_2O_3$; göthite, $Fe_2O_3 \cdot H_2O$; almandite, $Fe_3Al_2(SiO_4)_3$; andradite, $Ca_3Fe_2(SiO_4)_3$; ilmenite, $FeTiO_3$; and a large number of combinations with other elements such as manganese, magnesium, zinc, sodium, potassium, nickel, copper, tungsten, lead, arsenic, antimony, etc.

## DETECTION

*Ferric Iron.*—A hydrochloric acid solution of ferric iron is colored a pure yellow; at high concentrations of HCl (e.g., 6 *M*) a large part of the iron is most probably in the form of chloroferric acid, $HFeCl_4$.

*Potassium or Ammonium Thiocyanate* produces red-colored complex ions upon addition to a solution containing ferric iron; [1] ferrous iron yields no color with thiocyanate. The red color of the ferric thiocyanate complexes is stable to heat which is not true of the color produced by nitric or chloric acid. The color of the thiocyanate complexes, unless stabilized with persulfate $S_2O_8^{-2}$, or $H_2O_2$, fades with time. The red color of ferric iron with the cyanate is destroyed by mer-

---

* This chapter revised by Dr. Edward G. Moorehead of Harvard University.

[1] Bent, H. E., and French, C. L., J. Am. Chem. Soc., **63**, 568, 1947; Edmonds, S. M., and Birnbaum, N., *ibid.*, **63**, 1741, 1941; Gould, R. K., and Vosburgh, W. C., *ibid.*, **64**, 1631, 1942; Frank, H. S., and Oswalt, R. L., *ibid.*, **69**, 1321, 1947.

curic chloride and by phosphates, borates, certain organic acids and their salts, e.g., acetic, oxalic, tartaric, citric, malic and succinic acids.

*Thioglycollic (mercaptoacetic) acid, SHCH₂·CO₂H* when added as an ammoniacal solution to ferrous or ferric iron, forms a soluble reddish-purple complex ion; $\alpha,\alpha'$-bipyridyl reacts similarly.

*Potassium ferrocyanide, K₄Fe(CN)₆*, produces a deep blue color with solutions of ferric salts.

*Salicylic acid* added to the solution of a ferric salt containing no free mineral acid gives a violet color. Useful for detecting iron in alum and similar products.

*Ferrous Iron.*—Potassium ferricyanide, $K_3Fe(CN)_6$, gives a blue color with solutions of ferrous salts.

**Distinction between Ferrous and Ferric Salts.**—KCNS gives red color with $Fe^{+3}$ and no color with $Fe^{++}$.

$K_3Fe(CN)_6$ gives a blue color with $Fe^{++}$ and a brown or green with $Fe^{+3}$.

**NH₄OH, NaOH,** or **KOH** precipitates reddish-brown, $Fe(OH)_3$ with $Fe^{+3}$ and white, $Fe(OH)_2$ with $Fe^{++}$, turning green in presence of air due to oxidation.[2]

**Sodium peroxide** produces a reddish-brown precipitate of $Fe(OH)_3$ with either ferrous or ferric salt solutions, the former being oxidized to the higher valence by the peroxide. Chromium and aluminum remain in solution, if present in the sample.

**1,10-Phenanthroline** gives an orange-red color with ferrous iron and a light blue with ferric. The red color of the ferrous complex is best developed in the pH range 2–9; at pH less than 2, the color is weak and slowly formed.

## ESTIMATION

Iron is so widely diffused in nature that its determination is necessary in practically all complete analyses of ores, rocks, minerals, etc. It is especially important in the evaluation of iron ores for the manufacture of iron and steel.

In the process of wet analysis iron is generally obtained in solution, after separation of silica, as the ferric salt and is precipitated, together with aluminum, etc., as the hydrous oxide by addition of ammonia. It is determined most satisfactorily by a titration procedure, preferably on a separate sample from the aluminum precipitate. If the original valences are desired, one portion is run for total iron and another for ferrous or ferric iron, care being exercised to prevent oxidation or reduction in obtaining the solution.

### PREPARATION AND SOLUTION OF THE SAMPLE

The material should be carefully sampled and quartered down according to the general procedure for sampling. Ores should be ground to pass an 80-mesh sieve. In analysis of metals, both the coarse and fine drillings are taken.

The methods of attack used on iron containing ores and minerals are varied. The ores, etc., are usually brought into solution by treatment with HCl or $HNO_3$ or both, or by means of fluxes such as $K_2CO_3$ or $Na_2CO_3$ followed by HCl or by fusion with $KHSO_4$. The more recalcitrant ores may be fused with pyrosulfate or acid fluoride. Sulfides and arsenides or iron are best fused with an alkali flux, as the subsequent water extraction provides a good means for the separation of As, P, V, and Mo from base metals.

---

[2] The green salt is a hydrate of $Fe_3O_4$. The white precipitate can be obtained in absence of air or by using $H_2SO_3$ to take up oxygen in solution.

Ferrous iron may be oxidized with $Cl_2$, $Br_2$, $HNO_3$, or $H_2O_2$.

The following facts regarding solubility should be remembered: The element is soluble in hydrochloric acid and in dilute sulfuric acid, forming ferrous salts with liberation of hydrogen. It is insoluble in concentrated, cold sulfuric acid, but is attacked by the hot acid, forming ferric sulfate with liberation of $SO_2$. Moderately dilute, hot nitric acid forms ferric nitrate and nitrous oxide; the cold acid gives ferrous nitrate and ammonium nitrate or nitrous oxide or hydrogen. Cold, concentrated nitric acid forms "passive iron," which remains insoluble in the acid. The oxides of iron are readily soluble in hydrochloric acid, if not too strongly ignited, but upon strong ignition the higher oxides dissolve with extreme difficulty. They are readily soluble, however, by fusion with acid potassium sulfate followed by an acid extraction. Silicates are best dissolved by hot hydrochloric acid containing a few drops of hydrofluoric acid or by fusion with sodium and potassium carbonates, followed by hot hydrochloric acid.

**Soluble Iron Salts.**—Water solutions are acidified with HCl or $H_2SO_4$, so as to contain about 3% of the free acid. HCl is to be preferred, as this is less likely to interfere after the precipitation of the $H_2S$ elements.

**Ores.**—The samples should be pulverized to pass an 80- to 100-mesh sieve.

**Sulfides, Ores Containing Organic Matter.**—One- to 5-gram samples should be roasted in a porcelain crucible over a Bunsen flame for about half an hour, until oxidized. The oxide is now dissolved as directed in the following procedure.

**Oxides, Including Red and Brown Hematites, Magnetic Iron Ore, Spathose Iron Ore, Roasted Pyrites, and Iron Ore Briquettes.**—One to 5 grams of the ore, placed in a 400-ml. beaker, is dissolved by adding twenty times its weight of concentrated hydrochloric acid with a few drops of 5% stannous chloride solution. Addition of 4 or 5 drops of HF is advantageous if small amounts of silica are present. The solution is covered with a watch-glass and heated to 80° or 90°C. until solution is complete. Addition of more stannous chloride may be necessary, as this greatly assists solution. An excess sufficient to decolorize the solution completely necessitates reoxidation with hydrogen peroxide, hence should be avoided. If a colored residue remains, it should be filtered off, ignited, and fused with a mixture of $Na_2CO_3$ and $K_2CO_3$ in a platinum crucible. The fusion dissolved in dilute HCl is added to the main filtrate.

NOTE.—The ore placed in a porcelain boat in a red-hot combustion tube may be reduced with hydrogen (taking precaution first to sweep out oxygen with $CO_2$) and, after cooling in an atmosphere of hydrogen, the reduced iron may be dissolved in acid and titrated.

**Iron Silicates. Solution with Hydrofluoric Acid.**—One to 5 grams of the material, placed in a deep platinum crucible, is treated with ten times its weight of 60% HF and 3 to 4 drops of concentrated $H_2SO_4$. The mixture is evaporated nearly to dryness on the steam bath and taken up with dilute sulfuric acid or hydrochloric acid. The latter acid is the best solvent for iron.

**Fusion with Potassium Bisulfate.**—The sample is mixed with ten times its weight of the powdered bisulfate and 2–3 ml. of concentrated sulfuric acid added. A porcelain or silica dish will do for this fusion. The fusion should be made over a moderate flame and cooled as soon as the molten liquid becomes clear. Complete expulsion of $SO_3$ should be avoided. It may be necessary to cool and add more concentrated sulfuric acid to effect solution. Iron and alumina completely dissolve, but silica remains undissolved. The melt is best cooled by pouring it on a large platinum lid.

**Fusion with Carbonates of Sodium and Potassium.**—The residues insoluble in hydrochloric acid are fused with 5 parts by weight of the fusion mixture ($Na_2CO_3$ + $K_2CO_3$) in a platinum crucible. The Meker blast will be necessary. When the effervescence has ceased and the melt has become clear, the crucible is removed from the flame, a platinum wire inserted and the melt cooled. Upon gently reheating, the fused material may be readily removed by the wire in a convenient form for solution in dilute hydrochloric acid.

The bisulfate fusion is recommended for fusion of residues high in iron and alumina. It is an excellent solvent for ignited oxides of these elements. The carbonate fusions are adapted to residues containing silica.

## SEPARATIONS

Among the more important methods for the separation of iron from accompanying elements are the following:

1. Precipitation with $H_2S$ in a weakly acidic solution which separates iron from elements such as Hg, Pb, Bi, As, etc. Iron is left in solution.

2. Solution of the ammonium hydroxide precipitate in sulfuric acid followed by addition of tartrate, then precipitation of the iron (also Zn, Co, Ni, and some Mn, if these are present) with $H_2S$ in a solution made alkaline with ammonium hydroxide; aluminum remains in solution as the complexed tartrate. The iron sulfide is dissolved in HCl, $H_2S$ is then expelled by heating, and the metal determined.

3. Precipitation of iron with NaOH which separates it from such elements as V, W, Mo, As, Al, etc. (fusion with $Na_2CO_3$ and extraction with water accomplishes a similar separation).

4. Extraction with a nonaqueous solvent: iron may be extracted from a concentrated (6–8 $M$) HCl solution into ethyl, dichloroethyl, or isopropyl ether [3] saturated with HCl; as the 8-quinolinate [4] or cupferrate [5] into chloroform which separates iron from Mn, Ni, Cr, and Al; from concentrated HCl or LiCl solutions into Hexone.[6] Solvent extraction affords a means of separating large amounts of iron from solution.

In addition to the foregoing, several other methods of separating iron may be mentioned.

1. Homogeneous solution precipitation of ferric formate by hydrolysis of urea [7] to separate iron from Mn, Co, Ni, Cu, Zn, Cd, Mg, Ca, and Ba.

[3] Rothe, J. W., Stahl u. Eisen, **12,** 1052, 1892; Noyes, Bray, Spear, J. Am. Chem. Soc., **30,** 515, 1908; Swift, E. H., *ibid.,* **46,** 2378, 1924; Houben, J., and Fischer, W., J. prakt. Chem., **123,** 89, 1929; Dodson, R. W., Forney, G. J., and Swift, E. H., J. Am. Chem. Soc., **58,** 2573, 1936; Axelrod, J., and Swift, E. H., *ibid.,* **62,** 33, 1940; Meyers, R. J., Meltzler, D. E., and Swift, E. H., *ibid.,* **72,** 3767, 1950; Laurene, A. H., Campbell, D. E., Campbell, S. E., Wiberly, S. E., and Clark, H. M., J. Phys. Chem., **60,** 901, 1956; Saldick, J., *ibid.,* **60,** 500, 1956.

[4] Moeller, T., Ind. Eng. Chem., Anal. Ed., **15,** 271, 346, 1943; Gentry, C. H. R., and Sherrington, L. G., Analyst, **75,** 17, 1950; see Merritt, L. L., and Walker, J. K., Ind. Eng. Chem., Anal. Ed., **16,** 387, 1944, for the use of 2-methyl-8-quinolinol in separating Fe and Al.

[5] Furman, N. H., Mason, W. B., and Pekola, J. S., Anal. Chem., **21,** 1325, 1949.

[6] Riedel, K., Z. anal. Chem., **159,** 110, 1957; Specker, H., Arch. Eisenhuttenw., **29,** 467, 1958.

[7] Willard, H. H., and Sheldon, J. L., Anal. Chem., **22,** 1162, 1950.

2. Iron is completely separated from Cu, Cd, Ni, Zn, and Co by the addition of pyridine [8] to a solution slightly acidified with HCl.

3. Precipitation of iron cupferrate.

4. Separation by ion exchange.

5. Separation of iron from Al, Ti, Zr, P, V, and U by rapid electrolysis with a mercury cathode from a 1.0 $N$ $H_2SO_4$ solution.

In the usual course of analysis silica is removed by evaporating the acid solution to dryness, taking up with water, and filtering. Hg, Pb, Bi, Cu, Cd, As, Sb, Sn, Mo, and other elements precipitated from an acid solution as sulfides are removed as such by filtration and iron, after oxidation to the ferric state, is precipitated as $Fe(OH)_3$. In the majority of cases it may now be determined by titration.

**Ether Procedure for Removing Iron from a Solution.**—Ferric chloride dissolved in HCl (sp. gr. 1.1) is more soluble in ether than in this acid. Advantage is taken of this fact when it is desired to remove a greater portion of the iron in determining copper, nickel, cobalt, chromium, vanadium, and sulfur (as $H_2SO_4$) in steel. The hydrochloric acid solution of iron, etc., is evaporated to a syrupy consistency and then taken up with HCl (sp. gr. 1.1) and transferred by means of more of the acid to a separatory funnel. The cold acid solution is now extracted several times by shaking with ether, each time allowing the ether carrying the iron to separate before drawing off the lower layer for re-extraction. Three extractions are generally sufficient for removing the iron.

Since alkali salts cause trouble by crystallizing and clogging the borings of the stopcock, the use of alkalies should be avoided when this method of separation is used. The iron may be extracted from the ether by shaking this with water and drawing off the lower water layer. Since heat is generated by the mixing of ether and the ferric chloride-hydrochloric acid solution, cooling the mixture under the tap during mixing may be necessary. This heating is reduced by using a mixture of ether and hydrochloric acid. Concentrated hydrochloric acid (sp. gr. 1.19) is saturated with ether, an excess of ether separating out as an upper layer. One hundred ml. of the acid will absorb 150 ml. ether. (Dilute hydrochloric acid (sp. gr. 1.1) absorbs only 30 ml. ether.)

The ether should be free from alcohol and the solution extracted should not contain substances which decompose ether, e.g., $HNO_3$, $Cl_2$, etc. If copper and nickel are present at high concentration in the aqueous phase, there is danger that a small quantity will be extracted along with the iron. "Continuous extraction" of Fe(III) with diethyl ether affords a practically complete separation of this element; only a few micrograms remain in the aqueous layer. Fig. 25-1 shows the continuous extraction apparatus developed by Heberling which can be used for the separation of iron.

**The Extraction of Ferric Chloride from Hydrochloric Acid Solutions by Isopropyl Ether.**—The efficiency of the extraction with isopropyl ether is very dependent on the acid concentration; the optimum range is 7.75–8.25 moles HCl per liter, in which range the extraction of ferric chloride is 99.8–99.9% complete.

Isopropyl ether offers marked advantages over ethyl ether for the extraction of ferric iron from aqueous hydrochloric acid solutions, giving a more efficient extraction over a wider range of acid concentrations than does ethyl ether.

[8] Furman, N. H., Haight, Jr., G. P., and McDuffie, B., Atomic Energy Report A-1054 (CC-G), Aug. 31, 1944, Sec. 2-E.

A very satisfactory separation of iron from copper, cobalt, manganese, nickel, aluminum, chromium, zinc, vanadium(IV), titanium, and sulfur may be obtained. Large amounts of vanadium(V) are extracted; phosphoric acid, and molybdenum pass into the ether layer with ferric iron.

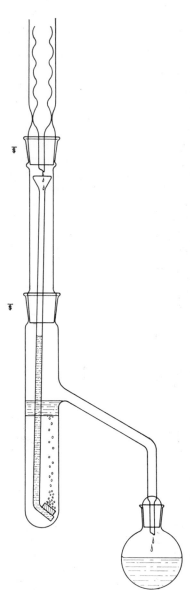

*Extraction of Ferric Cupferrate.*—Iron cupferrate is soluble to varying degrees in chloroform, diethyl ether, and esters (e.g., amyl acetate) among other solvents. Iron is an example of several metals that form insoluble cupferrates in acid solution, and advantage may be taken of this fact to separate iron from Al and Cu. Following is a series of cupferrate solubility product constants expressed as the negative logarithm: Cu(II)—16, Al—18.7, Fe(III)—25, Bi—27.2, Sn(IV)—34.1.

**Extraction of Ferric Cupferrate by Chloroform.**—The chloride solution containing the ferric iron is made acid (1:9) with HCl, cooled, then placed in a separatory funnel. A 6% solution of recrystallized cupferron is added in excess of the amount of iron present, and the aqueous phase extracted immediately with a convenient volume of chloroform (alternatively, the aqueous phase may be extracted directly with a chloroform solution of hydrogen cupferrate). It has been found that equilibrium is attained after shaking with the solvent for two minutes. Ordinarily, one extraction of the aqueous phase with an equal volume of chloroform is sufficient to remove all the iron. The iron may be recovered from the chloroform layer by evaporation followed by a treatment of the residue with nitric acid to destroy organic matter then with sulfuric acid to fumes of sulfur trioxide.

After separation from the chloroform, the iron is taken up with water and determined either by precipitation with ammonium hydroxide followed by ignition to the oxide or colorimetrically by the addition of 1,10-phenanthroline after reduction of the iron to the divalent state with hydroquinone or hydroxylamine hydrochloride. A large amount of chloride is to be avoided as this decreases the quantity of iron extracted.

FIG. 25-1. Apparatus for Continuous Extraction.

NOTE.—Chloroform may be used also to extract iron from (1:9) $H_2SO_4$ solutions.

Both cupferron and its chelates are unstable to heat, decomposing to form nitrobenzene. For this reason, cupferron is used in the cold. Decomposition may be retarded by addition of 50 mg. acetophenetidine to each 150 ml. of reagent solution.

*Separation of Iron with Cupferron.*—Details of the procedure are given under "Gravimetric Methods." Titanium, vanadium, and zirconium accompany the iron. Aluminum, cadmium, cobalt, chromium, manganese, nickel, and zinc are separated by this precipitation. The method is not commonly employed.

*Separation of Iron (with any Co, Mn, Ni, Zn) from Aluminum (with any U, V, Nb, Ta, Ti, P, Zr).*—Details of precipitation as FeS in presence of tartrate are given under "Gravimetric Methods."

Separation of iron from aluminum may also be effected by pouring the solution into a strong solution of a fixed alkali, NaOH or KOH, or $Na_2O_2$. In the latter reagent chromium also passes into solution with aluminum and as with the other reagents iron precipitates as the hydroxide.

## GRAVIMETRIC METHODS

The gravimetric determination of iron may be made from solutions practically free from other metals. A number of elements such as phosphorus, arsenic, molybdenum, tungsten, and vanadium, in neutral or slightly alkaline solutions, form fairly stable compounds with iron, whereas others such as lead, copper, nickel, cobalt, sodium, and potassium may be occluded in the ferric hydroxide precipitate and are removed only with considerable difficulty. Aluminum, chromium, and several of the rare earths are precipitated with iron, if present. When these facts are taken into consideration, the titrimetric methods are generally preferred as being more rapid and trustworthy.

### DETERMINATION OF IRON AS $Fe_2O_3$

Iron is precipitated as the hydrous ferric oxide and ignited to the oxide, $Fe_2O_3$, in which form it is weighed.

**Reactions.—**

$$2Fe^{+3} + 6NH_3 + (x + 3)H_2O \rightarrow Fe_2O_3 \cdot xH_2O + 6NH_4^+$$

$$Fe_2O_3 \cdot xH_2O \rightarrow Fe_2O_3 + xH_2O$$

*Procedure.*—A one gram sample, or a larger amount of material if the iron content is low, is brought into solution with hydrochloric acid, aqua regia, or by fusion with potassium carbonate or potassium acid sulfate, as the case may require. Silica is filtered off and the acid solution treated with $H_2S$ if elements of Groups I and II (i.e., lead, mercury, silver, copper, cadmium, bismuth, arsenic, antimony or tin) are present. If elements of Analytical Group III are present, two alternate procedures are available, depending on whether they include aluminum or chromium.

**Separation of Iron from Group III Elements Including Aluminum and Chromium.**—By the following procedure iron is separated from aluminum, chromium, niobium, phosphorus, tantalum, titanium, uranium, vanadium, and zirconium; however, cobalt, manganese, nickel, and zinc accompany the iron. Two to three grams of tartaric acid per 100 ml. of solution are added, followed by $NH_4OH$ until faintly alkaline; if a precipitate forms, it is dissolved by adding dropwise HCl and then more tartaric acid. The solution is saturated with $H_2S$, then made ammoniacal and again saturated with $H_2S$. The sulfide of iron is precipitated (together with Co, Mn, Ni, and Zn). The precipitate is filtered off and washed with water containing 1% of ammonium tartrate. It is generally advisable to dissolve the sulfide and reprecipitate it, when greater accuracy is desired. The sulfide is now dissolved in HCl, the solution boiled to expel $H_2S$ and the iron oxidized by addition of $H_2O_2$ or $Br_2$ water.

Iron is now precipitated as ferric hydroxide by addition of ammonium hydroxide, the precipitate is filtered off, and washed with water (if the solution contains sulfate, a large excess of ammonium hydroxide is to be avoided, as insoluble basic sulfates are likely to form). The precipitate is again dissolved in HCl and the ferric hydroxide reprecipitated to remove occluded substances. Dissolve the precipitate with the least amount of hot dilute hydrochloric acid and wash the paper free of iron. Add a few milliliters of 10% ammonium chloride solution and reprecipitate the hydroxide of iron by adding an excess of ammonium hydroxide, the volume of the solution being about 200 ml. Washing the precipitate by decantation is advisable. Three such washings, 100-ml. portions, followed by two or three on filter paper, will remove all impurities.

In place of ammonium hydroxide, powdered sodium peroxide is added in small portions until the precipitate first formed clears, the solution being cold and nearly neutral. It is diluted to about 300 ml. and boiled 10 to 15 minutes to precipitate the iron. Aluminum and chromium stay in solution. (Mn will precipitate with Fe, if present.) The precipitate is filtered onto a rapid filter and washed with hot water.

**Separation of Iron from Group III Elements Other Than Aluminum and Chromium.**—About 1.0 g. of $NH_4Cl$ or its equivalent in solution is added, the volume made to about 200 ml., and ammonia added in slight excess to precipitate the ferric hydroxide. The solution is boiled for about five minutes, then filtered through an ashless filter paper, and reprecipitated in accordance with the above.

**Burning and Ignition.**—The wet filter paper and precipitate are placed in a tared crucible over a low, carefully controlled flame (Bunsen burner) and the paper burned off. Care must be taken to prevent the gases in the crucible from igniting, as incomplete combustion has a reducing effect on the ferric oxide. After the paper has been removed, the temperature is increased to the full heat of the Meker burner for about 20 minutes to the reddish-brown color of $Fe_2O_3$. Prolonged blasting causes a color change to black, the color of the magnetic oxide, $Fe_3O_4$.

The crucible is cooled for about 40 minutes in a desiccator, is then weighed and $Fe_2O_3$ determined.

Factors.

$$Fe_2O_3 \times 0.6994 = Fe$$

$$\times 0.8998 = FeO$$

# PRECIPITATION OF IRON WITH AMMONIUM NITROSO-PHENYLHYDROXYLAMINE (CUPFERRON) [9]

Cupferron is very general in its ability to precipitate the heavy metals, but it may be used effectively for the separation of iron from acid solutions of Al, Ni,

[9] Furman, N. H., Mason, W. B., and Pekola, J. S., Anal. Chem., **21,** 1325, 1949; Baudisch, O., Chem. Ztg., **33,** 1298, 1905; *ibid.,* **35,** 913, 1911; Baudisch, O., and King, V. L., J. Ind. Eng. Chem., **3,** 627, 1911; Lundell, G. E. F., and Knowles, H. B., Ind. Eng. Chem., **12,** 344, 1920; see Baudisch, O., and Holmes, S., Z. Anal. Chem., **119,** 241, 1940, for the use of Neo-cupferron in the precipitation of iron; Cupferron and Neo-Cupferron, G. Frederick Smith Chemical Company, Columbus, Ohio, 1938.

Co, Cr, Cd, Mn, and Zn. Titanium, V, and Zr accompany iron if present, and Hg, Pb, Bi, Sn, and Ag may be partially precipitated.

Although the ammonium salt is freely soluble in water, the parent compound, nitrosophenylhydroxylamine, is a weak acid ($pK_a = 4.3$) and separates out of solution as fine white crystals in the presence of strong mineral acids. The free acid is very unstable and decomposes into nitrobenzene and other products, and for this reason the reagent is always used cold. The reagent is stable, however, in neutral or basic solutions; light promotes its decomposition. Precipitates are best formed in relatively strong acids, but excessively strong acids decompose them, as do hot acids.

*Procedure.*—The solution containing the iron in the form of the chloride or sulfate is made up to 200 ml., and sufficient $H_2SO_4$ is added to make the solution about 10% acid by volume. Permanganate may be added to insure complete oxidation of the iron. The solution is cooled to 10°C. and 6% cupferron added slowly with stirring until further addition produces a white, silky precipitate of excess cupferron. The precipitate, with a little filter pulp if necessary, is allowed to stand for about 15 minutes and then transferred to an ashless filter paper and washed with cold 10% sulfuric (or hydrochloric) acid containing about 1.5 g. of cupferron per liter. The precipitate is washed with 6 N ammonia to remove excess precipitant and to aid in converting the iron cupferrate to oxide. (Removal of the organic matter lessens the chance of Fe(III) being reduced during ignition.) The drained precipitate is burned carefully to char the paper, then is ignited with the Meker burner to convert the Fe to $Fe_2O_3$.

Factor. $Fe_2O_3 \times 0.6994 = Fe$.

Note.—The ammonium salt of nitrosonaphthylhydroxylamine (Neo-Cupferron) forms precipitates with metals which generally are less soluble than those of cupferron. This has permitted the determination of smaller quantities of iron in many cases.

## PRECIPITATION OF IRON WITH 8-HYDROXYQUINOLINE [10]

Many metals are precipitated with 8-hydroxyquinoline (oxine, 8-quinolinol) but some measure of selectivity can be obtained by close control of the acidity. An advantage lies in its large equivalent weight which is negated, of course, in the precipitation of iron, if the oxinate is converted to the oxide prior to the final weighing. The precipitate of Fe(III) is among the least soluble of the hydroxyquinolinates, and, as in the case of trivalent ions, contains no water of crystallization. Oxine is an amphoteric substance whose solubility in water is least at pH of 7.4. This fact should be borne in mind when making precipitations near the neutral point. Many metals precipitating close to the pH of iron (2.8) should be separated from solution prior to the treatment with oxine as they often interfere through coprecipitation.

*Procedure.*—The slightly acidic solution of oxidized iron is treated with a 5% solution (5 g. of oxine plus 12 g. glacial acetic acid diluted to 100 ml. volume with distilled water) of the reagent. One to two ml. of the reagent are added in excess (or until the solution above the precipitate turns a straw color) and the volume is made up to 200 ml. The solution containing the precipitate is digested at 60–80°C. on the steam bath for about 20 minutes, 2 N ammonium acetate is added to adjust the pH to about 3.5 (a pH of 7 is recommended if iron occurs alone) and

10 Churnside, R. C., Pritchard, C. F., and Rooksby, H. P., Analyst, **66**, 399, 1941; Berg, R., Z. Anal. Chem., **71**, 369, 1927; *ibid.*, **76**, 191, 1929; Zanko, A. M., and Butenko, G. A., Zavordkaya Lab., **5**, 415, 1936; Brit. Chem. Abstr., **A1**, 264, 1937.

the solution is allowed to stand for about 15 minutes. The iron quinolinate is transferred to a glass crucible having a fritted disk and is washed several times with the acetate buffer, after which the precipitate (without removing from the crucible) is dried at 130°C. for 2–3 hours.

**Calculation.**—Wt. of Fe = $(0.1144) \times$ (Wt. of $Fe(C_9H_6ON)_3$).

NOTES.—Among the derivates of 8-hydroxyquinoline which have been studied as possible analytical reagents, 5,7-dibromo-8-hydroxyquinoline and 2-methyl-8-hydroxyquinoline (8-hydroxyquinaldine) are possibly the foremost. The former has the advantage of a higher equivalent weight but its solubility in aqueous solutions is very low. The latter reagent is advantageous in offering a greater selectivity of separation. This results from the steric hindrance offered by the adjacent methyl group. Iron, for example, may be readily separated from aluminum by use of this precipitant.

## PRECIPITATION OF IRON WITH α-NITROSO-β-NAPHTHOL [11]

The use of α-nitroso-β-naphthol as an organic precipitant for cobalt is well known, but in weakly acidic solutions, it will also precipitate Cu, Fe(III), Pd, Zr, Bi, Cr(III), Ag, Sn(IV), Ti, W(VI), U(VI), and V(V); under these conditions it will not precipitate Al, Sb, As, Be, Cd, Ca, Pb, Mn, Hg, Ni, Zn, nor the alkaline earths, or alkali metals.

The reagent is soluble in acetic acid, alcohol and benzene but is insoluble in water, and for this reason the potassium salt is generally used instead of the neutral compound.

*Procedure.*—The solution containing up to 0.25 g. of the metal as the sulfate or chloride is neutralized with ammonia until the first permanent precipitate occurs which is then just dissolved with HCl. A volume of 50% acetic acid equal to the original volume is added and the iron then precipitated by slow addition of a solution of α-nitroso-β-naphthol prepared by dissolving 10 g. of the neutral compound (or its equivalent as the potassium salt) in 500 ml. hot 1:1 acetic acid and filtering when cool. The precipitate, after standing for several hours, is filtered through a fritted glass filter crucible, washed with 50% acetic acid, then water and ignited to the ferric oxide. Phosphates must be absent as they contaminate the precipitate.

Factor.

$$Fe(C_{10}H_7NO_2)_3 \times 0.0971 = Fe$$

$$Fe_2O_3 \times 0.6994 = Fe$$

NOTE.—Fe(III) may be precipitated with the reagent in the presence of zirconium provided oxalic acid is present.

Metal precipitates of α-nitroso-β-naphthol are readily soluble in chloroform.

## TITRIMETRIC METHODS

Because iron may exist as the stable divalent or trivalent form in aqueous solution, two general approaches are available for its determination:

*A.* Oxidation of ferrous ion to ferric ion by standard oxidizing agents.

*B.* Reduction of ferric ion to ferrous ion using standard reducing agents.

The sample is dissolved, as directed under "Preparation and Solution of the Sample," then reduced or oxidized according to whether the oxidation or reduction

[11] Ilinski, M., and von Knorre, G., Ber., **18**, 2728, 1885; Papish, J., and Hoag, L. C., J. Am. Chem. Soc., **50**, 2118, 1928.

methods are to be used. Ferrous iron in HCl or $H_2SO_4$ is but *slowly* oxidized in air at room temperature; it is somewhat more stable to air in sulfate solutions. The presence of $HNO_3$, $F^-$, $PO_4^{-3}$ or Cu, however, accelerates the conversion to the trivalent state, and these substances are to be avoided if a stable ferrous solution is desired.

## DETERMINATION OF IRON BY OXIDATION METHODS

Some modification of either the dichromate, permanganate, or ceric method is usually employed in the determination of iron by oxidation, and to accomplish this quantitatively, the iron must be reduced to the ferrous condition. This may be done in the following ways:

*Reduction by Hydrogen Sulfide.*—During the course of a complete analysis of an ore, $H_2S$ is passed into the acid solution to precipitate the members of that group (Hg, Pb, Bi, Cu, Cd, As, Sb, Sn, Pt, Au, Se, etc.). The filtrate contains iron in the reduced condition suitable for titration with either dichromate or permanganate, the excess of $H_2S$ having been boiled off. If the expulsion of $H_2S$ is conducted in an Erlenmeyer flask there is little chance for reoxidation of the iron during the boiling. Reduction by $H_2S$ is very effective and is frequently advisable. This is the case when titanium is present, since this is not reduced by $H_2S$, but by methods given below. Arsenic, antimony, copper, and platinum, which, if present, would interfere, are removed by this treatment.

Reaction.

$$2Fe^{+3} + S^= \rightarrow 2Fe^{++} + S$$

*Reduction with Stannous Chloride.*—$SnCl_2$ reduces iron rapidly in a hydrochloric acid solution of the ore and the conversion to the divalent state is easily noted by the disappearance of the yellow color. V, Mo, and W are also reduced. The excess $SnCl_2$ is oxidized readily to $SnCl_4$ on the addition of $HgCl_2$.

Reactions.

$$2Fe^{+3} + Sn^{+2} \rightarrow 2Fe^{+2} + Sn^{+4}$$

$$(excess)\ Sn^{+2} + 2Hg^{+2} \rightarrow Sn^{+4} + 2Hg^+$$

Only a slight excess of $SnCl_2$ is advisable, otherwise the $HgCl_2$ may be reduced to metallic mercury—indicated by a darkening of the silk-like calomel, causing a high result through the consumption of additional oxidant. For the same reason, the $HgCl_2$ should be cooled before being added quickly to the ferric solution. About 15–20 ml. of saturated $HgCl_2$ should be sufficient.

*Reduction by a Metal Such as Test Lead, Zinc, Magnesium, Cadmium, or Aluminum, in Presence of Either Hydrochloric Acid or Sulfuric Acid.*—The former acid is preferred with the dichromate titration and the latter with the permanganate. Two methods of metallic reduction are in common use—reduction by means of test lead, and reduction with amalgamated zinc by means of the Jones Reductor.

**Reduction with Test Lead.**—By this method copper is precipitated from solution and small amounts of arsenic and antimony expelled. Sufficient test lead is added to the acid ferric solution to cover the bottom of the beaker completely. The solution is covered and boiled vigorously until the yellow color has completely disappeared and the solution is colorless. The reduced iron solution is cooled and decanted into a 600-ml. beaker, the remaining iron washed out from the lead mat by several decantations with water; two or three 50-ml. portions of water should be sufficient; the washings are added to the first portion. If the solution becomes slightly colored, a few drops of stannous chloride, $SnCl_2$, solution are added, followed by 10 ml. of mercuric chloride, $HgCl_2$, solution. The sample is now ready for titration.

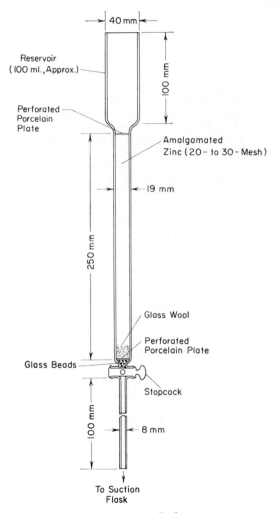

40 mm

Reservoir
( 100 ml., Approx.)

Perforated
Porcelain
Plate

100 mm

Amalgamated
Zinc ( 20 - to 30 - Mesh )

19 mm

250 mm

Glass Wool

Perforated
Porcelain Plate

Glass Beads

Stopcock

100 mm

8 mm

To Suction
Flask

FIG. 25-2. Jones Reductor.

**Reduction with Zinc Amalgam, Using the Jones Reductor.**[12]—The Jones Reductor (Fig. 25-2) as generally used in the laboratory consists of a glass tube 2 cm in diameter and 20–40 cm long, which is filled with 20-mesh zinc amalgamated with 0.1 to 5.0% mercury. The column of amalgamated zinc rests on a filtering pad

12 Hillebrand, W. F., Lundell, E. F., Bright, H. A., and Hoffman, J. I., Applied Inorganic Analysis, John Wiley and Sons, Inc., New York, 1953, 2nd ed., p. 108.

of glass wool or asbestos supported by a perforated porcelain plate or by platinum gauze. This is illustrated in Fig. 25-3 which shows the lower end of the reductor extending into a flask which is fitted with a stopper and tube to provide attachment of a vacuum, or admittance of an inert atmosphere.

The amalgam may be prepared rapidly by washing iron-free, 20-mesh zinc for 1 minute in enough 1.0 $N$ HCl to cover it completely, adding the correct amount

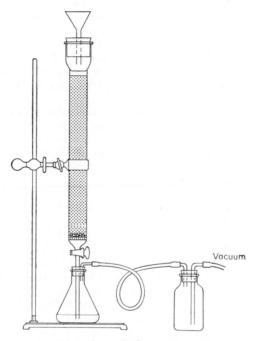

FIG. 25-3. Jones Reductor Assembly.

of 0.25 $M$ HgCl$_2$ (or nitrate) and stirring rapidly for three minutes. After decantation and washing with water, the shiny-looking amalgam is stored under water to which has been added a few drops of HCl. The ideal amalgam should give rapid and complete reduction with a minimum of hydrogen evolution. The required amount of mercury depends upon the metal to be reduced, the acidity of the solution, the length of the column, etc. For oxidants such as Fe(III), which react with mercury as well as with zinc, a 1% amalgam is sufficient.

The reductor containing the amalgam is *always* kept filled with enough water to cover the surface, otherwise basic salts will form which will tend to clog the column or result in channeling of the solution. Basic solutions or solutions containing ions which are easily reducible to the metal should, of course, not be admitted.

The Jones Reductor is capable of reducing Fe, Ti, Eu, Cr, Mo, V, U, W, Re, As, and Sb to lower oxidation states. In addition, nitric acid, polythionic acids, from reduction with H$_2$S, and organic matter must not be passed through the column. Nitric acid is reduced to hydroxylamine which would subsequently interfere, and acetanilide, frequently contained in commercial hydrogen peroxide, is often trouble-some.

**Reduction with the Silver Reductor.**[13]—Iron may be reduced readily by passing the ferric solution over particles of silver contained in a tube 2 cm. in diameter and 12 cm. in length that has attached at one end a reservoir of 50–75 ml. capacity. The tube is filled with about 18 g. of silver prepared by dissolving 29 g. of $AgNO_3$ in 400 ml. of water, adding a little $HNO_3$, then stirring rapidly with sheet copper, about 10 cm. square, until the silver has been completely deposited. Upon washing with dilute $H_2SO_4$, the silver is transferred to the tube of the reductor and washed again with dilute sulfuric acid until free from copper.

Between runs the reductor is kept filled with a molar solution of HCl. With continued use, the silver gradually becomes coated with AgCl which inhibits its effectiveness. This AgCl layer may be quickly reduced by placing a Zn rod in contact with the silver after filling the column with 0.1 $M$ $H_2SO_4$; after washing, the column is again ready for use.

Platinum salts must not be introduced into the reductor, as the reduced metal forms a new couple with the silver resulting in an increased power of reduction. Titanium, for example, may be reduced to the trivalent state should platinum be present. Greater care must be exercised in the regulation of pH with the silver reductor than with the zinc reductor, e.g., molybdenum is reduced to Mo(V) in 2 $M$ and to Mo(III) in 4 $M$ HCl.

Unlike the zinc reductor, the silver reductor does not reduce Re(VII), Cr(III), or Ti(IV), but it reduces other elements to the following valencies: Fe(II), Mo(III and V), V(IV), U(IV), and Cu(I).

**Reduction with Sulfur Dioxide.**—$SO_2$ gas is passed into a neutral solution of iron, since iron is not reduced readily in an acid solution by this method. The excess $SO_2$ is expelled by acidifying the solution and boiling. Although the action is slow, the method is a very accurate one; Cu, As, Sb, and V interfere. The $SO_2$ is best passed through $H_2SO_4$ prior to reduction.

**Reduction with Potassium Iodide,** the liberated iodine being expelled by heat.

In the solution of the ore with stannous chloride and hydrochloric acid, if an excess of the former has been accidentally added, it will be necessary to oxidize the iron before reduction. This may be accomplished by addition of hydrogen peroxide until the yellow color of ferric chloride appears (or by addition of $KMnO_4$ solution); the excess $H_2O_2$ may be removed by boiling. The iron may now be reduced by one of the above methods.

## DETERMINATION OF IRON BY OXIDATION WITH POTASSIUM DICHROMATE

This method depends upon the quantitative oxidation of ferrous salts in cold acid solution (HCl or $H_2SO_4$) to the ferric oxidation state by potassium dichromate; the following reaction takes place:

$$6Fe^{+2} + Cr_2O_7^{=} + 14H^+ \rightarrow 6Fe^{+3} + 2Cr^{+3} + 7H_2O.$$

Diphenylamine or, more often, potassium diphenylaminesulfonate is employed as the internal redox indicator. A slight excess of the oxidant causes the indicator to change to an intense reddish-violet color. As the standard oxidation potential

[13] Hillebrand, W. F., Lundell, E. F., Bright, H. A., and Hoffman, J. I., Applied Inorganic Analysis, John Wiley and Sons, Inc., New York, 1953, 2nd ed., p. 108.

of diphenylamine ($-0.76$ volt) and diphenylaminesulfonate ($-0.87$ volt) are quite close to the standard oxidation potential of the iron couple ($-0.77$ volt), it is necessary to add $PO_4^{-3}$ or $F^-$ to complex the Fe(III) causing it to be more readily oxidized; this serves also to remove the yellow color of Fe(III) which would interfere with the color change at the end point.

Each 0.1 ml. of 0.2% indicator will require 0.12 ml. of 0.01 $N$ oxidant, and this correction should be made when oxidants of this strength are used for the titration.

*Reagents.* **Standard Potassium Dichromate.**—It is evident from the stoichiometry of the above equation that a normal solution of dichromate contains one-sixth of the molecular weight of $K_2Cr_2O_7$ per liter, i.e., 49.04 g. For general use, it is convenient to have two strengths of this solution, 0.2 $N$ for ores high in iron content and 0.1 $N$ for products containing smaller amounts.

*Standardization.*—For the 0.2 $N$ solution, 9.807 g. of the recrystallized dehydrated salt are dissolved in water and made up to 1 liter; 0.1 $N$ $K_2Cr_2O_7$ contains 4.904 g. of the pure salt per liter. It is advisable to allow the solution to stand a few hours before standardization.

The iron equivalent of the solution, in g. of Fe per ml. is equal to the weight of Fe in g. in the sample taken divided by titration volume in ml. (corrected for the indicator).

$$\text{Wt. of Fe in g. equivalent to 1.0 ml. of solution} = \frac{(\% \text{ Fe in ore}) \times (\text{wt. of ore sample in g.})}{100 \times (\text{volume of oxidant})}.$$

**Stannous Chloride.**—Sixty grams of the crystallized salt dissolved in 600 ml. of concentrated HCl and made up to 1 liter with water. The solution should be kept well stoppered.

**Phosphoric Acid-Sulfuric Acid Mixture.**—150 ml. concentrated $H_2SO_4$, 150 ml. concentrated $H_3PO_4$ diluted with water to one liter.

**Mercuric Chloride.**—Saturated solution of $HgCl_2$ (60–70 g. per liter).

*Apparatus.* **Chamber Burette.**—This should read from 75 to 90 ml. in tenths and from 90 to 100 ml. in twentieths of a ml.

*Procedure for Iron Ores.*—The amount of sample taken should be such that the actual iron present would weigh between 0.9 and 1.1 g. This weight can be estimated by dividing 95 by the approximate percentage of iron present, e.g., for 50% Fe ore take $95/50 = 1.9$ g.; 95% iron material would require 1 g., whereas 20% Fe ore would require 4.75 g.

For samples containing less than 20% Fe, it is advisable to use 0.1 $N$ $K_2Cr_2O_7$ solution.

The sample should be finely ground (80-mesh).

**Solution.**—The hydrochloric acid method for solution of the oxidized ore with subsequent carbonate fusion of the residue is recommended as being suitable for iron ores, briquettes, and materials high in iron.

**Reduction of Iron.**—Iron may be rapidly and efficiently reduced with stannous chloride according to the procedure described on page 539; or alternatively, the acidified (HCl) iron solution may be reduced by boiling with test lead which serves to remove Cu, As, and Sb.

**Titration.**—The standard dichromate solution is run slowly into the flask containing the ferrous iron, to which has been added 15 ml. of $H_2SO_4$-$H_3PO_4$ mixture and 3–4 drops of indicator, to within 5–10 ml. of the estimated end point, then drop by drop until the green-colored solution changes sharply to a deep violet. If the solution contains considerable iron, the end point may be preceded immediately by an intermediate gray color. Once the region of the end point has been established, slightly greater accuracy may be obtained by adding the indicator to the solution a few ml. prior to the end point.

Wt. Fe in sample = (Volume $K_2Cr_2O_7$ sol. in ml.) $\times$ (Fe value per ml.).

NOTES.—In case an excess of dichromate has been added in the titration, back-titration may be made with ferrous ammonium sulfate, $(NH_4)_2SO_4 \cdot FeSO_4 \cdot 6H_2O$. 0.1 $N$ solution of this reagent may be prepared by dissolving 9.81 g. of the clear crystals in about 100 ml. of water, adding 5 ml. concentrated $H_2SO_4$ and making to 250 ml. volume. The resulting solution should be standardized against dichromate solution to get the equivalent values.

If diphenylamine is used for the indicator, a solution may be prepared by dissolving 1.0 g. of the reagent in 100 ml. of concentrated $H_2SO_4$. Three drops of the resulting indicator solution are sufficient for titrations in 100–250 ml. of test solution.

If 1.0% potassium ferricyanide is used as an *external* indicator, the iron must not be reduced with zinc as this reacts with ferrocyanide; furthermore, the ferricyanide test solution must be free of ferrocyanide as this forms a blue color with both ferric and ferrous iron. Ferricyanide is slowly reduced with time and test solutions should be prepared immediately prior to the titration.

Titration with diphenylamine or diphenylaminesulfonate has the advantage over titration with permanganate in that the end point does not fade in the presence of Zn, Al, Mn, Ni, Co, or Cr. Cu in quantities less than 1.0 mg. does not interfere (larger quantities assist the oxidation of ferrous iron by air). As(III) raises results as it is oxidized to As(V) by dichromate.

*p*-Phenetidine as a 1.0% solution may be used in place of the diphenylamine. The end point is characterized by a reddish-violet color.[14]

## CERIC SULFATE METHOD [15]

Standard ceric sulfate solution (see Appendix for Standard Solutions) is one of the most satisfactory reagents for the titration of ferrous iron, especially in solutions containing hydrochloric acid; sulfuric, perchloric, nitric, and acetic acids do not interfere with titrations by ceric sulfate; hydrofluoric and phosphoric acids may be present in fairly high concentrations. The iron is reduced by any conventional method, after which two drops of 0.025 $M$ *o*-phenanthroline indicator, or five drops of 0.1% aqueous solution of erioglaucine or eriogreen is added as indicator. *o*-Phenanthroline ferrous sulfate is the most satisfactory indicator for general use, changing from deep red to pale blue at the end of oxidation of ferrous iron. Erioglaucine (or eriogreen) is especially suitable for indication when the iron has been reduced by the stannous chloride-mercuric chloride method. The presence of calomel does not interfere with the action of the indicator, which changes to pale rose when all of the iron has been oxidized.[16]

## POTASSIUM PERMANGANATE METHOD

The method depends upon the quantitative oxidation of ferrous salts to the ferric condition when potassium permanganate is added to their cold solution; the following reaction takes place:

$$10Fe^{+2} + 2MnO_4^- + 16H^+ \rightarrow 10Fe^{+3} + 2Mn^{+2} + 8H_2O.$$

14 Szebelledy, L., Z. Anal. Chem., **81**, 97, 1930; Sarver, L. A., J. Am. Chem. Soc., **49**, 1473, 1927.
15 Smith, G. F., Cerate Oxidimetry, G. F. Smith Chemical Company, Columbus, Ohio.
16 Willard and Young, J. Am. Chem. Soc., **50**, 1334, 1928; **55**, 3260, 1933.

Hydrochloric acid in the presence of iron salts exerts a secondary, *induced* reaction on the permanganate, e.g.,

$$2KMnO_4 + 16HCl \rightarrow 2MnCl_2 + 5Cl_2 + 8H_2O + 2KCl$$

and/or

$$2KMnO_4 + 11HCl \rightarrow 2KCl + 2MnCl_2 + 5HClO + 3H_2O.$$

These reactions may be prevented by addition of large amounts of zinc or manganous sulfates together with an excess of phosphoric acid, or by large dilution. The sulfate solution is diluted, reduced with zinc amalgam in the Jones Reductor, and titrated as directed. In the presence of Ti, V, Cr, U, and As, reduction is accomplished by $H_2S$ in hydrochloric acid solution, or by $SO_2$ or $SnCl_2$.

Since potassium permanganate enters into reaction with acid solutions of Sb, Sn, Pt, Cu, and Hg, when present in their lower oxidation states (also with Mn in neutral solutions), and with $SO_2$, $H_2S$, $N_2O$, ferrocyanides, and with most soluble organic substances, these must be absent from the iron solutions to be titrated.

Potassium permanganate produces an intense pink color in solution so that it acts as its own indicator.

**Reagents.** **Standard Permanganate Solution.**—As in the case of potassium dichromate, it is convenient to have two standard solutions, 0.2 $N$ and 0.1 $N$. From the reaction given above, it is evident that one $KMnO_4$ molecule is equivalent to five $FeSO_4$; hence a normal solution would contain one-fifth of the molecular weight of $KMnO_4$, i.e., 31.61 grams of the pure salt.

Since commercial potassium permanganate is seldom pure (see Appendix for Standard Solutions), it is necessary to determine its exact value by standardization. This is commonly accomplished by any of the following methods: (a) by a standard electrolytic iron solution; (b) by ferrous salt solution (e.g., ferrous ammonium sulfate); (c) by oxalic acid or an oxalate; (d) by arsenious oxide plus iodide or iodate as a catalyst.

Standardization of $KMnO_4$ against arsenious oxide is recommended as the most accurate procedure.

*Reaction.*—$5H_2AsO_3^- + 2MnO_4^- + 6H^+ \rightarrow 5H_2AsO_4^- + 2Mn^{+2} + 3H_2O.$

*To Standardize.* 0.2 g. of pure $As_2O_3$, equivalent to $0.2/0.00495 = 40.5$ ml. of 0.1 $N$ solution, is dissolved in 10 ml. 3 $N$ NaOH (free from reducible substances). Fifteen ml. of 1:1 HCl are added and the solution is then diluted to 50 ml. with water. After addition of one drop of 0.002 $M$ $KIO_3$, the solution is titrated to the first permanent rose color of permanganate.

The number of arsenious oxide milliequivalents divided by the volume in ml. of $KMnO_4$ required equals the normality of the $KMnO_4$ solution. There is no induced oxidation of chloride when permanganate is used to determine arsenic.

NOTE.—The titration of Fe(II) with permanganate may be conducted in the presence of HCl by adding $MnSO_4$ and $H_3PO_4$ ("Zimmermann-Reinhardt reagent"), or by high dilution. (Reagent.—200 g. $MnSO_4 \cdot 4H_2O$ plus 100 ml. $H_2O$ plus 400 ml. syrupy $H_3PO_4$.)

**Procedure for the Determination of Iron by the Jones Reductor.** **Preparation of Sample.**—An amount of the sample is taken such that the iron content is between two- and three-tenths of a gram (0.2 to 0.3 g). If hydrochloric acid has been required to effect solution, or hydrochloric acid and nitric acid (25:1), as in case of iron and steel, four to five ml. of concentrated sulfuric acid is added, and the solution is evaporated to small bulk on the steam bath and to $SO_3$ fumes to remove hydrochloric acid. The iron is taken up with about 50 ml. dilute sulfuric acid, (1:4), heating if necessary, and filtering if an insoluble residue remains.

**Preparation of the Reductor.**—Cleaning out the apparatus. See Fig. 25-2 and Fig. 25-3. The stopcock of the reductor is closed, a heavy-walled flask or bottle is put into position at the bottom, and 50 ml. of dilute sulfuric acid is poured into the funnel. The cock is opened and the acid allowed to flow slowly through the zinc in the tube, applying gentle suction. Before the acid has drained out of the funnel, 50 ml. of water are added, followed by 50 ml. more of dilute sulfuric acid and 50 ml. of water in turn. The stopcock is turned off before the water has drained completely from the funnel so that the zinc is always covered by a solution of acid or water.

**Determination of the Blank.**—Fifty ml. of dilute sulfuric acid, (1:4), are passed through the reductor, followed by 250 ml. of distilled water, according to the directions given above. The acid solution in the flask is then titrated with 0.1 N $KMnO_4$ solution. If more than 3 or 4 drops of the permanganate are required, the operation must be repeated until the blank titration does not exceed this amount. The final blank obtained should be deducted from the regular determinations for iron. The end point of the titration is a faint pink, persisting for one minute.

**Reduction and Titration of the Iron Solution.**—The sample is diluted to 200 ml., and, when cold, is run into the funnel, the stopcock is opened and the solution drawn slowly through the column of zinc into the flask, about four minutes being required for 200 ml. of solution. Before the funnel has completely drained, rinsings of the vessel which contained the sample are added; two 50-ml. portions are sufficient, followed by about 50 ml. of water. The stopcock is closed before the solutions have completely drained from the funnel. The flask is removed and a 0.1 N solution of permanganate added until a faint pink color, persisting one minute, is obtained. The blank is deducted from the ml. reading of the burette.

One ml. 0.1 N $KMnO_4$ = 0.005585 g. Fe; or 0.007985 g. $Fe_2O_3$.

## OPTIONAL PERMANGANATE METHOD FOR IRON IN ORES

**Procedure. Solution of the Sample.**—0.5 gram of ore is weighed into an 8-oz. flask. With oxidized ores add 10–15 ml. of HCl and warm gently until the iron oxide is dissolved; then if sulfides are also present add 5 ml. of $HNO_3$ to decompose them also. With straight sulfides use 10 ml. of HCl and 5 ml. of $HNO_3$. When decomposition is complete, add 5 ml. of $H_2SO_4$ and boil over a free flame nearly to dryness.

**Refractory Ores.**—Certain silicates, oxides of iron furnace slags, etc., do not decompose with acid treatment. Decomposition may be accomplished by fusion methods followed by solution of the fused mass with water and hydrochloric acid. Fusions with $Na_2CO_3$ and $K_2CO_3$ are made in a nickel or platinum crucible and are recommended for materials high in silica. Fusions with an acid flux, $K_2SO_4$ (+5 ml. $H_2SO_4$, sp. gr. 1.84) or $KHSO_4$ are recommended for oxides. These latter fusions are conveniently carried out in Pyrex flasks held by a heavy wire clamp. About 10–15 g. of the solid flux is added to the ore in the flask and the fusion completed by heating until the mix becomes transparent. Oxides that do not readily decompose may be brought into solution, frequently, by adding a little piece of filter paper to the molten mass in the flask. The carbon thus furnished reduces the oxides, effecting decomposition. If decomposition is incomplete, the water and acid extraction is made, the soluble constituents are decanted off, and the residue is again fused with more $KHSO_4$ and filter paper. It may be necessary to follow $KHSO_4$ fusion by the $Na_2CO_3$ fusion on the insoluble residue remaining from the acid extraction of the $KHSO_4$ mass.

**Reduction.**—After cooling, add 30 ml. water, 10 ml. HCl and 6 g. of 20-mesh granulated zinc. It is not necessary to get salts into solution. Now add 3 ml. of a 4% copper sulfate solution. Allow to stand until the action has become feeble. Add 50 ml. of cold water and then 10 ml. of concentrated $H_2SO_4$ and allow to stand until the zinc is nearly all dissolved.

**Filtration from Insoluble Gangue and Excess Zinc.**—Prepare a filter by placing a rather thick wad of absorbent cotton in a funnel and wetting it into place. Place a battery jar, or a liter beaker containing about an inch of cold water, under the funnel. Have the beaker marked at the 700-ml. point. When the zinc in the flask has nearly all dissolved, filter the liquid through the absorbent cotton and wash out the flask at least 10 times with cold water, pouring through the filter. Use the wash bottle reversed to save time, and use enough water for each wash to completely cover the absorbent cotton. Allow to drain between washes. Continue the washing until the filtrate reaches the 700-ml. mark on the beaker.

**Titration of the Sample.**—Titrate at once with standard permanganate to a very faint tinge and take reading. A blank should previously be run on the zinc to determine any correction (usually due to a little iron) necessary. Deduct this correction from the above reading.

**Calculation.**—Multiply the volume in milliliters of permanganate used by the factor for iron.

## DIPHENYLAMINE OR DIPHENYLAMINESULFONATE INDICATOR IN PERMANGANATE TITRATIONS OF IRON [17]

As in the case of titrations of iron with potassium dichromate, diphenylamine or diphenylaminesulfonate may be used in potassium permanganate titrations. The advantage of the indicator is in the fact that titrations may be made in presence of considerable hydrochloric acid and in the presence of tin and mercury salts without a fading end point, obtained when permanganate is used alone. The blue color is more intense than the pink of potassium permanganate.

*Procedure.* **Decomposition and Reaction of Sample.**—The procedure given above applies also to this method.

**Titration.**—About 15 ml. of phosphoric-sulfuric acid mixture are added and the solution is diluted to about 100 ml. 0.2 ml. (four drops) of sodium diphenylaminesulfonate indicator is added and the titration now made with the standard potassium permanganate solution. The color becomes green deepening to a blue-green or grayish blue. The reagent is now added "dropwise" until an intense violet blue or dark blue color is obtained.

$$1 \text{ ml. } 0.1 \ N \ KMnO_4 = 0.005585 \text{ g. of Fe}$$

NOTES.—If 0.5585 g. of sample is taken, then 1 ml. of 0.1 $N$ potassium permanganate is equivalent to 1% of iron.

[17] Scott, Wilfred W., J. Am. Chem. Soc., **46**, 1396, 1924.

## FERRIC IRON BY TITRATION WITH A TITANOUS
## SALT SOLUTION [18]

The determination of iron in the ferric oxidation state may be made using one of several standard reducing agents, e.g., $Ti_2(SO_4)_3$, $TiCl_3$, $CrCl_2$, $CrSO_4$, or $VSO_4$; HCl, $H_2SO_4$, HF (provided $H_3BO_3$ is added to remove the $F^-$ as fluoroborate) may be present. $HNO_3$, certain organic compounds, Cu, Sb, Mo, Se, Pt, W, and V (which is reduced to $V_2O_3$) must be absent from solution.

The reagent is most commonly of 1% strength and may be prepared by diluting the commercially available 20% solution of $Ti_2(SO_4)_3$; alternatively, the trivalent titanium can readily be obtained by passage of $TiOSO_4$ (or chloride) through the Jones Reductor. The resulting solution must not be exposed to direct sunlight as it is very easily oxidized, nor should it be exposed to air for the same reason.

The iron solution is titrated cold using ammonium thiocyanate as the indicator. The solution remains red as long as thiocyanate complexes of Fe(III) are present. Methylene blue may also be used, but is not to be preferred over thiocyanate, as the former is not sensitive at room temperature unless salicylic acid is added; in addition, the organic acid prevents back titration of the solution with permanganate.

**Reagents.**    **Titanous Sulfate Solution.**—A 0.1 $N$ solution of the salt may be prepared by dissolving 16 g. of the basic tetravalent salt in 40 ml. of concentrated $H_2SO_4$, and diluting to one liter with cold, distilled water. The resulting solution is then passed through a Jones Reductor into a flask filled with oxygen-free nitrogen gas. The solution is stored in an apparatus such as that shown in Fig. 25-4; standardization against ferric ammonium sulfate is recommended.

**Potassium Thiocyanate Solution.**—One hundred grams of the crystals are dissolved in water, the resulting solution is filtered, and the clear filtrate is diluted to 1 liter.

**Ferric Ammonium Sulfate Solution.**[19]—Forty-eight grams of ferric alum crystals are dissolved in water, the solution is acidified with 50 ml. of concentrated sulfuric acid, and the volume is made up to 1 liter.

**Apparatus.**—The titanous sulfate solution, prepared as described above, is charged into the storage bottle S, Fig. 25-4, the volume being so regulated as to fill the container to its neck. The stopcock E is then turned so that the liquid rises in the burette B and continues upwards until hydrostatic equilibrium has been attained. With the hydrogen supply from the Kipp generator K turned on, the burette is allowed to empty itself by properly manipulating the cock, F, and a current of hydrogen is maintained through the apparatus till it is reasonably certain that all air has been displaced from within the system. It suffices to pass a slow stream of the protecting gas for about an hour; though it may be well also, after letting the solution stand for a day or two, to repeat the sweeping for a shorter interval (say 15 minutes). After each attempt to remove the air, the burette

[18] Knecht, E., and Hibbert, E., New Reduction Methods in Volumetric Analysis, pp. 10, 68, Longmans, Green and Company, New York, 1925; Thornton, Jr., W. M., and Chapman, J. E., J. Am. Chem. Soc., **43**, 91, 1921; Thornton, Jr., W. M., and Wood, A. E., J. Ind. Eng. Chem., **19**, 150, 1927; Knecht and Hibbert employ $TiCl_3$ which is equally satisfactory—see Kolthoff, I. M., and Tomicek, O., Rec. Trav. Chim., **43**, 776, 1924; Thornton, W. M., Jr., and Roseman, R., Am. J. Sci. (5), **20**, 14, 1930.

[19] The ferric ammonium sulfate solution will serve for a "back titration" in the analysis, and it will enable the operator to detect quickly any change in the reducing strength of the titanous solution.

is refilled, in which state it is ready for service. Glass connections should be used. If rubber connections are used, they should be wired and coated with shellac varnish. If the apparatus is carefully assembled, the standard reagent will show a change of titer considerably less than one part in a thousand per month; certainly, as far as the solution in the bottle is concerned.

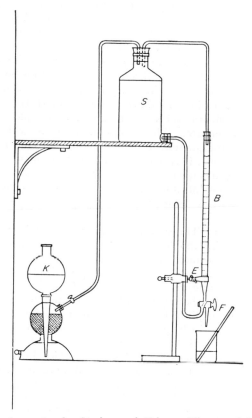

FIG. 25-4.   Apparatus for Storing and Using a Titanous Salt Solution.

*Standardization.*—Some specimens of ferrous ammonium sulfate, as procured in the market, contain very nearly the theoretical amount of iron (14.24%), this being the total quantity of iron and not simply that present in the ferrous condition; but it is hardly safe to make this assumption with samples of the salt that have not been tested.[20]   On the other hand, the iron ore,[21] which may be obtained from the Bureau of Standards, is a reliable standard.

**Against Ferrous Ammonium Sulfate.**—One and five-tenths grams of the analytical grade crystals are weighed into a 300-ml. beaker and dissolved in 90 ml. of water.   Ten ml. of sulfuric acid (1:1) are added, and the solution is titrated with

[20] Hillebrand, W. F., Lundell, G. E. F., Bright, H. A., and Hoffman, J. I., Applied Inorganic Analysis, John Wiley & Sons, Inc., New York, 1953, 2nd ed., p. 108.
[21] U. S. National Bureau of Standards certified Iron Ore.

0.1 $N$ potassium permanganate, which, by the way, need not have been standardized, until the end point is reached. After boiling for ten minutes,[22] the liquid is permitted to cool thoroughly, 5 ml. of the thiocyanate solution is introduced by a pipette, and (using the apparatus of Fig. 25-4) while hydrogen is passing through the apparatus, the titanous sulfate is added dropwise till there is no further diminution of color, allowing ample time, when nearing the end of the titration, for each portion to exert its full effect before introducing the next.

**Against Iron Ore.**—About 1.5 g. of the ore (previously dried at 100°C.) are weighed with exactness and dissolved in 10 ml. of concentrated hydrochloric acid, using for the dissolution a small Erlenmeyer flask fitted with a cut-off calcium chloride tube to serve as a trap,[23] and adding about 3 drops of hydrofluoric acid toward the end to decompose the silica (and silicates). This solution is transferred to a Pyrex evaporating basin, 25 ml. of sulfuric acid (1:1) are added, and the hydrochloric and hydrofluoric acids are removed, as completely as possible, by evaporating on the steam-bath. The residue is taken up with water, heating if necessary, the solution cooled, transferred to a 500-ml. volumetric flask; and, the volume being about 300 ml., it is oxidized with permanganate as described above, omitting, however, the subsequent boiling. The solution is then diluted to the mark and aliquot portions of 100 ml. each are taken with an accurate pipette. The remaining procedure is the same as that given under "Ferrous Ammonium Sulfate."

*Procedure.* **Ferric Iron.**—The solution, which may contain any amount of iron up to 0.28 g.,[24] and which should preferably occupy a small volume (not much greater than 100 ml.), is titrated with titanous sulfate, using the same quantities of reagents and in other respects proceeding as prescribed above.

**Total Iron.**—To determine the entire amount of iron in a given material, notwithstanding its state of oxidation, the whole of it must be oxidized to the ferric state. This may be accomplished in any one of three ways: (1) the solution is treated with ammonia and hydrogen peroxide and boiled to decompose the excess of peroxide and finally acidified with hydrochloric acid; (2) the sulfuric acid solution is titrated with permanganate until the pink color just becomes visible (see standardization); (3) the ferrous salt is oxidized with potassium chlorate by evaporation. The second method is generally to be preferred. Large amounts of hydrochloric acid may be expelled by evaporating on the steam bath with sulfuric acid in excess; but with small concentrations of that acid, its effect upon permanganate may be offset by adding a sufficient quantity of the Zimmermann-Reinhardt preventive reagent, leaving out, of course, the phosphoric acid.[25] This is prepared by dissolving 67 grams of manganous sulfate ($MnSO_4 \cdot 4H_2O$) in 500 ml. of water, adding 130 ml. of sulfuric acid (sp. gr. 1.82), and diluting to 1000 ml.

[22] Smith, G. F., Cerate Oxidimetry, G. F. Smith Chemical Company, Columbus, Ohio.
[23] Willard and Young, J. Am. Chem. Soc., **46**, 1396, 1924.
[24] Scott, Wilfred W., J. Am. Chem. Soc., **46**, 1396, 1924.
[25] Knecht, E., and Hibbert, E., New Reduction Methods in Volumetric Analysis, Longmans, Green and Co., New York, pp. 10, 68, 1925; Thornton, Jr., W. M., and Chapman, J. E., J. Am. Chem. Soc., **43**, 91, 1921; Thornton, Jr., W. M., and Wood, A. E., J. Ind. Eng. Chem., **19**, 150, 1927; Knecht and Hibbert employ $TiCl_3$ which is equally satisfactory—see Kolthoff, I. M., and Tomicek, O., Rec. Trav. Chim., **43**, 776, 1924; Thornton, Jr., W. M., and Roseman, R., Am. J. Sci. (5), **20**, 14, 1930.

## IODOMETRIC DETERMINATION OF IRON

Iron in the ferric form may be determined iodometrically, as in case of cupric ion determination. The reaction of the iodide ion with iron is:

$$2Fe^{+3} + 2I^- \rightarrow 2Fe^{++} + I_2$$

*Procedure.*—The solution, free from other substances liberating iodine from KI and containing about 2 ml. of 4 $N$ HCl per 10 ml., is treated with about 1–2 g. KI and titrated with standard solution of thiosulfate as in case of the copper determination, using starch as an indicator.

One ml. 0.1 $N$ thiosulfate is equivalent to 0.005585 g. Fe.

## ELECTROMETRIC AND ELECTROMETRIC END POINT METHODS IN THE DETERMINATION OF IRON [26]

The very interesting chemical and electrochemical reversibility of the ferric-ferrous couple have led to the development of many useful electrometric techniques in the determination of this element, some of which rival or exceed the convenience and/or accuracy of classical analytical procedures. Among the more common of these methods are potentiometric end point detection, amperometric end point detection, voltammetry at micro electrodes (polarography), potentiostatic or galvanostatic deposition from stirred solution, etc. However, because of the simplicity and great utility of the potentiometric technique, this method of end point detection will be discussed briefly here in connection with the determination of iron.

*Potentiometric End Point Detection in the Determination of Iron.*—The use of an inert gold or platinum wire electrode in conjunction with a reference electrode, e.g., calomel or quinhydrone, to determine the end point in the redox titration of iron eliminates the subjectiveness associated with a colored indicator, or the correction for oxidation of the indicator, and it has the further advantage of not being limited by the color of the test solution itself.

In practice, the potential of the cell, the inert electrode of which is immersed in the test solution, is followed with a potentiometer comprised, simply, of a battery, galvanometer, and slide wire resistance (a vacuum tube voltmeter will often suffice) as the oxidant is added by increments to the solution. The observed potential of the electrode is a reflection of the ratio of Fe(III)–Fe(II) in solution and exhibits a large break to more oxidizing values as the end point is reached. In the case of the symmetrical oxidation of Fe(II) with Ce(IV), the equivalence point occurs at the point of maximum slope on the volume-potential curve of the titration; should Fe(III) be present initially, the equivalence point potential occurs at values slightly more negative than the point of maximum inflection in the curve.

If the oxygenated reagents, $MnO_4^-$ and $Cr_2O_7^{-2}$, are used as oxidants, the end point potential is a function of pH, and because the reaction with Fe(II) is not symmetrical, the equivalence point lies at potentials more positive than that corresponding to the point of inflection of the curve.

As the end point potential depends upon the ratio of the two oxidation states, it is independent of the total quantity of iron present. At small concentrations of reductant, however, attainment of equilibrium in solution occurs slowly between

[26] For a general review of electrometric methods pertaining to iron, see, e.g., J. J. Lingane, Electroanalytical Chemistry, 2nd ed., Interscience Publishers, Inc., New York, 1958.

additions of titrant, but the error due to this lag can often be eliminated by setting the potentiometer to the previously determined end point potential, closing the switch, and following the current change to zero with a sensitive galvanometer as the titrant is added.

In addition to its use in the primary analysis, the potentiometric method is often of value in elucidating the simultaneous oxidation of previously unsuspected impurities in solution.

## COLORIMETRIC METHODS

The determination of iron colorimetrically is generally accomplished either by measuring the transmittancy of the red-colored *ferric* thiocyanate complexes or that of the red-colored complex formed between *ferrous* ion and 1,10-phenanthroline; the reddish-purple color produced by ferrous iron and mercaptoacetic acid at pH 10 serves to determine this metal in the presence of fluoride, phosphate, arsenate, etc. Other methods involve measurement of the yellow color of Fe(III) in constant boiling HCl; measurement of the amethyst-colored complex of Fe(III) with salicylic acid in acetic acid; the red-orange color produced by Fe(III) with salicylaldoxime at pH 7 and the reddish-purple color of the ferrous-2,2'-bipyridyl complex.

## DETERMINATION WITH THIOCYANATE [27, 28]

The intensity of color produced by the reaction of Fe(III) with thiocyanate depends upon the kind of acid present, complexing impurities, time of standing, and the amount of thiocyanate added in excess; in addition, exposure to light lessens the color due to the reduction of Fe(III) by thiocyanate. Metals which precipitate $SCN^-$ must, of course, be absent. This is true for metals that form stable complexes with thiocyanate, e.g., Cd and Hg. The absorption of light by the $Fe(SCN)_3$ at 450–480 m$\mu$ (depending upon the excess of $SCN^-$) does not, in general, follow Beer's Law above about 4 p. p. m. and for this reason a set of working standards is necessary, the composition of which must exactly duplicate the unknown sample.

Extraction of the $Fe(CN)_3$ into a nonaqueous solvent,[28, 29] e.g., amyl alcohol, amyl alcohol-ether, ethyl acetate, or isobutyl alcohol, has the advantage of concentrating the iron and in many cases enhancing the color. The latter solvent is recommended, as a large increase in the stability of the color is obtained.

*Reagents.* **Potassium Thiocyanate.**—Prepared from the colorless, analytically pure salt. The salt may be tested for iron by adding 1–2 ml. acetone to 2 g. of the solid; an absence of color shows the salt to be free from iron.

**Hydrochloric or Nitric Acid.**—Analytical reagent grade is adequate except for the determination of very small amounts of iron. The nitric acid should be free of oxides of nitrogen.

[27] Bent, H. E., and French, C. L., J. Am. Chem. Soc., **63**, 568, 1947; Edmonds, S. M., and Birnbaum, N., *ibid.*, **63**, 1741, 1941; Gould, R. K., and Vosburgh, W. C., *ibid.*, **64**, 1631, 1942; Frank, H. S., and Oswalt, R. L., *ibid.*, **69**, 1327, 1947.

[28] Woods, J. T., and Mellon, M. G., Ind. Eng. Chem., Anal. Ed., **13**, 551, 1941; Peters, C. A., MacMasters, M. M., and French, C. L., *ibid.*, **11**, 502, 1939; Peters, C. A., and French, C. L., *ibid.*, **13**, 604, 1941; Ovenston, C. J., and Parker, C. A., Anal. Chem. Acta, **3**, 277, 1949.

[29] See Winsor, H. W., Ind. Eng. Chem., Anal. Ed., **9**, 453, 1937, for the use of 2-methoxyethanol ("Methyl Cellosolve") to extract the Fe-SCN complex.

**Potassium Persulfate.**—2% solution prepared fresh every few days and stored in the cold.

**Isobutyl Alcohol.**—Obtained pure (b.p. 106–107°C.) by redistilling from Pyrex glassware.

**Standard Iron Solution.**—Dissolve 0.1000 g. of electrolytic iron in 50 ml. of 1:3 $HNO_3$, expel oxides of nitrogen by boiling, then dilute to one liter with iron-free distilled water. This solution may be further diluted with 0.2 $M$ $HNO_3$.

**Procedure.**—The acidity of the solution may vary from 0.05 to 1.0 $N$, and the solution can contain up to 10 p. p. m. Fe(III) if a photoelectric photometer is used (1.0-cm. cuvette).

Sufficient KSCN is added to make the final solution about 0.3 $M$ in this salt, and the transmittancy of the resulting solution is measured *at once* at 480 m$\mu$.

Alternatively,[30] to a 25-ml. aliquot of the iron solution in a 125-ml. separatory funnel, add, with swirling, 5.0 ml. concentrated HCl, 1.0 ml. 2% potassium persulfate, and 10.0 ml. of the prepared KSCN solution. Follow this with an addition of 25 ml. of the isobutyl alcohol and shake for 2 minutes. Transfer the alcohol layer to a 50-ml. beaker and add 0.1 g. of anhydrous sodium sulfate to remove all droplets of water. Determine the transmittancy at 485 m$\mu$; compare this with the standard.

## DETERMINATION OF FERROUS IRON
## WITH 1,10-PHENANTHROLINE [31]

This method for the determination of iron is sensitive and requires the formation of the orange-red complex, $(C_{12}H_8N_2)_3Fe^{+2}$, whose color is very dependent on pH in the range 2–9; below a pH of 2 the color is weak and develops slowly. The complex, which follows Beer's Law closely in its absorbance, is very stable and remains unchanged for many months.

Ferric iron may be reduced with hydroxylamine hydrochloride, sulfur dioxide, or hydroquinone. The latter reductant is to be preferred if the solution pH is adjusted with a citrate.[32] Ag and Bi give precipitates and are to be avoided; divalent metals which give stable complexes, e.g., Cd, Hg, and Zn, are also to be avoided. The maximum permissible concentrations, in p. p. m., of interfering elements follow: (Fe-2 p. p. m.); Cd, 50; Hg, 1; Zn, 10; Be, 50 (pH 3.0–5.5); W, 5 (tungstate decreases the color intensity); Cu, 10 (pH 2.5–4.0); Ni, 2; Co, 10 (pH 3–5); Sn(II), 20 (pH 2–3) and Sn(IV), 50 (pH 2.5). Fluoride does not interfere (500 p. p. m.) if the pH is above 4.0. Oxalate and tartrate do not interfere if the pH is above 6 and below 3 respectively. Phosphorus causes difficulty above 20 p. p. m., and should be considered carefully in the determination of iron in biological samples.

**Reagents. Hydroquinone.**—A 1% solution prepared by shaking the compound with distilled, iron-free water.

**Sodium Citrate.**—250 grams of the dihydrate in 1 liter of solution.

**1,10-Phenanthroline.**—0.5% solution of the monohydrate in water which may

[30] Thompson, J. B., Ind. Eng. Chem., Anal. Ed., **16**, 646, 1944.

[31] Saywell, L. G., and Cunningham, B. B., Ind. Eng. Chem., Anal. Ed., **9**, 67, 1937; Fortune, W. B., and Mellon, M. G., *ibid.*, **10**, 60, 1938; Thiel, A., Heinrich, H., and van Hengle, E., Ber. **71B**, 756, 1938.

[32] An acetate buffer can be used if interferences, e.g., phosphorus found in biological samples, are not present. Citrate is recommended by Cowling, H., and Benne, E. J., J. Assoc. Official Agr. Chem., **25**, 555, 1942, and Bandemer, S. L., and Schaible, P. J., Ind. Eng. Chem., Anal. Ed., **16, 317,** 1944.

be prepared by warming the compound to effect solution. *Keep in the dark* and discard if any color subsequently develops.

*Procedure.*—An aliquot portion of the sample containing 0.01–0.2 mg. Fe (1.0-cm. cuvette) and a little mineral acid is transferred to a 25-ml. volumetric flask. An amount of sodium citrate (determined with a corresponding aliquot by adjusting the pH to 3.5 with bromphenol blue) is then added together with 1.0 ml. each of hydroquinone and 1,10-phenanthroline. The mixture is allowed to stand for one hour (room temperature or above) then made up to the mark and the transmittancy determined at 508 m$\mu$. A filter may be used which passes a band at 480–520 m$\mu$.

The amount of iron present is determined, in the case of aqueous solutions, by comparing the transmittancy of the unknown with that of a set of standards; when measuring the transmittancy of the extracted complex either a set of standards may be used or the concentration of the iron may be calculated using the extinction coefficient previously determined.

## TITRIMETRIC-SPECTROPHOTOMETRIC DETERMINATION OF FERRIC IRON WITH ETHYLENEDIAMINETETRAACETIC ACID (EDTA) [33]

The exceptionally stable anionic complex formed between Fe(III) and EDTA make this reagent especially useful for the titrimetric determination of iron. The logarithms of stability constants of various EDTA complexes are: V(III), 25.9; Fe(III), 25.1; In(III), 24.95; Hg(II), 21.8; Ga(III), 20.27; Cu(II), 18.80; V(IV), 18.77; Ni(II), 18.62; Pb(II), 18.04; Zn(II), 16.50; Cd(II), 16.46; Co(II), 16.31; Al(III), 16.31; Mn(II), 13.79.

*Procedure.*[34]—Sweetser and Bricker used the Beckman Model B Spectrophotometer, with special titration cell, to follow the disappearance of the deep-colored complex formed between Fe(III) and the salicylic acid.

An aliquot of the moderately acid, oxidized iron solution is transferred to the titration cell and enough acetate buffer added to adjust the pH of the final solution to 1.7–2.3. The titration cell is next placed in the spectrophotometer, the instrument set at 525 m$\mu$ and the slit adjusted so that the absorbance reads 0.20. One ml. of 6% salicylic acid in acetone is then added and the solution titrated slowly with a 0.1 M solution of disodium dihydrogen EDTA, until the absorbance reads 1.80 (about 0.80 to 0.40 ml. prior to the end point), after which the reagent is added in 0.1 or 0.2 ml. increments. The end point is obtained by extrapolating the straight line segments of the volume-absorbance curve. The principal interferences are Pb(II), Bi(III), Co(II), Ni(II), and Cu(II).

**Standardization of Disodium EDTA.**—The reagent, disodium EDTA, may be standardized against a ferric solution of known strength prepared by dissolving the requisite amount of analytical grade ferric ammonium sulfate in sulfuric acid, adding a few drops of $H_2O_2$ to insure complete oxidation of the iron, then diluting to volume. The titration of the known iron is performed in the same manner as the unknown.

---

[33] For a review of the use of EDTA in the determination of iron and other metals, see Welcher, F. J., The Analytical Uses of Ethylenediamine Tetraacetic Acid, D. Van Nostrand Co., Princeton, N. J., 1958.

[34] Sweetser, P. B., and Bricker, C. E., Anal. Chem., **25**, 253, 1953.

## METHODS FOR IRON ANALYSES IN OTHER CHAPTERS

| | |
|---|---|
| Iron in Aluminum Alloys | See Analysis of Aluminum Alloys |
| Iron in Bauxite | See Analysis of Bauxite (Aluminum Chapter) |
| Iron in Hydrated Alumina | See Analysis of Hydrated Alumina |
| Iron in Calcined Alumina | See Analysis of Calcined Alumina |
| Iron in Fused Alumina | See Analysis of Fused Alumina |
| Iron in Arsenious Oxide | See Analysis of Arsenious Oxide |
| Iron in Barite | See Analysis of Barite (Barium Chapter) |
| Iron in Alloys by Ion Exchange | See Chromine Chapter |
| Iron in Magnesite | See Analysis of Magnesite (Magnesium Chapter) |
| Iron in Metallic Nickel | See Analysis of Metallic Nickel |
| Iron in Phosphorus Ores | See Analysis of Phosphorus Ores |
| Iron in Commercial Phosphates | See Analysis of Commercial Phosphates |
| Iron in Sodium Silicate | See Analysis of Sodium Silicate (Silicon Chapter) |
| Iron in Sand | See Analysis of Sand |
| Iron in Selenium | See Trace Analysis for Impurities in Selenium |
| Iron in Tellurium | See Determination of Selenium, Lead, Iron and Copper in Selenium (Selenium Chapter) |
| Iron in Titanium | See Analysis of Titaniterous Ores |
| Iron in Titanium Pigments | See Analysis of Pigments containing Titanium Dioxide |
| Iron in Slab Zinc | See Analysis of Slab Zinc |

# Chapter 26

# LEAD*

**Pb,** *at. wt.* **207.19;** *sp. gr.* **11.35 (at 20°C.);** *m.p.* **327.4°C.;** *b.p.* **1620°C.;** *oxides,* **Pb$_2$O, PbO, Pb$_2$O$_3$, Pb$_3$O$_4$, PbO$_2$**

The occurrence of lead in native state is rare and in comparatively small amounts. It occurs combined in a large number of minerals, principally as sulfide in galenite (galena), PbS. Among the other more common minerals: the carbonate, cerussite, PbCO$_3$; the sulfate, anglesite, PbSO$_4$; the phosphate, pyromorphite, PbCl$_2$·3Pb$_3$(PO$_4$)$_2$; minium, Pb$_3$O$_4$; wulfenite, PbMoO$_4$; crocoite, PbCrO$_4$; and also in sulfo-salts, silicates, vanadates, arsenates, etc. Galena, the chief source, is frequently associated with marcasite (white iron pyrites), zinc blende (sphalerite), ZnS and pyrite, FeS$_2$.

Lead was employed by man many centuries ago as is shown by the objects made of this metal that have been found in ancient ruins. It was employed as a roofing material during the Medieval Ages. It was used during the early periods and is still used for manufacture of pipes. It is employed in storage batteries, covering of cables, in chemical industries—lead chambers in sulfuric acid manufacture, lead crystallizing pans, etc.; it is employed in making shot and rifle bullets, and in alloys —pewter, type metal, Babbitt, and solder. The more recently developed uses of the metal include shielding from radiation, vibration-absorbing pads for high-speed machinery, etc. Compounds of lead are extensively used—paint pigments, drying agents for oils, lead glass, plumber's cement, covering of steel to prevent rusting, and for many other purposes. All lead compounds are cumulative poisons.

## DETECTION

*Hydrochloric acid* in cold, sufficiently concentrated solutions precipitates lead as PbCl$_2$, white, accompanied with silver and mercurous chlorides, if these are present. It is distinguished from the silver and mercury compounds by its solubility in hot water (solubility at 100°C. three times that at 20°C.).

*Potassium chromate* precipitates yellow PbCrO$_4$ when added to a neutral or faintly acetic acid solution of lead. The precipitate dissolves in free mineral acids. The mineral acid may be neutralized by sodium or ammonium acetate.

*Sulfuric acid* precipitates PbSO$_4$, white. The sulfate is soluble in hot concentrated HCl, HNO$_3$, or H$_2$SO$_4$. It is soluble in sodium or ammonium acetates and

* The original contributions to this Chapter in the previous edition of J. R. Sheppard, Consulting Chemist and Metallurgist, Saginaw, Mich., formerly Director of Research, The Eagle-Picher Lead Co., Joplin, Mo., and of W. J. Brown, Chief Analyst of the National Lead Co., to the preliminary revision of this chapter are acknowledged. Further additions were made by A. J. Nicklay, Research Chemist, The Eagle-Picher Lead Co. The testing of the accuracy of certain methods was carried out by Lenora White and S. M. Alldredge.

sodium thiosulfate. The solubility in water is decreased by addition of a little $H_2SO_4$ or by presence of an appreciable amount of alcohol.

*Hydrogen sulfide* precipitates PbS, black, when added to a solution containing lead. Traces of lead may be detected in presence of 1 ml. HCl (sp. gr. 1.19) per 100 ml. of solution. Three times this acidity, however, has an appreciable effect on precipitation, as PbS is soluble in HCl or $HNO_3$ solutions stronger than 0.3 $N$. The test is best made in HCl solutions. (*Caution:* other members of the $H_2S$ group should be absent.)

Sodium carbonate will convert $PbSO_4$ to $PbCO_3$, forming a precipitate easily soluble in hot dilute acid solutions. Spongy metallic lead may be precipitated from the solution by zinc.

*General Procedure.*—Lead is precipitated from a slightly acid solution as PbS, black. PbS is separated from As, Sb, Sn by its comparative insolubility in $(NH_4)_2S_x$; from HgS by its solubility in dilute $HNO_3$ and is converted to $PbSO_4$ by heating to fuming with $H_2SO_4$, separating it from Bi, Cu, and Cd. The $PbSO_4$ is converted to acetate by action of ammonium acetate, from which $PbCrO_4$, yellow, is precipitated by a soluble, neutral chromate ($K_2CrO_4$, $K_2Cr_2O_7$, etc.).

## ESTIMATION

In addition to the valuation of ores, such as galena, PbS, etc., the determination of lead is required in a large number of substances of commercial importance. It is determined in lead mattes; certain slags; drosses from hard lead; cupel bottoms; lead insecticides (lead arsenate, etc.); paint pigments (white lead, red lead, yellow and red chromates, etc.); it is determined in alloys such as solder, type metal, bell metal, etc. Its estimation is required in the analysis of a large number of ores, especially in minerals of antimony and arsenic. Traces of lead are determined in certain food products, where its presence is undesirable. Its use in the industry makes its determination of special importance.

If the ore is decomposed by HCl some of the lead may remain with silica and be volatilized as the chloride. That remaining in solution, unless provided for, will precipitate with the ammonia precipitate and will be reported as alumina. If $H_2SO_4$ is used in the decomposition of the ore, lead will remain with the silica as $PbSO_4$.

## PREPARATION AND SOLUTION OF THE SAMPLE

In dissolving the ores, alloys, or the metal lead, the following facts should be kept in mind. The metal is soluble in hot dilute nitric acid. Lead nitrate is comparatively insoluble in concentrated nitric acid, but dissolves readily upon dilution with water. Decomposition of an ore may generally be effected by treating with $HNO_3$ (1:1). (If HCl or $HNO_3$ is used, as may be advisable with certain sulfides, it is necessary to expel these acids with $H_2SO_4$ taking to fumes, cooling, adding a little water and again evaporating to fumes, otherwise low results will be obtained.[1]) In the process of analysis the lead is left with the residue, which may contain, in addition to the silica, $BaSO_4$, tin and antimony salts, which persist in holding up lead, preventing its complete solution in ammonium acetate. The National Lead Company employs fusion with $Na_2CO_3$, leaching, filtering off the

[1] Communicated to the Editor by W. J. Brown, Chief Analyst, National Lead Company.

$PbCO_3$ and $BaCO_3$, dissolving in HCl, heating to expel $CO_2$, and precipitating PbS with $H_2S$.

*Oxides and Carbonates.*—These are generally soluble in dilute nitric acid. Hydrogen peroxide, sodium nitrite, etc., must be added to dissolve lead peroxide or red lead.

*Sulfides.*—It is often desirable to start with HCl to expel $H_2S$ and follow this with $HNO_3$ or a mixture of $HNO_3$ and $H_2SO_4$; in any case taking to fumes with $H_2SO_4$. (See discussion above.) The residue may be extracted with ammonium or sodium acetate to dissolve $PbSO_4$. In presence of $BaSO_4$, a fusion, as given under the discussion above may be advisable.

*Silicates and Slags.*—These are decomposed by fusion with $Na_2CO_3$ and $K_2CO_3$, extracting the mass with water (traces of lead may dissolve), and converting the $PbCO_3$ formed to the nitrate, or to the chloride according to directions stated above. If preferred the ore may be treated with HF and $H_2SO_4$, taken to fumes to expel silicon tetrafluoride, and the lead determined in the residue.

*Alloys.*—These are best decomposed by treatment with dilute nitric acid. The lead may then be converted to sulfate as in case of the ores. Specific details are given in the body of the text. Alloys of lead, antimony, tin, and copper may be decomposed by the following method, which avoids formation of insoluble oxides of antimony and tin. A 0.5-g. sample is digested with 10 ml. of concentrated $H_2SO_4$ until a clear solution is obtained or at least until there is no residue of unattacked metal. The solution is cooled and then diluted with about 100 ml. of dilute (1 to 4) $H_2SO_4$. Five ml. of concentrated HCl are added. The solution is brought to a boil, allowed to cool, and stand 4 hours. Lead is precipitated as sulfate and the antimony, tin, and copper remain in solution. On the class of sample indicated, the lead sulfate may be determined gravimetrically.

## SEPARATIONS

*Separation as Lead Sulfate.*—Lead may be separated from a number of elements whose sulfates are soluble in water and dilute acid solutions by conversion to the sulfate, $PbSO_4$. Barium, niobium, silica, tantalum, and tungsten accompany lead. Antimony, bismuth, and silver may contaminate the lead sulfate and occasionally chromium and nickel may be found with this residue. In the presence of much bismuth or iron it is necessary to wash the residue with 10% sulfuric acid solution to keep the bismuth in solution and to prevent the formation of the difficultly soluble basic ferric sulfate. In absence of these contaminating substances, lead sulfate is best separated by adding to the dilute sulfuric acid solution an equal volume of alcohol before filtering to prevent a slight amount of the lead from dissolving, which would otherwise occur.

*Separation of Lead from the Acid Insoluble Residue—Extraction of Lead by Ammonium Acetate.*—Lead may be completely separated from silica, barium, tin, and antimony by extraction with ammonium acetate, provided a sufficient amount of this reagent is used. Separation from barium sulfate may be effected even when the amount of barium is 100 times that of lead.[2,3] Calcium, if present in the solution, will also be extracted to a considerable extent and will accompany the lead. Free sulfuric acid must be absent as it retards the extraction and will prevent

---

[2] Scott, W. W., and Alldredge, S. M., Ind. Eng. Chem., Anal. Ed., **3**, 32, 1931.
[3] 95% of the Pb is extracted when the ratio of Pb:Ba is 1:100.

this entirely if it is present to the extent of 10%. In the separation of lead from silica the presence of free acetic acid is desirable (20 g. of ammonium acetate and 3 ml. of 80% acetic acid per 100 ml. of extraction solution). Occasionally it is well to remove the silica by HF and $H_2SO_4$ treatment prior to the extraction of the lead. The filter containing the impure sulfate, obtained by one of the procedures for solution of the sample, is placed in a casserole and extracted with about 50 ml. of hot, slightly ammoniacal ammonium acetate, the stronger the acetate the better. The clear liquid is decanted through a filter and the extraction repeated until the residue is free from lead (i.e., no test is obtained for lead with $K_2Cr_2O_7$). A very effective method of extraction is by adding solid ammonium acetate directly to the sample on a filter and pouring over it a hot solution of ammonium acetate.

Lead sulfate containing arsenic should be dissolved in ammonium acetate, the extract made alkaline and lead precipitated as PbS. Arsenic remains in solution.

*Ammonium Carbonate Method.*—Lead may be separated from barium sulfate by digesting the mixed sulfates with ammonium carbonate solution, whereby the lead sulfate is transposed to lead carbonate and ammonium sulfate, while barium sulfate is not changed. The soluble ammonium sulfate may be washed out with ammonium solution followed by water. Since lead carbonate is slightly soluble in the ammonium salt, the filtrate is treated with hydrogen sulfide and the dissolved lead recovered as PbS. The residue containing lead carbonate and barium sulfate is treated with dilute nitric or acetic acid. Lead passes into solution, while barium sulfate remains insoluble.

*Separation of Lead from Calcium.*—Calcium, if present, will accompany lead in the acetate extract. The acetate solution of lead and calcium is evaporated to fumes with $H_2SO_4$. The cooled residue is taken up with water and NaOH added to dissolve the lead. The extract is filtered from calcium and lead determined in the filtrate, acidified with HCl.

If antimony is present, $PbSO_4$ carries down an appreciable amount of this element.

*Hydrogen Sulfide Method.* **Separation from Barium, Niobium, Tantalum and Members of the Ammonium Sulfide, Ammonium Carbonate, and Water Soluble Groups.**—Lead sulfide is precipitated from an acid solution containing tartaric acid.

*Separation from Tungsten.*—Advantage may be taken of the solubility of tungstic acid in ammonia and ammonium tartrate. Lead as sulfate remains in the residue. Any entrained lead in the tungsten filtrate may be precipitated as sulfide by $H_2S$, keeping the solution alkaline with $NH_4OH$.

NOTES.[4]—It is a good practice to effect solution with dilute $HNO_3$ (1:1) and proceed as directed in "Determination of Lead in an Ore." When the nature of ore is such as to necessitate the use of HCl, fume, cool, take up with a few milliliters of water, fume again, and repeat this operation. Experience indicates that HCl may not be expelled by a single fuming and unless it is, low results are obtained.

Another cause for low results is the effect that $BaSO_4$ and separated tin and antimony compounds have in holding up lead after the $PbSO_4$ has been treated with ammonium acetate. We separate the occluded lead from barium by a fusion with $Na_2CO_3$ and $K_2CO_3$, leach, filter off the $BaCO_3$ and $PbCO_3$, dissolve in HCl and boil to expel $CO_2$. The solution is neutralized with $NH_4OH$ and then made acid with acetic; $H_2S$ is passed to precipitate the lead. The occluded lead is separated from tin and antimony by a fusion of the treated residue with $S–Na_2CO_3$ mixture. After leaching, the tin and antimony are found in solution while the lead is present in the residue as PbS.

A cause for high results is the use of the theoretical factor 0.641 for the conversion of

---

[4] Brown, W. J., Chief Analyst, National Lead Company.

$PbCrO_4$ to Pb when the precipitate is heated to 100°C. and even to 110°C. An alloy having a lead content of 85% will invariably total 0.4% too high and examination of the $PbCrO_4$ will show the presence of water. Use the factor 0.6375, which is constant for all weights of precipitate.

# GRAVIMETRIC METHODS

## DETERMINATION OF LEAD AS LEAD SULFATE

This method is generally considered among the best of the gravimetric methods for the determination of lead.

*Reagents.* "Lead Acid."—Mix 300 ml. of $H_2SO_4$ (sp. gr. 1.84) and 1800 ml. of distilled water. Dissolve 1 g. of C.P. lead acetate in 300 ml. of distilled water and add this to the hot solution, stirring meanwhile. Let stand 24 hours and filter through a thick asbestos pad.

**Dilute Alcohol for Washing.**—Mix equal parts of denatured alcohol and distilled water.

*Procedure for Ores.*—The material is brought into solution according to the procedure outlined under the preparation and solution of the sample, the lead precipitated as $PbSO_4$ by addition of an excess of sulfuric acid, nitric or hydrochloric acid expelled by taking to fumes ($H_2SO_4$) and the impure sulfate filtered off and washed, first with water containing 10% of its volume of $H_2SO_4$ until free of soluble impurities, and then with 50% alcohol solution to remove the free acid.

**Purification.**—The lead sulfate is dissolved from the impurities of the residue by repeated extraction with a strong solution of ammonium acetate. The separation from barium sulfate is complete,[5] very little $SiO_2$ dissolves, calcium, if present, will accompany lead. The acetate solution is evaporated to dryness, taken up with water and a large excess of sulfuric acid added. Lead sulfate is again filtered and washed as before. Water is expelled by heating to 110°C. or by gentle ignition.

$$PbSO_4 \times 0.6832 = Pb$$

NOTE.—In presence of Ca, Bi, Si, W, Nb, Ta, Ba, Sb, Ag, washing with dilute alcohol will not remove these completely. The solubility of $PbSO_4$ is increased by the presence of HCl and $HNO_3$, hence the necessity for their removal.

In determining lead in alloys the sulfate precipitation generally gives $PbSO_4$ as a difficultly soluble salt free from impurities. In case of ores, however, $SiO_2$ will be present and an acetate extraction of the $PbSO_4$ is necessary (100 ml. of a saturated solution of ammonium acetate will dissolve a little over 3 g. of $PbSO_4$). The $PbSO_4$ is reprecipitated from the extract, after diluting with water, by adding a large excess of $H_2SO_4$ (acidity should be 10% $H_2SO_4$).

*Procedure for Determination of Lead in Alloys.*—In a covered 300-ml. Erlenmeyer flask dissolve 1 g. of the alloy in 20 ml. $H_2SO_4$ (sp. gr. 1.84); heat the solution nearly to boiling until the metal is completely decomposed and the $PbSO_4$ is white (this may take 30 minutes or more) and finally boil for several minutes. Allow to cool, but not below 60°C., and then add slowly 50 ml. of water while the solution is agitated. Heat to boiling for several minutes in order to insure complete solution of antimony sulfate. Allow the $PbSO_4$ to settle out until the solution is clear, not letting the temperature fall below 60°C. If the liquid does

---

[5] Alldredge, S. M., Research, Univ. So. Calif., 1930.

not clear quickly, it must be heated longer.  When clear, pour the solution through a weighed porcelain Gooch crucible with asbestos mat, decanting the solution as completely as possible without allowing more than a very small amount of $PbSO_4$ to go over into the crucible.  Now add 10 ml. more of $H_2SO_4$ (sp. gr. 1.84) to the $PbSO_4$ in the original flask, and boil for several minutes.  Cool, add slowly 30 ml. of water, and again heat to boiling for a few minutes; allow the solution to cool to about 60°C. and completely transfer the $PbSO_4$ to the Gooch crucible.  Wash the precipitate with lead acid reagent.[6]  Remove the beaker containing these solutions and wash out the lead acid with dilute alcohol; set the Gooch crucible inside a porcelain crucible; dry and ignite for five minutes over a Meker or Bunsen burner; cool and weigh as $PbSO_4$, which contains 68.33% lead.

NOTES.—Copper alloys are best decomposed by nitric acid, followed by sulfuric acid. The greater part of the acids are expelled by concentration to strong fumes, the solution is cooled and diluted with water.  In presence of lead, $PbSO_4$ remains as a precipitate while copper, tin, and zinc are in solution.

## LEAD AS THE MOLYBDATE, $PbMoO_4$

This method is rapid and has the following advantages: (a) the sulfation of lead is avoided; (b) the acetate extraction is eliminated; (c) the precipitate may be ignited; and (d) the ratio of lead to its molybdate compound is less than either lead to $PbSO_4$ or to $PbCrO_4$, lessening the magnitude of error through weighing.

Cobalt, calcium, strontium, and barium have little effect in presence of ammonium acetate.  In absence of this salt they interfere slightly.

The solution should be free from $CrO_4$, $AsO_4$, $PO_4$, Ti, and Sn.

*Procedure.*—The ore or alloy is decomposed with nitric acid or aqua regia as the case may require.  (Silica if present is eliminated by taking to dryness, dehydrating, taking up with dilute nitric acid, and filtering.)  To the clear liquid, 2 g. of ammonium chloride are added and then sufficient ammonium acetate to destroy the excess of free nitric acid, i.e., 2 g. per ml. of free $HNO_3$ present.

Lead is now precipitated by adding 40 ml. of ammonium molybdate solution (4 g. per liter + 10 ml. acetic acid), per 0.1 g. of lead present, stirring the mixture during the addition.  After boiling for two or three minutes the precipitated lead molybdate is allowed to settle; it is then filtered and washed with small portions of hot water containing 2% of ammonium nitrate and ignited over a Bunsen burner to dull red heat.

The cooled residue is weighed as $PbMoO_4$.  $PbMoO_4 \times 0.5644 = Pb$.

NOTES.—If antimony or other members of the group are present in the original sample, it is advisable to dissolve the residue in HCl and reprecipitate the lead with molybdate reagent.

If lead is in the form of the sulfide, as may be the case in a complete analysis of a substance, it is decomposed with hot dilute $HNO_3$ and precipitated as $PbMoO_4$.

Galena is best decomposed by treating with hydrochloric acid to expel sulfur as oxidation of sulfur to sulfate is not desirable in this method.  If lead sulfate has formed due to oxidation of sulfur, it is advisable to treat any residue, remaining from the acid extraction, with ammonium acetate, adding the acetate extract to the solution containing the lead.

The sample, evaporated to dryness, is treated with about 10 ml. of dilute nitric acid (1:1) and a little water, then it is heated and filtered.  About 2 g. of ammo-

[6] Washing the lead sulfate with lead acid prevents the solution of $PbSO_4$ by the wash solution.

nium chloride are added and for each ml. of free nitric acid (sp. gr. 1.42) two grams of ammonium acetate are necessary (total 10–15 g.). The precipitate generally appears a light canary yellow or yellowish white.

Washing the precipitate with water containing a little ammonium nitrate prevents the formation of colloidal lead molybdate, which would pass through the filter paper. (Use about 2 g. of nitrate per 100 ml.)

The pulp used is paper pulp made by breaking up ashless filter paper and agitating it thoroughly with hot water in a flask. Scott preferred omitting the pulp and using a fine-grained ashless filter paper; the washing of the precipitate being conducted with wash water containing ammonium nitrate. A filter crucible may be used in place of a paper filter.

## LEAD AS THE CHROMATE, $PbCrO_4$

This method is applicable to a large class of materials and is of special value in precipitation of lead from an acetic acid solution, the method depending upon the insolubility of lead chromate in weak acetic acid.

*Procedure.*—The solution of the sample, precipitation of the lead as the sulfate, and extraction of lead with ammonium acetate have been given in detail in the method, "Lead as Lead Sulfate."

The filtrate, containing all the lead in solution as the acetate, is acidified slightly with acetic acid and heated to boiling. Lead is precipitated by addition of potassium dichromate solution in excess (10 ml. of 5% $K_2Cr_2O_7$ solution are generally sufficient). The solution is boiled until the yellow precipitate turns to a shade of orange or red.[7] The precipitate is allowed to settle until the supernatant solution is clear. (This should appear yellow with the excess of dichromate reagent.) The $PbCrO_4$ is filtered into a filter crucible, washed with water, dried in an oven at about 110°C. and the cooled compound weighed as $PbCrO_4$.

$$PbCrO_4 \times 0.6411 = Pb[7]$$

Notes.—Impurities, such as iron, copper, cadmium, etc., in the acetate solution of lead seriously interfere in the chromate precipitation. These should be leached out with water containing a little sulfuric acid before extracting the lead sulfate with ammonium acetate.

## ELECTROLYTIC DETERMINATION OF LEAD AS THE PEROXIDE, $PbO_2$

An electric current passed through a solution of lead containing sufficient free nitric acid will deposit all the lead on the anode as lead peroxide. The method is excellent for analysis of lead alloys. The following substances interfere: Bi, Sn, Sb, Ag, Mn will contaminate the $PbO_2$ precipitate; Cl, Hg, As, Te, Se, P prevent complete deposition.

*Procedure.*—The sample containing not over 0.1 g. lead is brought into solution by heating with dilute nitric acid, 1:1. The solution is washed into a large platinum dish with unpolished inner surface. Twenty to 25 ml. of concentrated nitric acid (sp. gr. 1.42) are added and the solution diluted to about 150 ml.

---

[7] The yellow precipitate gives high results, since it is difficult to wash. The crystalline orange or red compound may be quickly filtered and washed.

If Bi is present add 2 g. of citric acid dissolved in a little hot water before filtering off the $PbCrO_4$.

The sample is electrolyzed in the cold with 0.5 to 1 ampere current and 2.0 to 2.5 volts, the platinum dish forming the anode of the circuit, a spiral platinum wire or a platinum crucible dipped into the solution being the cathode. Three hours are generally sufficient for the deposition of the Pb. Overnight electrolysis is advisable, a current of 0.05 ampere being used.

A rapid deposition of the lead may be obtained by heating the solution to 60–65°C. and electrolyzing with a current equivalent to 1.5 to 1.7 amperes per 100 sq. cm, the e.m.f. varying within wide limits. Stirring the solution with a rotating cathode aids in the rapid deposition of the $PbO_2$.

To ascertain whether all the lead has been removed from the solution, more water is added so as to cover a fresh portion of the dish with water. The electrolysis is complete if no fresh deposition of the peroxide takes place after half an hour.

The solution is siphoned off while more water is being added until the acid is removed, the current is then broken, the dish emptied of water and the deposits dried at 220°C. and weighed as $PbO_2$.

$$PbO_2 \times 0.8662 = Pb. \text{ (Empirical Factor)}$$

NOTE.—The deposit of lead peroxide may be removed by dissolving off with warm dilute nitric acid (1:3) and a little $H_2O_2$.
For titrimetric estimation of the peroxide $PbO_2$, see page 578.

## TITRIMETRIC METHODS

## FERROCYANIDE METHOD FOR THE DETERMINATION OF LEAD

Although the gravimetric methods for the determination of lead are considered the more accurate, titrimetric procedures may be frequently used with advantage. The ferrocyanide method was considered by Bull [8] to be the best of the procedures in use, the results being accurate.

*Procedure.*—Lead sulfate is obtained according to the method outlined under "Preparation and Solution of the Sample." The lead sulfate is transferred to a small beaker and gently boiled with 10 to 15 ml. of a saturated solution of ammonium carbonate, the liquid having been added cold and brought up to boiling. After cooling, the precipitate is filtered on the original filter paper from which the lead sulfate was removed. The lead carbonate is washed free of alkali with cold water. The filter with the precipitate is dropped into a flask containing a hot mixture of 5 ml. of glacial acetic acid with 25 ml. of water. The lead carbonate is decomposed by boiling and the solution diluted to 100 ml.

**Titration.**—The sample warmed to 60°C. is titrated with a standard solution of potassium ferrocyanide, using a saturated solution of uranium acetate as an outside indicator. The excess of ferrocyanide produces a brown color with the uranium acetate drop on the tile.

Free ammonia must be absent, as it reacts with uranium acetate and gives low results. $NH_4OH$ precipitates reddish brown, gelatinous uranous hydroxide, $U(OH)_4$.

The bulk of solution to be titrated should be as near as possible to 100 ml., including 5 ml. of glacial acetic acid.

[8] Chem. News, **87,** 53, 1903.

A 1% potassium ferrocyanide solution is used in the titration. This reagent is standardized against a known amount of lead in solution as an acetate.

A correction of 0.8 ml. is generally necessary on account of the indicator. This is determined by a blank titration.

Antimony, bismuth, barium, strontium, and calcium interfere only to a very slight extent, the error being negligible.

## THE PERMANGANATE METHOD [9]

The following method for the determination of lead in ores has proved very satisfactory in the great majority of cases. It depends upon the separation of the lead as sulfate, the conversion of the sulfate to carbonate, the solution of the carbonate in acetic acid, followed by the precipitation of the lead as oxalate. The lead oxalate is then decomposed in dilute sulfuric acid and the separated oxalic acid titrated with standard permanganate.

Ordinary constituents of lead ores do not interfere, with the exception of lime. As high as 10% of CaO in an ore, however, is without effect. Barium interferes only by forming a combination with lead that resists the reactions, with consequent low results. The remedy is easy and is described below.

*Procedure.*—Decompose 0.5 g. of the ore in a 250-ml., pear-shaped flask, such as is commonly called a "copper-flask." The treatment may usually be a very gentle boiling with 10 ml. of hydrochloric acid for a short time, then adding 5 ml. of nitric acid and continuing the gentle boiling until decomposition is complete. Now add 6 ml. of sulfuric acid and boil over a free flame to strong fumes. Allow to cool.

Add 100 ml. of cold water and 5 ml. of sulfuric acid and heat to boiling. Remove from the heat, add 10 ml. of alcohol (cautiously) and cool under the tap.

Fold a 9-cm filter with particular care to creasing the fold that will come next to the precipitate as thin as possible, so it will lie flat and not easily allow material to get under the edge. Filter the mixture through this. Return the first portions of the filtrate if not clear. Wash 6 times with cold water containing 10% of alcohol. Any trace of lead sulfate remaining in the flask will be recovered subsequently.

With a jet of hot water, using as little as possible, rinse the precipitate from the filter, through a short funnel, back into the flask. (In the known or assumed presence of barium, interpolate the following short procedure: Add 10 ml. of hydrochloric acid and boil over a free flame almost to dryness. Allow to cool, add 20 ml. of water and a few drops of ammonium hydroxide, sufficient to neutralize the acid.) Place the flask again under the original funnel and pour through the filter 10 ml. of a cold saturated solution of ammonium carbonate. Remove the flask and heat the contents just to boiling, then cool completely under the tap. Pour the cold mixture through the original filter. Wash out the flask well with cold water, pouring through the filter, and then wash filter and precipitate 10 times with cold water containing about 5% of the ammonium carbonate solution. Reject the filtrate.

Again using a jet of hot water, wash the precipitate from the filter into a small beaker. Add 5–6 ml. of glacial acetic acid and heat to boiling. Replace the flask under the funnel and pour the hot acid mixture through the filter. Wash

[9] By Albert H. Low.

out the beaker with hot water and then wash the filter 10 times with hot water slightly acidulated with acetic acid. (Small amounts of lead carbonate may be dissolved directly upon the filter, without previous transference to a beaker.)

Add to the filtrate 10 ml. of a cold saturated solution of oxalic acid, heat to boiling and then cool completely under the tap. Be particular to get it as cold as possible. Now filter the lead oxalate through a 9-cm filter. Using cold water, wash out the flask thoroughly and then wash filter and precipitate 10 times.

Place about 25 ml. of cold water in the flask, add 5–6 ml. of sulfuric acid, and then about 100 ml. of hot water. Drop the filter and precipitate into this. Wipe out any lead oxalate adhering in the funnel with a small piece of dry filter paper and drop into the flask. Heat the acid mixture nearly to boiling and then titrate it with standard potassium permanganate solution to a faint pink tinge. Calculate the result from the known lead value of the permanganate.

NOTES.—The permanganate commonly used for iron titrations will serve, although it is rather strong for lead. Theoretically, 1.857 times the iron factor will give the lead factor. Owing to slight losses of lead an empirical factor must be used. This is 1.879 times the iron factor. Based on this factor and on 0.5 g. of ore taken for assay, 1 ml. of a permanganate solution containing 1.544 g. per liter will equal 1% lead. It may be standardized directly on lead as follows: Convert about 0.250 g. of pure lead foil to sulfate by boiling with 6 ml. of sulfuric acid. Continue according to the above entire process. Finally, divide the percentage value of the lead taken by the ml. of permanganate required, to obtain the percentage value of 1 ml. in lead. A comparison of this figure with the iron value of the permanganate may be made, to check the conversion factor given above. The personal equation may cause a slight difference.

Metallic lead is converted to lead sulfate by boiling with strong sulfuric acid. The reaction takes place with the hot concentrated acid, the metal changing to the white lead sulfate solid, soluble in large excess of sulfuric acid; this is unnecessary, as decomposition is complete with the amount stated.

Conversion of lead sulfate to carbonate before changing to acetate appears at first thought to be an unnecessary step, but experience has shown that a direct conversion of sulfate to acetate by dissolving in ammonium acetate leaves sufficient sulfate in the solution to cause low results, as much as 10% of lead apparently escaping subsequent conversion to oxalate. In the procedure for converting the lead to carbonate any small amount of lead sulfate remaining does no harm. It frequently occurs that the carbonate formed does not completely dissolve in acetic acid. If a cloudy solution is obtained, a few drops of ammonia will furnish enough ammonium acetate to dissolve the small amount of sulfate remaining. The precipitation of lead oxalate is not interfered with by the ammonium salt present, a large amount of which, however, should be avoided. Ammonium oxalate may be added in place of oxalic acid.

## THE MOLYBDATE METHOD

Lead is precipitated from an acetic acid solution by a standard solution of ammonium molybdate, the termination of the reaction being recognized by the yellow color produced by the excess of reagent when a drop of the mixture comes in contact with a drop of tannin solution, used as an outside indicator. The method is rapid, but is not as accurate as the chromate-iodide method.

*Reagents.* **Ammonium Molybdate.**—4.26 g. of the salt are dissolved in water and diluted to 1000 ml. On a half-gram sample basis 1 ml. of the reagent is equivalent to about 1% lead.

*Standardization.*—Dissolve 0.2 g. of pure lead foil in 5 ml. of concentrated sulfuric acid by boiling gently in a 250-ml. pear-shaped flask. When the lead has been converted to sulfate, dilute (on cooling) with water and filter off the $PbSO_4$. Now follow the details of the procedure given below, after isolating the lead as sulfate. Note the ml. of molybdate reagent required and divide this into 0.2 to get the equivalent value in terms of lead per ml. of reagent. One ml. should be equivalent, approximately, to 0.005 g. Pb.

**Tannin Indicator.**—0.1 g. tannic acid per 20 ml. water. The reagent should be prepared fresh for each day's analysis.

*Procedure.* **Decomposition.**—Follow the usual procedure recommended for decomposing lead ores, using HCl, $HNO_3$ and finally $H_2SO_4$. Evaporate to strong sulfuric fumes, and take up with water. Filter off the lead sulfate and wash with a 10% sulfuric acid solution, to remove sulfates of the metals, and finally with water containing a little alcohol, remembering that $PbSO_4$ is slightly soluble in water.

The lead sulfate is now brought into solution as lead acetate by extraction with ammonium acetate slightly acidified with acetic acid. (Use a strong solution of the reagent.) In absence of calcium and barium, the writer prefers to convert the lead sulfate to carbonate by boiling with ammonium carbonate solution, according to the permanganate method for lead (p. 564), and then to the acetate by dissolving the lead carbonate in dilute acetic acid. Thus sulfates are eliminated. The addition of a few drops of ammonia to the acetic acid solution insures the solubility of the lead. ($PbSO_4$ may be present in small amount and does not readily dissolve in acetic acid.) The results are more concordant in absence of sulfate. The acetate solution of lead is now titrated with the standard molybdate solution.

**Titration.**—The solution is divided into two portions, one being kept in reserve. To one is added the standard solution of ammonium molybdate, from a burette, until a drop of the titrated solution, brought in contact with a drop of tannin indicator, on a white tile, or paraffined surface, gives a brown or yellow color. The reserve solution is now added in portions, the titration being continued, until the last portion has been used and the brown color obtained. This precaution avoids over-running the end point.

## THE CHROMATE METHOD

This method consists of precipitation of the lead as the chromate by addition of an excess of standard dichromate solution. The precipitate is filtered off, and the excess of dichromate is determined by titration with ferrous sulfate solution, or with potassium iodide and thiosulfate.

*Procedure.*—Lead sulfate is obtained according to the method outlined under "Preparation and Solution of the Sample." The lead sulfate is transferred to a small beaker and gently boiled with 10 to 15 ml. of a saturated solution of ammonium carbonate, the liquid having been added cold and brought up to boiling. After cooling, the precipitate is filtered on the original filter paper from which the lead sulfate was removed. The lead carbonate is washed free of alkali with cold water. The filter with the precipitate is dropped into a flask containing a hot mixture of 5 ml. of glacial acetic acid with 25 ml. of water. The lead carbonate is decomposed by boiling and the solution diluted to 100 ml. Acidify the solution slightly with acetic acid and heat to boiling. Add from a burette sufficient 0.025 $M$ potassium dichromate solution to precipitate all the lead and about one-third of the volume in excess is added to the hot solution. After boiling about two minutes the precipitate is filtered off quickly and washed several times with hot water.

**Titration.**—Titration of the excess chromate may be carried out in two ways: (a) after boiling about two minutes the precipitate is filtered off quickly and washed several times with hot water. The filtrate, or an aliquot part of it, is made acid with 5 ml. of concentrated sulfuric acid and titrated with standard ferrous sulfate at about 60°C., using potassium ferricyanide as an outside indicator; the end point is a blue color produced by the slight excess of the ferrous salt reacting with the indicator. (b) Filter as above and add 3 to 4 g. of solid potassium iodide, KI, to the solution diluted to about 500 ml. with water to which 15 ml. of concentrated sulfuric acid have been added. The liberated iodine is titrated with standard thiosulfate, with starch solution indicator. These titrations are described in detail in the following method. Bi, Sb, Ba, Sr, and Ca interfere slightly.

$$\text{One ml. } 0.025M \text{ K}_2\text{Cr}_2\text{O}_7 = 0.01036 \text{ g Pb}$$

$$\text{One ml } 0.5M \text{ K}_2\text{Cr}_2\text{O}_7 = 0.02072 \text{ g. Pb}$$

## THE CHROMATE-IODIDE METHOD

The method depends upon the action of chromates on potassium iodide with a resulting liberation of an amount of free iodine in direct ratio to the chromate present, which in turn is a measure of the amount of lead isolated as lead chromate. The liberated iodine is determined by titration with a standard solution of thiosulfate.

*Reagents.* **Ammonium Acetate Extraction Solution.**—A saturated solution of ammonium acetate, filtered to remove foreign matter if present, is diluted with twice its volume of distilled water and 30 ml. of 80% acetic acid is added per liter of solution.

**Hydrochloric Acid Mixture.**—To a liter of saturated salt solution, filtered if necessary, are added 150 ml. of distilled water and 100 ml. of concentrated hydrochloric acid.

**Potassium Dichromate.**—Saturated solution, filtered if not clear.

**Starch Solution.**

*Procedure.* **Solution of the Sample.**—Half a gram of the finely divided ore (if the factor weight 0.6907 g. is taken, 1 ml. 0.1 N reagent in final titration is equivalent to about 1% Pb) is dissolved in a beaker or a flask (Low's type) by adding 20 ml. of concentrated hydrochloric acid and heating gently until the action subsides. If the decomposition is incomplete, about 5 ml. of nitric acid are added and the heating continued.

About 5 ml. of sulfuric acid are added and the solution evaporated to strong fumes. After cooling, about 50 ml. of water are added and the solution is boiled to dissolve the soluble salts. If the ore is low grade, 5–10 ml. of ethyl alcohol are now added, the precipitate is allowed to settle and then washed by decantation three or four times with 1:15 sulfuric acid (i.e., about 7% solution), and finally transferred to the filter with the dilute acid and washed once with pure cold water.

By means of a fine jet from a wash bottle filled with ammonium acetate extraction reagent, heated to near boiling, the precipitate is transferred to the beaker or flask in which the precipitation was made. This may be done by carefully spreading out the filter in the funnel or by breaking the filter and washing the paper free of the lead sulfate with a fine stream of the reagent. If the precipitate does not go into solution, more of the acetate is added and heat gently applied until it dissolves. The solution is now diluted to 150 ml., heated to boiling and 10 ml. of the saturated dichromate solution added and the boiling continued ten minutes. The yellow color of the lead chromate precipitate changes to red. This is important to obtain a precipitate of definite composition.

The precipitate is filtered, the containing vessel washed out with hot dilute ammonium acetate wash solution (50 ml. of the extraction solution diluted to 1000 ml.) and the precipitate washed ten times with the reagent.

The original beaker or flask is now placed under the funnel and the lead chromate is dissolved on the filter by adding cold dilute hydrochloric acid mixture, stirring up the precipitate with a jet of the reagent, adding the acid until all the chromate has dissolved and the color has been completely removed from the filter. At least 50 ml. of the reagent should be used.

At this stage either of the following methods may be followed; both procedures give good results. The second method (J. Ind. Eng. Chem., **17**, 678, 1925) is less expensive.

## REDUCTION BY IODIDE

For low grade ores the entire solution is taken and treated with potassium iodide solution; in case of high grade ores, about half the solution is set aside in reserve, and upon completing the titration of the first portion, the reserve is added and the titration completed. This precaution is taken because a loss of iodine is apt to occur if much iodine is liberated at one time, free iodine being apt to escape as vapor from the easily saturated solution. (The solution is a poor solvent of iodine.) To the solution are added 5 ml. of 25% potassium iodide and the liberated iodine is titrated with 0.1 N sodium thiosulfate until the iodine color begins to fade; starch solution is now added in sufficient quantity to produce a distinct blue color and the titration continued until the blue color changes to pale green.

A background of white assists in recognition of the end point. A sheet of white paper placed under the beaker will do, if the base of the stand is not already white.

**Standardization of the Thiosulfate.**—This is best standardized against metallic lead. 0.6907 g. of pure lead should require 100 ml. of 0.1 N thiosulfate. 0.2 g. of lead is taken or a fraction of the factor weight (0.6907). The lead foil is dissolved in 5 ml. of sulfuric acid by bringing to vigorous boiling; upon cooling the residue is taken up with water and treated exactly according to the regular procedure described above. One ml. of 0.1 N thiosulfate is equivalent approximately to 0.0069 of lead.

NOTES.—If barium is present in the sample, the residue left from the acetate extraction may contain lead. This is treated with about 10 ml. of strong hydrochloric acid, evaporated to dryness, 25 ml. of the acetate reagent added, the mixture boiled, filtered and the residue washed. The filtrate contains the lead that remained with the residue.

In considering the reactions that take place it must be remembered that it is the combined chromate radical that is responsible for the liberated iodine. The equation represents what takes place:

$$2PbCrO_4 + 6KI + 16HCl \rightarrow 2PbCl_2 + 2CrCl_3 + 6KCl + 8H_2O + 3I_2$$

It is evident that Pb is equivalent to 3I. Therefore a normal equivalent of Pb is $\frac{1}{3}$ of its atomic weight, 207.21 divided by 3 = 69.07, hence 1 ml. of a 0.1 N solution will titrate iodine equivalent to .006907 g. Pb.

Since Fe equivalent is 55.85, Fe to Pb = 69.07 divided by 55.85 = 1.236, factor of iron to lead.

Example in Standardization of Sodium Thiosulfate.—If 0.2035 g. of lead required 30.05 ml. of thiosulfate solution, then 1 ml. would be equivalent to 0.00677 g. lead.

## REDUCTION BY FERROUS SULFATE

With experience the results are excellent. In the hands of the inexperienced analyst low results are obtained due to loss of $PbSO_4$ during the washing, incomplete extraction of the sulfate with acetate, loss of chromate and incomplete solution of $PbCrO_4$ before the final steps of titration.

*Reagents.* **Ferrous Solution.**—0.1 $N$ contains 39.3 g. ferrous ammonium sulfate hexahydrate per liter.

Standardize against 0.1 $N$ potassium dichromate.

**Potassium Dichromate.**—0.1 $N$ contains 4.903 g. per liter.

**Phosphoric-Sulfuric Acid Mixture.**—One volume 85% $H_3PO_4$ with 1 volume $H_2SO_4$ (1.84).

**Diphenylamine Indicator.**—One gram dissolved in 100 ml. $H_2SO_4$ (1.84).

*Procedure.*—The chromate solution is diluted to about 100 ml., 10 ml. of phosphoric-sulfuric acid mixture are added and 4–5 drops of diphenylamine indicator. The standard ferrous sulfate reagent is now run in until the yellow color changes to green. The excess of ferrous sulfate is oxidized by back titration with standard dichromate reagent until the green color changes to a deep blue. The difference between the two titrations (the ml. must be converted to a common basis of 0.1 $N$ by multiplying by the factors of the reagents before subtracting the $K_2Cr_2O_7$ titration from the $FeSO_4$ titration) is due to the ferrous sulfate oxidized by the chromate.

One ml. of 0.1 $N$ ferrous sulfate solution required by the chromate is equivalent to 0.006907 g. Pb.

NOTES.—If much HCl is present the blue color will not be obtained. Addition of 1 g. ammonium acetate per ml. HCl present will prevent this difficulty. If the end point is a dirty green in place of blue add the solid acetate until a blue color develops. Add additional standard ferrous sulfate until a green color is obtained and back titrate with dichromate to a blue color. Note the total ferrous and dichromate reagents used.

## COLORIMETRIC METHODS

### DITHIZONE METHODS

The shorter, one-color dithizone method for lead is described in the Chapter on Magnesium, where it is used for the determination of lead in magnesium metal and alloys. A simplified version of it is given later in this Chapter for the determination of lead in biochemical materials. Two widely-used dithizone methods are given below.

#### EXTRACTION AT HIGH pH WITH BISMUTH REMOVAL

In this method (the Cholak, Hubbard and Burkey modification of the Bambach-Burkey Method) most of the excess dithizone is removed when the buffered test solution at pH 10.5–11.5 is shaken with extraction dithizone solution. The resulting lead complex in the chloroform layer shows very little of the mixed color quality. The bismuth is separated from lead by means of a single wash with a buffer solution at pH 3.4. The method is applicable to the analysis of any material which can be placed in solution.

*Reagents.* **Ammonium Citrate Solution.**—Dissolve 400 g. of citric acid in water, and add sufficient reagent ammonium hydroxide to make the solution alkaline to phenol red. Dilute the solution to 1 liter with water and purify by shaking it with repeated portions of a solution of dithizone in chloroform until the dithizone retains its original green color. Remove excess dithizone by repeated extractions with chloroform.

Sodium citrate may be used in place of citric acid, thus eliminating the necessity of neutralizing with ammonium hydroxide. The solution is purified with dithizone as described in the preparation of ammonium citrate.

**Lead-Free Ammonium Hydroxide.**—Pass tank ammonia through 1300 ml. of double-distilled water cooled in an ice bath, using a sintered glass disperser to bubble the ammonia through the solution for 2.5–3 hours, by which time the volume of solution will increase to 2000 ml. or more. Measure the total volume and obtain the specific gravity (should be less than 0.900). Adjust the specific gravity to 0.900 with double-distilled water. The following formula may be used:

$$\frac{\text{Milliliters measured}}{\text{Final volume at sp. gr. 0.900 (in milliliters)}} = \frac{28.33}{\% \text{ NH}_3 \text{ at sp. gr. measured by Westphal balance}}$$

The number 28.33, in the above formula, is the percentage of ammonia in an ammonium hydroxide solution of specific gravity 0.900 at 15°C.

**Hydroxylamine Hydrochloride Solution.**—Twenty g. of hydroxylamine hydrochloride are dissolved in sufficient water to make about 65 ml. and a few drops of $m$-cresol purple indicator solution are added. Concentrated ammonium hydroxide is next added until a yellow color results. Sodium diethyldithiocarbamate in water (an approximate 4% solution) is added in sufficient quantity to combine with all the lead (and most other metals) present and to leave a considerable excess. After a few minutes, the organometallic complexes and the excess reagent are completely extracted with chloroform. The absence of a yellow color when the chloroform layer is shaken with a dilute solution of a copper salt indicates when this point has been reached. Distilled hydrochloric acid is then added to the hydroxylamine hydrochloride solution until the indicator turns pink, and double-distilled water is added to make the final volume 100 ml. It is not necessary to filter the solution.

**Potassium Cyanide Solution.**—A practically saturated solution containing 50 g. of potassium cyanide in sufficient water to make 100 ml. is repeatedly shaken with portions of a solution of dithizone in chloroform (30 mg. per liter) until the lead has been removed. Part of the dithizone dissolves in the aqueous phase but enough remains in the chloroform to color it and to indicate when the lead has been completely extracted. Most of the dithizone in the aqueous phase can be removed, if desired, by repeated extractions with pure chloroform. The concentrated solution of potassium cyanide is then diluted with double-distilled water to the proper strength (10 g. per 100 ml.). It is not necessary to filter the solution.

**Ammonia-Cyanide Solution.**—Each liter of mixture contains 20 g. of potassium cyanide (200 ml. purified 10% potassium cyanide) and 150 ml. lead-free ammonium hydroxide (sp. gr. 0.900), or its equivalent; it is brought to volume with double-distilled water. This solution should be kept in a cool place.

**Indicator Solutions.**—Phenol red, $m$-cresol purple, methyl red.

**Standard Lead Solution.**—A stock solution is prepared by dissolving 1.5984 g. recrystallized lead nitrate in 1 liter of 1% nitric acid (1 ml. = 1.0 mg. Pb). From the stock solution prepare by dilution with 1% nitric acid, standards containing 0.01 mg. lead per ml. and 0.001 mg. lead per ml. All solutions will keep indefinitely in glass-stoppered Pyrex containers.

**Standard (Extraction) Dithizone Solution.**—One liter of chloroform is shaken with 100 ml. of water containing about 0.5 g. hydroxylamine hydrochloride, which has been made alkaline to phenol red with ammonium hydroxide. The chloroform is drained off and 40 mg. of dithizone are dissolved in it. Approximately 5 ml. of alcohol are added to the solution if part of it is to be kept for several days. Filtration is not necessary. The quantity of dithizone solution to be used for one day is shaken with 100 ml. of dilute hydrochloric acid (1 ml. per 100 ml. solution) just before use.

**Buffer Solution (pH 3.4).**—Clark and Lubs potassium acid phthalate-hydrochloric acid buffer pH 3.4 is used. This solution is made by mixing 250 ml. of 0.2 $M$ potassium acid phthalate with 49.75 ml. of 0.2 $M$ hydrochloric acid and diluting to 1000 ml. with distilled water.

**Citrate-Cyanide-Hydroxylamine Solution.**—Seven hundred and fifty ml. of the ammonium citrate solution are mixed with 375 ml. of the potassium cyanide solution and 50 ml. of the hydroxylamine hydrochloride solution.

**High pH-Cyanide Solution.**—To 1 liter of ammonium hydroxide (sp. gr. 0.900) add 15 g. potassium cyanide. This solution should be kept in a cool place.

*Apparatus.*—Pyrex glassware should be used throughout; containers should all be glass stoppered. The extractions are most conveniently carried out in 125-ml. Squibb-type separatory funnels, graduated at 5 and 10 ml. and at 10-ml. intervals thereafter to 100 ml., with the aid of rotary funnel racks or other racks that permit the convenient handling of the funnels. White vaseline is used to grease the stopcocks, since it is practically lead-free.

Any photometer which can be used with cells of lengths varying from 10 mm. to 50 mm. is satisfactory. A glass filter with maximum transmission at 510 m$\mu$ is suitable.

*Procedure.*—Place 25 ml. of the citrate-cyanide-hydroxylamine mixture and 2 drops of phenol red in a 125-ml. Squibb-type separatory funnel and add an aliquot or the entire prepared sample.

Add ammonium hydroxide (15% by volume) dropwise until a pH 8.5 (red) is reached. Add 10 ml. extraction dithizone solution and shake.

Remove the extraction dithizone solution to a second separatory funnel and repeat the extraction of the aqueous solution with fresh 5 ml. quantities of extraction dithizone solution until no further color changes occur in the dithizone solution, and deliver each portion after extraction to the second separatory funnel. The amount of dithizone used is a rough measure of the quantity of lead present. (Each 5 ml. of dithizone is equivalent to 50 micrograms of lead when the color is cherry red.)

Add 50 ml. buffer solution (pH 3.4) and shake.

Allow the layers to separate, add 2 drops methyl orange indicator solution, adjust to pH 3.4 (pink) with 1 $N$ hydrochloric acid. (The color corresponding to pH 3.4 is obtained by comparing against a standard 50 ml. buffer solution (pH 3.4), to which 2 drops of methyl orange indicator solution have been added.) Again shake vigorously and allow the layers to separate.

Discard the dithizone solution. In the case of large quantities of lead, it is possible, at this point, to discard sufficient buffer solution (pH 3.4) to bring the lead in the sample to below 90 micrograms. The volume of solution should be readjusted to 50 ml. with fresh buffer solution (pH 3.4).

Add 5 ml. clear chloroform, shake, and discard the chloroform layer. Allow the chloroform drop floating on the surface to evaporate spontaneously or apply vacuum or a stream of air to remove it.

Add 15 ml. of dithizone extraction solution (use a volumetric pipette), 20 ml. of the high pH-cyanide solution, and shake vigorously for one minute.

If the quantity of lead is below 12 micrograms, run the chloroform into a cell with a 50-mm. optical path (Type D, American Instrument Company) and into a 10-mm. cell if the quantity of lead is between 12 and 90 micrograms. (Moisture should be removed by placing a pledget of cotton in the stem of the funnel and filtering the chloroform through the pledget.)

Place the cell in the optical path of any suitable photometer and measure the density or transmittancy at 510 m$\mu$. Carry known amounts of lead through the entire procedure. Two curves are prepared, one for the range 0–12 micrograms for the 50-mm. cell and 0–90 micrograms for the 10-mm. cell.

A rack blank should be obtained by handling all of the reagents in the same manner as the sample. The reading for this blank serves as the zero point of the calibration curves and automatically corrects for the amount of lead in the reagents.

## MIXED COLOR METHOD WHEN BISMUTH IS ABSENT
### (USPHS METHOD)

This method is a mixed color procedure in which the lead dithizonate is determined in the presence of excess dithizone. The method is especially convenient for the analysis of lead in the absence of bismuth.

*Reagents.* **Lead-Free Ammonium Hydroxide.**—See preceding method.

**Potassium Cyanide Solution.**—See preceding method.

**Extraction Dithizone Solution.**—Dissolve 16 mg. dithizone per 1000 ml. purified chloroform (see preceding method). Keep in brown bottle in refrigerator.

**Standard Dithizone Solution.**—Dissolve 8 mg. dithizone in 1000 ml. of purified chloroform. Keep in brown bottle in refrigerator and allow to warm to room temperature before using.

*m*-**Cresol Purple Indicator.**—Prepare a 0.1% aqueous solution.

**Phenol Red Indicator.**—Prepare a 0.1% aqueous solution.

**Ammonia Cyanide Mixture.**—Mix 200 ml. purified potassium cyanide with 150 ml. lead-free ammonium hydroxide (sp. gr. 0.900) and make to 1 liter with double-distilled water. (If the specific gravity of the distilled ammonia is not 0.900, the equivalent volume should be computed from tables of specific gravity versus percentage of ammonia.)

*Procedure.*—Transfer the dissolved sample to a 125-ml. Squibb-type separatory funnel.

Add 1 ml. hydroxylamine hydrochloride solution, 10 ml. ammonium citrate solution, and 1 drop phenol red indicator solution (25% sodium citrate solution purified by extraction with dithizone at pH 9–10 may be used in place of the ammonium citrate).

Titrate to a strong red color (pH 9–10) with lead-free ammonia.

Add 5 ml. potassium cyanide solution, and shake for 1–2 minutes with 5-ml. portions of dithizone extraction solution until a green extract indicates all of the lead has been removed.

Collect the chloroform extracts in a second funnel to which 30 ml. of 1% nitric acid has been added and shake for 2 minutes.

Discard the chloroform layer, and wash the aqueous layer with 5 ml. chloroform and discard the chloroform layer. Evaporate the last drop of chloroform floating on the surface of the aqueous portion by blowing air gently into the funnel.

Add 6 ml. of the ammonia-cyanide mixture and then exactly 15 ml. of the standard dithizone solution, and shake for 2 minutes.

Insert a pledget of cotton into the stem of the funnel.

Drain the chloroform layer into a dry photometer tube. (A set of matched test tubes 22 mm. x 175 mm. is convenient.)

Inspect for water droplets in the light path; if present, carefully decant the solution into another dry photometer tube, leaving the water behind.

Read the optical density at 510 m$\mu$ using the blank as a reference and refer to the standard curve for the quantity of lead.

**Standard Curve.**—The standard dithizone solution should be aged a day or two before using or standardizing and should be restandardized every month or two. Quantities of lead in graded amounts up to 25 micrograms in 30 ml. of 1% nitric acid are run through the procedure starting with the chloroform washing step above. The zero standard is used as the photometer reference, and the optical densities are plotted against micrograms of lead.

## SULFIDE METHOD

Estimation of small amounts of lead by the intensity of the brown coloration produced by the sulfide in colloidal solution was first proposed by Pelouze. The procedure was modified by Warington and by Wilkie to overcome the color produced by accompanying impurities, among these, iron, which is almost invariably associated with lead. The method is useful in determining traces of lead in drinking water, in food products, baking powders, canned goods, phosphates, alums, acids such as sulfuric, hydrochloric, citric, tartaric and the like. By this procedure on a gram sample one part of lead per million may be detected and as high as 50 parts may be estimated. For larger amounts of lead, a smaller sample must be taken. Nickel, arsenic, antimony, silver, zinc, tin, iron, and alumina, present in amounts such as commonly occur in these materials, do not interfere.

In order to obtain accurate results it is necessary to have the solutions under comparison possess the same general character. It must be remembered that the tint depends to a large extent on the size of the colloidal particles of lead, which in turn depend upon the nature of the salts in the solution and upon the way that the solution has been prepared. Vigorous agitation, salts of the alkalies and alkaline earths tend to coagulate the colloidal sulfide.

*Reagents.* **Standard Lead Solution.**—A convenient solution may be made by dissolving 0.1831 g. of lead acetate, $Pb(C_2H_3O_2)_2 \cdot 3H_2O$ in 100 ml. of water, clearing any cloudiness with a few drops of acetic acid and diluting to 1000 ml. If 10 ml. of this solution is diluted to 1000 ml., each ml. will contain an equivalent of 0.000001 g. Pb.

Harcourt suggests a permanent standard made by mixing ferric, copper, and cobalt salts. For example 12 g. of $FeCl_3$ together with 8 g. of $CuCl_2$ and 4 g. of $Co(NO_3)_2$ are dissolved in water, 400 ml. of hydrochloric acid added and the solution diluted to 4000 ml. One hundred and fifty ml. of this solution, together with 115 ml. of hydrochloric acid (1:2), diluted to 2000 ml. will give a shade comparable to that produced by the standard lead solution above, when treated with the sulfide reagent. The exact value per ml. may be obtained by comparison with the lead standard.

**Alkaline Tartrate Solution.**—Twenty-five grams of C.P. sodium potassium tartrate, $NaKC_4H_4O_6 \cdot 4H_2O$, is dissolved in 50 ml. of water. A little ammonia is added and then sodium sulfide solution. After settling some time the reagent is filtered. The filtrate is acidified with hydrochloric acid, boiled free of $H_2S$ and again made ammoniacal and diluted to 100 ml.

**Ammonium Citrate Solution.**—Ammonium citrate solution is prepared in the same way as the tartrate solution above, 25 g. of the salt being dissolved in 50 ml. of water.

**Potassium Cyanide.**—A 10% solution is made from the lead-free salt.

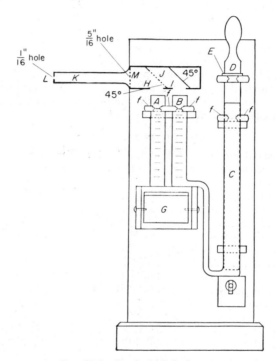

Fig. 26-1. Hurley's Colorimeter.

**Sodium Sulfide.**—A 10% solution, made from colorless crystals. Sodium sulfide may be made by saturating a strong solution of sodium hydroxide with hydrogen sulfide gas, and then adding an equal volume of the sodium hydroxide. The solution is diluted to required volume, allowed to stand several days, and filtered.

**Sodium Metabisulfite.**—The solid salt, $Na_2S_2O_5$.

*Apparatus.*—The color comparison may be made in Nessler tubes, or in a colorimeter. The Campbell and Hurley modification of the Kennicott-Sargent colorimeter is excellent for this purpose,[10] Fig. 26-1. The colorimeter is simple in construction and operation. Although this method is included with the original apparatus and procedure, analogous colorimeters are commercially available.

The tubes for holding the solutions to be compared are those of one of the well-known colorimeters, in which the unknown solution is placed in the left-

[10] J. Am. Chem. Soc., **33**, 1112, 1911.

hand tube while the color is matched by raising or lowering the level of a standard solution in the right-hand tube by means of a glass plunger working in an attached reservoir.

This accompanying diagram shows the essential features of construction of the colorimeter employed in the tests described below. The unknown solution is placed in the left-hand tube $A$, which is 19 cm. long, 3 cm. in diameter, and graduated for 15 cm. The standard solution is placed in the right-hand tube $B$, which is the same size as $A$, the graduated portion being divided into 100 divisions of 1.5 mm. each. The tube $B$ is permanently connected by a glass tube with the reservoir $C$ in which the glass plunger $D$ works, so that the level of the liquid in $B$ can be readily controlled by raising or lowering the plunger. As the tube $B$ and reservoir $C$ are made in one piece, the liquid used for the standard solution comes in contact with glass only, thus preventing any possibility of chemical change due to contact with the container. The plunger is provided with a rubber collar $E$, so placed as to prevent the plunger from accidentally striking and breaking the bottom of the reservoir. The tubes $A$ and $B$, with the connecting reservoir, rest on wooden supports, the one under $A$ and $B$ being provided with holes for the passage of the light, and are held in position by spring clips $ff$. This arrangement allows the glass parts to be readily removed for cleaning and filling. The light for illuminating the solution is reflected upward through the tubes $A$ and $B$ by means of the adjustable mirror $G$. The best results are obtained by facing the colorimeter toward a north window in order to get reflected skylight through the tubes, care being taken to avoid light reflected from adjacent objects. The black wooden back of the colorimeter serves the double purpose of a support for the parts of the instrument and of a screen, as it is interposed between the color tubes and the source of light.

The light, passing upward through the tubes $A$ and $B$, impinges on the two mirrors $H$ and $I$ cemented to brass plates sliding in grooves cut at an angle of 45° in the sides of the wooden box $J$. This box is supplied with a loosely-fitting cover, thus allowing easy access for the purpose of removing and cleaning the mirrors. The mirror $H$ is cut vertically and cemented in such a position as to reflect one-half of the circular field of light coming through the tube $A$. The light passing upward through $B$ is reflected horizontally by the mirror $I$, through a hole in the brass plate supporting the mirror $H$. One-half of the circular field of light from the tube $B$ is cut off by the mirror $H$, the vertical edge of which acts as a dividing line between the two halves of the circular field. The image of one-half of the tube $B$ is then observed in juxtaposition to the opposite half of the image of the tube $A$.

The juxtaposed images are observed through a tube $K$, 2.5 cm. in diameter and 16 cm. long, lined with black felt and provided with an eye-piece having a hole 1.5 mm. in diameter. At the point $M$ in the tube $K$ is placed a diaphragm having an aperture 8 mm. in diameter. All parts inside the box $J$ except the mirrors are painted black so that no light except that coming through the tubes $A$ and $B$ passes through the tube $K$. By having the apertures in the eye-piece and diaphragm properly proportioned only the image of the bottoms of the tubes $A$ and $B$ can be seen, thus preventing interference of light reflected from the vertical sides of the tubes $A$ and $B$.

A person looking through the eye-piece observes a single circular field divided vertically by an almost imperceptible line when the two solutions are of the same intensity. By manipulating the plunger $D$, the level of the liquid in $B$ can be easily raised or lowered, thus causing the right half of the image to assume a darker or lighter shade at will. In matching colors with an ascending column in *B*, that is, gradually deepening the color of the right half of the field, the usual tendency is to stop a little below the true reading while in a comparison with a descending column the opposite is the case.

*Procedure.*—If lead is between 10 to 50 parts per million a 1-g. sample is taken. If it is above or below these extremes the amount of sample is regulated accordingly. In materials containing organic matter it is not advisable to take more than a 1-g. sample.

Substances containing organic matter, such as starch in baking powder, should be decomposed by fusion with sodium peroxide, or with sodium or potassium sulfate containing a few drops of sulfuric acid. A Kjeldahl digestion with concentrated sulfuric acid and potassium bisulfate may occasionally be advisable. Sulfuric acid discolored by organic matter should be mixed with 4 to 5 g. of potassium bisulfate, taken to fumes and then diluted with water. The material may be extracted with ammonium acetate and lead determined in the extract. See Notes.

To the solution containing the sample are added 10 ml. of tartrate solution (or 20 ml. of citrate solution with phosphates of lime, etc.), 10 ml. of hydrochloric acid and the mixture brought to boiling. Small amounts of ferric iron are now reduced by adding 0.5 g. sodium metabisulfite. Sufficient ammonium hydroxide is added to neutralize the free acid and 5 ml. in excess; then 3 ml. potassium cyanide (to repress any copper color that may be present to reduce higher oxides), and the mixture heated until the solution becomes colorless. The entire solution or an aliquot portion is placed in the comparison cylinder, and diluted to nearly 100 ml. If the Kennicott-Sargent apparatus is used the standard color solution is forced into the adjacent cylinder, until the color in this cylinder matches the one containing the sample. The number of ml. of the standard is noted. This blank is due to the slight color that the solutions of the samples invariably have. Four drops of the sulfide reagent are added to the sample and this is mixed by means of a plunger, avoiding any more agitation than is absolutely necessary to make the solution homogeneous. After one minute the comparison is again made, the colored standard being forced into the cylinder until its color matches the sample. It is advisable to take several readings with ascending and descending columns of standard reagent, taking the average as the true reading.

**Calculation.**—Suppose the standard = 0.000001 g. Pb per ml., blank = 5 ml., total reading = 22 ml., one gram of sample being taken for analysis. Then $22 - 5 = 17$ ml. = 0.0017% Pb or 17 parts per million.

NOTES.—Iron must be completely reduced before adding ammonium hydroxide and potassium cyanide.

Allen's method of reducing iron with sodium metabisulfite is excellent. The salt may be made by passing $SO_2$ into a saturated solution of sodium carbonate at boiling temperature, until the liquor is just acid to methyl orange. The water evaporated during the treatment is replaced during the action. $Na_2S_2O_5$ separates and may be filtered off and the water removed by centrifuging.

If a separation from iron is desired, the lead may be extracted with ammonium acetate solution. Ten grams of the powdered material are mixed with 75 ml. of a 33% lead-free ammonium acetate solution (25 g. of the salt dissolved in 50 ml. $H_2O$), the reagent being added boiling hot. The mixture is diluted to 500 ml., a portion filtered, and the determination made on an aliquot part of the total, following the directions above.

The following may be present, if their amounts do not exceed the following limits: nickel 0.1%, arsenic 0.2%, zinc 0.2%, antimony 0.05%, copper 0.25%, iron 1.0%, aluminum 10%, tin 1.4%.

## DETERMINATIONS IN SPECIFIC SUBSTANCES

## DETERMINATION OF LEAD IN AN ORE AS
## LEAD CHROMATE [11]

*Reagents.* **Potassium Dichromate.**—Make up a hot saturated solution of $K_2Cr_2O_7$. Cool and reserve for use.

**Ammonium Acetate.**—Measure out 400 ml. of water and 400 ml. of $NH_4OH$ (sp. gr. = 0.9) into a large beaker and add 80% acetic acid until the solution is neutral; then add sufficient 80% acetic acid to make the solution 2% acid with 80% acetic acid.

**Acid Ammonium Chloride.**—Measure out 300 ml. of water and 300 ml. of $NH_4OH$ (sp. gr. = 0.9) into a large beaker; make just neutral with HCl (sp. gr. = 1.18) and then add sufficient HCl to make the solution 1% acid.

*Procedure.*—Weigh from 1 to 2 g. of the dried and finely ground ore into a 250-ml. beaker, add 20 ml. $HNO_3$ (1:1), digest in a warm place for one hour; add 10 ml. $H_2SO_4$ and evaporate to fumes. Cool, take up with 100 ml. water, boil for 5 or 10 minutes and allow to stand overnight in the cold. Filter and wash with dilute $H_2SO_4$ (1:9). Transfer the precipitate back to the original beaker, set under the funnel and pour through the paper about 60 ml. of boiling ammonium acetate solution.[12] Replace with a clean 300-ml. beaker; boil the solution containing the $PbSO_4$ and filter through the same paper. Wash well with hot water; dilute the filtrate to a volume of 150 ml., add 2 ml. 80% acetic acid, bring to boil, add 20 ml. of the $K_2Cr_2O_7$ solution, again bring to a boil, stir, and allow to stand in a warm place for two hours. Filter on a previously prepared and weighed porcelain Gooch crucible, washing two or three times by decantation using boiling water. Finally, transfer all of the precipitate to the Gooch crucible, wash three or four times with boiling water and finally with alcohol. Dry at 105–110°C. for one hour; cool and weigh. The increased weight is $PbCrO_4$. Multiply by 0.6375 for lead.[13] (Theoretical factor 0.6411.)

**Accuracy.**—Duplicate determinations should check within 0.1% of lead.

## DETERMINATION IN BASIC LEAD CARBONATE
## (CORRODED WHITE LEAD)

Basic carbonate, white lead ($2PbCO_3 \cdot Pb(OH)_2$) contains approximately 80% of combined lead and 20% carbonic acid and combined water, with traces of silver, antimony, free lead, and other metals. The analysis of basic carbonate, white lead can best be carried out by Walker's method.[14]

*Procedure.*—Weigh 1 g. of the sample, moisten with water, dissolve in acetic acid, filter, wash, ignite, and weigh the insoluble impurities. To the filtrate from the insoluble matter add 25 ml. of sulfuric acid (1:1), evaporate and heat until the acetic acid is driven off; cool, dilute to 200 ml. with water, add 20 ml. of ethyl alcohol, allow to stand for two hours, filter on a Gooch crucible, wash with

---

[11] Standard Method of the National Lead Company.

[12] When appreciable amounts of calcium are present, use 50 ml. of ammonium acetate solution and 50 ml. of acid ammonium chloride solution for the solution of the $PbSO_4$ as described above.

[13] Empirical factor.

[14] Walker, P. H., Bureau of Chemistry Bulletin No. 109, revised, U. S. Dept. of Agriculture, pp. 21 and 22.

1% sulfuric acid, ignite, and weigh as lead sulfate. Calculate to total lead ($PbSO_4 \times 0.6833 = Pb$) or calculate to basic carbonate of lead (white lead) by multiplying the weight of lead sulfate by 0.8526.

The filtrate from the lead sulfate may be used to test for other metals, though white lead is only rarely adulterated with soluble substances; test, however, for zinc, which may be present as zinc oxide.

Instead of determining the total lead as sulfate it may be determined as lead chromate by precipitating the hot acetic acid solution with potassium bichromate, filtering on a Gooch crucible, igniting at a low temperature, and weighing as lead chromate.

## LEAD PEROXIDE ($PbO_2$) AND TRUE RED LEAD ($Pb_3O_4$) IN COMMERCIAL RED LEAD BY THE THIOSULFATE IODIDE METHOD

(Method of Diehl [15] modified by Topf [16]—not applicable when substances are present, other than oxides of lead, that liberate iodine under conditions given.) [17]

*Reagents.* **Red Lead Solvent.**—Dissolve in a 1-liter beaker 600 g. of "Tested Purity" crystallized sodium acetate and 48 g. of KI in about 500 ml. of 25% acetic acid solution (made by mixing 150 ml. of glacial acetic acid with 450 ml. of distilled water). Warm the beaker and contents on a steam bath, stirring occasionally, until a clear solution is obtained. Cool this solution to room temperature, dilute to exactly 1000 ml. with the 25% acetic acid solution and mix thoroughly. If preferred, the red lead solvent may be prepared separately for each titration, as follows: Dissolve 30 g. of the "Tested Purity" crystallized sodium acetate and 2.4 g. of C.P. KI in 25 ml. of the 25% acetic acid solution, warming gently and stirring until a clear solution is obtained. Cool this solution to room temperature, dilute to 40 ml. with the 25% acetic acid solution, and mix thoroughly.

**Sodium Thiosulfate Solution (0.1 N).**—Dissolve 24.83 g. of C.P. sodium thiosulfate, freshly pulverized and dried between filter paper, and dilute with water to 1 liter at the temperature at which the titrations are to be made. The solution is best made with well-boiled water free from $CO_2$, or let stand 8 to 14 days before standardizing. Standardize with pure, resublimed iodine, as described in the Chapter on Iodine.

**Starch Solution.**—Stir up 2 to 3 g. of potato starch with 100 ml. of 1% salicylic acid solution, and boil the mixture till starch is practically dissolved, then dilute to 1 liter.

*Procedure.*—Weigh 1 g. of the finely-ground sample, transfer to a 200-ml. Erlenmeyer flask, add 10 ml. of a mixture of 7 parts by volume of chloroform and 3 parts by volume of C.P. glacial acetic acid; then add as quickly as possible 40 ml. of the red lead solvent at room temperature. Rub with the flattened end of a glass rod until nearly all of the red lead has been dissolved; add 30 ml. of water containing 5 or 6 g. of sodium acetate, and titrate at once with 0.1 N sodium thiosulfate, adding the latter rather slowly and keeping the liquid constantly in motion by whirling the flask. When the solution has become light yellow, rub-up

[15] Dinglers Polytech. J., **246**, 196, 1882.
[16] Z. anal. Chem., **26**, 296, 1887.
[17] Lead Peroxide.—If sample contains an appreciable amount of nitrite (nitrate has no effect on method), leach out water-soluble matter, dry residue and determine $PbO_2$ as above, calculating to basis of original sample.

any undissolved particles with the rod until free iodine no longer forms, wash off rod, add the sodium thiosulfate solution until *pale yellow,* add starch solution and titrate until colorless, add 0.1 $N$ iodine solution until blue color is just restored and subtract the amount used from the volume of sodium thiosulfate that had been added.

**Calculation.**—The iodine value of the sodium thiosulfate solution multiplied by $0.942 = PbO_2$; the iodine value multiplied by $2.7 = Pb_3O_4$; the $PbO_2$ value multiplied by $2.872 = Pb_3O_4$.

## LEAD PEROXIDE (PbO$_2$) AND TRUE RED LEAD (Pb$_3$O$_4$) IN COMMERCIAL RED LEAD BY HYDROGEN PEROXIDE– PERMANGANATE METHOD [18]

The following is a convenient and relatively accurate method which depends upon the interaction of lead peroxide and of hydrogen peroxide and a titration of the excess of the latter by potassium permanganate.

*Reagent.* **Standard Potassium Permanganate.**—It is necessary to have on hand a potassium permanganate solution with an iron value of exactly 0.005 if the method described for red lead is used. Dissolve 5.75 grams C.P. salt in two liters distilled water and store in a brown bottle in a dark place for a week or more. By this time all organic matter will have been oxidized and after filtering the solution through an asbestos filter the solution is ready for standardization. As small amounts of $MnO_2$ destroy the permanence of this solution, it is necessary that it be removed by filtering. The method described in Bureau of Standards Circular No. 40 should be used. This method is as follows:

In a 400-ml. beaker, 0.25 g. of sodium oxalate is dissolved in 200 to 225 ml. of hot water (80–90°C.) and 10 ml. of (1:1) sulfuric acid added. The solution is at once titrated with the solution of permanganate, the solution being stirred continuously and vigorously. The permanganate must be added at the rate of 10 to 15 ml. per minute and the last 0.5 to 1 ml. must be added drop by drop, each drop being allowed to decolorize fully before the next is added. The solution should not be below 60°C. by the time the titration is completed. With a permanganate solution having an iron value of 0.005 per ml., 41.66 ml. of the permanganate are required to react with 0.25 g. sodium oxalate.

If the first titration shows that the solution is too strong a small amount of distilled water should be added. To calculate exactly how much water to add divide 41.66 by the number of ml. required in the titration and multiply by the number of ml. remaining in the bottle. The difference between this product and the number of ml. in the bottle will be the volume of water to add, if the solution is too strong.

If the solution is too weak this difference multiplied by 0.00283 will be the grams of potassium permanganate salt to add. After the addition of water or salt the solution should again be titrated and if a titer of 41.66 is not obtained water or salt added until this titer is obtained. A solution carefully prepared in this manner should keep for months.

*Procedure.*—Treat 1 g. of the sample in a beaker with 15 ml. of nitric acid, sp. gr. 1.2 (110 ml. nitric acid, sp. gr. 1.42, plus 100 ml. of water). This solution should be aerated to free it from all nitrous fumes. Stir the sample until all trace

[18] Schaeffer, J. A., J. Ind. Eng. Chem., **8,** 237, 1916.

of red color has disappeared. Add from a calibrated pipette or burette exactly 10 ml. of dilute hydrogen peroxide (1 part of 3% hydrogen peroxide to 3.5 parts of water). Add about 50 ml. of hot water and stir until all the lead dioxide has passed into solution. In the case of some coarsely ground oxides the contents of the beaker may have to be heated gently to effect complete solution. After the oxide has passed into solution, dilute with hot water to about 250 ml., and titrate directly with a standard potassium permanganate solution, having an iron value of 0.005. Titrate to the faint pink permanganate color.

A blank titration on the hydrogen peroxide solution must now be made. Into a beaker pour 15 ml. of nitric acid (sp. gr. 1.2, as prepared above) and add exactly the same amount of hydrogen peroxide (10 ml.). Dilute to 250 ml. with hot water and titrate with standard potassium permanganate to a faint pink color.

The difference between the number of milliliters of potassium permanganate required for the blank titration and the number required for the red lead titration is the amount of potassium permanganate required for the hydrogen peroxide which reacted with the lead dioxide. The difference between the two amounts of potassium permanganate required multiplied by 3.058 gives the percentage of red lead present. To determine the lead dioxide present multiply this difference by 1.067.

The basis of the calculations depends on the fact that each milliliter of potassium permanganate solution (iron value, 0.005) is equivalent to 3.058% of true red lead on a 1-g. sample. A red lead or orange mineral having 100% true red lead content requires 32.7 ml. potassium permanganate solution of the above strength.

It is always advisable to make several blank determinations each day where this analysis is constantly made and when only occasionally used a blank titration should be made before each analysis. The strength of the hydrogen peroxide solution will vary but the permanence of the permanganate solution renders the method accurate over a long period of time.

NOTE.—Where numerous determinations ot true red lead must be made it is convenient to have a burette scaled directly to read in terms of percentage of $Pb_3O_4$ in the sample.

## RAPID METHOD FOR LEAD IN ZINC ORES OF THE SULFIDE TYPE [19]

The following procedure, a modification of the titrimetric molybdate method, is convenient and has proven accurate enough for control work on zinc ores of the sulfide type, such as are found in the Tri-State field, and on "roasted" or oxidized ore.

**Procedure for Zinc Sulfide Ore.**—Heat a 5-g. sample with 50 ml. dilute nitric acid until the ore is well oxidized. Add 15 ml. concentrated sulfuric acid and keep on hot plate till $SO_3$ fumes are copiously evolved. Cool and dilute with 300 ml. water. Boil and allow to settle for 4 hours.

Filter through a fine filter paper and wash well. Place the paper and contents in the beaker from which the filtration was made and add about 12 ml. of saturated ammonium acetate solution. Heat until all lead sulfate is dissolved and then add 100 ml. water. Titrate with standard ammonium molybdate solution (4.335 g. of the salt dissolved in water and diluted to 1000 ml.), using tannic acid (0.5% solution) as an outside indicator, the end point being the attainment of a

[19] By W. M. Bratton, Hillsboro Zinc Oxide Plant, Eagle-Picher Lead Co.

brownish coloration when a drop of the titrated solution is brought into contact with a drop of the indicator.

The size of the sample may be varied to suit its lead content. Thus if the latter is about 0.2%, a 10 g. sample is convenient; for a lead content of 5%, a 2 g. sample is recommended.

Although 1 ml. of molybdate solution made up as above theoretically equals 0.005 g. lead, the solution should be standardized either against assay litharge or pure lead foil.

**Procedure for "Roasted," or Oxidized Zinc Ore.**—Digest a 5 g. sample on hot plate with 40 ml. concentrated sulfuric acid until the ore is completely broken down and until dense fumes of $SO_3$ are evolved. Cool, add 300 ml. water, heat to complete dissolution of soluble matter, and allow to settle for 4 hours. Then proceed as from "Filter through a fine filter . . ." in the procedure above.

## SIMPLIFIED ONE-COLOR DITHIZONE METHOD FOR LEAD IN BIOCHEMICAL MATERIALS [20]

By substitution of alpha-naphtholphthalein as the indicator instead of phenol red and the use of a single Mojonnier extraction tube or Jacobs-Singer separatory flask instead of multiple separatory funnels, the manipulative steps of the one-color dithizone method for lead are simplified and improved.

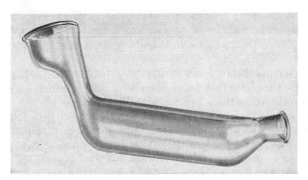

FIG. 26-2. Mojonnier Extraction Tube.

**Apparatus.**—The use of a spectrophotometer is necessary. In developing the method a Bausch and Lomb Spectronic 340 was used, readings being taken in 1"-diameter cuvettes.

An 03A Mojonnier extraction tube (Fig. 26-2) or Jacobs-Singer separatory flask (Fig. 26-3) is used, having a #16 pennyhead glass stopper, and a capacity of 104.5 ml. in the upper chamber and 21.5 ml. in the bottom one.

All glassware should be washed with dilute nitric acid before use.

**Reagents. Dithizone Solution.**—Dissolve 50 mg. of pure diphenylthiocarbazone in reagent grade chloroform and make up to 500 ml. with chloroform.

**Ammoniacal Sodium Citrate Solution.**—Dissolve 100 g. of reagent grade sodium citrate in distilled water and dilute to 500 ml. Add 150 ml. of ammonium hydroxide solution (1:1). Mix thoroughly.

[20] Jacobs, M. B., and Herndon, Jeanne. Am. Ind. Hyg. Assoc. J., October 1961.

**Potassium Cyanide Solution, 10%.**—Dissolve 20 g. of reagent grade KCN in distilled water in a 200-ml. volumetric flask and make up to volume with water. Transfer to a reagent bottle and keep in dark, storing it, for instance, in a full metal cabinet. If it becomes discolored discard it and make a fresh solution.

**Hydrochloric Acid (1:1).**—Dilute highest purity hydrochloric acid with an equal volume of distilled water.

**Hydroxylamine Hydrochloride, 20%.**—Dissolve 40 g. of hydroxylamine hydrochloride, $NH_2OH \cdot HCl$, in distilled water and dilute to 200 ml. in a volumetric flask. This solution can be purified by shaking out with dithizone extraction solution as detailed in the Dithizone Method, page 569.

**Ammonium Hydroxide Solution (1:1).**—Dilute one volume of concentrated ammonium hydroxide solution (sp. gr. 0.90) with an equal volume of distilled water.

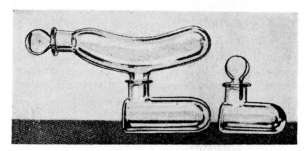

FIG. 26-3.   Jacobs-Singer Separatory Flask.

**Dithizone Extractive Solution.**—Transfer 5 ml. of 10% potassium cyanide solution and 15 ml. of concentrated ammonium hydroxide solution to a 500-ml. volumetric flask and dilute to the mark with distilled water.

**Indicator Solution.**—Weigh out 100 mg. of α-naphtholphthalein (National Aniline No. 249) and transfer to a 20-ml. beaker. Add 10 ml. of distilled water and stir to wet the indicator. Add 4 ml. of 0.01 N sodium hydroxide solution. The indicator dissolves to form a deep blue solution. Transfer to a 250-ml. volumetric flask, wash the beaker thoroughly with water and transfer the washings to volumetric flask. Add an additional 6 ml. of 0.01 N sodium hydroxide solution, make to the mark with distilled water, stopper and mix thoroughly. This is a 0.04% solution of α-naphtholphthalein. It is virtually colorless in acid solution and changes to a green to blue green at pH 8.

**Stock Standard Lead Solution.**—Weigh out accurately 1.598 g. of recrystallized lead nitrate, $Pb(NO_3)_2$ and transfer to a 1-liter volumetric flask. Dissolve in 0.1% nitric acid and make to the mark with this acid. One milliliter of this solution contains 1 mg. of lead.

**Standard Working Lead Solutions.**—Transfer 1 ml. of this stock standard solution to a 100-ml. volumetric flask and dilute to volume with distilled water. This solution contains 10 micrograms per milliliter. Transfer 10 ml. of this dilution to a 100-ml. volumetric flask and dilute to volume. This final dilution contains 1 microgram per milliliter.

*Preparation of Standard Curve.*—Transfer with the aid of pipettes 0, 0.25 ml., 0.5 ml., 1.0 ml., 2.0 ml., 4.0 ml., 6.0 ml., 10.0 ml., and 15.0 ml. of the 1 microgram per milliliter working standard solution to 100-ml. volumetric flasks. These volumes are equivalent to 0, 0.25, 0.5, 1.0, 2.0, 4.0, 6.0, 10.0, and 15.0 micrograms of lead, respectively. Add 15 ml. of hydrochloric acid and continue with the method as detailed in the procedure but omit the heating steps. Place the final chloroform solution in 1-inch tube cuvettes and read in the Bausch and Lomb spectrophotometer at 525 m$\mu$. Plot the micrograms of lead against the transmission.

*Procedure.*—Transfer 50 ml. of a solution prepared from the biochemical material to a Coors porcelain casserole, size 180-3A, and evaporate cautiously on a hot plate in a hood to dryness using low heat at first. After the biological material has been evaporated continue heating on the hot plate at high heat until the material chars. Transfer the casserole to a muffle furnace that has been adjusted to 550°C. and heat at that temperature for 10 minutes. Remove the casserole from the furnace and allow it to cool. Add 2 ml. of concentrated nitric acid and replace it on the hot plate in the hood and drive off the nitrogen oxides. Replace in the muffle furnace at 550°C. and again heat for 10 minutes. Do not permit the temperature to rise above this. Remove from the muffle furnace, allow to cool, add 15 ml. of hydrochloric acid to the casserole washing the sides with the acid, heat on the hot plate, and transfer to a 100-ml. volumetric flask. Add 10 ml. of distilled water to the casserole washing the sides of the dish with the water, heat on the hot plate, and transfer to the 100-ml. volumetric flask. Repeat this step using 15 ml. of ammoniacal sodium citrate solution. Repeat the washing again with 10 ml. of water and add the washing to the volumetric flask.

Allow the flask to cool to room temperature and add 1 ml. of 20% hydroxylamine hydrochloride solution and 0.5 ml. of $\alpha$-naphtholphthalein indicator solution. Add sufficient ammonium hydroxide solution (1:1) to turn the indicator blue. Add 5 ml. of 10% potassium cyanide solution and make to volume.

Place 10 ml. of chloroform solution in a Mojonnier tube and transfer the contents of the volumetric flask to the tube. Add 0.2 ml. of the dithizone solution, stopper the flask, and shake thoroughly, holding the stopper firmly. Set upright and release the stopper cautiously. Add additional volumes of dithizone solution 0.1 ml. at a time, shaking after each addition until the chloroform layer turns purple. Allow to stand until the phases separate. Pour off the supernatant solution to the constriction and discard. Add an additional 10 ml. of chloroform and discard most of the remainder of the aqueous layer.

Add 10 ml. of potassium cyanide-ammonium hydroxide extractive solution, stopper the tube, shake, and allow to separate. Pour off the supernatant as before. Repeat by adding an additional 10 ml. of this extractive solution. (If care is exercised in addition of the dithizone solution so that not too large an excess is added, only two washings with the cyanide-ammonia extractive solution will be required.) Add sufficient chloroform to raise the level of the chloroform layer to just above the middle of the constriction so that the water layer can be poured off completely.

Wet a 9- or 11-cm. Whatman No. 41H filter paper with chloroform and filter the chloroform layer into a 1-inch cuvette. Read the absorption at 525 m$\mu$. Obtain the concentration from the standard curve and compute the concentration on the basis of micrograms per liter.

## METHODS FOR LEAD IN ANALYSES IN OTHER CHAPTERS

Lead in Aluminum Alloys  See Analysis of Aluminum Alloys
Lead in Arsenious Oxide  See Analysis of Arsenious Oxide
Lead in Refined Copper  See Analysis of Refined Copper
Lead in Bullion  See Fire Assay in Gold Chapter
Lead in Magnesium Alloys  See Magnesium Chapter
Lead in Commercial Phosphates  See Analysis of Commercial Phosphates
Lead in Tellurium  See Determination of Selenium, Lead, Iron and Copper in Tellurium (Selenium Chapter)

Lead in Slab Zinc  See Analysis of Slab Zinc

## Chapter 27

# MAGNESIUM *

**Mg**, *at. wt.* 24.312; *sp. gr.* 1.74; *m.p.* 651°C.; *b.p.* 1107°C.; *oxide*, **MgO**.

Magnesium is one of the most abundant of the metals and is widely distributed in nature, occurring only in combined state. The following are the more important ores in which the element occurs: Magnesite, $MgCO_3$; dolomite, $CaCO_3 \cdot MgCO_3$; kieserite, $MgSO_4 \cdot H_2O$; kainite, $MgSO_4 \cdot KCl \cdot 6H_2O$; carnallite, $MgCl_2 \cdot KCl \cdot 6H_2O$; in the silicates, enstatite, $MgSiO_3$; talc, $H_2Mg_3(SiO_2)_4$; meerschaum, forsterite, $Mg_2SiO_4$; titanate, $MgTiO_3$; olivine, $Mg_2SiO_4 \cdot Fe_2SiO_4$; serpentine, $H_4Mg_3Si_2O_4$. It occurs as boracite, $4MgB_4O_7 \cdot 2MgO \cdot MgCl_2$. It is found in sea water, and in certain mineral waters. It occurs as a phosphate and carbonate in the vegetable and animal kingdoms.

The Romans were familiar with the oxide of magnesium, "magnesia alba." The sulfate was obtained by Grew from a natural spring in Epsom, England. The metal was obtained in impure form by Davy in 1808. The metal in powdered form is used in photographic flash lights, in flares, the ribbon is likewise used. The element is used in alloys, magnalium is an alloy of aluminum and magnesium; duraluminum, an alloy of aluminum, copper, silicon with a small percentage of magnesium. The alloys are employed where lightness and strength are required, for example in aircraft. The oxide magnesia is a refractory material and an insulator, magnesium oxychloride is used in stucco and as an insulator. Magnesium carbonate is the basis of silver polishes and certain toothpowders. The hydroxide, milk of magnesia, is a mild remedy for acidity of the stomach. Asbestos is a silicate of magnesium, likewise talc and soapstone. The carbonate and sulfate are valuable pharmaceutical products.

## DETECTION

In the usual course of analysis magnesium is found in the filtrate from the precipitated carbonates of barium, calcium, and strontium. The general procedure for removal of the preceding groups may be found in the section on "Separations" given below on pages 587 and 588. Magnesium is precipitated as white magnesium ammonium phosphate, $MgNH_4PO_4$, by an alkali phosphate, $Na_2HPO_4$, $NaNH_4HPO_4$, etc., in presence of ammonium chloride and free ammonia. The precipitate forms slowly in dilute solution. This is hastened by agitation and by rubbing the sides of the beaker during the stirring with a glass rod. Crystals soon appear on the sides of the beaker in the path of contact, and finally in the solution.

*Procedure.*—To the filtrate from calcium precipitation by ammonium oxalate add 5 ml. of 15 $N$ $NH_4OH$ and 25 ml. of $Na_2HPO_4$ solution and stir. If no

* Revision for the Sixth Edition with the assistance of U. D. Stenger and G. B. Wengert, of the Dow Chemical Co.

precipitate forms, let the mixture stand for at least half an hour, stirring frequently. A white crystalline precipitate indicates the presence of magnesium. Filter and wash the precipitate with alcohol. *Confirm* as follows:—Treat the precipitate or a small portion, if the amount is large, with 5 ml. of 2 $N$ $H_2SO_4$, and to the solution add 10 ml. of alcohol and stir vigorously. If a precipitate forms ($BaSO_4$, etc.) filter off, saving the filtrate. To the filtrate (or solution, if no precipitate forms) add 10 ml. of water, 20 ml. of $NH_4OH$ and 5 ml. of $Na_2HPO_4$ (10% solution) and let the mixture stand at least half an hour. A white crystalline precipitate confirms the presence of magnesium.

*Baryta or lime water* added to a solution containing magnesium produces a white precipitate of magnesium hydroxide.

Both the phosphate and the hydroxide of magnesium are soluble in acids.

*Delicate Colorimetric Test for Magnesium.*—Titan yellow G [1] has been proposed by Kolthoff [2] as a reagent for the detection of magnesium. To 10 ml. of the solution to be tested 0.1 to 0.2 ml. of a 0.1% solution of the indicator in water and about 0.25 to 1 ml. 4 $N$ sodium hydroxide are added. In the absence of magnesium the mixture has a brownish-yellow color; if 5 mg. magnesium per liter are present, the solution turns red, with 1 mg. of magnesium per liter orange. If a blank without Mg is used for comparison, 0.2 of a mg. of magnesium per liter can be detected (sensitivity). Small amounts of calcium intensify the color of the magnesium reaction product, which must be considered in the application of the reagent to the colorimetric determination of magnesium in presence of calcium salts. The reaction is very suitable for the detection and approximate estimation of traces of magnesium in alkali salts. Similarly it can be used for the detection of this element in calcium salts. In testing calcium carbonate for the presence of magnesium, the most delicate procedure is to dissolve this salt in a small excess of hydrochloric acid then add the indicator and make alkaline with 1 to 2 ml. 4 $N$ sodium hydroxide, a precipitate of calcium carbonate not interfering. Fifty mg. of calcium carbonate are treated with 4 drops 4 $N$ HCl, 10 ml. of water and 0.2 ml. 0.1% titan yellow, and 1 to 2 ml. 4 $N$ sodium hydroxide are added. In the presence of 0.1% magnesium in the calcium carbonate a bright red color appears and even 0.01% of magnesium can be detected by comparing with a blank. In the so-called "chemically pure" commercial products of calcium carbonate, the presence of magnesium is easily shown.

Nickel and cobalt must be absent as they give the same reaction as magnesium.

*Detection with* p-*Nitrophenylazoresorcinol.*[3] **Reagent.**—0.1 g. of the compound in 100 ml. of 1% NaOH. The reagent is stable for a few months.

**Procedure.**—All other metallic ions than magnesium and the alkalies should be removed; ammonium salts must be removed before the test is made. The solution (10 ml.) that may contain magnesium is treated with 1 drop of the reagent and then made strongly alkaline with NaOH. The presence of magnesium is indicated by a blue color or precipitate.

[1] Titan yellow G: Sodium salt of the diazoamino compound of dehydrothio-*p*-toluidinesulfonic acid (or the mixed diazoamino compound of dehydrothio-*p*-toluidine-sulfonic acid and primuline dehydrothio-*p*-toluidinesulfonic acid). (Schulz' Farbstofftabellen, No. 198, 1923; Rowe, F. M., Colour Index, No. 813, 1924.)

[2] Kolthoff, I. M., Biochem. Z., **185**, 344, 1927.

[3] Suitsu and Okuma, J. Soc. Chem. Ind. Japan, **29**, 132, 1926; Ruigh, J. Am. Chem. Soc., **51**, 1456, 1929; Engel, *ibid.*, **52**, 1812, 1930.

## ESTIMATION

The element is determined in the complete analysis of a large number of substances; in the analysis of ores, minerals, rocks, soils, cements, water, etc.

In analytical procedures magnesium passes into the filtrate with the alkalies after separating the elements of the HCl, $H_2S$, $(NH_4)_2S$, and $(NH_4)_2CO_3$ groups, where it is separated from the alkalies by precipitation as magnesium ammonium phosphate. Should arsenates or phosphates be present in excess of the amounts taken care of by the iron and aluminum (etc.) present, magnesium will come down with the ammonium precipitate and will be weighed as iron and aluminum oxides, unless provision is made to avoid this.

Decomposition of the substances containing magnesium and separation of the element are given in subsequent sections.

## PREPARATION AND SOLUTION OF THE SAMPLE

In solution of the material it will be recalled that the metal is soluble in acids and is also attacked by the acid alkali carbonates. It is soluble in ammonium salts. The oxide, hydroxide, and the salts of magnesium are soluble in acids. Combined in silicates, however, the substance requires fusion with alkali carbonates to bring it into solution.

**General Procedure for Ores.**—One gram of the ore is treated with 20 ml. of concentrated hydrochloric acid and heated gently until the material is decomposed. If sulfides are present, 5 to 10 ml. of concentrated nitric acid are added and the material decomposed by the mixed acids. If silicates are present and the decomposition is not complete by the acid treatment, the insoluble material is decomposed by fusion with sodium carbonate, or the entire sample may be fused with the alkali carbonate, the fusion is dissolved in hydrochloric acid and taken to dryness. Silica is dehydrated as usual by heating the residue from the evaporated solution. This is taken up with 50 ml. of water containing about 5 ml. concentrated hydrochloric acid, the silica filtered off and, after removal of the interfering substances according to procedures given under the next section on "Separations," magnesium is determined as directed in the sections on "Methods."

## SEPARATIONS

**Removal of Members of the Hydrogen Sulfide Group. Copper, Lead, Bismuth, Cadmium, Arsenic, etc.**—The filtrate from silica [4] is diluted to about 200 ml. and hydrogen sulfide gas passed in until the members of this group are completely precipitated. The sulfides are filtered off and washed with $H_2S$ water and the filtrate and washings concentrated by boiling. This treatment is seldom necessary in analysis of many silicates and carbonates in which these elements are absent.

**Removal of Iron, Aluminum, Manganese, Zinc, etc.**—The concentrated filtrate from the hydrogen sulfide group, or in case the treatment with hydrogen sulfide was not required, the filtrate from silica, is boiled with a few ml. of nitric acid to oxidize the iron (solution turns yellow), about 5 ml. of concentrated hydrochloric acid added, and the solution made alkaline to methyl orange by adding $NH_4OH$, drop by drop until a yellow color is obtained. If zinc, cobalt, and nickel

[4] See previous paragraph.

are present, these are best removed as sulfides by passing hydrogen sulfide into the ammoniacal solution.

*Separation of Magnesium from the Alkaline Earths.*—The alkaline earths are precipitated either as oxalates, recommended when considerable calcium is present, or as sulfates, recommended in presence of a large proportion of barium, the magnesium salts being soluble. A double precipitation is necessary to recover magnesium occluded by calcium oxalate. Magnesium is precipitated from the filtrates as a phosphate, according to directions given later. Details of the separation of magnesium from the alkaline earths may be found in the Chapter on Barium.

An excellent procedure for the separation by means of sulfuric acid is to evaporate the solution to dryness, concentrating first in a porcelain dish and finally to dryness in a platinum dish, and then adding about 50 ml. of 80% alcohol and sufficient sulfuric acid to combine with the alkaline earths and magnesium, with slight excess. This precipitates barium, strontium, and calcium as sulfates, while the greater part of the magnesium is in solution. After settling, the precipitate is filtered and washed free of sulfuric acid by means of absolute alcohol, then with 40% alcohol to remove any magnesium sulfate remaining with the precipitate. Magnesium is determined in the filtrate by expelling the alcohol by evaporation, and then precipitating as magnesium ammonium phosphate according to directions given for the determination of this element.

*Separation of Magnesium from the Alkalies.*—Members of the HCl, $H_2S$, $(NH_4)_2S$, and $(NH_4)_2CO_3$ groups being removed, magnesium is quantitatively precipitated as phosphate free from the alkalies by addition of a soluble phosphate ($Na_2HPO_4$, $NaNH_4HPO_4$, $(NH_4)_2HPO_4$, etc.) to the ammoniacal solution. Details are given under the gravimetric method that follows later.

*Separation of Magnesium by Precipitation with 8-Hydroxyquinoline.*[5]—The reagent precipitates the following elements in acid-acetate solution: Cu, Bi, Cd, Al, Zn, quantitatively, and Ag, Hg, Pb, Sb, V, U, Fe, Ta, Ti, Co, Ni, Nb, Mn, and Zr from acetic acid solution, with exception of Ag, all of above and in addition Ba, Be, Ca, Mg, and Sn in ammoniacal solution, effecting separation from the alkalies. After the removal of the interfering elements (see list above) by precipitation with HCl, $H_2S$, $(NH_4)_2S$ and removal of the alkaline earths, magnesium is precipitated by the reagent as follows:—The solution containing 0.1 g. MgO equivalent per 100 ml. and sufficient $NH_4Cl$ to prevent precipitation of $Mg(OH)_2$, is heated to about 70°C. and 8-hydroxyquinoline reagent (5 g. powder per 100 ml. 2 N acetic acid) is added to complete precipitation of magnesium and 10% excess to the feebly acid solution and then sufficient $NH_4OH$ to make the solution alkaline. (The excess of the reagent colors the solution yellow.) The solution is settled, filtered, washed with dilute $NH_4OH$ (1:40), dried at 130–140°C. and weighed as $Mg(C_9H_6ON)_2$, containing 12.91% of MgO.

*Separation of Magnesium from Iron and Aluminum.*—Magnesium phosphate is precipitated in presence of tartaric acid.

[5] Skraup, Z. H., Monatsh. chem., **2**, 139, 518, 1881; *ibid.*, **3**, 381, 531, 1882. Berg, R., J. prakt. Chem., **115**, 178, 1927; Robitschek, J., J. Am. Ceram. Soc., **11**, 587, 1928; Kolthoff, I. M., and Sandell, E. B., J. Am. Chem. Soc., **50**, 1900, 1928; Lundell, G. E. F., and Knowles, H. B., Bur. Standards J. Research, 1929.

## GRAVIMETRIC METHODS

### PRECIPITATION OF MAGNESIUM AS MAGNESIUM AMMONIUM PHOSPHATE AND ESTIMATION AS PYROPHOSPHATE [6]

Magnesium is determined in the filtrate from the alkaline earths after the removal of members of the HCl, $H_2S$, $(NH_4)_2S$, and the alkaline earths, which would interfere with its determination. Should phosphates be present in the original material, magnesium is apt to precipitate with iron and aluminum when the solution is made alkaline with $NH_4OH$. The phosphate radical may be removed by precipitation from an acid $(HNO_3)$ solution by ammonium molybdate. The phosphate is filtered off and washed with water containing 2% $HNO_3$. The free acid is neutralized by adding $NH_4OH$ in presence of methyl orange indicator until a yellow color develops. The solution should contain sufficient $NH_4Cl$ to prevent precipitation of $Mg(OH)_2$ by $NH_4OH$. If manganese is present it must be removed by precipitation with $H_2S$ or by Br in ammoniacal solution. Calcium is removed by a double precipitation as oxalate. If barium is present it is removed as $BaSO_4$ by precipitation with $H_2SO_4$. Should molybdenum be present it may be removed as sulfide. The solution should contain sufficient $NH_4Cl$ to prevent precipitation of $Mg(OH)_2$, but a large quantity is undesirable. Since the separations may lead to loss of magnesium through occlusion and adsorption, double precipitations should be made. Finally, the precipitation should be made under conditions that would give $MgNH_4PO_4 \cdot 6H_2O$ uncontaminated by $Mg_3(PO_4)_2$, $Mg(NH_4)_4(PO_4)_2$, or $Mg(OH)_2$. The first and last would lead to low results, the second to high results, and a mixture to an uncertain error. A double precipitation is recommended, the precipitations being made by adding the soluble phosphate reagent to a slightly acid solution and then making alkaline with $NH_4OH$. Diammonium phosphate is a satisfactory precipitant. It is interesting to note that a high concentration of $(NH_4)H_2PO_4$ and $NH_4Cl$ results in a precipitate (ammonium phosphate) forming which may be mistaken for magnesium. This dissolves on dilution. The magnesium salt is ignited to $Mg_2P_2O_7$.

Reactions:

$$(NH_4)_2HPO_4 + MgCl_2 + NH_4OH \rightarrow MgNH_4PO_4 + 2NH_4Cl + H_2O$$

$$MgNH_4PO_4 \xrightarrow{\Delta} 2NH_3 + H_2O + Mg_2P_2O_7$$

*Procedure.*—The combined filtrates from the double precipitation of calcium, free from interfering elements, are neutralized with HCl and made faintly acid. The solution is diluted so as to contain not over 0.1 g. MgO per 100 ml. and for each 100 ml. 20 ml. of a 10% solution of $(NH_4)HPO_4$ solution are added. The solution is stirred vigorously (avoiding touching the sides of the vessel with the stirring rod) and while stirring $NH_4OH$ is added dropwise (conveniently from a burette) until the free acid is neutralized and a further addition of 10 ml. per each 100 ml. of solution present. The precipitate is allowed to settle at least four hours, preferably overnight, and is filtered through filter paper and washed with cold dilute (1:20) solution of $NH_4OH$.

The precipitate is dissolved in warm dilute HCl (1:4), catching the solution in the beaker in which the precipitation was made, dissolving any magnesium pre-

[6] de Koninck, L. L., Z. anal. Chem., **29**, 165, 1890. Epperson, Alice W., J. Am. Chem. Soc., **50**, 324, 1928. McCandless, J. M., and Burton, J. I., J. Ind. Eng. Chem., **19**, 496, 1927.

cipitate adhering to the beaker and stirring rod. The solution is diluted to 100–150 ml., 1–2 ml. of the diammonium phosphate reagent added followed by $NH_4OH$ added drop by drop as before until the solution is alkaline and now 5 ml. in excess of each 100 ml. of solution. The precipitate is allowed to settle and stand for four hours or more and is filtered onto an ashless paper filter and washed with $NH_4OH$ (1:20), carefully cleaning out the beaker of all adhering precipitate, adding this to the filter. (Some of the phosphate is apt to adhere to the walls of the beaker, hence the precaution.)

The filter is folded and with its contents placed in a crucible that has been previously weighed. After drying in an oven the paper is charred by gentle heating over a low flame. The heat is gradually increased and finally to the full blast of a flame at a temperature of 1000°C. until a constant weight is obtained. The residue is $Mg_2P_2O_7$.

Factors.

$$Mg_2P_2O_7 \times 0.3622 = MgO$$

$$\times 0.2184 = Mg$$

$$\times 0.7577 = MgCO_3$$

$$\times 1.0817 = MgSO_4$$

$$\times 2.2149 = MgSO_4 \cdot 7H_2O$$

NOTES.—The ignition is conducted gently at first to oxidize the carbon that the precipitate contains gradually. With rapid ignition the particles are enclosed in the mass in a form that it is almost impossible to completely oxidize, so that the final residue is gray instead of white. L. L. de Koninck [7] considers that the blackening of the precipitate is frequently due to the presence of organic bases in commercial ammonia and its salts, rather than to the fibers of filter paper occluded in the mass. With caution, the filter and residue may be ignited wet, the heat being low until the filter completely chars and then being increased, with the cover removed, until the residue is white.

Impurities.—The precipitate may contain traces of lime that remained soluble in ammonium oxalate. This may be determined by dissolving the pyrophosphate in dilute sulfuric acid followed by addition of 9 to 10 volumes of absolute alcohol. Calcium sulfate, $CaSO_4$, precipitates and settles out on standing several hours. It may be filtered off, dissolved in hydrochloric acid and precipitated as oxalate in the usual way and so determined.

A residue remaining after treating the pyrophosphate with acid is generally $SiO_2$.

The presence of manganese may be detected by dissolving the magnesium pyrophosphate, $Mg_2P_2O_7$, in nitric acid and oxidizing with sodium bismuthate. (See method under Manganese.)

*Properties of Ammonium Magnesium Phosphate.*—Readily soluble in dilute acids. One hundred ml. of pure water at 10°C. will dissolve 0.0065 g. The presence of ammonia greatly decreases the solubility of the salt, e.g., 2.5% ammonia decreases the solubility to 0.00006 g. MgO per 100 ml. The presence of ammonium salts increase the solubility of the precipitate, e.g., 1 g. of ammonium chloride will increase the solubility to 0.0013 g. MgO.[8]

A large amount of $NH_4Cl$ tends to prevent precipitation of magnesium so that its removal may be advisable. This may be accomplished by J. Lawrence Smith method [9] by making the solution slightly acid with HCl and adding 2–3 ml. con-

[7] Z. anal. Chem., **29**, 165, 1890.

[8] Am. J. Sci. (3), **5**, 114, 1873.

[9] Am. J. Sci., **15**, 94, 1853.

centrated $HNO_3$ per gram $NH_4Cl$ present, covering the beaker until the evolution of gas has ceased and then evaporating to dryness.[10]

A pink color of the precipitate indicates contamination by Mn.

Hillebrand and Lundell [11] claim that asbestos should not be used as a filtering medium for the magnesium precipitate as some types are attacked by alkaline solvents containing soluble phosphates.

## THE OXINE METHOD

The details of the precipitation of aluminum by the method using 8-oxyquinoline has been described; in acids magnesium remains in solution. On making the solution alkaline magnesium precipitates with the addition of this reagent. Interfering elements must be absent, the alkalies may be present in the solution. The filtrate from the oxalate precipitation is taken for the determination of magnesium.

*Procedure.*—Fifty to one hundred ml. of solution containing the magnesium, free from interfering elements, and containing 1–2 ml. of 2 $N$ $NH_4Cl$ and about 1 ml. of free 6 $N$ $NH_4OH$ are heated to boiling and the oxine solution added, drop by drop, the precipitate allowed to settle, then filtered off, washed and weighed as $Mg(C_9H_6NO)_2$.

In an 0.001 $M$ solution magnesium can be determined by this method, accurately to 1% according to Kolthoff.

## TITRIMETRIC METHOD

### TITRATION OF THE MAGNESIUM AMMONIUM PHOSPHATE WITH STANDARD ACID

The procedure known as Handy's titrimetric method for magnesium,[12] depends upon the reaction:

$$MgNH_4PO_4 + H_2SO_4 \rightarrow MgSO_4 + NH_4H_2PO_4$$

An excess of standard sulfuric acid is added to the precipitate and the excess of acid titrated back with standard sodium hydroxide.

*Procedure.*—The method of precipitation of the magnesium ammonium phosphate is the same as has been described under the gravimetric method. The precipitate is washed several times by decantation with 10% ammonium hydroxide solution (1 part $NH_4OH$, sp. gr. 0.90 to 9 parts water), and finally on the filter. After draining, the filter is opened out, the moisture removed as much as possible by means of dry filter papers. The residue may be dried in the room for about forty-five minutes or in the air oven at 50 to 60°C. for fifteen to twenty minutes. When the filter has dried, ammonia will have been expelled. The substance is placed in a dry beaker, 0.1 $N$ sulfuric acid added in excess (methyl orange indicator), the solution diluted to 100 ml. and the excess of acid titrated with 0.1 $N$ sodium hydroxide.

One ml. 0.1 $N$ $H_2SO_4$ = 0.002016 gram MgO

[10] Smith, J. L., Am. Chemist, 111, 201, 1873. Langmuir, A. C., J. Am. Chem. Soc., 22, 104, 1900.
[11] Applied Inorganic Analysis, John Wiley & Sons, New York.
[12] Handy, James Otis, J. Am. Chem. Soc., 22, 31, 1900.

## DETERMINATIONS IN SPECIFIC SUBSTANCES

## CLEAVE'S METHOD FOR THE ANALYSIS OF CRUDE, CAUSTIC, AND DEAD-BURNED MAGNESITE [13]

*Sampling.*—In pulverizing *dead-burned* magnesite it should be kept in mind that this material is very abrasive and that any grinding between iron surfaces, such as in a disc pulverizer or on a bucking board, will result in contamination of the sample with a considerable quantity of iron.

The method of sampling used in this laboratory is as follows: The sample from the bin is cut to about 15 lbs. through a Jones Sampler. This sample is crushed through a small jaw crusher and cut through a Jones Sampler to about 1000 grams. This is crushed to pass an 8-mesh screen, using a Spiegel mortar made of case-hardened tool steel (Arthur H. Thomas, Cat. No. 7320). The material is crushed in the mortar by hammering the pestle, avoiding any grinding action. The sample is then cut to about 100 grams through the Jones Sampler, crushed to pass a 100-mesh screen, using the Spiegel mortar, and finally cut to about 25 grams by quartering on an oil cloth.

*Reagents.* **Dilute HCl.**—One part concentrated HCl to 3 parts water.

**Dilute NH$_4$OH.**—One part concentrated NH$_4$OH to 3 parts water.

**Dilute H$_2$SO$_4$.**—One part concentrated H$_2$SO$_4$ to 3 parts water.

**Rosolic Acid Solution.**—One gram rosolic acid in 100 ml. 75% grain alcohol.

**Ammonium Nitrate Wash Solution.**—Ten grams ammonium nitrate to a liter of water.

**Ammonium Oxalate Solution.**—Sixty grams ammonium oxalate to a liter of water. Keep solution warm with heat from a 100-watt electric light to prevent crystallization.

**Potassium Permanganate Solution.**—Strength of solution required is such that 1 ml. equals 0.001 g. CaO or 0.2% on a 0.5 g. sample. Dissolve 11 g. KMnO$_4$ to each liter of water; standardize with Bureau of Standards sodium oxalate, dilute to give required factor and restandardize.

**Paper Pulp.**—Make by moistening quantitative filter paper clippings with water, add concentrated HCl and stir vigorously. Add water, filter through Büchner funnel, wash with hot water to free from acid. Put pulp in container, add water, shake to disintegrate. Add water till consistency is right to pour easily.

### DETERMINATION OF IGNITION LOSS

*Procedure.*—Weigh 1 g. into a platinum crucible, weigh crucible and sample, heat in electric muffle at 1000°C. for 30 minutes, cool, and weigh. Loss in weight × 100 gives ignition loss in per cent.

### SILICA

*Procedure.*—Weigh 0.5 g. into a platinum crucible containing about 2 g. of anhydrous sodium carbonate, mix, cover, and fuse over a gas flame or in an electric muffle. Cool, loosen by squeezing the sides of the crucible, transfer to a 3-inch evaporating dish, cover with a watch glass, and add sufficient hot dilute HCl to dissolve the fusion. Dissolve the material remaining on the cover and in the crucible with a little hot dilute HCl, pour into the evaporating dish, and rinse crucible

[13] Method of the North West Magnesite Company.

and cover with warm water, using finger to loosen any silica which may cling to the crucible. When the fusion is dissolved remove and wash watch glass and evaporate solution to dryness over a water bath. If, when about half evaporated, any material remains undissolved on the bottom of the dish, stir it up with a stream of hot dilute HCl from a wash bottle. When dry bake in an oven at 110–118°C. until no odor of HCl can be detected. Do not heat above 118°C.; the silica may combine with the magnesia above this temperature, causing low results. When sufficiently baked, dissolve with a small quantity of hot dilute HCl, dilute with twice the quantity of hot water, heat to boiling, and filter through an 11-cm. Whatman No. 40 paper into a 250-ml. beaker, loosening silica clinging to the dish with a policeman and rinsing dish into filter with hot water. Wash filter 8 times with hot water, circling wash stream around top of paper. Burn the filter in a weighed platinum crucible, cool, and weigh. Moisten silica in crucible with a drop of water, add a drop of dilute $H_2SO_4$, add about 1 ml. of HF, evaporate on hot plate until free from $SO_3$ fumes, ignite in muffle at 1000°C., and weigh. Loss in weight multiplied by 200 gives the percentage of silica. Weight of residue in crucible, obtained by subtracting weight of empty crucible from weight of crucible after volatilization of silica, is added to weight of $R_2O_3$.

## IRON AND ALUMINA ($R_2O_3$)

*Procedure.*—To filtrate from the silica add about 4 g. of $NH_4Cl$ and a few drops of rosolic acid solution, heat to boiling, add a little paper pulp, make very slightly ammoniacal with dilute ammonia, as shown by faint pink color of rosolic acid, and filter through an 11-cm. Whatman No. 31 paper into a 600-ml. beaker. Without washing, transfer paper with precipitate back into same 250-ml. beaker, add about 25 ml. of hot dilute HCl, pulp paper by stirring with a glass rod, add about 100 ml. of hot water and a few drops of rosolic acid solution, and reprecipitate by making faintly ammoniacal with dilute ammonia. Filter through an 11-cm. Whatman No. 31 paper into previous filtrate, wash beaker and paper 4 times with 1% $NH_4NO_3$ solution. Transfer filter and precipitate to a No. 2 annealing cup and ignite in a muffle, cool, empty onto balance pan and weigh. Add weight of residue from silica determination to this weight, subtract weight of two 11-cm. Whatman No. 31 papers and multiply by 200 to get the percentage of $R_2O_3$.

## LIME

*Procedure.*—Make filtrate from above slightly acid, add about 8 g. of $NH_4Cl$, and 75 ml. of ammonium oxalate solution, stir to dissolve $NH_4Cl$, dilute to within ½ in. of top of beaker, make slightly ammoniacal and let stand overnight. Filter through an 11-cm. Whatman No. 30 paper, wash beaker and paper once with water, dissolve precipitate by filling funnel twice with hot, dilute HCl, letting solution run back into same 600-ml. beaker, wash paper at least 6 times or until volume of solution in beaker is about 300 ml., using hot water. Add ammonia until solution is faintly acid, heat to boiling, add about 25 ml. of ammonium oxalate solution, make faintly ammoniacal, remove to asbestos board on hot plate where solution will keep hot but will not boil. When precipitate has settled, remove from hot plate and when cool filter through an 11-cm. Whatman No. 30 paper. Wash beaker 3 times and paper 12 times more with water, circling wash stream around top of paper. To beaker add about 50 ml. of cold water, 25 ml. of dilute $H_2SO_4$, dilute to about 300 ml. with boiling water, drop paper containing calcium oxalate precipitate into beaker and stir, without pulping paper. Titrate to a faint pink with standard potassium permanganate solution. Milliliter of permanganate $\times$ lime factor $\times$ 200 gives percentage of lime.

## MAGNESIA

*Procedure.*—Ordinarily the difference between the sum of the above determinations and 100 is reported as magnesia. Where a direct determination of the magnesia is required the following is the method used: Make the combined filtrates from both lime precipitations up to 1000 ml. in a volumetric flask, and take a 200-ml. aliquot. Heat to 50°C., add from a pipette drop by drop, with stirring, 10 ml. of cold saturated ammonium phosphate solution. If a precipitate does not form with the first few drops add a little ammonia. In a few minutes stir and add about 10 ml. of paper pulp. Then, with stirring, add 25 ml. 1:1 $NH_4OH$. Let stand overnight, filter through an 11-cm. Whatman No. 40 paper. Dissolve precipitate with hot dilute HCl, letting solution run back into same beaker, wash with hot water until volume is about 150 ml., add a few drops of rosolic acid indicator, add 1 ml. ammonium phosphate solution, then make alkaline with dilute ammonia, stirring until precipitate forms. In a few minutes stir and add 10 ml. paper pulp. Then with stirring add 20 ml. 1:1 ammonia. Let stand overnight. Filter through an 11-cm. Whatman No. 40 paper. Wash with 2 funnels of cold 1:10 ammonia, drain well, place filter in a No. 2 annealing cup, place in front of muffle till charred and paper is burned, finish to 1000°C. Grams $Mg_2P_2O_7 \times$ 0.3621 $\times$ 1000 gives the percentage of MgO.

When lime is precipitated as oxalate, in the presence of considerable quantities of magnesia, the precipitate will be contaminated with magnesium oxalate, the amount of contamination increasing with increased concentration of undissociated magnesium oxalate. The ammonium oxalate added, if ionized will tend to prevent ionization of the magnesium oxalate, as the two salts contain a common ion. A considerable quantity of ammonium chloride is added, therefore, to decrease the ionization of the ammonium oxalate, thus decreasing the oxalate ions in the solution and increasing, as a result, the dissociation of the magnesium oxalate.

As dilution also increases the dissociation of the magnesium oxalate, as large a volume as possible within reason should be used when precipitating the lime. A volume of 550 ml. is used in the laboratory for the first precipitation and about 400 ml. for the second.

## PERCHLORATE METHOD FOR THE DETERMINATION OF CALCIUM IN BURNED MAGNESITE [14]

*Procedure.*—To a 1.000 g. sample in a 250-ml. Pyrex beaker add 5 ml. of water and 10 ml. of 60% perchloric acid, then heat on a steam bath until the solvent action is complete. Fume off the excess of $HClO_4$ by placing the beaker on a high temperature hot plate, the last traces of $HClO_4$ being removed by heating the wall of the beaker with a burner flame. No damage is done if some of the magnesium perchlorate is dehydrated or decomposed by this treatment. After cooling, dissolve the salts in about 20 ml. of water, filter off the silica, and wash successively with small portions of hot water. To save time in evaporation the volume of the wash water should not exceed 50 ml. The filtrate and washings are received in a 250-ml. beaker. Evaporate the solution to 9 ml., and add 1 ml. of dilute (1:4) sulfuric acid, cool and then add very slowly from a pipette 90 ml.

[14] Caley and Elving, Ind. Eng. Chem., Anal. Ed., **10**, 264, 1938.

of pure methanol ($CH_3OH$). Allow the vessel to stand at least one hour, then filter off the precipitated calcium sulfate on a weighed porcelain filter crucible. Wash with successive small portions of 90% $CH_3OH$. About 50 ml. will be required. A rubber policeman is used to transfer the last traces of the precipitate to the filter crucible. Wipe off the outside of the crucible with a cloth moistened with benzene to remove any rubber dissolved by the action of the $CH_3OH$ on the rubber crucible holder. Dry the crucible at 110°C. for 30 minutes, then place it in a muffle or crucible furnace and heat for 30 minutes at 400–500°C. Cool and weigh. The weight of $CaSO_4$ in grams $\times$ 41.19 gives the percentage of CaO in the sample.

The amount of sodium and potassium present should not exceed a few milligrams since they form slightly soluble double sulfates with calcium. The above procedure is valid when the $R_2O_3$ content of the material does not exceed 3–4%. With higher percentages of these oxides much longer periods of time may be necessary between precipitation and filtration.

The procedure for the determination of calcium in a limestone or dolomite is nearly the same as that for the determination of calcium in a burned magnesite. For all materials that contain more than 5% of calcium the following slight modification is advisable.

Remove the silica as described for calcined magnesia. To the filtrate and washings after the removal of the silica, add 1 or 2 ml. of the dilute sulfuric acid. Evaporate the solution to 5 ml., add 15 ml. of water and then add very slowly 180 ml. of pure $CH_3OH$ while stirring constantly. Filter after 1 hour.

## ANALYSIS OF MAGNESIA [15]

*Loss on Ignition.*—Ignite a 2.0000 g. sample to constant weight with a Fisher burner.

*Decomposition.*—Mix 1.0000 g. with approximately an equal weight of reagent $Na_2CO_3$ in a platinum crucible and sinter with a Bunsen burner. Dissolve the cake in an excess of dilute $HClO_4$ sufficient to provide an excess for refluxing to dehydrate the silica.

*Silica.*—Double dehydration with $HClO_4$ with intervening filtration. The silica is corrected for impurities with HF and $H_2SO_4$.

*$R_2O_3$.*—Double precipitation with $NH_4OH$.

*Iron.*—Reduce the iron to $Fe^{++}$ and titrate with $K_2Cr_2O_7$ using sodium diphenylaminesulfonate as an indicator.

*CaO.*—Separate calcium by triple oxalate precipitation.

*MgO.*—Ammonium salts in the combined filtrates from CaO destroyed with $HNO_3$. Solution made up to definite volume and aliquots equivalent to 0.2000 or 0.2500 g. MgO twice precipitated as phosphate, taking precautions suggested by Lundell and Hoffman.[16] The $Mg_2P_2O_7$ is corrected for CaO and MnO content.

More frequently MgO is not determined directly.

15 Outline of procedure used by the Norton Co., Worcester, Mass. Courtesy of M. O. Lamar.
16 Bur. Stand. Jour. Res., 5, 279, 1930.

# METHODS FOR THE ANALYSIS OF MAGNESIUM AND MAGNESIUM-BASE ALLOYS [17]

## *ALUMINUM BY THE BENZOATE-HYDROXYQUINOLINE (GRAVIMETRIC) METHOD*

This method is suitable for the determination of from 0.5–12% aluminum. Since this method is capable of giving very accurate results, it is recommended for referee analysis.

Aluminum is precipitated first as the benzoate and then as the oxinate, in buffered solutions. The aluminum oxinate is dried and weighed.

No appreciable interference is caused by the ordinary quantities of zinc, manganese, tin, or silicon found in magnesium alloys. Copper will remain largely insoluble in HCl, the amount going into solution being too small to cause serious interference. Zirconium and thorium would interfere if present, but are not usually encountered in magnesium-aluminum alloys. Zirconium and aluminum are incompatible. Iron can be removed by precipitation from the ammoniacal tartrate solution with $H_2S$ just before the precipitation with 8-hydroxyquinoline. Interference due to minor quantities of iron and cerium can be eliminated by the addition of hydroxylamine hydrochloride prior to the precipitation of the aluminum as the benzoate.

*Apparatus.* **Filtering Crucible.**—A 15-ml. fritted-glass crucible of medium porosity.

*Reagents.* **Ammonium Benzoate Solution (100 g. per liter).**—Dissolve 100 g. of pure ammonium benzoate ($NH_4C_7H_5O_2$) in 1 liter of warm water and add 1 mg. of thymol as a preservative.

**Ammonium Tartrate Solution (30 g. per liter).**—Dissolve 30 g. of ammonium tartrate (($NH_4)_2C_4H_4O_6$) in 500 ml. of water, add 120 ml. of $NH_4OH$ and dilute to one liter.

**Benzoate Wash Solution.**—To 100 ml. of the ammonium benzoate solution, add 900 ml. of warm water and 20 ml. of glacial acetic acid.

**8-Hydroxyquinoline (Oxine) Solution (50 g. per liter).**—Dissolve 50 g. of reagent grade 8-hydroxyquinoline ($C_9H_6NOH$) in 120 ml. of glacial acetic acid and dilute to one liter. Filter and store in a dark bottle.

*Procedure.*—Weigh, to the nearest milligram, a sample calculated to contain 0.2–0.3 g. of aluminum and transfer to a 400-ml. beaker containing 50 ml. of water. Dissolve the sample by adding, in small portions, a total of 10 ml. of HCl for each gram of sample. When dissolved, cool the solution to room temperature, and dilute to 500 ml. in a volumetric flask. Any residue of undissolved silica, which might contain some occluded aluminum, should be kept in suspension.

Pipette a 50.0-ml. aliquot into a 400-ml. beaker and dilute with 50 ml. of water. Neutralize the solution with $NH_4OH$ (1:1), by adding dropwise with stirring until the precipitate which forms as each drop strikes finally redissolves only very slowly; that is, until nearly all of the free acid is neutralized without permanent precipitation of $Al(OH)_3$. Add 1 ml. of glacial acetic acid, about 1 g. of $NH_4Cl$, and 20 ml. of ammonium benzoate solution. Heat the mixture to boiling while stirring, keep at gentle boiling for 5 minutes, then filter on a medium porosity

[17] From Methods of the Dow Chemical Company, West Analytical Laboratory, 3–143 Building, Midland, Mich. Courtesy of Mr. G. B. Wengert.

paper. Wash the precipitate 8 to 10 times with hot benzoate wash solution, making no effort to transfer all of the precipitate to the filter paper.

Dissolve the precipitate with five 10-ml. portions of hot ammonium tartrate solution, washing with hot water after each portion is added. Collect the solution in the original beaker and dilute to 150 to 200 ml. Heat the solution to 70–90°C., add 20 ml. of 8-hydroxyquinoline solution and digest for 15 minutes without boiling. Filter the solution through a tared, glass crucible and wash 8 times with hot water, transferring all of the precipitate.

Dry the precipitate for 2 hours at 120–130°C., cool, and weigh as aluminum oxinate $(Al(C_9H_6ON)_3)$.

**Calculation.**—Calculate the percentage of aluminum as follows:

$$\text{Aluminum, } \% = \frac{A \times 0.0587}{B} \times 100$$

where $A$ = grams of aluminum oxinate, and
$B$ = grams of sample in aliquot used.

### ALUMINUM BY THE POTENTIOMETRIC METHOD

This method is applicable to the determination of aluminum in concentrations of 2 to 13%.

The sample is dissolved in HCl, the excess acid is partially neutralized with $NH_4OH$ (1:2) and the neutralization is completed with 1 $N$ NaOH to a potentiometric end point. Aluminum is then titrated with 1 $N$ NaOH to a final potentiometric end point.

Bismuth interferes with the potential changes of the antimony electrode and may be removed, if present, by precipitation with $H_2S$ and expulsion of excess $H_2S$ by boiling before titration. Copper and silver lower the potentials of the end points but do not interfere with the deflections. The presence of abnormal amounts of dissolved silicic acid and ferric iron cause high results. Ceric cerium, thorium, zirconium, titanium, and tin must be absent. Zinc, cadmium, nickel, and manganese do not interfere.

**Apparatus. Apparatus for Potentiometric Titration.**—The titration assembly consists of an antimony electrode and a saturated calomel electrode with a KCl salt bridge terminating in a porous-glass or porcelain plug. These dip into a titration beaker, which is provided with a thermometer and a mechanical stirrer and is mounted on a support in such a way that it can be heated.

**Reagents. Bromphenol Blue Indicator Solution.**—Place 4.0 g. of bromphenol blue in a mortar, add 8.25 ml. of 1 $N$ NaOH and mix until solution is complete, adding one or more ml. of water if necessary. Dilute to one liter with water.

**Indicator-Buffer Solution.**—Add 8 ml. of bromphenol blue indicator solution to one liter of saturated $NH_4Cl$ solution.

**Sodium Hydroxide Standard Solution (1 $N$).**

**Procedure.**—Weigh, to the nearest milligram, a sample calculated to contain approximately 0.15 g. of aluminum and place it in a 250-ml. beaker containing 50 ml. of water. Add, in small portions, 7.5 ml. of HCl per gram of sample, and then 1 ml. in excess.

When the dissolution is complete, cool to room temperature, and add 20 ml. of the indicator-buffer solution. Place the beaker in the titration assembly, start the stirrer and titrate the excess acid with dropwise additions of $NH_4OH$ (1:2) until the potentiometer shows a rapid increase in deflection. Continue titrating with 1 N NaOH, using a two-drop increment, to the first potentiometric break, shown by a maximum deflection at a potential of 150 to 190 mv. and occurring very nearly at the color change from yellow to blue.

Heat the solution to 80°C. and, while maintaining the temperature of the solution at this level, titrate again with 1 N NaOH to a second end point as shown by a maximum deflection occurring at a potential of 275 to 300 mv.

**Calculation.**—The equation upon which this titration is based is believed to be as follows:

$$2AlCl_3 + 5NaOH \rightarrow Al_2(OH)_5Cl + 5NaCl.$$

The theoretical factor for this reaction is 0.01079.

Calculate the percentage of aluminum as follows:

$$\text{Aluminum, } \% = \frac{AB \times 0.0108}{C} \times 100$$

where $A$ = milliliters of NaOH solution required for titration of the sample from the first to the second potentiometric end point,

$B$ = normality of the NaOH solution, and

$C$ = grams of sample used.

### ALUMINUM BY THE 8-HYDROXYQUINOLINE (PHOTOMETRIC) METHOD

This method is applicable to the determination of aluminum in concentrations of less than 0.5%. It has been written for cells having a 1-cm. light path. Cells having other dimensions may be used, provided suitable adjustments can be made in the amounts of sample and reagents used.

Aluminum is separated from most metals by precipitation as the benzoate using zirconium as a carrier. Aluminum is determined by extracting the 8-hydroxyquinolate in chloroform. The photometric reading at 385 m$\mu$ is proportional to the aluminum concentration over the range of 0.010–0.200 mg. per 50 ml.

The recommended concentration range is from 0.025 to 0.100 mg. of aluminum for 50 ml. of solution using a cell depth of 1 cm.

The color of the aluminum oxinate is stable for an indefinite period if kept unexposed to light, especially sunlight.

Iron, zirconium, and cerium are the only metals carried through the benzoate separation with aluminum in amounts that are likely to cause interference. The addition of diammonium phosphate is sufficient to prevent interference by zirconium. Iron is removed by extraction as the 8-hydroxyquinolate in the pH range from 1.9 to 2.5 without extraction of aluminum. If cerium is present in small amounts, it is removed by extraction in the pH range above 12.2 without extraction of aluminum. Excess benzoate, which also interferes, is removed with the iron.

**Reagents. Aluminum Standard Solution (1 ml. = 0.010 mg. Al).**—Dissolve 0.100 g. of pure aluminum metal in 20 ml. of HCl (1:1). Transfer to a 500-ml. volumetric flask, add 100 ml. of HCl and make to volume. Pipette 25 ml. into a 500-ml. volumetric flask and make to volume.

**Ammonium Benzoate Solution (100 g. per liter).**—Dissolve 100 g. of pure ammonium benzoate $(C_6H_5CO_2NH_4)$ in one liter of warm water and add 1 mg. of thymol as a preservative.

**Benzoate Wash Solution.**—To 100 ml. of the ammonium benzoate solution add 900 ml. of warm water and 20 ml. of glacial acetic acid.

**Diammonium Phosphate Solution (150 g. per liter).**—Dissolve 15 g. of diammonium phosphate $[(NH_4)_2HPO_4]$ in 100 ml. of water.

**8-Hydroxyquinoline Solution (Oxine) (10 g. per liter).**—Dissolve 10 g. of 8-hydroxyquinoline $(C_9H_6NOH)$ in 1 liter of chloroform. Prepare fresh as needed.

**Sodium Hydroxide-Sodium Carbonate Buffer Solution.**—Dissolve 10 g. of sodium hydroxide and 45 g. of sodium carbonate in one liter of water.

**Zirconium Solution (1 ml. = 0.2 mg. Zr).**—Dissolve 0.356 g. of zirconyl chloride $(ZrOCl_2 \cdot 8H_2O)$ in about 100 ml. of water, add 100 ml. of HCl and dilute to 500 ml.

*1. Preparation of Calibration Curve.* (a) Calibration Solutions.—Transfer 2.5, 5.0, 7.5, and 10.0 ml. portions of the standard aluminum solution (1 ml. = 0.010 mg. Al) to 250-ml. separatory funnels. Dilute each solution to 100 ml. with water.

(b) **Reference Solution.**—Add 100 ml. of water to a 250-ml. separatory funnel and acidify with a few drops of HCl (1:1).

(c) **Color Development.**—Add 10.0 ml. of the 8-hydroxyquinoline solution, 3 drops of thymolphthalein indicator and just enough of the sodium hydroxide-sodium carbonate buffer solution to produce a blue color. Shake the mixture for one minute, allow the layers to separate thoroughly and draw off the lower chloroform layer into a dry 50-ml. volumetric flask containing about 1 g. of anhydrous $Na_2SO_4$. Repeat the extraction twice more, adding 15 ml. of chloroform each time. Dilute to volume with chloroform.

(d) **Photometry.**—Transfer a suitable portion of the reference solution to an absorption cell with a 1-cm. light path and adjust the photometer to the initial setting using a light band centered at approximately 385 m$\mu$. While maintaining this adjustment, take the photometric readings of the calibration solutions.

(e) **Calibration Curve.**—Plot the photometric readings of the calibration solutions against milligrams of aluminum per 50 ml. of solution.

*2. Procedure.* (a) Test Solution.—Weigh, to the nearest milligram, 1 to 2 g. of sample and place it in a 250-ml. beaker. Add 25 ml. of water and dissolve the sample by adding, in small portions, a total of 10 ml. of HCl for each gram of sample. When dissolution is complete, add $NH_4OH$ (1:1) dropwise, with stirring, until the solution is just basic to Congo Red indicator paper. Add 1 ml. of glacial acetic acid, about 1 g. of $NH_4Cl$, 10 ml. of zirconium solution and 10 ml. of ammonium benzoate solution. Heat the mixture to boiling while stirring, keep at a gentle boil for five minutes and then filter through a fine porosity filter paper. Wash 8 to 10 times with hot benzoate wash solution. Dissolve the precipitate back into the original beaker with hot HCl (1:1). Cool the solution, transfer it to a 250-ml. volumetric flask and dilute to volume with water. Pipette an aliquot containing 0.010 to 0.100 mg. of aluminum into a 250-ml. separatory funnel. Dilute to 100 ml. with water.

(b) **Reference Solution.**—Add 100 ml. of water to a 250-ml. separatory funnel and acidify with a few drops of HCl (1:1).

(c) **Color Development.**—Add 5.0 ml. of the 8-hydroxyquinoline solution and adjust the pH to 2.0 with the sodium hydroxide-sodium carbonate buffer solution (use Hydrion paper). Shake the mixture for one minute, allow the layers to separate, draw off and discard the lower chloroform layer. Repeat the extraction using 15 ml. of chloroform, discarding the lower organic phase. Add 10.0 ml. of the 8-hydroxyquinoline solution, 2 ml. of $(NH_4)_2HPO_4$ solution, 3 drops of thymolphthalein indicator and sufficient sodium hydroxide-sodium carbonate buffer solution to color the aqueous layer blue. Shake the mixture for one minute, allow the layers to separate thoroughly and draw off the lower chloroform layer into a dry 50-ml. volumetric flask containing about 1 g. of anhydrous $Na_2SO_4$. Repeat the extraction twice more, adding 15 ml. of chloroform each time. Dilute the solution to volume with chloroform and mix.

(d) **Photometry.**—Take the photometric reading of the test solution as described in Section 1(d).

(e) **Calculation.**—Convert the photometric reading of the test solution to milligrams of aluminum by means of the calibration curve. Calculate the percentage of aluminum as follows:

$$\text{Aluminum, } \% = \frac{A}{B \times 10}$$

where $A$ = milligrams of aluminum per 50 ml. of solution, and
$B$ = grams of sample represented in the aliquot taken.

## CALCIUM BY THE ETHYLENEDINITRILOTETRAACETATE (TITRIMETRIC) METHOD

This method is applicable to the determination of calcium in concentrations greater than 5% with a relative error of 1%. For alloys having calcium contents under 5%, the flame spectrophotometric procedure is usually employed.

Calcium is separated from the bulk of the magnesium as the tungstate. The calcium tungstate is then dissolved in sodium hydroxide and an excess of standard ethylenedinitrilotetraacetate (ethylenediaminetetraacetate) solution. The excess ethylenedinitrilotetraacetate is back titrated with a standard calcium solution using Cal-Red indicator.

Aluminum and iron would interfere, if present, but can be removed by precipitation as benzoates. Barium and strontium would be included with the calcium if they are present, but since these are not usually present in magnesium alloys, no interference would be expected from this source.

*Apparatus.* **Crucible.**—Filtering, Selas, #3001 or #4001.

**Magnetic Stirrer.**—With a Teflon-covered magnetic stirring bar.

*Reagents.* **Ammoniacal Wash Solution.**—Add 20 ml. of the buffer solution to water and dilute to one liter.

**Ammonium Benzoate Solution (100 g. per liter).**—Dissolve 100 g. of pure ammonium benzoate ($NH_4C_7H_5O_2$) in one liter of warm water and add 1 mg. of thymol as preservative.

**Ammonium Benzoate Wash Solution.**—To 100 ml. of the ammonium benzoate solution, add 900 ml. of water and 20 ml. of glacial acetic acid.

**Buffer Solution.**—Dissolve 67.5 g. of reagent grade $NH_4Cl$ in 300 ml. of water. Add 570 ml. of $NH_4OH$ and dilute to one liter with water.

**Calcium Standard Solution, 0.05 $M$ (1 ml. = 2.004 mg. Ca).**—Weigh 5.0050 g. of primary standard calcium carbonate and transfer it to a 400-ml. beaker. Add 50 ml. of water and dissolve in 10.6 ml. of HCl, added in small increments. When the dissolution is complete, boil the solution to remove carbon dioxide. Cool the solution to room temperature, transfer to a one-liter volumetric flask and dilute to volume with water.

**Cal-Red Indicator.**—Available from Scientific Service Laboratory, Inc., Dallas, Texas.

**EDTA Solution, 0.05 *M*.**—Dissolve 18.61 g. of disodium dihydrogen ethylene-dinitrilotetraacetate in water and dilute with water to one liter in a volumetric flask. Standardize this solution against known amounts of calcium standard carried through the entire procedure. From this standardization can be obtained the volume ratio of the EDTA to calcium solution and the gram calcium equivalent of the EDTA solution.

**Sodium Hydroxide Solution (500 g. per liter).**—Dissolve 500 g. of reagent grade sodium hydroxide (NaOH) in 400 ml. of water. Cool to room temperature and dilute to one liter with water. Store in a polyethylene bottle.

**Sodium Tungstate Solution (100 g. per liter).**—Dissolve 10 g. of reagent grade sodium tungstate ($Na_2WO_4 \cdot H_2O$) in water and dilute to 100 ml. with water. Prepare fresh as needed.

*Procedure.*—(a) Weigh, to the nearest milligram, 1 g. of sample and transfer it to a 400-ml. beaker. Add 50 ml. of water and dissolve the sample with 10 ml. of HCl, added in small increments. When dissolution is complete, cool the solution to room temperature. Transfer the solution to a 250-ml. volumetric flask and dilute to volume with water. Pipette an aliquot which will contain from 10–100 mg. of calcium but not more than 125 mg. of aluminum, if aluminum is present, into a 400-ml. beaker. If aluminum is not present, proceed in accordance with step (c) below.

(b) To the aliquoted solution which contains 10–100 mg. of calcium and not more than 125 mg. of aluminum, add $NH_4OH$ (1:1) dropwise, with stirring, until the precipitate that forms as each drop strikes redissolves only very slowly; that is, until nearly all the free acid is neutralized without permanent precipitation of aluminum hydroxide. Add 1 ml. of glacial acetic acid, about 1 g. of $NH_4Cl$ and 25 ml. of the ammonium benzoate solution. Heat the mixture to boiling while stirring, keep at a gentle boil for 5 minutes and then filter on a medium porosity paper (Whatman No. 40). Wash the beaker several times with the hot benzoate wash solution and the precipitate from eight to ten times as well. Make no effort to transfer all of the precipitate to the paper. Discard the precipitate and paper.

(c) To the filtrate from step (b), or the aliquot from step (a), add 25 ml. of the buffer solution and 15 ml. of the $Na_2WO_4$ solution. Heat the mixture to boiling and then digest, just under boiling, for five minutes. Cool the mixture to room temperature and filter the solutions on a #3001 or #4001 Selas filtering crucible, making no effort to transfer all of the precipitate to the crucible. Wash the beaker three to four times and the precipitate three to four times with the ammoniacal wash solution. Transfer the crucible containing the calcium tungstate to the original beaker. Add 100 ml. of water, 10 ml. of the NaOH solution and a measured amount of standard 0.05 *M* EDTA solution until there is a 10–15 ml. excess over the amount needed to sequesterize the calcium. Heat the mixture to boiling and digest just below boiling until all of the calcium tungstate is solubilized. (There is usually a small amount of magnesium which is co-precipitated with the calcium tungstate. The magnesium tungstate co-precipitated does not dissolve in the strongly alkaline solution, even in the presence of EDTA, and causes no interference.)

Remove the crucible from the solution and wash it well with water. Cool the solution to room temperature.

(d) Dilute the solution to about 200 ml. with water, insert a magnetic stirring bar and add about 0.2 g. of Cal-Red indicator. Titrate with the standard 0.05 *M* calcium solution from a color change of pure blue to wine red. (The back titration with the 0.05 $M$ calcium solution can be done spectrophotometrically on the Sargent-Malmstadt Automatic Titrator, Model SE. The additional conditions necessary are a flow rate of 5–6 ml. per minute for the first 10 ml., a polarity of one and a wavelength of 650 m$\mu$. The advantages of using the instrument are that the end points are more consistent and the accuracy better.)

(e) **Calculation.**—Calculate the percentage calcium as follows:

$$\text{Calcium}, \% = \frac{(A - BC) \times D \times 100}{E}$$

where $A$ = total milliliters of 0.05 $M$ EDTA solution added,

$B$ = milliliters of 0.05 $M$ calcium solution used in the back titration,

$C$ = EDTA equivalent of the 0.05 $M$ calcium solution expressed in milliliters of 0.05 $M$ EDTA solution per milliliter of 0.05 $M$ calcium solution,

$D$ = calcium equivalent of the 0.05 $M$ EDTA solution expressed in grams of calcium per milliliter of 0.05 $M$ EDTA solution and,

$E$ = grams of sample represented in the aliquot.

### CALCIUM, SODIUM, POTASSIUM, INDIUM, AND LITHIUM BY THE FLAME PHOTOMETRIC METHOD

This method is suitable for the determination of 0.01 to 1.0% of sodium, 0.01 to 1.0% potassium, 0.01 to 5.0% calcium, 0.01 to 1% indium, or 0.05 to 20% lithium in magnesium alloys. The procedure may be extended to a multi-component analysis. Other elements that are excited in a flame may also be determined by this method if their emissivity is high enough.

A sample is dissolved in a suitable acid and the solution is analyzed by flame photometry. The emission due to the component in question is compared with that of a standard synthetic sample.

*Apparatus.* **Oxygen and Acetylene Cylinders.**—Fitted with necessary regulators and gauges.

**Sample Cups, 5-ml. capacity.**

**Photometer.**—Fitted with flame attachment capable of making emission measurements at wavelengths between 220 and 1000 m$\mu$. This method describes the use of a Beckman Model DU Spectrophotometer with a Model 9200 flame attachment.

*Reagents.* **Calcium Chloride, Stock Solution (1 ml. = 1.00 mg. Ca).**—Dissolve 2.49 g. of reagent grade Iceland spar ($CaCO_3$) in 300 ml. of water and a minimum of HCl. Heat to boiling to evolve carbon dioxide, cool, and dilute to 1 liter with water. Store in a polyethylene bottle.

**Indium Chloride, Stock Solution (1 ml. = 2.00 mg. In).**—Dissolve 2.00 g. of pure indium metal in 25 ml. of water and a minimum of HCl. Mild heating and a few drops of $HNO_3$ will aid in dissolving the metal. Dilute to 1 liter with water and store in a polyethylene bottle.

**Lithium Chloride, Stock Solution (1 ml. = 10.00 mg. Li).**—Dissolve 53.24 g. of reagent grade, dried lithium carbonate ($Li_2CO_3$) in 300 ml. of water and a minimum of HCl. Heat to boiling on a hot plate to evolve carbon dioxide. Dilute to 1 liter with water and store in a polyethylene bottle.

**Magnesium Chloride, Stock Solutions (1 ml. = 50.0 mg. Mg).**—Dissolve 50.0 g. of pure magnesium metal in 300 ml. of water and a minimum of HCl added in small increments and dilute to 1 liter with water. Store in a polyethylene bottle.

**Potassium Chloride, Stock Solution (1 ml. = 1.00 mg. K).**—Dissolve 1.91 g. of pure, dried potassium chloride (KCl) in water and dilute to 1 liter with water. Store in a polyethylene bottle.

**Sodium Chloride, Stock Solution (1 ml. = 1.00 mg. Na).**—Dissolve 2.54 g. of pure, dried sodium chloride (NaCl) in water and dilute to 1 liter with water. Store in a polyethylene bottle.

*1. Preparation of Sample.*—(a) The sample weight to be taken depends upon the concentration of the element(s) in question and its emissivity (flame spectral intensity). The following table gives the approximate alloy sample weight to be taken.

| Element | Wavelength (mμ) | Per cent | Sample Weight (grams) |
|---|---|---|---|
| Sodium | 588.5 | 0.4 – 4 | 0.5 |
| | | 6.0 – 20 | 0.1 |
| Potassium | 767 | 0.4 – 4 | 0.5 |
| | | 6.0 – 20 | 0.1 |
| Calcium | 422.5 | 0.01 – 0.10 | 3.0 |
| | | 0.1 – 1.0 | 2.0 |
| Indium | 451.1 | 0.01 – 0.10 | 3.0 |
| | | 0.5 – 1.0 | 2.0 |
| | | 2.0 – 13 | 0.5 |
| Lithium | 671 | 0.4 – 4 | 0.5 |
| | | 6.0 – 27 | 0.1 |

(b) For a sample weight of less than 1 g., it is advisable to take a 1-g. sample and a suitable aliquot of the resulting solution. Dissolve the sample in 25 ml. of water and a minimum amount of HCl and dilute to 100 ml. with water.

*2. Preparation of Calibration Curve.* **(a) Calibration Solutions.**—Prepare a series of 5 standard solutions of the element to be determined. The following table is a generalization for the determination of lithium in the concentration range of 0.8 to 5.2% lithium. A sample weight of 0.500 g. per 100 ml. is assumed. Dilute 10 ml. of the lithium chloride stock solution to 100 ml. with water. Also dilute 100 ml. of the magnesium chloride stock solution to 500 ml. with water.

| Standard Solution No. | Volume | Lithium chloride, dilute solution ml. | mg. (Li) | Magnesium chloride, dilute solution ml. | gram (Mg) |
|---|---|---|---|---|---|
| 1 | 100 ml. | 4 | 4 | 49.6 | 0.496 |
| 2 | 100 ml. | 8 | 8 | 49.2 | 0.492 |
| 3 | 100 ml. | 14 | 14 | 48.6 | 0.486 |
| 4 | 100 ml. | 20 | 20 | 48.0 | 0.480 |
| 5 | 100 ml. | 26 | 26 | 47.4 | 0.474 |

**(b) Flame Photometry.**—After instrument warm-up on the red sensitive phototube, make the following settings: 50.0% emission, 0.03 mm. slit width, 671 mμ, 0.1 selector switch, resistor switch at No. 2 position, and sensitivity control at 1 turn off of counterclock-wise. Balance the dark current, ignite the burner, and adjust the gas pressures. Position a sample cup containing standard solution No. 3 under the burner and re-balance the galvanometer needle with the sensitivity control. Now read the other standard solutions against this setting maintaining dark current and sensitivity balance at all times. Flush the burner with water after each reading. The flame and solvent background should be determined. In this case for lithium, it should be zero. (The optimum slit width and sensitivity control setting should be determined by the analyst for his particular instrument. The exact wavelength setting is best determined by slowly rotating the wavelength dial either direction from the approximate wavelength setting until the galvanometer deflects the greatest distance to the left. The maximum deflection to the left of the galvanometer zero denotes the peak of the analytical line in question. If this is significantly different than the stated wavelength, check the calibration with a mercury or hydrogen discharge lamp.)

(c) **Calibration Curve.**—Plot the readings obtained above on log-log (i cycle) graph paper, concentration of lithium versus percentage emission.

**3. Procedure.** (a) **Test Solution.**—Prepare a test solution as described in Section 1.

(b) **Flame Photometry.**—Measure the percentage emission as described in Section 2 (b).

(c) **Calculation.**—Convert the emission reading of the test solution to milligrams of the element being determined by means of the calibration curve. Calculate the percentage of the element being determined as follows:

$$\text{Element, \%} = \frac{A}{B \times 10}$$

where $A$ = milligram of the element being determined per 100 ml. of solution, and
$B$ = grams of sample represented in 100 ml. of final solution.

## CALCIUM, SODIUM, POTASSIUM AND LITHIUM BY THE ALTERNATE (SPIKING-EXTRAPOLATION TECHNIQUE) FLAME PHOTOMETRIC METHOD

The following paragraphs are a description of the method using calcium as the element being determined. The necessary preparations and dilutions for the determination of sodium, potassium, and lithium can also be established.

A sample is dissolved in acid and diluted to a known volume. A rough determination of the calcium concentration is made by comparing an aliquot portion of the sample with calcium standards. From this comparison a suitable aliquot size is determined.

Four equal aliquots are pipetted into volumetric flasks of the desired size. The first aliquot is diluted to volume. The last three aliquots are spiked respectively with approximately 1, 2, and 3 times the quantity of calcium present in the sample aliquot taken. The samples are diluted to volume and the emission readings for the 4 solutions are determined. A curve is plotted, extrapolating to the horizontal axis to determine the true calcium content present in the sample.

The advantage in using this procedure is that a true background is always obtained for each sample. Also, since calcium is the only standard added, it is unnecessary to have a supply of other standards on hand.

The procedure is applicable in cases where the concentrations used are such that a linear or very nearly linear curve is obtained. If, however, the curve is found to vary greatly from linearity, errors may be encountered due to the resulting inaccuracy of the extrapolation.

*Procedure.* **Test Solution.**—Weigh, to the nearest milligram, 10 g. of sample and transfer it to a 400-ml. beaker containing 50 ml. of water. Dissolve the sample in a minimum amount of HCl, added in small increments. Dilute with water to 250 ml. in a volumetric flask. Pipette a 25-ml. aliquot into a 100-ml. volumetric flask and dilute to volume with water. Make a rough determination of the calcium present by comparing its emission at 422.5 m$\mu$ against calcium standards. From this data determine the aliquot size to be used in the procedure.

**Flame Photometry.**—Pipette four equal aliquots of the sample solution into 100-ml. volumetric flasks and label $A$, $B$, $C$, and $D$. To flasks $B$, $C$, and $D$ add respectively X mg., 2X mg. and 3X mg. of calcium (X = mg. of Ca present in the aliquot used) and dilute to volume with water. Make the necessary instrumental adjustments and determine the emission readings for the 4 solutions. Make duplicate readings on all solutions, adjusting the instrument whenever necessary. Obtain the true background emission by reading the emission of the solutions at wavelengths settings on either side of the calcium peak. This should give the same reading for both the spiked and the unspiked solutions. Subtract this background emission from the emission readings obtained for the solutions.

**Calculation.**—Plot the net emission readings for the 4 solutions on the vertical or Y-axis versus the mg. of calcium added on the horizontal or X-axis. ($A = 0$ mg., $B = $ X mg., $C = $ 2X mg. and $D = $ 3X mg.). Draw the curve. The curve will cross the X-axis to the left of the Y-axis. Call the point of intersection "R." The distance of the intersection point "R" from the origin represents the amount of calcium present in the sample. Transpose "R" to the right-hand side of the origin and read the number of milligrams of calcium present in the aliquot taken.

Calculate the percentage of calcium as follows:

$$\text{Calcium, } \% = \frac{A}{B \times 10}$$

where $A$ = milligrams of calcium present, and
$B$ = grams of sample represented in the aliquot taken.

## COBALT BY THE NITROSO-R (PHOTOMETRIC) METHOD

This method is applicable to the determination of cobalt in concentrations of less than 1.0%.

A hot sodium acetate buffered solution of cobalt forms an orange-colored complex with nitroso-R salt. Upon the addition of a controlled amount of $HNO_3$ the cobalt complex is stabilized and interfering complexes are destroyed. Photometric measurement is made at approximately 540 m$\mu$.

The recommended concentration range is from 0.01 to 0.08 mg. of cobalt per 100 ml. of solution, using a cell depth of 5 cm. (This method has been written for cells having a 5-cm. light path. Cells having other dimensions may be used, provided suitable adjustments can be made in the amounts of sample and reagents used.)

The color is stable for at least 30 minutes, and the elements ordinarily present in magnesium alloys do not interfere.

**Reagents. Cobalt Standard Solution $A$ (1 ml. = 0.10 mg. Co).**—Dissolve 0.100 g. of cobalt metal in 5 ml. of water and 5 ml. of $HNO_3$. After the action ceases, boil the solution until it is free of brown fumes. Transfer this solution to a 1-liter volumetric flask and dilute to volume.

**Cobalt Standard Solution $B$ (1 ml. = 0.01 mg. Co).**—Pipette 100 ml. of standard cobalt solution $A$ into a 1-liter volumetric flask and dilute to volume.

**Nitroso-R Salt Solution (7.5 g. per liter).**—Dissolve 0.75 g. of nitroso-R salt in water, filter the solution, and dilute to 100 ml. This solution is unstable and should not be used after one week.

**Sodium Acetate Solution (500 g. per liter).**—Dissolve 500 g. of reagent grade sodium acetate trihydrate in 600 ml. of water. Filter the solution and dilute to one liter.

*1. Preparation of Calibration Curve.* **(a) Calibration Solutions.**—Transfer 1.0-, 2.0-, 4.0-, 6.0-, and 8.0-ml. aliquots of cobalt solution *B* to five 150-ml. beakers. To each beaker add enough water to make a volume of 25 ml.

**(b) Reference Solution.**—Add 25 ml. of water to 150-ml. beaker and carry this through the procedure.

**(c) Color Development.**—To each solution, add 5 ml. of sodium acetate solution and 2.0 ml. of nitroso-R salt solution. The solutions should be stirred well after each addition. The solutions at this point should have a pH of approximately 5.5. Cover the beakers, heat the solutions to boiling, and then maintain the temperature just under boiling for one to two minutes. To each solution add 5.0 ml. of $HNO_3$ (1:2) and boil gently for one to two minutes. Cool the solutions to room temperature, transfer to 100-ml. volumetric flasks and dilute to volume.

**(d) Photometry.**—Transfer a suitable portion of the reference solution to an absorption cell with a 5-cm. light path and adjust the photometer to the initial setting using a light band centered at approximately 540 m$\mu$. While maintaining this adjustment, take the photometric readings of the calibration solutions.

**(e) Calibration Curve.**—Plot the photometric readings of the calibration solutions against milligrams of cobalt per 100 ml. of solution.

*2. Procedure.* **(a) Test Solutions.**—For alloys with cobalt contents under 0.008%, transfer 1 g. of sample, weighed to the nearest milligram, to a 150-ml. beaker. Add 15 ml. of water and 5.3 ml. of $HNO_3$, added in small portions. Dilute to 25 ml. with water.

For alloys containing over 0.008% cobalt, weigh, to the nearest milligram, 1 g. of sample and place it in a 150-ml. beaker. Add 15 ml. of water and 6 ml. of $HNO_3$, added in small portions. When dissolution is complete, cool, transfer to a volumetric flask and dilute to volume. Pipette an aliquot containing 0.01 to 0.08 mg. of cobalt into a 150-ml. beaker. Dilute to 25 ml. with water.

**(b) Reference Solution.**—Add 25 ml. of water to a 150-ml. beaker.

**(c) Color Development.**—Develop the color as described in Section 1 (c).

**(d) Photometry.**—Take the photometric reading of the test solution as described in Section 1 (d).

**(e) Calculation.**—Convert the photometric reading of the test solution to milligrams of cobalt by means of the calibration curve. Calculate the percentage of cobalt as follows:

$$\text{Cobalt, } \% = \frac{A}{B \times 10}$$

where $A$ = milligram of cobalt per 100 ml. of solution, and
$B$ = grams of sample represented in 100 ml. of final solution.

## COPPER BY THE NEO-CUPROINE (PHOTOMETRIC) METHOD

This method is applicable to the determination of less than 0.05% copper. It has been written for cells having a 5-cm. light path. Cells having other dimensions may be used, provided suitable adjustments can be made in the amounts of sample and reagents used.

Cuprous copper is separated from other metals by extraction of the Neo-cuproine complex with chloroform. Photometric measurement is made at approximately 455 m$\mu$.

The recommended concentration range is from 0.005 to 0.05 mg. of copper in 50 ml. of solution using a cell depth of 5 cm.

The color develops in aqueous media within five minutes and the extracted complex is stable for at least a week.

The elements ordinarily present in magnesium alloys do not interfere.

**Reagents.—Chloroform.**

**Copper Standard Solution (1 ml. = 0.01 mg. Cu).**—Dissolve 0.2000 g. of pure copper metal in 15 ml. of water and 3 ml. of $HNO_3$. When dissolution is complete, boil out all nitrogen oxide fumes, cool, dilute to one liter with water. Pipette 50 ml. of this solution into another one-liter flask, dilute to volume with water.

**Hydrogen Peroxide Solution, 30%.**

**Hydroxylamine Hydrochloride Solution (100 g. per liter).**—Dissolve 10 g. of hydroxylamine hydrochloride ($NH_2OH \cdot HCl$) in water and dilute to 100 ml.

**Neo-cuproine Solution (1 g. per liter).**—Dissolve 50 mg. of 2,9-dimethyl-1,10-phenanthroline hemihydrate in 50 ml. of absolute ethyl alcohol.

**Sodium Citrate Solution (100 g. per liter).**—Dissolve 100 g. of sodium citrate dihydrate ($Na_3C_6H_5O_7 \cdot 2H_2O$) in water and dilute to one liter.

*1. Preparation of Calibration Curve.* (a) **Calibration Solutions.**—Transfer 0.5, 1.0, 2.0, 3.0, and 5.0 ml. of standard copper solution (1 ml. = 0.01 mg. Cu) to 100 ml. beakers. Dilute to approximately 40 ml. with water and add HCl until the solution is acid to Congo Red paper. Proceed as directed in paragraph (c), below.

(b) **Reference Solution.**—Transfer 40 ml. of water to a 100-ml. beaker and add HCl until the solution is acid to Congo Red paper. Proceed as directed in paragraph (c), below.

(c) **Color Development.**—Add 5.0 ml. of hydroxylamine hydrochloride solution and stir. Add 5.0 ml. of sodium citrate solution and swirl. Neutralize the solution with ammonium hydroxide (1:1) until it is definitely alkaline to Congo Red paper. Add 4.0 ml. of the Neo-cuproine solution, stir and allow to stand for five minutes.

Transfer the solution to a 250-ml. separatory funnel and add 20 ml. of chloroform. Shake the mixture and allow the layers to separate. Place a glass wool plug which has been washed with chloroform in a small funnel and filter the organic layer, catching the filtrate in a dry 50-ml. volumetric flask. Add another ml. of the Neo-cuproine solution, shake, and re-extract with 20 ml. of chloroform. Filter the organic layer into the volumetric flask and make to volume with chloroform.

(d) **Photometry.**—Transfer a suitable portion of the reference solution to an absorption cell with a 5-cm. light path and adjust the photometer to the initial setting using a light band centered at approximately 455 m$\mu$. While maintaining this adjustment, take the photometric readings of the calibration solutions.

(e) **Calibration Curve.**—Plot the photometric readings of the calibration solutions against milligrams of copper per 50 ml. of solution.

*2. Procedure.* (a) **Test Solution.**—Weigh, to the nearest milligram, a sample calculated to contain from 0.005 to 0.05 mg. of copper and transfer it to a 100-ml.

beaker. Add 25 ml. of water and dissolve the sample by adding small portions of HCl. (Use 7.5 ml. of HCl per gram of sample.) When dissolution is complete, add a few drops of hydrogen peroxide solution, boil to remove excess peroxide, cool and dilute to approximately 40 ml. (In case there is insoluble material remaining and an exact analysis is desired, the solution should be filtered and the residue treated with hydrofluoric acid to eliminate silica. Fuse any remaining residue with potassium bisulfate and add the dissolved melt to the original filtrate.)

   (b) **Reference Solution.**—Transfer 40 ml. of water to a 100-ml. beaker and add HCl until the solution is acid to Congo Red paper.

   (c) **Color Development.**—Develop the color as directed in Section 1 (c).

   (d) **Photometry.**—Take the photometric reading of the test solution as directed in Section 1 (d).

   (e) **Calculation.**—Convert the photometric reading of the test solution to milligrams of copper by means of the calibration curve. Calculate the percentage of copper as follows:

$$\text{Copper, } \% = \frac{A}{B \times 10}$$

where $A$ = milligrams of copper found and,
   $B$ = grams of sample used.


## IRON BY THE 1,10-PHENANTHROLINE (PHOTOMETRIC) METHOD

   This method is applicable to the determination of iron in concentrations less than 0.1%. Larger percentages may be determined by taking an aliquot portion of the sample. This procedure has been written for cells having 5-cm. and 1-cm. light paths. Cells having other dimensions may be used, provided suitable adjustments can be made in the amounts of sample and reagents used.

   Ferrous iron, in a solution having a pH of about 5, forms an orange-red complex with 1,10-phenanthroline. Photometric measurement is made at approximately 510 m$\mu$. (A 1% alcoholic solution of 2,2'-bipyridine can also be used for color development. Photometric measurement should be made at approximately 520 m$\mu$.)

   The recommended concentration range is from 0.01 to 0.10 mg. and from 0.10 to 0.50 mg. of iron in 100 ml. of solution, using cell depths of 5 cm. and 1 cm. respectively.

   The color develops within 15 minutes and is stable for at least 2 hours.

   The elements ordinarily present in magnesium alloys do not interfere. Neodymium causes a slight positive interference when present in large amounts. Half a milligram of copper per 100 ml. of solution changes the hue of the solution but interferes only slightly when excess reagent is added. Zinc, nickel, and cadmium form complexes and consume 1,10-phenanthroline but do not interfere if sufficient reagent is used.

   **Reagents.   Acetate Buffer Solution (pH 5).**—Dissolve 272 g. of sodium acetate trihydrate ($NaC_2H_3O_2 \cdot 3H_2O$) in 500 ml. of water. Add 240 ml. of glacial acetic acid, cool, and dilute to 1 liter.

   **Hydroxylamine-Hydrochloride Solution (100 g. per liter).**—Dissolve 10 g. of hydroxylamine hydrochloride ($NH_2OH \cdot HCl$) in water and dilute to 100 ml.

   **Iron Standard Solution A (1 ml. = 0.100 mg. Fe).**—Dissolve 0.1000 g. of iron wire (primary standard) in 50 ml. of water, 25 ml. of HCl and 1 ml. of $HNO_3$. Dilute with water to 1 liter in a volumetric flask.

**Iron Standard Solution B (1 ml. = 0.010 mg. Fe).**—Pipette 100 ml. of standard iron solution *A* into a 1-liter volumetric flask, add 10 ml. of HCl and dilute to volume with water.

**Phenanthroline Solution (10 g. per liter).**—Dissolve 2.5 g. of 1,10-phenanthroline in methyl alcohol and dilute to 250 ml. with alcohol.

**1. Preparation of Calibration Curve.** **(a) Calibration Solutions.**—Transfer 1.0-, 2.0-, 3.0-, 4.0-, and 5.0-ml. portions of standard iron solution *A* (1 ml. = 0.100 mg. Fe) to five 100-ml. volumetric flasks. Dilute to 50 ml. with water and proceed in accordance with paragraph (c).

Transfer 1.0-, 3.0-, 5.0-, 8.0-, and 10.0-ml. portions of standard iron solution *B* (1 ml. = 0.010 mg. Fe) into five 100-ml. volumetric flasks. Dilute to 50 ml. with water.

**(b) Reference Solution.**—Transfer 50 ml. of water to a 100-ml. volumetric flask and proceed in accordance with paragraph (c).

**(c) Color Development.**—Add in order the following solutions, mixing after each addition: 4 ml. of hydroxylamine-hydrochloride solution, 10 ml. of acetate buffer solution and 10 ml. of phenanthroline solution. Dilute to volume with water and mix. Allow to stand for 15 minutes.

**(d) Photometry.**—Transfer a suitable portion of the reference solution to an absorption cell with a 5 cm. light path and adjust the photometer to the initial setting using a light band centered at approximately 510 m$\mu$. While maintaining this adjustment, take the photometric readings of the calibration solutions containing 0.01 to 0.10 mg. of iron.

Transfer a suitable portion of the reference solution to an absorption cell with a 1-cm. light path and adjust the photometer to the initial setting using a light band centered at approximately 510 m$\mu$. While maintaining this adjustment, take the photometric readings of the calibration solutions containing from 0.10 to 0.50 mg. of iron.

**(e) Calibration Curves.**—Plot the photometric readings of the calibration solutions against milligrams of iron per 100 ml. of solution.

**2. Procedure.** **(a) Test Solution.**—If the sample is in rod, bar, or sheet form, remove adventitious iron by immersing the entire sample in dilute HCl (1:9) for 5–10 seconds, washing with water, then with acetone, and drying. Transfer a sample, weighed to the nearest milligram and containing from 0.01 to 0.50 mg. of iron, to a 100-ml. beaker and add 25 ml. of water. Add HCl in small portions until 7.5 ml. per gram of sample have been added, and add 0.5 ml. in excess. When the dissolution is complete, heat the solution on a hot plate for a few minutes and filter if necessary. Reserve the filter paper and precipitate for the recovery of insoluble iron. Evaporate the filtrate on a hot plate or steam bath to a volume of approximately 25 ml. Cool and reserve the solution.

Transfer the filter paper containing the insoluble iron to a platinum crucible. Dry, char, and ignite the precipitate at 600°C. for 1 hour. Cool the crucible to room temperature, moisten the residue with a few drops of water, add 2 drops of $H_2SO_4$ and 1–2 ml. of HF. Evaporate to dryness. Cool the crucible and dissolve the residue with 3–5 drops of HCl and a minimum of water. Warm the crucible to hasten the dissolution, if necessary. Combine this solution with the original filtrate reserved above, and transfer the solution containing the total iron to a 100-ml. volumetric flask.

**(b) Reference Solution.**—Prepare a reagent blank for use as a reference solution.

**(c) Color Development.**—Develop the color as described in Section 1 (c).

**(d) Photometry.**—Take the photometric reading of the test solution as described in Section 1 (d).

**(e) Calculation.**—Convert the photometric reading of the test solution to milligrams of iron, using the appropriate calibration curve. Calculate the percentage of iron as follows:

$$\text{Iron, } \% = \frac{A}{B \times 10}$$

where $A$ = milligrams of iron found in 100 ml. of final solution and,
      $B$ = grams of sample used.

## LEAD BY THE ONE-COLOR DITHIZONE (PHOTOMETRIC) METHOD

This method is applicable to the determination of from 0.001 to 0.05% lead.

Lead reacts with diphenylthiocarbazone to form a pink-colored complex in a chloroform solution. The complex is separated from other metals by extraction with chloroform from an aqueous, ammonium citrate-cyanide solution. Photometric measurement is made at approximately 520 m$\mu$. This method has been written for cells having a 1-cm. light path. Cells having other dimensions may be used, provided suitable adjustments can be made in the amounts of sample and reagents used.

The recommended concentration is from 0.002 to 0.015 mg. of lead in 10 ml. of solution using a cell depth of 1 cm.

The color is stable if the solution is protected against evaporation and decomposition of the chloroform. Because of the nature of the solvent, it is advisable to make the reading promptly.

The elements ordinarily present in magnesium alloys do not interfere if their contents are under those usually found. Bismuth, thallium, indium, and stannous tin interfere but are not likely to be present in magnesium alloys. Bismuth can be determined and compensated for through the use of suitable calibration curves if another reading is made at 420 to 450 m$\mu$. Tin may be oxidized to the harmless stannic form by boiling the HCl solution with 1 ml. of $HNO_3$; the other components should then be reduced by boiling with a slight excess of hydroxylamine hydrochloride. The blank should receive the same treatment.

**Reagents. Ammonium Citrate Solution (50 g. per liter).**—Dissolve 40 g. of citric acid ($C_6H_8O_7$) in water, neutralize with $NH_4OH$ and dilute to one liter.

**First Extraction Solution.**—To 435 ml. of water, add 30 ml. of KCN solution (50 g. per liter), 30 ml. of ammonium citrate solution (50 g. per liter), and 5 ml. of $NH_4OH$.

**Dithizone Solution.**—Dissolve 0.0025 g. of diphenylthiocarbazone in 100 ml. of chloroform.

**Lead Standard Solution (1 ml. = 0.001 mg. Pb).**—Dissolve 0.1391 g. of lead chloride ($PbCl_2$) in water containing 1 ml. of HCl and dilute to one liter in a volumetric flask. Pipette a 10-ml. aliquot of this solution into another one-liter volumetric flask, add 0.5 ml. of HCl and dilute to volume. Prepare fresh as needed.

**Potassium Cyanide Solution (50 g. per liter).**—Dissolve 50 g. of potassium cyanide (KCN) in water and dilute to one liter.

**Second Extraction Solution.** To 500 ml. of water, add 10 ml. of KCN solution (50 g. per liter) and 5 ml. of $NH_4OH$.

**1. *Preparation of Calibration Curve*. (a) Calibration Solutions.**—Transfer 2.0-, 5.0-, 10.0-, and 15.0-ml. portions of the standard lead solution (1 ml. = 0.001 mg. Pb) to 125-ml. separatory funnels and add enough water to make a total volume of 15 ml. (All glassware used in this determination must be cleaned thoroughly with $HNO_3$ and rinsed well with water.) Add 15 ml. of the first extraction solution.

**(b) Reference Solution.**—Add 15 ml. of water and 15 ml. of the first extraction solution to a 125-ml. separatory funnel.

**(c) Color Development.**—From a burette, add dithizone solution in 1-ml. increments, introducing just enough so that after shaking and allowing the layers to separate, the lower layer has a noticeable purple to green color which indicates a slight excess of dithizone. From another burette, add chloroform to make a total volume of dithizone solution and chloroform of exactly 10 ml. Shake the mixture well and allow the layers to separate. Draw off the lower chloroform layer into another 125-ml. separatory funnel containing 20 ml. of the second extraction solution. Discard the aqueous solution in the first funnel. Shake the mixture in the second funnel well, allow the layers to separate, and drain off the lower chloroform layer into a third 125-ml. separatory funnel containing 20 ml. of the second extraction solution. Shake the mixture and allow the layers to separate thoroughly. Insert a small plug of cotton into the stem of the separatory funnel.

**(d) Photometry.**—Filter a suitable portion of the reference solution into an absorption cell with a 1-cm. light path and adjust the photometer to the initial setting using a light band centered at approximately 520 m$\mu$. While maintaining this adjustment, take the photometric readings of the calibration solutions. (The blank color may be due not only to lead but to oxidation products of the dithizone.)

**(e) Calibration Curve.**—Plot the photometric readings of the calibration solutions against milligrams of lead per 10 ml. of solution.

**2. *Procedure*. (a) Test Solution.**—Weigh, to the nearest milligram, a portion of sample calculated to contain 0.1 to 0.7 mg. of lead and transfer to a 250-ml. beaker. Add 30 ml. of water and dissolve the sample with HCl (1:1), using 20 ml. per gram of sample. When dissolution is complete, heat the solution to boiling and dilute to 200 ml. with water. (If the lead content is low, so that the aliquot taken contains appreciable aluminum, additional ammonium citrate may be required to prevent the precipitation of aluminum hydroxide. Since citrate hinders the extraction of lead, as little as possible should be used.) Proceed in accordance with paragraph (c), below.

**(b) Reference Solution.**—Carry a reagent blank through all of the steps of the procedure, starting with the same quantity of HCl (1:1) and evaporating most of it before diluting. Proceed as directed in paragraph (c), below.

**(c)** Cool the solution, transfer to a 500-ml. volumetric flask and dilute to volume with water. Pipette a 10-ml. aliquot into a 125-ml. separatory funnel. Pipette another 10-ml. aliquot into a small beaker and titrate with $NH_4OH$ (1:9) until alkaline to methyl red. To the aliquot in the separatory funnel, add 15 ml. of the first extraction solution and as much $NH_4OH$ (1:9) as was found necessary to neutralize the free acid in the duplicate aliquot.

**(d) Color Development.**—Develop the color as described in Section 1 (c).

**(e) Photometry.**—Take the photometric reading of the test solution as described in Section 1 (d).

**(f) Calculation.**—Convert the photometric reading of the test solution to milligrams of lead by means of the calibration curve. Calculate the percentage of lead as follows:

$$\text{Lead, } \% = \frac{A}{B \times 10}$$

where $A$ = milligrams of lead found in 10 ml. of final solution, and
$B$ = grams of sample represented in 10 ml. of final solution.

### MANGANESE BY THE PERIODATE (PHOTOMETRIC) METHOD

This method is applicable to the determination of manganese in concentrations less than 2.0%. It has been written for cells having a 1-cm. light path. Cells having other dimensions may be used, providing suitable adjustments can be made in the amounts of sample and reagents used.

Manganese in an acid solution is oxidized to permanganate by potassium periodate. Photometric measurement is made at approximately 545 m$\mu$.

The recommended concentration range is 0.10 to 1.5 mg. of manganese in 100 ml. of solution, using a cell depth of 1 cm.

The color develops within 15 minutes and is stable for several weeks providing excess periodate is present.

The elements ordinarily present in magnesium alloys do not interfere. At least ten times as much cerium as manganese can be present without causing interference.

**Reagents.** **Manganese Standard Solution (1 ml. = 0.10 mg. Mn).**—Dissolve 0.100 g. of high purity manganese in 5 ml. of water and 5 ml. of $HNO_3$. Boil to expel brown fumes. Cool, dilute to one liter in a volumetric flask.

*1. Preparation of Calibration Curve.* (a) **Calibration Solutions.**—Transfer 1.0-, 5.0-, 10.0-, and 15.0-ml. portions of the standard manganese solution (1 ml. = 0.10 mg. Mn) to 250-ml. beakers and dilute to approximately 40 ml. with water. Add 15 ml. of $H_2SO_4$ (1:4) and 25 ml. of $HNO_3$.

(b) **Reference Solution.**—Prepare a blank containing 40 ml. of water, 15 ml. of $H_2SO_4$ (1:4) and 25 ml. of $HNO_3$ for use as a reference solution.

(c) **Color Development.**—Heat the solution to boiling, cool slightly, and carefully introduce 0.5 g. of $KIO_4$. Boil for 3 minutes and then digest just below boiling for 15 minutes to develop the full intensity of color. Cool, dilute to 100 ml. in a volumetric flask.

(d) **Photometry.**—Transfer a suitable portion of the reference solution to an absorption cell with a 1-cm. light path and adjust the photometer to the initial setting using a light band centered at approximately 545 m$\mu$. While maintaining this adjustment, take the photometric readings of the calibration solutions.

(e) **Calibration Curve.**—Plot the photometric readings of the calibration solutions against milligrams of manganese per 100 ml. of solution.

*2. Procedure.* (a) **Test Solutions.**—For alloys with manganese content under 0.15%, transfer a 1.0-g. sample, weighed to the nearest milligram, to a 250-ml. beaker. Add 15 ml. of water and 25 ml. of $H_2SO_4$ (1:4) to dissolve the sample. When the action ceases, add 5 ml. $HNO_3$ and boil to dissolve any dark residue. If the solution is turbid, filter through a fine-porosity paper. Add 20 ml. of $HNO_3$.

For alloys with a manganese content over 0.15%, transfer, to a 250-ml. beaker, a sample weighed to the nearest milligram and calculated to contain 10 to 20 mg. of manganese, and add 15 ml. of water. Add 25 ml. of $H_2SO_4$ (1:4) for each gram of sample. When the action ceases, add 5 ml. of $HNO_3$ and boil to dissolve any dark residue. If the solution appears turbid, filter through a fine-porosity paper. Transfer the solution to a 500-ml. volumetric flask, dilute to volume with water and mix. Pipette an aliquot containing 0.2 to 1.5 mg. of manganese into a 250-ml. beaker. Add 15 ml. of $H_2SO_4$ (1:4) and 25 ml. of $HNO_3$.

(b) **Reference Solution.**—Prepare a reference solution as described in Section 1 (b).

(c) **Color Development.**—Develop the color as described in Section 1 (c).

(d) **Photometry.**—Take the photometric reading as described in Section 1 (d).

(e) **Calculation.**—Convert the photometric reading of the sample solution to milligrams of manganese by means of the calibration curve. Calculate the percentage of manganese as follows:

$$\text{Manganese, } \% = \frac{A}{B \times 10}$$

where $A$ = milligrams of manganese found in 100 ml. of final solution and,
$B$ = grams of sample represented in 100 ml. of final solution.

## NICKEL BY THE DIMETHYLGLYOXIME EXTRACTION (PHOTOMETRIC) METHOD

This method is applicable to the determination of nickel in the concentration range of 0.0005 to 0.005%. Larger percentages may be determined by taking an aliquot portion of the sample. This procedure has been written for cells having 5-cm. light paths. Cells having other dimensions may be used, provided suitable adjustments can be made in the amounts of sample and reagents used.

Nickel is separated from other metals by extraction of the dimethylglyoxime complex with chloroform. The nickel is re-extracted with acid, oxidized with bromine, and determined photometrically as nickelic dimethylglyoxime at approximately 530 m$\mu$.

The recommended concentration range is from 0.005 to 0.050 mg. of nickel in 100 ml. of solution, using a cell depth of 5 cm.

The color intensity increases slowly on standing. Readings should be made about 10 minutes after mixing.

The elements ordinarily present in magnesium alloys do not interfere if their content is under the limits usually found.

*Reagents.*—Bromine Water (saturated).

**Dimethylglyoxime Solution (10 g. per liter in alcohol).**

**Hydroxylamine-Hydrochloride Solution (50 g. per liter).**—Dissolve 5 g. of hydroxylamine hydrochloride ($NH_2OH \cdot HCl$) in water and dilute to 100 ml. Prepare fresh as needed.

**Nickel Standard Solution (1 ml. = 0.005 mg. Ni).**—Dissolve 0.1000 g. of pure nickel metal in 10 ml. of water and 5 ml. of $HNO_3$ in a 150-ml. beaker. When the dissolution is complete, boil the solution to remove the lower oxides of nitrogen. Cool the solution to room temperature, transfer to a one-liter volumetric flask, dilute to volume with water. Pipette 25.0 ml. of this solution into a 500-ml. volumetric flask, dilute to volume with water. Optionally, the original solution may be prepared from a nickel salt and standardized gravimetrically.

**Sodium Citrate Solution (88 g. per liter).**—Dissolve 100 g. of sodium citrate dihydrate ($Na_3C_6H_5O_7 \cdot 2H_2O$) in water, dilute to one liter and mix.

**1. Preparation of Calibration Curve.** (a) **Calibration Solutions.**—(1) Transfer 1.0-, 2.0-, 5.0-, 7.0-, and 10.0-ml. portions of the standard nickel solution (1 ml. = 0.005 mg. Ni) to 200-ml. separatory funnels containing 50 ml. of water. Add 2 ml. of $HNO_3$ and 10 ml. of sodium citrate to each funnel.

(2) Neutralize each solution to litmus by the dropwise addition of $NH_4OH$ and add a few drops in excess. Introduce 3 ml. of dimethylglyoxime solution, mix, and allow to stand for 5 minutes. Extract with three 10-ml. portions of $CHCl_3$ and combine the $CHCl_3$ layers in a clean separatory funnel. Wash the combined extracts with a 25-ml. portion of $NH_4OH$ (2:98) and draw off the $CHCl_3$ layer into another clean separatory funnel. Extract the ammoniacal wash layer with a 5-ml. portion of $CHCl_3$ and add this to the main portion which contains the nickel. Shake the combined $CHCl_3$ extracts for 1 minute successively with a 25-ml. and a 15-ml. portion of HCl (1:19). Draw off the $CHCl_3$ layer, separating it as completely as possible, and discard. Draw off both acid layers into a 100-ml. volumetric flask. Proceed in accordance with paragraph (c), below.

(b) **Reference Solution.**—To a 200-ml. separatory funnel, add 50 ml. of water, 2 ml. of $HNO_3$, and 10 ml. of sodium citrate solution and proceed in accordance with Section 1 (a), paragraph (2), above.

(c) **Color Development.**—To the combined acid extracts add 5 drops of saturated bromine water. Add $NH_4OH$ (1:1) dropwise until the bromine color is destroyed and then 3 or 4 drops in excess. Add 0.5 ml. of dimethylglyoxime, dilute to 100 ml. with water and mix. Allow the solution to stand exactly 10 minutes.

(d) **Photometry.**—Transfer a suitable portion of the reference solution to an absorption cell with a 5.0-cm. light path and adjust the photometer to the initial setting using a light band centered at approximately 530 m$\mu$. While maintaining this adjustment, take the photometric readings of the calibration solutions.

(e) **Calibration Curve.**—Plot the photometric readings of the calibration solutions against milligrams of nickel per 100 ml. of solution.

**2. Procedure.** (a) **Test Solution.**—Transfer a 1-g. sample, weighed to the nearest milligram, to a 250-ml. beaker. Add 25 ml. of water and dissolve the sample by gradually adding 10 ml. of HCl and 2 ml. of $HNO_3$. When the dissolution is complete, cool the solution to room temperature. If the sample contains 0.005% Ni or less, transfer the solution to a 200-ml. separatory funnel using as little water as possible so that the total volume does not exceed 60 ml. If the sample contains over 0.005% Ni, transfer the solution to a volumetric flask and dilute to volume. Pipette an aliquot calculated to contain 0.005 to 0.050 mg. of nickel into a 200-ml. separatory funnel and dilute to approximately 60 ml. with water. To the solution in the separatory funnel, add 10 ml. of sodium citrate solution, or more, if the aluminum is unusually high. If manganese is also present, add 5 ml. of hydroxylamine hydrochloride solution. Proceed as directed in Section 1 (a), paragraph (2).

(b) **Reference Solution.** To a 200-ml. separatory funnel, add 50 ml. of water, 2 ml. of $HNO_3$ and the amounts of sodium citrate solution and hydroxylamine hydrochloride solution used for the sample. Proceed as directed in Section 1 (a), paragraph (2).

(c) **Color Development.** Develop the color of the test solution as described in Section 1 (c).

(d) **Photometry.** Take the photometric reading of the test solution as described in Section 1 (d).

**(e) Calculation.** Using the calibration curve, convert the photometric reading of the test solution to milligrams of nickel. Calculate the percentage of nickel as follows:

$$\text{Nickel, } \% = \frac{A}{B \times 10}$$

where $A$ = milligrams of nickel found in 100 ml. of final solution, and
$B$ = grams of sample used.

## RARE EARTH ELEMENTS BY THE SEBACATE-OXALATE (GRAVIMETRIC) METHOD

This method is applicable to the determination of 0.2 to 10% rare earth elements.

Rare earth elements are precipitated with ammonium sebacate and the sebacates are ignited. The oxides formed are redissolved, precipitated as oxalates, ignited, and weighed as oxides.

Yttrium and scandium, if present, will be included with the rare earth elements. Thorium and rare earth combinations are not ordinarily present in magnesium alloys but may occur. If so, thorium may be precipitated by benzoic acid prior to the precipitation of the rare earth elements.

**Reagents. Ammonium Hydroxide Wash Solution (1:49).**—Mix 1 volume of $NH_4OH$ with 49 volumes of water.

**Ammonium Sebacate Solution (50 g. per liter).**—Dissolve 50 g. of sebacic acid $[COOH(CH_2)_8COOH]$ in 400 ml. of $NH_4OH$ and 300 ml. of water. Filter, dilute to 1 liter with water, and mix. Store in a polyethylene bottle.

**Bromphenol Blue (4 g. per liter).**—Place 0.40 g. of bromphenol blue in a mortar, add 8.25 ml. of sodium hydroxide solution (5 g. NaOH per liter), and mix until solution is complete. Dilute to 100 ml. with water and mix.

**Hydrogen Peroxide (30%).**

**Nitric Acid-Hydrogen Peroxide Solution.**—Dilute 1 volume of $H_2O_2$ (30%) with 5 volumes of water and 1 volume of $HNO_3$

**Oxalic Acid Solution (Saturated).**—Dissolve 150 g. of oxalic acid dihydrate $(C_2H_2O_4 \cdot 2H_2O)$ in 1 liter of warm water. Allow to cool and filter off any insoluble material.

**Oxalic Acid Wash Solution.**—Dilute 70 ml. of saturated oxalic acid solution to 500 ml. with water.

**Potassium Pyrosulfate ($K_2S_2O_7$)-Potassium Bisulfate, Fused Powder.**

**Procedure.**—Weigh, to the nearest milligram, a portion of sample containing from 10 to 100 mg. of rare earth elements. Transfer to a 400-ml. beaker containing 50 ml. of water and add HCl a little at a time until dissolution of the metal is complete (7.5 ml. of HCl will dissolve 1 g. of sample). Heat the solution to boiling on a hot plate, cool, and filter if necessary. (The residue, if any, will be mainly zirconium and in most cases can be ignored. For very exact work, however, traces of rare earth elements may be recovered by igniting the paper and residue, fusing with 0.5 g. of $K_2S_2O_7$, dissolving in water plus HCl, and filtering into the original filtrate.) Bring the combined filtrate to a volume of about 100 ml. with water.

Add 3 drops of bromphenol blue indicator solution to the prepared solution and adjust the acidity to the blue color with $NH_4OH$ (1:4). Heat the mixture to boiling on a hot plate, remove it from the heat, and allow to stand for 5 minutes with occasional stirring. Filter the mixture on medium paper and wash the precipitate thoroughly with hot water. The volume of filtrate at this point should be no greater than 250 ml. Reserve this filtrate, containing most of the rare earth elements. Dissolve the zirconium hydroxide precipitate, and any rare earths that may have been occluded, into the original beaker with 10 ml. of $HNO_3$-$H_2O_2$ solution and hot water. Evaporate the solution to approximately 25 ml. and reserve.

To the filtrate containing most of the rare earths, add 10 g. of $NH_4Cl$ and enough $NH_4OH$ to neutralize most of the free acid. Adjust the pH of the solution between 7.5 and 8.5 with a weaker solution of $NH_4OH$. If zinc is present, the pH should be raised to 8.5 to 9.5. (Indicator paper may be used to test the pH.) Warm the solution on a hot plate, remove from the heat, and, while stirring, add 20 ml. of ammonium sebacate solution. Allow the suspension to stand for 15 minutes with occasional stirring. Filter the mixture on medium paper, police the beaker, and wash it thoroughly with hot $NH_4OH$ wash solution. If zinc is present, wash the precipitate once more with 20 ml. of $NH_4OH$ (1:1). Transfer the precipitate and paper to a clean tared crucible. Dry, burn off the paper, and ignite at a temperature above 500°C.

Remove the crucible from the furnace, allow it to cool, and carefully wash the contents of the crucible into the beaker containing the reserved zirconium. Heat the mixture on a hot plate until dissolution of the rare earth oxides is complete. (An additional amount of $H_2O_2$ may be needed at this point.) Remove the beaker from the hot plate, wash down the sides of the beaker, and dilute the solution to approximately 125 ml. with water. While stirring the solution, slowly add 25 ml. of saturated oxalic acid solution. Place the beaker on a steam bath for half an hour or until small bubbles begin to form quite vigorously in the solution. Allow the mixture to stand overnight. Filter the precipitated rare earth oxalates on a fine paper. Police and wash the beaker thoroughly with oxalic acid wash solution.

Place the filter paper and precipitate in the original porcelain crucible, dry, burn off the paper, and ignite the residue at 950°C. to constant weight, cooling each time in a desiccator charged with anhydrous magnesium perchlorate [$Mg(ClO_4)_2$]. Weigh the rare earth oxides.

**Calculation.**—Calculate the percentage of rare earth oxides as follows:

$$\text{Rare earth oxides, } \% = \frac{A}{B} \times 100$$

where $A$ = grams of rare earth oxides found, and
$B$ = grams of sample used.

In order to calculate the rare earth oxides as metals, the following factors should be used: cerium, 0.8141; praseodymium, 0.8277; neodymium, 0.8574; lanthanum, 0.8527; mischmetal, 0.829; and didymium, 0.853. The factors for mischmetal and didymium were calculated from analyses of commercial mischmetal and a didymium salt. These factors may vary slightly with each new batch of mischmetal and didymium salt used, as the proportions of individual rare earth elements vary.

## CERIUM, NEODYMIUM, PRASEODYMIUM, AND LANTHANUM
### BY THE PHOTOMETRIC METHOD

This method is suitable for the determination of 0.5 to 20% total rare earths, 0.03 to 1.5% praseodymium, 0.1 to 4.0% neodymium, 0.2 to 10% cerium and 0.1 to 4.0% lanthanum. This method has been written for cells having 1-cm. and 10-cm. light paths. Cells having other dimensions can be used, provided suitable adjustments can be made in the amounts of sample and reagents used.

The sample is dissolved in HCl and the rare earths are precipitated, first as the sebacates and then as the oxalates. The oxalates are ignited and weighed as the oxides. The oxides are dissolved in $HClO_4$ and the individual elements are determined on the resulting solution. Cerium is determined by ultraviolet photometry, neodymium and praseodymium by absorption in the visible spectrum and lanthanum by flame photometry.

The recommended concentration range for praseodymium is from 15.0 to 60.0 mg. of praseodymium in 50 ml. of solution using a cell depth of 10 cm.

The recommended concentration range for neodymium is from 15.0 to 75.0 mg. of neodymium in 50 ml. of solution using a cell depth of 10 cm.

The recommended concentration range for cerium is from 2.5 to 15.0 mg. of cerium in 100 ml. of solution using a cell depth of 1 cm.

The recommended concentration range for lanthanum is from 0.25 to 1.0 mg. of lanthanum in 20 ml. of solution.

Scandium and yttrium, if present, will be included in the rare earth oxides. If thorium is present, it should be removed as the benzoate prior to precipitation of the rare earths.

*Apparatus.* **Spectrophotometer, Beckman Model DU.**—Equipped with a model 9200 flame attachment and a model 4300 photomultiplier attachment.

**Cells, Absorption, Quartz.**—With a 1-cm. light path.

**Cells, Absorption, Glass.**—With a 10-cm. light path.

**Oxygen and Acetylene Cylinders.**—With the necessary regulators and gauges.

*Reagents.* **Ammonium Acetate Solution (77 g. per liter).**—Dissolve 77 g. of reagent grade ammonium acetate ($NH_4C_2H_3O_2$) in water and dilute to one liter with water.

**Ammonium Hydroxide Wash Solution.**—Dilute 10 ml. of $NH_4OH$ to 500 ml. with water.

**Ammonium Sebacate Solution.**—Dissolve 50 g. of sebacic acid ($COOH(CH_2)_8$-COOH) in 400 ml. of $NH_4OH$ and 300 ml. of water. Filter and dilute to one liter with water. Store in a polyethylene bottle.

**Bromphenol Blue.**—Triturate 0.40 g. of bromphenol blue in a mortar with 8.3 ml. of 0.1 N sodium hydroxide. Dilute to 100 ml. with water.

**Cerium Standard Solution (1 ml. = 1.00 mg. Ce).**—Transfer 0.614 g. of freshly ignited, 99.9% ceric oxide ($CeO_2$) to a 250-ml. beaker and add 50 ml. of water. Add 10 ml. of $HClO_4$, 1 ml. of 30% hydrogen peroxide, and cover with a ribbed watch glass. Heat on a hot plate to effect dissolution, adding more hydrogen peroxide if necessary. Evaporate the solution to incipient dryness on the hot plate, then cool. Rinse the walls of the beaker first with 10 ml. of $HClO_4$ and then with water, and re-evaporate to incipient dryness to remove the last traces of hydrogen peroxide. Cool, rinse the walls of the beaker with 15 ml. of $HClO_4$ and boil 3 minutes to dissolve cerium perchlorate. Cool, wash the watch glass and beaker walls with water, transfer the solution to a 500-ml. volumetric flask and dilute to volume with water.

**Lanthanum Standard Solution A (1 ml. = 1.00 mg. La).**—Transfer 0.586 g. of freshly ignited, 99.9% lanthanum oxide ($La_2O_3$) to a 250-ml. beaker and add 50 ml. of water and 10 ml. of $HClO_4$. Heat on a hot plate to effect dissolution, cool, and transfer the solution to a 500-ml. volumetric flask. Dilute to volume with water.

**Lanthanum Standard Solution B (1 ml. = 0.100 mg. La).**—Pipette a 50.0-ml. aliquot of standard lanthanum solution A into a 500-ml. volumetric flask and dilute to volume with water.

**Methyl Isobutyl Ketone, Reagent Grade.**

**Neodymium Standard Solution (1 ml. = 3.00 mg. Nd).**—Transfer 1.750 g. of freshly ignited, 99.9% neodymium oxide ($Nd_2O_3$) to a 250-ml. beaker and add 50 ml. of water. Add 10 ml. of $HClO_4$, cover and heat on a hot plate. When dissolution is complete, cool, transfer the solution to a 500-ml. volumetric flask and dilute to volume with water.

**Nitric Acid-Hydrogen Peroxide Solution.**—Mix one volume of 30% hydrogen peroxide with five volumes of water and one volume of $HNO_3$.

**Oxalic Acid, Saturated Solution (150 g. per liter).**—Dissolve approximately 150 g. of oxalic acid ($C_2H_2O_4 \cdot 2H_2O$) in one liter of warm water. Allow to cool to room temperature and filter off any insoluble material.

**Oxalic Acid Wash Solution.**—Dilute 70 ml. of the saturated oxalic acid solution to 500 ml. with water.

**Praseodymium Standard Solution (1 ml. = 3.00 mg. Pr).**—Transfer 1.812 g. of freshly ignited, 99.9% praseodymium oxide ($Pr_6O_{11}$) to a 250-ml. beaker and add 50 ml. of water. Add 10 ml. of $HClO_4$, cover, and heat on a hot plate to effect dissolution. Cool, transfer the solution to a 500-ml. volumetric flask, and dilute to volume with water.

**2-Thenoyltrifluoroacetone (TTA) Solution (22 g. per liter).**—Dissolve 5.5 g. of technical grade 2-thenoyltrifluoroacetone in methyl isobutyl ketone and dilute to 250 ml. with additional solvent. Store in a cool, dark place.

*1. Preparation of Calibration Curve for Praseodymium and Neodymium.* (a) **Neodymium Calibration Solutions.**—To a series of four 50-ml., glass-stoppered volumetric flasks, add 5.0, 10.0, 15.0, and 25.0 ml. of the standard neodymium solution (1 ml. = 3.00 mg. Nd). Add 5 ml. of $HClO_4$ to each flask and dilute to volume with water.

**(b) Praseodymium Calibration Solutions.**—To a series of four 50-ml., glass-stoppered volumetric flasks, add 5.0, 10.0, 15.0, and 20.0 ml. of the standard praseodymium solution (1 ml. = 3.00 mg. Pr). Add 5 ml. of $HClO_4$ to each flask and dilute to volume with water.

**(c) Reference Solution.**—Use water as a reference solution.

**(d) Photometry.**—The wavelengths given below are for a particular photometer. Each analyst should determine the exact setting by rotating the wavelength dial slightly on either side of the given values. The peak absorbance is indicated by the maximum movement of the galvanometer needle to the right. Allow the photometer to warm up with the tungsten lamp on. Set the wavelength dial at 575 m$\mu$ and the slit width at 0.015 mm. Take the photometric readings of the four neodymium standard solutions in a 10-cm. glass absorption cell, zeroing the instrument on water. Reset the wavelength dial at 443.8 m$\mu$, change the slit width to 0.030 mm. and again adjust the photometer to the initial setting on water.

While maintaining this adjustment, take the photometric readings of the four praseodymium standard solutions using a 10-cm glass absorption cell. Determine cell corrections at both wavelengths for the cells used, and apply these corrections to the photometric readings.

(e) **Calibration Curves.**—Plot the photometric readings of the calibration solutions against milligrams of metal (neodymium or praseodymium) per 50 ml. of solution.

**2. Preparation of Calibration Curve for Cerium.** (a) **Cerium Calibration Solutions.**—To a series of four 100-ml., glass-stoppered volumetric flasks, add 2.5, 5.0, 10.0 and 15.0 ml. of the standard cerium solution (1 ml. = 1.00 mg. Ce). Add 10 ml. of $HClO_4$ to each flask and dilute to volume with water.

(b) **Reference Solution.**—Use water as a reference solution.

(c) **Photometry.**—With the hydrogen discharge lamp on, allow the photometer to warm up. Set the wavelength dial at approximately 254 m$\mu$ and the slit width at 0.36 mm. Transfer a suitable portion of the standard solution to a 1-cm quartz absorption cell and, with the photometer adjusted to the initial setting on water, take photometric readings of the four standard cerium solutions. Determine cell corrections for the cells at the wavelength specified and apply these corrections to the photometric readings.

(d) **Calibration Curve.**—Plot the photometric readings of the calibration solutions against milligrams of cerium per 100 ml. of solution.

**3. Preparation of Calibration Curve for Lanthanum.** (a) **Lanthanum Calibration Solutions.**—To a series of three 125-ml. separatory funnels, add 2.5, 5.0 and 10.0 ml. of the standard lanthanum solution $B$ (1 ml. = 0.100 mg. La). Dilute the solutions to 20 ml. with water.

(b) **Reference Solution.**—Transfer 20 ml. of water to a 125-ml. separatory funnel and carry this through the procedure.

(c) **Extraction.**—To each funnel add 20 ml. of ammonium acetate solution and adjust the solution to pH 5 with $NH_4OH$. Add 20.0 ml. of the TTA solution with a volumetric pipette and shake vigorously for one minute. Allow the layers to separate, drain off, and discard the lower aqueous phase. Filter the organic layer through a small funnel containing a tightly packed plug of cotton and collect the filtrate in a clean, dry test tube. Stopper the test tube to prevent evaporation.

(d) **Photometry.**—Allow the photometer to warm up observing the following settings: selector switch 0.1, wavelength 743 m$\mu$, slit width 0.30 mm. and red sensitive phototube. The optimum slit width and sensitivity control setting should be determined by the analyst for his particular instrument. Using an oxygen pressure of 6.5 lb. per square inch and an acetylene pressure of 1.5 lb. per square inch, ignite the burner and adjust the flame to the desired height. Balance the dark current before each reading. Place a sample cup containing the 1.00 mg. lanthanum standard under the burner and, using the sensitivity control, adjust the photometer to read 50% emission. Flush the burner with methyl isobutyl ketone after each reading. Compare the other standard solutions with the 1.00 mg. lanthanum standard and record their emission readings.

(e) **Calibration Curve.** Plot the emission readings of the calibration solutions against milligrams of lanthanum per 20 ml. of solution.

**4. Procedure.** (a) **Preparation of Sample.**—(1) Select a sample size to contain from 100 to 250 mg. of rare earth elements (not to exceed 20 g. of sample). Weigh the sample to the nearest milligram, transfer it to a 400-ml. beaker and add 75 ml. of water. Add HCl in small portions until the metal is completely dissolved (*ca.*

8 ml. of HCl per gram of sample). Heat the solution to boiling and cool. Filter the solution through a fine-porosity paper (Whatman No. 42). The residue, if any, will be mainly zirconium and in most cases can be ignored. For very exact work, however, traces of rare earth elements may be recovered by igniting the paper and residue, fusing with 0.5 g. of $KHSO_4$, dissolving in water plus HCl, and filtering into the original filtrate.

(2) Add 3 drops of bromphenol blue indicator to the solution and adjust it to the blue color with $NH_4OH$ (1:1). Heat the solution to boiling, remove it from the hot plate and allow it to stand for 5 minutes with occasional stirring. Filter the mixture on a medium-porosity paper (Whatman No. 40) and wash the precipitate well with hot water. If zinc is present, wash with 20 ml. of $NH_4OH$ (1:1) and hot water. The volume of filtrate at this point should be no greater than 250 ml. Reserve the filtrate containing most of the rare earth elements. Dissolve the zirconium hydroxide precipitate and any occluded rare earths into the original beaker with 10 ml. of nitric acid-hydrogen peroxide solution and hot water. Boil the zirconium solution down to approximately 25 ml. and save.

(3) To the filtrate containing most of the rare earth elements, add 10 g. of $NH_4Cl$ and adjust to a pH of 7.5 to 8.5 with $NH_4OH$ (1:1) (indicator paper may be used to test the pH). If zinc is present, the pH should be raised to 8.5 to 9.5. Warm the solution on a hot plate, remove from the heat and add 20 ml. of ammonium sebacate solution while stirring. Allow the suspension to stand for 15 minutes with occasional stirring. Filter the mixture on a medium-porosity paper (Whatman No. 40), police the beaker, and wash thoroughly with hot $NH_4OH$ wash solution. If zinc is present, wash the precipitate once more using 20 ml. of $NH_4OH$ (1:1). Transfer the precipitate and paper to a clean, tared crucible. Dry, burn off the paper and ignite at temperature above 500°C. for half an hour. Remove the crucible from the furnace and allow it to cool. Carefully wash the contents of the crucible into the beaker containing the redissolved zirconium, police the crucible with the aid of water and a few drops of $HNO_3$ and transfer any remaining oxides to the beaker. Heat on a hot plate until dissolution is complete, adding more hydrogen peroxide, if necessary. Remove the beaker from the hot plate, wash down the sides and dilute the solution to approximately 100 ml. with water. Add 25 ml. of saturated oxalic acid solution slowly, while stirring. Digest the mixture on a steam bath for 30 minutes and let the mixture stand overnight. Filter the mixture on a fine-porosity paper (Whatman No. 42), police the beaker, and wash the precipitate thoroughly with oxalic acid wash solution. Place the paper and precipitate in the original porcelain crucible, dry, burn off the paper and ignite the residue at 950°C. to constant weight, cooling each time in a desiccator loaded with magnesium perchlorate $(Mg(ClO_4)_2)$. The net weight is total rare earth oxides. Transfer the ignited rare earth oxides to a 150-ml. beaker with water, police the crucible with the aid of water and a few drops of $HClO_4$. Add 5 ml. of $HClO_4$ and 1 ml. of 30% hydrogen peroxide, cover with a ribbed watch glass and evaporate to dryness on a hot plate. Allow the beaker to cool slightly, add another 5 ml. of $HClO_4$ and fume for 2–3 minutes. Cool slightly, rinse the sides of the beaker and the watch glass down with a few milliliters of water, replace the watch glass and re-evaporate to dryness on the hot plate to remove the last traces of hydrogen peroxide. Cool, add 5 ml. of the $HClO_4$, and boil at dense fumes for 3 minutes to render the salts soluble. At this point, any slight turbidity remaining is due to traces of silica present in the ignited oxides. Allow the solution to cool, rinse the watch glass and beaker with water and filter the solution through a fine-porosity paper (Whatman No. 42),

collecting the filtrate in a 50-ml. glass-stoppered volumetric flask. Dilute to volume with water.

**(b) Procedure for Praseodymium and Neodymium.** **(1) Test Solution.**—Use the solution in the 50-ml. volumetric flask prepared in the section above.

**(2) Reference Solution.**—Water is used as the reference solution.

**(3) Photometry.**—Take the photometric readings of the test solution for both praseodymium and neodymium as described in Section 1 (d). Save the solution for the determination of cerium and lanthanum.

**(c) Procedure for Cerium.** **(1) Test Solution.**—Pipette a 5.0-ml. aliquot of the solution reserved from the determination of praseodymium and neodymium into a 100-ml. glass-stoppered volumetric flask. Add 9.5 ml. $HClO_4$ and dilute to volume with water.

**(2) Reference Solution.**—Water is used as a reference solution.

**(3) Photometry.**—Take the photometric reading of the cerium test solution as described in paragraph (c) of Preparation of Calibration Curve for Cerium.

**(d) Procedure for Lanthanum.** **(1) Test Solution.**—Pipette a 5.0-ml. aliquot of the solution reserved from the determination of praseodymium and neodymium into a 100-ml. volumetric flask and dilute to volume with water. Pipette a 10.0-ml. aliquot of this diluted solution into a 125-ml. separatory funnel. Dilute the solution to 20 ml. with water.

**(2) Reference Solution.**—Add 20 ml. of water to a 125-ml. separatory funnel and carry through a reagent blank for use as a reference solution.

**(3) Extraction.**—Extract the solution as described in Section 3 (c).

**(4) Photometry.**—Take the photometric reading of the test solution as described in Section 3 (d).

**Calculation.** (a) *Total Rare Earth Oxides.*—Calculate the percentage of total rare earth as follows:

$$\text{Total Rare Earth Oxides, } \% = \frac{A}{B} \times 100$$

where $A$ = grams of rare earth oxide weighed, and
$B$ = grams of sample taken.

(b) *Praseodymium.*—Convert the photometric reading of the test solution to milligrams of praseodymium by means of the calibration curve. Calculate the percentage of praseodymium as follows:

$$\text{Praseodymium, } \% = \frac{A}{B \times 10}$$

where $A$ = milligrams of praseodymium in 50 ml. of solution, and
$B$ = grams of sample represented in 50 ml. of final solution.

(c) *Neodymium.*—Convert the photometric reading of the test solution to milligrams of neodymium by means of the calibration curve. Calculate the percentage of neodymium as follows:

$$\text{Neodymium, } \% = \frac{A}{B \times 10}$$

where $A$ = milligrams of neodymium in 50 ml. of final solution, and
$B$ = grams of sample represented in 50 ml. of final solution.

(d) *Cerium.*—Convert the photometric reading of the cerium test solution to milligrams of cerium by means of the calibration curve. Calculate the percentage of cerium as follows:

$$\text{Cerium, } \% = \frac{A}{B \times 10}$$

where $A$ = milligrams of cerium found in 100 ml. of final solution, and
      $B$ = grams of sample represented in 100 ml. of final solution.

(e) *Lanthanum.*—Convert the photometric reading of the lanthanum test solution to milligrams of lanthanum by means of the calibration curve. Calculate the percentage of lanthanum as follows:

$$\text{Lanthanum, } \% = \frac{A}{B \times 10}$$

where $A$ = milligrams of lanthanum found in 20 ml. of final solution, and
      $B$ = grams of sample represented in 20 ml. of final solution.

## SILICON BY THE PERCHLORIC ACID (GRAVIMETRIC) METHOD

This method is applicable to the determination of silicon in concentrations greater than 0.1%.

The sample is dissolved in $HNO_3$ and the silica is dehydrated with $HClO_4$. The dehydrated silica is ignited, weighed, and volatilized with HF. The residue is ignited and weighed. The loss in weight represents $SiO_2$.

The metals ordinarily present in magnesium alloys do not interfere if their contents are under the limits usually found.

**Procedure.** Weigh, to the nearest milligram, a sample calculated to contain 0.010–0.075 g. of silicon, transfer it to a 400-ml. beaker and add 50 ml. of water. Cautiously add $HNO_3$ in small portions until the sample is dissolved. When dissolution is complete, warm the solution on a hot plate to dissolve any dark residue, cool, and add 10 ml. of $HClO_4$ for each gram of alloy present. Evaporate the solution on a hot plate to dense white fumes of $HClO_4$ and then continue the heating for an additional 15 minutes.

Cool the mixture, add 75 ml. of water and warm to dissolve the metallic salts. Filter the solution through an ashless, fine-porosity paper containing filter-paper pulp, and wash the precipitate once with hot water and then five times with $H_2SO_4$ (1:99) using a total of 75 ml. of the $H_2SO_4$ solution. Finally, wash the precipitate several times with hot water using a total of about 250 ml. It is imperative that the $HClO_4$ be completely removed prior to drying the precipitate, otherwise a sudden deflagration may occur. When the precipitate has been thoroughly washed, place the filter paper in a platinum crucible, dry, char the paper at a low temperature and ignite at 900–1000°C. for 1.5 hours. Cool in a desiccator and weigh.

To the residue in the platinum crucible, add a few drops of $H_2SO_4$ (1:1) and about 5 ml. of HF. Evaporate carefully to dryness on a hot plate, ignite at 900–1000°C., cool in a desiccator and weigh. Repeat the treatment with HF and ignite to constant weight. The loss in weight represents $SiO_2$.

Make a blank determination, following the same procedure and using the same amounts of all reagents.

**Calculation.**—Calculate the percentage of silicon as follows:

$$\text{Silicon, } \% = \frac{(A - B) \times 0.4672}{C} \times 100$$

where $A$ = grams of $SiO_2$

$B$ = correction for blank, in grams, and

$C$ = grams of sample used.

## SILICON BY THE MOLYBDISILICIC ACID (PHOTOMETRIC) METHOD

This method is applicable to the determination of silicon in concentrations less than 0.1%. This method has been written for a cell having a 5-cm. light path. Cells having other dimensions may be used, provided suitable adjustments can be made in the amounts of sample and reagents used.

Silicic acid in a true (not colloidal) solution reacts with molybdate to form a soluble yellow-colored molybdisilicic acid. Photometric measurement is made at approximately 420 m$\mu$.

The recommended concentration range is from 0.1 to 0.5 mg. of silicon in 100 ml. of solution, using a cell depth of 5 cm.

The color is stable for about 1 hour.

The elements ordinarily present in magnesium alloys do not interfere if their content is under the limit usually found. Phosphates cause a yellow color that interferes. (It appears from the literature that a given weight of phosphorus yields slightly less than half as much color as the same weight of silicon. The possible interferences from elements such as tin, arsenic, or cerium have not been investigated.)

*Reagents.* **Ammonium Molybdate Solution (80 g. per liter).**—Dissolve 40 g. of ammonium molybdate tetrahydrate $[(NH_4)_6Mo_7O_{24} \cdot 4H_2O]$ in 500 ml. of water.

**Boric Acid Solution (saturated).**

**Silicon Standard Solution (1 ml. = 0.05 mg. Si).**—Fuse 0.1070 g. of $SiO_2$ with 1.0 g. of $Na_2CO_3$ in a platinum crucible. Cool the melt, dissolve completely in water, and dilute to 1 liter in a volumetric flask. The solution should be stored in a polyethylene bottle, or prepared fresh as needed.

*1. Preparation of Calibration Curve.* (a) **Calibration Solutions.**—Transfer 2.0, 5.0 and 10.0 ml. of the standard silicon solution (1 ml. = 0.05 mg. Si) to 100-ml. volumetric flasks. To each flask, add 40 ml. of water, 1.0 ml. of $H_2SO_4$ (1:4) and 10 g. of $MgSO_4 \cdot 7H_2O$. Swirl the flask to dissolve the $MgSO_4$.

(b) **Reference Solution.**—Prepare an additional 100 ml. volumetric flask containing 40 ml. of water, 1.0 ml. of $H_2SO_4$ (1:4) and 10 g. of $MgSO_4 \cdot 7H_2O$ for use as a reference solution. Swirl the flask to dissolve the $MgSO_4$.

(c) **Color Development.**—To each flask, add 5.0 ml. of ammonium molybdate solution, dilute to 100 ml. and mix. (The yellow color ordinarily develops within 5 minutes and should be read within 1 hour after addition of molybdate, since fading takes place after a longer time.)

(d) **Photometry.**—Transfer a suitable portion of the reference solution to an absorption cell with a 5-cm. light path and adjust the photometer to the initial setting using a light band centered at approximately 420 m$\mu$. While maintaining this adjustment, take the photometric readings of the calibration solutions.

(e) **Calibration Curve.**—Plot the photometric readings of the calibration solutions against milligrams of silicon per 100 ml. of solution.

*2. Procedure.* (a) **Test Solutions.** (1) *Soluble Silicon.*—Transfer to a 150-ml. beaker, a sample weighed to the nearest milligram and calculated to contain less than 0.5 mg. of silicon and not more than 2 g. of magnesium. Add 25 ml. of water and 5 ml. of the boric acid solution. Add, in small quantities, 11.7 ml. of freshly prepared $H_2SO_4$ (1:4) per gram of sample, meanwhile keeping the beaker in a cold water bath to prevent losses of silicon as the hydride. Add 1.0 ml. of $H_2SO_4$ (1:4) in excess. When the sample is dissolved, introduce 0.1 g. of $K_2S_2O_8$ to oxidize ferrous iron or other reducing agents. Allow to stand for at least 10 minutes, dilute to about 60 ml. with water and filter through a fine, low-ash paper, catching the filtrate in a 100-ml. volumetric flask. Rinse the beaker and paper with enough water to dilute the filtrate to approximately 90 ml. Continue as described in paragraph (c) below.

(2) *Insoluble Silicon.*—Place the filter paper in a clean platinum crucible and ignite at approximately 500°C. Add 0.1 g. of $Na_2CO_3$ and fuse at approximately 850°C. Dissolve the residue in water with enough freshly prepared $H_2SO_4$ (1:4) to neutralize the $Na_2CO_3$, plus 1.0 ml. in excess, and filter through a fine, low-ash paper into another 100-ml. volumetric flask. Rinse the beaker and paper with enough water to dilute the filtrate to approximately 90 ml. Proceed in accordance with paragraph (c) below.

(b) **Reference Solutions.**—Prepare two reagent blanks, one for the soluble silicon portion and the other for the insoluble silicon portion for use as reference solutions. These blanks should contain all of the reagents, including the filter paper, except that only 1 ml. of $H_2SO_4$ (1:4) shall be used per 100 ml. of solution, since the color is affected by the acidity.

(c) **Color Development.**—To each flask add 5.0 ml. of ammonium molybdate solution. If a green color develops due to the presence of reducing agents, add 0.1 g. of $K_2S_2O_8$. Dilute to volume and mix.

(d) **Photometry.**—Take the photometric readings of the test solutions as described in Section 1 (d).

**Calculation.**—Convert the photometric readings of the test solutions to milligrams of silicon by means of the calibration curve. Add together the amounts found in the soluble and insoluble silicon portions. Calculate the percentage of silicon as follows:

$$\text{Silicon, } \% = \frac{A}{B \times 10}$$

where $A$ = total milligrams of silicon found, and
$B$ = grams of sample used.

## SILVER BY THE TITRIMETRIC THIOCYANATE METHOD

This method is applicable to the determination of from 1.0 to 10.0% silver.

The magnesium alloy is dissolved with $HNO_3$ and the silver is titrated with an ammonium thiocyanate solution.

Mercury, palladium, and chlorides interfere, but they are not usually encountered in magnesium alloys. Nitrous acid interferes but can be removed by boiling the solution.

**Reagents. Ammonium Thiocyanate Standard Solution, 0.1 N.**—Dissolve 7.6124 g. of ammonium thiocyanate ($NH_4CNS$) in water and dilute to one liter. Standardize against a standard silver nitrate solution, using Volhard indicator.

**Volhard Indicator.**—Dissolve 106.6 g. of ferric alum ($FeNH_4(SO_4)_2$) in 13.3 ml. $HNO_3$ and water. Dilute the solution to one liter.

**Procedure. Test Solution.**—Transfer a portion of sample, weighed to the nearest milligram and calculated to contain 100 to 150 mg. of silver, to a 250-ml. Erlenmeyer flask. Add 50 ml. of water and dissolve the alloy by carefully adding 5 ml. increments of $HNO_3$. The reaction is vigorous and care must be taken to add the additional $HNO_3$ only after the previous reaction has subsided. After the alloy has dissolved, add 2 ml. of $HNO_3$ and boil the solution to expel the lower oxides of nitrogen.

**Blank Solution.** Add 50 ml. of water and 2 ml. of $HNO_3$. Boil the solution to remove nitrous oxide.

Cool the solutions and add 3 ml. of Volhard indicator to each. Titrate the solutions with standard 0.1 $N$ $NH_4CNS$ solution until a faint pink color persists after vigorous stirring. Care must be exercised to avoid under-titration since the color is but slowly removed at the end point.

**Calculation.**—Calculate the percentage of silver as follows:

$$\text{Silver, } \% = \frac{(A - B) \times 0.01078 \times 100}{C}$$

where $A$ = milliliters of standard 0.1000 $N$ $NH_4CNS$ solution used to titrate the test solution,

$B$ = milliliters of standard 0.1000 $N$ $NH_4CNS$ solution required for the blank and,

$C$ = grams of sample taken.

## THORIUM BY THE BENZOATE-OXALATE (GRAVIMETRIC) METHOD

This method is applicable to the determination of 0.2 to 25% thorium.

Thorium, along with zirconium if present, is precipitated as the benzoate. The combined benzoate precipitate is dissolved and thorium is precipitated as the oxalate, ignited to the oxide, and weighed.

Provision is made in the method to take care of all elements ordinarily present in magnesium-thorium alloys.

**Reagents. Benzoic Acid Solution (20 g. per liter).**—Dissolve 2 g. of benzoic acid ($C_6H_5COOH$) in hot water and dilute to 100 ml.

**Benzoic Acid Wash Solution (2.5 g. per liter).**—Dissolve 2.5 g. benzoic acid ($C_6H_5COOH$) in hot water and dilute to 1 liter.

**Bromphenol Blue (4 g. per liter).**—Place 0.40 g. of bromphenol blue in a mortar, add 8.25 ml. of NaOH solution (5 g. NaOH per liter), and mix until solution is complete. Dilute to 100 ml. with water.

**Hydroxylamine Hydrochloride ($NH_2OH \cdot HCl$).**

**Oxalic Acid Solution (saturated).**—Dissolve 150 g. of oxalic acid dihydrate ($C_2H_2O_4 \cdot H_2O$) in 1 liter of warm water. Allow to cool, and filter off any insoluble material.

**Oxalic Acid-Hydrochloric Acid Wash Solution.**—Dilute 70 ml. of saturated oxalic acid solution to 500 ml. with water and add 5 ml. of HCl.

**Procedure.**—Weigh, to the nearest milligram, a portion of sample containing from 10 to 100 mg. of thorium and transfer to a 400-ml. beaker. Add 50 ml. of water, and dissolve the metal by adding HCl a little at a time until dissolution is complete (7.5 ml. of HCl dissolves 1 g. of sample). Heat the solution to boiling on a hot plate, cool, filter through a fine paper, and wash with water. Dilute the solution to 100 ml. with water.

If rare earth elements are present, add 1 g. of hydroxylamine hydrochloride to reduce any ceric cerium. Add 3 drops of bromphenol blue and adjust the acidity with either $NH_4OH$ (1:4) or HCl (1:4) until the solution is just basic to bromphenol blue. Add 10 g. of $NH_4Cl$, place the beaker on a hot plate, and heat the solution to boiling. Pour 100 ml. of hot benzoic acid solution into the sample solution, while stirring, and continue to heat for 10 minutes. Set the beaker aside until the precipitate settles and then filter the solution through a rapid, hardened paper. Police the beaker and wash thoroughly with hot benzoic acid wash solution.

Punch a hole in the filter paper and wash the benzoate precipitate back into the original beaker with 50 ml. of hot water. Wash the filter paper with 10 ml. of HCl (1:4) and 50 ml. of hot water. Place the beaker on a hot plate and heat the solution to boiling. Remove the beaker from the hot plate and add 25 ml. of saturated oxalic acid solution while stirring. Allow the mixture to stand overnight and then filter on a fine paper. Police and wash the beaker thoroughly with oxalic acid-hydrochloric acid wash solution. Transfer the precipitate and paper to a clean, tared, porcelain crucible. Dry, burn off the paper, and finally ignite at 950°C. to constant weight, cooling each time in a desiccator charged with anhydrous magnesium perchlorate [$Mg(ClO_4)_2$].

**Calculation.**—Calculate the percentage of thorium as follows:

$$\text{Thorium, } \% = \frac{A \times 0.8788}{B} \times 100$$

where $A$ = grams of thorium oxide ($ThO_2$), and
$B$ = grams of sample used.

## THORIUM BY THE THORON (PHOTOMETRIC) METHOD

This method is applicable to the determination of from 0.04 to 1.0% thorium. This method has been written for cells having a 1-cm. light path. Cells having other dimensions may be used, provided suitable adjustments can be made in the amounts of sample and reagents used.

Thorium is determined through the formation of a colored complex with the disodium salt of o-(2-hydroxy-3,6-disulfo-1-naphthylazo)benzenearsonic acid in an acid solution. Photometric measurement is made at approximately 545 m$\mu$.

The recommended concentration range is from 0.1 to 1.0 mg. of thorium per 100 ml. of solution using a cell depth of 1 cm.

The color develops within 5 minutes and is stable for at least 24 hours.

Aluminum, manganese, and zinc do not interfere when present in concentrations of less than 10 mg. per 100 ml. of solution. Five mg. of either praseodymium, neodymium, lanthanum, or mischmetal per 100 ml. of solution cause no interference. In concentrations greater than 5 mg. per 100 ml., there is a slight positive interference. Anions such as phosphate, fluoride, citrate, tartrate, and oxalate will interfere if present. Zirconium is complexed with mandelic acid.

**Reagents.** **Mandelic Acid Solution (80 g. per liter).**—Dissolve 8.0 g. of reagent grade DL-mandelic acid in water and dilute to 100 ml. with water. Prepare fresh as needed.

**Thorium Standard Solution A (1 ml. = 1.0 mg. Th).**—Dissolve 2.38 g. of reagent grade thorium nitrate tetrahydrate ($Th(NO_3)_4 \cdot 4H_2O$) in 50 ml. of water and 50 ml. of HCl. Dilute to 1 liter with water. Standardize this solution by precipitating the thorium in aliquot portions with oxalic acid and by igniting the thorium oxalate to the oxide.

**Thorium Standard Solution B (1 ml. = 0.1 mg. Th).**—Pipette 50.0 ml. of thorium standard solution A into a 500-ml. volumetric flask, add 22.5 ml. of HCl and dilute to volume with water.

**Thoron Dye Solution (3 g. per liter).**—Dissolve 3.0 g. of the disodium salt of o-(2-hydroxy-3,6-disulfo-1-naphthylazo)benzenearsonic acid (Eastman Kodak Company) in one liter of water. Filter if necessary.

*1. Preparation of Calibration Curve.* (a) **Calibration Solutions.**—Transfer 1.0-, 3.0-, 5.0-, 7.0-, and 10.0-ml. portions of standard thorium solution *B* (1 ml. = 0.1 mg. Th) into 100-ml. volumetric flasks. Add enough HCl, so that each flask contains a total of 3.5 ml. of HCl. Add 10 ml. of mandelic acid solution and dilute to approximately 90 ml. with water.

(b) **Reference Solution.**—To a 100-ml. volumetric flask containing approximately 75 ml. of water, add 3.5 ml. of HCl and 10 ml. of mandelic acid solution.

(c) **Color Development.**—Add 5.0 ml. of the Thoron dye solution to each flask and dilute to volume with water. Shake the solutions and allow them to stand for 5 minutes.

(d) **Photometry.**—Transfer a suitable portion of the reference solution to an absorption cell with a 1-cm. light path and adjust the photometer to the initial setting using a light band centered at approximately 545 m$\mu$. While maintaining this adjustment, take the photometric readings of the calibration solutions.

(e) **Calibration Curve.**—Plot the photometric readings of the calibration solutions against milligrams of thorium per 100 ml. of solution.

*2. Procedure.* (a) **Test Solution.**—Weigh, to the nearest milligram, 2.5 g. of sample, place it in a 400-ml. beaker and add 75 ml. of water. Dissolve the sample by adding HCl in small increments until there is a 25-ml. excess (7.5 ml. of HCl dissolves 1 g. of sample). When dissolution is complete, cool the solution, and transfer it to a 500-ml. volumetric flask, filtering if necessary. Dilute the solution to volume with water. Pipette an aliquot containing from 0.1 to 1.0 mg. of thorium into a 100-ml. volumetric flask. Add sufficient HCl, so that the flask contains a total of 3.5 ml. of HCl (a 10-ml. aliquot of the sample solution contains 0.5 ml. of HCl).

(b) **Reference Solution.**—Prepare a reference solution as described in Section 1 (b).

(c) **Color Development.**—Develop the color as described in Section 1 (c).

(d) **Photometry.**—Take the photometric reading of the test solution as described in Section 1 (d).

(e) **Calculation.**—Convert the photometric reading of the test solution to milligrams of thorium by means of the calibration curve. Calculate the percentage of thorium as follows:

$$\text{Thorium, } \% = \frac{A}{B \times 10}$$

where $A$ = milligrams of thorium per 100 ml. of solution, and
$B$ = grams of sample represented in the aliquot taken.

### TIN BY THE TITRIMETRIC IODINE METHOD

This method is applicable to the determination of tin in concentrations greater than 0.5%. (Tin in lower concentrations may be determined by this procedure using a 0.01 $N$ iodine solution.)

The sample is dissolved in HCl in an inert atmosphere and the stannous tin is titrated with a standard iodine solution to the starch-iodide end point.

Any element that, after dissolving, will be present in a reduced form which is oxidizable by iodine will interfere. Such elements are not likely to be present in the usual magnesium alloys.

*Apparatus.* See **Fig. 27-1.**

*Reagents.* **Iodine Standard Solution (1 ml. = 0.006 g. Sn, approximately 0.1 $N$).**—Standardize against weighed amounts of tin and tin-free magnesium in accordance with the procedure described in Section on "Procedure."

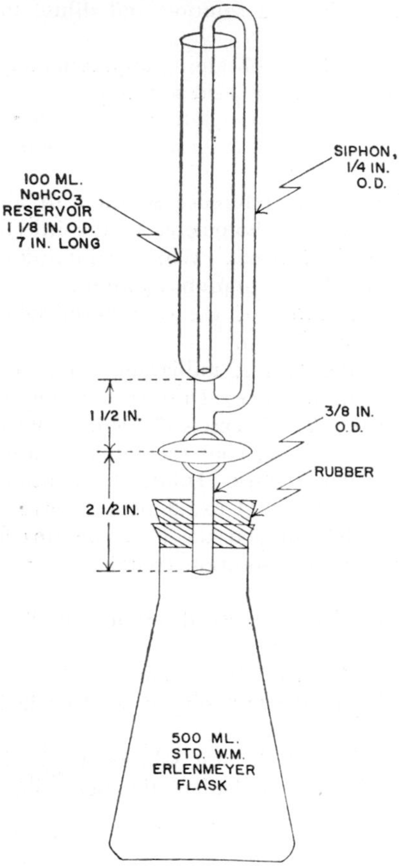

**Magnesium Metal (tin-free).**

**Sodium Bicarbonate Solution (Saturated).**

**Starch Solution (10 g. per liter).**

*Procedure.*—Weigh, to the nearest milligram, a sample containing from 0.025 to 0.10 g. of tin, transfer to a reduction flask, and add 20 ml. of water. Add concentrated HCl in small increments until a total of 100 ml. have been added. If the metal is finely divided or the sample weight is large, place the flask and contents in an ice bath during the dissolution.

After the sample has dissolved, cool and cautiously add 1.0 g. of tin-free magnesium metal. Stopper as shown in Fig. 27-1, and dip the outlet into saturated $NaHCO_3$ solution.

After the magnesium metal disappears, heat on a hot plate until the solution becomes clear (except for silica particles). Allow to cool. The $NaHCO_3$ solution will draw back sufficiently to maintain an atmosphere of $CO_2$ in the flask.

When the solution is cold, remove the head quickly and rinse down the sides of the flask with water through which $CO_2$ has been bubbled. Add a couple of marble chips, 2 or 3 ml. of starch solution and close with a one-hole rubber stopper. Titrate at once through the stopper with 0.1 $N$ iodine solution to a blue color.

Make a blank determination, following the same procedure and using the same amounts of all reagents.

Fig. 27-1. Apparatus for the Determination of Tin. (Courtesy of The Dow Chemical Company, Midland, Michigan.)

**Calculation.**—Calculate the percentage of tin as follows:

$$\text{Tin, } \% = \frac{(A - B)C}{D} \times 100$$

where $A$ = milliliters of iodine solution required for titration of the sample.

$B$ = milliliters of iodine solution required for titration of the blank,

$C$ = tin equivalent of the iodine solution, in grams per milliliter, and

$D$ = grams of sample used.

## ZINC BY THE TITRIMETRIC ETHYLENEDIAMINETETRAACETATE METHOD

This method covers the determination of zinc in magnesium-base alloys in the range from 0.3 to 20%. The zinc thiocyanate complex is extracted with methyl isobutyl ketone to effect a separation from magnesium. The zinc is then removed from the organic extract as the ammonia complex. Zinc and other bivalent metals are complexed with potassium cyanide. Finally, the zinc is selectively released from the cyanide complex and titrated with standard sodium ethylenediaminetetraacetate solution. None of the metals ordinarily present in magnesium-base alloys interfere with this method. This method also affords a separation of zinc from cadmium in the event that they are encountered together.

*Apparatus.* **500-ml. Separatory Funnels, pear-shape.**

**Magnetic Stirrer.**—Equipped with a Teflon-covered magnetic stirring bar.

*Reagents.* **Ammonium Thiocyanate Solution (500 g. per liter).**—Dissolve 500 g.. of ammonium thiocyanate ($NH_4CNS$) in water and dilute to 1 liter.

**Ammonium Thiocyanate-Hydrochloric Acid Wash Solution.**—Add 100 ml. of $NH_4CNS$ solution to approximately 700 ml. of water and mix. Add 8.3 ml. of HCl, 3.3 ml. of $HNO_3$, and dilute to 1 liter with water.

**Buffer Solution.**—Dissolve 65.5 g. of $NH_4Cl$ in water, add 570 ml. of $NH_4OH$, and dilute to 1 liter with water.

**Buffer Solution, Dilute.**—Dilute 400 ml. of the buffer solution to 1 liter with water.

**Formaldehyde (37%).**

**Indicator Solution.**—Dissolve 0.4 g. of Eriochrome Black-T (1-(1-hydroxy-2-naphthylazo)-6-nitro-2-naphthol-4-sulfonic acid, sodium salt) in a mixture of 20 ml. of ethyl alcohol and 30 ml. of triethanolamine. This solution is stable for at least 3 months when kept in a tightly closed polyethylene dropping bottle.

**Methyl Isobutyl Ketone.**

**Potassium Cyanide Solution (50 g. per liter).**—Dissolve 5 g. of potassium cyanide (KCN) in water containing 3 ml. of $NH_4OH$ and dilute to 100 ml. *Caution:* The preparation, storage, and use of potassium cyanide solutions requires care and attention. Avoid inhalation of fumes and exposure of skin to the chemical or its solutions. Work in a well-ventilated hood.

**Sodium Ethylenediaminetetraacetate (EDTA) Standard Solution (0.01 *M*).**—Dissolve 4.0 g. of disodium ethylenediaminetetraacetate dihydrate in water. Add to this solution 0.1 g. of magnesium chloride ($MgCl_2 \cdot 6H_2O$) and dilute to volume in a 1-liter volumetric flask. Standardize this solution against a standard zinc solution as described in Section 1 (c) through (d).

**Zinc, Standard Solution (1 ml. = 1.00 mg. Zn).**—Dissolve 1.000 g. of pure zinc in 50 ml. of water and 22.6 ml. of HCl. Dilute to volume in a 1-liter volumetric flask.

*1. Procedure.*—(a) For alloys with a zinc content under 1.0%, transfer a sample, weighed to the nearest 1 mg. and containing preferably from 4 to 10 mg. of zinc (but in no case more than 1.5 g.), to a 250-ml. beaker. Add 25 ml. of water and dissolve the alloy by the addition of 7.5 ml. of HCl per gram of sample. Cool and continue as described in paragraph (c).

(b) For alloys with a zinc content over 1.0%, transfer a portion of the sample, weighed to the nearest 1 mg. and containing from 40 to 100 mg. of zinc, to a 250-ml. beaker. Add 25 ml. of water and dissolve the sample by the addition of 7.5

ml. of HCl per gram of sample. Cool, transfer to a 500-ml. volumetric flask, dilute to volume, and mix. Continue as described in paragraph (c).

(c) Transfer the solution from either paragraph (a), or an aliquot portion of the solution from paragraph (b) containing from 4 to 10 mg. of zinc, to a 500-ml. separatory funnel. Add 2.5 ml. of HCl, 1.0 ml. of $HNO_3$, dilute to 300 ml., and mix. Add 30 ml. of $NH_4CNS$ solution and mix. Add 50 ml. of methyl isobutyl ketone and shake well. Allow the layers to separate, and draw off and discard the lower aqueous layer. To the solvent extract, add 100 ml. of ammonium thiocyanate-hydrochloric acid wash solution. Shake, allow the layers to separate, and draw off and discard the lower aqueous layer. To the organic layer add 40 ml. of the buffer solution. Cautiously shake, allow the layers to separate, and draw off the lower ammoniacal layer into a 500-ml. Erlenmeyer flask. Add 25 ml. of the dilute buffer solution to the solvent extract and shake. Allow the layers to separate, and draw off and add the lower ammoniacal layer to the Erlenmeyer flask. Discard the organic layer.

(d) Dilute to approximately 300 ml. with water, add 10 ml. of KCN solution, a few drops of indicator solution, and a Teflon-covered stirring bar. Place the flask on a magnetic stirrer and stir at a fairly fast rate. To the blue solution, add 3 ml. of formaldehyde and titrate from wine-red to pure blue with 0.01 $M$ EDTA solution.

**Calculation.**—Calculate the percentage of zinc as follows:

$$\text{Zinc, }\% = \frac{AB}{C \times 10}$$

where $A$ = milliliters of standard EDTA solution used,
      $B$ = equivalent of the standard EDTA solution in milligrams of zinc per milliliter, and
      $C$ = grams of sample in the aliquot used.

### ZINC BY THE POTASSIUM FERROCYANIDE (POTENTIOMETRIC) METHOD

This method is suitable for the determination of from 1.0 to 10% zinc in magnesium alloys which do not contain aluminum.

The alloy is dissolved in $H_2SO_4$ (1:4) and the zinc is titrated potentiometrically with potassium ferrocyanide using platinum-calomel electrodes and a Macbeth titrator.

Aluminum decreases the sensitivity of the electrodes. Silver, nickel, mercury, cobalt, copper, iron, lead, and tin might interfere, but are usually not present in magnesium alloys in more than trace quantities.

*Apparatus.* **Macbeth Titrator** (Model T, Macbeth Corp., Newburgh, N. Y.), or equivalent.

**Platinum and Calomel Electrodes.**

*Reagents.* **Potassium Ferrocyanide Solution.**—Dissolve 18 g. of potassium ferrocyanide $(K_4Fe(CN)_6)$ in one liter of water and allow to stand for 3 weeks or more (for immediate use, 0.3 g. of potassium ferricyanide $(K_3Fe(CN)_6)$ can be added, but such a solution may change gradually). Standardize this solution each time it is used by titrating 10.0 ml. of the standard zinc solution as described under "Procedure," below. Calculate the number of grams of zinc equivalent to 1 ml. of $K_4Fe(CN)_6$ solution.

**Sodium Sulfate, Anhydrous.**

**Zinc Standard Solution (1 ml. = 5.0 mg. Zn).**—Weigh out accurately about 5 g. of pure zinc metal and dissolve in $H_2SO_4$ (1:4). Dilute to 1 liter with water and calculate the zinc content in grams per milliliter.

*Procedure.*—Weigh, to the nearest milligram, a sample to contain from 0.04 to 0.10 g. of zinc into a 400-ml. beaker. Dissolve, using 25 ml. of $H_2SO_4$ (1:4) per gram of sample. Adjust the volume to 150 ml. with water, add 4 g. of sodium sulfate. Place the sample in the electrode assembly, heat to 65–75°C. and titrate with $K_4Fe(CN)_6$ solution, using two-drop increments, to the greatest change in potential. Keep the temperature at 65–75°C. while titrating.

**Calculation.**—Calculate the percentage of zinc as follows:

$$\text{Zinc, } \% = \frac{A \times B}{C} \times 100$$

where $A$ = milliliters of $K_4Fe(CN)_6$ solution used,
$B$ = zinc equivalent of the $K_4Fe(CN)_6$ solution expressed in grams of zinc per milliliter of $K_4Fe(CN)_6$ solution, and
$C$ = grams of sample taken.

## ZIRCONIUM BY THE ALIZARIN RED (PHOTOMETRIC) METHOD

This method covers the determination of acid-soluble and acid-insoluble zirconium, in amounts from 0.03 to 1.0%.

The acid-soluble and acid-insoluble zirconium are separated by dissolving the alloy in dilute hydrochloric acid. The insoluble fraction is brought into solution by fusion with potassium bisulfate. Zirconium in each solution is determined photometrically through the formation of a colored complex with alizarin red S at a pH of 0.6 to 0.7. Photometric measurement is made at approximately 510 m$\mu$. This procedure has been written for cells having a 5-cm. light path. It has been found necessary to use these deep cells in order to avoid interference in the analysis of samples containing appreciable amounts of thorium. In the absence of unfavorable thorium to zirconium ratios, smaller cell depths can be used, in this case using 5 ml. of 0.10% dye solution and adjusting the sample aliquot to accommodate the larger range of zirconium concentration.

The recommended concentration range is from 0.05 to 0.25 mg. of zirconium in 100 ml. of solution, using a cell depth of 5 cm.

The color develops rapidly for 15 minutes and increases very slowly thereafter.

Rare earths, zinc, aluminum, manganese, copper, iron, nickel, and lead, in concentrations likely to be found in magnesium alloys, do not interfere with the method. Thorium does not interfere at pH values of 0.6 to 0.7, but may cause interference at a higher pH. Hafnium is included as zirconium in this method. Sulfate and phosphate retard the rate of color development, but in concentrations of less than 0.08 g. per 100 ml. the color intensity is at a maximum after 1 hr.; in greater concentrations full color intensity does not develop. Fluoride in concentrations greater than 0.01 mg. per 100 ml. interferes quantitatively by reacting with zirconium. Very high neodymium could interfere at 510 m$\mu$, but the interference would be less at 500 m$\mu$.

**Reagents. Alizarin Red S Solution (0.5 g. per liter).**—Dissolve 0.125 g. of alizarin red S in water and dilute to 250 ml.

**Ferric Chloride Solution (1 ml. = 2.5 mg. Fe).**—Dissolve 0.25 g. of iron wire in 10 ml. of HCl and 2 ml. of $HNO_3$. Boil off the fumes and dilute to 100 ml. with water.

**Potassium Pyrosulfate (K₂S₂O₇)-Potassium Bisulfate, Fused Powder.**

**Zirconium, Standard Solution (1 ml. = 0.05 mg. Zr).**—Dissolve 0.177 g. of zirconyl chloride (ZrOCl₂·8H₂O) in about 100 ml. of water, add 100 ml. of HCl, and dilute to 1000 ml. with water. One milliliter contains approximately 0.05 mg. of zirconium and 0.1 ml. of HCl. Standardize by analyzing 200 ml. gravimetrically by the phosphate method.

*1. Preparation of Calibration Curve.* **(a) Calibration Solutions.**—Transfer 1.0, 2.0, 3.0, 4.0, and 5.0 ml. of standard zirconium solution (1 ml. = 0.05 mg. Zr) to 100-ml. volumetric flasks. Add sufficient HCl to give a total of 2.8 ml. of HCl in each flask and dilute to about 90 ml.

**(b) Reference Solution.**—Transfer the equivalent of 2.8 ml. of HCl to a 100-ml. flask, dilute to about 90 ml. with water.

**(c) Color Development.**—Add 5 ml. of alizarin red S solution to each flask, dilute to the mark, and mix. Allow to stand for 15 minutes.

**(d) Photometry.**—Transfer a suitable portion of the reference solution to an absorption cell with a 5-cm. light path and adjust the photometer to the initial setting using a light band centered at approximately 510 mμ. While maintaining this photometer adjustment, take the photometric readings of the calibration solutions.

**(e) Calibration Curve.**—Plot the photometric readings of the calibration solutions against milligrams of zirconium per 100 ml. of solution.

*2. Procedure.* **(a) Test Solution.** (1) *Rod, Sheet, or Bar.*—Transfer 1.5 g. of the sample into a 400-ml. beaker. Dissolve by adding 125 ml. of HCl (1:4). The acid should all be added at one time to prevent the possibility of some of the zirconium hydrolyzing because of a deficiency of acid. Filter through a fine filter paper into a 500-ml. volumetric flask. Wash 4 to 5 times with hot water. Cool, dilute the filtrate to volume, and mix. This represents the acid-soluble zirconium. Proceed as directed in paragraph (a)(3).

(2) *Drillings, Millings, or Pellets.*—Transfer 1.5 g. of the sample into a 400-ml. beaker. Add 50 ml. of water and dissolve the sample by adding HCl in 3 ml. increments until a total of 25 ml. has been added. The increments of acid should be added rapidly and continuously without allowing the reaction to become too vigorous.

NOTE.—The procedure in paragraph (a)(1) is that recommended for dissolving magnesium-zirconium alloys. The more vigorous treatment of paragraph (a)(2) is necessary with an alloy that is finely divided because zirconium will hydrolyze to some extent as the alloy dissolves. This can be seen as a white turbidity in the solution and should disappear upon heating.

Heat the solution to 95°C. Remove immediately from the heat, cool, and filter through a retentive paper into a 500-ml. volumetric flask. Wash 4 to 5 times with hot water, cool, and dilute the filtrate to volume and mix. This represents the acid-soluble zirconium.

(3) Place the paper containing the insoluble residue in a porcelain crucible and char slowly. Heat at 950°C. for 30 minutes, cool slightly, add about 1 g. of K₂S₂O₇, and fuse. Cool and dissolve the melt in 100 ml. of water containing 1 ml. of HCl and 1 ml. of FeCl₃ solution. Add NH₄OH until all the iron and zirconium are precipitated. Filter through a moderately rapid paper and wash the precipitate with hot water. Dissolve the hydroxide from the filter paper with 15 ml. of hot HCl (1:1). Transfer the solution to a 250-ml. volumetric flask, dilute to volume, and mix. This represents the zirconium from the acid-insoluble fraction.

(4) From each flask, transfer an aliquot containing from 0.05 to 0.25 mg. of zirconium to a 100-ml. volumetric flask. Calculate the amount of acid present (a 10-ml. aliquot will contain about 0.3 ml.) and add sufficient acid to give a total of 2.8 ml. of HCl. Dilute to about 90 ml.

(b) **Reference Solution.**—Carry along a reagent blank containing the same amount of all reagents for use as a reference solution.

(c) **Color Development.**—Develop the color as directed in Section 1 (c).

(d) **Photometry.**—Take the photometric readings of the test solutions as directed in Section 1 (d).

**Calculation.**—Convert the photometric readings of the test solutions to milligrams of zirconium by means of the calibration curve. Calculate the percentage of zirconium in each fraction as follows:

$$\text{Zirconium, } \% = \frac{A}{B \times 10}$$

where $A$ = milligrams of zirconium found in 100 ml. of each final solution, and
$B$ = grams of sample represented in 100 ml. of the same solution.

### ZIRCONIUM BY THE ALIZARIN RED (PHOTOMETRIC) METHOD (SEMIMICRO METHOD)

This method is applicable to the determination of from 0.0005 to 0.05% zirconium. This method has been written for cells having a 5-cm. light path. Cells having other dimensions may be used, provided suitable adjustments can be made in the amounts of sample and reagents used.

Zirconium is concentrated by chloroform extraction of its cupferron complex and is determined photometrically by the alizarin red S method. Photometric measurement is made at approximately 510 m$\mu$.

The recommended concentration range is from 0.025 to 0.25 mg. of zirconium in 100 ml. of solution using a cell depth of 5 cm.

The color develops rapidly for 15 minutes and increases very slowly thereafter.

None of the normal alloying agents used in magnesium alloys interferes with this method. Fluorides, organic acids, and greater than trace amounts of sulfate or phosphate ions will interfere if present. Hafnium is included as zirconium in this method.

*Reagents.* **Alizarin Red S Solution (0.5 g. per liter).**—Dissolve 0.125 g. of alizarin red S in water and dilute to 250 ml. with water. Filter if necessary.

**Chloroform.**

**Cupferron Solution (50 g. per liter).**—Dissolve 5 g. of the ammonium salt of N-nitroso-N-phenylhydroxylamine in water and dilute to 100 ml. with water. Prepare fresh as needed.

**Iron Solution.**—Dissolve 1.0 g. of pure iron wire in 50 ml. of water and 100 ml. of HCl. Add a few drops of hydrogen peroxide to oxidize the iron and boil to remove excess peroxide. Cool and dilute to 1 liter with water.

**Perchloric Acid, 70%.**

**Potassium Pyrosulfate (potassium bisulfate fused powder).**

**Zirconium Standard Solution (1 ml. = 0.05 mg. Zr).**—Dissolve 0.177 g. of zirconyl chloride ($ZrOCl_2 \cdot 8H_2O$) in about 100 ml. of water, add 100 ml. of HCl and dilute to 1 liter with water. Standardize by analyzing 200 ml. gravimetrically by the phosphate method.

**1. Preparation of Calibration Curve.** (a) **Calibration Solutions.**—Transfer 0.5-, 1.0-, 3.0-, and 5.0-ml. portions of the standard zirconium solution (1 ml. = 0.05 mg. Zr) to 100-ml. volumetric flasks. Add enough HCl to make a total of 2.8 ml. and dilute each solution to approximately 90 ml. with water.

(b) **Reference Solution.**—Add 2.8 ml. of HCl to a 100-ml. volumetric flask containing 90 ml. of water.

(c) **Color Development.**—Add 5.0 ml. of the alizarin red S solution and dilute to volume with water. Allow for complete color development (15 minutes).

(d) **Photometry.**—Transfer a suitable portion of the reference solution to an absorption cell with a 5-cm. light path and adjust the photometer to the initial setting using a light band centered at approximately 510 m$\mu$. While maintaining this adjustment, take the photometric readings of the calibration solutions.

(e) **Calibration Curve.**—Plot the photometric readings of the calibration solutions against milligrams of zirconium per 100 ml. of solution.

**2. Procedure.** (a) **Test Solutions.**—(1) Weigh, to the nearest milligram, 5 g. of sample and place it in a 400-ml. beaker. Add 50 ml. of water and HCl in small portions until a total of 45.0 ml. has been added. When the dissolution is complete, heat the solution to 95°C. and filter through a retentive filter paper, catching the filtrate in a 400-ml. beaker. The filtrate contains the soluble zirconium. Proceed in accordance with paragraph (3) below.

(2) Place the paper containing the insoluble zirconium in a porcelain crucible and char slowly. Heat to 950°C. for 30 minutes. Cool, add approximately 1 g. of potassium pyrosulfate and fuse. When the crucible and melt are cool, dissolve the melt in 100 ml. of water containing 7.5 ml. of HCl.

(3) Cool the solutions from paragraphs (1) and (2) to room temperature and transfer to 250-ml. separatory funnels. Dilute each solution to about 170 ml. with water.

(b) **Reference Solution.**—Add 7.5 ml. of HCl to a 250-ml. separatory funnel containing about 160 ml. of water.

(c) Add 1.0 ml. of the iron solution and shake the mixture. Introduce 2.0 ml. of cupferron solution and shake to coagulate the combined zirconium-iron precipitate. Extract the cupferrates with two 15-ml. portions of chloroform, drawing the organic layer into a 50-ml. Erlenmeyer flask. Place the flask on a steam bath and evaporate the solution to dryness. Moisten the residue in the flask with 3 drops of $H_2SO_4$ and 3 drops of $HNO_3$. Place the flask on a hot plate in a fume hood, and carefully add one drop of $HClO_4$ to the residue. Allow time for reaction and then add another drop of $HClO_4$. Continue with the dropwise addition until all of the organic material is decomposed. When decomposition is complete, wash down the sides of the flask with $HClO_4$ and heat for 5 minutes. Wash the contents from the flask into a porcelain crucible and place the crucible on a hot plate. Evaporate the acid to dryness to insure loss of excess sulfate. Allow the crucible to cool, and add 2.8 ml. of HCl and 5 ml. of water. Warm the crucible to dissolve the residue.

(d) If the zirconium content is greater than 0.005%, make the solution from the crucible to volume and pipette an aliquot containing 0.15 mg. of zirconium into a 100-ml. volumetric flask. Add sufficient acid to make a total of 2.8 ml. of HCl. If the zirconium content is less than 0.005%, wash the contents of the crucible into a 100-ml. volumetric flask.

(e) **Color Development.**—Develop the color as described in Section 1 (c).

(f) **Photometry.**—Take the photometric readings of the test solutions as described in Section 1 (d).

**Calculation.**—Convert the photometric readings of the test solutions to milligrams of zirconium by means of the calibration curve. Calculate the percentage of zirconium as follows:

$$\text{Zirconium, } \% = \frac{A}{B \times 10}$$

where $A$ = milligrams of zirconium per 100 ml. of solution, and
   $B$ = grams of sample represented in 100 ml. of final solution.

### ZIRCONIUM BY THE PHOSPHATE (GRAVIMETRIC) METHOD

This method is applicable to the determination of zirconium in magnesium alloys containing 30 to 60% of metallic or acid-insoluble zirconium.

The sample is treated with dilute acid and the insoluble portion is removed by filtration. The zirconium in solution is precipitated as the phosphate from the filtrate, which has been adjusted to 10% $H_2SO_4$ concentration. The zirconium in the residue is put into solution with $H_2SO_4$, $HNO_3$, and $KHSO_4$. This method avoids loss and danger caused by the pyrotechnic properties of finely divided metallic zirconium during ignition prior to a dry fusion. The dissolved zirconium is precipitated as zirconium phosphate from 10% $H_2SO_4$ solution.

Silica, cerium, and titanium would interfere in this method but have not been encountered. Silica may be removed by adding a limited quantity of HF to the $H_2SO_4$ solution before heating. Cerium and titanium can be held in solution by adding hydrogen peroxide before precipitating with phosphate. Hafnium is included as zirconium.

**Reagents. Ammonium Nitrate Wash Solution (50 g. per liter).**—Dissolve 50 g. of ammonium nitrate ($NH_4NO_3$) in a liter of water.

**Diammonium Phosphate Solution (150 g. per liter).**—Dissolve 15 g. of diammonium phosphate (($NH_4)_2HPO_4$) in water and dilute to 100 ml.

**Potassium Pyrosulfate-Potassium Bisulfate (fused powder).**

**Procedure.**—Weigh, to the nearest milligram, 2.5 g. of sample; place in a 400-ml. beaker with 50 ml. of water, and dissolve by adding small quantities of $H_2SO_4$ (1:4), until 15 ml. per gram of sample has been added. (The large sample weight taken may cause some difficulty in effecting solution, but is desirable because the samples may not be homogeneous. Duplicate portions should be run and reported separately, for the same reason.)

Heat, filter the solution through fine-porosity paper (Whatman No. 42) and wash the precipitate and paper thoroughly with hot water.

To the filtrate, which contains the part of the zirconium that is soluble in dilute acid, add 10 ml. of $H_2SO_4$ and dilute in a beaker to a volume of 175 ml. Heat the solution nearly to boiling and add 10 ml. of ($NH_4)_2HPO_4$ solution while stirring. Keep warm for 30 minutes and let stand overnight.

Place the wet filter paper containing the insoluble zirconium in a 500-ml. Erlenmeyer flask, add 30 ml. of $H_2SO_4$ and place on a hot plate in the hood. (The filter paper and acid-insoluble zirconium *must not be allowed to become dry*. Finely divided, dry zirconium will react violently with $H_2SO_4$.)

From time to time carefully add small quantities of $HNO_3$ until the paper is destroyed and all the metal is dissolved. If difficulty is encountered in effecting solution add 5 g. of $KHSO_4$ and heat at higher temperatures until the zirconium is dissolved and the precipitated zirconium salts are white. Allow the solution to cool and cautiously dilute with water. Cool, transfer to a 500-ml. volumetric flask and dilute to volume with water. Pipette an aliquot containing approximately 50 mg. of zirconium into a 400-ml. beaker and dilute to 200 ml. with water. Add 15 ml. of $H_2SO_4$, heat nearly to boiling and add 10 ml. of $(NH_4)_2HPO_4$ solution while stirring. Keep warm for 30 minutes and let stand overnight.

Filter the precipitates on Whatman No. 40 paper. Carefully wash the beakers and paper with 250 ml. of $NH_4NO_3$ wash solution. Place the filter paper containing the precipitate in a tared porcelain crucible. Dry the precipitate carefully and burn off the paper at a low temperature. Ignite for two hours at 950°C., cool in a desiccator, and weigh.

**Calculation.**—Calculate the percentage of zirconium as follows:

$$\text{Zirconium, } \% = \frac{A \times 0.344 \times 100}{B}$$

where $A$ = grams of zirconium pyrophosphate weighed, and
$B$ = grams of sample represented in the aliquot.

## RAPID METHOD FOR DETERMINATION OF TOTAL MAGNESIUM IN MAGNESIUM ALLOYS

In the marketing of certain magnesium alloy scrap, it is necessary to have a control method to indicate when the material meets the guarantee for percentage total Mg. Two general methods are available for this, namely a potentiometric titration, or a modification of the rapid method for determination of magnesium oxide in dolomitic limestone.

Because the potentiometric titration gives low and variable results and because in the rapid limestone method the results are found to be more consistent, this method is used. Magnesium is determined by this method by estimating the amount of NaOH necessary to precipitate it. In this case, the aluminum will interfere, as well as such metals as copper, zinc, cadmium, manganese, and tin. In order to prevent this interference, a solution of $Na_2S$ is added to precipitate the interfering metals.

### LIME METHOD

*Reagents.* **30% NaOH.**—30 g. C.P. NaOH dissolved in 70 ml. of water.

**$Na_2S$ Solution.**—Dissolve one g. $Na_2S \cdot 9H_2O$ in 100 ml. of water. 10 ml. of this solution should be titrated with $N$ HCl to determine its acid equivalent.

*Procedure.*—Weigh a sample of between 0.4 and 0.5 g. of the alloy and add 25 ml. of water. Dissolve with 5 ml. of concentrated HCl. Transfer to a 250-ml. volumetric flask and add 10 ml. of aqueous methyl red indicator. Add dropwise, from a pipette, a solution of 30% NaOH with vigorous shaking between each addition until the aluminum has been precipitated, but allow a good red color to remain. Stopper the flask and shake violently for 3 minutes. Continue the neutralization with $N$ NaOH, shaking violently between each small addition, to the yellow end point. Add 10 ml. of the $Na_2S$ solution and shake well. Neutralize with $N$ HCl, but leave slightly on the alkaline side; this should not require as much as the acid equivalent of the $Na_2S$ added. Run in from a burette 50 ml. of $N$ NaOH and make to volume. Shake well and filter through a fluted filter paper, using a dry funnel and beaker. Discard the first 25 ml. of solution. Pipette a 25-ml. aliquot of the filtered solution into a flask and titrate with 0.1 $N$ HCl to the methyl red end point. The difference between the $N$ NaOH and the 0.1 $N$ HCl used for back-titration is equivalent to the $N$ NaOH used to precipitate the magnesium. The percentage magnesium is calculated as

$$\frac{(\text{ml. } N \text{ NaOH} - \text{ml. } 0.1 N \text{ HCl}) \times 0.0122 \times 100}{\text{Weight of sample}} = \% \text{ magnesium.}$$

## METHODS FOR MAGNESIUM IN ANALYSES IN OTHER CHAPTERS

Magnesium in Aluminum Alloys — See Analysis of Aluminum Alloys

Magnesium in Bauxite — See Analysis of Bauxite

Magnesium in Fused Alumina — See Analysis of Alumina

Magnesium in Barite — See Analysis of Barite (Barium Chapter)

Magnesium in Beryllium Metal — See Analysis of Beryllium Metal

Magnesium in Water — See Determination of Calcium (and Magnesium) in Water (Calcium Chapter)

Magnesium in Gypsum — See Standard Method for Test Gypsum (Calcium Chapter)

Magnesium in Phosphorus Ores — See Analysis of Phosphorus Ores

Magnesium in Commercial Phosphates — See Analysis of Commercial Phosphates

Magnesium in Sodium Silicate — See Analysis of Sodium Silicate (Silicon Chapter)

Magnesium in Sand — See Analysis of Sand

# Chapter 28

# MANGANESE*

Mn, *at. wt.* 54.9380; *sp. gr.* 7.2; *m.p.* 1260°C.; *b.p.* 1900°C.; *oxides*, MnO, $Mn_2O_3$, $Mn_3O_4$, $MnO_2$, $MnO_3$, $Mn_2O_7$

Manganese occurs associated with iron in many rocks. As oxide it is found in sandstones and limestones, especially in rocks high in iron. In these the percentage seldom exceeds 0.5%. The more important minerals are: pyrolusite, black oxide of manganese, $MnO_2$, the chief source; manganite, $Mn_2O_3 \cdot H_2O$; psilomelane, a hydrous manganese manganate; rhodochrosite, $MnCO_3$; rhodenite, $MnSiO_3$ and spessartite, $Mn_3Al_2(SiO_4)_3$.

Manganese compounds were thought to be those of iron until Scheele (1774) proved these to be distinct. The metal is used largely in alloys of iron—speigeleisen, ferromanganese, manganese steel. Manganese bronze is an alloy of manganese and copper; manganin, an alloy of copper, nickel and manganese. In the analysis of manganese compounds, titrimetric methods take advantage of the varying valences of the element (see oxides above). Certain compounds are valuable analytical reagents.

## DETECTION

*General Procedure.*—In the usual course of analysis manganese is found in the filtrate from the hydroxides of iron, alumium, and chromium, and previous groups having been removed with hydrochloric acid, hydrogen sulfide, and ammonium hydroxide in the presence of ammonium chloride. Manganese, cobalt, nickel, and zinc are precipitated as sulfides in an ammoniacal solution. The sulfides of manganese and zinc are dissolved by cold dilute hydrochloric acid, $H_2S$ expelled by boiling and manganese precipitated as the hydroxide by addition of potassium hydroxide in sufficient amount to dissolve the zinc (sodium zincate). Manganese is now confirmed by dissolving this precipitate in nitric acid and adding a strong oxidizing agent such as sodium bismuthate, potassium periodate, red lead, or lead peroxide to the concentrated nitric acid solution. A violet-colored solution is produced in presence of manganese. Chlorides should be absent.

Manganese in soils, minerals, vegetables, etc., is detected by incinerating the substances, treating with nitric acid, and adding perchloric acid, and evaporating the solution to strong fumes of $HClO_4$ to destroy organic matter. $HNO_3$ (sp. gr. 1.135) is added, the solution is boiled to expel free chlorine, followed by the addition of ammonium persulfate, silver nitrate, and boiling, etc. A pink color is produced in the presence of manganese.

* Based on a chapter in the Fifth Edition, revised and rewritten by Arnold R. Gahler, Research and Development Analytical Laboratory, Union Carbide Metals Co., Niagara Falls, New York.

*Manganese compounds heated with borax* in the oxidizing flame produce an amethyst red color. The color is destroyed in the reducing flame.

*Fused with sodium carbonate and nitrate* on a platinum foil manganese compounds produce a bluish-green opaque fusion.

## ESTIMATION

The titrimetric bismuthate and pyrophosphate (Lingane-Karplus)[1] methods are now most generally used for manganese in high grade manganese ores, ferromanganese, and manganese metal. The gravimetric method is of interest in connection with special problems. Very small quantities of manganese are best estimated colorimetrically after the manganese has been converted into permanganic acid.

Speigeleisen or ferromanganese is an important alloy for the steel industry. The element is determined in certain paint pigments—green and violet manganous oxides, in dryers of oils, etc. It occurs in a number of alloys.

In analyses, manganese passes into the filtrate from the double ammonia precipitation and is in part precipitated with calcium and the remainder as manganese ammonium phosphate with magnesium, unless provision is made for its separation and estimation.

### PREPARATION AND SOLUTION OF THE SAMPLE

In dissolving the sample the following facts are important: The metal dissolves in dilute acids, forming manganese salts. The oxides and hydroxides of manganese are soluble in hot hydrochloric acid. Manganous oxide is soluble in nitric or in sulfuric acid; the dioxide is insoluble in dilute or concentrated nitric acid, but is soluble in hot concentrated sulfuric acid.

*Ores of Manganese.*—A sample of powdered ore weighing 1 g. is brought into solution by digesting with 25 to 50 ml. of hydrochloric acid (sp. gr. 1.19) for 15 to 30 minutes on the steam bath. If much silica is present 5 to 10 ml. hydrofluoric acid will assist solution. Five ml. of sulfuric acid is added and the mixture evaporated and heated until fumes of sulfur trioxide are evolved. The residue is taken up with a little water and warmed until the sulfates have dissolved. If decomposition is incomplete and a colored residue remains, this is filtered off, ignited in a platinum dish and fused with a little potassium bisulfate. The fusion is dissolved in water containing a little nitric acid and the solution added to the bulk of the sample.

*Sulfide Ores—Pyrites, etc.*—The sample may be treated with $HNO_3$ and evaporated with $HClO_4$; the residue is taken up with $HNO_3$ (sp. gr. 1.135), the solution is boiled to expel free chlorine.

*Slags.*—These may best be decomposed by treating with $HNO_3$ (sp. gr. 1.135) plus a few drops of HF and evaporation with $HClO_4$.

*Iron Ores.*—May be treated in the same fashion as slags.

*Manganese Alloys.*—Ferromanganese or silicomanganese (0.2 g.) is dissolved in a mixture of 20 ml. of dilute nitric acid (sp. gr. 1.25), 10 ml. of $HClO_4$, and 8 to 10 drops of HF. After addition of boric acid, the solution is evaporated to fumes of perchloric acid and chromium is volatilized by dropwise addition of HCl. Oxides of manganese are dissolved by boiling with HCl and $H_2O_2$ and the manganese determined titrimetrically by the pyrophosphate method.

[1] Lingane, J. J., and Karplus, R., Ind. Eng. Chem., **18,** 191, 1946.

*Manganese Alloys.*—One gram of ferromanganese is dissolved in 50 ml. of dilute nitric acid (sp. gr. 1.135) and treated with sodium bismuthate and the solution heated to boiling. The solution is cleared with $H_2SO_3$, cooled and diluted to 500 ml., and 10 to 25 ml. is treated with about 30 ml. of dilute nitric acid for the subsequent determination of manganese.

*Manganese Bronze.*—The sample may be dissolved in $HNO_3$ (sp. gr. 1.135).

*Ferrotitanium Alloy.*—This is best decomposed by fusion with sodium peroxide in a pure iron crucible, the fusion is taken up in water and rendered slightly acid with $HNO_3$. Sufficient $HNO_3$ (sp. gr. 1.42) is added to give a specific gravity of 1.135.

*Manganese in Ferrochrome and Metallic Chromium.*—Fuse one or two grams of the 35-mesh sample of low carbon ferrochromium or of the 100-mesh high carbon ferrochromium in a pure iron crucible with 8 to 12 grams of $Na_2O_2$, dissolve the melt in water, filter and wash the residue with water. The iron residue containing the manganese is dissolved in nitric acid (sp. gr. 1.135).

*Ferroaluminum.*—The method used for steel is suitable for this substance.

*Vanadium Alloys.*—For vanadium alloy, fuse the sample cautiously with $Na_2O_2$ in a pure iron crucible, dissolving the melt in water, add a little $Na_2O_2$, boil for three minutes and filter. The residue is dissolved in $HNO_3$ (sp. gr. 1.135) plus a small amount of $H_2SO_3$.

*Molybdenum Alloys.*—The manganese in these alloys may be determined in the same way as in steels.

*Tungsten Alloys and Ferrotungsten.*—Dissolve the sample in HF and a little $HNO_3$ in a platinum dish, add $HClO_4$ and evaporate to fumes of $HClO_4$. Transfer to a 250-ml. beaker with 100 ml. of water, boil to expel free chlorine, filter and wash with 1% $HNO_3$. Add sufficient $HNO_3$ (sp. gr. 1.42) to give a nitric acid solution of 1.135 specific gravity and finish by the bismuthate method. The tungstic acid residue may be tested by treating with a 5% excess of 10% NaOH solution and a little $Na_2O_2$, boiling and filtering. Any residue is dissolved in $HNO_3$ (sp. gr. 1.135) plus a little $H_2SO_3$, and added to the main solution.

*Ferrosilicon.*—Dissolve the sample in HF and $HNO_3$ and add either $H_2SO_4$ or $HClO_4$ and evaporate to fumes of sulfur trioxide or of $HClO_4$, take up with $HNO_3$ (sp. gr. 1.135), and boil in case $HClO_4$ was used.

*Titanium Alloys.*[2]—For titanium alloys containing less than 0.1% manganese, add 80 ml. of water, 20 ml. of HCl (sp. gr. 1.19), and 20 ml. of $H_2SO_4$ (sp. gr. 1.49) to a one-gram sample. Heat to boiling, add about 1 ml. of HF, and heat gently to dissolve the sample. Oxidize the titanium by dropwise addition of $HNO_3$ (sp. gr. 1.42), evaporate to fumes of sulfuric acid to remove chlorides, cool, and dilute with water. The manganese is oxidized with ammonium persulfate and the permanganate titrated with standard sodium arsenite solution.

For titanium alloys containing less than 0.2% manganese, dissolve 0.5 g. of the sample in 150 ml. of $H_2SO_4$ (sp. gr. 1.34). After the sample is in solution, add 25 ml. of 3% $H_2O_2$ and evaporate to dense fumes. Cool, add 100 ml. of water, and oxidize the manganese by boiling the solution with $KIO_4$. The permanganate color is measured photometrically.

*Iron and Steel.*—From 0.2 to 1 gram of steel is dissolved by heating with 30 to 50 ml. of dilute nitric acid (sp. gr. 1.135). The colorimetric method by oxidation

[2] Methods for chemical Analysis of Metals, A.S.T.M., p. 443, 1956.

with potassium periodate is generally recommended, no separations of other substances being required, as manganese may be determined directly in the sample.

**Pig and Cast Iron.**—One gram of the drillings is dissolved in 30 ml. of dilute nitric acid (sp. gr. 1.135), and as soon as the action has ceased the sample is filtered through a 7-cm. filter and the residue washed with 30 ml. more of the acid. The filtrate containing the manganese is now treated according to the procedure for steel.

## SEPARATIONS

Frequently the isolation of manganese is not necessary, since it may be determined titrimetrically in presence of a number of elements, which would interfere in its gravimetric determination. The analyst should be sufficiently familiar with the material to avoid needless manipulations, which not only waste time, but frequently lead to inaccurate results.

**Removal of Elements of the Hydrogen Sulfide Group.**—This separation may be required in the analysis of certain alloys where a separation of manganese from copper is required.

The acid solution containing about $4\%$ of free hydrochloric acid (sp. gr. 1.2), is saturated with hydrogen sulfide and the sulfides filtered off. Manganese passes into the filtrate. This treatment will effect a separation of manganese from mercury, lead, bismuth, cadmium, copper, arsenic, antimony, tin, and the less common elements of the group.

**Separation of Manganese from the Alkaline Earths and the Alkalies.**—The separation is occasionally required in the analysis of clays, limestone, dolomite, etc. It is required in the complete analysis of ores. In the usual course of a complete analysis of a substance, the filtrate from the hydrogen sulfide group is boiled free of $H_2S$ and is treated with a few milliliters of nitric acid to oxidize the iron. The solution is made slightly ammoniacal in the presence of ammonium chloride, whereby iron, aluminum, and chromium are precipitated as hydroxides. The filtrate is treated with hydrogen sulfide or colorless ammonium sulfide, whereby manganese, nickel, cobalt, and zinc are precipitated as sulfides and the alkaline earths and alkalies remain in solution.

**Separation of Manganese from Nickel and Cobalt.**—The free acid of the sulfate or chloride solution of the elements is neutralized with sodium carbonate and a slight excess added. It is now made strongly acid with acetic acid and 5 g. of ammonium acetate added for every gram of nickel and cobalt present. The solution is now diluted to about 200 ml. and saturated with hydrogen sulfide, whereby nickel and cobalt are precipitated as sulfides and manganese remains in solution.

**Separation of Manganese as Manganese Dioxide.**—Manganese is precipitated as $MnO_2$ from acid solution by $KClO_3$, $KBrO_3$ and from alkaline solution by Cl, Br, etc. Reducing agents should be absent. If the precipitate of $MnO_2$ is large, appreciable amounts of Fe, Co, Sb, and V will be occluded. The oxides of W, Si, Nb, and Ta will precipitate with $MnO_2$. See details under the "Gravimetric Methods."

**Separation of Manganese from Iron and Aluminum, Basic Acetate Method.**— The procedure effects a separation of iron, aluminum, titanium, zirconium, and vanadium from manganese, zinc, cobalt, and nickel.

The separation depends upon the fact that solutions of acetates of iron, aluminum, titanium, zirconium, and vanadium are decomposed when heated and the insoluble basic acetates precipitated, whereas the acetates of manganese, zinc, cobalt, and nickel remain undecomposed when boiled for a short time.

$$Fe(C_2H_3O_2)_2 + 2H_2O \rightarrow 2HC_2H_3O_2 + Fe(OH)_2 \cdot C_2H_3O_2$$

The solvent action of the liberated acetic acid is prevented by the addition of sodium acetate which checks ionization of the acid. The method requires care and is somewhat tedious, but the results obtained are excellent.

**Procedure.**—To the cooled acid solution of the chlorides is added a concentrated aqueous solution of sodium carbonate from a burette with constant stirring until the precipitate that forms dissolves slowly. A dilute solution of the carbonate is now added until a slight permanent opalescence is obtained. With the weak reagent and careful addition of the carbonate drop by drop the proper neutralization of the free acid is obtained. With considerable iron present the solution appears a dark red color, fading to colorless as the quantity of iron decreases to a mere trace in the solution. Three ml. of acetic acid (sp. gr. 1.044) are added to dissolve the slight precipitate. The more perfect the neutralization before heating the less amount of reagent required for precipitating iron—an excess of reagent does no harm. If this does not clear the solution in two minutes, more acetic acid is added a drop at a time until the solution clears, allowing a minute or so for the reaction to take place with each addition. The solution is diluted to about 500 ml. and heated to boiling and 6 ml. of a 30% sodium acetate solution added. The solution is boiled for one minute and removed from the flame. (Longer boiling will form a gelatinous precipitate, difficult to wash and filter.) The precipitate is allowed to settle for a minute or so, then filtered, while the liquid is hot, through a rapid filter and washed with hot, 5% sodium acetate solution three times. The apex of the filter is punctured with a glass stirring rod and the precipitate washed into the original beaker in which the precipitation was made with a fine stream of hot, 1:1 hydrochloric acid solution from a wash bottle. (Dilute $HNO_3$ may be used in place of HCl.)

*A second precipitation* with neutralization of the acid and addition of sodium acetate is made exactly as directed above. It is advisable to evaporate the solution to small volume to expel most of the free mineral acid before addition of $Na_2CO_3$ to avoid large quantities of this reagent. The filtrates contain manganese, zinc, cobalt, and nickel; the precipitate iron, aluminum, titanium, zirconium, and vanadium.

## GRAVIMETRIC METHODS

### SEPARATION OF MANGANESE AS MANGANESE DIOXIDE

Manganese is oxidized to $MnO_2$ in neutral solution of the manganous salt by chlorine, bromine, hypochlorite, hypobromite, ferricyanide; in acid solution by ammonium or potassium persulfate, potassium bromate, or potassium perchlorate. The reaction with bromate follows:

$$5Mn^{++} + 2BrO_3^- + 4H_2O \rightarrow 5MnO_2 + Br_2 + 8H^+$$

Iron may be present up to 100:1 but in excess of this hinders precipitation. In presence of large amounts of iron precipitation with hydrated zinc sulfate is advisable. A high concentration of ferric iron and a low concentration of manganese favor the formation of permanganate. In presence of iron under definite conditions results are reproducible and an empirical factor has been worked out. The National Bureau of Standards recommends multiplying the theoretical by 1.028. Kolthoff and Sandell apply a slightly lower factor under conditions given below. These authors recommend precipitation of $MnO_2$ by means of potassium bromate in presence of dilute acid, giving preference to this method over persulfate, since this reagent is not decomposed by boiling as is the persulfate and the precipitation of $MnO_2$ is more certain in presence of iron. Details of the method follow.

## POTASSIUM BROMATE METHOD FOR DETERMINATION OF MANGANESE [3]

Convenient quantities for the separation range from 20 to 150 mg. of manganese. The method is useful in determining comparatively large amounts of manganese.

The ore is brought into solution preferably by treating the finely ground sample with HCl and $KClO_3$. If iron is not already present an amount about equal to that of the manganese is added in form of ferric nitrate or sulfate. The presence of this iron makes it possible to get consistent results. Zinc sulfate may be added in place of iron; a slightly higher empirical factor is then necessary.

*Separation of Manganese.*—To a volume of about 50 ml., containing 20 to 150 mg. manganese, sufficient dilute sulfuric or nitric acid is added to make the solution 0.8 to 1.0 $N$ with respect to acid. Iron or zinc should be present for consistency of the empirical factor as stated above. One to 2 grams of potassium bromate are then added and the solution is heated to boiling and the boiling continued from 10 to 20 minutes according to the amount of iron present. (Samples containing a large ratio of iron require longer boiling than those in which the ratio is small.) If the iron content is more than 100:1 the period of precipitation is increased to such an extent that it is advisable to use the bismuthate method. Water is added to replenish that lost by boiling. The precipitate is filtered through ashless filter paper, passing the first portion again through the filter if it is turbid. Wash the dioxide thoroughly with hot water, using 6–10 portions of about 10 ml. each. The manganese may now be determined either gravimetrically or titrimetrically. If it is determined gravimetrically the oxide is ignited and weighed as $Mn_3O_4$. The oxide may be dissolved in $H_2SO_4$, the excess of acid expelled and the residue weighed as $MnSO_4$. The results for Mn should be multiplied by 1.02 if zinc is present and iron absent, or by 1.01 if iron alone is present. (See also under "Titrimetric Methods" for the details that follow at this stage.)

Manganates of zinc or calcium will be precipitated if present in large amounts.

Manganese may also be precipitated by ammonium persulfate in an ammoniacal solution or by potassium chlorate and chloride of lime in presence of zinc chloride in a neutral solution.[4]

## DETERMINATION OF MANGANESE AS PYROPHOSPHATE

Manganese is precipitated as ammonium manganese phosphate, $NH_4MnPO_4$, and then ignited to pyrophosphate, $Mn_2P_2O_7$.[5]

[3] Volumetric Determination of Manganese as Dioxide, by I. M. Kolthoff and E. B. Sandell, Ind. Eng. Chem., Anal. Ed., **1**, 181, 1929.
[4] Pattinson, J., J. Chem. Soc., **35**, 365, 1899.
[5] Gibbs, Chem. New, **17**, 195, 1868.

*Procedure.*—The cold solution of manganese chloride [6] obtained as directed in previous sections, should be diluted so as to contain not over 0.1 g. of manganese oxide equivalent per 100 ml. of solution. A cold saturated solution of ammonium sodium phosphate (170 g. per liter; 9 ml. precipitates an equivalent of 0.1 g. of the oxide) is now added in slight excess. The solution is made strongly ammoniacal and heated to boiling, the boiling being continued until the precipitate becomes crystalline. After allowing to settle until cold, the precipitate is filtered off (the filtrate being tested with more of the precipitating reagent to assure that an excess had been added), and dissolved in a little dilute hydrochloric or sulfuric acid.

**Reprecipitation of the Phosphate.**—The free acid is neutralized with ammonia added in slight excess until the odor is quite distinct, the solution heated to boiling, and a few milliliters of additional phosphate reagent added. The crystalline precipitate is filtered into a weighed Gooch crucible, washed free of chlorides with very dilute ammonia ($AgNO_3 + HNO_3$ test), dried and ignited to the pyrophosphate. The ignition is conducted, as in case of magnesium, by heating first over a low flame and gradually increasing the heat to the full power of the burner. The final residue will appear white or a pale pink.

$$Mn_2P_2O_7 \times 0.4999 = MnO$$

$$\times 0.3871 = Mn$$

NOTES.—Zinc, nickel, copper, and other elements precipitated as phosphates should be absent from the solution. The separation from iron is generally made by the basic acetate method and manganese precipitated from the filtrate, free of other elements, as the peroxide $MnO_2$, by means of bromine added to the ammoniacal solution. Other oxidizing reagents may be used, as has been stated. The dioxide is dissolved in strong hydrochloric acid and the above precipitation effected.

## TITRIMETRIC METHODS

### VOLHARD'S METHOD FOR MANGANESE [7]

The method is based on the principle that when potassium permanganate is added to a neutral manganese salt all of the manganese is oxidized and precipitated. When this stage is reached any excess of permanganate is immediately evident by the color produced. The calculation of results may be based on the reaction,

$$3MnSO_4 + 2KMnO_4 + 2H_2O \rightarrow 5MnO_2 + K_2SO_4 + 2H_2SO_4,$$

or

$$5ZnSO_4 + 6MnSO_4 + 4KMnO_4 + 14H_2O \rightarrow 4KHSO_4 + 7H_2SO_4 + 5ZnH_2 \cdot 2MnO_3,$$

the ratio in either case being $2KMnO_4 = 3Mn$.

*Procedure.*—The material decomposed with hydrochloric and nitric acid and taken to fumes with sulfuric acid, as stated for the preparation of the sample, is

---

[6] Some analysts prefer to add the phosphate reagent to the strongly ammoniacal solution, boiling hot.

(N.B. also F. A. Gooch and M. Austin, Am. J. Sci. (IV), **6,** 233, 1898. A. Blair, The Chemical Analysis of Iron, 8 ed., p. 106.)

[7] Applicable for high-grade ores.

cooled and boiled with 25 ml. of water until all salts have dissolved; then continue as follows: Transfer the mixture to a 500-ml. volumetric flask and add an emulsion of zinc oxide in slight excess to precipitate the iron.

Agitate the flask to facilitate the precipitation and see that a slight excess of zinc oxide remains when the reaction is complete. Now dilute the contents of the flask up to the mark with cold water, mix thoroughly and allow to stand a short time and partially settle. By means of a graduated pipette draw off 100 ml. of the clear supernatant liquid and transfer it to a 250-ml. flask. While the precipitate in the 500-ml. flask may appear large, it actually occupies but a very small space, and any error caused by it may consequently be neglected. Likewise the error in measurement due to change of temperature during the manipulation is insignificant. Heat the solution in the small flask to boiling, add two or three drops of nitric acid (which causes the subsequent precipitate to settle more quickly) and titrate with a standard solution of potassium permanganate. The permanganate causes a precipitate which clouds the liquid and it is therefore necessary to titrate cautiously and agitate the flask after each addition, and then allow the precipitate to settle sufficiently to observe whether or not the solution is colored pink. A little experience will enable one to judge by the volume of the precipitate formed, about how rapidly to run in the permanganate. The final pink tinge, indicating the end of the reaction, is best observed by holding the flask against a white background and observing the upper edges of the liquid. When this point is attained, bring the contents of the flask nearly to a boil once more and again observe if the pink tint still persists, adding more permanganate if necessary. In making this end test avoid actually boiling the liquid, as a continual destruction of the color may sometimes thus be effected and the true end point considerably passed. When the color thus remains permanent the operation is ended. Observe the number of milliliters of permanganate solution used and calculate the result.

It is customary to use the same permanganate solution for both iron and manganese. Having determined the factor for iron, this may be multiplied by 0.2952 [8] to obtain the factor for manganese. It will be observed that $2KMnO_4$ are required for 3Mn, and in the reaction for iron that $2KMnO_4$ are required for 10Fe.

## BISMUTHATE METHOD [9]

The determination of manganese by the bismuthate method is generally conceded to be one of the most accurate analytical procedures for determination of this element. It is simple and rapid, and generally can be accomplished without a previous separation being necessary. The principle of the process depends upon the fact that under certain conditions bivalent manganese can be quantitatively oxidized to permanganic acid by sodium bismuthate. This permanganic acid can be titrated by a standard reducing agent such as sodium arsenite or ferrous sulfate. A typical method illustrating this procedure follows:

### DETERMINATION OF MANGANESE IN MANGANESE ORE

This method is designed for standard manganese ores containing approximately 50% manganese. The steps involved are: solution in HCl and $HClO_4$, expulsion of HCl by fuming, and recovery of any insoluble residue by fusion with $Na_2S_2O_8$.

---

[8] An empirical factor 0.2984 is recommended by Cir. No. 26, National Bureau of Standards, in place of 0.2952 to obtain the manganese factor from iron.
[9] Cunningham, C. R., and Cotton, R. W., Ind. Eng. Chem., **16,** 58, 1924.

After adjusting the volume and acidity, the manganese is oxidized with $NaBiO_3$ and titrated with $FeSO_4$.

*Reagents.* **Potassium Permanganate (0.1 $N$).**—Dissolve 3.18 g. of $KMnO_4$ in 300 ml. of $H_2O$, heat to boiling, and boil 10 to 15 minutes; cool and filter through acid-washed and ignited asbestos, avoiding contact with rubber or dust. Dilute to 1000 ml. and mix thoroughly. Make a preliminary standardization, adjust to 0.1 $N$, then make a second comparison with sodium oxalate. The standardization against sodium oxalate is carried out as follows:

Transfer 0.3000 g. of sodium oxalate (dried at 105°C.) to a 600-ml. beaker. Add 250 ml. of diluted sulfuric acid (5:95) previously boiled for 10 to 15 minutes and then cooled to 27°C. ± 3°. Stir until the oxalate has dissolved. Add 39 to 40 ml. of 0.1 $N$ potassium permanganate at a rate of 25 to 35 ml. per minute, while stirring slowly. (0.3000 g. of sodium oxalate will require 44.78 ml. of 0.1 $N$ $KMnO_4$.) Let stand until the pink color disappears (about 45 seconds). If the pink color should persist because the permanganate is too strong, discard, and begin again, adding a few ml. less of the $KMnO_4$ solution. Heat to 55 to 60°C. and complete the titration by adding permanganate until a faint pink color persists for 30 seconds. Add the last 0.5 to 1 ml. dropwise with particular care to allow each drop to become decolorized before the next is introduced.

Determine the excess of permanganate required to impart a pink color to the solution. This can be done by matching the color by adding permanganate to the same volume of the specially treated dilute sulfuric acid at 55 to 60°C. This correction usually amounts to 0.03 to 0.05 ml. For further details consult National Bureau of Standards Journal of Research, **15**, 493, 1935.

The standardization is based on the following reaction:

$$5C_2O_4^= + 2MnO_4^- + 16H^+ \rightarrow 2Mn^{++} + 10CO_2 + 8H_2O$$

Theoretically, 44.78 ml. of 0.1 $N$ $KMnO_4$ are required for 0.3000 g. of $Na_2C_2O_4$.

**Standard Ferrous Ammonium Sulfate.**—Mix thoroughly 500 g. of fine crystal $FeSO_4 \cdot (NH_4)_2SO_4 \cdot 6H_2O$ and standardize as follows:

Transfer 250 ml. of $HNO_3$ (sp. gr. 1.135) to a 750-ml. Erlenmeyer flask, add approximately 2 g. of $NaBiO_3$, shake for 1 minute, dilute to 500 ml. with cold water, and filter on a sintered glass funnel covered with a layer of asbestos. Add 5.000 g. of the $FeSO_4 \cdot (NH_4)_2SO_4$ to the filtrate and titrate immediately with 0.1 $N$ $KMnO_4$ to a faint permanent pink end point. *o*-Phenanthroline-ferrous ion may be used to locate this end point. The excess $KMnO_4$ to give a pink color must be determined by matching with the color of a like amount of acid and water in another beaker.

Thus, the strength of the $FeSO_4 \cdot (NH_4)_2SO_4$ is obtained in terms of ml. of 0.1 $N$ $KMnO_4$. If the salt is kept in a well-stoppered bottle, its composition will change only very slowly, so that once a quantity of the salt has been carefully mixed and standardized, it may be used for a considerable period without being restandardized.

*Procedure.*—Transfer approximately 0.50 g. of the 200-mesh sample to a 10-ml. weighing bottle and dry for 1 hour at 120°C. Cool in a desiccator and weigh the bottle and contents, loosening the stopper momentarily to equalize the pressure. Dump the contents of the weighing bottle into a 250-ml. beaker, stopper the bottle, and reweigh to obtain the exact weight of ore taken for analysis. (Note 1.)

Add 25 ml. of HCl and 20 ml. of $HClO_4$ to the beaker and digest until the sample is all dissolved except for a light-colored silicious residue. (Note 2.) Then evaporate to dense fumes of $HClO_4$ and fume for a few minutes. Cool somewhat and rinse the cover and sides of the beaker with a little water. Again heat to dense fumes of $HClO_4$. Cool, add 50 ml. of water and boil for about 5 minutes to expel free chlorine. Add sufficient $H_2SO_3$ to dissolve any separated oxides of manganese, boil for a few minutes, then filter through a 9-cm. Whatman No. 40 filter paper into a 750-ml. Erlenmeyer flask. Wash the paper and residue about 20 times with hot water. Reserve the filtrate.

Ignite the residue in a platinum crucible until the filter paper is oxidized, cool, treat with a few drops of $H_2SO_4$ and 2 ml. of HF and evaporate to dryness. Fuse the residue with 1 to 2 g. of $Na_2S_2O_7$, dissolve the melt in 25 ml. of $H_2O$, and add to the reserved filtrate. (Note 3.)

Add 75 ml. of $HNO_3$ and sufficient $H_2O$ to the filtrate to bring the solution to a total volume of 250 ml. Add 1 g. of $NaBiO_3$ and a few glass beads, then heat to boiling, and boil for several minutes. Clear the solution with a sufficient volume of $H_2SO_3$, boil for 5 minutes to expel oxides of nitrogen, and cool. Readjust the volume to 250 ml. with water and cool to between 10° and 15°C. in a refrigerator.

Add approximately 7 g. of $NaBiO_3$ (26 g. for each g. of manganese present), agitate the solution for 1 minute, dilute with 250 ml. of water (10° to 15°C.), and filter immediately through a thin layer of acid-washed asbestos on a medium-porosity, fritted-glass funnel (Corning Catalog No. 36060) using moderate suction. Wash the filter and residue with cold $HNO_3$ (3:97), prepared from colorless $HNO_3$, until the washings are colorless. At no time should the filter be allowed to suck dry until the washings are colorless lest manganese be retained in the residue.

Add 9.000 g. of the standard $FeSO_4 \cdot (NH_4)_2SO_4 \cdot 6H_2O$ to the filtrate, stir until the salt is dissolved, then back-titrate the excess with 0.1 $N$ $KMnO_4$ to a permanent pink end point as was used above to standardize the ferrous ammonium sulfate. Convert the ferrous ammonium sulfate to ml. of 0.1 $N$ $KMnO_4$, subtract the back titration, and calculate the manganese content.

$$1 \text{ ml. } 0.1 \ N \ \text{KMnO}_4 = 0.0010988 \text{ g. of manganese}$$

NOTES.—1. Manganese ores are frequently so hygroscopic as to render necessary the procedure described. The use of a 0.5-g. sample is based on the assumption that the ore contains approximately 50% manganese. If the percentage of manganese should vary 3% or more in either direction from 50%, a larger or smaller weight of sample should be taken in order that the weight of manganese will be approximately 0.2500 g.

2. The sample can be decomposed by treating with 50 ml. of $HNO_3$ (sp. gr. 1.135) and 10 ml. of 3% $H_2O_2$ instead of HCl and $HClO_4$. The insoluble residue is treated as described for the $HCl$-$HClO_4$ procedure.

3. Any barium in the ore will precipitate when the sulfuric acid solution of the residue is added to the main solution, but the barium sulfate does not interfere with the subsequent operations.

4. Small amounts of chromium (less than 2%) do not interfere with the determination. Larger amounts of chromium interfere to some extent and should be separated prior to the oxidation with bismuthate.

## DETERMINATION OF MANGANESE IN FERROMANGANESE AND MANGANESE METAL

This method is applicable to all grades of ferromanganese and manganese metal. Chromium under 2% does not interfere. Results in two laboratories on the same sample should not differ by more than 0.20% manganese. The sample is decomposed with $HNO_3$ and carbon destroyed by fuming with $HClO_4$. Alternatively, especially for high-carbon material, the sample may be fused with $Na_2O_2$. The manganese is then oxidized to $HMnO_4$ with $NaBiO_3$ under carefully controlled conditions of temperature, acidity, and concentration. The $HMnO_4$ is reduced with $FeSO_4$-$NH_4SO_4$, and the excess ferrous ion back-titrated with standard $KMnO_4$.

*Reagents.* **Sodium Bismuthate.**—The sodium bismuthate shall contain enough active oxygen to correspond to at least 75% $NaBiO_3$.

**Nitric Acid (3:97).**—Boil 40 ml. of $HNO_3$ until decolorized, cool, and pass in a current of clean air for 5 minutes. Mix 30 ml. of this acid with 970 ml. of water, add 1 g. of $NaBiO_3$, shake, and allow to settle. Use the clear supernatant liquid for wash solution.

**Ferrous Ammonium Sulfate.**—Mix the contents of a bottle of fine crystals of $FeSO_4 \cdot (NH_4)_2SO_4 \cdot 6H_2O$ thoroughly and determine the manganese value as follows: Add 250 ml. of $HNO_3$ (1:3) to a 750-ml. Erlenmeyer flask containing approximately 2 g. of $NaBiO_3$. Agitate the solution vigorously for one minute, dilute with 250 ml. of ice water, and filter on a layer of acid-washed asbestos or a fritted-glass filtering funnel. Add 5.000 g. of the ferrous ammonium sulfate to the filtrate and titrate the resulting solution immediately with 0.1 $N$ $KMnO_4$. $o$-Phenanthroline can be used as the indicator in which case the color change is from pink to clear green or the pink of excess $KMnO_4$ can be used as the end point and the excess $KMnO_4$ determined by matching with a blank of the same volume and acidity. Calculate the titer of the solid ferrous ammonium sulfate. One ml. of 0.1 $N$ $KMnO_4$ is equal to 0.0010988 g. of manganese. If the ferrous ammonium sulfate is kept in a well-stoppered bottle, it may be used for at least a week without restandardizing.

$o$-**Phenanthroline Indicator.**—Dissolve 1.5 g. of $o$-phenanthroline monohydrate in 100 ml. of water containing 0.7 g. of $FeSO_4 \cdot 7H_2O$.

*Procedure.* **Solution in $HNO_3$.**—Transfer 0.2500 g. of the 100-mesh sample to a 750-ml. Erlenmeyer flask with a mark at 250 ml. Add 15 ml. of $HNO_3$ (1:3) and digest until solution is complete. Add 10 ml. of $HClO_4$, cover the flask, and boil gently so that $HClO_4$ refluxes on the sides of the flask and no great amount is lost by volatilization. Continue the heating until manganese dioxide separates from the solution. Cool, add 10 ml. of water and 50 ml. of $HNO_3$ (1:3), again heat to boiling, and boil for about 5 minutes to expel free chlorine. Add $H_2SO_3$ or $NaNO_2$ solution dropwise until the $MnO_2$ redissolves, then boil the solution for 5 minutes to expel oxides of nitrogen. Cool to room temperature, dilute to 250 ml. with $HNO_3$ (1:3), and cool to 10 to 15°C. (Note 1.)

**Fusion with $Na_2O_2$.**—Transfer 0.2500 g. of the sample to a new iron crucible containing approximately 5 g. of dry $Na_2O_2$. Mix the contents thoroughly (*put on goggles*) and fuse by rotating the crucible in the outer edge of the flame of a laboratory burner until the mixture blackens. Finally heat at a bright red heat for one or two minutes.

Cool, cover the crucible, and tap on a solid object to loosen the fusion as a cake. Transfer the cake and crucible to a dry 600-ml. beaker. Cover and add 25 ml. of water. When the vigorous action ceases, add 10 ml. of $H_2SO_3$, then $HNO_3$ until the precipitate just dissolves. Add an excess of 10 ml. of $HNO_3$ and remove and rinse the crucible. Boil the solution for 5 minutes, cool, add 50 ml. of colorless $HNO_3$, and transfer to a 750-ml. Erlenmeyer flask with a mark at 250 ml. Wash any iron scale by decantation and discard. Dilute to 250 ml. with water and cool to 10 to 15°C.

**Oxidation of Manganese.**—Add approximately 7 g. of NaBiO$_3$ (26 g. of NaBiO$_3$ are required for each gram of manganese) to the solution prepared by either procedure. Agitate the solution briskly for one minute, dilute with 250 ml. of cold water, and immediately filter on a layer of acid-washed asbestos supported on a 2-inch porcelain plate resting in a large glass funnel or on a medium-porosity, fritted-glass funnel (Corning Catalog No. 36060). Wash the flask, filter, and residue with the HNO$_3$ wash solution until the washings are entirely colorless. Add 9.000 g. of the ferrous ammonium sulfate to the filtrate, stir until the salt is dissolved and the reduction is complete, then titrate the excess ferrous ammonium sulfate with 0.1 $N$ KMnO$_4$ using $o$-phenanthroline as the indicator until the color changes from pink to clear green.

NOTES.—The conditions necessary for securing complete oxidation of large quantities of manganese by bismuthate and for preventing the permanganic acid from undergoing any appreciable decomposition during the subsequent filtration are summarized below.

**Concentration of Nitric Acid.**—The manganese should be present in a solution containing from 11% (sp. gr. 1.062) to 22% (sp. gr. 1.135) by weight of nitric acid. If the concentration of nitric acid falls much below 11%, the oxidation of the manganese will not be complete unless the time of shaking be increased to more than 1 minute.

**Concentration of Manganese.**—A solution of permanganic acid containing about 0.05 g. of manganese per 100 ml. has the maximum stability, but the weight of manganese can be increased to 0.1 g. in 100 ml. without danger of any material decomposition occurring during the time required for filtering off the excess of bismuthate. When the concentration of manganese rises much above 0.10 g. per 100 ml., the rate of decomposition of the permanganic acid is unduly rapid.

**Amount of Sodium Bismuthate Necessary.**—Approximately 26 g. of sodium bismuthate (79% NaBiO$_3$) must be used for 1 g. of manganese.

**Time of Oxidation.**—Shaking for 1 minute is sufficient to insure complete oxidation of the manganese to permanganic acid provided the foregoing conditions are adhered to strictly.

Chlorides should be removed by taking the solution to fumes with H$_2$SO$_4$. The residue is dissolved in a small amount of water and the solution is evaporated to fumes a second time to insure the removal of every trace of chloride.

The only common metals that seriously interfere with the determination are cerium, cobalt, and Cr(VI). A method for the determination of cerium outlined by Metzger is exactly the same in principle as the bismuthate method for manganese. Any cerium present must therefore be separated as oxalate in acid solution, and the oxalic acid in the filtrate destroyed by evaporation with sulfuric and nitric acids as a preliminary to the determination of manganese.

The pink color produced by large amounts of cobalt interferes with the titration of permanganic acid. This can be overcome by separating the manganese from the bulk of the cobalt by precipitating it with sodium or potassium chlorate.

While trivalent chromium is in hot solution oxidized to the Cr(VI) state by bismuthate and by permanganic acid, the error caused by small amounts of trivalent chromium is not appreciable provided the solution is kept cold (10°C.), and is oxidized, filtered, and titrated as rapidly as possible. When more than a small percentage of chromium is present, it should be separated from the manganese by one of the several methods that have been proposed. Precipitation of the manganese from a nitric acid solution with sodium or potassium chlorate with subsequent filtration does not effect complete removal of chromium, but is useful in some cases. Fusion with sodium peroxide followed by filtration will give a complete separation, manganese remaining in the residue as oxide and chromium passing into the filtrate as sodium chromate. Watters precipitates chromium and ferric iron with zinc oxide and determines manganese in the filtrate, while Cain precipitates chromium and vanadium from a ferrous solution with cadmium carbonate and analyzes the filtrate for manganese. Cr(VI) interferes with the determination of manganese by the bismuthate method and must be reduced to the trivalent condition prior to the final oxidation with bismuthate.

Although any vanadium present is reduced by the ferrous sulfate added during the determination, it is re-oxidized by an equivalent amount of permanganic acid during the back titration, the manganese titration as a consequence being unaffected.

## PYROPHOSPHATE (POTENTIOMETRIC) METHOD

In recent years this method has replaced the bismuthate procedure to a great extent for titration of high concentrations of manganese. Lingane and Karplus [10] titrated manganese(II) potentiometrically in a pyrophosphate solution at a pH near 6.5 to manganese(III) with a standard solution of potassium permanganate.

$$4Mn^{++} + MnO_4^- + 8H^+ + 15H_2P_2O_7^= \rightarrow 5Mn(H_2P_2O_7)_3^{-3} + 4H_2O$$

This method has been applied to the determination of manganese in manganese alloys such as ferromanganese and silicomanganese, and manganese ores. A typical procedure illustrating this method follows:

### DETERMINATION OF MANGANESE IN FERROMANGANESE AND SILICOMANGANESE

**Apparatus.** **Beckman pH Meter, Model G or Equivalent.**—Equipped with a platinum, calomel-shielded electrode (Note 1), and a glass electrode.

**Reagents.** **Standard KMnO$_4$ Solution (0.05 N).**—Standardize against N.B.S. (National Bureau of Standards) sodium oxalate. Take 0.26 g. of oxalate for standardization of KMnO$_4$; this requires 77.61 ml. of 0.05 N KMnO$_4$. This is approximately the volume used in titration of standard ferromanganese and silicomanganese samples.

**Sodium Pyrophosphate, Na$_4$P$_2$O$_7$·10H$_2$O, Saturated Water Solution.**—The reagent must be free from impurities. Each lot should be tested by analyzing a solution containing a known amount of manganese in the form of a standard manganese solution. If the results are erratic, the sodium pyrophosphate should be purified by recrystallization.

**Procedure.**—Transfer 0.2000 g. of the sample to a 600-ml. beaker (Note 2). Add 15 ml. of HNO$_3$, 10 ml. of HClO$_4$, and 8 to 10 drops of HF, cover, and heat gently to complete dissolution. Add 1 g. of H$_3$BO$_3$ and evaporate to dense fumes of HClO$_4$ (Note 3). Volatilize any chromium present by dropwise addition of HCl. When the chromyl chloride has been expelled, as shown by the disappearance of the orange vapors, replace the cover and evaporate to dense fumes of HClO$_4$. Cool and rinse the cover and sides of the beaker with approximately 25 ml. of water. Add 2 or 3 drops of sulfurous acid to reduce the manganese and boil for five minutes. Cool to room temperature and add approximately 350 ml. of saturated sodium pyrophosphate solution.

Place the beaker on a magnetic stirrer, insert the glass and calomel electrodes in the solution, and adjust the pH to 6.5 with freshly prepared NaOH solution (200 g./liter) and H$_2$SO$_4$ (1:1) if the solution becomes too basic. Replace the glass electrode with the platinum electrode, turn the meter on, and let stand for 5 minutes (Note 4) at 20°C. After stable potential has been reached, titrate potentiometrically with 0.05 N KMnO$_4$, add the KMnO$_4$ rapidly until the first deflection of the galvanometer is noted and then dropwise to the equivalence point. Calculate the amount of manganese in the sample.

One ml. of 0.05 N KMnO$_4$ = 0.0021972 g. of manganese

NOTES.—1. Calomel electrodes that have been allowed to dry out will give very poor results.

2. For silicomanganese, use 0.2500 g. of the sample and dissolve in 15 ml. of HNO$_3$ plus

[10] Lingane, J. S., and Karplus, R., Analytical Chemistry, **18,** 191, 1946.

20 drops of HF (previously mixed). Add 10 ml. of $HClO_4$ and proceed as described. For manganese metal, dissolve 0.1500 g. in $HNO_3$ and $HClO_4$ as described for ferromanganese.

3. Avoid prolonged fuming which will precipitate manganese as oxide from the solution.

4. This waiting period gives a more stable initial potential (usually from +200 to +350 millivolts). The first drop that gives a potential change of 50 mv. or more is the best end point.

## IODOMETRIC METHOD

Manganese is precipitated as dioxide according to the procedure described under the "Gravimetric Methods—Bromate Method." The dioxide placed in the flask in which the precipitation is made is treated with 50–75 ml. of water and 5 ml. of 20% solution of $KF \cdot 2H_2O$ and 5 ml. 4 $N$ $H_2SO_4$ and about 1–2 g. of KI. The liberated iodine is titrated with 0.1 $N$ $Na_2S_2O_3$ solution. Use a weaker solution of $Na_2S_2O_3$ if the amounts of Mn are small. Near the end point the flask should be shaken and the titration completed.

Empirical factors—Zinc present and iron absent: 1 ml. 0.1 $N$ $Na_2S_2O_3$, 0.002747 × 1.02 = 0.002801 g. Mn. Iron present: 1 ml. 0.1 $N$ $Na_2S_2O_3$, 0.002747 × 1.01 = 0.002774 g. Mn.

## FERROUS SULFATE METHOD

Separate manganese as dioxide according to the method described under "Gravimetric Methods—Bromate Method." To the washed precipitate add dilute sulfuric acid and an excess of standard ferrous sulfate. Titrate the excess with standard potassium permanganate. Convert the two solutions to equivalent volumes and multiply the difference ($FeSO_4 - KMnO_4$) by the empirical factors given above under "Iodometric Method."

NOTES.—Kolthoff and Sandell [11] state that chromium does not affect results. Molybdates, except in small amounts, give results that are too low; tungsten to a less extent gives low results. Phosphoric acid in appreciable quantities interferes. Cobalt and iron may be present to the extent of 70 mg. with 75 mg. Mn. Small amounts of lead, nickel and bismuth may be present. Chlorides are oxidized by the bromate and do not interfere. Ammonium salts should not be present in quantity. Vanadium is absorbed by the $MnO_2$, but does not interfere with the Ferrous Sulfate Method.

## FORD-WILLIAMS METHOD FOR MANGANESE

In this method manganese dioxide is precipitated by potassium chlorate from a nitric acid solution. Chlorine dioxide gas that is formed by the reaction is boiled off, the manganese dioxide is dissolved by an excess of ferrous sulfate or oxalic acid and the excess of the reducing agent is titrated with standard potassium permanganate.

*Reagents.*—0.03 $N$ solutions of potassium permanganate, ferrous sulfate (or oxalic acid or sodium oxalate). See "Manganese in Steel" for preparation of reagents, Chapter on Iron.

*Procedure.*—A sample of about 3 g. of steel is dissolved in 60 ml. of dilute nitric acid (sp. gr. 1.2). (For ores see "Preparation and Solution of the Sample.") The solution is evaporated to about 50 ml. and 50 ml. concentrated nitric acid added and about 3 g. of potassium chlorate. The solution is boiled for about 15 minutes and the flask removed from the source of heat. ($KClO_3$ added to boiling $HNO_3$ will cause an explosion.) Fifty ml. more of nitric acid (sp. gr. 1.42) are added and 3 g. of $KClO_3$ and the solution again boiled. After cooling under water of a tap, the precipitated $MnO_2$ is filtered onto asbestos (an asbestos mat over a plug

[11] Ind. Eng. Chem., Anal. Ed., **1**, 181, 1929.

of glass wool in a funnel), and is washed with concentrated nitric acid until free from iron and then with water until free from acid.

The precipitate is now placed in a flask, together with the asbestos, 50 ml. of the standard ferrous sulfate are added and the solution diluted to about 200 ml. The mixture is shaken to dissolve the $MnO_2$ and the excess of 0.03 $N$ ferrous solution is titrated with 0.03 $N$ potassium permanganate.

**Calculation.**—If the permanganate is standardized against sodium oxalate, the oxalate equivalent of 1 ml. of the permanganate solution multiplied by 0.4099 will give the equivalent manganese per ml., according to theory (see note).

NOTE.—The nitric acid must be free from nitrous acid as this reduces $MnO_2$.

The permanganate equivalent is $\frac{5}{3}$ of the permanganate equivalent of the Volhard's method, in which the valence of manganese is reduced from 7 to 4. Here the valence is reduced to 2. It is advisable to get the value of the reagents in terms of manganese on standard samples of manganese.

## DETERMINATION OF MANGANESE IN STEELS AND CAST IRON BY THE PERSULFATE-ARSENITE METHOD [12]

This method is applicable to all steels and cast irons with cobalt $<5\%$ and manganese $<1.5\%$. Cerium interferes. The principle of the method is solution in $HNO_3$-$H_3PO_4$-$H_2SO_4$ followed by oxidation of the manganese with $(NH_4)_2S_2O_8$-$AgNO_3$. The $HMnO_4$ is titrated with $Na_3AsO_3$ either visually or potentiometrically. Modifications are given for chromium and tungsten steels.

**Reagents.** **Acid Mixture.**—Dissolve 8 g. of $AgNO_3$ in 525 ml. of water, add 100 ml. of $H_2SO_4$, cool somewhat, and add 125 ml. of $H_3PO_4$ and 250 ml. of $HNO_3$.

**Sodium Arsenite Solution.**—Transfer 3.4 g. of $As_2O_3$ to a 600-ml. beaker, add 250 ml. of water, 15 g. of NaOH, and stir until solution is complete. Saturate with $CO_2$, then dilute to 5000 ml.

**Procedure.**—Transfer 1.000 g. of the sample to a 400-ml. beaker, add 30 ml. of the acid mixture (see Notes for modification for chromium and tungsten steels), and heat until action ceases. Cool, add 200 ml. of water, 15 ml. of freshly prepared 25% $(NH_4)_2S_2O_8$ solution, and a few glass beads. Heat to boiling and boil vigorously for 60 to 90 seconds. Cool to $<20°C.$, dilute to 300 ml. with ice water, and titrate rapidly with the standard arsenite solution to a clear yellow end point which does not change on the addition of more arsenite.

The titration can be made potentiometrically. In this case, titrate to the first large change in potential after the disappearance of the pink color.

Both end points are empirical and the arsenite must be standardized with a N.B.S. standard steel containing approximately the same amount of manganese put through all steps of the procedure.

NOTES.—1. If the manganese content is greater than 1.5%, the end point is difficult to locate, so better results are obtained if the size of the sample is reduced so that not more than 15 mg. of manganese are present.

2. If the steel contains more than 2% chromium, dissolve the sample in 20 ml. of HCl and 10 ml. of $HNO_3$. When solution is complete, add 10 ml. of $HClO_4$, evaporate to fumes of $HClO_4$, and continue the fuming until the chromium is oxidized. Cool, add 30 ml. of water, heat to boiling, and boil a few minutes to expel free chlorine. Add sufficient (13%) $Pb(NO_3)_2$ solution to precipitate the chromium (1 ml. will precipitate 2% chromium), boil one minute, and cool to $<20°C$. Stir until the precipitate becomes crystalline, allow to settle, and filter through a 9-cm. Whatman No. 40 paper catching the filtrate in a 250-ml. beaker. Wash the paper about 10 times with $HClO_4$ (1:99).

[12] Jour. Res. NBS, **3,** 573, 1929.

Add 5 ml. of $H_2SO_4$ (1:1) to precipitate lead, stir well, and filter through a 9-cm. Whatman No. 40 paper catching the filtrate in a 400-ml. beaker. Add 5 ml. of $H_3PO_4$ and 5 ml. of 0.5% $AgNO_3$ to the filtrate, adjust the volume to 125 ml., and oxidize the manganese as described for plain steels.

3. If the steel contains tungsten, treat the sample with 50 ml. of $H_2SO_4$ (1:9) and 5 ml. of $H_3PO_4$. Heat until action ceases, then add 40 ml. of water and 5 ml. of $HNO_3$, boil until the carbides dissolve, then proceed with the oxidation.

Cast irons are treated as steels. It is not necessary to remove the graphite.

## COLORIMETRIC/PHOTOMETRIC METHODS

## OXIDATION WITH $KIO_4$ [13] (WILLARD-GREATHOUSE METHOD)

Manganous ion is oxidized to $HMnO_4$ in nitric acid solution by a slight excess of $KIO_4$. The color is stable for a long period of time.

*General Procedure.*—The substance to be examined is brought into a solution containing per 100 ml. at least 10 ml. of concentrated $H_2SO_4$ and 10 ml. of concentrated $HNO_3$, or 5 to 10 ml. of concentrated $H_3PO_4$. Reducing substances should be removed by prior oxidation with $HNO_3$ or $HClO_4$ or by adding a little persulfate if carbon compounds are present as in steels. Chloride must be removed by evaporation to fumes of $SO_3$. Then 0.2 to 0.4 g. of $KIO_4$ is added and the solution is boiled for 10 minutes, cooled, diluted to a proper volume, and the absorbance of the solution measured with a spectrophotometer or photometer.

If iron is present, either sulfuric or phosphoric acid must be present. Ferric periodate is insoluble in fairly concentrated nitric acid but dissolves in the other acids.

Ammonium salts or $HClO_4$ do not interfere nor do the metallic ions that are commonly present unless they are colored. Colored ions such as chromium, nickel, cobalt, and copper interfere but may be compensated for by use of a suitable reference solution. If much chromium is present, it is advisable to measure the colored system in an instrument with a narrow band width (less than 30 m$\mu$). The absorbance is measured at 545 m$\mu$ or 575 m$\mu$ rather than at 525 m$\mu$ to eliminate much of the absorption from the chromate ion.

For the determination of large concentrations of manganese, the differential spectrophotometric method may be used in which an oxidized manganese solution is compared with a standard permanganate solution placed in the reference beam of the spectrophotometer.

The method is applicable to the determination of manganese in water, soil, ores, alloys, and other materials in which the element is present in small amounts.

## DETERMINATION OF MANGANESE IN STEELS AND CAST IRONS (SPECTROPHOTOMETRIC METHOD WITH PERIODATE OXIDATION)

The procedures in this method are applicable for the determination of manganese in trace concentrations to several per cent in steels. This method is based on solution of the sample in $HNO_3$, $H_3PO_4$, $HClO_4$, or mixtures of the three acids with a small addition of HF to decompose carbides and to remove silicon, followed by oxidation of the manganese to $HMnO_4$ with $KIO_4$. The manganese is then determined spectrophotometrically.

Colored ions such as chromium, nickel, cobalt, and copper interfere with the

[13] Young, I. G., and Hiskey, C. F., Anal. Chem., **23,** 506–8, 1951; Cooper, M. D., Anal. Chem., **25,** 511, 1953.

measurement of the colored system. These can be compensated for by the use of a prepared reference solution for the blank. Chromium may be removed by volatilization with HCl.

The concentration range for the manganese colored solution obeys Beer's Law from 0.1 to 2.0 mg. of manganese in 100 ml. of solution using 1-cm. cells. The absorbance may be read at 525 or 545 m$\mu$.

*Reagents.* **Standard Manganese Solution (0.05 mg. of manganese per ml. of solution).**—Dissolve 1.0 g. of high-purity manganese metal in 40 ml. of $HNO_3$ by heating. Cool, dilute to one liter in a volumetric flask. Transfer 50 ml. of this solution to a one-liter volumetric flask, add 50 ml. of $HNO_3$, and dilute to volume.

*Preparation of Calibration Graph.*—Transfer aliquots containing from 0 (blank) to 2.0 mg. of manganese in 250-ml. beakers. Add water and dilute to a volume of about 75 ml. Add 1 ml. of $H_2SO_4$, 1 ml. of $HNO_3$, 20 ml. of $H_3PO_4$, and 0.3 g. of solid $KIO_4$. Heat the solution just below boiling for 15 minutes, cool, dilute to 100 ml. in a volumetric flask, and mix. Measure the absorbance at 545 m$\mu$ versus the blank in the reference beam of the spectrophotometer.

*Procedure.* **Plain Carbon, Cast Irons, and Low-Alloy Steels.**—Transfer 1 g. to a 400-ml. beaker, add 15 ml. of $HNO_3$ (1:2), and heat gently until dissolved. Then add 2 to 3 drops of 48% HF (about 1 ml. for cast irons) and 20 ml. of 70% $HClO_4$, and evaporate to dense fumes of $HClO_4$.

Cool, add 100 ml. of water, 25 ml. of 85% $H_3PO_4$, and 20 ml. of $H_2SO_4$ (1:1), and heat to boiling for 5 minutes. Cool, transfer to a 250-ml. volumetric flask, and dilute to volume. Transfer an aliquot containing from 0.1 to 2.0 mg. of manganese to a 100-ml. volumetric flask, add 20 ml. of $H_3PO_4$ (Note 1), dilute to volume, and reserve for the reference solution. Transfer a similar size aliquot to a 250-ml. beaker and add 20 ml. of $H_3PO_4$ (Note 1). Dilute to about 75 ml. with water, add 0.3 g. of $KIO_4$, and heat the solution just below boiling for at least 15 minutes. Cool, transfer to a 100-ml. volumetric flask and dilute to volume. Determine the absorbance at 545 m$\mu$ using the reference solution in the reference beam of the spectrophotometer.

**Tungsten, Niobium, or Tantalum Steels.**—Transfer 1 g. to a 400-ml. beaker containing 3 or 4 glass beads and add 30 ml. of 70% $HClO_4$, 25 ml. of 85% $H_3PO_4$, and 10 drops (0.5 ml.) of 48% HF. Heat to boiling and boil or fume gently until the sample is in solution. When dissolution appears to be complete, add 20 ml. of $H_2SO_4$ (1:1) and heat strongly until the chromium is completely oxidized. Then proceed with the determination as described for "Plain Carbon, Cast Irons, and Low-Alloy Steels." If the solution after the oxidation with $KIO_4$ is turbid due to the presence of separated niobic, tantalic, or tungstic acids, cool, filter through a fritted-glass crucible into a 250-ml. flask, wash with cold water, dilute to the mark, and mix thoroughly.

NOTE.—1. If a large aliquot is taken, less $H_3PO_4$ acid may be added. The final colored system should contain from 10 to 20 ml. of $H_3PO_4$ per 100 ml. of solution.

## DETERMINATION OF MANGANESE IN STAINLESS STEEL (SPECTROPHOTOMETRIC BY PERIODATE OXIDATION) [14]

This method is designed for Types 304, 316, 347, and similar 18-8 steels. Solution of the sample in $HClO_4$, $H_3PO_4$, and HF, oxidation of the chromium, and

[14] Fowler, R. M., and Culbertson, J. B., Steel, **122**, 108, 1948.

boiling with very dilute HCl to reduce traces of oxidized manganese. An aliquot is treated with $KIO_4$, the manganese converted to $KMnO_4$ and determined colorimetrically.

*Caution.*—Goggles must be worn when making additions to hot or fuming acids. Strict adherence to the given procedures for additions to hot or fuming acids is necessary; otherwise, the analyst may be burned by splashing acid, or the determination spoiled by loss due to the spattering of the hot solutions.

*Reagent.* $H_2SO_4$-$HClO_4$ Mixture.—Add 250 ml. of 70% $HClO_4$ to 500 ml. of $H_2SO_4$ (1:1).

*Preparation of Calibration Graph.*—Treat various weights of a suitable standard such as N.B.S. 121a containing from 0.1 to 2.0 mg. of manganese according to the procedure. Measure the absorbance of the solution at 575 m$\mu$ in 1-cm. cells with a spectrophotometer with a narrow band width.

*Procedure.*—Transfer 1 g. of the sample to a 750-ml. Erlenmeyer flask containing 3 or 4 glass beads and add 30 ml. of 70% $HClO_4$, 10 ml. of $H_3PO_4$, and 0.5 ml. (10 drops) of HF. Heat to boiling and boil or fume gently until the sample is in solution. When solution appears to be complete and before chromium oxidation begins, add 20 ml. of $H_2SO_4$-$HClO_4$ mixture and continue heating strongly over a free flame until the chromium is oxidized. About 30 seconds after the solution turns orange-red is usually sufficient to oxidize the chromium completely. Immediately grasp the flask with a pair of metal tongs, swirl the contents vigorously for about 10 seconds in such a way that centrifugal force causes the liquid to wash much of the sides of the flask and pour into the thickest layer of the swirling solution 30 ml. of $H_3PO_4$ (1:1) (Note 1). Continue the vigorous swirling and cautiously direct a stream of water against the inside of the neck of the flask, adding about 5 ml. in this way. Swirl until the violent bubbling ceases, then with continued swirling, slowly add 100 ml. of water containing about 0.35 ml. of HCl, and swirl over a free flame until boiling begins. Boil for 5 minutes or longer, if necessary, to completely reduce any oxidized manganese. Cool to room temperature, dilute to 500 ml., and mix thoroughly.

Transfer a 100-ml. aliquot of the solution to a 400-ml. beaker, add 0.3 g. of $KIO_4$, and boil for 10 minutes. Cool to room temperature and dilute to 100 ml. Determine the absorbance of this solution in a spectrophotometer versus the solution of the sample in the reference cell. Convert the absorbance into manganese content from a calibration graph.

Note.—1. If oxidation of the chromium is complete, some of the manganese will oxidize to give a permanganate color in the flask after the phosphoric acid addition.

## METHODS FOR MANGANESE IN ANALYSES IN OTHER CHAPTERS

| | |
|---|---|
| Manganese in Aluminum Alloys | See Analysis of Aluminum Alloys |
| Manganese in Bauxite | See Analysis of Bauxite (Aluminum Chapter) |
| Manganese in Fused Alumina | See Analysis of Fused Alumina |
| Manganese in Beryllium Metal | See Analysis of Beryllium Metal |
| Manganese in Magnesium Alloys | See Magnesium Chapter |
| Manganese in Metallic Nickel | See Analysis of Metallic Nickel |
| Manganese in Phosphorus Ores | See Analysis of Phosphorus Ores |

*Chapter* **29**

# MERCURY

Hg, *at. wt.* 200.59; *sp. gr.* 13.546; *m.p.* −38.87°C.; *b.p.* 356.9°C.; *oxides,* Hg₂O, HgO.

The element is not abundant, nor widely distributed. The metal is found in the upper portions of cinnabar deposits, a mineral HgS, the chief source of the element. The element has been found in quartz, sandstone, schists, iron pyrites, bituminous substances, eruptive and sedimentary rocks of all ages. It occurs as chloride in horn silver. It is occasionally associated with zinc ores. It is generally found locally concentrated. The minerals that are more common are: cinnabar, HgS; calomel, Hg₂Cl₂; coloradoite, HgTe; amalgam, Ag·Hg; livingstonite, HgSb₄O₇; tiemannite, HgSe.

There is evidence that the knowledge of metallic mercury dates back to 1600 B.C. Aristotle refers to mercury as "fluid silver." Mercury was used by the ancients in gilding; the sulfide was employed as a pigment. Today mercury finds use in thermometers and barometers. It is employed in vacuum pumps and as a confining liquid for gases. It is used in mercury vapor lamps. It forms amalgams with metals; silver and tin amalgams are employed in filling teeth, sodium amalgam is used as a reducing agent. The element is extensively used in the extraction of gold from its ores by formation of gold amalgam. Mercury salts which are at all soluble are poisonous, as well as the vapor of mercury. Compounds of mercury are used for skin diseases, as eczema, and for increasing secretions of internal body fluids.

Organic mercurials are widely used as antiseptics, fungicides, slimicides, and related agents.

## DETECTION

Metallic mercury is recognized by its physical properties. It is the only metal with the exception of gallium (m.p. *ca.* 30°C.), which is a liquid at ordinary temperatures. The element forms a convex surface when placed on glass.

Mercury in the mercurous form is precipitated by hydrochloric acid as white mercurous chloride, Hg₂Cl₂. This compound is changed by ammonium hydroxide to the black precipitate of metallic mercury and ammono-mercuric chloride.

Mercury in the mercuric form is not precipitated by hydrochloric acid but the sulfide of the element is from an acid solution as black HgS. The precipitate first appears white, changing to orange-yellow, then brown, and finally to black, as the H₂S gas is passed into the solution. The element is distinguished from the other members of the group by the insolubility of its sulfide in yellow ammonium sulfide and in dilute nitric acid.

If the mercury sulfide is dissolved in aqua regia, the nitric acid expelled by taking to dryness, then adding hydrochloric acid and evaporating again to dryness, the residue taken up with a little hydrochloric acid, diluted with water, and treated with a solution of stannous chloride, a white precipitate of mercurous chloride is first formed, which is further reduced to metallic mercury by an excess of the reagent.

## ESTIMATION

In preparation of the sample for analysis, the volatility of mercury and its compounds, especially the chloride, the iodide, and sulfide, must be borne in mind. This volatilization takes place even in boiling solutions, unless provision is made for carrying out the decomposition in flasks with condensers. Fusions with appropriate fluxes are made in combustion tubes with provision to absorb the evolved gases.

Mercury amalgams are best decomposed by nitric acid. The oxides are soluble in acids, the mercurous oxide forming the difficultly soluble mercurous chloride with HCl.

Decomposition of the sulfide of mercury is accomplished by treating in a flask, carrying a short-stemmed funnel, with sulfuric acid and potassium permanganate, according to Low's Method given under "Titrimetric Thiocyanate Method" later in this chapter. Mercuric sulfide is readily soluble in constant-boiling HI.

Decomposition of ores may be effected in a combustion tube, drawn out at one end and bent at right angles, so as to dip into water. Hillebrand and Lundell recommend mixing the material with copper oxide and anhydrous quicklime and inserting well into the tube. Ignited calcium oxide, asbestos plug and copper plug are placed on either side of the charge, in the order named, this completes the packing of the tube. Carbon dioxide is conducted into the straight end of the tube, the tube is heated and the mercury swept into water and dilute nitric acid, in flasks connected in series. Mercury is converted to nitrate and determined according to the "Titrimetric Thiocyanate Method"—page 662.

Direct decomposition is accomplished in a specially constructed apparatus, a description of which is given under "Gravimetric Methods."

The volatility of mercury compounds, especially the chloride, makes it necessary to use great care in decomposing substances in which it is contained. Fusion of compounds with sodium carbonate will completely volatilize mercury. Volatilization also takes place in evaporations by boiling solutions containing the mercury compounds. The loss that occurs is dependent on the form of apparatus. In flasks this is the least volatile (approximately 5%) while in open dishes this may reach nearly 50% of the mercury originally present.[1] Decompositions, therefore, cannot be carried out in open vessels, and must be conducted in combustion tubes, with special precautions for absorbing the volatilized mercury, or in flasks with provision for condensing the evolved mercury compounds. The matter is dealt with later.

## SEPARATIONS

*Direct Volatilization.*—See under "Gravimetric Methods."

*Separation of Mercury from the Iron and Zinc Groups, or from the Alkaline Earths and the Alkalies.*—Mercury is precipitated as a sulfide from an acid solution

[1] Hillebrand and Lundell, Applied Inorganic Analysis, John Wiley and Sons.

of the mercuric salt by hydrogen sulfide, together with the members of the hydrogen sulfide group. Sufficient acid should be present to prevent the precipitation of zinc sulfide. Iron, aluminum, chromium, manganese, cobalt, nickel, zinc, the alkaline earths, and the alkalies remain in solution.

*Separation of Mercury from Arsenic, Antimony, and Tin.*—The sulfides obtained by passing hydrogen sulfide into an acid solution, preferably of the chlorides, are digested with yellow ammonium sulfide solution. Arsenic, antimony, and tin dissolve, whereas mercury sulfide remains insoluble. Sulfides of the fixed alkalies dissolve mercury as well as arsenic, antimony, and tin, so cannot be used in effecting a separation.

*Separation from Lead, Bismuth, Copper, and Cadmium.*—These elements remain with mercury after removal of arsenic, antimony, and tin by treatment of the sulfides with ammonium sulfide. (CuS slightly soluble.) The precipitated sulfides are transferred to a porcelain dish and boiled with dilute nitric acid, sp. gr. 1.2 to 1.3. After diluting slightly with water the solution is filtered and the residue of mercuric sulfide washed with dilute nitric acid and finally with water. If much lead is present in the solution it is apt to contaminate the residue by a portion being oxidized to lead sulfate and remaining insoluble. In this case the residue is treated with aqua regia, the solution diluted and mercury chloride filtered from $PbSO_4$ and free sulfur. Mercury is best determined as HgS by the "Ammonium Sulfide Method" described later. Traces of lead do not interfere, as lead is completely removed by remaining insoluble in potassium hydroxide, whereas mercury sulfide dissolves.

*Separation from Selenium and Tellurium.*—The mercury selenide or telluride is dissolved in aqua regia, chlorine water added and the solution diluted to 600 to 800 ml., phosphorous acid is added and the solution allowed to stand for some time; mercurous chloride is precipitated, selenium and tellurium remaining in solution. Selenium and tellurium will precipitate in hot concentrated solutions when treated with phosphorous acid, but not in dilute hydrochloric acid solutions.

*Mercury in Organic Substances.*—The material is decomposed by heating in a closed tube with concentrated nitric acid, or by heating in a flask with filter funnel (short-stemmed), with 10% $H_2SO_4$ and sufficient $(NH_4)_2S_2O_8$, added in small portions until the organic matter is decomposed.

## GRAVIMETRIC METHODS

### DETERMINATION OF MERCURY BY PRECIPITATION WITH AMMONIUM SULFIDE

The following method, suggested by Volhard, is generally applicable for determination of mercury. The element is precipitated by ammonium sulfide as HgS. The precipitate dissolved in caustic is again thrown out by addition of ammonium nitrate to the thio salt solution of mercury.

$$Hg(SNa)_2 + 2NH_4NO_3 \rightarrow 2NaNO_3 + (NH_4)_2S + HgS$$

*Procedure.*—The acid solution of the mercuric salt is nearly neutralized by sodium carbonate, and is then heated with a slight excess of ammonium sulfide reagent, freshly prepared. Sodium hydroxide solution is added until the dark-colored liquid begins to lighten. The solution is now heated to boiling and more sodium hydroxide added until the liquid is clear. If lead is present it will remain undissolved and should be filtered off. Ammonium nitrate is now added to the solution in excess and the mixture boiled until the greater part of the ammonia has been expelled. The clear liquid is decanted from the precipitate through a weighed Gooch crucible and the precipitate washed by decantation with hot water and finally transferred to the crucible and washed two or three times more. The mercuric sulfide is dried at 110°C. and weighed as HgS.

$$HgS \times 0.8622 = Hg$$

$$\times 0.9310 = HgO$$

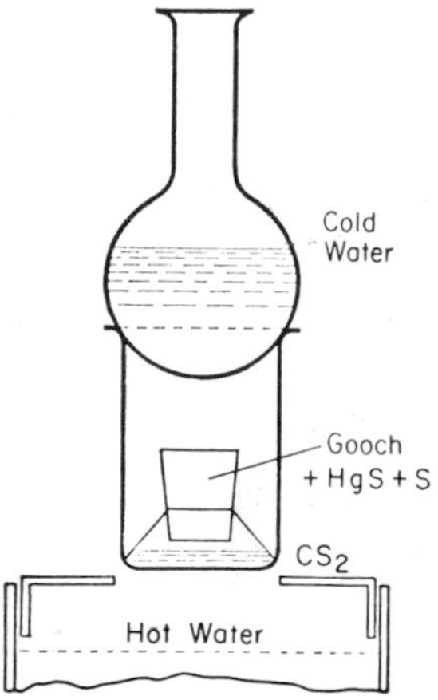

NOTES.—Alumina and silica are apt to be present in caustic.

Free sulfur may be removed, if present, by boiling with sodium sulfite, $Na_2SO_3 + S = Na_2S_2O_3$. The sulfur may be extracted with carbon disulfide. The Gooch crucible is placed upon a glass tripod in a beaker, containing carbon disulfide and a round-bottomed flask filled with cold water is placed over the mouth of the beaker to serve as a condenser, Fig. 29-1. By gently heating over a water bath for an hour the sulfur is completely extracted from the sulfide. Carbon disulfide is removed from the precipitate by washing once with alcohol followed by ether. The residue is now dried and weighed.

If the mercuric sulfide is collectd on a glass or porcelain filter crucible, the sulfur present may be determined after weighing the impure HgS–S mixture by adding cold constant-boiling HI, stirring, washing with four 5-ml. portions of 5–10% HI, then with cold water, drying for 2 hours in a vacuum desiccator and weighing.[2]

FIG. 29-1. Sulfur Extraction Apparatus.

## DETERMINATION OF MERCURY AS THE METAL BY THE AMALGAMATION METHOD

This excellent direct method for determining mercury in ores depends upon the distillation of the metal from the dry material, reducing the material, if necessary, by means of iron filings or lime, and collecting the metal on a weighed sheet of gold or silver. For purpose of effecting a reduction of the mercury Eschka[3] suggested the use of iron; Erdmann and Marchand recommended lime; in ores containing arsenic, zinc oxide is recommended. By the method 50 mg. may readily be determined, and as much as 100 mg. if gold is used to collect the volatilized mercury. If iron filings are used, these should be fairly fine and free of dust. Grease should be removed by treating the filings with alcohol, followed by ether, and then drying thoroughly.

*Apparatus.*—A thin-spun iron or nickel crucible with a rim to which the sheet of gold or silver will fit snugly is recommended. The crucible is inserted in a circular opening in an asbestos board, just large enough for the crucible to fit snugly and protrude about half its height above the board. This prevents the flame from heating the upper portion. The disc of gold or silver is cooled by contact with a cylindrical condenser, through which cold water circulates. An Erlenmeyer flask may be used as is shown in Fig. 18-1 (Chapter on Fluorine). The Whitton apparatus is shown in Fig. 29-2.

[2] Caley and Burford, Ind. Eng. Chem., Anal. Ed., **8,** 43, 1936.
[3] Eschka, A., Dinglers Polytech. J., **204,** 47, 1872. Holloway, G. T., Analyst, **31,** 66, 1906.

The Whitton apparatus possesses novel features which render the assay more accurate and reliable, the manipulation simpler and the time rapid. It consists of a steel retort with a cover of sheet silver, and above these a flat-bottomed cooling dish of brass; all clamped tightly together. Thus the distillation is performed in a closed retort, which prevents the escape of mercury vapor, and renders careful regulation of the heat unnecessary.

An important advantage lies in the use of the steel retort. It should be recognized that mercury vapors will condense upon any surface below the boiling point of mercury, 357.82°C., whether that surface be ore with which they will amalgamate

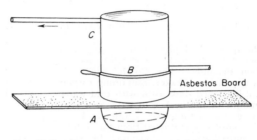

FIG. 29-2. Apparatus for Determining Mercury.

$A$ = Crucible for distillation of mercury; $B$ = Sheet of silver foil for deposition of condensed mercury; $C$ = Cooling dish to condense mercury.

or not. The steel retort is a good conductor of heat, and thus all portions of it are readily brought above this temperature, while the foil is kept below this temperature by its contact with the bottom of the cooling dish; thus the vapor must condense upon the foil and not upon any other portions of the exposed inner surface of the retort. The silver foil used in the apparatus can easily be replaced at a very small expense. One piece of foil will last for from five to ten assays.

The time required for an assay is about thirty minutes. By using two sets of apparatus and four foils, weighing up the first pair of foils while the second pair is in use, it may be made in fifteen minutes.

*Procedure.*—The sample is weighed and placed in the crucible $A$ of the apparatus. Not over 0.1 g. of mercury should be present in the amount of material taken. Five to 10 grams of iron filings are intimately mixed with the product in the crucible and additional filings sprinkled over the surface. Sulfide ores should be mixed with about twice their weight of a flux of zinc oxide and sodium carbonate in the proportion of 4:1, and about five times the weight of iron filings added, mixing well. The silver foil is weighed and placed between the crucible and cooler at $B$.

The bottom of the crucible is gradually heated with a small flame of a Meker or burner of similar type, being careful not to overheat. The top of the crucible should remain cold, otherwise mercury will be lost. After heating for thirty minutes, the apparatus is allowed to cool without disconnecting the condenser. The foil is now removed, dipped in alcohol and dried in a desiccator over fused calcium chloride. The increase in weight of the foil is due to metallic mercury.

NOTE.—It is advisable to repeat the test with a clean foil to be sure that all mercury has been obtained from the sample. The mercury may be removed from the foil by heat. Gold is preferable to silver for on its surface minute amounts of mercury are visible and gold absorbs a larger amount on its surface than will silver. The silver foil, however, is very satisfactory.

**Determination of Mercury in Cyanide Solutions.**—The procedure recommended by W. J. Sharwood with use of the apparatus described above is given in the later portion of this chapter.

## DETERMINATION OF MERCURY BY ELECTROLYSIS

Mercury is readily deposited as a metal from slightly acid solutions of its salts.

*Procedure.*—The neutral or slightly acid solution of mercuric or mercurous salt is diluted in a beaker to 150 ml. with water and 2 to 3 ml. of nitric acid added. The solution is electrolyzed with a current of 0.5 to 0.1 ampere, and an e.m.f. of 3.5 to 5 volts. A gauze cathode is recommended, or a platinum dish with dulled inner surface may be used. One gram of mercury may be deposited in about fifteen hours (or overnight). The time may be shortened to about three hours by increasing the current to 0.6 to 1 ampere.

The metal is washed with water without interrupting the current and then with alcohol. After removing the adhering alcohol with a filter paper, the cathode is placed in a desiccator containing fused potash until dry, and then weighed.

The increased weight of the cathode is due to metallic mercury.

NOTES.—In the electrolysis of mercuric chloride turbidity may be caused by formation of mercurous chloride by reduction, but this does no harm, as the reduction to metallic mercury follows.

Mercury may be electrolyzed from its thio-salt solutions, obtained by dissolving its sulfide in concentrated sodium sulfide solution.

## TITRIMETRIC METHODS

### SEAMON'S METHOD [4]

The principle of this method is solution of the sample in acid (even the more refractory mercury ores yield to treatment with hydrochloric acid followed, if necessary, by the addition of nitric acid). After precipitation of the bismuth, if present, with neutralization by ammonium hydroxide, it is acidified with nitric acid and titrated with potassium iodide solution, using starch solution as an outside indicator.

*Procedure.*—Weigh 0.5 g. of the finely ground ore into an Erlenmeyer flask of 125 ml. capacity. Add 5 ml. of hydrochloric acid (sp. gr. 1.19) and allow it to act for about 10 minutes at a temperature of about 40°C., then add 3 ml. of nitric acid (sp. gr. 1.4) and allow the action to continue for about 10 minutes longer. The mercury should now all be in solution. Now if lead is present, add 5 ml. of concentrated sulfuric acid; it may be omitted otherwise. Dilute with 15 ml. of water and then add ammonia cautiously until the liquid is slightly alkaline. Bismuth, if present, will be precipitated. Acidify faintly with nitric acid, filter, receiving the filtrate in a beaker, and wash thoroughly.

Add to the filtrate 1 ml. of nitric acid (sp. gr. 1.4) that has been made brownish in color by exposure to the light, and titrate with a standard solution of potassium iodide until a drop of the liquid brought into contact with a drop of starch liquor, on a spot-plate, shows a faint bluish tinge. It is a good plan to set aside about

[4] Manual for Assayers and Chemists.

one-third of the mercury solution and add it in portions until the end point is successively passed, finally rinsing in the last portion and titrating to the end point very carefully.

Deduct 0.5 ml. from the burette reading and multiply the remaining milliliter used by the percentage value of 1 ml. in mercury to obtain the percentage in the ore.

The standard potassium iodide solution should contain 8.3 g. of the salt per liter. Standardize against pure mercuric chloride. Dissolve a weighed amount of the salt in water, add 2 ml. of the discolored nitric acid and titrate as above. One ml. of standard solution will be found equivalent to about 0.005 g. of mercury, or about 1% on the basis of 0.5 g. of ore taken for assay.

The precipitate of red mercuric iodide which forms during the titration may not appear if the amount of mercury present is very small, but this failure to precipitate does not appear to affect the result.

Iron, copper, bismuth, antimony, and arsenic, when added separately to the ore, did not influence the results in Seamon's tests. Silver interferes. Duplicate results should check within 0.1 to 0.2 of 1%.

## THIOCYANATE METHOD [5]

*Reagents.* **Ferric Indicator.**—Make a saturated solution of ferric ammonium sulfate or ferric sulfate. Add sufficient nitric acid (freed from nitrous acid by heating) to clear the solution and produce a pale yellow color. Three to five ml. of this solution are used in the test. Ferric nitrate may be used if the sulfate is not available.

**Thiocyanate Solution.**—A 0.1 $N$ solution may be made by dissolving 7.4 g. of $NH_4CNS$ or 9.2 g. of KCNS in water and diluting to a liter. The solution may be standardized against a standard silver solution, containing 0.01079 g. silver per ml.

Forty ml. of the silver solution is measured into a beaker or Erlenmeyer flask and diluted to about 100 ml. The ferric indicator is added and the solution is titrated with the thiocyanate solution. Each addition of the thiocyanate will produce a temporary red color, which fades out as long as there is silver uncombined with thiocyanate. A drop in excess of the thiocyanate produces a permanent faint red color.

The thiosulfate may be standardized against pure mercury dissolved in dilute $HNO_3$ following the procedure given above.

*Procedure.*—A sample containing 0.1 to 0.5 g. of mercury placed in a flask is decomposed by adding 10 ml. of dilute $H_2SO_4$ (1:1) and about 0.5 g. of $KMnO_4$ crystals. The mixture is agitated and heated to fumes. The solution is cooled and diluted to 50 ml. with cold water, then boiled and the $MnO_2$ dissolved by adding a few crystals of oxalic acid (small portions at a time).

The solution is filtered, and any residue washed with dilute (1:10) $H_2SO_4$. The sulfide group is now precipitated with $H_2S$ and filtered off. The precipitate, transferred to a flask, with short-stemmed funnel, is digested for some time with dilute $HNO_3$ (2:1), the solution then diluted with hot water and filtered and the HgS washed with dilute $HNO_3$ (1:1).

The HgS is transferred to a flask with a few ml. of hot water and then 5 ml. of strong $H_2SO_4$ and 0.5 g. $KMnO_4$ are added and the mixture heated to fumes.

5 Low, A. H., Chemist-Analyst, **29**, 13, 1929.

Oxalic acid crystals are added until the $MnO_2$ dissolves and the mixture again heated to fumes to destroy the excess of oxalic acid. The solution, cooled, is diluted to 100 ml. (It should now be clear.)

About 5 ml. of a saturated solution of ferric ammonium sulfate solution (acidified with $HNO_3$) is added and the solution titrated with 0.1 $N$ thiocyanate solution.

One ml. 0.1 $N$ thiocyanate = 0.01003 g. Hg

## OTHER TITRIMETRIC METHODS

Mercurous ion may be oxidized by potassium permanganate or by ceric sulfate in excess.[6] Potassium iodate may be used for the direct oxidation of calomel under iodine monochloride conditions (see Appendix on Standard Solutions). Mercury may be precipitated as zinc mercuric thiocyanate and the thiocyanate titrated with standard iodate solution. Mercurous mercury may be titrated with standard chloride or bromide solution using bromphenol blue as adsorption indicator.[7] Mercuric chloride may be titrated with standard potassium iodide to the appearance of a permanent red turbidity. Mercuric ion may be precipitated as mercuric pyridine bichromate and weighed, or the bichromate may be titrated by conventional methods.[8]

## COLORIMETRIC METHODS

### COLORIMETRIC DETERMINATION OF MERCURY BY DITHIZONE

The basis of this method is the orange to yellow color formed with dithizone by mercury(II) compounds in the pH range 1–2. The complex formed is insoluble in water but is soluble in $CCl_4$ and $CHCl_3$. Chloride in moderate concentration interferes, and therefore sulfuric acid is used in acidification. Organic matter interferes and must be absent from the solution of the sample.

**Reagents. Dithizone Solution.**—Dissolve in 1 liter of analytical-reagent chloroform 10 mg. of specially-purified dithizone, which is supplied by the Eastman Kodak Co. If the commercial grade of dithizone is used, it must be purified as follows: Dissolve about 1 g. of dithizone in 60 ml. of chloroform, filtering if necessary. Extract with four 100-ml. portions of 1:100 redistilled concentrated ammonia. Discard the chloroform layer. Filter the combined aqueous extracts through cotton into a large separatory funnel. Acidify to litmus with 1:1 HCl. The dithizone precipitates. Extract it with three 20-ml. portions of chloroform. Combine these extracts, wash them with water, and discard the water. Evaporate the chloroform solution on the steam bath, and dry the purified dithizone for 1–2 hours at 50°C. *in vacuo.*

**Sulfuric Acid Solution (1:17).**—Add 10 ml. concentrated $H_2SO_4$, slowly and with stirring, to 170 ml. of water.

[6] The latter method is very satisfactory. Willard and Young, J. Am. Chem. Soc., **52**, 557, 1930.

[7] Zombory, Z. anal. Chem., **184**, 237, 1929; Zombory and Pollak, *ibid.*, **215**, 255, 1933; Kolthoff and Larson, J. Am. Chem. Soc., **56**, 1881, 1934.

[8] Spacu and Dick, Z. anal. Chem., **76**, 273, 1929; Furman and State, Ind. Eng. Chem., Anal. Ed., **8**, 467, 1936.

*Procedure.*—Because the color is sensitive to light, work in relatively dim daylight or in artificial light. Place in a separatory funnel an aliquot of sample containing 0.01–0.02 mg. of mercury. Neutralize with 1:1 ammonia, dilute to 20 ml., and add 20 ml. of 1:17 $H_2SO_4$. Add 5 ml. of the dithizone solution in $CHCl_3$. Shake for one minute and let the solvent separate. If the color of the solution is not green, indicating excess reagent (or red-violet, due to the presence of copper) add another 5 ml. of dithizone solution and shake again. If necessary, continue to add reagent until the green color (A) or the red-violet color (B) appears.

**(A) Copper Absent.**—Draw off the solvent layer. If it is not clear, centrifuge it in a stoppered tube. Expose to light as little as possible and read the transmittance at once. Read the mercury dithizonate at 500 m$\mu$ and check by reading the excess dithizone at 625 m$\mu$.

**(B) Copper Present.**—Draw off the chloroform layer (discarding the aqueous layer) and shake it with 10 ml. 6 N $H_2SO_4$, adjust pH to 1.5–2.0 by slow addition of 1:1 ammonia, then add 5 ml. of an .001 M sodium ethylenediaminetetraacetate solution.[9] Shake again, and discard the chloroform layer.

To the aqueous layer, add 20 ml. of 1:17 $H_2SO_4$, and 5 ml. of the dithizone solution in chloroform. Then proceed from this point as directed in procedure.

## DETERMINATIONS IN SPECIFIC SUBSTANCES

### DETERMINATION OF MERCURY IN ZINC AMALGAM

The method is applicable to the determination of mercury in "battery zincs" in which mercury is present to the extent of 1–3%.

*Procedure.*—Accurately weigh about 5 g. of the finely divided alloy, place in a beaker and dissolve in about 75 ml. of dilute HCl (1:1) and heat gently for about 3 hours. The zinc goes into solution, whereas the mercury and lead remain undissolved as metals. Decant off the solution and wash the metals several times with hot distilled water by decantation. Transfer to a weighed porcelain crucible, carefully decanting off the water. Expel the remaining water by drying in an oven at 100°C. Cool in a desiccator and weigh. Now gently ignite at a dull red heat. Cool in a desiccator and again weigh. The loss of weight is due to the volatilization of mercury.

NOTES.—Conduct the ignition under a hood for 3–5 minutes. The usual run of battery zincs contain sufficient lead to absorb the mercury, otherwise the zinc must be plated with lead by the addition of sufficient soluble lead salt prior to dissolving with HCl.

### DETERMINATION OF MERCURY IN AMALGAMATED ZINC [10]

*Procedure.*—Remove the rolling compound from the surface with appropriate solvents and cut the dry zinc into small pieces. Weigh about 20 g. into a 300-ml. beaker. Dissolve the metal with HCl (1:1), facilitating the solution process by decanting the spent acid through a hard filter before a fresh portion is added.

When no more H is evolved compress the residue in the bottom of the beaker with a flattened glass rod and drain off the liquid through the filter. Wash with hot water by decantation until acid free. Dry the filter at 100°C. and brush from it the small amount to the main residue in the beaker. There is little danger of

9 Friedeberg, H., Anal. Chem., **27**, 305, 1955.

10 Kundert, Alfred, Research and Development Department, French Battery Co., Madison, Wisconsin. From the Chemist-Analyst.

mercury loss to this point in the procedure provided there be sufficient lead present to absorb the mercury, but great care must be taken when this amalgam is dissolved.

Cover the beaker with a watch glass and dissolve the residue without heat in 2 or 3 ml. $HNO_3$ (1:1). Add a slight excess of Br water and rotate until dissolved, then add 25 ml. $H_2O$. Ignore any white undissolved salt but be certain that Hg is all converted. Add dropwise a concentrated solution $Na_2CO_3$ until a slight flocculent precipitate persists. Carry out all steps in a hood.

Add a drop of phenolphthalein and 10% NaCN until pink, then 10 ml. in excess. Dilute to 200 ml. Stir and let settle. Filter $PbCO_3$ and wash with 1% NaCN until Hg free. Precipitate HgS by passing $H_2S$ for about 5 minutes then heat to 60°C., continue $H_2S$ for 5 minutes more, and let settle.

Prepare a Gooch crucible with a thin asbestos floor, wash with 10% NaCN, HCl (1:2), and finally with $H_2O$, then heat and weigh. Decant the clear liquid into the crucible with gentle suction and finally transfer the sulfide with acidulated $H_2S$ water. Purify the sulfides by washing with cold HCl (1:2), then wash with alcohol and dry.

Purify with $CS_2$ and alcohol, then dry to constant weight at 100°C. Volatilize HgS and reweigh. Calculate Hg from loss.

NOTES.—If there are more than a few milligrams of nonvolatile residue, or for exceptionally accurate results, this residue should be redetermined as the sulfide in the same manner as above.

## DETERMINATION OF MERCURY IN CYANIDE SOLUTIONS AND IN CYANIDE PRECIPITATES [11]

*Procedure for Cyanide Solutions.*—Measure 1000 ml. of solution into a 2500-ml. acid-bottle, give the contents a rotary motion and add 0.5 gram of the finest aluminum powder. Shake the bottle violently for half a minute, then give it a rapid rotary motion and allow to stand for a half to one minute; by this means the solution continues moving most of the time. Repeat the violent shaking, etc., at least 6 times—a total of 5 to 10 minutes. Meanwhile prepare a porcelain Gooch crucible, covering the perforated bottom with a layer of fine asbestos, and connect with an empty 2500 ml. bottle attached to a good vacuum-pump. Shake the solution again and pour it all through a large funnel into a 1000-ml. narrow-necked flask. Rinse the bottle twice with a little water and catch the washings in a small beaker. Pour the washings into the flask until nearly full, and pour the remainder upon the Gooch filter. Invert the flask over the filter with the mouth at least half an inch below the rim, clamp it in that position, and then allow the liquid to filter, using a good vacuum. It may require two or three hours to pass through. Remove the empty flask, rinse any adhering particles into a beaker, and transfer to the filter. Wash once with distilled water. When sucked dry, wash once with alcohol, using a pipette to rinse down the sides of the crucible; when drained, wash twice with a little ether to remove any oil, etc. Remove the crucible and heat gently till thoroughly dry; transfer the asbestos filter-pad and contents to the mercury apparatus with a weighed gold foil, and proceed exactly as with ores. See procedure on page 659 "Determining Mercury as the Metal by the Amalgamation Method."

Using 1000 ml. of solution, every milligram found corresponds to one part per million, and half a milligram of mercury is easily visible on gold foil. If the solu-

[11] Recommended by W. J. Sharwood, Mining Sci. Press, Oct. 30, 1915.

tion is very low in alkali and in cyanide a gram of caustic soda may be added; much more is undesirable. In case of doubt there is no harm done by using additional aluminum powder.

Zinc-dust is not a satisfactory substitute for aluminum; the excess of zinc must be removed by hydrochloric acid, and the cadmium it contains also interferes.

*Procedure for Cyanide Precipitates.*—The precipitate, obtained by treatment of cyanide solution with zinc-dust or shaving, may contain mercury in the metallic state or as sulfide.

Metallic mercury probably exists mainly as amalgam, in combination with gold or silver, or with unaltered metallic zinc. Sulfuric acid refining leaves both mercuric sulfide and the metal in the residue.

In using the apparatus for collecting mercury upon silver foil, the quantity of material taken for analysis should not contain over 0.10 g. of mercury, and preferably 0.025 to 0.050 g. From 1 to 2 g. of precipitate is usually a safe amount, but some slime and concentrate precipitates have yielded over 10% mercury when raw, and considerably more after acid refining.

Place the weighed sample in a 150-ml. beaker with watch-glass cover, moisten, and add 10 or 15 ml. dilute hydrochloric acid. When action slackens add more acid and finally heat gently until action ceases. All the lime, practically all the zinc and cadmium, and some copper and lead pass into solution. Dilute with warm water, stir, and allow to settle, and pass the clear liquid through an asbestos Gooch filter, using gentle suction. Heat the residue with a little more acid, dilute and filter as before; finally transfer all the residue to the filter and wash with hot water till all chlorides are removed. The filtrate may be used for the determination of calcium and zinc, and for cadmium if the residue has been thoroughly extracted with acid.

The residue contains all the mercury. As soon as it is sucked dry, wash once with about 10 ml. of alcohol (denatured may be used), using a pipette to rinse the sides of the Gooch crucible; then wash at least twice with ether to remove grease, asphaltum, etc. These washings are discarded unless the organic matter extracted is to be determined by evaporation in a watch-glass. Disconnect the Gooch crucible and dry it in an oven or on a hot plate, avoiding a high temperature. Transfer the asbestos mat and residue to the mercury apparatus with a weighed disk of silver or gold foil. Wipe out the crucible with a wisp of dry asbestos and add to the residue in the retort. Add 5 g. clean iron filings or crushed steel and a little well-burned quicklime, and grind up with the residue, using a stout glass rod. Cover with 2 or 3 g. of iron or lime. Clamp foil and cooler upon retort, heat for about 20 minutes, etc., exactly as with ores, and weigh the foil with condensed mercury.

## DETERMINATION OF MERCURY IN ORGANIC MATERIAL BY PRECIPITATION AS THE SULFIDE

*Procedure.*—The compound is decomposed by the method of Carius by heating in a closed tube (see Chapter on Chlorine) with concentrated nitric acid (sp. gr. 1.42). The amount of nitric acid used should not exceed 3 ml. per 50 ml. tube, otherwise an explosion may result.[12] The acid solution is neutralized by addition of sodium hydroxide and sufficient excess of the alkali added to insure a slight excess. Pure potassium cyanide is now added in quantity sufficient to dissolve the mer-

12 Fresenius, Quantitative Chemical Analysis, 2, 118, 1915.

curic oxide precipitate, and the solution saturated with $H_2S$ gas. Ammonium acetate is added and the solution boiled until nearly all the $NH_3$ has been expelled. The precipitate is allowed to settle and then filtered off and washed with hot water, and then with hot dilute HCl and again with water. The precipitate is dried at 110°C. and weighed as mercuric sulfide, HgS.

NOTE.—Should free sulfur be present its removal is accomplished by extraction with pure $CS_2$, see Notes on page 659.

## DETERMINATION OF MERCURY IN BIOCHEMICAL MATERIAL BY ULTRAVIOLET PHOTOMETRY [13]

The method presented here, combining cold incomplete digestion, extraction with dithizone, decomposition of the mercury dithizone complex by heating to produce mercury vapor, and subsequent estimation of the mercury by ultraviolet photometry, is relatively rapid and simple compared with the methods presently available. It is suitable for amounts of mercury in blood of the order of milli-

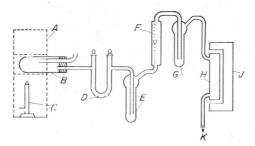

FIG. 29-3. Apparatus for the Microdetermination of Mercury.

$A$ = Wire enclosure of heating chamber; $B$ = Ignition tube; $C$ = Bunsen burner; $D$ = U-tube containing absorbent cotton; $E$ = Cold trap; $F$ = Rotameter; $G$ = Cold trap; $H$ = Optical cell; $J$ = Mercury vapor meter; $K$ = To water aspirator pump.

microgram concentrations, that is, $10^{-9}$ gram of mercury in one millilter of blood, or in corresponding amounts of other biochemical materials.

*Apparatus.*—The apparatus, Fig. 29-3, comprises a heating chamber, connected to a U-tube containing absorbent cotton and followed by a cold trap, a rotameter, an additional trap, a modified Beckman mercury vapor meter Model 23 and a water aspirator pump. The mercury vapor meter is modified by altering the grille so that it can be removed easily and be replaced by an optical cell. This cell is a cylinder 23 cm. in length and 4 cm. in diameter. It has removable silica end windows, and is fitted with inlet and outlet ports for the air stream drawn by the aspirator pump. A calibrated Fischer and Porter rotameter equipped with both glass and steel floats is used to measure the air flow.

The heating chamber consists of a Bunsen burner mounted in a Nichrome wire cage 3¾ x 3¾ x 12 inches. Two cylindrical openings having a diameter of one inch capable of snugly accepting a 25 x 200-mm. Pyrex ignition tube are cut in opposite faces of the unit about 6½ inches from the bottom and about 2 inches above

[13] Jacobs, Yamaguchi, Goldwater and Gilbert, Amer. Indus. Hygiene Jour., **21**, 475, 1960; Jacobs, Goldwater, and Gilbert, *ibid.*, **22**, 276, 1961.

the top of the burner. A 25-mm. diameter wire cylinder fits between the two openings, and the ignition tube passes through this cylinder.

*Reagents.* **Potassium Permanganate Solution, 6%.**—Dissolve 60 g. of reagent grade potassium permanganate in distilled water with the aid of heat, and dilute to one liter with distilled water.

**Sulfuric Acid.**—From concentrated reagent grade sulfuric acid prepare a 0.25 $N$ solution in the customary manner.

**Dithizone Extraction Solution.**—Weigh out accurately 6 mg. of purified diphenylthiocarbazone and dissolve in reagent grade chloroform. Transfer to a 1-liter volumetric flask. Make to volume with chloroform.

**Hydroxylamine Hydrochloric Solution, 20%.**—Dissolve 200 g. of reagent grade $NH_2OH \cdot HCl$ in 650 ml. of distilled water and purify as follows: Add a few drops of *m*-cresol purple indicator solution. Add ammonium hydroxide solution until the mixture turns yellow. Add one ml. of 5% sodium diethyldithiocarbamate solution and extract with chloroform until the metal complexes and all the excess diethyldithiocarbamate have been removed. Test for complete extraction of the reagent by the addition of a small amount of dilute copper solution to a small portion of the purified hydroxylamine hydrochloride reagent. If the extraction is complete no yellow color is produced. Add pure hydrochloric acid until the *m*-cresol purple indicator turns pink. Then transfer the purified reagent to a one-liter volumetric flask and dilute to volume with distilled water.

**Standard Stock Mercury Solution.**—Weigh out exactly 0.1354 g. of mercuric chloride and dissolve in 0.25 $N$ sulfuric acid. Transfer to a 100-ml. volumetric and dilute to the mark with 0.25 $N$ sulfuric acid. This solution contains 1 mg. of mercury per milliliter.

**Standard Working Mercury Solution.**—Transfer, with the aid of a pipette, 1 ml. of the stock standard to a 100-ml. volumetric flask. Dilute to the mark with distilled water. This solution contains 10 micrograms of mercury per milliliter. Transfer 1 ml. of the 10 $\mu$g./ml. solution to a 100-ml. volumetric flask and dilute to volume with distilled water. This working standard solution contains 0.1 micrograms per milliliter. These solutions must be prepared fresh as required.

*Preparation of Standard Curve.*—Place 250 ml. of 0.25 $N$ sulfuric acid in a separatory funnel with a dry stem. Add 1 ml. of the standard mercury solution containing 10 micrograms of mercury per milliliter and mix. Extract with 5 ml. of dithizone extraction solution shaking for 1 full minute and allowing the phases to separate completely. Swirl the separatory funnel to make sure all of the chloroform solution is brought to the bottom of the funnel. Release the pressure of the chloroform through the mouth of the funnel and not through its stopcock. Transfer the clear extract to a 100-ml., glass-stoppered volumetric flask, being careful not to draw any of the aqueous layer into the flask. Repeat the extraction twice with 5-ml. portions of the dithizone extraction solution and then once more with 5 ml. of chloroform. Add these extracts to the volumetric flask and then complete to volume with chloroform. Mix thoroughly. This solution contains 0.1 microgram of mercury per milliliter. Transfer with the aid of pipettes 0.2 ml. of dithizone extraction solution to each of two 25 x 200-mm. Pyrex combustion tubes to serve as the blank. Transfer 0.1-, 0.2-, 0.3-, and 0.4-ml. portions of the chloroform solution containing 0.1 microgram of mercury (as mercury dithizonate) per ml. in duplicate to separate Pyrex combustion tubes. The tubes will then contain respectively 0, 0.01, 0.02, 0.03, and 0.04 microgram of mercury in duplicate. Place the tubes into a beaker of hot water and evaporate off the chloroform completely at 70–80°C. Continue as detailed in the procedure. Plot the maximum arbitrary scale reading in mg./m.³ against the micrograms of mercury of the standard to obtain the standard curve. An alternative method is to plot one-half the product of the time interval from the start of movement of the meter pointer to its return to zero by the maximum arbitrary scale reading in mg./m.³ against micrograms of mercury in the standard. The average curve obtained with results for five series of tests are shown in Fig. 29-4.

*Procedure.*—Transfer 0.5 ml. of blood or a corresponding amount of other biochemical material, with the aid of a pipette to a 125-ml. glass-stoppered Erlenmeyer flask. Place in a pan containing ice and water and add cautiously 2 ml. of concen-

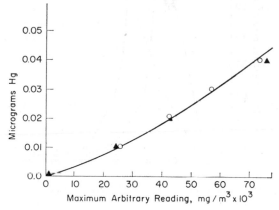

Fig. 29-4. Standard Curve.

trated sulfuric acid and swirl. Warm on a hot plate at low heat (do not boil). Place in the ice bath again. Add 10 ml. of 6% potassium permanganate solution. Warm on a hot plate, remove from hot plate, swirl and allow to stand for 15 minutes. Repeat the warming on the hot plate, removing, swirling, and cooling two more times. Allow to stand until the supernatant solution is clear or for a total elapsed time of one hour. Dissolve the precipitate with 0.5 ml. of 20% hydroxylamine hydrochloride solution. Swirl to assist in dissolving the precipitate. Stopper the flask, shake, cautiously release the pressure. Add 20% hydroxylamine hydrochloride solution drop by drop if more is required to dissolve the precipitate and allow to stand for 10 minutes. Dilute with 20 ml. of water.

Transfer the solution to a dry 125-ml. separatory funnel with a dry stem. Wash the Erlenmeyer flask with three 10-ml. portions of distilled water, add the washings to the separatory funnel, and mix. Add 5 ml. of the dithizone extraction solution. Stopper the separatory funnel and shake vigorously for one minute. Release the pressure through the mouth. Swirl to bring down any chloroform droplets and allow to stand until the phases separate completely. Draw off the chloroform layer into a glass-stoppered, 25-ml. graduated cylinder, being careful not to draw off any of the aqueous layer. Repeat the extraction with 5 ml. more of dithizone extraction solution and then wash with 3 ml. of pure chloroform. Add the chloroform wash to the graduated cylinder. Add sufficient chloroform directly to the cylinder to make the total volume 15 ml.

Transfer with the aid of a pipette and a safety pipetter, 1 ml. of the chloroform solution of mercury dithizonate to a Pyrex ignition tube 25 x 200 mm. and place in a hot water bath. Evaporate off the chloroform completely at 70–80°C.

While the chloroform is being evaporated check the apparatus, turn on the Beckman mercury vapor meter, turn on the aspirator pump so that the air flow is about 3300 ml. per minute, and allow the instrument to come to equilibrium.

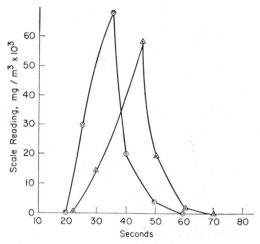

Fɪɢ. 29-5.  Comparative Areas of Mercury Determinations.

Check the span of the instrument. After all the chloroform has evaporated, dry the outside of the tube and insert the ignition tube into the heating unit placing it so that the flame will heat the bottom end of the tube. Light a match, insert it into the lighting opening, turn on the gas, allow it to ignite, remove the match, and start a stop watch. Record the starting time, in seconds, of the movement of the meter needle, the maximum deflection of the meter needle, the meter readings at 10-second intervals, if possible, and the time of return of the meter needle to zero. Plot the scale readings against time, as in Fig. 29-5, which shows two such plots. From the maximum scale reading, obtain the concentration from the standard curve.

Multiply this reading by 15 to obtain the concentration in micrograms of mercury in 0.5 ml. of blood and subsequently by 200 to express the result in micrograms per 100 ml. of blood.

## Chapter 30

# MOLYBDENUM *

**Mo**, *at. wt.* 95.94; *sp. gr.* 10.2; *m.p.* 2620°C.; *b.p.* 4800°C.; † *oxides*, $Mo_2O_3$, $MoO_2$, $MoO_3$

Molybdenum frequently occurs in granite in the form of sulfide, molybdenite; it is associated as molybdate with iron, lead and calcium. The commercial minerals are molybdenite, $MoS_2$; wulfenite, $PbMoO_4$. Molybdenite is a bluish gray mineral with metallic lustre, opaque, foliated masses or scales like graphite, easily separated and soft, streak bluish. Wulfenite is a yellow to orange-red mineral with resinous lustre. It may contain vanadium, chromium, arsenic and tungsten. Molybdite is an earthy yellow mineral, opaque to translucent, streak yellow. It is an alteration product of molybdenite, occurring in small proportions with it and is not a commercial ore.

Molybdenum is a common element in steel and alloys. It is also frequently determined in concentrations in the parts-per-millions range in high purity metals and inorganic compounds.

The metal is employed in alloy steels, being added to the steel in form of ferromolybdenum. It is employed in high-temperature resistor furnaces, in supports for tungsten filaments in lamps, and in dentistry for tooth plugs. Ammonium molybdate is valuable in the analytical laboratory for determination of phosphorus.

### DETECTION

Molybdenum appears in the hydrogen sulfide group; it is precipitated from acid solution by $H_2S$ as a dark brown sulfide, mostly $MoS_3$. The sulfide is dissolved by digestion with alkali or ammonium sulfides, forming thio-molybdates which impart a deep brown-red color to the solution. In the formation of soluble thio-salts it behaves like arsenic, tin and antimony, but the thiomolybdates of these metals are not deeply colored. When acid solutions of molybdenum are treated with metallic zinc, molybdenum is reduced to a lower valence, imparting various colors to the liquid as reduction progresses. It remains in solution, whereas tin and antimony, if present in the liquid, are reduced to metals. Arsenic, if present, is in part eliminated as arsine. Neither tin, antimony nor arsenic give colored solutions upon reduction with zinc.

*Sodium thiosulfate* added to a slightly acid solution of ammonium molybdate produces a blue precipitate with a supernatant blue solution. With more acid a brown precipitate is formed.

* Based on a chapter in the Fifth Edition revised and rewritten by Arnold R. Gahler, Research and Development Analytical Laboratory, Union Carbide Metals Co., Niagara Falls, N. Y.

† Handbook of Chemistry and Physics, 42nd Ed., 1960–61.

*Sulfur dioxide* produces a bluish-green precipitate if sufficient molybdenum is present, or a colored solution with small amounts.

Molybdenum present as molybdate is precipitated by phosphates as yellow ammonium phosphomolybdate from a nitric acid solution. The precipitate is soluble in ammonium hydroxide.

A pinch of powdered mineral on a porcelain lid, moistened with a few drops of concentrated sulfuric acid, stirred and heated to fumes, then cooled, will produce a blue color when breathed upon. The color disappears on heating, but reappears on cooling. Water destroys the color.

Molybdenite is very similar to graphite in appearance. It is distinguished from it by the fact that nitric acid reacts with molybdenite, $MoS_2$, leaving a white residue, but has no action upon graphite. The blowpipe gives $SO_2$ with molybdenite and $CO_2$ with graphite.

Spot tests have been proposed with thiocyanate and stannous chloride, potassium xanthate, phenylhydrazine, and methylene blue with hydrazine.[1]

## ESTIMATION

The determination is required in the analysis of molybdenum ores; also in iron and copper ores containing molybdenum.

The metal is determined in certain steels, alloys, and metals.

The reagents ammonium molybdate and the oxide-molybdic acid, $MoO_3$, are valuable for analytical purposes. Tests of their purity may be required.

Molybdenum is precipitated from acid solution as sulfide by $H_2S$, soluble in alkalies. If it is not thrown out with the hydrogen sulfide group it will remain in solution and pass into the soluble alkali group and probably escape detection.

The ores are easily decomposed by acids or by alkali fusion. Details follow below.

### PREPARATION AND SOLUTION OF THE SAMPLE

In dissolving the substance the following facts should be kept in mind: The metal is easily soluble in aqua regia; soluble in hot concentrated sulfuric acid, soluble in dilute nitric acid, oxidized by excess to $MoO_3$. It is dissolved by fusion with sodium carbonate and potassium nitrate mixture. It is insoluble in hydrochloric, hydrofluoric and dilute sulfuric acids.

The oxide $MoO_3$ is soluble in concentrated mineral acids becoming much less soluble on ignition; soluble in alkalies.

Molybdates of the heavy metals are insoluble in water, the alkali molybdates are soluble.

*Ores.*—Molybdenum residues are treated as described in the procedure for the "Determination of Molybdenum in Ores." Molybdenum ores may be decomposed with nitric and sulfuric acids. They may also be decomposed by fusion with a mixture of sodium carbonate and potassium nitrate, or with sodium peroxide, in an iron crucible, 0.5 g. of the sample being taken and 10 times its weight of fusion mixture. The melt is disintegrated with about 150 ml. of water, the alkali partly neutralized with $NH_4Cl$ and filtered. The molybdenum is in the filtrate, the iron remains in the residue.

It is advisable to dissolve the residue in a little dilute HCl; pour this solution

[1] Feigl, F., Spot Tests in Inorganic Analysis, p. 111 to 115, Elsevier Publishing Co., 1954.

into a hot solution of an excess of NaOH and again filter off the iron hydroxide, adding the filtrate to the first lot.

The combined filtrates and washings are treated with about 5 ml. of a 50% tartaric acid solution or its equivalent in crystals (preventing W and V from separating out) and the solution saturated with $H_2S$. The thiomolybdate solution is made slightly acid with $H_2SO_4$ (1:2) and $MoS_3$ precipitates.

*Steel and Iron.*—One gram of drillings is dissolved in 20 ml. of $HNO_3$ (1:1) and 15 ml. of $HClO_4$. Add a little HF for high-silicon alloys and evaporate to perchloric acid fumes. Determine the molybdenum colorimetrically with thiocyanate.

*Stainless Steel.*—Dissolve 0.25 to 0.5 gram in 30 ml. of $HClO_4$, 10 ml. of $H_3PO_4$, and 0.5 ml. of HF. Evaporate to perchloric acid fumes and determine the molybdenum colorimetrically with thiocyanate.

## SEPARATIONS

*Separation of Molybdenum from Iron and the Other Elements present in Steels.*[2] —Knowles found that α-benzoinoxime precipitates molybdenum from solutions containing as much as 20% by volume of $H_2SO_4$ or 5% by volume of either HCl or $HNO_3$ or $H_3PO_4$. The only other elements precipitated in mineral acid solutions by the reagent are Cb, W, Pd, Cr(VI), V(V), and Ta. The reagent is, therefore, very useful for the determination of molybdenum in steel and in other alloys.

*Separation from the Alkaline Earths.*—Fusion of the substance with sodium carbonate and extraction of the melt with water gives a solution of molybdenum, whereas the carbonates of barium, calcium and strontium remain undissolved.

*Separation from Lead, Copper, Cadmium and Bismuth.*—The sulfides of the elements are treated with sodium hydroxide and sodium sulfide solution and are digested by gently heating in a pressure flask. Molybdenum dissolves, whereas lead, copper, cadmium and bismuth remain insoluble. If the solution of the above elements is taken, made strongly alkaline, and treated with $H_2S$, the sulfides of the latter elements are precipitated and molybdenum remains in solution. The precipitates are filtered off and the filtrate containing molybdenum is made slightly acid with sulfuric acid and the mixture heated until the liquid appears colorless, $MoS_3$ is precipitated and may be converted into the oxide as described later.

*Separation of Molybdenum from Iron, Aluminum, Chromium, Nickel, Cobalt, Zinc, Manganese, Alkaline Earths and Alkalies.*—Molybdenum is precipitated from an acid solution, preferably a mixture of $H_2SO_4$ and HCl—1 and 2 ml. respectively in a volume of 50 ml. After saturating with $H_2S$, the solution is diluted with an equal volume of water and again saturated with $H_2S$ and the sulfides filtered and washed as usual. Members of the $H_2S$ group will be present, if in the original solution.

*Separation from Vanadium* is effected by a molybdenum sulfide precipitation in acid solution.

*Separation from Arsenic.*—(a) Arsenic, present in the higher state of oxidation, is precipitated by magnesia mixture, added to a slightly acid solution (5 ml. of concentrated hydrochloric acid per 100 ml. of solution for each 0.1 gram arsenic). The solution is neutralized with ammonia (methyl orange), and the arsenic salt filtered off. $MoS_3$ is now precipitated with $H_2S$ in presence of free sulfuric acid in

[2] Knowles, H. B., Bur. Standards J. Research, **9**, 1, 1932.

a pressure flask. (*b*) Arsenic is reduced to arsenous form and distilled as AsCl₃ separating it from molybdenum.

*Separation from Phosphoric Acid.*—Phosphoric acid is precipitated from an ammoniacal solution as magnesium ammonium phosphate. Molybdenum may then be precipitated as the sulfide from the filtrate.

*Separation from Titanium.*—Ammonia will separate molybdenum from titanium. The metals of the ammonium sulfide group and titanium are precipitated by adding ammonium hydroxide and ammonium sulfide. Molybdenum remains in solution and passes into the filtrate. H₂S is passed into the solution until it appears red; sulfuric acid is then added until the solution is acid, when molybdenum sulfide precipitates.

*Separation from Tungsten.*—Molybdenum may be precipitated by H₂S as MoS₃ in presence of tartaric acid. Tungsten does not precipitate.

MoS₃ may be precipitated from a formic acid solution by H₂S, tungsten remains in solution.[3] The alkaline solution is neutralized with concentrated formic acid and an excess of ammonium sulfide added followed by more formic acid with 5 ml. excess per each 100 ml. of solution. After standing for half an hour or more the MoS₃ is filtered off and washed with a 5% solution of formic acid.

*Separation (and Determination) of Nickel, Chromium, Cobalt, Iron, Titanium, Tungsten, Molybdenum, Niobium, and Tantalum by Anion-Exchange.*[4]—Molybdenum can be separated by an anion-exchange procedure involving a series of elutions with solutions of varying composition. See Chapter on Tungsten for the procedure.

*Separation from Rhenium.*[5]—These elements may be separated by ion-exchange. A sodium hydroxide solution containing rhenium and molybdenum is passed through an Amberlite resin, IR-400, perchlorate form. Molybdenum is eluted with a 1 *M* potassium oxalate solution, the rhenium remaining in the column, to be removed with 7 *N* HCl.

# GRAVIMETRIC METHODS

## PRECIPITATION AS LEAD MOLYBDATE

This method, suggested by Chatard,[6] has been pronounced by Brearly and Ibbotson to be "one of the most stable processes found in analytical chemistry." "It is not interfered with by the presence of large amounts of acetic acid, lead acetate, or alkali salts (except sulfates). The paper need not be ignited separately and prolonged ignition at a much higher temperature than is necessary to destroy the paper does no harm. From faintly acid solution lead molybdate may be precipitated free from impurities in the presence of copper, cobalt, nickel, manganese, zinc, magnesium and mercury salts." It may be readily separated from coprecipitated iron and chromium. Barium, strontium, uranium, arsenic, cadmium and aluminum do not interfere if an excess of hydrochloric acid has been added to the solution followed by lead acetate and sufficient ammonium acetate to destroy the free mineral acid.

[3] Böhm and Vostrebal, Z. anorg. Allgem. Chem., **110**, 81, 1920.
[4] Hague, Brown, and Bright, Jour. Research, N.B.S., **53**, 261, 1954; Wilkins, Talenta, **2**, 355, 1959.
[5] Fisher and Meloche, Anal. Chem., **24**, 1100, 1952; Meloche and Preuss, Anal. Chem., **26**, 1911, 1954.
[6] Chatard, Am. J. Sci. (3), **1**, 416, 1871.

The method is not adapted to use with molybdenite, $MoS_2$, because of the sulfate that forms on oxidation.

Vanadium and tungsten, if present, must be removed. Fe, Cr, Si, Sn, Ti, Bi, and Sb will contaminate the precipitate if present.

*Reagents.* **Lead Acetate.**—A 4% solution is made by dissolving 20 g. of the salt in 500 ml. of warm water. A few ml. of acetic acid are added to clear the solution.

*Procedure.*—The solution acidified with acetic acid (5 ml. per 200 ml.) and free from iron, is heated to near boiling and the lead acetate reagent added slowly until no further precipitation occurs and then about 5% excess. (One ml. of the 4% lead acetate reagent will precipitate about 0.01 g. of molybdenum.) The precipitate is allowed to settle a few minutes and filtered hot into a weighed Gooch crucible or into a filter paper. (Refiltering first portion if cloudy.)[7] The precipitate is washed with hot water until free of chlorides and the excess of the lead acetate.

The precipitate dried and ignited in a porcelain crucible at red heat for about twenty minutes is weighed as $PbMoO_4$.

$$PbMoO_4 \times 0.2613 = Mo \qquad PbMoO_4 \times 0.3921 = MoO_3$$

$$Mo \times 3.8266 = PbMoO_4 \qquad MoO_3 \times 2.5506 = PbMoO_4$$

## PRECIPITATION AND WEIGHING AS SILVER MOLYBDATE

Silver molybdate is an excellent form in which to precipitate and weigh molybdate. The procedure is useful for standardization of solutions of molybdenum and for checking the amount of $MoO_3$ extracted by ammonia from the crude oxide as obtained in many analytical procedures.[8] 100 ml. of water dissolved 0.0044 g. $Ag_2MoO_4$ at 25°C., but the precipitate is practically insoluble when an excess of silver is present. The latter may be washed out with alcohol.

*Procedure.*—To 150 ml. of the ammonium or other alkali molybdate solution is added a drop of methyl orange and enough sulfuric acid to change the color to red. One g. of $NaC_2H_3O_2 \cdot 3H_2O$ is dissolved in the solution; heat to boiling and add $AgNO_3$ solution to complete precipitation. The precipitate is filtered on a filter crucible, washed with a solution of 5 g. $AgNO_3$ per 1000 ml. of $H_2O$. The excess of $AgNO_3$ is removed by $C_2H_5OH$; wash with three 5-ml. portions of $C_2H_5OH$ (95%). Dry the precipitate to constant weight at 250°C.

## SEPARATION WITH ALPHA-BENZOINOXIME AND DETERMINATION AS THE OXIDE[9]

Molybdenum is precipitated with α-benzoinoxime in cold, dilute sulfuric, hydrochloric, nitric, acetic, or phosphoric acid solutions. The precipitate cannot be weighed directly upon drying, but is ignited to form the oxide, $MoO_3$.

Aluminum, antimony, arsenic, bismuth, cadmium, chromium(III), cerium, cobalt, copper, iron, lead, manganese, mercury, nickel, silver, tin, titanium, uranium, vanadium(IV), zinc, and zirconium do not interfere.

Niobium, silicon, palladium, tantalum, and tungsten must be removed before precipitation of the molybdenum or else determined in the $MoO_3$ and the amount

---

[7] Addition of ammonium nitrate to the solution tends to prevent formation of colloidal $PbMoO_4$. Paper pulp (ashless) may be added to assist rapid filtration.

[8] McCay, L. W., J. Am. Chem. Soc., 56, 2548, 1934.

[9] Knowles, Natl. Bur. Standards J. Research, 9, 1, 1932; A.S.T.M., Chemical Analysis of Metals, 1960.

present deducted. Hydrofluoric and tartaric acids cause incomplete precipitation.

**Reagents.—Boric Acid Solution (40 g. per l.).**

**Alcohol Solution of Alpha-Benzoinoxime (20 g. per l.).—**Dissolve 10 g. of alpha-benzoinoxime in 500 ml. of ethanol or methanol. Filter if not clear.

**Alpha-Benzoinoxime Wash Solution.—**Dilute 25 to 50 ml. of alpha-benzoinoxime (20 g. per l.) to 1 liter with cold $H_2SO_4$ (1:99). This solution shall be freshly prepared before using.

**Cinchonine Solution.—**Dissolve 125 g. of cinchonine in 1 liter of HCl (1:1).

**Cinchonine Wash Solution.—**Dilute 30 ml. of cinchonine solution to 1 liter.

### PROCEDURE FOR MOLYBDENUM STEELS

(a) Transfer 1 to 3 g. of the sample to a 600-ml. beaker, add 50 ml. of $H_2SO_4$ (1:6), and warm until action ceases. Carefully add just enough $HNO_3$ to decompose carbides and to oxidize iron and molybdenum. Add 2 to 4 drops of HF, mix, and then add 10 ml. of boric acid (40 g. per l.).[10] Boil for a few minutes, and filter if the solution is not perfectly clear.[11]

(b) With some chromium steels, the acid-insoluble residue may contain small amounts of molybdenum. In this case, filter, ignite at as low a temperature as possible, and fuse slowly (below 500°C.) with $K_2S_2O_7$. Dissolve the melt in the main solution.

(c) Dilute to 100 ml. with water, cool to 25°C., and add sufficient $FeSO_4$ (0.5 g. is usually sufficient) to reduce vanadic and chromic acids. Cool to 5°C., stir, and slowly add 10 ml. of the ethanol solution of alpha-benzoinoxime (20 g. per l.) and then 5 ml. more for each 0.01 g. of molybdenum present. Continue to stir the solution, add 5 to 10 ml. of bromine water, and then add a few more milliliters of the alpha-benzoinoxime solution. Allow the beaker and contents to remain in the cooling mixture 10 minutes, while stirring occasionally. Stir in a little macerated filter pulp, and filter through a rapid paper. If the first 50 ml. or so are not entirely clear, filter this portion again. Wash the precipitate with 200 ml. of cold alpha-benzoinoxime wash solution. On standing, needlelike crystals will appear in the filtrate if sufficient reagent has been used.

(d) Transfer the precipitate and paper to a platinum crucible and dry cautiously. Char, without inflaming, and ignite at 500 to 525°C. Cool, weigh, and repeat the heating until the weight remains constant. Treat the ignited residue with 5 ml. of $NH_4OH$, digest, and filter through a small paper. Wash well with $NH_4OH$ (1:99). Ignite the paper and contents in the original crucible, cool, and weigh. The difference in weights represents the $MoO_3$ present.

(e) Tungsten is also precipitated. If present, the ammoniacal filtrate is treated as follows: Add 5 ml. of $H_2SO_4$ (1:1) and evaporate to dense white fumes. Cool, dilute to 25 ml. with water, and add 1 to 2 ml. of cinchonine solution. Digest at 80 to 90°C., or preferably overnight at room temperature. Filter through a close-texture paper containing a little paper pulp and wash with cinchonine wash solution. Transfer the paper and contents to a platinum crucible, char the paper,

---

[10] With larger samples (5 to 6 g.) of silicon steel it is best to evaporate the solution, dehydrate, and remove $SiO_2$ before treatment with the alpha-benzoinoxime.

[11] If the sample is insoluble in this treatment it may be dissolved in a mixture of HCl and $HNO_3$, $HClO_4$ added, and the solution evaporated to white fumes. The solution is then diluted and sufficient $H_2SO_3$ added to reduce the chromium. After boiling out the excess $SO_2$ and filtering off any silica, the solution is cooled and molybdenum then precipitated.

and ignite at 750 to 850°C. to constant weight. Cool and weigh. In very accurate work, dissolve any residue obtained here and test for molybdenum by the "Thiocyanate Method," page 687.

(*f*) Calculation.—Calculate the percentage of molybdenum as follows:

$$\text{Molybdenum, } \% = \frac{(A - B) \times 0.667}{C} \times 100$$

where $A$ = grams of $MoO_3$ (paragraph (*d*)),
  $B$ = correction for impurities (paragraph (*e*)), in grams, and
  $C$ = grams of sample used.

(*g*) With high-molybdenum, medium-tungsten steel (8% molybdenum, 2% tungsten) the ignited oxides may be weighed, dissolved, and molybdenum determined by the $MoS_3$-$MoO_3$ method (after reprecipitation of the sulfide). Tungsten is then obtained by difference.

(*h*) If molybdenum is present in very small amounts (carbon steels), the ignited alpha-benzoinoxime precipitate should be dissolevd in $NH_4OH$ and the molybdenum determined by the photometric method.

### PROCEDURE FOR CAST IRON

(*a*) Transfer 1 to 5 g. of the sample to a 600-ml. beaker, add 100 ml. of $H_2SO_4$ (1:4), and warm. When action ceases, add $HNO_3$ drop by drop until rapid effervescence ceases (usually 2 to 5 ml.), and then add 2 to 3 drops in excess. Evaporate the solution to dense white fumes, cool somewhat, and add 100 ml. of water. Warm until salts are dissolved and filter through a rapid paper. Wash the paper with warm water.

(*b*) Dilute the filtrate to 150 ml. and cool to 25°C. Add sufficient $FeSO_4$ to reduce any chromium or vanadium that may have been oxidized by the above treatment, cool to 5°C., and complete the determination as described in "Procedure for Molybdenum Steels."

### PROCEDURE FOR OPEN-HEARTH IRON AND WROUGHT IRON [12]

Determine molybdenum in accordance with the procedure described in "Procedure for Molybdenum Steels."

## MOLYBDENUM BY PRECIPITATION AS SULFIDE AND WEIGHING AS OXIDE

**Reagents.** **Ammonium Persulfate Solution (250 g. per l.).**
**Hydrogen Sulfide Wash Solution.**—Saturate $H_2SO_4$ (1:99) with $H_2S$.

### PROCEDURE FOR MOLYBDENUM STEELS CONTAINING NO TUNGSTEN

(*a*) Transfer 2 to 10 g. of the sample (approximately 0.03 g. of molybdenum) to a 600-ml. beaker, add 100 ml. of $H_2SO_4$ (1:5), and warm. When action ceases, add 20 ml. of $(NH_4)_2S_2O_8$ (250 g. per l.) and boil the solution for 8 to 10 minutes to oxidize the molybdenum and part of the iron. Cool somewhat, add 5 g. of tartaric acid, neutralize with $NH_4OH$, and add $H_2SO_4$ (1:1) until acidified and then 10 ml. in excess for each 100 ml. of solution.

[12] The small amounts of molybdenum normally encountered in these materials are preferably determined by the photometric method.

(b) Heat to boiling and pass in a rapid stream of $H_2S$ for 10 minutes. Dilute with an equal volume of hot water, and pass in $H_2S$ for 5 minutes. Digest at 50 to 60°C. for 1 hour. Filter, and wash the sulfur and sulfides with $H_2S$ wash solution.[13]

(c) Place the paper and precipitate in the original beaker, add 5 ml. of $H_2SO_4$ and 20 ml. of $HNO_3$, cover, and heat to dense white fumes. Cool somewhat, add 10 ml. of $HNO_3$, and again evaporate to dense white fumes. If the solution is not clear and of a light color, repeat the treatment with $HNO_3$. Cool, dilute to 100 ml., and add a slight excess (ten to twelve drops) of NaOH (200 g. per l.). Heat to boiling and set aside for 5 minutes. Filter, and wash the paper and residue with hot water.

(d) Heat the filtrate to boiling and pass in $H_2S$ for 10 minutes. Add $H_2SO_4$ (1:1) until acidified and then a 4 ml. excess per 100 ml. of solution. Pass $H_2S$ into the solution for 5 minutes and digest at 50 to 60°C. for 1 hour. Filter through a 9-cm. close-texture paper, and wash thoroughly with $H_2S$ wash solution.[14]

(e) Transfer the precipitate to a small porcelain crucible, and heat carefully until carbon is destroyed and then at 500 to 525°C. to constant weight.[15] Weigh as $MoO_3$.

(f) Test the ignited oxide for impurities by treating with $NH_4OH$. If copper is indicated, determine its amount colorimetrically, and calculate to CuO. If a residue remains, filter, wash with water, ignite, and weigh.[16]

(g) Calculation.—Calculate the percentage of molybdenum as follows:

$$\text{Molybdenum, } \% = \frac{(A - B) \times 0.667}{C} \times 100$$

where $A$ = grams of $MoO_3$ (paragraph (e)),
$B$ = correction for impurities (paragraph (f)), in grams, and
$C$ = grams of sample used.

### PROCEDURE FOR TUNGSTEN STEELS

(a) Dissolve 2 to 10 g. of the sample (approximately 0.03 g. of molybdenum) in 100 ml. of HCl (1:1), cautiously add 20 ml. of $HNO_3$ (1:1), and then boil gently until the tungstic acid becomes bright yellow. Dilute to 150 ml. and heat to boiling. Filter, and wash the residue with HCl (1:9). Reserve the precipitate.

[13] In umpire analyses the filtrate should be boiled to expel $H_2S$ and its molybdenum content determined colorimetrically, or the unprecipitated molybdenum (usually not in excess of 0.5 mg.) should be recovered as follows: Boil the filtrate to expel $H_2S$ and to reduce the volume to about 450 ml. Add 20 ml. of $(NH_4)_2S_2O_8$ (250 g. per l.), boil for 8 to 10 minutes, and then pass in a rapid stream of $H_2S$ for 10 to 15 minutes. Digest for 1 hour, filter, wash, and combine with the main precipitate.

[14] Precipitation of molybdenum is usually complete, but it is well to test the filtrate by boiling to expel $H_2S$, oxidizing with bromine water, boiling to expel bromine, and again passing $H_2S$ into the solution.

[15] Molybdenum oxide volatilizes at temperatures above 500°C. but the rate is very slow at temperatures below 600°C. The heating may be done in a muffle, using a pyrometer for temperature control, or in a "radiator" consisting of a 50-ml. porcelain crucible containing a disk of asbestos board, 4 mm. thick on the bottom and fitted with a nichrome triangle which is bent to fit the inside of the crucible and supported by bending the end wires over the rim. The crucible shall be placed so that the bottom is 8 cm. above the top of a Tirrill burner and heated by a flame 12.5 cm. high.

[16] If residual amounts of molybdenum are being determined, the determination should be checked by testing the solution of the oxide.

(b) Add 15 ml. of $H_2SO_4$ to the filtrate, evaporate to fumes of $H_2SO_4$, cool, and add 100 ml. of water. Digest until soluble salts are in solution. If any tungstic acid separates, filter through a small filter, wash with a little $H_2SO_4$ (1:99), and combine with the reserved tungstic acid precipitate (paragraph (a)). Small amounts of tungsten will not precipitate, but will form a complex with the molybdenum and be held in solution.

(c) Add 5 g. of tartaric acid to the clear filtrate and neutralize with $NH_4OH$. Add $H_2SO_4$ (1:1) until acidified, then 10 ml. in excess per 100 ml. of solution, and pass in $H_2S$ as described in (b) of preceding section.

(d) Some molybdenum is always carried down by the tungstic acid and should be recovered as follows: Dissolve the combined tungstic acid residues in a hot solution of NaOH (50 g. per l.), and wash the papers with a little water and then with a little hot $H_2SO_4$ (1:99). Add 5 g. of tartaric acid, then $H_2SO_4$ until the solution contains 5 ml. per 100 ml., and precipitate with $H_2S$ as described in (b) of the preceding section. Filter, wash, combine with the main sulfide precipitate, and complete the determination as described in the preceding section, (c) to (g).

## PROCEDURE FOR CAST IRON

(a) Transfer 2 to 5 g. of the sample to a 600-ml. beaker, add 100 ml. of $H_2SO_4$ (1:4), and warm. When action ceases, add $HNO_3$ (1:1) drop by drop until rapid effervescence ceases (usually 5 to 10 ml.), and then add three to five drops in excess. Evaporate the solution to dense white fumes. Cool somewhat, add 100 ml. of warm water, stir, and heat until salts are dissolved. Filter through a rapid paper, catching the filtrate in a 600-ml. beaker. Wash the paper well with hot water.

(b) Add 5 g. of tartaric acid to the filtrate and neutralize the solution with $NH_4OH$. Add 10 ml. of $H_2SO_4$ (1:1) for each 100 ml. of solution, heat to boiling, and pass in a rapid stream of $H_2S$ for 10 minutes. Dilute with an equal volume of hot water, and pass in $H_2S$ for 5 minutes. Digest at 50 to 60°C. for 1 hour. Filter, and wash the sulfur and sulfides with $H_2S$ wash solution.

(c) Complete the determination as described above.

## PROCEDURE FOR CARBON STEELS, OPEN-HEARTH IRON, AND WROUGHT IRON

Determine molybdenum in accordance with the procedure described above.

## SEPARATION OF MOLYBDENUM FROM TUNGSTEN [17]

Procedure.—To a solution of sodium tungstate and sodium molybdate in 10–15 ml. is added 10 ml. of 50% ammonium formate, 10 ml. of 30% tartaric acid and 100 ml. of water saturated at zero with $H_2S$, and 10 ml. of 2 $M$ formic acid. At this point, the solution has a pH of 2.9. Heat the mixture at 60°C. on a water bath for 1 hour, having a flask stoppered with a one-hole stopper, the outlet of which is closed with a glass ball held in place by a stout rubber band. The stopper is also held in place by a second rubber band which is carried around the bottom of the flask. Add a small quantity of filter paper pulp and add 10 ml. of 24 $M$ formic acid to complete the precipitation of the molybdenum sulfide. Keep the mixture at 60°C. for 30 minutes longer, filter through a Gooch or porcelain filter and crucible, and wash the precipitate with 5–10 ml. portions of a mixture

[17] Yagoda and Fales, J. Am. Chem. Soc., 58, 1494, 1936.

of 5 ml. 50% ammonium formate, 5 ml. of 24 $M$ formic acid and 100 ml. of water. The molybdenum sulfide is converted to the oxide in an electric muffle at a temperature of 500–550°C.

The filtrate is concentrated and treated with 25 ml. of 16 $M$ HNO$_3$. The ammonium salts are destroyed by evaporation and the precipitation of the WO$_3$ is completed using the customary cinchonine reagent. The WO$_3$ is brought to constant weight by heatings at a final temperature of 750°C. in an electric muffle.

## SEPARATION AS MERCUROUS MOLYBDATE AND DETERMINATION AS THE OXIDE

Especially applicable for small amounts of molybdenum where fusion with an alkali carbonate has been required.

*Procedure.*—One gram of the ore is fused with 4 grams of fusion mixture, (Na$_2$CO$_3$ + K$_2$CO$_3$ + KNO$_3$), and the cooled melt extracted with hot water.

If manganese is present, indicated by a colored solution, it may be removed by reduction with alcohol, the manganese precipitate filtered off and washed with hot water, the solution evaporated to near dryness and taken up with water, upon addition of nitric acid as stated below.

The solution containing the alkaline molybdate is nearly neutralized by adding HNO$_3$, the amount necessary being determined by a blank, and to the cold, slightly alkaline solution, a faintly acid solution of mercurous nitrate is added until no further precipitation occurs. The precipitate consists of mercurous molybdate and carbonate (chromium, vanadium, tungsten, arsenic and phosphorus will also be precipitated if present). The solution containing the precipitate is boiled and allowed to stand 10–15 minutes to settle, the black precipitate is filtered off and washed with a dilute solution of mercurous nitrate. The precipitate is dried, and as much as possible transferred to a watch-glass. The residue on the filter is dissolved with hot dilute nitric acid, and the solution received in a large weighed porcelain crucible. The solution is evaporated to dryness on the water bath and the main portion of the precipitate added to this residue, and that product heated cautiously over a low flame [18] until the mercury has completely volatilized. The cooled residue is weighed as MoO$_3$.

$$MoO_3 \times 0.6665 = Mo$$

NOTE.—If Cr, V, W, As or P are present a separation must be effected. Molybdenum should be precipitated in an H$_2$SO$_4$ solution in a pressure flask as the sulfide by H$_2$S as given in the following method, and arsenic if present removed by magnesia mixture as indicated in the procedure for separation of arsenic from molybdenum. If these impurities are present the molybdenum oxide may be fused with a very little Na$_2$CO$_3$, and leached with hot water and the filtrate treated with H$_2$S as directed.

## TITRIMETRIC METHODS

### THE IODOMETRIC REDUCTION METHOD [19]

When a mixture of molybdic acid and potassium iodide in presence of hydrochloric acid is boiled, the volume having defined limits, free iodine is liberated

---

[18] The oxide, MoO$_3$, sublimes at bright red heat. At 500–550°C. the loss is only 0.1 mg. per hour. M. P. Brinton and A. F. Stoppel, J. Am. Chem. Soc., **46**, 2454, 1924.

[19] Gooch and Fairbanks, Am. J. Sci. (4), **2**, 160, 1896.

and expelled and the molybdic acid reduced to a definite lower oxide; by titrating with a standard oxidizing agent the molybdic acid is determined.

**Reaction.**—$2MoO_3 + 4KI + 4HCl = 2MoO_2I + I_2 + 4KCl + 2H_2O$.

**Reagents.**—0.1 $N$ solutions of iodine, sodium arsenite, potassium permanganate.

**Procedure.**[20] **Reduction.**—The soluble molybdate in amount not exceeding an equivalent of 0.5 g. $MoO_3$ is placed in a 150-ml. Erlenmeyer flask, 20 to 25 ml. of hydrochloric acid (sp. gr. 1.19) added together with 0.2 to 0.6 gram potassium iodide. A short stemmed-funnel is placed in the neck of the flask to prevent mechanical loss during the boiling. The volume of the solution should be about 600 ml. The solution is boiled until the volume is reduced to exactly 25 ml. as determined by a mark on the flask. The residue is diluted immediately to a volume of 125 ml. and cooled. Either reoxidation, below, may now be followed.

**Reoxidation by Standard Iodine.**—A solution of tartaric acid, equivalent to 1 g. of the solid, is now added, and the free acid nearly neutralized with sodium hydroxide solution (litmus or methyl orange indicator) and finally neutralized with sodium acid carbonate, $NaHCO_3$, added in excess. A measured amount of 0.1 $N$ iodine is now run in. The solution is set aside in a dark closet for two hours, in order to permit complete oxidation, as the reaction is slow. The excess iodine is now titrated with 0.1 $N$ sodium arsenite.

One ml. 0.1 $N$ iodine = 0.0144 g. $MoO_3$ = 0.0096 g. Mo

On long standing a small amount of iodate is apt to form. This is determined by making acid with dilute HCl and titrating with 0.1 $N$ sodium thiosulfate.

**Reoxidation of the Residue by Standard Permanganate.**—To the reduced solution about 0.5 g. of manganese sulfate in solution is added, followed by a measured amount of 0.1 $N$ permanganate solution, added from a burette until the characteristic pink color appears. A measured amount of standard 0.1 $N$ sodium arsenite, equivalent to the permanganate is then run in and about 3 g. of tartaric acid added. The acid is neutralized by acid sodium or potassium carbonate, the stopper and the sides of the flask rinsed into the main solution. The residual arsenite is now titrated by 0.1 $N$ iodine, using starch indicator.

NOTES.—Tartaric acid prevents precipitation during the subsequent neutralization with $NaHCO_3$.

The addition of manganese salt in the reoxidation of the residue by standard permanganate is to prevent the liberation of free chlorine by the action of $KMnO_4$ on HCl. In addition to the oxidation of the lower oxides to molybdic acid, potassium permanganate added as above liberates free iodine from HI, it produces iodic acid, and forms the higher oxides of manganese. The standard arsenite, on the other hand, converts free iodine and the iodate to HI and reduces the higher oxides of manganese.

# DETERMINATION BY REDUCTION WITH JONES REDUCTOR AND OXIDATION BY STANDARD PERMANGANATE SOLUTION (INCLUDING COLORIMETRIC PROCEDURE) [21]

The procedure depends upon the reduction of hexivalent molybdenum to the trivalent form by passing its acidified solution through a column of amalgamated zinc. Since the reduced molybdenum compound is sensitive to the oxygen of the air, resulting in partial oxidation,[22] the reduced compound is caught in an excess

[20] Gooch and Pulman, Am. J. Sci. (4), **12**, 449, 1901.
[21] A.S.T.M. Methods Chemical Analysis of Metals, 1956, 1960.
[22] Randall, D. L., Am. J. Sci. (4), **24**, 313, 1907.

of ferric solution, whereupon an equivalent amount of ferrous ion plus $Mo^{+5}$ is formed. Titration of the reduced solution by means of standard permanganate establishes the amount of molybdenum reduced by the zinc.

$$2MoO_4^= + 3Zn + 16H^+ \rightarrow 2Mo^{+3} + 3Zn^{++} + 8H_2O$$

$$5Mo^{+3} + 3MnO_4^- + 8H_2O \rightarrow 5MoO_4^= + 3Mn^{++} + 16H^+$$

*Apparatus.* **Jones Reductor.**—The reductor tube to be used is of the dimensions shown in Fig. 30-1 and set up as shown in Fig. 25-3, page 541, in the Chapter on Iron. It is prepared by shaking 800 g. of 20–30 mesh zinc (as free of iron as possible), with 400 ml. of $HgCl_2$ (25 g. per l.) in a 1-liter flask for 2 minutes. Wash several times with $H_2SO_4$ (2:98), and then thoroughly with water. The reductor, when idle, should always be kept filled with distilled water to above the top of the zinc.

*Reagents.* **Ammonium Sulfide Wash Solution.**—Saturate $NH_4OH$ (1:99) with $H_2S$.

**Tartaric Acid Wash Solution.**—Dissolve 10 g. of tartaric acid in 1 liter of $H_2SO_4$ (1:99) and saturate with $H_2S$.

**Potassium Permanganate Solution (25 g. per l.).**

**Zinc.**—The zinc should preferably be 20 mesh and should not contain more than 0.002% of iron.

**Ferric Phosphate Solution.**—Dissolve 100 g. of $Fe_2(SO_4)_3$ in 1 liter of water to which 150 ml. of 85% $H_3PO_4$ and 20 ml. of $H_2SO_4$ (1:1) have been added. Add $KMnO_4$ (25 g. per l.) until the solution is just tinted pink, due to the excess of $KMnO_4$.

**Standard Potassium Permanganate Solution (0.1 N).**

**Sodium Thiocyanate Solution (50 g. per l.).**

**Stannous Chloride Solution.**—Transfer 350 g. of $SnCl_2 \cdot 2H_2O$ to a 500-ml. Erlenmeyer flask, add 200 ml. of HCl (1:1), and boil gently until solution is practically complete. Transfer the solution to a 1-liter bottle, and dilute to 1 liter with freshly boiled water. Add a few pieces of metallic tin, and stopper.

**Ferric Sulfate Solution.**—Dissolve 80 g. of $Fe_2(SO_4)_3$ in 1 liter of $H_2SO_4$ (1:4).

**Standard Molybdenum Solution (1 ml. = 0.0005 g. Mo).**—Dissolve 0.5 g. of pure $Na_2MoO_4 \cdot 2H_2O$ in 1 liter of water containing 5 ml. of $H_2SO_4$. To standardize this solution, pipette 100 ml. of it into a 250-ml. beaker, add 10 ml. of $H_2SO_4$ (1:1), and reduce it in the Jones Reductor as follows: If the reductor has been standing idle, pass 100 ml. of $H_2SO_4$ (5:95) through it, then some water, and discard the wash solution. Add 30 ml. of ferric phosphate solution to the receiver, and then enough water so that the tip of the reductor dips beneath the surface of the solution. (To prepare the ferric phosphate solution, dissolve 100 g. of $Fe_2(SO_4)_3$ in 1 liter of water to which 150 ml. of $H_3PO_4$ and 20 ml. of $H_2SO_4$ (1:1) have been added. Add $KMnO_4$ (25 g. per l.) until the solution is just tinted pink.) Draw the molybdenum solution, by gentle suction, through the reductor. Just before the surface of the liquid reaches the zinc, add a 50-ml. portion of water, and finally rinse by adding two more 50-ml. portions, each time just before the surface of the solution reaches the zinc. Close the stopcock, disconnect, and raise the reductor as a little water is allowed to run through the stem. Rinse the stem and titrate the solution with 0.1 N $KMnO_4$. Make a blank determination, following the same procedure and using the same amounts of all reagents.

**Isopropyl Ether.**—Shake isopropyl ether in a separatory funnel with 100 ml. of $H_2SO_4$ (1:9), 10 ml. of the $Fe_2(SO_4)_3$ solution, 10 ml. of the NaCNS (50 g. per l.), and the 10 ml. of $SnCl_2$ solution.

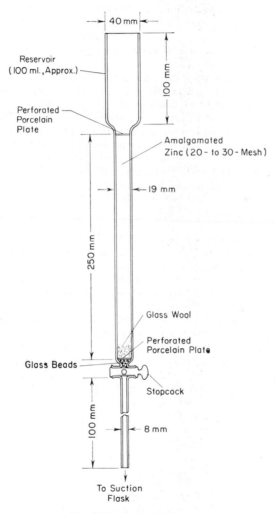

40 mm

Reservoir
(100 ml., Approx.)

100 mm

Perforated
Porcelain
Plate

Amalgamated
Zinc (20- to 30-Mesh)

19 mm

250 mm

Glass Wool

Perforated
Porcelain Plate

Glass Beads

Stopcock

100 mm

8 mm

To Suction
Flask

Fig. 30-1. Jones Reductor.

**Procedure.**—Transfer 0.5 g. of the sample to a 150-ml. beaker, cover, add 10 ml. of $HNO_3$ (1:3), and warm to complete solution. If the sample dissolves with difficulty, add a drop or two of HF. When reaction is complete, cautiously add 10 ml. of $H_2SO_4$ (1:1) and evaporate to dense white fumes. Cool, add 40 ml. of water, and warm until all salts have dissolved. Rinse and remove the cover. Filter, and wash the paper and residue 12 to 15 times with hot water, 3 to 4 times with hot $NH_4OH$ (1:3), and finally 4 to 5 times with hot water, and washings being allowed to run into the main filtrate. Discard the residue.

Cool the filtrate, add $NH_4OH$ until it is difficult to avoid a red tint, and heat the slightly acid solution to boiling. Slowly pour the solution, while stirring vigorously, into 75 ml. of nearly boiling $NH_4OH$ (1:5) in a 600-ml. beaker. Rinse the beaker that held the filtrate with a little water and then with a little hot $NH_4OH$ (1:5), and add the rinsings to the main solution. Add a little paper pulp, filter into a 600-ml. beaker, and wash the precipitate with hot water. Set the filtrate aside.

Dissolve the precipitate in a slight excess of hot $H_2SO_4$ (1:4), nearly neutralize with $NH_4OH$, and pour into $NH_4OH$ (1:5) as before. Filter into the reserved filtrate. Dissolve the precipitate and repeat the operation.

Dissolve the precipitate of $Fe(OH)_3$ in a slight excess of hot $H_2SO_4$ (1:4), wash the filter with hot water, and reserve the filtrate for further treatment.†

Add 3 g. of powdered tartaric acid to the combined ammoniacal filtrates, stir until dissolved, and saturate the solution with $H_2S$. If a precipitate appears, filter, and wash with $(NH_4)_2S$ wash solution. Warm the filtrate, cover the beaker, and add $H_2SO_4$ (1:1) until the solution contains 10 ml. of $H_2SO_4$ in excess for each 100 ml. of solution. Heat the solution just to boiling and let stand at the side of a steam bath (about 40°C.) for 15 minutes, until the precipitate has settled. Filter, and wash thoroughly with tartaric acid wash solution. Reserve the filtrate.*

Transfer the paper and precipitate ($MoS_3$) to the original 600-ml. beaker. Place a glass stirring rod in the beaker, cover, and add 6 ml. of $H_2SO_4$ and 10 ml. of $HNO_3$. Cautiously heat to dense white fumes. Let cool, add 5 ml. of $HNO_3$, again heat to dense white fumes, and repeat the treatment until the yellow color due to organic matter has disappeared. Cool, rinse, and remove the cover. Rinse the inside of the beaker, and add $KMnO_4$ (25 g. per l.) very cautiously until a permanent red tint is obtained. Again evaporate to dense white fumes. Cool, and add 75 ml. of water. Boil for a few minutes, add 2 g. of 20-mesh zinc, and continue the boiling until any copper has been reduced to the metallic form. Filter through a 9-cm. paper and wash with hot water. Add a slight excess of $KMnO_4$ (25 g. per l.).

If the Jones Reductor has been standing idle, pass 100 ml. of warm (40 to 50°C.) $H_2SO_4$ (5:95) through it and then a little cold water. Discard the wash solution. Add 35 ml. of ferric phosphate solution to the receiver, and then enough water so that the tip of the reductor dips well beneath the surface of the solution when the receptacle is connected with the reductor. Draw the cool (about 20°C.) solution of molybdenum, which should be about 100 ml. in volume and contain about 5 ml. of $H_2SO_4$, through the reductor, while gently swirling the solution in the receiving flask. Just before the surface of the liquid reaches the zinc, add 50 ml. of cold $H_2SO_4$ (5:95) and finally rinse twice more by adding 50 ml. of water each time just before the surface of the solution reaches the zinc.

Close the stopcock while a portion of the last washing solution remains in the reductor funnel. Disconnect and raise the reductor as a little water is allowed to run through the stem and rinse the outside of the stem. Titrate the solution with 0.1 $N$ $KMnO_4$.

**Blank.**—Make a blank determination, following the procedure up to this point.

Boil down the filtrate reserved in the paragraph marked with the asterisk to a volume of about 75 ml., and combine with the solution reserved in accordance with the paragraph marked with the dagger.

Add 1 to 2 g. of $(NH_4)_2S_2O_8$, boil down to a volume of 100 ml., and cool to 15°C. Add sufficient $H_2SO_4$ (1:1) to give a solution containing approximately 10% $H_2SO_4$ by volume. The sodium-molybdenum thiocyanate amber to reddish-brown color is best developed in a solution containing 10% $H_2SO_4$ by volume.

Cool to 25°C. and transfer to a 500-ml. separatory funnel. Add 10 ml. of NaCNS (50 g. per l.) and 10 ml. of $SnCl_2$ solution. Stopper and shake vigorously for several minutes. Add 50 ml. (or more if needed) of isopropyl ether, and shake for 1 to 2 minutes longer. Allow the extract to separate, draw off the lower layer, and set it aside. Transfer the extract to a 150-ml. Nessler, Julian, or similar colorimeter tube. Return the lower acid layer to the separatory funnel and shake again with approximately 25 ml. of ether. Should the upper layer have an amber to reddish-brown color, add it to the solution in the colorimeter tube.

Prepare a color standard containing approximately the same concentration of molybdenum as the sample solution. Transfer 25 ml. of $Fe_2(SO_4)_3$ solution to a 250-ml. separatory funnel containing 10 ml. of cold water, and add molybdenum solution (1 ml. = 0.0005 g. Mo) from a burette. Cool the solution to about 25°C., and proceed as described in the preceding paragraph.

Allow both the sample solution and the color standard to stand for several minutes before comparing. Dilute the darker of the two solutions with isopropyl ether and mix thoroughly until the sample and the standard match exactly. The colorimetric determination is limited to solutions containing not more than 0.05 mg. of molybdenum per milliliter.

**Calculation.**—Calculate the percentage of molybdenum as follows:

$$\text{Mo}\% = \frac{[(A - B)C \times 0.032] + D}{E} \times 100$$

where $A$ = milliliters of $KMnO_4$ solution required for titration of the reduced molybdenum solution,
$B$ = milliliters of $KMnO_4$ solution required for titration of the blank,
$C$ = normality of the $KMnO_4$ solution,
$D$ = grams of molybdenum determined colorimetrically, and
$E$ = grams of sampled used.

## DETERMINATION BY REDUCTION WITH MERCURY AND OXIDATION WITH CERIC SULFATE [23]

The molybdenum solution is made approximately 3 $N$ in HCl and is shaken vigorously with 25 ml. of mercury in a glass-stoppered vessel. The reduced solution is filtered to remove calomel and 1:5 HCl is used for washing the latter, and the Mo(V) is titrated with standard ceric sulfate using o-phenanthroline indicator (2 drops of 0.025 $M$ indicator are used, and the volume must be 300 ml. if 0.25 g. of Mo are present before adding the indicator). As much as 0.25 g. of either phosphate or arsenate does not interfere. The acidity of the solution must not be as high as 4 $N$ in HCl during the reduction because partial reduction to Mo(III) occurs at acidities of 4 $N$ and higher. Copper, even in quantities of the order of 0.1–1 mg. causes serious interference by catalyzing the autoxidation of the reduced solution by air. The copper must be excluded, or alternatively oxygen must be excluded.

Ceric sulfate may also be used for the titration of the ferrous solution produced when Mo(III) is led from a Jones Reductor into an excess of ferric sulfate.

[23] Furman and Murray, J. Am. Chem. Soc., **58**, 1689, 1936.

## METHOD FOR DETERMINING MOLYBDENUM AND VANADIUM IN A MIXTURE OF THEIR ACIDS

The procedure depends upon the fact that vanadic acid alone is reduced by $SO_2$ [24] in a sulfuric acid solution, whereas both vanadic and molybdic acids are reduced by amalgamated zinc, in each case the reducing agents forming definite lower oxides which are readily oxidized to definite higher oxides by $KMnO_4$.

**Reactions.—**

$SO_2$ Reduction:

1. $V_2O_5 + SO_2 \rightarrow V_2O_4 + SO_3$.   (No action on $MoO_3$.)

Zn Reduction:

2. $V_2O_5 + 3Zn \rightarrow V_2O_2 + 3ZnO$.
3. $2MoO_3 + 3Zn \rightarrow Mo_2O_3 + 3ZnO$.

$KMnO_4$ Oxidation:

4. $5V_2O_4 + 2KMnO_4 + 3H_2SO_4 \rightarrow 5V_2O_5 + K_2SO_4 + MnSO_4 + 3H_2O$.
5. $5V_2O_2 + 6KMnO_4 + 9H_2SO_4 \rightarrow 5V_2O_5 + 3K_2SO_4 + 6MnSO_4 + 9H_2O$.
6. $5Mo_2O_3 + 6KMnO_4 + 9H_2SO_4 \rightarrow 10MoO_3 + 3K_2SO_4 + 6MnSO_4 + 9H_2O$.

From reactions 4 and 5 it is seen that three times the amount of $KMnO_4$ is required to oxidize $V_2O_2$ to $V_2O_5$ as is required in the case of $V_2O_4$, hence, total milliliters $KMnO_4$ required in oxidation of the zinc-reduced oxides minus three times the milliliters $KMnO_4$ required in oxidizing the tetroxide of vanadium formed by the sulfur dioxide reduction = ml. $KMnO_4$ required to oxidize $Mo_2O_3$ to $MoO_3$. From these data molybdenum and vanadium may readily be calculated.

*Procedure.* **Vanadic Acid.**—The solution containing the vanadic and molybdic acids in a 250- to 300-ml. Erlenmeyer flask, is diluted to 75 ml., acidified with 2 to 3 ml. of sulfuric acid (1.84), heated to boiling and the vanadic acid reduced by a current of $SO_2$ passed into the solution until the clear blue color indicates the complete reduction of the vanadic acid to $V_2O_4$. The boiling is now continued and $CO_2$ passed into the flask to expel the last trace of $SO_2$.

Standard 0.1 $N$ $KMnO_4$ is now run into the reduced solution to the characteristic faint pink. From reaction 4, vanadic acid may be calculated.

One ml. 0.1 $N$ $KMnO_4$ = 0.009095 g. $V_2O_5$ = 0.005095 g. vanadium

**Molybdic Acid.**—The reduction by Jones' Reductor, and titration of the combined acids reduced by amalgamated zinc with 0.1 $N$ potassium permanganate solution, is carried out exactly as described in the determination of molybdic acid alone. In this case 50 ml. of 10% ferric alum and 8 ml. of the phosphoric acid is placed in the receiving flask.

**Calculation.**—Total permanganate titration in molybdic acid minus three times the titration in vanadic acid gives the permanganate required to oxidize $Mo_2O_3$ to $MoO_3$. From equation 6 the molybdic acid may now be calculated.

$$\text{One ml. 0.1 } N \text{ } KMnO_4 = \frac{0.014395}{3} \text{ g. } MoO_3 = \frac{0.009595}{3} \text{ g. molybdenum}$$

[24] Reduction of vanadium by $SO_2$ in presence of molybdenum, Graham Edgar, Am. J. Sci. (4), **25**, 332, 1908. No reduction of $MoO_3$ when 0.4 g. is present with 5 ml. $H_2SO_4$ in 25-ml. volume.

## COLORIMETRIC/PHOTOMETRIC METHODS

### THIOCYANATE METHOD

Molybdenum forms an orange-red color with thiocyanate in acid solution in the presence of a reducing agent such as stannous chloride. The colored complex may be measured in the aqueous solution, in an aqueous-soluble organic solution, or in an immiscible organic solvent after extraction. There are several advantages in extracting the complex with an immiscible solvent: concentration of the molybdenum, separation of molybdenum from colored ions, and better color stability. Organic liquids commonly used are isopropyl ether, ethyl ether, butyl acetate, isoamyl alcohol, and methyl isobutyl ketone.

The presence of a small amount of iron or copper is necessary for full color development for both aqueous and organic solvent systems.

Acidity may vary from 0.25 to 2.5 $N$ and the stannous chloride concentration from 0.02 to 1% without effect on the molybdenum extraction and color development when isopropyl ether is used for extractant. The colored solution measured at 470 m$\mu$ follows Beer's Law over the range 0.01 to 0.5 mg. of molybdenum in 100 ml. of isopropyl ether using 1-cm. cells.

Interference from tungsten is eliminated or greatly reduced depending upon the amount of tungsten by addition of citrate or tartrate to the solution before extraction. Of 68 elements tested only rhenium, platinum, palladium, rhodium, vanadium, and tellurium interfere.[25]

The thiocyanate method with modification has been applied to the determination of molybdenum in a wide variety of materials including steels, beryllium,[25] titanium metal and alloys,[26] zirconium, uranium alloys and compounds, ores,[27] scheelite concentrates,[28] and silicate rocks.[29] Up to 9% molybdenum in titanium alloys may be determined with reasonable accuracy.[26]

**Reagents.** **Sodium Thiocyanate Solution (50 g. per l.).**

**Stannous Chloride Solution (350 g. per l.).**—Transfer 350 g. of $SnCl_2 \cdot 2H_2O$ to a 500-ml. Erlenmeyer flask, add 200 ml. of HCl (1:1), and warm (60 to 70°C.) until solution is practically complete. Cool and dilute to 1 liter in a volumetric flask with freshly boiled and cooled water. Add a few pieces of metallic tin, and stopper.

**Butyl Acetate or Isopropyl Ether:**

(1) Saturate technical butyl acetate with NaCNS and $SnCl_2$ by shaking, and keep in a dark bottle.

(2) Shake 50 ml. of butyl acetate or isopropyl ether with 25 ml. of $Fe(SO_4)_3 \cdot 9H_2O$ (80 g. per l.), 10 ml. of NaCNS (50 g. per l.), and 10 ml. of $SnCl_2 \cdot 2H_2O$ (350 g. per l.). Draw off and discard the lower or acid layer. Prepare the butyl acetate or isopropyl ether by this method immediately prior to use.

**Ferric Sulfate Solution (80 g. per l.).**—Dissolve 80 g. of $Fe_2(SO_4)_3 \cdot 9H_2O$ in water and dilute to 1 liter.

**Standard Molybdenum Solution (1 ml. = 0.0002 g. Mo).**—For the solution of strength 1 ml. = 0.0005 g. Mo see page 1331. Place 400 ml. of it in a 1-liter volu-

[25] Hibbits, Davis, Menke, and Kallmann, Talanta, **4**, 104, 1960.
[26] A.S.T.M. Methods of Chemical Analysis of Metals, 1960.
[27] Ward, Anal. Chem., **23**, 788, 1951.
[28] Hope, Anal. Chem., **29**, 1053, 1957.
[29] Sandell, Colorimetric Determination of Traces of Metals, p. 654, Interscience Publishers, Inc., New York, 1959.

metric flask and make up to volume. Aliquots of this solution may be diluted to suitable strength for use.

*Procedure for Molybdenum in Steel.*[30]—(*a*) Transfer 0.1 g. of the sample (for steels and irons containing from 0.02 to 0.4% of molybdenum) to a 150-ml. Erlenmeyer flask. Add 10 ml. of $HClO_4$ (1:1), warm until the sample has dissolved, and then add 1 ml. of $HNO_3$. Heat to boiling, cover, and fume until all carbonaceous matter has been destroyed. Cool somewhat, add 25 ml. of water, and boil for a few minutes to expel free chlorine. For steels and irons containing higher percentages of molybdenum, use proportionate amounts of sample and reagents.

(*b*) If the steel contains less than 0.02% of molybdenum, dissolve 0.5 to 1.0 g. of the sample in 20 ml. of $HNO_3$ (1:3), add 8 ml. of $HClO_4$, and evaporate to fumes. In the case of high-silicon steel, add 0.5 ml. of HF before evaporating to white fumes. Cool, wash down the sides of the flask with water, and again evaporate to white fumes. Cool somewhat, add 25 ml. of water, and boil for a few minutes to expel free chlorine.

(*c*) To the cooled solution (paragraph (*a*) or (*b*)), add 2 g. of tartaric acid and a slight excess of NaOH (200 g. per l.). About 30 ml. will be required. Heat to about 80°C. for a few minutes, remove from the source of heat, and cool somewhat. Neutralize to litmus with $H_2SO_4$ (1:1), and then add an excess of 2 ml. for each 8 ml. of solution, which will give a solution containing 10% of $H_2SO_4$ by volume. Cool the solution to 25°C. and transfer to a 250-ml. cylindrical-type separatory funnel, rinsing the flask twice with 5-ml. portions of cool $H_2SO_4$ (1:9).

(*d*) Add 10 ml. of NaCNS (50 g. per l.) and shake 0.5 minute. Add 10 ml. of $SnCl_2 \cdot 2H_2O$ (350 g. per l.) (20 ml. for 1 g. of the sample), and shake vigorously for 1 minute. Add 50 ml. of butyl acetate or preferably isopropyl ether (treated similarly) from a transfer pipette, stopper the funnel, and shake vigorously for several minutes. Allow the layers to separate; then draw off the lower acid layer. Next draw off the upper or ether layer into a 100-ml. volumetric flask. Return the acid layer to the separatory funnel, add 40 to 50 ml. of butyl acetate or isopropyl ether, stopper, and repeat the shaking. Draw off the lower layer and discard. Add the upper or ether layer to that in the 100-ml. volumetric flask and dilute to the mark with butyl acetate or isopropyl ether. Mix thoroughly and allow the solution in the flask to stand for 2 or 3 minutes.

(*e*) Transfer a portion of the clear extract to an absorption cell and measure the absorbance or transmittance in a photoelectric photometer, using a green filter (540 m$\mu$) and a blank (on the reagents) to set the zero. Determine the percentage of molybdenum from a previously prepared calibration curve obtained by adding varying portions of standard molybdenum solution to molybdenum-free steels and proceeding as in the method.

## MISCELLANEOUS COLORIMETRIC METHODS

Several other colored systems have been useful for specific applications. Dithiol (toluene-3,4-dithiol) forms a complex with molybdenum in 4 *N* HCl which can be extracted with organic solvents such as isoamyl acetate [31] or carbon tetrachloride [32] and measured at 670 m$\mu$. It has been applied to the analysis of molybdenum in steels,[33] ores,[31] and in uranium trioxide.[32] An aqueous-*n*-butyl alcohol

[30] A.S.T.M. Method for Chemical Analysis, 1960.
[31] Clark and Axley, Anal. Chem., **27**, 2000, 1955.
[32] Ashbrook, Chemist-Analyst, **48**, 5, 1959.
[33] Wells and Pemberton, Analyst, **72**, 185, 1947.

dithiol system has been described for analysis of molybdenum in uranium and in molybdenum-columbium alloy.[34]

Molybdenum in plutonium alloys can be determined by the color reaction with chloranilic acid [35] in about 1.4 $M$ perchloric acid. Hydrogen peroxide reacts in dilute acid solutions to form a peroxymolybdic acid complex.[36]

Phenylhydrazine [37] reacts with molybdenum(VI) to form a red complex in an aqueous-isopropanol-chloroform solution. This method is particularly applicable for the determination of molybdenum in tungsten metal and compounds because it is free from interference of large amounts of tungsten.

## DETERMINATIONS IN SPECIFIC SUBSTANCES

## DETERMINATION OF MOLYBDENUM IN ORES AND CONCENTRATES

This procedure is suitable for molybdic oxide, molybdenum sulfides, and with modification, for other molybdenum-containing materials. The sample is decomposed with $HNO_3$, $H_2SO_4$ added, and the $HNO_3$ expelled. The insoluble is removed and treated to recover any molybdenum it may contain. Arsenic is removed by precipitation with $Fe_2(SO_4)_3$ and $NH_4OH$, iron by precipitation with $H_2S$ in $NH_4OH$ tartrate solution, molybdenum precipitated as the sulfide, converted to the sulfate, reduced from $Mo^{+6}$ to $Mo^{+3}$ with zinc and reoxidized with $KMnO_4$. Unprecipitated molybdenum is recovered and measured colorimetrically with thiocyanate.

*Apparatus.* **Nine-Inch Jones Reductor.**—Place a perforated porcelain plate in the bottom of the reductor tube, followed by a small wad of glass wool. Fill to the neck with 20- to 30-mesh zinc amalgamated as follows: shake 800 g. of zinc with 400 ml. of $HgCl_2$ (25 g. per l.) in a liter flask for 2 minutes. Wash several times with $H_2SO_4$ (1:49) and then thoroughly with water. Keep the reductor filled with water when not in use.

**Filter Photometer or Spectrophotometer.**

*Reagents.* **Ferric Phosphate Solution.**—Dissolve 100 g. of $Fe_2(SO_4)_3 \cdot NH_2O$ in a mixture of 150 ml. of $H_3PO_4$, 20 ml. of $H_2SO_4$ (1:1), and 850 ml. of water. Add just sufficient $KMnO_4$ to produce a faint tint in the solution.

**1,10-Phenanthroline Indicator.**—Dissolve 1.49 g. of 1,10-phenanthroline in 100 ml. of water containing 0.7 g. of $FeSO_4 \cdot 7H_2O$.

**Stannous Chloride.**—Dissolve 350 g. of $SnCl_2$ in 200 ml. of HCl (1:1) and dilute to 1 liter with cold water.

**Standard Molybdenum Solution.**—Dissolve 0.5 g. of $Na_2MoO_4 \cdot 2H_2O$ in 1 liter of water containing 5 ml. of $H_2SO_4$. Standardize by treating a 100-ml. aliquot by the reduction procedure described below.

**Sodium Diphenylamine Sulfonate.**—Dissolve 0.273 g. of sodium diphenylamine sulfonate in 100 ml. of water.

*Procedure.*—The optimum range for this method is 0.2 to 0.3 g. of molybdenum.

[34] Granger, Analyst, **83**, 609, 1958.
[35] Waterbury and Bricker, Anal. Chem., **29**, 129, 1957.
[36] Telep and Boltz, Anal. Chem., **22**, 1030, 1950; Bacon and Milner, Analytica Chimica Acta, **15**, 573, 1956.
[37] Goldstein, Chemist-Analyst, **45**, 47, 1956.

| Material | Sample Weight |
|---|---|
| Molybdenite | 0.5000–1.000 g. |
| Molybdenum trisulfide | 1.000 g. |
| Wulfenite | 1.000 g. |
| Low-grade ores and tailings | 5.00 g. |

Transfer the appropriate amount of the sample ground to pass a 100-mesh sieve and dried at 105 to 110°C. to a 400-ml. beaker. Moisten with 5 ml. of water, then add 10 to 15 ml. of $HNO_3$ and 10 ml. of $H_2SO_4$ (1:1) for each gram of sample taken. Cover and warm at about 75°C. with stirring until decomposition appears to be complete. Then evaporate cautiously to fumes of sulfur trioxide.

Cool, add 50 ml. of water, stir, and warm to dissolve the sulfates. (For wulfenite and similar materials, see Note 1). Filter the hot solution through a 9-cm. No. 40 Whatman filter catching the filtrate in a 400-ml. beaker. Wash the residue about 10 times with hot water, 5 times with $NH_4OH$ (1:3), and finally 5 times with hot water. Reserve the residue for treatment by Note 2. (For ores containing more than traces of arsenic, treat the filtrate as described in Note 3.)

Add 6 ml. of tartaric acid solution (500 g. per l.) and an excess of 5 ml. of $NH_4OH$. Pass a *brisk stream* of $H_2S$ into the ammoniacal solution for from 20 to 30 minutes. Filter on a 9-cm. paper containing a little paper pulp into an 800-ml. beaker, and wash about 15 times with $(NH_4)_2S$ water containing 1% of ammonium tartrate. Reserve the precipitate (Note 1).

Add some paper pulp to the filtrate and then carefully add small amounts of $H_2SO_4$ (1:1) with stirring until the solution is acid, finally adding an excess of 20 ml. Care should be exercised to avoid any loss of the molybdenum solution by spraying. Heat to boiling, allow to settle, then filter on a 12.5-cm. paper containing a little paper pulp into an 800-ml. beaker. Wash the paper and precipitate about 15 times with dilute $H_2SO_4$ (1:99) containing 50 g. of tartaric acid per liter. Reserve the filtrate (Note 1).

Transfer the $MoS_3$ precipitate and paper to the original 800-ml. beaker (containing a glass stirring rod), add 6 ml. of $H_2SO_4$, 20 ml. of $HNO_3$, and 2 ml. of $HClO_4$, cover, and evaporate to dense fumes of sulfur trioxide. Cool, add 5 ml. of $HNO_3$, and from 1 to 2 ml. of $HClO_4$, and again evaporate to dense fumes of sulfur trioxide. If necessary, repeat the treatment with $HNO_3$ and $HClO_4$, evaporation, etc., until the yellow color due to organic matter has disappeared. Cool, rinse the sides of the beaker with 10 ml. of water, add a slight excess of $KMnO_4$ solution (25 g. per l.) and again evaporate to dense fumes of sulfur trioxide. Cool.

Add 75 ml. of water, 2 g. of 20-mesh zinc, and heat until the zinc has dissolved. If any copper is precipitated, filter through a 9-cm. paper into a 600-ml. beaker, and wash the paper about 20 times with hot water. Discard the precipitate.

Adjust the volume of the molybdenum solution to approximately 100 ml., and the acidity to about 6 ml. of $H_2SO_4$. Add an excess of $KMnO_4$ solution (25 g. per l.) and cool to room temperature. Prepare the Jones Reductor by passing 100 ml. of $H_2SO_4$ (1:19) followed by 100 ml. of water through it. Discard these solutions, then pass the molybdenum solution through the reductor into 30 ml. of ferric phosphate solution in the receiver. Wash the reductor with 100 ml. of cold $H_2SO_4$ (1:19), followed by 100 ml. of cold water. The tip of the reductor tube should dip just beneath the surface of the solution when the receiver is connected to the reductor. Finally disconnect and raise the reductor so that a little water is allowed to run through the stem. Rinse the outside of the stem and transfer the solution to an 800-ml. beaker.

Titrate with 0.1 $N$ KMnO$_4$ to a clear green which persists for at least 30 seconds, using a few drops of 1,10-phenanthroline as the indicator (Note 4). Run a blank by passing 100 ml. of cold H$_2$SO$_4$ (1:19) plus the wash solutions used through the reductor into 30 ml. of ferric phosphate solution, and titrate as described.

Calculate the percentage of molybdenum as follows:

$$\frac{((A - B) \times C \times 0.03198) + D}{E} \times 100 = \% \text{ Mo}$$

where $A$ = ml. of KMnO$_4$ required to titrate the sample,

$\quad\quad B$ = ml. of KMnO$_4$ required to titrate the blank,

$\quad\quad C$ = normality of KMnO$_4$,

$\quad\quad D$ = grams of Mo determined colorimetrically (Note 1), and

$\quad\quad E$ = weight of sample in grams.

NOTES.—1. Cool the solution in cold water to 15 to 20°C., filter through a 9-cm. Whatman No. 40 paper containing a little paper pulp into a 250-ml. beaker, and wash the residue of silica, lead sulfate, and possibly tungstic acid, about 20 times with cold H$_2$SO$_4$ (1:49). Treat the filtrate with tartaric acid solution, NH$_4$OH and H$_2$S as in "Procedure." Return the paper and residue to the beaker, add 50 ml. of ammonium acetate solution (prepared by mixing 18 ml. of NH$_4$OH with 20 ml. of water and 12 ml. of acetic acid), stir well, and digest at a temperature just short of boiling for at least 5 minutes. Filter on an 11-cm. paper containing a little ashless paper pulp and wash about 20 times with hot ammonium acetate solution (50 g. per l.) containing several drops of NH$_4$OH per liter. Ignite in porcelain at a temperature not higher than 450°C. to burn off the paper, and transfer to a 30-ml. platinum crucible. Add 1 ml. of H$_2$SO$_4$ (1:1), 2 ml. of HNO$_3$, 5 ml. of HF, and evaporate to fumes of sulfur trioxide, and treat by Note 2.

2. The small amount of molybdenum occluded by the iron sulfide and that unprecipitated with H$_2$S can be recovered as follows:

Transfer the iron sulfide precipitate to a 250-ml. beaker, add 5 ml. of H$_2$SO$_4$ and HNO$_3$ dropwise until the paper is destroyed, finally evaporate to strong fumes of sulfur trioxide. Cool and add to the filtrate from the molybdenum sulfide precipitation which has been evaporated to about 100 ml. Cool and transfer to a 500-ml. separatory funnel.

Add sufficient H$_2$SO$_4$ (1:1) to give a solution containing 10% H$_2$SO$_4$ by volume, and cool to 20°C. Next add 10 ml. of NaCNS solution (100 g. per l.) and 10 ml. of SnCl$_2$ solution. Stopper the funnel and shake well. Add 50 ml. of isopropyl ether, shake vigorously for several minutes, and allow to stand until the solution has separated into two distinct layers. Draw off the lower layer into the original beaker. Then draw off the upper layer into a 100-ml. volumetric flask. Return the acid layer to the separatory funnel, add 25 ml. of the isopropyl ether, again shake the solution vigorously for several minutes, and allow to separate into two distinct layers. Discard the lower layer and add the upper layer to the 100-ml. flask.

Dilute to the mark with ether that has just previously been shaken with 100 ml. of cold (20°C.) ferric sulfate solution (10 g. per l.) containing 10 ml. of H$_2$SO$_4$, 10 ml. of NaCNS, and 10 ml. of SnCl$_2$. Stopper the flask, mix well, transfer a portion to a filter photometer cell and measure the absorbance with a spectrophotometer.

Prepare a calibration graph by carrying known amounts of molybdenum preferably from a standard steel through all steps of the procedure. The usual range for this curve is to cover amounts of molybdenum ranging from 0.2 to 2.0 mg. in 100 ml. of ether. Read the amount of molybdenum from this curve and add to the molybdenum found by reduction.

3. To the filtrate add sufficient ferric sulfate to provide approximately 10 times as much iron as there is arsenic present. From 0.3 to 0.4 g. of ferric sulfate is usually ample to ensure the retention of arsenic by the ferric hydroxide. Nearly neutralize the solution

with $NH_4OH$ but do not add enough to impart a permanent red tint to the clear yellow solution. Heat nearly to boiling, and pour very slowly, with vigorous stirring, into 75 ml. of nearly boiling $NH_4OH$ (1:5) contained in a 400-ml. beaker.

4. The reduced solution may also be titrated with 0.1 $N$ $K_2Cr_2O_7$ to a permanent purple, using a few drops of sodium diphenylaminesulfonate as indicator. Run a blank by passing 100 ml. of cold $H_2SO_4$ (1:19) plus the wash solutions used, through the reductor into 30 ml. of ferric phosphate solution, add a few drops of the sodium diphenylaminesulfonate indicator and titrate to a permanent purple end point with 0.1 $N$ $K_2Cr_2O_7$.

## DETERMINATION OF MOLYBDENUM IN STEELS AND CAST IRONS

This method is designed for steels and cast irons with molybdenum content in the range from 0.1 to 1%. The method gives precise and accurate results. The results at the 1.0% level should not vary more than ±0.02% using a spectrophotometer. The method can be extended to the determination of molybdenum in stainless steels (1 to 3% or higher molybdenum). The sample is dissolved in $HNO_3$ and $HClO_4$. After adding tartaric acid and adjusting the acidity, the molybdenum thiocyanate complex is extracted with isopropyl ether. The absorbance of the red colored system is measured at 470 m$\mu$. The range using a 1-cm. cell is from 0.01 to 0.5 mg. in 100 ml. of organic solvent.

*Apparatus.*—Filter Photometer or Spectrophotometer.

*Reagents.* **Tartaric Acid.**—Dissolve 500 g. of tartaric acid in 1 liter of water.

**Ferric Sulfate.**—Dissolve 80 g. of $Fe_2(SO_4)_3$ in 1 liter of water containing 10 ml. of $H_2SO_4$.

**Sodium Thiocyanate.**—Dissolve 100 g. of NaCNS in 1 liter of water.

**$SnCl_2$.**—Dissolve 375 g. of $SnCl_2 \cdot 2H_2O$ in 100 ml. of HCl and dilute to 1 liter.

**Isopropyl Ether.**—Purify by shaking with activated carbon and then pouring through a dry paper.

*Preparation of Calibration Graph.*—Carry varying amounts of a similar National Bureau of Standards' sample through all steps of the procedure as outlined below. Plot absorbance versus milligrams of molybdenum. N.B.S. 36a which contains 0.922% molybdenum is a convenient standard to use for this purpose.

*Procedure.*—Transfer 1 g. of the sample to a 400-ml. beaker, add 20 ml. of $HNO_3$ (1:1) and 15 ml. of $HClO_4$, and heat gently until the sample is in solution. Evaporate to fumes of perchloric acid. Cool, add 150 ml. of water, boil to remove traces of chlorine, cool, and transfer to a 250-ml. volumetric flask.

Dilute to volume, mix thoroughly, and withdraw an aliquot containing 0.01 to 0.5 mg. of molybdenum to a 250-ml. beaker (see Note). Add 10 ml. of tartaric acid, 2 ml. of $Fe_2(SO_4)_3$ and make slightly alkaline with NaOH (100 g./l.). Neutralize to litmus with $H_2SO_4$ (1:1) and then add an excess of 2 ml. for each 8 ml. of solution which will give a solution 10% $H_2SO_4$ by volume.

Add 10 ml. of NaCNS solution and stir for at least 2 to 3 minutes. Cool to 20°C. or less and transfer to a 300-ml. separatory funnel, rinsing the beaker with $H_2SO_4$ (1:9). Add 10 ml. of $SnCl_2$ solution and shake thoroughly. Add 100 ml. of isopropyl ether, stopper, and shake vigorously for 2 to 3 minutes. Remove the stopper and allow to stand until the solution has separated into two distinct layers. Draw off the lower layer into another separatory funnel. Dry the funnel stem with a piece of filter paper. Transfer the ethereal layer into a dry 100-ml. volumetric flask. Add 5 to 10 ml. of isopropyl ether to the separatory funnel containing the aqueous phase, shake, let separate, and use this ether for dilution of the first ether extract to 100 ml.

Mix thoroughly and measure the absorbance at 470 m$\mu$ in 1-cm. cells. Null the instrument with water.

Obtain the concentration of molybdenum by referring to the absorbance-concentration graph.

NOTE.—For molybdenum contents between 0.1 and 0.5%, use a 25-ml. aliquot; for 0.5 to 1.0% use a 10-ml. aliquot.

## DETERMINATION OF MOLYBDENUM IN STAINLESS STEELS

The method is identical to that for the determination of molybdenum in steels and cast irons with the exception of the sample dissolution.

*Procedure.*—Transfer 0.25 to 0.50 g. of the sample depending on the molybdenum content to a 400-ml. beaker. Add 30 ml. of $HClO_4$, 10 ml. of $H_3PO_4$, and 0.5 ml. of HF, heat to boiling, and boil or fume gently until the sample is in solution. When dissolution is complete, continue heating until the chromium is oxidized. Cool, add 400 ml. of water, transfer to a 500-ml. volumetric flask, and dilute to volume. Mix thoroughly and withdraw an aliquot containing from 0.01 to 0.5 mg. of molybdenum to a 250-ml. beaker. Continue with the procedure as described under "Determination of Molybdenum in Steels and Cast Irons."

## DETERMINATION OF MOLYBDENUM IN 65% MOLYBDENUM-ALUMINUM

After dissolution with $HNO_3$-HF and fuming with $H_2SO_4$, the molybdenum is reduced in the Jones Reductor and titrated with $KMnO_4$. Iron is determined separately and the $KMnO_4$ titration corrected.

*Apparatus.* **Nine-inch Jones Reductor.**—Place a perforated porcelain plate in the bottom of the reductor tube, followed by a small wad of glass wool. Fill to the neck with amalgamated zinc. Prepare the zinc as follows: shake 800 g. of 20- to 30-mesh zinc with 400 ml. of $HgCl_2$ (25 g. per liter) in a liter flask for 2 minutes. Wash several times with $H_2SO_4$ (1:49) and then thoroughly with water. Keep the reductor filled with water when not in use.

*Reagents.* **1,10-Phenanthroline Indicator.**—Dissolve 1.49 g. of 1,10-phenanthroline in 100 ml. of water containing 0.7 g. of $FeSO_4 \cdot 7H_2O$.

**Ferric Phosphate Solution.**—Dissolve 100 g. of $Fe_2(SO_4)_3 \cdot xH_2O$ in a mixture of 150 ml. of $H_3PO_4$, 20 ml. of $H_2SO_4$ (1:1), and 850 ml. of water. Add $KMnO_4$ dropwise to produce a faint pink tint to the solution.

**Mercuric Chloride.**—Add 7.0 g. of $HgCl_2$ to 100 ml. of water, bring to a boil, then cool.

**Stannous Chloride.**—Dissolve 100 g. of $SnCl_2$ in 100 ml. of water and 200 ml. of HCl, bring to a boil, cool, and dilute to 1000 ml. (The solution becomes cloudy if it is diluted while warm.) Add some tin shot to the bottle.

**Sodium Diphenylamine Sulfonate Indicator.**—Dissolve 0.273 g. of sodium diphenylamine sulfonate in 50 ml. of cold water and dilute to 100 ml.

**0.1 N Potassium Dichromate.**—Dissolve 4.9032 g. of $K_2Cr_2O_7$ in 500 ml. of hot water. Cool, dilute to 1000 ml., and standardize against 0.1 N ferrous ammonium sulfate which has been standardized against 0.4 g. of $K_2Cr_2O_7$ (N.B.S.) (1 g. of $K_2Cr_2O_7$ = 203.95 ml. of 0.1 N ferrous ammonium sulfate).

**0.1 N Potassium Permanganate.**—Dissolve 6.25 g. of $KMnO_4$ in 50 ml. of boiling water. While still hot, filter through glass wool into a 100-ml. volumetric flask and dilute to volume. Filter 54.0 ml. of the solution into a 1000-ml. volumetric flask through burned-off asbestos and dilute to volume.

*Standardization.*—Weigh 0.3000 g. of sodium oxalate (N.B.S.) into a 600-ml. beaker. Add 250 ml. of $H_2SO_4$ (1:19) which has been boiled and cooled to 27°C. Stir until dissolved and add 39 to 40 ml. of $KMnO_4$ solution. Stir slowly and allow to stand until the pink color disappears. Heat to 55 to 60°C. and complete titration at this temperature. The end point should remain for 30 seconds. Determine a blank using the same volume of $H_2SO_4$ (1:19) and subtract. Calculate the normality, adjust to 0.1 $N$ $KMnO_4$ with water, and restandardize.

(0.3000 g. of sodium oxalate (N.B.S.) is equivalent to 44.78 ml. of 0.1 $N$ $KMnO_4$.)

*Procedure.*—Transfer a 0.5000-g. sample to a large platinum dish. Add 15 ml. of $HNO_3$, cover, and add HF dropwise until solution is complete. Heat gently to aid solution. When the reaction is complete, carefully add 15 ml. of $H_2SO_4$ (1:1) and evaporate to fumes of sulfur trioxide. Rinse down the cover and sides of the dish and refume. Cool, add 50 ml. of water, and heat until all the salts have dissolved. Transfer to a 400-ml. beaker, rinse the dish well, and add the rinsings to the beaker.

Add 2 g. of 20-mesh zinc, heat until dissolved, filter off any residue through a 9-cm. Whatman No. 42 paper into a 400-ml. beaker. Wash the paper about 20 times with hot water and discard the residue.

Adjust the volume of the molybdenum solution to about 100 ml. and the acidity to about 6 ml. of $H_2SO_4$. Add $KMnO_4$ solution (25 g. per liter) dropwise until a faint pink color is present. Cool to room temperature.

Prepare the Jones Reductor by passing 100 ml. of $H_2SO_4$ (1:19) followed by 100 ml. of water through it. Discard these solutions. Add 30 ml. of the ferric phosphate solution to the filter flask receiver and pass the molybdenum solution through the reductor into it. Wash the reductor with 100 ml. of cold $H_2SO_4$ (1:19) followed by 100 ml. of cold water. The tip of the reductor tube should dip just beneath the surface of the solution when the receiver is connected to the reductor. Finally, disconnect and raise the reductor so that a little water is allowed to run through the stem. Rinse the outside of the stem and transfer the solution to an 800-ml. beaker.

Add a few drops of 1,10-phenanthroline indicator and titrate to a clear green color with 0.1 $N$ $KMnO_4$. The color must hold at least 30 seconds.

Run a blank by passing 100 ml. of $H_2SO_4$ (1:19) plus the wash solutions used through the reductor into 30 ml. of ferric phosphate solution and titrate as described.

**Iron Correction.**—(This method is titrimetric; however, spectrophotometric methods may also be used.)

Transfer a 5.0000-g. sample to a 400-ml. beaker. Add 20 ml. of $H_2SO_4$ (1:1), cover, and add $HNO_3$ dropwise until solution is complete. Dilute to approximately 100 ml., neutralize with NaOH (50 g. per 100 ml.) and add 10 ml. excess. Add 1 to 2 g. of sodium peroxide, bring to a boil, and boil for 10 minutes. Cool, filter through an 11-cm. filter paper, and wash 15 to 20 times with NaOH solution (10 g. per liter). Discard the filtrate.

Dissolve the precipitate through the paper into a 250-ml. beaker with 20 ml. of hot HCl (1:9). Wash the paper 20 times with hot HCl (1:99). Dilute to about 100 ml., neutralize with $NH_4OH$, and add 2 to 3 ml. excess $NH_4OH$. Boil for 2 to 3 minutes, allow the precipitate to settle, filter through an 11-cm. Whatman No. 40 filter paper and wash 15 to 20 times with hot $NH_4Cl$ (1 g. per 100 ml. of solution). Discard the filtrate.

Wash the precipitate through the paper into a 400-ml. beaker with 20 ml. of hot HCl (1:9). Wash the paper 10 times with hot HCl (1:99) and 10 times with hot water. Discard the paper and residue.

Heat the filtrate to boiling, add stannous chloride dropwise until the yellow color disappears, dilute to 200 ml., and cool to below 10°C. Add 5 ml. of $H_3PO_4$, 10 ml. of $HgCl_2$, 3 to 4 drops of sodium diphenylamine sulfonate and titrate with 0.1 $N$ $K_2Cr_2O_7$ to a purple end point.

**Calculations.**—Calculate as follows:

$$\frac{A \times 0.005585}{B} \times 100 = \% \text{ Iron}$$

where $A$ = ml. of 0.1 $N$ $K_2Cr_2O_7$ titration,
$\quad B$ = weight of sample used for iron determination.

Then $C$ = ml. of 0.1 $N$ $KMnO_4$ required for iron contained in sample used in molybdenum determination

$$= \frac{\% \text{ iron} \times \text{wt. of sample used in molybdenum determination}}{100 \times 0.005585}$$

$$\frac{(D - E - C) \times F \times 0.03198}{G} \times 100 = \% \text{ Molybdenum}$$

where $D$ = ml. of $KMnO_4$ required for sample,
$\quad E$ = ml. of $KMnO_4$ required for blank,
$\quad F$ = normality of $KMnO_4$,
$\quad C$ = ml. of $KMnO_4$ required for iron, and
$\quad G$ = weight of sample used in molybdenum determination.

## METHODS FOR MOLYBDENUM IN ANALYSES IN OTHER CHAPTERS

Molybdenum in Alloys by Ion Exchange    See Method in Chromium Chapter
Molybdenum in Tungsten Alloys           See Tungsten Chapter

# Chapter 31

# NICKEL *

**Ni, *at. wt.* 58.71; *d.* 8.9; *m.p.* 1455°C.; *h.p.* 2900°C.; *oxides,* NiO, Ni$_2$O$_3$, Ni$_3$O$_4$**

Nickel occurs native in meteoric iron and in the minerals josephinite, FeNi$_3$ and awaurite, FeNi$_2$. It occurs in arsenates, antimonates, silicates, sulfides and phosphates, together with cobalt, iron, copper, chromium, and zinc.

Nickel was discovered by Cronstedt in 1751 in the mineral niccolite, NiAs. Metallurgists of that day had vainly attempted to extract copper from this mineral, thinking that it contained this element, and in disgust had named it kupfernickel (Old Nick's copper). Cronstedt's effort to solve the difficulty led to his discovery. Nickel is extensively used either as the metal or its alloys. Nickel plated articles, nickel coating on copper or iron, are in daily evidence. In finely divided form it serves as a valuable catalyst in the hydrogenation of oils. The alloys, Monel metal (Ni, Cu, Fe, Mn); German silver (Cu, Ni, Zn); Nichrome (Ni, Cr); the U. S. nickel coin, are familiar uses of this metal.

## DETECTION

The H$_2$S group having been removed in acid solution and iron oxidized to trivalent state, NiS is precipitated with other elements of its group by H$_2$S passed into its ammoniacal solution. NiS is practically insoluble in cold, dilute HCl (sp. gr. 1.035), a property useful in effecting its separation (together with CoS) from other elements of the group. The sulfide dissolves on addition of an oxidizing agent such as KClO$_3$ and nickel then is readily identified by the dimethylglyoxime or alpha-benzildioxime test.

*Dimethylglyoxime* will precipitate nickel as oxime from an acetic acid solution containing sodium acetate and in this manner separate it from cobalt, manganese, and zinc. After precipitating iron, aluminum, and chromium and filtering them off, the solution is slightly acidified with hydrochloric acid, then is neutralized with sodium hydroxide, and acidified with acetic acid. A solution of dimethylglyoxime is added, when nickel, if present, will be precipitated as a flocculent red precipitate.

Nickel may be detected in the presence of cobalt by adding a solution of sodium hydroxide to the solution of cobalt and nickel until a slight precipitate is formed, then somewhat more potassium cyanide than is necessary to redissolve the precipitate and finally two volumes of bromine water. Warm gently and allow to stand for some time. If a precipitate of nickel hydroxide separates, filter, wash, and test with the borax bead.

Nickel may also be detected in the presence of cobalt by precipitating the cobalt as nitrite, as described in the Chapter on Cobalt, and then precipitating the nickel as hydroxide with sodium hydroxide and bromine water and testing the precipitate with the borax bead.

* Chapter revised for Sixth Edition by C. Manning Davis, International Nickel Co.

*Alpha-Benzildioxime* added to an ammoniacal solution of nickel precipitates an intensely red salt having the composition $C_{28}H_{22}N_4O_4Ni$. This precipitate is very voluminous. Silver, magnesium, chromium, manganese, and zinc do not interfere with this reaction.

## ESTIMATION

The determination of nickel is required, principally, in the analysis of ores, metallic nickel and its alloys, but is also required in the analysis of metallic cobalt and cobalt products as well as in a host of miscellaneous materials.

In the majority of cases the results of a nickel determination are calculated in terms of metallic nickel.

In analytical separations nickel is precipitated with the ammonium sulfide group. Small amounts may pass into the later groups where it separates with calcium and magnesium, if care is not taken in its previous removal.

Nitric acid is the best solvent for ores containing nickel. Details of attack are given in a later section.

## PREPARATION AND SOLUTION OF THE SAMPLE

The materials in which nickel occurs ordinarily, may, in general, be brought into solution by treatment with acids, but in the case of some refractory ores and alloys, a fusion is required first to make the acid treatment effective. When treating ores containing sulfides or arsenides a strong oxidizing treatment is necessary to break up these compounds. Metallic nickel may be dissolved easily in nitric acid, more slowly in hydrochloric acid and still more slowly by sulfuric. Nickel alloys may be dissolved in a mixture of hydrochloric acid and nitric acid.

*General Procedure for Ores.*—One gram of the finely powdered ore is weighed into a porcelain dish and mixed intimately with 3 g. of powdered potassium chlorate. The dish is covered with a watch glass and 40 ml. concentrated nitric acid added slowly. The dish is allowed to stand in a cool place for a few minutes, then placed on a water bath and digested until the sample is completely decomposed, stirring the mixture frequently with a glass stirring rod, and adding a little potassium chlorate from time to time until the decomposition is complete. The watch glass is then removed and any particles that may have spattered on it are washed back into the dish and the evaporation continued to dryness. This evaporation to dryness is repeated with the addition of 10 ml. of concentrated hydrochloric acid, and the silica dehydrated by heating for an hour or more in an air oven at 110°C. The dry residue is moistened with concentrated hydrochloric acid and the sides of the dish washed down with hot water, the mixture heated to boiling and allowed to boil for a few minutes, then withdrawn from the heat and filtered hot, after the insoluble matter has settled.

Treat the filtrate for the removal of interfering elements as directed under "Separations."

*Fusion Method.*—If it is necessary to make a complete analysis it is usually advisable to fuse the sample with a sodium and potassium carbonate mixture containing a little potassium nitrate and then treat in the usual manner to determine silica.

**Potassium Bisulfate Fusion.**—In the treatment of nickel and cobalt oxides these are ground to a fine powder and a representative sample of 1 g. is fused with 10 g.

of potassium bisulfate. This may be done in a porcelain or silica crucible or dish. The melt is extracted with water and the silica filtered off.

*Solution of Metallic Nickel and Its Alloys.*—From 1 to 5 g. of the well-mixed drillings are treated with a minimum quantity of nitric acid and 20 ml. (1:1) sulfuric acid added and the solution evaporated to fumes of sulfur trioxide. Allow the fuming to continue for 10 minutes. Dilute carefully with a little water and filter off the insoluble. Continue as directed in the following detailed analyses.

It may be necessary to use a mixture of nitric and hydrochloric acids to bring certain alloys into solution, after which the procedure is the same as above.

## SEPARATIONS

*Separation of Nickel from Mercury, Lead, Bismuth, Copper, Cadmium, Arsenic, Tin, Antimony, Molybdenum.*—The elements are precipitated in acid solution by $H_2S$ as sulfides, nickel remains in solution.

*Separation of Nickel from Iron, Aluminum, Chromium, Cobalt, Manganese, and Zinc.*—Separation of nickel by precipitation as oxime by dimethylglyoxime affords a rapid and quantitative separation. Details of the procedure are given under the "Gravimetric Methods." [1]

In the separation from cobalt neutralization of the acid solution by sodium acetate is generally recommended. This procedure also applies to the separation from manganese.

Separation from zinc may be effected by precipitation of nickel oxime in acetic acid solution; or better in ammoniacal citrate solution.

Separation of nickel from zinc may be effected by precipitating ZnS by means of $H_2S$ passed into an 0.01 $N$ sulfuric acid solution or a solution acidified with formic acid. Nickel remains in solution.

*Separation of Nickel from Iron.*—Two modifications of the oxime method may be used.

(1) The iron, if present as a ferric salt, is converted into a complex salt by adding from 1 to 2 g. of tartaric acid, and the solution diluted to 200 or 300 ml., boiled and the nickel precipitated as the oxime in an ammoniacal solution by the prescribed method. Iron forms no oxime under these conditions.

The iron may be precipitated from this filtrate by colorless ammonium sulfide and the sulfide converted to ferric oxide ($Fe_2O_3$) by ignition.

(2) Ferric iron is reduced to the ferrous condition by warming with sulfurous acid, in a nearly neutral solution. If the original solution has an excess of acid, it is treated with a solution of sodium hydroxide until a permanent precipitate is formed. This is dissolved with a few drops of hydrochloric acid and the iron reduced by adding from 5 to 10 ml. of a saturated solution of sulfur dioxide or by passing $SO_2$ through the solution. The solution is diluted to 200 or 300 ml. and the solution of dimethylglyoxime added in slight excess, followed by sodium acetate until a permanent precipitate of nickel oxime is formed. After adding 2 g. more of sodium acetate the solution is filtered immediately. The iron is precipitated from the filtrate by oxidizing with bromine water and adding ammonium hydroxide to precipitate the basic acetate of iron.

Modification (1) is suitable for the determination of nickel in iron and steel.

[1] Teschugaeff, L., Z. anorg. allgem. Chem., **46,** 144, 1905. Ber., **38,** 2520, 1905.

**Cupferron Method.**—Small quantities of iron may be precipitated with cupferron in acid solution, the nickel remaining in solution. See Chapter on Iron.

**Separation of Nickel from Aluminum.**—This method is the same as modification (1) given above.

**Separation of Nickel from Chromium.**—This separation cannot be carried out in an acetic acid solution. From 1 to 2 g. of tartaric acid are added and followed by from 5 to 10 ml. of a 10% ammonium chloride solution. The solution is made ammoniacal, but no precipitate should form. If the solution becomes cloudy, it is acidified with hydrochloric acid and additional ammonium chloride added and again made ammoniacal and the nickel precipitated as oxime according to directions given from this precipitation.

## GRAVIMETRIC METHODS

### ALPHA-BENZILDIOXIME METHOD

The alcoholic solution of alpha-benzildioxime gives an intensely red precipitate of $C_{28}H_{22}N_4O_4Ni$, when added to ammoniacal solutions containing nickel. The reaction is more characteristic for nickel than is that with dimethylglyoxime and is more delicate. In a volume of 5 ml. (according to Atack [2]), 1 part of nickel in 2,000,000 parts of water may be detected. In the presence of 100 times as much as cobalt only a faint yellow color is produced by the cobalt. One part of nickel per million of water will cause precipitation with the compound, whereas no precipitate is formed with dimethylglyoxime under the same conditions. With glyoxime iron produces a pink color, with alpha-benzildioxime ferrous salts give a faint violet color, hence do not interfere in the detection of nickel. Silver, magnesium, chromium, manganese, and zinc do not interfere. Since the nickel precipitate with this reagent is exceedingly voluminous it is advisable to have not more than 0.025 g. of nickel in the solution in which the nickel is being determined. The method is adapted to the detection and determination of traces of the element and small amounts up to 10% nickel.

**Reagent. Alpha-Benzildioxime.**—This may be prepared by boiling 10 g. of benzil (not necessarily pure) with 8 to 10 g. of hydroxylamine hydrochloride in methyl alcohol solution. After boiling for 3 hours the precipitate is filtered off and dried, washed with hot water and then with a small amount of 50% alcohol, and dried. This dried precipitate consists of pure benzildioxime (m.p. 237°C.). A further yield may be obtained by boiling the filtrate with hydroxylamine hydrochloride. The reagent is prepared by dissolving 0.2 g. of the salt per liter of alcohol to which is added ammonium hydroxide to make 5% solution, sp. gr. 0.96 (50 ml. per liter).

**Procedure.**—A slight excess of the warmed solution of the above reagent is stirred into the ammoniacal solution containing nickel and the whole heated on the water bath for a few moments to coagulate the precipitate. Quantitative precipitation is complete after one minute. The liquid is filtered through a Gooch crucible, with suction, or onto a filter paper, for which a counterpoise has been selected. The counterpoise paper is treated in exactly the same manner as the one containing the precipitate. The precipitate is washed with 50% alcohol, followed by hot water, and is then dried at 110°C. In weighing the precipitate the counterpoise filter is

---

[2] Method by F. W. Atack, Analyst, **38**, 448, 318. Cockburn, Gardiner and Black, Analyst, **38**, 439, 443.

placed in the weight pan of the balance. The precipitate contains 10.93% nickel. Weight of $C_{28}H_{22}N_4O_4Ni \times 0.1093 = Ni$.

NOTES.—Acetone may be used instead of alcohol as a solvent of the reagent. The compound is more soluble in acetone than in alcohol.

The precipitate does not pass through the filter as does the compound with dimethylglyoxime.

The method is affected by the presence of nitrates, hence these must be removed by evaporation of the solution with sulfuric acid to fumes, before the addition of the reagent to the nickel solution.

In the presence of cobalt an excess of the reagent must be used, as in the case of the dimethylglyoxime precipitation.

In the presence of iron and chromium Rochelle salt, sodium citrate or tartaric acid are added to prevent precipitation of the hydroxides of these metals upon making the solution alkaline.

In the presence of manganese a fairly large excess of the reagent is required, the solution being slightly acid with acetic acid.

Zinc and magnesium are kept in solution by addition of ammonium chloride.

Large amounts of copper must be removed by precipitating with hydrogen sulfide before addition of the reagent.

The process is applicable to the determination of nickel in the filtrate obtained in the separation of zinc after the removal of the hydrogen sulfide, formic acid, etc.

## DIMETHYLGLYOXIME METHOD

This method has been demonstrated by Brunck to be a very accurate and expeditious procedure known for nickel.[3] By this method 1 part of nickel may be detected when mixed with 5000 parts of cobalt or 1 part of nickel may be detected in 400,000 parts of water. The nickel precipitate with this reagent is almost completely insoluble in water and is only very slightly soluble in acetic acid, but is easily decomposed by strongly dissociated acids, so that the precipitation is incomplete in neutral solutions of nickel chloride, sulfate, or nitrate. If, however, the free acid formed is neutralized with sodium, potassium, or ammonium hydroxides or by addition of the acetate salts of these bases, nickel will be completely precipitated, not even a trace being found in the filtrate.

The quantitative determination of nickel in the presence of other metals is a simple operation. The nickel should be in the form of a convenient salt.

The concentration of the solution does not matter; the precipitation can take place either in a solution of the greatest concentration, or in a very dilute solution. The reaction is not hindered by the presence of ammonium salts.

Iron, aluminum, chromium, cobalt, manganese and zinc do not interfere. Theoretically, 4 parts of dimethylglyoxime, added as a 1% alcoholic solution, are necessary; a certain excess does no harm provided the alcohol volume does not exceed more than half that of the water solution containing the nickel salt, as alcohol has a solvent action on the oxime. The compound is very stable and volatilizes undecomposed at 250°C.

An excess of ammonium hydroxide is also to be avoided in the solution in which the precipitation takes place.

It has been observed that the precipitate of nickel with dimethylglyoxime may be safely ignited to the oxide NiO without loss, if the filter is first carefully charred without allowing it to take fire, then gradually heated to redness.

*Procedure.*—Such an amount of the sample should be taken that the nickel be not over 0.1 g., as glyoxime of nickel is very voluminous and a larger amount would

[3] Brunck, O., Z. angew. Chem., **20**, 1844, 1907.

be difficult to filter.[4]  If cobalt is present it should not exceed 0.1 g. in the sample taken.[5]

If hydrogen sulfide has been used to precipitate members of the second group, it is expelled by boiling the acid solution and the volume brought to 250 ml.

One or 2 grams of tartaric acid are added to prevent the precipitation of the hydroxides of iron, aluminum, and chromium by ammonium hydroxide (this treatment is omitted if these are absent), and 5 to 10 ml. of a 10% solution of ammonium chloride added to keep zinc and manganese in solution, should they be present.  Ammonium hydroxide is now added until the solution is slightly alkaline. If a precipitate forms, ammonium chloride is added to clear the solution, followed by ammonium hydroxide to neutralize the acid.  The solution should remain clear after this treatment, otherwise the ammonium chloride is added in solution or as salt until the solution of the sample will remain clear.  It is then heated to nearly boiling and the alcoholic solution of dimethylglyoxime added until the reagent is approximately seven times, by weight, the weight of nickel present. Ammonium hydroxide is now added until the solution has a distinct odor of this reagent.  The precipitation of the scarlet red nickel salt is hastened by stirring. It is advisable to place the mixture on the steam bath for fifteen to twenty minutes to allow the reaction to go to completion before filtering.  The precipitate is filtered off, into a platinum sponge Gooch crucible, sometimes known as a Neubauer Gooch crucible.  (Other forms of Gooch crucible are used for this purpose, but the Neubauer crucible has been found to be most satisfactory.)  The precipitate is dried for about 2 hours at 110 to 120°C. and weighed as $C_8H_{14}N_4O_4Ni$, which contains 20.31% Ni.

Weight of precipitate $\times$ 0.2031 = weight of nickel.

## ELECTROLYSIS METHOD

The solution is freed from members of the $H_2S$ group by precipitation of these in acid solution by $H_2S$.  Zinc is removed by $H_2S$ in a 0.01 $N$ solution, preferably of $H_2SO_4$ or HCOOH.  Nickel is now deposited by electrolysis.[6]

This deposition is conducted in exactly the same manner as the one described under Cobalt by Electrolysis, and requires that the same precautions be exercised.

In the presence of cobalt the two elements may be determined together by electrolysis as described below and the deposited metal redissolved and nickel determined as oxime.  Cobalt is obtained by difference.

*Procedure.*—After the sample has been brought into solution by one of the methods outlined under "Preparation and Solution of the Sample," the solution

[4] Mr. C. Sterling of the International Nickel Co. states that it is their practice to precipitate as much as 0.25 g. or even 0.5 g. of Ni as the glyoxime salt.  The precipitate produced in a perchlorate solution containing chromate is comparatively compact, and by dissolving a weighed amount of the reagent in a small volume of hot alcohol the use of large volumes and losses due to solubility of the precipitate in alcohol are avoided. The practical precipitating power of the reagent is 0.25 g. of Ni per g. and a reasonable excess should be allowed.  It is therefore possible to use the reagent in the analysis of alloys containing high percentages of Ni.

[5] If the sample contains more than 0.1 g. of cobalt, a large excess of ammonium hydroxide and dimethylglyoxime is necessary to prevent its precipitation, hence it is advisable to take such weights of samples that the cobalt content will be less than this weight. A sample containing 0.03 g. Ni or less is satisfactory—5 ml. of 1% alcoholic glyoxime per 0.01 g. Ni are advisable.

If much copper is present it should be removed.

[6] Marsh, W. J., J. Phys. Chem., **18**, 705, 1914.

is evaporated with 20 ml. of 1:1 sulfuric acid for every gram of metal in the sample. The evaporation is continued until the solution has fumed strongly for 10 minutes. Cool carefully and dilute with 20 ml. of water. Heat the solution to nearly boiling and pass hydrogen sulfide for 1 hour to precipitate members of the second group. This long treatment is necessary to insure complete precipitation of arsenic. Filter and boil to expel hydrogen sulfide. Add 5 ml. $H_2O_2$ to insure oxidation of iron compounds to the ferric state and add ammonium hydroxide until just slightly alkaline. Filter off the ferric hydroxide and wash with water containing a small quantity of ammonium hydroxide. To recover occluded nickel dissolve the precipitate in hydrochloric acid and reprecipitate the iron with addition of a little hydrogen peroxide. Combine the filtrates. Evaporate to about 250 ml. and add 50 ml. of concentrated ammonium hydroxide and electrolyze as described under Cobalt.

The increase in weight of the electrode is the weight of cobalt and nickel in the sample. The percentage of cobalt and nickel in the sample is found by multiplying the increase in weight of the electrode by 100 and dividing by the weight of the sample.

NOTE.—The deposition of cobalt and nickel by the above method has been found to be the most accurate of the electrolytic methods. In the solutions containing the organic acids there is always more or less carbide deposited on the cathode with the metal. This causes high results.

## TITRIMETRIC METHOD

### MODIFIED DIMETHYLGLYOXIME METHOD

This method, as described by Parr and Lindgren,[7] and especially useful for alloys, consists of a modification of the gravimetric dimethylglyoxime method. The precipitation takes place in the usual manner, the precipitate is dissolved in sulfuric acid, and the excess titrated with a standard solution of potassium hydroxide.

*Procedure.*—The alloy is dissolved in nitric or hydrochloric acid and if iron, aluminum, or chromium are present, twice their weight of tartaric acid is added to prevent their precipitation. If chromium is present, ammonium chloride is also added. If manganese or zinc is present, hydrochloric acid should be used and most of the free acid evaporated. Add a few milliliters of hydrogen peroxide to oxidize any ferrous iron to the ferric state. Dilute to 300 or 400 milliliters and neutralize the free acid by sodium acetate. Heat the solution nearly to boiling and add five times as much dimethylglyoxime, in 1% alcoholic solution, as the nickel present. Then completely neutralize with ammonium hydroxide, using a very slight excess (or the solution may be neutralized with sodium acetate). Heat until all the nickel is precipitated. Filter and wash. Place the precipitate and filter in a beaker, add an excess of 0.05 N sulfuric acid, dilute to 200 ml., heat until solution is complete, and titrate back with 0.1 N potassium hydroxide solution, taking the first faint yellowish tinge as the end point. The solutions are standardized against pure nickel.

NOTE.—Cobalt should not exceed 0.1 g. per 100 ml. and an excess of the dimethylglyoxime should be used.

[7] Parr, S. W., and Lindgren, J. M., Trans. Am. Brass Founders' Assoc., **5**, 120, 1912.

## COLORIMETRIC METHOD

### POTASSIUM DITHIOOXALATE METHOD

Very small amounts of nickel may be determined by the use of this method.[8] The nickel is separated from iron and, if necessary, from cobalt. Its concentration is then determined by the formation of magenta-colored nickel dithiooxalate.

*Procedure.*—Evaporate, dry, and char the specimen (if organic in nature) in a porcelain dish. Ash at low red heat, being careful not to fuse the ash. Cool, add 15 ml. of hydrochloric acid (1:1) and sufficient water, if necessary, to cover the residue. Cover the dish with a watch glass and heat to boiling. Filter, and extract 2 more times with hot water. If a clean ash has not been obtained, return the filter paper and its residue to the original ashing dish, dry, and re-ash in a muffle. Extract as directed above. Combine all the filtrate-extracts and washings, and neutralize the hydrochloric acid with ammonium hydroxide, using methyl orange as indicator. Add a few drops of hydrochloric acid until the solution is just acid. Saturate the cold solution with hydrogen sulfide and allow to stand overnight. Filter and wash the precipitate with hydrogen sulfide water. Combine the filtrate and washings, which contain the nickel, and boil until free of hydrogen sulfide. Add bromine water to oxidize iron to the ferric state.

If cobalt is present, proceed as directed below. If cobalt is absent, it is necessary to free the solution only of iron, which interferes with the determination. To the cold, slightly acid solution, add 10 ml. of 50% ammonium acetate solution and 0.5 ml. of glacial acetic acid. Under these conditions, iron is precipitated in the cold. Warming should be avoided to prevent reduction of iron to the ferrous state. Filter the cold solution through quantitative filter paper into a volumetric flask. Dilute to a known volume depending upon the nickel concentration. Transfer 50 ml. of this solution to a Nessler tube and add a small amount of potassium dithiooxalate. If nickel is present a clear magenta color develops at once. If nickel is absent no color will develop except a slight yellow.

**Procedure in the Presence of Cobalt.**—If cobalt is present, it must be separated from the nickel. To do this both calcium and magnesium are precipitated as oxalate and phosphate respectively and can be estimated as detailed above.

To the nickel solution, add 10 ml. of 20% sodium citrate solution to prevent precipitation of iron. Add saturated ammonium oxalate solution to precipitate calcium. When precipitation is complete, add dilute ammonium hydroxide solution slowly to precipitate ammonium magnesium phosphate in the same solution. Filter. Dissolve the precipitates in hydrochloric acid and then reprecipitate calcium and magnesium as oxalate and phosphate as above. Filter and combine this filtrate with the main filtrate. This step recovers any nickel occluded on the calcium and magnesium precipitates. To the alkaline filtrate, add an excess of α-benzildioxime, filter and wash the nickel precipitate, dissolve in aqua regia, and evaporate the acid solution to dryness in a porcelain dish. Dissolve in a few drops of dilute hydrochloric acid and make to volume in a volumetric flask. Determine nickel colorimetrically with potassium dithiooxalate.

Standards containing from 0.005 to 0.05 mg. of nickel can be prepared by dissolv-

[8] Jones and Tasker, J. Chem. Soc., **95**, 1905, 1909; Fairhall, J. Ind. Hyg., **8**, 528, 1926; Drinker, Fairhall, Ray, and Drinker, J. Ind. Hyg., **6**, 346, 1924; Yoe and Wirsing, J. Am. Chem. Soc., **54**, 1866, 1932.

ing a weighed portion of nickel dimethylglyoxime, which contains 20.32% of nickel, in aqua regia, evaporating, redissolving in hydrochloric acid, evaporating again, redissolving in hydrochloric acid, and making up to a known volume. To prepare standards make further dilutions. Higher concentrations of nickel can be matched in a colorimeter.

## DETERMINATIONS IN SPECIFIC SUBSTANCES

### NICKEL IN STEEL BY DIMETHYLGLYOXIME METHOD *

*Apparatus.* **Filtering Crucible.**—A Gooch crucible or a fritted-glass crucible or other suitable type of porous filtering crucible.

**Electrodes for Electroanalysis.**—The electrodes should consist of a platinum-gauze cathode and a spiral platinum-wire anode. Platinum cathodes may be formed either from plain or perforated sheets or from wire gauze, and may be either open or closed cylinders. Gauze cathodes are recommended, and should be made preferably from gauze containing approximately 400 meshes per sq. cm. (50 meshes per linear inch). Gauze for cathodes should be woven from wire of approximately 0.0085 in. (0.21 mm.) in diameter. The cathode should be stiffened by doubling the gauze for about 3 mm. at the top and the bottom of the cylinder or by reinforcing the gauze at the top and bottom with a platinum band or ring. The cylinder should be approximately 30 mm. in diameter and 50 mm. in height. The stem should be made from a platinum alloy wire, such as platinum-iridium, platinum-rhodium, or platinum-ruthenium, having a diameter of approximately 1.30 mm. It should be flattened and welded the entire length of the gauze. The over-all height of the cathode should be approximately 130 mm. Cathodes should be sandblasted.

Platinum anodes may be of the spiral type when anodic deposits are not being determined, or if the deposits are small (as in the electrolytic determination of lead when it is present in amounts not over 0.2%). When used in analyses where both cathodic and anodic plates are to be determined, the anodes should be of wire gauze. Spiral anodes should be made from 1.00-mm. or larger platinum wire formed into a spiral of seven turns having a height of approximately 50 mm. and a diameter of 12 mm., the over-all height being approximately 130 mm. The spiraled section should be sandblasted. Platinum gauze anodes should be made of the same material and of the same general design as platinum gauze cathodes. The anode cylinder should be approximately 12 mm. in diameter and 50 mm. in height and the over-all height of the anode should be approximately 130 mm. Platinum gauze anodes should be sandblasted.

*Reagents.* **Tartaric Acid Solution (250 g. per l.).**—Dissolve 250 g. of tartaric acid in 600 ml. of water, filter, add 10 ml. of $HNO_3$, and dilute to 1 liter.

**Alcohol Solution of Dimethylglyoxime (10 g. per l.).**

**Tartaric Acid Solution (20 g. per l.).**—Dilute 80 ml. of tartaric acid (250 g. per l.).

**Potassium Thiocarbonate Solution.**—Saturate 125 ml. of KOH (50 g. per l.) with $H_2S$. Add 125 ml. of KOH (50 g. per l.) and 10 ml. of $CS_2$ and heat moderately. Decant the dark red liquid from the undissolved $CS_2$ and keep in a tightly closed flask.

**Ethyl Ether.**

* A.S.T.M. Chemical Methods of Analysis, 1960.

*PROCEDURE FOR NICKEL STEELS CONTAINING 0.05 TO 3.5% NICKEL*

(*a*) Transfer 1 g. of the sample [9] to a 400-ml. beaker, cover, and add 60 ml. of HCl (1:1).[10] Warm until decomposition is complete, and then cautiously add 10 ml. of $HNO_3$ (1:1). Boil until iron and carbides are oxidized and brown fumes have been expelled. Dilute to 200 ml. with hot water. Add 20 ml. of tartaric acid (250 g. per l.), neutralize with $NH_4OH$, and add 1 ml. of $NH_4OH$ in excess. Filter, and wash the paper and residue with hot water containing a little $NH_4OH$ and $NH_4Cl$. Add HCl until slightly acid, warm to about 60 to 80°C., and add 20 ml. of dimethylglyoxime solution (10 g. per l.). Add $NH_4OH$ until slightly alkaline, and digest for 30 minutes at about 60°C. Cool to room temperature.[11]

(*b*) Complete the determination by the gravimetric procedure (paragraphs (*c*) to (*f*)) or the electrolytic procedure (paragraphs (*g*) to (*l*)).

*Gravimetric Procedure.*—(*c*) Filter through a weighed Gooch crucible under light suction, but do not allow the mat to run dry; wash the precipitate thoroughly with cold water. Fritted-glass or other porous crucibles may also be used. If fritted-glass crucibles are used, it is advisable to allow a thin mat of the precipitate to form before strong suction is applied. Add 5 ml. of dimethylglyoxime (10 g. per l.) and 0.5 ml. of $NH_4OH$ to the filtrate and washings. Stir, and allow to stand to determine whether precipitation is complete.

(*d*) If appreciable cobalt (over 1%) or copper (over 4%) is present, add sufficient dimethylglyoxime to take care of them as well as the nickel, and preferably reprecipitate the nickel as follows: When the precipitate has been washed, discontinue the suction, place the original beaker under the funnel, and add a hot mixture of 20 ml. of HCl (1:1) and 5 ml. of $HNO_3$. After 1 minute, apply suction until dry, repeat the treatment with 25 ml. of the HCl-$HNO_3$ mixture, drain, and wash thoroughly with 50 ml. of hot tartaric acid (20 g. per l.). Nearly neutralize the absolutely clear solution with $NH_4OH$ and precipitate with dimethylglyoxime and $NH_4OH$ as before. A dimethylglyoxime precipitate contaminated by cobalt is a darker red than a pure nickel dimethylglyoxime.

(*e*) Dry the precipitate (paragraph (*c*) or (*d*)) at 150°C. to constant weight. Cool in a desiccator and weigh as nickel dimethylglyoxime.

(*f*) **Calculation.**—Calculate the percentage of nickel as follows:

$$\text{Nickel, } \% = \frac{A \times 0.2031}{B} \times 100$$

where $A$ = grams of nickel dimethylglyoxime, and
$B$ = grams of sample used.

*Electrolytic Procedure.*—(*g*) Filter the nickel dimethylglyoxime precipitate (paragraph (*a*)) on a 12- or 15-cm. paper and wash thoroughly 18 to 20 times with hot water.

---

[9] If the steel contains under 1% of nickel, 2- or 3-g. samples may be used with correspondingly larger amounts of tartaric acid. For steels containing more than 3.5% of nickel, either a sample equivalent to about 0.035 g. of nickel, or a suitable aliquot of a larger sample may be used.

[10] If the percentage of chromium is under 0.5%, the sample may be dissolved in 50 ml. of hot $HNO_3$ (1:3).

[11] If the amount of nickel is small (under 0.2%), or if much cobalt is present, the solution should be allowed to stand at room temperature overnight and filtered cold.

(*h*) Dissolve the precipitate in hot $HNO_3$ (1:3) and wash the filter thoroughly with hot water. Add 20 ml. of $H_2SO_4$ (1:1) and evaporate to dense white fumes. Cool somewhat, add 10 ml. of $HNO_3$, and repeat the evaporation to dense white fumes. Rinse the cover and sides of the beaker with water and heat the solution to white fumes again to insure the expulsion of every trace of the $HNO_3$. Cool, add 50 ml. of cold water, and heat until salts are dissolved.

(*i*) Neutralize with $NH_4OH$ and add an excess of 25 ml. of $NH_4OH$. Dilute to 175 ml. and electrolyze at a current density of from 1 to 2 amperes per sq. dm. Continue the electrolysis until the solution has become colorless (5 to 8 hours). The solution may be tested for complete electrolysis by adding one or two drops of it to 1 ml. of potassium thiocarbonate solution. A pink or red color indicates the presence of nickel.

(*j*) When deposition of the nickel is complete, lower the electrolytic beaker quickly, with the current still on, while rinsing the cathode with water from a wash bottle. Turn off the current, quickly detach the cathode and rinse it in a beaker of water, and then dip it in two successive baths of ethanol or methanol. Dry in an oven at 110°C. for 3 to 5 minutes, cool (preferably in a desiccator), and weigh the deposit as metallic nickel.

(*k*) In very accurate work, dissolve the deposit in warm $HNO_3$, wash the cathode with water, then alcohol, dry for a few minutes at 110°C., and reweigh.

(*l*) **Calculation.**—Calculate the percentage of nickel as follows:

$$\text{Nickel, } \% = \frac{A}{B} \times 100$$

where $A$ = grams of nickel, and
$B$ = grams of sample used.

### PROCEDURE FOR HIGH-CHROMIUM, HIGH-NICKEL STEELS (20% CHROMIUM, 20% NICKEL; 18% CHROMIUM, 8% NICKEL; ETC.)

Transfer 0.35 to 0.5 g. of the sample to a 400-ml. beaker, and add 20 ml. of HCl (1:1) and 20 ml. of $HNO_3$ (1:1). Heat until solution is complete, add 20 ml. of $HClO_4$, and evaporate to fumes (for low-carbon, low-silicon alloys this latter step may be omitted). Cool somewhat, and add 100 ml. of water. Warm until salts dissolve, filter, and complete the determination as described for Steels Containing 0.05–3.5% Nickel, adding sufficient dimethylglyoxime (10 g. per l.) to precipitate all of the nickel (20 to 40 ml.).

### PROCEDURE FOR CARBON STEELS AND OTHER STEELS CONTAINING UNDER 0.05% NICKEL

(*a*) Transfer 5 g. of the sample to a 400-ml. beaker and add 40 ml. of HCl (1:1). Heat until solution is complete, and then carefully add 15 ml. of $HNO_3$ (1:1). Evaporate to a volume of about 15 ml. and add 50 ml. of HCl (1:1).

(*b*) Transfer to a 200-ml. separatory funnel, rinsing the beaker with several 15-ml. portions of HCl (1:1). Cool to 10°C., add 120 ml. of ethyl ether, and carefully shake for 1 to 2 minutes in a stream of cold water. Let settle for several minutes and then draw off the lower clear solution into the original beaker.

(*c*) Gently heat the solution in the beaker to expel the ether (avoid free flames). Add 0.3 g. of $KClO_3$, boil until the $KClO_3$ is decomposed, dilute to 100 ml., and add 3 g. of tartaric acid. Make the solution alkaline with $NH_4OH$ and filter.

Acidify with HCl and complete the determination as described for Steels Containing 0.05–3.5% Nickel.

## PROCEDURE FOR CAST IRON AND HIGH-SILICON STEELS

(a) Dissolve 5 g. of the sample in 40 ml. of HCl (1:1), carefully add about 15 ml. of $HNO_3$ (1:1) to oxidize the iron, and evaporate to dryness. Drench the hot, dried mass with 10 ml. of HCl and then dilute with 75 ml. of hot water. Filter, wash with HCl (1:1), and evaporate the filtrate to a sirupy consistency.

(b) Add 50 ml. of HCl (1:1), transfer to a 200-ml. separatory funnel, rinse the beaker with several small portions of HCl (1:1), add 120 ml. of ethyl ether, and complete the determination as described for Carbon Steels and Others Containing Under 0.05% Nickel.

## PROCEDURE FOR HIGH-NICKEL, CHROMIUM ALLOY CAST IRON (15% NICKEL, 6% COPPER, 2% CHROMIUM; ETC.)

(a) Transfer 2.5 g. of the sample to a 400-ml. beaker or flask and add a mixture of 25 ml. of HCl and 25 ml. of $HNO_3$. When solution is complete, add 30 ml. of $HClO_4$ and 5 to 10 drops of HF, and fume for 10 to 15 minutes after the chromium has been oxidized. Cool somewhat, add 100 ml. of water, and heat to boiling. Filter and wash well with HCl (5:95), catching the filtrate and washings in a 250-ml. volumetric flask.[12] Mix the contents, cool to room temperature, dilute to the mark, and mix thoroughly.

(b) Pipette 50-ml. aliquots and proceed by the dimethylglyoxime-electrolytic method as in "Procedure for Steels Containing 0.05–3.5% Nickel (a), (b), and (g) to (l)." Either dissolve and reprecipitate the nickel dimethylglyoxime (d), or determine any occluded copper in the deposit and correct the results accordingly.

## PROCEDURE FOR OPEN-HEARTH IRON AND WROUGHT IRON

Determine nickel in accordance with the procedure described under "Procedure for Carbon Steels."

## PROCEDURE FOR NICKEL WROUGHT IRON

Determine nickel as in "Procedure for Steels Containing 0.05–3.5% Nickel." Dissolve the first dimethylglyoxime precipitate and again precipitate nickel with dimethylglyoxime as directed in (d).

# NICKEL IN STEEL BY THE CYANIDE TITRATION METHOD

**Reagents.** **Sulfuric-Citric Acid Mixture.**—Dissolve 200 g. of citric acid in 1 liter of cool $H_2SO_4$ (1:9).

**Standard Silver Nitrate Solution (1 ml. = 0.001 g. Ni).**

**Potassium Iodide Solution (100 g. per l.).**

**Standard Potassium Cyanide Solution (1 ml. = 0.001 g. Ni).**—Dissolve 4.5 g. of KCN in 1 liter of water containing 1 g. of KOH and standardize against the standard $AgNO_3$ solution. The KCN solution changes with age, so it must be standardized frequently.

**Ethyl Ether.**

**Hydrogen Sulfide Wash Solution.**—Saturate HCl (1:99) with $H_2S$.

[12] The residue sometimes contains appreciable amounts of nickel. This may be recovered by igniting, treating with HF, evaporating, fusing the residue with a small amount of $K_2S_2O_7$, dissolving, and adding to the main solution.

## TITRATION FOLLOWING A PRELIMINARY PRECIPITATION WITH DIMETHYLGLYOXIME [13]

**Procedure.**—(a) Precipitate the nickel in 1 g. of the sample as in "Procedure for Steels Containing 0.05–3.5% Nickel" (a). Dissolve the washed precipitate with a hot mixture of 20 ml. of HCl (1:1) and 5 ml. of $HNO_3$ in a 400-ml. beaker.[14] Evaporate the solution to 50 ml. or until free of dimethylglyoxime and oxidizing gases. Cool the solution and add 10 ml. of sulfuric-citric acid mixture. Make nearly alkaline with $NH_4OH$, again cool, dilute to 200 ml., and complete the neutralization as follows: Add exactly 2 ml. of $AgNO_3$ (1 ml. = 0.001 g. Ni) and, if no precipitate appears, add HCl (1:10) until a precipitate of AgCl forms. Then add $NH_4OH$ (1:1) drop by drop, while stirring constantly, until the precipitate just dissolves. Add 3 ml. of $NH_4OH$ and 2 ml. of KI (100 g. per l.) and titrate with KCN (1 ml. = 0.001 g. Ni), while stirring constantly, until the solution becomes perfectly clear.

(b) Determine the volume of KCN solution equivalent to exactly 2 ml. of the $AgNO_3$ solution.

**Calculation.**—Calculate the percentage of nickel as follows:

$$\text{Nickel, } \% = \frac{(A - B)C}{D} \times 100$$

where $A$ = milliliters of KCN solution required for titration of the sample,

$B$ = milliliters of KCN solution equivalent to the $AgNO_3$ solution added,

$C$ = nickel equivalent of the KCN solution, in grams per milliliter, and

$D$ = grams of sample used.

## TITRATION FOLLOWING A PRELIMINARY EXTRACTION WITH ETHER [15]

**Procedure.**—(a) Transfer 1 g. of the sample to a 150-ml. beaker, cover, and add 20 ml. of HCl (5:2). When reaction ceases, carefully add 4 ml. of $HNO_3$ (5:2), and boil until brown fumes have been expelled.

(b) Cool, transfer the solution to a 200-ml. separatory funnel, and rinse the beaker with HCl (5:2). Cool to 10°C., add 40 ml. of ethyl ether (perform this operation away from open flames or hot plates), and shake gently for a few minutes. Let settle for 2 minutes, and draw off the acid layer into a 250-ml. beaker. Add 5 ml. of HCl (5:2) to the ether portion. Cool, shake, let settle for 1 minute, draw off the acid layer, and add it to the main extract.

(c) Heat gently to expel dissolved ether, add 0.2 g. of $KClO_3$, and boil until the chlorine is driven off. Dilute to 100 ml. with water, neutralize with $NH_4OH$, add an excess of 3 to 4 ml., and boil for a few minutes. Filter and wash with hot water. Add 10 ml. of HCl to the filtrate, heat just short of boiling, and pass $H_2S$ into the solution. Filter and wash with $H_2S$ wash solution.

(d) Boil to expel $H_2S$. Cool, dilute to 200 ml., add 10 ml. of the sulfuric-citric acid mixture, and complete the determination as described in the preceding titration.

[13] This method may be applied to steels containing cobalt, copper, and tungsten.

[14] If the steel contains more than 4% of copper or 2% of cobalt, the nickel should be reprecipitated with dimethylglyoxime.

[15] This method is not applicable to steels containing cobalt or more than 1% of tungsten.

## NICKEL IN COBALT AND COBALT OXIDE

The dimethylglyoxime precipitation is used in combination with the electrolytic precipitation. See Chapter on Cobalt.

## NICKEL IN NICKEL-PLATING SOLUTIONS

In most cases it is unnecessary to separate the cobalt from the nickel in making this determination and, as the principal impurity is usually iron, the best practice is to follow the procedure given under "Electrolytic Method," Chapter on Cobalt.

If chlorides or organic matter are present in the solution the preparation of the solution for electrolysis is accomplished in the following manner:

*Procedure.*—From the well-stirred solution in the plating tank, withdraw about 200 ml. and place in a small beaker. Prepare a 100-ml. burette by thoroughly cleaning it with the sulfuric acid and potassium dichromate mixture and distilled water. Wash finally with a few milliliters of the nickel solution and fill the burette with the solution from the plating tank.

Run 66.7 ml. into an evaporating dish and add 2 ml. (1:1) sulfuric acid. Evaporate to fumes of sulfur trioxide and allow to fume strongly for ten minutes. Dissolve in a little water. Dilute to 200 ml. carefully, neutralize with a solution of ammonium hydroxide and add 50 ml. of concentrated ammonium hydroxide and electrolyze.

The increase in weight of the cathode in grams multiplied by 2 gives the weight in ounces of nickel in one United States gallon of the plating solution.

## THE ANALYSIS OF METALLIC NICKEL [16]

Nitric acid is the general solvent for nickel. The strength of the acid may be varied in accordance with the determination in view: concentrated acid is used for gravimetric sulfur; 1:4 acid facilitates the determination of manganese in high silicon material; and 1:9 acid may be used for residue analyses.

Solution of the sample in dilute HBr saturated with $Br_2$ followed by evaporation to dryness and baking will remove As, Sb, and Sn.[17] The bromide residue is decomposed by $HNO_3$, fumed with $H_2SO_4$ or $HClO_4$, and the usual procedures are followed.

Silicon may be removed by dehydration with HCl, $H_2SO_4$, or $HClO_4$ followed by filtration. Addition of HF to the $HNO_3$ solution followed by evaporation with $H_2SO_4$ is useful in many cases. The operation may be carried out in glass if elements introduced by corrosion of the reaction vessel do not interfere in subsequent operations and determinations.

Most of the elements found in very small amounts may be gathered by precipitation with $NH_4OH$. Ferric ion may be added to the solution if necessary. In general, the techniques developed for the analysis of refined copper are applicable. The use of $MnO_2$ in dilute acid solution would probably apply, although the presence of Co should not be overlooked.[18]

The ammonia precipitate will contain all the Fe, Al, Ti, Zr, Ta, Nb, and Sn, and, if conditions are properly regulated, all of small quantities of P, As, Sb, Bi,

---

[16] Outline prepared by Mr. C. Sterling, Research Chemist, International Nickel Co.
[17] Anonymous, Chemistry and Industry, **53,** 615, 1934.
[18] Park and Lewis, Ind. Eng. Chem., Anal. Ed., **5,** 182, 1933; Park, Ind. Eng. Chem., Anal. Ed. **6,** 189, 1934.

Se, Te, Pb, Cr, V, and W.　Manganese divides, but may be retained in the precipitate by the addition of an oxidizing agent.　Ca and Mg will be found in the filtrate containing the bulk of the Cu and Ni; they may be precipitated together from this solution as phosphates and subsequently separated and purified.[19]

Precipitation by $NH_4OH$ in the presence of perchlorates must be done in a large volume of hot solution with only a slight excess of reagent.　$Ni(NH_3)_6(ClO_4)_2$ crystallizes readily and will contaminate the precipitate if proper precautions are not observed.　It is interesting to note that Ni and Co may be nearly quantitatively precipitated in cold, strongly ammoniacal perchlorate solutions.　Tartrate does not interfere.　Co is readily oxidized to a soluble form even by exposure to air.

Cyanide solutions offer possibilities for a number of separations.　Fe and Al may be sharply separated from Ni by $NH_4OH$ in the presence of the complex cyanide.[20]　Evans precipitates ZnS in a buffered cyanide solution,[21] and it seems probable that some useful separations by 8-hydroxyquinoline could be made in this medium.[22]　Extraction by dithizone will probably be of service when optimum conditions have become established.

The routine analysis of metallic nickel involves determinations of C, Si, S, Cu, Mn, and Fe.　Nickel (plus cobalt) is found by difference.　Direct determinations of Ni + Co + Cu by electrolysis from ammoniacal sulfate solutions give high values and the deposit will contain Mn if it is present.

## DETERMINATION OF CARBON

*Procedure.*—Carbon is determined on 3 g. samples by direct combustion in the usual type of train used for steel analysis.　A temperature of 1200°C. is advisable and the period of burning should be at least 20 minutes.　Ingot iron may be used as a flux to decrease the time needed for the combustion.

## SILICON AND SULFUR

*Procedure.*—These determinations are conveniently combined on 10 g. samples. The sample is mixed with 1 g. of $KClO_3$ and dissolved with $HNO_3$.　The $HNO_3$ is removed by two evaporations to dryness with HCl.　The chlorides are moistened with 2–3 ml. of HCl, dissolved in water, and the silica is filtered off and determined. Sulfur is precipitated in the filtrate with $BaCl_2$ solution and is determined as usual after standing 18–24 hours.

Sulfur may be determined by the evolution method.　The fine drillings or sawings are dissolved by concentrated HCl in an all-glass evolution flask equipped with a water-cooled reflux condenser.　The evolved gases are passed through a gas-washing bottle containing water before entering the absorption medium.

Silicon in high silicon nickel should be determined on 1-gram samples after dehydration with 15 ml. of 70% $HClO_4$.

## COPPER

*Procedure.*—Copper in ordinary amounts is determined by direct electrolysis. When it is very low it is best to concentrate it by double precipitation with $H_2S$

[19] Hillebrand and Lundell, Applied Inorganic Analysis.

[20] Lundell, Hoffman and Bright, Chemical Analysis of Iron and Steel, p. 278; Chirnside, Analyst, **59**, 278, 1934.

[21] Evans, Analyst, **60**, 464, 1935.

[22] T. Heczko, Chem. Ztg., **58**, 1032, 1934; Analyst, **60**, 120, 1935, abstract.

and determine it colorimetrically. To determine Cu by direct electrolysis 5 grams of sample are dissolved in $HNO_3$. The excess of acid is removed by evaporation to a syrup. After dilution, $NH_4OH$ is added until a precipitate forms and is followed by 10–15 ml. of 1:1 $H_2SO_4$. The solution is diluted to 250 ml. to prevent crystallization and electrolyzed for Cu.

## MANGANESE

**Procedure.**—Routine determinations of Mn are made by the bismuthate method applied directly to $HNO_3$ solutions of 1 g. samples. A correction must be applied to the titration to compensate for the excess $KMnO_4$ used to overcome the color of the nickel nitrate.

Umpire determinations are made by the bismuthate method after precipitating the Mn from $HNO_3$ solutions of 5-g. samples by means of $NH_4OH$ and $(NH_4)_2$-$S_2O_8$. A fairly large excess of $HN_4OH$ is necessary to secure a good separation of Co.

## IRON

**Procedure.**—Iron is gathered from $HNO_3$ solution of 5-g. samples by double precipitation with $NH_4OH$. The ammonia precipitate is dissolved in HCl, the Fe is reduced with $SnCl_2$ and titrated with dilute $K_2Cr_2O_7$, using diphenylamine as an internal indicator.

## ALUMINUM

**Procedure.**—Aluminum may be concentrated by precipitation with $NH_4OH$ and freed from most impurities by electrolysis in a Hg cathode cell. The method of determination depends on the amount of Al and elements associated with it. Provision should be made for Si, Mn, and P; also such elements as Ti, V, Zr, Be, U, and Ce. The ammonia, phosphate, quinolate, or colorimetric methods have been used.[23]

## NICKEL

**Procedure.**—Dissolve 0.3 g. of drillings in an 800 ml. beaker with $HNO_3$. Add 15 ml. of 70% $HClO_4$ and evaporate cautiously to fumes. HF may be added to high silicon material. Boil gently for 10–15 minutes. Cool and add 400 ml. of water. Add 10 ml. of 25% ammonium citrate solution. Neutralize with $NH_4OH$ and add 1–2 ml. excess. Dilute to 500 ml. and heat to 90°C. Precipitate the nickel with 1.5 g. of dimethylglyoxime dissolved in 40 ml. of hot alcohol. Stir vigorously and allow to stand for 30 minutes to 1 hour.

Filter the nickel dimethylglyoxime on a 15-cm. paper and wash with hot water. Transfer the precipitate to a 600-ml. beaker and dissolve it with 15 ml. of $HNO_3$ and 15 ml. of HCl. Add 20 ml. of 1:1 $H_2SO_4$ and evaporate to fumes. Add $HNO_3$ dropwise to the fuming residue until all organic matter is destroyed. Continue fuming until nitric acid is removed. Cool, dissolve salts in 100 ml. of water. Neutralize with $NH_4OH$ and add 25 ml. excess. Dilute to 200 ml. and determine Ni by electrolysis.

This method is satisfactory for all ordinary purposes. For work of the highest accuracy it is recommended that the nickel dimethylglyoxime be reprecipitated with

23 Peters, Chemist-Analyst, **24**, No. 4, 1935.

the usual dilute reagent, filtered on fritted glass, dried, and weighed. The combined filtrates should be concentrated, the organic matter destroyed, and the residual nickel recovered.

## COBALT

*Procedure.*—The titrimetric method of Sarver [24] may be applied to a solution of the crude cobalt obtained by direct precipitation with nitroso beta naphthol. The usual small amounts of Fe and Cu present do not interfere. Titrimetric methods based on oxidation of Co in ammoniacal citrate solution by means of potassium ferricyanide will probably prove to be satisfactory.[25]

The following procedure is suitable for occasional accurate determinations:

Dissolve 3 g. of drillings in 25 ml. of nitric acid and evaporate the solution to a syrup. Add 50 ml. of hydrochloric acid and evaporate to dryness. Again add 50 ml. of hydrochloric acid and evaporate to dryness. Drench the residue with 10 ml. of hydrochloric acid and dilute to 100 ml. with warm water. Heat until salts are in solution, filter and wash with hot water.

Ignite the paper and contents in a platinum crucible, cool and add 1 drop of 1:1 sulfuric acid and a little hydrofluoric acid. Evaporate until fumes of sulfuric acid are given off, then fuse the residue with a pinch of sodium bisulfate. Dissolve the melt in water and add to the reserved filtrate.

Dilute the solution to 200 ml., heat to boiling, and pass a rapid stream of hydrogen sulfide for 30 minutes. Allow the sulfides to settle for 1 hour, filter and wash with 1:99 hydrochloric acid saturated with hydrogen sulfide. Discard the precipitate and boil the hydrogen sulfide off from the filtrate. Oxidize with a pinch of ammonium persulfate and evaporate to 100 ml.

Neutralize the solution with ammonia and add 20 ml. excess of hydrochloric acid. Dilute to 200 ml., cool to 10°C., and add an excess of cool 6% cupferron solution. Filter and wash with cold 5:95 hydrochloric acid. Discard the precipitate and dilute the filtrate and washings to 400 ml.

Add one and one-half times as much nitroso-beta-naphthol as is required to precipitate the cobalt. (1 g. of the reagent dissolved in 15 ml. of glacial acetic acid and filtered. 15 ml. precipitate approximately 0.06 g. of cobalt.) Heat to 60°–70°C. by digesting on steam bath for 20 minutes and allow to stand for several hours.

Filter and wash with hot 1:3 hydrochloric acid and then with hot water. Ignite in a porcelain crucible. Transfer the oxides to a beaker, dissolve in hydrochloric acid and evaporate to dryness. Add 15 ml. of hydrochloric acid, dilute to 300 ml., and heat to 90°C. Precipitate the cobalt with nitroso-beta-naphthol, let stand several hours, filter and wash as before. Ignite to constant weight at 750°–850°C. and weigh as $Co_3O_4$.

The weighed oxide should be corrected by a blank carried through all steps in the determination, or it may be dissolved in hydrochloric acid and any impurities found deducted. (Mainly iron from the reagent.)

[24] Sarver, Ind. Eng. Chem., Anal. Ed. **5,** 275, 1933.

[25] Dickens and Maassen, Mitt. Kaiser-Wilhelm Inst. Eisenforsch. Düsseldorf, **17,** 191, 1935; Tomicek and Freiberger, J. Am. Chem. Soc., **57,** 801, 1935.

## METHODS FOR NICKEL IN ANALYSES IN OTHER CHAPTERS

| | |
|---|---|
| Nickel in Aluminum Alloys | See Analysis of Aluminum Alloys |
| Nickel in Arsenious Oxide | See Analysis of Arsenious Oxide |
| Nickel in Beryllium Metal | See Analysis of Beryllium Metal |
| Nickel in Alloys by Ion Exchange | See Method in Chromium Chapter |
| Nickel in Refined Copper | See Analysis of Refined Copper |
| Nickel in Magnesium Alloys | See Magnesium Chapter |

*Chapter 32*

# NIOBIUM AND TANTALUM*

Nb, *at. wt.* 92.906; *d.* 8.57; *m.p.* 2468°C.; *b.p.* 3700°C.; *oxides,* $Nb_2O_3$, $Nb_2O_5$.
Ta, *at. wt.* 180.948; *d.* 16.6; *m.p.* 996°C.; *b.p.* 4100°C.; *oxide,* $Ta_2O_5$.

The most important minerals in commerce are tantalite and niobite, the two end members of the isomorphous tantalo-niobite series $(Ta,Nb)_2O_5 \cdot (Fe,Mn)O$. With the advent in recent years of new methods of separating niobium from tantalum the intermediate members of this series, which at one time were only diffi-cultly marketable, are now of considerable commercial importance. Pyrochlorite deposits in East Africa, Canada, and Norway have also assumed importance as a source of niobium.

The chief deposits of high-grade tantalite occur in Western Australia, but Nigeria is the principal source of high-grade niobite, which is a by-product of the mining of cassiterite.

Both metals are now available commercially in the form of bars, sheet, and wire produced by powder metallurgy techniques. They resist the action of all acids and combinations of acids except hydrofluoric acid and mixtures containing this acid, but are more readily attacked by alkaline reagents. Both metals readily absorb gases (nitrogen, oxygen, hydrogen) at temperatures above about 300°C. and become brittle. They can, however, readily be worked cold since they work-harden only relatively slightly. All annealing must be done in a high vacuum under which conditions absorbed gases are rapidly removed.

Tantalum is used for plating chemical apparatus used for handling highly cor-rosive acid liquors, as one electrode in current rectifiers, and for radiation shields and crucibles in high-temperature vacuum furnaces. Niobium has nuclear prop-erties which appear to render it useful in cladding fuel elements for fast reactors. otherwise its chief use is as an alloying element in certain high-temperature alloys for jet engines, and in stainless steels for stabilizing them against weld-decay.

## DETECTION

Most minerals containing tantalum and niobium are heavy and usually dark-colored (black or brownish-black) but microlite (calcium tantalite), and stibio- and bismuthotantalite are yellowish to light brown. Titania is a minor constituent of most tantalites and niobites, but is a major constituent of the titanoniobite min-erals which also contain the rare earths and frequently uranium. Some varieties of ilmenite and rutile contain appreciable percentages of the earth acids. The tantalum-niobium minerals are not attacked by digestion in the finely powdered state with hot hydrochloric acid, whereas the tungsten minerals, with which they

---

* Chapter by A. R. Powell, F.R.S., Metallurgical Chemist, Wembley, England.

714

might be confused, either dissolve completely or become coated with a yellow deposit of tungstic acid. Cassiterite may be distinguished from other heavy dark-colored minerals by stirring it, without crushing, with zinc powder and hydrochloric acid, which treatment causes it to become coated with a gray deposit of metallic tin.

Tantalum and niobium may be detected in a mineral that fails to respond to a test for tungsten or tin as follows:—

*Schoeller's Test.*—The powdered mineral is fused with potassium bisulfate in a silica crucible, and the melt spread round the sides to cool. It is then moistened with a few drops of sulfuric acid, and just fused again, avoiding excessive loss of acid. The cold melt is dissolved in hot 20% tartaric acid, and the filtered solution boiled for 10 minutes with one-third its volume of concentrated hydrochloric acid. A white flocculent precipitate is a specific and sensitive indication of the presence of earth acid. (In this chapter the term "mixed pentoxides" is used to denote $(Ta, Nb)_2O_5$, and the term "earth acid" to denote a mixture of the hydrated oxides.)

If the mineral contains tungsten it may be tested for the presence of tantalum and niobium as follows:—

*Powell's Test.*[1]—The finely powdered mineral is fused with potassium hydroxide in a nickel crucible or with potassium carbonate in a platinum crucible. The cold melt is leached with hot water and the extract filtered. The cold filtrate is stirred while sufficient solid powdered sodium chloride is added to give an almost saturated solution of this salt. A white crystalline precipitate indicates the presence of earth acids, tungsten giving no precipitate. The crystals may be collected on a loose filter, washed with cold saturated sodium chloride solution, and rinsed back into the original beaker with hot water; on adding hydrochloric acid to the beaker and boiling a white flocculent precipitate of the earth acids is obtained.

If the mineral contains much titanium as shown by the usual hydrogen peroxide test on a dilute sulfuric acid solution of the bisulfate melt the presence of tantalum and niobium may be detected as follows:—

*Tannin Test.*[2]—The bisulfate fusion of the mineral is extracted with a hot 2% solution of tannin in 2 N sulfuric acid; a red to orange residue indicates the presence of earth acids and an orange solution the presence of titanium. This test may be made on only a few milligrams of mineral.

In all of the above tests the precipitate obtained is a mixture of earth acids. The following tests are applied to detect the presence of each separately, but the precipitate must first be ignited to obtain the mixed pentoxides.

*Marignac's Test* (does not detect the presence of small quantities of tantalum in presence of much niobium).—The oxides are digested in platinum with 40% hydrofluoric acid and the solution is evaporated almost dry on the steam bath. The residue is dissolved in the minimum of water containing a few drops of hydrofluoric acid. A few drops of a saturated solution of potassium fluoride are added to the hot solution which is then allowed to cool slowly. The presence of tantalum is indicated by the separation of acicular rhombic prisms of potassium fluotantalate, $K_2TaF_7$, soluble in 200 parts of cold water. On evaporation of the filtrate the niobium separates as flat plates of potassium fluoxyniobate $K_2NbOF_5, H_2O$, soluble in 12 parts of water.

*Gile's Test* [3] (sensitive for small amounts of niobium).—The oxides are fused

[1] Modified process based on Schoeller and Jahn, Analyst, **52,** 513, 1927.
[2] Schoeller, Analyst, **54,** 453, 1929.
[3] Gile, Chem. News, **95,** 1, 1907.

with potassium carbonate in platinum and the cold melt is dissolved in the minimum of water. The solution is heated with a large excess of phosphoric acid until clear and zinc dust is added; a brownish to inky black color develops according to the amount of niobium present. Tantalum gives no coloration.

*Powell and Schoeller's Test* [4] (applicable to the characterization of both elements when mixed in any proportions).—The oxides are fused with bisulfate in a silica crucible, and the melt is dissolved in 50 ml. of hot 5% ammonium oxalate solution. To the boiling solution tannin is added (0.1–0.2 g. dissolved in a little water) followed by 0.5 N ammonia until a flocculent precipitate forms. If this is pale to bright yellow the presence of tantalum is proved; if orange to red, niobium is present with tantalum either absent or present in more or less subordinate amount. An orange or red precipitate is collected, washed with hot 2% ammonium chloride solution, rinsed back into the beaker, boiled with 25 ml. of ammonium oxalate solution, and dissolved by addition of N sulfuric acid. The clear solution is boiled with 0.1 g. of tannin and 0.5 N ammonia added dropwise until a flocculent precipitate is again obtained; this will now be yellow if the amount of tantalum is not too small, but if again orange the process must be repeated once more.

If the first precipitate was yellow the presence of niobium is readily detected by boiling the filtrate with more tannin and an excess of ammonium acetate; an orange-red to vermilion precipitate indicates niobium.

*Other Tests.*—The chromatographic and colorimetric tests described later in this chapter may also be used for the detection of the two elements.

## ESTIMATION

*Fusion with Bisulfate.*—Although many materials containing tantalum and niobium may be brought into solution by digestion with hydrofluoric acid, fusion with alkali bisulfate is generally preferable, the potassium salt being the most convenient, except when rare earths are present. Opaque silica crucibles should be used for the fusion in preference to platinum to avoid contamination of the solution with that metal. The material must be finely ground, preferably in an agate mortar, and the fusion should be made at as low a temperature as possible, and continued until frothing has completely ceased and crystals of neutral potassium sulfate separate on the surfate of the melt. The mass is then spread in a thin layer round the sides of the crucible, left to cool, and moistened with 0.5 to 1 ml. of concentrated sulfuric acid. The fusion is then repeated at a low temperature; this should always be done even if the first fusion appears to give a complete attack on the material. With this technique attack on the crucible is insignificant and any silica present in the material remains completely insoluble. In analyzing ores and minerals the crucible should be weighed before and after fusion so that an allowance can be made for silica if necessary.

*Leaching the Bisulfate Melt.*—This should always be done in the crucible, at least until the melt becomes completely detached from the sides; this occurs quite readily if the melt has been spread round the sides in a thin layer, but may take a considerable time if the melt has been allowed to solidify as a thick cake at the bottom. The solvents used are either a hot 4% solution of ammonium oxalate or a hot 20 to 30% solution of tartaric acid. The former dissolves the earth acids

4 Powell and Schoeller, Analyst, **50**, 494, 1925.

rapidly and completely, leaving a residue of siliceous material and, if present, rare earths (as oxalates; thorium and yttria earth oxalates are, however, soluble in excess of ammonium oxalate). If tartaric acid is used as solvent the liquid is warmed on the water bath and solution hastened by stirring with a thin glass rod. The liquid is then transferred to a small beaker with hot water and filtered; the residue is washed with hot water, ignited in the same silica crucible, and fused with bisulfate exactly as before. The second cake is extracted with a smaller volume of the same tartaric acid solution and the extracts are combined. The re-treatment of the residue is recommended to ensure that attack is complete and to bring into solution small quantities of tantalic acid which may have been precipitated by hydrolysis in the first leaching, especially if the material being analyzed is poor in, or free from, niobium.

Should a clear tartrate liquor not be obtained, as may happen in the analysis of tantalum-rich materials low in niobium, it is not necessary to start afresh. The turbid solution—and filter paper, if filtration has been started—is evaporated with an excess of nitric acid and a restricted amount of sulfuric acid until the organic matter is destroyed; the residual acid sulfate mass will dissolve to a clear liquid in tartaric acid solution.

*Destruction of Tartaric (Citric) Acid, Tannin, and Filter Paper.*—A moist filter, containing a precipitate, dissolves when dropped into a few milliliters of sulfuric acid giving a black turbid solution. To destroy the organic matter the covered beaker is placed on the hot plate and about 20 ml. of concentrated nitric acid and 2 ml. of 70% perchloric acid are added. As the liquid gets hot, copious brown fumes are evolved and the solution gradually becomes light brown in color. Gentle boiling is continued until brown fumes cease to appear and the brown color of the liquid vanishes. The cover is then removed and the liquor allowed to evaporate slowly until fumes of perchloric acid appear; the heat is then raised and evaporation continued until copious fumes of sulfuric acid are emitted. After cooling the acid is diluted with cold water and the analysis continued. This process can be used for destroying organic acids or tannin and is more rapid and reliable than the older method of evaporation with sulfuric acid until foaming ceases followed by dropwise addition of nitric acid. No foaming occurs when perchloric acid is used with a large excess of nitric acid.

*Filtration and Washing of Amorphous Precipitates.*—Earth acid precipitates, when properly precipitated, are as readily filtrable as is ferric hydroxide, which they resemble in physical properties and tendency to adsorption. The same remark applies to tannin precipitates of tantalum, niobium, titanium, zirconium, vanadium, and aluminum which are very voluminous, a property invaluable in microwork, but undesirable for the treatment of substantial quantities of the elements. This inconvenience may be overcome by filtration under gentle suction, which reduces the bulk of the precipitate to such an extent that 0.1 g. of titania can be collected on an 11-cm. paper. For this purpose an ordinary filter funnel is fitted through a rubber bung or short rubber washer into the neck of a vacuum suction flask, a small perforated platinum cone is inserted in the apex of the funnel, and a folded 5.5-cm. Whatman No. 40 paper or its equivalent is placed in the cone, followed by a folded 9-, 11-, or 12.5-cm. paper of the same texture in such a way that the threefold thickness of the inner paper lies over the single thickness of the outer, so that in effect a fourfold thickness of paper is present round the whole of the lower part of the funnel. This arrangement will withstand the full suction of an ordinary water pump and will retain even the finest precipitate if filter-pulp has first been beaten up with it. The precipitate on the paper should not be pulled dry enough to crack or pull away from the paper until washing is completed. It is advisable, however, to rinse the precipitate back into the beaker after two or three washings, beat it up with fresh wash solution and re-filter, finishing with a few more washings on the paper. After this, precipitate and paper can be sucked as dry as possible before transferring them to the crucible for ignition.

If filtration is to be made under atmospheric pressure a loose-textured paper is perfectly safe. The precipitate should be allowed to settle as much as possible and the clear supernatant liquid decanted through the paper. The precipitate is then intimately mixed with filter-pulp and transferred to the filter. After two or three washes it is rinsed back into the beaker, beaten up with more wash solution, and re-filtered and washed. The beaker is finally cleaned with a little filter-pulp on the end of a rubber-tipped glass rod. The wash liquor should always contain an electrolyte, preferably ammonium chloride or nitrate, and also a little tannin if that reagent has been used for the precipitation.

*Ignition of Precipitates.*—All earth acid precipitates should contain either filter-pulp or tannin and should be ignited in a porcelain crucible without previous drying. In this way the oxides are obtained as a soft loose powder which can readily be redissolved by dilute hydrofluoric acid, or by fusion with sodium bisulfate, followed by treatment with water. The ignited precipitates tend to be contaminated with small quantities of alkali salts, sulfur trioxide, and perhaps iron oxide and lime. They should therefore always be purified before weighing. This can be done by digesting the ignited oxides with dilute hydrochloric acid in the crucible on the water bath for 10 to 15 minutes, transferring the contents of the crucible to a small beaker, neutralizing the acid with ammonia, adding 6 drops of 1:1 hydrochloric acid and boiling with a little tannin to precipitate traces of niobium oxide which may dissolve. The precipitate is collected in a small filter, washed with hot 2% ammonium chloride solution containing a little tannin, ignited in the original crucible, and weighed. The oxides are then dissolved by bisulfate fusion, the melt leached with 4% ammonium oxalate solution containing 5% of tartaric acid, the solution made just ammoniacal and some hydrogen sulfide water added. The dark precipitate is allowed to flocculate by digestion at gentle heat, collected, well washed with slightly ammoniacal 2% ammonium nitrate solution, ignited, and weighed as $SiO_2 + Fe_2O_3 + CaO$; the weight is deducted from that of the oxide previously obtained.

In all work with the earth acids special precautions should be taken to use only the purest reagents free from glass splinters or gritty matter. This particularly applies to the bisulfate.

## PREPARATION AND SOLUTION OF THE SAMPLE

Most of the difficulties encountered in earth acid analysis are due to the fact that tantalum and niobium form very few water-soluble compounds. The fluorides are very soluble, but can be handled only in platinum or polyethylene ware; their aqueous solutions hydrolyze on evaporation to dryness but there is no loss by volatilization although the pure pentafluorides are themselves volatile. The residue from evaporating fluoride solutions can be ignited without loss and no loss occurs if the fluoride solution is evaporated with sulfuric acid and the latter expelled by heating.

The water-soluble compounds of importance in analytical work are as follows:

(1) **The Tartaric Acid Complexes.**—These are prepared as described in the previous Section (under "Leaching the Bisulfate Melt"). They are more stable in ammoniacal than in acid solution and the tantalum complex dissociates more readily than the niobium in acid solution although both complexes hydrolyze readily on boiling with a large excess of hydrochloric acid, the earth acids being precipitated. Citric acid also forms soluble earth acid complexes.

(2) **The oxalic acid complexes** are obtained by dissolving the precipitated earth acids in hot oxalic acid solution or by dissolving the bisulfate melt in hot ammonium oxalate solution. The niobium complex is more stable than that of tantalum, a fact of which advantage is taken in the separation of the two elements.

(3) **The per-acids** are obtained when a bisulfate melt of the earth acids is dissolved in sulfuric acid and hydrogen peroxide. If the acid is concentrated the niobium per-acid imparts a yellow color to the solution but the tantalum per-acid gives no color. In dilute acid neither compound produces a color (distinction from titanium).

(4) **The Potassium Salts.**—Fusion of the earth acids or their minerals with potassium carbonate or hydroxide yields the 4:3 (or "hexa") salts, $4K_2O \cdot 3(Ta,Nb)_2O_5$, which are soluble in water and may be crystallized. The tantalate hydrolyzes much more readily than the niobate but hydrolysis may be repressed by addition of potassium hydroxide to the solution. If a solution of the potassium salts is saturated with sodium chloride crystalline precipitates of the following sodium salts are obtained:

$$4Na_2O \cdot 3Ta_2O_5, \quad 4:3 \text{ sodium tantalate.}$$

$$7Na_2O \cdot 6Nb_2O_5, \quad 7:6 \text{ sodium niobate.}$$

The soda in these precipitates can be determined by titration with standard acid, which gives a measure of the earth acid combined with it. Since the two compounds are not of similar composition the titers obtained with mixed earth acid salts are not sufficiently reliable for an accurate estimation of tantalum and niobium by the "indirect" method.

*Treatment of Minerals.*—From the above discussion of the behavior of the earth acids it will be obvious that their minerals can be decomposed by three procedures, namely (1) digestion with hydrofluoric acid; (2) fusion with alkali bisulfate; or (3) fusion with potassium hydroxide or carbonate. The subsequent treatment of the solution varies with the method of attack adopted and will therefore be described in each case as part of the analytical process. Before proceeding to a description of these processes it is necessary to consider methods of separating the earth acids from their mineral associates, the most common of which are silica, tin, tungsten, iron, titanium, zirconium, thorium, the rare earths, and uranium.

## SEPARATIONS

*From Silica.*[5]—(a) Fusion of earth acid minerals or of a mixture of oxides low in silica with potassium bisulfate and extraction of the melt with 4% ammonium oxalate solution leaves all the silica in the insoluble residue which is then treated as (b) below.

(b) To detect and determine small quantities of earth acids in silica, the ignited and weighed oxides are transferred to a platinum dish, moistened with a little

---

[5] Schoeller and Powell, Analyst, **53,** 258, 1928.

20% sulfuric acid, and evaporated with an excess of hydrofluoric acid. The residue remaining after expulsion of both acids is heated strongly for some time after fumes cease to be evolved, cooled, and weighed, the silica being taken by difference. The fixed residue is fused with bisulfate, the cold melt extracted with ammonium oxalate solution, and the filtered liquid added to the main solution obtained as under (a) above.

*From Tin.*[6]—Many earth acid minerals contain small amounts of tin oxide either as cassiterite inclusions or actually in the molecule of the mineral, and earth acids are also found as minor constituents of some cassiterites. Two cases have, therefore, to be considered:

(a) Earth acid minerals containing or associated with tin oxide are fused with bisulfate and the melt extracted with hot 20 to 30% tartaric acid (see "Notes on Analytical Technique," above). Most of the tin oxide remains insoluble but a small amount of tin goes into solution; this is recovered by treating the unfiltered solution with hydrogen sulfide after adding a few drops of saturated mercuric chloride solution. The precipitate of tin sulfide is much more readily flocculated and filtered if co-precipitated with mercuric sulfide and has no tendency to peptize during washing. The precipitate and insoluble residue are collected, washed with slightly acidified hydrogen sulfide water and ignited cautiously in the fusion crucible. The residue is again fused with bisulfate, and the whole process repeated to ensure complete separation of the earth acids. The second ignition residue is analyzed as usual for tin after weighing. If silica is present this will all be in the tin oxide residue and may be estimated by the usual hydrofluoric acid-sulfuric acid treatment.

Ammonium oxalate solution must not be used to extract the bisulfate melt since oxalate inhibits precipitation of tin as sulfide. Also the wash water used in this separation must be free from chlorides to avoid loss of tin by volatilization during the ignition.

(b) Cassiterite and tin oxide containing small quantities of rare earths should be reduced by heating to redness in a stream of hydrogen and the reduced tin dissolved in hydrochloric acid. The residue from this treatment is collected, ignited, and fused with bisulfate and the analysis continued as under (a) above.

*From Tungsten.*—Tungstic acid behaves similarly to the earth acids in hydrolytic precipitation reactions; although, unlike the earth acids, it is soluble in ammonia and ammonium sulfide, digestion of a mixed hydrolysis precipitate with either of these reagents fails to effect complete extraction of the tungsten. Fusion of the mixed oxides with sodium carbonate and sulfur also gives an unsatisfactory separation. Accurate results are, however, obtained by either of the following methods.

(a) **Small Amounts of Tungstic Acid from Much Earth Acid.**[7]—The mixed oxides are fused with 3 g. of potassium carbonate in a platinum crucible and the cold melt is digested with hot water containing 0.5 g. of potassium hydroxide. The extract is transferred to a small beaker and solid sodium chloride is slowly stirred in until the liquid is saturated. Next day the crystalline precipitate of sodium tantalate and niobate is collected on a small loose-textured paper and well washed with half-saturated sodium chloride solution. The small quantity of earth acid that fails to precipitate as the sodium salt is recovered by neutralizing the

6 Schoeller and Webb, Analyst, **56,** 795, 1931.
7 Schoeller and Jahn, Analyst, **52,** 506, 1927.

filtrate to phenolphthalein with dilute hydrochloric acid and heating on the water bath, adding more acid from time to time until the pink color of the indicator ceases to return. After several hours on the water bath the earth acid precipitate will have flocculated and settled; it is collected and washed in the same way as the sodium salts. Both filter papers and precipitates are returned to the last beaker, beaten up with hot water, and treated with a slight excess of dilute hydrochloric acid (methyl red). When the precipitate of earth acids and filter pulp has completely flocculated it is collected, washed thoroughly with 2% ammonium nitrate solution, and ignited; the residue is weighed as $(Ta,Nb)_2O_5$.

The filtrate from the second precipitate contains all the tungstic acid. It is treated with a solution of 0.5 g. of tannin, made distinctly acid with dilute hydrochloric acid, heated nearly to boiling, and stirred with 10 ml. of 2.5% cinchonine hydrochloride solution. After cooling for 6 hours or overnight the brown precipitate is collected with the acid of a little filter pulp, washed very thoroughly with a cold 2% solution of ammonium chloride containing a little tannin, dried in a tared porcelain crucible and ignited to $WO_3$, which is weighed.

(b) **Small Amounts of Earth Acid in Tungsten Trioxide.**—One gram of the oxide is fused for 1 minute with 2 g. of sodium hydroxide in a clean nickel crucible and the melt is extracted with 10 ml. of hot 15% sodium chloride solution. After cooling for some hours the extract is filtered through a small dense pad of filter pulp in the apex of a narrow-bore funnel, the pad is washed repeatedly with 1 ml. portions of the same sodium chloride solution until the washings are neutral (litmus), and pad and precipitate are rinsed into a small beaker in which they are digested with a few drops of hydrochloric acid on the water bath. Pulp and precipitate are then collected on a small filter, washed with 2% ammonium nitrate solution, and ignited to $(Ta,Nb)_2O_5$.

(c) **Separation of Tungsten from Tantalum, Niobium, Titanium, and Zirconium.**[8]—The oxide mixture is fused with 4 g. of potassium carbonate in a platinum crucible, the cold melt disintegrated by gentle boiling and stirring with a glass rod to break up any lumps, and the whole transferred to a 400-ml. beaker. The hot solution (150–200 ml.) is stirred while adding dropwise 25 ml. of a slightly ammoniacal solution containing 1 g. of magnesium sulfate and 2 g. of ammonium chloride; it is then placed on the steam bath for half an hour for the precipitate to flocculate, after which the liquid is filtered and the precipitate washed with hot 5% ammonium chloride solution. The tungsten in the filtrate is determined by the tannin-cinchonine method described in (a) above.

The precipitate produced by the magnesia reagent is rinsed back into the original beaker, the paper ignited, the ash brushed into the beaker, and the hot liquid (150 ml.) made just acid with dilute hydrochloric acid (methyl red). After adding an equal volume of 25% ammonium chloride solution and dilute ammonia until the free acid is almost neutralized, the solution is boiled and treated with a fresh solution of tannin until the precipitate flocculates and settles readily, after which it is collected, washed with hot 2% ammonium chloride solution, and ignited to $(Ta,Nb)_2O_5 + (Ti,Zr)O_2$.

*From Iron.*[9]—The elements are obtained in tartaric acid solution, e.g., by fusion of the mineral with bisulfate and extraction of the melt with tartaric acid. If much earth acid is present the solution is boiled with 30 ml. of concentrated

8 Powell, Schoeller, and Jahn, Analyst, **60,** 506, 1935.
9 Schoeller and Webb, Analyst, **54,** 709, 1929.

hydrochloric acid as described below under "Separation from Titanium (a)." The well-washed earth-acid precipitate, which is free from iron, is ignited and weighed. The filtrate that contains all the iron and a small quantity of earth acid, or the original solution if it contains only a little earth acid, is made slightly ammoniacal, treated with 5 g. of ammonium chloride and some filter-pulp, and then with hydrogen sulfide, and heated on a covered water bath until the ferrous sulfide has coagulated and settled. The precipitate is collected, washed as usual, and redissolved in hydrochloric acid; the iron is then recovered as ferric hydroxide, which is ignited to $Fe_2O_3$.

The filtrate from the ferrous sulfide is boiled with hydrochloric acid to expel hydrogen sulfide, neutralized with dilute ammonia (methyl red) and boiled with a solution of 1 g. of tannin, 5 g. of ammonium chloride, 5 g. of ammonium acetate then being added to complete the precipitation of the earth acids. The precipitate is collected, well washed with hot 2% ammonium chloride solution containing a little tannin, and ignited to $(Ta,Nb)_2O_5$. Its weight is added to that of the oxides recovered by acid hydrolysis of the tartrate solution if this step was used.

*From Zirconium, Thorium, Uranium, Rare Earths, Iron, Aluminum, and the Alkaline Earths.*[10]—Fusion with bisulfate of a mineral containing these elements in association with the earth acids and titania, followed by leaching of the melt with ammonium oxalate yields a solution containing the earth acids, titanium, zirconium, iron, aluminum and some or all of the thorium and rare earths (yttria group), together with a crystalline oxalate precipitate containing part of the rare earths (cerium group), a little thorium, and most of the alkaline earths. Hexavalent uranium goes into solution, tetravalent uranium is mainly in the precipitate. The solution is filtered, and the precipitate washed with 2% ammonium oxalate solution and ignited at a low temperature to oxides; these are digested with concentrated hydrochloric acid in which they should dissolve completely unless they consist mainly of thoria (a very rare occurrence). The acid solution is diluted, nearly neutralized with dilute ammonia, and boiled with a little tannin. Any precipitate is collected, washed, ignited, and fused with bisulfate; the melt is extracted with ammonium oxalate solution, the solution filtered, and the filtrate added to the first filtrate which then contains all the earth acids. This combined filtrate is neutralized with dilute ammonia, added dropwise, re-acidified with 4 drops of 1:1 hydrochloric acid, diluted with an equal volume of saturated ammonium chloride solution, and heated to boiling. Addition of a 4% tannin solution until no further turbidity forms then precipitates almost all the earth acids and titania, leaving the other elements in solution. After 10 minutes on the steam bath the precipitate is collected under suction and washed as described in the preceding section entitled "Estimation"; it is then ignited to oxides which are weighed as $(Ta,Nb)_2O_5 + TiO_2$. The filtrate may still contain small quantities of earth acids and titania; it is therefore heated to boiling and treated with a little more tannin followed by 1:10 ammonia added dropwise with vigorous stirring until the small orange precipitate first formed begins to be contaminated with the violet iron-tannin complex. At this stage two drops of 1:1 hydrochloric acid are added to redissolve the violet compound leaving a small flocculent orange precipitate which contains the last traces of niobium and titanium. This precipitate is collected, washed as before, and ignited; the oxide residue is weighed and added to the main fraction.

10 After Powell and Schoeller, Analyst, **50**, 485, 1925.

The violet filtrate from the tannin separation is combined with the acid filtrate from the retreatment of the rare earths and the combined solution is made just ammoniacal, treated with tannin solution until no further turbidity is produced, boiled, and filtered. The precipitate contains all the other elements originally present, either as tannin complexes or as oxalates; it is collected by suction, washed with hot slightly ammoniacal 2% ammonium nitrate solution and ignited to obtain the mixed oxides, which are analyzed by any suitable conventional method.

*From Titanium.*—Until quite recently this separation was the most difficult problem associated with the analysis of earth acid materials; it engaged the attention of Schoeller and his co-workers for many years and although they devised three methods (published between 1929 and 1932) which gave sufficiently accurate results for most purposes, all three were time-consuming and two of the three depended for their apparent accuracy on a compensation of errors, a small quantity of titania being left with the earth acid product and a corresponding quantity of niobium pentoxide contaminating the titania. These methods, with minor modifications, constituted standard practice for about 20 years. In 1952, however, the chemists at the Chemical Research Laboratory (now the National Chemical Laboratory) at Teddington, England, discovered that the ammonium fluoro-salts of tantalum and niobium could be eluted from a cellulose column with a mixture of hydrofluoric acid and methyl ethyl ketone, whereas the corresponding titanium and zirconium compounds remained stationary at the top of the column. The only interfering element was found to be tungsten; this is partly eluted and partly retained in the column but can be readily removed before proceeding to the chromatographic separation by the methods described earlier in this section, or it may subsequently be determined colorimetrically in the earth acids eluted from the column. Since the chromatographic method can be applied directly to the analysis of ores without preliminary separations it is described fully in the section on Gravimetric Methods. The older chemical methods of separation devised by Schoeller are given below in their most recent modified form:

(a) **Tartaric Hydrolysis Method.**[11]—Serviceable results are obtained rapidly by this method when the weight of mixed oxides to be analyzed does not exceed about 0.05 g., and, since the reaction is specific for tantalum and niobium, the presence of these elements can be confirmed with certainty.

The mixed oxides (about 0.05 g.) are fused with 1 g. of bisulfate and the cold melt is dissolved in 10 ml. of hot 20% tartaric acid solution. The clear solution is diluted to 100 ml. and gently boiled for 10 minutes with 20 ml. of concentrated hydrochloric acid. The white flocculent precipitate of earth acids is mixed with filter pulp, collected, washed with hot 5% ammonium chloride and ignited to $(Ta,Nb)_2O_5$ for weighing. It contains a little titania but a little earth acid (chiefly niobia) escapes precipitation, the two errors compensating one another.

(b) **Pyrosulfate-Tannin Method for Small Amounts of Earth Acid in Much Titania.**[12]—The titania is fused with 2–3 g. of bisulfate and the melt spread around the sides of the crucible to cool; it is then extracted with a hot 1% solution of tannin in 2 $N$ sulfuric acid whereby the titania dissolves as the sulfate while the earth acids remain insoluble as their tannin complexes. When detached, the contents of the crucible are transferred to a 150-ml. beaker, and the crucible rinsed with the extraction solution. The liquid is heated to boiling, stirred until

11 Schoeller and Jahn, Analyst, **54**, 321, 1929.
12 Schoeller, Analyst, **54**, 455, 1929.

all the melt has dissolved, and set aside overnight to allow the precipitate to settle. Next day the small orange precipitate is collected, well washed with cold $N$ sulfuric acid containing a little tannin, ignited, and weighed as the mixed pentoxides. The small titania content of the oxides may be estimated colorimetrically; if a specific earth-acid test is required the ignited oxides may be examined by method (a) above.

(c) **Oxalate-Salicylate Method.**[13]—This is the most accurate chemical process for the separation of large amounts of earth acid from titania.

The bisulfate melt derived from 0.2 to 0.3 g. of mixed oxides is dissolved in a hot solution of 2 g. of ammonium oxalate in a 600-ml. beaker and the liquid cautiously neutralized with 1:10 ammonia (methyl red), re-acidified with exactly 3 drops of 1:1 hydrochloric acid and treated with 5 g. of sodium salicylate which produces a yellow to orange solution. This is diluted to 250 ml., boiled, and stirred while adding slowly a 20% solution of calcium chloride in moderate excess to convert all the oxalate to calcium oxalate, which brings down with it the earth acids leaving the titania complexed with the salicylate. After a few minutes gentle boiling and stirring, the boiling-hot solution is filtered under slight suction, the precipitate washed with hot 2% sodium salicylate solution until the washings are colorless and then rinsed back into the beaker with hot water, and the paper cleaned with 50 ml. of 1:1 hydrochloric acid and ignited. The ash and washings are added to the beaker and the acid liquid boiled gently while adding a 4% solution of permanganate to destroy the oxalic acid, followed by a little sulfur dioxide water until the solution is colorless. It is now diluted to about 200 ml., boiled, neutralized with ammonia (methyl red), made just acid with 3 drops of 1:1 hydrochloric acid, and boiled for 5 minutes with 1 g. of tannin. The precipitate, which contains most of the earth acids and a little titania, is collected, washed with hot 2% ammonium chloride solution containing a little tannin, and ignited. The oxide residue is fused with bisulfate and the whole process repeated to give a mixed pentoxide containing less than 10 mg. of titania and suitable for the separation of the two earth acids from one another.

The combined salicylate filtrate is boiled with 10 g. of ammonium acetate and a 4% tannin solution added until no further red precipitate forms, then a 10 ml. excess of the reagent. The precipitate is collected under suction, washed with hot 10% ammonium chloride solution, and ignited in silica. The resulting oxide is fused with bisulfate and the melt treated by method (b) above to recover its small content of niobium pentoxide as the tannin complex. This is collected, washed, ignited, and added to the bulk of earth acids obtained from the calcium oxalate precipitate. The titania may be recovered from the orange acid filtrate by adding more tannin, neutralizing with ammonia and boiling with ammonium chloride and acetate. The washed tannin precipitate is ignited to titanis for weighing.

Both the final earth oxide and the titania residues from the ignitions should be leached and tested for purity as explained under "Estimation."

*From Zirconium and Hafnium.*—If the mixed oxides contain only small quantities of earth acids, precipitation of these from an almost neutral oxalate solution provides an efficient and rapid separation from zirconia. If, however, the amount of earth acid present greatly exceeds that of the zirconia it is preferable to remove the bulk of the former by fusing the mixture with potassium carbonate and leach-

13 Schoeller and Jahn, Analyst, **57**, 75, 1932.

ing out the soluble potassium salts, the zirconia remaining in the residue which is then subjected to the bisulfate fusion-tannin precipitation process to recover the last small quantity of earth acid.[14]

(a) **Small Amounts of Earth Acid from Much Zirconia.**[14]—The mixed oxides are fused with bisulfate and the melt leached with a 4% solution of ammonium oxalate. The solution is boiled and made just neutral to methyl red with very dilute ammonia, two drops of 1:1 hydrochloric acid are added, and the solution gently boiled while adding a 2% solution of tannin until no further orange precipitate forms. If the solution remains colored yellow to orange a little more tannin is added followed dropwise with stirring by very dilute ammonia until no further colored precipitate forms. If a dirty white precipitate of the zirconium-tannin complex forms it will readily redissolve on addition of 1 or 2 drops of acid. Finally the hot solution is treated with 5 g. of ammonium chloride and set on the water bath to allow the precipitate to settle; it is then collected, washed with hot 2% ammonium chloride solution, and ignited to $(Ta,Nb)_2O_5$ for weighing. The zirconia can be recovered from the filtrate by adding more tannin and dilute ammonia. The dirty white precipitate is well washed with 2% ammonium chloride solution, rinsed back into the beaker, and digested with 0.05 N hydrochloric acid containing 1% of tannin and 2% of ammonium chloride. The mixture is again filtered through the same paper, washed with the same solution, and ignited to $ZrO_2$ for weighing.

(b) **Large Amounts of Earth Acid from Zirconia.**—The mixed oxides are fused with 5 times their weight of potassium carbonate in a platinum crucible and the melt is leached with hot water containing 0.5 g. of potassium hydroxide. The liquid is transferred with hot water to a small beaker, mixed with filter pulp and filtered on a close-textured paper that is then washed with hot 2% potassium carbonate solution. Paper and residue are returned to the beaker, a little hydrochloric acid is added, the paper pulped with a stirring rod, and the mixture made just ammoniacal and filtered. After washing with 2% ammonium nitrate solution, the paper is ignited, and the residue of zirconia weighed; it is then treated according to (a) above to recover its small earth acid content.

The alkaline filtrate containing the major fraction of the earth acid is made just acid with hydrochloric acid, then feebly ammoniacal, boiled with a little filter pulp and filtered. The precipitate is washed with 2% ammonium nitrate solution and ignited; the residue is leached with dilute acid, again collected, ignited strongly, and weighed.

## GRAVIMETRIC METHODS

### A. HYDROFLUORIC ACID METHOD (J. LAWRENCE SMITH)

This method is suitable for decomposing minerals containing the rare earths, but not for tantalite or columbite.

*Procedure.*—The finely crushed mineral (0.25 to 0.5 g.) is mixed with a few milliliters of water in a platinum dish and, while stirring with a short platinum wire or polyethylene rod and warming on the water bath, 5 to 10 ml. of 40% hydrofluoric acid are slowly added, more acid being added later if the mineral does not completely decompose. When the reaction has finished about 10 volumes of water are added and the mixture set aside to cool overnight and allow the precipi-

[14] Schoeller and Powell, Analyst, **57**, 550, 1932.

tate of thorium, uranium(IV), and rare earth fluorides to settle. The clear liquid is then decanted through a close-textured paper in a hard rubber or polyethylene funnel and the filtrate collected in a polyethylene beaker. The residue is then rinsed on to the paper with 5% hydrofluoric acid (polyethylene "squeeze" wash-bottle) and well washed with the same acid. The filtrate is evaporated under an infrared lamp to a low volume and then transferred with hot water to a platinum dish containing 15 ml. of 1:1 sulfuric acid. The liquid is evaporated on the hot plate until fumes of sulfuric acid are freely evolved. After cooling, the sides of the dish are rinsed down with water and the fuming repeated until about half the acid has been removed. The cold acid mixture is diluted with 10 ml. of water containing 3 g. of tartaric acid and warmed until a clear solution is obtained; this contains the earth acids, titania, tungsten, tin, and the common metals and is treated as described under "B" below, starting at the second paragraph.

## B. TARTARIC ACID METHOD FOR TANTALITE AND NIOBITE [15]

*Procedure.*—The finely powdered mineral (0.5 g.) is fused with alkali bisulfate and a tartaric acid solution of the melt prepared exactly as described under "Estimation."

This solution, without filtering, is treated with a few drops of mercuric chloride solution and saturated with hydrogen sulfide to remove the tin [see "Separation from Tin, (a)"].[16]

The filtrate is diluted or concentrated to 150 ml. and boiled for 3 minutes with 25 ml. of hydrochloric acid. The white flocculent precipitate, constituting the major earth-acid fraction $P_1$, is collected, washed, ignited, and treated for the removal of tungsten, if present, as described under "Separation from Tungsten, (a) or (c)."

The minor earth-acid fraction is recovered as described under "Separation from Iron, (a)"; the small tannin precipitate $P_2$ obtained in this process is ignited and added to $P_1$; it contains the balance of the earth acids. The weight of the combined precipitate represents $(Ta,Nb)_2O_5 + TiO_2$.

Since the tungsten content of high-grade ores is generally very small its separation can be omitted in commercial analysis, but the percentage of titania should always be determined by a separate test on a 0.1 g. sample. This is fused with bisulfate, the melt dissolved in ammonium oxalate solution, the liquid acidified with sulfuric acid and treated with hydrogen peroxide, and the resulting color compared with that of a standard prepared from the same quantities of reagents and an appropriate amount of ferric sulfate solution to which a titanium sulfate solution (0.1 g. of $TiO_2$ per l.) is added.

If the titania is less than about 1% of the weight of mixed oxides the tantalum may be separated directly from the niobium by the tannin process, and the final tantalum precipitate tested for titania colorimetrically.

If the titania is greater than 1%, the mixed oxides must be subjected to the oxalate-salicylate method [see "Separation from Titania, (c)"]. Only one treatment by this process is necessary unless the titania content of the mixed oxides exceeds 3%.

The chromatographic method given under "D" below provides a more rapid

[15] Schoeller and Waterhouse, Analyst, **53**, 515, 1928.
[16] Schoeller and Webb, Analyst, **59**, 669, 1934.

and efficient separation of the earth acids from titania and is recommended when the amount present is more than 1% of the mixed oxides.

## C. AMMONIUM OXALATE METHOD [17]

This is the most rapid method of recovering the earth acids and titania from most minerals, but the precipitate is very voluminous and must always be collected by suction using a 12.5-cm. paper, and the quantity of material worked on must be such as to give not more than 0.2 g. of mixed oxides, $(Ta,Nb)_2O_5 + TiO_2 +$ (if present) $WO_3$. Hence for high grade tantalites and niobites a 0.25-g. sample should be used.

*Procedure.*—The mineral is fused with 4 g. of bisulfate, the cold melt extracted with 100 ml. of hot 4% ammonium oxalate solution, and any insoluble material (silica, tin oxide, rare earth, or alkali earth oxalates or sulfates) filtered off and washed with hot water.

The boiling filtrate in a 600-ml. beaker is diluted to 200 ml. and cautiously neutralized with very dilute ammonia until a faint permanent turbidity is formed; this is cleared by dropwise addition of 1:1 hydrochloric acid, and the liquid diluted with an equal volume of saturated ammonium chloride solution. The mixture is again boiled and treated with a filtered solution of 2.5 g. of tannin in 25 ml. of water while gently stirring and boiling for 3 minutes. A voluminous yellow to orange precipitate of the tannin complexes of the earth acids, titania, and tungsten is produced; this precipitate will also contain any small quantity of tin dissolved by the fusion. After 30 minutes on the water bath the solution is filtered by gentle suction and the precipitate well washed with hot 5% ammonium chloride solution as described under "Estimation." After the final wash the filter is filled with saturated ammonium chloride solution, sucked dry, and ignited, slowly at first so as to allow any traces of tin present to be volatilized while the filter and precipitate are charring, and then at a good red heat; the residue is weighed as $(Ta,Nb)_2O_5 + TiO_2 (+ WO_3$ if present).

The filtrate from the tannin precipitate may contain a small quantity of niobium and titanium due to the increase in acidity arising from the removal of the bulk of the earth acids from their oxalate complexes by the tannin. It should, therefore, be heated to boiling with a little more tannin and cautiously neutralized by dropwise addition of very dilute ammonia until a test on Universal Indicator paper shows a pH of about 5; after boiling to flocculate the small orange precipitate a few drops of dilute hydrochloric acid are added to bring the pH to 4 thus preventing contamination of the precipitate with iron. The purple solution is filtered through a small loose-textured paper and the precipitate washed as before, ignited, and added to the bulk of the oxides for weighing.

If tungsten is present the combined mixed oxides are fused with potassium carbonate in a platinum crucible and the earth acids and titania recovered by the sodium chloride method [see "Separation from Tungsten, (a)"], ignited, and weighed.

Before proceeding to separate the earth acids from one another an approximate determination of the titania content of the mineral should be made as described under "Tartaric Acid Method, (b)" above.

---

[17] Modified procedure based on Schoeller and Powell, Analyst, **57**, 550, 1932.

## D. SEPARATION AND GRAVIMETRIC ESTIMATION
## OF TANTALUM AND NIOBIUM

Two methods of separating the earth acids from one another are now available. The older, due to Powell and Schoeller,[18] depends on the greater ease with which tantalo-oxalic acid dissociates in the presence of tannin; in slightly acid oxalate solution the yellow absorption complex of tantalic acid and tannin is precipitated, whereas the bright vermilion complex of niobic acid and tannin precipitates completely only from neutral solution in presence of excess of tannin. Since this difference in behavior is not sufficiently marked for a clean-cut separation to be obtained in one operation the procedure is one of fractionation. The presence of niobium in the tantalum precipitate is clearly indicated by the color; the niobium-free complex is pure yellow, but a slight admixture of niobium imparts to it a more or less pronounced orange color. If niobium predominates in the mixed oxides an orange to red precipitate is obtained at first, but in the second or third precipitation a yellow precipitate will be obtained if tantalum is present. Titania interferes in the separation by discoloring the tantalum precipitate to a buff to brownish yellow color rather than to orange. The method works normally if the titania does not exceed 1% of the tantalic oxide present, the titania being estimated colorimetrically in the tantalic oxide finally obtained and the necessary correction made.

The newer separation method, due originally to Burstall and Williams,[19] but later modified by Mercer and Wells,[20] can be used for separating the earth acids not only from one another, but also from all other metals except tungsten. Its great advantage is that it rapidly and efficiently separates the earth acids from any admixture with titania. It depends on the following facts:

(a) When a concentrated solution of the ammonium fluoro-salts is absorbed on a pad of cellulose fibre which is then placed on top of a short column of the same material and eluted with a 85:15 volume mixture of methyl ethyl ketone and 40% hydrofluoric acid, the earth acids pass into the eluate as the $(NH_4)_2(Ta,Nb)F_7$ compounds, whereas the titanium, in the form of $(NH_4)_2TiF_6$, moves only a short distance down the column.

(b) When a fluoride solution of the earth acids containing a small excess of ammonium fluoride and very little free hydrofluoric acid is placed on the cellulose column and eluted with water-saturated methyl ethyl ketone the $(NH_4)_2NbF_7$ is hydrolyzed to $(NH_4)_2NbOF_5$ that moves very little, whereas the $(NH_4)_2TaF_7$ remains unchanged and is readily eluted.

(c) If tungsten is present it forms the compound $(NH_4)_2WOF_6$ that moves somewhat slowly down the column under either of the above conditions, and part is eluted before elution of the earth acids is complete. Hence the final earth acid precipitate must be tested for tungsten (e.g., colorimetrically), or the tungsten must first be removed by one of the methods described under "Separation from Tungsten."

(d) Other metals remain on the cellulose column either as simple fluorides or as double fluorides or oxyfluorides with ammonium fluoride.

(1) *Procedure for Separation by Tannin.*—The mixed oxides, derived from any of the above methods of separating them from the mineral, are fused with bisulfate

18 Powell and Schoeller, Analyst, **50**, 485, 1925; Schoeller, *ibid.*, **57**, 750, 1932.
19 Barstall and Williams, J. Chem. Soc., 1952, 3399.
20 Mercer and Wells, Analyst, **79**, 339, 1954.

and the melt is dissolved in a hot 4% solution of ammonium oxalate, and the solution (about 200 ml.) boiled with 10 ml. of freshly prepared 2% tannin solution; 0.5 N ammonia is then added dropwise with stirring until a permanent strong turbidity results. If the incipient precipitate is pure yellow, more of the tannin reagent is added slowly with stirring until a transient orange precipitate forms which disappears only slowly on stirring, but the addition should be interrupted before the precipitate becomes permanently tinted with orange, and 10 g. of ammonium chloride added while boiling for a further few minutes. The yellow precipitate is collected by suction, washed with 2% ammonium chloride, and ignited in porcelain; the residue is reserved. The filtrate is evaporated to 250 ml., treated with a little more tannin, and further neutralized. If the precipitate is still yellow it is collected, washed, and ignited, and the oxide added to that previously obtained, but if orange the ignited oxide from it is fused with bisulfate and the oxalate leach of the melt treated as described below.

Orange to red precipitates obtained either from the original tannin precipitation or from the retreatment of the filtrate from yellow tantalum precipitates indicate that the amount of niobium in the solution is small, but, provided that enough ammonia and tannin are added to give a good red precipitate, this will contain all the tantalum. Such precipitates are collected, washed, and ignited, and the resulting small oxide residue is fused with a little bisulfate, the melt dissolved in a small volume of 4% ammonium oxalate solution, and the tannin precipitation repeated as before but on a smaller scale. Any yellow precipitate is collected, washed, and ignited, and the oxide added to the tantalum fraction. If the precipitate is still orange the oxide obtained from it is subjected to a repetition of the process. The operations are uniform throughout the process and result in three products, viz. (1) yellow precipitates which are ignited as the final $Ta_2O_5$, (2) orange precipitates which are retreated, and (3) tantalum-free niobium filtrates. After a few fractionations a yellow precipitate is no longer obtained and the weight of the intermediate fraction (2) becomes negligible.

**Determination of Tantalum.**—The oxide obtained from all the yellow fractions is digested in the crucible with 1:1 hydrochloric acid and an excess of ammonia added; the precipitate is collected, washed, ignited, and weighed as $Ta_2O_5$. It should be tested for impurities by fusion with bisulfate and dissolution of the melt in ammonium oxalate solution; any insoluble is collected, ignited, and weighed and the filtrate tested colorimetrically for titania with hydrogen peroxide. The sum of any insoluble material and titania is deducted from the original weight.

**Determination of Niobium.**—This may be taken by difference or the combined filtrates from the tantalum fractions may be treated with more tannin, and neutralized with ammonia to pH 5, the resulting vermilion niobium complex being collected, washed, and ignited in the same way as the tantalum. The residual oxide is weighed and purified like the tantalum oxide.

*(2) Procedure for Separation by Chromatography.*—The weighed mixed oxides, preferably freed from tungsten, are dissolved by warming with a few milliliters of hydrofluoric acid in a platinum dish on the water bath, and the solution is evaporated just to dryness. The residue is dissolved in 6 ml. of 10% hydrofluoric acid, 1 g. of ammonium fluoride is added, and the residue gently warmed while stirring with a polyethylene rod until a clear solution is obtained; this is mixed with 4 g. of Whatman coarse-grade cellulose powder to obtain a damp friable mass for transfer to the chromatographic column.

The apparatus consists of a polyethylene tube 2 cm. in diameter and about 15 cm. in length, the top being opened out to form a funnel and the bottom drawn down to a 5 to 6 mm. tube that is closed at its lower end with a rubber tube and pinchcock. At the junction of the narrow tube with the wider tube, indentations are provided as a support for the cellulose column. Coarse grade cellulose powder is slurried in a polyethylene beaker with a 15:85 volume mixture of 40% hydrofluoric acid and purified methyl ethyl ketone (see Notes at end of this section) and the slurry is poured into the wider tube a little at a time while agitating with a polyethylene plunger to eliminate all air bubbles; sufficient slurry is used to provide a cellulose column 6–8 cm. long after settling. The ketone is allowed to drain out of the tube until the liquid level reaches the top of the cellulose and the latter is gently tamped down with the plunger to ensure even packing. The cellulose powder containing the fluorides is then transferred to the top of the column and beaten up with the plunger so as to form a continuous column of cellulose, the dish is rinsed several times with a few milliliters of the acid-ketone mixture, and the washings are transferred to the column. The pinchcock is then opened and the eluate allowed to drip slowly into a 600-ml. polyethylene beaker until the liquid level in the column reaches the top of the cellulose. This procedure is repeated with 20 ml. additions of acid-ketone mixture to the top of the column until the total eluate amounts to 400 ml., when all the earth acids should have passed out of the column leaving the titania retained in the cellulose as $(NH_4)_2TiF_6$. The beaker is placed on the water bath and a stream of air blown over the surface of the liquid until all the ketone has evaporated and the volume of liquid in the beaker has been reduced to about 20 ml. The contents of the beaker are then rinsed into a platinum dish with warm water, 10 ml. of 1:1 sulfuric acid are added, and the liquid is evaporated under an infrared lamp until strong fumes of the latter acid are evolved. The sides of the dish are rinsed down with a little water and the contents then rinsed into a 400-ml. beaker with cold water, made just ammoniacal, and boiled. The precipitate of earth acids is mixed with filter-pulp, collected, washed with very dilute ammonia, ignited, and weighed as $(Ta,Nb)_2O_5$.

Alternatively, the acid residue from fuming may be mixed with 5 g. of ammonium oxalate in 100 ml. of water, the solution warmed and partly neutralized with ammonia until clear, and the earth acids separated by tannin fractionation. If the first tannin precipitate shows that the earth acids are either mostly tantalum or mostly niobium then the total earth acids can be precipitated with tannin and ammonium acetate, the precipitate washed, ignited to mixed oxides, and the minor constituent determined colorimetrically (see "Colorimetric Methods" below).

For the chromatographic separation of tantalum from niobium, the mixed oxides from the titania separation are brought into solution with 8 ml. of 10% hydrofluoric acid, the solution is mixed with 6 g. of cellulose powder, and the mixture is transferred to the top of a 20-cm. cellulose column contained in a 40-cm. long polyethylene tube and moistened with methyl ethyl ketone saturated with water. Elution of the tantalum requires the passage of 250 to 300 ml. of water-saturated ketone, the whole test being carried out exactly as for the titanium separation, the only difference being the longer tube and cellulose column used. The tantalum is recovered from the eluate in exactly the same way as the mixed earth acids, and the pentoxide weighed. Niobium pentoxide is taken by difference.

Notes. **Purification of Methyl Ethyl Ketone.**—Five gallons of the commercial grade of ketone are refluxed for 2 hours with 3 liters of water containing 60 g. of potassium permanganate and 100 g. of sodium bicarbonate. After cooling overnight, the ketone layer is siphoned off, dried over anhydrous calcium chloride, then over caustic soda pellets, and redistilled. The eluant for the separation from titania is prepared by mixing 850 ml. of purified ketone with 150 ml. of 40% hydrofluoric acid (A. R. grade); it is stored in a polyethylene bottle. The eluate for separating the tantalum is prepared by shaking 1 liter of purified ketone with 125 ml. of water, allowing the mixture to settle overnight, and withdrawing the water layer.

## DETERMINATION OF EARTH ACIDS IN LOW-GRADE ORES AND ALLOYS

*Procedure in Pyrochlore Ores.*—The finely crushed and dried ore (2 to 5 g.) is digested on the hot plate with 25 ml. of hydrochloric acid, and the solution evaporated to dryness to dehydrate silica. The residue is moistened with a few drops of 1:1 hydrochloric acid and boiled with 50 ml. of water and 2 g. of hydroxylamine hydrochloride to reduce ferric chloride to ferrous chloride. Some filter pulp is stirred in, 0.5 g. of tannin added, and the hot solution filtered on loose-textured paper. The precipitate and residue are washed with 2% ammonium chloride solution, and ignited in a platinum dish. Silica is then removed by the usual hydrofluoric-sulfuric acid evaporation, and the residue is fused with bisulfate until everything dissolves except, perhaps, a few clear crystals of zircon. The cold melt is extracted with boiling $N$ sulfuric acid containing 2% of tannin and the solution is allowed to cool overnight. The precipitate is collected, washed with 0.5 $N$ sulfuric acid, and ignited in silica. The residue is fused with bisulfate, the melt leached with ammonium oxalate, and the solution filtered. The filtrate is neutralized to methyl red with dilute ammonia, boiled with tannin and 5 g. of ammonium chloride, and the tannin complexes of the earth acids are collected, washed, and ignited to mixed oxides. Traces of titania can be determined colorimetrically, or removed by a second bisulfate fusion and acid tannin leach.

A more rapid procedure is to fuse the residue from the hydrofluoric acid removal of the silica with bisulfate, extract the melt with ammonium oxalate, neutralize the filtered solution with ammonia, and recover the earth acids and titania with tannin; the washed and ignited precipitate of $TiO_2 + (Ta,Nb)_2O_5$ is then dissolved in hydrofluoric acid for a chromatographic separation of the earth acids from titania (see section on "Procedure for Separation by Chromatography"). The mixed oxides recovered from the eluate are analyzed colorimetrically for tantalum and niobium as described in the following section on "Colorimetric Methods."

If the earth acids in the ore are mainly niobium pentoxide with a very small tantalum pentoxide contamination the niobium may be determined rapidly as follows: [21]

A one-gram sample is evaporated with 5 ml. of hydrofluoric acid to dryness on the water bath in a platinum dish, the residue is stirred (polyethylene rod) with 2 ml. of 10% hydrofluoric acid delivered from a polyethylene pipette, and, after 30 minutes, 0.01 ml. is transferred by means of a glass capillary pipette to one end of a Whatman No. 1 filter-paper strip. Standard niobium solutions (0.01 ml.) are added to a series of similar strips, all the strips are allowed to dry for 1 hour over saturated potassium carbonate solution, and then placed with the spots downward in a polythene beaker containing 20 ml. of a mixture of 4 ml. of 40% hydrofluoric acid, 8 ml. of water, and 88 ml. of purified methyl ethyl ketone. When the solvent has diffused upwards to the top of the strips, they are removed, allowed to dry in the air, and then exposed to ammonia vapor, and sprayed with 2% tannin

---

[21] Hunt and Wells, Analyst, **79**, 351, 1954.

solution from an atomizer (e.g., of the scent spray type). An orange band develops at the top of the strips (solvent front), the width and depth of color of which is a measure of the niobium content of the sample. If the niobium contents of the standards used vary in steps of 1 microgram when the niobium content of the sample can be estimated within 0.5 microgram.

To prepare a series of paper strips large sheets are cut into rectangles 9 in. x 4½ in., and slots 3¾ in. long and 1/16 in. wide are cut parallel to the short side, leaving ⅜ in. uncut at each end. The slots are cut at ¾ in. intervals to produce 11 strips ¾ in. wide and a strip at one end slightly narrower; only the 10 center strips are used, the two end strips being clipped together to make the whole into a cylinder for immersion in the solvent. In this way ten trials can be made at one time; these may all be standards or all ore samples, or they may be a mixture of both. The ketone is purified as described under "Separation from Titanium."

**Procedure for Chromatographic Estimation of Niobium in Steels.**—The sample (0.3 g.) is dissolved in a platinum dish in 10 ml. of 1:1 nitric acid and 2 ml. of hydrofluoric acid, and the solution evaporated to dryness. The residue is dissolved in 5 ml. of 40% hydrofluoric acid, and the solution again evaporated to expel nitric acid. The second residue is dissolved as before, 0.3 g. of pure iron wire added to reduce any molybdenum to a lower valence, and the solution again evaporated. This residue is moistened with 2 ml. of 10% hydrofluoric acid, and used for chromatography as described immediately above.

**Procedure for Gravimetric Estimation of Niobium in Steels and Magnet Alloys.**[22] —The alloy (1 to 2 g. of turnings or millings) is simmered with 20 ml. of hydrochloric acid and solution completed by dropwise addition of nitric acid, avoiding more than a small excess. The solution is evaporated just to dryness, the residue moistened with 2 ml. of 1:1 hydrochloric acid, and the mixture boiled with 100 ml. of water and 2 g. of hydroxylamine hydrochloride to reduce ferric to ferrous chloride. The reduced solution is then boiled with 5 g. of ammonium chloride and 1 g. of tannin in 20 ml. of water, a little filter-pulp is added, and the precipitate collected, washed with hot 5% ammonium chloride solution containing 2 ml. of hydrochloric acid per liter, and ignited. The residue is fused in silica with a little bisulfate, the melt leached with 50 ml. of 4% ammonium oxalate solution, and the filtered solution boiled with an equal volume of 25% ammonium chloride solution, neutralized with dilute ammonia (methyl red), and re-acidified with 2 drops of 1:1 hydrochloric acid. The earth acids and titania are then precipitated with tannin, and the washed and ignited precipitate is weighed as $TiO_2$ + $(Nb,Ta)_2O_5$. Titania may be estimated colorimetrically and the $Nb_2O_5$ found by difference; any tantalum present is very small and may generally be neglected.

Alternatively the titanium may be separated chromatographically or by the bisulfate-tannin method (see "Separation from Titanium").

## TITRIMETRIC METHODS

No titrimetric method of estimating tantalum has been devised; but various suggestions have been made for estimating niobium in the mixed earth acids, all depending on the reduction of this element to a lower valence state in the presence of a complexing agent to prevent hydrolysis of the pentavalent earths. Several metals have been suggested as reductants, but none give consistent results

[22] Author's method.

probably owing to partial hydrolysis of the niobic acid complex before it is reduced. Since tantalic acid complexes hydrolyze readily and their hydrolysis induces partial hydrolysis of the corresponding niobium complex, the degree of reduction of niobium is generally the smaller the higher is the tantalum:niobium ratio in the mixed acids. Again titanium is almost always present to a greater or lesser extent in earth acid minerals, and is readily reduced stoichiometrically to the tervalent state by all the reductants that reduce niobium, so that the results for the latter are erratic since no method is known of estimating either titanium or niobium in the presence of the other. For these reasons titrimetric methods are never used in commercial analysis.

## COLORIMETRIC/PHOTOMETRIC METHODS

*Niobium* gives three reactions that have been used as the basis of a colorimetric estimation: (1) In a 80:20 volume mixture of concentrated sulfuric acid and 88% phosphoric acid, niobic acid gives a yellow coloration with hydrogen peroxide;[23] the presence of phosphoric acid suppresses the color attributable to iron and titanium. Tungsten and molybdenum interfere but can be separated from the earth acids by the sodium chloride process (see Separation from Tungsten). Maximum absorption of the niobium peroxy-complex occurs at 365 m$\mu$.

(2) A tartaric acid solution of niobium pentoxide when reduced with stannous chloride in the presence of ammonium thiocyanate gives a yellow color, intensified by the presence of acetone or ether and extractible by ether;[24] the solution has a maximum absorption at 385 m$\mu$ but good results can be obtained by measuring the absorption at 405 m$\mu$ in the Hilger Spekker absorptiometer or equivalent instrument using suitable filters. Tungsten and titanium interfere, as also do a number of other metals which, however, are readily separated during the normal procedure for isolating the earth acids from low-grade ores.

(3) An oxalate solution of the bisulfate melt adjusted to pH 7 to 8 with sodium sulfite solution gives a yellow color with pyrogallol which is measured in a quartz-prism spectrophotometer at 410 m$\mu$.

*Tantalum* gives only one useful color reaction: An oxalate solution of the bisulfate melt, adjusted to pH 1 to 2 gives a yellow color with acid pyrogallol having a maximum absorption at 400 m$\mu$.

The most useful of these reactions are those with pyrogallol which can be applied to the estimation of small quantities of either earth acid in a mixture free from titanium and tungsten, such as that obtained by eluting the earth acids from a cellulose column.

*Procedure.*[25]—Twenty-five milligrams of mixed oxides free from titanium and tungsten, are fused with 0.5 g. of bisulfate in a silica crucible and the cold melt is dissolved by warming with 1 g. of ammonium oxalate and 10 ml. of water in the crucible. The resulting solution is rinsed into a 25-ml. calibrated flask, cooled, and diluted to the mark.

For the estimation of tantalum, 5 ml. of the solution are pipetted into another 25-ml. volumetric flask together with 4 ml. of potassium bisulfate solution (0.1 g. per ml.), 0.8 g. of finely ground ammonium oxalate, 10 ml. of water, and, after shaking to obtain complete solution, 2 ml. of a 20% solution of resublimed pyro-

23 Pickup, Colonial Geology and Mineral Sources, **3**, 358, 1953.
24 Marzys, Analyst, **79**, 327, 1954.
25 Hunt and Wells, Analyst, **79**, 395, 1954.

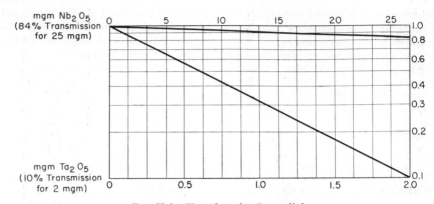

FIG. 32-1.  Tantalum by Pyrogallol.

gallol in 3% by volume of sulfuric acid.  The mixture is diluted to the mark and the transmission at 400 mμ is read against a reagent blank prepared by dissolving 0.5 g. of potassium bisulfate and 1 g. of ammonium oxalate in 20 ml. of water, adding 2 ml. of the pyrogallol solution and diluting to 25 ml.

**For the estimation of niobium,** 1 ml. of the solution is pipetted into a 50-ml. volumetric flask, followed by 5 ml. of potassium bisulfate solution (0.1 g. per ml.), 20 ml. of 4% ammonium oxalate solution, and 20 ml. of a filtered solution of 1 g. of pyrogallol in freshly prepared 20% sodium sulfite solution.  After diluting to the mark and mixing well, the transmission of the solution is measured at 410 mμ.

Standard curves are calibrated from solutions of the pure oxides prepared exactly as described above.  Since niobium gives a small reading under the conditions of the tantalum test, and tantalum a small reading under those of the niobium a correction must be applied in analyzing mixed oxides.  For example, to find the true reading for tantalum the apparent concentration is read from the tantalum graph (Fig. 32-1) and this weight of pentoxide is deducted from the weight of mixed oxides to give the apparent weight of niobium pentoxide; the transmission

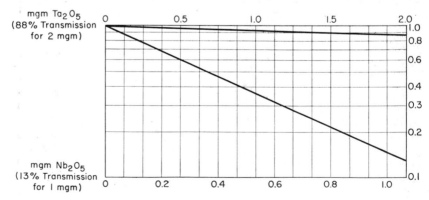

FIG. 32-2.  Niobium by Pyrogallol.

equivalent to this is read on the niobium graph (Fig. 32-2), and deducted from the apparent tantalum transmission; the weight of tantalum pentoxide equivalent to this transmission is then read on the tantalum graph. In each of these figures, the top graphs being used for making the corrections to the readings in the lower.

It is essential, in order to obtain accurate results, that all reagents should be accurately weighed, and solutions measured with a pipette, not a measuring cylinder. The solution for the tantalum estimation must have a pH of 1 to 2, and that for the niobium estimation a pH of 7 to 8.

## METHODS FOR NIOBIUM AND TANTALUM IN ANALYSES IN OTHER CHAPTERS

| | |
|---|---|
| Niobium and Tantalum by Ion Exchange | See Method in Chromium Chapter |
| Niobium in Tungsten Alloys | See Tungsten Chapter |
| Tantalum in Alloys by Ion Exchange | See Method in Chromium Chapter |
| Tantalum in Tungsten Alloys | See Tungsten Chapter |

# Chapter 33

# NITROGEN

N, *at. wt.* 14.0067; *d.* (*air*) 0.9674; *m.p.* −210°C.; *b.p.* −195.8°C.; *oxides*, $N_2O$, $N_2O_2$, $N_2O_3$, $N_2O_4$, $N_2O_5$.

Nitrogen was established as an element by Lavoisier who named the gas azote (lifeless), the name by which nitrogen is known in France.

Nitrogen occurs free in air to extent of 78%+ by volume and 76%− by weight. Weight of 1 liter of nitrogen at S. T. P. = 1.293 g.

Nitrogen is found combined in nature as potassium nitrate (saltpeter), $KNO_3$; sodium nitrate (Chile saltpeter), $NaNO_3$, and to a lesser extent as calcium nitrate, $Ca(NO_3)_2$. It occurs in plants and in animals, in the protein-bearing materials, blood, muscle, nerve substance, in fossil plants (coal), in guano, ammonia, and ammonium salts.

*Free nitrogen* is estimated in the complete analysis of gas mixtures. In illuminating gas the other components are removed by combustion and absorption and the residual gas is measured as nitrogen.

*Total nitrogen* in organic substances is best determined by decomposition of the materials with sulfuric acid as described in a subsequent section, and estimating the nitrogen from the ammonia formed.

*Combined nitrogen* in the form of ammonia and nitric acid specially concerns the analyst. In the evaluation of fertilizers, feedstuffs, hay, fodders, grain, etc., the nitrogen is estimated after conversion to ammonia. Ammonia, nitrates, and nitrites may be required in an analysis of sewages, water, and soils. Nitric acid is determined in Chili saltpeter, in the evaluation of this material for the manufacture of nitric acid or a fertilizer, the nitrate being reduced to ammonia and thus estimated.

NOTES.—The determination of nitrogen is required in tests of a large number of compounds containing nitrogen in combination, such as the azo compounds, antipyrine, amides, imides, brucine, hydrazine, cyanide, phenylhydrazine, isatin, atropine, caffeine, strychnine, nicotine, cinchonidine, cocaine, etc.

## DETECTION

*Element.* **Organic Nitrogen.**—Organic matter is decomposed by heating in a Kjeldahl flask with concentrated sulfuric acid as described under "Preparation and Solution of the Sample." Ammonia may now be liberated from the sulfate and so detected.

**Nitrogen in Gas.**—Recognized by its inertness towards the reagents used in gas analysis. The element may be recognized by means of the spectroscope.

*Ammonia.*—Free ammonia is readily recognized by its characteristic odor. A glass rod dipped in hydrochloric acid and held in fumes of ammonia produces a white cloud of ammonium chloride, $NH_4Cl$.

**Moist red litmus paper** is turned blue by ammonia. Upon heating the paper the red color is restored, upon volatilization of ammonia (distinction from fixed alkalies).

**Nessler's Test.**[1]—Nessler's reagent added to a solution containing ammonia, combined or free, produces a brown precipitate, $NHg_2I \cdot H_2O$. If the ammoniacal solution is sufficiently dilute a yellow or reddish-brown color is produced, according to the amount of ammonia present. The reaction is used in determining ammonia in water.

**Salts of ammonia** are decomposed by heating their solutions with a strong base such as the hydroxides of the alkalies or the alkaline earths. The odor of ammonia may now be detected.

*Nitric Acid.* **Ferrous Sulfate Test.**—About 1 to 2 ml. of the concentrated solution of the substance is added to 15 to 20 ml. of concentrated sulfuric acid in a test tube. After cooling the mixture, the test tube is inclined and an equal volume of a saturated solution of ferrous sulfate is allowed to flow slowly down over the surface of the acid. The tube is now held upright and gently tapped. In the presence of nitric acid a brown ring forms at the junction of the two solutions.

The test for nitrate may be made according to the quantitative procedure given for determining nitric acid (see later). It should be remembered that ferrous sulfate should be present in excess, otherwise the brown color is destroyed by the free nitric acid. Traces of nitric acid in sulfuric produce a pink color with the sulfuric acid solution of ferrous sulfate.

Ferro- and ferricyanides, chlorates, bromides and bromates, iodides and iodates, chromates and permanganates interfere.

**Diphenylamine Tests for Nitrates.**—$(C_6H_5)_2NH$ dissolved in sulfuric acid is added to 2 or 3 ml. of the substance in solution on a watch glass. Upon gently warming a blue color is produced in presence of nitrates. Nitric acid in sulfuric acid is detected by placing a crystal of diphenylamine in 3 or 4 ml. of the acid and gently warming. Cl(V), Br(V), I(V), Mn(VII), Cr(VI), Se(IV), Fe(III), and other oxidizing agents interfere.

**Copper** placed in a solution containing nitric acid liberates brown fumes.

*Detection of Nitrous Acid.* **Acetic Acid Test.**—Acetic acid added to a nitrite in a test tube (inclined as directed in the nitric acid test with ferrous sulfate), produces a brown ring. Nitrates do not give this. If potassium iodide is present in the solution, free iodine is liberated. The free iodine is absorbed by chloroform, carbon tetrachloride or disulfide, these reagents being colored pink. Starch solution is colored blue.

Nitrous acid reduces iodic acid to iodine. The iodine is then detected with starch, or by carbon disulfide, or carbon tetrachloride.

**Potassium Permanganate Test.**—A solution of the reagent acidified with sulfuric acid is decolorized by nitrous acid or nitrite. The test serves to detect nitrous acid in nitric acid. Other reducing substances *must be* absent.

**Sulfanilamide Test.**—The well-known method of Griess-Ilosvay,[2] in which α-naphthylamine hydrochloride and sulfanilic acid are used for the detection and determination of nitrite, depends upon the diazotization of the sulfanilic acid by the nitrite present, with subsequent coupling of α-naphthylamine and the forma-

---

[1] The reagent is made by dissolving 20 g. of potassium iodide in 50 ml. of water, adding 32 g. of mercuric iodide and diluting to 200 ml. To this is added a solution of potassium hydroxide—134 g. KOH per 260 ml. $H_2O$.

[2] Griess, Ber., **12**, 427, 1879; Ilosvay, Bull. Soc. Chim., **3**, 2, 317, 1889.

tion of a red dye. The color produced is proportional to the amount of nitrite present. It has been shown by Germuth [3] and others that the α-naphthylamine complex is not stable. Other substances such as dimethyl-α-naphthylamine, $C_{10}H_7N(CH_3)_2$, have been suggested as substitutes to overcome this disadvantage.

## ESTIMATION

The methods of estimating nitrogen are discussed first for organic substances and then for inorganic substances. The former includes, of course, foods, soils, and fertilizers. The latter includes ammonium salts, nitrates and nitrites and free ammonia.

In general nitrogen is more accurately and easily measured as ammonia, to which form it is converted by reduction methods. Large amounts are determined by titration, whereas small amounts are estimated colorimetrically. Nitric acid and nitrates may be determined by direct titration by the Ferrous Sulfate Method outlined later. The procedure is of value in estimation of nitrates in mixed acids. The nitrometer method for determining nitrates (including nitrites), and the free acid in mixed acids, is generally used by manufacturers of explosives. Compounds of ammonia and of nitric acid are generally soluble in water. All nitrogen compounds, however, are not included. Among those which are not readily soluble the following deserve mention: compounds of nitrogen in many organic substances; nitrogen bromophosphide, $NPBr_2$; nitrogen selenide, $NSe$; nitrogen sulfide, $N_4S_4$; nitrogen pentasulfide, $N_2S_5$; ammonium antimonate, $NH_4SbO_3 \cdot 2H_2O$; ammonium iodate, $NH_4IO_3$ (2.6 g. per 100 ml. $H_2O$); ammonium chloroplatinate, $(NH_4)_2PtCl_6$ (0.67 g.); ammonium chloroiridate, $(NH_4)_2IrCl_6$ (0.7 g.); ammonium oxalate, $(NH_4)_2C_2O_4 \cdot H_2O$ (4.2 g.); ammonium phosphomolybdate, $(NH_4)_3PO_4 \cdot 12MoO_3$ (0.03 g.); nitron nitrate, $C_{20}H_{16}N_4 \cdot HNO_3$.

## ORGANIC SUBSTANCES

The estimation of nitrogen is generally done by a modified Kjeldahl digestion method. This digestion should be done only in a hood with a good draught. This method depends upon the decomposition of organic nitrogen compounds by boiling with sulfuric acid. The carbon and hydrogen of the organic material are oxidized to carbon dioxide and water. A part of the sulfuric acid is simultaneously reduced to sulfur dioxide which in turn reduces the nitrogenous material to ammonia. The ammonia combines with the sulfuric acid and remains as ammonium sulfate, a substance with a high boiling point. The ammonia is subsequently liberated by the addition of sodium hydroxide; is distilled into a known amount of standard acid and the excess acid is estimated by titration with standard alkali. In the method detailed in the next section of this chapter, that is, the Kjeldahl-Gunning-Arnold Method, copper sulfate or mercury is added to act as a catalyst. Potassium sulfate or sodium sulfate is added in order to raise the temperature of the reaction mixture and thus hasten the digestion.

Gerritz and St. John [4] recommend the addition of 10 g. of anhydrous dipotassium phosphate or 12 g. of dipotassium phosphate trihydrate to be substituted for ⅝ths of the potassium or sodium sulfate to obtain more rapid digestion.

*Selenium Catalyst for Kjeldahl Digestions.*—Lauro [5] reported that 0.1–0.2 g. of

[3] Germuth, Ind. Eng. Chem., Anal. Ed., 1, 28, 1929.
[4] Gerritz and St. John, Ind. Eng. Chem., Anal. Ed., 7, 380, 1935.
[5] Lauro, Ind. Eng. Chem., Anal Ed., 3, 401, 1931.

selenium in the form of oxychloride or the element itself might be used as a catalyst instead of the usual copper or mercury catalyst, with the advantage of a very considerable shortening of the period necessary for the conversion of the nitrogen to ammonium salt and the destruction of the organic matter. The use of both selenium and mercuric oxide gives the same results for % N as the use of HgO alone and results in a 25% saving of time for various classes of materials.[6] A solution of selenium dioxide in 1:1 $H_2SO_4$ is a convenient form in which to add the catalyst. 0.1–0.2 g. of selenium and 0.7 g. of HgO is a good combination catalyst for macro determinations.

*Ter Meulen Semimicro Method.*—In brief outline the method is as follows: The organic substance (20–50 mg.) is mixed with 1–2 g. of catalytic nickel and heated in a stream of hydrogen, and the partially hydrogenated material is passed over a 25-cm. packing of asbestos and nickel catalyst held at about 250°C. in a 1.5-cm. quartz combustion tube. The carbon is converted to methane, the oxygen to water and the nitrogen to $NH_3$. The latter is absorbed in standard acid and determined by titration.[7]

## INORGANIC NITROGEN COMPOUNDS

**Soils. Available Nitrates.**—Five hundred to 1000 grams of the air-dried soil is extracted with 1 to 2 liters of water containing 10 to 20 grams of glucose. Fifteen to twenty hours of leaching is sufficient. An aliquot portion is taken for analysis.

*Ammonium Salts.*—The sample is placed in the distillation flask with splash bulb as described in the modified Kjeldahl procedure for organic substances, and the material decomposed with ammonia-free caustic solution. The ammonia is distilled into an excess of standard acid or a saturated solution of boric acid (neutral to methyl orange), and the ammonia determined as usual, either by titration of the excess of acid, or by direct titration with acid, according to the absorbent used.

*Nitrates.*—The sample, broken down as fine as possible, is dissolved in water, decomposed with Devarda alloy and distilled as described by the modified Devarda methods given later.

*Nitrites.*—The material, dissolved in water, is determined by the "Colorimetric Method" or the "Titrimetric Permanganate Method" given later in this chapter.

*Mixtures of Ammonium Salts, Nitrates, and Nitrites.*—Ammonia is determined by distillation with caustic as usual. The nitrite is titrated with permanganate. Total nitrogen is determined by the modified Devarda methods. Nitric acid is now estimated by difference, e.g., from the total nitrogen is deducted the nitrogen due to ammonia together with the nitrogen of the nitrite and the difference calculated to the nitrate desired. The nitrate may be determined in presence of nitrite and ammonia by direct titration with ferrous sulfate. The detailed procedures may be found under "The Titrimetric Determination of Nitrates."

[6] A critical comparison of the use of (1) Se catalyst; (2) HgO; (3) Se and HgO; (4) Se and $CuSO_4$ indicates that (3) is the most effective mixture for all varieties of material, according to Osborn and Krasnitz, J. Assoc. Official Agr. Chem., **16**, 110, 1933; **17**, 339, 1934. Other investigators report successful operation and saving of time either with Se alone or Se and $CuSO_4$ catalyst. See, for example: Illaraonov and Soloveva, Z. anal. Chem., **101**, 254, 1935; Kurtz, Ind. Eng. Chem., Anal. Ed., **5**, 260, 1933; Täufel, Thaler and Starke, Z. angew. Chem., **48**, 191, 1935; Hartley, Ind. Eng. Chem., Anal. Ed., **6**, 249, 1934.

[7] See Alsberg and Griffing, J. Am. Chem. Soc., **53**, 1037, 1931, for details about the speed and accuracy of the method.

*Nitric Acid in Mixed Acid.*—This is best determined by the ferrous sulfate method for nitric acid, cited above. The nitrometer method is also excellent.

NOTE.—P. H. Carter, Southern Fertilizer and Chemical Company,[8] recommends the following procedure:
Weigh the nitrate sample, put it into a Kjeldahl flask, then add 2 g. dry salicylic acid and the usual amount of potassium sulfate, mix well, by shaking the flask. Then add 5 ml. sulfuric acid (this gives a 40% salicylic acid concentration), this mixture is set aside a short time to insure proper solution and absorption, then add the remaning 25 ml. sulfuric acid and proceed with the regular method.

## SEPARATIONS

*Ammonia.*—No special separation need be considered in the determination of ammonia. The general method has already been mentioned by which ammonia is liberated from its salts by a strong base and volatilized by heat. This effects a separation from practically all substances.

*Nitric Acid.*—The compound may be isolated as the fairly insoluble, crystalline nitron nitrate, $C_{20}H_{16}N_4 \cdot HNO_3$ by the following procedure.[9]

Such an amount of the substance is taken as will contain about 0.1 g. nitric acid, and dissolved in about 100 ml. of water with addition of 10 drops of dilute sulfuric acid. The solution is heated nearly to boiling and about 12 ml. of nitron acetate solution added (10 g. of nitron in 100 ml. of 50% acetic acid).[10] The solution is cooled and placed in an ice pack for about two hours, and the compound then transferred to a Gooch or Munroe crucible (weighed crucible if gravimetric method is to be followed), and after draining, it is washed with about 10 to 12 ml. of ice-water added in small portions. The nitrate may now be determined gravimetrically by drying the precipitate to constant weight at 110°C., 16.52% of the material being due to $NO_3$.

The base 1,4-diphenyl-3,5-endanilodihydrotriazole (nitron) also precipitates the following acids: nitrous, chromic, chloric, perchloric, hydrobromic, hydriodic, hydroferro- and hydroferricyanic, oxalic, picric, and thiocyanic acids. Hence these must be absent from the solution if precipitation of nitric acid is desired for quantitative estimation.

**Removal of Nitrous Acid.**—Finely powdered hydrazine sulfate is dropped into the concentrated solution. (0.2 g. substance per 5 or 6 ml.)

**Chromic acid** is reduced by addition of hydrazine sulfate.

**Hydrobromic acid** is decomposed by chlorine water added drop by drop to the neutral solution, which is then boiled until the yellow color has disappeared.

**Hydriodic acid** is removed by adding an excess of potassium iodate to the neutral solution and boiling until the iodine is expelled.

## DETERMINATION OF NITROGEN IN ORGANIC MATERIALS

### KJELDAHL-GUNNING-ARNOLD METHOD [11]

*Procedure.*—Transfer a weighed portion of about 0.7–3.5 g. of the material according to its nitrogen content into a digestion flask, Fig. 33-1. This may be done

[8] Chemist-Analyst, 19 (2), 15, 1930.
[9] Busch, M., Ber., **38**, 861, 1905; Treadwell and Hall, Analytical Chemistry.
[10] Keep nitron reagent in a dark-colored bottle.
[11] Jacobs, Chemical Analysis of Food and Food Products, 3rd edition, Van Nostrand, 1958.

by weight, by difference or by weighing the material directly on filter paper or ungummed cigarette paper and transferring the paper and its contents to the flask. If the material is moist, a convenient method is to support a weighed piece of filter paper on the balance pan by means of a watch glass and rubber washer or gasket of a mason jar. Then weigh the material directly and rapidly on the filter paper and, after recording the weight, transfer the paper and contents to the flask. The rubber washer prevents the filter paper from touching the watch glass and thus prevents any loss of moisture by wetting the watch glass.

Weigh out and add 18 g. of anhydrous potassium sulfate or anhydrous sodium sulfate or an equivalent amount of the crystallized hydrated salts, 1 g. of crystallized copper sulfate, $CuSO_4 \cdot 5H_2O$, or approximately 0.7 g. of mercuric oxide, HgO, or its equivalent of metallic mercury and 25 ml. of sulfuric acid. Do not add mercuric oxide or mercury if it is possible to carry out the digestion easily without these materials, for then the subsequent addition of potassium or sodium sulfide solution may be avoided. Heat the mixture gently until frothing ceases, then boil briskly and continue the digestion for a time after the mixture is colorless or nearly so, or until the oxidation is complete. The digestion usually requires at least 2 hours and the flask should be rotated at intervals during the digestion. Cool, add about 200 ml. of water, and, if mercuric oxide or metallic mercury has been used, add also 50 ml. of potassium sulfide solution (40 g. $K_2S$ per liter), or

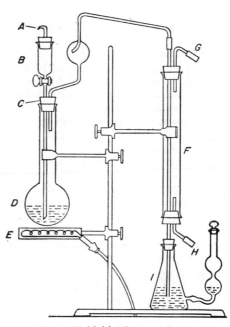

Fig. 33-1. Kjeldahl Nitrogen Apparatus.

sodium sulfide solution (40 g. $Na_2S$ per liter), or sodium thiosulfate solution (80 g. $Na_2S_2O_3 \cdot 5H_2O$ per liter). Then make strongly alkaline by pouring 70–75 ml. concentrated sodium hydroxide solution (454 g. NaOH plus 1 liter of water) down the side of the flask so that it does not mix at once with the acid solution. Add a pinch of zinc dust to prevent bumping and reduce frothing. Connect the flask to the condenser by means of a Kjeldahl connecting bulb, taking care that the tip of the condenser extends below the surface of the standard acid in the receiver and that the contents of the flask are mixed completely by shaking the flask at first carefully and cautiously and then vigorously. Distill until all of the ammonia has passed over into a measured quantity of standard acid. The first 150 ml. of the distillate will generally contain all the ammonia. Titrate with standard alkali using methyl red indicator (1 g. of the dye in a mixture of 50 ml. 95% alcohol plus 50 ml. of water).

The Winkler [12] modification of the Kjeldahl method is very useful. In this method the ammonia is distilled as usual but is fixed in 50 ml. of a saturated solu-

---

[12] Winkler, Z. angew. Chem., **26**, 231, 1913.

tion of pure recrystallized boric acid with the formation of ammonium borate. The ammonia may then be titrated directly with standard acid, because the boric acid is too weak an acid to affect the hydrogen-ion concentration to an appreciable extent during the titration. The advantages of this method are that it needs only one standard solution, namely, acid; it saves time and the boric acid need be measured only approximately. Care must be taken, however, that the receiver of the distillate be kept cool during the distillation, for ammonium borate is somewhat volatile.

## PREGL-PARNAS-WAGNER MICRO METHOD

In this method, which is a modification [13] of the Pregl-Parnas-Wagner method,[14] as in the macro method detailed above, protein and other forms of nitrogen are converted to ammonia and fixed as ammonium sulfate by digestion with sulfuric acid. The ammonia is liberated by the addition of sodium hydroxide solution, is distilled, trapped in standard hydrochloric acid, and the excess hydrochloric acid is estimated titrimetrically with standard sodium hydroxide solution. The apparatus used is shown in Fig. 33-2.

*Procedure.*—Dilute an aliquot portion of the material being analyzed, if necessary, or use a weighing variation as detailed in the macro method, so that the amount of protein nitrogen or other form of nitrogen will be 1 or 2 mg. per ml. Transfer 1 ml. to a micro Kjeldahl digestion flask. Add 1 ml. of concentrated sulfuric acid, 1 ml. of a 4% copper sulfate solution to act as the catalyst, and 0.8 g. of potassium sulfate, and digest in a digestion oven. Raise the heat slowly, boil vigorously, and after the material has been digested, as evidenced by a clear, straw yellow or light green color, reduce and cut off the heat. This process generally takes about 20 minutes. If the mixtures does not clear in this time, reduce the heat, carefully add 2 to 3 drops of 30% hydrogen peroxide, and then continue heating for 5–10 minutes. Allow to cool, add 4 ml. of water, and stir to dissolve the salts.

Add 7.0 ml. of 0.01 N hydrochloric acid, accurately measured (generally transferred by use of a reservoir type micro or semimicro burette) to a 25-ml. flask and add a trace of methyl red indicator solution. Allow the water in the steam generator to boil gently and open the pinch clamp or stopcock at the bottom of the steam trap so that the steam can escape. Transfer the digest from the micro Kjeldahl digestion flask to the distillation tube through the small funnel. Wash out the micro Kjeldahl digestion flask with two 2-ml. portions of water and add these washings to the distillation tube. Place the receiving flask under the condenser so that the tip of the silver tube condenser is below the standard acid. Add with the aid of a pipette 7 ml. of 30% sodium hydroxide solution to the mixture in the distillation tube through the small funnel.

Close the stopcock or pinch clamp of the small funnel and on the steam trap, thus compelling the steam to pass through the distillation tube. Distill for exactly 3 minutes. Lower the receiving flask so that the tip of the condenser is about 1 cm. above the surface of the distillate. Continue the distillation for another minute. Rinse the tip of the condenser tube with a few drops of water. Add another trace of methyl red indicator solution, if this is necessary. Titrate with standard 0.01 N sodium hydroxide solution. One ml. of standard hydrochloric acid is equivalent

[13] Jacobs, and Jacobs and Shepard, J. Am. Pharm. Assoc., Sci. Ed., **40**, 151, 154, 1951.
[14] Parnas and Wagner, Biochem. Z., **125**, 253, 1931.

to 0.14 mg. of nitrogen. Run a blank and subtract the blank from the volume of standard hydrochloric acid used.

Clean the distillation flask by removing the flame under the steam generator. This creates a vacuum in the steam trap and the material in the distillation tube is sucked into the trap. Open the steam trap to reject this mixture. Replace the

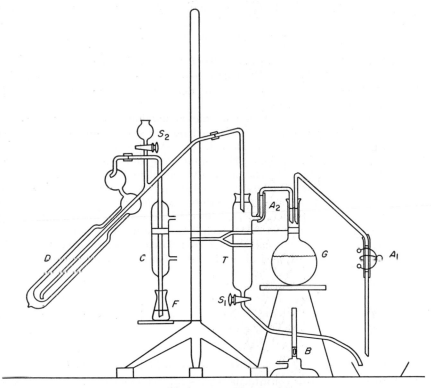

Fig. 33-2. Modified Parnas-Wagner Apparatus.

$A_1$ = Position *1* of pinch clamp; $A_2$ = Position *2* of pinch clamp; $B$ = Burner; $C$ = Condenser; $D$ = Distillation tube; $F$ = Receiving flask; $G$ = Steam generator; $S_1$ = Stopcock attached to steam trap; $S_2$ = Stopcock attaching funnel to distillation tube; $T$ = Steam trap.

flame. Add about 10 ml. of water to the distillation tube through the small funnel and repeat the cleaning process.

The modified Parnas-Wagner apparatus shown in Fig. 33-2 permits the water in the generator to boil continuously, for the flame need not be removed in order to induce a vacuum. This speeds up the operations considerably. Placing the pinch clamp in position $A_2$ causes a vacuum while at the same time the steam being generated can escape through the vent. Placing the pinch clamp in position $A_1$ forces the steam through the apparatus for distillation. The distillation tube can be cleaned more rapidly following this procedure.

**The Winkler modification** detailed above can also be adapted to this method.

## DETERMINATION OF NITROGEN COMPOUNDS

### AMMONIA

Methods for determining ammonia have already been given as part of the two preceding methods for nitrogen in organic materials. Of the other available methods, the titrimetric procedures for determination of ammonia are preferred to the gravimetric on account of their accuracy and general applicability. The following gravimetric method may occasionally be of use:

*GRAVIMETRIC DETERMINATION BY PRECIPITATION AS AMMONIUM PLATINOCHLORIDE, $(NH_4)_2PtCl_6$*

Ammonia in ammonium chloride may be determined gravimetrically by precipitation with chloroplatinic acid.

*Procedure.*—The aqueous solution of the ammonium salt is treated with an excess of chloroplatinic acid and evaporated on the steam bath to dryness. The residue is taken up with absolute alcohol, filtered through a weighed Gooch crucible, and washed with alcohol. The residue may now be dried at 130°C. and weighed as $(NH_4)_2PtCl_6$, or it may be gently ignited in the covered crucible until ammonium chloride has been largely expelled and then more strongly with free access of air. The residue of metallic platinum is weighed. If the ignition method is to be followed, the ammonium platinic chloride may be filtered into a small filter, the paper with the washed precipitate placed in a porcelain crucible, then gently heated until the paper is charred (crucible being covered) and then more strongly with free access of air until the carbon has been destroyed.

Factors. $(NH_4)_2PtCl_6 \times 0.2410 = NH_4Cl$
$$\times 0.08128 = NH_4$$
$$\times 0.07673 = NH_3$$
$$Pt \times 0.5484 = NH_4Cl$$
$$\times 0.1849 = NH_4$$
$$\times 0.1746 = NH_3$$

### *TITRIMETRIC ANALYSIS OF AQUA AMMONIA*

Provided no other basic constituent is present, free ammonia in solution is best determined by direct titration with an acid in presence of methyl red indicator.

*Procedure.*—About 10 g. of the solution in a weighing bottle with glass stopper is introduced into an 800-ml. Erlenmeyer flask containing about 200 ml. of water and sufficient 0.5 $N$ sulfuric acid to combine with the ammonia and about 10 ml. in excess. The flask is stoppered and warmed gently. This forces out the stopper in the weighing bottle, the ammonia combining with the acid. Upon thorough mixing, the solution is cooled, and the excess of acid is titrated with 0.5 $N$ sodium hydroxide solution.

One ml. 0.5 $N$ H₂SO₄ = 0.008515 g. NH₃

NOTE.—The aqua ammonia exposed to the air will lose ammonia, hence the sample should be kept stoppered. This loss of ammonia is appreciable in conc. ammoniacal solutions.

## TITRIMETRIC DETERMINATION OF COMBINED AMMONIA IN AMMONIUM SALTS

Strong bases decompose ammonium salts, liberating ammonia. This may be distilled into standard acid or into a saturated solution of boric acid (neutral to methyl orange) and titrated.

*Procedure.*—About 1 g. of the substance is placed in a distillation flask and an excess of sodium or potassium hydroxide added and the ammonia distilled into a saturated solution of boric acid or an excess of standard sulfuric acid. Ammonia in boric acid solution may be titrated directly with standard acid (methyl red indicator) or in case a mineral acid was used to absorb the ammonia, the excess of acid is titrated with standard caustic solution.

One ml. 0.5 $N$ sulfuric acid = 0.008515 g. $NH_3$

One ml. $N$ acid = 0.017031 g. $NH_3$

## NITRITES AND NITROGEN OXIDES

### COLORIMETRIC METHOD

The sulfanilamide-$N$-(1-naphthyl)-ethylenediamine dihydrochloride method for the determination of nitrite has been adapted [15] with but slight modification for estimating nitrite (especially in meat, water, etc.) for a range extending from less than 1 p. p. m. to over 1000 p. p. m. of nitrite with the same set of standards. Dyer [16] adapted it for the determination of nitrite in fish.

This method has the marked advantage over the Griess-Ilosvay procedure that maximum color development is obtained in 10 minutes and the color produced remains constant for about 2 hours.

*Reagents.* **Sulfanilamide Solution.**—Prepare a saturated solution of $p$-amino-benzenesulfonamide in water. This solution contains about 0.4 g. per 100 ml.

**Coupling Agent.** *N-(1-Naphthyl)-ethylenediamine Dihydrochloride.*—Dissolve 0.2 g. of this substance in water and dilute to 200 ml. Store in an amber-colored bottle in a refrigerator.

**Hydrochloric Acid.**—Dilute a volume of concentrated hydrochloric acid with an equal volume of water. This is approximately 6 $N$.

**Standards.** *Stock Solution A.*—Dissolve 1.00 g. of reagent sodium nitrite in water and dilute to 1 liter. This contains 1.0 mg. $NaNO_2$ per ml.

*Stock Solution B.*—Dilute 50 ml. of solution A to 500 ml. (0.1 mg. per ml.).

*Stock Solution C.*—Dilute 5 cc. of solution B to 500 ml. (0.001 mg. per ml.). Add 6–7 drops of chloroform to each solution to act as a preservative.

*Procedure.*—Weigh 5 g. of the sample into a 50-ml. flask. Dilute with hot water to about 300 ml. Allow to stand on a steam bath for 2 hours. Add 5 ml. of saturated mercuric chloride solution while the mixture is still hot. Swirl vigorously, allow to stand for 5 minutes, dilute almost to the mark, cool under running water, make to the mark, shake by inverting and filter through a dry filter.

To analyze liquid or dissolved samples, transfer 1 ml. to a 500-ml. flask, dilute with water and, after the addition of 5 ml. of saturated mercuric chloride solution, proceed as above. Water may be treated similarly, if badly polluted, or may be tested directly.

[15] Jacobs, work performed 1941–1942.
[16] Dyer, J. Fisheries Research Board Can., **6,** 414, 1945.

Transfer a 1-ml. and a 10-ml. aliquot of the sample filtrate to 100-ml. Nessler tubes. Dilute to 100 ml. with distilled water. Add 1 ml. of 6 $N$ hydrochloric acid, 2 ml. of saturated sulfanilamide solution and 1 ml. of the coupling reagent. Invert each tube 3 times to mix and allow to stand for at least 10 minutes. Compare with standards prepared at the same time.

**Standards.**—Transfer 0.5, 1.0, 1.5, 2.0, 2.5, and 3.0 ml. of Standard Solution C to Nessler tubes. Dilute to 100 ml. and treat as directed in the method. These solutions contain respectively 0.0005, 0.001, 0.0015, 0.002, 0.0025, 0.003 mg. of sodium nitrite.

**Calculation of Results.**—Each milliliter of test solution is equivalent to 10 mg. of sample. If 1 ml. of test solution develops a color that is stronger than 0.003 mg. standard, it is necessary to repeat the determination with a smaller aliquot, say, 0.5 ml. It is unnecessary to prepare new standards since they are stable for at least 2 hours. If the 10 ml. aliquot is too weak, use 25 ml., 50 ml., or 100 ml. of the sample solution for comparison.

### GRAVIMETRIC METHOD OF BUOVOLD [17]

One and one-fourth to 1.5 grams of $AgBrO_3$ are dissolved in 100 ml. of water and 110 ml. of 2 $N$ acetic acid, in an Erlenmeyer flask. Two hundred ml. of the nitrite solution (1 g. $NaNO_2$) are added from a burette, stirring the mixture during addition of the nitrite. A pale green precipitate is obtained. Thirty ml. of $H_2SO_4$ (1:4) are added, the mixture warmed to 85°C. When the yellow precipitate settles it is filtered on a Gooch crucible and washed with hot water, then dried and weighed as $AgBr + AgCl$. Chloride is determined on a separate portion and AgCl deducted. $AgBr \times 1.102 = NaNO_2$. The method is specially applicable to nitrites high in chlorine.

### TITRIMETRIC PERMANGANATE METHOD

Potassium permanganate reacts with nitrogen trioxide or a nitrite as follows:

$$5N_2O_3 + 4MnO_4^- + 12H^+ \rightarrow 5N_2O_5 + 4Mn^{++} + 6H_2O$$

$$5NO_2^- + 2MnO_4^- + 6H^+ \rightarrow 5NO_3^- + 2Mn^{++} + 3H_2O$$

1 ml. $N$ $KMnO_4$ = 0.0190 g. $N_2O_3$
= 0.0345 g. $NaNO_2$

Organic matter is also oxidized by $KMnO_4$; hence will interfere if present.

**Reagents.** **0.2 $N$ Potassium Permanganate.**—The solution contains 6.322 g. $KMnO_4$ per liter.

**0.2 $N$ Sodium Oxalate.**—The solution contains 13.400 g. $Na_2C_2O_4$ per liter.

**Procedure.** **Soluble Nitrites.**—Ten grams of the nitrite are dissolved in water and made to 1000 ml.; 10 ml. contain 0.1 g. of the sample.

**Water-insoluble Nitrites.**—0.5 to 1.0 g. of the nitrite according to the amount of nitrous acid present is taken for analysis. An excess of $KMnO_4$ solution is added, followed by dilute $H_2SO_4$ and the excess standard permanganate titrated with sodium oxalate according to directions given under "Titration of Nitrite" below.

**Nitrous Acid in Nitric Acid and Mixed Acids.**—This is present generally in very small amounts so that a large sample is taken. The amount and details of the procedures are given under the special subject.

[17] Buovold, Chem. Ztg., **38**, 28, 1914; C. A. **8**, 1250, 1914.

For routine work where a number of daily determinations are made, a 50-ml. burette is generally preferred.

**Trial Run.**—If the approximate strength of the salt is not known the following test may be quickly made to ascertain whether more than 50 ml. of solution is necessary and the approximate amount of $KMnO_4$ required for oxidation.

Ten ml. of the solution together with 100 ml. of water are placed in a 4-in. casserole and about 10 ml. of dilute $H_2SO_4$, 1:1, added. Standard $KMnO_4$ from a 50-ml. burette is now run into the sample until a permanent pink color is obtained. The milliliter of $KMnO_4$ multiplied by 5 = the approximate amount of permanganate solution required for oxidation of 50 ml. of sample. An excess of 5 to 10 ml. should be taken in the regular run.

**Titration of Nitrite.**—Sufficient standard 0.2 $N$ $KMnO_4$ to oxidize the sample to be titrated (as ascertained by the trial run) and 10 ml. excess are placed in a casserole. The solution is acidified with 10 ml. of dilute (1:4) $H_2SO_4$ and 50 ml. of the nitrite solution is added slowly with constant stirring. The sample is placed on a hot plate until the mixture reaches a temperature of 70° to 80°C. and 25 ml. more of the dilute $H_2SO_4$ added. The excess permanganate is now titrated with 0.2 $N$ $Na_2C_2O_4$, the oxalate being added slowly until the permanganate color is destroyed. Five ml. excess of the oxalate are added and the exact excess determined by titrating the hot solution with 0.2 $N$ $KMnO_4$ to a faint pink color. The total permanganate solution taken minus the oxalate titration = ml. $KMnO_4$ required by the nitrite.

Standard ferrous sulfate, $FeSO_4$, may be used, in place of sodium oxalate. The titration then may be conducted in the cold.

One ml. 0.2 $N$ $KMnO_4$ = 0.0038 g. $N_2O_3$, or 0.0069 g. $NaNO_2$, or 0.0085 g. $KNO_2$.

*Detection of a Nitrate in a Nitrite Salt.*—Iridium salts are colored blue by $HNO_3$ but no color is produced by $HNO_2$. Use a 0.025% solution of $IrO_2$ or $(NH_4)_2IrCl_6$ per 100 ml. of 98–99% $H_2SO_4$ and heat to boiling. The solution should be kept in a stoppered bottle. Into the hot reagent in a test tube is dropped the solid substance tested. A blue color is produced by nitrates. If the nitrite is in solution, make alkaline with KOH, evaporate to dryness and test the residue. Chlorine interferes, but not $FeCl_3$.

## NITRIC ACID AND NITRATES

### GRAVIMETRIC METHOD FOR DETERMINATION AS NITRON NITRATE

As in case of ammonia the titrimetric methods are generally preferable for determining nitric acid, combined or free. Isolation of nitric acid by precipitation as nitron nitrate may occasionally be used. The fairly insoluble, crystalline compound, $C_{20}H_{16}N_4 \cdot HNO_3$ is formed by addition of the base diphenylendianilohydrotriazole (nitron) to the solution containing the nitrate as directed under Separations. The precipitate washed with ice-water is dried to constant weight at 110°C. 16.52% of the compound is $NO_3$.

NOTE.—Solubility of less soluble nitron salts in 100 ml. of water. Nitron nitrate = 0.0099 g., nitron bromide = 0.61 g., iodide = 0.017 g., nitrite = 0.19 g., chromate = 0.06 g., chlorate 0.12 g., perchlorate = 0.008 g., thiocyanate = 0.04 g.

## DIPHENYLAMINE COLORIMETRIC METHOD [18]

*Procedure.*—A series of standards is prepared each containing 10 g. of potassium chloride and 0.1, 0.2, 0.3, 0.4, 0.5, 1.0, 2.0, 3.0, 4.0, 5.0 mg. of nitrate ion, respectively, per liter. To the aqueous solution of the nitrate to be analyzed is added potassium chloride to a concentration of 8–12 g. per liter. If one does not know the approximate concentration of the unknown, a preliminary experiment with standards containing 0.5, 1.0 and 3.0 mg. of nitrate per liter is run.

The mixtures are prepared in the following way: to 10 ml. of the nitrate-chloride solution is added 10 ml. of sulfuric acid from a pipette. Immediately after addition of the acid the flask is put into cold water and stirred sufficiently to mix its content. After cooling to room temperature 0.1 ml. of a 0.006 $M$ sodium diphenylaminesulfonate solution is added and the whole carefully mixed. The colors are compared in a colorimeter as soon as the more dilute of the two standards between which the unknown appears to belong has become sufficiently colored.

## DETERMINATION OF NITRATES BY REDUCTION TO AMMONIA. MODIFIED DEVARDA METHOD [19]

An accurate procedure for the determination of nitrogen in nitrates is Allen's modification of the Devarda method. The method is based upon the quantitative reduction of nitrates to ammonia in an alkaline solution by an alloy consisting of aluminum, copper, and zinc. The ammonia evolved is distilled into standard sulfuric acid and thus estimated. The method, originally designed for the valuation of sodium or potassium nitrates, is also of value in the determination of nitric acid, nitrites or ammonia. In the latter case the alloy is omitted.

*Reagents.* **Devarda's Alloy.**—Forty-five parts aluminum, 50 parts copper and 5 parts zinc. The aluminum is heated in a Hessian crucible in a furnace until the aluminum begins to melt, copper is now added in small portions until liquefied and zinc now plunged into the molten mass. The mix is heated for a few moments, covered and then stirred with an iron rod, allowed to cool slowly with the cover on and the crystallized mass pulverized.

**Standard Sulfuric Acid.**—This is made from the stock C.P. acid by dilution so that 1 ml. is equal to 0.0057 g. $H_2SO_4$, 100 ml. of acid of this strength being equivalent to approximately 1 g. of sodium nitrate. (A 0.1 $N$ acid will do, a smaller sample being taken for analysis.) Since it is necessary to standardize this acid against a standard nitrate, it is advisable to have an acid especially for this determination rather than a common reagent for general use.

*Standardization of the Acid.*—11.6 g. of standard potassium nitrate, equivalent to about 9.6 g. of $NaNO_3$, is dissolved and made to volume in the weighing bottle (100 ml.), and 10 ml. is placed in the Devarda flask, reduced, and the ammonia distilled into 100 ml. of the acid, exactly as the following method describes. The temperature of the acid is noted and its value in terms of $H_2SO_4$, $KNO_3$ and $NaNO_3$ stated on the container. The acid expands or contracts 0.029 ml. per 100 ml. for every degree centigrade above or below the temperature of standardization.

**Standard Potassium Nitrate.**—The purest nitrate that can be obtained is recrystallized in small crystals, by stirring, during the cooling of the supersaturated concentrated solution, and dried first at 100°C. for several hours and then at 210°C.

[18] Kolthoff, I. M., and Noponen, G. E., J. Am. Chem. Soc., **55**, 1448, 1933.
[19] Allen, W. S., Eighth International Congress of Applied Chemistry.

to constant weight. Chlorides, sulfates, carbonates, lime, magnesia and sodium are tested for and if present are determined and allowance made.

**Standard Sodium Hydroxide.**—This should be made of such strength that 1 ml. is equal to 1 ml. of the standard acid, 2 ml. methyl red being used as indicator. Ten ml. of the acid are diluted to 500 ml. and the alkali added until the color of the indicator changes from a red to a straw color.

**Methyl Red Solution.**—0.25 g. of methyl red is dissolved in 2000 ml. of 95% alcohol; 2 ml. of the indicator is used for each titration. As the indicator is sensitive to $CO_2$, all water used must first be boiled to expel carbon dioxide.

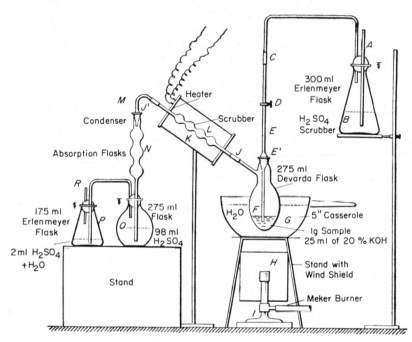

FIG. 33-3. Devarda's Apparatus.

**Sodium Hydroxide—28%.**—Pure sodium hydroxide is dissolved in distilled water and boiled in an uncovered casserole with about 1 g. of Devarda's alloy to remove ammonia. This is cooled and kept in a well-stoppered bottle.

**Apparatus.**—This is shown in the accompanying illustration, Fig. 33-3. It consists of the Devarda flask connected to the scrubber $K$, filled with glass wool. This scrubber is heated by an electric coil or by steam passed into the surrounding jacket. The scrubber prevents caustic spray from being carried over into the receiving flask $O$. The form of the apparatus can best be ascertained from the sketch.

Weighing bottle with graduation at 100 ml. and a 10-ml. dropper with rubber bulb is used for weighing out the sample in solution. See Fig. 33-4.

**Procedure.**—It is advisable to take a large sample if possible, e.g., 100 g. of $NaNO_3$, 119 g. of $KNO_3$ or about 80 g. of concentrated $HNO_3$ (95%) or more if the acid is dilute. Solids are taken from a large sample, all lumps being broken down. After dissolving in water the sample is made up to 1 liter. (Scum is broken up by addition of a little alcohol.) One hundred ml. of this solution is placed in the weighing bottle, which has been previously weighed, being perfectly clean and dry. The difference is the weight of the 100-ml. sample. All parts of the apparatus are washed out with $CO_2$-free water. All water used in this determination should be boiled to expel $CO_2$. Ninety-eight ml. of the standard acid is placed in flask $O$ and washed down with 2 to 3 ml. of water. Two ml. of the standard acid are placed in flask $P$ and washed down with 10 ml. of water and 13 to 14 drops of methyl red indicator added. Connections are made between the flasks and the scrubber. (The correction is made for the acid, the temperature being noted at the time of withdrawal.) A casserole, filled with cold water, is placed under $F$ (see illustration). The stem $E$ is removed from the Devarda flask and 10 ml. (or more) of the nitrate added by means of the dropper in the weighing bottle, a funnel having been inserted in the flask. The bottle reweighed gives the weight of the sample removed, by difference. The nitrate is washed down with 10 ml. of water and 25 ml. of 20% caustic added (free from $NH_3$), the alkali washed down with 10 ml. more of water and then 3 g. of Devarda alloy placed in the flask by means of dry funnel. The stem $E$ is quickly replaced, the stopcock being turned to close the tube. The reaction begins very soon. If it becomes violent, the reaction may be abated by stirring the water in the casserole, thus cooling the sample. After the energetic action has abated (five minutes), the casserole with the cold water is removed and the action allowed to continue for twenty minutes, meantime heat or steam is turned on in the scrubber. $E$ is connected at $C$ to the flask $B$ containing caustic to act as a scrubber. It is advisable to have a second flask containing sulfuric acid attached to the caustic to prevent ammonia from the laboratory entering the system. A casserole with hot water is placed under $F$ and the burner lighted and turned on full. A gentle suction is now applied at $R$, the stopcock $D$ being turned to admit pure air into the evolution flask; the rate should be about 5 to 6 bubbles per second. The suction is continued for thirty minutes, hot water being replaced in the casserole as the water evaporates. The heat is now turned off and the apparatus disconnected at $M$ and $J$. The contents of this elbow and the condenser are washed into the flask $O$. The acid in $O$ and $P$ poured into an 800-ml. beaker and rinsed out several times. The volume in the beaker is made up to 500 ml., 1 ml. of methyl red added, and the free acid titrated with the standard caustic. The end point is a straw yellow.

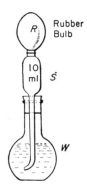

FIG. 33-4.
Weighing Bottle
and Dropper.

**Calculation.**—The volume in milliliters of the back titration with caustic being deducted, the volume of the acid remaining (e.g., combined with ammonia) is corrected to the standard condition. Expansion or contraction per 100 ml. is 0.029 ml. per each degree C. above or below the temperature at which the acid was standardized. If the acid is exactly 0.057 g. $H_2SO_4$ per ml., the result multiplied by 0.989 and divided by the weight of the sample taken gives per cent nitrate. (In terms of $NaNO_3$.) Ten times the difference of the weighings of the bottle $W$ before and after removal of the 10 ml. and the product divided by the weight of the 100 ml. of the solution equals the weight of solid taken.

**Example.**—Weight of the bottle + 100 ml. sample = 218 grams. Weight of the bottle = 112 grams, therefore weight of 100 ml. sample = 106 grams.

Weight of the bottle + 100 ml. sample = 218. Weight after removal of 10 ml. = 207.4 grams, therefore sample taken = 10.6 grams, including the added water. Now from above the weight of the actual sample taken = $10.6 \times 10 \div 106 = 1$ gram.

*Temperature Correction.*—Temperature of standardization = 20°C. Temperature of the sulfuric acid when taken for the analysis = 31°C. Back titration of the caustic = 2 ml. The correct volume = $(100 - 2) - ((31 - 20) \times 0.029) = 97.681$ ml. $H_2SO_4$ combined with ammonia from the reduced nitrate. $97.681 \times 0.989 \div 1 = 96.62\%$ $NaNO_3$.

Factors. $H_2SO_4 \times 2.0618 = KNO_3$ or $H_2SO_4 \times 1.7333 = NaNO_3$ or
$H_2SO_4 \times 1.2850 = HNO_3$.
$H_2SO_4 \times 0.9587 = HNO_2$ or $H_2SO_4 \times 0.3473 = NH_3$.
$NH_3 \times 3.7000 = HNO_3$ or $NH_3 \times 4.9907 = NaNO_3$ or $NH_3 \times 4.0513 = NaNO_2$.
$NaNO_3 \times 1.1896 = KNO_3$ and $KNO_3 \times 0.8407 = NaNO_3$.

## DETERMINATION OF NITRATES BY REDUCTION TO AMMONIA. VAMARI-MITSCHERLICH-DEVARDA METHOD

This method has found particular usefulness in determining nitric nitrogen in soil samples. The required apparatus is a greatly simplified version of that required for the previous method.

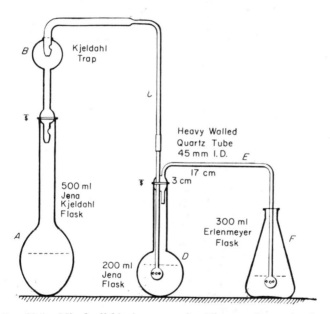

FIG. 33-5. Mitscherlich's Apparatus for Nitrogen Determination.

**Procedure.**—Forty ml. of water, a small pinch of magnesia and one of magnesium sulfate are added to flask $D$ of the Mitscherlich apparatus (Fig. 33-5). Twenty-five ml. of standard acid and 60 ml. of neutral redistilled water are placed in flask $F$; 250 or 300 ml. of aqueous soil extract are placed in a 500-ml. Kjeldahl flask, 2 ml. of 50% sodium hydroxide added, the mouth of the flask closed with a small funnel to prevent spattering, and the contents of the flask boiled for thirty minutes. The water which has boiled off is replaced, and, after cooling, 1 g. of Devarda's alloy (60-mesh), and a small piece of paraffin are added and the flask connected with the apparatus; reduction and distillation are carried on for forty minutes. The receiver contents are then cooled, 4 drops of 0.02% solution of methyl red added, the excess acid is nearly neutralized, the liquid boiled to expel $CO_2$, cooled to 10 to 15°C. and the titration completed.

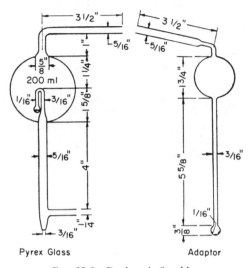

Pyrex Glass                    Adaptor

FIG. 33-6. Davisson's Scrubber.

Davisson,[20] recommends an improved form of scrubber, shown in Fig. 33-6 to be used in place of the Kjeldahl trap (Fig. 33-5). The bulb and adaptor are made of Pyrex glass. Steam condenses in the bulb and the condensate acts as a scrubber preventing alkali mist from being carried over with the ammonia. During the test ammonia is completely volatilized into the absorption flask. The bulb of the adaptor prevents back suction into the distillation flask.

### NITRATES IN FOODS AND OTHER ORGANIC MATERIALS BY XYLENOL METHOD

In this method,[21] nitrates and the nitric acid formed from them are used for the simultaneous nitration of *m*-xylenol. The 4-hydroxy-1,3-dimethyl-5-nitrobenzene formed is separated from the reaction mixture by distillation after making it alkaline and the amount formed is estimated colorimetrically, by an evaluation of the deep yellow color produced, which obeys the Beer-Lambert law.

*Procedure.*—Transfer a 5-ml. aliquot of the extract of the sample obtained by heating it with, successively, one 100-ml. portion and four 50-ml. portions of water to a 250-ml. standard-taper flask. Dilute with an equal volume of water. Add 0.1 ml. of 1% *m*-xylenol dissolved in either triethylene or propylene glycol, which is adequate for 100 micrograms of potassium nitrate, stopper, and cool under running water. Add 17 ml. of concentrated sulfuric acid dropwise with constant

[20] Davisson, B. S., J. Ind. Eng. Chem., **11,** 465, 1919.
[21] Yagoda and Goldman, J. Ind. Hyg. Toxicol., **25,** 440, 1943.

cooling so that the temperature does not exceed 35°C. Allow to stand for 10 minutes. Dilute the mixture by the addition of 150 ml. of cold water, add a few chips of porcelain, and connect the flask to the distillation apparatus (Fig. 33-7).

Bring the solution to the boiling point and reduce the size of the flame to about 2 cm. so that the distillate comes over at a rate of about 1 ml. per minute. Collect the distillate in a water-cooled 25-ml. graduated cylinder containing 1 ml. of 2% sodium hydroxide solution. The bulk of the nitroxylenol should come over in the first few drops of distillate. Quantitative separation is achieved by stopping the distillation when the condensate reaches the 10-ml. mark on the cylinder. Mix the contents of the receiver and set aside for comparison.

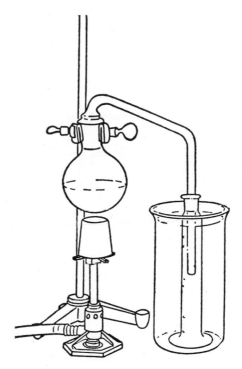

Prepare a blank by distilling a system consisting of 5 ml. of the glycol used, 5 ml. of water, 0.1 ml. of 1% m-xylenol in the glycol, and 17 ml. of concentrated sulfuric acid, following the identical procedure used for the unknown. Prepare a standard by substituting 5 ml. of 0.002% potassium nitrate, containing 100 micrograms of $KNO_3$, for the 5 ml. of water used in the blank, add the other reagents, and proceed with the method. When the sample and the standard are of similar intensities, the concentration of the unknown can be evaluated by a comparison of the solutions with the aid of a suitable (e.g., Duboscq-type) colorimeter. When the concentration falls

FIG. 33-7. Distillation Apparatus for Xylenol Method.

below 50 micrograms of potassium nitrate, compare the unknown with a series of dilute standards prepared by distilling 10, 20, 30, and 40 micrograms of potassium nitrate.

## IODOMETRIC DETERMINATION OF NITRATES— METHOD OF GOOCH AND GRUENER [22]

By this method the nitrate to be estimated is treated, in an atmosphere of carbon dioxide, with a saturated solution of crystallized manganous chloride in concentrated hydrochloric acid, the volatile products of the reaction (nitrogen dioxide, chlorine, etc.) are now distilled and caught in a solution of potassium iodide. The iodine set free is titrated by a standard solution of thiosulfate.

*Procedure.*—The nitrate and the manganous mixture (saturated solution of crystallized manganous chloride and concentrated hydrochloric acid—20 ml. per 0.2-g. sample) following it are introduced into the pipette shown in Fig. 33-8

22 Gooch, F. A., Gooch, F. A. and Gruener, H. W., Methods in Chemical Analysis, Am. J. Sci. (3), **44**, 117, 1892.

(marked *C*) suction being applied, if necessary, at the end of the absorption train (*D*). The current of $CO_2$ is started immediately after putting in the mixture. When the air has been replaced by $CO_2$, heat is applied to the retort (*C*) and the distillation continued until nearly all the liquid has passed over into the receiver

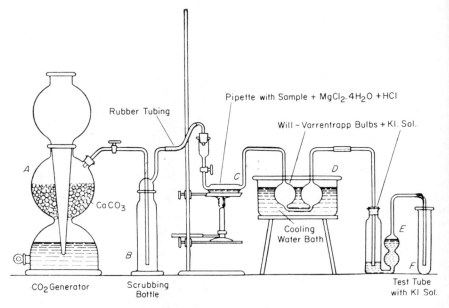

Fig. 33-8. Gooch-Gruener Apparatus.

(*D*), which is cooled by water. (See Fig. 33-8.) The contents of the receivers are united and the bulbs washed out by passing the wash water directly through *C* and *D*. Introduction of manganous chloride into the distillate does not influence the accuracy of the titration. The liberated iodine is titrated with standard sodium thiosulfate as soon as possible after admitting air to the distillate, since traces of dissolved nitric oxide reoxidized by the air would react with the iodide liberating more iodine.

### THE TITRIMÉTRIC DETERMINATION OF NITRATES WITH FERROUS SULFATE AS REDUCING AGENT [23]

*Procedure.*—A 0.1–0.2-g. sample of nitrate is introduced into the 250-ml. Erlenmeyer flask; 25 or 50 ml. 0.18 *N* ferrous iron solution are added (an excess of approximately 50% of ferrous iron is recommended) and 70 ml. 12 *N* hydrochloric acid. Then 3 to 5 g. of solid sodium bicarbonate is added carefully in small portions to displace the air from the flask and immediately thereafter the flask is closed with the stopper, from which a rubber tube leads to a suspension to 50 g. of sodium bicarbonate in 100 ml. of water. The dropper fitted into the other hole of the stopper contains 3 ml. of 1% ammonium molybdate solution. The solution is heated and the catalyst added after two or three minutes' boiling.

[23] Kolthoff, I. M., Sandell, E. B., and Moskovitz, B., J. Am. Chem. Soc., **55,** 1454, 1933.

The boiling is continued for ten minutes, the sodium bicarbonate suspension then replaced with a fresh saturated solution, the flask removed from the flame and immersed in cold water. After cooling to room temperature the flask is *unstoppered* and 35 ml. of 6 $N$ ammonium acetate for every 50 ml. of solution to be titrated and 3 to 5 ml. 85% phosphoric acid are added. The acetate reduces the concentration of the strong acid to between 1 and 2 $N$. The solution, which should have a volume of 100 to 150 ml., is slowly titrated with 0.1 $N$ dichromate using 6 to 8 drops of diphenylamine sulfonate (or diphenylamine or diphenylbenzidine) as indicator. The ferrous iron solution is standardized under the same conditions as described above.

One ml. of 0.1000 $N$ iron is equivalent to 3.370 mg. of potassium nitrate or 2.067 mg. of $NO_3$.

## DETERMINATION OF NITROGEN OF NITRATES (AND NITRITES) BY MEANS OF THE NITROMETER

The nitrometer is an exceedingly useful instrument employed in the accurate measurement of gases liberated in a great many reactions and has therefore a number of practical applications. It may be used in the determination of carbon dioxide in carbonates; the available oxygen in hydrogen peroxide; in the evaluation of nitrous ether and nitrites; in the evaluation of nitrates and nitric acid in mixed acids.

The method for the determination of nitrogen in nitrates depends on the reaction between sulfuric acid and nitrates in presence of mercury:

$$2KNO_3 + 4H_2SO_4 + 3Hg \rightarrow K_2SO_4 + 3HgSO_4 + 4H_2O + 2NO$$

The simplest type of apparatus is shown in the illustration, Fig. 33-9. The graduated decomposition tube has a capacity of 100 ml. It is connected at the base by means of a heavy-walled rubber tubing with an ungraduated leveling tube, $B$. At the upper portion of $A$ and separated from it by a glass stopcock, $S_1$, is a bulb, $C$, of about 5-ml. capacity; a second stopcock, $S_2$, enables completely enclosing the sample, as may be necessary in volatile compounds. The glass stopcock, $S_1$, directly above the graduated chamber, is perforated so as to establish connection with the tube $D$ when desired and the graduated cylinder $A$.

**Procedure.**—Tube $B$ is filled with mercury and the air in $A$ now displaced by mercury, by turning the stopcock to form an open passage between $A$ and $D$ and then raising $B$. A sample of not over 0.35 g. potassium nitrate or a corresponding amount of other nitrates, is introduced into $C$, the material being washed in with the least amount of water necessary (1 to 2 ml.). By lowering $B$ and opening the stopcock $S_1$ the solution is drawn into the decomposition chamber, taking care that no air enters. This is followed by about 15 ml. of pure, concentrated sulfuric acid through $S_2$ and $S_1$, avoiding admitting air as before. NO gas is liberated by the heat of reaction between the sulfuric acid and the water solution. When the reaction subsides, tube $A$ is shaken to mix the mercury with the liquor and the NO completely liberated. The gas is allowed to cool to room temperature and then measured, after raising or lowering $B$ so that the column of mercury is the calculated excess of height above that in $A$ in order to have the gas under atmospheric pressure. The excess of height is obtained by dividing the length of the acid layer in $A$, in millimeters, by 7 and elevating the level of the mercury in $B$ above that in $A$ by this quotient; i.e., if the acid layer = 21 mm. the mercury in $B$

would be 3 mm. above that in $A$. The volume of gas is reduced to standard conditions by using the formula

$$V' = \frac{V(P - w)}{760(1 + 0.00367t)}$$

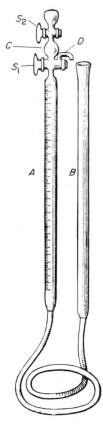

Fig. 33-9.
Nitrometer.

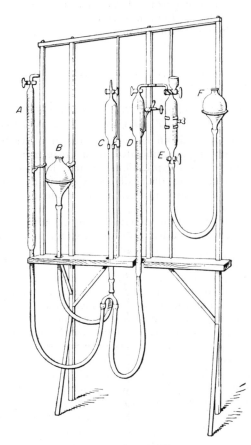

Fig. 33-10. DuPont's Nitrometer.

$V'$ = volume under standard conditions; $V$ = observed volume; $P$ = observed barometric pressure in mm. of mercury; $w$ = tension of aqueous vapor at the observed temperature, expressed in mm. of mercury; $t$ = observed temperature.

One ml. gas = 4.62 mg. of $KNO_3$, or 3.8 mg. $NaNO_3$ or 2.816 mg. $HNO_3$

## DU PONT NITROMETER METHOD [24]

The Du Pont nitrometer, Fig. 33-10, is the most accurate apparatus for the volumetric determination of nitrates. By use of this, direct readings in percentages

[24] See paper by J. R. Pitman, J. Soc. Chem. Ind., **19**, 983, 1900.

may be obtained, without recourse to correction of the volume of gas to standard conditions and calculations such as are required with the ordinary nitrometers.

The apparatus consists of a generating bulb of 300-ml. capacity $E$ with its reservoir $F$ connected to it by a heavy-walled rubber tubing. $E$ carries two glass stopcocks as is shown in illustration. The upper is a two-way stopcock connecting either the cup or an exit tube with the chamber. $D$ is the chamber-reading burette, calibrated to read in percentages of nitrogen, and graduated from 10 to 14%, divided in 1/100%. Between 171.8 and 240.4 ml. of gas must be generated to obtain a reading. $A$ is also a measuring burette, that may be used in place of $D$ where a wider range of measurement is desired. It is used for the measurement of small as well as large amounts of gas. It is most commonly graduated to hold 300.1 milligrams of NO at 20°C. and 760 mm. pressure and this volume is divided into 100 units (subdivided into tenths) each unit being equivalent to 3.001 milligrams of NO. When compensated, the gas from ten times the molecular weight in milligrams of any nitrate of the formula $RNO_3$ (or five times molecular weight of $R(NO_3)_2$) should exactly fill the burette. This simplifies all calculations; for example the per cent of nitric acid in a mixed acid would be

$$\frac{R63.02}{100W} = \% \text{ HNO}_3$$

$R$ = burette reading, $W$ = g. acid taken.[25] $C$ is the compensating burette very similar in form to the chamber burette $D$. $B$ is the leveling bulb, by the raising or lowering of which the standard pressure in the system may be obtained. The apparatus is mounted on an iron stand. As in the more simple form of apparatus, previously described, mercury is used as the confining liquid. The parts are connected by heavy-walled rubber tubing, wired to the glass parts.

*Standardizing the Apparatus.*—The apparatus having been arranged and the various parts filled with mercury, the instrument is standardized as follows: 20 to 30 ml. of sulfuric acid are drawn into the generating bulb through the cup at the top, and at the same time about 210 ml. of air; the cocks are then closed, and the bulb well shaken; this thoroughly desiccates the air, which is then run over into the compensating burette until the mercury is about on a level with the 12.30% mark on the other burette, the two being held in the same relative position, after which the compensating burette is sealed off at the top. A further quantity of air is desiccated in the same manner and run into the reading burette so as to fill up to about the same mark; the cocks are then closed, and a small piece of glass tubing bent in the form of a U, half filled with sulfuric acid (not water), is attached to the outlet of the reading burette; when the mercury columns are balanced and the enclosed air cooled down, the cock is again carefully opened, and when the sulfuric balances in the U-tube, and the mercury columns in both burettes are at the same level, then the air in each one is under the same conditions of temperature and pressure. A reading is now made from the burette, and the barometric pressure and temperature carefully noted, using the formula

$$V_t = \frac{V_0 P_0 (273 + t)}{(P_t)(273)}$$

the volume this enclosed air would occupy at 29.92 ins. pressure and 20°C. is found. The cock is again closed and the reservoir manipulated so as to bring the

25 Betts, A. W., Chemist, E. I. du Pont de Nemours Powder Co., private communication.

mercury in both burettes to the same level, and in the reading burette to the calculated value as well. A strip of paper is now pasted on the compensating burette at the level of the mercury, and the standardization is then complete.

Another rapid method of standardizing is to fill the compensating chamber with desiccated air as stated in the first procedure and then to introduce into the generating chamber 1 gram of pure potassium nitrate dissolved in 2 to 4 ml. of water, the cup is rinsed out with 20 ml. of 66° Bé. sulfuric acid, making three or four washings of it, each lot being drawn down separately into the bulb. The generated gas formed after vigorous shaking of the mixture, as stated under procedure, is run into the measuring burette. The columns in both burettes are balanced so that the reading burette is at 13.85 (= % N in $KNO_3$). A strip of paper is pasted on the compensating burette at the level of the mercury, and standardization is accomplished. By this method the temperature and pressure readings, and the calculations are avoided.[26]

**Procedure for Making the Test. Salts.**—One gram of sodium or potassium nitrate, or such an amount of the materials as will generate between 172 to 240 ml. of gas, is dissolved in a little water and placed in the cup of the generating bulb.

**Liquid Acids.**—The acid is weighed in a Lunge pipette and the desired amount run into the funnel of the generating bulb, the amount of acid that is taken being governed by its nitrogen content.

The sample is drawn into the bulb; the funnel is then rinsed out with three or four successive washings of 95% sulfuric acid, the total quantity being 20 ml.

To generate the gas, the bulb is shaken well until apparently all the gas is formed, taking care that the lower stopcock has been left open, this cock is then closed and the shaking repeated for two minutes. The reservoir is then lowered until about 60 ml. of mercury and 20 ml. of acid are left in the generating bulb. There will remain then sufficient space for 220 ml. of gas.

NOTE.—If too much mercury is left in the bulb, the mixture will be so thick that it will be found difficult to complete the reaction, a long time will be required for the residue to settle and some of the gas is liable to be held in suspension by the mercury, so that inaccurate results follow.

The generated gas is now transferred to the reading burette, and after waiting a couple of minutes to allow for cooling, both burettes are balanced, so that in the compensating tube the mercury column is on a level with the paper mark as well as with the column in the reading burette; the reading is then taken.

If exactly one gram of the substance is taken the percentage of nitrogen may be read directly, but in case of other amounts being taken, as will invariably be the case in the analysis of acids, the readings are divided by the weight of the substance and multiplied by 4.5 to obtain the per cent of nitric acid monohydrate present.

The procedure may be used for determining nitrites as well as nitrates.

## DETERMINATION OF $HNO_3$ IN OLEUM BY DU PONT NITROMETER METHOD [27]

About 10 ml. oleum are weighed in a 30-ml. weighing bottle, 10 ml. 95% reagent sulfuric acid added and mixed by shaking. This mixture is transferred to

---

[26] Standardization with "C.P. $KNO_3$ is the better, as it is less tedious and is not subject to the correction errors that cannot be escaped when standardizing with air. The $KNO_3$ must be of undoubted purity."—A. W. Betts.

[27] By courtesy of E. I. du Pont de Nemours Powder Co.

the nitrometer reaction tube and the weighing bottle and nitrometer cup rinsed with three 5-ml. portions of the reagent sulfuric acid which is drawn into the reaction tube. This is vigorously shaken for three minutes and the gas then passed to the measuring tube and allowed to stand for about five minutes, after which the mercury levels are adjusted and the reading taken.

It is obvious that this determination includes any nitrous acid in the oleum.

## DETERMINATION OF HYDROXYLAMINE— METHOD OF RASCHIG [28]

Hydroxylamine in hot acid solutions reduces ferric salts to ferrous condition quantitatively according to the reaction:

$$2NH_2OH + 4Fe^{+3} \rightarrow 4Fe^{++} + 4H^+ + N_2O + H_2O$$

The amount of ferrous iron formed is a measure of the hydroxylamine originally present.

*Procedure.*—Approximately 0.1 g. of hydroxylamine salt is dissolved in a little water in an Erlenmeyer flask and 30 ml. of cold saturated solution of ferric-ammonium alum added, followed by 10 ml. of dilute sulfuric acid (1:4). The solution is heated to boiling and kept at this temperature for five minutes, then diluted to 300 ml. and titrated immediately with standard permanganate solution.

One ml. 0.1 $N$ KMnO$_4$ = 0.001652 g. NH$_2$OH

## DETERMINATION OF PYRIDINE IN AMMONIUM NITRATE [29]

*Procedure.*—Dissolve 250 g. of sample in 300 ml. of distilled water, using a 1000-ml. Kjeldahl or Florence flask. Add a few drops of methyl orange and neutralize with 10% sodium hydroxide solution. Then add 15 ml. excess of 10% sodium hydroxide solution. Set up apparatus, note Fig. 33-11, using 300 ml. hypobromite solution in the second flask and receiving the distillate in 25 ml. 0.1 $N$ sulfuric acid. Distill until 100 ml. of distillate have been collected. The heating should be very slow until all the ammonia driven off has been destroyed. This point will be indicated first by an acid reaction of the methyl orange in the first flask and second by the gradual reduction of the amount of nitrogen given off, in very small bubbles, in the hypobromite. At this point the hypobromite flask should not be warm enough to burn the hand (not above 70° to 75°C.). It is now safe to increase the heat so that boiling occurs in the hypobromite in 10 to 15 minutes and 100 ml. of distillate comes over in 20 to 25 minutes after active boiling starts.

Titrate the liquid in the receiver, using 0.1 $N$ sodium hydroxide solution with methyl orange as the indicator.

[28] Hydroxylamine may also be determined by reduction with an excess of titanous salt in acid solution with exclusion of air, and the excess titrated with permanganate.

$$2NH_2OH + Ti_2(SO_4)_3 \rightarrow (NH_4)_2SO_4 + 4TiOSO_4 + H_2SO_4$$

For discussion of the two methods see paper by Wm. C. Bray, Miriam E. Simpson, and Anna A. MacKenzie, J. Am. Chem. Soc., **41**, 9, 1362, 1919.
[29] Ladd, R. M., J. Ind. Eng. Chem., **11**, 552, 1919.

Record the end point; add ½ ml. of phenolphthalein (1:1000) solution and continue the titration until a red color which will persist for 30 seconds appears.

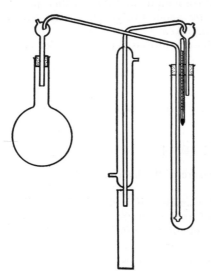

Subtract the methyl orange end point from that obtained with phenolphthalein, and multiply the difference by 0.0079. The result is the pyridine bases in grams. Methyl orange indicates pyridine plus ammonia. Phenolphthalein indicates ammonia. Difference is due to pyridine.

NOTES.—Because of the fact that the methyl orange and phenolphthalein end points are never quite the same and because an absorption of carbon dioxide by the sodium hydroxide solution may bring it about that they vary still more widely, it is necessary to standardize the solutions used to both end points and to make a correction for their normal difference. This correction should be checked by a new standardization at least once a week.

In case it is desired to use a sample of a different size, maintain the proportions indicated above, except that the total solution in the first flask should always be about 500 ml.

The hypobromite solution is made up as follows: 100 g. sodium hydroxide are dissolved in 800 ml. of water, 25 ml. of liquid bromine are added, and the mixture shaken until the bromine

FIG. 33-11.   Apparatus for Pyridine.

is entirely dissolved and made up to 1000 ml. The solution should be made up a day in advance. It will maintain its strength for at least a week if kept in a stoppered, dark bottle. It will be brown in color. Should the brown color disappear during the distillation it would mean that an excess of ammonia is present. This should also be indicated and eliminated from the calculations by the double end point called for, but in case this happens it is well to repeat the test, using more of the hypobromite solution.

The reactions involved are indicated in the following equations:

$$NaOH + NH_4NO_3 \rightarrow NH_3 + H_2O + NaNO_3$$

$$2NH_3 + 3NaBrO \rightarrow 3H_2O + N_2 + 3NaBr$$

$$2NaOH + Br_2 \rightarrow NaBrO + NaBr + H_2O$$

# HYDROCYANIC ACID, CYANIDES, AND COMPLEX CYANIDES

## TITRIMETRIC DETERMINATION OF HYDROCYANIC ACID [30]

The method depends upon the decolorization of the blue ammoniacal solutions of cupric salts by a soluble cyanide, the reduction to cuprous condition making possible for an accurate quantitative estimation of the cyanide.

*Reagent.* **Standard Copper Sulfate.**—Twenty-five grams of copper sulfate, $CuSO_4 \cdot 5H_2O$ are dissolved in a 1000-ml. flask with 500 ml. of distilled water and ammonium hydroxide added until the precipitate that first forms dissolves and a deep blue solution is obtained. Water is now added to make the volume exactly 1000 ml. The cupric solution is standardized by running a portion into a solution containing 0.5 g. pure potassium cyanide, KCN, per 100 ml. of water and 5 ml. of

[30] McDowell, J., Chem. News, **89**, 229, 1904.

ammonium hydroxide until a faint blue color is evident. Chlorides do not interfere.

*Procedure.*—0.5 gram of the soluble cyanide is dissolved in 100 ml. of water and 5 ml. concentrated ammonium hydroxide added. The standard cupric sulfate solution is now added until the blue color is obtained. The milliliters required multiplied by the factor of the copper salt in terms of the salt sought gives the weight of that salt in the sample.

### LIEBIG'S METHOD FOR HYDROCYANIC ACID. SOLUBLE CYANIDES [31]

Silver nitrate reacts with an alkali cyanide in neutral or alkaline solution as follows: $AgNO_3 + 2KCN = KAg(CN)_2 + KNO_3$. The potassium silver cyanide is soluble, hence the precipitate that first forms immediately dissolves on stirring as long as the cyanide is present in excess or in sufficient quantity to react according to the equation. A drop of the silver salt in excess will produce a permanent turbidity, owing to the following reaction:

$KAg(CN)_2 + AgNO_3 = 2AgCN + KNO_3$, the insoluble AgCN being formed.

*Procedure.*—The alkali cyanide contained in a beaker placed over a sheet of black glazed paper, is treated with 4 to 5 ml. of 10% KOH solution and diluted to 100 ml. The liquid is now titrated with standard silver nitrate, with constant stirring, until a faint permanent turbidity is obtained.

One ml. 0.1 $N$ AgNO$_3$ = 0.013024 g. KCN

### VOLHARD'S METHOD FOR CYANIDE

The method involves Volhard's method for determining halogens, the procedure depending upon the fact that the silver salts of cyanides are insoluble in dilute cold nitric acid solutions.

*Procedure.*—The neutral cyanide solution is treated with an excess of silver nitrate reagent, slightly acidified with nitric acid, and diluted to a definite volume in a measuring flask. A portion of the solution is now filtered through a dry filter, and a convenient aliquot portion of this is titrated with standard thiocyanate solution, using ferric alum as indicator (see page 769) to determine the silver nitrate present. From this calculate the excess silver nitrate reagent added and ascertain that combined with the cyanide.

One ml. 0.1 $N$ AgNO$_3$ = 0.006512 g. KCN or 0.002602 g. CN

### CYANIDE AND THIOCYANATE IN PRESENCE OF ONE ANOTHER

*Procedure.*—The cyanide is determined preferably by Liebig's method (above), and the milliliters of AgNO$_3$ required recorded. To the alkaline or neutral solution is added an excess of standard AgNO$_3$ and the solution acidified with HNO$_3$, then made to definite volume and a portion filtered. The silver nitrate in a convenient amount of the filtrate, an aliquot portion of the whole, is determined by titrating with standard thiocyanate solution, using ferric alum indicator. From this titration the excess of AgNO$_3$ added is determined, and the amount of reagent required for the thiocyanate is known.

One ml. 0.1 $N$ AgNO$_3$ = 0.006512 g. KCN or 0.002602 g. CN or 0.005808 g. CNS

In place of the above method the following may be used: One portion of the solution is treated with nitric acid and the thiocyanic acid oxidized to sulfate.

[31] Ann. Chem. und Pharm., **77**, 102, 1851.

By adding $Ba(NO_3)_2$ solution $BaSO_4$ is precipitated, and the equivalent thiocyanic acid may be calculated; also the equivalent 0.1 $N$ $AgNO_3$ that would be required to precipitate this. In another portion an excess of 0.1 $N$ $AgNO_3$ is added and the thiocyanate and cyanide precipitated. The excess of the silver nitrate may now be determined by Volhard's method described above and the amount required by CN and CNS thus ascertained. The amount of reagent required for CNS is subtracted from this total and that required by CN thus obtained. The factors are given above.

For determination of cyanide in presence of the halogens see the Chapter on Chlorine.

### SCHULEK'S METHOD FOR HYDROCYANIC ACID [32]

By this method, hydrocyanic acid may be determined in presence of chlorides, bromides, sulfides, sulfites, and thiosulfates. The cyanide may be separated from thiocyanate by addition of boric acid and distillation of the cyanide.

*Procedure.*—The solution containing 0.1 to 40 mg. hydrocyanic acid, placed in a bottle with a tightly fitting glass stopper, is acidified with 5 ml. of 20% phosphoric acid and bromine water added to a persistent deep yellow color. The excess of bromine is removed by addition of 2 ml. of 5% phenol solution and the mixture allowed to stand for fifteen minutes. 0.5 g. KI is added and the sample shaken repeatedly. The mixture is set aside, shielded from light for half an hour, and then titrated with 0.01 $N$ or 0.1 $N$ thiosulfate. When the solution is decolorized it is set aside for 5–10 minutes and again titrated to a definite end point, if the color returns.

### SOLUBLE FERROCYANIDE BY TITRATION

*Procedure.*—One gram of the (soluble) ferrocyanide in 100 ml. of water acidified with 10 ml. of sulfuric acid is titrated in a casserole with standard potassium permanganate to a permanent pink color. The end point is poor, so that it is advisable to standardize the permanganate against pure potassium ferrocyanide.

Reaction: $5Fe(CN)_6^{-4} + MnO_4^- + 8H^+ \rightarrow 5Fe(CN)_6^{-3} + Mn^{++} + 4H_2O.$

One ml. $N$ $KMnO_4$ = 0.3683 g. $K_4Fe(CN)_6$

### SOLUBLE FERRICYANIDE BY TITRATION

*Procedure.*—Ten grams of (soluble) ferricyanide are dissolved in water, the solution made alkaline with KOH and heated to boiling and an excess of ferrous sulfate solution added. The yellowish brown ferric hydroxide turns black with excess of ferrous salt. The solution is diluted to exactly 500 ml. and 50 ml. of a filtered portion titrated with potassium permanganate.

One ml. $N$ $KMnO_4$ = 0.3292 g. $K_3Fe(CN)_6$

## DETERMINATIONS IN SPECIFIC SUBSTANCES

### ANALYSIS OF NITRATE OF SODA

The following impurities may occur in nitrate of soda: $KNO_3$, $NaCl$, $Na_2SO_4$, $Na_2CO_3$, $NaClO_3$, $NaClO_4$, $Fe_2O_3$, $Al_2O_3$, $CaO$, $MgO$, $SiO_2$, $H_2O$, etc. In the

---

[32] Schulek, E., Z. anal. Chem., **62**, 337, 1923; Kolthoff and Furman, Volumetric Analysis, Vol. II, p. 404, J. Wiley and Sons.

analysis of sodium nitrate for determination of $NaNO_3$ by difference, moisture, $NaCl$, $Na_2SO_4$ and insoluble matter are determined and their sum deducted from 100, the difference being taken as $NaNO_3$. Such a procedure is far from accurate, the only reliable method being a direct determination of niter by the Devarda method given in detail. The following analysis may be required in the evaluation of the nitrate of soda.

## DETERMINATION OF MOISTURE

*Procedure.*—Twenty grams of sample are heated in a weighed platinum dish at 205–210°C. for fifteen minutes in an air bath or electric oven. The loss of weight multiplied by 5 = % moisture. (Save sample for further tests.)

## INSOLUBLE MATTER

*Procedure.*—Ten grams are treated with 50 ml. of water and filtered through a tared filter crucible. The weight of the dried residue (100°C.) multiplied by 10 = % insoluble matter. (Save filtrate.)

## SODIUM SULFATE

*Procedure.*—The moisture sample is dissolved in 20 ml. hot water and transferred to a porcelain crucible. It is evaporated several times with hydrochloric acid to dryness to expel nitric acid. (Until no odor of free chlorine is noticed when thus treated.) Fifty ml. of water and 5 ml. of hydrochloric acid are now added and the sample filtered. Any residue remaining is principally silica. The filtrate is heated to boiling, 10 ml. of 10% barium chloride solution added, and the precipitated sulfate filtered off, ignited, and weighed.

$$BaSO_4 \times 3.0429 = \% Na_2SO_4$$

## IRON, ALUMINA, LIME, AND MAGNESIA

*Procedure.*—These impurities may be determined on a 20-g. dried sample, the material being dried and evaporated as in case of the sodium sulfate determination. The filtrate from silica is treated with ammonium hydroxide and $Fe(OH)_3$ and $Al(OH)_3$ filtered off. Lime is precipitated from the iron and alumina filtrate as oxalate and magnesia determined by precipitation as phosphate from the lime filtrate by the standard procedures.

## SODIUM CHLORIDE

*Procedure.*—The filtrate from the insoluble residue is brought to boiling and magnesia, MgO (Cl free), is added until the solution is alkaline to litmus. 0.5 ml. of 1% potassium chromate ($K_2CrO_4$) solution is added as an indicator and then the solution is titrated with a standard solution of silver nitrate until a faint red tinge is seen, the procedure being similar to the determination of chlorides in water by silver nitrate titration. The ml. $AgNO_3 \times$ factor for this reagent $\times 10 = \%$ NaCl.

Silver nitrate is standardized against a salt solution.

## CARBONATES

This determination is seldom made. $CO_2$ may be tested for by addition of dilute sulfuric acid to the salt. Effervescence indicates carbonates. Any evolved gas may be tested by lime water, which becomes cloudy if $CO_2$ is present.

## ANALYSIS OF AMMONIACAL LIQUOR

The crude liquid by-product from coal gas in addition to ammonia contains hydrogen sulfide, carbon dioxide, hydrochloric acid, sulfuric acid, combined with ammonia, also sulfites, thiosulfates, thiocyanates, cyanides, ferrocyanides, phenols.

### DETERMINATION OF AMMONIA

*Volatile Ammonia.*—This is determined by distillation of the ammonia into an excess of standard sulfuric acid and titrating the excess of acid. With the exception that caustic soda is omitted in this determination, the details are the same as those for total ammonia as stated in the next paragraph.

*Total Ammonia.*—The true value of the liquor is ascertained by its total ammonia content. Ten to 25 ml. of the sample are diluted to about 250 ml. in a distilling flask with a potash connecting bulb, as previously described, 20 ml. of 5% sodium hydroxide are added and about 150 ml. of solution distilled into an excess of sulfuric acid. The excess is then titrated according to the standard procedure for ammonia.

$$\text{One ml. } N \text{ H}_2\text{SO}_4 = 0.01703 \text{ g. NH}_3$$

*Fixed ammonia* is the difference between the total and the volatile ammonia.

### CARBON DIOXIDE

*Procedure.*—Ten ml. of the liquor are diluted to 400 ml. and 10 ml. of 10% ammoniacal calcium chloride added and the mixture, placed in a flask with Bunsen valve, is digested on the water bath for two hours. The precipitated calcium carbonate is washed, placed in a flask and an excess of 0.5 $N$ HCl added and the excess acid titrated with 0.5 $N$ NaOH.

$$\text{One ml. } 0.5 \text{ } N \text{ HCl} = 0.01100 \text{ g. CO}_2$$

### HYDROCHLORIC ACID AND CHLORIDES

*Procedure.*—Ten ml. of the liquor are diluted to 150 ml. and boiled to remove ammonia. Now hydrogen peroxide is added to oxidize organic matter, etc., the mixture being boiled to remove the excess of the peroxide. Chloride is titrated in presence of potassium chromate as indicator by 0.1 $N$ silver nitrate after neutralizing with dilute nitric acid.

$$\text{One ml. } 0.1 \text{ } N \text{ AgNO}_3 = 0.003646 \text{ g. HCl}$$

### HYDROGEN SULFIDE

*Procedure.*—To 10 ml. of the liquor is added an excess of ammoniacal zinc chloride or acetate, the mixture diluted to about 80 ml. and warmed to 40°C. After settling for half an hour the zinc sulfide is filtered off and washed with warm water (40 to 50°C.); the precipitate is washed from the filter into an excess of 0.1 $N$ iodine solution, the sulfide clinging to the paper is washed into the main solution with hydrochloric acid. The mixture is acidified and the excess iodine titrated with 0.1 $N$ sodium thiosulfate.

$$\text{One ml. } 0.1 \text{ } N \text{ I} = 0.001704 \text{ g. H}_2\text{S or } 0.001603 \text{ g. S}$$

## SULFURIC ACID AND SULFATES

*Procedure.*—250 ml. of the liquor are concentrated to 100 ml., 2 ml. of concentrated hydrochloric added and the mixture heated to decompose any thiosulfate, sulfide, or sulfite present. The concentrate is extracted with water, filtered, and made to 250 ml. The sulfates are now precipitated in an aliquot portion with barium chloride.

$$BaSO_4 \times 0.4202 = H_2SO_4, \text{ or } BaSO_4 \times 0.1373 = S \text{ present as } H_2SO_4$$

## TOTAL SULFUR

*Procedure.*—Fifty ml. of the liquor are run by means of a pipette into a deep beaker (250-ml. capacity), containing an excess of bromine covered by dilute hydrochloric acid. The mixture is evaporated to dryness on the steam bath and the residue taken up with water and diluted to 250 ml. Sulfur is now precipitated as barium sulfate as usual, preferably on an aliquot portion.

## ANALYSIS OF CYANAMIDE [33]

### SAMPLING

The sample shall consist of at least two pounds of the material taken from every other bag composing the lot or shipment, by means of a tube which shall remove a core from the top to the bottom of the container. Pass all through a 48-mesh Tyler screen, grinding any oversize if necessary. Mix the portions thoroughly by rolling on a clean oil cloth or paper and quarter until the desired amount is obtained. Place the final sample in two containers and seal airtight. One is for analysis and one for referee.

### DETERMINATION OF NITROGEN

Determine the total nitrogen according to the Kjeldahl-Gunning-Arnold Method described in the text. Report the nitrogen found, as ammonia ($NH_3$).

### CALCIUM CARBIDE

Determine by weighing a convenient quantity of the material and transferring to an apparatus equipped to measure the volume of acetylene liberated by addition of water to the sample.

### OIL

Weigh a 2-g. portion into the thimble of a Soxhlet apparatus and extract the oil with carbon tetrachloride. Collect the extract in a weighed flask and evaporate off the carbon tetrachloride on a water bath. Complete the removal of the solvent by heating 15 minutes in a drying oven at 105°C. Weigh and calculate the percentage of oil.

## ANALYSIS OF CALCIUM CYANIDE [34]

### SAMPLING

Ten drums in each lot of 4000 lbs. shall be sampled. The portions removed shall have a combined weight of approximately 1 pound. The sample shall be

[33] Courtesy of American Cyanamid Co.
[34] By courtesy of American Cyanamid Co.

taken as soon as the drum is filled, by inserting a long sampling rod or tryer the full depth of the drum and depositing the sample in a suitable container.

A portion of the sample is removed at the laboratory for analysis and the container is sealed air tight and retained for 6 months as a reference sample.

## DETERMINATION OF TOTAL CYANIDE CONTENT

**Reagents.** **Standard Silver Nitrate Solution.**—Dissolve 17 g. of silver nitrate in 200 ml. of distilled water, filter, and dilute to one liter.

**Soda-Lead Mixture.**—Dissolve 200 g. of anhydrous sodium carbonate in 700 ml. of distilled water and filter. Dissolve 20 g. of lead acetate ($Pb(CH_3CO_2)_2 \cdot 3H_2O$) in 200 g. of distilled water, filter and add the filtrate to the solution of sodium carbonate. Dilute to one liter. Shake the solution well each time before using.

**Alkaline Iodide Indicator.**—Dissolve 30 g. of potassium iodide in 1 liter of 10% sodium hydroxide solution.

**Standardization of Reagents.** **Standard Silver Nitrate Solution.**—Standardize the solution against an accurately weighed sample of pure sodium chloride, previously dried for 1 hour at 105°C., using potassium chromate indicator.[35]

**Procedure.**—Place 200 ml. of distilled water in a 500-ml. volumetric flask and carefully dry the neck of the flask. Weigh rapidly and accurately a 5-g. sample of the flake cyanide or "Cyanogas" and transfer it to the flask. Wash down the sides of the flask and thoroughly mix the sample with a whirling motion. Agitate the solution at intervals for 15 minutes, then add 30 ml. of the soda-lead mixture, mixing the latter well before measuring it. Thereafter agitate the solution every 5 minutes for 0.5 hour. Then make the solution up to volume, mix thoroughly, and filter through a dry filter paper into a dry beaker. Reject the first 25 ml. of filtrate, rinsing the beaker with the rejected portion. Now continue filtration, collecting at least 150 ml. of filtrate. Measure out 100 ml. with a calibrated pipette, place in an 800-ml. beaker, dilute to 400 ml., and add 5 ml. of the alkaline iodide indicator. Titrate with the standard silver nitrate solution until a faint blue opalescence shows permanently against a black background. Calculate the per cent calcium cyanide in the sample.

$$1.0 \text{ ml. } 0.1 \ N \text{ AgNO}_3 = 0.00921 \text{ g. Ca(CN)}_2$$

## TOTAL SULFUR

Weigh accurately 2 grams of the flake cyanide and transfer to a 400-ml. beaker containing 50 ml. of distilled water. Add 25 ml. of a saturated solution of bromine in concentrated nitric acid. Stir the mixture for 5 minutes and then boil down to dryness. Moisten the residue thoroughly with concentrated hydrochloric acid and evaporate to dryness again. Add 10 ml. of concentrated hydrochloric acid and then 150 ml. of water, boil, filter, and wash thoroughly. Heat the filtrate to 90°C. and add with constant stirring 5 ml. of 10% solution of barium chloride. After digesting the solution at 90°C. for 1 hour on a water bath, filter the barium sulfate through an ashless filter paper, and wash the precipitate thoroughly with hot (80°C.) distilled water. Transfer the filter paper containing the precipitate to a weighed platinum crucible, and ignite in a muffle with free access of air. Cool and weigh the barium sulfate and calculate the percentage of sulfur in the sample.

[35] See page 769.

## ANALYSIS OF HYDROCYANIC ACID [36]

### SAMPLING

**Procedure.**—Each official sample for analysis shall consist of at least 1 pound of material taken in the following manner: During the filling of the first cylinder, the last and one or more intermediate cylinders depending on the number composing the shipment, draw off through a by-pass in the filling line, about 25 ml. of the liquid into an iced container. After all the samples have been taken, close the container and agitate gently to secure the proper mixing of the contents. All of the succeeding determinations are to be made in open air, not in a laboratory, after which the sample may be disposed of in any suitable manner.

### DETERMINATION OF TOTAL HYDROCYANIC ACID

**Procedure.**—Place a portion of the sample in an iced hydrometer jar, determine the specific gravity by means of a calibrated hydrometer and note the temperature of the liquid. Determine the hydrocyanic acid content from the specific gravity— by use of the following table:

Specific Gravity of Aqueous Solutions of HCN at $15°/4°C$

| Sp. gr. | Percent HCN |
|---------|-------------|
| 0.998 | 1 |
| 0.996 | 2 |
| 0.993 | 4 |
| 0.989 | 6 |
| 0.984 | 8 |
| 0.978 | 10 |
| 0.971 | 12 |
| 0.964 | 14 |
| 0.956 | 16 |

### TOTAL ACIDITY

**Procedure.**—Dilute a 50-ml. portion of the sample with 300 ml. of distilled water. Add 3 drops of 1% methyl red indicator and titrate until nearly colorless with 0.1 N sodium hydroxide solution. Add two drops more of the indicator and titrate to the appearance of a yellow color. Calculate the acidity in terms of sulfuric acid.

## ANALYSIS OF SODIUM FERROCYANIDE [37]

### SAMPLING

**Procedure.**—Each official sample sent to the laboratory shall consist of at least 2 pounds of material taken in the following manner: Take approximately 0.5 pound of the crystals from a few inches below the surface of every third barrel comprising the lot or shipment. Thoroughly mix the several portions together on a clean oil cloth or paper, reduce by quartering to the quantity of sample required, and place in an air-tight container.

[36] By courtesy of American Cyanamid Co.
[37] By courtesy of American Cyanamid Co.

## DETERMINATION OF MOISTURE

*Procedure.*—Heat 20 g. of the crystals for six hours at 105°C. Cool in a desiccator and weigh. Grind this dried sample rapidly in a mortar. Heat 3 g. of the powder to constant weight at 105°C. Calculate the total water content and subtract from it the water of crystallization equivalent to the sodium ferrocyanide content of the sample as determined below and calculate to $Na_4Fe(CN)_6 \cdot 10H_2O$. The difference is the free moisture in the sample.

## TOTAL SODIUM FERROCYANIDE

*Reagents.* **Standard Potassium Permanganate Solution.**—Dissolve 3.2 g. of potassium permanganate in 500 ml. of distilled water. Place the solution in a stoppered bottle and allow it to stand in the dark for 2 days. Filter the solution through a Gooch crucible, using an asbestos mat, and dilute the filtrate to 1 liter.

**Standard Potassium Ferrocyanide Solution.**—Dissolve 42 g. of pure potassium ferrocyanide, $K_4Fe(CN)_6 \cdot 3H_2O$ in 500 ml. of distilled water, filter, and dilute the filtrate to 1 liter.

**Standard Zinc Chloride Solution.**—Dissolve 10 g. of pure zinc in a mixture of 150 ml. of concentrated hydrochloric acid and 300 ml. of distilled water. Dissolve 200 g. of ammonium chloride in the zinc chloride solution, filter, and dilute the filtrate to 1 liter.

**Potassium Chloride Solution.**—Dissolve 100 g. of pure potassium chloride in 600 ml. of distilled water, filter, and dilute the filtrate to 1 liter.

**Uranium Nitrate Indicator.**—Dissolve 3 g. of uranyl nitrate $UO_2(NO_3)_2 \cdot 6H_2O$ in 50 ml. of distilled water.

*Standardization of Reagents.* **Standard Potassium Permanganate Solution.**—Dissolve 0.25 g. of pure sodium oxalate $(Na_2C_2O_4)$ obtained from the U. S. Bureau of Standards, in 175 ml. of distilled water, and add 25 ml. of dilute sulfuric acid (1:4). Heat the solution to 80°C. and titrate with the standard potassium permanganate solution until the solution assumes a faint pink color.

**Standard Potassium Ferrocyanide Solution.**—Measure out 25 ml. of solution, dilute to 500 ml. and add 5 ml. of concentrated sulfuric acid. Titrate with the standard potassium permanganate solution until the solution assumes a faint pink color. Calculate the quantity of sodium ferrocyanide $Na_4Fe(CN)_6 \cdot 10H_2O$ equivalent to one ml. of the potassium ferrocyanide solution.

$$\text{One ml. } 0.1 \ N \ K_4Fe(CN)_6 = 0.4841 \text{ g. } Na_4Fe(CN)_6 \cdot 10H_2O$$

**Standard Zinc Chloride Solution.**—Measure out 25 ml. of solution with a calibrated burette, add 10 ml. of 10% potassium chloride solution and dilute to 200 ml. Heat the solution to 90°C. (do not boil the solution) and titrate with the standard potassium ferrocyanide solution until a drop of uranyl nitrate solution, used on a spot plate as an outside indicator, turns faintly brown. Add the ferrocyanide solution rapidly with constant stirring until near the end point (within 1 to 4 ml.). The zinc chloride solution is blue at first, but turns almost white at the end point. When near the end point, add the ferrocyanide solution in 0.5-ml. portions, and stir for at least 15 seconds before testing with the indicator. When the end point has been passed, add 0.5 ml. of standard zinc chloride solution, and again titrate with the standard potassium ferrocyanide solution, testing the solution with the indicator after the addition of each drop of the ferrocyanide solution. Make a check determination. Calculate the amount of the potassium ferrocyanide solution exactly equivalent to 25 ml. of the zinc chloride solution.

*Procedure.*—Weigh accurately a 30-g. sample of sodium ferrocyanide, dissolve in distilled water and dilute to one liter. Measure accurately 25 ml. of the standard zinc chloride into a 400-ml. beaker, add 10 ml. of the 10% potassium chloride solution and 165 ml. of distilled water. Heat the solution to 90°C. (do not boil the solution) and titrate with constant stirring with the sodium ferrocyanide solution using uranyl nitrate as an outside indicator, following the procedure given for the standardization of the zinc chloride solution.

The value of the zinc chloride solution has been determined in terms of sodium ferrocyanide. From this value calculate the sodium ferrocyanide $Na_4Fe(CN)_6 \cdot 10H_2O$ present in the sample.

## TOTAL SODIUM CHLORIDE

**Reagents. Standard Silver Nitrate Solution.**—Dissolve 8.5 g. of silver nitrate in water, filter and dilute the filtrate to 1 liter.

**Standard Ammonium Thiocyanate Solution.**—Dissolve 3.8 g. of ammonium thiocyanate in approximately 100 ml. of water, filter, and dilute to 1 liter.

**Zinc Nitrate Solution.**—Dissolve 100 g. of zinc nitrate in 500 ml. of distilled water, filter, and dilute to one liter.

**Ferric Ammonium Sulfate Solution.**—Saturate 100 ml. of distilled water with ferric ammonium sulfate, at room temperature (20°C.). Filter and add just enough nitric acid to remove the turbidity and to change the color from red to pale yellow.

**Potassium Chromate Solution.**—Prepare a saturated solution of the C.P. salt in distilled water.

**Standardization of Reagents. Standard Silver Nitrate Solution.**—Weigh accurately 0.20 g. of pure sodium chloride, previously dried at 105°C. for one hour, and dissolve it in 50 ml. of distilled water. Add 2 drops of potassium chromate indicator and titrate with the silver nitrate solution to the appearance of a brown coloration. Calculate the amount of silver nitrate equivalent to the sodium chloride and then calculate the normality of the standard solution.

**Standard Ammonium Thiocyanate Solution.**—Measure accurately from a burette, 35 ml. of the standard silver nitrate solution, add 2 ml. of concentrated nitric acid, and dilute to 150 ml. with distilled water. Titrate with the ammonium thiocyanate solution, using 1 ml. of the ferric ammonium sulfate indicator. Calculate the volume of the ammonium thiocyanate solution equivalent to 1 ml. of the standard silver nitrate solution.

*Procedure.*—Heat 100 ml. of the sample solution under "Total Sodium Ferrocyanide" to 80°C. and add with constant stirring 50 ml. of a hot (80°C.) 10% solution of zinc nitrate, to precipitate the ferrocyanide as zinc ferrocyanide. Filter and wash the precipitate. To the filtrate add 2 ml. of concentrated nitric acid and 15 ml. of standard silver nitrate solution. Filter and wash the precipitate. Titrate the excess silver nitrate with the standard ammonium thiocyanate solution, using the ferric ammonium sulfate indicator, and calculate the per cent sodium chloride in the sample.

## TOTAL SODIUM SULFATE

**Reagents. Zinc Chloride Solution.**—Dissolve 100 g. of zinc chloride in 500 ml. of distilled water, filter and dilute to 1 liter.

**Barium Chloride Solution.**—Dissolve 100 g. of barium chloride ($BaCl_2 \cdot 2H_2O$) in 500 ml. of distilled water, filter, and dilute to 1 liter.

*Procedure.*—Heat 100 ml. of the sample solution (from "Total Sodium Ferrocyanide—Procedure") to 80°C. and add with constant stirring 50 ml. of a hot (80°C.) 10% solution of zinc chloride, to precipitate the ferrocyanide as zinc ferrocyanide. Filter and wash the precipitate. Acidify the filtrate with concentrated hydrochloric acid and then add 2 ml. in excess. Heat the solution to boiling, add with constant stirring 15 ml. of the 10% barium chloride solution, and digest at 90°C. for two hours. Filter the precipitate through an ashless filter, wash with 2% hydrochloric acid until the residue is white, and then follow with successive portions of hot (60°C.) water until the filtrate is free from chloride by the silver nitrate test. Place the filter and the precipitate in a platinum crucible and ignite for 0.5 hour in a muffle with free access of air. Cool the crucible in a desiccator, weigh, and report the percentage of sodium sulfate.

## FOREIGN MATTER

*Procedure.*—Dissolve 50 g. of the material in 300 ml. of hot water and filter off the insoluble matter on a weighed Gooch crucible. Wash the residue thoroughly with hot water. Dry the crucible in an oven at 105°C. and weigh. Calculate the percentage of insoluble or foreign matter.

## DETERMINATION OF NITROGEN IN STEEL [38]

For the determination of nitrogen in steel, a modification of the method first published by A. H. Allen and modified by Prof. J. W. Langley is used.

By the following method the sample and standard distillates are prepared under similar conditions, and when treated with Nessler reagent, develop colors nearly identical in quality or tone, but proportional in intensity to the ammonia present.

If the Nessler reagent is carefully prepared and works properly, the color in sample and standard will develop almost instantly and is fully developed in less than one minute. The solutions treated with such reagent remain clear or do not cloud appreciably on standing for ten minutes; however, the comparison is best made after standing one minute, and all difficulty due to clouding is avoided.

The difficulties of comparison are also reduced to a minimum by using an aliquot part of the distillate in the manner to be described instead of that corresponding to the whole sample.

*Reagents.* **Hydrochloric acid** of 1.1 sp. gr., free from ammonia, which may be prepared by distilling pure hydrochloric acid gas into distilled water free from ammonia. To do this, take a large flask connected with a separatory funnel-tube and an evolution-tube, fill it half full of strong hydrochloric acid, connect the evolution-tube with a wash-bottle connected with a bottle containing the distilled water. Admit concentrated sulfuric acid free from nitrous acid to the flask through the funnel-tube, apply heat as required, and distill the gas into the prepared water.

Test the acid by admitting some of it into the distilling apparatus, described farther on, and distilling it from an excess of pure caustic soda, or determine the amount of ammonia in a portion of hydrochloric acid of 1.1 sp. gr., and use the amount found as a correction.

NOTE.—The ammonia-free hydrochloric acid may also be prepared as follows:
Dilute concentrated hydrochloric acid to specific gravity 1.10 and without addition of sulfuric acid distill it.
Hydrochloric acid of this strength distills without change in concentration.
The first 100-ml. distillate from one liter of acid will usually contain all the ammonia

[38] Methods of Analysis used in Laboratories of the Titanium Alloy Manufacturing Co. Contributed by L. E. Barton.

and is rejected; the portions distilled thereafter being collected for use but must, of course, be tested as usual to make sure it is free from ammonia.

Solution of caustic soda, made by dissolving 300 g. of fused caustic soda in 500 ml. of water and digesting it for 24 hours at 50°C. on a copper zinc couple, made, as described by Gladstone and Tribe, as follows:

Place from 25 to 30 g. of thin sheet zinc in a flask and cover with a moderately concentrated, slightly warm solution of copper sulfate. A thick, spongy coating of copper will be deposited on the zinc. Pour off the solution in about ten minutes and wash thoroughly with cold distilled water.

**Nessler Reagent.**—Dissolve 35 g. of potassium iodide in a small quantity of distilled water, and add a strong solution of mercuric chloride little by little, shaking after each addition until the red precipitate formed dissolves. Finally the precipitate formed will fail to dissolve, then stop the addition of the mercury salt and filter. Add to the filtrate 120 g. of caustic soda dissolved in a small amount of water, and dilute until the entire solution measures 1 liter. Add to this 5 ml. of saturated aqueous solution of mercuric chloride, mix thoroughly, allow the precipitate formed to settle, and decant or siphon off the clear liquid into a glass-stoppered bottle.

**Standard Ammonia Solution.**—Dissolve 0.0382 g. of ammonium chloride in 1 liter of water. One ml. of this solution will equal 0.01 milligram of nitrogen.

**Distilled Water Free from Ammonia.**—If the ordinary distilled water contains ammonia, redistill it, reject the first portions coming over, and use the subsequent portions, which will be found free from ammonia. Several glass cylinders of colorless glass of about 160-ml. capacity are also required.

The best form of distilling apparatus consists of an Erlenmeyer flask of about 1500-ml. capacity, with a rubber stopper, carrying a separatory funnel-tube and an evolution-tube, the latter connected with a condensing-tube around which passes a constant stream of cold water. The inside tube, where it issues from the condenser, should be sufficiently high to dip into one of the glass cylinders placed on the working table.

*Procedure.* **Distillation of Sample.**—In a distilling flask of 1000- to 1500-ml. capacity, fitted with separatory funnel and connected with condenser, place 40 ml. prepared caustic soda solution; add 500 ml. distilled water and distill until the distillate gives no reaction with Nessler reagent.

Dissolve a 5-g. sample of the steel in 40 ml. of ammonia-free hydrochloric acid, and by means of the separatory funnel add the solution slowly to the contents of the distilling flask, washing in finally with ammonia-free water.

Distill and collect 150 ml. of distillate in a graduated flask. Cork the flask and set aside. Experience has shown that 150 ml. of distillate will contain all the nitrogen in the sample.

**Preparation of Standard.**—After distilling the sample—the apparatus then being free from ammonia but containing the residue of sample and reagents—25 ml. of standard ammonium chloride solution and 150 ml. of ammonia-free water are added to the contents of the flask, and distillation continued until a standard distillate of 150 ml. is collected in a graduated flask.

As before, the single distillate will contain all the ammonia from 25 ml. of standard solution.

To the standard distillate is added 6 ml. of Nessler reagent; and since the standard ammonium chloride solution is equivalent to 0.00001 g. nitrogen per ml., 1 ml. prepared standard distillate is equivalent to $\dfrac{25 \times 0.00001}{156} = 0.0000016$ g., nitrogen per ml. = 0.00016% nitrogen when using a 1-g. sample.

**Comparison and Determination.**—To make the determination, 30 ml. of sample distillate, equal to 1 g. of sample, are placed in one of a pair of Nessler jars and the color developed by addition of 1 ml. Nessler reagent.

The standard and sample are allowed to stand one minute to develop the color fully.

Into the other jar the standard distillate is run from a burette until the colors in standard and sample jars are of the same intensity; the final comparison being made after bringing the contents of the jars to the same volume by addition of ammonia-free water to one or the other.

The number of milliliters of standard distillate multiplied by 0.00016 gives the percentage of nitrogen in the steel.

## CONTINUOUS SAMPLING AND ULTRAMICRODETERMINATION OF NITROGEN DIOXIDE IN AIR [39]

The following simple and convenient method is designed for the continuous sampling and ultramicrodetermination of nitrogen dioxide in urban atmospheres, important in air pollution studies.

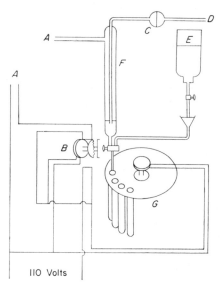

Fig. 33-12. Automatic Sequence Sampler for Nitrogen Dioxide.

$A$ = To pump; $B$ = Hour clock; $C$ = Dust filter; $D$ = To sampling point; $E$ = Reservoir; $F$ = Fritted bubbler; $G$ = 24-hour clock.

**Apparatus. Air Sampler.**—Fig. 33-12 shows a modified Wilson 24-hour automatic air sampler. It is equipped with a filter paper trap 11 inches in diameter in the sample line, and a meter capable of registering 2 liters per hour.

**Spectrophotometer.**—This should be of the type similar to Coleman No. 14, with matched cuvettes 20 × 40 mm.

**Reagents. Absorbing Reagent.**—0.1 $N$ sodium hydroxide solution with 2 ml. of butynol alcohol per liter.

**Coupling Reagent.**—0.1% solution of $N$-(1-naphthyl)-ethylenediamine dihydrochloride (1 ml. is equivalent to 1 mg.).

**Diazotizing Reagent.**—Prepare by dissolving 20 g. of sulfanilamide in 1 liter of water containing 50 ml. of phosphoric acid.

**Hydrogen Peroxide.**—1% solution.

**Standard Sodium Nitrite Solution.**—Prepare by dissolving 150 mg. of sodium nitrite in 1 liter of water and diluting 10 ml. of this solution to 100 ml. (1 ml. = 10 micrograms $NO_2$).

**Procedure.**—Aspirate air at 1.3 liters per minute through 30 to 35 ml. of absorbing reagent in the automatic air sampler apparatus. Twenty-four 40-minute samples are obtained in this manner. Transfer the samples to 50-ml. Nessler tubes, add 1 drop of hydrogen peroxide reagent, and mix to oxidize the dissolved sulfur dioxide to sulfate. Add 10 ml. of diazotizing reagent

[39] Jacobs and Hochheiser, Anal. Chem., **30**, 426, 1958.

and then 1 ml. of *N*-(1-naphthyl)-ethylenediamine dihydrochloride reagent.  Dilute to 50 ml. and mix.  Allow to stand for 30 minutes and determine the absorbance in the spectrophotometer at 550 m$\mu$ using the reagent blank as the reference.

To calibrate, add 0.2, 0.4, 0.6, 0.8, and 1.0 ml. of standard sodium nitrite solution to 35 ml. of absorbing reagent in five 50-ml. Nessler tubes.  Add 1 drop of hydrogen peroxide solution, 10 ml. of diazotizing reagent, 1 ml. of coupling reagent, and dilute to 50 ml.  Read in the spectrophotometer at 550 m$\mu$ (found to give the maximum absorption) using the reagent blank as the reference.

**Calculations.**—Nitrogen dioxide can be expressed as parts per hundred million of the air sample.  For a 52-liter air sample at 760 mm. of mercury and 25°C., 1 microgram of nitrogen dioxide is equivalent to 1 p. p. h. m.

NOTE.  **Effect of Sulfur Dioxide.**—In a 52-liter air sample having a concentration of 5 p. p. h. m. of nitrogen dioxide, 1 p. p. m. of sulfur dioxide caused a 50% reduction in color after one-half hour.  One drop of 1% hydrogen peroxide oxidized the sulfur dioxide to sulfate, but did not interfere with the intensity of the nitrite color when determined after 30 minutes.

## Chapter 34

# OXYGEN

**O,** *at. wt.* 15.9994; *b.p.* −183.0°C.; *wt. per l.* 1.429 g. (at 0°C.); (liquid, *d.* 1.14)

Oxygen is a colorless, tasteless, odorless gas. It is found free in the atmosphere to the extent of about 21% by volume. Combined with hydrogen it is a constituent of water (88.8% by weight). It is an exceedingly active element and combines with all elements except fluorine. It is a constituent of a great number of minerals and an important constituent of animal and vegetable matter. About half our globe is oxygen, combined or free.

Priestly, Scheele, and Lavoisier are generally credited with the discovery and isolation of oxygen. Lavoisier named the element oxygen (1777)—acid producer—from his erroneous belief that it was a constituent of all acids.

## DETECTION

Free oxygen is recognized by its activity in combining with substances when heated. A lighted taper plunged into oxygen gas burns brilliantly. The burning of the taper in the air is due to oxygen.

Hydrogen passed over a highly heated oxide, in a majority of simple compounds, combines with it forming water.

Certain oxides and salts heated decompose giving off oxygen, for example $2HgO$ decomposes to $2Hg$ and $O_2$, $2KClO_3$ to $2KCl$ and $3O_2$.

Carbon combines with oxygen at kindling temperature forming $CO_2$, a gas detected by means of lime water  (See Chapter on Carbon.)

## ESTIMATION

The determination of oxygen in a gas mixture is accomplished by the combination and subsequent absorption of oxygen, the gas contraction being due to oxygen. Pyrogallic acid is commonly used for this purpose.

The determination of combined oxygen is difficult and seldom attempted. It is frequently estimated by difference after determining the other constituents of the substance, after definitely establishing the presence of oxygen.

A number of analyzers are on the market for determining the proportion of oxygen in gas mixtures by measuring their paramagnetism. Some types are actuated by the cooling effect upon heat resistance elements of conduction currents induced by a magnetic field; they are usually designed to cancel out the effect of thermal conduction currents by use of a reference resistance element. Other types measure the magnetic susceptibility of the gas directly by a magnetic torsion balance.

## METHODS OF DETERMINATION

## DETERMINATION OF FREE OXYGEN IN GAS

### POTASSIUM PYROGALLATE METHOD

*Procedure.*—One hundred ml. of gas are measured out as with the Orsat apparatus, the burette being allowed to drain two minutes. The rubber connectors upon the burette and pipette are filled with water, the capillary tube inserted, as far as it will go, by a twisting motion, into the connector upon the burette, thus

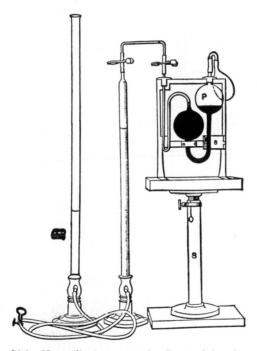

Fig. 34-1. Hempel's Apparatus for Determining Oxygen.

filling the capillary with water; the free end of the capillary is inserted into the pipette connector, the latter pinched so as to form a channel for the water contained in it to escape, and the capillary twisted and forced down to the pinchcock. There should be as little free space as possible between the capillaries and the pinchcock. Before using a pipette, its connector (and rubber bag) should be carefully examined for leaks, especially in the former, and if any found the faulty piece replaced.

The pinchcocks on the burette and the pipette (Fig. 34-1) are now opened, the gas forced over into the potassium pyrogallate solution (*P*), and the pinchcock on the pipette closed. After allowing it to stand for fifteen minutes, the residue is drawn back into the burette and the reading taken. Before setting aside the pyrogallate pipette, the number of cubic centimeters of oxygen absorbed should be noted upon the slate $S$ on the stand. This must never be omitted with any pipette save possibly that for potassium hydroxide, as failure to do this may result in the ruin of an important analysis. The reason for the omission in this case is found in the large absorption capacity—four to five liters of carbon dioxide—of the reagent.

### EXPLOSION WITH HYDROGEN METHOD

*Procedure.*—Forty-three ml. of gas and 57 ml. of hydrogen are measured out, passed into the small explosion pipette, Fig. 34-2, the capillary of the pipette filled

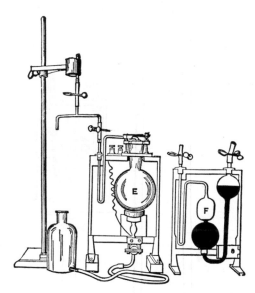

FIG. 34-2.   Explosion Pipette (left); Hample Gas Pipette (right).

with water, the pinchcocks and glass stopcock all closed, a heavy glass or fine wire gauze screen placed between the pipette and the operator, the spark passed between the spark wires, and the contraction in volume noted. *The screen should never be omitted, as serious accidents may occur thereby.* The oxygen is represented by one-third of the contraction. For very accurate work the sum of the combustible gases should be but one-sixth that of the non-combustible gases, otherwise some nitrogen will burn and high results will be obtained; [1] that is $(H + O):(N + H)::$ 1:6.

### DETERMINATION OF TRACES OF OXYGEN IN GASES

The apparatus designed by J. G. Dely is shown in the accompanying drawing. The procedure is of special value in the determination of traces of oxygen in the nitrogen-hydrogen gases used in the synthetic catalytic fixation of nitrogen by the Haber or Claude processes or their modifications.

The method depends upon the blue color produced by the action of oxygen on colorless ammoniacal cuprous chloride, and matching with a standard.

[1] This is shown in the work of Gill and Hunt, J. Am. Chem. Soc., **17,** 987, 1895.

Details of the apparatus are shown in Fig. 34-3.  The globe *A* is filled with pure copper drillings.  The cylinder *G* contains fine granulated copper.  Cupric chloride is reduced in *A* and mixed with the necessary amount of ammonium hydroxide.  Complete reduction is effected by slowly flowing the desired portion of the

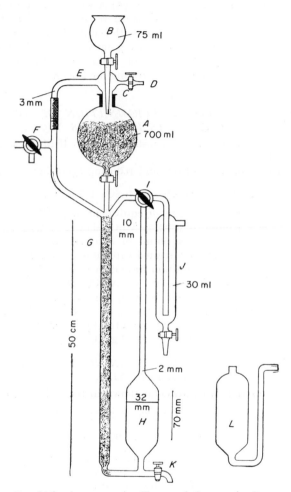

Fig. 34-3.  Apparatus for Traces of Oxygen in Gases.

solution through *G* into *H*.  Solution in *J* acts as a seal preventing contamination of air.

Gas in measured quantity is allowed to flow through the solution in *H* until a blue color develops that matches the intensity of color in the standard solution in *L*.  The standard has been prepared by passing a known quantity of oxygen through colorless ammoniacal cuprous chloride, under conditions closely matching those of the tested gas.

## AVAILABLE OXYGEN

The determination of the available oxygen in a substance such as manganese dioxide is sometimes demanded on account of the use of an oxidizing agent in various processes, for example in the production of chlorine from hydrochloric acid.

Two procedures are commonly employed: (A) A weighed amount of the dioxide is reduced by a measured amount of standard reducing agent and the excess of the reducing agent determined by titration with standard potassium permanganate, thus establishing the exact amount of reducing agent required by the dioxide.

(B) Indirect method by the liberation of iodine from hydriodic acid by the peroxide ($MnO_2$, $BaO_2$, $PbO_2$, etc.) and titrating the liberated iodine with standard thiosulfate.

### DIRECT METHOD FOR DETERMINATION OF AVAILABLE OXYGEN IN PEROXIDES

**Procedure.**—The sample is dried to constant weight. If $MnO_2$ a temperature of 120°C. is permissible.

The theoretical reaction with $MnO_2$ and reducing agent $FeSO_4$ is as follows:

$$MnO_2 + 2FeSO_4 + 2H_2SO_4 \rightarrow MnSO_4 + Fe_2(SO_4)_3 + 2H_2O$$

Hence 1 ml. of 0.1 N reducing agent is equivalent to 0.00435 g. $MnO_2$. On the basis of a pure oxide not more than 0.2 g. $MnO_2$ should be taken. The sample is placed in a 250-ml. Erlenmeyer flask, 50 ml. of water added and 2–5 ml. of concentrated sulfuric acid. The solution is treated with 50 ml. of 0.1 N $FeSO_4$ (or 0.335 g. $Na_2C_2O_4$) standard reagent, the solution heated to near boiling and the excess of $FeSO_4$ titrated immediately with standard 0.1 N $KMnO_4$.

If the normalities of the $FeSO_4$ and $KMnO_4$ are not exactly equivalent, convert to a common basis by titration of, say, 10 ml. of $FeSO_4$ acidified with $H_2SO_4$ by $KMnO_4$. From this ascertain the $FeSO_4$ required by the $MnO_2$.

One gram mole of $MnO_2$ is equivalent to 32 g. O.

### INDIRECT METHOD FOR DETERMINING AVAILABLE OXYGEN IN A PEROXIDE

**Procedure.**—The reaction with $MnO_2$ is shown in the following equation:

$$MnO_2 + 4HCl \rightarrow MnCl_2 + 2H_2O + Cl_2$$

$$2KI + Cl_2 \rightarrow 2KCl + I_2$$

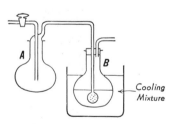

FIG. 34-4. Apparatus for Available Oxygen.

In a flask, $B$, Fig. 34-4, place 15–20 ml. of 20% solution of potassium iodide. Insert in this receiver the side arm a second flask carrying a glass stopper. Place in this second flask about 0.2 g., carefully weighed, of the peroxide ($MnO_2$). The receiving flask ($B$, see illustration) is cooled by means of ice water. Now add to flask $A$ about 30 ml. of concentrated hydrochloric acid, quickly replacing the glass stopper. Warm the acid gently, distilling the liberated chlorine into the receiving flask containing the KI. Raise the temperature gradually until the acid boils and continue the heating for about five minutes. Without removing the flame lower the flask, $B$. Discontinue heating and titrate the liberated iodine in *B* with standard 0.1 *N* thiosulfate reagent, using starch indicator.

A blank should be run on the same volume of iodide used in the determination above, diluting to 100 ml., adding 5 ml. HCl and titrating any liberated iodine with standard thiosulfate. This blank should be subtracted from the test above.

Calculate the available oxygen. See procedure for "Direct Method," above.

A stream of nitrogen or $CO_2$ is used to transfer the chlorine to the KI solution.

## THE DETERMINATION OF OXYGEN IN ORGANIC COMPOUNDS

### SEMI-MICRO COMBUSTION METHOD

In this method the amount of oxygen consumed during the combustion of an organic compound gasometrically is determined and thus it is possible to analyze for carbon, hydrogen, and oxygen in one operation.

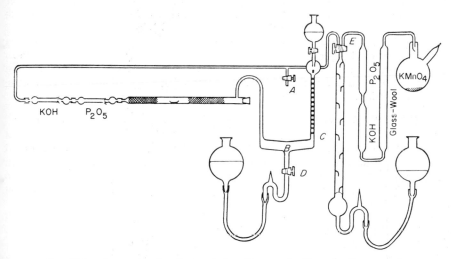

Fig. 34-5. Apparatus for Determining Oxygen in Organic Compounds.

*Apparatus.*—The apparatus used is shown in Fig. 34-5. Oxygen is made from solid potassium permanganate and measured (N. T. P.) in a Ramsay burette. The combustion tube contains platinized asbestos only. The use of copper oxide is avoided following a suggestion of Professor W. H. Hunter. It is possible that copper oxide wire reduced to copper during the combustion may not be reoxidized to the same extent as it had been originally. The sample is weighed on an ordinary analytical balance, as are the absorption tubes.

*Procedure.*—At the beginning of an analysis the apparatus is brought to atmospheric pressure by opening stopcock *A*. Sample and absorption tubes are, of course, in place. The mercury in vessel *B* is placed on the mark *C* and stopcock *D* is closed. Room temperature and barometer are noted. Oxygen sufficient for the combustion is transferred to the vessel *B* so that all of it would take part in the flow through the combustion tube. The circulation is started by causing the

Sprengel pump to operate. By a previous calibration the proper rate of dropping the mercury should be determined so as to produce the usual flow of oxygen through the combustion tube. Forty-five minutes for complete combustion and fifteen minutes for further sweeping is allowed.

At the end of the experiment the apparatus is brought into its initial condition by removing the three pieces of triangular iron which comprised the furnace and all the hot asbestos shields and allowing room temperature to be attained. The remaining oxygen is now removed from vessel B, which is again filled with mercury to the mark C. Stopcock D was closed. The gas is thus transferred to the Ramsay burette, which is set to atmospheric pressure and stopcock E is closed. The oxygen remaining in the burette is measured and the absorption tubes are removed and weighed. An analysis can be carried out in two hours.

Blank experiments are run which showed some consumption of oxygen and gain of weight in the potassium hydroxide and pentoxide absorption tubes. However, oxygen thus treated and run through a second blank shows a negligible decrease in volume and the gains in the absorption tubes are also negligible. In further work we expect to pretreat the oxygen as it comes from the generator, thus avoiding the necessity of making blank experiments.

A very important feature of the apparatus is that the system is closed and any gases due to cracking or incomplete combustion (such as methane and carbon monoxide) are carried back through the hot combustion tube several times in the period allowed for the combustion. Thus the method tends to insure complete combustion.

### CARBON MONOXIDE METHOD (UNTERZAUCHER METHOD)

In this method [2] the sample is heated in an atmosphere of nitrogen until pyrolysis is complete, the exit gases being passed through a column of powdered graphite or pelleted carbon at a temperature of 1150°C. Under these conditions, all the carbon dioxide and steam (water vapor) in the exit gases is converted to CO, which is oxidized to carbon dioxide by iodine pentoxide and the equivalent amount of iodine liberated is determined photometrically.

*Apparatus.*—A diagram of the apparatus is shown in Fig. 34-6. The furnace B must be of sufficient capacity to maintain a temperature of 1120°C. in the oxidation tube (see Fig. 34-8 for details of tube packing).

To make sure that the evolved iodine is swept completely into the adjoining Vigreux absorption tube, K, the ground-glass joint is likewise kept at an elevated temperature inside the furnace.

A Fisher high-temperature burner, C, is adequate for pyrolysis of the sample. To confine the flame, a small U-shaped hood constructed of Nichrome gauze, with asbestos ends, is permanently fastened to the top of the burner. A roll of Nichrome wire gauze is also coiled around the reaction tube and maintained in position directly above the burner. In addition, a section of Transite is placed between the burner and the cap, F, as a heat shield. By this means a temperature of 1000°C. is easily maintained in the end section of the tube where the sample is pyrolyzed.

The burner should be moved by automatic propulsion (at a rate of about 0.3 cm./minute). Some type of motorized reducer should be used for this purpose.

[2] Schütze, Z. anal. Chem., **118**, 241, 1939; Zimmermann, Z. anal. Chem., **118**, 258, 1939; Unterzaucher, Ber., **73**, 391, 1940; Aluise *et al.*, Anal. Chem., **19**, 347, 1947. It has been found by various analysts that the per cent of oxygen may be accurately determined from the weight of the $CO_2$ that is formed by oxidation of the CO by the iodine pentoxide.

It is necessary to remove all traces of oxygen from the nitrogen before using it in this determination. This can be effected by passing it over a 10-cm. section of copper ribbon, or copper particles of 40–60 mesh, heated to 500°C. in a Pyrex tube.

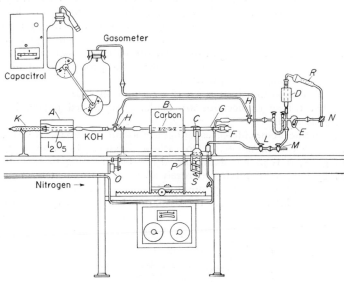

FIG. 34-6. Diagram of Apparatus for Direct Determination of Oxygen in Organic Compounds.

$A$ = Oxidation furnace; $B$ = Reaction furnace; $C$ = Movable Burner; $D$ = Purification unit; $E$ = Bubble counter; $F$ = Quartz tube cap; $G$ = Quartz tube; $H$, $H'$ = Reverse stopcocks; $K$ = Vigreux Absorption tube; $L$ = Three-way stopcock; $O$ = Motorized reduced. The joints in this apparatus are spherical or 12/5 standard taper throughout.

The bubble counter, $E$, contains concentrated sulfuric acid; the adjacent arm of the U-tube, Ascarite; and the other, phosphorus pentoxide.

The quartz reaction tube, $G$, should be tested for leaks by using vacuum and a Tesla spark coil. The detailed dimensions are shown in Fig. 34-7. Its design and connections permit reversal of the flow of nitrogen through the tube, in order to prevent the entrance of air during introduction of the sample, and sweeps out,

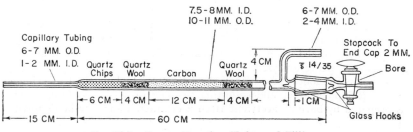

FIG. 34-7. Quartz Reaction Tube and Filling.

through the stopcock on the closing cap, *F*, the air in the platinum boat containing the sample.

Once assembled, precautions should be taken to prevent air from entering the apparatus. On overnight standing, a slow stream of nitrogen, one or two bubbles per second, is passed through the apparatus directly from the cylinder, by adjusting the gas pressure regulator and reducing valve. For long periods of idleness it is convenient to use a gasometer, which is designed to maintain the apparatus under pressure of nitrogen, the end of the tube containing the iodine pentoxide being closed. The gasometer is filled with nitrogen through the three-way T-stopcock, *L*.

A Mariotte bottle is used to aid in maintaining the proper flow of nitrogen and reaction products through the apparatus.

The platinum combustion boat is 4 x 12 x 2.5 mm. in size.

Where rubber tubing connections are made, heavy-walled paraffin-impregnated rubber tubing is used.

**Reagents. Iodine Pentoxide.**—Reagent-grade iodine pentoxide is satisfactory for conversion of the carbon monoxide to carbon dioxide. In order to permit the free flow of gases, it is prepared for use either by screening to exclude particles finer than 100 mesh, or by mixing as received, with approximately one-fifth of its weight of water-washed and dried pumice stone, 20- to 30-mesh. The prepared iodine pentoxide is introduced into the oxidation tube (Fig. 34-8) and conditioned

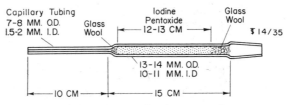

FIG. 34-8. Oxidation Tube and Filling.

in a stream of dry nitrogen for 24 hours or more at 230 to 240°C. followed by 40 to 50 hours at 150 to 160°C. After cooling in a stream of nitrogen, the contents of the tube should be packed firmly by repeated tapping in order to avoid formation of channels during service. When this oxidant is used, the temperature of the oxidation tube furnace, *A*, is set at 120–121°C.

**Sodium Hydroxide.**—A 20% solution of C.P. pellets in distilled water.

**Bromine.**—C.P. grade.

**Potassium Acetate-Glacial Acetic Acid.**—A 10% solution of C.P. potassium acetate in glacial acetic acid.

**Sodium Acetate.**—A 20% solution of C.P. sodium acetate in distilled water.

**Formic Acid.**—C.P. formic acid, 90%.

**Potassium Hydroxide.**—Reagent-grade pellets are crushed to 8- to 10-mesh and tightly packed into the carbon monoxide scrubber tube for removal of interfering gaseous products formed when elements, such as halogens and sulfur, are present in the substance being analyzed.

**Carbon.**—Benzene soot is prepared in the laboratory by burning a wick immersed in benzene (thiophene-free), and collecting the soot on a glass surface. Acetylene soot is prepared by burning acetylene from a cylinder, using a welder's torch with no auxiliary air or oxygen, and collecting the soot on a glass surface. These carbons and a commercial carbon are pelleted at a pressure of 3500 lb./in.$^2$ A suitable commercial carbon is Aerofloted Arrow carbon black (J. M. Huber, Inc., New York). The pellets are then cut into small pieces (30–80-mesh) and dried at 150°C.

The sieved carbon is placed in a tube and heated in a slow stream of nitrogen, the temperature being gradually increased to 550°C. and maintained for a period of several hours. This treatment removes volatile constituents and sinters the carbon, thereby preventing channeling when the carbon is used later in the reaction tube.

*Procedure.*—The reaction tube is packed with quartz chips, 6- to 10-mesh, quartz wool, carbon, and a second section of quartz wool, as shown in Fig. 34-7, with repeated tapping in order to avoid channeling in service. The apparatus is assembled as shown in Fig. 34-6. The copper in the preheater furnace, *D*, is reduced *in situ* by a slow stream of hydrogen introduced through the three-way T-stopcock, *M*; the gas stream escapes through the three-way T-stopcock, *N*. The temperature of the preheater furnace is maintained at 500°C. With the reaction furnace, *B*, at room temperature, a slow stream of nitrogen is passed through the apparatus for several hours. The furnace is then turned on and the temperature gradually raised to 1150°C. After nitrogen has been passed through the apparatus overnight at this temperature, it is ready for use.

Before starting an analysis, the Mariotte flask is connected to the apparatus and the valve on the nitrogen cylinder is adjusted to provide a flow of 8 to 10 ml. per minute through the system, with the furnace *B* at the operating temperature. A gauge pressure of 4 to 6 pounds is sufficient to maintain this rate, which can be checked as required by observing the bubble counter. The platinum boat is flamed just before use and cooled in a desiccator, and a sample containing 1.0 to 1.3 mg. of oxygen is weighed into the boat. Liquid samples are weighed in small capillaries and placed in the boat.

By means of the three-way T-stopcocks, *H* and *H'*, the nitrogen is passed in the reverse direction through the reaction tube, *G*, and out through the stopcock of the cap, *F*. This cap is then removed and the sample boat pushed into position 9 to 10 cm. in front of *B* by means of a flamed glass rod provided with a platinum hook. *F* is immediately replaced, with its stopcock open to the atmosphere, and the reverse flow of nitrogen continued for 10 minutes in order to expel all air that has entered during introduction of the sample. During this sweeping period, the inside of the Vigreux absorption tube, *K*, is moistened with a 20% sodium hydroxide solution, by dipping the capillary end into the solution, filling by suction to the ground joint, and allowing to drain. The tube is connected to the oxidation tube containing iodine pentoxide, using a rotary motion so that the two joints are firmly seated. (No lubricant should be used.) The Mariotte flask is then attached to the absorption tube. At the end of the reverse sweeping period the stopcock of *F* is closed to the atmosphere, *H* and *H'* are immediately adjusted so that nitrogen enters the reaction tube through its side arm, and the side arm of the Mariotte flask is quickly lowered to a horizontal position.

After the movable burner has been placed 4 or 5 cm. from the sample boat, the automatic propulsion device is started, the burner lighted, and the flame slowly increased so that the Nichrome gauze around the tube is brought to a white heat, indicating a temperature of 900° to 1000°C. within the tube. As the burner advances, the sample is gradually pyrolyzed, and the decomposition products are swept into the hot carbon inside the furnace. When the automatic movement has ceased and the burner contacts $B$ (40 to 50 minutes), the furnace is moved about 5 cm. (2 inches) to the left. The burner is then advanced manually and that portion of the tube previously protected by the insulating wall of the furnace is heated for 5 minutes. The burner is moved back and the furnace immediately returned to its original position. This ensures complete pyrolysis of any decomposition products that may have condensed on the cool portion of the tube.

The burner is turned off and the sweeping continued for about 15 minutes. The absorption tube, $K$, is then removed, and the contents are immediately rinsed with about 125 ml. of distilled water into a beaker containing 10 drops of bromine and 10 ml. of a 10% solution of potassium acetate in glacial acetic acid. After stirring, the contents of the beaker are transferred to a 250-ml. Erlenmeyer flask containing 10 ml. of a 20% solution of sodium acetate in water, and the excess bromine is destroyed by slowly adding, with shaking, 15 to 20 drops of 90% formic acid. After 4 or 5 minutes, about 0.3 g. of potassium iodide and 5 ml. of 10% sulfuric acid are added and the flask is gently swirled. The liberated iodine is titrated immediately with 0.02 $N$ sodium thiosulfate, using starch indicator.

A blank run is made by introducing into the reaction tube an empty platinum boat and proceeding exactly as above using 500 to 600 ml. of nitrogen. The percentage of oxygen is calculated as follows:

$$\frac{(Y - b) \times \text{normality of Na}_2\text{S}_2\text{O}_3 \times 0.1333 \times 100}{0.0200 \times \text{milligrams of sample}} = \% \text{ Oxygen}$$

where $Y$ = ml. of $\text{Na}_2\text{S}_2\text{O}_3$ required for sample;

$b$ = ml. of $\text{Na}_2\text{S}_2\text{O}_3$ required for blank; and

0.1333 = mg. of oxygen equivalent to 1 ml. 0.0200 $N$ $\text{Na}_2\text{S}_2\text{O}_3$

## DETERMINATION OF DISSOLVED OXYGEN IN WATER

The Alsterberg azide method is a modification of the Winkler process for the determination of dissolved oxygen, and the principle is the same. The method depends on the formation of a precipitate of manganous hydroxide. The oxygen dissolved in the water is rapidly absorbed by manganous hydroxide, forming a higher oxide, which may be in the following form:

$$\text{MnSO}_4 + 2\text{KOH} \rightarrow \text{Mn(OH)}_2 + \text{K}_2\text{SO}_4$$

$$2\text{Mn(OH)}_2 + \text{O}_2 \rightarrow 2\text{MnO(OH)}_2$$

$\text{Mn(OH)}_2$ floc acts as a "gathering" agent for oxygen; therefore, the floc is passed twice through the solution to insure quantitative reaction.

Upon acidification in the presence of iodide, iodine is released in a quantity equivalent to the dissolved oxygen present.

$$\text{MnO(OH)}_2 + 2\text{KI} + \text{H}_2\text{O} \xrightarrow{\text{H}^+} \text{Mn(OH)}_2 + \text{I}_2 + 2\text{KOH}$$

The liberated iodine is then titrated with a standard sodium thiosulfate solution using starch as the indicator.

$$\text{I}_2 + 2\text{S}_2\text{O}_3^= \rightarrow \text{S}_4\text{O}_6^= + 2\text{I}^-$$

Oxidizable organic matter consumes iodine and thereby causes low results. This effect of organic matter can be minimized if the liberation of iodine is followed immediately by the titration with thiosulfate. Any readily oxidizable or reducible constituents interfere by reaction with either the iodine or thiosulfate. Oxidizable substances cause low results and reducible substances, high results. The magnitude of the net effect is, of course, proportionate to the absolute and relative concentrations of the different interferences.

In the procedure given, sodium azide eliminates the interference of nitrite, and potassium fluoride overcomes the effect of ferric salts, provided the ferric iron concentration does not exceed 200 mg. per liter and there is no delay in titration. The ferrous iron concentration should not exceed 1 mg. per liter. High concentrations of suspended solids, which interfere, are removed by alum flocculations.

When the method given is used on water which is not heavily polluted, the results are generally reproducible to ±0.01 mg., except that at low concentrations (below 0.1 mg.) the error may be ±50%.

*Apparatus.*—Burette, 25-ml.

*Reagents.* **Alum Solution, 6%**.—Dissolve 10 g. $AlK(SO_4)_2 \cdot 12H_2O$ in water and dilute to approximately 100 ml.

**Potassium Fluoride Solution, 25%**.—Dissolve 40 g. $KF \cdot 2H_2O$ in water and dilute to approximately 100 ml.

**Manganous Sulfate Solution, 32%**.—Dissolve 49 g. $MnSO_4 \cdot 4H_2O$ or 40 g. $MnSO_4 \cdot 2H_2O$ or 36 g. $MnSO_4 \cdot H_2O$ in water, filter, and dilute to approximately 100 ml.

**Alkaline-Iodide Reagent.**—Dissolve 50 g. NaOH or 70 g. KOH and 13.5 g. NaI or 15 g. KI in water and dilute to 100 ml.

**Alkaline-Iodide Sodium Azide Solution.**—Dissolve 1 g. $NaN_3$ in 4 ml. water. Add this solution with constant stirring to 95 ml. alkaline iodide reagent. The reagent should not give a color with starch indicator when diluted and acidified.

**Sulfuric Acid, Concentrated (sp. gr. 1.84).**

**Starch Indicator, Stable.**

**Sodium Thiosulfate, 0.025 N.**—Dissolve 6.205 g. $Na_2S_2O_3 \cdot 5H_2O$ in carbon dioxide-free water, add 1 g. $Na_2CO_3$, and dilute to 1000 ml. Store the thiosulfate in a glass-stoppered bottle which has been cleaned with dichromate-sulfuric acid cleaning solution and rinsed with hot water. Standardize the $Na_2S_2O_3$ against $KIO_3$ as follows: Dry approximately 1 g. $KIO_3$ for 2 hours at 180°C. Dissolve 0.8918 g. in water and dilute to 1000 ml. Pipette 25.000 ml. of the $KIO_3$ into a 250 ml. iodine flask, then add successively 75 ml. water and 2 g. KI. After solution is complete, add 10 ml. 20% $H_2SO_4$. Allow the stoppered flask to stand 5 minutes in the dark. Titrate with $Na_2S_2O_3$ using 2 ml. starch indicator as end point is approached.

$$\text{Normality of } Na_2S_2O_3 = \frac{\text{Vol. in ml. } KIO_3}{\text{Vol. in ml. } Na_2S_2O_3} \times 0.025$$

*Procedure.*—The method of sampling is critically important in the accurate determination of dissolved oxygen, or other dissolved gases, in water. The sampler itself should be chosen of a type suitable for the depth to be sampled, or if an integrated sample is desired, a depth integrating sampler should be used. The sample is then transferred to a narrow-mouthed, biological-oxygen-demand bottle which has a pointed glass stopper to avoid entrapment of air. However, if the sample must be transferred to a distant point, a pressure-sealed sample bottle should be used.

The bottle should be filled by a 2-fold or 3-fold displacement from the bottom.

To the sample bottle add 10 ml. of the alum solution and 1–2 ml. of concentrated $NH_4OH$. Mix by inversion and allow the flocculated material to settle. Decant into a smaller biological-oxygen-demand bottle until it overflows. Add successively 1 ml. of the potassium fluoride solution, 2 ml. of the manganese sulfate solution and 2 ml. of the alkaline-iodide sodium azide solution; on all three additions being made below the liquid surface. Stopper and mix by inversion. Allow the precipitate to settle and then repeat the mixing and settling processes. Add 2 ml. concentrated $H_2SO_4$ by allowing the acid to run down the neck of the bottle. Mix by gentle inversion until solution is complete.

From this treated sample withdraw by a pipette a volume that represents less than 2.0 mg. of oxygen (not exceeding 200 ml.). Titrate with the 0.25 N $Na_2S_2O_3$ to a pale straw color. Add 1–2 ml. starch indicator and continue the titration to the first disappearance of the blue color. Subsequent recoloration should be disregarded. Correct the sample volume reacted with $MnSO_4$ as follows:

$$\text{ml. Sample} = \frac{300 \times \text{ml. taken for flocculation}}{\text{ml. taken for flocculation} + \text{ml. of alum solution}}$$

$$\text{p. p. m. } O_2 = \frac{1}{\text{density}} \times \frac{1000}{\text{ml. sample}} \times \frac{(\text{ml. treated aliquot} + 7)}{\text{ml. treated aliquot}} \times \text{ml. } Na_2S_2O_3 \times 0.2$$

Report dissolved-oxygen concentration to 1 decimal place.

## DETERMINATIONS IN PROCESS MATERIALS AND PRODUCTS

### DETERMINATION OF DISSOLVED OXYGEN IN CYANIDE SOLUTIONS [3]

The method described is a modification of Schutzenberger's whereby the solution in titrations and the standards are protected from the atmosphere by a layer of kerosene. Indigo-disulfonate is the indicator and sodium hydrosulfite the standard. The method is rapid and delicate. It has been tried on a variety of mill solutions and mill men have found the method of value.

The important part that dissolved oxygen plays in the cyanide treatment of gold and silver ores is commonly recognized by most metallurgists and mill men. The method herein described was devised for the use of the mill man. It is a modification of the Schutzenberger method and depends on the reducing action of a sodium hydrosulfite solution on a solution of indigo blue (indigotindisulfonate). The method determines oxygen accurately to tenths of a milligram per liter of solution or one part of oxygen in 10,000,000 parts of solution on a 250-ml. solution sample, with a proportionately greater degree of accuracy on larger amounts of solution samples.

*Saturation of Oxygen in Solution.*—The saturation of oxygen in solution is taken as that maximum quantity of oxygen which dissolves from free air, which

[3] By A. J. Weinig, E.Met., Director of Experimental Plant, Colorado School of Mines, and Max W. Bowen, Golden, Colo.

is very much less than the quantity of oxygen that dissolves in pure water from an atmosphere of pure oxygen. The amount of oxygen that dissolves in water depends on the atmosphere from which it is derived and, except in the case of hydrogen, this solubility is well explained by Dalton's law of partial pressures of gases. Salts dissolved in the water also affect the oxygen solubility but, under the usual concentrations found in practice, this is relatively unimportant. The oxygen content of air-saturated water is a function of the pressure and tempera-

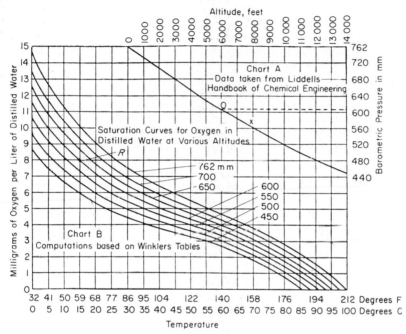

FIG. 34-9. Saturation Curves for Oxygen in Distilled Water.

ture; Winkler's results are shown in Fig. 34-9. From this chart, the saturation point can be quickly determined for all localities and temperatures.

*Altitude-Pressure and Standard Saturation Curves.*—Chart *A*, Fig. 34-9, is used to determine barometric pressures at various altitudes; chart *B* is used to determine standard saturation values for various temperatures and pressures. In chart *A*, altitudes, in feet, are plotted on the horizontal axis and pressures, in millimeters, on the vertical axis. To find the pressure corresponding to a certain altitude, follow the elevation line downward to its intersection with the curve *X* then horizontally to the right and read the pressure. For example, if the elevation is 6000 ft., the 6000-ft. line is followed to its intersection *O* with the curve *X* then the corresponding pressure, 607 mm., is obtained from the right-hand side of the chart.

In chart *B*, temperatures are plotted on the horizontal axis and the amount of oxygen, in milligrams per liter of distilled water, is plotted on the vertical axis; various pressure curves also are plotted, as shown. To find the saturation value for a certain temperature and pressure follow the temperature line upwards until the point corresponding to a given pressure is reached, then follow horizontally across to the left-hand side of the chart and read off the amount, in milligrams, of oxygen per liter of solution. For example, to determine the amount of oxygen in a solution having a temperature of 59°F., at an elevation of 6000 ft. It has already been found that at an elevation of 6000 ft. the pressure is 607 mm.; therefore the 607-mm. pressure curve must be used; that is, it is necessary to interpolate between the 600-mm. and the 650-mm. curves. The 59°F. line is followed to its intersection $R$ with the 607-mm. curve, then from the left-hand side of the chart is read off 8 mg. of oxygen per liter. The same procedure is used for the various pressures, using the curve corresponding to the particular pressure. For any particular plant, a solubility curve for that elevation should be plotted.

*Oxygen-Saturated Water or Solution.*—The standard for comparison is air-saturated water or solution. This is best made by placing 1 liter of water or solution in a 2-liter Winchester bottle and violently blowing air through it. With distilled water or pure tap water, 20 to 30 minutes' aeration will insure saturation; but with mill solutions that contain hydrogen, saturation can only be attained by aerating at least for an hour. Solutions fresh from precipitation saturate with great difficulty; it may take several hours aeration to wash out the dissolved hydrogen before complete oxygen saturation can be attained. After this aeration is completed, the solution should remain for ½ hour or longer at a constant temperature to insure the complete elimination of finely disseminated undissolved air bubbles, which would otherwise interfere. When using water for this standardization, it is well to add a little lime before aeration so as to produce alkalinity similar to the conditions found with cyanide solutions. This alkalinity does not materially affect the solubility of oxygen but is desirable so that the following procedure may be as near like that of cyanide solution as possible. When convenient, it is desirable to use distilled water.

*Apparatus.*—The apparatus required for this test are: Two Winchester acid bottles $A$, $B$, Fig. 34-10, 2.5-liters capacity; one 250-ml. flask $C$, one 50-ml. burette $D$ with side connection; one common 50-ml. burette $E$; one clamp stand $F$ to hold burettes in position; one 400-ml. beaker with the 250-ml. point marked on it; one special glass stirring rod, shown in Fig. 34-11; glass or lead tubing ($\frac{3}{16}$ in.) for connections; rubber tubing for connections; one pinchcock $G$ for bottom of rubber connection on burette that contains standard hydrosulfite solution; one container for kerosene to be used in the procedure.

When setting up the apparatus, the relative position of the different parts shown in Fig. 34-10 must be closely followed. As there is a siphoning action from bottle $A$ to bottle $B$ and from bottle $B$ to the burette $D$, the bottom of bottle $A$ must be above the top of bottle $B$ and also above the top of the burette $D$; also the bottom of the flask $C$ should be above top of the burette $D$, for convenience. Bottle $B$ contains the standard solution; as this standard deteriorates very rapidly, if exposed to the air, the bottle must be sealed air tight. This may be done in the following manner: Place a cork—not rubber—with two holes for the tubing in the neck of the bottle so that there is about 1″ between the top of the cork and the top of the neck of the bottle, as shown in $A$, Fig. 34-10. Place the tubing in the cork as shown, then pour melted shellac above the cork so as to fill the space completely. Care must be taken not to break the tubing or the neck of the bottle with the hot shellac; this danger may be avoided by having the glass perfectly dry and heating it before pouring in the hot shellac.

The bottles are filled in the following manner: Remove the connection $X$ and place a cork in the top of the burette $D$ so that no solution can overflow. Place a bottle containing 2.5 liters of kerosene so that its bottom is above the top of bottle $A$ and connect this bottle to the bottom of the burette $D$ with a siphon.

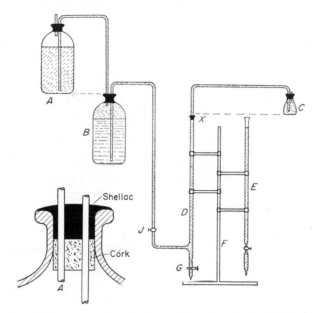

FIG. 34-10. Apparatus for Determining Oxygen in Solution.

Open the pinchcock $G$ and the stopcock $J$ and allow kerosene to siphon into bottle $B$ until it is filled. Replace the bottle which contained kerosene by a bottle containing the standard solution of hydrosulfite. This solution should always be covered with a layer of kerosene; siphon the standard solution into bottle $B$, the kerosene being forced from bottle $B$ over into bottle A automatically. As soon as the standard hydrosulfite solution has reached to within 1″ or 2″ of the top of bottle $B$, close both the pinchcock $G$ and the stopcock $J$. After the flask $C$ has been nearly filled with kerosene, place the connection $X$ in top of the burette $D$ and seal with dry shellac dissolved in alcohol. Open the stopcock $J$, the pinchcock $G$ being kept closed, and allow the standard solution to pass into the burette $D$ until it just enters the flask $C$; then close the stopcock $J$, open the pinchcock $G$, and allow the standard solution to drain out completely; its action as a siphon will draw the kerosene over into the burette $D$. The standard solution is now drained off so as to eliminate any possibility of its being exposed to air and to give it a cover of kerosene in the burette $D$. Close the pinchcock $G$, open the stopcock $J$, and allow the burette $D$ to fill to the zero mark. The layer of kerosene prevents the admission of air during this procedure. Then the apparatus is ready for use. Fill the burette $E$ with the indigo disulfonate solution and place a test tube or glass cover over the top to prevent evaporation.

FIG. 34-11. Stirrer.

*Reagents.*—A very convenient amount of standard sodium hydrosulfite solution is made up as follows. Fill a Winchester acid bottle, 2.5-liter capacity, with distilled water. Preferably it should be freshly distilled so as to be as free from oxygen as possible but this is not essential. Dissolve 5 g. of sodium hydroxide in this bottle by gently revolving. When all the sodium hydroxide is dissolved, add 5 g. of sodium hydrosulfite to the solution and immediately place a layer of kerosene over the solution. When all the salts are dissolved, siphon into the bottle *B* for standard solution. The caustic soda preserves the hydrosulfite and enters into the reaction during titration.

The indicator, indigotin disulfonate, is made up as follows: Place in a casserole 7 g. of indigotin and add 30 ml. of concentrated sulfuric acid. Place over water bath and heat to 90°C. for 1.5 hours, or until all lumps disappear. Then dilute to 2 liters with distilled water. Neutralize the acidity by adding powdered limestone, small portions at a time and allowing it to stand for a few minutes between additions, until all action has ceased. Filter without washing, place in a corked bottle, and use as necessary in the procedure. It is convenient to dilute this solution so that 1 ml. of the indicator is equivalent to 0.25 mg. of oxygen per liter of solution. This will indicate 1 g. per liter when a solution sample of 250 ml. is taken for titration.

**Standardization of Solutions.**—Into the clean, dry, graduated 400-ml. beaker place one drop of phenolphthalein indicator and cover with a ¾" layer of kerosene. Care should be used to avoid entrapping air bubbles. The oxygen-saturated water is now siphoned into the beaker below the kerosene. The line of demarcation between the kerosene and the solution is made distinct by the red color produced with the indicator in the alkaline water; thereby a close measurement of the water can be attained. When 250 ml. of water have been measured out beneath the kerosene, the alkalinity is neutralized with dilute sulfuric acid from a burette, the tip of which extends below the surface of the solution; 1 ml. of the indigotin disulfonate solution is then run in beneath the kerosene. The solution is now titrated with the hydrosulfite solution. The tip of the burette must dip beneath the kerosene so that, by constant stirring with the special stirring rod (Fig. 34-11), any entry of air is avoided. In the titration the hydrosulfite first reacts with the dissolved oxygen; as the end point is reached the hydrosulfite decolorizes the indigotin disulfonate and the end point is yellow or yellowish white. When this point is reached, the burette is read and noted and 5 ml. of indigotin disulfonate solution is run in, all of the above precautions being taken; this is again followed by titration with the hydrosulfite. This operation gives the required relationships between the various solutions.

Assume that the water showed a saturation of 8 mg. per liter for the particular temperature and pressure, and that the titration gave 9 ml. hydrosulfite standard followed by 5.5 ml. more, after 5 ml. of the indigotin disulfonate standard was added. Then 5 ml. indigotin = 5.5 ml. hydrosulfite; and 1 ml. indigotin = 1.1 ml. hydrosulfite. Also, as 1 ml. of the indigotin was used at the start, one must correct the first hydrosulfite titration for the 1 ml. indigotin used, which is 1.1 ml.

The amount of hydrosulfite then consumed on the dissolved oxygen is, 9.0 ml. − 1.1 ml. = 7.9 ml. Now, 7.9 ml. hydrosulfite = 8 mg. oxygen per liter, or 1 ml. hydrosulfite = 8.0 ÷ 7.9 = 1.01 mg. oxygen per liter, when 250 ml. of the saturated water is titrated. Also, 1 ml. indigotin disulfonate standard is equivalent to $\dfrac{1.1 \times 1.01}{4} = \dfrac{1.11}{4} = 0.28$ mg. oxygen.

The indigotin disulfonate does not deteriorate and may be kept in a well-stoppered bottle. When once standardized, it may be used to check the standard hydrosulfite solution instead of making up aerated water. In this case, sufficient water should be added to the indigotin disulfonate solution until 1 ml. exactly equals 0.25 mg. oxygen.

*Titration of Mill Solutions.*—When once the hydrosulfite and indigotin disulfonate solutions are standardized, the procedure with routine solution titrations is simple. The solution is siphoned over beneath the kerosene into the 400-ml. beaker until 250 ml. are obtained, the alkalinity is then neutralized with dilute sulfuric acid, 1 ml. or less of indigotin disulfonate is added as an indicator, and titration is completed with the hydrosulfite. Following this, the necessary correction is made for the indicator and the result is converted to milligrams of oxygen per liter of solution, or per cent saturation as may be desired. The kerosene may be used several times by pouring the contents of the beaker into a large bottle, after titration, then siphoning off the kerosene for reuse after sufficient accumulation.

Fig. 34-12. Sampling Device for Mill Solutions.

**Precautions.**—After the aeration of the solution in the standardization process, sufficient time must be allowed for all entrapped air bubbles to escape before titration or the end point will "go back" rapidly and erroneous results are obtained.

When stirring the solution during titration, care must be taken not to introduce air into the solution. This stirring is done by revolving the special stirring rod between the thumb and fingers, holding it vertically.

A cover of kerosene should always be kept over the solution.

When mill solutions are used to standardize the hydrosulfite solution, care must be taken that they are thoroughly saturated as they saturate much more slowly than tap or distilled water. It sometimes requires more than an hour to saturate them completely.

The end point in clear solutions is a slight yellow; but if solutions contain certain salts, or are cloudy, the end point color may be white or milky, or sometimes gray.

All connections through which the standard solution pass must be sealed airtight. This is best done with shellac.

When neutralizing the alkalinity of the solution for titration, care must be taken that it is just neutral to phenolphthalein. If it is too acid, the titration will be low; if it is too alkaline, the titration will be too high.

Manipulation in the procedure must be as rapid as possible without sacrificing accuracy, for notwithstanding the cover of kerosene, there will be a slow absorption of oxygen through the kerosene.

If the end point is over-run, back titration can be made with the standard indigotin sulfonate; or, if more desirable, an excess of hydrosulfite solution may be run in and the excess titrated with indigotin disulfonate standard.

*Sampling of Mill Solutions.*—Reasonably clear mill solutions are best sampled by using a bottle, as shown in Fig. 34-12. This bottle forms part of a siphon, into which a sample may be safely transported to the laboratory. When sampling, the end of the tube that reaches to the bottom of the flask is connected through a pinchcock and tubing to the tank, launder, or other source of solutions to be tested. The tube that just reaches through the cork is also connected to rubber tubing and has a pinchcock. The connections are made as shown and the siphon started by suction. After the bottle is filled with solution, the apparatus is allowed to run for a while to replace any contaminated solutions. The pinchcocks are then closed and the bottle may be transported to the place for titration.

Pulps require settlement before the solutions can be removed for titrations. In this case, it is best to fill a Winchester bottle completely with pulp, close the bottle with its cork, and allow the whole to stand until the solution can be siphoned off.

Examinations made of many operating plant solutions give the following ranges of results:

|  | Per cent of maximum oxygen saturation |
|---|---|
| General circulating plant solutions................ | 7 to 75 |
| Agitator solutions.............................. | 0 to 50 |
| Leaching-plant effluent......................... | 0 to 50 |
| Crowe vacuum operation removes as a rule, one-half of the oxygen contained in its feed. | |
| Precipitation plant barrens...................... | 0 |
| Concentrate treatment agitator solutions.......... | 0 |

## DETERMINATION OF OXYGEN IN STEEL

The properties of steel are affected by the presence of oxygen so that its determination is being recognized as an essential one in the analysis of this product. It occurs in steel as occluded oxygen and as combined oxygen, i.e. oxides of iron, aluminum, manganese, silicon, titanium, etc. The following method determines the occluded oxygen and the oxygen combined with iron, but does not determine that combined with manganese, aluminum, and silicon, as these oxides are not reduced by hydrogen.

The method depends upon the combination of hydrogen with the oxygen of iron when the latter is heated in a current of hydrogen; the water formed is absorbed and weighed and the oxygen calculated.

The apparatus shown in Fig. 34-13 operates in such a way that the hydrogen generated by the action of HCl on zinc is purified by passing through the wash bottles $B$, $C$, $D$, containing KOH and $H_2SO_4$, oxygen in the gas is removed by passing through a preheated tube containing platinum gauze or palladiumized asbestos, the water formed being absorbed in the $P_2O_5$ in $G$. The pure hydrogen now combines with the oxygen of the sample and the water formed is absorbed in $P_2O_5$ in the tube $J$.

*Procedure.*—The apparatus is connected up as shown in Fig. 34-13 and hydrogen gas passed through for 5 to 10 minutes. The $P_2O_5$ tube is now weighed as in regular test (see "Notes"), the tube being disconnected from $K$, which is used as a guard to prevent moisture being absorbed by an accidental back suction of air.

The sample of 20 to 30 g. of the steel borings are placed in a nickel boat ($\frac{1}{2}'' \times \frac{1}{2}'' \times 6''$) and this inserted quickly through the opening at "$a$" into the combustion tube, the current of hydrogen flowing through the tube. The absorption tube $J$ and its guard are connected up and the heat turned on. (All connections should be air tight.) The temperature of bright-red heat (850°C.)

is desired. The hydrogen is passed at a rate of about 100 ml. per minute, the rate having been previously established by the speed of bubbles in *D*. After 30 minutes the heat is turned off, the top of the hinged furnace lifted, and the tube raised and allowed to cool, hydrogen gas still passing. A blast of air assists the cooling.

The cocks *"c"* and *"d"* of *J* are turned off in the order named, the exit end of the guard *K* closed and the two connected placed in the balance for about 10

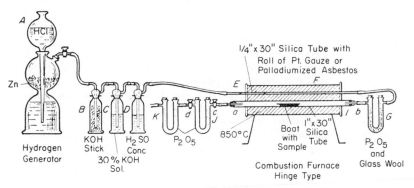

FIG. 34-13. Apparatus for Determining Oxygen in Steel.

minutes. The exit end of the guard is now opened, the cock *"d"* quickly opened and shut, thus obtaining atmospheric pressure in the tube *J* without intake of air. The guard is now disconnected and *J* is weighed. The increase of weight due to absorbed water is multiplied by 0.889 to obtain the weight of occluded oxygen and the oxygen combined with iron.

NOTES.—The tube *J* is weighed before and after the test filled with hydrogen under atmospheric pressure and at the same temperature, so that it is not necessary to aspirate air through the tube as is sometimes recommended. The preliminary run for obtaining the initial weight should be conducted under conditions the same as in the final test, the tubes *J* and *K* being closed, transferred to the balance and *J* finally weighed as stated at the end of the procedure, so that the conditions will be the same in regard to the inclosed hydrogen or the tube.

The $P_2O_5$ tubes are charged by packing alternate layers of $P_2O_5$ and glass wool, beginning and ending with the latter, otherwise the powder will pack and prevent the passage of gas.

The drilling of the samples should be done slowly to prevent heating, the drills being free of grease or oil. The sample should be taken from several sections of the ingot, whose surface has been cleaned by a cutting tool or by emery.

The apparatus should be tested for leaks as described under "Determination of Hydrogen in Steel" in the Chapter on Hydrogen.

## INSTRUCTIONS FOR THE ANALYSIS
## OF COMMERCIAL OXYGEN [4]

A method for the determination of oxygen in gas mixtures containing from 95 to 100% oxygen is based on the fact that clean bright copper oxidizes rapidly in the presence of ammonia vapor. The oxide that is formed is dissolved by a saturated solution of ammonium chloride, thus exposing fresh copper to the remaining gas.

[4] Standard method of the Linde Company, Division of Union Carbide Corp.

*Apparatus.*—The apparatus for the determination of oxygen in commercial oxygen is shown assembled in Fig. 34-14. The various units making up this assembly are designated by letters and these will be used in identifying the pieces of equipment in this description.

The sample is measured in burette *A* and transferred through the transparent tubing *S* and the connecting tube *E* to the absorption pipette *B*. The displaced pipette solution passes into the storage pipette *C* by means of the tee tube *D*.

The aspirator bottle *F* is connected to the burette *A* by means of about 42 inches of rubber tubing *J*. The aspirator bottle and the burette both contain distilled water and transference of the gas sample from the burette to the pipette is accomplished by raising and lowering of the aspirator bottle.

The Bakelite support *T* is used to adjust the level of the copper coils in *B* and is held in position by friction on the sides of the hole in rubber stopper *V*. Clip *M* is used to hold this stopper in position.

The glassware is mounted on a metal frame *L* by means of the clamps *R*, *P* and *N*. This frame is secured to a base *K* and the whole structure keyed to the shaft of a pendulum shaking apparatus.

*Preparation of Solutions.*—The absorption liquid for use in the pipette *B* consists of a solution of equal volumes of ammonium hydroxide ($NH_4OH$) and distilled water, saturated with ammonium chloride ($NH_4Cl$).

The ammonium hydroxide shall be of C.P. grade of 0.90 specific gravity. The ammonium chloride should be of the grade technically known as white ammonium chloride. Water used in the preparation of the pipette solution and in the burette should be distilled water. Electrically "purified" and other special waters still contain impurities that might introduce errors in the results obtained and therefore must not be used.

*Procedure.*—Measure out 6 quarts of distilled water and pour it into a clean 5-gallon bottle. Measure out 6 quarts of ammonium hydroxide and add it to the distilled water in the 5-gallon bottle. Weigh out 9 pounds of ammonium chloride and add it to the solution of water and ammonium hydroxide in the 5-gallon bottle.

Stopper the 5-gallon bottle containing the mixture with a rubber stopper and agitate by shaking the bottle every 10 minutes for a period of 2 hours. Allow the bottle and its contents to stand for a period of 8 hours. Pour off the quantity of solution required for immediate use, being careful not to stir up the material that has settled to the bottom. Restopper the 5-gallon bottle with a rubber stopper and store it in a cool place.

Distilled water is used as the burette liquid.

*Preparation of Apparatus for Test.*—Prepare copper spirals by winding about two feet of clean No. 20 copper wire on a rod ¼" in diameter. Fill pipette *B* with the spirals to within one inch of the opening for the stopper *V*. Insert the Bakelite support *T* through the hole in the center of the rubber stopper *V* and place the stopper in the position shown in Fig. 33-14. Adjust the Bakelite support until the copper spirals reach to about ¼" from the top of the pipette.

Install the pipettes and the burette on the metal frame and make all connections as shown in Fig. 34-14. Grease the three-way stopcock on the burette *A*, applying the stopcock grease sparingly so as to avoid plugging the passages. Remove the rubber stopper *G* from the pipette *C*; close off the pipettes by means of the three-way stopcock on burette *A*. Fill the pipette *C* with ammonium chloride pipette solution. Replace stopper *G* and open the pipettes to the air by turning the

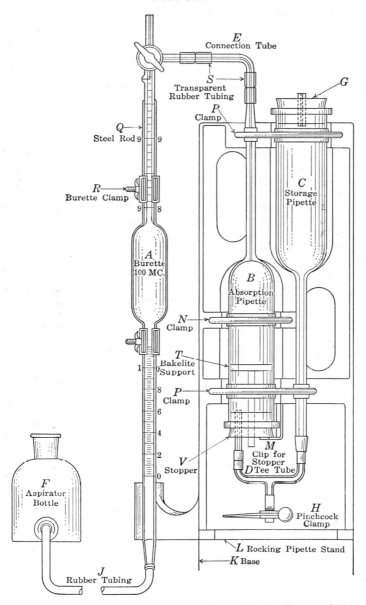

FIG. 34-14.  Apparatus for the Determination of $O_2$ in Commercial $O_2$.

$A$ = 100-ml. oxygen burette; $B$ = Absorption pipette; $C$ = Storage pipette; $D$ = Glass T-tube; $E$ = Glass connection tube; $F$ = Aspirator bottle, 250 ml. $G$ = No. 10 rubber stopper; $H$ = Mohr pinchcock clamp, small size; $J$ = $5/16''$ outer diameter rubber tubing; $K$ = Base for rocking pipette stand; $L$ = Rocking pipette stand; $M$ = Clip for absorption pipette stopper; $N$ = Clamp with wing nuts; $P$ = Clamps with wing nuts (2 required); $Q$ = $7/16''$ steel rod, $16\frac{1}{2}''$ long; $R$ = Burette clamps (2 required); $S$ = Transparent rubber tubing of 5 mm. bore, $1\frac{3}{4}$ mm. wall; $T$ = Bakelite support; $V$ = No. 10 rubber stopper.

stopcock on *A*. The pipette liquid should then stand above the constrictions in both pipettes.

Connect the aspirator bottle *F* to the burette *A* by means of 42″ of tubing *J*, and fill the bottle with 150 ml. of distilled water. Turn the burette stopcock so that the burette and the pipette are connected, and draw over into the burette any gas in the pipette by lowering the aspirator bottle. Turn the stopcock to open the burette to the air, and, by raising the aspirator bottle, force out this gas, at the same time filling the burette with water from the aspirator bottle until it flows from the short tube above the stopcock, which hereafter will be called the *sampling connection*.

"Season" the pipette solution by transferring five samples of approximately 100 ml. each of commercial oxygen from the burette to the pipette. Shake for three minutes and then draw the residual gases back into the burette as before. Open the burette to the air and by raising the aspirator bottle force the gas out of the burette until the water from the bottle flows out of the sampling connection. Close the stopcock and the apparatus is ready for accurate testing.

*Procedure.*—Purge the sampling hose and the source of supply by starting a flow of gas through the rubber hose connected to this source. Attach the rubber tubing to the sampling connection, open the stopcock quickly to permit the oxygen to flow into the burette only. Take a sample of slightly over 100 ml. before closing the stopcock. Allow 15 seconds for the water to drain down the walls of the burette; then adjust the volume of the gas to exactly 100 ml. by holding the aspirator bottle so that its liquid level is on a line with the zero graduation of the burette, gradually opening the stopcock to the atmosphere, discharging the excess gas until the meniscus of the liquid is also even with the zero mark. Close the stopcock immediately to prevent too much sample being discharged or air being drawn in. Turn the stopcock so as to connect the burette with the pipette and, by raising the aspirator bottle, pass the entire sample over into the absorption pipette. Be sure that the last bubble of gas has been forced into the pipette and that the liquid fills the entire capillary tube; then close the stopcock.

Set the apparatus in motion and allow it to shake for exactly 3 minutes. Stop the apparatus and immediately turn the stopcock to connect the burette and pipette; draw the remaining gas back into the burette by lowering the aspirator bottle. Be sure that no bubbles of gas remain in the pipette or connecting tube; also be careful to pass the least possible amount of pipette solution into the burette. Then close the stopcock. Allow 15 seconds for drainage of liquid down the walls of the burette. Remove the aspirator bottle from its stand and hold it so that the liquid in it and in the burette is at exactly the same level and take the burette reading at the lower edge of the meniscus. This reading gives directly the volume of oxygen in milliliters that was contained in the sample, and as the total sample taken was 100 ml. the reading indicates the percentage of oxygen in the gas.

A fresh solution should be good for from 60 to 70 tests on commercial oxygen before it becomes spent.

The solution need not be changed until brown solid matter is deposited on the glass of the absorption bottle.

The precipitate deposited in the pipette serves as a warning, but the solution will still give correct results for a few additional tests. Change the burette water at the same time as the pipette solution.

**Precautions.**—Be sure that the glass bottle used for storage of the pipette solution is tightly stoppered to prevent loss of ammonia. A rubber or ground-glass stopper should be used. Corks should never be used with ammonia.

Be sure that the water used in the preparation of the solution is distilled water.

Do not allow the solutions to come near the mouth, nose or eyes, as painful injury may result.

Be sure that the copper coils are kept within $\frac{1}{4}''$ of the top of the pipette but that enough free space is allowed to eliminate the trapping of bubbles in this zone.

The upper part of the burette is graduated in one-tenth milliliters (0.1 ml.), so that the reading may be made directly to this amount and it should always be estimated to one-half division, or the five one-hundredths of a milliliter (0.05 ml.). Thus if the lower edge of the meniscus is halfway between the 99.50 and the 99.60 marks, the reading is 99.55.

Inspect the burette frequently for accumulations of dirt and grease, and, if these are noted, remove and clean the burette. In order to clean a burette the stopcock plug is first removed. The larger particles of grease can then be easily removed by means of a piece of soft copper wire bent at the end. This wire is admitted to the burette through the opening into the stopcock and is moved around until a lump of grease adheres to it. It is then removed, wiped off, and the process repeated. After most of the grease has been removed, a grease film will generally remain on the glass. A small swab of absorbent cotton moistened with carbon tetrachloride and wound tightly around a piece of wire will remove this film. Failure to keep the top of the burette clean may result in errors as great as 0.1%.

# Chapter 35

# PHOSPHORUS *

*P, at. wt.* 30.9738; *two crystalline allotropes of* white P, *three to five crystalline and one amorphous allotropic modifications of* red P, *and a crystalline and an amorphous modification of* black P; *one liquid form of the element,* $P_4$. *Well-established oxides,* $P_4O_6$, $(PO_2)_x$, *and three crystalline, one amorphous, and two liquid forms of* $(P_2O_5)_x$. *Established acids,* $H_3PO_2$, $H_3PO_3$, $H_4P_2O_5$, $H_4P_2O_6$, $H_3PO_4$, $H_{n+2}P_nO_{3n+1}$ *with n* = 2, 3, 4, 5, . . . , *ca.* $10^5$, $H_3(PO_3)_3$, $H_4(PO_3)_4$.

Although the Arabian alchemists probably isolated elemental phosphorus as early as the Twelfth Century, discovery of this element is usually attributed to Brand in 1669. The name phosphorus, meaning light-bearer, was first applied to all substances that glowed in the dark but was later restricted to this element. About nine-tenths of the phosphorus (combined or uncombined) commercially utilized in the United States goes into the production of fertilizers, primarily superphosphates. Phosphate fertilizers are usually made by direct treatment of the ore with acids. Over a half billion pounds of elemental phosphorus are produced annually by electric furnaces in the United States. The majority of this phosphorus is converted into phosphoric acid, a large part of which is used in the manufacture of sodium and calcium salts. Sodium tripolyphosphate and tetrasodium pyrophosphate are the main detergent builders. In addition, phosphoric acid and its sodium and calcium salts are widely used in foodstuffs and for a large variety of other applications. Phosphorus is also employed in metal technology.

Phosphorus occurs to some extent in nearly all igneous rocks but is commonly mined from secondary deposits of marine origin. Phosphorus is essential to all living matter and is found in high concentration in bones and teeth. The metabolism of all known forms of life is believed to involve phosphorus, and, hence, this element is widely distributed in plant and animal tissues. Except for a few rare minerals found only in meteorites, phosphorus, in both inorganic and organic matter, is always present in nature as the phosphate, the most stable oxidation state. Of the more than one hundred established phosphate minerals, the following are important: fluor- and hydroxyapatites, $Ca_5F(PO_4)_3$, $Ca_5(OH)(PO_4)_3$; pyromorphite, $Pb_5Cl(PO_4)_3$; wavellite, $Al_3(OH)_3(PO_4)_2 \cdot 5H_2O$; turquoise, $H_5Al_6$-$Cu(OH)_{13}(PO_4)_4$; vivianite, $Fe_3(PO_4)_2 \cdot 8H_2O$; and monazite, (Ce, La, Di) $PO_4$.

* This chapter has been prepared by Editha Karl-Kroupa, Research Analyst, Monsanto Chemical Company, Dayton, Ohio; John R. Van Wazer, Assistant Director of Research, Monsanto Chemical Company, Dayton, Ohio and Cecil H. Russell, Chief Plant Chemist, Monsanto Chemical Company, Trenton, Michigan. These three contributors wish to acknowledge their indebtedness to many other investigators, notably the chief chemists and analytical staffs of various Monsanto plants. In particular, the laboratories at the Monsanto, Tennessee (Albert B. Finley, Chief Chemist) and the Trenton, Michigan (Cecil H. Russell, Chief Chemist) plants have made important contributions.

Until the last few years, misunderstanding as to the nature of the various condensed phosphates and their acids was nearly universal. Most analytical papers, even including some of today's publications, follow the obsolete notation of Thomas Graham, in which all phosphates are considered to be either ortho- ($H_3PO_4$), pyro- ($H_4P_2O_7$), or meta- ($HPO_3$) phosphates. It is now unequivocally known [1] that the materials that Thomas Graham classified in 1833 as metaphosphates or mixtures of meta- and pyrophosphates consist of three general types of condensed phosphates: a series of chain phosphates, which are called polyphosphates (general formula of the acids: $H_{n+2}P_nO_{3n+1}$); the ring phosphates for which the term metaphosphate should still be used (general formula of the acids: $H_m(PO_3)_m$); and highly branched structures called ultraphosphates. Since the ultraphosphates are extremely unstable in aqueous solution, they are not of interest to the analyst.

It should be noted that as $n$ becomes very large, the polyphosphate formula approaches the empirical composition of the metaphosphate formula, and thus the long-chain phosphates were formerly erroneously classified as "metaphosphates." For $n$ equaling 1, 2, 3, and 4, the polyphosphate formula gives, respectively, the orthophosphate ($H_3PO_4$), the pyrophosphate ($H_4P_2O_7$), the triphosphate—often called tripolyphosphate—($H_5P_3O_{10}$), and the tetraphosphate ($H_6P_4O_{13}$). Thus, the orthophosphate is the monomer of the polyphosphate series, and the pyrophosphate is the dimer of the series, or the first truly chain phosphate. Crystalline sodium triphosphate is an important article of commerce, and lead tetraphosphate has also been crystallized. The vitreous sodium phosphates of commerce consist of mixtures of variously sized polyphosphates. In general, vitreous sodium phosphates have an average value of $n$ in the polyphosphate formula ranging from 4–200. There are also several varieties of crystalline sodium phosphates having high molecular weights, corresponding to $n$ as great as 20,000. Two ring metaphosphates are known. These are the trimetaphosphate ($m = 3$) and the tetrametaphosphate ($m = 4$). In this chapter, the correct, modern notation will be used exclusively; but in turning to the literature, the reader is cautioned about the obsolete terminology which he will probably find there.

## DETECTION

The general procedure for detecting phosphorus in any compound is based on the reaction between orthophosphoric acid and molybdate to give a yellow precipitate in strongly acid solution (pH below 2). After the sample is brought into soluble form, it is fumed with aqua regia almost to dryness to oxidize lower oxidation states of phosphorus that might be present. Add 10 ml. of 1 $N$ $HNO_3$ and boil gently for 10–20 minutes, in order to convert condensed phosphates (chain and ring structures) to the orthophosphate form. To half of this solution, add an equal volume of the acid molybdate solution described on p. 814. If a yellow precipitate occurs, phosphorus and/or arsenic are present. In this case, precipitate any arsenic with $H_2S$ from the second portion of the solution being tested, filter, remove $H_2S$, and again add the acid molybdate solution. A yellow precipitate indicates the presence of phosphorus.

[1] Van Wazer, J. R., Encyclopedia of Chemical Technology (Kirk and Othmer, Editors), Vol. **X,** pp. 403–510, Interscience, N. Y., 1953.

*Element.*—Phosphorus may be detected by its property of burning in air to give white fumes. The white varieties are spontaneously combustible at room temperature, but both the red and black varieties have to be heated to cause ignition.

Since white phosphorus and its vapors are highly poisonous, a sensitive method for detection of small amounts of this material is often used. This method consists of steam distilling the phosphorus from an aqueous slurry of the sample which was adjusted to a pH of about 3 with tartaric acid. The slurry is placed in a closed flask, and the vapors are led into a water-cooled glass condenser pointing downwards. In a darkened room, the appearance of flashes of light in the condenser indicates the presence of white phosphorus. To avoid interference from phosphorus sulfides, it is advisable to introduce live steam into the flask, rather than heating it directly. Boiling should be continued for an appreciable length of time, since certain interfering substances may prevent detection of phosphorus during the first part of the run. Minute traces of white phosphorus can be detected by this method.

*Various Oxidation States.*—Mixtures of the acids and/or salts of phosphorus in various states of oxidation have been separated and detected by electrophoretic and diffusion paper chromatography.[2]

Phosphites and hypophosphites can be distinguished from phosphates by the ignitable phosphine gas formed when acid solutions of the former are treated with metallic zinc.

*Phosphates.*—Orthophosphates form yellow precipitates with ammonium molybdate in cold (4°C.) acid solution; whereas, neither the poly-(chain) nor meta-(ring) phosphates show this behavior. Silver nitrate at pH 3–4 gives a yellow precipitate with orthophosphates, white precipitates with polyphosphates, and no precipitates at reasonably dilute concentrations with the ring metaphosphates. When 2 ml. of an albumin solution, made either by saturating distilled water with fresh egg white or by adding 1% of crystalline albumin to distilled water, is mixed with 3 ml. of a 0.2 N acetic acid solution containing a trace of the phosphate under test, a turbid or flocculant precipitate forms with long-chain phosphates but not with orthophosphates or ring metaphosphates. With increasing phosphate concentration in the solution, shorter chain phosphates can be detected. Chains as short as the pyro- and triphosphates do not coagulate egg albumin. This test is sensitive to the molecular weight of the albumin used, as well as to the molecular weight of the polyphosphate.

Two-dimensional paper chromatography is the best qualitative technique for identifying constituents in mixtures of orthophosphates with ring and short-chain phosphates. A droplet (ca. 0.005 ml.) of solution containing from 1 to 20 mg. of the phosphate mixture is placed on a pencil-marked spot an inch from both edges at one corner of a 9″ by 9″ sheet of S&S 589, Orange Ribbon, filter paper. The sheet is formed into a cylinder, keeping the opposite edges of the filter paper apart by platinum wire clips and considering the end near the marked spot as the bottom of the cylinder. The cylinder is placed in a closed glass jar and exposed for two hours to the vapors of the chromatographic solvent to be used. An alkaline chromatographic solvent consisting of 40 ml. of isopropyl alcohol, 20 ml. of isobutyl alcohol, 39 ml. of water, and 1 ml. of concentrated ammonium hydroxide is then allowed to diffuse evenly upward through the paper cylinder which is still kept in the closed jar. Before the solvent reaches the upper edge of the

[2] Klement, R., and Frieser, H., Angew. Chem., **66**, 138, 1954 and Volmar, Y., Ebel, J. P., and Bassili, Y. F., Bull. soc. chim. France, **20**, 1085, 1953.

paper (about 8 hours), the paper is removed from the jar, dried in a freely hanging position, and again coiled into a cylinder, the axis of which is at right angles to that of the original cylinder. The marked spot should be at the bottom, and exposure to vapor must again be used before the second solvent is allowed to diffuse. This solvent is acidic and is composed of 75 ml. isopropyl alcohol, 25 ml. water, 5 g. trichloroacetic acid, and 0.3 ml. concentrated ammonium hydroxide. After the acid solvent has diffused up the paper cylinder (as made up for the second time) for about 8 hours, the paper is again dried and then sprayed with an acid molybdate solution made from 1 g. $(NH_4)_2MoO_4$, 5 ml. 72% $HClO_4$, 1 ml. concentrated HCl, and 100 ml. $H_2O$. Dry for a few minutes at 70–80°C. and irradiate with a short-wave ultraviolet light to make the phosphates visible as blue spots.

By using reference substances of ortho-, pyro-, tri-, trimeta-, tetrameta-, and perhaps tetraphosphate, the procedure is calibrated. Use of reference phosphates applied between the first (alkaline) and the second (acid) runs gives a one-dimensional chromatogram on the same sheet of paper. This aids in interpreting the two-dimensional pattern. Since the chain phosphates move relatively faster in the acidic solvent than do the ring phosphates having the same number of phosphorus atoms, the rings and chains are found to form separate series of spots. Employing the eight-hour runs described here, chain phosphates as large as the heptaphosphate can be differentiated when using reference standards.

Acid phosphates of any type can be distinguished from normal phosphates by the addition of neutral silver nitrate and subsequent test for free acid (pH meter or litmus paper). The silver precipitate releases the weakly acidic hydrogens, which then appear in the form of free nitric acid.

## ESTIMATION

Quantitative determination of total phosphorus, often reported as phosphorus pentoxide and sometimes, in the case of fertilizers, as bone phosphate of lime (BPL), is required for a great variety of materials. The main substances on which analyses for total phosphorus are routinely carried out in a number of laboratories are the following: phosphate ores; fertilizers; soils; slags; industrial waters, especially boiler and cooling waters; commercial phosphate salts, including the sodium, calcium, and ammonium phosphates; alloys, especially those of iron and copper; foodstuffs; pharmaceuticals; and various organic compounds, including the organo-phosphorus plasticizers, lubricant additives, and insecticides.

By far the large majority of quantitative determinations for total phosphorus are based on precipitation with acid molybdate solution. However, one of the most accurate procedures is the magnesium pyrophosphate method, which suffers from the disadvantages of being lengthy and having interference from a large number of ions. In fact, the number of compounds which interfere with precipitation of phosphorus as magnesium ammonium phosphate is so large that the precipitation must usually follow a preliminary separation of the phosphate with molybdate.

In this chapter, the highly accurate magnesium pyrophosphate procedure, the pH titration technique, and a very satisfactory titrimetric molybdate procedure are described for analysis of large samples. By standardizing the titrimetric method solutions against very similar samples of known phosphorus content, the precision of the titrimetric molybdate method can also be made to approach that of the magnesium pyrophosphate method. The gravimetric molybdate procedure is briefly mentioned but is not recommended because it is difficult to obtain a dried compound of the right composition, and the procedure offers no advantages over the titrimetric technique. Colorimetric procedures are described for small amounts of phosphorus.

The separation and quantitative determination of various oxidation states and of mixtures of phosphates (ortho, chain, and ring) are discussed, as is the separation of phosphorus from other elements.

Particular analytical schemes are described for the following materials: (1) ores and slag, (2) water and soils, (3) fertilizers, (4) organic substances, (5) commercial phosphate salts, and (6) alloys.

There are a large number of analytical procedures for phosphorus and its compounds which have not been described here. These are surveyed in the chapter on phosphorus written by R. Klement in *Handbuch der Analytischen Chemie* (Fresenius and Jander, Editors), Springer, Heidelberg, 1953, Part 3, Vol. V ab.

## PREPARATION AND SOLUTION OF THE SAMPLE

Although most of the alkali metal and ammonium phosphates are sufficiently soluble in water for all analytical purposes, some of the high molecular-weight alkali metal and ammonium salts are either insoluble or very slowly soluble in water. These materials can be dissolved in salt solutions containing alkali metal ions other than the ones present in the phosphate sample. In some cases the salt solution must be boiled for 1 hour or so to effect complete dissolution. Acid salts of polyvalent cations, including the alkaline earth metals, are sometimes sufficiently soluble in water for analytical purposes. However, these materials and the more insoluble normal salts can often be dissolved in strong mineral acids, with boiling sometimes being required. When insoluble residues, attributable to the presence of silica, are found, these residues can usually be completely dissolved by fuming with hydrofluoric acid in platinum. In extreme cases, fusion with alkaline fluxes in platinum is necessary. Following the alkaline fusion, the phosphorus can be extracted with water. It should be noted that the presence of reducing substances, such as carbonaceous materials, in melts containing phosphates, leads to destruction of the platinum. In general, oxidation states of phosphorus lower than the phosphate should never be allowed to come in contact with heated platinum.

Use of high-capacity, synthetic, cation-exchange resins (such as Dowex-50) have proved profitable in certain cases in dissolving difficultly soluble phosphates for analysis. In this technique, 1 g. of the finely powdered phosphate is mixed with 100 g. of the ion-exchange resin, and sufficient water (about 150 ml.) is added to give a free-flowing slurry, which is mechanically stirred for about a half hour to effect dissolution of the phosphate.[3] The advantages of using cation-exchange resins in dissolving difficultly soluble phosphates are that (1) condensed phosphates are not appreciably hydrolyzed and (2) cations which might interfere in subsequent determinations are removed by the resin.

## ORES, PHOSPHATE ROCK, AND MINERALS

*Acid-Soluble Material.*—Transfer 0.1000 g. of the powdered and homogenized sample (80-mesh) to a 500-ml. wide-mouth Erlenmeyer flask, add 20 ml. of concentrated HCl, and evaporate to dryness. Bake for a few minutes, cool, and add

---

[3] Van Wazer, J. R., and Holst, K. A., J. Am. Chem. Soc., **72**, 641, 1950.

5 ml. of concentrated HCl and 30 ml. of concentrated $HNO_3$. Boil until the brown fumes have been expelled. Add 50 ml. of water, cool to room temperature, and take this solution for analysis.

**Ion-Exchange Technique for Sample Preparation.** *Helrich and Rieman's Procedure.*[4]—Prepare a 40-cm column containing 170 ml. of Amberlite IR-100-H. Backwash with tap water and regenerate the resin with 500 ml. of 1 N HCl. Wash with 300 ml. of distilled water. Control the rate of flow so that the total 800 ml. of volume of acid and water takes about 20 minutes to pass through the column.

Boil the sample (450–550 mg. of phosphate rock) with 15 ml. of concentrated HCl for 30 minutes in a 150-ml. beaker. Boil gently and keep the beaker covered. Transfer to a steam bath, evaporate to dryness, and keep there for one more hour (during this time the column is prepared as described in the above paragraph).

Add 2 ml. of 6 N HCl and 98 ml. of $H_2O$ and pass the solution through the column. Wash with 300 ml. of distilled water. Control the flow rate so that it takes 10 minutes to percolate these 400 ml. Catch the filtrate and the washings in a 1-liter dish. The solution is ready for titration of the weak acid function of the phosphoric acid either potentiometrically or using color indicators and reference buffers of pH 4.5 and 8.2 (see pages 816 and 817).

*Procedure Using Wofatit KS.*—If Wofatit KS is used,[5] the resin is soaked overnight, treated with 2 N HCl several times, and washed carefully with distilled water. It is transferred into a water-filled column of 16-mm. diameter and 500-mm. height. There must not be any air bubbles in the column.

At a pH of about 1, the resin removes Fe, Al, and many heavy metals, but the concentration of cations must not greatly exceed the concentration of phosphate.

Dissolve 20 g. of the phosphate in 100 ml. of concentrated HCl and 50 ml. of concentrated $HNO_3$. Evaporate to dryness, dissolve the residue in 100 ml. of water and 15 ml. of concentrated HCl, filter, wash, and dilute to 1000 ml. in a measuring flask. A 50-ml. aliquot (corresponding to 1 g.) is applied to the column with a percolation rate of 4–5 ml. per minute (for the dimensions of the given column discard the first 80 ml., which is always free of phosphoric acid). Wash with 300–400 ml. of distilled water. Use the solution passed through the column for the phosphorus determination.

Treat the column with 250–300 ml. of 2 N HCl and collect the percolate containing the cations. This percolate can be used for subsequent determination of the cations. After washing again with 2 N HCl and then with distilled water, the column again is ready for use.

**Refractory Material (Fluorine-Containing Materials). Fusion.**—Weigh a 1.000-g. sample (fine powder) into a 30-ml. platinum crucible, add 5–6 g. of sodium carbonate-boric acid flux (obtained by mixing 4.5 g. of anhydrous $B_2O_3$ and 5.5 g. of $Na_2CO_3$), and mix carefully. Cover with 2–3 g. of the flux and heat in a furnace at 1000°C. for about 7 minutes. Remove from the furnace, chill the outside of the crucible with cold water, and place the crucible while still hot into a 400-ml. beaker which contains a hot mixture of 30 ml. 70–72% $HClO_4$ and 65 ml. water. As soon as the melt comes loose from the crucible, remove the crucible and rinse it with hot water. Cover the beaker with a "Speedy Vap" watch glass. Evaporate contents of the beaker almost to dryness (the mass should solidify upon cooling). Cool, add 30 ml. of concentrated HCl and about 100 ml. of hot water. Cover

4 Anal. Chem., **19,** 651, 1947.
5 Samuelson, O., Svensk. kem. Tidskr., **52,** 241, 1940.

with the watch glass and boil for about 10 minutes. Filter off the silica, using a small amount of ashless paper pulp, wash ten to twelve times with hot water, and dilute the filtrate to 500 ml. Mix well and take aliquots for the determination of phosphorus, calcium, aluminum, and iron.

NOTES.—Samples containing organic matter and phosphate should not be fused directly with $Na_2CO_3$ in a platinum crucible (see p. 802). Extraction of the sample with $HNO_3$ or aqua regia and fusion of any residue which is insoluble in acid will usually yield complete decomposition of the sample.

If fluorine is present besides organic material, and silica has to be determined, special procedures are necessary. (See section on "Organic Material" on p. 805.)

## ELEMENTARY PHOSPHORUS AND PHOSPHORUS CHLORIDES

The handling of different kinds of samples is reported in the paragraphs under "Lower Oxidation States" (see pp. 823 and 827).

## SLAGS

The procedures for dissolving ores, rock, and minerals can be applied (see p. 802). If moist slag is under analysis, take a 2-g. sample, the water content of which will be about 25%. Transfer it into a mortar, add exactly 10 ml. of dilute $HNO_3$ (sp. gr. 1.2), grind finely so that the slag decomposes and silica gel separates. Add slowly exactly 65 ml. more of the dilute $HNO_3$ while constantly stirring, and use a 10-ml. aliquot of this solution for colorimetric determination as phospho-vanadomolybdate. A 10-ml. aliquot would correspond to 0.2 g. of dry sample, if the moisture were exactly 25%. The actual sample weight is calculated, using the analytical value found for the moisture.

## WATER AND SOILS

Mineralization of any organic material and removing of silica will sometimes be necessary when preparing water samples for determination of total phosphorus (see p. 805). Coprecipitation of phosphate is possible with ferric hydroxide as collector (see p. 810). It represents a procedure for concentrating $P_2O_5$ from large volumes or separating it from excessive amounts of alkali salts.

Residues from soils obtained after removing organic material by ashing (see p. 805) will be treated like minerals (see p. 802). Only total $P_2O_5$ can be gathered from this type of analysis. For specification of soils, discrimination between available and unavailable $P_2O_5$ is required. Procedures are reported on p. 845.

## FERTILIZERS

The procedures used for minerals (see p. 802) apply to fertilizers and will yield total $P_2O_5$. The technique to be chosen for dissolving samples varies widely with the content of organic material. Boiling with $HNO_3$ or aqua regia will be suitable for samples containing only a minor percentage of carbonaceous material, while some of the usual fertilizers, high in organic matter, should be treated as directed for organic material on p. 805 below.

Any residue insoluble in acid will usually require fusion with sodium carbonate, but it also may be made soluble by fuming with HF and $HNO_3$ if silica content need not be determined in the sample.

## DETERGENTS

Organic material should be destroyed and silica removed before determination of total $P_2O_5$ (see section on "Organic Material," on the next page).

## COMMERCIAL PHOSPHATE SALTS

Dissolution of the sample for obtaining total $P_2O_5$ is accomplished with water or acid. The complete reversion of condensed phosphates is indispensable for quantitative precipitation of $P_2O_5$ as orthophosphate and is discussed on p. 812. For the dissolving effect of alkali salt solutions which is due to ion exchange, see p. 802.

## ORGANIC MATERIAL

**Catalytic Wet Oxidation.**[6]  **Oxidation Mixture.**—35 g. of sodium molybdate dihydrate is dissolved in 150 ml. of water. First, 150 ml. of concentrated $H_2SO_4$ and, after cooling, 200 ml. of 70–72% $HClO_4$ are added.

**Procedure.**—Transfer 5 ml. of the oxidation mixture into a 500-ml. Kjeldahl flask and add the sample of organic phosphate (0.25–0.30 g.) without spreading it over the inside walls of the flask. Introduce 10 ml. of concentrated $HNO_3$, 10–20 glass beads, several boiling stones, and boil for 15 minutes. Add 2 ml. of $HClO_4$ and continue to boil until dense, white fumes have been visible for 1 minute. It takes about 15 minutes. Cool, transfer to a 250-ml. volumetric flask, and dilute to the mark (dispose of the beads and boiling stones by filtering through a Gooch crucible). Use aliquots for determining phosphoric acid by colorimetric or titrimetric procedure. For the colorimetric determination, a blank is carried out with 5 ml. of catalytic oxidation reagent, 10 ml. of concentrated $HNO_3$, and 2 ml. of $HClO_4$ by evaporating to fumes and making up to 250 ml.

**Wet Oxidation with Hydrogen Peroxide. Procedure.**—Transfer a sample of appropriate weight into a 300-ml. Kjeldahl flask and avoid getting the sample spread over the walls of the flask. Add 3 ml. of concentrated $H_2SO_4$ and a 6-mm. glass bead and mix the contents by swirling the flask. Char by warming gently with a microburner, meanwhile directing a stream of cool air against the neck of the flask. Increase the heat while reducing the air stream until dense, white fumes appear, apply cool air again, and drop 1 ml. of $HNO_3$ slowly into the boiling solution. Keep boiling and repeat adding 1 ml. of $HNO_3$ in the same way, as soon as white fumes show up again. Continue with this stepwise oxidation until the digestion mixture becomes a light straw color. Almost all organic matter has been oxidized by that time.

Cool slightly, add 0.5 ml. of 30% hydrogen peroxide, heat until dense, white fumes are given off, and while boiling, add 1 ml. more of concentrated $HNO_3$ dropwise. Boil off the $HNO_3$ until white fumes reappear and repeat the hydrogen peroxide-$HNO_3$ treatment until the mixture is colorless (usually about four times), which means complete oxidation of organic material.

Cool the flask, wash mouth and neck down with about 5 ml. of water, and mix well. Heat again until dense, white fumes are evolved and repeat this procedure several times for removing traces of hydrogen peroxide.

Cool, determine by visual observation the volume of $H_2SO_4$ left, dilute, and make to volume. Calculate the acidity and make allowance for it in the subsequent phosphorus determination in a suitable aliquot of the solution.

Record the amounts of reagents required and carry out a blank for each sample, using the same amounts of acids and hydrogen peroxide.

**Mineralization, Using Zinc Oxide.**—Transfer a weighed sample (0.5–1 g.) into a porcelain crucible and cover with an excess of zinc oxide (2 g. in most cases). Dry

6 Simmons, W. R., and Robertson, J. H., Anal. Chem., **22**, 294, 1177, 1950.

on a hot plate for 30 minutes. Ignite slowly over a small flame in the hood and finally heat with a blast burner or in a muffle until all the carbon has been burned off. After cooling, transfer the residue to a 250-ml. beaker, removing it from the bottom of the crucible as much as possible. Place the crucible in the beaker, add 10 ml. of 10 $N$ $HNO_3$ and 20 ml. of water, and heat until the residue has completely dissolved. Remove and wash the crucible (the resulting volume should not exceed 50 ml.) and use this solution for precipitating the phosphomolybdate.

**Mineralization by Sodium Peroxide** [7] (**Bomb Combustion**). **Apparatus.**—A nickel bomb (this nickel contains about 0.3% of manganese) with about 10 ml. combustion space is used (see Fig. 35-1). A rubber washer, $W$, and steel jacket, $J$,

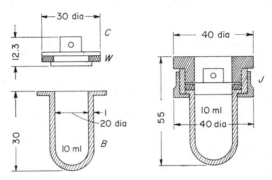

Fig. 35-1.   Combustion Bomb.

are provided for keeping the cap, $C$, tight. A protecting case for the heating procedure is necessary. For heating, the bomb is placed on an asbestos sheet in a circular hole cut into the center of the sheet. The diameter of this hole is 2 mm. smaller than the diameter of the bomb. The sheet rests on a tripod. Thus, the bottom of the bomb can be heated by the flame of a burner without overheating the walls.

**Handling of Different Sample Materials.**—Powders are weighed into a weighing bottle and transferred into the bomb, the exact sample weight (0.1–0.5 g.) being determined by reweighing the bottle. Very fluffy materials can be pressed to pills. (Mixing of sample and sodium peroxide is not necessary.) Materials not in powder form may be cut or torn into very small pieces and handled as directed for powders. Liquids are sealed into tiny vials (the neck must not protrude from the peroxide during the melting procedure), and these are bedded upright into the peroxide, so that the glass does not touch the walls of the bomb. Pastes are put into little glass jars (twice the capacity of the sample), and the space in the jars not required by the sample is filled up with dry $Na_2CO_3$. In this case, $Na_2O_2$ is added to cover the glycol in the bomb cup (see below) before the little jar containing the sample is added.

If reaction between sample and peroxide takes place in the cold (this has to be checked in a preliminary experiment), the sample is covered with a layer of

[7] Procedures for macro, semimicro, and micro amounts are reported by Wurtzschmitt, B., and Zimmermann, W., Fortschr. chem. Forsch., **1,** 485, 1949/50; Wurtzschmitt, B., Mikrochemie, **36/37,** 769, 1951.

$Na_2CO_3$ so that it does not touch the peroxide before the heating starts. The technique of weighing the sample into a gelatin capsule and bedding it in the center of the peroxide is very convenient for many sample materials.

**Preparation for Fusion.**—(*Wear goggles!*) Transfer 8 drops of ethylene glycol (160 mg.) to the bottom of the carefully dried bomb cup, *B*. Put the sample on top and fill with $Na_2O_2$ up to 2 mm. below the top of the cup. About 11 g. of $Na_2O_2$ are necessary. Tap the cup, *B*, slightly against the table while filling. Close the bomb and tighten carefully with the steel screw jacket, *J*.

**Fusion and Removing of the Chilled Melt.**—The bomb is inserted into the heating stand and heated by putting a microburner under the bottom. Ignition with sodium peroxide and ethylene glycol takes place at 56°C. The combustion is completed about 1 minute later. While still hot, the closed bomb is dipped into cold distilled water and allowed to cool in a clean porcelain dish. After cooling, the bomb is opened (*Wear goggles!*), and the contents are inspected. The material must have the appearance of a chilled melt. If the substance appears to be unchanged, the heat applied was insufficient, and the bomb must be closed and heated again. *Adding water in this case may cause an explosion.*

If melting has taken place, pick up the washer with tweezers, rinse carefully with distilled water to collect all particles of the fused mass, and put it aside. Transfer the cup and the cap (*B* and *C*) of the bomb into a porcelain casserole, cover with a watch glass, and add distilled water until only half of the cup emerges from the water. Use the water that was employed for rinsing the washer. Warm slightly, stopping as soon as the dissolving reaction starts. After solution is complete, remove cup and cap and rinse them well with water. The solution must not be brown. If this happens, the fusion was probably carried out at too low a temperature and must be repeated with a new sample. A few small particles of carbon are not of any significance.

Remove $H_2O_2$ by boiling the alkaline solution for 10 minutes and add $HNO_3$ (sp. gr. 1.4) until strongly acid. Evaporate to dryness, moisten the residue with 5 ml. of concentrated $HNO_3$, and evaporate again. Bake the residue at 130°C. for one hour. Moisten with 10 ml. of $HNO_3$ (1:1), heat for a short time, and add 100 ml. of water. Remove $SiO_2$ and determine $P_2O_5$ after precipitation as molybdenum complex.

Run a blank, using the reagents without a sample, and deduct the results.

### ALLOYS

As a general rule, it should be kept in mind that dissolution without oxidizing agent (e.g., treatment only with HCl) will result in a loss of phosphorus, if it is present as phosphide or any lower oxidation state than phosphate. Treatment with concentrated $H_2SO_4$ will avoid such loss.

Alloys containing tin will yield a precipitate of stannic acid when treated with $HNO_3$. Since, as is well known, stannic acid always carries down phosphate, this precipitate has to be analyzed (see "Procedure for Phosphor Tin" below), or precipitation of stannic acid has to be avoided by using mixtures of $HNO_3$ and HCl.

**Copper and Brass. Procedure.**—Dissolve 1–5 g. of the sample in a 500-ml. Erlenmeyer flask in concentrated $HNO_3$ (apply 2 ml., plus 5 ml. for each gram of sample). Remove nitrogen oxides by gentle heating, dilute with 100 ml. of water, and bring to a boil. Drop in a 2.5% solution of $KMnO_4$ until a purple tint persists, boil for 5 minutes, and reduce higher manganese oxides by dropping in a 10% solution of $NH_4NO_2$ until the color of the solution shows a clear blue again.  Boil for 5 minutes, cool, and precipitate phosphoric acid as phosphomolybdate.

*Phosphor Tin.*  **Procedure.**—Transfer a sample of 0.6–0.8 g. to a porcelain dish of medium size, cover, and add 2 ml. of water and 8 ml. of concentrated $HNO_3$. Evaporate to dryness (avoid decomposition of the nitrates) and grind the residue with a glass rod to a fine powder.  Add 5–6 g. of crystallized sodium sulfide (hydrate) and 0.2–0.3 g. of powdered sulfur, mix well, and melt carefully, using a very small flame (keep covered with a watch glass).  Stir occasionally with a glass rod.  Only a little water is lost during the melting procedure.

After cooling, dissolve in 100 ml. of a hot 2% solution of $NH_4NO_3$, and keep almost boiling for half an hour.  A residue consisting of sulfides (usually the sulfides of copper, iron, bismuth, zinc) remains undissolved.  Filter; wash first with very dilute sodium sulfide solution and later with a 2% solution of $NH_4NO_3$ saturated with $H_2S$.

Acidify the filtrate containing tin and phosphorus with acetic acid and precipitate tin with $H_2S$.  Phosphate remains in solution and is precipitated as magnesium ammonium phosphate.

*Phosphor Copper.*  **Procedure.**—Moisten the sample (0.4–0.6 g.) with water and dissolve in concentrated $HNO_3$.  Evaporate almost to dryness and fume with a little HCl and $HNO_3$ on a steam bath.  Add water and evaporate again.  Dissolve in 5 ml. of concentrated HCl, add 150 ml. of water, and precipitate copper (and traces of lead) as sulfide.  Evaporate the filtrate and precipitate phosphorus as the molybdenum complex.

*Iron (Pig Iron, Wrought Iron, Cast Iron) and Steel.*  **Procedure.**—Transfer the sample (2 g. of steel, 0.5–2 g. of cast iron, and 1 g. of wrought iron or pig iron [8]) into a 300-ml. Erlenmeyer flask and dissolve in 65 ml. of $HNO_3$ (1:3).  In the case of cast iron, filter through a filter of loose texture to remove silica and wash with very dilute $HNO_3$ (1:49) and hot water.  Adding a few drops of HF prevents moderate amounts of silica from precipitating.  Oxidize with 10 ml. of 2.5% $KMnO_4$ and boil for 3 minutes.  If manganese dioxide does not separate, add permanganate in slight excess and boil again.  Drop in aqueous $SO_2$ until the manganese precipitate is dissolved.  Boil to remove oxides of nitrogen.  After cooling, the solution is ready for precipitation of the phosphomolybdate.

*Ferrophosphorus.*  **Procedure.**—Transfer a 1-g. sample (120-mesh) into a 250-ml. beaker.  Add 20 ml. of concentrated $H_2SO_4$, cover with a watch glass, and boil on a hot plate for 30 minutes.  Let cool, first in air for about 3 minutes, and then in water (shallow pan) to room temperature.  Rinse the cover and beaker sides with cold water, using about 75 ml. and 25 ml. of HCl, and boil for 10 minutes (stir to avoid bumping).  After removing from the heat, dilute with 75 ml. of cold water, filter, and wash twice with dilute HCl (1:3) and eight times with hot water.  The residue consisting of silica is ready for ignition and determination of $SiO_2$.  Dilute the filtrate with distilled water to exactly 500 ml. in a measuring flask and mix well. Use a 25-ml. aliquot for precipitating the phosphomolybdate.

*Alloy Steels Containing Ti, Zr, Nb, Ta, V, Cr, Mo, W, and Ferroalloys with Si, Mn, Al, Co, Mo, W, V, Ti, Cr, Nb, Ta, Se.*—Procedures for dissolving and analyzing these materials are given on pp. 863–865.

[8] Phosphorus contents fall between 0.03 and 0.08% for steels, and 0.1 and 0.3% for wrought iron and pig iron; cast iron may contain more than 0.3% P.

## SEPARATION FROM OTHER ELEMENTS

*Separation of Phosphoric Acid as Ammonium Phosphomolybdate.*—Precipitation of the yellow molybdenum complex accomplishes separation from most of the other anions and cations. Exceptions are listed and discussed on p. 816. A procedure for removing $P_2O_5$ by extraction of the molybdenum complex with a solvent mixture is reported on p. 858.

*Separation of Phosphoric Acid as Magnesium Ammonium Phosphate from Fe(III), Al, Ti, Zr, Zn, Se, Te, V, Sn, and Ca.*—The separation is carried out in the presence of citric acid, using a large excess of magnesia mixture.

**Procedure.**—To the solution which contains less than 100 mg. $P_2O_5$ in 100-ml. volume, add 3 g. of citric acid and 100 ml. of a magnesia mixture that is 1 molal in magnesium chloride and 3 molal in $NH_4Cl$ and precipitate with ammonia (see p. 812). Filter after 12–24 hours, dissolve in dilute acid, and reprecipitate after adding 0.5 g. of citric acid and 1 ml. of the magnesia mixture. Let settle at least 6 hours before filtration.

As a precaution, the filter paper that was extracted with acid to remove the precipitate (and also the one that was extracted with ammonia, if the phosphoric acid were separated first as phosphomolybdate) should be ignited and the ash fused with $Na_2CO_3$. The aqueous extract of this melt will then contain any undissolved phosphorus left on the paper. It has to be united with the main solution (see paragraphs on separation by fusion or precipitation on p. 810 and coprecipitation of phosphates with iron or aluminum hydroxide on p. 810). If a turbid solution results in the course of the procedure, it is filtered (if necessary, using paper pulp), and the filter ignited and treated for recovery of any phosphate, as described.

*Separation of Phosphoric Acid as Magnesium Ammonium Phosphate from W(VI), V(V), and Mo(VI).*—A fairly good separation is possible by precipitating the magnesium ammonium phosphate in a tartrate solution. Any vanadium present is reduced previously by adding $SO_2$ and boiling.

**Determination of Phosphorus in Tungsten and Ferrotungsten.**—Transfer a 2-g. sample into a platinum dish with flat bottom (about 8 cm. in diameter, provided with a lip for pouring and a well-fitting platinum cover), add 15 ml. of concentrated $HNO_3$ and 3 ml. of HF. Cover the dish and start the decomposition by gentle heating. After violent action is over, add 3 ml. more of HF, let react, boil, and continue adding HF and boiling until decomposition is complete. After that, rinse and remove the cover and evaporate to about 10 ml. Add 10–12 drops of a 2.5% $KMnO_4$ solution and concentrate until crusts of tungstic acid begin to form. Add 10 ml. of concentrated $H_2SO_4$ and evaporate to dense, white fumes (avoid strong heat which would cause refractory crusts to form on the bottom of the dish).

Cool, add 25 ml. of water, and boil, agitating over a flame until disintegration of the crusts is complete. Pass $SO_2$ slowly through the solution until the higher manganese oxides are reduced (the pink color is discharged), and boil for a minute or two. Add 2 g. of tartaric acid, cool to about 50°C., and pour ammonium hydroxide (1:1) slowly into the solution until the precipitated tungstic acid has dissolved completely and a clear solution results.

Add 4 g. of $MgSO_4 \cdot 7H_2O$ dissolved in 10 ml. of water to the hot solution, transfer it to a glass-stoppered bottle, and cool thoroughly while open in iced water. Drop 4 or 5 glass beads (6-mm. diameter) into the bottle, stopper tightly, and shake violently for 10 minutes or more in a shaking machine. The phosphoric acid begins to separate as magnesium ammonium phosphate free from tungsten. The precipitation is made complete by adding 15 ml. of ammonium hydroxide (1:1) and cooling overnight in a refrigerator.

Filter the magnesium ammonium phosphate, wash thoroughly with small portions of dilute ammonium hydroxide (1:20), dissolve in 40 ml. of $HNO_3$ (1:3), and precipitate as molybdenum complex (for final determination see p. 814).

**Separation of Phosphoric Acid from Mo, W, Cu, Ni, Cr(VI), and Alkali Salts by Coprecipitation with Iron or Aluminum Hydroxide.**—Traces of phosphoric acid can be separated and collected from large volumes by the aid of a multifold excess (0.1 g. or more) of ferric or aluminum salt. By adding ammonium hydroxide in very slight excess, the phosphate is carried down completely, together with the iron or aluminum hydroxide.

**Removing Phosphoric Acid with Barium Hydroxide.**—Precipitation of barium phosphate is applied successfully for separating traces of aluminum and boron from large amounts of phosphoric acid (see pp. 856 and 858).

**Removing Phosphoric Acid with Zinc Carbonate.**—The procedure is described on p. 840 in connection with the determination of sodium in minerals.

**Removing Phosphoric Acid from Ca, Sr, Ba, Mg (also Zn, Mn, Co, Ni) and Alkali Metals in Acetate Buffered Medium.**—The separation is made possible by adjusting the pH of the solution to about 5 with ammonium acetate. Complete precipitation of phosphoric acid free of alkaline earths is accomplished by adding an excess of ferric chloride.

**Procedure.**—Neutralize the free acid in the sample solution (the volume should not be more than 50 ml. in a 600-ml. beaker) with a solution of ammonium carbonate, until a slight precipitate persists or until the solution is alkaline to methyl orange. Then just acidify by dropping in dilute HCl (any precipitate dissolves and a clear solution results). Add a few grams of crystalline ammonium acetate and dissolve completely by stirring. Gradually add a strong solution of ferric chloride. Ferric phosphate precipitates. Continue adding ferric chloride until a brown color in the supernatant liquid indicates a considerable excess of iron. Dilute with boiling water to 400 ml., keep boiling for 1 minute while stirring, and filter while still hot through a fluted filter. Wash with hot water which contains a little ammonium acetate. The resulting solution is free of phosphoric acid.

**Separation of Phosphoric Acid from V, Fe, Zn, Cu, Pb, (As) as Zirconium Phosphate.**—Add zirconyl chloride in excess to the strongly hydrochloric acid solution of the sample, evaporate, and take up the residue with 40 ml. of a mixture of HCl and HBr (3:1). Boil and evaporate again to complete dryness (arsenic volatilizes upon this treatment). Bake the residue, dissolve all soluble salts by adding about 50 ml. of HCl (1:1), boiling down to 20 ml., and diluting with enough boiling water to obtain a 0.2 $N$ HCl. Digest for half an hour at 50–60°C., filter the insoluble zirconium phosphate while hot, with the aid of filter pulp, and wash with hot dilute HCl. The filter is ignited, and the phosphorus separated from zirconium as described in the paragraphs on separation of phosphoric acid by fusion with $Na_2CO_3$ (see below) and coprecipitation of phosphate with iron or aluminum hydroxide, page 810, above.

**Separation of Phosphoric Acid from Fe, Ti, Zr, Cr(III), Ni, and Co by Fusion or Precipitation. Fusion.**—The dry sample or the powdered residue obtained after some evaporation is fused with $Na_2CO_3$. The melt is leached with water. After filtration, the residue is extracted with a dilute solution of $Na_2CO_3$. Phosphate, together with other similar anions which might have been present, as e.g., arsenate and vanadate, go into solution. If several centigrams or more of the sample are under analysis, repeated fusion will be necessary. Between fusions, careful extraction with water is recommended.

When dehydrating silica as usual in analysis, the precipitate obtained may be contaminated by the phosphates of Ti, Zr, Th, Sn, and also by iron and aluminum phosphate. Therefore, fusion of the residue left after fuming with HF may be necessary. The aqueous extract of this melt will contain practically all the co-precipitated phosphorus, besides other elements forming soluble sodium salts or colloidal solutions as e.g., Sn, W, Nb, Ta, Mo, V, As, if any of them had been present in the sample and were carried down with the silica. The small amount of phosphate contained in the aqueous extract of the melt can conveniently be precipitated, using coprecipitation with iron or aluminum hydroxide (see paragraph on p. 810).

**Precipitation.**—A special procedure involving use of NaOH containing some $Na_2CO_3$ is described in connection with the determination of small amounts of nickel in phosphates on p. 861.

**Removal of the Hydrogen Sulfide Group.**—The elements of the hydrogen sulfide group are precipitated from acid solution with $H_2S$. Phosphoric acid remains in solution. The separation from molybdenum is not satisfactory with $H_2S$ and therefore is better accomplished by precipitating magnesium ammonium phosphate from a solution containing tartrate (see paragraph on p. 809).

**Removal of Fe, Zn, Co, Ni, and Mn with Ammonium Sulfide.**—The separation is accomplished by precipitating the sulfides from a solution which contains an excess of tartaric acid. Al, Ti, Zr, and Th form stable complexes with tartrate and therefore would remain in the solution together with the phosphate. Ca, Sr, Ba, and Mg, if present, would precipitate as phosphates.

**Procedure.**—Add a solution of 2 g. of tartaric acid to the acid solution of the sample. Saturate with $H_2S$ by bubbling the gas through the solution and neutralize with a slight excess of ammonium hydroxide. Let settle overnight in a stoppered flask filter, and wash with water containing a little ammonium sulfide.

**Removal of As and Ge by Volatilization.**—The separations can be accomplished by distillation of the chlorides of As and Ge according to the respective chapters or simply by fuming off these elements with HCl or HF in case their determination is not required. Arsenic must be reduced previously to the trivalent state, e.g. by adding HBr.

**Removal of Metals by Electrolysis with a Mercury Cathode.**—Most metals such as Fe, Cu, Ni, Co, Zn, Ga, Ge, Ag, Cd, In, Sn, Sb, Cr, Pb, Bi, As, Se, Te, Re, Hg, Tl, Rh, Pd, Os, Ir, Pt, Mo, and Au can be separated from phosphoric acid by electrolytic deposition on a mercury cathode. Elements which remain in the solution with the phosphoric acid are V, B, U, Be, Al, Ti, Zr, and rare earths (0.1 $N$ $H_2SO_4$ as electrolyte).

**Separation of Phosphoric Acid from Other Ions by the Aid of Ion Exchangers.**—Application of this technique is detailed in the analysis of phosphate ores (see p. 803).

**Removal of Ti, W, and Al with Special Reagents.**—A precipitation of titanium free from phosphorus by use of tannin and antipyrine in acid medium was worked out by Moser, Neumayer, and Winter.[9] Thornton[10] used cupferron for this purpose.

[9] Moser, Neumayer and Winter, Monatsh. Chem., 55, 96, 1930.
[10] Thornton, Amer. J. Sci. (4), 37, 407, 1914.

Tungsten can quantitatively be precipitated in the presence of phosphoric acid by the use of tolidine hydrochloride according to Knorre.[11]

Precipitation with 8-hydroxyquinoline in ammoniacal solution carries down aluminum free of phosphate (see Chapter on Aluminum).[12]

## TOTAL PHOSPHORUS

*Lower Oxides of Phosphorus.*—If the material being analyzed contains lower oxides of phosphorus, such as $H_3PO_2$ and $H_3PO_3$, the sample must be treated with an oxidizing agent to assure that all of the phosphorus is in the form of phosphates before an analysis for total phosphorus can be carried out. In this case, the sample can be dissolved in approximately 10 ml. of water to which 10 ml. each of $HNO_3$ and $HClO_4$ are then added. The solution is then gently heated and fumed nearly to dryness. It is then cooled somewhat, diluted to 100 ml., and boiled to convert all condensed phosphates to the orthophosphate form, as described in the next section.

As an alternative to the procedure given above, the sample may be fumed with aqua regia or an equivalent mixture of bromine and $HNO_3$. It should be noted that many of the lower oxidation states of phosphorus, including both inorganic and organic compounds, react very slowly with all but the strongest oxidizing agents. The lower oxyacids of phosphorus are strong reducing agents, but some of them react only with extreme slowness with oxidizing agents. In a later section (see pp. 828–830) concerned with the differential analysis of these acids, reference will be given to a procedure in which the large differences in the rates of oxidation of certain of these acids are used to differentiate between them.

*Reversion of Condensed Phosphates.*—In order to carry out an analysis for total phosphorus, it is necessary to have all of the phosphate present as the orthophosphate ion. This means that the condensed ring or chain structures must be degraded by hydrolysis. Under ordinary conditions, hydrolysis of the condensed phosphates proceeds very slowly, but when condensed phosphates are subjected to the combined action of low pH and high temperature, their rate of hydrolysis is greatly accelerated. For analytical purposes, complete reversion of the condensed phosphates to the orthophosphate form can be achieved by gently boiling the sample in a 1 $N$ $HNO_3$ solution for 30 minutes.

## GRAVIMETRIC DETERMINATION OF ORTHOPHOSPHATE AS MAGNESIUM PYROPHOSPHATE

*Magnesia Mixture.*—110 g. of magnesium chloride ($MgCl_2 \cdot 6H_2O$) are dissolved in a small amount of water. To this are added 280 g. of ammonium chloride and 700 ml. of ammonia (sp. gr. 0.90); the solution is now diluted to 2000 ml. with distilled water. The solution is allowed to stand several hours and then filtered into a large storage bottle having a glass stopper. For every 0.1 g. $P_2O_5$ present in the sample analyzed, 10 ml. of the solution should be used. As the reagent ages, it will be necessary to filter off the silica that gradually accumulates from the reagent bottle.

*Procedure.*—The ammonium phosphomolybdate, obtained as directed on p. 815, is filtered onto a filter paper and washed four or five times with 1% $HNO_3$. The precipitate is now dissolved from the filter by a fine stream of hot ammonium

11 Knorre, Z. Anal. Chem., **47,** 37, 1908.
12 Lundell and Knowles, J. Research Nat. Bur. Standards, **3, 91,** 1929.

hydroxide (1:1), with the solution being caught in the beaker in which the precipitation was made. The solution and washings should be not over 100–150 ml. in volume. Then HCl is added to the cooled solution to neutralize the excess of ammonium hydroxide, the yellow precipitate formed during the neutralization dissolving with difficulty when sufficient acid has been added. To the cooled solution, cold magnesia mixture is added drop by drop (2 drops per second) with constant stirring. A quantity of 10 ml. of the reagent will precipitate 0.1 g. $P_2O_5$. When the solution becomes cloudy, the stirring is discontinued and the precipitate allowed to settle 10 minutes. Ammonium hydroxide is added until the solution contains about one-fourth its original volume of concentrated ammonia (e.g., 25 ml. $NH_4OH$ per 90–100 ml. of solution). The solution is stirred during the addition of the ammonium hydroxide and then allowed to settle for at least 2 hours. It is filtered through a porcelain filter crucible with a porous bottom or through filter paper, and the precipitate is washed with dilute ammonium hydroxide (1:4). Filter paper is recommended for the first filtration and a filter crucible for the second when the compound is reprecipitated as is generally advisable. The reprecipitation is accomplished by dissolving the precipitate in dilute acid, then adding 1 ml. of the magnesia mixture and ammonium hydroxide as indicated below, for solutions free of interfering ions. The filter crucible containing the precipitate is then dried in an oven at 100°C. for a half hour and placed in a cold electric furnace which is slowly heated (30–60 minutes) to 1000°C.

If filter paper was used for the final filtration, the precipitate should be placed in a porcelain crucible, a few drops of saturated solution of $NH_4NO_3$ added and the precipitate heated over a low flame till decomposed (or until the paper chars). The lumps of residue are broken up with a platinum rod and again ignited over a Meker burner, the heat being gradually increased to 1100°C.

If the heating is properly conducted, the resultant ash will be white or light gray, otherwise it will be dark. The addition of solid $NH_4NO_3$ aids the oxidation in obstinate cases, but there is danger of slight mechanical loss.[13] The crucible is cooled in a desiccator and the residue weighed as magnesium pyrophosphate.

$$Mg_2P_2O_7 \times 0.6378 = P_2O_5$$
$$\times 0.2783 = P$$

**Accuracy.**—If the procedure is followed painstakingly, so that a magnesium ammonium phosphate of the stoichiometric composition is obtained, this procedure gives results that have an absolute accuracy of $\pm 0.05\%$. It is assumed that no less than 0.1 g. of the pyrophosphate is weighed on a properly calibrated, sensitive, analytical balance. For accurate results on smaller precipitates, a microanalytical balance and microtechniques must be used.

*Alternate Procedure for Orthophosphates in Absence of Interfering Ions.*—In the absence of those metals, the phosphates of which are insoluble in ammoniacal solution, the magnesia mixture may be added directly to the slightly acid solution containing the orthophosphate without previous precipitation of ammonium phosphomolybdate. Then the solution can be made strongly ammoniacal by neutralizing it slowly with ammonium hydroxide while stirring, and by adding a large excess (one-fourth of the original volume of concentrated ammonia), while still

---

[13] McNabb, W. M. (J. Am. Chem. Soc., **49**, 891, 1927) has shown that loss of $P_2O_5$ occurs if ignition of $MgNH_4PO_4$ is carried on with free $HNO_3$, but no loss in presence of free $NH_4OH$. Therefore, moistening the residue with $HNO_3$ should not be done, as is sometimes recommended.

stirring. The magnesium ammonium phosphate is washed and ignited, according to directions given above, and weighed as magnesium pyrophosphate. Consult also the Chapter on Magnesium.

## GRAVIMETRIC DETERMINATION OF ORTHOPHOSPHATE AFTER PRECIPITATION AS PHOSPHOMOLYBDATE

The gravimetric determination of the molybdate complex after precipitation according to the procedure given below can be made as follows:

*Procedure.*—Precipitate the complex as directed under "Procedure" on p. 815. After 2 hours, transfer the precipitate into a filter crucible (be careful not to lose any particles adhering to the sides of the flask) and wash with 1% $HNO_3$ containing about 2% of $NH_4NO_3$ and finally with 1% $HNO_3$. Dry at 105°C. and weigh the yellow compound $(NH_4)_3PO_4 \cdot 12MoO_3 \cdot H_2O$.

$$\text{Weight of precipitate} \times 0.03751 = P_2O_5$$
$$\times 0.01637 = P$$

An alternate possibility is to heat to 450°C. very slowly. Ammonia and water are expelled completely, and the dark greenish-blue anhydrous complex $P_2O_5 \cdot 24MoO_3$ can be weighed.

$$\text{Weight of precipitate} \times 0.03947 = P_2O_5$$
$$\times 0.01723 = P$$

This method is not recommended for accurate results or rapidity.

## TITRIMETRIC DETERMINATION OF ORTHOPHOSPHATE AFTER PRECIPITATION AS PHOSPHOMOLYBDATE

**Reagents. Ammonium Molybdate.**—Dissolve 118 g. of 85% molybdic acid in a mixture of 400 ml. of distilled water and 80 ml. of concentrated ammonium hydroxide solution. Cool, filter if necessary, and pour, while stirring, into a cool mixture of 400 ml. of concentrated $HNO_3$ and 600 ml. of water. Add about 0.05 g. of $Na_2HPO_4$ which is dissolved in a little water. Mix and let settle 24 hours. Use the clear supernatant liquor, filtering if necessary. Storage in a cool, dark place is advised. (According to Hillebrand, Lundell, Bright, and Hoffman, 56 mg. of $MoO_3$ per 1 mg. P is usually required, but larger excesses do no harm and are sometimes advisable.)

**Standard Alkali and Acid.**—0.324 $N$ NaOH and $HNO_3$ solutions. 1 ml. of 0.324 $N$ NaOH equals 0.001 g. $P_2O_5$ when titrating ammonium phosphomolybdate. This solution is prepared from $CO_2$-free water. The NaOH is standardized against Bureau of Standards benzoic acid, and the $HNO_3$ is standardized against the NaOH. The benzoic acid standardization can be modified according to the results obtained on standard phosphorus samples as described below.

**Other Reagents.**—0.1% solution of methyl orange in water; 1.0% solution of phenolphthalein in a 50–50 water ethyl alcohol mixture (dissolve phenolphthalein in alcohol before adding the water); 1% solution of $KNO_3$.

**Comparison Standard.**—As a standard phosphate, it has been found that monopotassium orthophosphate is very satisfactory. This material, known as Sørensen's salt, has no hydrate and can be readily dried at 110°C. to constant weight. For a C.P. grade sample having a $K_2O/P_2O_5$ mole ratio of exactly unity, corresponding to the $KN_2PO_4$ composition, the pH of a 0.1 $N$ solution is 4.51 ± 0.01 when compared in $CO_2$-free distilled water blanketed with $CO_2$-free air to a pH 4.00 standard buffer, using a glass electrode. Such a sample of $KN_2PO_4$ contains 52.15% $P_2O_5$ when dried to constant weight. An increase or decrease of 0.1 pH-unit from the 4.51 value corresponds to an inversely proportional variation of about 0.2% in the $P_2O_5$-content of the monopotassium orthophosphate. This means that the $P_2O_5$-content of the $KH_2PO_4$ can be corrected according to the pH of its 0.1 $N$ aqueous solution as follows: % $P_2O_5 = 53.34 - 0.263$ pH, for $52.13 < \%$ $P_2O_5$ $< 52.18$.

If the pH is appreciably different from 4.51, or if there is any other reason for doubting the purity of the monopotassium orthophosphate, it is recommended that the standard sample be carefully analyzed by the magnesium pyrophosphate procedure described above.

*Procedure.*—Transfer an aliquot portion of the sample, equivalent to approximately 0.05 g. $P_2O_5$, to a 400-ml. beaker. (The method is reasonably accurate for quantities as low as 1 mg. $P_2O_5$.) Dilute to 100 ml., add 1 drop of a 0.1% solution of methyl orange indicator and just neutralize the excess acid with concentrated ammonia. Add 5–8 g. of ammonium nitrate crystals, cool to room temperature, stirring until the ammonium nitrate is dissolved. Add 60 ml. of the molybdate reagent while stirring. If the quantities of $P_2O_5$ are very small, stir vigorously for a period of 3 minutes, using a crosswise stroke. Otherwise, stirring for only a moment or two is needed. In either case, the sample need not stand for 15 minutes, as is often recommended, but can be filtered within 5 or 6 minutes. If filtration is within 6 minutes, the 3-minute stirring should always be used. During the 15-minute period of standing, the sample should be stirred intermittently. It is then filtered with suction through a ¼″ paper-pulp filter pad supported on a 1″ perforated porcelain plate into a 500-ml. suction flask, using about 5″ of vacuum. The filter pad should be coated with a portion of a suspension of a good analytical filter aid (purified diatomaceous earth). The paper pulp for the filter pad is easily prepared by vigorously shaking Whatman No. 4 paper, or its equivalent, in a little hot water. If desired, filtration can be carried out on a filter paper coated with a small amount of filter aid. In this case, the filter paper should be supported by a platinum cone. After the contents of the beaker have been transferred to the filter, rinse the beaker with about 25 ml. of 1% $KNO_3$, and pour this onto the filter. This rinsing operation should be repeated five times. Finally, carefully rinse the filter five times more with the $KNO_3$ solution.

Return the filter pad and its contents to the beaker and add about 150 ml. of distilled water. Then add the standard NaOH until the yellow precipitate is dissolved and an excess of 5–8 ml. of base is present. Add 5–10 drops of 1.0% phenolphthalein indicator solution and discharge the pink color with standard $HNO_3$. Finally, titrate to a perceptible pink with the NaOH. The total NaOH added, minus the $HNO_3$ used, equals the volume of the alkali required to react with the molybdate complex.

**Calculations and Accuracy.**—For work of average precision, the percentage of total $P_2O_5$ can be calculated on the basis that 1 ml. of the net standard alkali is equivalent to 0.001 g. of $P_2O_5$ ($0.436_5$ mg. of P). This relationship is calculated on the basis of one P equivalent to 23 NaOH according to the following approximate equation:

$$(NH_4)_3PO_4 \cdot 12MoO_3 + 23NaOH \rightarrow$$

$$NaNH_4HPO_4 + (NH_4)_2MoO_4 + 11Na_2MoO_4 + 11H_2O$$

Use of this factor has been found to give results correct to about 1% of the absolute value for a variety of samples. For phosphates containing from 30–75% $P_2O_5$, replicate determinations can be made to within about 0.1% of the average value. In order to obtain a higher absolute accuracy, which can be made to approach that of the magnesium pyrophosphate method given above, it is advisable to standardize the base against a standard sample with an exactly known phosphorus content and having a composition very similar to that of the unknowns being analyzed. It has proved very satisfactory in the case of the analysis of commercial phosphate salts to run a comparison sample of monopotassium orthophosphate, standardized as described on p. 814. In this technique, an amount of the standard $KH_2PO_4$ to give a volume of phosphomolybdate precipitate nearly equal to that of the unknown is employed, and the results on all samples are corrected to give the correct percentage of $P_2O_5$ for the $KH_2PO_4$. It should be noted that the $KH_2PO_4$ sample should contain about the same amount of chloride and sulfate ion as the unknowns (see following section on Interferences).

**Interferences.**—Separation from almost all other anions and cations is accomplished when the orthophosphate ion is precipitated as the phosphomolybdate complex. However, interference is found in the case of bismuth, tin, and zirconium because of coprecipitation of highly insoluble phosphate and in the case of lead because of coprecipitation of a molybdate. Pentavalent arsenic can substitute for phosphorus in the molybdate complex, whereas vanadium and tungsten act in a manner similar to molybdate to form heteropoly acids with phosphates. Titanium and silicon also interfere, the latter mainly because of coprecipitation of gelatinous hydrated silica. Selenium and tellurium interfere seriously by delaying the precipitation and contaminating the precipitate. Interference from organic matter is common; and fluoride, chloride, and sulfate anions delay the precipitation of the phosphomolybdate complex.

Interference from lead, tin, and bismuth can be overcome by precipitating these elements with $H_2S$ under the proper conditions. Arsenic can also be removed by $H_2S$ precipitation, or it can be separated by distillation of the trichloride. In the usual method of sample preparation, which includes a step of fuming with acid, silicon, zirconium, tin, and tungsten are removed as insoluble residues before the beginning of the molybdate precipitation. It should be noted that these precipitates usually contain some phosphorus. Specific techniques for avoiding interference from titanium, vanadium, zirconium, and tungsten are reported in the latter part of this chapter concerned with analysis of alloys (see pp. 863 and 864). The organic material is customarily removed by oxidation (ashing) in the sample preparation. In the case of a number of different organic acids, it has been shown that interference can be eliminated by adding more $HNO_3$ and a considerable excess of the molybdate. Interference from hydrofluoric acid can be overcome by use of boric acid, which complexes the fluorine. In the presence of chloride and sulfate, the amount of molybdate used has to be increased to obtain a quantitative precipitation. Even in this case, precipitation may be delayed. Potassium ions may interfere if gravimetric evaluation of the yellow precipitate is intended, since the ammonium ion in the complex is likely to be partly replaced by potassium.

## TITRIMETRIC DETERMINATION OF TOTAL PHOSPHORUS
## BY pH TITRATION

There is one strongly acidic hydrogen for each phosphorus atom in every acid of phosphorus, regardless of the molecular weight of the acid (see p. 799) or its oxidation state. In mixtures containing only the acids of phosphorus and their salts, removal of cations by passage through an ion-exchange resin, followed by pH titration to the first end point (near pH 4.5) is a measure of the total phosphorus. On the other hand, by conversion of lower oxidation states to the phosphate, followed by hydrolysis of condensed phosphates to the orthophosphate (see p. 812), the total phosphorus can be obtained by titrating the orthophosphoric acid and/or its salts between the end points near pH 4.5 and 9. Obviously, if no lower oxides (and also normal esters of phosphoric acid) are present, the oxidation step can be omitted. Phosphine, phosphonium salts, and normal esters of the acids of phosphorus will not be included in the determination unless the oxidation step is used.

A precise procedure based on titration of the strictly acidic hydrogen has not yet been reported. However, a procedure that can be applied to sodium and potassium salts with an error of less than 0.5% has been described by Van Wazer and Holst.[14]

Titration between the two end points of orthophosphoric acid forms the basis of the quantitative method described below. For routine analysis of soluble salts, this procedure for total $P_2O_5$ is the most rapid and convenient of all.

*Procedure.*—This procedure can be used in the presence of strong acids, strong bases, and their salts if the salts which may be present are soluble at any pH. After fuming the sample under analysis with aqua regia and boiling to hydrolyze any condensed phosphates which might be present (following the procedure described on p. 812), an aliquot containing approximately 0.5 g. of the sample is made up to 100 ml. before beginning the titration, the pH of the sample must be adjusted to approximately 3, at which pH it is most convenient to start the titration. Adjustments of pH by adding alkali should always be made with carbonate-free NaOH, since carbonic acid and other weak acids or bases interfere in this titration.

It is recommended that the titration be carried out with a glass-electrode pH meter. If a continuous recording pH meter is not used, then a number of points should be taken in the two pH ranges of 3.0–5.5 and 7.0–10.0; pH values outside of these ranges are unessential. The end points near pH 4.5 and 9 are precisely measured by bisecting the straight portion of the S-shaped curves at the end points or a $\Delta$pH—ml. plot may be used.

This titration can be carried out with indicators instead. In this case, twice the amount of sample is originally employed, and it is divided into two aliquots, one of which is titrated, using bromcresol green as the indicator, and the other of which is titrated with thymol blue after addition of 20 g. of crystalline $NaNO_3$ to the 100-ml. aliquot. The use of comparison standards to obtain an end point at pH 4.5 with the bromcresol green indicator and an end point at pH 8.2 with the thymol blue indicator in presence of $NaNO_3$ gives reasonably precise results for most samples. However, to obtain the highest accuracy with the colorimetric procedure, it is necessary to determine the end point electrometrically and find what color of the indicator exactly corresponds to the electrometric end point.

This titration is based on neutralization of the second hydrogen of orthophosphoric acid, as illustrated by the following equation for the sodium salt.

$$H_2PO_4^- + OH^- \rightarrow HPO_4^= + H_2O$$

**Accuracy.**—With the Precision-Dow Recording Titrometer (Precision Scientific Company, Chicago, Illinois) the readings have an accuracy of $\pm 0.05$ ml. For a

[14] Van Wazer and Holst, J. Am. Chem. Soc., **72**, 641, 1950.

titration in which 25 ml. of base is employed, the precision is then 0.2%. Considerably less deviation in reproductibility is obtained with a machine which titrates to a given pH. For the Beckman Autotitrator (Beckman Instruments, Inc., South Pasadena, California) the readings are reproducible to $\pm 0.01$ ml. and 50-ml. burettes are employed.

## COLORIMETRIC DETERMINATION OF ORTHOPHOSPHATE BY THE MOLYBDENUM BLUE REACTION

*Reagents.*  **Ammonium Molybdate.**—Dissolve 2.5 g. of ammonium molybdate in distilled water.

**Perchloric Acid.**—60–72% reagent-grade $HClO_4$.

**Reducing Agent.**—Transfer 0.5 g. of 1-amino-2-naphthol-4-sulfonic acid (recrystallized [15]), 29.3 g. of anhydrous $Na_2S_2O_5$, 1.0 g. of anhydrous $Na_2SO_3$, and 200 ml. of distilled water into an Erlenmeyer flask. Warm on a water bath until solution is complete and filter. The reagent becomes yellow upon standing and should not be kept longer than one week.

**Standard Phosphate Solutions.**—Dissolve exactly 0.4393 g. of pure $KH_2PO_4$ (for specification, see p. 814) and make up to 1 liter with distilled water in a volumetric flask. This solution contains 0.1 mg. (100 micrograms) of phosphorus in 1 ml. Use this solution for preparing more dilute solutions containing 10 and 1 micrograms, respectively, in 1 ml., by dilution in the exact proportions. A more concentrated stock solution which contains 1 mg. P/ml. is obtained by dissolving 4.393 g. $KH_2PO_4$ in 1 liter of water.

*Procedure.*[16]—Transfer the solution of the sample which should not contain more than 100 or less than 10 micrograms of phosphorus to a 25-ml. volumetric flask and add 1 ml. of $HClO_4$. Allowance has to be made for the acid already present in the sample solution ($H_2SO_4$ may be used as well, but a special calibration curve has to be employed). Add 2 ml. of ammonium molybdate solution, dilute to about 20 ml. with distilled water, add 1 ml. of the reducing agent, make to volume, and mix well (the resulting pH is about 0.75). Let stand at room temperature for exactly 15 minutes and read the optical density against a blank made up at the same time with the sample, using only distilled water and the same amounts of reagents. Read at 660 m$\mu$ (a red filter should be used). Prepare a standard curve employing varying amounts of the orthophosphate solution.

**Modified Procedure for Determining Less Than 15 Micrograms of Phosphorus.**—By reducing the volumes of the sample and the reagents to one-fifth while working in microbeakers (or small porcelain crucibles) and adjusting the final volume of the solution to be measured colorimetrically within 0.05 ml. (by weighing on a balance accurate to 0.05 g.), as little as 0.2 micrograms of phosphorus can be measured. Four samples and one blank can be measured in a given series. The sequence of making up the solutions and performing the measurements has to be

[15] Recrystallization of 1-amino-2-naphthol-4-sulfonic acid: Heat 1 liter of water to 90°C. and dissolve in it 150 g. of $NaHSO_3$ and 10 g. of $Na_2SO_3$. To this mixture, add 15 g. of the crude sulfonic acid, stir or shake until all of the material but the amorphous impurities has dissolved. Filter the hot solution through a large paper, cool the filtrate to room temperature, and add 10 ml. concentrated HCl. Filter the precipitate with suction, wash with about 300 ml. water, and finally with alcohol until the washings are colorless. Dry in air without exposure to light, powder, and store in a brown bottle.

[16] Fiske, C. H., and SubbaRow, Y., J. Biol. Chem., **66**, 375, 1925, and King, E. J., Biochem. J. (London), **26**, 292, 1932.

carried out in the same succession, in order to achieve a uniform time delay for each sample. The blank is made up as the first solution, and all four samples are compared to it.

**Oxidation of Lower Oxidation States and Mineralization of Organic Material.—** Procedures are described on p. 812 and p. 805, respectively. A suitable aliquot of the resulting solution has to be applied, and allowance has to be made for the acid left over after the fuming procedure or any molybdenum used as catalyst in the mineralization process. Reversion of condensed phosphates is accomplished by boiling, as indicated on p. 812. Instead of $HNO_3$, however, the proper amount of $HClO_4$ (or $H_2SO_4$) required for the development of the blue color is applied. The operation can be carried out in the 25-ml. volumetric flask (or the micro-beaker in the lower range) by immersing it into a boiling water bath. The blank must be run with the sample through the whole procedure.

**Accuracy.—**The solution obeys Beer's Law, and the accuracy is usually limited by the reproducibility of the readings on the colorimeter. When strictly keeping to the procedure used for setting up the standard curve, the errors ordinarily range from 0.5–1 microgram P per 25-ml. volumes and from 0.2–0.4 microgram P for 5-ml. volumes, with the smaller errors occurring at the lower concentrations.

## COLORIMETRIC PHOSPHORUS DETERMINATION IN IRON AND STEEL [17]

*Reagents.* **Ammonium Molybdate Solution.—**300 ml. of concentrated $H_2SO_4$ and 500 ml. of water are mixed and cooled. 20 g. of ammonium molybdate, $(NH_4)_6Mo_7O_{24} \cdot 4H_2O$, is dissolved in the mixture. It is made up to 1000 ml.

**Molybdate Hydrazine Sulfate Reagent.—**25 ml. of ammonium molybdate solution is diluted to 80 ml. with water. 10 ml. of 0.15% hydrazine sulfate solution is added. The mixture is made up to 100 ml. This mixture is unstable and must be prepared as needed.

*Procedure.—*Transfer a 50-mg. sample to a 125-ml. Erlenmeyer flask, add 5 ml. of $HNO_3$ (sp. gr. 1.2), and heat until the sample has dissolved. For samples insoluble in $HNO_3$, add 3 ml. of HCl (sp. gr. 1.1). Add 3 ml. of 60% $HClO_4$, evaporate the solution to fuming, and fume gently until all of the $HNO_3$ is removed (3–4 minutes). Cool, dilute with 10 ml. of water, add 15 ml. of 10% sodium sulfite solution, and boil gently for 20–30 seconds. Add 20 ml. of molybdate hydrazine reagent, and keep the mixture at 90°C. for 4–5 minutes. Increase heating just to boiling temperature, cool rapidly, transfer to a measuring flask, and dilute to 50 ml. with a mixture of 1 part of molybdate hydrazine reagent and 4 parts of water. After mixing carefully, determine percentage of transmission at 830 m$\mu$ or 650 m$\mu$ after setting the photometer to 100% of transmission for distilled water. Evaluate the readings by the aid of a calibration curve which is obtained by carrying standard samples of exactly known phosphorus contents through the entire analysis. (One determination takes only 20 minutes, if the calibration curve has been prepared.)

**Analysis of Cast Iron.—**Since a smaller sample weight is required, dissolve 100 mg. of cast iron in 25 ml. of $HNO_3$ (sp. gr. 1.2), expel nitrous fumes by boiling, cool, and dilute to exactly 100 ml. Allow the graphite to settle, pipette a 5-ml. aliquot into a 125-ml. Erlenmeyer flask, add 3 ml. of $HClO_4$, and proceed as indicated.

[17] Hague, J. L., and Bright, H. A., J. Research Natl. Bur. Standards, **26**, 405, 1941.

**Interfering Constituents.**—A correction for the absorption due to more than 2% of chromium, 5% of vanadium, or 35% of nickel is necessary. For this purpose, a 50-mg. sample is carried through all the steps of the analysis, but 20 ml. of diluted $H_2SO_4$ (8:92) is substituted for the molybdate hydrazine sulfate reagent, and the solution is made up to 50 ml., using distilled water instead of diluted reagent. Arsenic contents exceeding 0.05% must be eliminated. In this case, add 5 ml. of dilute HBr (1:4) to the cooled $HClO_4$ solution, evaporate to fuming, and fume gently to remove the HBr (the procedure is satisfactory for samples containing up to 0.25% of arsenic).

**Accuracy and Application for Extremely Low Phosphorus Percentages.**—The usual deviations are

$$\pm 0.02\% \text{ for } 0.25\text{–}0.8\% \text{ of phosphorus}$$

$$\pm 0.003\% \text{ for } 0.01\text{–}0.11\% \text{ of phosphorus.}$$

Microamounts of phosphorus in high purity iron (0.0001% P) are determined by Gates,[18] using the above colorimetric procedure. A mercury cathode is employed to separate the bulk of the iron.

## ALTERNATE COLORIMETRIC DETERMINATIONS OF ORTHOPHOSPHATE

### PHOSPHOVANADOMOLYBDATE PROCEDURE FOR PHOSPHORUS DETERMINATION IN COPPER-BASE ALLOYS

**Reagents. Ammonium Vanadate.**—2.5 g. of ammonium vanadate is dissolved in 500 ml. of boiling water. 20 ml. of concentrated $HNO_3$ is added. The solution is made up to 1000 ml.

**Ammonium Molybdate.**—Dissolve 10 g. of ammonium molybdate in 100 ml. of water.

**Standard Curve.**—Prepare a curve by adding known amounts of phosphate to low-phosphorus copper, using exactly the procedure recommended for the sample. The technique is feasible for 0.1–2 mg. P, corresponding to 0.01–0.2% of P in the alloy.

**Procedure.**—Transfer a 1-g. sample (fine drillings or sawings) into a 150-ml. beaker. For a blank, prepare 1 g. of low-phosphorus copper in another beaker of the same size. A correction for the iron content of the samples has to be considered. (The error can also be eliminated by using the sample material itself as a blank and all reagents except molybdate.)

Dissolve in 15 ml. of an acid mixture (32 ml. concentrated $HNO_3$, 12 ml. concentrated HCl, and 50 ml. water are mixed; after cooling, make up to 100 ml. with water), and add a few grains of SiC. Heat the covered beakers moderately until dissolution is complete.

Add 1 ml. of 3% hydrogen peroxide and boil gently for 3–5 minutes without losing appreciable amounts of acid. The acidity of the solution is very important for the development of the color. It should be maintained as closely as possible throughout the standards and samples. Remove from heat, add 5 ml. of the ammonium vanadate solution, cool, and transfer to a 50-ml. volumetric flask. Add 5 ml. of the ammonium molybdate solution, make to volume, mix well, and meas-

18 Gates, Anal. Chem., **26**, 730, 1954.

ure the per cent transmission at least 5 minutes later at 470 m$\mu$ against the blank (the color is stable for about 1 hour).

NOTE.—A comprehensive study on development of a highly precise phosphovanado-molybdate method was published by Gee and Deitz.[19]

### COLORIMETRIC METHODS RECOMMENDED FOR PHOSPHORUS DETERMINATION IN IRON AND STEEL

Kitson and Mellon [20] use the yellow-orange phosphovanadomolybdate complex $(NH_4)_3PO_4 \cdot NH_4VO_3 \cdot 16MoO_3$ and measure transmission at 460–480 m$\mu$ (blue filter). Tristrychnine molybdate is recommended by Koch.[21]

## LOWER OXIDATION STATES

## DETERMINATION OF PHOSPHINE

Phosphine, $PH_3$, is a gas with a garlic-like odor, which burns in air and is spontaneously flammable when it contains small amounts of diphosphine, $P_2H_4$. Several kinds of determinations have been recommended for phosphine. For large amounts of phosphine in gases, absorption in solutions of heavy metals such as copper, silver, gold, and mercury has been recommended. For lesser amounts, absorption by oxidizing solutions is used. When phosphine is absorbed in strongly oxidizing reagents, autoignition of the gas has to be taken into consideration. Therefore, the hypochlorite procedure given below should not be applied to gases containing more than 25% of $PH_3$. A very good method for determining traces of phosphine in gases (or traces of phosphides in solid materials) consists of continuous combustion of the gas in a special burner and determination of the resulting phosphoric acid.

### DETERMINATION OF PHOSPHINE BY ABSORPTION IN HYPOCHLORITE

*Procedure.*—A gas sampling bottle can be filled with the gas in question, which is slowly displaced by suitable means through a gas-scrubbing bottle containing a 5% solution of sodium hypochlorite. After the absorption period, the sodium hypochlorite solution is acidified with HCl. The resulting solution is boiled until all chlorine is expelled. All or part of the resulting solution is then analyzed for total phosphorus by the magnesium pyrophosphate method.

Dennis and O'Brien have used a procedure similar to the above one in determining the amount of calcium phosphide present in calcium carbide.[22] In this procedure, the calcium carbide is reacted with a solution of NaCl, and the resulting gas passed through the solution of sodium hypochlorite.

### DETERMINATION OF PHOSPHINE BY ADSORPTION IN MERCURIC CHLORIDE

The procedure described here is usually used for detecting traces of phosphine in air.

*Procedure.*—Bubble 50–100 liters of air through two absorption bottles that each contain 100 ml. of 5% mercuric chloride solution. Maintain a flow rate of about

[19] Gee and Deitz, Anal. Chem., **25**, 1320, 1953.
[20] Kitson and Mellon, Ind. Eng. Chem., Anal. Ed., **16**, 379, 1944.
[21] Koch, Tech. Mitt. Krupp. A. Forschungsber., **1938**, 37, 1938.
[22] Dennis and O'Brien, Ind. Eng. Chem., **4**, 834, 1912.

600 l. per hour when approximately 1 mg. of $PH_3$ is expected to be contained in 1 liter of air. For obtaining a satisfactory distribution of gas in the absorbent solution, the inlet tube should terminate in a bulb with several tiny holes. The resulting precipitate of $P(HgCl)_3$ is white or yellow and forms mainly in the first absorption bottle.

Add enough solid KI to the liquid in the bottles to dissolve the $HgI_2$ initially formed and a 100% excess of standard iodine solution (twice the theoretical amount) to dissolve the mercury-phosphorus compound. Back titrate the excess of iodine with thiosulfate, choosing the normality of the standardized iodine and thiosulfate according to the phosphorus content of the gas being analyzed. In this procedure, 1 ml. of 0.1 $N$ iodine is equivalent to 0.4255 mg. $PH_3$, based on the following equation:

$$P(HgCl)_3 + 4I_2 + 4H_2O \rightarrow H_3PO_4 + 3HgI_2 + 2HI + 3HCl.$$

The error is less than 1%.

### DETERMINATION OF PHOSPHINE BY COMBUSTION (DETERMINATION OF PHOSPHORUS IN ALUMINUM)

*Apparatus.*—The special apparatus is shown in Fig. 35-2.

*Procedure.*—Transfer 200 ml. of water and 2 ml. of NaOH (1:3), to each of the wash bottles, $F_1$ and $F_2$ shown in Fig. 35-2, and place a sample of 30–50 g. of the

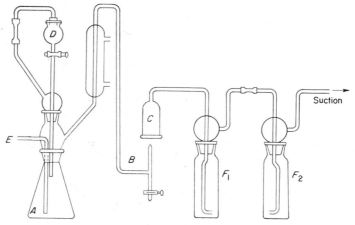

FIG. 35-2. Apparatus for Determining Phosphorus in Aluminum.

aluminum (chips) into the Erlenmeyer flask, $A$. Add enough water to cover the sample in $A$ and replace the air in the apparatus by connecting the tube, $E$, to a hydrogen source. The hydrogen gas has to be washed previously with diluted NaOH. Light the hydrogen at $B$ (a pilot light is arranged very close to $B$ because a varying pressure in the apparatus is apt to extinguish the flame). Sufficient suction is applied so that none of the combustion gas is lost (adjust $B$ to such a height that the flame burns inside the wide glass tube, $C$). Warm the flask, $A$, to about 80°C. and let HCl (1:1) drip from the dropping funnel, $D$. Control the flow of HCl so that the little flame will always have a height of 2–3 cm. After the sample has dissolved completely, sweep for half an hour more with hydrogen gas while contents of $A$ are kept boiling.

Transfer contents of $F_1$ and $F_2$ to a beaker containing 4 ml. of $H_2SO_4$ (1:1) and concentrate to a small volume. Rinse $C$ containing a residue of phosphorus pentoxide and silica with 50 ml. of a 3% solution of HF, so that the connecting tube, including the sieve plate in $F_1$, is washed 3 times (there is not much etching of the glass by this procedure). Transfer this solution to a platinum dish, add the concentrated $H_2SO_4$ solution, evaporate, and fume to dryness, keeping the temperature as low as possible. Excessive heating causes a loss of $P_2O_5$. Dissolve the residue in 2 ml. of hot concentrated $HNO_3$ and not more than 50 ml. of water, boil gently for an hour, keeping the water level approximately constant,[23] transfer to a beaker, and precipitate with ammonium molybdate (see p. 814). A blank must be run through the entire procedure, and the resulting correction has to be subtracted from the analysis.

NOTE.—Treadwell and Hartnagel, Helv. Chim. Acta., **15**, 1023, 1932, adopted this procedure for determining microgram amounts of phosphorus in aluminum (1–60 micrograms P, using 0.1–1.0 g. of sample).

## ANALYSIS OF WHITE PHOSPHORUS

Autoignition takes place when pieces of elemental phosphorus are taken from immersion in water or organic solvents as soon as the evaporation of the solvent is complete. Nearly saturated solutions of phosphorus in benzene smoke heavily. Solutions should, therefore, never be more than two-thirds saturated.

The procedure given below can be used for analyzing purified white phosphorus, as well as for extracting and determining small percentages of white phosphorus in crude phosphorus and sludges. Samples containing red and white phosphorus in all proportions can be analyzed.

**Sample Preparation.**—White phosphorus is cut under water and transferred into an acetone bath, or it can be granulated by melting it under water in a stoppered flask and cooling it in running water while shaking vigorously. Samples that contain enough white phosphorus so as to oxidize rapidly in air should also be handled the same way.

Samples of aqueous phosphorus sludges are shaken thoroughly and transferred into centrifuge tubes. By centrifuging for about 10 minutes at 2500 r.p.m. liquid and solid are separated. After determining the ratio of volumes, the liquid may be discarded. The solids are rinsed out of the tubes with water into a small beaker and analyzed.

For sampling procedures yielding samples strictly representative of the material initially sampled see Aldred:[24]

**Apparatus.**—The apparatus consists of a boiling flask of 250- to 500-ml. capacity, an extractor, a calibrated water trap, and a condenser. The extractor-condenser system (see Fig. 35-3) is connected to the flask by the ground-glass connection at $G_1$. $S$ represents a sintered glass disk of medium porosity (small pores could be sealed by water originating from the sample, so that the benzene flow is impeded). The upper joint, $G_2$, connects the extractor with the water trap, $T$. This water trap

---

[23] Boiling is recommended for complete hydrolysis of any condensed phosphates that might be formed during the fuming process.
[24] Aldred, Ind. Eng. Chem., Anal. Ed., **13**, 390, 1941.

supports the condenser, *C*. A stopper is kept ready for $G_2$ and an adapter and a cap for $G_1$.

*Procedure.*—The extractor, together with the stopper and cap, is dried at 105°C. and weighed. Then it is clamped in upright position ($G_2$ on the top). By the aid of the adapter, the lower joint, $G_1$, is connected with a nitrogen cylinder, and the extractor is swept with nitrogen for 2–3 minutes (flow rate about 1 l./hour). Without stopping the stream of nitrogen, the moist sample containing not more than 3 g. of phosphorus is transferred into the extractor, without coming in contact

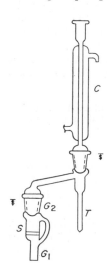

with the upper joint, $G_2$, through use of a protecting metal shield. If the sample contains considerable water or is contaminated with an organic solvent, it is dried in a current of dry nitrogen. The upper stopper is inserted, the adapter removed from the lower joint, $G_1$, and replaced by the cap. The extractor is weighed accurately to 0.5 mg. to obtain the weight of the dry sample.

After weighing the extractor and sample, the cap is removed, the dried sample covered with benzene, and the flask containing 70 ml. of benzene for every gram of sample is attached to $G_1$ (the final solution must certainly not contain more than 2.4 g. of phosphorus in 100 ml.; solutions higher in phosphorus have to be diluted before transferring).

The stopper is removed from $G_2$, and the water trap, *T*, with the condenser, *C*, is connected. The sample is extracted completely by maintaining the benzene in the flask boiling on a water bath for 2 hours or more, depending upon the nature of the sample. After completion of the extraction, the benzene solution is cooled, transferred to a volumetric flask, and made to volume (250 ml. for a 3-g. sample).

FIG. 35-3.
Extractor-
Condenser System.

A sufficient excess of a 25% copper nitrate solution is transferred to a 250-ml. Erlenmeyer flask (20 g. of $Cu(NO_3)_2$ for 1 g. of phosphorus; after the copper has precipitated and the phosphorus and this precipitate have settled, the solution must show a distinct greenish color). An aliquot of the benzene-phosphorus solution is added by the aid of a safety pipette to the copper nitrate solution. The flask is stoppered and shaken vigorously at 2-minute intervals for about 15 minutes. The stopper and sides of the flask are washed down with water, and benzene is removed by heating on a water bath under a hood (glass beads prevent bumping). To the remaining aqueous residue, 5 ml. of concentrated $HNO_3$ is added cautiously, and the precipitate is dissolved by heating. After cooling, the clear solution is made up to 250 ml. with distilled water. An aliquot representing 15 mg. or less of P is transferred to a 500-ml. wide-mouthed Erlenmeyer flask. Then 10–15 ml. of 60% $HClO_4$ is added. The solution is digested on a hot plate and fumed down to 2–3 ml. The rate of heating is controlled by the condensing $HClO_4$ in the neck of the flask. The condensing acid has to be visible 2.5–3.3 cm. below the top.

By this procedure, phosphorus is completely oxidized to orthophosphoric acid.

The solution is cooled, neutralized, and phosphorus is determined by precipitation as the molybdenum complex, as described on p. 814.

## DETERMINATION OF WATER AND THE PERCENTAGE OF INSOLUBLE MATTER

*Procedure.*—The water volume in the water trap, $T$, is read. This value can be used to correct the sample weight to an anhydrous basis, and it represents the water content if the sample were not dried. The extractor containing the benzene-insoluble residue is dried in a stream of nitrogen at 105°C. for 1 hour, stoppered on both sides, and weighed.

*Accuracy.*—The deviation of the percentage of soluble phosphorus plus insoluble residue from 100% usually amounts to several tenths of a per cent. This difference includes the inaccuracies of the method and the benzene-soluble non-phosphorus compounds (usually oil).

## DETERMINATION OF WHITE PHOSPHORUS IN MUD

Phosphorus mud and press cakes or similar materials containing not more than 40% of phosphorus on a dry basis can be analyzed, using the procedure described below. Materials higher in phosphorus should be pressed on a laboratory pressure filter to remove part of the phosphorus before extraction. A certain amount of phosphorus mud is formed in all manufacturing operations for making elemental phosphorus. The mud is composed primarily of dust and hydrolyzed silicon tetrafluoride which is carried over with the phosphorus vapors from the furnace.

*Procedure.*—Transfer a weighed sample containing about 5 g. of white phosphorus to a mortar and, after adding water, grind to break up any lumps. Transfer into a 1-liter round-bottomed flask and let settle overnight. Remove the clear, supernatant water layer by the aid of a safety pipette. Attach the flask to a descending condenser, using a stopper which also carries a separatory funnel and a device for sweeping the system with $CO_2$. Replace the air in the apparatus with $CO_2$, introduce about 600 ml. of toluene, and distill until all water has been driven out (more than 600 ml. of toluene can be used for large amounts of water; some toluene left over does not interfere with the extraction).

Increase the $CO_2$ stream, cool, and replace the cooling system by a reflux condenser.

Separate water and toluene in the distillate and retain the toluene, which will contain a little phosphorus.

Make the volume in the flask to about 600 ml. with benzene and reflux for 1 hour, while slowly sweeping with $CO_2$. Increase the $CO_2$ stream again and cool. Filter, using a Buechner funnel, wash with benzene (loosen all material sticking to the flask), and save the filtrate, which contains most of the phosphorus. The filtrate may smoke a little if it is still warm when the filtration is carried out. But if the volume and the sample weight were chosen as directed, it will not catch fire (spilling of the filtrate, on the other hand, represents a serious danger).

Transfer the residue on the filter with 500 ml. benzene back into the flask, sweep with $CO_2$, and reflux for 1 hour more, as before. Filter, wash, and save the filtrate, which contains the remainder of the white phosphorus.

Collect, dry, and save the residue. It contains the red phosphorus, iron, aluminum, lime, carbon, silica, potassium, and fluorine.

Unite the two filtrates and the toluene layer from the water-toluene distillation, mix thoroughly, and read the volume. Take 100 ml. of it as an analytical sample and burn the rest.

Transfer a 10-ml. fraction of the mixture to a 250-ml. wide-mouthed Erlenmeyer flask, add 50–100 ml. of 25% copper nitrate solution (according to the phosphorus present), stopper, and shake at intervals for 15 minutes. Remove benzene by boiling and dissolve the precipitate by adding slowly and carefully 25 ml. of concentrated $HNO_3$. After the reaction has ceased, add 25 ml. of concentrated HCl, boil until nitrous fumes are removed, and cool. Dilute to 250 ml. and determine phosphoric acid in an aliquot (usually 100 ml.). The amount of precipitate may be used for estimating roughly the aliquot required.

## DETERMINATION OF OIL IN PHOSPHORUS

*Procedure.*—Measure 200 ml. of $PCl_3$ into a 3000-ml. three-necked flask and replace the air by sweeping with carbon dioxide or nitrogen. Transfer 150 ml. of molten phosphorus by the aid of a calibrated tube that is equipped with a stopcock for stopping delivery and which has a sufficiently long stem to reach to the bottom of the flask containing the trichloride. Avoid transferring water with the phosphorus.

Connect a Friedrich's condenser with standard taper joint to one neck of the flask and insert a cork stopper carrying a 7-mm. glass tube with reduced end (to 2 mm.) and bent at a 90° angle into another neck. Connect this tube to a chlorine cylinder and provide a safety pressure seal in case the delivery tube becomes plugged. Close the third neck with a ground-glass joint.

Introduce chlorine at a moderate rate until $PCl_5$ crystals begin to form (the end of the chlorine delivery tube has to be kept just above the top of the phosphorus and well below the surface of the phosphorus chloride).

Replace the chlorine stream by carbon dioxide or nitrogen and control the flow rate so that the solution is kept agitated. Insert a separatory funnel containing water in the third neck and allow the water to drop in slowly until all of the chloride is hydrolyzed. Much of the HCl developed in this step may be absorbed by water in bottles connected to the outlet of the condenser (*do not dip the HCl delivery tubes into the water!*). After hydrolysis is complete, add more water to the flask, so that the specific gravity of the solution contained therein will be below that of $CCl_4$, and let cool. Transfer the contents of the flask to a large separatory funnel, rinse the flask with redistilled $CCl_4$, and extract the oil by repeated shaking with $CCl_4$ in the separatory funnel. As soon as the $CCl_4$ remains colorless after shaking, all oil has been extracted.

Evaporate the combined $CCl_4$ extracts to about 50 ml., filter into a tared 250-ml. beaker, and wash the paper with $CCl_4$. Evaporate at low temperature (below 100°C.) until all $CCl_4$ has gone. Cool and weigh.

A blank has to be run, and a corresponding correction is applied.

## ANALYSIS OF RED PHOSPHORUS

### DETERMINATION OF TOTAL PHOSPHORUS IN RED PHOSPHORUS

*Procedure.*—Transfer a 2.000-g. sample of red phosphorus to a 500-ml. widemouthed Erlenmeyer flask and add 40 ml. of concentrated $H_2SO_4$. Cover with a watch glass and dissolve by heating on a hot plate at moderate heat for about 30 minutes. Increase heat until the $H_2SO_4$ starts to fume and condenses on the cooler upper walls of the flask. Maintain this temperature for about 5 minutes. Cool to room temperature and add, little by little, 150 ml. of water while swirling the flask. Boil for 1 hour (the volume must not be reduced below 100 ml.), cool, and dilute to exactly 500 ml. with distilled water in a volumetric flask.

Dilute a 100-ml. aliquot of the well-mixed solution to 500 ml. in another measuring flask, mix thoroughly, and transfer a 100-ml. aliquot representing 0.08 g. of sample to a 400-ml. beaker. Precipitate magnesium ammonium phosphate in the presence of citric acid, as described on p. 809.

## DETERMINATION OF ACIDITY IN RED PHOSPHORUS

Prepare a water extract and titrate with standard base to the strong and weak acid end points.

NOTES.—Acids in red phosphorus were determined by Tolkatschoff and Portnoff,[25] and Korinfsky.[26] Determinations of the lower acids of phosphorus in the presence of each other are reported by Krjukowa.[27]

## ANALYSIS OF MIXTURES OF WHITE PHOSPHORUS, PHOSPHOROUS, AND PHOSPHORIC ACIDS [28]

An aqueous solution of this nature is obtained when a sample containing P, $PCl_3$, and $POCl_3$ is treated with water for 15 minutes. The procedure was developed for the analysis of 3–5 g. of a mixture of P, $PCl_3$, and $POCl_3$ which was hydrolyzed for 15 minutes with 200 ml. of water. Red phosphorus would remain as insoluble residue. For samples with high phosphorus contents, a sufficiently large volume of benzene must be used. (See remarks on p. 823 concerning autoignition.)

*Extraction.*—Extract the aqueous solution of about 200-ml. volume in a groundglass Erlenmeyer flask by shaking with 75 ml. of benzene for 1 minute. Transfer to a 500-ml. separatory funnel, wash the flask twice with 20 ml. of water and 20 ml. of benzene, and add the washings to the contents of the funnel. Shake for 2 minutes, let separate, and transfer the aqueous phase into a second separatory funnel. Add 50 ml. of benzene to the aqueous phase, shake for 2 minutes, draw the aqueous layer into a third funnel, and wash again. Transfer the aqueous phase into a 500-ml. volumetric flask. Collect all the benzene phases in the first funnel and wash both the second and third funnels once with 20 ml. of water and 20 ml. of benzene. Unite these washings also with the contents of the first funnel. Shake for 1 minute and add the aqueous layer to the volumetric flask. Wash the benzene by shaking twice with 20 ml. of water, add the water to the other aqueous phases in the volumetric flask, and make up to volume.

## DETERMINATION OF WHITE PHOSPHORUS

*Procedure.*—Transfer the benzene-phosphorus solution to 50 ml. of 25% copper nitrate solution in a 500-ml. Erlenmeyer flask with ground-glass stopper. If more than 40 mg. of phosphorus was extracted, the benzene solution is first made to volume, and an aliquot is added to the copper nitrate solution. Wash the funnel two times with 10 ml. of benzene, and add these washings to the flask containing the copper nitrate. Proceed with oxidation, precipitation, and titration, as described above for phosphorus determination in benzene extracts (see pp. 825 and 826).

[25] Tolkatschoff and Portnoff, Z. anal. Chem., **82**, 122, 1930.
[26] Korinfsky, Zavodskaya Lab., **8**, 861, 1940.
[27] Krjukowa, Zavodskaya Lab., **6**, 47, 1937.
[28] Keeler, R. A., Anderson, C. J., Satriana, D., Anal. Chem., **26**, 933, 1954.

### DETERMINATION OF PHOSPHOROUS ACID

**Procedure.**—Transfer an aliquot of the aqueous solution (corresponding to 0.2 g. of $PCl_3$) to a mixture of 50 ml. of 0.1 $N$ iodine solution (standardized) and 50 ml. of a saturated sodium bicarbonate solution. Let react for a half hour in the dark, and titrate the excess of iodine with standard arsenious solution (1 ml. of 0.1 $N$ iodine solution corresponds to 1.549 mg. of trivalent phosphorus).

### DETERMINATION OF PHOSPHORIC ACID BY DIFFERENCE

**Procedure.**—Transfer an aliquot of the water solution to a 600-ml. beaker. Add 15 ml. of concentrated $HNO_3$ and 10 ml. of 70% $HClO_4$, heat to white fumes, and keep fuming for 5 minutes. Cool and determine phosphoric acid by precipitation and titration of the molybdenum complex. Deduct the phosphorus due to phosphorous acid.

## ANALYSIS OF MIXTURES OF HYPOPHOSPHOROUS ACID, ORTHOPHOSPHOROUS ACID, HYPOPHOSPHORIC ACID, AND ORTHOPHOSPHORIC ACID [29]

### QUALITATIVE DETECTION

**Procedure.**—Add 2–3 drops of 10% NaOH to the neutral sample solution and drop in 1 or 2 drops of 0.1 $N$ $KMnO_4$. Prepare a reference solution by adding the same amounts of reagents to the same volume of pure water. A green tint showing up after 2–3 minutes indicates phosphorous or hypophosphorous acid, or both. Even 6 micrograms of these reducing acids can be detected in this manner.

Hypophosphoric acid is detected by adding thorium nitrate to a hydrochloric acid solution of the sample. A precipitate of $ThP_2O_6$ is formed.

### ORTHOPHOSPHOROUS ACID

**Procedure.**—Transfer an aliquot of the neutral solution into a 250- to 500-ml. flask with ground-glass stopper. Add 50 ml. of 0.2 $M$ sodium bicarbonate solution which had been saturated previously with $CO_2$. Introduce an excess of standardized 0.1 $N$ iodine solution (about 50% excess over the theoretical amount, but at least 10 ml. of the 0.1 $N$ solution, is satisfactory). Insert the stopper and allow to react for 40–60 minutes. Titrate back the excess of iodine with arsenite solution or thiosulfate solution of corresponding normality. If exactly 0.1 $N$ iodine solution is used, 1 ml. corresponds to 4.10 mg. of phosphorous acid ($H_3PO_3$).

### HYPOPHOSPHOROUS ACID

**Procedure.**—Transfer an aliquot of the neutral solution into a flask with a ground-glass stopper, add 10 ml. of 15% $H_2SO_4$, and an excess of standardized 0.1 $N$ iodine solution. Insert the stopper and allow to react for 10 hours.

Add a pasty suspension of sodium bicarbonate in small portions until the solution becomes neutral, as shown by cessation of the $CO_2$ development. Add 50 ml. of 0.2 molal sodium bicarbonate, saturated with $CO_2$, stopper, allow to react for 1 hour, and titrate the excess of iodine with sodium thiosulfate. The sum of phosphorous acid originally present plus the phosphorous acid formed by oxidation of the hypophosphorous acid in acid solution is determined. The iodine consumption due to phosphorous acid originally present must be deter-

[29] Wolf, L., and Jung, W., Z. anorg. Chem., **201**, 347, 353, 1931.

mined, as directed under "Orthophosphorous Acid," and has to be deducted from the volume of 0.1 $N$ iodine solution used. Following this procedure, 1 ml. of 0.1 $N$ iodine solution corresponds to 1.65 mg. of hypophosphorous acid ($H_3PO_2$).

## HYPOPHOSPHORIC ACID

*Procedure.*—To an aliquot of the solution that has been neutralized against phenolphthalein, add 2 drops of a 10% acetic acid solution, 20–25 ml. of a 20% sodium acetate solution, and 25 ml. of a barium nitrate solution prepared by saturating water with the chloride-free salt at room temperature. Separate the precipitate by centrifuging 20–30 minutes. Wash by stirring the precipitate with water and centrifuge again. Discard the solutions. Dissolve the precipitate, which is free of hypophosphite and consists of the barium salts of orthophosphorous, hypophosphoric, and orthophosphoric acids, in 20–25 ml. of 10% phosphoric acid.

Add a few milliliters of ether and precipitate silver hypophosphate by adding a 100% excess of standardized 0.1 $N$ AgNO$_3$. Mix well by shaking and filter immediately under very slight suction into a 250-ml. ground-glass stoppered flask (use filter paper disks on a sintered glass filter), wash with distilled water several times by decantation, and finally wash the precipitate several times more on the filter. Acidify the filtrate without delay and titrate the excess of silver with ammonium thiocyanate. In the above procedure, 1 ml. of 0.1 $N$ AgNO$_3$ corresponds to 8.099 mg. of hypophosphoric acid ($H_4P_2O_6$).

NOTES.—Silver orthophosphate does not precipitate in phosphoric acid of the concentration used. The whole procedure must be carried through without delay, so that phosphorous acid present cannot reduce appreciable amounts of silver salt. An error up to 1 mg. must be expected with small amounts of hypophosphoric acid. Grundman and Hellmich [30] consider Wolf and Jung's procedure as not very accurate in the presence of phosphorous acid, because of the rather time-consuming filtration, during which silver salt could be reduced by phosphorous acid. Therefore, a potentiometric titration for hypophosphoric acid was worked out which is feasible in the presence of phosphorous acid (hypophosphorous acid must be absent).

## ORTHOPHOSPHORIC ACID

*Procedure.*—Transfer an aliquot of the original neutral solution into a porcelain dish, evaporate after adding HNO$_3$ and HCl, and fume several times with a mixture of these acids. Determine the sum of phosphorus as orthophosphate (pp. 814 or 817) and deduct the amounts of phosphorus due to the lower oxidation states.

Another convenient procedure is to weigh approximately 1 g. of the acid mixture from a weighing bottle on an analytical balance into a 250-ml. flask and to add 25 ml. of aqua regia. Then, the flask is heated until the evolution of brown fumes has ceased, and the volume is reduced to about 5 ml. The flask is cooled, and the solution is then diluted to the mark, mixed, after which total $P_2O_5$ is determined by the molybdate procedure (see p. 814) on an aliquot portion equivalent to about 0.05 g. $P_2O_5$.

## ALTERNATE METHODS

Mixtures containing orthophosphorous acid, hypophosphoric acid, and orthophosphoric acid were analyzed by Van Name and Huff,[31] using the following

[30] Grundman and Hellmich, J. prakt. Chem., **143,** 100, 1935.
[31] Van Name and Huff, Amer. J. Sci., (4), **45,** 91, 1918.

three steps: (1) determination of orthophosphorous acid with iodine (see p. 828), (2) splitting of hypophosphoric acid into orthophosphorous acid and phosphoric acid by boiling with concentrated HCl; determination of the sum of orthophosphorous acid originally present and the fraction formed by splitting hypophosphoric acid; the orthophosphorous acid originally present must be accounted for in the evaluation of the iodine consumption; and (3) determination of the total phosphorus as orthophosphate; deduction of the calculated amounts due to orthophosphorous acid and hypophosphoric acid yields the orthophosphoric acid present.

A procedure for determination of hypophosphite and phosphite using cerium(IV) in sulfuric acid solution has been reported by Bernhart.[32]

## PHOSPHATE MIXTURES

Although considerable effort has been spent during the last fifty years on developing traditional wet-chemical methods for determining the various species of phosphates in the presence of one another, none of these methods has proved generally satisfactory. This fact has been clearly demonstrated for mixtures of pyro- and tripolyphosphate by Dewald.[33] It should be noted that the procedures in this category that are most popular in the United States are those of Jones [34] and Bell.[35] Both the Jones and Bell procedures are satisfactory for routine determinations on a given industrial product, although the absolute values may be considerably in error.

## ORTHOPHOSPHATE IN THE PRESENCE OF OTHER PHOSPHATES

It has been adequately demonstrated by a number of authors that the only phosphate which forms a complex with molybdate is the orthophosphate. Therefore, a molybdate analysis under conditions where the condensed phosphates are not too rapidly hydrolyzed to the orthophosphates will give a direct determination of orthophosphate in the presence of any other phosphate. In addition, orthophosphoric acid is different from all of the other phosphoric acids, in that it has a third replaceable hydrogen ion per phosphorus atom. The condensed phosphates have two or less replaceable hydrogens per phosphorus atom. Although the third hydrogen of orthophosphoric acid is extremely weak, it can be released by precipitating the normal phosphate of heavy metals.

### MOLYBDATE METHOD (PRECIPITATION OF THE COMPLEX)

**Reagents. Special Ammonium Molybdate Solution.**—For Solution $A$, dissolve by gentle warming 59 g. of 85% molybdic acid in 150 ml. of distilled water containing 60 ml. of concentrated ammonium hydroxide. Add 190 ml. of distilled water and cool. For Solution $B$, mix 150 ml. of concentrated $HNO_3$ with 450 ml. of distilled water and 10 g. of crystalline $NH_4NO_3$. This solution should be cooled also. Then, add Solution $A$ to Solution $B$ while stirring; cool; let stand for 24 hours in a cool, dark place; filter before using, if the mixture is not perfectly clear. This

[32] Bernhart, Anal. Chem., **26,** 1798, 1954.
[33] Dewald, Fette u. Seifen, **56,** 105, 1954.
[34] Jones, Ind. Eng. Chem., Anal. Ed., **14,** 536, 1942.
[35] Bell, Anal. Chem., **19,** 97, 1947; *ibid.,* **24,** 1997, 1952.

reagent should not be used once it has started to deteriorate through formation of a precipitate.

All reagents other than the ammonium molybdate are the same as those described on p. 814.

*Procedure.*—Pipette or weigh directly 0.1–0.2 g. of the phosphate mixture being analyzed to a 250-ml. beaker. Dilute to 60 ml., add 5 g. of crystalline $NH_4NO_3$, and cool to $8°C \pm 2°$ in a cooling bath (crushed ice-salt water is usually used here). Add 60 ml. of the special molybdate solution (also cooled to 8°C.) and stir vigorously with a crosswise motion for 3 minutes. A motor-driven stirrer can be used here. At the end of 6 minutes, remove the beaker from the cooling bath, and filter as quickly as possible through the type of filter previously described on p. 815 for the phosphomolybdate complex. Proceed as described under "Titrimetric Determination of Orthophosphate after Precipitation as Phosphomolybdate" on p. 815. The results are computed in terms of phosphorus or $P_2O_5$ present as the orthophosphate, and these numbers divided by the total phosphorus or total $P_2O_5$, respectively, give the fraction of the total phosphorus present as orthophosphate.

## COLORIMETRIC METHOD

*Reagents.* **Molybdate Solution.**—Dissolve 50 g. of ammonium molybdate in 400 ml. of 10 $N$ sulfuric acid and dilute to 1 l. with water.

**Isobutyl Alcohol and Benzene.**—Mix equal volumes of isobutyl alcohol and thiophene-free benzene (analytical grade).

**Stannous Chloride Solution.**—Dissolve 10 g. of $SnCl_2 \cdot 2H_2O$ in 25 ml. of concentrated HCl and store in a glass-stoppered brown bottle. Prepare the reagent by diluting 1 ml. of this stock solution to 200 ml. with approximately $N$ sulfuric acid as needed (this dilute reagent is not stable longer than 1 day).

**Sulfuric Acid in Ethyl Alcohol.**—Dissolve 20 ml. of concentrated sulfuric acid in 980 ml. of 99.5% ethyl alcohol (check this reagent with respect to the stability of the molybdenum blue color; instability is due to some contamination of the alcohol and a new batch should be tried).

*Standard Curve.*—Use standard phosphate solutions (see p. 818) for plotting a calibration curve which covers 1 to 75 micrograms P when 1-cm. cells are used for measuring optical density and keep exactly to the procedure given below.

*Procedure.*—Transfer a suitable aliquot, which contains not more than 0.2 mg. ortho-$P_2O_5$ and the volume of which should be determined in a preliminary test, into a 100-ml. test tube or cylinder. Make to 15 ml. with distilled water, add exactly 25 ml. of isobutyl alcohol-benzene solution and 5 ml. of molybdate reagent, stopper, and immediately shake for 15 seconds. Let the phases separate and withdraw 10 ml. of the supernatant organic liquid into a 25-ml. volumetric flask. Rinse the pipette and dilute with alcoholic sulfuric acid to 20 ml., add 1 ml. of freshly prepared dilute stannous chloride, and make to volume with the alcoholic sulfuric acid. Mix and measure at 625 m$\mu$ (red filter) against a blank that has been carried through the whole procedure.

## TITRIMETRIC METHOD (SILVER SALT PRECIPITATION)

*Reagents.* **Silver Nitrate Solution.**—170 g. reagent-grade $AgNO_3$ is dissolved in water and diluted to 1 liter. An $AgNO_3$ solution which is approximately 1 $N$ results.

**Sodium Hydroxide.**—0.15 $N$ NaOH, free of $CO_2$, is made up and standardized against acid potassium phthalate.

*Potentiometric Procedure.*—An aliquot of the sample solution, containing an appropriate amount of $P_2O_5$ (see "Calculations" below), is adjusted to a volume of about 100 ml. and a pH of about 3. It is then titrated by the aid of a glass electrode and a pH meter or an automatic Titrometer just beyond the first end point at a pH of about 4.5. The titration is stopped, and 50 ml. of the 1 $N$ $AgNO_3$ solution is added. The titration is now continued very slowly (about 0.5 ml. of base per minute) until the pH curve shows complete neutralization of the hydrogen ions that were set free by precipitating the silver salt (pH of the end point about 5).

Another equal aliquot is titrated with base starting at pH 3 until the second end point is passed (see pp. 817 and 833).

*Alternate Procedure with Color Indicators.*—The aliquot is titrated to the bromcresol green end point at pH 4.5 with a comparison color standard (see p. 817). An excess of $AgNO_3$ and 0.5 ml. of a 0.2% methyl red solution as indicator are added. The titration is then carried through to the methyl red end point. The use of color indicators always requires a slight correction, which is best accomplished by running a standard phosphate sample with every set of unknown samples.

**Calculations.**—In the above method, the titration of the acid sample solution is carried through the first end point, so that the strong acid function of all acids has been neutralized before $AgNO_3$ is added (see following section). One hydrogen ion is therefore titrated for every end group phosphorus atom in the chain phosphates and two hydrogen ions for each molecule of orthophosphoric acid present, after the $AgNO_3$ has been added (see p. 830).

Hence, the volume of base, equivalent to the third (and weakest) hydrogen ion of the orthophosphoric acid, and representing a measure of the orthophosphoric acid present, can be calculated. The base equivalent to the second hydrogen of the end groups (see next paragraph) and to the second hydrogen of the orthophosphoric acid is found by titrating the other aliquot between the two end points at pH 4.5 and pH 9. Deduction of this volume from the base consumed in the silver precipitation procedure gives the volume in milliliters of base due to the third hydrogen of the orthophosphoric acid. This value multiplied by the normality of the base give the milliequivalents of ortho-$P_2O_5$, which are called $S$ in the formula below.

$$\% \ P_2O_{5(ortho)} = \frac{(7.1)S}{\text{Weight of sample}}$$

## TITRIMETRIC DETERMINATION OF END GROUPS

As previously stated, there is one strongly acid hydrogen for each phosphorus atom in any phosphoric acid. Ring phosphates (true metaphosphoric acids) have only this one strongly ionized hydrogen for each phosphorus atom and exhibit no weakly ionized hydrogens. Chain phosphates (polyphosphoric acids) have one strongly ionized hydrogen for each phosphorus atom and, in addition, have a weakly ionized hydrogen at each end of the chain. By titrating this weak hydrogen, it is possible to determine the number of end groups present in a mixture of chains and rings. The two-membered chain (pyrophosphoric acid) has, according to the above statement, one strongly and one weakly acidic hydrogen per phosphorus atom.

The orthophosphoric acid plays an anomalous role, in that it has in addition to its one strongly ionized hydrogen, a moderately weak (like the end group) and an extremely weak hydrogen. Therefore, titrations for end groups in mixtures of chain and ring phosphates must be corrected for the presence of orthophosphate.

*Procedure.*—Dissolve 0.5 g. of the sample in 100 ml. of water, to which sufficient NaOH ($CO_2$-free) was added in the case of acidic materials to keep the pH above 6, or take an aliquot of a larger sample treated as directed. If the sample dissolves promptly, it is not necessary to control the pH. Lower the pH to about 3 (HCl is suggested) and titrate electrometrically with base through the end point near pH 4.5 and continuing beyond the second end point near pH 9, as described on p. 817. The number of milliequivalents of base, $A$, used between the two end points in this titration correspond to the weakly acidic function of the end groups and of the orthophosphoric acid. As described on p. 817, indicators may be used in this titration, or an automatic titrating machine which stops at a set pH can be employed, if the exact pH of the end point has been determined electrometrically before. To obtain precise results, it is important to complete the titration as rapidly as possible after the pH is lowered to 3, since in acid solution the condensed phosphates hydrolyze at an appreciable rate. In order to avoid hydrolysis, the steps in this procedure should all be carried out at room temperature or below. *Do not boil* the solutions of the sample under any circumstances before carrying out an end group titration.

**Total phosphorus** may be gathered from titration of the weakly acidic function in another sample of the same weight or an aliquot, after complete hydrolysis according to the procedure on p. 817. Between the end points at pH 4.5 and pH 9, $A_h$ milliequivalents of base are consumed.

**Orthophosphoric acid** is determined according to p. 831 in a third sample of the same weight or an aliquot. The milliequivalents of $P_2O_5$ present as ortho, $S$ are obtained (see p. 832).

**Calculations and Accuracy.**— In the hands of a careful worker, end groups can be determined to better than 0.5%.

**The percentage of total phosphorus present as end groups** is calculated as follows:

$$\% \text{ of total } P_2O_5 \text{ as end groups} = \frac{A - S}{A_h} \times 100$$

This formula holds true if exactly the same sample weights (aliquots of a solution) are analyzed or if all milliequivalents are calculated for the same sample weight by the aid of proportions.

*Average Chain Length.*—In a sample that contains only chain phosphates, the number average chain length (degree of polymerization) of the phosphate, $\bar{n}$, can be calculated from the following equations:

$$P_2O_{5\,(total)} : P_2O_{5\,(end)} = \bar{n} : 2$$

since every chain is limited by two end groups. Total $P_2O_5$ can be expressed by the number of milliequivalents of weakly acidic function after complete hydrolysis, $A_h$ (titration between pH 4.5 and pH 9). On the other hand, $P_2O_{5\,(end)}$ is represented by the number of milliequivalents, $A$, obtained for the weakly acidic function without hydrolysis, as described on p. 832. Therefore, the following relations hold true:

$$\bar{n} = 2 \frac{P_2O_{5(total)}}{P_2O_{5(end)}} = 2 \frac{A_h}{A}$$

For compositions of the formula $M_2O \cdot P_2O_5$, where $M_2O$ may stand for $Na_2O$, $K_2O$, $H_2O$ of composition, $CaO$, etc., or mixtures of these constituents, the average chain length can be calculated from the proximate composition. If only chains (no ortho, rings, or branched structures) are present, the following equation applies:

$$M_2O/P_2O_5 = \frac{\bar{n} + 2}{\bar{n}}$$

Thus, for a commercial sodium phosphate glass containing 63.41% of $P_2O_5$, 35.71% of $Na_2O$, and 0.88% of $H_2O$ of composition, one can solve for $\bar{n}$ from the above equation as follows:

$$\frac{\bar{n} + 2}{\bar{n}} = \frac{(35.71/62.0) + (0.88/18.0)}{(63.41/142.0)}$$

or $\bar{n} = 5.01$, which means that this glass has an average formula of $Na_7P_5O_{16}$ (from $Na_{n+2}P_nO_{3n+1}$) and an average molecular weight of 571.88.

When ring phosphates and orthophosphate are present, the average chain length is obtained by changing the equation as follows:

$$\bar{n} = 2\frac{P_2O_{5(total)} - P_2O_{5(ring)} - P_2O_{5(ortho)}}{P_2O_{5(end)} - P_2O_{5(ortho)}} = 2\frac{A_h - R - S}{A - S}$$

$S$ = number of milliequivalents of ortho-$P_2O_5$ in the sample
$R$ = number of milliequivalents of ring-$P_2O_5$ in the sample (must be known).

The reader is referred to the article by L. T. Jones,[36] for an approximate procedure for determining rings. It should be noted that in the Jones' article, ring phosphates are called "trimetaphosphate."

As there are no satisfactory traditional wet-chemical methods for separating and characterizing a mixture of chain phosphates, such as is found in the sodium phosphate glasses of commerce (Calgon, Oilfos, etc.), the characterization of mixtures of chain phosphates in terms of their number average chain length, $\bar{n}$, is extremely valuable. In modern practice, this average chain length is used to describe many of the amorphous phosphates.

## ANALYSIS OF MIXTURES OF ORTHO-, PYRO-, AND TRIPHOSPHATE

### ION-EXCHANGE METHOD

Higher polymerized phosphates do not interfere in the ion-exchange technique, since these compounds appear in the eluant later than triphosphate. If a column has been prepared, and the proper elution curve has been determined, it is ready for continuous use. Yet, careful regeneration which removes any higher-molecular phosphates left in the column from a previous separation is essential before every run. The time-consuming collection of the fractions may be simplified by use of an automatic sampler.

*Apparatus.* **Column.**—A 30-cm. glass tube with an inside diameter of 12.8 mm. is clamped in vertical position and fitted at the bottom with a one-hole stopper, carrying a stopcock. Some glass wool is packed into the bottom to support the resin. An amount of resin which corresponds to 9.2 g. of anhydrous material is

36 Jones, Ind. Eng. Chem., Anal. Ed., **14**, 536, 1942.

necessary. By stirring the resin to a slurry, it is transferred into the tube without any air bubbles. The resulting bed height is about 21 cm. In the top end of the tube, a stopcock with Tygon tubing bearing a pinch clamp is inserted. It connects the column with the elevated reservoir of the eluant.

**Resin.**—Nalcite SBR (8% cross-linked) is air dried, and the +80-mesh particles are removed by screening. The moisture is determined on a 2-g. sample at 110°C.

**Eluting Solution.**—An aqueous solution, which is 0.15 $N$ in $NH_4Cl$ and 0.15 $N$ in ammonia, is used. The buffering capacity of this solution keeps the pH constant.

**Elution Curve.**—By running a sample in the manner described below on a carefully filled and regenerated column, collecting the eluate in fractions of 10 ml. and by analyzing every fraction for its phosphorus content, a microgram P *versus* ml. curve can be drawn on graph paper. The sections in the curve which show no phosphorus between the peaks (attributable to ortho-, pyro-, and triphosphate) indicate the volumes which have to be collected for obtaining total ortho-, total pyro-, and total triphosphate. This procedure must be followed whenever a newly filled column is put in operation.

**Procedure.**—Regenerate the column by passing 200 ml. of 2 $N$ $NH_4Cl$ and by following with 500 ml. of eluting solution at a moderate rate. Check the last few milliliters to make sure that no background phosphorus is present. Remove the stopper at the top of the column, draw the liquid level just to the top of the resin bed, and pipette 5 ml. of sample solution, containing 5–10 mg. P into the column. Draw the liquid level again down to the top of the resin bed. Drop a layer of about 5 cm. eluant on top of the resin, insert the top stopper, and start the elution at a rate of 0.5 ml./minute, while the liquid level is maintained about 5 ml. above the top of the resin bed. The eluate is collected in 3 fractions, the exact volume of which is read from the elution curve. For the column dimensions recommended, about 150 ml. for ortho-, 250 ml. for pyro-, and 350 ml. for triphosphate will result.

In suitable aliquots of these fractions phosphorus is determined colorimetrically after hydrolysis (see p. 818).

**Alternate Procedures.**—In the absence of higher chain or ring phosphates, a combination of selective procedures can furnish data for calculating the percentages of ortho-, pyro-, and triphosphate. The following scheme must be followed: Analyze for orthophosphate by one of the methods shown on pp. 830–832. Analyze for total phosphorus by one of the methods shown on pp. 812–818. Analyze for triphosphate, which can be done by precipitation with tris(ethylenediamine)cobalt(III) chloride and determination of the excess reagent. Selective hydrolysis of triphosphate in alkaline medium yields 1 mole orthophosphate for each mole of triphosphate and leads also to the estimation of triphosphate.

A very good procedure consists in analyzing for orthophosphate and total phosphorus (see above), and in carrying out an end group titration according to p. 832. The results are evaluated as follows: Calculate number of milliequivalents from the above analyses for one sample weight and call them $S$ for ortho-$P_2O_5$, $A_h$ for total $P_2O_5$, and $A$ for the $P_2O_5$ having a weak acid function. Thus, we have the following equations:

Milliequivalents of $P_2O_5$ as orthophosphate $= S$
Milliequivalents of $P_2O_5$ as end groups $= A - S$
Milliequivalents of $P_2O_5$ as middle groups $= A_h - A$

Milliequivalents of $P_2O_5$ as triphosphate $= 3(A_h - A)$

Milliequivalents of $P_2O_5$ as pyrophosphate $= A_h - S - 3(A_h - A) = 3A - 2A_h - S$

Percentage of total $P_2O_5$ as orthophosphate $= \dfrac{S}{A_h} \cdot 100$

Percentage of total $P_2O_5$ as pyrophosphate $= \dfrac{3A - 2A_h - S}{A_h} \cdot 100$

Percentage of total $P_2O_5$ as triphosphate $= \dfrac{3A_h - 3A}{A_h} \cdot 100$

## DETERMINATIONS IN SPECIFIC SUBSTANCES

## ANALYSIS OF ORES, PHOSPHATE ROCK, AND MINERALS [37]

### DISSOLUTION AND DETERMINATION OF SILICA

If the sample is treated with acid, and the silica is made insoluble by baking (according to p. 802), any acid insoluble residue is filtered off, together with silica. For analysis of this type of silica-containing residues, see p. 810. Presence of appreciable amounts of fluorine would cause low results for silica in this procedure.

The fusion procedure described on p. 803 is feasible in the presence of moderate amounts of fluorine and yields a purer silica than the acid treatment. Yet, the result for silica may turn out a little too high, due to boric acid remaining with the silica precipitate, since this boric acid is volatile as $BF_3$ in the usual fuming process with HF. (For a procedure that eliminates boron by treating the melt with methyl alcohol, previously saturated with HCl gas, see Hillebrand, Lundell, Bright, and Hoffman, *Applied Inorganic Analysis*, 2nd ed., p. 849.) Furthermore, contamination of the silica with small amounts of Fe, Al, Ti, Zr, and other elements must still be expected, and for very accurate analyses, the silica should be treated as indicated on p. 810.

A very reliable but rather time-consuming method for determination of $SiO_2$ in phosphates containing fluorine was worked out by Hoffman and Lundell.[38] They recommend two successive fusions with $Na_2CO_3$ and careful leaching with water. The insoluble residue is treated with $HNO_3$ and $HClO_4$ after adding boric acid, and $SiO_2$ is separated from this solution by dehydration. Silica in the alkaline solutions is precipitated by the aid of zinc nitrate and zinc hydroxide dissolved in ammonia. For the final determination of silica, see Chapter on Silicon.

### PHOSPHORUS

*Procedure.*—Transfer to a 400-ml. beaker a 50-ml. aliquot of the solution which is obtained after fusing the sample according to p. 803 and which contains 0.1 g. of the sample. Add 50 ml. of water, 2 drops of methyl orange indicator, and ammonium hydroxide until alkaline; then dilute $HNO_3$ dropwise, until the solution is just acid to the indicator. Phosphoric acid is precipitated as molybdate complex and determined as indicated on p. 814.

[37] Phosphorus determination in iron ores is described by Kassner and Ozier, Anal. Chem., **22**, 194, 1950 and later by Grindley, Burden, and Zaki, Analyst, **79**, 95, 1954. The latter use ether extraction for removing iron. A colorimetric procedure for determination of $P_2O_5$ as phosphovanadomolybdate is reported by Willard and Carter, Ind. Eng. Chem., Anal. Ed., **13**, 81, 1941.

[38] Lundell, J. Research Nat. Bur. Standards, **20**, 621, 1938.

NOTES.—In the analysis of rocks and superphosphate, Hoffman and Lundell [39] have replaced the molybdenum method by precipitating magnesium ammonium phosphate in the presence of citric acid. Methods for getting highly accurate phosphate analyses were reported.

## CALCIUM

*Procedure.*—Transfer to a 400-ml. beaker a 100-ml. aliquot of the filtrate obtained according to p. 803 and corresponding to 0.2 g. of the sample. Add 200 ml. of water and 4–5 drops of methyl orange indicator. Drop in ammonium hydroxide until faintly alkaline, and then adjust with HCl dropwise until the indicator shows the amber mixed-color.

Bring to a boil, add 15 ml. of 10% oxalic acid solution and about 2 g. of ammonium oxalate. Boil gently for 3–4 minutes, let settle, and filter through filter paper. Wash the beaker and the filter 8–10 times with hot water, return the paper and the precipitate to the beaker in which the precipitation was carried out, and add about 200 ml. of hot water. After addition of 10 ml. of $H_2SO_4$ (1:1), calcium is titrated with standard $KMnO_4$ (see Chapter on Calcium).

## ALUMINUM

*Reagent.* **Buffer.**—Dissolve 150 g. ammonium acetate in 150 ml. of water; add 8 ml. of 80% acetic acid.

*Procedure.*—Transfer a 100-ml. aliquot of the filtrate from silica which was obtained in the procedure described on p. 803 (corresponding to 0.2 g. of sample) into a 600-ml. beaker. Add 300 ml. of distilled water, 30 ml. of 10% diammonium phosphate, and 2 drops of methyl orange indicator. Neutralize with ammonium hydroxide and then acidify by adding exactly 2 ml. of HCl (3:1, sp. gr. 1.14).

Add 50 ml. of 20% sodium thiosulfate solution and a small amount of macerated ashless filter paper and heat until it starts to boil. Add 25 ml. of the acetate-acetic acid buffer, boil for 10 minutes, allow the precipitate to settle, and filter. Wash with cold water until free from chlorides, ignite at 800°C., and weigh as $AlPO_4$ (containing 41.78% of aluminum).

## IRON

*Procedure.*—Transfer 100 ml. of the solution obtained as directed on p. 803 (corresponding to 0.2 g. of the sample) to a 250-ml. beaker, add 10 drops of a saturated solution of $KMnO_4$, and boil until the red color disappears. Remove from the heating plate and titrate iron according to Zimmerman-Reinhardt (reduction with stannous chloride, titration with $KMnO_4$ in HCl solution).

## TITANIUM

*Procedure.*—Transfer a 1.0000-g. sample into a platinum dish, add 10–15 ml. 48% HF, 5–10 ml. of concentrated $HNO_3$, and 15 ml. of 70% $HClO_4$. Evaporate just to dryness, rinse the sides with 10–15 ml. of hot water, and add 15 ml. of the $HClO_4$. Bring to dryness, take up with 10 ml. of concentrated $H_2SO_4$ and 50 ml. of water, and digest on a hot plate for about 10 minutes. Filter into a 100-ml. volumetric flask and cool to room temperature. Make to volume, mix well, and transfer 20 ml. of the solution into an absorption cell as a blank. To the 80 ml. remaining in the flask and representing 0.8 g. of the sample, add 5 ml. of hydrogen

[39] Hoffman and Lundell, J. Research Nat. Bur. Standards, **19**, 59, 1937; **20**, 607, 1938.

peroxide and fill to the mark with water. Mix and measure the color in a photometer, using the blank for setting the instrument to 100% of transmittancy.

## CHROMIUM AND VANADIUM

*Procedure.*—Weigh a 20-g. sample into a 600-ml. beaker. Add 20 ml. of concentrated $HNO_3$, 20 ml. of concentrated HCl, 5 ml. of 48% HF, 5 ml. of 72% $HClO_4$, and 20 ml. of $H_2SO_4$ (1:1). Evaporate on a steam bath as far as possible, transfer to a hot plate, and fume almost to dryness (avoid complete dryness). Repeat fuming after adding 20 ml. of concentrated $H_2SO_4$. Cool, add 125 ml. of water, and boil until all solids are decomposed, while breaking lumps with a glass rod. Filter with suction through filter paper on a Buechner funnel, wash with hot water, and transfer the filtrate to a 400-ml. beaker.

**Titration of Chromium.**—To the warm solution (having a volume of about 250 ml.), add 8–10 ml. of 0.5% solution of $AgNO_3$, 6–8 drops of 2.5% $KMnO_4$ solution, and 3–5 g. of ammonium persulfate to oxidize the chromium present. Boil for at least 5 minutes, until the permanganate color shows up again (after all trivalent chromium is oxidized, the manganese is oxidized by the persulfate). Introduce 20 ml. of 10% NaCl solution and boil until all higher oxidation products of manganese have been reduced. Unless it is accomplished after 3 minutes, add 10 ml. additional 10% NaCl and continue boiling. Filter and wash 6 times with hot water. Cool to room temperature, treat with 3 ml. of phosphoric acid (sp. gr. 1.73), and add 0.1 $N$ ferrous ammonium sulfate in excess. Titrate back with $KMnO_4$ solution of corresponding normality, while stirring vigorously until a faint pink color stays for 30 seconds. Calculate the chromium contents from the difference between milliequivalents of ferrous salt solution and permanganate.

**Titration of Vanadium.**—While vigorously stirring, add $KMnO_4$ solution to the above solution until a strong pink color remains for 30 seconds. Then add about 0.05 $N$ ferrous ammonium sulfate solution while stirring until a drop of the solution, when added to a 1% $K_3(Fe(CN)_6)$ solution on a spot plate, develops a blue color immediately, thus showing an excess of ferrous ion. Introduce 10 ml. more of the ferrous ammonium sulfate and stir for 1 minute. The excess of ferrous salt over the amount necessary for reducing the vanadium is oxidized by adding 8 ml. of ammonium persulfate and vigorously stirring for 1 minute. Under these conditions, vanadium is not oxidized together with the ferrous salt. Vanadium is then titrated with 0.05 $N$ $KMnO_4$ with constant stirring until a faint pink color remains for 30 seconds.

In this procedure, 1 ml. of 0.05 $N$ $KMnO_4$ is equivalent to 2.547 mg. of vanadium.

## MANGANESE

*Procedure.*—Transfer a 1-g. sample into a crucible and ignite for 30 minutes. Cool and transfer it into a 250-ml. Erlenmeyer flask. Add 10 ml. of concentrated HCl, evaporate almost to dryness, cool, and add 10 ml. of concentrated $HNO_3$. Evaporate to about 3 ml., cool, wash down the sides of the flask with water (the resulting volume should be about 30 ml.), and add 10 ml. of concentrated $HNO_3$. Put on a hot plate, add 15 ml. of 0.1 $N$ $AgNO_3$, and boil for 5 minutes. Filter, using a little paper pulp, into a 100-ml. Kohlrausch flask, and wash with hot water.

Bring to a boil, remove from heating plate, and add carefully about 1 g. of ammonium persulfate. Boil for 30 seconds and cool. Make to volume and read transmittancy of the solution on a photometer, using a green filter. Evaluate by the aid of standard samples with known manganese content, which have been treated in the same way.

## MAGNESIUM

**Procedure.**—Transfer a 2.000-g. sample to a 250-ml. beaker and add 15 ml. of diluted HCl (2:1) and 5 ml. of concentrated $HNO_3$. Dissolve by boiling gently for 10–15 minutes (keep the beaker covered), add 6 ml. $H_2SO_4$ (1:1), and evaporate until fumes of $H_2SO_4$ appear. Cool, wash down the walls of the beaker with a jet of water, and evaporate again until fumes of $H_2SO_4$ show up. Cool, add 10 ml. of water, stir thoroughly, and digest on a steam bath for 10–15 minutes. Cool and separate calcium sulfate by adding 100 ml. of 95% alcohol. Stir well and allow to stand for at least 30 minutes. Filter by suction through a tight plug of filter paper in a Gooch crucible, and wash five times with 5-ml. portions of 95% alcohol containing 1 ml. of $H_2SO_4$ in 100 ml.

Evaporate the alcoholic filtrate on a steam bath as far as possible, transfer the remaining solution to a 250-ml. Erlenmeyer flask, and make up to 75–100 ml. Add 2 g. of citric acid and 15 ml. of a 25% solution of diammonium phosphate. Make alkaline to litmus by adding ammonium hydroxide and add 10 ml. of concentrated ammonium hydroxide in excess. Add a few glass beads, stopper the flask tightly, and shake on a shaking machine for 1 hour or more. Let settle 4 hours or longer in a cool place, filter, using a little filter pulp, and wash with very diluted ammonium hydroxide (1:19) containing 5% of diammonium phosphate.

Dissolve the precipitate by passing 25 ml. of hot diluted HCl (1:19) through the filter into the flask in which the precipitation was made, and transfer the solution, without the beads, quantitatively to a 150-ml. beaker (rinsing filter and flask carefully with diluted HCl).

Add to the solution (50–75 ml.) 0.5 ml. of a 25% solution of diammonium phosphate, cool, and add ammonium hydroxide while stirring until reaction is alkaline to litmus. Stir for a few minutes, add 3–4 ml. ammonium hydroxide, and let stand for at least 4 hours. Filter through a small filter and wash with diluted ammonia (1:19).

Ignite and weigh as $Mg_2P_2O_7$.

## POTASSIUM AND SODIUM

**Procedure.**—Transfer a 2.0000-g. sample into a 250-ml. beaker. Add 20 ml. of HCl and evaporate almost to dryness. Add 10 ml. of HCl and 50 ml. of water and boil. Cool, filter, and wash 5 or 6 times with hot water. Save the filtrate and ignite the residue in a platinum dish. Dissolve the residue in HF and HCl, and evaporate to dryness. Fume three times with 2 ml. of HCl to get rid of all HF. Dissolve the residue in the dish in 5 ml. of hot HCl (1:1) and 15–20 ml. water, and unite with the previous main filtrate. Evaporate to dryness, cool, add 25 ml. of hot water, and boil for 1–2 minutes. Filter into a 100-ml. volumetric flask and make to volume. Use 50 ml. for the $K_2O$ determination, and transfer the remaining 50 ml. into a 100-ml. beaker for the determination of $Na_2O$.

**Potassium Oxide.**—To the 50-ml. aliquot, add 5 ml. of 5% platinum chloride solution. Evaporate carefully on a hot plate until a scum forms and cool under tap water. Upon cooling, the mass in the beaker should solidify. Add 15 ml. of alcohol containing 2% by volume of HCl and warm gently until the crust loosens and a granular precipitate becomes visible. (If the crust is gummy, add a little more platinum chloride and warm. Upon standing, the precipitate will become granular.) Grind the residue finely and let settle in the cold for about 30 minutes.

Filter through filter paper (it has to be pretreated by washing twice with acidified alcohol in the funnel) and wash carefully with not more than 60 ml. of the acidic alcohol in many small portions. The precipitate is rather soluble in the wash liquid.

Dissolve the soluble part of the precipitate by applying small jets of hot water onto the filter paper, catching the filtrate in a beaker of 250-ml. capacity. Wash until 125 ml. of filtrate are obtained, add 2–3 ml. of HCl, and heat nearly to boiling. Insert a clean magnesium rod into the beaker and allow the reduction of platinum to go for 30 minutes at a warm temperature (add some HCl if the reaction stops). Remove the magnesium rod, wash it off into the beaker with hot water, and let the reduced platinum coagulate on a hot plate. Add 5 ml. of HCl, boil for 2 minutes, and filter while hot. Wash with hot water and transfer the filter into a porcelain crucible. Char and ignite at about 800°C. for 20–30 minutes. The $K_2O$ is calculated by multiplying the weight of the platinum residue with the factor 0.4826.

NOTE.—An excess of platinum chloride over the $K_2O$ present must be applied. If the solution becomes clear just before it reaches the gummy stage, all of the platinum is used up and more reagent must be added.

**Sodium Oxide.** *Reagent.*—90 g. of $UO_2(CH_3COO)_2 \cdot 2H_2O$ plus 60 g. of concentrated acetic acid are dissolved in 1 liter of water; 600 g. of $Mg(CH_3COO)_2 \cdot 4H_2O$ plus 60 g. of concentrated acetic acid are dissolved in 1 liter of water; equal volumes of both solutions are mixed to make the reagent as needed. After mixing, the reagent is kept at 20°C. for 24 hours. Following filtration, it is ready for use.

*Procedure.*—Slightly acidify the solution in the 100-ml. beaker with 8–10 drops of HCl. Add 5 g. of $ZnCO_3$ to precipitate the phosphates, let stand for 5 minutes, and filter into a 250-ml. Erlenmeyer flask (wash with cold water). Add HCl until just acid to methyl orange and evaporate to 1–5 ml. (1 ml. for 1 mg. of sodium or less, 2–5 ml. for up to 25 mg. of sodium). Precipitate the complex acetate, $CH_3COONa \cdot (CH_3COO)_2Mg \cdot 3UO_2(CH_3COO)_2 \cdot 6H_2O$, by adding 100 ml. or more of magnesium uranyl acetate reagent, insert a rubber stopper, and shake vigorously for about 30 seconds. Cool in water to 20°C. for 45 minutes, shaking vigorously every 5 minutes. Filter through a fritted-glass crucible and wash the precipitate and flask 2 or 3 times with 5-ml. portions of the reagent. Then wash the flask and precipitate with small jets of alcohol that has been previously saturated with the sodium magnesium uranyl acetate (30–40 ml. of alcohol will be sufficient). Dry to constant weight at 103–107°C. It takes about 45 minutes. The precipitate contains 2.06% $Na_2O$ (1.53% Na).

NOTES.—A blank must be run through each step of the analysis, and its result should be used for correcting the percentage found. As not more than 25 mg. of sodium should be present, the sample weight must be chosen according to the sodium content. 100 ml. of reagent is used if 10 mg. or less of sodium has to be precipitated. For larger amounts, employ 10 ml. of reagent for each mg. of sodium oxide. Turbidity in the filtrate is due to solubility reduction of the salts in the filtrate, caused by addition of the alcohol washings. Decomposition takes place when the precipitate is heated beyond 110°C.

## *IGNITION LOSS*

*Procedure.*—Ignite the sample at 1000°C. for about 1 hour and let cool in a desiccator. Repeat the procedure until constant weight is obtained.

## INSOLUBLES IN PHOSPHATE ORES

**Procedure.**—Transfer a 0.50-g. sample of finely powdered material into a 250-ml. beaker. Add 50 ml. of HCl (1:1) that contains 1 g. of boric acid, cover with a watch glass, and evaporate on a hot plate to about 5 ml. Add 10 ml. of $HClO_4$ and fume down to 2–3 ml. Cool for a few minutes (the residue becomes solid upon cooling), add 20 ml. of HCl and about 50 ml. of water, and boil until solution of the salts is complete. Remove from hot plate, filter, and transfer all particles adhering to the beaker to the filter. Wash 6 to 8 times with hot water and ignite for 25–30 minutes at about 1000°C.

## CARBON IN PHOSPHATE ORES

The determination consists of a combustion procedure similar to the technique for ultimate organic analysis using oxygen as oxidizing gas.

**Apparatus.**—A purifying jar filled with soda lime, held between glass wool, is placed between the needle valve of the oxygen cylinder and the inlet of the combustion tube. The outlet of the combustion tube is connected to a purifying jar filled with granular zinc of 30-mesh size (descending gas flow). The outlet at the bottom of the jar which is filled with zinc is connected with a Fleming purifying jar about half-filled with concentrated $H_2SO_4$. The outlet of the Fleming purifying jar is connected to the bottom of a 25-cm. purifying jar filled with anhydrous magnesium perchlorate between glass wool. Its top is connected with the inlet of a Stetser-Norton $CO_2$-absorption bulb filled with Ascarite, followed by a 2.5-cm. layer of anhydrous magnesium perchlorate for catching the water freed in the $CO_2$-absorption process with the Ascarite.

**Procedure.**—Prepare the combustion boat by placing a layer of abrasive grain in the bottom of the boat, spreading the sample evenly over the abrasive, and covering with more abrasive grain.

Pass oxygen through the apparatus and heat the furnace to about 1000°C. for 2–3 minutes. Disconnect the absorption bulb and weigh. Replace the absorption bulb, insert the combustion boat into the hot zone of the combustion tube, and close the combustion tube immediately. Carry out the combustion in a flow of oxygen of medium speed for 15 minutes. Disconnect the absorption bulb and weigh again. The gain in weight represents the $CO_2$ absorbed.

Run several blanks, using the same amount of abrasive grain, and subtract the average of the results from the $CO_2$ in the sample. Choose the sample weight according to the carbon content. Usually 2 g. of a phosphate rock will be satisfactory.

## CARBON DIOXIDE IN PHOSPHATE ORES

**Apparatus.**—A round-bottomed flask of about 250-ml. capacity is fitted with a two-hole stopper which carries a 60-ml. dropping funnel and an upright condenser of 200-mm. length. The top of the condenser is connected to a Fleming wash bottle filled with concentrated $H_2SO_4$. The outlet of the wash bottle is attached to a U-tube filled with calcium chloride. It leads to a straight drying tube filled with dehydrite. The $CO_2$-absorption bulb (Stetser-Norton), filled with Ascarite and magnesium perchlorate as usual, is connected to the drying tube. A purifying jar, filled with soda lime, held between glass wool, is inserted between an oxygen source and the top stopper of the dropping funnel.

**Procedure.**—Weigh the absorption bulb filled with oxygen. Then weigh a 2-g. sample into the 250-ml. flask, assemble as described above, and sweep the whole apparatus with oxygen. Remove the top stopper of the dropping funnel (carrying the oxygen inlet tube), place 20 ml. of HCl (1:1) into the funnel, and replace the stopper. Insert the weighed absorption bulb into the apparatus. Open the stopcock of the dropping funnel and apply a small pressure of oxygen to force the HCl into the extraction flask at a moderate rate. Heat the contents of the flask while maintaining a slow flow of oxygen, and boil for about 1 minute. Stop heating, increase the flow of oxygen, and transfer all $CO_2$ into the absorption bulb by sweeping for 15 minutes with the oxygen. Disconnect the absorption bulb and weigh.

### SULFUR IN PHOSPHATE ORES

*Procedure.*—Transfer a 2-g. sample into a 250-ml. beaker and decompose by adding 25 ml. of bromine water and 15–20 ml. of concentrated $HNO_3$. Evaporate to 5–10 ml., add 15 ml. of HCl, and evaporate again to a small volume. Fume again with HCl to expel $HNO_3$. Cool, add 5 ml. of concentrated HCl and 100 ml. of water, and boil for 2–3 minutes. After cooling, filter into a 400-ml. beaker, using paper pulp. Wash the residue with hot water. Bring the filtrate to boil, add 15 ml. of 10% barium chloride solution, and boil for 5 minutes. Let settle for 30 minutes, and filter through a close-textured filter, using a little ashless pulp. Wash 8 times with hot water. Ignite to constant weight at 800°C.

NOTE.—Sulfate originally present as barium or strontium sulfate will remain mainly insoluble. It is found in the residue after fuming with HF for removing $SiO_2$. If this is the case, fusion of the residue with $Na_2CO_3$ (see p. 810) must be made in order to get a water-soluble sulfate for the analysis.

### FLUORINE IN PHOSPHATE ORES

*Apparatus.*—The delivery tube of a 250-ml. modified Claisen flask is connected to a condenser. The other neck of the flask is fitted with a two-hole rubber stopper in which is inserted a thermometer and a 6-mm. glass tube extending almost to the bottom of the flask. The tube is connected to a steam generator. The flask is heated on a small hot plate equipped with a refractory having a 1½″ hole. The distillate is caught in a 200-ml. volumetric flask.

*Procedure.*—Weigh a 0.1-g. sample into the flask, add 50 ml. of water and 30 ml. of 70–72% $HClO_4$. Heat to boiling and boil until the temperature of the liquid rises to 135°C. Introduce steam and maintain the temperature at 135°C. by adjusting the temperature of the hot plate until 200 ml. of distillate have been collected.

Mix the contents of the receiving flask and pipette 20 ml. into a 100-ml., tall-form beaker. Add 1.5 ml. of 0.02% aqueous sodium alizarin-sulfonate and 0.05 N NaOH dropwise until a deep violet color appears. Drop in 0.03 N HCl until a yellow color is obtained, and adjust to a pH of about 3.5 by adding Hoskins-Ferris buffer solution, which consists of an equimolar mixture of monochloroacetic acid and its sodium salt in 48% ethyl alcohol (the most favorable concentration of the buffer in the solution under analysis is 0.02 M). Add 30 ml. of neutral alcohol (Formula 3A).

Prepare a blank, using 20 ml. of distilled water, and treat exactly as directed above. Add 0.1 ml. of 0.01 N standard thorium nitrate solution.

Titrate the sample with 0.01 N thorium nitrate until the color of the sample matches exactly that of the blank. Subtract the thorium nitrate used in the blank from the consumption required for the sample.

1 ml. 0.01 $N$ Th(NO$_3$)$_4$ is equivalent to 0.19 mg. F

NOTE.—Free sulfur and pyritic sulfur interfere in the thorium nitrate titration, causing too high results. Redistillation or previous ignition of the sample at a low temperature in a silica dish is reported to overcome this difficulty.[40]

## ANALYSIS OF SLAGS

In general, the procedures given for minerals can be used. Chilled slags are easily decomposed by acid (see preparation of the sample, p. 804). The phosphorus determination in materials which are low in P$_2$O$_5$ is best accomplished colorimetrically, using the molybdenum blue method (p. 818) or the phosphovanadomolybdate procedure (p. 820). Since different elements, which are not encountered in the natural materials discussed so far, may be contained in these artificial products, additional determinations must be considered. Zinc, copper, lead, cobalt, nickel, sulfur, and others can be expected in different samples. It is recommended that the chapters dealing with these elements be consulted for their determination (see also section on "Impurities in Commercial Phosphates" on p. 855).

## ANALYSIS OF WATER AND SOILS

### DETERMINATION OF PHOSPHATES IN WATER

**Titrimetric Procedure for High Phosphorus Contents.**—Transfer a 500-ml. sample into a porcelain dish, add 10 ml. of HNO$_3$, and slowly evaporate to about 10–20 ml. (30 minutes or more should be used for evaporation if condensed phosphates from water treatment are present). Take up with water, filter, neutralize with ammonium hydroxide and barely made acid with HNO$_3$. Precipitate with ammonium molybdate, filter, and titrate as directed on pp. 814–816.

**Colorimetric Procedure for Low Orthophosphate Content.**—(Content below 0.3 mg. P$_2$O$_5$/liter). Neutralize a 500-ml. sample of the water against methyl orange, evaporate in a porcelain dish to a volume of 10 ml., filter, and add 1 ml. of 15% NaHSO$_3$ solution. Determine orthophosphoric acid according to p. 818. The pH value of the original sample must be watched.

NOTES.—It is necessary to specify the species of phosphorus compounds which should be determined. The following may be distinguished in both natural and industrial waters: dissolved inorganic phosphorus, dissolved organic phosphorus, inorganic phosphorus in the suspended solid, organic phosphorus in the suspended solid, and total phosphorus which represents the sum of all these compounds. Separation of dissolved and suspended phosphorus can be effected by filtration (bacteria filter, if desired). The direct colorimetric determination yields the inorganic orthophosphate. Natural waters contain no other inorganic phosphorus compounds. Total phosphorus can be obtained after evaporation and mineralization of the residue according to p. 804 (as there are usually only very small amounts of organic matter present in water, fractions of the amounts of reagents recommended will accomplish complete destruction of the organic matter). A simple procedure for mineralization of phosphorus in water with HClO$_4$ was reported by Robinson.[41]

**Interfering Ions.**—Extremely high silica contents must be removed. Pentavalent arsenic yields a corresponding blue compound. Prior reduction of As(V) to As(III) with sodium bisulfite in hot acid solution was reported satisfactory by Pett.[42]

[40] Hoffman and Lundell, J. Research Nat. Bur. Standards, **20**, 610, 1938.
[41] Robinson, Ind. Eng. Chem., Anal. Ed., **13**, 465, 1941.
[42] Pett, Biochem. J. (London), **27**, 1672, 1933.

Thiourea (20 mg./25 ml. of the final solution ready for reading the color) is recommended for this purpose by Kalle.[43]

Nitrite interferes too. It can be destroyed by $H_2SO_4$, added in a concentration of 10 g./liter of the acid molybdate reagent.[44]

**Glassware and Blank.**—All glassware has to be cleaned carefully *without using phosphate built detergents*. They also must be steamed. A blank carried out with all reagents should be run with every determination.

**Analysis of seawater** was accomplished using extraction of the complex molybdophosphoric acid with ethyl acetate by Stoll.[45] Using 50-ml. samples, 5–40 micrograms $P_2O_5$/liter were determined.

**Deeply colored industrial water** can be decolorized with active carbon. Slightly yellowish water may be tested using a blank, the color of which is adjusted with a dyestuff to the same tint as the water sample. See also decolorizing of soil extracts, below.

## DETERMINATION OF PHOSPHORUS IN SOIL

**Total phosphorus** can be determined after mineralization according to pp. 805–807.

**Selective Extraction.**—For classifying soils, procedures for selective extraction have to be applied in order to match the conditions of $P_2O_5$ take-up by plants. Widely used for this purpose is a calcium lactate buffer solution of a pH value 3.5–3.7.

**Calcium Lactate Buffer.**—Dissolve 30.82 g. pure calcium lactate in 300 ml. of distilled water while warming. Add 20 ml. of 5 N HCl and make to 400 ml. Add 1 droplet of $CHCl_3$. The resulting stock solution has a pH of 3.2 and can be stored for about one week. By diluting 40 ml. of this stock solution with 960 ml. distilled water, the required solution of a pH 3.7 is prepared as needed. (This solution cannot be stored!)

**Procedure.**—Transfer 5 g. of the air-dried soil into a 1-liter bottle, add 250 ml. of the lactate buffer solution, stopper, and shake 1½ hours at 15–20°C. Filter, discard the first portion of the filtrate, and use an aliquot of the solution for colorimetric determination of the phosphoric acid (see p. 818). A special colorimetric procedure in connection with the lactate extraction was worked out by Herrmann and Lederle.[46]

NOTES.—Extraction of available phosphorus from soil by the aid of ion exchange (Zeolite) was carried out by Møller and Mogenson.[47] The authors claim to imitate best the reactions taking place in the earth between soil colloids and phosphates.

Sodium acetate (pH 4.85) was used for extraction by Atkinson, Bishop, and Levick.[48]

*Decolorizing Extracts.*—For decolorizing soil extracts the following procedure was recommended by Hibbard.[49] To 50 ml. of the colored solution, add 5 ml. of a saturated aqueous bromine solution (more, if very dark solutions must be decolorized) and enough of 5 N NaOH to make alkaline (the brown color disappears). Add 5 N acid until the solution is acid (free bromine should appear;

[43] Kalle, Am. Hydrogr. Maritime Meterol., **62**, 95, 1934; *ibid.*, **63**, 58, 1935.
[44] Greenberg, Weinberger, and Sowyer, Anal. Chem., **22**, 499, 1950.
[45] Stoll, Z. anal. Chem., **112**, 81, 1938.
[46] Herrmann and Lederle, Z. Pflanzenernähr. Dung. Bodenk., **34**, 1, 1944.
[47] Møller and Mogenson, Soil Sci., **76**, 297, 1953.
[48] Atkinson, Bishop and Levick, Sci. Agr., **30**, 61, 1950.
[49] Hibbard, Ind. Eng. Chem., Anal. Ed., **4**, 283, 1932.

otherwise addition of bromine and base must be repeated) and then a little sodium sulfite solution until all free bromine is reduced.

**Semiquantitative Field Test for Soils. Reagent.**—Dissolve 4 g. of ammonium molybdate in 500 ml. of distilled water and add slowly with constant stirring a mixture of 63 ml. of concentrated HCl and 437 ml. of distilled water.

**Procedure.**—Transfer 10 ml. of the reagent into a test tube, add a carefully measured amount of soil (¼ level teaspoon for greenhouse and garden soils, ½ level teaspoon for other soils), and shake vigorously for 1 minute. Partial extraction and hydrolysis of phosphates take place. Filter into a funnel tube and collect at least 5 ml. of this sample solution. Prepare a solution of stannous salt by dissolving in 5 ml. of distilled water ¼″ of powdered and dried stannous chloride or stannous oxalate adhering to the end of a toothpick. Add small portions of this reducing agent to the solution under test and mix well by rotating the tube after each addition until the blue coloration no longer increases. Avoid adding too large an excess of stannous salt, because a brownish color can develop that will spoil the test. Evaluate the color produced in the sample solution (blue to light yellow) by comparison with a standard test chart. Such charts are obtainable from the Agricultural Experiment Station, Purdue University, Lafayette, Indiana.

NOTES.—Frothing upon addition of the soil to the acid reagent indicates basic soils. The values obtained for these are generally too high. Any rock phosphate present will cause high results, owing to partial dissolution in the acid reagent under the conditions applied.

The procedure can be applied for estimation of $P_2O_5$ in plant material as well and can be used for judging the actual $P_2O_5$ requirement of the plant. The tissue selected (the main stem or the leaf petiole of actively growing plants should be used) is cut into small pieces of $\frac{1}{16}$″ thickness or less by the aid of a razor blade. One level teaspoon of this material is tested, as described for soils.

## ANALYSIS OF FERTILIZERS

**Procedure for Total $P_2O_5$.**—The total $P_2O_5$ in any of the different materials which are used as fertilizers can be determined by a conventional procedure (pp. 812–819) after preliminary treatment for getting phosphorus into solution as orthophosphate. The procedures recommended for dissolution of minerals and organic material will apply (see pp. 802 and 805). Depending upon the amount of phosphorus present, a titrimetric (or gravimetric) method or a colorimetric procedure will be chosen. However, total phosphorus content is not of prime importance in fertilizer specification, since only that part of the phosphorus, which is available to the plants, determines the value of phosphorus fertilizers. Special procedures have been worked out and are now official for measuring the percentages of phosphorus present in the various states of availability.

### AVAILABLE PHOSPHORUS (AOAC METHODS)

**Water-Soluble $P_2O_5$. Procedure.**—Place 1 g. of sample on a 9-cm filter and wash with successive small portions of water until the filtrate measures about 250 ml. Allow each portion of wash water to pass through the filter before adding more and use suction if the washing would not otherwise be complete within 1 hour. If the filtrate is turbid, add 1–2 ml. of $HNO_3$ to it, dilute to a convenient volume, mix well, and determine $P_2O_5$ in the aqueous extract.

**Citrate-Insoluble $P_2O_5$. Reagent.**—An ammonium citrate solution which should have a specific gravity of 1.09 at 20°C. and a pH of 7.0, as determined by electrometric pH measurement or by colorimetric procedure with phenol red. Dissolve

370 g. of crystalline citric acid in 1500 ml. of water and nearly neutralize by adding 345 ml. of ammonium hydroxide (28–29% $NH_3$). If the concentration of ammonia is less than 28%, add a correspondingly larger volume and dissolve the citric acid in a correspondingly smaller volume of water. Cool, and adjust to a pH of exactly 7.00 by adding ammonia dropwise and using a glass electrode. If the end point is overshot, citric acid can be used to return to it. The use of a pH meter obviates the need for the tedious procedure for preparing this reagent which is recommended by the AOAC.

Dilute the solution to the proper density of 1.09 at 20°C. and keep in tightly stoppered bottles (check the pH from time to time).

**Procedure.**—Within less than an hour after removing the water-soluble $P_2O_5$, transfer the filter paper containing the residue to a 200- or 250-ml. flask containing 100 ml. of ammonium citrate solution previously heated to 65°C. Close the flask tightly with a smooth rubber stopper, shake vigorously until the filter paper is reduced to pulp, relieve pressure by momentarily removing stopper, and proceed by one of the following methods: (1) Loosely stopper the flask to prevent evaporation, place in a water bath so regulated as to maintain the contents of the flask at exactly 65°C., keep the level of the water in the bath above that of the citrate solution in the flask, and shake every 5 minutes; or (2) continuously agitate contents of the stoppered flask by means of an apparatus equipped to maintain the contents of the flask at exactly 65°C.

At the expiration of exactly 1 hour from the time the filter paper and residue were introduced, remove the flask from the bath or apparatus and immediately filter as rapidly as possible by suction through a Whatman No. 5 filter paper or other paper of equal speed and retentiveness, using a Buchner funnel or an ordinary funnel with platinum or other perforated cone. Wash with water at 65°C. until the volume of the filtrate is about 350 ml., allowing time for thorough draining before adding new portions of water. (If the sample gives a cloudy filtrate, wash with 5% $NH_4NO_3$ solution).

Determine $P_2O_5$ in the citrate-insoluble residue.

NOTE.—In the analysis of nonacidulated samples, 1 g. of the material is directly treated with the citrate solution without the preceding water extraction.

*Citrate-Soluble $P_2O_5$.*—Subtract the sum of water-soluble and citrate-insoluble $P_2O_5$ from total $P_2O_5$.

*Available $P_2O_5$.*—Subtract citrate-insoluble $P_2O_5$ from total $P_2O_5$.

## ANALYSIS OF ORGANIC MATERIAL

The determination of total phosphorus is accomplished after oxidation of the carbonaceous matter, as directed on p. 805.

### SPECIFICATION OF PHOSPHATES IN BIOLOGICAL MATERIALS

In biological analyses, values for "7-minute" or "10-minute" phosphorus are often reported. By boiling in acid for the specified length of time, the so-called labile phosphorus compounds are distinguished from those that are stable to acid hydrolysis. These labile phosphorus compounds generally consist of two classes: (1) organic and inorganic phosphates which hydrolyze by splitting of P—O—P linkages and (2) phosphate esters of aldehydes or ketones in the "enol" form, which hydrolyze by splitting of the C—O—P linkage. Thus, adenosine triphosphate has two labile phosphorus atoms (which hydrolyze to orthophosphate by splitting of the P—O—P linkages) and one that does not hydrolyze and remains with the organic radical, as adenylic acid (an orthophosphate). In glucose-1-phosphate, the phosphorus is labile, since it is linked to the "enol" oxygen. Glucose-6-phosphate is an example of the large class of nonlabile orthophosphates.

*Procedure.*—Weigh a 1.000 g. sample into a 250-ml. beaker, add 100 ml. of 1 N HCl, cover with a watch glass, bring to a boil, and boil gently for 10 minutes. Filter, and wash the paper and any residue with 1 N HCl. Measure the orthophosphate content of the filtrate colorimetrically (see p. 818) and carry out a similar colorimetric determination on a water extract of the original material.

$$\% \text{ of total P as "10-minute P"} = \frac{100 \times P_2O_{5(ortho)}}{P_2O_{5(total)}}$$

$$\% \text{ of total P as labile P} = \frac{100 \times \Delta P_2O_{5(ortho)}}{P_2O_{5(total)}}$$

where $\Delta P_2O_{5(ortho)}$ is the difference between amounts of orthophosphate found in the above two measurements. All results are to be calculated for the same sample weight.

Note.—A procedure for determining alkali labile phosphate was reported by Axelrod, Saltman, Bandursky, and Baker.[50]

## TETRAETHYL PYROPHOSPHATE IN INSECTICIDES

*Procedure.* **Selective Hydrolysis.**—Transfer 20 ml. of a 9% NaCl solution into a separatory funnel and adjust the temperature to 30°C. by running water of this temperature over the surface of the funnel. Add from a weighing bottle 1.0–2.5 g. of sample (depending on the tetraethyl pyrophosphate content of the sample; the exact sample weight is obtained by weighing the weighing bottle before and after taking the sample) and shake until a homogeneous solution results. The higher polyphosphate esters are hydrolyzed in this procedure.

**Extraction.**—Let the emulsion stand for exactly 5 minutes from the time the sample was added, then add 20 ml. of benzene and shake vigorously for 30 seconds. Let separate and draw off the aqueous layer into another separatory funnel. Prevent the benzene from entering the stopcock bore. Wash the benzene layer with 5 ml. of 9% NaCl by shaking 10 seconds and again draw off the aqueous layer to the other funnel. This time the benzene interface should pass just into the stopcock bore.

The combined aqueous layers are extracted with 10 ml. of benzene for 10 seconds and the layers allowed to separate. Discard the aqueous layer, which contains most of the acid hydrolysis products, keeping the benzene above the stopcock bore. Wash the benzene with 5 ml. of 9% NaCl by shaking 10 seconds, and after separation draw off and discard the aqueous layer (the interface should just pass into the stopcock bore).

Combine the benzene layer with the benzene layer left in the first separatory funnel by draining it into this first funnel.

**Assay.**—Wash the combined benzene layers with 20 ml. of ice-cold distilled water by shaking for 10 seconds. Separate the layers and drain the aqueous layer into a 250-ml. Erlenmeyer flask, keeping the interface above the stopcock bore. Add 5–10 drops of bromothymol blue indicator (0.1% aqueous solution of the sodium

[50] Axelrod, Saltman, Bandursky, and Bauer, J. Biol. Chem., **197**, 89, 1952.

salt) and neutralize immediately with 0.5 $N$ NaOH to the first definite blue shade. Drain the benzene from the funnel into the neutralized wash water in the Erlenmeyer flask. Rinse the funnel that was used for collecting the aqueous phases with 5 ml. of benzene, transfer this wash benzene into the funnel that contained the benzene layers, rinse the walls, and drain also into the Erlenmeyer flask.

Add a large excess of 0.5 $N$ NaOH (about twice the stoichiometric amount; that is, 27 ml. of 0.5 $N$ NaOH for each gram of tetraethyl pyrophosphate expected) and stir or shake for 1 hour vigorously enough to obtain good mixing of the two phases. After that time, titrate with 0.5 $N$ HCl, while swirling the flask to mix the layers. When close to the end point, let the layers separate completely after each addition of acid or base. Since the first blue is considered as end point, it is more accurate to overtitrate the end point with acid to a definite yellow and to titrate back to the blue end point with 0.5 $N$ NaOH. The base that was required to neutralize the wash water must not be included in the reading of base consumption.

**Calculations.**—Under the conditions given and in the presence of benzene, the base hydrolyzes only the tetraethyl pyrophosphate to diethyl acid orthophosphate without affecting any triethyl phosphate present. But since only 97.8% of the tetraethyl pyrophosphate present is recovered with the above technique, a correction factor must be used in the calculation. The following relation results:

$$\% \text{ tetraethyl pyrophosphate} = \frac{\text{ml. of } 0.5 \ N \text{ NaOH} \times 7.255}{\text{Weight of sample} \times 0.978}$$

The precision of the method is ±0.5% of the tetraethyl pyrophosphate content.

NOTE.—A different procedure for the same purpose, which includes selective hydrolysis in aqueous acetone and removing of acid hydrolysis products with a resin, followed by alkaline hydrolysis of the tetraethyl pyrophosphate, was published by Wreath and Zickefoose.[51] In all of these procedures, pyrophosphate formed by hydrolysis of the higher polyphosphate esters is included in the assay for pyrophosphate.

## MISCELLANEOUS PROCEDURES

For the purpose of attributing percentages of phosphorus to different phosphorus compounds or distinguishing between various states of availability, numerous special procedures have been suggested. Selective extraction procedures for specifying soils, fertilizers, and plant material are reported on pp. 844 and 845.

Pons and Guthrie [52] accomplished determination of inorganic phosphorus from plant material after extraction with trichloroacetic acid. Interference of different organic compounds was studied and reported.

Procedures for determining inorganic phosphate, phosphocreatine, and adenosine triphosphate in the presence of each other in biological material by selective hydrolysis are reported by Griswold, Humoller, and McIntyre.[53]

Separation and determination of different phosphoric esters by the technique of paper chromatography are reported by Hanes and Isherwood; [54] see also R. Bandursky and B. Axelrod.[55] Another application of paper chromatography for separating phosphate esters (thiamine) in extracts of biological materials was pub-

[51] Wreath and Zickefoose, Anal. Chem., **21**, 808, 1949.
[52] Pons and Guthrie, Ind. Eng. Chem., Anal. Ed., **18**, 184, 1946.
[53] Griswold, Humoller, and McIntyre, Anal. Chem., **23**, 192, 1951.
[54] Hanes and Isherwood, Nature, **164**, 1107, 1949.
[55] Bandursky and Axelrod, J. Biol. Chem., **193**, 405, 1951.

ished by Kiesling and Lindell.[56] Paper electrochromatography for fractionating phosphoric esters and separating from inorganic phosphate in tissue extracts was also employed.[57]

## ANALYSIS OF COMMERCIAL PHOSPHATE SALTS

Dissolution and preparation of the sample is reported on page 805.

### DETERMINATION OF THE MAIN CONSTITUENTS

*Total Phosphorus.*—The titrimetric determination after precipitation of the phosphomolybdate complex is convenient and is recommended (see p. 814).

*Total Water in Salts of Nonvolatile Bases (Metals).* **Procedure.**—Weigh about 2.5 g. of ZnO into a medium-sized crucible. Heat it to 600°C. for 1 hour. Cool in a desiccator and weigh to 0.1 mg. on an analytical balance. Put the powdered sample (about 0.5 g.) on top of the ZnO and mix carefully by stirring with a platinum wire. Avoid losses by dusting. Collect any particles adhering to the wire by brushing them into the crucible. Weigh to 0.1 mg. on the analytical balance. Heat crucible and contents to 550°C. for 45 minutes. Cool in a desiccator and weigh. Check by heating and weighing again. The weight loss is equal to the water content of the sample.

This method measures the sum of water of composition, water of hydration, and adsorbed water. These three types of water can be distinguished in many cases. Thus, in mono- and disodium orthophosphates, the sum of water of hydration plus adsorbed water can be determined separately by heating (without ZnO) at 110°C. and 120°C., respectively. In the determination with ZnO, volatile constituents such as ammonia show up as a loss in weight and might be counted as water.

In the special case of trisodium orthophosphate the ZnO procedure is not recommended. However, tetrasodium pyrophosphate can be used in place of the ZnO, as shown in the alternate procedure given below. This alternate procedure will work on any phosphate.

**Alternate Procedure for Total Water.**—Transfer 5 g. of $Na_4P_2O_7$ into a porcelain crucible, heat to constant weight at 600°C., cool in a desiccator, and weigh to 0.1 mg. on an analytical balance. Mix in carefully 0.5 g. of powdered sample using the technique indicated for the ZnO procedure above, weigh accurately to 0.1 mg. and heat at 600°C. until constant weight is obtained. The loss of weight corresponds to the content of water.

*Ammonium.*—No special pretreatment is necessary for determining ammonia in ammonium orthophosphates by the Kjeldahl method. The ammonium polyphosphates sometimes require fuming with $H_2SO_4$, followed by a 20-minute boiling period prior to distillation.

*Calcium.*—The precipitation as oxalate without removing $P_2O_5$, which has been described in the analysis of minerals, can be applied (see p. 837). This procedure gives satisfactory results for commercial calcium phosphates when reversion to the ortho state is accomplished previously by HCl digestion.

*Potassium.*—The tetraphenyl boron method can be recommended as being very fast and accurate. This procedure can also be used for determining traces of $K_2O$, if an exactly known amount (5 mg.) is added to the sample and then deducted from the total $K_2O$ obtained. Reversion and removal of the phosphoric acids are not

[56] Kiesling and Lindell, Art. Kemi., **6**, 271, 1953.
[57] Turba and Enenkel, Naturwissenschaften, **38**, 189 (1951), Schild and Maurer, Naturwissenschaften, **38**, 303 (1951), Neil and Walker, Biochem. J., **56**, XXVII (1954).

necessary. Ammonium ion interferes by precipitating with the reagent. For separation of ammonium and potassium after common precipitation as tetraphenyl boron compounds, see G. H. Gloss, Chemist Analyst, 42, 50, 1953.

**Reagent.**—Prepare a 0.6% solution of sodium tetraphenylboron by dissolving 1.5 g. in 250 ml. of distilled water, add 0.5–1.0 g. of reagent-grade aluminum hydroxide and stir for 5 minutes. Filter, refiltering the first 20 ml. of reagent if necessary. The clear reagent is stable for some time.

**Wash Solution.**—Precipitate about 250 mg. of pure potassium tetraphenylboron with a slight excess of reagent as directed under procedure below, filter, and wash with distilled water. Dry in a desiccator at room temperature. Saturate 250 ml. of distilled water with some of this precipitate by shaking vigorously for at least 10 minutes at room temperature. Add 0.5–1.0 g. of reagent-grade aluminum hydroxide, stir a few minutes, and filter as indicated for the reagent, so that a clear solution results.

**Procedure.**—Transfer an aliquot of the sample solution, which contains about 10 mg. $K_2O$, to a 250-ml. beaker. Dilute to 40 ml. and add 0.5 ml. of concentrated HCl. While stirring, let drop in slowly from a burette 10 ml. of the reagent for each 5 mg. of $K_2O$, and allow to stand a few minutes. Filter through a weighed glass filter crucible of medium porosity and wash with small portions of the wash solution. Dry at 105°C. to constant weight.

$$\text{Wt. of Precipitate} \times 0.1091 = \text{Wt. of K}$$
$$\times 0.1314_4 = \text{Wt. of } K_2O$$

**Sodium.**—After reversion of condensed phosphates and removal of $P_2O_5$ by the aid of $ZnCO_3$, sodium can be determined as the sodium magnesium uranyl complex (see p. 840). The procedure is also convenient for the determination of traces of $Na_2O$ (0.02%) in calcium phosphates, when an exactly known amount of sodium (5 mg. $Na_2O$) is added to the sample and then deducted from the total $Na_2O$ obtained.

$$\text{Wt. of Precipitate} \times 0.0153 = \text{Na}$$
$$\times 0.0206 = Na_2O$$

NOTE.—An error which must always be less than 2%, may come from contamination of the precipitated complex with the corresponding sodium zinc uranyl acetate. This error may be avoided completely by titration of the uranium content of the precipitate. Such a titration is carried out by reduction of the uranium to the tetravalent state and oxidation with standardized $KMnO_4$.

## SPECIAL PROCEDURES FOR SPECIFIC PRODUCTS

**Calcium Phosphates.**—Determination of CaO, $H_2O$, and $P_2O_5$, as well as the trace of impurities, are usually required (see pp. 849 and 855). Extraction with 2% HCl will give the percentage of acid insoluble. (For determination of any silica, magnesium, and sulfate present see pp. 836, 839, and 842).

**Free Acid in Commercial Monocalcium Phosphate.**[58] **Procedure.**—Weigh about 3 g. of sample into a dry, narrow-mouth, 250-ml. Erlenmeyer flask and, to this, add 60 ml. of acetone which is free from water, using a dry, graduated cylinder. Stopper the flask with a dry rubber stopper, then shake the flask on an automatic

[58] This procedure can be used to measure free acid in any mixture of calcium phosphates.

shaker for about 15 minutes. Remove the flask from the shaker, rinse the stopper with acetone, catching the rinsings in the flask. Filter the slurry through a fine glass-fritted crucible, or a dry Gooch filter. Wash the flask and its residue 3 times with 2–3 ml. portions of acetone and wash the residue twice more, keeping the total volume of acetone below 75 ml. It is not necessary to have a completely dry receiving flask. Remove the funnel from the receiving flask that has been attached to suction, and wash the filtrate into an Almquist flask with distilled water.

Dilute the solution in the flask to 100 ml. with distilled water, add 0.5 ml. of 0.4% water-soluble bromcresol green indicator, and titrate to pH 4.6 with NaOH. The end point can be determined by comparing the color of the solution in the side arm of the flask with a LaMotte pH 4.6 color standard. Calculate free $P_2O_5$ on the basis that 1 ml. of 0.1409 $N$ NaOH equals 0.01 g. $P_2O_5$.

*Neutralizing Value of Phosphate Leavening Agents.*—The neutralizing value of a leavening acid is defined as the weight in grams of sodium bicarbonate that will react with 100 g. of the leavening acid to give a satisfactory baked product. This value can be determined accurately only by making tests in which various ratios of sodium bicarbonate (baking soda) and leavening acid are used. For each specific type of baked goods (biscuits, doughnuts, various types of cakes, etc.), there is an optimum final pH of the crumb, and the neutralizing value is computed from the sodium bicarbonate/acid ratio which yields this crumb pH.

A rapid semiquantitative measure of the neutralizing value can be obtained by titrating the leavening acid with NaOH to a phenolphthalein end point. For the two important phosphate leavening agents, monocalcium orthophosphate and sodium acid pyrophosphate, this simple test gives neutralizing values that are about 25% lower than the ones obtained from baking tests. To circumvent this difficulty, the solution of monocalcium phosphate is titrated at boiling temperature, and the sodium acid pyrophosphate is titrated in a nearly saturated solution of NaCl.

*Specification of Leavening Phosphates by Dough Reaction Rate.*[59]—By processing procedures, the phosphate leavening agents are made to have various rates of reaction with baking soda in batters and doughs. These reaction rates are measured by a special testing procedure described below. For different types of leavening acids, some variations in the details of the test method (such as stirring and reading period, stirring direction, and sample weight) have been used. In any case, the procedure must be strictly duplicated to every minor detail in all applications of a given test. Otherwise, the figures obtained cannot be compared successfully. The equipment described below can be used for testing all kinds of leavening acids. The procedure given is the one which is usually specified for sodium acid pyrophosphate (SAPP).

**Apparatus.**—A cylindrical mixing bomb (see Fig. 35-4) made of brass (inside height 4¼″, inside diameter 3¼″) has 4 brass rods standing upright on the bottom (2½″ long, ⅛″ diameter), equidistant from each other, and ¾″ from the sides of the bomb. The cover of the bomb fits tightly by the aid of a 1″ flange and is closed with four machine bolts and a rubber-type gasket to form a gas-tight seal. The cover is provided with a mercury well through which a mixing drive-arm extends into the bomb. By the aid of a crosspiece, two specially arranged stirring paddles 3½″ long and of different widths (½″ and ¾″) are fastened to the drive. When in motion, one of them covers the entire space between the rods and sides

59 The technique is based on Barackman's publication in Cereal Chem., **8**, 423, 1931.

and the other one clears exactly the space inside the rods, so that thorough mixing of the sample is achieved. There are two copper tubes extending from the cover that are connected to a water-jacketed Chittick gasometer and a water-jacketed burette (4-mm. bore stopcock), respectively. The top of the burette is connected with the gas system of the gasometer. A constant speed motor set at 180 r.p.m. is connected to the drive arm. The bomb is immersed into a constant-temperature

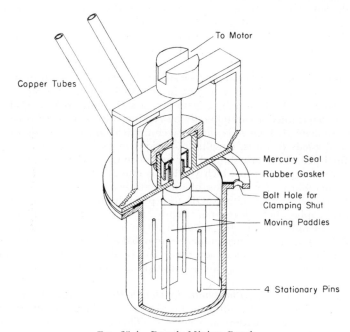

FIG. 35-4. Dough Mixing Bomb.

water bath at 27°C. which contains pumps for circulating the water through the jackets of the burette and gasometer, keeping them at 27°C.

The liquid used to confine the gas in the Chittick gasometer is made by adding 100 g. NaCl to 350 ml. water, followed by 1 g. $NaHCO_3$ and 2 ml. of 0.1% methyl orange solution, and sufficient $H_2SO_4$ (1:5) to give a decided pink coloration. This displacement liquid is stirred until all the free $CO_2$ is removed and is then ready for lengthy service.

The bomb must be cleaned extremely carefully after each experiment, in order to obtain reproducible conditions in every run.

**Procedure.**—To a 16-oz. wide-mouth glass bottle, transfer 57.0 g. of bleached flour (short patent soft wheat, from a stock supply which was sifted four times and is stored in a screw cap gallon bottle), add 5.0 g. of powdered skim milk (Breadlac), 1.0 g. of salt, 0.755 g. of sodium bicarbonate (granulation: 100% − 80, 90% + 200), and an amount of leavening agent equal to 0.01480 times the neutralizing value obtained from baking tests (for sodium acid pyrophosphate this equals

1.057 g.). Mix these ingredients by tumbling for 3 minutes using rotational movement about 2 axes of the jar plus minor shaking to prevent adherence to the side of the jar.

Place the mixture in a mixing bowl and cut in 6.0 g. of solid vegetable shortening (Crisco, Spry) with 50 downward strokes, using a table fork. Clean down the sides of the bowl and the fork and mix again with 50 downward strokes of the fork.

Transfer this mixture into the dry bomb, previously adjusted to 27°C., close it with the stirring paddles in the same position in every run, and place it in the water bath at 27°C. After 5 minutes, the ingredients have attained 27°C. Fill the proper amount of distilled water into the burette (43 ml., if flour of 12.5% moisture is used; for another percentage of moisture, the corrected figure for the water must be calculated) and connect the bomb to the gasometer system. Adjust the leveling bulb filled with brine to the zero mark in the gas burette, while the system is open to the atmosphere. After 5 minutes, close the stopcock leading to the atmosphere and reduce the pressure by lowering the leveling bulb. Add the water from the burette as quickly as possible (within 4 seconds), start the motor stirrer immediately in clockwise direction, and start a stop watch at the same time. Stop stirring exactly 3 minutes later.

Read gas volume with the leveling bulb at the gas level after ½, 1, 1½, 2, 3, 4, 5, 6, 7, and 8 minutes.

A reference standard sample is run with each group of determinations. A blank (called the "soda-blank") with all ingredients except the leavening acid precedes every series of determinations and acts as a conditioning procedure for the bomb and also as a rough standard.

*Calculations.*—The percentage of gas produced after 8 minutes of the stoichiometric amount of $CO_2$ (corresponding to the sample weight of leavening acid taken) is a measure for the reaction rate.

The volume of $CO_2$ read at 27°C. and at the prevailing pressure multiplied by a conversion factor, which contains density of $CO_2$ over stoichiometric amount of $CO_2$, and therefore varies with the pressure, $p$, yields the percentage of $CO_2$.

$$\% \ CO_2 = 0.000573 \ ml. \ CO_2 \ (p \ in \ mm.)$$

The result is corrected according to the reference sample run with the series.

*Sodium and Potassium Phosphates.*—For determination of $Na_2O$, $K_2O$, $H_2O$, and $P_2O_5$ see p. 849. Analyses for traces of different impurities are dealt with below (see p. 855). The procedures given under "Phosphate Mixtures" on p. 830 are suitable for assaying these compounds.

*Alkalinity of Detergent Phosphates.*—The term "alkalinity as $Na_2O$" is used in the detergent industry to describe the ability of a given compound to buffer against addition of acid. By definition the "alkalinity as $Na_2O$" can be determined by titrating the sample with acid to the end point at pH 4.5 and computing the results in terms of the weight percentage of $Na_2O$ stoichiometrically equivalent to the acid titrated. The alkalinity can also be computed from the proximate composition of a sodium phosphate as follows:

$$\% \ Alkalinity \ as \ Na_2O = \% \ Total \ Na_2O - 0.4367 \ (\% \ total \ P_2O_5)$$

Note.—For assaying phosphates by determining titratable $Na_2O$, contamination with carbonates must be taken into consideration. Therefore, the consumption of acid is not necessarily equivalent to neutralized weak acid function of phosphates.

*Temperature Rise Test for Crystal Form-I in Sodium Triphosphate.*—There are two types of sodium triphosphate, both of which may be found in commercial samples. The ratio of Form-I to Form-II can be determined by X-ray analysis and an empirical test, based on the fact that Form-I hydrates more rapidly than Form-II, has also been developed. This test, called the temperature rise test, has been calibrated by X-ray procedures and is described below.

**Special Apparatus (see Fig. 35-5).**—A narrow, tall-form beaker of 180-ml. capacity (Cat. No. 1140, Corning Glass Works) is inserted up to the top rim into the

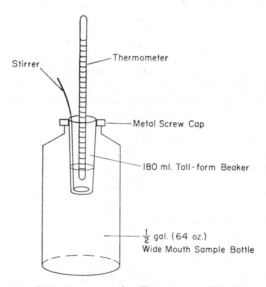

Stirrer

Thermometer

Metal Screw Cap

180 ml. Tall-form Beaker

$\frac{1}{2}$ gal. (64 oz.)
Wide Mouth Sample Bottle

FIG. 35-5. Apparatus for Temperature Rise Test.

neck of a wide-mouth half-gallon sample bottle. It is fitted into a circular hole cut into the metal screw cap of the bottle (considerable insulation is accomplished by this arrangement). A stirrer having two $1\frac{3}{8}''$ diameter rings attached $1''$ apart to a handle is made up from $\frac{1}{8}''$ stainless steel welding rod. In addition a thermometer (ASTM D 460, $-2$ to $+68°C$., 45 mm. immersion) and a timing device are provided. The equipment must be at room temperature when the test is started and must have the specified dimensions, as well as the form shown in the figure.

**Procedure.**—Weigh $50.0 \pm 0.1$ g. of dry C.P. glycerin, which is at room temperature and has a sp. gr. of 1.249–1.250 (25°C.), into the dry beaker and put the weighed sample of powdered sodium triphosphate ($50.0 \pm 0.1$ g., also at room temperature) on top of the glycerin. Suspend the beaker in the neck of the bottle, insert the dry stirrer, and begin the test by stirring exactly 2 minutes with vertical strokes, starting the timer simultaneously. Prevent dusting and losses of sample by moving the stirrer only slowly for the first few seconds, until powder and glycerin are well mixed. Then increase the stirring rate quickly to 240 complete cycles a minute and maintain this rate for the last 90 seconds (a complete cycle always means lifting the bottom ring from the bottom of the beaker just to the surface of the mixture and pushing it back down until it touches the bottom again; scraping of the sides is desirable). Stop stirring, clamp the dry thermometer in a central position with the tip 10 mm. above the bottom of the beaker (lower it until it touches the bottom and lift 10 mm., checking the height by the aid of the thermometer scale). Read and record the temperature of the glycerin-sample mixture exactly 4¾ minutes after starting the test (initial temperature). Precisely 5 minutes after the start of the test, rapidly add 25.0 ± 0.3 ml. of distilled water (at room temperature) and resume stirring at the rate of 240 complete cycles per minute (2 seconds are supposed to cover these operations). Stir for 30 seconds, push the stirrer down to the bottom of the beaker, and stop stirring. Observe the temperature without stirring until it has reached a maximum and has decreased again at least 0.1°C. Deduct the initial temperature from the maximum temperature reading and report the figure obtained (degrees centigrade) as temperature rise, T.R.

*Calculation:* The following empirical relation yields the sodium tri(poly)phosphate (I) content:

$$\% \text{ STP (I)} = (\text{T.R.} - 6) \times 4$$

For reliable results it is essential to follow exactly the standard procedure.

**Insoluble Sodium Metaphosphate in Commercial Sodium Triphosphate. Procedure.**—Add slowly while swirling, a 10-g. sample into 100 ml. of distilled water contained in a narrow-neck, 500-ml. Erlenmeyer flask. Stopper, and shake 10 minutes on a flask shaker. Then filter on a tared, ignited Gooch crucible. Rinse the contents of the flask into the crucible, with 2 or 3 small washings of distilled water. Then wash the crucible until free of soluble phosphate Dry at 110°C. to constant weight. It is believed that a porcelain crucible coated with fine Gooch asbestos, followed by a little Johns-Manville filter aid makes the best filter.

Report the insoluble content as insoluble sodium metaphosphate. If there is a question about the presence of insoluble calcium salts, silicates, etc., run a semiquantitative spectrographic analysis on the precipitate and check for strong lines of polyvalent metals. With commercial triphosphates of American manufacture, the insoluble content is nearly wholly attributable to insoluble sodium metaphosphate.

The presence of insoluble sodium metaphosphate is usually reported in terms of turbidity, using a 5% solution and silica standards for comparison.

**Ammonium Phosphates and Salts of Other Weak Bases.**—The pH titration procedures for phosphate mixtures (see p. 832) and for total phosphorus (see p. 816) can be carried out on these compositions after passage through an ion-exchange column to replace the weakly basic cation with either sodium or hydrogen (see pp. 803 and 816).

## IMPURITIES IN COMMERCIAL PHOSPHATES

It is often necessary to determine aluminum, arsenic, boron, calcium, chloride, chromium, copper, fluorine, iron, lead, magnesium, nickel, sulfate, and zinc in commercial phosphates. Since $P_2O_5$ generally interferes with the standard procedures, it seems necessary to say something about the analysis for these important trace elements in phosphates.

In general, all of the tests are made after the reversion of the phosphate to the ortho state. The polyphosphates are very strong complex-forming (sequestering) compounds, and this tendency should be overcome before analysis.

*Aluminum.*—Small amounts of $Al_2O_3$ in phosphoric acid, ammonium, potassium, and sodium phosphates can be determined by the Aluminon method, but $P_2O_5$ must first be removed in this case of very unfavorable $Al/P_2O_5$ ratio. Trace amounts of aluminum may be separated from $P_2O_5$ by barium hydroxide precipitation, though it is not possible with larger amounts.

**Reagents.** *Barium Hydroxide.*—24 g./liter $Ba(OH)_2 \cdot 8H_2O$. Store in a Pyrex bottle with a Pyrex pipette. Do not employ aged solutions; use the clear supernatant liquid only.

*Wash Solution.*—Dilute 20 ml. of barium hydroxide reagent to 1 liter. Use fresh solution only.

*Ammonium Carbonate Solution—Fresh.*—Dissolve 153.6 g. powdered C.P. reagent and make to 1 liter with distilled water.

**Procedure.**—Weigh 2 g. of phosphate into a volumetric flask, add about 100 ml. of distilled water, and adjust so as to be just acid to Congo red paper, using HCl or ammonium hydroxide. Then add 2.5 ml. of concentrated ammonium hydroxide from a pipette, stopper, and let stand until any turbidity (in such materials as $Na_2H_2P_2O_7$) has disappeared. Dilute to the mark, mix, and transfer a 10-ml. aliquot to a platinum dish or crucible. Add, while swirling, 20 ml. of the barium hydroxide reagent (mix by allowing a stream of reagent to run down one side of the platinum dish), bring to a boil, allow to settle 3 to 5 minutes, then filter by suction through a S&S No. 597 paper or its equivalent containing a little paper pulp and supported by a platinum cone into a 100-ml. Pyrex beaker. Wash the dish and filter twice, and then wash the filter once more with small portions of cold wash solution. The volume of the filtrate should be about 50 ml.

Add an excess of $(NH_4)_2CO_3$ to the filtrate while swirling. This removes barium and the last traces of iron. Filter into a 100- to 150-ml. low-form Pyrex beaker. Carefully wash the beaker twice and the filter once more with hot water (volume about 70 ml.). Make the filtrate slightly acid to Congo red paper with HCl and carefully concentrate the solution to 10–15 ml. on the hot plate or under an infrared heat bulb.

Determine aluminum in this solution colorimetrically with Aluminon (see Chapter on Aluminum, and Snell and Snell, *Colorimetric Methods of Analysis,* Volume II, p. 248, D. Van Nostrand Co., Inc., 1949; Volume IIA, p. 175, D. Van Nostrand Co., Inc., 1959.

*Arsenic.*—The Gutzeit method (see Chapter on Arsenic) is a very good micromethod for arsenic in phosphates after making the slight modifications described below.

In general, the sample should be in the ortho state. Condensed phosphates can be reverted by boiling 20 minutes with 2 $N$ $H_2SO_4$. A total of 10 ml. of concentrated acid is used in the generator, either HCl, $H_2SO_4$, $H_3PO_4$, or $HClO_4$ or a mixture of them. HCl and $H_2SO_4$ are preferred. Phosphates are neutralized to methyl orange previously.

**Apparatus.**—The usual 2-oz., wide-mouth reagent bottle fitted with a No. 5, one-hole rubber stopper is used as generator.

Although the absorption tubes normally described are satisfactory, the following is recommended. The absorption tube is 11 cm. long and has a 10-mm. inside diameter. Each end is fitted with a No. 00, one-hole rubber stopper. The bottom end is joined to the stopper that fits into the generator bottle by a short piece of glass tubing with a bulb blown in the center. The bulb prevents acid bubbles from entering the absorption tube. A piece of glass tubing 12 cm. long and of

3-mm. inside diameter is fitted through the rubber stopper at the top of the 11-cm. piece of tubing and is used to hold the mercuric bromide paper strip. The round bulb between the absorption tube and the generator is left empty. The bottom of the 10-mm. tube is packed with a pleated roll of filter paper 2.5 cm. long that has been treated with a 5% solution of lead acetate and dried. The top of the tube contains a pleated roll of moist lead acetate paper (treated with a 10% solution) 5.5 cm. long. The wet paper must not touch the dry paper. A calcium chloride tube having a round bulb on the bottom may be used for the bottom portion of the absorption apparatus.

**Reagents.** *Potassium Iodide Solution.*—40% aqueous solution.

*Stannous Chloride Solution.*—40% solution in concentrated HCl.

*Ferric Alum Solution.*—Dissolve 120 g. of ferric ammonium sulfate in water containing 25 ml. of concentrated $H_2SO_4$, add 10 g. of NaCl, and dilute to 1 liter.

*Standard Arsenic Solution.*—Dissolve 1 g. of $As_2O_3$ in 25 ml. of 20% NaOH solution, dilute to about 500 ml., neutralize with $H_2SO_4$, and add 10 ml. of $H_2SO_4$ (1:1) in excess. Dilute to 1 liter with fresh distilled water and mix well (1 ml. contains 0.001 g. of $As_2O_3$). Dilute 10 ml. of this to 1 liter with distilled water containing 10 ml. of $H_2SO_4$ (1:1). Of this second solution, 1 ml. is equivalent to 0.01 mg. $As_2O_3$. Further dilutions may be made if necessary.

*Zinc.*—Arsenic-free pellets of about 6 g. are required. If arsenic-free stick zinc is used, mold into pellets by the aid of a stainless steel mold.[60]

*Mercuric Bromide Paper.*—Sheets of Whatman No. 4 filter paper are soaked 1 hour in 5% alcoholic mercuric bromide solution. Dry the sheets of paper by hanging in a vertical position and turning around occasionally in an atmosphere free from $H_2S$. When dry, trim off 2.5 cm. of the outer edge, then cut the remainder in strips exactly 2.5 mm. wide and about 12 cm. long. Store in a dry, tightly stoppered bottle. Make fresh every 30 days. (To avoid cutting strips, one may purchase Hanford-Pratt Arsenic Strips for impregnation.)

**Procedure for Phosphoric Acid.**—The method given here assumes that there may be trace quantities of $H_3PO_2$ and/or $H_3PO_3$ present. The $KMnO_4$ treatment is to remove $H_2S$ and oxidize these lower acids of phosphorus to $H_3PO_4$. $HNO_3$ must be removed by $H_2SO_4$ or $HClO_4$ fuming, followed by acid digestion for reversion.

Pipette 5 ml. of phosphoric acid into the generator bottle, add an excess of 3% $KMnO_4$ solution, and dilute to 20 ml. Heat to 90°C. for 10 minutes, cool, and add 5 ml. of concentrated HCl and 0.5 ml. of ferric alum solution. Dilute to about 35 ml. While swirling, add 2 ml. of the potassium iodide reagent, stir, and add 0.5 ml. of the 40% $SnCl_2$ solution. Mix again, dilute to about 40 ml., and cool to 25°C. Add 2 pellets of zinc and insert the absorption tube containing a strip of the mercuric bromide paper. The mercuric bromide paper extends into the top of the 3-mm. bore tube about 7.5 cm.

Place the generator in a 25°C. water bath for 20 minutes, remove, and let the reaction proceed for an hour or longer at room temperature. Remove the stained paper strip, drop it in paraffin, attach it to the proper record sheet, measure, and compute the $As_2O_3$ by comparison with standard stains run under the same conditions, which include the use of the same amount of $P_2O_5$ in the generator. It is convenient to set up a graph giving the micrograms of $As_2O_3$ versus mm. of stain length.

60 Mills, J. Assoc. Offic. Agr. Chemists, **18**, 506, 1935.

*Boron.*—In water-soluble phosphates, boric acid can be determined by alkali titration in the presence of mannitol after $P_2O_5$ is removed. Silica and sulfate, if present, must also be removed by special procedures. (See Chapters on Silica and Sulfur.) If there is no ring metaphosphate present, then it is not necessary to revert polyphosphates before their removal. The sample taken should be such that less than 0.05 g. of boron is present.

*Procedure.*—Weigh a sample (0.2–0.5 g.) into a 250-ml. beaker, dissolve in 100 ml. of water, add 2 or 3 drops of 1% phenolphthalein indicator, and adjust to a deep red color by dropwise addition of about 0.3 N NaOH. Then add 2 g. or more, if necessary, of reagent-grade barium hydroxide. Boil 1 minute and filter by suction through a Whatman No. 42 paper or equivalent containing a little paper pulp into a second 250-ml. beaker. Wash the beaker and filter twice, and wash the filter two additional times, with distilled water containing 0.5 g./l. barium hydroxide. The wash solution should be protected from $CO_2$ and can be delivered by siphon. Add 1 or 2 drops of methyl red indicator to the filtrate, make just acid with N HCl, and add 0.5 ml. in excess. Cover with a watch glass and boil very gently for 5 or 10 minutes to remove $CO_2$. Cool and just neutralize to the methyl red indicator with 0.1 N NaOH. Add 2 g. of mannitol and a few drops of phenolphthalein indicator solution and titrate to the phenolphthalein end point with 0.1 N NaOH.

*Calcium and Magnesium.*—Titration with disodium ethylenediaminetetraacetate (EDTA) after removal of $P_2O_5$ is feasible.

**Procedure for Removal of $P_2O_5$.**—Pipette an aliquot of the neutral sample solution into a separatory funnel and add 1 ml. of concentrated HCl for each 20 ml. of sample solution. Add 20 ml. of a *n*-butanol-chloroform mixture (1:1) and 10 ml. or more of a 20% sodium molybdate solution. Shake the funnel fairly vigorously for about a minute, let separate for a minute, and drain off the yellow bottom layer. Repeat the extraction until a colorless extract is obtained.

Determine calcium and magnesium in the aqueous phase by titration with EDTA (see Chapters on Calcium and Magnesium).

*Chloride.*—In phosphates, 0.005% or more chlorine can be determined by titrating a sample of 10–20 g. Dilute to 200 ml. and titrate in the presence of 7 ml. excess $HNO_3$ with 0.1 N $AgNO_3$, using an electrical titration assembly.

Chlorides in the p. p. m. range can be determined turbidimetrically.

*Procedure.*—Pipette or weigh 0.1–1.0 g. of the phosphate into a clean volumetric flask. Make to about 10–15 ml. and adjust to pH 4.6 with $HNO_3$ if necessary. Dilute to 22 ml. with distilled water and add 1 ml. of 0.3 $HNO_3$. Mix, add 1 ml. of 0.03% $AgNO_3$ and dilute to the 25-ml. mark. Mix by inverting only once and allow to stand in the dark for 30 minutes.

Transfer to a cylindrical absorption cell, and determine "Scale A" reading on a Fisher Electrophotometer with color filter No. 425 B (blue). The micrograms corresponding to the "Scale A" reading are obtained from a calibration graph.

If very accurate results are required, the standardization should be made in the presence of the same amount of phosphate as present in the sample. The results obtained upon addition of known amounts of chloride to pyrophosphate are satisfactory. Hydrolysis of the pyrophosphate to orthophosphate gives a slightly higher chloride reading.

*Chromium.*—After oxidation with $HClO_4$, traces of chromium in the microgram range are determined colorimetrically using diphenylcarbizide. The method can be used on sodium, potassium, calcium, and ammonium phosphates with no difficulty. The quantity of iron usually found in a pure commercial sodium phosphate furnishes no serious interference. If iron is present in large quantities, then special separations are required.

**Procedure.**—Transfer a sample equivalent to not more than 1.75 g. $P_2O_5$ to a 125-ml. Erlenmeyer flask. Add 10 ml. of 70% $HClO_4$ and cover with a small watch glass supported by a bent glass tube which is 1–2 mm. in diameter. Place the flask on a hot plate and heat until the solution in the bottom of the flask turns yellow and dense white fumes rise to the top of the flask. Then heat an additional 3 minutes (or 5 minutes after fumes first appear at the surface of the solution).

At the end of the heating period, raise the watch glass on the flask with rubber-tipped tongs and quickly add 10–20 mg. $KMnO_4$ crystals from a small porcelain or Pyrex spoon. Quickly replace the cover and swirl until a deep purple color indicates an excess of $KMnO_4$ in the solution. Remove the flask at once from the hot plate and place it in an ice-water bath, swirling constantly. Just as soon as the temperature of the flask has dropped to about 100°C., remove from the water bath and quickly add 40 ml. of distilled water and 1 ml. of concentrated HCl. Swirl, add 2 or 3 chromium-free glass beads, bring to a boil, and boil 3 to 5 minutes to remove the last traces of $KMnO_4$ and chlorine.

Remove the flask from the hot plate, cool to room temperature in a water bath, and carefully transfer contents to a 100-ml. volumetric flask. Dilute the solution in the volumetric flask nearly to the mark, add 4 drops of a fresh 1% alcoholic solution of diphenylcarbizide, make to mark, mix, and determine the chromium by reading the optical density 3 5 minutes later on an electrophotometer.

The apparatus is standardized by adding known amounts of chromium to chromium-free phosphates and then proceeding as given for the sample.

**Procedure for Larger Amounts.**—If larger amounts of chromium (more than 0.1%) are present in phosphates, oxidize in the same fashion as given for traces and titrate with $FeSO_4$ and $KMnO_4$ at room temperature in the presence of excess $H_3PO_4$ and $H_2SO_4$ (see p. 838).

**Copper.**—Trace amounts of copper are determined colorimetrically with sodium diethyldithiocarbamate after separation as copper sulfide (see Chapter on Copper). Conditions for quantitative separation of minute amounts of copper sulfide are reported.[61]

If phosphoric acid is under analysis, pipette 2 ml. of the sample into a thoroughly cleaned 15-ml. Pyrex centrifuge tube with tapered bottom. Dilute to 5 ml., add 1 drop of thymol blue indicator, and then add ammonium hydroxide dropwise until the solution turns from pink to orange. Cool in a water bath and readjust to the orange color. Add 0.5 ml. of 20% HCl, dilute to 10 ml. (HCl concentration equal to 1%), and precipitate with $H_2S$.

When testing salts (such as ammonium, calcium, sodium, and potassium phosphates), weigh 1–2 g. into a clean centrifuge tube, add 5 ml. of distilled water and 1 drop of thymol blue and adjust to 1% acid as given above. If the sample is insoluble in 10% HCl, or is a polyphosphate, add enough HCl at 5-ml. volume to dissolve and revert the sample by heating the tube in a hot water bath. Then readjust to 1% HCl at 10 ml. volume. If insoluble material is present after the

61 Conn, Johnson, Trebler, and Kampenko, Ind. Eng. Chem., Anal. Ed., **7,** 19, 1935.

foregoing treatment, centrifuge and transfer the solution at 10-ml. volume to a clean centrifuge tube.

*Fluorine.*—For determining traces of fluorine, the distillation procedure followed by titration with thorium nitrate is satisfactory (see p. 842). In general, most of the phosphates containing fluorine are soluble in either $HClO_4$ or $H_2SO_4$. The phosphates are generally distilled with $H_2SO_4$ (or $HClO_4$ as described on p. 842).

*Iron.* **Procedure for Larger Amounts of Iron.**—The method depends on the quantitative oxidation of ferrous salts in HCl and/or $H_2SO_4$ to the ferric condition by potassium dichromate. All phosphates must be in the ortho state before the analysis is begun.

*Procedure.*—Transfer 10–20 g. of sample to a 250-ml. wide-mouth Erlenmeyer flask containing about 50 ml. of water. Add an excess of 3% $KMnO_4$ solution, acidify with $H_2SO_4$, then add about 2–5 ml. in excess. Add a few clean glass beads to the flask and boil until consumption of $KMnO_4$ ceases. Add 15 ml. of concentrated HCl, continue heating until the $KMnO_4$ color is completely destroyed, chlorine is expelled, and all phosphate is in the ortho form. If an orthophosphate is being analyzed, boiling 5 minutes with HCl is sufficient; but if a polyphosphate is being tested, then boiling with HCl must be continued for at least 20 minutes. Reduce and then titrate the iron, as indicated in the Chapter on Iron.

**Procedure for Traces of Iron.**—The colorimetric *o*-phenanthroline procedure of Saywell and Cunningham,[62] is suggested if the quantities of iron are in the range below 20 p. p. m. The procedure depends on the reduction of iron to the ferrous state by treating with hydroxylamine hydrochloride, followed by the addition of *o*-phenanthroline and formation of the ferrous *o*-phenanthroline complex.[63]

Weigh or pipette the sample (0.1–2 g. of phosphoric acid, sodium, or potassium orthophosphate) into a 50-ml. beaker, dilute to 15 ml., and add 0.5 ml. of concentrated $H_2SO_4$. When polyphosphates are under analysis, hydrolyze 2.5 g. by boiling 30 minutes with 5 ml. of concentrated HCl in a volume of 40–50 ml. Dilute this stock solution to 50 ml. in a volumetric flask, mix, and use 10 ml. for analysis.

Heat the sample solution until near boiling, add 1 ml. of a 10% hydroxylamine hydrochloride solution, stir, and add 0.5 ml. of a 1.5% *o*-phenanthroline solution in alcohol. Then add concentrated ammonium hydroxide dropwise until a light red or pink color develops. Drop in a very small piece of Congo red paper and continue the addition of ammonium hydroxide, while stirring gently, until the Congo red paper is distinctly pink. Remove the Congo red paper. Cool in a water bath and carefully transfer to a 25-ml. volumetric flask, dilute to the mark, mix well, and let stand 25–30 minutes for maximum development of color. Use a blue filter for reading the optical density.

*Interferences.*—If it is suspected that more than a few micrograms of aluminum are present, add citric acid to prevent the precipitation of $AlPO_4$ upon addition of ammonium hydroxide. Large amounts of copper and lead should be removed by $H_2S$ precipitation. Copper interferes by forming a bluish-green complex with *o*-phenanthroline, and lead precipitates as lead phosphate at pH 3.5–4.5. Large amounts of chromium and nickel cause an objectionable green color. Chromium can be removed by oxidation to chromate before precipitating iron as the hy-

[62] Saywell and Cunningham, Ind. Eng. Chem., Anal. Ed., **9**, 67, 1937.
[63] See Chapter on Iron and Ind. Eng. Chem., Anal. Ed., **18**, 554, 1946.

droxide, as indicated on p. 862. For precipitation and separation of iron and nickel see p. 862 and the respective chapters.

It is necessary to wait 30 minutes before measuring the color of the solution, because orthophosphate slows up the formation of the colored complex. It is therefore also necessary to have essentially the same amount of phosphate in the standard as in the sample.

**Lead.**—Regardless of the method chosen to determine traces of lead, the lead is usually separated from a large sample of phosphate by precipitating it as the sulfide at a pH of about 3.0 with copper added as a collector. If desired, the lead can be determined electrolytically or determined colorimetrically by either the dithizone method or by the colloidal sulfide procedure. The dectrolytic method will handle 0.05–10.0 mg., and the dithizone method is generally used for 0.001–0.2 mg. Pb (see Chapter on Lead). If the sample is a polyphosphate, then it should be reverted to the ortho state by boiling with HCl. One p. p. m. or more of arsenic interferes and should be removed by precipitation as the sulfide in a 6 $N$ HCl solution. The arsenic sulfide is filtered out. The excess $H_2S$ should be boiled off before continuing the determination.

**Pretreatment.**—For analyzing ammonium, sodium, and potassium phosphates, weigh 50 g. of sample into a clean 600-ml. beaker containing 1 g. of citric acid (it is assumed that the sample is already in the ortho form). Dilute the sample in the beaker to 200 ml. and add a slight excess of concentrated HCl. Warm until all of the salts are dissolved. Add 4 drops of 0.4% thymol blue indicator solution. Cool, add concentrated ammonium hydroxide while stirring until the pink color is changed to orange, cool in a running water bath, and dilute to 450–500 ml. Add concentrated ammonia from a burette until the solution is yellow, and then 0.5–1.0 ml. in excess (pH 2.8–3.4; check, if necessary, by glass electrode). Add 0.5 ml. of a 2% $CuSO_4$ solution, precipitate with $H_2S$, filter, and wash with wash solution (water, adjusted to pH 3 with HCl and ammonium acetate, and then saturated with $H_2S$ gas).

When calcium phosphates are being analyzed, weigh 25 g. of sample into a 600-ml. beaker, add 200 ml. distilled water, warm, and dissolve by adding HCl. (If there is acid-insoluble material present, it may be removed and discarded or made soluble by a fusion procedure and added to the sample, if total $P_2O_5$ is required.) Analyze for acid-soluble lead as directed above after neutralizing the main fraction of acid with concentrated ammonium hydroxide and accomplishing the final adjustment to pH 3 using a 33% sodium citrate solution.

**Nickel.**—An amount of 5–10 p. p. m. of nickel will cause phosphoric acid to have a greenish color and will impart a greenish cast to the ordinary ammonium, sodium, and potassium phosphates. Generally, for trace analysis, 1 p. p. m. or less is being considered. Separation from $P_2O_5$ is accomplished by precipitation with NaOH.

In the analysis of calcium phosphates, the calcium must be removed previously (see removal of calcium as sulfate, p. 839).

If copper and arsenic are present, remove as follows. Weigh a 5-g. sample into a 250-ml. beaker, dilute to 30–40 ml., make acid to thymol blue indicator, and then add ammonium hydroxide until the solution just turns orange. Add 2.5 ml. of 25% HCl and dilute to 50 ml. Heat to 80–90°C. and precipitate by saturating with $H_2S$ for 10 minutes.

Chromium may be removed by adding an oxidizing agent to the beaker during the NaOH precipitating process (see below).

**Removal of the Phosphoric Acid.**—To the copper-free solution that was boiled to expel $H_2S$ and treated with bromine to oxidize iron, add 0.2–0.5 ml. of a 1% ferric-iron solution (nickel-free, prepared from pure iron wire) and 4 drops of methyl orange indicator. Neutralize with 15% NaOH which contains about 1% $Na_2CO_3$ until the solution is barely acid to methyl orange, dilute to 100 ml., and add 50 ml. of the 15% NaOH solution, while stirring with a Pyrex stirring rod. Boil 1 minute and digest at 60–70°C. for 30 minutes. Filter the warm solution through a Whatman No. 42 paper supported by a platinum cone, using suction as necessary. A little paper pulp and analytical filter aid on the filter paper is beneficial. (Wash the filter with a little 5% NaOH before starting the filtration.) Rinse the beaker twice and the filter six times with 1–3% $Na_2CO_3$ solution which may contain 1% NaOH. Discard the filtrate.

Transfer the filter to a clean suction flask and dissolve the nickel and iron precipitate with 2–3 alternate washings of hot dilute HCl (1:5) and hot water. Allow the filter to stand a minute or so before applying suction. Cool the filtrate and dilute to 50 ml. in a volumetric flask. Determine nickel colorimetrically with dimethylglyoxime in an aliquot of this solution (see Chapter on Nickel).

**Sulfate. Procedure for Larger Amounts.**—The gravimetric barium sulfate method can be used when the $SO_3$ content is 0.005% or more.

Weigh the sample (usually 10 g.) into a 250-ml. beaker. Dissolve in 100 ml. of distilled water. If the sample is alkaline, make just acid to methyl orange indicator with concentrated HCl and add 10 ml. in excess. Bring to a boil and filter to remove the insoluble matter. If the material being tested is a polyphosphate, boil 20 minutes in the acid solution before the filtration. Dilute the filtrate to 150 ml. with distilled water, heat to boiling, and add 10 ml. of 10% barium chloride solution slowly, while stirring vigorously. Digest at about 70°C. for at least an hour or preferably overnight. Filter through a tared Gooch crucible, or a fine-porosity, fritted-porcelain crucible, wash with hot water and ignite in the crucible at about 800°C. to constant weight.

$$\text{Wt. of Precipitate} \times 0.343 = \text{Wt. of } SO_3$$

**Procedure for Traces of $SO_3$.**—The micromethod described below takes advantage of the reducibility of sulfate to $H_2S$.

The reduction is carried out by boiling the sample with a mixture of $H_3PO_2$, HCl, and HI. The acids (160 ml. HI of sp. gr. 1.70, 160 ml. concentrated HCl, 45 ml. 50% $H_3PO_2$) are mixed and boiled for 5 minutes. After cooling, the mixture is stored in a brown, glass-stoppered bottle. An appropriate reduction flask is made from a glass-stoppered washing bottle (250-ml. capacity) by straightening the long tube and sealing to it the top of a thistle tube with stopcock and by sealing to the other arm a Pyrex tube that is long enough (after being bent downwards) to extend into a 300-ml. Erlenmeyer flask. This Erlenmeyer flask represents the receiver. It contains 150 ml. 0.2% cadmium chloride solution in 2.5% ammonium hydroxide to absorb the hydrogen sulfide evolved and is kept in ice during the absorption process.

Transfer the sample (50 ml. of phosphoric acid or 20 g. of phosphate) into the reduction flask and insert the stopper. Adjust the receiver so that the delivery tube is immersed in the cadmium chloride solution. Add 35 ml. of the acid mixture and boil for 8 minutes. The heating must be conducted carefully, so that not enough acid is carried over to neutralize the ammonium hydroxide in the receiving flask completely. To prevent bumping, SiC grains may be added or a gas stream (nitrogen or helium) may be bubbled through the boiling solution.

Remove the receiver, cool it in ice to 10°C., add 20 ml. of concentrated HCl, and swirl just once. Add an excess of $1/600$ $M$ potassium iodate solution which contains NaOH (1 gram/liter) and KI (5 grams/liter). Stopper the flask and shake vigorously. Back titrate the excess of iodine with standardized 0.01 $N$ sodium thiosulfate (starch is added as indicator). A blank is carried out under the same conditions.

When $1/600$ $M$ potassium iodate solution is used, 1 ml. corresponds to 0.4003 mg. of $SO_3$ (0.4803 mg. of $SO_4$).

*Zinc.*—Occasionally, it is necessary to determine trace quantities of zinc in phosphates. This is accomplished after separation of the zinc as sulfide. Any arsenic and lead are removed previously by precipitating them with $H_2S$ from a rather strong acid solution.

**Procedure.**—Weigh a 10-g. sample into a 250-ml. beaker and dilute to 100 ml. with distilled water. Adjust to about 0.5 $N$ with respect to HCl or $H_2SO_4$ before introducing $H_2S$ to remove the interfering metals. Pass a rapid stream of $H_2S$ gas for 5 minutes. While sulfiding, add about 0.5 ml. of concentrated ammonium hydroxide to start precipitation of the lead. After filtration of the sulfides, remove $H_2S$ by boiling the filtrate, add 5 g. of crystalline sodium citrate, and dilute to 100 ml.

Cool, add 3 drops of 0.2% thymol blue indicator, then add concentrated ammonium hydroxide from a burette until the yellow color is just obtained. Cool again, add 4 drops of 0.2% bromphenol blue indicator, and continue to add ammonium hydroxide dropwise until a light green color is obtained (pH 3.0–3.4). Add a pinch of analytical filter aid to the beaker, then pass a rapid stream of $H_2S$ gas for 15 minutes. Filter through a double thickness of Whatman No. 42 paper or its equivalent using vacuum. Wash the beaker and filter four times each with $H_2S$ water which has been adjusted to pH 3.0.

Discard the filtrate and dissolve the precipitate through the filter into the original beaker by applying 4 successive rinsings of warm $N$ HCl followed by 1 washing of hot water. Determine zinc by a convenient micromethod (see Chapter on Zinc).

## PHOSPHORUS DETERMINATION IN ALLOY STEELS AND FERROALLOYS

### *ALLOY STEEL WITH MORE THAN 0.1% OF Ti OR Zr*

**Procedure.**—Dissolve the sample as described for iron (see p. 808). An insoluble precipitate results. Filter and wash the residue containing silica, Ti, and Zr, ignite in a platinum crucible, and fume with HF and $H_2SO_4$ on a steam bath. Fuse the residue, which still contains a little $H_2SO_4$, with $Na_2CO_3$ (not a mixture of $Na_2CO_3$ and $K_2CO_3$!). Dissolve the melt in hot water, filter from insoluble sodium titanate and sodium zirconate, and wash with diluted $Na_2CO_3$ solution. Add an excess of $HNO_3$ (1:1) to the filtrate and combine with the main filtrate. Precipitate phosphorus as molybdenum complex.

NOTE.—A procedure using HF and boric acid to prevent incomplete precipitation of the molybdenum complex by any titanium present in the solution is reported by West.[64]

64 West, *Analyst*, **70**, 82, 1945.

### ALLOY STEEL CONTAINING Nb AND Ta

**Procedure.**—Dissolve the sample as indicated for iron and steel (see p. 808), make up to 100 ml., and filter insoluble niobic and tantalic acids, using a dry filter. Precipitate phosphoric acid in a 50-ml. aliquot.

### ALLOY STEEL CONTAINING V

**Procedure.**—Dissolve a 4-g. sample, as indicated for iron and steel. Cool to 25°C., add a slight excess of ammonia, and dissolve the resulting precipitate by adding dropwise HCl (1:1). After adding 25 ml. of a 10% solution of ferrous sulfate, precipitate with acidic ammonium molybdate solution (see p. 814) and shake. Keep at 30–35°C. for 60–100 minutes before filtering.

### ALLOY STEEL CONTAINING Cr

**Procedure.**—Transfer a 4-g. sample into an Erlenmeyer flask. Dissolve by heating with 60 ml. of $HNO_3$ (1:1) and slowly adding HCl (1:1), a few milliliters at a time, and boiling after each addition. 10–20 ml. of the HCl are necessary to dissolve the sample. Add 20 ml. of concentrated HCl in excess, evaporate until the liquid becomes a syrup, add 40 ml. of concentrated $HNO_3$, and evaporate again. Dissolve in 60 ml. of $HNO_3$ (1:1), make up to 100 ml., filter through a dry filter, and use a 50-ml. aliquot of the filtrate for the phosphorus determination.

### ALLOY STEEL CONTAINING Mo

**Procedure.**—Dissolve the sample as indicated for iron and steel (see p. 808) and filter, in case a precipitate containing molybdic acid separates. Wash this precipitate with diluted $HNO_3$ (1:100), ignite it in a platinum crucible at low temperature, and then fuse with a mixture of $Na_2CO_3$ and $K_2CO_3$. Dissolve the melt in hot water, filter, and wash with diluted $Na_2CO_3$ solution. Acidify the filtrate with $HNO_3$. Add 0.2 g. of alum as collector (if over 3 mg. P is expected, additional alum should be used), and precipitate by adding ammonium hydroxide to the hot solution. Filter, wash the precipitate with a diluted hot solution of $NH_4Cl$, dissolve in $HNO_3$, and add to the main filtrate. Precipitate phosphorus as phosphomolybdate.

If no precipitate containing molybdic acid is formed in the first place, the analysis is carried out in the usual fashion (see p. 808).

### ALLOY STEEL CONTAINING W

**Procedure.**—Dissolve a 2-g. sample (chips) in 60 ml. of $HNO_3$ (1:1), adding a few drops of HF. Boil and evaporate to dryness. After cooling, dissolve the residue in 100 ml. of concentrated HCl and boil. (Tungstic acid dissolves first but reprecipitates upon boiling. This second precipitate is free of P, V, and As.) Concentrate to 20 ml., add 50 ml. of water, boil, and filter, using a filter with paper pulp, and wash with diluted HCl (1:100). Evaporate to a small volume, add 80 ml. of concentrated $HNO_3$, and evaporate again. Dissolve in 50 ml. of $HNO_3$ (1:1), transfer into an Erlenmeyer flask, and precipitate the phosphomolybdate complex after oxidizing as indicated for iron and steel (see p. 808).

## ALLOYS CONTAINING Fe, Si, Mn, Al, AND Ca IN VARYING COMBINATIONS

**Procedure.**—Transfer a 2-g. sample into a platinum dish and add 50 ml. of $HNO_3$ (1:1) and 20 ml. of HF (phosphorus free) in small portions. Evaporate almost to dryness. After adding 30 ml. of $HNO_3$ (1:1), evaporate again. Dissolve in 30 ml. of $HNO_3$ (1:1), heat to 90°C., add 25 ml. of a hot saturated solution of sodium tetraborate ($BF_3$ is volatile), and keep at this temperature for 10 minutes. Transfer into a flask, oxidize, and precipitate phosphorus as phosphomolybdate.

If titanium and/or zirconium is present, dissolve a 2-g. sample in $HNO_3$ and HF, and fume to dryness after 15 ml. of $H_2SO_4$ (1:3) have been added. Transfer the residue into a silver crucible, fuse with sodium peroxide, extract the cooled melt with water, make up to 500 ml., and filter (titanate and zirconate remain insoluble). To 400 ml. of the filtrate (corresponding to 1.6 g. of sample), add $HNO_3$ and 10 ml. of a 5% solution of alum (only if the sample itself does not contain any aluminum). Precipitate by adding ammonium hydroxide to the hot solution. Filter, dissolve the residue in $HNO_3$, and determine phosphorus in the solution as recommended above.

## FERROTITANIUM, FERROCHROMIUM, FERRONIOBIUM, FERROTANTALUM, AND FERROSELENIUM

**Procedure.**—In a silver crucible, fuse 2.5 g. of the alloy with 10 g. of sodium peroxide. The cooled melt is treated with water in a porcelain dish. Boil for 5 minutes, make up to 500 ml., and filter through a fluted filter. To 400 ml. of the filtrate, corresponding to 2 g. of sample weight, add $HNO_3$ until slightly acid, heat until it starts to boil (keep boiling for 15 minutes when niobium and tantalum are present, then filter out the precipitates of niobic and tantalic acid and wash with dilute $HNO_3$), and precipitate with ammonium hydroxide. Dissolve the precipitate in $HNO_3$ and, after adding 10 ml. of a 5% solution of ferric chloride (ferrotitanium usually contains aluminum, therefore no hydroxide-forming compound need be added), precipitate again with ammonium hydroxide. Filter and wash with a hot 2% solution of $NH_4NO_3$. Dissolve the residue in 30 ml. of $HNO_3$ (1:1) and determine phosphorus after precipitation as phosphomolybdate.

## FERROPHOSPHORUS

**Procedure.**—Dissolve the sample and make to volume as directed on p. 808. Transfer a 25-ml. aliquot of the solution to a 500-ml. wide-mouth Erlenmeyer flask and neutralize with ammonium hydroxide against methyl orange. Add 25 ml. of concentrated $HNO_3$, 40 ml. of water, 40 ml. of ammonium hydroxide (sp. gr. 0.96), and 40 ml. of molybdate solution (see p. 814). Shake occasionally for 10 minutes and let settle for another 10 minutes. Filter, wash with dilute $HNO_3$, and dissolve the phosphomolybdate complex in dilute ammonium hydroxide. Reprecipitate after adding 25 ml. of molybdate solution with $HNO_3$. Filter, wash, and determine titrimetrically according to p. 814.

*Chapter 36*

# THE PLATINUM METALS*

The members of the platinum group—platinum, palladium, iridium, rhodium. ruthenium, and osmium—occur in nature in alloyed form chiefly in the metallic state with the base metals copper and iron, and sometimes with native gold. However, platinum arsenide and ruthenium and osmium sulfides are found in nature but these are rare. The mineral sperrylite, platinum arsenide $PtAs_2$, has a tin-white metallic luster and is found in the nickel ores of Sudbury, Ontario, Canada. The mineral laurite, ruthenium sulfide $Ru_2S_3$, has a metallic luster and is found in the platinum washings of Borneo. Platinum deposits of commercial importance occur in the Ural Mountains, British Columbia, and South America.

The assay method by fusion with a litharge flux, similar to the method for gold and silver ores, is used in evaluation of the original ores. Analysis, however, generally deals with concentrates, alloys, jewelers' sweeps, pen-point material, scrap, catalyst masses, etc. A very large amount of alloy in which ruthenium and osmium predominate has replaced the original osmiridium grains for tipping fountain pen-points.

The entire group of platinum metals can be brought into solution by fusing with a mixture of barium peroxide and barium nitrate, and extracting with dilute hydrochloric acid.

Hydrogen sulfide precipitates all metals from hot solutions with a hydrochloric acid content up to about 5%; iridium solutions should have about 20% hydrochloric acid. Platinum from platinum ammines cannot be completely precipitated by hydrogen sulfide or ammonium chloride. All sulfides are soluble in aqua regia. The sulfides of palladium, rhodium, and osmium are insoluble in ammonium sulfide, whereas, the sulfides of iridium, platinum, and ruthenium are soluble, the latter two with difficulty. The ignition of the sulfides yields metal in the case of platinum, oxidized residues with ruthenium. iridium, rhodium, palladium, and the volatile tetroxide with osmium. Some sulfur will be retained in all cases.

Concentrated sulfuric acid will attack palladium and finely divided osmium, but less so than nitric acid. In both cases the osmium goes off as the tetroxide.

When the metals are alloyed with lead and dissolved in dilute nitric acid, some rhodium and platinum will go into solution with the lead, and by treating the wet residue with dilute aqua regia or concentrated sulfuric acid, the remaining rhodium and platinum will dissolve leaving the iridium insoluble. These treatments provide a clean separation of iridium and rhodium.

Mercuric cyanide, $Hg(CN)_2$, gives a white precipitate of palladium cyanide, $Pd(CN)_2$, while the other metals are not affected.

Chlorine will distill ruthenium and osmium both from ruthenate and osmate solutions; nitric acid will distill osmium only. Care should be taken not to have

* Chapter by R. E. Hickman.

the solution too strong with nitric acid as there is a tendency for a small amount of ruthenium to be carried over. Organic matter should not be present when osmium is distilled with nitric acid.

Zinc will precipitate all metals from the chloride solutions, iridium being very difficult to precipitate completely. The precipitates will always contain a small amount of zinc. Magnesium and aluminum are somewhat cleaner.

Reactions of Salts of Platinum Metals

| | Ruthenium (RuCl₃) | Rhodium (RhCl₃) | Palladium (PdCl₂) | Osmium (OsCl₄) | Iridium (IrCl₄) | Platinum (PtCl₄) |
|---|---|---|---|---|---|---|
| Color | Dark brown | Red | Brownish yellow | Yellow | Dark brown | Yellow |
| Hydrogen sulfide at 80°C | Azure-blue color on prolonged treatment | Brownish black ppt., $Rh_2S_3$ | Brownish black ppt., PdS | Brownish black ppt., $OsS_2$ | Brownish black ppt., $Ir_2S_3$ | Brownish black ppt., $PtS_2$ |
| Ammonium sulfide | Dark brown ppt., difficulty soluble in excess | Dark brown ppt., $Rh_2S_3$ insoluble in excess | Black ppt., PdS, insoluble in excess | Dark ppt., insoluble in excess | Brown ppt., $Ir_2S_3$, soluble in excess | Brown ppt., $PtS_2$, soluble in excess to $(NH_4)_2PtS_3$ |
| Caustic alkalies | Black ppt. of hydrated oxide insoluble in excess | Yellow-brown ppt., $Rh(OH)_3$, soluble in excess | Yellowish brown basic salts soluble in excess | Brownish red $OsO_2 \cdot 2H_2O$ | Green solution Brownish black double chloride ppt. | Dark ppt. of $PtO_2 \cdot xH_2O$ |
| Ammonium hydroxide on warming | Greenish coloring | Slow decolorization | Decolorized | Yellowish brown ppt. | Bright color | Slow decolorization |
| Saturated NH₄Cl solution | Brown ppt. | No ppt. | No ppt. | Red ppt. | Black ppt. | Yellow ppt., $(NH_4)_2PtCl_6$ |
| Saturated KCl solution | Violet cryst. ppt. of $K_2RuCl_5$ | Red cryst. ppt., $K_2RhCl_5$ | Red ppt. of $K_2PdCl_4$ | Brown cryst. ppt., $K_2OsCl_6$ | Brownish red ppt. of $K_2IrCl_6$ | Yellow ppt. $K_2PtCl_6$ |
| KI solution (1:1000) | No change | No change | Dark ppt. | No change | Yellow color | Slow red-brown color |
| Hg(CN)₂ solution | No change | No change | White ppt., $Pd(CN)_2$ | No change | No change | No change |
| KCNS, 1% solution | Dark violet color | Yellow color | Unchanged | Unchanged | Decolorized | Increased yellow color |
| Hydrazine in hydrochloric acid solution | Yellow color | Yellow color | Black ppt., metallic Pd | No change | Yellow color | Black ppt., metallic Pt |
| Dimethyl glyoxime | No change | No change | Yellow ppt. | No change | No change | No change |
| Metallic zinc | Ppt., Ru | Ppt., Rh | Ppt., Pd | Ppt., Os | Ppt., Ir | Ppt., Pt |

Quantitative Separation of the Elements of the Platinum Group

Dissolve the material in aqua regia and filter off the insol. Ignite the residue and fuse in a nickel crucible with $Na_2O_2$. Cool, place in a beaker containing a little water and acidify with HCl. Combine the solutions, place in a distillation flask, make alkaline with NaOH and distill with a current of chlorine gas, catching the distillate in NaOH.

**Distillate: Ru, Os.** Acidify with HCl and pass in $H_2S$. Filter off sulfides and ignite in a boat in a combustion tube in a current of oxygen, catching the volatile $OsO_4$ in a solution of NaOH and alcohol. Determine Os in this solution, and weigh $RuO_2$ remaining in the boat.

The remaining solution is boiled to expel chlorine and then concentrated $NH_4Cl$ solution is added and sufficient 95% alcohol to double the volume of the solution.

**Precipitate: Pt, Ir, some Rh, traces of Pd.** Ignite in an atmosphere of hydrogen, extract residue with dilute aqua regia (1 part acids to 4 parts water).

- **Residue: Ir, Rh.** Fuse with $KHSO_4$, extract with water and dilute $H_2SO_4$. Repeat fusion and extraction. Combine filtrates, washing residue.
  - **Residue: Ir, trace Rh.**
  - **Solution: (A) Rh.** Boil with $Na_2CO_3$, then acidify with HCl and filter. Ignite residue and combine with Rh from (B) and (C).
- **Solution: Pt with traces of Pd, Ir, Rh.**

**Filtrate: Rh, Pd, some Pt, Ir, and any Fe, Ni, Cu that was present in sample.** Nearly neutralize with $NH_4OH$ and pass in $H_2S$ gas.

- **Precipitate: sulfides of Pd, Rh, Au, Cu.** Ignite and digest with HCl, filter and repeat ignition and extraction of residue. Combine extracts.
  - **Residue (C):** Rh. Combine with (A) and (B).
  - **Filtrate:** Pd, Cu. Add KCl and alcohol. If Pd is present, it will precipitate as $K_2PdCl_4$.
- **Filtrate: Ni, Fe, some Au and Rh.** Evaporate to dryness with $HNO_3$ and ignite. Extract Fe and Ni with HCl. Ignite residue (B) and combine with (A) and (C).

Combine residues (A), (B) and (C) containing Au and Rh. Dissolve out Au by extraction with aqua regia. Rh is left as a residue.

# PLATINUM

**Pt, *at. wt.* 195.09; *d.* 21.37; *m.p.* 1770°C.; *b.p.* 4300°C.; *oxides*, PtO, PtO$_2$**

## DETECTION

*Platinum* is a gray, lustrous, soft and malleable metal. It is not altered by ignition in the air, but fuses in the oxyhydrogen flame. It does not dissolve in any of the single acids, but a fusion with acid potassium sulfate attacks the metal slightly. The action of chlorine in general, and nitrohydrochloric acid (aqua regia), the main solvent, converts the metal to hydrochloroplatinic acid, H$_2$PtCl$_6$, which forms many double salts, or platinichlorides. If platinic chloride is gently heated it breaks up into platinous chloride, PtCl$_2$, and chlorine.

If, however, the platinum is alloyed with silver, it dissolves in nitric acid to a yellow liquid, provided sufficient silver is present in the alloy.

The oxides can be formed by carefully igniting the corresponding hydroxides. These are very unstable, decomposing into metal and oxygen by gentle ignition.

The chlorides are the most important compounds of platinum. Two complex acids are formed with hydrochloric acid when the metal is dissolved in aqua regia.

$$PtCl_4 + 2HCl = H_2PtCl_6 \text{ (chloroplatinic acid), orange-red crystals}$$

$$PtCl_2 + 2HCl = H_2PtCl_4 \text{ (chloroplatinous acid), only known in solution}$$

An aqueous solution of the former is yellowish-orange, while an aqueous solution of the latter is dark brown, the former being by far the more important.

*Potassium iodide* precipitates platinum iodide, but it dissolves readily, giving a pink to a dark blood-red liquid, depending on the concentration of the solution. Nitric acid should be absent. Heat destroys this color, as well as hydrogen sulfide, sodium thiosulfate and sulfite, sulfurous acid, and certain other reducing reagents.

*Hydrogen sulfide* precipitates black platinum disulfide, PtS$_2$, with the other elements of the hydrogen sulfide group. The solution should be hot, as precipitation takes place more quickly. It is difficultly soluble in ammonium sulfide. It will be found in the extract with the arsenic, antimony, tin, gold, molybdenum, etc., and is precipitated with these elements upon addition of hydrochloric acid. Platinum sulfide is soluble in aqua regia. Addition of MgCl$_2$ solution prevents formation of colloidal PtS$_2$.

*Ammonium chloride* added to a concentrated solution of platinum chloride precipitates yellow (NH$_4$)$_2$PtCl$_6$, which is slightly soluble in water, and less so in dilute ammonium chloride solution and alcohol.

*Potassium chloride* precipitates yellow K$_2$PtCl$_6$, which is slightly soluble in water, but insoluble in 75% alcohol.

*Ferrous sulfate* precipitates metallic platinum on boiling from a neutral solution. Neutralize with Na$_2$CO$_3$. Free mineral acids (except dilute H$_2$SO$_4$) prevent the precipitation (difference from gold).

*Stannous chloride* does not reduce platinum chloride to metal, but reduces chloroplatinic acid to chloroplatinous acid.

$$H_2PtCl_6 + SnCl_2 = H_2PtCl_4 + SnCl_4$$

870

*Oxalic acid* does not precipitate platinum (difference from gold).

*Sodium hydroxide with glycerin* reduces chloroplatinic acid on warming to black metallic powder.

*Formic acid* precipitates from neutral boiling solutions all the platinum as a black metallic powder.

*Thallous oxide* precipitates from the platinum dichloride solution a pale yellow salt, thallium platinochloride. When the salt is heated to redness it leaves an alloy of thallium and platinum.

*Sodium hydroxide* added to platinic chloride and then acidified with acetic acid produces a pale yellow to orange precipitate of platinic hydroxide, $Pt(OH)_4$. This dissolves in acids readily, except acetic acid.

*Metallic zinc, magnesium, iron, aluminum and copper* are the most important metals that precipitate metallic platinum.

$$H_2PtCl_6 + 3Zn = 3ZnCl_2 + H_2 + Pt$$

## ESTIMATION

Platinum may be present under the following conditions:

1. Native grains usually accompanied by the other so-called platinum metals, iridium, palladium, ruthenium, rhodium, osmium, and gold and silver (alloyed with one or more of the allied metals).

Ore concentrates containing the native grains as above with the base metals, iron, copper, chromium, titanium, etc. The associated minerals high in specific gravity in the gravels may be expected to appear with the platinum nuggets, such as chromite, magnetite, garnet, zircon, rutile, small diamonds, topaz, quartz, cassiterite, pyrite, epidote, and serpentine; with gold in syenite; ores of lead and silver.

2. Scrap platinum containing, oftentimes, palladium, iridium, gold, silver, and iron.

3. Small amounts of platinum in the presence of large amounts of iron, silica, carbon, magnesia; platinum residues, nickel and platinum contacts, photographic paper, jewelers' filings and trimmings, dental and jewelers' sweeps and asbestos, etc.

4. Platinum alloyed with silver, gold, tungsten, nickel, copper, lead, etc.

5. Platinum solutions and salts.

## PREPARATION AND SOLUTION OF THE SAMPLE

The best solvent for platinum is aqua regia. The metal is also acted upon by fusion with the fixed alkalies—sodium or potassium hydroxide and sodium peroxide or potassium or sodium nitrate; also by chlorates in the presence of HCl. Platinum, when highly heated, alloys with other metals, as lead, tin, bismuth, antimony, silver, gold, copper, etc. The element dissolves in nitric acid when alloyed with silver. This gives a method for the determination of gold in the presence of silver and platinum alloy.

All salts of platinum are soluble in water. The less soluble salts are the chloroplatinates of potassium, ammonium, rubidium, and cesium. Heat increases the solubility while the presence of alcohol decreases the solubility.

*Ores.*—When the free grains of platinum, gold, and osmiridium are desired the following method is recommended: Five to 10 g. of the ore are taken from a well-mixed, pulverized sample and placed in a large platinum dish. Twenty-five to 50 ml. of strong hydrofluoric acid together with 5 to 10 ml. of concentrated sulfuric acid is mixed with the ore in the dish and evaporated on the water bath, when $SiF_4$ and the excess of HF are expelled. The material is gently heated until $SO_3$ fumes are given off. This is repeated with HF if necessary. The material is washed into a casserole with about 200 ml. of hot water and digested over a water bath for 15 or 20 minutes, and is then washed by decantation, several times pouring the supernatant liquor through a filter to save any floating material that might be washed out. The filter is cautiously burned and the residue is added to the unattacked material. This is treated with aqua regia and filtered. The platinum and a small amount of iridium that dissolves with the platinum on account of its being alloyed can be precipitated with ammonium chloride. The residue is cautiously ignited and treated with HF and $H_2SO_4$ in a platinum dish as described above. After washing and drying the bright grains are weighed as osmiridium. The sand and osmiridium can also be fused with silver and borax, then extracted with dilute nitric acid, leaving the osmiridium grains *free* from sand.

*Platinum Scrap.*—One-half gram to a gram is dissolved in aqua regia and evaporated with HCl to get rid of the $HNO_3$.

If the platinum is alloyed with a large amount of copper, silver, lead, and other impurities, a sample of 1 to 5 g. is dissolved in 15 to 25 ml. of $HNO_3$, whereby the copper, silver, lead, and other impurities alloyed with the platinum as well as a large amount of platinum will dissolve. The residue after washing will be platinum and gold. These are dissolved in aqua regia as described above and the platinum precipitated with ammonium chloride. The platinum is recovered from the nitric acid solution and added to the aqua regia solution and the whole is evaporated to get rid of the $HNO_3$.

*Small Amounts of Platinum in the Presence of Large Amounts of Iron, Iron Scale, $Fe_2O_3$; Iron Sulfate, Magnesia, Magnesium Sulfate, Silica, etc.*—The material is carefully weighed and the coarse scales are separated from the finer material containing the platinum by passing the fines through a 20-in. mesh or finer wire sieve. The coarse scale seldom contains platinum, but it is advisable to quarter this down to 1 kilogram or a fairly good-sized sample and test for platinum on a portion of the ground sample. This can be tested by a wet or a fire assay. The fines are quartered down to about 1 kilogram and ground to pass a 60- to 80-in. mesh sieve. One hundred to 500 grams of the material are taken for analysis. This is placed in one or more casseroles, depending on the amount taken. Each 100-g. portion is extracted by digestion on the steam-bath with about 300 to 400 ml. of 10% $H_2SO_4$. The iron, magnesia, etc., soluble in $H_2SO_4$ will go into solution, leaving the platinum with the insoluble residue. Filter (a Buechner funnel may be necessary) and wash the residue with water. Test the filtrate for platinum and if any is present precipitate with zinc as described below.

After the filter is ignited in a large platinum dish, the residue is moistened with $H_2SO_4$ and HF is added completely covering the material. The solution is evaporated on the water bath until $SO_3$ fumes are given off. If necessary, repeat the treatment with $H_2SO_4$ and HF until all the silica is driven off as $SiF_4$. The residue is transferred to a casserole and digested with aqua regia according to directions given under "Ores" and "Platinum Scrap." It is sometimes very difficult to precipitate all of the platinum in the presence of a large amount of iron, magnesia, etc., not having the solution concentrated enough for the platinum. It is advisable to reduce the platinum by iron or zinc, filter, wash with water, and redissolve the black metallic platinum in aqua regia. The $HNO_3$ is expelled by evaporation and adding concentrated HCl from time to time and finally the platinum is precipitated with ammonium chloride.

## SEPARATIONS

A careful review of the paragraphs on "Detection" will be very helpful oftentimes in making separations from other metals and substances.

*Separation of Platinum from Gold.*—(1) The platinum is precipitated first with ammonium chloride, as $(NH_4)_2PtCl_6$. After the precipitate has settled it is filtered and washed free from gold with 20% ammonium chloride solution and alcohol. The gold is precipitated with a concentrated solution of ferrous sulfate or chloride as metallic gold. (See also page 471.)

(2) Oxalic acid precipitates gold, leaving the platinum in solution. The oxalic acid is added and the solution heated until the gold is entirely precipitated. Filter and wash the precipitate of metallic gold free from platinum. The filtrate is evaporated as far as possible without crystallizing, and the platinum is precipitated with ammonium chloride as $(NH_4)_2PtCl_6$, or it may be reduced with zinc and the black dissolved in aqua regia and treated as described above.

*Separation of Platinum from Iridium.*—The platinum and the iridium are precipitated by iron or zinc and the black residue is washed free from impurities and the platinum is dissolved in dilute aqua regia with gentle heating, leaving the iridium as metallic iridium. The platinum solution is evaporated as described above and precipitated with $NH_4Cl$ as $(NH_4)_2PtCl_6$.

If the platinum and iridium are precipitated together, the salts are filtered and washed with ammonium chloride solution and finally ignited. The sponge is redissolved and evaporated as above to expel the $HNO_3$. The platinum and the iridium are precipitated with NaOH, which brings down the platinum and iridium as $Pt(OH)_4$ and $Ir(OH)_4$. Boil this mixture with alcohol, which reduces the $Ir(OH)_4$ to $Ir(OH)_3$, but does not affect the $Pt(OH)_4$. Dissolve these hydroxides in HCl, forming $PtCl_4$ and $IrCl_3$ in solution, and the platinum is precipitated with $NH_4Cl$ free from iridium.

See "Deville-Stas-Gilchrist Method" on page 891, also "Separations" on page 890.

*Separation of Platinum from Palladium.* Platinum is precipitated with ammonium chloride, and palladium is precipitated from the filtrate by means of 1% alcoholic dimethylglyoxime solution.

Palladium may be precipitated in presence of platinum by adding a 1% solution of dimethylglyoxime (1% salt in 95% alcohol) to the cold, slightly acid chloride solution of the elements. If the solution is hot the palladium precipitate will be badly contaminated with platinum.

*Separation of Platinum from Ruthenium.*—From the chloride solution of platinum and ruthenium the metals are precipitated with ammonium or potassium chloride and filtered. The filter is washed with dilute ammonium chloride solution and alcohol until free from ruthenium. If a large quantity is handled it may be necessary to ignite to platinum sponge and dissolve in aqua regia, expel the $HNO_3$ as described above, and reprecipitate with $NH_4Cl$, filter, and wash free from ruthenium. (See also page 895.)

*Separation of Platinum from Rhodium.*—The separation is accomplished by adding freshly precipitated barium carbonate to the chloride solution of platinum and rhodium, previously brought nearly to the neutral point by addition of sodium hydroxide. After boiling for 2 or 3 minutes rhodium hydroxide precipitates. The precipitate is filtered off, dissolved in HCl, the solution again nearly neutralized and the rhodium precipitation repeated.

Other platinum metals will also precipitate if present. These should be removed prior to the separation of platinum and rhodium. (E. Wichers.) See Section on Rhodium.

*Separation of Platinum from Osmium.*—Both metals are reduced with zinc as a fine black powder. The metallic residue is washed and carefully ignited at a high temperature under a hood, as the fumes are poisonous and disagreeable like chlorine. The osmium will be converted into $OsO_4$, which is very volatile. The residue is dissolved in aqua regia and the platinum is precipitated with $NH_4Cl$. See Section on Osmium.

## GRAVIMETRIC METHODS

### WEIGHING AS METALLIC PLATINUM

1. When the platinum contains only a small amount of impurities a sample of 0.1 g. or more is taken and dissolved in aqua regia. The solution is gently heated until all is dissolved, adding another portion of aqua regia if necessary. The solution is evaporated, adding HCl from time to time in order to expel the $HNO_3$. Filter and evaporate again to concentrate the solution. Precipitate with ammonium chloride. After stirring, let stand until the precipitate, $(NH_4)_2PtCl_6$, settles, overnight if convenient. Filter, wash with alcohol or ammonium chloride solution and alcohol, and ignite to metal very slowly. Cool in a desiccator and weigh as metallic platinum.

$$\frac{\text{Wt. of Pt found}}{\text{Wt. of sample taken}} \times 100 = \text{Percentage of Pt in the material}$$

2. When the platinum solution contains a large amount of impurities, as iron, nickel, magnesia, etc., it is advisable to reduce the platinum to black metallic platinum with zinc, iron, or magnesium as follows: The solution is made acid (2 to 5% free HCl) by adding HCl. The Zn, Fe or Mg is added in small quantities at a time until the solution becomes colorless or until the platinum is completely precipitated.[1] After action has ceased the platinum black metal is filtered onto an ashless filter paper and washed with warm dilute HCl to remove any excess Zn, Fe, or Mg that might be present. The filter and its contents are carefully ignited and afterwards dissolved in aqua regia and treated as directed under 1.

3. If none of the other Hydrogen Sulfide Group metals is present the platinum can be precipitated by hydrogen sulfide, filtered, washed with hot water and ignited to metal.[2] If impurities are present in the sulfide, dissolve in aqua regia and proceed as under the first paragraph. The solution should be boiling and have an acidity of 3% HCl or $H_2SO_4$.

4. After distilling off the osmium and ruthenium as described under these metals, the solution containing the other platinum metals in the distilling flask is transferred to a liter beaker. HCl is added cautiously and the contents evapo-

---

[1] $FeCl_3$ in presence of HCl has a solvent action on platinum, hence the iron should be completely reduced.

[2] The ignition should be finished at a high temperature as it is very difficult to get rid of all the sulfur.

rated several times with additional HCl. If the flask is stained by $IrO_2$, clean it by adding 5 to 10 ml. of aqua regia and evaporate several times with HCl to get rid of the $HNO_3$. Add this to the main solution and evaporate it as far as possible on the steam bath and then dilute to 200 ml. with water.

Heat the solution containing platinum, palladium, rhodium, and iridium to boiling, and add to it 20 ml. of a filtered 10% solution of sodium bromate. Carefully add a filtered 10% solution of sodium bicarbonate until the dark green solution shows evidence of the formation of a permanent precipitate. Test the acidity of the hot solution from time to time by allowing a drop of bromcresol purple indicator solution (0.01%) to run down the stirring rod into the drop which clings to it as it is lifted from the solution. Enough bicarbonate has been added when the color of the indicator changes from yellow to blue. At this stage, add 10 ml. more of the bromate reagent and boil the solution for 5 minutes. Increase the pH of the solution slightly by carefully adding dropwise bicarbonate solution until a faint pink color is produced in the test drop by a drop of cresol red indicator solution (0.01%). Again add 10 ml. of the bromate reagent and boil for fifteen minutes.

On removing the beaker from the source of the heat, the mixed precipitate will settle quickly, leaving a mother liquor containing the platinum. Filter the solution by suction, using a porcelain filtering crucible having solid walls and a porous base.

It is highly desirable to avoid the use of filter paper when repeated precipitations are to be made. The material of which the paper is composed undoubtedly reacts with acids and probably forms small quantities of organic compounds with the platinum metals which are not easily hydrolyzed. Iridium dioxide, which dissolves much less readily than either palladium or rhodium dioxide, tends to stain paper pulp. The stain cannot always be removed by washing. These difficulties are avoided if the porcelain filtering crucible is used. Furthermore, such crucibles have the advantage that concentrated HCl can be used to dissolve the hydrated dioxides, and considerable time is saved in preparing the solution for subsequent treatment.

Pour the supernatant liquid through first, then transfer the precipitate. Rinse the beaker and wash the precipitate with a hot 1% solution of sodium chloride, the acidity of which has been adjusted to between pH 6 and 7. Place the crucible with the precipitate, and also the stirring rod, in the beaker used for the precipitation. It may be necessary to remove a small amount of the precipitate which has crept over the lip of the beaker during filtration. It is preferable to do this with moistened crystals of sodium chloride, on the finger, rather than to use paper or a rubber policeman. Replace the watch glass and add from 10 to 20 ml. of HCl, pouring most of it into the crucible. Place the covered beaker on the steam bath. The rhodium and palladium compounds will dissolve quickly, the iridium dioxide much more slowly. Carefully lift the crucible with the stirring rod, wash it with water and place it in a 250-ml. beaker. Pour 5 ml. of HCl into the crucible. Cover the beaker with a watch glass and set it on the steam bath. This treatment will usually leach out the small quantity of metal chlorides in the porous bottom. This operation should be repeated with fresh acid to ensure complete removal. Combine the leachings with the main portion of the dissolved precipitate, add 2 g. of sodium chloride, and evaporate to dryness on the steam bath. Add 2 ml. of HCl, dilute the solution to 300 ml. with water, and repeat the precipitation of the hydrated dioxides. Two such precipitations are sufficient ordinarily to effect the complete separation of platinum from palladium, rhodium and iridium.

Add 20 ml. of HCl to each of the filtrates obtained from the hydrolytic precipitation of the dioxides of palladium, rhodium, and iridium. Carefully warm the solutions until they become quiescent. Partially concentrate the filtrates, combine them and then evaporate to dryness. Make certain that all of the bromate is destroyed, by evaporation with HCl. Dilute the yellow platinum solution somewhat and filter it. Wash the filter with diluted HCl (1:99). Dilute the filtered solution to about 400 ml. with water and have it contain 5 ml. of HCl in each 100 ml. volume.

Precipitate the platinum, in a hot solution, with hydrogen sulfide, using a rapid stream. Continue the passage of hydrogen sulfide as the solution cools somewhat, to ensure complete precipitation.

Filter the solution and wash the precipitate with diluted HCl (1:99). Ignite the dried filter and precipitate in a porcelain crucible. Leach the metal residue with diluted HCl, transfer it to a filter and wash it thoroughly with hot water. Ignite the filter and metal again strongly in air. Weigh the residue as metallic platinum.[3]

## WEIGHING AS A SALT

1. The procedure is the same as described above. The $(NH_4)_2PtCl_6$ precipitate is washed on a weighed Gooch crucible with alcohol. The crucible and contents are dried at a temperature below 100°C. Cool in a desiccator and weigh as $(NH_4)_2PtCl_6$.

Wt. of $(NH_4)_2PtCl_6$ found $\times \dfrac{195.09}{443.91} \times \dfrac{100}{\text{Wt. of sample}}$ = Percentage of Pt in material[4]

2. After proceeding as described under "Weighing as Metallic Platinum," the platinum is precipitated with potassium chloride as $K_2PtCl_6$. Transfer to a weighed Gooch crucible and wash well with alcohol. Dry below 100°C., cool in a desiccator and weigh as $K_2PtCl_6$.

Wt. of $K_2PtCl_6$ found $\times \dfrac{195.09}{486.03} \times \dfrac{100}{\text{Wt. of sample}}$ = Percentage of Pt in material[5]

## DETERMINATION OF IRIDIUM, PALLADIUM, PLATINUM, AND RHODIUM IN DENTAL GOLD ALLOYS [6]

The alloys are usually in the form of wires, bands or plates. These should be rolled out to a ribbon or sheet 0.003 to 0.005 inch thick. These rolled pieces are then clipped to short lengths or small squares one-sixteenth to one-eighth of an inch in size.

A sample of 0.5 gram to 2 grams is taken at random from these small pieces, and dissolved at a low temperature in about 25 ml. of dilute aqua regia (1 part aqua regia to 1 part $H_2O$) in a 250-ml. beaker. Silver chloride will remain as an insoluble residue, which should be broken up from time to time with a glass rod until the alloy is completely decomposed. Add 150 to 200 ml. of water and digest

---

[3] Gilchrist and Wichers, J. Am. Chem. Soc., **57**, 2565, 1935.
[4] Factor $(NH_4)_2PtCl_6$ to Pt = 0.4395.
[5] Factor $K_2PtCl_6$ to Pt = 0.4014.
[6] Swanger, William H., Bureau of Standards. Scientific Papers of the Bureau of Standards, No. 532, 1926.

for about an hour. Set aside to cool until the supernatant liquid is perfectly clear, then the silver chloride is filtered off, washed well with water, and hot dilute $NH_4OH$ (1:1) is poured on the paper in successive portions until no more of the silver chloride can be seen. The iridium will be left on the paper as a black metallic residue. The platinum, rhodium, and palladium that were present will be in solution with the silver chloride. After washing the paper and iridium residue several times with hot 1% $NH_4OH$, place the paper and residue in a small beaker, add 15 to 25 ml. of dilute $NH_4OH$, and digest for half an hour. Filter through a small paper and wash well with hot 1% $NH_4OH$. Transfer the paper and residue to a weighed porcelain crucible for the determination of iridium. This residue is ignited in air to burn off the paper, then reduced in hydrogen and weighed as metallic iridium.

When the weight of the residue amounts to not more than 0.2 or 0.3% of the sample, the amount of platinum that is with the iridium is so small that it may be neglected. When larger amounts of iridium are present it is usually necessary to separate the platinum in the residue from iridium. (See page 891—"Method of Deville and Stas.")

Unite the two ammoniacal filtrates and acidify with $HNO_3$ to reprecipitate the silver chloride. This is filtered off and washed well with warm water. The filtrate is evaporated to dryness and cautiously add HCl, and again evaporate the residue to a small volume and transfer to a porcelain crucible where the residue is evaporated to dryness. Add about 10 grams of sodium pyrosulfate and fuse the mixture for about a half hour at a red heat, cool, and dissolve the melt in hot water. Pass $H_2S$ through the solution for about a half hour while it is heated to incipient boiling on the hot plate. Filter off the platinum, rhodium, and palladium sulfides, wash and ignite to metal in a porcelain crucible. Dissolve the residue in the crucible in a few milliliters of dilute aqua regia, filter off any silica, and add the solution to the main portion of the samples before the determination of the metals is made. If the original alloy contains no tin the above solution is evaporated to dryness and taken up with a little water followed by 10 ml. HCl. Dilute to about 200 ml., add about 50 ml. of a saturated solution of $SO_2$ in water and digest for about an hour. Additional $SO_2$ solution (10 to 20 ml.) is added and the solution is set aside to cool. The supernatant liquid is poured through a tight paper which has been treated with filter paper pulp. Wash the gold thoroughly in the beaker by decantation with hot 1% of HCl. The paper is washed thoroughly and together with the small amount of gold caught on it, is returned to the beaker. This gold precipitate is dissolved in 20 ml. of dilute aqua regia, filtered and washed with hot 1% HCl. The solution is then evaporated to dryness at a low temperature. Take up with 2 or 3 ml. HCl and again evaporate to dryness. Repeat until $HNO_3$ is eliminated. The residue is taken up with 5 ml. HCl, 8 to 10 drops $H_2SO_4$, and 150 ml. $H_2O$. Fifty ml. of a saturated solution of oxalic acid is added and the solution is boiled for not more than 15 minutes as prolonged boiling will precipitate some of the platinum or palladium. Ten ml. more of the oxalic acid is added and the solution is boiled for a minute or two, then is set on the steam bath for not less than four hours. Filter off the gold precipitate on a paper that has been treated with filter-paper pulp. Wash the beaker and the paper with the gold precipitate thoroughly with hot water.

The filtrate is evaporated to dryness, 5 ml. $H_2SO_4$ is added and again evaporated on the hot plate until nearly all the $H_2SO_4$ has been driven off. The oxalic acid will thus be eliminated.

The residue is digested with 10 ml. dilute aqua regia until all of the precipitated metals are again dissolved. The solution is filtered off from any silica (from the glassware) and added to the filtrate from the first precipitation of the gold. This solution is evaporated to dryness at a low temperature and the residue is digested with 10 ml. dilute aqua regia until all of it is in solution. Dilute to about 250 ml. and cool to room temperature. Enough of a 1% solution of dimethylglyoxime in alcohol is added to precipitate all of the palladium. The solution must not be heated as some of the platinum may be precipitated. After standing for one hour the precipitate is filtered off on a paper of suitable size and washed well with hot water. Additional reagent is added to the filtrate to ascertain whether or not all of the palladium has been precipitated. The precipitate with the paper is returned to the beaker and dissolved, on the steam bath, in 25 ml. of dilute aqua regia. The paper pulp is filtered off, washed with hot water, and ignited in a porcelain crucible. Any metallic residue is dissolved in the crucible with a few ml. of dilute aqua regia and the solution is added to the main solution of the palladium. This solution is diluted to about 250 ml. and the palladium is precipitated as before. The precipitate is filtered on a Gooch crucible, washed thoroughly with hot water, dried at 110°C., and weighed. The weight of the precipitate multiplied by 0.3167 gives the weight of palladium.

The precipitate can be filtered on a paper, and after washing and allowing to drain, the paper with the precipitate is removed from the funnel and carefully wrapped in another ashless filter paper. The whole is placed in a porcelain crucible and dried at a temperature not exceeding 110°C. Heat gently in hydrogen to decompose the compound. Ignite the paper in air and the residue is reduced to metallic palladium by heating strongly for several minutes in an atmosphere of hydrogen, and letting it cool very gradually. Weigh as metallic palladium.

The filtrates from the precipitation of palladium are united and evaporated to dryness. The excess of dimethylglyoxime is destroyed by adding about 5 ml. $HNO_3$ and digesting on the steam bath. The solution is again evaporated to dryness and the residue digested with 10 ml. HCl and enough water to dissolve the salts present.

The copper is precipitated at this time as cuprous thiocyanate. Palladium shows some tendency to contaminate the precipitate of cuprous thiocyanate. For this reason it is recommended that palladium be separated before the determination of copper is made. If the cuprous thiocyanate is contaminated with platinum the precipitate should be dissolved and reprecipitated.

The filtrate or filtrates from the precipitation of copper are evaporated to dryness. The excess of thiocyanate is destroyed by adding 5 to 10 ml. $HNO_3$ and digesting the mixture at a low temperature for about half an hour. The solution is again evaporated to dryness. The $HNO_3$ is completely expelled by heating the residue on the hot plate with 5 or 10 ml. $H_2SO_4$ until fumes of $H_2SO_4$ appear. The residue is cooled and digested with 29 ml. of dilute HCl. The solution is finally diluted to about 100 ml. and boiled to put all of the platinum compounds in solution. The solution will usually contain a small amount of silica. This is filtered off and ignited in a porcelain crucible. The residue is leached with dilute aqua regia to dissolve the small amount of platinum it usually contains. This solution is evaporated separately to expel the $HNO_3$ and is then taken up with HCl and added to the main solution containing the platinum. This solution contains the platinum as well as rhodium and impurities.

Precipitate the platinum and the rhodium with $H_2S$ as described before. If rhodium is absent the platinum sulfide is filtered off, ignited to metal and weighed as platinum.

When great accuracy is desired, this ignited sponge is dissolved in 10 ml. of dilute aqua regia and the solution is evaporated to dryness on the steam bath. $HNO_3$ is expelled by adding 2 or 3 ml. HCl and repeating the evaporation to dryness. The residue is taken up with 20 ml. of dilute HCl and 2 or 3 ml. $H_2SO_4$. The solution is diluted to about 300 ml. and the precipitation of the platinum with $H_2S$ is repeated. In this way any error due to the presence of alkali salts in the first precipitate is eliminated.

If rhodium is present the sulfides of platinum and rhodium are filtered off and ignited, first in air, then in hydrogen, and weighed as metallic platinum plus rhodium.

The weighed sponge is transferred to a beaker and digested on the steam bath with 15 to 20 ml. of aqua regia. A little of the acid should be poured into the crucible in which the sponge was ignited to dissolve any metal adhering to the walls. The sponge generally dissolves completely. If there is a residue the solution is poured off and the residue is washed by decantation. Fresh portions of acid are added until it is certain that no more of the residue will dissolve. The residue may be considered to be rhodium. It is filtered off and ignited in the weighed porcelain crucible that is to be used for the determination of rhodium.

The solution of platinum and rhodium is evaporated nearly to dryness to expel most of the excess acids and is then diluted to about 200 ml. The free acid in the solution is neutralized with sodium hydroxide solution, using 4 to 8 drops of a 0.4 solution of cresol red as indicator. The alkaline color of the indicator need not persist for more than a few seconds. A freshly prepared mixture consisting of 5 ml. of a solution containing 90 g. of crystallized barium chloride per liter, and 5 ml. of a solution containing 36 grams of anhydrous sodium carbonate per liter is added to precipitate the rhodium. After the suspension of barium carbonate is added the solution is rapidly heated to boiling and boiled for two minutes. The residue is filtered off, washed several times with a hot 2% solution of sodium chloride, returned, together with the paper, to the beaker, and digested with 25 ml. HCl (1:4) until solution is complete. The presence of barium carbonate with the rhodium hydroxide may be noted by the evolution of $CO_2$ when the acid is added. If no barium carbonate is present the platinum-rhodium solution should be given a second treatment. If the first precipitate contains barium carbonate the filtrate may be acidified with HCl and set aside for the subsequent recovery of platinum.

After the mixture of barium carbonate and rhodium hydroxide has dissolved in HCl, the solution is diluted somewhat and filtered from the paper pulp. The solution is again treated with barium carbonate exactly as before. Care should be taken not to add an excess of NaOH in the preliminary neutralization. If the amount of rhodium present is very small, it is better to leave the solution slightly acid before adding barium carbonate. The period of boiling should be extended to three minutes. The precipitate is handled as before and a third precipitation made if desired. For mixtures of platinum and rhodium containing 1% or less of rhodium, two precipitations should be sufficient, unless the first precipitate was for some reason unduly contaminated with platinum.

The final solution of rhodium chloride and barium chloride is diluted to about 150 ml. It contains about 5 ml. HCl. Rhodium is precipitated as sulfide by passing a fairly rapid stream of $H_2S$ for 30 to 45 minutes while the solution is heated to incipient boiling on the hot plate. The precipitated rhodium sulfide should be filtered off at once. If the solution is allowed to stand for some time after precipitation is completed, some of the barium present may be converted to sulfate and be included with the rhodium sulfide. The precipitate is washed with a hot 1% solution of $NH_4Cl$. The filtrate and wash water are discarded. The precipitate and paper are ignited in the crucible containing the insoluble residue from the solution of the mixed platinum-rhodium sponge. The ignited sulfide is finally reduced and cooled in an atmosphere of hydrogen. The residue is weighed as metallic rhodium. It should have a clean, light-gray color. The weight of rhodium thus obtained is subtracted from the weight of the mixed sponge of platinum and rhodium to get the weight of platinum in the sample.

The determination of Ag, Sn, Au, Cu, Zn, Ni, Mn, Fe, and Mg have been omitted. If these metals are desired, consult the original reference.[6]

# PALLADIUM

Pd *at. wt.* 106.4; *d.* 12.16; *m.p.* 1549°C.; *b.p.* 2200°C.; *oxides*, PdO, PdO$_2$

## DETECTION

This metal is also found associated with platinum and iridium as well as ruthenium, rhodium, and osmium. It occurs in the metallic state sometimes with gold and silver. It resembles platinum as to luster and color. Palladium sponge when heated slightly gives a rainbow effect due to the formation of oxides. Hydrogen passed over the sponge restores it to the original color. It dissolves in HNO$_3$ and boiling H$_2$SO$_4$. HCl has little action upon it. It is readily soluble in aqua regia, forming PdCl$_2$. PdCl$_4$ is unstable.

Palladium monoxide, PdO, is formed by a long-continued heating of the spongy metal in a current of oxygen at a temperature from 700 to 840°C. or by heating a mixture of a palladium salt with potassium carbonate. The pure hydrated oxide is best prepared by the hydrolysis of the nitrate.

It turns diphenylamine blue; and it reduces hydrogen peroxide with difficulty.[7]

Palladium dioxide, PdO$_2$, is obtained in an impure hydrated form as a brown precipitate by the addition of caustic soda to potassium chloropalladate. This is soluble in acids, but becomes less soluble when preserved. It can be obtained free from alkali and basic salts by the anodic oxidation of the nitrate, but it is not quite free from monoxide. The dioxide very readily decomposes into the monoxide and oxygen, and cannot be obtained in the anhydrous state. It acts as a vigorous oxidizing agent and decomposes hydrogen peroxide.

*Alkalies* precipitate in a concentrated solution a dark-brown precipitate soluble in an excess of the reagent. If boiled a brown palladous hydroxide is precipitated. The anhydrous oxide is black.

*Ammonium hydroxide* added to a concentrated solution gives a flesh-red precipitate, Pd(NH$_3$)$_4$Cl$_2$·PdCl$_2$, soluble in excess of ammonium hydroxide. If HCl is added to this solution, the yellow compound of palladosammine chloride, Pd(NH$_3$Cl)$_2$, is deposited.

*Sulfur dioxide* precipitates the metal from the nitrate or sulfate solution but not from the chloride.

*Cuprous chloride* precipitates the metal from the sulfate, nitrate and chloride solutions when they are not too strongly acid.

*Mercuric cyanide* precipitates a yellowish-white gelatinous precipitate, Pd(CN)$_2$, insoluble in dilute acids, but dissolving in ammonia and in potassium cyanide to K$_2$Pd(CN)$_4$.

*Potassium iodide* precipitates black palladous iodide, PdI$_2$, insoluble in water, alcohol, and ether, but soluble in an excess of reagent.

*Hydrogen sulfide* precipitates black palladous sulfide, PdS, soluble in HCl and aqua regia, but insoluble in (NH$_4$)$_2$S.

[7] A Comprehensive Treatise on Inorganic and Theoretical Chemistry, J. W. Mellor, Vol. XV, p. 656, 1936.

*Ferrous sulfate* slowly produces a black precipitate of metallic palladium from the nitrate.

*Ammonium chloride* precipitates palladium as $(NH_4)_2PdCl_4$ from the nitrate.

*Formic acid, zinc and iron* reduce it to metallic palladium.

*Soluble carbonates* precipitate brown palladous hydroxide, $Pd(OH)_2$, soluble in excess, and reprecipitated on boiling.

*Phosphine* precipitates palladium phosphide. (Difference from Pt, Rh, and Ir).

*Alcohol* precipitates, on boiling metallic palladium.

*Alkaline tartrates and citrates* form yellow precipitates in a neutral solution from the nitrate.

*Stannous chloride* produces a brownish-black precipitate, soluble in hydrochloric acid to an intense green solution.

*Potassium bisulfate* attacks the metal readily.

*An alcoholic solution of iodine* dropped on the metal will turn black.

*Acetylene gas* passed through an acidified solution containing Pd produces a brown precipitate which, upon ignition, yields Pd. In this way Pd may be quantitatively separated from Cu.

## ESTIMATION

Palladium is determined in alloys, ores, jewelers' sweeps, etc.

## PREPARATION AND SOLUTION OF THE SAMPLE

The solubility of palladium has been taken up under "Detection." Palladium when alloyed with platinum, or an alloy of platinum, iridium and palladium, dissolves with the other metals in aqua regia as the chloride. When palladium is alloyed with silver the palladium and silver are dissolved in $HNO_3$, from which the silver can be separated.

## SEPARATIONS

*Separation of Palladium from Platinum and Iridium.*—The chlorides of palladium, platinum, and iridium in solution must be free from $HNO_3$. The platinum and the iridium are precipitated with $NH_4Cl$, leaving the palladium in solution. The precipitate is put on a filter and washed free from Pd with $NH_4Cl$ solution and alcohol.

*Separation of Palladium from Silver and Gold.*—By weight at least three times as much silver as gold should be present in the alloy in order to separate the silver and palladium from the gold. The silver and the palladium will dissolve in $HNO_3$, leaving the gold as the residue. This is filtered off and the silver may be precipitated with HCl. The silver chloride is filtered off and washed with hot water acidulated with HCl until free from palladium. Since AgCl tends to retain palladium it is advisable to redissolve the silver with $HNO_3$ after reduction of AgCl and reprecipitate the chloride to obtain a complete separation of palladium.

*Separation of Palladium from Platinum.*—The chlorides of platinum and palladium being free from $HNO_3$ and having an excess of HCl are diluted with water. A 10% solution of potassium iodide is added until all of the palladium is precipitated. Avoid adding a large excess. The precipitate of $PdI_2$ is filtered off and washed free from platinum and alkali with water slightly acidulated with HCl.

The filter is ignited to metallic sponge in a current of hydrogen. See "Dimethylglyoxime Method," below.

## GRAVIMETRIC METHODS

### ZINC-AMMONIUM CHLORIDE METHOD

*Procedure.*—The palladium is precipitated from the solution by granulated zinc, the solution having a small amount of free hydrochloric acid. The residue, after the zinc is dissolved, is put on a filter and washed free from impurities. Ignite the filter and dissolve in a small amount of aqua regia and evaporate to a syrupy consistency. Dilute with a small amount of water and add a few drops of $HNO_3$; precipitate the palladium with $NH_4Cl$ crystals. Heat for a few minutes and let cool. Filter, wash with alcohol, and ignite. Reduce in hydrogen or moisten with formic acid to reduce to metal any oxide that may have formed. Dry and weigh as metallic Pd.

### IODIDE METHOD

*Procedure.*—With the solution containing about one-fifth the volume of free HCl, the palladium is precipitated with 10% KI solution. Heat nearly to boiling, filter, wash free from iron, etc., with 1:4 HCl. Ignite, cool, reduce in hydrogen or moisten with formic acid, dry, and weigh as metallic Pd.

### DIMETHYLGLYOXIME METHOD FOR PALLADIUM

*Procedure.*—The filtrate from the platinum precipitation or the nearly neutral solution containing the Pd is made to about 150 ml., and the Pd is precipitated by adding a solution of dimethylglyoxime (1% solution in alcohol). Bring to boiling and let stand overnight if convenient. Filter on a weighed Gooch crucible and wash with hot water slightly acidified with HCl, then with alcohol. Dry and weigh as $(C_8H_{14}N_4O_4)Pd$, which contains 31.69% Pd.

### DIMETHYLGLYOXIME METHOD FOR PALLADIUM, RHODIUM, AND IRIDIUM

*Procedure.*—The hydrated dioxides of palladium, rhodium, and iridium, after separating the platinum, are dissolved in HCl. Filter the solution and dilute it to a volume of about 400 ml. Add a sufficient volume of a 1% solution of dimethylglyoxime in 95% ethyl alcohol to precipitate all of the palladium (2.2 g. of the solid reagent is required for 1 g. of palladium). An excess of the reagent amounting to 10% should be added to ensure complete precipitation. Let the solution stand for one hour and then filter it. The manner of filtration will depend upon the form in which the palladium is to be determined. Wash the precipitate with dilute HCl (1:99), and finally with hot water. The precipitate can be washed with a considerable volume of water without a trace of it dissolving. A single precipitation of the palladium is sufficient to separate it completely from rhodium and iridium.

Palladium dimethylglyoxime is sufficiently stable and constant in composition to be dried and weighed. If the determination is to be made in this manner, catch the precipitate in a porcelain or glass filtering crucible, using suction. Wash the precipitate as previously directed and dry it at 110°C. for one hour. Calculate the quantity of palladium, using the theoretical factor, 0.3167.

If the palladium is to be determined as metal, catch the precipitate on an ashless filter. Wipe the inner walls of the beaker and also the glass rod with a small piece of ashless paper. Wrap the filter and precipitate in a second filter and place them in a porcelain crucible. Dry them and ignite them carefully in the air. Only sufficient heat should be supplied to keep the papers smoking gently. Ignite the charred residue strongly in air and then in hydrogen. Ignite the metallic palladium in $CO_2$ for two minutes and cool it in $CO_2$. Weigh the residue as metallic Pd.[8]

## CYANIDE METHOD

*Procedure.*—The nitric acid in the palladium solution is expelled by evaporating with HCl. Neutralize the chloride solution almost completely with sodium carbonate and mix the solution with a solution of mercuric cyanide, $Hg(CN)_2$, and heat gently for some time. Let stand until cool, overnight if convenient. A yellowish-white precipitate of $Pd(CN)_2$ is formed. Filter, wash with 1% $Hg(CN)_2$ solution, ignite and reduce in hydrogen to metal, or reduce with formic acid, dry, and weigh as metallic Pd.

## FORMIC ACID METHOD

*Procedure.*—The filtrate from the platinum precipitation is made neutral or slightly alkaline with $Na_2CO_3$ solution and an excess of formic acid is added. Boil until all the palladium is precipitated or the solution becomes clear. Filter, wash with hot water, ignite, reduce in hydrogen or with formic acid and weigh as metallic Pd.

## NIOXIME (1,2-CYCLOHEXANEDIONE DIOXIME) METHOD

*Procedure.*—Adjust the volume of the solution containing from 5 to 20 mg. of palladium to approximately 200 ml. The pH of the solution may vary from 1 to 5, depending upon other cations present. Heat the solution to about 60°C. Add slowly from a pipette with stirring 0.43 ml. of 0.8% Nioxime (1,2-cyclohexanedione dioxime) for each milligram of palladium present. Digest the solution with occasional stirring for 30 minutes at 60°C., filter through a weighed filter crucible of medium porosity, and wash with five portions of hot water. Dry at 110°C. for 1 hour and weigh. The factor for palladium is 0.2737.

The reagent offers several advantages over dimethylglyoxime as a precipitant for palladium. Nioxime is soluble in water, in contrast to dimethylglyoxime which must be dissolved in alcohol, and the possibility of contamination of the palladium precipitate with excess reagent is eliminated. Palladium nioxime, $Pd(C_6H_9O_2N_2)_2$, is very insoluble and may be filtered from a hot solution after a brief digestion period, which is a great saving of time with no sacrifice of accuracy.[9]

## DETERMINATION OF PLATINUM AND PALLADIUM IN BULLION, SILVER, AND GOLD [10]

### GOLD BULLION

*Procedure.*—Dissolve a 100-g. sample in aqua regia, and expel the nitric acid by evaporation and the addition of small amounts of hydrochloric acid. Take

[8] Gilchrist and Wichers, J. Am. Chem. Soc., **57**, 2565, 1935.
[9] Voter, Roger C., Banks, Charles V., and Diehl, Harvey, Analytical Chemistry, **20**, 7, 652, 1948.
[10] Contributed by F. Jaeger, Chemist, Nichols Copper Co.

up with a few milliliters of dilute hydrochloric acid.  If there should be present a large amount of reduced gold, add a few drops of nitric acid and heat the solution for a few minutes.  Dilute to 800 ml. with water and let it stand in a cool place until solution clears.  Filter off silver chloride and wash it with cold water.  Pass sulfur dioxide gas through the filtrate to reduce the gold (palladium, etc., is also reduced).  Decant the clear solution on a  Whatman No. 42 filter paper, and wash several times with hot water by decantation.  Then pour over the gold in the beaker, 50 ml. of nitric acid, and boil for a few minutes to dissolve the reduced palladium.  Add 50 ml. of hot water and filter on the same filter paper and wash several times with hot water.  Add 15 ml. of sulfuric acid to the filtrate, evaporate, and heat to heavy fumes.  Cool, dilute to 200 ml. with water, and boil for a few minutes, and filter off any gold and lead sulfate if present. Now pass hydrogen sulfide gas through the hot solution to precipitate the sulfides of platinum and palladium, etc.  Filter and wash with hot water.  Place the filter paper with the precipitate in a porcelain crucible, dry, burn, and ignite.  Now touch the residue with the reducing flame of a Bunsen burner to reduce to metal any oxide of palladium that may have formed.  Dissolve the residue with a few milliliters of aqua regia, and transfer the solution to a tall 300-ml. beaker, and evaporate carefully to dryness on a steam or sand bath.  Then moisten the residue with hydrochloric acid and evaporate to dryness again.  Moisten the dry residue once more with hydrochloric acid and evaporate to dryness.

Now take up with 16 ml. of hydrochloric acid and 4 ml. of water, cover beaker, and boil gently for a moment.  Fiter on a small filter paper and wash with a small stream of hot water.  Discard the residue.  Dilute filtrate to 60-ml., cover beaker, and heat to near boiling point.  Then add 16 g. of ammonium chloride and heat gently to near boiling until all ammonium chloride is in solution.  Remove beaker from the hot plate and let it stand overnight in a cool place.  Filter rapidly (using suction) on a tight, double filter paper, and wash with ammonium chloride solution (200 g. per liter of water).  As the ammonium chloroplatinate is somewhat soluble if exposed to air, the precipitate should be covered with the wash solution all the time during filtration.  Then before the ammonium chloride solution is all sucked through, wash once or twice with 95% ethyl alcohol.  Save filtrate for palladium determination.  Place the filter paper with the precipitate in a porcelain crucible, so that the precipitate does not come in contact with the sides of the crucible; if it does, a platinum mirror will form, which cannot be removed.  Dry gently and smoke off the filter paper (without burning it with a flame), and finally ignite at a bright red heat.  Cool and weigh metallic Pt.

Add to the filtrate from the ammonium chloroplatinate precipitate, 16 ml. of nitric acid, stir, cover beaker, placing a glass triangle under the watch glass, and let it stand overnight on steam plate.  When the solution is supersaturated, as indicated when half of the solution is filled with ammonia salts, remove the beaker from the steam plate and cool the solution.  Filter off the ammonium chloropalladate just like the platinum salt and wash with ammonium nitrate solution (200 g. per liter of water).  Finally wash with 95% grain alcohol.  The solubility of ammonium chloropalladate is greater than of the platinum salt when exposed to air, therefore great care must be taken in filtering it.  Place the precipitate with the filter paper in a porcelain crucible, dry, smoke off filter paper, and finally ignite at a bright red heat.  When cool, reduce any oxide that may have formed with the reducing flame of a Bunsen burner.  Cool and weigh metallic Pd.

To confirm that all platinum and palladium is precipitated, neutralize the filtrate from the ammonium chloropalladate with a saturated solution of sodium carbonate, then add 30 ml. of formic acid, and boil for about one hour. Any platinum or palladium if still present will be precipitated as black powder.

NOTE.—All evaporations should be made on a steam or sand bath; if not, incomplete precipitation of platinum will be obtained.

## REFINED SILVER

*Procedure.*—Weigh out 1000-g. sample and dissolve it with dilute nitric acid. Filter off the gold and any undissolved platinum, and then separate the gold from the platinum as described under "Gold Bullion," and add the solution to the main filtrate. Dilute the filtrate from the gold residue, so that there will be 10 g. of silver per liter of solution, and then add a slight excess of hydrochloric acid to precipitate all the silver. Stir well and let it settle. Decant the clear solution and wash the precipitate on a Buechner funnel with cold water. Evaporate the filtrate to a small volume. Now mix the silver chloride, with about ten times its weight, with soda ash (which contains a small amount of corn starch) and dry. Place the mass in 30-g. crucibles, and fuse for about 30 minutes. Pour in molds. When cool, hammer off excess of slag, and finally boil with hydrochloric acid to clean the silver buttons. Then dissolve with dilute nitric acid and precipitate silver as silver chloride as already described. Another silver chloride precipitation will be necessary to separate all platinum and palladium from the silver.

Combine all filtrates and evaporate to dryness on steam plate. Take up with a few milliliters of hydrochloric acid and water, filter off the silver chloride, and wash with cold water. This small amount of silver chloride carries down considerable platinum and palladium. Therefore place the filter paper with the silver chloride in a 3-inch scorifier, dry, add 40 g. of test lead and a pinch of borax and scorify. Then cupel the lead button. Dissolve the silver buttons with dilute nitric acid and reprecipitate silver with hydrochloric acid. Finally when the pure white color of the silver chloride indicates that it is free from platinum and palladium, evaporate the filtrate to dryness on steam plate. Take up with 16 ml. of hydrochloric acid and 4 ml. of water. Boil for a minute, filter, and precipitate platinum and palladium as described under "Gold Bullion."

## REFINED GOLD [11]

*Procedure.*—The sample may be in the shape of drillings, but from a bar it is easier to roll the gold into a thin ribbon.

Fifty grams [12] of gold sample is sufficient for gold which has been parted with sulfuric and nitric acids.

Dissolve sample in a 1500-ml. beaker with 50 ml. of nitric acid (sp. gr. 1.42) and 150 ml. of hydrochloric acid (sp. gr. 1.19) using no water. Heating is not necessary. After complete solution of the sample, evaporate solution to a syrup of about 40 ml. volume, taking care not to evaporate too far, otherwise, some gold will become reduced and separate out; add 100 ml. of hydrochloric acid and re-evaporate the solution to syrup, repeating this operation four times in order to remove all nitric acid.

[11] Contributed by S. Skowronski, Chemist, Raritan Copper Works, Perth Amboy, N. J.
[12] For gold which has been electrolytically refined by the Wohlwill process, 100 g. of gold should be taken as a sample, doubling the quantity of acid necessary for the solution.

After the last evaporation, dilute with hot water, boil, add about 50 ml. hydrochloric acid (sp. gr. 1.19) to clear up solution. The volume of solution should be about 500 ml.

To the boiling solution [13] gradually add a mixture of 50 g. ammonium oxalate and 50 g. oxalic acid, which should precipitate all the gold, but should there be any doubt add more of the mixture of the salts. Dilute the solution to about 1000 ml. in volume and allow to settle in a warm place overnight.

Filter off the gold, washing by decantation into a 1500-ml. beaker. For extreme accuracy, this gold may be redissolved, re-evaporated, and reprecipitated, this time with sulfur dioxide gas. This is more of a precautionary measure, for as a rule, no platinum or palladium will be found with the gold.

To the solution from the gold add 5 g. of 30-mesh C.P. zinc. This precipitates any gold left in the solution along with the silver, platinum, palladium, tellurium, copper, etc.

Filter as soon as precipitation is complete and wash by decantation keeping as much of the precipitate in the beaker as possible. Ignite filter paper and transfer residue and precipitate to a 250-ml. beaker, dissolve in 10 ml. aqua regia and after complete solution, add 5 ml. sulfuric acid (sp. gr. 1.84), evaporate to fumes of $SO_3$ and fume well,[14] cool, dilute to 100 ml., bring solution to boiling, and add 1 drop of hydrochloric acid to precipitate the silver, filter in a 400-ml. beaker, dilute filtrate to 200 ml. volume, add 5 ml. hydrochloric acid (sp. gr. 1.19), and precipitate palladium with 0.5 gram of dimethylglyoxime dissolved in 50 ml. of boiling water.[15]

Palladium dimethylglyoxime, canary yellow in color, which possesses the same physical characteristics as the corresponding nickel salt, at once separates out. Allow to settle in a warm place for about five minutes. Filter in a Gooch crucible, wash with hot water, dry at 110°C. and weigh. Factor 0.3161.

To the filtrate from the palladium add 2 g. of 30-mesh C.P. zinc, which precipitates the platinum. Filter, ignite precipitate, and dissolve in aqua regia. Remove nitric acid by three evaporations with hydrochloric acid (sp. gr. 1.19), taking care not to evaporate solution to dryness.[16] After the last evaporation, take up with not more than 10 ml. of water and a few drops of hydrochloric acid. If necessary, filter, keeping volume of 10 ml., add 2 g. of ammonium chloride, stir well, add 10 ml. of alcohol, and let stand one hour with an occasional stirring.

[13] Sulfur dioxide gas is not recommended for the precipitation of gold as gold bullions contain a trace of tellurium, and in the presence of tellurium, palladium is precipitated as a telluride by sulfur dioxide gas. The gold precipitated with oxalic acid is free from palladium telluride and therefore may be reprecipitated with sulfur dioxide gas if a reprecipitation is thought necessary.

[14] The platinum and palladium after solution in aqua regia, and addition of sulfuric acid, should be well fumed, in order to reduce any gold remaining in the solution to the metallic condition. It is very essential that all the gold is removed at this stage, otherwise it is liable to contaminate the palladium dimethylglyoxime.

[15] Palladium is best precipitated with dimethylglyoxime in a 3–5% acid solution; gold if present will be reduced to the metallic condition and should be removed beforehand. Alcohol is not recommended as the solvent for the dimethylglyoxime, as it slows up the precipitation of the palladium. A hot water solution works quicker, and should be filtered to remove insoluble matter before addition to the palladium solution.

The precipitation should be carried out in a cold solution, since platinum will contaminate the palladium precipitate if the dimethylglyoxime reagent is added to a hot solution.

[16] Any solutions containing platinum should never be evaporated to dryness, as platinum is easily reduced in baking to the "platinous" condition which is not precipitated with ammonium chloride.

Filter off ammonium chloroplatinate in small Gooch crucible and ignite to platinum in the usual manner.

**Separation of Platinum and Gold.**—In place of the procedures given on page 873 it is often preferable to precipitate gold first by means of sulfur dioxide, then reprecipitating with oxalic acid from weakly acid solution to obtain gold free from platinum.

**Separation of Platinum and Ruthenium.**—According to Deville and his coworkers the ammonium chloride separation is unsatisfactory owing to contamination of the ammonium chloroplatinate with ruthenium. The ruthenium may be separated by volatilization with chlorine passed into the alkaline solution of platinum and ruthenium. See page 895.

# IRIDIUM [17]

Ir *at. wt.* 192.2; *d.* 22.4; *m.p.* 2454°C.; *b.p.* 4800°+C.; *oxides*, $IrO_2$, $Ir_2O_3$

## DETECTION

Iridium is found associated with platinum. The element is insoluble in all acids, including aqua regia. Chlorine is the best reagent which forms the chlorides of iridium. If the element is heated in a stream of chlorine in the presence of potassium chloride there forms a salt, $K_2IrCl_6$, which is sparingly soluble and is used in the separation of iridium.

The oxide, $Ir_2O_3$, is formed when $K_2IrCl_6$ is mixed with sodium carbonate and gently fused at a dull red heat.

$$2K_2IrCl_6 + 4Na_2CO_3 \rightarrow Ir_2O_3 + 8NaCl + 4KCl + 4CO_2 + O$$

The fusion is dissolved in water containing ammonium chloride. Filter the residue and after igniting to expel the ammonium chloride, treat with dilute acid in order to remove the small quantity of alkali. A bluish-black powder is thus obtained which begins to decompose when heated above 800°C., and at temperatures somewhat above 1000°C. is completely broken up into oxygen and the metal.[18]

The dioxide, $IrO_2$, is a black powder obtained by heating the hydroxide in a current of carbon dioxide. It is insoluble in acids.[18]

*Caustic alkalies* produce in a boiling solution a dark-blue precipitate of $Ir(OH)_4$ insoluble in all acids except HCl.

*Potassium chloride* forms the double salt of $K_2IrCl_6$, which is black and is difficultly soluble in water.

*Ammonium chloride* precipitates black $(NH_4)_2IrCl_6$, which is difficultly soluble in water.

*Hydrogen sulfide* precipitates black $Ir_2S_3$, soluble in $(NH_4)_2S$.

*Metallic zinc* precipitates from an acid solution black metallic iridium.

*Formic acid and sulfurous acid* precipitate black metallic iridium from hot solutions.

*Lead acetate* gives a gray-brown precipitate.

## ESTIMATION

Substances in which iridium is determined are: platinum scrap, jewelers' sweeps, contact points, ores. Iridium is weighed as the metal.

### PREPARATION AND SOLUTION OF THE SAMPLE

Platinum scrap and contact points, etc., containing iridium dissolve with difficulty in aqua regia, depending on the amount of iridium present. The alloy is dissolved more quickly if it is rolled or hammered to a very thin sheet or ribbon.

[17] Chapter contributed by R. E. Hickman.
[18] Treatise on Chemistry, Roscoe and Schorlemmer.

The alloy of platinum and iridium with an iridium content up to 10% dissolves in aqua regia slowly; an alloy of iridium content of 15% dissolves in aqua regia very slowly and the aqua regia will likely have to be replenished from time to time. An alloy of 25% iridium is practically insoluble in aqua regia. The filings from sweeps, etc., can be dissolved by aqua regia the same as the scrap. After expelling the $HNO_3$ the platinum and the iridium are precipitated together with $NH_4Cl$ as $(NH_4)_2PtCl_6$ and $(NH_4)_2IrCl_6$. The iridium imparts a pinkish to a scarlet color to the salt.

If the iridium content is too high to be dissolved in aqua regia the metal can be mixed with NaCl, heated to a dull red heat in a porcelain or silica tube, and moist chlorine passed over the mixture. The iridium will be in the form of a double chloride which dissolves in water. After filtering the solution and evaporating with HCl, the iridium as well as the platinum is precipitated with $NH_4Cl$ or $H_2S$. This is a convenient way on a larger scale to dissolve osmiridium in ores.

When the iridium is contaminated with a large amount of impurities, it may be reduced from the solution with zinc, and the impurities dissolved by $HNO_3$ and dilute aqua regia; the residue is washed and dried as iridium.

Clean osmiridium grains are also brought into solution by sintering with $BaO_2$ and $Ba(NO_3)_2$ and dissolving in water acidulated with HCl. A fusion can be made with $KNO_3$, $NaNO_3$, or $Na_2O_2$ and NaOH or KOH yielding a soluble ruthenate and osmate, and leaving the iridium and rhodium as insoluble oxides.

## SEPARATIONS

*Separation of Iridium from Platinum.*—See "Separation of Platinum from Iridium" in Section on Platinum.

If the platinum and iridium are alloyed with at least ten times their weight of silver or lead and the alloy dissolved in $HNO_3$, the silver or lead and the platinum dissolve, leaving the iridium insoluble. After washing the residue, treat with a small amount of dilute aqua regia to dissolve any platinum that may be present. If the alloy contains more than a few milligrams of platinum, it will be necessary to add fine gold when cupelling to prevent the platinum from becoming colloidal.

If the alloy is made with silver only, hot concentrated $H_2SO_4$ can be used in place of $HNO_3$ to dissolve the silver. The iridium and platinum which are insoluble are treated with dilute aqua regia to remove the platinum leaving a residue of iridium and a small amount of silver chloride.

*Separation from Osmium.*—Osmium is removed by distillation. See Section on Osmium.

For other separations see Sections on Rhodium and Ruthenium.

## GRAVIMETRIC METHODS

### BY IGNITING THE SALT $(NH_4)_2IrCl_6$

*Procedure.*—The percentage of iridium in the salt may be judged fairly well by the color, by comparing with standard iridioplatinum salts. The salt is filtered, washed with alcohol and carefully ignited and weighed as iridioplatinum sponge metal. The percentage of iridium in the sample can be calculated from the weight of the iridium obtained. The two metals are treated as stated below.

## METHOD OF DEVILLE AND STAS
## (MODIFIED BY GILCHRIST [19])

*Procedure.* **Lead Fusion.**—Fuse the carefully sampled platinum alloy with 10 times its weight of granular test lead for a period of one hour at a temperature of about 1000°C. A covered crucible, whose outside dimensions are 4 cm. in diameter and 7 cm. in height, machined from Acheson graphite, is suitable for fusions made with 20 to 40 grams of lead. The inside of the crucible should possess a slight taper to facilitate the removal of the cooled ingot. Do not pour the fusion from the crucible, but allow it to solidify, since the iridium has largely settled to the bottom of the crucible. The crucible is best heated in an electric furnace.

**Disintegration with Nitric Acid.**—Brush the cooled lead ingot free from carbon with a camel's hair brush and place it in a beaker. Add dilute nitric acid (1 volume of nitric acid (sp. gr. 1.42) to 4 volumes of water), using 1 ml. of acid per gram of lead. Place the beaker on the steam bath or on a hot plate, which maintains the temperature of the solution at about 85°C. Disintegration of the lead ingot is usually complete in about 2 hours and leaves a rather voluminous, grayish-black mass. Dilute the solution to twice its volume and decant the liquid through a double filter, consisting of a 9-cm. paper of fine texture, on which is superimposed a 7-cm. paper of looser texture. Wash the residue thoroughly with hot water and pass the washings through the filters. The residue is not transferred to the filters at this point. The lead nitrate solutions and washings are best caught in an Erlenmeyer flask to make easier the detection of the presence of any residue which has passed through the filters. This is done by whirling the liquid in the flask. Return the filters to the beaker without ignition.

**Solution of the Lead-Platinum Alloy with Aqua Regia.**—Add, in order, 15 ml. of water, 5 ml. of hydrochloric acid (sp. gr. 1.18) and 0.8 ml. of nitric acid (sp. gr. 1.42) for each gram of the platinum-alloy sample taken. Heat the solution in the beaker on the steam bath or on a hot plate which maintains the temperature at about 85°C. The lead-platinum alloy is usually completely dissolved within 1.5 hours. Dilute the solution with twice its volume of water and filter through a double filter similar to the one used for the lead nitrate solution; the iridium, insoluble in aqua regia, is in the form of fine crystals, possessing a bright metallic luster and having a high density. Pass the clear solution through the filter first and then transfer the thoroughly macerated paper. It is very important to examine the beaker to see that no iridium remains. To do this the interior of the beaker is wiped with a piece of filter paper to collect any metal adhering to the sides. Then by whirling a small quantity of water in the beaker any iridium remaining gravitates towards one place whence it can be removed with a piece of paper. Wash the filters and iridium thoroughly, first with hot water, then with hot dilute hydrochloric acid (1:100), and lastly with hot water. The chloroplatinic acid filtrate and washings should be examined for iridium, which may have passed through the filters, in the manner described under the nitric acid treatment. The last washings should be tested for the absence of lead.

**Ignition and Reduction of the Iridium.**—Place the washed filters and iridium in a porcelain crucible and dry, before igniting in air. After the destruction of the filter paper, ignite the iridium strongly with the full heat of a Tirrill burner. After all the carbon is burned out, cover the crucible with a Rose lid, preferably of quartz. Introduce in the crucible a stream of hydrogen, burning from the tip of a

[19] Gilchrist, R., J. Am. Chem. Soc., **45**, 2820, 1923.

Rose delivery tube (a quartz tube preferred). After 5 minutes remove the burner and a few minutes later extinguish the hydrogen flame by momentarily breaking the current of hydrogen. This is best done by having a section of the rubber delivery tube replaced by a glass tube, one end of which can easily be disconnected. Allow the iridium to cool in an atmosphere of hydrogen and then weigh as metallic iridium.

NOTES.—In commercial analysis no effort is made to correct the weight of iridium for small amounts of ruthenium. Correction, if desired, can be made according to the original directions of Deville and Stas. ("Procés-verbaux, Comité International des Poids et Mesures," pp. 162, 191, 1877.) The correction for iron can be made by the procedure suggested by W. H. Swanger, U. S. Bureau of Standards. The iridium is fused with zinc, the excess zinc removed with hydrochloric acid, and the zinc-iridium alloy fused with potassium pyrosulfate. The fusion is digested with dilute sulfuric acid, which leaves a residue of iridium free from iron but contaminated with silica. Silica is now removed by the usual manner and pure iridium remains. This purification is necessary if iron is present in the sample since this separates with iridium. Palladium, rhodium and gold have no effect in the determination. Ruthenium separates quantitatively with the iridium. The loss of weight of iridium during the ignition periods is insignificant.

## DETERMINATION OF IRIDIUM BY PRECIPITATION AS THE HYDRATED DIOXIDE

Iridium may be determined in either of two ways. If the solution containing both rhodium and iridium can be divided conveniently into aliquot parts, the determination of iridium is greatly simplified and the precipitations of titanium by cupferron avoided. (See "Gravimetric Methods" for Rhodium.) The rhodium and iridium in one portion of the solution can be recovered by hydrolytic precipitation as described in the procedure for the separation of platinum. If this is done, the mixed precipitate of rhodium and iridium dioxides is washed with a hot 1% solution of ammonium chloride, neutral to bromthymol blue (pH 7), instead of with a solution of sodium chloride. The dried filter and precipitate are impregnated with a few drops of a saturated solution of ammonium chloride, in order to prevent deflagration, and carefully ignited to a mixture of the anhydrous oxides. The oxidized residue is ignited and cooled in hydrogen, and weighed as a mixture of metallic rhodium and metallic iridium. In order to calculate the quantity of iridium, it is necessary, in addition, to determine rhodium in a separate portion of the solution. (See "Gravimetric Methods" for Rhodium.)

If the iridium cannot be determined in this way, it is necessary to recover it from the filtrates resulting from the precipitation of rhodium by titanous chloride.

*Procedure.*—Dilute the combined filtrates from the precipitation of rhodium by titanous chloride to 800 ml. Cool the solution by placing the beaker in crushed ice. Add a chilled, filtered, freshly prepared 6% solution of cupferron (ammonium salt of nitrosophenylhydroxylamine, $C_6H_5N \cdot NO \cdot ONH_4$) in slight excess. Filter the solution and wash the titanium precipitate with chilled diluted $H_2SO_4$ (2.5:97.5) containing some cupferron. The cupferron precipitate is usually slightly contaminated by iridium, but the amount does not exceed 1 mg. when about 0.2 g. of iridium is being handled. Return the filter and precipitate to the beaker, add 20 ml. of $HNO_3$, and heat until the precipitate is mostly decomposed. Add 20 ml. of $H_2SO_4$ and heat the solution until vapors of $H_2SO_4$ appear. Destroy the remaining organic matter by adding $HNO_3$, and heating. Dilute the resulting solution to 800 ml. and repeat the precipitation of the titanium. Unite the filtrates from the cupferron precipitations and evaporate until approximately 10 ml. of

$H_2SO_4$ remains.  Ensure the destruction of all organic matter.  Dilute the solution somewhat and filter it.

Dilute the solution to 200 ml. with water and neutralize most of the acid contained in it with a filtered solution of sodium bicarbonate.  Heat the solution to boiling and complete its neutralization with bicarbonate to the end point of bromcresol purple, as described in the procedure for the separation of platinum. Add 20 ml. of a filtered 10% solution of sodium bromate, and boil the solution for 20 to 25 minutes.  Be sure that sufficient bromate is present to oxidize all of the iridium to the tetravalent state.  Filter the solution and wash the precipitate thoroughly with a hot 1% solution of ammonium chloride.

Place the filter and precipitate in a porcelain crucible.  Dry them somewhat and then moisten them with a few drops of a saturated solution of ammonium chloride.  Ignite the filter and precipitate carefully in the air and then in hydrogen. Leach the metallic residue with diluted HCl, then transfer it to a filter, and wash with hot water.  Ignite the filter and metallic residue in air.  Finally, ignite the resulting oxidized metal in hydrogen, cool it in hydrogen and weigh it as metallic iridium.[20]

[20] Gilchrist and Wichers, J. Am. Chem. Soc., **57**, 2565, 1935.

# RUTHENIUM

Ru *at. wt.* 101.07; *d.* 12; *m.p.* 2450°C.; *b.p.* 2700°+C.; *oxides,* $Ru_2O_3$, $RuO_2$, $RuO_4$

## DETECTION

This element is found in platinum ores, and as laurite, $Ru_2S_3$. It is barely soluble in aqua regia and insoluble in acid potassium sulfate. It dissolves when fused with KOH and $KNO_3$. The solution of the fusion when dissolved in water forms potassium ruthenate, $K_2RuO_4$, from which $HNO_3$ precipitates the hydroxide, which is soluble in HCl. The treatment with chlorine and KCl at a high temperature yields a salt, $K_2RuCl_6$. The salts that are most common are $K_2RuCl_5$ and $K_2RuCl_6$.

The oxide, $Ru_2O_3$, is formed when finely divided ruthenium is heated in the air, forming a blue powder which is insoluble in acids. It can also be obtained by heating the trihydroxide, $Ru(OH)_3$, in dry carbon dioxide which forms a black, scaly mass.

Ruthenium dioxide, $RuO_2$, is obtained by roasting the disulfide or sulfate in contact with air. It is likewise formed when the metal is fused in an oxidizing atmosphere, when it burns with a sparkling smoky flame, and evolves an ozone-like smell.

Ruthenium tetroxide, $RuO_4$, is formed in small quantities when the metal is heated at 1000°C. in a current of oxygen, although when heated alone it decomposes at about 106°C. It is prepared by passing chlorine into a solution of potassium nitrosochlororuthenate, potassium ruthenate or sodium ruthenate (prepared by fusing the metal with sodium peroxide); the liquid becomes heated and the tetroxide distills over and is deposited in the receiver. The moist oxide quickly decomposes. In the dry state it is fairly stable, but decomposes in sunlight with the formation of lower oxides. It dissolves slowly in water, and the solution when it contains free chlorine or HCl may be kept without alteration for some days if light be excluded, but when pure slowly deposits a black precipitate.

In addition to the above oxides, salts corresponding to the acidic oxides $RuO_3$ and $Ru_2O_7$ have been prepared.

*Potassium hydroxide* precipitates a black hydroxide easily soluble in HCl.

*Hydrogen sulfide* slowly produces brown $Ru_2S_3$.

*Ammonium sulfide* precipitates a brownish black sulfide.

*Metallic zinc* precipitates metallic ruthenium, the solution first turning blue.

*Potassium thiocyanate* gives on heating a dark brown solution.

*Silver nitrate* gives a rose red precipitate.

*Mercurous nitrate* produces a bright blue precipitate.

*Zinc chloride* produces a bright yellow precipitate which darkens on standing.

*Potassium iodide* after heating precipitates the black sesqui-iodide.

*p-Nitrosophenol* yields a deep violet coloration on warming with a solution of ruthenium trichloride.[21]

[21] Ogburn, Jr., S. C., J. Am. Chem. Soc., **48**, 2493, 2507, 1926.

**Sodium thiosulfate** according to C. Lea, is mixed with ammonium hydroxide, and a few drops of solution of ruthenium chloride are added, and the whole boiled. A reddish-purple liquid is produced, which, unless the solutions are very dilute, is black by transmitted light. The coloration is permanent, and the liquid may be exposed to the air without alteration. This reaction is far superior to any known test for ruthenium.

## ESTIMATION

Ruthenium is generally estimated in alloys and ores or residues.

## PREPARATION AND SOLUTION OF THE SAMPLE

When ruthenium is alloyed with platinum or gold, aqua regia dissolves these metals, forming the chlorides of platinum, gold, and ruthenium. The ruthenium in ores is in the form of an alloy with platinum or osmiridium. This is fused with $KNO_3$ and KOH in a silver crucible, the osmium and the ruthenium forming salts as described above, while the iridium remains as an oxide.

## SEPARATIONS

**Separation of Ruthenium from Platinum.**—The two metals are precipitated with KCl and the potassium chlororuthenate is dissolved out with cold water containing a very small amount of KCl and alcohol. The ruthenium is then precipitated from an acid solution by additions of granulated zinc.

A separation may be made by alloying with silver and dissolving the platinum and silver in $HNO_3$, the ruthenium remaining as the residue. Gold should be added to the alloy to prevent the platinum from becoming colloidal. Treat with dilute aqua regia to remove the gold and a small amount of platinum. The residue will be ruthenium with a small amount of silver chloride.

From a concentrated solution of these metals precipitate the platinum with $NH_4Cl$. Evaporate the filtrate with potassium nitrate to dryness and boil the residue with alcohol when the residual platinum will remain behind while the ruthenium goes into solution.

**Separation of Ruthenium from Iridium.**—The two metals are fused with KOH and $KNO_3$ as described above, the ruthenium forming a salt soluble in water and the iridium remaining as an oxide.

To the solution of the two metals, sodium nitrite is added in excess, with sufficient sodium carbonate to keep the liquid neutral or alkaline. The whole is boiled until an orange color appears. The ruthenium and the iridium are converted into soluble double nitrites. Sodium sulfide is then added, small quantities at a time until the precipitated ruthenium sulfide is dissolved in the excess of alkaline sulfide. At first the addition of the sulfide gives the characteristic crimson tint due to ruthenium, but this quickly disappears and gives a bright chocolate-colored precipitate. The solution is boiled for a few minutes, and allowed to become perfectly cold and then dilute HCl cautiously added until the dissolved ruthenium sulfide is precipitated and the solution is faintly acid. The solution is filtered and the precipitate washed with hot water. The filtrate will be free from ruthenium.

The fusion with KOH and $KNO_3$ as described above is dissolved in water in a flask or retort; chlorine is passed through this solution and thence into two or three flasks containing a solution of KOH and alcohol. The two or three flasks that form the condensing apparatus should be kept as cold as possible. The ruthenium is transformed into volatile $RuO_4$ that condenses in the flasks, while the iridium remains in the retort.

*Separation of Ruthenium from Rhodium.*—The mixed solution of the two metals is treated with potassium nitrite as described above. The orange-yellow solution is evaporated to dryness upon the water bath and treated with absolute alcohol. The rhodium remains undissolved and can be filtered off and washed with alcohol. The rhodium salt can be ignited with $NH_4Cl$ and after washing yields metallic rhodium. See "Separation of Rhodium from Ruthenium."

*Separation of Ruthenium from Osmium.*—The tetroxides from the chlorine distillation are caught in HCl. After heating to about 70°C., air should be drawn through the distillate for about half an hour to eliminate the osmium. See "Gravimetric Methods" in the Section on Osmium.

## GRAVIMETRIC METHODS

Ruthenium is weighed as the residue or metallic ruthenium after it has been separated from the other metals.

### DISTILLATION INTO POTASSIUM HYDROXIDE

*Procedure.*—The residue containing ruthenium or osmiridium is fused in a silver crucible with 5 g. KOH and 1 g. $KNO_3$ at a low temperature from one-half to one hour. The mass is cooled and extracted with water. The orange-colored solution containing potassium ruthenate is gently distilled in a current of chlorine whereby the volatile ruthenium tetroxide passes over into the receivers, which are charged with 200 ml. 10–15% KOH solution and 50 ml. of alcohol. All connections should be ground glass so that no Ru will be reduced in the joints. The solution in the distilling flask must be kept alkaline to prevent iridium chloride from distilling over with the Ru. Add a small piece of KOH to the distillate and repeat the distillation. (Some residues retain part of the ruthenium after the fusion and extraction so that it, as well as the distillation, must be repeated.) Pass chlorine through the alkaline solution of the distillate until all effervescence ceases. Disconnect the chlorine and draw air through the apparatus, heating the solution nearly to boiling.

This alkaline solution containing the ruthenium tetroxide distillate is evaporated to a smaller volume and the ruthenium is precipitated by boiling with absolute alcohol. Filter, wash well with hot water, dilute HCl and again with hot water. Ignite, reduce in hydrogen and weigh as metallic Ru.

*Alternate Procedure.*—The alkaline solution from the receivers is made acid with HCl and the Ru is precipitated from the hot solution with hydrogen sulfide gas. Filter, wash, ignite at a high temperature, reduce in hydrogen and weigh as metallic Ru.

### DISTILLATION INTO HYDROCHLORIC ACID

*Procedure.*—This method is identical with the preceding one except that the receivers are charged with 3 N HCl instead of alcoholic KOH. This acid solution containing the ruthenium tetroxide distillate is heated to nearly boiling and the ruthenium is precipitated with hydrogen sulfide gas as above.

*Alternate Procedure.*—The acid solution containing the Ru is evaporated to a concentrated solution and transferred to a weighed porcelain crucible. Evaporate to dryness, bake, and ignite. Reduce in hydrogen and weigh as metallic Ru.[22]

## BY PRECIPITATION WITH MAGNESIUM

*Procedure.*—Ruthenium may be estimated by precipitation with magnesium from solutions of its salts. The precipitate is washed with dilute sulfuric acid to remove excess of magnesium, dried, ignited in a current of hydrogen, cooled in carbon dioxide and weighed as metal.[23]

Evaporate to a moist residue on the steam bath. Add 10 ml. of HCl and digest the solution for one-half hour. Add 50 ml. of water and heat the solution to boiling in order to complete the dissolving of the somewhat difficultly soluble ruthenium compound. When the ruthenium compound is completely dissolved, filter the solution and wash the filter with diluted HCl (1:99). The solution is filtered to ensure the elimination of a small amount of silica which may be present. Dilute the ruthenium solution to 200 ml., heat it to boiling, and add a filtered 10% solution of sodium bicarbonate until a precipitate begins to form. Add the bicarbonate solution dropwise until the acidity of the solution reaches a value of pH 6 as indicated by the change in color from yellow to blue of bromcresol purple indicator present in the solution. Boil the solution for 5 to 6 minutes and filter it.

Wipe the inner walls of the beaker and also the glass rod with a small piece of ashless filter paper. Thoroughly wash the filter and precipitate with a hot 1% solution of ammonium sulfate. Finally wash them 3 or 4 times with a cold 2.5% solution of ammonium sulfate.

Place the filter and precipitate in a porcelain crucible, dry them, and char the filter slowly. The dried filter will usually char completely when once it begins to smoke. This operation should be done carefully in order to prevent loss of ruthenium by deflagration. Ignite the residue strongly in air and then in hydrogen. Cool the resulting metal in hydrogen and leach it well with hot water. This is done to ensure complete removal of soluble salts. It is well to leach the residue in the crucible first and then to transfer it to a filter. Ignite the filter and metal in air and in hydrogen. Cool the residue in hydrogen and weigh it as metallic ruthenium.[24]

[22] A correction should be made for impurities in the HCl used.
[23] Friend, J. N., Text Book of Inorganic Chemistry, Vol. IX, Part I.
[24] Gilchrist, Raleigh, Research Paper 654, J. Research Nat. Bur. Standards, **12,** 1934.

# RHODIUM

Rh *at. wt.* 102.905; *d.* 12.5; *m.p.* 1966 ± 3°C.; *b.p.* 2500°C.; *oxides,* RhO, $Rh_2O_3$, $RhO_2$

## DETECTION

Rhodium is found only in platinum ores. It is a white metal, difficultly fusible, and insoluble in acids. Rhodium, however, dissolves in aqua regia when alloyed with platinum, to a cherry-red solution. It is also soluble in molten phosphoric acid and dissolves when fused with acid potassium sulfate with the formation of $K_3Rh(SO_4)_3$. If the metal is treated with chlorine in the presence of sodium chloride there forms a soluble salt, $Na_3RhCl_6$.

Rhodium monoxide, RhO, is obtained by heating the hydroxide $Rh(OH)_3$; by cupellation of an alloy of rhodium and lead, or by igniting the finely-divided metal in a current of air. It is a gray powder with a metallic appearance, and is not attacked by acids. When heated in hydrogen it is reduced with evolution of light.

The oxide, $Rh_2O_3$, is obtained as a gray iridescent spongy mass by heating the nitrate. It is also formed as a crystalline mass when sodium rhodochloride is heated in oxygen. It is perfectly soluble in acids.

Rhodium dioxide, $RhO_2$, is obtained by repeated fusions of the metal with KOH and $KNO_3$. It is attacked neither by alkalies nor by acids and is reduced by hydrogen only at a high temperature.

*Hydrogen sulfide* precipitates rhodium sulfide, when passed into a boiling hot solution containing rhodium.

*Potassium hydroxide* precipitates at first a yellow hydroxide, $Rh(OH)_3 \cdot H_2O$ soluble in an excess of the reagent. If boiled, a dark gelatinous precipitate separates. A solution of $Na_3RhCl_6$ does not show this reaction immediately, but the precipitate appears in the course of time. Addition of alcohol causes a black precipitate immediately.

*Ammonium hydroxide* produces a precipitate which dissolves in excess $NH_4OH$ on heating. Addition of HCl now produces a yellow precipitate, insoluble in HCl but soluble in $NH_4OH$.

*Potassium nitrite* precipitates from hot solutions a bright yellow precipitate of double nitrite of potassium and rhodium.

*Zinc, iron, and formic acid* precipitate rhodium as a black metal.

*Hydrogen* reduces rhodium salts.

To detect small amounts of rhodium in the presence of other metals, evaporate the solution and displace with a fresh solution of sodium hypochlorite; the yellow precipitate formed is soluble after an addition of acetic acid. After a long agitation the solution changes to an orange-yellow color and after a short time the color passes and finally a gray precipitate settles and the solution turns sky-blue.

## ESTIMATION

Rhodium is estimated mainly in ores, platinum group metal scrap, and salts.

## PREPARATION AND SOLUTION OF THE SAMPLE

When rhodium is estimated in scrap thermocouple wire or other alloys of platinum and rhodium the sample is rolled to a thin ribbon and dissolved in aqua regia. (An alloy containing 30% of Rh is practically insoluble in aqua regia.) Both metals will go into solution, forming the chlorides of rhodium and platinum. The aqua regia will have to be replaced from time to time, as the alloy dissolves slowly.

The rhodium from salts is precipitated with zinc and the black metallic rhodium cleaned with dilute aqua regia, filtered, washed, ignited, and reduced with hydrogen. If platinum is present with the rhodium the residue will invariably contain a small amount of platinum after the aqua regia treatment. If all the platinum is desired it will be necessary to alloy with silver as described on page 890.

Some alloys and ores are alloys with silver and some platinum, which are dissolved in $HNO_3$. The residue is cleaned with aqua regia, dried, and weighed as metallic rhodium.[25] If the residue is ignited, reduce with hydrogen.

The material or residue containing rhodium is fused with $KHSO_4$, or with $K_2S_2O_7$, for some time at a red heat and the mass leached with hot water acidified with HCl. The rose-red solution contains the rhodium. Several fusions are generally necessary.

## SEPARATIONS

*Separation of Rhodium from Platinum.*—Alloys and ores containing platinum and rhodium dissolve slowly in aqua regia as stated above. After expelling the $HNO_3$ add $NH_4Cl$. The precipitate is filtered and washed with dilute ammonium chloride solution, which dissolves the rhodium salt. A very small amount of rhodium will color the filtrate pink to a rose-red color, depending on the amount of rhodium present. A green tinge in the ammonium chloroplatinate indicates the presence of rhodium.

A solution of NaOH is added to the HCl solution of the two metals until yellow rhodium hydroxide begins to separate. After neutralizing, the volume of the solution should be so adjusted that the estimated total content of Pt and Rh does not exceed 1 g. per 100 ml. A mixture of equal volumes of solutions containing 90 g. of crystallized barium chloride and 36 g. of anhydrous sodium carbonate per liter, respectively, is added. Not less than 5 ml. of each solution is taken. After the suspension of barium carbonate is added, the solution is rapidly heated to boiling and boiled for two or three minutes. The residue is filtered off and washed several times with a hot 2% solution of sodium chloride, after which it is returned, with the filter paper, to the original beaker and digested with 25 ml. HCl (1:4) until solution is complete. Dilute with water and filter off the paper pulp. Adjust the volume to about 150 ml., heat to incipient boiling for 30 to 45 minutes while a current of hydrogen sulfide is passed in. After the precipitation the rhodium sulfide is filtered off at once, washed with water con-

---

[25] See Separations in Section on Iridium.

taining a little ammonium chloride, and ignited in a weighed porcelain crucible. The ignited sulfide is reduced and cooled in hydrogen, and weighed as metallic Rh.[26]

An alternate method is to chlorinate the rhodium-platinum ore or ground alloy at 600°C., and treat with aqua regia. $RhCl_3$ is insoluble in that reagent, and may be filtered off and weighed as $RhCl_3$, or by ignition, as metallic Rh.

*Separation of Rhodium from Iridium.*—A separation can be made by adding sodium nitrite in excess to the solution of the two metals, with a sufficient quantity of sodium carbonate to make the solution neutral or alkaline; this is boiled until the solution assumes a clear orange color. The rhodium and iridium are converted into soluble double nitrites. A solution of sodium sulfide is added in slight excess and the liquid made slightly acid. The rhodium is precipitated as dark-brown rhodium sulfide.

A solution of rhodium and iridium is evaporated with HCl and displaced with a large excess of acid sodium sulfite, $NaHSO_3$, and allowed to stand some time when a pale yellow double salt of rhodium and sodium sulfite slowly separates out while the solution becomes nearly colorless. Wash out the precipitate, and heat with hot concentrated $H_2SO_4$ till the sulfurous acid is driven off. Heat the material in a crucible until rid of all free sulfuric acid. Then the iridium is dissolved out as a sulfate with a deep chrome-green color, while a double salt of sodium sulfate and rhodium oxide remains behind. This is flesh colored, insoluble in water and acids. Boil with aqua regia, wash, dry, and heat to decompose the salt into rhodium and sodium sulfate. Leach out the latter with water, dry and weigh the Rh.[27]

Rhodium can also be separated from iridium, when the latter is present as an iridic salt such as $Ir(SO_4)_2$, by precipitating the mixed salts with caustic potash, dissolving the hydroxides in dilute sulfuric acid and adding cesium sulfate. The sparingly soluble rhodium cesium-alum separates in the cold, and can readily be purified by recrystallization and then by electrolysis.

The residue of rhodium and iridium is melted or scorified with test lead.. The lead button is cleaned and dissolved in dilute $HNO_3$. After filtering and washing the residue, do not ignite, but wash the contents of the filter into a beaker and fume with $H_2SO_4$ from 1 to 3 hours. When cool, dilute with water and let stand overnight. The residue contains the iridium and a small amount of $PbSO_4$, while the solution contains the rhodium as the sulfate. To make a further separation from impurities present, the sulfate solution is made alkaline with NaOH and boiled. Let stand until cold and filter off the rhodium hydroxide. Digest with HCl until all the hydroxide has dissolved. Filter and wash with hot water. Evaporate the filtrate to dryness, dissolve in hot water and add about 15 ml. of sodium nitrite solution (40% $NaNO_2$). Heat until all action ceases, then add sodium carbonate to the hot solution until no more precipitate forms. Let cool, filter and wash with hot water. Acidify the filtrate with dilute acetic acid and add potassium chloride solution (20% KCl) until all the Rh is precipitated. Let stand overnight at 50 to 60°C. When cold, filter the white precipitate, washing with 20% KCl solution containing a little $NaNO_2$. The white precipitate of potassium rhodium nitrite is digested with HCl, filtered and washed with hot water. Evaporate the HCl solution to dryness, add ammonium formate and heat

26 Wichers, Edward, J. Am. Chem. Soc., **46**, 1818, 1924.
27 Dammer, O., Handbuch der Anorganischen Chemie. F. Enke, Stuttgart.

until dry. Ignite, wash free from salts with hot water, reduce in hydrogen, cool in $CO_2$, and weigh as metallic Rh.

***Separation of Rhodium, Platinum, and Palladium.***—After dissolving the material as above, precipitate the platinum with $NH_4Cl$ as described under "Platinum." After filtering off the $(NH_4)_2PtCl_6$ precipitate, and after neutralizing the filtrate with $Na_2CO_3$ add mercuric cyanide to separate the palladium as $Pd(CN)_2$ as described under "Palladium." The filtered solution is evaporated to dryness with an excess of HCl. On treating the residue with alcohol, the double chloride of rhodium and sodium is left undissolved as a red powder. By heating this in a tube through which hydrogen is passed the rhodium is reduced to the metallic state and the sodium chloride is washed out with water leaving a gray powder of metallic rhodium.

The residue containing these three metals is scorified with test lead, and the resultant lead button cupelled with silver. The silver bead is dissolved in dilute $HNO_3$; the solution filtered, washed with hot water, ignited, and the residue treated with dilute aqua regia to dissolve any platinum or palladium that may be present. Filter, wash with hot water, ammonia water, and again with hot water. Ignite and reduce in hydrogen as metallic Rh.[28] (See "Separations" in Section on Iridium.)

***Separation of Rhodium from Ruthenium.***—The solution containing the two metals is treated with sodium nitrate as above and evaporated to dryness. The residue is powdered and treated in a flask with absolute alcohol. After filtering and washing with alcohol the rhodium remains undissolved.

The substance or residue containing the rhodium and ruthenium may be fused with $KHSO_4$ in a porcelain or platinum crucible causing the rhodium to go into solution as already described. The ruthenium remains insoluble, and is determined by distillation by method in Section on Ruthenium.

## GRAVIMETRIC METHODS

### BY PRECIPITATION WITH ZINC

The solution containing rhodium is treated with zinc and the residue is washed well with hot water acidulated with HCl. The residue is then cleaned with dilute aqua regia and the black metallic rhodium is filtered off, dried, and ignited in hydrogen. Cool and weigh as metallic rhodium.[29]

### BY PRECIPITATION AS SULFIDE

The rhodium solution containing about 5% free acid is treated for one-half to one hour with a rapid stream of $H_2S$ while the solution is kept boiling on the hot plate. Let settle overnight, filter, wash well with hot water, ignite, reduce in hydrogen, cool in $CO_2$ and weigh as metallic rhodium.

### BY PRECIPITATION WITH FORMIC ACID

The solution containing the rhodium is made alkaline with KOH and then acid with formic acid, boil, and the rhodium will be precipitated as finely divided

[28] Very often this Rh contains lead in amounts varying from a trace to 35%.
[29] This weight may be somewhat high due to contamination with Zn, as well as other impurities either from the solution or reagent.

metallic rhodium.   After filtering wash well with hot water, ignite, clean with dilute aqua regia and finish in the usual manner.

## BY FUSION WITH PYROSULFATE

After the platinum and the palladium are eliminated, the residue of Ir, Rh and Ru is fused with $K_2S_2O_7$ in a porcelain crucible and the melt dissolved in water.   Filter, wash with hot water, and after acidulating with HCl the Rh is precipitated with C.P. powdered zinc, hydrogen sulfide gas or both.   Filter, wash with hot water and ignite.   Clean the residue with dilute $HNO_3$, then with dilute aqua regia, wash with hot water, ignite in hydrogen and weigh as metallic Rh.[29]

## BY FUSION WITH KOH AND KNO₃

The residue containing Ir, Rh, Ru and Os is fused with 5 g. KOH and 1 g. $KNO_3$, and the Ru and Os are distilled with chlorine as explained under ruthenium.   The solution from the distilling flask is filtered, washed with water and the filtrate is made acid, treated thoroughly with zinc, filtered, joined with the original residue and the whole ignited.   The residue of impure Ir and Rh is scorified with test lead, the lead button dissolved in dilute $HNO_3$ and the residue treated with $H_2SO_4$, as explained under "Separation of Rh from Ir."   The clear rhodium sulfate solution is treated with C.P. powdered zinc, hydrogen sulfide gas or both, and the precipitate is treated as explained above and weighed as metallic Rh.[29]

## BY PRECIPITATION WITH ZINC, SOLUTION IN H₂SO₄, AND REPRECIPITATION

The solution from the distilling flask is treated with zinc as explained above. The residue is filtered, washed, ignited and boiled with a few ml. of $HNO_3$ and then boiled with $H_2SO_4$ for one to three hours.   Cool, dilute with three times its volume of water, filter, and wash thoroughly with hot water.   The rhodium sulfate solution is made alkaline with KOH and boiled with alcohol until all the rhodium is precipitated and the solution is clear.   Filter, wash with hot water, dilute $HNO_3$ and again with hot water.   Ignite, reduce in hydrogen, and weigh as metallic Rh.

## BY PRECIPITATION WITH MAGNESIUM

Rhodium is conveniently estimated by precipitation with magnesium from solutions of its salts.   The precipitate is washed with dilute $H_2SO_4$ to remove excess of magnesium, dried, ignited in a current of hydrogen, cooled in carbon dioxide and weighed as metal.[30]

## BY PRECIPITATION WITH TITANOUS CHLORIDE

A solution containing the rhodium and iridium as chlorides, together with the excess of dimethylglyoxime remaining from the precipitation of palladium is placed in a 500-ml. Erlenmeyer flask.   (See "Gravimetric Methods" for Palladium). Place a short-stemmed funnel in the mouth of the flask.   Add 10 ml. of $H_2SO_4$ and 2 to 3 ml. of $HNO_3$, and evaporate until heavy vapors of $H_2SO_4$ are evolved.   To ensure complete destruction of organic matter, add a small quantity of $HNO_3$ from time to time and continue to heat over a free flame, keeping the solution in constant motion.   Dilute the cooled solution with 20 ml. of water and again

30 Friend, J. N., Text Book of Inorganic Chemistry, Vol. IX, Part I.

evaporate it until vapors of $H_2SO_4$ appear. This is done to destroy nitroso compounds which may interfere in the precipitation of rhodium by titanous chloride.

Transfer the sulfate solution to a clean, unetched beaker, dilute it to 200 ml., and heat it to boiling. Add dropwise a solution of titanous chloride (a 20% solution of this reagent may be purchased) until the supernatant liquid appears slightly purple. If the solution is placed over a 100-watt light and stirred, observation of the end point is greatly facilitated. The metallic rhodium that is precipitated quickly coagulates into a spongy mass. If much iridium is present, the end point can be determined by the lack of formation of any further precipitate and the appearance of an orange color in the solution. Boil the solution for two minutes and filter it. Wipe the walls of the beaker and also the stirring rod with a piece of ashless filter paper. Wash the filter and precipitated metal thoroughly with cold (room temperature) diluted $H_2SO_4$ (2.5:97.5).

Place the filter with its contents in a 500-ml. Erlenmeyer flask, add 10 ml. of $H_2SO_4$, char gently, add 5 ml. of $HNO_3$, and digest the solution on a hot plate. Usually, the rhodium dissolves fairly readily. Complete the solution of the rhodium by heating the flask over a free flame, keeping the contents of the flask in constant motion. Ensure the destruction of organic matter and the elimination of nitroso compounds. If some black specks remain, dilute the solution, filter it and return the filter to the flask. Wipe down the walls of the flask with a piece of ashless filter paper. Add 5 ml. of $H_2SO_4$, char the paper, and destroy all organic matter with $HNO_3$. Heat the solution until heavy vapors of $H_2SO_4$ are evolved. This treatment will dissolve any remaining metal and will leave only a slight deposit of colorless silica.

Precipitate the rhodium a second time in the manner described above. Redissolve the rhodium as before, dilute the $H_2SO_4$ solution with 20 ml. of water and 10 ml. of HCl and boil the resulting solution for 15 minutes. This treatment is necessary to convert the rhodium into a form that will allow complete precipitation by hydrogen sulfide. During this treatment, the color of the solution will change from yellow to rose. Filter the solution and wash the filter with diluted HCl (1:99). Finally, dilute the solution to a volume of from 400 to 500 ml.

Precipitate the rhodium with $H_2S$ as directed under 2. Filter the solution and wash the precipitate with diluted $H_2SO_4$ (2.5:97.5), and finally with diluted HCl (1:99). Place the filter with the sulfide precipitate in a porcelain crucible. Ignite the dried precipitate carefully in air. Finally, ignite the oxidized residue in hydrogen, cool the resulting metal in hydrogen and weigh it as metallic rhodium.[31]

[31] Gilchrist and Wichers, J. Am. Chem. Soc., **57**, 2565, 1935.

# OSMIUM

Os *at. wt.* 190.2; *d.* 22.48; *m.p.* 2700°C.; *b.p.* 5300°C.; *oxides*, OsO, $Os_2O_3$, $OsO_2$, $OsO_4$

## DETECTION

Osmium occurs with platinum ores as a natural alloy with iridium (osmiridium) and remains undissolved in the form of hard, white metallic-looking grains when the ores are treated with aqua regia. The chlorides, $OsCl_2$ and $OsCl_4$, combine with the alkali chlorides. Through the action of $HNO_3$, aqua regia, or heating in a stream of moist chlorine, osmic tetroxide is formed. $OsO_4$ is volatile and the fumes are poisonous. It is detected readily by the odor when heated, as the fumes are highly corrosive and disagreeable like chlorine. Chlorine passed over hot osmium mixed with KCl gives $K_2OsCl_6$, which dissolves in cold water.

The oxyhydrogen flame oxidizes the metal but does not melt it. When strongly heated in contact with air, the finely divided osmium burns and is converted into $OsO_4$, commonly called osmic acid.

Osmium monoxide, OsO, is obtained when the corresponding sulfite mixed with sodium carbonate is ignited in a current of carbon dioxide. It is a grayish-black powder insoluble in acids.

The oxide, $Os_2O_3$, is a black insoluble powder obtained by heating its salts with sodium carbonate in a current of carbon dioxide.

Osmium dioxide, $OsO_2$, is obtained from its salts in a similar way to the foregoing oxides. It is likewise formed when its hydroxide is heated in a current of carbon dioxide.

Osmium tetroxide, $OsO_4$. Very finely-divided metallic osmium oxidizes slowly at the ordinary temperature, and at about 400°C. takes fire with formation of $OsO_4$. The denser the metal the higher is the temperature needed for oxidation.

*Hydrogen sulfide* precipitates dark brown osmium sulfide, $OsS_2$, but only in the presence of some strong mineral acid; from an aqueous solution of osmic acid there forms a dark brownish-black sulfide, $OsS_4$. These are insoluble in ammonium sulfide.

*Potassium hydroxide* precipitates reddish-brown osmium hydroxide, $Os(OH)_4$.

*Ammonium hydroxide* precipitates osmium hydroxide $Os(OH)_4$.

*Zinc and formic acid* precipitate black metallic osmium.

*Hydrogen* reduces osmium compounds to the metal.

*Potassium nitrite* added to a solution of osmic acid reduces it to osmous acid which unites with an alkali forming a beautiful red salt.

*Sodium sulfite* yields a deep violet coloration and a dark blue osmium sulfite separates out gradually.

*Phosphorus* reduces osmium from an aqueous solution.[32]

*Mercury* precipitates osmium from a hydrochloric acid solution of osmic acid.

[32] Ogburn and Miller, J. Am. Chem. Soc., **52**, 42, 1930.

*Stannous chloride* produces a brown precipitate, dissolving in HCl to give a brown fluid.

*β-Naphthylamine hydrochloride* produces a blue color upon reacting with a sodium or potassium osmate solution. This is a delicate and characteristic test which can be used in the presence of ruthenium.[33]

*Thiourea*, $CS(NH_2)_2$, when added to a solution containing $OsO_4$ or $K_2OsCl_6$ acidified with a few drops of HCl and heated for a few minutes, causes a deep red or rose color to appear.[34]

## ESTIMATION

Osmium is estimated mainly in osmiridium, synthetic alloys for pen-point material, spark points, and platinum residues.

### PREPARATION AND SOLUTION OF THE SAMPLE

After the platinum is extracted, the residue or osmiridium is mixed with two or three times its weight of common table salt. The mixture is put in a porcelain or silica tube and heated to a dull red heat; moist chlorine is then passed through the tube and thence through receivers containing KOH and $C_2H_5OH$ to catch the Os and Ru that pass over. The mass is cooled and dissolved with water. After several treatments the entire group of platinum metals will be in solution.

The osmium material may also be fused with KOH and $KNO_3$ and the melt dissolved in water. The osmium will be in solution as potassium osmate, $K_2OsO_4$, while the iridium remains as residue.

Cold selenic acid has no appreciable action on osmium; at about 120°C., however, the metal is dissolved to a colorless solution which contains selenious acid and $OsO_4$, but no selenate.[34]

### SEPARATIONS

In most cases osmium is separated from the other metals present by distillation or volatilization. See "Gravimetric Methods."

### GRAVIMETRIC METHODS

#### DISTILLATION WITH $HNO_3$

The residue containing osmium is fused with 5 grams KOH and 1 gram $KNO_3$ in a silver crucible as explained under ruthenium. Add $HNO_3$ slowly to the distilling flask which is connected to receivers containing NaOH solution and alcohol (10% NaOH and 10% $C_2H_5OH$). Draw the distillate over gently with the aid of the vacuum, the same as for the chlorine distillation under ruthenium. Continue the $HNO_3$ until strongly acid and then boil for a short time.

#### PRECIPITATION WITH $H_2S$ AND REDUCTION WITH $H_2$

Transfer the alkaline solution containing the $OsO_4$ distillate to a beaker and pass in hydrogen sulfide gas while the solution is heating until saturation; then add HCl until the solution is distinctly acid and continue to saturate the hot acid solution with hydrogen sulfide gas. Let stand overnight, filter through a weighed Gooch

[33] Chugaev, L., Compt. rend., **167**, 235, 1918.
[34] Hradecky, K. See C. A., **12**, 657, 1918.

crucible, washing well with hot water. Ignite in hydrogen, cool in $CO_2$ and weigh as metallic Os.

NOTES.—The ignition of the sulfide precipitate in hydrogen leaves the osmium containing some sulfur. A correction can be made, however, by dissolving the residue in aqua regia and precipitating the sulfur with barium as the sulfate.

The hydrogen used in the reduction of the osmium should be displaced with $CO_2$ before the air is admitted, to prevent explosion caused by the catalytic action of the metal.

## PRECIPITATION WITH ALUMINUM

The osmate solution from the receivers is heated gently and strips of aluminum are plunged in; the osmium will be deposited in metallic form, while the aluminum dissolves in the soda. Care must be taken not to add too much aluminum, as an aluminate might be precipitated which is troublesome. When the solution is decolorized, the dense precipitated osmium is washed by decantation with water to remove the sodium aluminate, and then with 5% $H_2SO_4$ solution to remove the excess aluminum. The osmium is dried in a bell-jar filled with hydrogen, then heated to a dull redness and cooled in a current of hydrogen. The osmium is weighed as the metal. As a check the osmium may be driven off in the form of $OsO_4$ by heating to redness with plenty of air, or better, in a current of oxygen and weighing again.

## REDISTILLATION WITH HCl AND AIR OR OXYGEN

The osmate solution from the condensing receivers or from the fusion of KOH and $KNO_3$ containing the ruthenium and osmium is placed in a retort and HCl is added. A slow current of air or oxygen is passed through the retort and thence through receivers containing KOH and alcohol similar to the ones mentioned above. These receivers are kept as cold as possible. The osmium is distilled over as $OsO_4$ while the ruthenium remains in the retort. Combine the solutions in the receivers and proceed to determine the osmium as described below.

## PRECIPITATION WITH $H_2SO_4$

The potassium or sodium osmate solution from the receivers above or where osmium tetroxide is dissolved in potassium hydroxide solution and alcohol is heated at 40 or 50°C. to form potassium osmate. A slight excess of dilute sulfuric acid is added and then 10 ml. more of alcohol in order to prevent reoxidation. After 10 or 12 hours, a bluish-black deposit settles, while the supernatant liquid is colorless and free from osmium. The precipitate is filtered, washed with aqueous alcohol, and converted into metallic osmium by reduction in a current of hydrogen.

After the osmium is removed with $HNO_3$ as described above, the ruthenium can be distilled after making the contents of the flask alkaline with KOH. Proceed then as described under the distillation of ruthenium.

## PRECIPITATION AS STRYCHNINE SALT

The sodium osmate solution from the receivers above is treated with concentrated HCl until slightly acid. Heat to the boiling point to change the sodium osmate to sodium chloroosmate. An excess of a saturated aqueous solution of strychnine sulfate is added and warmed on the water bath to coagulate the canary-yellow precipitate. Filter immediately through a prepared Gooch crucible and after washing thoroughly with warm water to remove the chlorides, dry at 105°C.

Weigh as $(C_{21}H_{22}O_2N_2)_3Os$ and calculate the percentage of Os in the salt, using the empirical factor 0.1758.

The other platinum metals also precipitate with strychnine sulfate, but that of ruthenium is soluble in boiling 95% ethyl alcohol. This affords a ready method of separating osmium from ruthenium. Precipitate both metals with a small excess of a saturated solution of strychnine sulfate and add an equal volume of 95% ethyl alcohol. Boil the mixture until the precipitates dissolve. Upon cooling, the osmium compound reprecipitates and after standing for 1.5 hours, is filtered through a prepared Gooch filter as explained above.[35]

## TREATMENT WITH $SO_2$, FOLLOWED BY HCl, PRECIPITATION AS HYDRATED DIOXIDE, AND REDUCTION WITH $H_2$

The osmium is distilled from the distilling flask as $OsO_4$ by adding $HNO_3$ as described above. The distillate is caught in receivers containing 150 ml. of dilute HCl (1:1), freshly saturated with $SO_2$, in the first receiver, and 50 ml. of the same reagent in each of the other two absorbing flasks.

Unite the portions of the absorbing solution and evaporate as far as possible on the steam bath in a clean, unetched beaker. It is important, in precipitating the platinum metals hydrolytically, that the beakers used do not have an etched surface. An etched beaker often becomes stained with the precipitate, and this stain cannot always be removed readily. Digest the residue with 10 ml. of HCl for fifteen minutes, and evaporate a second time. Repeat the digestion with HCl and the evaporation three times more. This is done to ensure complete decomposition of any sulfite compounds of osmium. Dissolve the residue from the last evaporation in 150 ml. of water. Heat the resulting solution to boiling, and add to it a filtered 10% solution of sodium bicarbonate until a precipitate appears and suddenly coagulates. Add a few drops of bromphenol blue indicator solution (0.04%) to the hot solution. This indicator changes from yellow to blue at pH 4. Add the bicarbonate solution dropwise until the indicator assumes a faint bluish color. Finally, boil the solution from five to six minutes to ensure complete precipitation of the hydrated osmium dioxide.

Filter the solution through a Munroe platinum crucible, carefully pouring the supernatant liquid through first. Transfer the precipitate, and wipe the inner walls of the beaker and also the glass rod with a rubber policeman which has been thoroughly wetted so that the precipitate will not cling to it. It should be borne in mind that filter paper must not be used to wipe the beaker, although it is used when handling precipitates of any of the other five platinum metals. Wash the precipitate thoroughly with a hot 1% solution of ammonium chloride, and then cover it with solid ammonium chloride. Moisten the ammonium chloride with a few drops of the wash solution and saturate the precipitate by applying suction. If desired, a saturated solution of ammonium chloride may be used to impregnate the precipitate. Continue the suction until the bottom of the crucible is coated with solidified ammonium chloride. Wipe off this coating of salt and place the platinum cap on the bottom of the crucible.

Cover the crucible with a Rose lid, preferably of quartz. Ignite a stream of hydrogen from a Rose delivery tube, likewise of quartz, and regulate the stream so that a very small flame is produced. Then insert the tube through the opening in the lid. The hydrogen flame will probably become extinguished by this

[35] Ogburn, Jr., S. C., and Miller, L. F., J. Am. Chem. Soc., **52**, 42, 1930.

operation and must be reignited. This is done by momentarily placing a burner flame under the crucible. The hydrogen will now burn as it emerges from under the lid at the edge of the crucible. The ignited hydrogen generates the requisite amount of heat to dehydrate the osmium compound without causing deflagration. After 5 minutes, gradually heat the crucible with the burner flame until all of the ammonium chloride is expelled. Ignite the osmium residue strongly in hydrogen for 10 minutes. Remove the burner and allow the crucible to cool somewhat. Extinguish the hydrogen flame by momentarily breaking the current of hydrogen, and allow the crucible to cool to room temperature. Finally, displace the hydrogen with a current of $CO_2$, without even momentary access of air. If the hydrogen is not displaced by an inert gas, such as $CO_2$, the reduced metal will be rapidly attacked when first exposed to the air, with significant loss of osmium. Weigh the residue as metallic osmium.[36]

[36] Gilchrist and Wichers, J. Am. Chem. Soc., **57**, 2565, 1935.

*Chapter* **37**

# RADIUM*[1]

**Ra,** *m.p.* 700°C.; *half life,* 1620 years; *chloride,* $RaCl_2$

Belgium Congo, Africa—pitchblende, torbernite, curite and kasolite; Western Colorado and Eastern Utah—carnotite; Canada and Joachimsthal, Czechoslovakia—pitchblende.

## DETECTION

Radium and its radioactive decay products are detected by means of the alpha, beta and gamma rays that they emit. The means of detection are (1) the ionization which these radiations produce in a gas, (2) the excitation of phosphorescent crystals, or (3) the effect in darkening a photographic plate. Radium is distinguished from other radioactive constituents of ores by the half life, 3.825 days, of the radon gas which is a decay product of the radium.

## ESTIMATION

Radium may be estimated by a variety of procedures, such as (1) the rate at which a sample causes the gold leaf of an electroscope to discharge, (2) the emission rate of radiation counted by a Geiger-Müller counter, (3) the amount of the blackening of a photographic plate, or (4) the rate of production of scintillations in a phosphor.

## DETERMINATION OF RADIUM

The procedures for determining radium are conveniently grouped by the kind of radiation or product measured, e.g. alpha-ray methods, beta-ray methods, gamma-ray methods, and radon methods.

**Standards.**—For quantitative determinations, all methods require suitable standards. Radium standards of all types are based ultimately on the International Standards, consisting of radium salts of the highest purity which have been weighed to determine the amount of radium present to an accuracy of $\pm 0.3\%$. Radium solutions, containing $10^{-9}$ gram of radium in 200 ml. of solution, for calibration of equipment using the radon method, are available from the National Bureau of Standards.

---

* Revision for the Sixth Edition by Dr. Leon Curtis of the National Bureau of Standards.
[1] Bulletin 70, U. S. Bureau of Mines; Bulletin 104, U. S. Bureau of Mines; Radioactivity and Geology, Joly, John, A. Constable and Co., London; Curtiss, L. F., Measurements of Radioactivity, National Bureau of Standards Circular 479, 1949; Curtiss, L. F., The Geiger-Müller Counter, National Bureau of Standards Circular 490, 1950; Rodden, C. J., Anal. Chem., **21**, 327, 1949.

## ALPHA-RAY METHOD

*Procedure.*—The estimation of radium by the alpha rays—formerly used as a rough method of estimating ores at mines—requires the ore to be finely pulverized. This powder is placed in a metal tray in a gold-leaf electroscope, as shown in

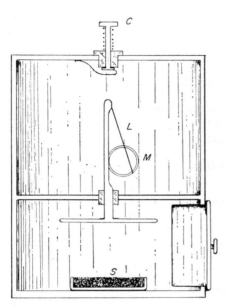

Fig. 37-1, and the rate of discharge of the leaf determined by timing its motion between two divisions on a micrometric scale in the low power microscope used to magnify the leaf. This device is calibrated by similar samples of ore for which the radon content has been determined by the radon method. Observations are made of the background rate of the motion of the leaf, when no sample is present, and this rate is subtracted from the rates observed with a sample or a standard. These corrected rates are directly proportional to the amounts of radium present, assuming no radioactive elements other than radium or its decay products to be present in the ore.

Fig. 37-1. Alpha-ray Electroscope.

C = Charging button; L = Gold leaf; M = Microscope; S = Sample.

## BETA-RAY METHOD

*Procedure.*—The beta-ray method is very similar in principle to the alpha-ray method, the main difference being that an end-window Geiger-Müller tube with amplifier and scaler is substituted for the gold-leaf electroscope to detect the beta rays from the sample. Each beta ray entering the tube is recorded by the scaler and the observation consists in determining the counting rate by recording the total number of particles in a measured interval of time. As in the alpha-ray method, it is essential that all samples to be compared should be as closely as possible of the same physical and chemical nature as the standard and of the same geometrical shape. The arrangement is shown in Fig. 37-2.

## GAMMA-RAY METHOD

*Procedure.*—This method is less sensitive than the preceding but is effective for ores of moderately high radium content and is customarily used for comparison of concentrated preparations of radium. The ore may be in a coarser state and is placed at a standard position from one or more gamma-ray type Geiger-Müller counter tubes, having metal walls of a thickness great enough to exclude all of the alpha rays and practically all of the beta rays. The counting procedure is identical with that for beta-ray counting and appropriate standards are required for calibrating the apparatus. An arrangement of four gamma-ray tubes in a square is shown in Fig. 37-3. In this geometry the counting rate is relatively independent of the position of the sample.

Where the more elaborate electronic equipment cannot be used, there are available portable, dry-cell operated, Geiger-Müller counters provided with headphones

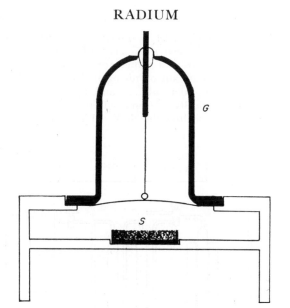

FIG. 37-2. Beta-ray end-window Geiger-Muller Tube.
$G$ = Geiger-Muller tube; $S$ = Sample.

for detection of the pulses produced by the radiation. At low counting rates, the pulses may be counted by ear for a given time interval to obtain approximate values of the amount of radium in the sample. Such equipment is now commonly used in prospecting for radium ore.

## RADON METHOD

The most sensitive and convenient as well as reliable and accurate method for the determination of radium in ore samples is provided by the measurement of the radon produced from the radium. By identification of the characteristic half life of the radon, this method insures that only the radium is measured.

*Procedure.*—A weighed sample of the ore is treated with nitric acid, which usually will dissolve a large part of the ore. The residue is treated with hydrofluoric acid, to remove silica, followed by a carbonate fusion. This melt is dissolved in nitric acid and added to the solution obtained from treating the ore directly with nitric acid. This procedure can be followed for nearly all radium-bearing minerals or sludges. In every case it is important to end up with an absolutely clear solution, free of suspended silica, on which radon is often readily adsorbed.

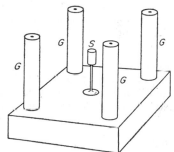

FIG. 37-3. Four Gamma-ray Counter Tubes, connected in parallel and arranged in a square.

$G$ = Gamma-ray tubes; $S$ = Sample.

The radon generated by the radium in this solution may be measured according to a method described in the Journal of Research of the National Bureau of

Standards, **31**, 181, 1943.  In Fig. 37-4 is shown a diagram of the essential components of the equipment.  The clear nitric acid solution is placed in the flask, $S$, attached by a ground glass joint to a reflux condenser.  The solution is boiled at a reduced pressure while a stream of nitrogen, freed of radon by storing for 30 days, bubbles through the inlet tube $A$ and up through $T_2$.  After 15 or 20 minutes the radon is practically all removed from the solution and the stopcocks, $T_1$ and $T_2$, are closed sealing the flask.  The radon is now permitted to

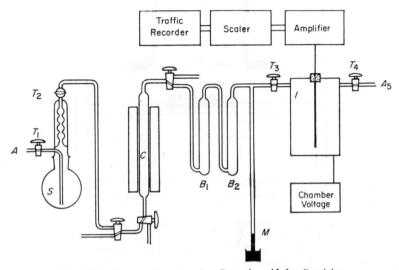

Fig. 37-4.  Radon Chamber for **Counting Alpha** Particles.

$I$ = Ion-pulse chamber; $B_1$ = Drierite; $B_2$ = $P_2O_5$; $C$ = Hot, reduced copper; $S$ = Radium solution; $M$ = Mercury manometer.

accumulate in the solution for a measured interval of time (considerably longer than the time required to remove the radon initially by boiling).  One-half the maximum equilibrium amount collects in 3.825 days and it is usually unnecessary to use collection periods longer than this.

The accumulated radon is transferred to the ion-counting chamber, $I$, by evacuating the chamber and connecting tubing up to the stopcock, $T_2$, and then closing $T_4$, closing off the connection to the vacuum pump.  With the reduced copper in the tube, $C$, hot, the solution in the flask, $S$, is again boiled at reduced pressure, as $T_2$ is gradually opened, and a stream of nitrogen is admitted through $T_1$.  The hot, reduced copper removes traces of oxygen from the nitrogen (which is necessary because the oxygen has an adverse affect on counting characteristics of the ion-counting chamber).  Drierite in the bulb, $B_1$, and $P_2O_5$ in the bulb, $B_2$, serve to remove water vapor which would impair the electrical insulation in the ion chamber.  When the pressure of nitrogen in the chamber has reached atmospheric, as indicated by the manometer, $M$, stopcock $T_3$ is closed.

It is convenient to wait approximately three hours for the immediate decay products of radon to come into transient equilibrium before starting the counting.  Each alpha particle ejected from a radioactive nucleus produces a trail of ions which, when collected on the central electrode by the applied electric field, produces a voltage pulse on this electrode which is sufficiently amplified by the linear amplifier to actuate the electronic scaler. It is sometimes advantageous to use some type of automatic recorder when a large number of chambers are operated simultaneously. The apparatus is calibrated by substituting for the flask, $S$, a similar one containing a known amount of radium and repeating the operations described above. Under ordinary conditions this calibration need be repeated only at infrequent intervals since the calibration factor is a constant, determined only by the dimensions and operating conditions of the chamber. Each use of the chamber leaves a small deposit of solid radon decay products on the interior surfaces. This deposit decays rather promptly to RaD ($Pb^{210}$) which then continues to decay with a half life of about 22 years. Consequently the background counting rate increases gradually with use and when it becomes of sufficient magnitude to limit the accuracy of the measurements the interior of the chamber must be cleaned, by careful machining, or the chamber replaced.

This method of determining radium can be illustrated by a hypothetical numerical example to demonstrate the various steps in the procedure. The calibration is made by use of a radon standard, available from the National Bureau of Standards, containing $10^{-9}$ grams of radium in a 200 ml. solution, introduced into a solution-flask of the apparatus according to the instructions accompanying the standard. Assume that the standard is then deemanated at 4:00 P.M. and at 8:00 A.M. the following day the accumulated radon is transferred to the ion chamber. Three hours later the alpha particles are counted for one hour, yielding 14,380 counts. This number is sufficient for the relative standard deviation, $\sqrt{N}/N$ (where $N$ is the total number of counts recorded) to be less than 1% of the observed counts, which will be assumed to be of sufficient accuracy for the purpose in hand. It will also be assumed that the background counting rate is of the order of 50 counts per hour and therefore negligible for this degree of accuracy. The counting rate, within ±1%, is 240 counts per minute. This should be corrected for the decay of the radon during the 3 hours it stood in the chamber before counting began and for its average decay during the counting process. The correction factor for the decay of radon in three hours is $e^{0.0226}$ which is approximately 1.023. The average decay during counting is given by

$$\frac{e^{-\lambda t}}{1 - e^{-\lambda t}}$$

This fraction is so near unity for $t =$ one hour that this correction also may be neglected in this instance. Therefore the corrected counting rate is $240 \times 1.023 = 245$ counts per minute from the radon at the time of its removal from the solution. The collection time of 16 hours permitted a fraction of the equilibrium amount given by $1 - e^{-0.121} = 0.114$ of the radon to grow in the solution. Therefore the calibration constant of the chamber may be expressed as $245/0.114 = 2149$ counts per minute per $10^{-9}$ curie of radon.

Next assume that 1.38 mg. of ore was used to make a solution and that 0.01 of this solution was introduced into another flask at $S$, deemanated, and allowed to accumulate radon for 36 hours, after which the radon was transferred to the chamber and counted, again after a delay of 3 hours, and yielded 14,915 counts in 30 minutes, or 497 counts per minute. At the time of transfer, this counting rate would have been $497 \times 1.023 = 508$ counts per minute. Therefore the amount of radon removed from the solution is $508/2149 \times 10^{-9}$ or $0.236 \times 10^{-9}$ curies. In 36 hours, 0.238 of the equilibrium amount of radon had accumulated, hence the amount of radium in the solution is given by $0.236/0.238 = 0.99 \times 10^{-9}$ grams. This was contained in 0.01 of the total ore sample weighed initially, from which the amount of radium per gram of ore is computed as $99/1.38 \times 10^{-9} = 7.2 \times 10^{-8}$ grams of radium per gram of ore.

*Chapter 38*

# RHENIUM AND TECHNETIUM*

Re, *at. wt.* 186.2; *d.* 21; *m.p.* 3180°C.; *b.p.* 2053°C.; *oxides,* $Re_2O_7$, $ReO_3$, $ReO_2$, $Re_2O_3$

$Tc^{99}$ and other isotopes; *oxides,* $Tc_2O_7$, $TcO_3$, $TcO_2$

Rhenium was not characterized until 1925 and its rarity properly places it among "less familiar" elements. Sulfidic copper ores, certain platinum ores, and some molybdenites may contain several tenths part per million of rhenium; rhenium-bearing minerals rarely exceed a Re content of 20 p. p. m. Chemically, the element is unlike its congener manganese, and manganese ores are relatively poor sources for rhenium. The perrhenate ion is but a weak oxidant and represents the most characteristic state of this element in solution.

The intermediate element, technetium, occurs primarily as the man-made, weakly beta-active $Tc^{99}$; its chemistry is more closely similar to that of rhenium than to manganese. The radiochemical assay of specific Tc isotopes is usual. Should conventional measuring steps be applied for the gross assay of isotopic mixtures of Tc, the isotopic history of the sample would be prerequisite to calculating percentage composition.

While gravimetric assay methods are available for the determination of large amounts of rhenium, the analytical chemistry of this element has emphasized the development of isolation techniques, particularly from molybdenum, and the measurement of low concentrations by colorimetric or spectrophotometric means. Few sensitive qualitative tests for rhenium are sufficiently selective for application without prior separations or concentration.

## DETECTION

Rhenium(VII) can be caused to concentrate in the acid insoluble sulfide group of classical separation schemes if the acidity is augmented. The separation of brown-black $Re_2S_7$ is both slow and critically dependent on the acidity. At least 1 hour of saturation with hydrogen sulfide should be employed. The recovery is quantitative only if the acidity is about 3.5 to 9.0 N, in the case of HCl. Less than 50% of the rhenium is precipitated from acid concentrations below 1.2 N.

The sulfide is readily dissolved on warming with 5% NaOH solution and adding 30% $H_2O_2$ dropwise as needed. Insoluble hydrous oxides should be filtered off, and the filtrate may be concentrated to a small volume prior to testing by one or more of the following methods.

1. A portion of the filtrate may be adjusted to about 4 N in HCl and treated with 1/10 its volume, each, of 20% sodium thiocyanate and 20% stannous chloride

* Chapter by Charles L. Rulfs, Department of Chemistry, University of Michigan, Ann Arbor, Michigan.

solutions. A permanent yellow to red color, persisting beyond 40 minutes, indicates the presence of rhenium. For closer observation, a faint coloration may be concentrated by extraction into a small volume of ether. A red color that fades appreciably indicates the presence of molybdenum and specific Mo/Re separations are advisable before drawing any further conclusions. A quantitative estimation via thiocyanate, but following a tetraphenylarsonium perrhenate extraction from molybdenum, is described later. Alternatively, molybdenum(VI) may be precipitated and either filtered off or extracted as its oxinate or as its cupferrate (see details below).

2. The microscopical observation of bipyramidical $CsReO_4$ formed from a drop of the test solution and a crystal of CsCl may be possible. This test is not very sensitive.

3. The blue-green color of $ReCl_6^{-2}$ ion may be discernible if a portion of the test solution is acidified to 50% HCl and warmed with 0.5 g. of $N_2H_4 \cdot 2HCl$. With critical samples the solution may be examined spectrophotometrically in the ultraviolet region (see details below) giving a much more sensitive and more selective test.

4. With an instrument of good dispersion, the rhenium concentrate can be examined by emission spectrography. The most persistent lines are at 3460.5 A (very wide, a triplet) and the blue line at 4889.2 A. Two green lines at 5271.0 A and 5275.6 A are also prominent.

5. The perrhenate catalyzed reduction of tellurates by stannous chloride [1] and a catalytic polarographic wave of thioperrhenate [2] are claimed to be sensitive tests. Not much is known of their general reliability and selectivity, however. No very satisfactory flame or bead tests have been reported for rhenium.

## ESTIMATION

Concentrates or products containing rhenium as a major component are encountered only infrequently. Even in such cases the rhenium must be essentially isolated prior to gravimetric assay with nitron or with tetraphenylarsonium chloride; though the latter has been shown to be moderately selective. The appreciable solubility of $TlReO_4$ and the incompleteness of formation or inexactness of stoichiometry of $Re_2S_7$, $ReO_2$, and electrodeposited Re make these forms unsuited for gravimetry. No good titrimetric techniques are available for rhenium.

The usual occurrence of rhenium will range from the minor constituent to the trace concentration level. Selective isolation via distillation of $HReO_4$, chelation and liquid-liquid extraction, or ion-exchange separations must precede measurements by colorimetric or spectrophotometric means. The ubiquitous thiocyanate plus stannous reduction has been the classical color forming method with rhenium; its greatest limitation in this role being the prominent interference of molybdenum which commonly accompanies rhenium. Perfect separation steps can overcome this difficulty, but more selective spectrophotometric measurements (e.g., of $ReCl_6^{-2}$ in the ultraviolet) contribute greatly to the reliability.

A technetium(V) thiocyanate color can also become the basis of measurement for this element.[3] Careful control of the conditions of color development permits discrimination from rhenium and some discrimination from molybdenum. The

[1] Anisimov, B. S., J. Applied Chem. (U.S.S.R.), **17**, 658, 1944.
[2] Heyrovsky, J., Nature, **135**, 870, 1935.
[3] Crouthamel, C. E., Anal. Chem., **29**, 1758, 1957.

radiochemical measurement of $Tc^{99}$ ($\beta$, 0.31 Mev.), or of other active isotopes, would often comprise the most appropriate type of measuring step.

The polarographic reduction of perrhenate gives a well-defined wave at $-0.38$ volt (versus saturated calomel electrode) in 4 $N$ $HClO_4$ solution and should sometimes be of value.

## PREPARATION AND SOLUTION OF SAMPLE

Alkaline reagents are preferable whenever their use is not too cumbersome. Any rhenium material may be converted to a soluble perrhenate by fusion with $Na_2O_2$. Fusion with $Na_2CO_3$, or with $Na_2CO_3$ plus $NaNO_3$, is about equally general as a mode of attack and has the advantage that platinum crucibles may be employed. The disulfide of rhenium is one of the few Re compounds resistant to dissolution in aqueous NaOH plus $H_2O_2$; this mixture readily dissolves the metal.

All modes of acid attack, while sometimes useful, invite more or less danger of loss of some volatile perrhenic acid (or, of rhenium heptoxide from anhydrous fusions). Any acid most appropriate to the bulk of the sample may serve; but an oxidizing acid, like $HNO_3$, is most desirable with metallic Re or with $ReO_2$. The use of a very efficient reflux condenser or of an alkaline effluent trap system should be considered in careful work whenever an acid dissolution is necessary. Organic materials to be wet-oxidized should be protected in a similar fashion. The dry combustion of rhenium-containing organic materials might or might not be a safe practice in the initial stages, but would certainly be unsafe beyond the point of removal of reducing materials unless alkaline agents are added.

## SEPARATIONS

While rhenium is mercury insoluble, it will quantitatively deposit in or on a mercury cathode under the usual conditions of this separation but with the addition of anode separation. In moist air, however, the deposit is rapidly reoxidized at the surface of the mercury to a water-soluble state.

Several hours of saturation with hydrogen sulfide in a 3.5 to 9.0 $N$ HCl medium are advisable to insure the quantitative precipitation of $Re_2S_7$. The separation is not complete at either higher or lower acidities. The addition of milligram amounts of $As^{+3}$ (or, $Cu^{+2}$, $Hg^{+2}$ or $Sb^{+3}$) as gatherer has been used in the collection of trace levels of rhenium. The heptasulfide readily dissolves in $NH_3$ or NaOH solution to which $H_2O_2$ is added as needed. While a qualitatively useful solubilization of Mo sulfide from $Re_2S_7$ may be achieved by digesting this precipitate with aqueous $Na_2S$, it is never certain that some rhenium will not be lost as thioperrhenate. A lower level of acidity, about 1.5 to 7.5 $N$ in HCl, may be suggested for the isolation of $Tc_2S_7$.

The classical techniques for separating rhenium from gross impurities amount to variations of a steam distillation of $HReO_4$ from different acidic media,[4] one example of which will be described below. Systematic studies have been reported on the vapor pressures of $Re_2O_7$, $HReO_4$ [5] and of $Tc_2O_7$, $HTcO_4$ [6] systems. The

[4] Hiskey, C. F., and Meloche, V. W., Ind. Eng. Chem., Anal. Ed., **12**, 503, 1940; Hoffman, J. I., and Lundell, G. E. F., J. Research Natl. Bur. Standards, **23**, 497, 1939; Hurd, L. C., and Hiskey, C. F., Ind. Eng. Chem., Anal. Ed., **10**, 623, 1938.

[5] Smith, W. T., Line, L. E., and Bell, W. A., J. Am. Chem. Soc., **74**, 4964, 1952.

[6] Smith, W. T., Cobble, J. W., and Boyd, G. E., *ibid.*, **75**, 5773, 1953.

cumbersome and tedious character of such separations favors their replacement by various liquid-liquid extractions.

Tetraphenylarsonium perrhenate is quantitatively extracted into chloroform from aqueous molybdate solutions, using a pH range of 7 to 13. Unfortunately, back-extraction is not feasible and the destruction of excess reagent in the organic phase is difficult.

Ether extracts an ethyl xanthate compound of Mo(VI) from Re solutions, but partial reduction of the Mo necessitates its reoxidation and reextraction.[7] The chloroform extraction of molybdenum cupferrate from aqueous perrhenate will be described in a subsequent procedure.

Useful separations by ion exchange include the use of Dowex-1 for Mo/Tc or for W/Re separation [8] and of Dowex-2 for the resolution of Re/Tc.[9] Amberlite IRA-400 has been found to retain perrhenate from 10% NaOH solutions while passing up to 3000-fold excesses of molybdate.[10]

## GRAVIMETRIC METHODS

The quantitative electrodeposition of Re is possible but difficulties attending the ready oxidation of the deposit prevent its use.[11] The nitron precipitation of perrhenate [12] has been largely supplanted by the tetraphenylarsonium perrhenate procedure.[13]

Rhenium concentrates resulting from the alkaline peroxide dissolution of separated $Re_2S_7$, or other sources, may be used in the following procedure. Most acids, except $HNO_3$ or $HClO_4$, do not interfere in concentrations up to 0.5 $M$, and up to 6 $M$ $NH_4OH$ may be used as the medium. Up to 0.2 g. of Mo can be tolerated in the presence of tartaric acid or using the ammonia medium. Interferences include the ions of Hg, Sn, Bi, $VO^{++}$, $Br^-$, $I^-$, $SCN^-$, $MnO_4^-$, $IO_4^-$, $NO_3^-$ and $ClO_4^-$.

*Procedure.*—Adjust the neutral perrhenate solution containing from 0.5 to 100 mg. of rhenium to a total volume of 25 to 60 ml. In general, this solution may be about 0.5 $M$ in NaCl (but the media previously noted may be used where desired) and should contain a moderate excess of the tetraphenylarsonium chloride reagent. The reagent may be added as the solid to minimize dilution. Digest hot and let the solution stand for several hours or overnight, stirring several times. Filter with suction through a tared glass frit or Gooch crucible. Wash several times with cold water and dry at 110 to 125°C. The factor to perrhenate is 0.3950, or 0.2940 to the metal.

[7] Malouf, E. E., and White, M. G., Anal. Chem., **23,** 497, 1951.

[8] Huffman, E. H., Oswalt, R. L., and Williams, L. A., J. Inorg. Nuclear Chem., **3,** 49, 1956.

[9] Atteberry, R. W., and Boyd, G. E., J. Am. Chem. Soc., **72,** 4805, 1950.

[10] Meloche, V. W., and Preuss, A. F., Anal. Chem., **26,** 1911, 1954.

[11] Lundell, G. E. F., and Knowles, H. B., J. Research Natl. Bur. Standards, **18,** 629, 1937.

[12] Geilmann, W., and Voigt, A., Z. anorg. Chem., **193,** 311, 1930; Scott, Standard Methods of Chemical Analysis, 5th Ed., Van Nostrand, 1939.

[13] Willard, H. H., and Smith, G. M., Ind. Eng. Chem., Anal. Ed., **11,** 305, 1939.

## TITRIMETRIC METHODS

No very popular titrimetric procedures for rhenium have been described. Its redox behavior permits a variety of oxidation levels and several disproportionation reactions are possible; but few clean-cut transitions have been claimed. Lundell and Knowles eight-electron zinc-column reduction of acidic Re(VII) to "equivalent" rhenide (as likely, rhenium hydride as Re$^-$) is as promising a basis as any redox reaction yet reported. Any standard oxidant of moderate strength can be used as the titrant. Only very dilute (less than millimolar) perrhenate solutions are quantitatively reduced, however; and the technique has other complicating features such as the need for a water-jacketed reductor, nitrogen atmosphere, etc.

An indirect tetraphenylarsonium procedure has been described [14] based on the back-titration with iodine of an excess of the reagent. In most cases it seems to offer little advantage over the gravimetric technique.

The electrodeposition of metallic Re on platinum is possible, but the rapid oxidation to $Re_2O_7$ complicates the gravimetric treatment. However, complete reoxidation (either in moist air or in neutral $H_2O_2$) and dissolution as $HReO_4$ permits a neutralimetric measurement.

## COLORIMETRIC AND SPECTROPHOTOMETRIC METHODS

This represents the most generally appropriate class of measurement for practical rhenium analyses. Three procedures are described in detail, including one volatilization and two different extraction techniques as representative of typical preliminary separations. Some modifications will suggest themselves and it is obvious that instrumental readings could well replace visual comparison in the first two procedures. Because of its special importance, appropriate spectrophotometric data are shown in Fig. 38-1. Further detail on the development of the rhenium thiocyanate color with time as well as on the application of this technique for the determination of technetium is available in the literature.[3]

### DISTILLATION AND THIOCYANATE COLOR (AQUEOUS) [4]

*Procedure.*—Add 20 ml. of concentrated nitric acid to 4 g. of pulverized molybdenite contained in a 250-ml. Erlenmeyer flask. Allow to react and add 5 ml. of fuming nitric acid, shaking at intervals. Warm on a hot plate below the boiling point until the disappearance of red fumes and cautiously add 50 ml. of concentrated hydrochloric acid. Evaporate, replacing the hydrochloric acid as needed (about 150 ml. are required) until chlorine is no longer evolved. Concentrate to about 25 ml., cool, and very carefully add 75 ml. of concentrated sulfuric acid. Transfer the suspension to a 300-ml. all-glass distilling flask and distill at 260–270°C. The distilling flask should contain an inlet tube extending nearly to its bottom, an internal thermometer, and a coiled air-condenser exit tube, followed by a water condenser. Pass a continuous stream of one part air or carbon dioxide and two parts dry steam through the solution. Collect about 250 ml. of distillate in an ice-cooled receiver over a period of 2.5 hours.

Add aqueous bromine in bromide solution to the distillate dropwise until a faint yellow color indicates the destruction of any sulfur dioxide. Add 100 ml.

14 Willard, H. H., and Smith, G. M., Ind. Eng. Chem., Anal. Ed., 11, 186, 1939.

of concentrated hydrochloric acid to the distillate and to each of three standards containing 0.01, 0.05, and 0.1 mg. of rhenium. Cool and add 10 ml. of 20% sodium thiocyanate solution and 10 ml. of 20% stannous chloride solution. Mix and let stand about 45 minutes to allow for the fading of any molybdenum com-

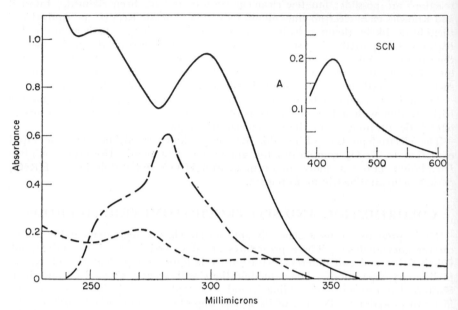

FIG. 38-1. Absorption Spectra of Rhenium(IV), Molybdenum(V), and Hydrazine in 4 N Hydrochloric Acid.

_____ Molybdenum(V), 0.5 mM.
_ _ _ _ _ _ Rhenium(IV), 0.05 mM.
_ _ _ _ _ _ Hydrazine, 0.05 M.

Spectrum of Re Thiocyanate Complex in Ether (1 mg. Re/L. ether).

plex. Dilute each solution to any convenient common volume, such as 500 ml. Using 100-ml. Nessler tubes, compare the sample with an appropriate standard using suitable volumes to match intensities. Calculate from measurements of the heights at balance. Check the match after an additional 30 minutes to be certain that any molybdenum color has faded.

## TETRAPHENYLARSONIUM PERRHENATE EXTRACTION AND THIOCYANATE COLOR [15]

*Procedure.*—React 1 g. of powdered molybdenite with 10–15 ml. of fuming nitric acid. Destroy the nitrate by repeated evaporations with hydrochloric acid, evaporating finally to about 2 ml. volume. Neutralize the excess acid with 10 M sodium hydroxide and adjust the pH to 8–9 by adding solid sodium bicarbonate. Dilute to 40–50 ml. volume.

Add 15–20 mg. of tetraphenylarsonium chloride and shake with 15–20 ml. of

[15] Tribalat, S., Anal. Chim. Acta, **3,** 113, 1949.

chloroform.   Carefully separate the chloroform layer and shake it with powdered anhydrous calcium chloride; filter through paper that has been moistened with chloroform.   With low amounts of rhenium it is advisable to repeat this operation in order to remove traces of trapped aqueous solution containing molybdenum.

Evaporate the chloroform extract on a water bath to a volume of 1 ml.   Transfer to a suitable test tube or color comparison tube and add 2 ml. of concentrated hydrochloric acid and 0.2 ml. of 20% ammonium thiocyanate.   Shake, and mix in 0.2 ml. of 10% stannous chloride in concentrated hydrochloric acid.   Extract with 1 ml. of isoamyl alcohol.   With very low rhenium (less than 1 microgram) only a faint yellow coloration is obtained and 0.5 ml. of alcohol may be used. When over 10 micrograms of Re is present, 2 ml. of alcohol is desirable.

## CUPFERRON EXTRACTION AND REDUCTION TO $[ReCl_6]^{-2}$ [16]

*Procedure.*—Adjust the perrhenate solution ("ores" my be converted to perrhenate by means of a sodium peroxide fusion) to a volume of about 25 ml. and make 2 $N$ in sulfuric acid.   Transfer to a 125-ml. separatory funnel and shake for 2–3 min. with 50 ml. of cupferron in chloroform solution.   (Use only white C.P. cupferron.   Aged cupferron may be recrystallized from ethanol.   0.5 g. of cupferron in dilute sulfuric acid is shaken with 50 ml. of chloroform to prepare fresh solution as needed.)   Separate and discard the chloroform layer.   Repeat the extraction if the aqueous layer is still colored.   Finally, extract the molybdenum-free aqueous layer once with 30–50 ml. of pure chloroform to remove the last traces of cupferron.

Transfer the aqueous layer to a beaker and neutralize the solution with sodium hydroxide.   Cover and evaporate to about 5 ml. volume.   Add 25 ml. of concentrated hydrochloric acid and 1 g. of hydrazine dihydrochloride.   Boil for 50–60 minutes.   Cool and transfer to a 50-ml. volumetric flask, dilute to the mark.   Read in a quartz cell at 281.5 m$\mu$ against a blank containing equivalent amounts of acid and hydrazine.   Calibration will show that Beer's Law is valid for the system for solutions up to 0.1 millimolar, and solutions as dilute as 0.002 m$M$ are easily read in 1-cm cells.

As shown in Figure 38-1, the absorbance of hydrazine is relatively weak at 281.5 m$\mu$ and stronger at 265 m$\mu$, where the rhenium curve has a shoulder.   One may treat the system as a two-component mixture reading at these two wavelengths against a hydrochloric acid blank, instead of the acid plus hydrazine blank.   The figure also shows that similarly treated molybdenum has only a moderate and a quite different absorbance than rhenium, permitting two-component analysis, using readings at 281.5 m$\mu$ and about 298 m$\mu$.   In this way, equal parts or more of molybdenum may be tolerated without recourse to the cupferron separation.

Meloche [17] describes an alternative reduction procedure in which 0.05 to 1.5 mg. of Re as perrhenate in less than 10-ml. volume are treated with 25 ml. of concentrated hydrochloric acid in a 50-ml. volumetric flask.   While nitrogen is passed, 1 ml. of about 0.05 $M$ chromous chloride is added and reacted for 2 minutes.   Air is bubbled for 2–3 minutes to oxidize the excess chromous ion.   After diluting to volume, the solutions are read as prescribed above, except that a blank of aerated chromous ion in acid is employed.

16 Meyer, R. J., and Rulfs, C. L., Anal. Chem., **27**, 1387, 1955.
17 Meloche, V. W., and Martin, R. L., Anal. Chem., **28**, 1671, 1956.

# Chapter 39

# SCANDIUM *

Sc, *at. wt.* 44.956; *sp. gr.* 3.02 (at 10°C.); *m.p.* 1200°C.; *b.p.* 2400°C. (calculated); *oxide*, $Sc_2O_3$

Scandium is very widely distributed in minute quantities in almost all rocks, but it is found in appreciable quantity only in very few minerals. Micas, cassiterite, and wolframite from some localities, euxenite and keilhauite contain a few tenths per cent of scandia; wiikite contains a little over 1% and thortveitite, the only mineral of which scandia is an essential constituent, over 30%.

## DETECTION

In qualitative analysis scandium is found in the iron group as precipitated by ammonium hydroxide. This is dissolved in hydrochloric acid, any ferric chloride present is reduced by passage of hydrogen sulfide, and the solution neutralized with sodium carbonate, avoiding a permanent precipitate. Scandium, thorium, zirconium, and titanium are then precipitated by boiling the solution for an hour with 5 g. of sodium thiosulfate. The washed precipitate is extracted with hot hydrochloric acid, the sulfur filtered off, and the filtrate neutralized with ammonia. Five grams of ammonium tartrate are added, followed by a few drops of hydrochloric acid to ensure a clear solution; this is boiled and treated dropwise with ammonia until it smells faintly of ammonia. The gradual separation of a crystalline precipitate indicates the presence of scandium.

If the amount of zirconia and titania present is large, these elements should be removed by precipitation with cupferron before applying the tartrate test; excess of cupferron may be removed by shaking the solution with chloroform.

In the examination of mixtures of the rare earths for traces of scandia, the mixed oxides obtained by ignition of the oxalates (see Chapter on Cerium and the Rare Earth Metals) are dissolved by boiling with hydrochloric acid and the scandia is concentrated by the thiosulfate method described above, but several drops of a 1% solution of hydrazine carbonate are added after the solution has been boiled for an hour. The washed precipitate is digested with hot hydrochloric acid, the sulfur removed, and the solution tested by the tartrate method or concentrated and examined by spark spectrography; the most sensitive scandium lines are 3613.83 A, 3630.74 A, and 3642.78 A. Alternatively the precipitate may be ignited and 20 mg. inserted in the positive crater of an arc, the resulting spectrum being examined for the line 3911.81 A.

* Chapter by A. R. Powell, Research Manager, Johnson, Matthey & Co., Ltd., London, England.

## ESTIMATION

### PREPARATION AND SOLUTION OF THE SAMPLE

Minerals containing the rare earths are decomposed by treatment with hydrochloric or sulfuric acids. Euxenite and similar minerals containing titanium, tantalum, and niobium can be decomposed by cautiously treating the moistened, finely powdered sample with 40% hydrofluoric acid; after the violent action has subsided the acid is evaporated almost to dryness on the water bath, the residue extracted with boiling water, and the insoluble material collected in a polyethylene funnel and dissolved by heating with concentrated sulfuric acid in a platinum dish. Wolfram, which sometimes contains scandia, is decomposed by digestion of the slimed mineral with aqua regia; the acid is almost completely evaporated on the water bath and the soluble bases are extracted from the tungstic acid residue with boiling water.

### DETERMINATION

*Procedure.*—The solution obtained by any of the above methods is saturated with hydrogen sulfide to remove heavy metals, and the filtrate nearly neutralized with sodium carbonate, avoiding a permanent precipitate. After addition of 10 g. of sodium thiosulfate the liquid is boiled for one hour, 1 ml. of a 1% solution of hydrazine carbonate is added and the precipitate is collected on a loose paper and well washed with hot water; it is then rinsed back into the beaker with a minimum of hot water and boiled with 10 ml. of hydrochloric acid, the separated sulfur being removed by filtering the solution through the same paper. The filtrate is evaporated to expel most of the free acid, diluted to 100 ml., nearly neutralized with dilute ammonia, avoiding a permanent precipitate, and poured into 100 ml. of 20% ammonium tartrate solution. If the solution is not clear a few drops of hydrochloric acid are added until any turbidity disappears. The solution is boiled and 10% ammonium hydroxide added drop by drop with stirring until the liquid smells faintly of ammonia. After cooling overnight the precipitate of scandium ammonium tartrate is collected and washed with 2% ammonium tartrate solution. To eliminate traces of impurities, particularly the metals of the yttria group, the precipitate should be redissolved in hydrochloric acid and the precipitation repeated exactly as before. The precipitate can be ignited directly to obtain $Sc_2O_3$ for weighing.

If the mineral contains large quantities of rare earths and scandia and appreciable quantities of titania and zirconia, the original solution should be treated with oxalic acid to recover the rare earths and scandia (see Chapter on Cerium and the Rare Earths). The oxides resulting from ignition of the oxalate precipitate are dissolved in hydrochloric acid and the solution is evaporated on the water bath to a moist crystal mass which is dissolved in 60 ml. of 0.5 N hydrochloric acid. After addition of 53 g. of ammonium thiocyanate crystals the solution is diluted to 100 ml. and shaken with 100 ml. of ether; the aqueous layer is removed and extracted twice more with 80 ml. of ether, 5 ml. of 2 N hydrochloric acid being added each time for each 100 ml. of aqueous layer. The ether extract contains the whole of the scandium and is free from thorium and the rare earth metals; it is treated with a little hydrochloric acid and the ether distilled off. The residual acid solution is cautiously heated with concentrated hydrochloric acid and then boiled with nitric acid to destroy the yellow derivatives of thiocyanic acid. After evaporation of most of the acid the solution is diluted to 150 ml. and the scandia precipitated with ammonium hydroxide. The ether extraction method can be used for testing the purity of the scandia obtained by the tartrate method; the ignited precipitate is dissolved in hydrochloric acid, the solution neutralized with ammonium hydroxide, treated with thiocyanate and shaken with ether.

The acid chloride solution obtained from the decomposition of wolfram is nearly neutralized with sodium carbonate and boiled with the cautious addition of hydrazine hydrochloride until the iron is reduced to the ferrous state. The solution is then treated with more sodium carbonate until almost neutral avoiding a permanent precipitate, and the scandia is recovered by boiling with thiosulfate and hydrazine carbonate; the precipitate is purified by the tartrate or ether-thiocyanate process.

# Chapter 40

# SELENIUM AND TELLURIUM*

Se, *at. wt.* 78.96; *sp. gr.* $\left\{ Cryst. \begin{cases} \textbf{\textit{Gray}} \textbf{4.79} \\ \alpha \textit{ form } 4.49, \beta \textit{ form } 4.41 \\ \textit{Amorph. } 4.26 \end{cases} \right\}$; *m.p.* 217°C.; *b.p.* 684.8°C.;

oxides, SeO, SeO$_2$, SeO$_3$

Te, *at. wt.* 127.60; *sp. gr.* 6.24; *m.p.* 450°C.; *b.p.* 990°C.; *oxides,* TeO$_2$, TeO$_3$

Selenium, which was discovered in 1817 by Berzelius in the flue dust of pyrite burners, is found in copper and iron pyrites, meteoric iron, and in the minerals clausthalite, PbSe; tiemannite, HgSe; guanajuatite, Bi$_2$Se$_3$; klockmannite, CuSe; eucairite, CuAgSe; crookesite (Cu,Tl,Ag)$_2$Se. The commercial source of selenium (and tellurium) is the slimes in the electrolytic copper refining cells.

Tellurium, which was discovered in 1782 by Muller, occurs in tellurides and arsenical iron pyrites and is frequently associated with gold, silver, lead, bismuth, and iron. Minerals in which tellurium is found include altaite, PbTe; calaverite, AuTe$_2$; coloradoite, HgTe; rickardite, Cu$_4$Te$_3$; petzite, Ag$_3$AuTe$_2$; sylvanite, (Ag,Au)Te$_2$; tellurite, TeO$_2$ (tellurium ochre); tetradymite, Bi$_2$Te$_3$S. Tellurium has also been found as the native metal.

Selenium is used as a decolorizer of glass to counteract the green ferrous shade; as selenium or sodium selenite to produce clear red glass, and for red enamels on ceramic ware and steel ware; in vulcanized rubber—the presence of 1–3% selenium notably increases the resistance to abrasion. The allotropic red crystalline form of selenium is used in microscopy as an imbedding substance. Selenium is used in the xerographic process (photo-printing). It is also used in photoelectric cells, electrical rectifiers, and as a stabilizer of lubricating oils. Many selenium compounds are extremely toxic.

Tellurium also finds uses as a coloring substance in the glass and ceramic industries, and as a (secondary) vulcanizing agent for rubber. It is also used in certain alloys of lead, iron and steel, one of which is a variety of stainless steel.

## DETECTION

Selenium and tellurium are commonly detected by precipitation with sulfur dioxide in hydrochloric acid solution. A solution of tetravalent or hexavalent selenium containing strong hydrochloric acid in the cold gives with either sulfur dioxide or an aqueous solution of the gas red amorphous selenium which, on

* Chapter revised by W. Charles Cooper, Chief Chemist, Canadian Copper Refiners, Limited, Montreal East, Quebec, Canada. The reviser wishes to acknowledge his indebtedness to Mr. Herbert Marshall, of Canadian Copper Refiners, Ltd., who developed many of the procedures; and to Mr. Stanislaus Skowronski, Retired Research Engineer, International Smelting and Refining Co., for valuable assistance.

warming, goes over to the gray, crystalline form. Solutions of tellurous or telluric tellurium in the presence of dilute hydrochloric acid when gassed with sulfur dioxide yield black, elementary tellurium.

Hydrogen sulfide gives with selenious acid solution a lemon yellow precipitate of selenium sulfide which on standing dissociates into sulfur and red amorphous selenium. Similarly the red brown tellurium sulfide, which is formed when hydrogen sulfide reacts with tellurous acid, dissociates into tellurium and sulfur. Both of the sulfides are soluble in alkaline sulfide solutions.

Stannous chloride, ferrous sulfate, hydroxylamine hydrochloride, hydrazine sulfate, phosphorous acid, or hypophosphorous acid added in the cold to solutions of tetravalent selenium give red elementary selenium. Selenite is reduced to elemental selenium by thiocyanate in 6 $N$ hydrochloric acid solution. As little as 0.05 p. p. m. of selenium can be detected by this reaction.[1] Potassium iodide added in excess to a hydrochloric acid solution of a selenate or selenite gives in the cold red selenium together with iodine. On warming the iodine distills and the red selenium goes over to the gray form.

A solution of Te(IV) or Te(VI) yields black elementary tellurium when treated with stannous chloride, hypophosphorous acid, hydrazine hydrochloride or with aluminum amalgam, zinc, or magnesium.

Neutral selenious solutions give with barium chloride a precipitate of barium selenite which is soluble in hydrochloric acid. Neutral selenates yield with barium chloride insoluble barium selenate, which, like all selenates, is decomposed on heating with the evolution of oxygen and subsequent reduction to the selenite. Precipitations of silver selenite and mercuric selenite have been employed for the quantitative estimation of selenium.[2]

The few soluble alkaline tellurites give with barium chloride a white precipitate of barium tellurite which is soluble in hydrochloric acid. Barium tellurate is analagous to barium selenate in its formation and decomposition.

*Sulfuric Acid Test.*—Selenium or a selenide with concentrated sulfuric acid, gently warmed, or with fuming sulfuric acid in the cold gives a green color the intensity of which varies from a light green to an almost opaque greenish black depending on the amount of selenium present. When the green solution is added to water, red elementary selenium is precipitated. The green color in the concentrated sulfuric acid is destroyed by warming the solution a few minutes. The test is not applicable to an oxidized selenium compound.

Tellurium or a telluride, but not oxidized tellurium compounds, gives in the cold with fuming sulfuric acid or with warm concentrated sulfuric acid a red color, the intensity of which depends on the amount of tellurium present. When the red solution is poured into water, black elementary tellurium is precipitated. When the red solution is warmed, sulfur dioxide is evolved, the red color disappears, and if much tellurium is present, white crystals of basic tellurium sulfate separate out. The sulfuric acid test has been applied to the spectrophotometric determination of selenium and tellurium,[3] and to the detection of tellurium in minerals.[4]

[1] Ljung, H. A., Ind. Eng. Chem., Anal. Ed., **9**, 328, 1937.

[2] Ripan-Tilici, R., Z. anal. Chem., **117**, 326, 1939; Deshmukh, G. S., and Sankaranarayanan, K. M., J. Indian Chem. Soc., **29**, 527, 1952.

[3] Wiberley, S. E., Bassett, L. G., Burrill, A. M., and Lyng, H., Anal. Chem., **25**, 1586, 1953.

[4] Goudey, H., Am. Minerol., **27**, 592, 1942.

*Detection of Selenium and Tellurium in Complex Mixtures.*—The substance in question is treated with aqua regia or with a mixture of hydrochloric acid and potassium chlorate, and the free chlorine expelled at a temperature below boiling in order to avoid loss of volatile chlorides. (Materials not decomposed in any acid or combination of acids may require fusion with an alkaline oxidizing flux. For this purpose nickel crucibles should be used since platinum vessels are seriously attacked.) The solution is then diluted and filtered to remove insoluble matter. Should tellurous acid precipitate on diluting with water, it can be redissolved by hydrochloric acid. The acid solution is treated with sulfur dioxide gas, the formation of a precipitate indicating the possible presence of selenium, tellurium, or gold. If the precipitate is allowed to settle, the liquid decanted, and the precipitate warmed with concentrated nitric acid, selenium and tellurium will dissolve leaving the gold insoluble. The nitric acid solution can be carefully evaporated with hydrochloric acid to destroy the nitric acid and then treated in concentrated hydrochloric acid solution with sulfur dioxide gas. If selenium is present it will appear as a red precipitate. The solution is then filtered through asbestos and the filtrate diluted with water and gassed with sulfur dioxide. A black precipitate indicates the presence of tellurium. The sulfur dioxide precipitate containing possible selenium, tellurium, and gold can, after washing, be treated directly with hot concentrated sulfuric acid in order to obtain, if possible, the characteristic selenium or tellurium colors.

## ESTIMATION

In the determination of selenium and tellurium where special precautions are not taken in regard to these elements, losses may occur due to coprecipitation or volatilization. Both elements may be coprecipitated with hydrous oxides of bismuth, antimony, iron, zinc, zirconium, titanium; hence such impurities should be solubilized. Volatilization loss is most pronounced with selenium which will distill in various acid vapors. With nitric acid solutions the loss may be prevented by oxidation to selenate with excess potassium bromate. With hydrochloric acid the loss is intensified in solutions greater than 6 $N$. Fortunately in most cases volatilization may be greatly minimized by a refluxing action made possible by the use of covered beakers or by evaporation below 100°C. Sulfuric acid fuming may be used to eliminate selenium from a selenium-tellurium mixture. However, dry tellurium sulfate is slowly volatile above 400°C. and should not be heated strongly in the absence of an alkali bisulfate.

The presence of organic matter in a solution from which selenium is to be precipitated may cause either a colloidal precipitate that cannot be filtered or a precipitate contaminated by organic matter. If there is a difficult organic component in the sample, it should be completely destroyed by the use of nitric acid and potassium chlorate or following nitric acid treatment by evaporation at 100°C. with a 1:1 sulfuric-perchloric acid mixture.

## SEPARATION

Volatilization in halogen or hydrohalide vapors may be employed to effect separations of selenium and tellurium from other elements not volatile in this manner. Thus selenides or tellurides may be distilled in chlorine. Heating selenites or tellurites in a stream of hydrogen chloride gas results in the formation of volatile

$SeO_2 \cdot 2HCl$ or $TeO_2 \cdot 2HCl$ while selenates and tellurates give chlorine in addition. Alternatively a sulfuric acid solution containing selenium may be distilled with hydrobromic acid to give a distillate of selenium relatively free from tellurium, iron, and copper but containing usually all the arsenic, antimony, and germanium impurities.

In solution selenium and tellurium may be separated from a large number of elements first by reduction to the tetravalent form and then to the elements by certain reducing agents in hydrochloric acid medium. Sulfur dioxide is the preferred reducing agent. If the solution is very impure, the elements are generally precipitated together and separated later. When solutions are highly impure and the amount of selenium and tellurium low, separation of the selenium and tellurium can be realized conveniently by precipitating basic zirconium selenite and tellurite along with zirconium hydroxide at pH 2. By this means a concentrate may be obtained which is remarkably free from iron, copper, and most other metals but containing all the arsenic and antimony present in the original solution.

## SEPARATION OF SELENIUM FROM TELLURIUM

**Keller's method** is to separate the selenium and tellurium from each other making use of the principle that selenium is completely precipitated by sulfur dioxide from concentrated hydrochloric acid solution while tellurium is not.

**Procedure.**—The two elements are separated from the other elements by sulfur dioxide in dilute hydrochloric acid solution. The washed precipitate is dissolved in nitric acid and the solution evaporated to dryness on the water bath. The residue is dissolved in 200 ml. of hydrochloric acid and the solution warmed to expel all free nitric acid. The solution is then saturated with sulfur dioxide gas at 15–20°C. The selenium is filtered off through a Gooch crucible, washed with water, then alcohol, and dried at 105°C. Following filtration the tellurium is precipitated in the filtrate by diluting with water, adding more sulfur dioxide and hydrazine hydrochloride as in the gravimetric method for tellurium. The tellurium is finally washed with water, then alcohol, dried at 90°C. and weighed.

The foregoing method parallels that of Lenher and Kao.[5]

**Distillation Method of Lenher and Smith.[6]**—This method is based on the fact that selenium chloride volatilizes from sulfuric acid solution when treated with hydrochloric acid gas while tellurium chloride is nonvolatile under the same conditions. None of the common elements naturally associated with selenium forms a volatile chloride under the conditions of the determination.

## GRAVIMETRIC METHODS FOR SELENIUM

Selenium is most commonly determined by precipitation as the element with sulfur dioxide. Hydroxylamine and hydrazine are also employed as reductants. This reduction to the element at the same time separates the selenium from most of the elements except gold, or in weaker hydrochloric acid concentrations, tellurium, also. When hydroxylamine hydrochloride or hydrazine hydrochloride is the precipitating agent, the material is usually most conveniently brought into hydrochloric acid solution and the selenium converted into the selenious state. From this selenious solution, which may be acid, neutral, or ammoniacal, these reducing agents on boiling precipitate elementary selenium which can be transferred

5 Lenher, V., and Kao, C. H., J. Am. Chem. Soc., **47**, 769, 1925.
6 Lenher, V., and Smith, D. P., J. Ind. Eng. Chem., **16**, 837, 1924.

to a Gooch crucible, washed, dried at 105°C., and weighed. Alternatively the crucible and precipitate may be weighed, the selenium volatilized and the crucible reweighed, the loss in weight being the weight of the selenium in the sample. (Conversion of the primary red amorphous precipitate of selenium to the black granular form by hot water is not recommended since a significant positive error may be introduced by permanent water occlusion.)

## SULFUR DIOXIDE METHOD

*Procedure.*—The addition of sulfur dioxide to a solution of selenious acid or a selenite which is stronger than 3.4 $N$ or 28% by volume in hydrochloric acid is one of the oldest and best methods of precipitating elementary selenium. A selenate or selenic acid must first be reduced to selenious acid by warming with hydrochloric acid, after which sulfur dioxide can be introduced as the gas or as a saturated solution in water or methyl alcohol.

The common sources of error in this method are: (1) the production of selenium monochloride as a result of too slow gassing, too high a temperature during gassing, or the presence of nitric acid; (2) the permanent enclosure of water or mother liquor in the precipitate brought about by too high a solution temperature. Where samples are prepared by evaporation to fumes with a sulfuric-nitric mixture, it is desirable to remove the residual nitric acid by the addition of solid sulfamic acid to the hot sulfuric acid. Most of the errors are removed by rapid gassing of the solution, filtration as soon as possible after gassing, and preliminary drying at 50°C. for 30 minutes before final treatment at 105°C. The solution temperature during precipitation should be about 15–20°C. A minimum of 6 $N$ hydrochloric acid is advisable to achieve the separation of selenium from tellurium present in small amounts, but the maximum acid concentration is recommended when large amounts are involved. Utmost accuracy in this method is obtained by deposition of the selenium precipitate on a base of suspended asbestos whereby the sources of error are still further reduced. It must not be forgotten that the selenium precipitate is very voluminous, and therefore coprecipitates finely divided silica and organic matter. Therefore the initial purity of the solution must be considered. As a general principle, the selenium should be filtered on an asbestos padded Gooch crucible and after drying at 105°C., weighed, ignited, and reweighed. Any error from gold and most of the errors due to occlusions are thus eliminated.

## TITRIMETRIC METHODS FOR SELENIUM

Numerous direct and indirect titrimetric procedures have been advanced for the determination of selenium. Many of these methods require conditions that are difficult to maintain and which render them unsuitable for routine analysis. A commendable permanganate method is that of Gooch and Clemons [7] as extended by Schrenk and Browning [8] and Barabas and Cooper.[9] In this method selenium and tellurium are oxidized in sulfuric acid medium from Se(IV) or Te(IV) to Se(VI) or Te(VI) by an excess of permanganate, the excess being determined by back titration with ferrous ammonium sulfate. Disodium phosphate is added to prevent the precipitation of manganese dioxide.

[7] Gooch, F. A., and Clemons, C. F., Am. J. Sci., **50,** 51, 1895.
[8] Schrenk, W. T., and Browning, B. L., J. Am. Chem. Soc., **48,** 2550, 1926.
[9] Barabas, S., and Cooper, W. C., Anal. Chem., **28,** 129, 1956.

## TITRIMETRIC PERMANGANATE METHOD

Schrenk and Browning's titrimetric permanganate method may be applied to the estimation of selenium in refined selenium, sodium selenite and selenate, and iron selenide.[9] Procedural details for the first three determinations are given under "Determinations in Specific Substances."

## COLORIMETRIC/PHOTOMETRIC METHODS FOR SELENIUM

The determination of micro amounts of selenium is at times accomplished colorimetrically on colloidal selenium following reaction with a reducing agent such as sulfur dioxide, phenylhydrazine,[10] or stannous chloride.[11] A selenium hydrosol stable for 5 days and obedient to Beer's Law in the concentration range 1 to 10 micrograms of selenium per milliliter has been reported.[11]

It is difficult to avoid a turbidimetric component even with gum arabic or polyvinyl alcohol as sol stabilizer. On the other hand, the turbidimetric component may be accentuated and stabilized through the use of methylcellulose thereby permitting a nephelometric estimation of selenium. This determination is useful in the range 0.7–4.5 micrograms per milliliter and no interference on the part of copper, iron, or tellurium is encountered.

## DIAMINOBENZIDINE METHOD

A widely used colorimetric method for selenium employs the 3,3'-diaminobenzidine reaction whereby the compound diphenylpiazselenol is formed. The compound is partially extracted by toluene at pH below 3 but quantitatively extracted at pH above 5. The extraction procedure makes the method more selective, because the colored salt solution does not interfere. Most common ions do not react with diaminobenzidine. The reaction can be carried out in the presence of ethylenediaminetetraacetic acid, which may be used for masking the polyvalent metals. Selenium is determined satisfactorily in the presence of iron, copper, molybdate, tritanium, chromium(III), nickel, cobalt, tellurium, and arsenic, and up to 5 mg. of vanadium(V). The strong oxidizing and reducing agents must be absent. The limit of sensitivity of the method is 50 p. p. b. with a 1-cm absorption cell.

*Apparatus.* **Beckman Spectrophotometer, Model B. Beckman pH Meter, Model N, or similar meter.**

*Reagents.* **3,3'-Diaminobenzidine Hydrochloride Solution, 0.5% in water.**—Store in a refrigerator.

**Standard Selenium Solution.**—A solution containing 1 mg. of selenium per ml. is prepared by dissolving 1.6337 g. of selenous acid ($H_2SeO_3$) in 1 liter of water. This stock solution is standardized gravimetrically. A 10-p. p. m. selenium solution is prepared by diluting the stock solution.

**Formic acid, 2.5 *M*.**

**EDTA Solution, 0.1 *M*.**—The disodium salt of (ethylenedinitrilo) tetraacetic acid (ethylenediaminetetraacetic acid) is used.

*Procedure.*—Place an aliquot containing not more than 50 micrograms of selenium in a 100-ml. beaker. Dilute to approximately 50 ml. with water after adding 2 ml. of 2.5 *M* formic acid. Adjust the pH to 2 to 3. Add 2 ml. of 0.5% diamino-

10 Dolique, R., Giroux, J., and Roca, S., Bull. soc. Chem., **10**, 49, 1943.
11 Shakhov, A. S., Zavodskaya Lab., **11**, 893, 1945.

benzidine solution and let stand for 30 to 50 minutes. Adjust the pH to 6 to 7 with 7 $M$ ammonium hydroxide. Transfer to a 125-ml. separatory funnel, add exactly 10 ml. of toluene, and shake vigorously for 30 seconds. Centrifuge the toluene portion for a few minutes. Separate and determine the absorbance at 420 m$\mu$, using a reagent blank. The calibration curves follow Beer's Law over the range of 5 to 25 micrograms of selenium per 10 ml. of toluene at the wave lengths 340 and 420 m$\mu$, 1 to 10 micrograms of selenium per 6 ml. of toluene (5-cm cell), and 10 to 100 micrograms of selenium per 10 ml. of toluene at 420 m$\mu$.

## ALTERNATE METHOD FOR TRACE AMOUNTS OF Se

This is a fluorometric modification of the foregoing procedure suitable for determining as little as 0.02 micrograms of Se in plant and other materials.

*Reagents.* *m*-Cresol Purple.—0.1% solution in 50% ethyl alcohol.

3,3'-Diaminobenzidine.—0.5% aqueous solution, freshly prepared from the tetrahydrochloride.

Zinc Dithiol.—1% suspension of the zinc complex of toluene-3,4-dithiol in 96% ethyl alcohol.

*Procedure.*—Dry the sample in a draft of air at 30 to 40°C. Transfer an amount of the finely ground material containing not less than 0.02 g. of selenium into a 6" x 1" borosilicate glass test tube. Add 10 ml. of nitric acid and leave it to digest at room temperature, preferably overnight. Heat carefully on a microburner rack. Add more nitric acid where necessary to prevent charring. After most of the material has been digested, add 5 ml. of 72% perchloric acid. When the volume of acid reaches 7 ml., reflux the mixture by standing the tube in an upright rack and inserting a funnel in a mouth of the tube. After oxidation is complete, remove the funnel and turn down the gas flame. Withdraw the acid fumes through a glass tube connected to a water pump until white fumes of perchloric acid are evolved. Cool, add a little water, and evaporate down to fumes of perchloric acid again to expel the last trace of nitric acid which would react with the dithiol. Warm with about 15 ml. of water and 4 ml. of 96% ethyl alcohol, and cool to room temperature to allow crystals of potassium perchlorate to separate out. Filter into a 100-ml. separating funnel and wash the paper with water to give a final volume of 35 ml.

Add 50 ml. of concentrated hydrochloric acid and 4 ml. of the suspension of zinc dithiol and let stand for 15 minutes. Extract the selenium complex into 10 ml. of a 50% mixture of ethylene chloride and carbon tetrachloride. Collect the organic phase in a 6" x 1" borosilicate glass-stoppered test tube. Extract again with 5 ml. of solvent and add to the first extract. To this add 1 ml. of 72% perchloric acid, 10 drops of nitric acid, and a glass ball. Boil off the organic solvent by placing the tubes in a 5-liter beaker containing boiling water. Digest the residue and heat of fumes of perchloric acid as before; then add water, and boil off to remove traces of nitric acid. Finally add about 20 ml. of water.

Add 2 ml. of 2.5 $M$ formic acid, 1 drop of *m*-Cresol Purple solution, and 7 $M$ ammonium hydroxide solution until the indicator just changes to yellow. Add 2 ml. of diaminobenzidine solution, dilute to about 45 ml., and let stand for 30 to 40 minutes. Add 7 $M$ ammonium hydroxide dropwise until the indicator just changes to purple, and dilute to 50 ml. Extract the selenadiazole into 10 ml. of toluene. Remove the toluene into a glass-stoppered tube by means of a teat-pipette and shake with a small amount of anhydrous calcium chloride.

Irradiate the selenadiazole in toluene, using a source emitting light in the region of 420 m$\mu$, and measure the resulting fluorescence within the band 550 to 600 m$\mu$. Calculate the amount of selenium by reference to a standard amount of 0.5 micrograms, the voltage on the multiplier phototube having been adjusted to give a full scale deflection on the microammeter with this amount.

## GRAVIMETRIC METHODS FOR TELLURIUM

Tellurium can be determined gravimetrically and separated from most of the elements except selenium and gold by a number of reducing agents. The oldest method, that of Berzelius, involves the precipitation of elementary tellurium with sulfur dioxide from dilute hydrochloric acid solution (1.2 to 5 $N$ or approximately 10 to 42% by volume). Complete precipitation is much delayed especially when the solution is warm and does not occur at all if the hydrochloric acid concentration is greater than 8.8 $N$. The hydrochloric acid solution of tellurium should always be allowed to stand 24 hours to insure complete precipitation. The tellurium is then transferred to a Gooch crucible, washed, and dried at 90°C. as quickly as possible in order to avoid the slight superficial oxidation which always takes place with tellurium which has been precipitated in this manner. It is desirable that the initial gassing be made in the cold when there is much copper present to avoid excessive formation of cuprous telluride.

Hydrazine hydrochloride used as a reducing agent for the precipitation of elementary tellurium gives fairly good results but as with sulfur dioxide complete precipitation is somewhat delayed. The use of sulfur dioxide and hydrazine hydrochloride together affords an accurate and rapid gravimetric estimation of tellurium and is applicable to both tellurites and tellurates, as well as to the free acids. It should be noted that this method does not effect a separation of tellurium from selenium.

### HYDRAZINE HYDROCHLORIDE-SULFUR DIOXIDE METHOD

*Procedure.*—The tellurium, either as a derivative of the dioxide or as a tellurate, should be present in a solution which has an acidity of approximately 10% free hydrochloric acid. The solution is saturated in the cold with sulfur dioxide, then 10 ml. of a 15% solution of hydrazine hydrochloride are added and the solution again gassed with sulfur dioxide. The solution is now boiled to coagulate the precipitate. The precipitated tellurium is transferred to a Gooch crucible, washed with hot distilled water until all the chlorides are removed, after which the water is displaced by isopropyl alcohol, the crucible and contents dried at 90°C., and weighed to constant weight.

## TITRIMETRIC METHODS FOR TELLURIUM

The oxidation of tellurous acid by ceric sulfate in hot sulfuric acid solution in the presence of chromic ion as catalyst affords a convenient titrimetric method for the determination of tellurium.[12] Selenious acid does not interfere if the sulfuric acid concentration is not too high. Excess ceric sulfate is added, the excess being titrated with ferrous ammonium sulfate.

Since permanganate readily oxidizes tellurous acid, its use as a self-indicating

[12] Willard, H. W., and Young, P., J. Am. Chem. Soc., **52**, 553, 1930.

oxidant has been carefully investigated.[13]  The principal reaction that occurs is:

$$4H_2TeO_3 + 2KMnO_4 + 5H_2SO_4 + 4H_2O \rightarrow 4Te(OH)_6 + 2KHSO_4 + Mn_2(SO_4)_3.$$

However, in the oxidation manganese(IV) is produced which either colors the solution strongly or precipitates as manganese dioxide.  Removal of most of the manganese(IV) may be effected by the addition of fluoride.  By using less than 10% sulfuric acid solution with a fluoride addition, a fairly constant Mn(III):Mn(IV) ratio is realized.  Under these conditions a temperature variation of from 20–55°C. has a negligible effect.  However, an upper concentration limit of 0.12 g. of tellurium per 400 ml. must be imposed.  Silver in high concentration induces a higher manganese(IV) concentration but this effect may be overcome by a larger fluoride addition.

Dissolution of the sample and its preparation for titration must be carried out so that tellurium is maintained in the Te(IV) state while other elements are fully oxidized.  This is accomplished by a combined sulfuric acid evaporation and bisulfate fusion.  Elements that may interfere in the determination include arsenic, antimony, and gold.  Arsenic and antimony are readily removed by volatilization as fluorides from hot concentrated sulfuric acid.  When gold is present, the sample must be treated so that gold remains undissolved as by the use of sulfuric acid alone.  Alternatively gold may be selectively reduced by oxalic acid during the analysis.

## CERIC SULFATE METHOD

The titrimetric ceric sulfate method of Willard and Young is best applied in cases where an accurate tellurium determination is required in tellurium-rich materials such as refined tellurium or tellurium compounds.  The detailed procedure for tellurium in refined tellurium given under "Determinations in Specific Substances" is applicable to numerous other substances.

## PERMANGANIMETRIC DETERMINATION OF TELLURIUM

*Procedure.*—Weigh out or pipette into a 400-ml. beaker a convenient amount of sample containing not more than 0.10 g. of tellurium.  Dissolve solid samples in concentrated nitric acid to limit the formation of telluric acid and to prevent the dissolution of gold.  Where necessary solution samples should be oxidized with a little concentrated nitric acid.

Now add 10–20 ml. of concentrated sulfuric acid and 3 g. of potassium bisulfate and evaporate the solution to dryness at maximum hot plate temperature.  Carry out a second fuming with 10 ml. of concentrated sulfuric acid to volatilize any remaining selenium.  When selenium films on the walls of the beaker are suspected, the walls should be washed down with a sulfuric-nitric acid mixture (4:1) and the fuming and evaporation to dryness repeated.  In all cases heat the sulfate residue strongly for 30 minutes before removing the beakers from the plate.

Now add 10 ml. of concentrated sulfuric acid while the beaker is still hot and fume until the bisulfate cake is completely dissolved.  Remove beaker from the plate, cool somewhat, but before crystallization occurs, dilute solution cautiously with 150 ml. of distilled water.  Boil solution until all salts are dissolved.  Remove solution from hot plate.  Dilute to 300 ml. with distilled water and add 3 g. of sodium fluoride.  Titrate with standard potassium permanganate solution (3.485 g.

[13] Marshall, H., Canadian Copper Refiners Limited, Montreal East, Quebec, Canada.

$KMnO_4$ per liter and standardized against pure tellurium or telluric acid [14]) to the first permanent pink lasting 30 seconds. A slight darkening of the solution precedes the end point and if much silver is present, a more gradual darkening due to manganese(IV) is produced. This effect may be overcome by the addition of more sodium fluoride. Should the end point drag or not be permanent for 30 seconds, significant amounts of arsenic or antimony may be suspected. The titration required to produce a similar end point in pure sulfuric acid solution (10 ml. $H_2SO_4$ in total volume of 300 ml.) may be taken as the blank requirement and is usually of the order of 0.1 ml.

**Standardization of Potassium Permanganate Solution.**—Prepare the potassium permanganate solution (3.485 g. $KMnO_4$ per liter) observing the usual precautions.

**Against Tellurium.**—Transfer 0.1 g. of pure powdered tellurium to a 400-ml. beaker and add 10 ml. of distilled water and 5 ml. of concentrated nitric acid. When the tellurium has dissolved completely, add 2 grams of potassium bisulfate and 10 ml. of concentrated sulfuric acid. Evaporate solution to dryness at maximum plate temperature. Repeat the evaporation with another 10 ml. of sulfuric acid. Complete the determination treating the residue from the evaporations as described above.

**Against Telluric Acid ($H_2TeO_4 \cdot 2H_2O$).**—Transfer 0.2 g. of pure telluric acid [15] to a 400-ml. beaker and add 10 ml. of concentrated hydrochloric acid. Cover the beaker with a raised watch glass and boil solution gently until all the chlorine has been expelled. Remove the watch glass, add 2 g. of potassium bisulfate and 10 ml. of concentrated sulfuric acid. Evaporate solution to dryness and complete the determination treating the residue as described above.

## COLORIMETRIC/PHOTOMETRIC METHODS FOR TELLURIUM

The determination of micro amounts of tellurium(IV) may be carried out spectrophotometrically on the tellurium hydrosol [16] or on the iodotellurite complex.[17] Johnson *et al.* recommend a red sol formed by reduction with hypophosphite and stabilized with gum arabic. Red sols are superior in conformance to Beer's Law, reproducibility and stability against agglomeration. However, the interferences are such, e.g., substances like selenium which also produce sols with hypophosphite, that a preliminary separation of tellurium is demanded in most applications.

The applicability of the iodotellurite complex, $TeI_6^=$, to the estimation of small amounts of tellurium is indicated by the fact that at 335 m$\mu$ the complex obeys Beer's Law over the concentration range of 0.2 to 2 p. p. m. Since selenite is reduced to elemental selenium by iodide, a prior separation of selenium, e.g., by repeated sulfuric acid-bisulfate fuming to dryness, is mandatory. Precautions must be taken to prevent the oxidation of iodide to free iodine.

[14] This solution will have a tellurium equivalence close to 0.005 g. Te per milliliter. For samples low in tellurium ($<0.1\%$) a standard solution with an equivalence of 0.001 g. Te per milliliter is recommended, with appropriate reduction in the volume of the solution titrated.

[15] The purest telluric acid usually obtained may analyze 55.70% tellurium (theoretical value 55.58%) because of traces of a polymer or of tellurous acid. Care should be taken that the telluric acid is free of nitric acid since this impurity causes reversibility in the reduction of the tellurium to the tellurous state. The purity of the telluric acid must be established before it is employed as a standard substance.

[16] Johnson, R. A., Kwan, F. P., and Westland, D., Anal. Chem., **25**, 1017, 1953.

[17] Johnson, R. A., and Kwan, F. P., *ibid.*, **23**, 651, 1951.

## SPECTROPHOTOMETRIC DETERMINATION OF TRACES OF TELLURIUM

The determination of small amounts of tellurium in selenium bearing materials can be carried out conveniently by volatilizing the selenium completely by repeated sulfuric acid-bisulfate fuming and evaporation to dryness and estimating the tellurium as the hydrosol using stannous chloride as reducing agent. Procedural details for this estimation, which has been employed successfully on a routine basis, are given under "Determinations in Specific Substances." Following the complete elimination of selenium, the procedure of Johnson and Kwan should also be suitable.

## DETERMINATIONS IN SPECIFIC SUBSTANCES

### SELENIUM IN SULFIDE ORES AND COPPER CONCENTRATES

The usual approaches to the dissolution of sulfide ores such as the use of nitric and sulfuric acid (Bruckner method),[18] sulfuric acid,[19] or bromine [20] are really limited to samples not greater than 5 grams. Such procedures tend to leave sulfur undissolved with the possible entrapment of selenium and/or are otherwise inconvenient. Edwards and Carlos [21] employed a potassium chlorate-nitric acid mixture to which mercuric oxide was added, this dissolution method having the advantage that volatility loss is entirely prevented since selenium is oxidized to the hexavalent state. Because the selenium content of ores and concentrates, although small, may vary rather widely, it is important that the dissolution procedure and the final method of determination be flexible. With this in mind the use of 15% fuming sulfuric acid is recommended since it makes for ease of sample dissolution, less manipulation, and a larger sized sample.

The separation of selenium by precipitation with sulfur dioxide and hydrazine, hydrazine sulfate, or hydroxylamine hydrochloride [22] as well as by distillation from hydrobromic acid solution has been customary. The distillation method [23,24] adapted to pyrite is undoubtedly the most suitable method of separation. However, it is impossible not to carry over certain other elements such as copper and iron which color the distillate. Gravimetric,[18] titrimetric,[19,25] and colorimetric [20,21] procedures have all been employed for the final estimation of selenium. Each of the methods cited has its peculiar disadvantages. Marshall [15] has introduced a microgravimetric procedure in which the loss upon ignition of the precipitated selenium in a 3-ml. Gooch crucible is determined to 0.01 mg. This method is recommended for precision, accuracy, and flexibility down to 20 p. p. m. for a 20-g. sample. A nephelometric determination at 627 mμ is accurate provided a suitable protective colloid such as methylcellulose is added to ensure a stable sol. The most desirable concentration range for this determination is between 20 and 250 p. p. m. for a

[18] Bruckner, K., Z. Anal. Chem., **94**, 305, 1933.
[19] Sill, C. W., and Peterson, H. E., U. S. Bureau of Mines, Report of Investigations 5047, May 1954.
[20] Volkov, S. T., Trans. All Union Sci. Research Inst. Econ. Mineral, No. 98, 1936.
[21] Edwards, A. B., and Carlos, G. C., Proc. Australian Inst. Min. Met., **172**, 1954.
[22] Zemel, V. K., Zavodskaya Lab., **5**, 1433, 1936.
[23] Gooch, F. A., and Pierce, A. W., Am. J. Sci. (4), **1**, 181, 1896.
[24] Robinson, W. O., Dudley, H. C., Williams, K. T., and Byers, H. G., Ind. Eng. Chem., Anal. Ed., **6**, 274, 1934.
[25] McNulty, J. S., Center, E. J., and MacIntosh, R. M., Anal. Chem., **23**, 123, 1951.

20-g. sample. Lower concentrations may be estimated if special absorption cells are used. Color comparison methods are not too accurate because of the difficulty in preparing the standards under the same conditions as the sample.

*Procedure.*—Weigh accurately a 20-g. sample and transfer to a dry, 300-ml., round-bottom flask. Add an excess of fuming, 15% sulfuric acid (150–250 ml.) and mix thoroughly to ensure that all the sample is wetted. Connect flask to a water-cooled, short, 3-bulb Allihn condenser and heat with a very low flame. The primary oxidation gives a milky white ferric sulfate suspension and a heavy black sediment. On no account should more heat be applied until this sediment is dissolved.

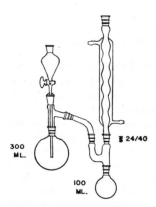

300 ML.

100 ML.

$ 24/40

FIG. 40-1. Apparatus for Hydrobromic Acid Distillation of Selenium in Ores and Concentrates.

Once the sediment has dissolved raise the heat slowly. If this operation is done cautiously, no globules of sulfur will be formed. Finally reflux the sample at high temperature until no further sulfur dioxide or sulfur is evident. Drain the condenser and allow the excess sulfur trioxide to escape via the open end of the condenser. Discontinue heating and disconnect the flask from the condenser.

Connect the flask to the distillation apparatus, Fig. 40-1. Heat to a suitable temperature (approx. 200°C. but under the boiling point of the solution) and add 10 ml. of 4% bromine in 48% hydrobromic acid at a rate not exceeding the rate of distillation. To ensure against loss of bromine vapor and anhydrous hydrobromic acid, occasional spurts of water may be added at the top of the condenser. Finally raise the temperature to the distillation point for sulfuric acid while boiling out the bromine from the 100-ml. collecting flask (allow water jacket of condenser to heat up above the boiling point of bromine). Discontinue heating and tap distillation and collecting flasks loose.

Cool distillate to room temperature and transfer to a 50-ml. beaker. Make volume up to 40 ml. with hydrochloric acid. Saturate solution with sulfur dioxide gas. If the selenium precipitate is so minor as to be uncoagulated, allow solution to stand for 18 hours. Filter through a micro Gooch crucible (3-ml. size), wash precipitate with dilute hydrochloric acid and distilled water. Dry at 110°C. for 1 hour, weigh to 0.01 mg., ignite, and reweigh crucible. Loss in weight gives weight of selenium in the sample.

NOTE.—Amounts of selenium below 30 micrograms per 40 ml. may not precipitate for 2 to 3 days. Such amounts are retained with difficulty on almost every type of filter. The difficulty in coagulating and filtering micro amounts of selenium sets a practical lower concentration limit of around 20 p. p. m. of selenium for a 20-gram sample. Heating the solution may aid in the detection or complete precipitation of the selenium.

Micro amounts of selenium may be detected colorimetrically by careful evaporation at low plate temperature to a small volume. If re-gassing with sulfur dioxide in low volume is carried out, a 1:1 dilution of concentrated hydrochloric acid is advised to minimize the effect of copper or iron.

## SELENIUM IN FLUE DUSTS

Selenium is more conveniently determined in smelter dusts by dissolving the sample in sulfuric acid in a Knorr arsenic still and distilling the selenium from hydrobromic acid-bromine solution. Sulfur is commonly formed during the dissolving operation causing contamination of the distillate with sulfur mono- and dibromide. If this effect is not very severe, it may be prevented by a tellurium addition. In other cases, notably with balloon and header dusts, the additional change from sulfuric to fuming sulfuric acid becomes necessary.

Hydrobromic acid distillation of the selenium should be made so that the hydrogen bromide distills off as added. When the vapor becomes colorless, the distillation should be discontinued before significant quantities of antimony and tin distill as would be expected in the case of balloon dust. The distillation of tin is especially to be avoided, because it catalyzes the reduction of sulfur dioxide to sulfur later when the precipitation and isolation of selenium is performed. Final determination of the selenium colorimetrically rather than nephelometrically is not recommended when accurate results are required. The colorimetric determination is rendered inaccurate by the possible presence in the distillate of iron, cuprous bromide, and other contaminants which impart a yellow color to the solution. The final estimation of the selenium is best made microgravimetrically.

The above technique is recommended from the viewpoint of flexibility and the small number of operations. Its principal advantages are to be found in the absence of losses occasioned by solution transfers and filtrations, of dissolution difficulties with sulfur-selenium globules, and of coprecipitation of bismuth, antimony, and tin with the selenium.

*Procedure.*—An adequate weight of sample is transferred to the dry Knorr flask. For amounts up to 2 g., add 20 ml. of sulfuric acid and for a 5-g. sample, 30 ml. of acid.[26] Replace the dropping funnel with the stopper closed. A 50-ml. Erlenmeyer flask serves best for collection of the distillate and is kept well immersed in a beaker of cold water. The flask contents are now gradually raised to boiling until all sulfur dioxide and water of reaction are evolved. After removing the flame, the funnel stopcock is opened to the air, and the flask contents are allowed to cool to about 150°C. The stopcock is then closed.

Add 10 ml. of 48% hydrobromic acid containing 4% bromine to the funnel. Apply some measure of heat to the flask and add the acid at the rate of about 1 drop every 3 seconds. The applied heat is adjusted so that the distillation keeps pace with the added hydrobromic acid. If there is a deficiency of water in the collection flask, the hydrobromic acid or the bromine fails to be absorbed, a situation that should be corrected. When all the acid has been added, the stopper is closed and all bromine fumes are driven over by more vigorous boiling, i.e., the bromine fumes are used as an indication that the selenium distillate is completely swept out from the flask and condenser.

The distillate is now transferred to a 50-ml. beaker with concentrated hydrochloric acid to give a final volume not exceeding 25–30 ml. Gas the solution with sulfur dioxide and allow to stand as long as required for adequate coagulation of the precipitate. Minor amounts of selenium, i.e., less than 1 mg., usually require about 18 hours standing but if desired the coagulation may be somewhat hastened by the use of a fine asbestos suspension in concentrated hydrochloric acid. As before the selenium is determined microgravimetrically by loss upon ignition.

[26] Where there is a tendency for released sulfur to cloud the apparatus as may happen with balloon and header dusts, about 0.5 g. of basic tellurium sulfate (selenium free) should be added before dissolving the sample. If this expedient fails, the sulfuric acid is replaced by 15% fuming sulfuric acid, the addition of the tellurium salt being maintained. In the second case, boiling during the dissolution should be continued until excess sulfur trioxide is distilled off, which distillation may require a larger addition of water to the distillate flask.

## SELENIUM IN SMELTER SLAGS

Since smelter slags contain a larger proportion of ferrous silicate in crystallized form, they cake rather than dissolve in sulfuric acid. This situation is not remedied by raising the temperature through the addition of potassium bisulfate. The slags are not decomposed appreciably by hydrochloric or hydrobromic acids.

Dissolution may be effected conveniently by a sodium peroxide fusion. However, when the melt is dissolved in water, the presence of colloidal silica renders impossible a satisfactory selenium determination. The best approach is nitric acid oxidation followed by sulfuric acid fuming and hydrobromic acid distillation. This procedure may be carried out in the Knorr still with as much as a 5-g. sample, not, however, without some bumping trouble in the case of reverberatory slag. This approach does not provide a final answer because even here a minor amount of magnetic iron oxide remains undissolved. Also, since a nitric acid distillate must be discarded, there is always the possibility of a slight volatility loss of selenium in this distillate.

*Procedure.*—An accurately weighed 5-g. sample is placed in the Knorr distillation flask and boiled gently with 20 ml. of nitric acid until oxides of nitrogen are no longer evolved. Add 30 ml. of sulfuric acid and boil to complete the expulsion of nitric acid vapors. After the nitric acid vapors have been swept out of the condenser, the distillate is discarded.

The flask is now boiled until strong fumes appear. After a suitable cooling period, distillation of the selenium is accomplished with 10 ml. of hydrobromic acid containing 4% bromine. Finally the selenium is recovered in the same manner as for smelter dusts and estimated microgravimetrically.

## SELENIUM AND TELLURIUM IN BLISTER AND REFINED COPPER

In order to determine the small amounts of selenium and tellurium in copper, particularly refined copper, determinable quantities of these elements must be separated from a large sample. Ferric hydroxide has commonly been used to effect this separation by coprecipitation. Zirconium sulfate in ammoniacal solution has also been employed successfully. Selenium and tellurium may be precipitated directly from acid solution with sodium hypophosphite. Such a separation is claimed to be more satisfactory than any based on the precipitation of selenium and tellurium with ferric hydroxide.[27] Noakes [28] has employed sodium hypophosphite for a second precipitation of selenium and tellurium after an initial precipitation with hydrazine hydrochloride and stannous chloride.

The method employed for the final estimation depends, of course, on the amounts of the elements present. Gravimetric and titrimetric procedures may be used for the relatively larger amounts of the elements in blister copper. In refined copper where selenium and tellurium are present in the order of a few parts per million, colorimetric, microgravimetric or particularly sensitive titrimetric methods are in order. Skowronski has successfully adapted the sensitive titrimetric method of Sill and Peterson [19] to the titration of microgram quantities of selenium from a 100-g. sample of copper. Noakes [28] reported excellent results for 0.001% to 0.1% selenium and tellurium by titrimetric iodometric methods on 5- to 20-g. samples.

[27] Challis, H. J. G., Analyst, **67**, 186, 1942.
[28] Noakes, F. D. L., *ibid.*, **76**, 542, 1951.

*Procedure for Selenium.*—Transfer a 50-g. sample to a 1000-ml. beaker, and dissolve in 200 ml. of nitric acid added in small portions to avoid too violent a reaction. When the sample has dissolved, boil the solution to expel oxides of nitrogen and the excess of acid until a slight green precipitate has formed on the surface. Cool and dilute to 400 ml. Start a blank containing a few drops of nitric acid.

Bring the solution nearly to boiling, neutralize with dilute ammonium hydroxide (1:50) to a faint opalescence indicating an incipient precipitation of basic copper nitrate, then dilute the solution to 900 ml. Now bring the solution to boiling and add cautiously and in small portions 1 g. of zirconium sulfate. (Alternatively, instead of zirconium sulfate, 100 ml. of a 40% solution of ferric ammonium sulfate may be added.)

Boil solution for 5–10 minutes, allow precipitate to settle, then filter through a 15-cm Reeve Angel No. 230 or Whatman #40 filter paper. Wash precipitate several times with hot distilled water and reject the filtrate. Transfer filter paper and precipitate to original beaker and add 100 ml. of hydrochloric acid to dissolve the precipitate. Now macerate the paper and precipitate with the aid of a glass rod, and allow to stand for about 1 hour. Filter solution through glass wool or asbestos to remove the filter paper, wash residue several times with distilled water collecting the filtrate in a 300-ml. Berzelius beaker. Dilute the filtrate to 200 ml. with hydrochloric acid and gas with sulfur dioxide to precipitate all the selenium. (The solution should contain 80% by volume of concentrated hydrochloric acid.)

Allow the precipitate to stand overnight, wash a few times with hydrochloric acid, then transfer to a Gooch crucible.[29] Retain the filtrate for the tellurium determination. In the case of blister copper, dry precipitate at 110°C., cool and weigh, and determine the selenium by loss upon ignition. In the case of refined copper, filter the selenium precipitate through either a Gooch crucible with a fresh asbestos mat or through a fast filter paper, such as S. & S. Sharkskin, and compare the coloration with a set of standards containing 0.0001, 0.0002, and 0.0003 g. of selenium.

*Alternative Procedure.*—This procedure for the estimation of selenium, which has been used successfully by Skowronski,[30] involves the application of Sill and Peterson's [19] titrimetric method.

Filter the precipitated selenium in a Gooch crucible, wash with water until free from chlorides in the usual manner. Remove the asbestos pad with the selenium and place in a 250-ml. beaker. To the crucible add slowly 2 ml. of nitric acid along the side of the crucible to dissolve any adhering selenium, allowing the acid to run into the beaker. In a like manner add 7 ml. of sulfuric acid allowing the acid to enter the beaker. Stir the asbestos pad into the acid until all the selenium has dissolved.

To decompose the nitric acid, add cautiously 1 g. of urea to avoid too violent a reaction. When the reaction has subsided, add an additional 2 g. of urea and mix well. Wash the crucible with 90 ml. of distilled water, adding this water to the beaker.

---

29 Some selenium precipitates have a tendency to pass through the Gooch crucible. In order to reduce selenium losses to a minimum, it is recommended that during filtration the asbestos mat be kept covered with solution. The precipitate should be washed by decantation 5 or 6 times with hydrochloric acid. The precipitate is then transferred to the Gooch crucible with distilled water and the aid of a rubber policeman.

30 Skowronski, S., Raritan Copper Works, Perth Amboy, N. J., private communication.

To the solution add 5 g. of ammonium chloride, and cool to room temperature. Add 0.5 ml. of starch-glycerol indicator.[31] Now carefully add 1% potassium iodide solution until a moderately deep blue color is produced. Do not add sufficient iodide to render the solution opaque. Titrate the solution with 0.01 $N$ sodium thiosulfate (1 ml. = 0.0002 g. Se or 0.0001% Se in a 200-g. sample) while stirring continuously. When the blue color has nearly gone, add just sufficient 1% potassium iodide solution to restore the blue color once more and continue the titration as before. When the discharge of blue color occurs sharply in local areas, the end point is near. Now on the next addition of potassium iodide solution add sufficient to make the total added during the entire titration 5 ml.

The end point is easily observed with 0.02 ml. of 0.02 $N$ thiosulfate and the solution will be colorless or at most a pale yellow if the minimum quantities of potassium iodide were added during the main part of the titration. The reaction is exactly stoichiometric and the normality of the thiosulfate solution obtained from a standardization against iodate may be used to calculate the selenium content.

*Procedure for Tellurium.*—In order to determine tellurium add slowly to the filtrate from the selenium precipitation 50 ml of mixed acid ($H_2O$, $H_2SO_4$, $HNO_3$ = 1:1:1). Allow the solution to stand until the reaction has subsided, add 3 g. of potassium bisulfate, then evaporate carefully to dryness, add 10 ml. of sulfuric acid and again evaporate to dryness.

In the case of blister copper, allow beaker to cool and add 100 ml. of distilled water and 10 ml. of sulfuric acid. Heat to dissolve all the salts and titrate with potassium permanganate solution (1 ml. = 0.005 g. tellurium) standardized against pure tellurium or telluric acid.

For refined copper, after the beaker has cooled, add 1 ml. of hydrochloric acid and 25 ml. of distilled water. Heat to dissolve the residue, transfer solution to a test tube, add about 0.1 g. of potassium iodide and gas with sulfur dioxide. Compare the black coloration due to tellurium with standards containing 0.0001, 0.0002, and 0.0003 g. of tellurium.

*Alternative Procedure.*—Evaporate the filtrate from the selenium determination to a suitable volume, dilute with an equal volume of distilled water and saturate with sulfur dioxide in the cold. Warm solution to about 60°C. and again saturate with sulfur dioxide. Let solution stand overnight. Transfer the precipitate to a Gooch crucible, wash with cold distilled water, and finally with alcohol. Dry at 90°C. for 1 hour, and weigh as elemental tellurium.

In order to apply this procedure to the determination of small amounts of tellurium such as are found in refined copper, duplicate 100-g. samples may be filtered through one Gooch crucible, thereby obtaining a weight on a 200-g. sample.

## SELENIUM AND TELLURIUM IN ELECTROLYTIC COPPER SLIMES

*Procedure.*—To determine selenium transfer a 0.5-g. sample to a 50-ml. beaker and add 10 ml. of 1:1 mixed nitric-sulfuric acids. If necessary, add a few crystals of potassium chlorate to facilitate dissolution of the sample or to destroy any organic matter. Cover beaker and evaporate to light fumes. Cool and wash down beaker cautiously with a little distilled water. Add 1 drop of hydrochloric acid to precipitate silver, filter and wash precipitate with distilled water, collecting the filtrate and washings in a 200-ml. tall-form beaker. To the filtrate add sufficient

---

[31] Sill, C. W., and Peterson, H. E., Anal. Chem., **21**, 1268, 1949.

concentrated hydrochloric acid to constitute 80% of the total volume, and saturate solution with sulfur dioxide gas. Filter selenium onto a Gooch crucible, wash, dry at 105°C. and determine selenium by loss upon ignition.

Tellurium may be determined gravimetrically on the filtrate from the selenium estimation following evaporation and dilution with an equal volume of distilled water. Alternatively tellurium may be determined by the titrimetric permanganate method using a 1-g. sample. The same procedure as for tellurium in refined selenium may be followed except that an additional 3 g. of sodium fluoride are added prior to the titration to offset the effect of the silver present.

## REFINED SELENIUM

### SELENIUM

**Procedure.**—Transfer a 1-g. sample to a 300-ml., tall-form beaker, add 20 ml. of mixed acid ($H_2O$, $H_2SO_4$, $HNO_3$ = 1:1:1) and allow solution to simmer under the boiling point. When all the nitrogen oxides have been driven off and the solution has turned colorless, cool, and dilute to the mark in a 500-ml. volumetric flask.

Run a 25-ml. aliquot from a burette into a 250-ml. Erlenmeyer flask. Add 20 ml. of 18 N sulfuric acid, 100 ml. of distilled water, and 12 g. of disodium phosphate. Stir the solution to dissolve the phosphate and add from a burette 20 ml. of 0.1 N potassium permanganate solution. Let solution stand for 30 minutes then back-titrate the excess permanganate with 0.1 N ferrous ammonium sulfate. One drop of o-phenanthroline ferrous sulfate indicator is added near the end point which is detected by the color change from pale blue to bright red.

It is recommended that the titer of the permanganate and ferrous ammonium sulfate solutions be checked carefully with each set of determinations by duplicate analyses of high-purity selenium.

NOTE.—In a number of refineries a direct estimation of selenium is not carried out, the selenium being determined by difference. In one case % Se = 100 − (% Ash + % Te) while in another instance % Se = 100 − [(% Te + % nonvolatile residue − % $TeO_2$ in NVR) + (% S − % S in NVR)].

### TELLURIUM

**Procedure.**—Dissolve a 10-g. sample in 35 ml. of nitric acid in a 400-ml. beaker, expel nitrogen oxide fumes, cool slightly, and add approximately 2.5 g. of potassium bisulfate and 20 ml. of sulfuric acid. Evaporate solution to dryness, heating at maximum hot plate temperature until no more fumes are evolved. Repeat this evaporation twice with 20-ml. portions of sulfuric acid to make sure that no traces of selenium remain. To the residue from these evaporations add 100 ml. of distilled water and 10 ml. of sulfuric acid. Boil solution until all salts are dissolved. After cooling, add 1 g. of sodium fluoride, and titrate with a standard solution of potassium permanganate (1 ml. = 0.005 g. tellurium). Subtract indicator blank.

The permanganate solution contains 3.485 g. of $KMnO_4$ per liter and is standardized against pure tellurium or telluric acid in the manner described under "Titrimetric Methods for Tellurium." For refined selenium low in tellurium (<0.1%), a standard solution having a tellurium equivalence of 0.001 g. of tellurium per milliliter is recommended, using 2 ml. of sulfuric acid and 60 ml. of distilled water.

The direct titrimetric procedure is superior to the more conventional gravimetric methods which depend on a prior separation of selenium by precipitation or on a precipitation of both selenium and tellurium together coupled with a separate selenium determination.

## TRACE ANALYSIS OF IMPURITIES IN SELENIUM [32]

### *DETERMINATION OF COPPER*

*Procedure.*—Transfer a 2-g. sample to a 20-ml. beaker and add 10 ml. of 1:1 mixed nitric and sulfuric acids. Warm at very low heat on a hot plate and when the dissolution is about complete, raise the temperature slowly until the excess nitric acid is expelled and fuming commences. Finally evaporate the solution to dryness at maximum plate temperature. If the copper is expected to be below 0.2 p. p. m., an acid blank must be run in which all procedural details are exactly reproduced. Care should be taken that films of condensate do not remain on the upper part of the beaker, especially near the pouring lip.

Add 1 drop of 3.6 N sulfuric acid and 2 ml. of distilled water free of organic matter and copper. The rigid exclusion of tap distilled water is mandatory in all future additions. Warm gently to complete solution, then remove beaker from the plate and cool to 25°C. (important).

Add 7 drops of 1% aqueous solution of 1-naphthol-4-sulfonic acid sodium salt and 5 drops of ammonia. Now add purified distilled water to bring the volume to 5 ml. After mixing add 1 drop of dilute hydrogen peroxide (one part 30% $H_2O_2$ to 100 parts pure $H_2O$) and mix thoroughly.

Transfer the solution to an absorption cell, let stand for 15 minutes (important), then measure the absorbancy at 680 m$\mu$ versus the acid blank. Determine the amount of copper present from a previously prepared working curve. Although 1-naphthol-4-sulfonic acid is one of the most favorable reagents for this estimation, it does impose a practical upper concentration limit of $4.0 \times 10^{-7}$ gram per milliliter of copper.

High iron, copper from laboratory tap distilled water, and substances liable to give turbidity or precipitates, such as finely divided silica, interfere in the determination.

### *IRON*

*Procedure.*—As in the copper determination, a 2-g. sample is employed with the dissolution effected by mixed nitric-sulfuric acids. Also an acid blank is carried through the procedure.

Dissolve the residue (obtained upon dissolution of the sample and subsequent evaporation to dryness) in 1 drop of hydrochloric acid and 2 ml. of distilled water (tap distilled water may be used). Warm to effect solution, remove beaker from the plate, and cool.

Add 5 drops of 10% sulfosalicylic acid, mix thoroughly, then add 5 drops of ammonium hydroxide and dilute to 5 ml. Mix solution thoroughly, transfer to an absorption cell, and measure the absorbancy at 530 m$\mu$ versus the acid blank. Determine the amount of iron present from a previously prepared working curve. Iron concentrations up to $9 \times 10^{-6}$ gram per milliliter have been found to obey

[32] The fate of finely divided silica is sometimes of importance in the determination of small amount of impurities in selenium. If the amount of silica is excessive, it may contribute turbidity, and constitute a source of error in colorimetric estimations. In such cases a careful filtration on a microbuechner funnel is recommended.

Beer's Law. Copper interferes in the determination. However, if the amounts of copper and iron are comparable, the interference on the part of copper is not serious.

## TELLURIUM

*Procedure.*—Transfer a 3-g. sample to a 50-ml. beaker and add 25 ml. of 1:1 mixed nitric-sulfuric acids and 3 drops of 30% lithium nitrate solution. Effect dissolution and evaporation to dryness as in the copper determination.

Since the tellurium determination is dependent on the complete removal of selenium, the final volatilization of selenium must be effected by 2–3 further evaporations to dryness with about 2 ml. of sulfuric acid at maximum hot plate temperature. Upon completion of these evaporations, remove beaker from the plate and cool.

Add 6 drops of hydrochloric acid and 2 ml. of distilled water. Heat carefully to effect complete solution of tellurium. Remove beaker from the plate, add an amount of distilled water just sufficient to destroy any yellow color and allow solution to cool.

Transfer solution to a 5-ml. graduated cylinder and make volume up to 3.7 ml. Add 1.25 ml. of 25% potassium iodide solution and 1 drop of 10% stannous chloride solution in 3 N hydrochloric acid. Transfer solution, the volume of which is now exactly 5 ml., to an absorption cell, mix thoroughly, and measure the absorbancy at 415 m$\mu$ versus a reagent blank. Determine the amount of tellurium present by reference to a previously prepared working curve.

## SULFUR

The determination of small amounts of sulfur in selenium can be realized most satisfactorily by oxidizing the sulfur to sulfate, precipitating barium sulfate, and estimating its amount gravimetrically or, with some experience, visually. The oxidation may be accomplished by dissolving the sample in 10% bromine in hydrobromic acid. The selenium is then removed from the sulfate by distillation as the tetrabromide. A superior procedure is to dissolve the selenium in nitric acid and precipitate the barium sulfate from the selenious acid solution thereby eliminating the selenium removal step. However, in this procedure the nitric acid concentration must be controlled carefully to prevent the precipitation of barium selenite. Also in spite of an optimum acid concentration barium selenite may precipitate if the solution is allowed to stand for an extended period, say beyond two hours. The following procedure permits the determination of 50 p. p. m. of sulfur. The accurate determination of amounts as small as 10 p. p. m. would demand a sensitive nephelometric procedure.

*Procedure.*—Transfer a 3-g. sample to a 300-ml., tall-form beaker and add 20 ml. of nitric acid. Dissolve sample gently and completely on a low temperature plate. Make volume to 250 ml. with distilled water, bring the solution to an incipient boil, and add slowly and with stirring 5 ml. of 10% barium chloride solution. After boiling the solution gently for about 15 minutes, allow the precipitate of barium sulfate to settle. If the precipitate is very slight, the amount of sulfur may be estimated visually. If the precipitate is present in larger amounts, it may be filtered onto a Gooch crucible, washed, dried, ignited, and weighed to constant weight in the customary manner.

A slight difference exists between the observation of sulfur as barium sulfate in hot and cold solutions. The observation is better made in hot solution, since the possibility of a slight precipitation of barium selenite after the solution has cooled cannot be ruled out.

## SPECTROGRAPHIC ANALYSIS OF SELENIUM

The production of high purity selenium and its use in the manufacture of selenium rectifiers has required the development of rapid and accurate procedures for the estimation of trace impurities such as arsenic, tellurium, copper, iron, nickel, mercury, and other metals. The estimation of nonmetallic elements such as sulfur, halogens, and oxygen has also been demanded. Although sensitive chemical procedures have been developed for the important impurities (see previous section), such procedures are too time-consuming to be suitable for production control. Consequently appropriate spectrographic methods have been devised.

Mellichamp [33] has developed a semiquantitative procedure in which a 50-mg. sample is burned to completion in a 10-ampere D.C. arc. 23 elements are determined from one spectrogram in the region 2200–4400 A using the background as internal standard.

Peterson and Currier [34] have devised a D.C. arc procedure for the quantitative determination of aluminum, bismuth, copper, lead, magnesium, silver, and zinc in selenium with detection limits considerably less than those given by Mellichamp. In this procedure a 0.50-g. sample to which 4 micrograms of palladium have been added as internal standard is burned in the D.C. arc for 35 seconds at 5 amperes. The analytical working curves were obtained from standards prepared by adding 0.05 ml. of standard impurity solution to pure selenium previously melted in the electrode crater. Following evaporation of the solution to dryness, additional selenium was added to fill the crater and the whole mass melted prior to excitation to ensure homogeneity. The accuracy of $\pm 20\%$ claimed for this procedure was established by analyzing "unknowns" prepared by adding the impurities in solution or as metallic selenides.

The disadvantages of the method of Peterson and Currier can be overcome by the use of external comparison standards. The comparison of the spectra of the samples with those of carefully prepared standards recorded on the same plate permits the rapid and accurate estimation of metallic impurities in high purity selenium.

In this procedure, which was developed by N. Tomingas of Canadian Copper Refiners Limited, a 200-mg. sample, generally in the form of shot, is excited in an A.C. arc (9.5 amperes) for 30 seconds at 100% transmission. The lower electrode is a 0.242″ diam. graphite rod with $\frac{3}{16}$″ crater while the upper electrode is a $\frac{1}{8}$″ diam. graphite rod. The electrode spacing is 4 mm. To accommodate the impurities estimated by this procedure (tellurium, lead, iron, copper, arsenic, antimony, tin, bismuth, nickel, chromium, aluminum, titanium, zinc, cadmium, indium, silver, sodium, magnesium, mercury, and silicon), two wavelength ranges must be employed viz., 2275–2970 A and 2480–4000 A. A double exposure is made on the first range at a 30-micron slit width to permit the accurate determination of very small amounts of tellurium. A single exposure is run on the second range at a slit width of 20 microns. Eastman Spectrum Analysis No. 1 plates are employed with the spectra of both samples and standards appearing on the same plate.

[33] Mellichamp, J. W., Applied Spectroscopy, **8**, 114, 1954.
[34] Peterson, G. E., and Currier, E. W., ibid., **10**, 1, 1956.

Duplicate spectra are recorded for both samples and standards on each range. The standards used are actual production samples or samples to which known amounts of impurities have been added. The concentrations of the significant impurities in all standards were determined by chemical analysis.

## SELENIUM IN SODIUM SELENITE

*Procedure.*—Dissolve 1.0000 g. of sample in 50 ml. of warm distilled water and dilute to the mark in a 500-ml. volumetric flask. Run a 50-ml. aliquot of the sample solution from a burette into a 250-ml. Erlenmeyer flask. Acidify with 20 ml. of 18 $N$ sulfuric acid, dilute with 100 ml. of distilled water and add 12 g. of disodium phosphate ($Na_2HPO_4 \cdot 7H_2O$). After the phosphate has dissolved, add from a burette 20 ml. of 0.1 $N$ potassium permanganate solution. Let the solution stand for 30 minutes to complete the oxidation. Back-titrate the excess of permanganate with 0.1 $N$ ferrous ammonium sulfate. One drop of $o$-phenanthroline ferrous sulfate indicator is added near the end point which is detected by the color change from pale blue to bright red.

## SELENIUM IN SODIUM SELENATE

*Procedure.*—Dissolve a 1.0000-g. sample in 15 ml. of 18 $N$ sulfuric acid at moderate heat. Cool solution and make up to the mark in a 250-ml. volumetric flask. Take a 25-ml. aliquot in a 250-ml. Erlenmeyer flask and add 1 g. of hydroxylamine hydrochloride. Boil gently for 10 minutes until all the selenium has precipitated. Cool and dissolve the selenium in 20 ml. of mixed acid ($H_2O$, $HNO_3$, $H_2SO_4$ = 1:1:1) added cautiously to avoid violent reaction. Heat just under the boiling point to expel nitrogen oxide fumes. Now proceed with the cool solution in the same manner as prescribed for the aliquot of the sodium selenite sample.

## REFINED TELLURIUM

*Procedure.*—Transfer a 1-g. sample to a 300-ml., tall-form beaker, add 30 ml. of mixed acid ($H_2O$, $H_2SO_4$, $HNO_3$ = 1:1:1) and cover. Bring to boiling and boil gently until all nitrogen oxide fumes have been driven off. Now keep the solution under the boiling point at a temperature at which no bumping occurs and bring to heavy fumes, continuing fuming for 15 minutes. Cool the solution and dilute with 30 ml. of distilled water. Stir and warm to dissolve all soluble salts. Lead sulfate, if present, will not dissolve and must be filtered off. Wash the precipitate of lead sulfate carefully by decantation with 5 small portions of 1:20 sulfuric acid. Add to the filtrate 20 ml. of 18 $N$ sulfuric acid, transfer solution to a 250-ml. volumetric flask, dilute to the mark and make homogeneous. Since tellurium sulfate may precipitate out if the solution is allowed to stand, the procedure must not be discontinued at this point. Hence, immediately transfer a 50-ml. aliquot to a 250-ml. Erlenmeyer flask, add 15 ml. of 18 $N$ sulfuric acid, and 75 ml. of distilled water and run in from a burette 40 ml. of 0.1 $N$ ceric sulfate. The ceric sulfate solution contains 1 g. $K_2Cr_2O_7$ per liter as catalyst. Heat to near boiling and simmer for 15 minutes. Cool and back-titrate with 0.1 $N$ ferrous ammonium sulfate. The end point is detected in the presence of one drop of $o$-phenanthroline ferrous sulfate solution by the color change from pale blue to bright red.

## DETERMINATION OF SMALL AMOUNTS OF SELENIUM. LEAD, IRON, AND COPPER IN TELLURIUM

### DETERMINATION OF SELENIUM

**Procedure for Amounts > 0.1%.**—Dissolve a 1-g. sample in 20 ml. of 1:1 nitric acid in a 200-ml., tall-form beaker. Evaporate almost to dryness at low plate temperature or on a steam bath. Dissolve the residue in 20 ml. of hydrochloric acid with warming to aid the decomposition of any remaining nitric acid. Make volume up to 15 ml. with additional hydrochloric acid and saturate solution with sulfur dioxide. Filter precipitated selenium onto a Gooch crucible, dry and weigh. Ignite crucible and reweigh. Loss in weight is the weight of selenium in the sample.

The gravimetric determination of selenium in the presence of a large excess of tellurium possesses the disadvantage of a possible induced precipitation of tellurium. After the volatilization of the selenium, the crucible should be examined for tellurium dioxide residue to determine if any tellurium was coprecipitated with the selenium.

**Procedure for Amounts < 0.1%.**—Transfer a 1- to 3-g. sample to the boiling flask of a Knorr arsenic distillation apparatus. Add 20 ml. of sulfuric acid and bring to a boil collecting the distillate in a dry flask. Allow the flask to cool somewhat and add 10 ml. of bromine-hydrobromic acid mixture (4% bromine in 48% hydrobromic acid) at a rate not exceeding the rate of distillation. Distill off the selenium. Continue the distillation until tellurium tetrabromide begins to distill appearing as a yellow condensate. The issuing vapors serve to scrub the condenser.

Add 30 ml. of hydrochloric acid to the distillate and saturate the solution with sulfur dioxide. Allow the solution to stand overnight, then filter off the selenium onto a microgooch crucible and determine selenium by loss upon ignition.

### LEAD

The ease with which tellurium(IV) solutions hydrolyze is responsible for the ready coprecipitation of lead tellurite over a wide pH range (0–12). Since the hydrolysis of tellurite solutions does not occur in concentrated sodium hydroxide solution, this medium is suitable for the separation of lead as sulfide (and telluride) and for the subsequent polarographic determination of lead.

**Procedure.**—Dissolve a 5-g. sample of tellurium in 40 ml. of 1:1 mixed nitric-sulfuric acid in a 250-ml. beaker. Carefully evaporate the solution to dryness and dissolve the dry cake of basic tellurium sulfate in 50 ml. of 20% sodium hydroxide solution. Boil to effect complete dissolution. Dilute solution to 230 ml. and add 12 drops of 10% thioacetamide solution. Bring solution to a boil. The presence of lead will be shown by the formation of a yellow coloration and of a black precipitate of lead sulfide, if at least 50 micrograms of lead are present. Add additional drops of thioacetamide solution until no further reaction is observed. To ensure the complete precipitation of lead as sulfide and telluride, precipitate some tellurium to serve as a carrier by adding 1 drop of 70% thioglycolic acid solution. Filter the precipitate on a small Buchner funnel and wash with distilled water. Transfer paper and precipitate to a 100-ml. beaker. Dissolve precipitate and destroy paper with 10 ml. of fuming nitric acid and 10 ml. of sulfuric acid. Evaporate the solution to dryness. Dissolve residue in a small quantity of 0.5 M sodium hydroxide, make volume up to a suitable known value with the same solution and polarograph between −0.2 and −0.9 volt versus mercury pool. Small amounts of residue dissolve readily in 7 ml. of 0.5 $M$ sodium hydroxide which is then evaporated to 5 ml. and the polarogram recorded using a micro-polarographic cell.

This procedure has been applied for lead in tellurium as low as 2 p. p. m.

### IRON

Iron may be determined in the hydrous ferric oxide precipitate remaining from the sodium hydroxide solution in the lead procedure. However, the separation of iron by extraction is to be preferred.

Extraction of the iron with diethyl ether or acetylacetone from a (1:1) hydrochloric acid solution is not possible since tellurium tetrachloride is also extracted. Isopropyl ether and cyclohexanone are suitable for extractions from (2:1) and (1:2) hydrochloric acid solutions respectively. The most satisfactory results were obtained using dichlorodiethyl ether.

*Procedure.*—A suitable sample (1–10 g.) is dissolved in a 250-ml. beaker with 20 ml. of sulfuric acid and 20 ml. of fuming nitric acid. Evaporate solution to dryness. Dissolve the residue in 35 ml. of cold 6 $N$ hydrochloric acid and extract the solution with three successive 5-ml. portions of dichlorodiethyl ether. Now back-extract the iron from the ether into 50 ml. of 0.67 $N$ hydrochloric acid. To this solution add 2 g. of ammonium thiocyanate and extract with 10 ml. of $n$-butanol. Filter the butanol layer through a filter paper directly into an absorption cell and measure the absorbancy versus $n$-butanol at 480 m$\mu$. Determine the amount of iron in the sample by reference to a previously prepared working curve.

### COPPER

*Procedure.*[35]—Dissolve a 5-g. sample of tellurium in a 250-ml. beaker with 20 ml. of sulfuric acid and 20 ml. of fuming nitric acid. Evaporate solution to dryness. Add 35 ml. of distilled water and boil until the residue becomes finely divided. Filter into a 50-ml. beaker and evaporate the filtrate to dryness. Add 10 ml. of distilled water and 1 drop of 1:10 sulfuric acid. Bring the solution to a boil, boil for a few minutes, then filter into a 10-ml. beaker and evaporate filtrate to dryness. Add 3 ml. of distilled water and 1 drop of 1:10 sulfuric acid to the residue. Again bring to a boil and filter into a 10-ml. beaker. Now add 5 drops of ammonium hydroxide, heat to coagulate the hydrous ferric oxide precipitate, filter and boil down filtrate to 3 ml.

Cool solution to 25°C., add 7 drops of 1% 1-naphthol-4-sulfonic acid solution, 5 drops of ammonium hydroxide, and 1 drop of dilute hydrogen peroxide (1 part 30% $H_2O_2$ to 100 parts pure water). Allow solution to stand for 15 minutes then measure the absorbancy at 680 m$\mu$ versus a reagent blank similarly prepared. Determine the amount of copper in the sample by reference to a previously prepared working curve.

### SELENIUM IN ORGANIC MATERIAL [36]

The following method developed by Robinson, Dudley, Williams, and Byers [37] is based on the fact that selenium may be separated from all other elements except

[35] Copper-free double distilled water must be used throughout this procedure.
[36] Jacobs, M. B., Chemical Analysis of Food and Food Products, 3rd Ed., D. Van Nostrand, 1958.
[37] Robinson, Dudley, Williams and Byers, Ind. Eng. Chem., Anal. Ed., **6**, 274, 1934.

arsenic and germanium by distillation with concentrated hydrobromic acid. The selenium must be in, or be converted into, the hexavalent condition before distillation in order to insure its distillation with the acid will be complete. In most cases the conversion may be accomplished by the use of bromine. The excess of bromine distills at a low temperature and the hydrobromic acid then reduces the selenium to the tetravalent condition. In this form it readily distills along with the hydrobromic acid. The selenium is subsequently estimated in the distillate by reduction with hydroxylamine hydrochloride and sulfur dioxide.

*Preparation of Sample.* **Vegetable Matter.**—Stir 100 g. of the well-ground and mixed vegetation into a concentrated solution of 25 g. of magnesium nitrate, and add 5 g. of magnesium oxide. Dry the mass over a water bath and finally in an oven at 105°C. Ignite the dried material slowly in a muffle until the ash is a uniform gray color. After ignition, triturate the ash with 100 ml. of concentrated hydrobromic acid, capable of being completely decolorized with sulfur dioxide, and 2 ml. of bromine, transfer to a distilling flask and estimate as detailed below.

William and Lakin [38] recommend the following procedure for preparation of the sample prior to the selenium distillation. To prepare a sample of air-dry vegetation, grind it to pass a 2-mm. mesh sieve, then mix and quarter. Stir a weighed sample, usually 10 g., into a mixture of 50 ml. of sulfuric acid and 100 ml. nitric acid in a 600-ml. Pyrex beaker. Stir the mixture with a thermometer until it becomes homogeneous, after the first few minutes with gentle heating, without allowing the temperature to rise above 100°C. After all frothing has ceased, raise the temperature of the mixture to a maximum of 120°C. until all evolution of nitrogen peroxide has ceased. The end of the operation is marked also by an incipient carbonization of the mixture, although longer heating at 120°C. does little harm. After the mixture has cooled, transfer it to the all-glass distilling flask, described below, and add 100 ml. of hydrobromic acid and 1 ml. of bromine and collect 75 ml. of the distillate. Care must be taken that the first portion of the distillate contains a small excess of bromine.

**Animal Matter.**[39]—Place the material in a suitable state of subdivision in a beaker of 400- to 600-ml. capacity, cover with 150 to 200 ml. of nitric acid, and allow to stand at room temperature for from 2 to 3 hours, during which period stir it vigorously at intervals. Add 50 ml. of hydrogen peroxide, 30% by weight, and allow the mixture to stand overnight. If frothing occurs on the addition of the hydrogen peroxide, foaming over is prevented by vigorous stirring of the foam. After standing overnight, warm the mixture slowly on the steam bath until frothing ceases, after which add 50 ml. more of hydrogen peroxide, together with 20 ml. of sulfuric acid. Evaporate the mixture essentially to complete dryness on the steam bath or hot plate. Treat the cooled black paste with 100 ml. of concentrated hydrobromic acid to which has been added sufficient bromine to make it deep yellow in color. Transfer the material to the distillation flask.

*Apparatus.*—The apparatus, Fig. 40-2, consists of a Pyrex 500-ml. round-bottom flask fitted with a ground-glass stopper into which has been sealed a thistle tube with a stem long enough to reach within 5 mm. of the bottom of the flask. The ground-glass stopper also has a side arm with a ground-glass end fitted into a condenser whose end is drawn out into a long adapter, bent, and provided with a capillary tip so that it may fit easily into a 100-ml., wide-mouth Erlenmeyer flask, which acts as the receiver.

[38] Williams and Lakin, Ind. Eng. Chem., Anal. Ed., **7**, 409, 1935.
[39] Dudley and Byers, Ind. Eng. Chem., Anal. Ed., **7**, 3, 1935.

*Procedure.*—Connect the distillation apparatus with the adapter just below the surface of 2 to 3 ml. of bromine water in the receiver flask and apply heat gradually. One or 2 g. of bromine should distill over in the first few milliliters of distillate. If insufficient bromine has been added to produce this quantity of bromine, more must be added through the thistle tube. A somewhat greater excess of bromine does no harm, but too great an excess is to be avoided because of the formation of too much sulfuric acid later. Collect 30 to 50 ml. of the distillate by increasing the heat. Make a second, or even third distillation with intervening additions of hydrobromic acid and bromine through the thistle tube, unless it is certain from experience that all the selenium is in the first distillate. Remove the

distillate and pass in sulfur dioxide until the yellow color due to bromine is discharged. Add 0.25 to 0.5 g. of hydroxylamine hydrochloride, stopper the flask loosely, put on the steam bath for an hour, and allow to stand overnight at room temperature. If selenium is present, it will appear as a characteristic pink or red precipitate. If much selenium is present it will shortly turn black.

Collect the precipitated selenium on an asbestos pad in a porcelain crucible, and wash slightly with hydrobromic acid containing a little hydroxylamine hydrochloride. Dissolve the selenium on the pad by passing through 10 to 15 ml. of a solution of 1 ml. of bromine in 10 ml. of hydrobromic acid in small quantities and wash into a 25-ml. measuring flask if the quan-

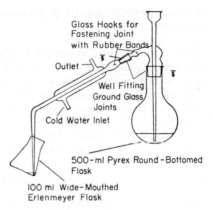

Glass Hooks for Fastening Joint with Rubber Bands

Outlet

Well Fitting Ground Glass Joints

Cold Water Inlet

500-ml Pyrex Round-Bottomed Flask

100 ml Wide-Mouthed Erlenmeyer Flask

Fig. 40-2. Selenium Distillation Apparatus.

tity is small and is to be estimated colorimetrically. If over 0.5 mg., filter into a small beaker, precipitate as before, gather on an asbestos pad as before, wash with hydrobromic acid containing a little hydroxylamine hydrochloride, and then with water. Prepare a tare in the same way. Dry at 90°C. for 1 hour, place in a vacuum desiccator, and exhaust the air while the crucibles are still hot. Cool 0.5 hour. Allow the air to enter the desiccator, cool an additional 0.5 hour, and weigh against the tare. Check the weight by drying again.

*Colorimetric Procedure.*—If the quantity is small and is to be estimated colorimetrically, add 1 ml. of a solution containing 5% gum arabic and precipitate the selenium by sulfur dioxide and hydroxylamine hydrochloride. Prepare comparison solution containing known quantities of selenium in exactly the same manner and allow them to stand overnight. Shake the standard and test solutions and compare the depth of color in Nessler tubes. This comparison is best carried out in sunlight. It is difficult to match solutions containing more than 0.5 mg. of selenium in 25 ml. and the color comparison is most satisfactory when 0.01 to 0.1 mg. is present.

# Chapter 41

# SILICON

**Si**, *at. wt.* **28.086** (±0.001); *sp. gr. amor.* **2.00**; *crys.* **2.42**; *m.p.* **1420°C.**; *b.p.* **2355°C.**; *oxides*, SiO, SiO$_2$

Silicon stands next to oxygen in abundance, occurring only in combined form. The oxides quartz, tridymite (silica), SiO$_2$ occur in great quantities. Silicates occur in all of the common rocks except in carbonates. It has been estimated that the earth's crust is composed of more than 27% silicon, combined in one form or other.

Silicon was first obtained in 1823 by Berzelius by the action of potassium on silicon tetrachloride. It may be made by reduction of SiO$_2$ with carbon at high temperature. It is used alloyed with iron (Duriron) in acid resisting materials, and in small amounts in steel used for transformer coils.

## DETECTION

The finely ground sample together with a small quantity of powdered calcium fluoride is placed in a small lead cup 1 cm. in diameter and depth (see Fig. 41-1),

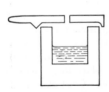

FIG. 41-1. Lead Cup for Silica Test.

and a few drops of concentrated sulfuric acid added. A lead cover, with a small aperture, is placed on the cup, and the opening covered with a piece of moistened black filter paper. Upon this paper is placed a moistened pad of ordinary filter paper. The cup is now gently heated on the steam bath. At the end of about ten minutes a white deposit will be found on the under side of the black paper, at the opening in the cover, if an appreciable amount of silica is present in the material tested.

A silicate, fused with sodium carbonate or bicarbonate in a platinum dish and the carbonate decomposed by addition of hydrochloric acid with subsequent evaporation to dryness, will liberate silicon as silicic anhydride, SiO$_2$. The silica placed in a platinum dish is volatilized by addition of hydrofluoric acid, the gaseous silicon fluoride being formed. A drop of water placed in a platinum loop, held in the fumes of SiF$_4$, will become cloudy owing to the formation of gelatinous silicic acid and fluosilicic acid,

$$3SiF_4 + 3H_2O \rightarrow H_2SiO_3 + 2H_2SiF_6$$

If a silicate is fused in a platinum loop with microcosmic salt, the silica floats around in the bead, producing an opaque bead with weblike structure upon cooling.

## ESTIMATION

The gravimetric procedure is the most satisfactory general method for the estimation of silica, except in small quantities. The substance in which the element is combined as an oxide or as a silicate is decomposed by acid treatment or by fusion with an alkali carbonate or bicarbonate, the material taken to dryness with addition of hydrochloric acid, whereby the compound silica is liberated. If other elements are present the silica is volatilized by addition of hydrofluoric acid and estimated by the loss of weight of the residue.

Combined as $SiO_2$ and in silicates the element is very widely distributed in nature and is a required constituent in practically every complete analysis of ores, minerals, soils, etc. It is present in certain alloys, ferrosilicon, silicon carbide, etc.

The element is scarcely attacked by single acids, but is acted upon by nitric-hydrofluoric acid mixture. It dissolves in concentrated alkali solutions. Silica is decomposed by hydrofluoric acid and by fusion with the fixed alkali carbonates or hydroxides.

Silicon is isolated as $SiO_2$ in the initial stage of analysis and if present in the material examined boron, niobium, tantalum, and tungsten will accompany silica. Lead, barium, and calcium will be found with this residue if sulfates are present. Tin, antimony, and bismuth are apt to contaminate the silica if these are present. Silica is determined by difference after volatilization with HF and $H_2SO_4$ treatment.

## PREPARATION AND SOLUTION OF THE SAMPLE

The natural and artificially prepared silicates may be grouped under two classes: 1. Silicates which are decomposed by acids. 2. Silicates not decomposed by acids. The minerals datolite, natrolite, olivine, and many basic slags are representative of the first class, and feldspar, orthoclase, pumice, and serpentine are representative of silicates not decomposed by acids. (See more complete list under "List of Most Important Silicates," page 952.) The first division simply require an acid treatment to isolate the silica, the latter class require fusion with a suitable flux.

In technical analysis, in cases where great accuracy is not required, the residue remaining, after certain conventional treatments with acids, is classed as silica. This may consist of fairly pure silica or a mixture of silica, undecomposed silicates, barium sulfate, and certain acid insoluble compounds. For accurate analyses this insoluble residue is not accepted as pure silica, unless impurities, which are apt to be found with the silica residue, are known to be absent from the material under examination.

Although the procedure for isolation of silica is comparatively simple, errors may arise from the following causes:

(1) Imperfect decomposition of the silicate.

(2) Loss of the silica by spurting when acid is added to the carbonate fusion.

(3) Slight solubility of silica, even after dehydration, especially in presence of sodium chloride and magnesia.

(4) Loss due to imperfect transfer of the residue to the filter paper.

(5) Mechanical loss during ignition of the filter and during the blasting, due to the draft whirling out the fine, light silica powder from the crucible.

(6) Error due to additional silica from contaminated reagents or from the porcelain dishes or glassware in which the solution was evaporated. A blank of 0.01%

on the sodium carbonate will make an error of 0.1% per g. sample in an ordinary fusion where 10 g. of the flux are required.

(7) Error due to loss of weight of the platinum crucible during the blasting.

(8) Incomplete removal of water, which is held tenaciously by the silica. Furthermore, weighing of the residue should be done quickly, as the finely divided silica tends to absorb moisture. Ignition to constant weight at 1200°C. is necessary.

(9) Expulsion of products by HF other than silica such as trivalent arsenic and boron. These substances should be removed before the HF treatment of the residue.

(10) Formation of silicates in the residue, not originally present, for example the change of $KAlSi_3O_8$ to $K_2SiO_3$ and $Al_2O_3$.

(11) Combination of substances with silica preventing its volatilization. For example alkaline earths forming silicates during the heating of the residue. When fusions are made with alkali salts, care should be exercised to remove these completely during the acid treatment of the silica.

(12) In presence of fluorides loss of silica will occur during the acid attack of the material, so that special treatment is necessary to prevent loss. If boron is present it is volatilized as $B(OCH_3)_3$ by treating the ore with methyl alcohol and sulfuric acid previous to the dehydration of silica. If tungsten is present the volatilization of silica must be conducted at a temperature below 850°C. at which temperature tungsten oxide volatilizes.

Decomposition of silicates is best effected by fusions with alkali fluxes followed by attack with acids.

## PREPARATION OF THE SUBSTANCE FOR DECOMPOSITION

If the material is an ore or mineral it is placed on a steel plate within a steel ring and broken down by means of a hardened hammer to small lumps and finally to a coarse powder. A quartered portion of this is air dried and ground as fine as possible in an agate mortar and preserved in a glass-stoppered bottle for analysis.

Analyses are based on this air-dried sample. If moisture is desired it may be determined on a large sample of the original material. Hygroscopic moisture is determined on the ground, air-dried sample, by heating for an hour at 105 to 107°C.

**List of Most Important Silicates.** *Silicates Decomposed by Acids.*—Allanite; allophane; analcite; botryolite; brewsterite; calamine; chabasite; croustedtitite; datolite (hydrated silicate and borate of Ca with Al and Mg); dioptase; eulytite; gadolinite; gahlenite; helvite; ilvaite (silicate ferrous and ferric iron with $Al_2O_3$, CaO, and MgO); laumonite; melinite; natrolite (hydrated silicate of Al and Na with Fe and CaO); okenite; olivine (silicate of Fe and Mg); pectolite; prehenite (hydrated Al and Ca silicate with Fe, Mn, K, Na, etc.); teproite; wernerite; woolastonite; zaolite.

*Silicates Not Decomposed by Acids.*—Albite; andalusite; augite; axinite; beryl; carpholite; cyanite; diallage; epidote (silicate of Fe, Al, and Ca with FeO, Mn, Mg, K, Na); euclase; feldspar (silicate of K, Na, Al, Fe, Ca, and Mg); garnet; iolite; labradorite; (micas of K and Mg); orthoclase; petalite; pinite; prochlorite; pumice; serpentine; sillimanite, talc, topaz, tourmaline ($Fe_2O_3$, FeO, Mn, Al, Ca, Mg, K, Na, Li, $SiO_2$, $B_2O_3$, $P_2O_5$, F); vesuvianite.

## DECOMPOSITION OF THE MATERIAL, GENERAL PROCEDURES

### *SILICATES DECOMPOSED BY ACIDS*

**Acid Extraction of the Silicates.**—0.5 to 1 g. of the finely pulverized material placed in a beaker or casserole is treated with 10 to 15 ml. of water and stirred thoroughly to wet the powder.[1] It is now treated with 50 to 100 ml. of concentrated hydrochloric acid and digested on the water bath for 15 or 20 minutes with the beaker or casserole covered by a watch glass. If there is evidence of sulfides (pyrites), etc., 10 to 15 ml. of concentrated nitric acid are now added and the containing vessel again covered. After the reaction has subsided, the glass cover is raised by means of riders and the mixture evaporated to dryness on the water bath. (This evaporation may be hastened by using a sand bath, boiling down to small bulk at comparatively high temperature, then to dryness on the water bath. Decomposition is complete if no gritty particles remain. A flocculent residue will often separate out during the digestion, due to partially dehydrated silicic acid; hydrated silicic acid, $Si(OH)_4$ is held in solution.) The silicic acid is converted to silica, $SiO_2$, the residue taken up with dilute hydrochloric acid, silica filtered off, washed with water acidified with hydrochloric acid, and estimated according to the procedure given later.

### *SILICATES NOT DECOMPOSED BY ACIDS*

**Fusion with Sodium Carbonate or Sodium Bicarbonate.**—0.5 to 1 g. of the air-dried, pulverized sample is placed in a large platinum crucible or dish in which has been placed about 5 g. of anhydrous sodium carbonate. The sample is thoroughly mixed with the carbonate by stirring with a dry glass rod, from which the adhering particles are brushed into the crucible. A little carbonate is sprinkled on the top of the mixture and the receptacle covered. It is heated to dull redness for 5 minutes and then gradually heated up to the full capacity of a Meker burner. When the mix has melted to a quite clear liquid, which generally is accomplished with 20 minutes of strong heating, a platinum wire with a coil on the immersed end is inserted in the molten mass, and allowed to cool. The fusion is removed by gently heating the crucible until the outside of the mass has melted, when the charge is lifted out on the wire, and after cooling disintegrated by placing it in a beaker containing about 75 ml. dilute HCl (1:2), covering the beaker to prevent loss by spattering. The crucible and lid are cleaned with dilute hydrochloric acid, adding this acid to the main solution. When the disintegration is complete, the solution is evaporated to dryness and silica is estimated according to directions given later.

If decomposition is incomplete, gritty material will be found in the beaker upon treatment of the fusion with dilute acid. If this is the case, it should be filtered off and fused with a second portion of sodium carbonate, and the fusion treated as directed above.[2]

---

[1] Water is added to the sample and then acid, as concentrated acid added directly would cause partial separation of gelatinous silicic acid, which would form a covering on the undecomposed particles, protecting them from the action of the acid.

[2] Fusions with soluble carbonates are generally best effected with the sodium salt, except in fusions of niobates, tantalates, tungstates, where the potassium salt is preferred

## SPECIAL PROCEDURES FOR DECOMPOSING THE SAMPLE

*Treatment of Iron and Steel for Silica.*—One gram of pig-iron castings, or 5 g. of steel are taken for analysis, both the fine and coarse drillings being taken in about equal proportion. (Fine particles contain more silicon than the coarse chips.) Twenty to 50 ml. of dilute nitric acid (sp. gr. 1.135) are added to the sample in a 250-ml. beaker or small casserole, and this covered. If the action is violent, cooling, by placing the beaker in cold water until the violent action has subsided, is advisable. Twenty ml. of 50% sulfuric acid are added and the solution evaporated on the hot plate to $SO_3$ fumes. After cooling, 150 ml. of water are added and 2 to 5 ml. dilute sulfuric acid. The mixture is heated until the iron completely dissolves and the silica is filtered off onto an ashless filter, washed with hot dilute hydrochloric acid (sp. gr. 1.1), and with hot water until free from iron. The residue is ignited and the silica estimated according to the procedure given later.

Pig iron and cast iron may be decomposed by digestion with a mixture of 8 parts by volume of $HNO_3$ (sp. gr. 1.42), 5 parts of $H_2SO_4$ (sp. gr. 1.84), and 17 parts of water.

Steel and wrought iron may be disintegrated by a mixture of 8 parts by volume of $HNO_3$ (sp. gr. 1.42), 4 parts $H_2SO_4$ (sp. gr. 1.84), and 15 volumes of water.

*Ferrosilicons.*—Dilute hydrochloric acid, 1 volume of acid (sp. gr. 1.19), with 2 volumes of water is a better solvent than the concentrated acid.

*Steels Containing Tungsten, Chromium, Vanadium, and Molybdenum.*—Fusion with potassium acid sulfate, $KHSO_3$, in a platinum dish, or sodium peroxide in a nickel crucible will generally decompose the material. Sodium peroxide is of special value in decomposing chromium alloys.

*Silicon Carbide, Carborundum.*—This is best brought into solution by fusion with potassium hydroxide in a nickel crucible or by fusion with $Na_2O_2$ in a pure iron crucible. Sulfuric, hydrochloric, nitric acids, or aqua regia have no effect upon this refractory material.

*Sulfides, Iron Pyrites, etc.*—These require oxidation with concentrated nitric acid or a mixture of bromine and carbon tetrachloride, followed by nitric acid, exactly according to the procedure given for solution of pyrites in the determination of sulfur. The sample is taken to dryness and then hydrochloric acid added and the solution again evaporated. The residue is dehydrated and silica determined as usual.

*Slags and Roasted Ores.*—Digestion with hydrochloric acid according to the first general procedure is best. The addition of nitric acid to decompose sulfides may be necessary.

Decomposition of silicates by fusion with lead oxide (method of Jannasch), and calcium carbonate and ammonium chloride (method of Hillebrand), are of value on account of the greater solubility of the potassium compounds. Sodium alone has an advantage over the mixed carbonates, $Na_2CO_3 + K_2CO_3$, as silica has a high melting-point and a flux, which fuses at 810°C., is more apt to cause disintegration of the silicate than the mixture, which melts at 690°C.

Prolonged blasting is undesirable, as it renders the fusion less soluble. Aluminum and iron are also rendered difficultly soluble, when their oxides are heated to a high temperature for some time.

If the melt is green, it is best to dissolve out the adhering melt from the crucible with dilute nitric acid, as a manganate (indicated by the color), if present, will evolve free chlorine by its action on HCl and this would attack the platinum.

when sodium is desired on the same sample. The procedures are given in the Chapter on the Alkali Metals.

NOTE.—$K_2CO_3$ is preferred to $Na_2CO_3$ for fusion of tungstates, niobates, and tantalates because of the greater solubility of the potassium salts. For corundum and alumina silicates $Na_2CO_3$ is preferred as double salts of potassium and aluminum are less soluble than the sodium salts.[3]

Fluorides of silicon are fused with boric acid, $BF_3$ is volatilized, $SiF_4$ is not formed. Jannasch.[4]

*Fluorides.*[5]—In presence of fluorides the melt is extracted with water (an acid extraction would volatilize some of the silica), and the extract filtered off from the insoluble carbonates. To the filtrate is added about 5 g. of solid ammonium carbonate, and the mix warmed to 40°C. and allowed to stand for several hours. The greater part of the silica is precipitated. This is filtered off and washed with water containing ammonium carbonate. Preserve this with the insoluble carbonate for later treatment. The filtrate, containing small amounts of silicic acid, is treated with 1 to 2 ml. of ammoniacal zinc oxide solution (made by dissolving C.P. moist zinc oxide in ammonia water). The mixture is boiled to expel ammonia and the precipitate of zinc silicate filtered off. The precipitate is washed into a beaker through a hole made in the filter, and the adhering material dissolved off with dilute HCl, enough being added to dissolve the remaining residue. This is evaporated to dryness and silica separated as usual. Meantime the insoluble carbonate is dissolved with HCl, evaporated to dryness and any silica it contains recovered. Finally all three portions of silica are combined, ignited, and silica estimated as usual.

## SEPARATIONS

*Separation of Silicon.*—This is accomplished in the initial steps of the general procedure of analysis by dehydration by means of sulfuric acid or perchloric acid. Silica is now treated with HF and volatilized and determined by loss of weight of the acid insoluble residue.

*Separation of Lead.*—Lead sulfate present in the insoluble residue may be extracted by a solution of concentrated ammonium acetate slightly acid with acetic acid. Silica remains undissolved.

*Insoluble Residue.*—After removal of silica and lead there may remain a residue which may contain niobium, tantalum, titanium, tungsten, barium, calcium, strontium, antimony, bismuth, tin, etc.

*Boron.*—The presence of boron in the residue will cause an error in the silicon determination since it will volatilize with the HF treatment. This may be separated by volatilization as $B(OCH_3)_3$ with methyl alcohol and acid before expulsion of silica with HF. See Chapter on Boron.[6]

*Silicon in Fluorspar.*—A special procedure will be found later in this chapter. The presence of fluoride requires a special procedure to avoid loss of silica during decomposition of the material.

[3] Smith, J. L., Am. J. Sci. (2), **40**, 248, 1865. Chem. News, **12**, 220, 1865.
[4] Jannasch, P., Ber., **28**, 2822, 1896.
[5] Sodium bicarbonate may be used in place of the carbonate with excellent results. See also "Determination of Silica in Presence of Fluorspar," later in this chapter.
[6] In presence of tungsten the temperature should be kept below 850°C. during volatilization of silica with HF.

## GRAVIMETRIC METHODS

## HYDROCHLORIC ACID METHOD

As has been stated, the gravimetric method for determination of silica is the most satisfactory general procedure for estimation of this substance, except in small quantities.

*Extraction of the Residue.* **First Evaporation.**—The residue, obtained by evaporation of the material after decomposition of the silicate, by acids or by fusion, as the case required, is treated with 15–25 ml. of hydrochloric acid (sp. gr. 1:1) covered and heated on the water bath 10 minutes. After diluting with an equal volume of water, filtration is proceeded with immediately, and the silica is washed with a hot solution consisting of 5 ml. hydrochloric acid (sp. gr. 1:2) to 95 ml. of water and finally with water. This filtration may be performed with suction. The filtrate and washings are evaporated to small volume on a sand bath and then to dryness. This contains the silica that dissolved in the first extraction.

**Second Evaporation.**—The residue obtained from evaporation of the filtrate is dehydrated for 2 hours at 105–110°C.[7] and extracted with 10 ml. of hydrochloric acid (sp. gr. 1:1) covered and heated on the water bath for 10 minutes diluted to 50 ml. with cold water and filtered immediately, without suction. The residue is washed with cold water containing 1 ml. concentrated hydrochloric acid to 99 ml. water, the washed residue containing practically all[8] the silica, that went into solution in the first extraction, is combined with the main silica residue. This is gently heated in a platinum crucible until the filters are thoroughly charred, and then ignited more strongly to destroy the filter carbon and finally blasted over a Meker burner for at least 30 minutes, or to constant weight, the crucible being covered. After cooling, the silica is weighed. For many practical purposes this residue is accepted as silica, unless it is highly colored. For more accurate work especially where contamination is suspected (silica should be white), this residue is treated further.

*Estimation of True Silica.*—Silica may be contaminated with $BaSO_4$, $TiO_2$, $Al_2O_3$, $Fe_2O_3$, $P_2O_5$ combined (traces of certain rare elements may be present). The weighed residue is treated with 3 ml. of water, followed by several drops of concentrated sulfuric acid and 5 ml. of hydrofluoric acid, HF (hood). After evaporation to dryness, the crucible is heated to redness and again cooled and weighed. The loss of weight represents silica, $SiO_2$.[9]

---

[7] Dehydration of silica is aided by the presence of lime and retarded by magnesia. In presence of the latter a soluble magnesium silicate will form if the dehydration is conducted at a temperature much above 110°C., hence it is better to avoid this by taking more time and heating to 100 or 105°C. as recommended.

Sodium chloride has a solvent action on silica, the reaction of HCl on sodium silicate being reversible; $2HCl + Na_2SiO_3 \rightleftharpoons 2NaCl + H_2SiO_3$. An evaporation of the filtrate to dryness will recover the greater part of the silica thus dissolved.

[8] Not more than 0.1% of the original $SiO_2$ may still be in solution.

[9] Silicic acid cannot be completely dehydrated by a single evaporation and heating, nor by several such treatments, unless an intermediate filtration of silica is made. If, however, silica is removed and the filtrate again evaporated to dryness and the residue heated, the amount of silica remaining in the acid extract is negligible. (See W. F. Hillebrand, J. Am. Chem. Soc., 24, 368, 1902.) Boron, if present, will volatilize with silica. Its removal with methyl alcohol should be made before dehydration of silica. See Introductory Section.

NOTES.—Lenher and Truog make the following observations for determining silica.[10]

1. In the sodium carbonate fusion method with silicates, there is always a nonvolatile residue when the silica is volatilized with hydrofluoric and sulfuric acids.

2. The nonvolatile residue contains the various bases, and should be fused with sodium carbonate and added to the filtrate from the silica when the bases are to be determined.

3. In the dehydration of the silica from the hydrochloric acid treatment of the fusion, the temperature should never be allowed to go above 110°C.

4. Dehydrated silica is appreciably soluble in hydrochloric acid of all strengths. With the dilute acid used, this error is almost negligible.

5. Dehydrated silica is slightly soluble in solutions of the alkaline chlorides. As sodium chloride is always present from the sodium carbonate fusion, an inherent error is obviously thus introduced.

6. The dehydrated silica along with the mass of anhydrous chlorides must not be treated first with water, since hydrolysis causes the formation of insoluble basic chlorides of iron and aluminum, which do not dissolve completely in hydrochloric acid.

7. Hydrochloric acid (sp. gr. 1:1) in minimum amount should be used first to wet the dehydrated chlorides and should be followed by water to bring the volume to about 50 ml., after which the silica should be filtered off as quickly as possible.

8. Pure silica comes quickly to constant weight on ignition. Slightly impure silica frequently requires long heating with the blast flame in order to attain constant weight, and is then commonly hydroscopic.

9. Evaporations of the acidulated fusion in porcelain give practically as good results as when platinum is used.

10. Filtration of the main bulk of the silica after one evaporation is desirable, inasmuch as the silica is removed at once from the solutions which act as solvents.

11. Dehydration of the silica under reduced pressure has no advantages over the common evaporation at ordinary atmospheric pressure.

12. Excessive time of dehydration, viz., four hours, possesses no advantages.

13. Excessive amounts of sodium carbonate should be avoided, since the sodium chloride subsequently formed exerts a solvent action on the silica. The best proportions are 4–5 sodium carbonate to 1 of silicate. Less than 4 parts of sodium carbonate is frequently insufficient completely to decompose many silicates.

14. The nonvolatile residue has been found to be invariably free from sodium. Pure silica, on fusion with sodium carbonate, subsequently gives no nonvolatile residue.

## PERCHLORIC ACID METHOD [11]

*Procedure for Metals and Alloys.*—Weigh out a sample corresponding to about 10 mg. of silica, using a 100- or 150-ml. beaker. Dissolve it in either nitric or hydrochloric acid, depending on which reagent is more suitable for effecting solution. For steel, 20 to 40 ml. of dilute nitric acid (sp. gr. about 1.17) will be found convenient. After the action has ceased add 8 to 10 ml. of perchloric acid (60 to 70%) for each gram of metal dissolved. (Care!! Perchloric acid presents an explosion hazard.) The amount of acid required depends upon the solubility of the metal perchlorate in hot concentrated perchloric acid. In the case of aluminum and its alloys it is necessary to use as much as 15 ml. of perchloric acid per gram of sample. Support the cover glass on glass hooks to facilitate evaporation, place the beaker on the hot-plate and evaporate to copious fumes of perchloric acid. Remove the glass hooks to prevent unnecessary loss of acid and boil 15 to 20 minutes, so that the acid refluxes down the side of the beaker. Especial care must be taken never to allow the boiling contents of the beaker to become solid, since if this occurs the separation of silica is always incomplete. If there is a tendency for much insoluble perchlorate to separate out, either the heating is not properly regulated or insufficient acid is present. In the case of aluminum, however, there is always a considerable amount of insoluble perchlorate. As the

10 Lenher, Victor, and Truog, Emil, J. Am. Chem. Soc., **38**, 1050, 1916.
11 Willard and Cake, J. Am. Chem. Soc., **42**, 2208, 1920.

solution cools it usually becomes completely solid. Dilute with 4 or 5 times its volume of water, heat to boiling, filter off the silica, wash it with very dilute hydrochloric acid and finally with water, ignite and weigh as usual. Treat the precipitate with hydrofluoric and sulfuric acids, ignite and weigh the residue to determine the weight of pure silica. This correction is usually very small.

High percentage ferrosilicon is not decomposed by perchloric acid.

*Procedure for Limestone and Soluble Silicates.*—In a 100- to 150-ml. beaker dissolve about 0.5 g. of the material in a mixture of 5 ml. perchloric acid and 10 ml. of water. If the silica content is very high, it is advisable to use more acid. Evaporate to dense fumes of perchloric acid and follow the procedure for metals described above. Insoluble silicates must first be fused with sodium carbonate as usual.

## FUSION METHOD (HAWLEY METHOD)

*Procedure.*—Weigh 0.5 g. of pulp into a 30-ml. nickel crucible and add one scoopful (about 4 g.) of flux composed of equal parts of sodium peroxide and sodium hydroxide. Mix the pulp and flux, and if the sample is known to contain over 50% of $SiO_2$ put on a cover to prevent loss. Fuse at a low temperature, beginning much below redness and increasing very slowly until a dull red is reached.

When the fusions are made as described the nickel crucibles can be used from 20 to 40 times, but if the temperature is too high, or if there is too much sodium peroxide in the flux, they will burn out more quickly.

Remove the crucibles and partly cool; place in 4″ casseroles, and cover the crucibles with 2″ watch glasses so placed that a slight opening is left on one side. Through this opening squirt in 2 or 3 ml. of warm distilled water from a wash bottle. This should start a vigorous reaction between the water and the flux. As soon as the action has somewhat diminished add 3 or 4 ml. more water and continue to do this until the fused mass is disintegrated. Toward the end the water should be added with enough force to stir the contents thoroughly. If the crucible gets too cold or the water is not hot enough, the action may cease before the melt is loosened from the crucible; and if too hot the contents may boil over. With a little practice the right conditions are readily found. As soon as the action ceases and the crucible is a little over half full, rinse off the watch glass and from a large burette add about 10 ml. of 60% HCl in small portions so as to avoid too violent reaction; then add 90% HCl until it is in excess. The crucible should now be about full and everything in solution except possibly a little gelatinous silica.

With the fingers or platinum-tipped tongs, remove the crucible, rinse, and place the casserole on the hot plate to evaporate. No harm is done if it boils gently at first. When about half evaporated, place the casserole on an iron or aluminum ring so made that the bottom of the casserole is kept about one-quarter inch above the hot plate. These rings are very beneficial in preventing spitting. When the residue has become dry, cover with a watch glass and bake at about 125°C. for 30 minutes; remove and when cool add 15 ml. of 60% HCl and turn about so as to moisten all parts of the residue. Allow to stand a short time and then put on the hot plate, and with cover still on, boil for 3 minutes. Remove and allow to cool, rinse the sides down with the minimum amount of warm distilled water, and swirl around to loosen any crust still adhering to the sides. The NaCl does not all dissolve, but will readily do so in the wash water.

It is very necessary that the casserole should not be heated after rinsing down the sides with water. After standing a few minutes, transfer the contents to a filter and wash twice with warm water; then once with hot dilute HCl and add a little to the casserole. Rub the sides and bottom of the casserole to loosen any adhering $SiO_2$ and rinse into the filter. This $SiO_2$ is ground rather fine by the rubbing and has a tendency to clog the filter, hence it is better to add this after the main portion has been partly washed. Wash the filter twice again with water, place in a crucible, partly dry, and ignite strongly for ten minutes. Weigh the $SiO_2$ as soon as cool, for it is hygroscopic. A correction is now made for the $SiO_2$ lost in solution, which under these conditions will amount to about 0.4%. A deduction is made for impurities in the $SiO_2$ and the $SiO_2$ from the flux. These gains about balance the solubility loss. Occasional tests should be made to check these losses and gains.

## DETERMINATION OF SILICA IN PRESENCE OF FLUORSPAR

When a silicate containing a fluoride is fused with boric oxide no loss of silica occurs, since the fluorine is expelled as boron trifluoride.[12] The method is based on this principle.

The procedure recommended by Schrenk and Ode [13] is as follows:

*Procedure.*—A 0.5-gram sample of finely ground material is treated with 15 ml. of 20% perchloric acid saturated with boric acid at 50°C. The ore is digested with this solution in a Pyrex beaker and heated until fumes of perchloric acid are evolved for 4–5 minutes. A few milliliters of water are now added and the fuming repeated for 4–5 minutes. The residue is diluted with about 75 ml. of water and the solution heated and the silica and insoluble matter filtered off. The filter paper is washed, first with dilute solution of perchloric acid and finally with hot water to remove free calcium salts (as shown by tests with ammonium oxalate). The paper and residue is ignited in a platinum crucible, two drops of concentrated sulfuric acid added and the residue ignited to constant weight. The silica is now volatilized by treatment with hydrofluoric acid by the customary procedure for silica, and silica estimated by the loss of weight.

NOTES.—The method is rapid and accurate and solves a problem that was formerly considered a difficult one and entailed a laborious procedure for separation, as the customary methods could not be employed, since the presence of HF would cause a loss of silica.

By the Berzelius-Hillebrand Method [14] the material (0.5 g.) is fused with $Na_2CO_3$ in a platinum crucible, the cooled cake extracted of silica by digesting with water (100 ml.) and the insoluble carbonates filtered off. The silica in the water extract is precipitated by addition of an excess of solid ammonium carbonate (5 g. or more), and allowing to stand for several hours, and filtering. The silica that still remains in the filtrate is recovered by precipitation with ammoniacal zinc oxide solution, this precipitate is filtered off, and dissolved in dilute HCl, then taken to dryness and the silica separated in the usual way. The silica remaining in the water insoluble carbonate and that precipitated by the ammonium carbonate is now obtained by dissolving the precipitates in HCl, evaporating to dryness and separating the silica by the usual procedure. The total silica residues are now weighed.

## RAPID METHOD FOR DETERMINATION OF SILICON

*Procedure.*—A two (0.9344 g.) to five (2.3360 g.) factor weight sample is transferred to a 300-ml. porcelain casserole and dissolved by addition of from 30 to

---

12 Jannasch and Weber, Ber., **32**, 1670, 1899.
13 Schrenk, W. T., and Ode, W. H., Ind. Eng. Chem. Anal. Ed., **1**, 201, 1929.
14 Hildebrand, W. F., U. S. Geol.. Survey Bull. 700, p. 222, 1919.

50 ml. of hydrochloric acid (sp. gr. 1.19), the casserole being covered with a clock-glass cover and warmed until the reaction is complete. Several milliliters of nitric acid (sp. gr. 1.42) and from 40 to 60 ml. of sulfuric acid (1.1) are added and the solution evaporated until fumes of sulfur trioxide are evolved. The solution is allowed to cool somewhat, 200 ml. of warm water are added and the liquid is boiled for several minutes or until all salts have dissolved. The silica is filtered on an 11-cm. blue ribbon paper, containing some ashless paper pulp, and washed thoroughly with hot water.

The paper and precipitate are ignited in a small platinum crucible, first at a low temperature until the carbon of the filter paper has been oxidized, and finally at 1050 to 1100°C. The crucible and its contents are cooled in a desiccator and weighed. One or two drops of sulfuric acid (sp. gr. 1.84) and several milliliters of pure 48% hydrofluoric acid are added and after having evaporated the solution until all sulfuric acid has been expelled the crucible is again ignited and weighed. The difference between the first and second weights, divided by 2 or 5 and multiplied by 100, gives the percentage of silicon in the sample.

If desired, 60% perchloric acid may be used to dehydrate the silica in place of the sulfuric acid, in which case 20 ml. of the 60% acid are required for a two factor weight sample. Since the perchlorate salts are readily soluble and cause no trouble during the evaporation to fumes, a determination may be completed in about one-half the time as when using sulfuric acid. Perchloric acid serves to render soluble any insoluble chromium carbide present. Also, the results obtained by the use of perchloric acid are of a higher degree of accuracy than those with sulfuric acid. The sample may be dissolved by direct treatment with the perchloric acid and the solution evaporated to strong fumes of perchloric acid. The cover glass and sides of the casserole are rinsed down with water, and the evaporation to strong fumes of perchloric acid is repeated. The residue is taken up with 100 ml. of water, the solution filtered and the determination completed as described in the second paragraph.

## COLORIMETRIC/PHOTOMETRIC METHODS

### SILICA AS THE SILICOMOLYBDATE

In moderately acid solutions, silica forms a yellow molybdenum complex, of the probable composition $H_5Si(Mo_2O_7)_6 \cdot H_2O$. The mole ratio of silica to molybdic oxide is 1:12, and only a slight excess of the molybdate is necessary to carry the reaction to completion. This method in various modifications has been used for the determination of silicon in fresh water,[15] in sea water,[16] in boiler feed water,[17] in iron and steel,[18] and in aluminum and magnesium base alloys.[19] The following method is for the determination of silicon in copper-base alloys.[20]

[15] Dienert and Wandenbulcke, Compt. rend., **176**, 1478, 1923; Jolles and Neurath, Z. angew. Chem., **11**, 315, 1898; Knudson, Juday, and Meloche, Ind. Eng. Chem., Anal. Ed., **12**, 270, 1940.

[16] Robinson and Spoor, Eng. Chem., Anal. Ed., **8**, 455, 1936; Thayer, Ind. Eng. Chem., Anal. Ed., **2**, 276, 1930; Thompson and Houlton, *ibid.*, **5**, 417, 1933.

[17] Schwartz, *ibid.*, **6**, 364, 1934; **14**, 893, 1942.

[18] Pinsi, Arch. Eisenhuttenw., **9**, 223, 1935.

[19] Aluminum Co. of America, Chemical Analysis of Aluminum, 2nd Ed., p. 64, 1941; Dow Chemical Co., Dowmetal Laboratory Methods, Bull. DM41, p. 21, 1941; Hadley, Analyst, **66**, 468, 1941; **67**, 5, 1942; Pinsi, Z. Metallkunde, **27**, 107, 1935.

[20] Case, Ind. Eng. Chem., Anal. Ed., **16**, 309–11, 1944.

*Reagents.* **Dilute Nitric Acid (1 to 2).**—Dilute 1 volume of reagent grade nitric acid with 2 volumes of water.

**Hydrofluoric Acid (48%) Reagent Grade.**—Even the best grades of hydrofluoric acid appear to contain a small amount of fluosilicic acid.

**Boric Acid (Saturated Solution).**—Dissolve 65 g. of reagent boric acid crystals, $H_3BO_3$, in 1 liter of hot water. Cool to room temperature.

**Ammonium Molybdate (10%).**—Dissolve 100 g. of reagent grade ammonium molybdate crystals, $(NH_4)_6Mo_7O_{24} \cdot 4H_2O$, in hot water. Cool and dilute to 1 liter. Filter if the solution is not clear.

**Citric Acid (10%).**—Dissolve 100 g. of reagent grade citric acid crystals, $C_6H_8O_7 \cdot H_2O$, in water and dilute to 1 liter.

**Standard Silica Solution.**—This standard solution may be prepared by the following method, which yields a solution containing 0.1 mg. of silicon per milliliter. Fuse 0.2141 g. of pure anhydrous silica, $SiO_2$, with 2 g. of sodium carbonate in a platinum crucible. Heat at slightly above fusion temperature for about 15 minutes, cool, and dissolve the melt in warm water, using a platinum dish for a container. Cool the solution and transfer to a 1000-ml. volumetric flask. Dilute to the mark and mix thoroughly. Store the solution in a wax or hard-rubber bottle.

*Procedure.* **Preparation of Calibration Curve (for alloys containing up to 0.20% silicon).**—Weigh portions of high-purity copper equivalent to the amount of copper (±25 mg.) present in a 1-g. sample of the alloy under test. Very fine pieces of metal (35-mesh) and light, feathery drillings should be avoided, as they react too vigorously with the dissolving acid. Transfer to platinum crucibles of at least 20-ml. capacity fitted with covers. Somewhat larger crucibles are preferable if available. To each portion of metal add 10 drops of hydrofluoric acid (0.3 to 0.4 ml.) followed by an amount of dilute nitric acid (1:2) equivalent to 0.6 ml. for each 100 mg. of metal plus 6 ml. in excess. Cover the crucibles and let stand until the vigorous reaction has subsided, when they may be placed on the steam plate to complete solution. With the aid of a long-stemmed hard-rubber or plastic funnel, transfer the contents of the crucibles to 200-ml. volumetric flasks containing 25 ml. of boric acid solution. Rinse the crucibles and sides of the flasks and immediately swirl the flasks to mix the solutions thoroughly. From a microburette add amounts of standard silicate solution to cover the desired range of silicon in steps of 0.2 mg. Cool the solutions to room temperature and add 10 ml. of ammonium molybdate solution to each. Dilute to the mark and mix thoroughly. Let the solutions stand for 15 minutes and read the transmission or relative density of the color with a photometer at approximately 410 m$\mu$. Plot the photometer readings against milligrams of silicon, or percentage of silicon. The curve approximates a straight line. Alternately, a calibration curve may be plotted by using several carefully analyzed samples of the alloy under test as standards, covering as wide a range of silicon content as possible.

While this method of calibration automatically compensates for the reagent blank, this blank may vary for different lots of reagents, and it is desirable to run either a synthetic standard or an analyzed sample of the alloy under test to determine whether or not a correction should be applied each time a new lot of reagents is used.

**Analysis of Sample.**—Treat a 1- to 1.0050-g. sample of the alloy under test exactly as described above, omitting addition of the standard silicate solution. Read the percentage of silicon directly from calibration curve.

The method of solution causes no significant loss of silicon volatilized as silicon tetrafluoride, provided the crucibles are covered and the pieces of sample metal are not so fine as to cause an exceedingly vigorous reaction which would bring the metal to the surface of the solution. Samples of silicon bronze containing as high as 15 mg. of silicon have been dissolved in this way with no significant loss of silicon.

The amount of hydrofluoric acid added in dissolving the sample should be kept to the minimum necessary for complete solution of the silicon (and tin if present); 0.3 to 0.4 ml. is ample for amounts of silicon up to 15 mg. This amount of hydrofluoric acid (48% reagent grade) may contain as much as 0.1 mg. of silicon as fluosilicic acid.

The amount of boric acid solution used is not critical, provided enough is present to react with the excess hydrofluoric acid. Using the technique described in the proposed method, 25 ml. of a saturated solution of boric acid are ample for inactivating the excess hydrofluoric acid. If desired, 1 g. of dry boric acid crystals may be added directly to the sample contained in the platinum crucible after solution is complete, the crucible being heated gently until the boric acid dissolves. Alternately, the solution of the sample may be mixed with a saturated boric acid solution in a platinum dish. The last two techniques obviate the necessity for using a funnel of nonsilicate material in transferring to the volumetric flask.

The amount of diluted nitric acid (1:2) used in dissolving the sample affects the color developed considerably; 12 to 14 ml. of acid for a 1-g. sample diluted to 200 ml. give the most intense color.

Eight to 10 ml. of 10% ammonium molybdate solution in a total volume of 200 ml. give the maximum color development. Less molybdate retards the color development, but amounts in excess of 10 ml. do not appreciably increase the intensity of the color.

## SILICA AS MOLYBDENUM BLUE [21]

Very small amounts of silicon can be determined by this method. In fact the range of concentration for which it should be used is 0.002–0.02 mg. of Si per 100 ml. of solution, assuming a transmission depth in the colorimetric cell of 1 cm.

In this method, silica is determined as molybdenum blue, by reduction of preformed yellow silicomolybdate complex. The latter is formed as the acid at a pH of 1.6 and after its reduction to the molybdenum blue, the transmittance of the latter can be read at various levels, preferably at 820 m$\mu$. In this determination plastic beakers and containers should be used, especially for standard silicon solutions.

*Reagents.* **Ammonium Molybdate Solution.**—Dissolve 75 g. of ammonium molybdate in water to which have been added 322 ml. of 1:9 sulfuric acid, and dilute to 1 liter.

**Reducing Solution.**—Dissolve 7 g. of anhydrous sodium sulfite in 100 ml. of water and add 1.5 g. of 1-amino-2-naphthol-4-sulfonic acid. When this is dissolved, add to the solution a solution of 90 g. of sodium bisulfite in 800 ml. of water, and dilute to 1 liter.

**Tartaric Acid Solution.**—Dissolve 16.8 g. of tartaric acid in 75 ml. of water and dilute to 100 ml.

**Standard Silicon Solution.**—Dissolve 5.0 g. of sodium metasilicate monohydrate in 200 ml. of water, and dilute to 1 liter. This solution should be standardized

[21] Boltz and Mellon, Anal. Chem., **19**, 873–7, 1947.

gravimetrically by the procedure on page 961, and stored in a paraffin-lined or plastic bottle.

*Procedure.*—Prepare a series of standards by transferring the desired amount of standard silica solution to a 100-ml. volumetric flask, diluting to about 94 ml., and adding 1 ml. of the ammonium molybdate solution. After letting it stand for 5 minutes, add 4% of the tartaric acid solution and mix. Then add 1 ml. of the reducing solution, dilute to 100 ml. and, after 20 minutes, read the transmittancy at 820 m$\mu$.

If sample is in solution, dilute to a concentration of 0.001–0.01 mg. of Si per 50 ml. of solution. If silicon is present as a solid sample, heat about 1 g. of it with 6–7 ml. of concentrated HCl in a platinum dish. When dissolved, add 5 ml. of perchloric acid and evaporate as far as possible without crystallization. Let stand for 5 minutes and dilute to 30 ml. with 1% HCl. Filter through a filter stick. Add 6 ml. concentrated $HNO_3$ and 3 ml. $HClO_4$ and heat until paper is oxidized. Wash sides of dish with a little water, evaporate to dryness and ignite. Fuse with 1 g. $Na_2CO_3$. After cooling, neutralize and adjust pH to 4.5–5.0, using silica-free $NH_4OH$ and 6 $N$ $H_2SO_4$. Heat until bubbling ($CO_2$) stops, filter, and dilute to 50 ml. Take an aliquot containing about 0.001–0.01 mg. of Si and dilute with water to 50 ml.

To the 50 ml. of solution of sample, add 1 ml. of ammonium molybdate solution. If phosphate ions are present, add after 5 minutes, 4 ml. of the tartaric acid solution. Reduce with 1 ml. of the reducing solution, dilute to 100 ml., and after 20 minutes, read the transmittance at 820 m$\mu$. For higher concentrations (up to 0.03 mg. Si per 50 ml. of original solution) allow a longer period (up to 30 minutes) for full color development.

## DETERMINATIONS IN SPECIFIC SUBSTANCES

## DETERMINATION OF SILICON IN SILICONES [22]

To the chemist who has not actually carried out a determination of silicon in silicones, it would seem reasonable that silicon could be determined by simply burning the sample to $SiO_2$. In practice this is seldom possible for at least two reasons: (a) heating often results in partial degradation to silicon-containing fragments which tend to volatilize, and (b) ignition may turn some of the carbon into a form which is extremely difficult to burn quantitatively.

Fusion with fluxes, such as sodium carbonate or potassium hydrogen sulfate, which are normally used to decompose silicates, is unsatisfactory for silicones. However, decomposition with sodium peroxide gives excellent results if carried out in a Parr bomb under proper conditions. Under improper conditions, use of sodium peroxide can be very hazardous.

Hydrochloric and nitric acids are of no use in decomposing silicones, but the use of concentrated sulfuric acid, which cleaves the Si—C bonds, is the basis for a procedure which, when properly carried out on nonvolatile silicones, usually leads to complete recovery of silicon in the form of $SiO_2$.

The problem in determining Si in silicones lies in the proper decomposition of the sample. Once this has been accomplished, the determination of the $SiO_2$ produced by the decomposition, and therefore of Si in the original sample, is

[22] Contribution by Howard B. Bradley, Research Laboratories, Linde Company and Silicones Division, Union Carbide Corporation, Tonawanda, New York.

routine. Two methods are given below for carrying out the decomposition of the sample. The first is the simpler and more direct, and should in general be tried first unless the sample is sufficiently volatile so that there would be evaporation losses when it is heated with sulfuric acid. The second method should be used for the more volatile samples and for any other samples for which the sulfuric acid method does not give good results.

## DIRECT SULFURIC ACID METHOD

*Procedure.*—Weigh sample in 50-ml. tared platinum crucible. Sample weight should be 250 mg. or more. Place crucible containing the sample in dry ice for about 5 minutes. Add enough fuming sulfuric acid to cover the sample. Remove crucible from dry ice and allow it to come to room temperature. Then start heating the crucible, increasing the temperature gradually and cooling if frothing of the sample commences. When the sample has been charred, or when decomposition appears complete, increase the temperature and evaporate to dryness. Ignite gradually to 1000°C. Cool, weigh, add HF + 1:1 $H_2SO_4$, evaporate to dryness, ignite, and reweigh, taking the loss in weight as $SiO_2$.

## PARR BOMB-PEROXIDE METHOD

*Reagents.*—1:1 Sulfuric Acid.
Nitric Acid.
Gelatin Capsules (Size 00).
Sodium Peroxide.
Petroleum Jelly.
*Apparatus.* Parr Peroxide Sulfur Apparatus (Flame Ignition No. AC-15B).—Use of an electrically fired bomb is easier, but reactions are frequently incomplete.
Safety Shield (or equivalent).
Apparatus for lifting the Parr bomb from flame and dipping the hot bomb into water. The apparatus consists of a hook (for holding the bomb) on the end of a long wire running over a pulley so that the wire can be pulled by the analyst from in front of the safety shield, and a metal tank partly filled with water at room temperature.
Weighing Bottle with cork insert having hole to serve as seat for gelatin capsule.
Forceps, Burner, and General Laboratory Equipment.
*Procedure.*—Thoroughly mix 15 g. dry $Na_2O_2$ and 0.7 g. sucrose in a Parr fusion cup. Obtain tare weight of weighing bottle containing cork insert plus capsule. Add sample to capsule, making sure that everything is inside the capsule; cover and obtain sample weight by difference. Sample should not weigh more than 0.35 g., and for convenience should weigh about 0.25 g. Using forceps, press capsule into surface of $Na_2O_2$-sucrose mixture; do not submerge the capsule, and make sure the sample does not spill into the flux lest a premature, and possibly violent, reaction occur. Immediately cover the crucible, place in casing, and tighten casing with Parr vise and wrench. Smear a little petroleum jelly on the side of the crucible, place the crucible over the burner behind the safety shield, and put the wire hook in place on the bomb. Heat the bottom of the crucible with the tip of a flame until a puff of smoke from the petroleum jelly indicates that the crucible temperature is high enough to start the reaction in the bomb. Allow the bomb to remain in contact with the flame for a full minute longer, then pull on the wire. This lifts the bomb and puts it in place over the tank of water.

Quickly let the wire go back over the pulley, thus quenching the bomb in the water. Remove bomb from the water and disassemble; wash outsides of crucible and cover with distilled water. Remove cover and wash and police it, allowing washings to run into a nickel or stainless steel beaker. Place the crucible on its side in the nickel beaker and add water until the bomb is ⅔ covered. Place nickel cover on beaker and boil gently for a few minutes. Remove crucible from beaker, washing thoroughly. Transfer contents of nickel beaker to porcelain casserole; cover casserole and add 1:1 $H_2SO_4$ cautiously until effervescence ceases. Add an additional 30 ml. 1:1 $H_2SO_4$ and evaporate to strong fumes. Dilute with water, filter, ignite the silica, weigh, treat with HF, and weigh again as in the usual method of determining $SiO_2$.

## ANALYSIS OF SODIUM SILICATE

### DETERMINATION OF $Na_2O$

*Procedure.*—Five grams of the sample are dissolved in about 150 ml. of water and heated; 1 ml. of phenolphthalein is added and then an excess of standard sulfuric acid from a burette. The excess acid is titrated with standard sodium hydroxide to a permanent pink.

$$H_2SO_4 \text{ (by weight)} \times 0.6319 = Na_2O \text{ (by weight)}$$

### SILICA

*Procedure.*—Ten grams of the sample are acidified with hydrochloric acid and evaporated to dryness on the steam bath. The treatment is repeated with additional hydrochloric acid and then the residue taken up with 5 ml. of the acid and 200 ml. of water. The residue is digested to dissolve the soluble salts, filtered, washed, and ignited. Silica is determined by loss of weight by volatilization of the silica with hydrofluoric and sulfuric acids. The filtrate is made to 1 liter.

### IRON AND ALUMINA

*Procedure.*—Five hundred ml. (5 grams) of the filtrate from the silica determination are oxidized with $HNO_3$ and the iron and alumina precipitated with ammonia, washed, ignited, and weighed as $Al_2O_3$ and $Fe_2O_3$. The residue is dissolved by digestion with hydrochloric acid or by fusion with sodium acid sulfate, and subsequent solution in hydrochloric acid. Iron is determined by titration in a hot hydrochloric acid solution with standard stannous chloride, $SnCl_2$, solution as usual. If only a small amount of precipitate of iron and alumina is present, as is generally the case, solution by hydrochloric acid is preferable to the fusion with the acid sulfate. The latter is used with larger amounts of the oxides.

### LIME, CaO

*Procedure.*—This is determined in the filtrate from iron and alumina by precipitation as the oxalate and ignition to CaO.

### MAGNESIA, MgO

*Procedure.*—This is determined in the filtrate from lime by precipitation with sodium ammonium phosphate. The precipitate is ignited and weighed as $Mg_2P_2O_7$ and calculated to MgO. Precipitate $\times$ 0.3622 = MgO.

## COMBINED SULFURIC ACID

**Procedure.**—One hundred ml. of the filtrate from the silica determination (= 1 gram) is treated with $BaCl_2$ solution and sulfuric acid precipitated as $BaSO_4$.

$$BaSO_4 \times 0.4202 = H_2SO_4 \text{ or } BaSO_4 \times 0.3433 = SO_3$$

## SODIUM CHLORIDE

**Procedure.**—Ten grams of the silicate of soda are dissolved in 100 ml. of water and made acid with $HNO_3$ in slight excess and then alkaline with MgO. Cl is titrated with standard $AgNO_3$ solution.

## WATER

**Procedure.**—This is determined either by difference or by taking 10 grams to dryness and then heating over a flame and blasting to constant weight.

# ANALYSIS OF SAND, COMMERCIAL VALUATION

## DETERMINATION OF SILICA

**Procedure.**—Two grams of the finely ground material are fused in a platinum crucible with 10 g. of fusion mixture ($K_2CO_3 + Na_2CO_3$) by heating first over a low flame and gradually increasing the heat to the full flame of a Meker blast lamp. When the fusion has become clear it is cooled by pouring on a large platinum cover. The fused mass on the cover and that remaining in the platinum crucible are digested in a covered beaker with hot hydrochloric acid on the steam bath. The solution is now evaporated to dryness, taken up with a little water and 25 ml. of concentrated HCl and again taken to dryness. Silica is now determined by the procedure outlined under the general method on page 956.

## FERRIC OXIDE AND ALUMINA

**Procedure.**—The filtrate is oxidized with crystals of solid potassium chlorate, $KClO_3$, and iron and aluminum hydroxides precipitated with ammonia. The precipitate is filtered, washed, ignited and weighed as $Al_2O_3 + Fe_2O_3$.

## CALCIUM OXIDE

**Procedure.**—To the ammoniacal filtrate 10 ml. of ammonium oxalate solution are added, the solution heated to boiling and the precipitate allowed to settle until cold. The solution should not be over 200 ml. The calcium oxalate is filtered off, washed and ignited. The residue is weighed as CaO.

## MAGNESIUM OXIDE

**Procedure.**—The filtrate from the lime is made strongly ammoniacal and 10 ml. of sodium ammonium phosphate added. The solution during the addition is allowed to stand cold for some time, three to four hours. The precipitate is filtered and washed with dilute ammonia (1 of reagent to 3 parts of water), then ignited and weighed as $Mg_2P_2O_7$. This weight multiplied by $0.3622 = MgO$.

# DETERMINATION OF SILICON IN CAST IRON AND STEEL

**Procedure.**—One gram of pig iron, cast iron, or high silicon iron, or 5 grams of steel, wrought iron, or low silicon iron are taken for analysis. (By taking multiples of the factor weight 0.4693, $SiO_2$ to Si, the final calculation is simplified.) The sample is placed in a 250-ml. beaker and 20 to 50 ml. of dilute nitric acid added. If the action is violent, cooling the beaker in water is advisable. When the reaction subsides, 20 ml. of dilute sulfuric acid (1:1), are added, the mixture placed on the hot plate and evaporated to dense white fumes. The residue is taken up with 150 ml. of water containing 2 to 5 ml. of sulfuric acid and heated until the iron completely dissolves.

The solution is filtered and the silica residue washed first with hot dilute hydrochloric acid (sp. gr. 1.1), and then with hot water added in small portions to remove the iron sulfate. The residue is now ignited and weighed as silica.

NOTE.—If the ash is colored by iron oxide, silica is determined by difference, after expelling the silica by adding 4 to 5 ml. of hydrofluoric acid and a few drops of sulfuric, taking to dryness and igniting the residue.

The following acid mixtures are recommended by the U. P. Ry. For steel, wrought iron and low silicon iron, 8 parts by volume of $HNO_3$, sp. gr. 1.42; 4 parts of concentrated $H_2SO_4$, sp. gr. 1.84; 6 parts HCl, sp. gr. 1.2 and 15 parts by volume of water.

## ANALYSIS OF FERROSILICON AND REFINED SILICON [23]

### *DETERMINATION OF SILICON*

This determination is based on decomposition of the sample by fusion with sodium peroxide in a pure iron crucible, acidification with hydrochloric acid, and dehydration and determination of the silica by the usual procedures. While the method is simple in theory, it requires more than ordinary care and attention to details if accurate results are to be obtained. A majority of the chances for error due to careless manipulation are of a character which result in loss of silica, consequently it is very usual for low silicon results to be obtained.

*Procedure.*—Into a 30 ml. iron crucible there is weighed 0.4672 g. of the sample of ferrosilicon or refined silicon which has been ground to at least 200-mesh in an agate mortar. The fine pulverization of the sample is necessary in order to secure complete decomposition by the subsequent fusion. The crucibles are stamped from No. 20 gauge (0.038″ thickness) "Armco" iron. This iron (called "Ingot Iron") contains only a trace of silicon and the crucibles made from it are more satisfactory for this particular purpose than nickel crucibles (which always contain some silicon) and cost only a fraction as much. Approximately 8 g. of dry sodium peroxide are added, the contents are mixed thoroughly with a small iron or nickel rod, and the mixture is covered with a layer of about 2 g. additional sodium peroxide.

The contents of the crucible are carefully fused over the flame of a laboratory burner. Instead of a gas flame, an electric crucible furnace or other source of heat may be employed, but the former is preferable. The fusion is best accomplished by holding the crucible with a pair of tongs and slowly revolving it around the *outer edge of the flame* until the contents have melted down quietly, care being taken not to raise the temperature so rapidly as to cause spattering. When the fusion is molten, a slight rotary motion is imparted to the crucible to stir up any unattacked particles of alloy on the bottom or sides, the crucible and contents being maintained at a low red head. Just before completion of the fusion, which only requires three or four minutes, the temperature is increased to bright redness for a minute. If these directions are followed carefully, a very quiet fusion without any spattering will result, and complete decomposition will be obtained. In

[23] Contributed by Thos. R. Cunningham.

event of a violent reaction, due usually to too rapid heating, use of insufficient sodium peroxide, or to lack of thorough mixing, appreciable loss will occur and the work should be repeated.

When the tightly covered crucible has cooled a sufficiently long time for the fusion to solidify, but before it has reached room temperature, it is tapped on an iron plate several times to loosen the fused mass from the crucible in a solid cake. When the melt has cooled, it is transferred to a large (275 ml.), covered platinum dish, to which there is cautiously added 50 ml. of cold water. As soon as the reaction is over the dish and its contents are allowed to cool somewhat, 10 ml. of sulfurous acid and approximately 50 ml. of hydrochloric acid (more is used if necessary) are introduced which should render the liquid acid and result in the solution of everything except a few particles of magnetic iron oxide which will dissolve during the subsequent evaporation. The solution is evaporated to dryness on a sand or water bath and heated for about 30 minutes at a temperature approximating but not exceeding 110°C. More prolonged heating, or heating at higher temperatures, is disadvantageous since it renders the iron oxide more insoluble. The use of a platinum rather than a porcelain dish is a matter of considerable practical importance. It is very difficult to remove all silica from a porcelain dish whereas this is easily accomplished with platinum. On the other hand, alkaline chlorides attack a porcelain dish after a few evaporations, when the glaze has worn off, introducing an error which leads to high results. For these reasons platinum, when available, should always be employed.

After having allowed the dish to cool, 20 ml. of hydrochloric acid (sp. gr. 1.19) are introduced and heat is applied for about 5 minutes, any hard lumps being broken up with a glass rod. Approximately 150 ml. of water are then added and the solution is heated just sufficiently long to dissolve most of the sodium chloride, when it is filtered on an 11-cm. ashless paper and washed 10 or 12 times with hot 2% hydrochloric acid and then thoroughly with hot water. The filtrate and washings are reserved. Dehydrated silica is appreciably soluble in hydrochloric acid of all strengths and also in solutions of sodium chloride. The important factors affecting this solubility are the strength and volume of acid used, its temperature, and the length of time the silica is exposed to the action of the acid and sodium chloride solution. The most important of these factors is the volume of acid employed. Adherence to the conditions described will result in a minimum of silica being dissolved. When the silica has been washed thoroughly it is reserved for further treatment.

To the combined filtrate and washings from the silica, there are added 60 ml. of sulfuric acid (sp. gr. 1.84) and the solution is evaporated in a porcelain dish or casserole until dense fumes of sulfur trioxide are freely evolved. Use of porcelain at this point is permissible because the glaze is not appreciably attacked under these conditions and silica which has been dehydrated by sulfuric acid is gelatinous and can be easily removed from a porcelain surface. After having allowed the residue of ferric sulfate, sodium sulfate, etc. to cool, 250 ml. of water are added and the solution is boiled until the sulfates are in solution, when it is immediately filtered on an 11-cm. ashless paper and the silica washed 10 to 12 times with cold 1% hydrochloric acid and then thoroughly with hot water. The small amount of silica that passes into the filtrate may be neglected.

The paper and silica from the second dehydration are placed in a large covered crucible and the paper is burned. The paper containing the silica from the first dehydration is then added and ignited very carefully at a very low red heat until the carbon has burned. Great care should be exercised in igniting the paper as the current of air produced by a burning filter paper is sufficient to carry finely divided silica out of the crucible. Carelessness at this point may result in loss of several per cent of silicon. When the carbon of the filter paper has burned completely, the crucible and its contents are ignited to constant weight with a blast lamp or in an electric muffle furnace at from 1100° to 1150°C.

After the crucible has been cooled in a desiccator and weighed, the precipitate is moistened with water, 2-3 drops of sulfuric acid (sp. gr. 1.84) and from 5 to 10 ml. of pure 48% hydrofluoric acid are added and the solution is evaporated on a sand bath until the acids have been expelled, when the crucible is again ignited for a few minutes and weighed. The difference between the two weights, less the "blank" on the sodium peroxide, multiplied by 100, gives the percentage of silicon.

A factor weight (0.4672 g.) of the 100-mesh sample of 15% ferrosilicon is fused with approximately 10 g. of sodium peroxide in an Armco iron crucible. The solution is acidulated with 80 ml. of sulfuric acid (1:1) and evaporated to fumes of sulfur trioxide.

Sodium peroxide usually contains only very small amounts of silica, but as a precaution a "blank" should be run on each new can that is employed. This is done by dissolving 10 g. of the reagent in water in a platinum dish, acidifying the solution with hydrochloric acid, evaporating to dryness, etc., as previously described. The amount of silica found in this way is usually negligible when compared to the errors to which the method is subject.

## CONDUCTIVITY METHOD FOR DETERMINING SILICON IN MAGNETIC SHEET STEEL [24]

*Apparatus.* **Resistivity Comparison Instrument.**—Shown in circuit diagram (Fig. 41-2) and photograph (Fig. 41-3).

*Procedure.*—The method consists simply of measuring the resistivity (reciprocal conductivity) of the sample and reading its silicon content from a standard graph.

Electrolytic iron has a resistivity of approximately 10 microhms per cm.[3] but it was found that commercial grades of magnetic sheet containing practically no silicon and obtained from several different sources had a resistivity of 14 or 15 microhms per cm.[3]; it will be observed that this is the starting point of the curve.

With this data it has been possible to construct a very dependable instrument for making silicon determinations; the wiring scheme for the instrument is presented in Fig. 41-2.

Fig. 41-3 shows the instrument with the sample of steel inserted for testing. Fig. 41-4 gives resistance as of function of the percentage of silicon.

There are two features incorporated in the instrument which deserve special mention: the first is the "Comparator" which is made of silicon steel (about 2.5% silicon) and is protected from corrosion by a coating of G. E. No. 880 protective paint baked on at a temperature of 100°C.

Since this "Comparator" is used in controlling the current and as it is constructed of the same material as the samples under test, it has the effect of compensating the instrument for temperature changes. Samples have been tested over a wide range of temperature and no appreciable errors have been noted in the indications.

The second feature is the "Graduated Rheostat" which makes it possible, by

[24] Contributed by P. L. Stapleton, General Electric Co.

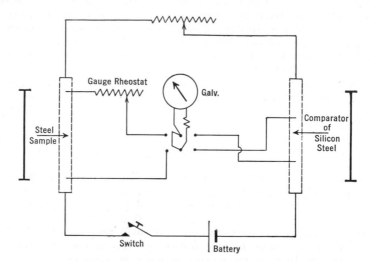

FIG. 41-2.

FIG. 41-3.

manual setting of the dial, to test steel of various thicknesses ranging from .013″ to .026″ and accurately to ⅕ of a mil. This eliminates entirely all computations and multiplying factors, and reduces the testing of the steel to a purely manual operation.

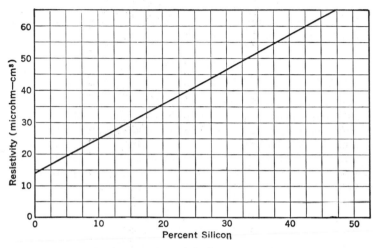

FIG. 41-4.

Instructions for operating the instrument are as follows:

1. Insert the strip of steel in the current clips and tighten the potential contact points against it.

2. Adjust the "Graduated Rheostat" to the thickness of the steel to be measured.

3. Close switch at right of instrument; then close switch at left to position marked "Comp.," and adjust galvanometer pointer to the red line on the scale by turning the lower rheostat.

4. Close switch at left to position marked "Samp.," and read the percentage of silicon directly from the position of the galvanometer pointer.

## ANALYSIS OF SILICON CARBIDE [25]

### UMPIRE METHOD

**Decomposition of Sample.**—The silicon carbide, powdered to pass through a 150-mesh screen, is dried at 110°C. for one hour to remove hygroscopic water. All analyses are made on the dried sample.

Weigh out approximately 0.5000 gram of sample and transfer to a platinum crucible of about 30-ml. capacity, somewhat larger if available. Mix thoroughly with 5 g. of the purest sodium carbonate, anhydrous, and place over a small flame of a Bunsen burner. Start with the bottom of the crucible at dull red heat and *very slowly* increase the temperature. It is important that this operation not be hurried for violent spattering will ensue and particles of SiC will be carried onto the cover and remain unattacked. As soon as the reaction of decomposition starts,

[25] Methods used by the Norton Co., Worcester, Mass., through the courtesy of M. O. Lamar.

ascertained by carefully lifting the cover for an instant, maintain that temperature for half an hour or more. The mass should be semipasty and not too fluid Finally, with great care increase the temperature to full heat of the burner and continue the fusion for half an hour. If these conditions are rigidly adhered to it is unnecessary to add any sodium or potassium nitrate to the fusion. Keep the flame of the burner oxidizing and do not envelop the crucible with a large semi reducing flame. The platinum crucible is not attacked more than in an ordinary sodium carbonate fusion of a rock or clay.

## TOTAL SILICA

*Procedure.*—When the fusion is complete transfer the contents of the crucible to a 400-ml. dish, preferably of platinum, cover with a watch glass, add 150 ml. of hot water and then 35 ml. of 1:1 hydrochloric acid. When all effervescence is over, rinse off the watch glass into the dish, clean the crucible and cover in a similar manner and evaporate the contents of the dish on the steam bath to complete dryness. Cool, drench the residue with 10 ml. of concentrated HCl, let stand five minutes, add 100 ml. of hot water, digest 10 minutes on the steam bath, filter off the silica, and wash free from chlorides with warm water. Evaporate the filtrate to dryness in the same dish, heat to 100 to 120°C. for one hour and repeat the silica filtration and washing.

Ignite the two papers in a platinum crucible, blast to constant weight and correct the silica for impurities with hydrofluoric acid and sulfuric acid according to the standard procedure.

The residue in the crucible is fused with a pinch of bisulfate, dissolved in water and added to the filtrate from the second silica. Heat the filtrate to 80–90°C. and gas thoroughly with $H_2S$. Let stand one-half hour at least, filter off the platinum sulfide, and wash with acidulated $H_2S$ water. Boil out the $H_2S$ from the filtrate and oxidize the iron by the addition of bromine water to a distinct yellow color. Finally boil out the bromine and bring the volume of the solution to 150 ml. by evaporation. The solution is now ready for the determination of iron oxide, alumina, titania, etc.

## TOTAL AMMONIA PRECIPITATE

*Procedure.*—Add a few drops of methyl red to the boiling hot solution and then dilute, carbonate-free, freshly prepared or redistilled ammonium hydroxide until the indicator changes to yellow. Boil one or two minutes and filter, washing the precipitate with hot 2% neutral ammonium chloride solution. Dissolve the precipitate in a few milliliters of hot dilute acid, wash the paper thoroughly and reprecipitate with the same precautions as above. Reserve the precipitate. Combine the two filtrates, make slightly acid, and concentrate to a volume of 100 ml. Make faintly ammoniacal, add bromine water and digest 1–2 hours on the steam bath, keeping the solution ammoniacal. Filter off any manganese precipitate which may have separated, wash, and dissolve in dilute $HNO_3$ containing a pinch of sulfite. (Note: If desired, determine Mn by any acceptable method. The amount is so small that color methods suffice.)

## LIME AND MAGNESIA

*Procedure.*—Determine lime and magnesia by the usual methods, making a double precipitation in each case. Allow the first precipitate of calcium oxalate and mag-

nesium ammonium phosphate to stand overnight. The second precipitate need
stand only about six hours, though longer does no harm.

## SEPARATION OF $Fe_2O_3$, $TiO_2$, ETC., FROM $Al_2O_3$

*Procedure.*—(a) The weighed total ammonia precipitate is fused with a small
amount of pyrosulfate and taken up in 2% sulfuric acid. Gas with $H_2S$ to remove
traces of Pt and filter if any appears. Add one gram of tartaric acid, pass in more
$H_2S$, make ammoniacal and continue gassing for 5–10 minutes. Let stand warm
for one-half hour and filter off FeS, washing with 2% $NH_4Cl$ solution containing
some colorless ammonium sulfide. Reserve the filtrate. Dissolve the precipitate
in hot 1:3 hydrochloric acid containing a pinch of potassium chlorate. Wash the
paper thoroughly and boil the chlorine out of the filtrate. Precipitate the iron
with ammonium hydroxide from the boiling hot solution, wash the precipitate
with hot 2% ammonium chloride solution and weigh as $Fe_2O_3$.

(b) The filtrate from the $H_2S$ precipitation is made acid with $H_2SO_4$ and
boiled down to a small volume. Titania can be determined either colorimetrically
with $H_2O_2$ or precipitated along with whatever $ZrO_2$ that may be present by
means of cupferron from an ice-cold solution containing 10% by volume of
sulfuric acid.

From the sum of the $Al_2O_3 + Fe_2O_3 + TiO_2$ precipitate, $Al_2O_3$ is found by
difference. This ignores the possible presence of several other elements ($P_2O_5$, for
example) but the minute amounts present do not usually warrant separate determinations. Calculate the oxides to metals.

## FREE CARBON

*Procedure.*—This determination is the least satisfactory of all, since it is very
difficult to burn out free carbon without some oxidation of the silicon carbide.
Best results are obtained when a weighed, dry sample is ignited in a boat in an
inclined tube furnace at 950°C. for 15 minutes. The loss in weight is assumed
to be carbon. No better results are obtained if the $CO_2$ is weighed after absorption
in Ascarite or other such materials.

## TOTAL CARBON

*Procedure.*—Weigh out 0.2500 of the dry sample, mix thoroughly by shaking in
a small weighing bottle with 1.50 grams of the very best $Pb_3O_4$. Transfer to a
combustion boat lined with RR Alundum, rinse out the bottle with RR Alundum
and pour on top of the sample. Cover with more alundum if necessary. Burn
the sample at 1000 1100°C. in a combustion furnace with oxygen, absorbing the
$CO_2$ exactly as for steel analyses. All $Pb_3O_4$ contains some carbonaceous matter;
therefore run several careful blank determinations using exactly the same conditions. If there are indications that all the sample did not burn, crush the fusion
in a clean mortar, add more $Pb_3O_4$, and reburn the sample. This condition
sometimes arises.

*Calculations.*—From the percentage of total carbon, subtract "free carbon," obtaining the per cent of combined carbon. Calculate this to SiC which gives the
percentage of silicon carbide in the sample. Next calculate the $SiO_2$ equivalent
of the SiC and subtract the result from the total silica found. The difference is
"total free silica." From the total summation of the analysis subtract 100.00%;
the difference is excess oxygen. Excess $O_2$ times the factor $SiO_2/O_2$ gives the

amount of silica equivalent to the excess oxygen. Subtract this figure from the "total silica"; the difference is the *free* silica present. The "total free silica" minus the "free silica" gives the $SiO_2$ derived from the free silicon present. Calculate to Si by the factor $Si/SiO_2$.

Iron, aluminum, and titanium are reported as metals, for it is a reasonable assumption that they are present in the lowest state of oxidation. Calcium and magnesium are reported as their respective oxides.

It is apparent that the summation of the analysis should be exactly 100.00% since some of the constituents ($SiO_2$ and Si, for example) are calculated on the basis of that assumption.

## THE ACETIC ANHYDRIDE METHOD FOR DETERMINING SILICA IN CEMENT AND CLINKER

Mr. R. M. Willson, the chief chemist of the Southwestern Portland Cement Company at Victorville, California, has developed the following method of procedure for the determination of silica in cement and clinker. This method is a modification of the glacial acetic acid method.

*Procedure.*—Weigh 0.5 g. of sample in 150-ml. Pyrex beaker. Rotate beaker while adding to it a mixture of 5.5 ml. of acetic anhydride, and 4.5 ml. of distilled water. Place on hot plate and rotate until violent action ceases. Remove the beaker to an asbestos pad which was previously heated and placed by the side of the hot plate. When action has ceased and the solution assumes a uniform reddish color, add a very small amount of 1:1 hydrochloric acid (not more than 5 ml.). Heat to clear yellow. Add 10 ml. of distilled water, and filter silica. Proceed identically as in "Gravimetric Methods."

## DETERMINATION OF FREE SILICA

The health hazard of free silica in a dust gives great importance to its determination, not only in dusts themselves, but in rocks encountered by construction workers, quarrymen, miners, etc. The most widely used chemical method is that of Knopf,[26] which consists of successive treatments of the dust or ground rock (through 150-mesh) with hydrochloric acid, hydrofluosilicic acid (cold), and hydrofluoric acid. The principle of the method is that the hydrochloric acid decomposes the carbonates, the hydrofluosilicic acid, the silicates, leaving the free silica essentially unaffected, to be dissolved by the hydrofluoric acid.

*Procedure.*—Weigh out a 0.5-g. sample of dust or ground rock. If it contains oil, extract with petroleum ether. Place the sample in a platinum dish. If it contains organic matter, ignite for 30 minutes until combustion is complete. Cool, and if carbonates are present, add concentrated hydrochloric acid and warm. After evolution of $CO_2$ has ended, filter (using ashless filter paper), wash with water and return the residue and paper to the platinum dish. Dry, ignite and cool to 20°C. or below. Add hydrofluosilicic acid, cover the dish, and set it in a spot where the ambient temperature does not exceed 20°C. Let it stand for a period of 1–3 days, depending on the expected amount of silicates. (Until this is known, it is well to run two or more samples.) Filter (using ashless filter paper) washing all the residue from the dish onto the filter, and continuing washing until the wash water is free from hydrofluosilicic acid. (It should give no precipitate with a mixture of 5% aqueous KCl solution and alcohol.) Return the residue and paper

[26] Knopf, U. S. Public Health Reports, **48**, 183, 1933.

o the platinum dish, dry, ignite, and weigh. The loss in weight due to the hydrofluosilicic acid treatment is silicate. If only one sample is being run, the hydrofluosilicic acid treatment should be repeated for another day to ensure that there
s no further loss in weight due to silicate. (See NOTE below.)

To the silicate-free residue, in the platinum dish, add 2–3 ml. of 48% hydrofluoric acid. When action has ceased, heat until all the acid has volatilized, ignite,
cool and weigh. The loss in weight due to the hydrofluoric acid treatment is
free silica. Repeat this treatment to constant weight.

NOTE.—The results for free silica by this method are always somewhat low due to the
fact that hydrofluosilicic acid has a slow solvent action on free silica. The results may
be corrected by adding 0.7% per day for each day of treatment with hydrofluosilic acid to
the weight of free silica found.

## METHODS FOR SILICON IN ANALYSIS IN OTHER CHAPTERS

# Chapter 42

# SILVER

**Ag,** *at. wt.* 107.870; *sp. gr.* 10.50–10.57; *m.p.* 960.5°C.; *b.p. about* 1950°C.; *oxides* $Ag_2O$, $Ag_2O_2$

Silver occurs native as metallic silver, but more commonly in combination as silver glance or argentite, $Ag_2S$; as antimonide, arsenide, bismuthide, bromide, chloride, iodide, selenide, sulfide, telluride, and in thio salts. It is found associated with sulfide of lead, with native gold and copper, with antimony, mercury, bismuth, and platinum. Among the more important minerals are:—native silver, argentite, hessite, proustite, pyrargyrite, cerargyrite (horn silver, AgCl). Traces of silver occur in sea water.

Silver has been known from prehistoric times and has been employed as a standard of value in coins many centuries before the Christian era and still continues in the currency of all civilized countries of the World. Copper is now added to increase the durability of the coins, the United States coinage containing 10% of copper, British coins 7.5% copper. The element is used in silver-plating, making of mirrors, table silverware, and jewelry and ornaments. The nitrate and various colloidal preparations are used in medicine, the chloride and bromide salts are employed in photography.

## DETECTION

A trace of silver in most substances is detected with greatest certainty by furnace assay methods.

*The wet method* of detection of silver most commonly practiced, depends upon observation of the properties of the precipitate formed by the addition of a not excessive amount of alkali chloride to a cold nitric or sulfuric acid solution of the substance undergoing examination. One-tenth milligram of silver precipitated as silver chloride in a cold 200-ml. acid solution gives a very perceptible opalescence to the liquid.

*Silver chloride* is white when freshly precipitated, tinted pink when palladium is present; in colorless liquids on exposure to light it turns brown, violet, blue, or black. By agitation, heating, or long standing the precipitate becomes coagulated or granular and in such a state is retained by an ordinary filter. The presence of some forms of organic matter prevents coagulation.

Silver chloride is dissolved by concentrated hydrochloric acid; raising the temperature of the acid assists the action. It is dissolved by sodium thiosulfate, alkali cyanides, mercuric nitrate, and alkali chlorides.

From mercurous chloride, silver chloride, except when constituting a small proportion of the precipitate, is distinguished by its solubility without decomposition in ammonium hydroxide. Precipitation from its ammoniacal solution is accomplished by acidifying. Lead chloride, precipitable also by hydrochloric acid, is not flocculent, does not coagulate, but dissolves quite freely by heating. Addition of hydrochloric acid to a solution of silicon, tellurium, thallium, tungsten, or molybdenum may produce a precipitate, in each case, easily distinguishable from that of silver chloride, but may mask traces of the salt.

Silver, in a cold solution containing free nitric acid, only a small amount of colored salts and no mercury, may be detected through the formation of a white precipitate, similar in appearance to silver chloride, by addition of a slight excess of an alkali thiocyanate.

When a solution of silver salt is added to a mixture of 20 ml. ammonium salicylate (20 g. salicylic acid neutralized with ammonium hydroxide, a slight excess added and the whole made up to 1000 ml.) and 20 ml. of a 5% solution of ammonium persulfate added, an intense brown color is produced, which will indicate the presence of a 0.01 milligram of silver. Lead does not affect the test.

When it appears that the chloride or thiocyanate test for silver is not positive because of the presence of other precipitable elements, the precipitate, after it settles, is filtered through the finest quality paper, and the mixture of the ash of the incinerated filter with dry potassium carbonate is heated on charcoal with a mouth blowpipe. If silver is present and not associated with a large amount of palladium, there will be found on the charcoal pellicles of the color characteristic of silver, which have no white or yellow sublimate when melted in the oxidizing flame of the blowpipe. The pink palladium salts of silver precipitated by a chloride or thiocyanate before the blowpipe produces metal which is dull in appearance and not readily melted.

NOTES.—Silver may be recognized in a solution of concentration 1 to 240,000 by the reduction of its salts with alkaline formaldehyde. Whitby's method of detection and estimation of small amounts of silver depends upon the formation of a yellow color through addition of sucrose and sodium hydroxide. Ammonium ion interferes, but bismuth, cadmium, copper, mercury of either valence, lead or zinc, in amounts equal to that of the silver, do not. Maletesta and De Nola add to the solution to be tested a few drops of a solution of chromium nitrate and then potassium hydroxide to alkalinity. A brownish turbidity or black precipitate of silver oxide forms. The limit of sensitiveness is 0.5 mg. in 100 ml.

Feigl [1] has described a very delicate test for silver with *p*-dimethylaminobenzylidene-rhodanine as a reagent. This reagent gives in weakly acid, neutral, and ammoniacal solutions, a flocculent red precipitate with silver. In 5 ml. of a weakly

acid solution, one part of silver in 5,000,000 of solution can be detected. In working with 10 ml. of solution, to which 0.5 ml. of 4 N nitric acid and 0.3 ml. of a saturated solution of the rhodanine [2] in alcohol were added, the same sensitivity

[1] Feigl, F., Z. anal. Chem., **74**, 380, 1928.

[2] The reagent is prepared according to the procedure given by Feigl. Instead of using a 0.03% solution of the rhodanine in acetone as described by Feigl, a saturated solution in alcohol (about 0.02%) may be taken.

was found.[3] A solution with 1 mg. of silver in a liter produces a distinct reddish brown color (10 ml. of solution, conditions as above); with 0.5 mg. of silver per liter a weakly reddish color was noticed; with 0.2 mg. per liter the solution showed a very weak pink color after ten minutes' standing, distinctly different from the blank, which was slightly yellow. In ammoniacal solution (10 ml. of solution + 1 ml. of 6 $N$ ammonia and 0.1 ml. of indicator) the color in the presence of silver is reddish-brown and in very dilute solutions orange-brown. The sensitivity in this case is about 2 mg. of silver in a liter.

In acid medium the reagent is so sensitive toward silver that it even cannot be used as an indicator for the titration of iodide with silver solution. A weakly acid solution of 0.01 $N$ potassium iodide to which some reagent is added gives a dark red precipitate after addition of a few drops of 0.01 $N$ silver nitrate. Even the silver in the complex potassium silver cyanide reacts with the rhodanine.

Feigl's reagent may also be applied to the estimation of traces of silver in water by colorimetric technique. Soft glass should not be used. Resistant glass is better, but vessels of fused silica are best. Silver ion is adsorbed on the surface of soft glass.[4]

**Dithizone** may be used to detect silver or to determine it colorimetrically in the absence of Cu, Hg, Au, Pd, and Pt(II). The acidified solution of the silver is extracted with dithizone in $CCl_4$ (see Lead Chapter for general technique). The silver salt of the reagent is yellow.[5]

## ESTIMATION

Silver is determined in copper, lead, silver, sulfur, or other ores, in copper and lead furnace by-products, and in lead by furnace assay methods, in which a preliminary acid treatment of the sample is rarely employed; in native copper ore, in copper, copper alloys, gold, gold alloys, and in the slime from the electrolytic refining of copper or lead by furnace methods, in which a preliminary acid treatment of the sample is employed, in silver alloys by titrimetric or gravimetric methods; in mercury by a gravimetric method; in cyanide mill solution or solutions containing much organic matter by furnace process on the residue obtained by evaporation or precipitation; in silver plating electrolyte by electrolysis.

**Solubility.**—Nitric acid, dilute or concentrated, attacks silver rapidly when hot. The presence of a soluble chloride, iodide, or bromide in the solvent or substance will retard and may prevent solution. Unless oxidizing agents are present, dilute sulfuric acid has practically no action on massive silver, but hot, concentrated acid commences to be an active solvent at a concentration of 75% $H_2SO_4$. Hydrochloric acid attacks silver superficially. The action of alkali hydroxides or carbonates in solution is inappreciable; in a state of fusion, slight.

**Furnace Assay Methods.**—These are described in the Chapter on Gold.

In procedures where HCl has been employed and precautions have not been taken for obtaining silver, practically all of this will remain with the silica residue, generally reduced to metallic form. In presence of silver the dehydration of silica must be done with sulfuric acid and the silver then extracted as sulfate, and precipitated from acid solution as sulfide.

[3] Kolthoff, I. M., J. Am. Chem. Soc., **52**, 2222, 1930.
[4] Schoonover, I. C., J. Research Natl. Bur. Standards, **15**, 377, 1935.
[5] Fischer, Leopoldi and von Uslar, Z. anal. Chem., **101**, 1, 1935.

Silver bearing ores are best extracted with nitric acid followed by fusion of the acid residue.

## SEPARATIONS

Silver is quantitatively precipitated as chloride in acid solution. Elements that require separation, if present, are lead, univalent mercury, copper, and thallium. Bismuth and antimony form precipitates of oxychlorides with sufficient dilution. Cyanides and thiosulfates dissolve the AgCl, and must be absent. Oxidation in the preliminary treatment prevents the co-precipitation of Hg, Cu, and Tl. $PbCl_2$ is soluble in hot water while AgCl is but slightly soluble. In 0.01 $N$ chloride solutions the solubility of AgCl at 25°C. is 0.002 mg. per liter. $Ag_2S$ is quantitatively precipitated by $H_2S$ in acid or alkaline solution, facts affording methods of separation of Ag from the $(NH_4)_2S$ and $(NH_4)_2CO_3$ groups and from As, Sb, and Sn, respectively.

## GRAVIMETRIC METHODS

### PRECIPITATION AS SILVER CHLORIDE [6]

Although silver might be determined as an iodide or bromide, the fact that these halides are more sensitive to light than the chloride, and decompose more readily, with liberation of the halide and the formation of subhalides, has led to the precipitation of silver as the chloride.

The reaction is $Ag+ + Cl^- \rightarrow AgCl$.

*Reagents.* **Hydrochloric Acid.**—One volume of concentrated HCl (sp. gr. 1.19) diluted with five volumes of water (sp. gr. of dilute HCl 1.035); 1 ml. contains 0.074 g. of HCl, equivalent to 0.219 g. of Ag.

**Nitric Acid.**—One volume of concentrated $HNO_3$ diluted with 1.6 volumes of water (sp. gr. of acid is 1.2); 1 ml. contains 0.38 g. of $HNO_3$ which would dissolve 0.64 g. of Ag.

*Preparation of the Sample.* **Silver Alloys.**—Place 0.5–1.0 g. of the alloy in an Erlenmeyer flask and add 5 ml. of the dilute nitric acid. Heat gently until the alloy is dissolved and the brown fumes are expelled. The solution is now diluted to about 100 ml. and the silver precipitated as stated below.

**Soluble Silver Salts.**—The salt is weighed into a weighing bottle; 1.0–2.0 g. are sufficient for a determination. The solution is now diluted to about 100 ml. and the silver precipitated as stated below.

**Halides of Silver.**—These are best brought into solution by fusion with about six times the weight of the sample of sodium carbonate. This converts the silver into the carbonate and the halide combines with sodium and is dissolved out in water. The silver carbonate is washed free of the halide and then dissolved out in dilute nitric acid.

**Ores of Silver.**—These may be brought into solution by digestion with nitric acid, the residue remaining is treated as stated above under halides of silver. Unless the ore is very high in silver, it is preferable to make the analysis by Fire Assay.

*Precipitation of Silver Chloride.*—Heat the solution to boiling and add from a burette, drop by drop, 5 ml. of dilute hydrochloric acid. This is sufficient to pre-

[6] Based on a chapter contributed originally by Wilfred W. Scott.

cipitate over 1 g. of silver. The excess of acid is desired as the chloride is less soluble in free hydrochloric acid.

NOTE.—The chloride is soluble in concentrated hydrochloric acid, hence a large excess is undesirable. Shaking or vigorously stirring the mixture will clear a cloudy solution. This is necessary to coagulate the silver chloride, as the fine suspended silver chloride will pass through the filter paper.

*Procedure.*—A filter crucible with either a glass or a porcelain filter bed is washed with ammonium hydroxide, distilled water, dilute nitric acid, water, and dried to constant weight by heating at 110°C. Record the weight.

Wash the precipitate by decantation, pouring the washings through the filter crucible, with application of suction. Transfer the chloride to the crucible and wash free of chlorides.

Finally wash once with alcohol and dry at 110°C. to constant weight.

Calculate the percentage of silver using the factor Ag/AgCl = 0.7526.

NOTES.—Solubility of the silver halides in milligrams of salt per 100 ml. of water are AgCl, 0.00017; AgBr, 0.00004; AgI, 0.00001.

Antimony, mercury, and lead interfere and should be removed if present.

Strong light will affect the salt causing the formation of the subhalide of silver and the liberation of chlorine. A drop of nitric acid followed by a drop of hydrochloric acid will restore the original form. This treatment is necessary only when a dark-colored salt is obtained by the action of light.

It is frequently advisable to dissolve larger samples than stated. The solution is made to 500 ml. and a portion taken for analysis.

## DETERMINATION AS SILVER CYANIDE

*Procedure.*—In the analysis of mercury, the nitric acid solution of the metal is nearly neutralized with a solution of sodium carbonate. Potassium cyanide solution is then added until the precipitate, which first forms, is dissolved. Then under a hood with strong draft, dilute nitric acid is added in slight excess of the quantity required to combine with the base in the amount of potassium cyanide present. The precipitate of silver cyanide, practically insoluble in dilute nitric or hydrocyanic acid, is coagulated by stirring or long standing and filtered from the cold solution of mercuric nitrate by use of a tared paper-bottomed Gooch crucible. The precipitate is washed with cold dilute nitric acid (1:10) until a test of the washings with hydrogen sulfide shows the absence of mercury. The crucible is dried at 100°C. to constant weight.

$$AgCN \times 0.8057 = Ag$$

NOTES.—Determination of silver as metal through precipitation with hypophosphorous acid [7] as silver sulfide or as silver chromate [8] are methods of doubtful technical application.

## ELECTROLYTIC METHOD FOR ELECTROPLATING SOLUTIONS [9]

*Procedure.*—According to the strength of the silver bath 10 or 20 ml. are filtered into a tared 200-ml. platinum dish and according to the greater or smaller excess of cyanide present, 0.5 to 1.0 g. of potassium cyanide in solution is added. The electrolyte diluted to about a half inch from the edge of the dish is kept, by a

[7] Mawrow and Mollow, Z. anorg. allgem. Chem., **61,** 96, 1909.
[8] Gooch and Bosworth, Am. J. Sci., **27,** 241, 1909.
[9] Langbein, Electro-Deposition of Metals, 6th Edition.

heater underneath, at a temperature of 60°–65°C. during the period of electrolysis using a current of 0.8 amperes.

Complete precipitation, which requires from 3 to 3.5 hours, is recognized by test with ammonium sulfide. Remove the solution, after the electrolysis, without breaking the current. If a siphon is used, care is taken to fill it and operate it without allowing the cyanide to come into contact with any part of the operator's body. The solution is displaced by adding distilled water. If a gauze electrode is used, the washing is more conveniently done by lowering the beaker and washing the electrode with the aid of a polyethylene wash bottle. The dish is rinsed with alcohol and ether, dried at 100°C., weighed and silver obtained calculated to grams per liter or cubic foot.

NOTES.—Benner and Ross [10] deposit 0.15 g. in 20 minutes with a current of 3 amperes from 50 ml. of electrolyte containing 8 g. potassium cyanide and 2 g. potassium hydroxide on a 9 g. platinum gauze cathode.

Exner,[11] using a platinum dish as the cathode and a 2″ diameter bowl-shaped spiral anode revolving 700 r.p.m., deposited 0.4900 g. from about 125 ml. of a hot electrolyte containing 2 g. potassium cyanide in 10 minutes using a current of 2 amperes.

The above methods presume the absence of other metals precipitable under conditions mentioned.

## BROMIDE ELECTROLYTIC METHOD FOR SILVER IN COPPER

This method resembles the classic chloride procedure closely but appears to yield somewhat more accurate (higher) values, especially in the assay of samples very low in Ag.

While large weights of sample must be treated for material very low in Ag (viz., 100 g. for 0.5 oz./ton, or under), ordinary silver-bearing copper containing up to 30 ounces is usually assayed on a 50-g. portion.

*Procedure.*—The clean copper (freed from oil and other extraneous material) is covered with water in a 1500-ml. beaker and dissolved cautiously in 185 ml. of concentrated $HNO_3$. When all metal is in solution, heat for a few minutes until brown fumes are no longer given off. Dilute to at least 800 ml., heat to boiling, and add potassium bromide dissolved in a little hot water. The quantity of KBr is important; in no case may it exceed 0.2 g., the optimum proportion being KBr: Ag::3.3:1. (It is convenient to prepare a reagent solution of known strength.) Boil about 3 minutes, remove from the heat source, and set aside in a dark place to settle overnight.

Filter (cool) on a clean asbestos-packed Gooch, leaving the bulk of the AgBr precipitate in the beaker. Wash sides and bottom of the beaker 3 times with cold 2% $HNO_3$, then twice with water. Wash the Gooch twice with water, filling it each time to two-thirds of its capacity, and finally giving a wash to its exterior. Remove the filter crucible to a watch glass, wash the filter funnel thoroughly, and substitute a clean suction flask of about 200-ml. capacity for the one that received the Cu solution.

Dissolve the washed AgBr by washing down the sides of the precipitation beaker 3 times with 12-ml. portions of a 5% solution of KCN, heating to boiling after each addition and pouring into the crucible, which is again mounted on the filtering apparatus. Suck through to the flask each time, after the KCN solution has stood in the Gooch 2 to 3 minutes. Finally, wash the beaker twice with hot water and the interior of the Gooch likewise.

10 Benner and Ross, J. Am. Chem. Soc., **33**, 1106, 1911.
11 Exner, J. Am. Chem. Soc., **25**, 900, 1903.

Transfer the cyanide solution of the AgBr to a small electrolysis beaker and deposit the Ag on a small weighed platinum cathode, preferably with agitation at about 0.5 ampere.

Notes.—The bromide reagent may be added only in definitely measured quantities. A large excess used in this method will hold more Ag in solution than will the same excess of chloride in the alternate method.

## TITRIMETRIC METHODS

### VOLHARD'S THIOCYANATE METHOD [12]

This method is especially adapted to the determination of silver in cold dilute nitric acid solution. The method is based on the greater affinity of silver ions than ferric for thiocyanate ions. When the silver has been precipitated as thiocyanate, the ferric indicator reacts with the thiocyanate producing the characteristic red color.

Reactions.

$$Ag^+ + CNS^- \rightarrow AgCNS$$

$$Fe^{+3} + 3CNS^- \rightarrow Fe(CNS)_3, \text{ red}$$

Note.—Mercury and palladium, highly colored salts of cobalt and nickel, copper if over 60% in the sample, nitrous acid, and chlorine interfere and should be absent.

*Reagents.* **Ferric Indicator.**—Make 100 ml. of a saturated solution of ferric ammonium sulfate or ferric sulfate. Add sufficient $HNO_3$ (freed from nitrous acid by heating) to clear up the solution and produce a pale yellow color, 0.5 ml. of this reagent is used in a test. Ferric nitrate may be used in place of sulfate.

**Thiocyanate Reagent.**—Dissolve 7.4 g. $NH_4CNS$ or 9.2 g. of KCNS in water and dilute to 1000 ml. Standardize the solution against the standard silver solution.

**Standard Silver Solution.**—This solution contains 0.25 g. of Ag in 50 ml. It is prepared in the following way.

Dissolve 1.0 g. of pure silver foil in 10 ml. of dilute $HNO_3$ (1:1.6) (sp. gr. 1.2). Boil to expel the nitrous oxides and dilute to 200 ml. One ml. will contain 0.005 g. of silver.

*Standardization.*—Measure 50 ml. of the standard silver solution into a beaker or an Erlenmeyer flask and dilute to 100 ml. Add 0.5 ml. of the ferric indicator. Titrate with the thiocyanate reagent until a permanent red tint is obtained. Each addition of the reagent will produce a temporary red color which fades immediately as long as any silver remains uncombined with the thiocyanate. A trace of excess of the reagent produces a permanent faint red color. Note the volume required and calculate the value of 1 ml. in terms of silver. Fifty ml. of the standard silver solution contains 0.25 g. of Ag.

Some prefer to have the thiocyanate exactly equal in strength to the silver solution. Should this be desired, dilute to the necessary volume and again standardize against the silver solution.

*Procedure.*—Weigh 0.25–0.3 g. of the alloy and dissolve in an Erlenmeyer flask by addition of 5 ml. of dilute $HNO_3$ (sp. gr. 1.2). Heat to expel lower oxides.

Cool, dilute to about 100 ml. and add 5 ml. of the ferric indicator.

Titrate with the standard thiocyanate reagent to a permanent faint red color.

[12] Contributed by Wilfred W. Scott.

From the milliliters of the reagent used, calculate the amount of silver present in the sample taken.

Divide the result by the amount of sample taken and multiply by $100 = \%$ Ag in the alloy.

## FAJANS' BROMIDE-ABSORPTION INDICATOR METHOD [13]

*Procedure.*—The nitric acid solution of the silver, in which the acidity does not exceed 0.5 $N$, is treated with a few drops of rhodamine 6G ($C_{26}H_{27}O_3N_2Cl$) indicator and then titrated with a standard solution of potassium bromide. As long as the silver ion is in excess, the basic dyestuff is not appreciably absorbed by silver bromide. At the end point the precipitate changes to a blue-violet color. The color change is distinct to a dilution as low as that of a 0.01 $N$ solution of silver.

## DENIGE'S CYANIDE METHOD [14]

Silver which has been precipitated as chloride may be determined titrimetrically by dissolving the precipitate with a measured quantity of a standard solution of potassium cyanide of about decinormal strength.

$$AgCl + 2CN^- \rightarrow Ag(CN)_2^- + Cl^-$$

Potassium iodide is then added and the excess of standard potassium cyanide solution determined by titration to the first appearance of a permanent precipitate with decinormal silver nitrate.

$$Ag^+ + I^- \rightarrow AgI; \quad AgI + 2CN^- \rightarrow Ag(CN)_2^- + I^-$$

NOTES.—If the last portion of the precipitate of silver chloride dissolves with difficulty in the potassium cyanide, the liquid may be decanted into another beaker and solution completed with ammonium hydroxide. The solutions are then combined.

## MISCELLANEOUS TITRIMETRIC METHODS

Although most of the older methods have been displaced by potentiometric indication or other physical methods, the following methods are of chemical interest.

Silver may be determined by addition from a burette of a portion of a known volume of its neutral or slightly acid solution to a standard solution of sodium chloride which contains a little potassium chromate or dichromate and sufficient chlorine-free magnesium oxide to neutralize free acid. The end point is indicated by the formation of a reddish or brown precipitate.

*By Pisani's Method* [15] a standard starch iodide solution is added to a very dilute neutral solution of nitrate of silver until the fluid becomes permanently blue.

*By Vogel's Modification of Pisani's Method,* [16] the silver solution, which may contain free acid, is titrated with standard starch iodide solution after addition of nitric acid containing nitrous acid.

*By Andrews' Modification,* [17] the standard starch iodide solution is added to a solution of silver nitrate which contains so much ferrous nitrate or sulfate that iron will be in excess of the silver present.

$$2Ag^+ + 2Fe^{+2} + I_2 \rightarrow 2AgI + 2Fe^{+3}$$

[13] Fajans, K., and Wolff, H., Z. anorg. allegem. Chem., **137,** 241, 1924.
[14] Clennell, The Cyanide Handbook, 433, London, 1911.
[15] Robière, Bull. soc. chim., **17,** 306, 1915; J. Soc. Chem. Ind., **34,** 1073, 1915.
[16] Fresenius, Quantitative Analysis.
[17] Z. anorg. allgem. Chem., **26,** 175, 1901.

*By Gooch and Bosworth's Method,*[18] silver is determined by precipitating with an excess of potassium chromate, dissolving the precipitate in ammonia, reprecipitating by boiling to low volume and determining iodometrically either the chromate ion combined with the silver, or that remaining after precipitating the silver with a known amount of standard potassium chromate.[19]

## NEPHELOMETRIC METHOD

This method is practicable for the determination of a small concentration of silver in a clear and colorless liquid. Less than 2 mg. of silver can be estimated with considerable accuracy by matching the opalescence produced by a drop of hydrochloric acid with that from a known quantity in a liquid of the same volume, depth and temperature. Intensity of opalescence attains the maximum in about five minutes after precipitation. Standard silver solution is made by dissolving 500 mg. standard silver (see "Preparation" at close of chapter) with several milliliters of dilute nitric in a liter flask and making the solution up to the mark. For most technical determinations the apparatus may consist of clear glass cylinders (color tubes) of suitable size. Greater accuracy can be achieved by use of a nephelometer of refined construction, for example [20] the combination of a projection lantern and a Duboscq colorimeter.

## DETERMINATIONS IN SPECIFIC SUBSTANCES

### GAY-LUSSAC METHOD FOR SILVER BULLION

This very accurate method is especially adapted to the valuation of silver bullion, but may be applied in principle to the determination of silver in a nitric acid solution which contains as little as 100 milligrams of the metal, providing the volume of the solution is not so large or color so deep as to make a precipitate of silver chloride equivalent to 0.1 milligram of silver indistinguishable. Metals that interfere are mercury and tin.

The method is founded upon the extremely low solubility of silver chloride or bromide in cold dilute nitric acid and the property of the precipitate becoming so completely coagulated through agitation that it settles speedily, leaving a liquid sufficiently clear to permit of observance of any precipitate produced by further addition of precipitant.

Reactions.

$$Ag^+ + Cl^- \rightarrow AgCl$$

$$Ag^+ + Br^- \rightarrow AgBr$$

The use of a bromide is preferable to a chloride salt as a reagent, chiefly because on account of the greater insolubility of silver bromide, the end point of the operation of titration is more sharply defined.

The presence of free sulfuric acid is prejudicial to a very close determination, because of the volume of liquid required to keep silver sulfate in solution, and

[18] Am. J. Sci., **27,** 302, 1909.
[19] C. A., **13,** 1735, 1909.
[20] Wells, Am. Chem. J., **35,** 99, 508, 1906; Richards, Am. Chem. J., **35,** 510, 1906; Dienert, Compt. rend., **158,** 1117, 1914.

also because the result of agitation after addition of precipitant is apt to be a fine precipitate which does not readily settle.

The factor of volume change per degree change of temperature from 15 to 21°C. is approximately 0.00012; from 20 to 26°C., 0.00019; from 25 to 31°C., 0.00024.

Although the approximate precipitating value should be known by previous test, it is the better practice to determine the exact value by running two or more checks of pure silver simultaneously with each batch of assays than to apply the temperature correction factor.

*Apparatus.*—The apparatus required consists of a pipette which will deliver approximately 100 ml. with an accuracy of not over 5 mg. variation in weight of the standard solution at constant temperature between successive deliveries, 10-ml. burettes with glass stopcocks; and 8-oz. narrow-mouth, round, flint-glass bottles with high, tightly fitting stoppers; the assay bottles should be of a quality which will endure heating in a steam bath or on a hot plate.

Since the end point by the Gay-Lussac method depends upon the observance of cessation of precipitation, it is evident, in order to avoid undue tediousness in its operation, that the silver content of the amount of sample taken for assay should be known within a few milligrams.

*Procedure.*—See "Procedure" under the "U. S. Mint Modification of the Gay-Lussac Method," below.

## U. S. MINT MODIFICATION OF THE GAY-LUSSAC METHOD [21]

This method, used in all of the United States Mints and the U. S. Assay Office, New York City, for determining silver in ingots and fine silver, has been found very satisfactory both as regards speed and accuracy.

*Standard Solutions.*—Two standard salt solutions are regularly used in the determinations. The first is called a "normal" and the second a "decimal" solution.

The "normal" solution is made of such concentration that 100 ml. of it will precipitate exactly 1002 milligrams of silver. 5.43 grams of C.P. sodium chloride are dissolved in water and diluted to make one liter of solution. It is kept in a large 40-liter carboy and is siphoned off as needed.[22]

The decimal solution is made by diluting 100 ml. of the "normal" solution to a liter.

*Standardization.*—The "normal" solution must be standardized at frequent intervals because of temperature changes which affect the concentration of the solution. The factor of volume change per degree change of temperature from 15 to 21°C. is approximately 0.00012; from 20 to 26°C., 0.00019; from 25 to 31°C., 0.00024.

The standardization is carried out as follows:

*Solution and Precipitation.*—A "proof" of 1004 milligrams of fine silver is carefully weighed out, placed in a glass-stoppered 8-oz. bottle and dissolved in 10 ml. of 1:1 nitric acid on a hot plate. Then 100 ml. of "normal" salt solution, sufficient to precipitate 1002 grams of silver, are added from an upright stationary pipette. The pipette is filled by means of a siphon controlled by a stopcock convenient to the right hand. After filling, the left forefinger is placed over the pipette, the rubber hose connection removed from the bottom, and the bottle containing the dissolved proof placed underneath, when the forefinger is removed, allowing the

---

[21] Communicated by F. C. Bond, Humid Assayer, Denver Mint, Colorado.

[22] Forty liters are made up at one time by the Denver Mint. The strength of the solution may be regulated by the size of the pipette used. At the Denver Mint 4.82608 grams per liter are taken of the C.P. NaCl, since the pipette delivers more than 100 ml.

contents to drain into the bottle, shaking the bottle once or twice to mix the solution. Then 2 ml. of the decimal solution are added by means of a small pipette graduated in ml. and held in the hand, and the stoppered bottle is placed in the shaker.

The shaker violently agitates the solution and causes the precipitate to coagulate and settle. The bottle is removed after four minutes.

More agitation than is absolutely necessary should be avoided, due to the increasing tendency of the precipitate to become granular and settle slowly.

**Titration.**—The bottle containing the coagulated precipitate is best placed upon a shelf in a window through which only reflected light enters, at such a height that the top of the solution is upon a level with or slightly above the eye. The shelf is backed by a blackened board which covers the window under the shelf and extends nearly to the top of the bottle.

The bottle stands a moment to allow the precipitate to settle and 1 ml. of the decimal salt solution is added from the hand pipette. The solution is shaken by moving the top of the bottle through a small arc once or twice and the reading is taken after 10 seconds. A slight white cloud forming at the top of the solution and more pronounced when viewed from below constitutes a "show" and indicates that only a small portion of the milliliter added was needed to precipitate the remaining silver. This is the desired condition for a proof.

The reading is taken as a "show," "quarter," "half," "three quarters," and "one"; according to the portion of the milliliter of salt solution necessary to precipitate the remaining silver. If the cloud is deep enough to indicate that all of the milliliter has been used, the bottle should be placed in the shaker and the precipitate coagulated, after which another milliliter is added and the reading taken as before with the addition of one milliliter.

The assignment of the proper value to the precipitate is difficult for the novice and experience in comparison is of much more value than any description could be. However it may be stated that a slight precipitate extending through the upper half of the solution after a slight uniform shake should be called a "quarter," a precipitate of the same appearance throughout the solution is a "half," a heavier precipitate throughout is called "three quarters," while a still denser precipitate is read "one" and should be confirmed by shaking and adding another milliliter, which should yield a "show," a very faint cloudiness.

The "show" of the proof influences the reading of the determinations and its appearance should be kept constantly in mind, since a "quarter" on a determination means that one quarter of a milliliter more of the decimal salt solution was used in precipitating silver than was used in the proof. Thus the proof reading or "show" is taken as zero and the concentration of the "normal" solution should be adjusted so that the proof gives as light a show as possible.

**Procedure.**—In the following determinations it is advisable to run a standard of proof silver side by side with the sample bullion for comparative purposes.

**Fine Silver.**—For silver bullion 998 parts fine or above a sample of 1005 mg. is weighed out, dissolved, precipitated and titrated as described under "Standardization."

In case 1 ml. was added, gave a heavy precipitate, was agitated and a second ml. added which gave a "half," the reading would be 1½ and the silver would be

$$\frac{1002 + 1\frac{1}{2}}{1005} = \frac{1003.5}{1005} = 998.5 \text{ fine}$$

In case a large number of samples are to be run, tables may be prepared for each fourth of a milliliter which will make the above calculation unnecessary.

**Coin Ingots.**—In determining the silver in silver coins or in silver coin ingots as they come from the melting room, which are usually within 1½ points of 900 fine, the sample weighed is 1115 mg. The color given to the solution by the copper base need not interfere with the titration.

NOTES.—Determinations may be made on silver bullion of almost any grade if the approximate fineness is previously determined by fire assay or the Volhard method. It is ordinary practice to weigh up the sample at the next figure even five mg. above that calculated. Thus if it is found from preliminary assay that 1082 mg. of bullion will contain approximately 1002 mg. of silver, 1085 mg. will be weighed out for a sample.

Interfering Elements.—There are very few substances which will be found in bullion in sufficient quantity to interfere with the process. The presence of free sulfuric acid is detrimental to a very close determination.

The use of a bromide is considered as preferable to a chloride as a reagent but the chloride is commonly used.

An eyeshade assists in making the readings accurately.

The chloride precipitate is reduced to a blue subchloride on standing in the sunlight so that the bottle should be exposed to the light as little as possible.

A set of twelve samples, with the bottles transported in a suitable wire frame, is usually run at one time.

A decimal solution of silver nitrate of equal strength with the decimal salt solution may be used for back titration, however the end point is less distinct and it is advisable to weigh out a larger sample.

Duplicates are commonly run.

Tables giving the fineness for different classes of materials examined for each reading facilitate calculations and are recommended for use.

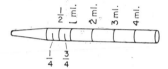

FIG. 42-1. Pipette.

To determine the ¼, ½ and ¾, a beginner should have a pipette, graduated in milli liters, holding 5 to 7 ml., of a suitable length for hand use, and with one ml. divided into ¼, ½, and ¾ milliliters, and he should use the same until he is familiar with the density of precipitates produced by one ml. with silver equivalent to the above fractions.[23]

Weight Taken 1115 Mg.

| | 0 | 1 | 2 | 3 | 4 | 5 | 6 |
|---|---|---|---|---|---|---|---|
| 0 | 896.9 | 897.7 | 898.6 | 899.6 | 900.4 | 901.3 | 900.2 |
| ¼ | 897.1 | 898.0 | 898.9 | 899.8 | 900.7 | 901.6 | 902.5 |
| ½ | 897.3 | 898.2 | 899.1 | 900.0 | 900.9 | 901.8 | 902.7 |
| ¾ | 897.5 | 898.4 | 899.3 | 900.2 | 901.1 | 902.0 | 902.9 |

In the following table the left hand column represents the milligrams of bullion to be taken, the top line indicates the milliliters of decimal solution required in addition to the 100 ml. of normal solution, the figures at the intersecting lines give the fineness of the bullion.

[23] No pipette is of use in the practice of the Gay-Lussac method that shows any tendency to spatter at the beginning or ending, or yields a quickly following or clinging drop at the completion of discharge. The film of liquid adherent to the inner surface of the body of a good pipette will drain without sign of rivulet effect and be retained by the capillary of the discharge tube for at least a minute.

High Grade Bullion

| Milligrams of bullion | 0 | 1 | 2 | 3 | 4 | 5 | 6 | 7 | 8 | 9 | 10 |
|---|---|---|---|---|---|---|---|---|---|---|---|
| 1000 | 1000.0 | | | | | | | | | | |
| 1005 | 995.0 | 996.0 | 997.0 | 998.0 | 999.0 | 1000.0 | | | | | |
| 1010 | 990.1 | 991.1 | 992.1 | 993.1 | 994.1 | 995.0 | 996.0 | 997.0 | 998.0 | 999.0 | 1000.0 |
| 1015 | 985.2 | 986.2 | 987.2 | 988.2 | 989.2 | 990.1 | 991.1 | 992.1 | 993.1 | 994.1 | 995.1 |
| 1020 | 980.4 | 981.4 | 982.4 | 983.3 | 984.3 | 985.3 | 986.3 | 987.2 | 988.2 | 989.2 | 990.2 |
| 1025 | 975.6 | 976.6 | 977.6 | 978.6 | 979.5 | 980.5 | 981.5 | 982.4 | 983.4 | 984.4 | 985.4 |
| 1030 | 970.9 | 971.8 | 972.8 | 973.8 | 974.8 | 975.7 | 976.7 | 977.7 | 978.6 | 979.6 | 980.6 |
| 1035 | 966.2 | 967.1 | 968.1 | 969.1 | 970.0 | 971.0 | 972.0 | 972.9 | 973.9 | 974.9 | 975.8 |
| 1040 | 961.5 | 962.5 | 963.5 | 964.4 | 965.4 | 966.3 | 967.3 | 968.3 | 969.2 | 970.2 | 971.1 |
| 1045 | 956.9 | 957.9 | 958.8 | 959.8 | 960.8 | 961.7 | 962.7 | 963.6 | 964.6 | 965.5 | 966.5 |
| 1050 | 952.4 | 953.3 | 954.3 | 955.2 | 956.2 | 957.1 | 958.1 | 959.0 | 960.0 | 960.9 | 961.9 |
| 1055 | 947.9 | 948.8 | 949.8 | 950.7 | 951.7 | 952.6 | 953.5 | 954.5 | 955.4 | 956.4 | 957.3 |

Silver Coin Bullion

| | 0 | 1 | 2 | 3 | 4 | 5 | 6 | 7 | 8 | 9 | 10 |
|---|---|---|---|---|---|---|---|---|---|---|---|
| 1095 | 913.2 | 914.2 | 915.1 | 916.0 | 917.0 | 917.8 | 918.7 | 919.8 | 920.5 | 921.5 | 922.4 |
| 1100 | 909.1 | 910.0 | 910.9 | 911.8 | 912.7 | 913.6 | 914.5 | 915.4 | 916.4 | 917.3 | 918.2 |
| 1105 | 905.0 | 905.9 | 906.8 | 907.7 | 908.6 | 909.5 | 910.4 | 911.3 | 912.2 | 913.1 | 914.0 |
| 1110 | 900.9 | 901.8 | 902.7 | 903.6 | 904.5 | 905.4 | 906.3 | 907.2 | 908.1 | 909.0 | 909.9 |
| 1115 | 896.9 | 897.8 | 898.6 | 899.5 | 900.4 | 901.3 | 902.2 | 903.1 | 904.0 | 904.9 | 905.8 |
| 1120 | 892.9 | 893.7 | 894.6 | 895.5 | 896.4 | 897.3 | 898.2 | 899.1 | 900.0 | 900.9 | 901.8 |
| 1125 | 888.9 | 889.8 | 890.7 | 891.6 | 892.4 | 893.3 | 894.2 | 895.1 | 896.0 | 896.9 | 897.8 |
| 1130 | 885.0 | 885.8 | 886.7 | 887.6 | 888.5 | 889.4 | 890.3 | 891.1 | 892.0 | 892.9 | 893.8 |
| 1135 | 881.1 | 881.9 | 882.8 | 883.7 | 884.6 | 885.5 | 886.3 | 887.2 | 888.1 | 889.0 | 889.9 |
| 1140 | 877.2 | 878.1 | 878.9 | 879.8 | 880.7 | 881.6 | 882.5 | 883.3 | 884.2 | 885.1 | 886.0 |
| 1145 | 873.4 | 874.2 | 875.1 | 876.0 | 876.9 | 877.7 | 878.6 | 879.5 | 880.3 | 881.2 | 882.1 |
| 1150 | 869.6 | 870.4 | 871.3 | 872.2 | 873.0 | 873.9 | 874.8 | 875.7 | 876.5 | 877.4 | 878.3 |

Ascertain the approximate fineness by a preliminary assay, consult the 0 column for the nearest corresponding figure slightly higher, the figure on the left of this is the weight of bullion to be taken. Now if the test required, in addition to the 100-ml. normal solution, 4 ml. decimal solution and 1115 mg. of bullion were taken, the fineness of the bullion would be 900.4. See table under Silver Coin Bullion.

# RECOVERY OF SILVER FROM SILVER RESIDUES

Convert the residues to silver chloride by treating with hydrochloric acid and filtering off the chloride and washing. Dissolve the chloride in ammonium hydroxide added in slight excess. Add sodium hyposulfite, $Na_2S_2O_4$ (not thiosulfate, $Na_2S_2O_3$). Metallic silver is formed. Thiosulfate gives silver sulfide. Photographers' residues containing "hypo" yield silver sulfide.

# COMBINATION METHODS

Combination of the operations of the Gay-Lussac and Volhard methods have been devised to avoid the tediousness incident to the performance of the Gay-Lussac method by the unexperienced. By the modified methods the amount of sample to be weighed out is determined by preliminary assay, and is dissolved in the same manner as in the practice of the Gay-Lussac method, but with the added precaution to decompose nitrous acid in the silver solution by gentle boiling when completion of the titration is to be accomplished by the Volhard method.

The operation of the combination methods consists briefly of precipitation of all but a few milligrams of silver by a standard solution of alkali thiocyanate, chloride or bromide added from the Stas pipette and estimation of the excess of silver with a decimal solution of thiocyanate or by a colorimetric or nephelometric method.

A favored procedure is to use a standard solution of potassium bromide as the pipette precipitant. After the liquid is cleared by shaking, it is decanted as completely as possible into a 500-ml. Erlenmeyer flask. The precipitate is washed by five 30 ml. portions of water containing a little nitrous-free nitric acid, each portion being shaken before decanting. Using the same amount of ferric indicator as in the check assays, decimal thiocyanate solution is added until not a very deep tint remains permanent after vigorous agitation. Decinormal silver solution is then added until the tint is discharged. When the assay is sufficiently free of copper or other colored salts to permit accurate matching of tints, the decanted liquid, which may contain particles of silver bromide without interference, is titrated with decimal thiocyanate to the appearance of a tint which will match that of the check assays. Except when colored salts are present in such quantity as to make recognition of the point of bleaching of the ferric thiocyanate coloration uncertain, the extreme range of error is 0.3 part per 1000.

# NEPHOLEMETRIC DETERMINATION OF SILVER [24] AS SILVER CHLORIDE IN SILVER BEARING COPPER

This method is useful for silver concentrations in the range 0.005–0.10%. While not to be confused with accurate gravimetric methods of silver assays where 50- or 100-g. samples are used, the following method has the advantage of being extremely fast. Where the problem is one of mass analysis of a large number of samples and the need for accuracy is such that an analytical error of $\pm0.005\%$ or one to two ounces per ton, the analyst may run about ten samples per hour. The method follows.

*Apparatus.* **Absorption Test Tube.**—Specially selected 7″ x ⅞″ tubes for the Evelyn Photoelectric Colorimeter, calibrated at 25 ml.

**Evelyn Photoelectric Colorimeter fitted with a No. 40 filter.**

*Reagents.* **Standard Silver Nitrate Solution.**—Dissolve 1.575 g. pure $AgNO_3$ crystals in water and dilute to 1 liter. Pipette 50 ml. of this solution into a 250-ml.

[24] Method of the Anaconda Copper Co.

volumetric flask and make up to the mark. One ml. of this solution contains 0.0002 g. of silver.

**0.05 N Hydrochloric Acid.**—Take 4.3 ml. concentrated HCl and dilute to 1 liter.

*Preparation of Calibration Curve.*—Transfer six 1.00-g. portions of pure electrolytic copper as silver-free as possible to 200-ml. beakers. From a microburette add 1-, 2-, 3-, 4-, and 5-ml. portions of standard $AgNO_3$ solution corresponding to 0.2, 0.4, 0.6, 0.8, and 1.0 mg. of silver, reserving one for a blank. Add sufficient distilled water to each sample so that the total volume for that sample is 5 ml. Now add 5 ml. concentrated $HNO_3$ to each sample and dissolve slowly over gentle heat until all oxides of nitrogen have been expelled, remove, allow to cool slightly, and wash into the calibrated tubes with about 10 ml. of distilled water. The tubes should then be placed in a rack or box that shades them from any direct light. The colorimeter should be readily accessible and previously turned on for one or two minutes and set for 100 with a water blank. Now to the blank add 1 ml. of 0.05 N HCl from a 1-ml. pipette graduated in tenths. Make up to the mark with distilled water, stopper with a No. 4 rubber stopper and invert ten times. Replace in the shaded receptacle and treat the second sample (containing 0.0002 gram of silver) the same as the first. Place the second tube in the receptacle, remove the first and read the percentage transmission against distilled water. Proceed with the preparation of the third sample before reading the second, and continue until the last one has been prepared and read. The elapsed time between preparation and reading of a sample should be between 30 seconds and 1 minute.

*Procedure.*—Transfer 1.00-gram samples of the metal to be analyzed to 200-ml. beakers. Dissolve in 10 ml. of 1:1 $HNO_3$ and treat the solution exactly as described in the preparation of the calibration curve. Obtain the percentage silver from the colorimeter reading or reference to the calibration curve or chart.

NOTES.—The importance of a standardized technique cannot be too strongly emphasized. Thus each analyst should not only prepare his own calibration curve but several of them. The method is only accurate to the extent that the mixing rate and time of standing before reading is duplicated with precision. The colorimeter should be carefully checked for instrumental deviation. Reading within a few seconds after the sample is prepared will sometimes give high results. After one or two minutes the opacity of the sample decreases rather rapidly. The timing technique suggested gives the greatest dispersion consistent with good duplication. The solution temperatures should be watched carefully so that they are consistent. Warmer solutions will give slightly higher results.

Various portions of the calibration curve should be redetermined carefully using more standards in that range and plotting the curve on an enlarged scale.

Since silver is generally referred to in troy ounces per ton it is convenient to make a chart directly converting colorimeter readings to ounces per ton.

# PREPARATION OF PURE SILVER

The titrimetric methods used for the determination of high percentages of silver employ solutions which should be standardized by metal of the highest purity. For the preparation of this metal, the electrolytic method as described below is preferred by laboratories which are suitably equipped.

For the manufacture of a large quantity—several pounds—a basket-like support for the anode is made of several glass rods bent so that they will hang from the rim of a tall 1000-ml. or larger beaker or battery jar and dip into the receptacle about an inch.

Smaller anodes may be supported by the positive wire or by a cloth bag fixed in place by a string under the flare of the rim of the beaker. In any arrangement for the support of the anode, allowance of room should be made for the introduction and free movement of an L-shaped stirring rod.

The cathode may consist of sheet silver or of platinum foil, and lies flat on the bottom of the beaker. The immersed length of the silver or platinum wire leading from the cathode should be covered with rubber tubing.

Commercial silver, usually about 999 fine, may be used for the anode, but by retreatment of the deposit, very impure silver may be used, providing that the quantity of tellurium present is very low. The presence of tellurium will exhibit itself in the impossibility of obtaining the desired coarsely crystalline deposit.

Tellurium in moderate quantities may be removed by melting the silver in a crucible or scorifier, adding niter, permitting the silver nearly to freeze, raising the temperature and pouring into a hot crucible or scorifier in which the operation is repeated, preferably in a muffle furnace, until the surface of the silver is without streaks or spots when cooled to near freezing. An oxidizing atmosphere about the molten metal should be maintained. On the basis of 172 g. silver per cubic inch an anode mould for any convenient amount of silver may be shaped from 4-in. pieces of 1-in. square rod on a smooth iron plate. Just before the anode bar sets in the mould, a silver terminal strip or wire is plunged into it.

After coating the contact wire or strip and the surface of the anode about it with sealing wax, the anode is wrapped with filter paper, held firmly in place by string or rubber bands. If the anode weighs half a pound or more, the anode is also wrapped with cotton flannel which has been washed with water until free of chloride. A porous dish, cylinder or filter cone can be used instead of filter paper and cloth.

The electrolyte contains about 4% of C.P. silver nitrate and 0.5% of chlorine-free nitric acid in distilled water, and fills the beaker or jar so it wets only the lower surface of the anode.

The current, of about 0.1 ampere per square inch of cathode surface at the start, is raised after deposition has proceeded for a few minutes to the limit at which a coarsely crystalline deposit can be maintained.

Inasmuch as the electrolysis proceeds at a rate of 4 g. per ampere hour, some attention is required to break up short circuits and to pack down the rather bulky deposit. The deposit, if coarse, can be washed very easily free of electrolyte, and after heating to near redness is in the form preferred for use by many assayers.

Other methods which may be employed consist of dissolving the crude silver with nitric acid about 1.20 sp. gr. or with hot concentrated sulfuric acid, if platinum is present, separating the gold and platinum by filtration, precipitating AgCl with not too large an excess of HCl, stirring the precipitate until it coagulates, washing repeatedly with hot water until a washing is obtained which shows no precipitate with $H_2S$, reducing the silver chloride by contact with pure zinc, wrought iron, or the silver terminal of a carbon-silver couple aluminum foil, and washing with hot dilute HCl until a test of the decanted liquid indicates absence of the precipitating element. The dried silver, mixed with about 1% of dry sodium carbonate, is packed into a clay crucible, the inside of which has been glazed with borax glass and covered with a layer of crushed charcoal.

The sodium carbonate is omitted in case it is desired to melt silver refined by electrolysis.

The silver melted in the tightly covered crucible is poured into an iron mould which has been chalked or black leaded.

By Knorr's method, a solution of silver nitrate from which excess of nitric acid has been removed by evaporation is freed of metallic impurities by adding enough sodium carbonate to precipitate one-tenth of the silver, boiling and filtering. The silver in the filtrate is precipitated by sodium carbonate and the precipitate decomposed without addition of reducing reagent, by melting in a crucible. Excess sodium carbonate carried down with the precipitate of silver carbonate will cover the fusion and such as adheres tightly to the metal is readily removed by hydrochloric acid. The metal should be smelted under charcoal.

If the cover of the charcoal is omitted or burned away during the fusion, the molten metal is capable of absorbing oxygen from the atmosphere to the extent of about 0.25% of its weight. This gas is expelled during the passage of the metal into the solid state and produces a casting which cannot be rolled into smooth sheets.

The most convenient size and shape of castings for rolling is but little larger than a lead pencil. Before rolling, the casting is cleaned of particles of the mould wash. After rolling to about cardboard thickness, the sheets may be cut up into strips of convenient size and length, then digested with dilute hydrochloric acid (1:5 of water) washed with ammonia and finally with pure water.

The silver then should be dried and annealed by heating to redness. It is best preserved in a glass-stoppered bottle and should be exposed to laboratory atmosphere as little as possible.

The purity of each batch of silver made should be compared by use of the Gay-Lussac method with standard silver, the purity of which has been determined by analysis of a 50- or 100-g. portion for Se and Te, As, Sb, Pb, Cu, Au, and the element employed in reducing silver chloride, if the reduction method was followed in the manufacture of the metal.

A considerable portion of this section was contributed by W. G. Derby, who for many years was chief assayer and research chemist of the Nichol's Copper Company, New York.

## METHODS FOR SILVER IN ANALYSES IN OTHER CHAPTERS

| | |
|---|---|
| Silver in Ores and Bullion | See Fire Assay in Gold Chapter |
| Silver in Magnesium Alloys | See Magnesium Chapters |

# Chapter 43

# STRONTIUM *

Sr, *at. wt.* 87.62; *sp. gr.* 2.63 (at 20°C.); *m.p.* 757°C.; *b.p.* 1360°C.; *oxides,* SrO, $SrO_2$

Strontium, which never occurs alone as the free element in nature, is chiefly found in the minerals celestite, $SrSO_4$, and strontianite, $SrCO_3$. It occurs as the least abundant of the alkaline earth metals but is occasionally found as high as 0.4% in some rocks. The element usually accompanies calcium in the various forms of calcite and is found along with barium as a silicate in the mineral brewsterite, $Al_2O_3 \cdot H_4(Ba,Sr)O_3 \cdot (SiO_2)_6 \cdot 3H_2O$. It may occur artificially as the beta-emitting isotope $Sr^{90}$ in the debris of nuclear and thermonuclear explosions. Its isotopes range in mass from 81 through 94. Strontium-97 also occurs, but it has only a short half-life. Strontium-88 is the most abundant of the naturally occurring isotopes (82.74%) followed by $Sr^{86}$ (9.75%) and $Sr^{84}$ (0.55%).

Strontium was discovered in the mineral strontianite found in strontian in Argyllshire by Cruikshank (1787). Davy isolated the metal (1807) by electrolysis of the chloride.

The compounds of strontium are used for medicinal purposes, for red fire in pyrotechnics; for the manufacture of iridescent glass; the dioxide for bleaching purposes; the sulfide for luminous paint; the hydroxide for refining of beet-root sugar, being preferable to lime, as the saccharate of strontia is more granular.

## DETECTION

In the usual scheme of analysis strontium is precipitated, along with barium and calcium, from the ammoniacal filtrate of the ammonium sulfide group by addition of ammonium carbonate. The barium is usually separated by dissolving the combined precipitate in acetic acid and reprecipitating it as the chromate by the addition of potassium dichromate. The strontium and calcium contained in the filtrate are separated from the excess potassium dichromate by reprecipitation with ammonium carbonate. The precipitate is again dissolved in acetic acid and the excess neutralized with ammonium. Strontium may now be precipitated by addition of a concentrated solution of $(NH_4)_2SO_4$.

*Sodium Sulfate Test.*—If a saturated solution of sodium sulfate is added to a solution containing strontium chloride acidified with acetic acid and the resulting solution boiled, a white precipitate will separate if strontium exceeds 0.0015 molar. Calcium will not precipitate unless it is in excess of 1.3 molar.

*Potassium Rhodizonate Test.*—Strontium may be detected by placing a drop of the solution containing the element on a strip of filter paper previously saturated with a 0.4% solution of potassium rhodizonate. A dark reddish-brown precipitate

---

* Revised by Edward D. Moorhead.

indicates the presence of strontium. Barium interferes, for it also produces a precipitate of this color.

*Flame Test.*—The flame spectrum of strontium is characterized by three bands at 6600, 6628, and 6747 A respectively. The first is most intense. In addition, the line at 4608 A is often used as a spectroscopic calibration.

The element may be detected in the Bunsen flame according to the following procedure: the sulfate is first reduced on a platinum wire ring in the luminous flame of the burner, moistened with hydrochloric acid and again held in the flame. A brilliant crimson coloration of the flame indicates the presence of strontium. Lithium and calcium color the flame red and yellowish-red respectively.

*Spectrum of Strontium.*—Eight bright bands are characteristic of the emission spectrum: six red, one orange and one blue. Two of these, known as strontium $\beta$ and $\gamma$, are red. The orange is strontium $\alpha$ and the blue strontium $\delta$. The sensitivity of the test is about 0.6 mg. of strontium per milliliter. The test is much more sensitive with the arc spectra yielding an accuracy of 0.03 mg. per milliliter. This subject is discussed in the Chapter on Barium.

## ESTIMATION

The following facts regarding solubility may be of value in the determination of strontium or its separation from similar metals of this periodic group:

Some Solubilities of Ca, Sr, and Ba (g./100 ml. $H_2O$)*

| Salt | Calcium | Strontium | Barium |
|------|---------|-----------|--------|
| carbonate | 0.0015(25°C.) | 0.0011(25°C.) | 0.002(20°C.) |
| sulfate | 0.209 | 0.0113(0°C.) | 0.0002(18°C.) |
| oxalate | 0.00067(13°C.) | 0.0051(18°C.) | 0.0093(18°C.) |
| fluoride | 0.0016(18°C.) | 0.011(0°C.) | 0.17(10°C.) |
| iodate | 0.10(0°C.) | 0.03(15°C.) | 0.022 |
| molybdate | insoluble | 0.0104(17°C.) | 0.0058(18°C.) |
| sulfite | 0.0043(18°C.) | 0.0033(17°C.) | 0.02(20°C.) |
| hydroxide | 0.185(0°C.) | 0.41(0°C.) | 5.6(15°C.)—Ba(OH)$_2$·8H$_2$O |
|  | 0.0077(100°C.) | 21.83(100°C.) | |

*Figures represent solubility at the temperatures noted.

In addition, the monohydrogen phosphates, the selenates, and pyrophosphates are but slightly soluble. To these may be added the slightly soluble salts of several long-chain fatty acids, e.g., stearic and palmitic acids. The reddish-brown rhodizonates of strontium and barium are also insoluble. It will be noted from the Table above that Sr(OH)$_2$ increases in solubility as the temperature is increased. The reverse is true of Ca(OH)$_2$, and this fact may be utilized when effecting separations of these elements. The water solubility of the nitrates of Ca, Sr, and Ba decreases as the atomic weight of the element increases. The calcium salt, however, is soluble in both acetone and ethanol, but the nitrates of strontium and barium are not. This important property is often used in the preliminary separation of calcium from strontium and barium.

Strontium sulfate dissolves in concentrated sulfuric acid and is appreciably soluble in HCl, HNO$_3$, CH$_3$COOH, NH$_4$CL, NH$_4$NO$_3$, NaCl, and MgCl$_2$. The sulfate may be dissolved in HI which reduces the sulfate group to the corresponding sulfide. The carbonates and oxalates may be dissolved in strong mineral acids. The rhodizonate may be dissolved in 6 $M$ HCl.

In the presence of sulfate, strontium may be partly retained with the silica, or, should the ammonia reagent be contaminated with carbonate, the strontium will be precipitated along with the iron and aluminum group. The same would be true should phosphate or fluoride occur in excess of that required to combine completely with the iron.

The procedure for treatment of ores and strontium products is the same as for calcium and barium, and the reader is referred to the chapters describing these elements for detailed solution procedures.

## SEPARATIONS

Strontium, as a member of the alkaline earth group, may be separated initially from the interfering elements of other groups in the usual manner by treatment with hydrogen sulfide in acid solution, ammonia and ammonium sulfide. In addition, interfering metallic cations may be converted, by a suitable complexing agent to the soluble complex anion and separated from the strontium group by ion exchange. Alternatively, many interfering metals when present under suitable solution conditions may be separated from strontium by extraction by the proper organic solvent. A classical example of the latter procedure is the separation of strontium from calcium which is described in detail in a subsequent section.

The advent of refined electrical methods in analytical chemistry has made it possible by the use of controlled potential deposition to separate strontium from barium as well as from a great number of other elements of the periodic table. Controlled potential deposition on a mercury pool electrode is an especially desirable procedure for the clean-cut separation of strontium from other elements.

*Separation of Strontium from Magnesium and the Alkalies.*—The general procedure for the separation of the alkaline earths from magnesium and the alkalies is discussed in detail in the Chapter on Barium.

Either precipitation as the oxalate or precipitation of strontium as the sulfate in the presence of ethanol will effect this separation. If the latter procedure is used, it will be necessary to avoid the presence of the alkalies (except perhaps for lithium) for their sulfates are insoluble in ethanol. Solution of the strontium sulfate is effected by fusing it with a basic flux (e.g., $Na_2CO_3$) or treating it with hydriodic acid.

*Separation of Strontium from Calcium.*—Strontium and calcium are converted to the nitrates, taken to dryness and all water expelled by heating to 140°C. for an hour or more. The dried nitrates are now extracted with equal parts of absolute ethanol and anhydrous ether or by boiling with amyl alcohol at 130°C. (the combined nitrates may also be separated by extraction with concentrated nitric acid). Strontium remains insoluble, but the calcium goes into solution as the nitrate. The resulting strontium nitrate may require additional cycling to remove the calcium completely, especially should this element be present in large excess. The strontium nitrate is then dissolved in water and determined according to one of the procedures given later.

*Separation of Strontium from Calcium with Potassium Rhodizonate.*—This procedure which is applicable to the analysis of $Sr^{90}$ applies only in the absence of barium [other interfering elements: Ag(I), Hg(I), Pb(II), Cu(II), Hg(II), Cd(II),

Zn(II), Bi(III), U(VI)]. Strontium may be separated in high yield from accompanying calcium by precipitating the brownish-red strontium rhodizonate (barium also gives a brownish-red precipitate).

**Procedure.**—A solution of the potassium rhodizonate is added to 100 ml. of the neutral solution containing the calcium and strontium and the strontium rhodizonate separated by centrifugation. The resulting precipitate is washed with about 45 ml. of water and it is then dissolved in 1–2 ml. of concentrated hydrochloric acid. The strontium at this stage may be metathesized to the oxalate by the addition of 20 ml. of concentrated ammonia, 5 ml. of 10% oxalic acid, and 5 ml. of 30% $H_2O_2$.

**Alternative Procedure.**—Saturate the mother liquor above the strontium rhodizonate with acetone. This lessens the competitive effect of the dissolved calcium for the potassium rhodizonate and allows an eight-fold increase in the amount of calcium which can be tolerated. Maximum separation is achieved when the rhodizonate-strontium ratio is greater than four and the calcium to strontium ratio does not exceed 15.

*Separation of Strontium from Calcium with Fuming Nitric Acid.*—This method is described fully in "AEC Method for Strontium-90," given later in this chapter.

*Separation of Strontium from Barium.*—The dissolved strontium and barium nitrates obtained from the ether-alcohol extraction (see above) are separated by precipitating the barium as the chromate by adding potassium dichromate to the weakly acidic solution containing an excess of ammonium acetate. Strontium remains in solution.

If preferred, barium may first be removed from the calcium-barium-strontium mixture by precipitating it as the chromate. Strontium and calcium are then precipitated from an ammoniacal solution of $(NH_4)_2CO_3$ as the carbonates. The carbonates are converted to the nitrates and strontium separated from the calcium according to the ether-alcohol or amyl alcohol procedure described previously. Details of the procedure are given in the Chapter on Barium.

Strontium may be separated from barium using the method of descending paper chromotography.

**Procedure.**—Strontium and barium may be separated on strips of paper (e.g., Whatman No. 1), 30–60 cm. in length, 1–25 cm. in width by elution with a solution of 100 parts ethanol plus 5 parts concentrated HCl. The bands of strontium-barium are developed on the air-dried paper by treatment with potassium rhodizonate solution. The ethanol-HCl eluant yields $R_f$ values of 0.1 and 0.3 for barium and strontium respectively. The strontium to barium $R_f$ ratio is three under these conditions and results in an excellent separation without appreciable overlapping.

## GRAVIMETRIC METHODS

Strontium may be conveniently determined either as the sulfate, the carbonate, or the oxide. The first procedure is considered best by authorities.

## DETERMINATION AS STRONTIUM SULFATE, $SrSO_4$

*Procedure.*—A 10:1 excess of dilute sulfuric acid (1:1) is added with stirring to the neutral solution of strontium. An equal volume of ethanol is then added. The mixture is stirred well and allowed to settle for at least 12 hours, or overnight, if more convenient. The precipitate, $SrSO_4$, is filtered onto an ashless filter and

washed first with 50% ethanol containing a little sulfuric acid, then with absolute ethanol until acid-free. The precipitate is dried and the paper and the greater
part of the salt ignited separately in a platinum crucible, then combined, and
weighed as $SrSO_4$.

Factors: $SrSO_4 \times 0.4770 = Sr$
$\times 0.8037 = SrCO_3$
$\times 0.5641 = SrO$

## DETERMINATION AS STRONTIUM CARBONATE

Strontium carbonate is not readily decomposed by ignition as is calcium carbonate, and its determination in this form may be made satisfactorily.

*Procedure.*—Strontium carbonate is precipitated by adding ammonium carbonate
in slight excess to the nearly boiling, ammoniacal solution of strontium. The
solution containing the precipitate is allowed to stand for several hours and then
filtered cold. The washed strontium carbonate and filter are ignited gently and
the cooled residue weighed as $SrCO_3$ (stable from 410 to 1100°C. according to
C. Duval).

Factors: $SrCO_3 \times 0.5935 = Sr$
$\times 1.2442 = SrSO_4$
$\times 0.7019 = SrO$

## DETERMINATION AS STRONTIUM OXIDE

Strontium is precipitated as the oxalate by addition of ammonium oxalate to
the slightly ammoniacal strontium solution. The precipitate is filtered and washed
with water containing ammonium oxalate. The residue is then ignited and
weighed as SrO.

Factors: $SrO \times 0.8456 = Sr$
$\times 1.7727 = SrSO_4$
$\times 1.4248 = SrCO_3$

## TITRIMETRIC METHODS

The titrimetric methods for the determination of strontium presuppose its isolation from other elements.

## ALKALIMETRIC METHOD, TITRATION
## WITH STANDARD ACID

Either the carbonate or the oxide of strontium may be titrated with standard
hydrochloric or nitric acids. The compound is treated with a known amount of
standard acid added in excess, using methyl orange as the indicator. The solution
is heated below boiling to complete the reaction, and upon cooling the excess acid
is titrated with standard alkali.

One ml. of normal acid = 0.04381 g. Sr; or 0.05181 g. SrO; or 0.07381 g. $SrCO_3$.

## TITRATION OF THE CHLORIDE WITH SILVER NITRATE

Strontium chloride, free of interfering substances which might react with the
silver, may be determined indirectly by titration of its combined chloride with
silver nitrate by Mohr's method, using potassium chromate as the end-point indicator. One ml. $N$ $AgNO_3$ = 0.04381 g. Sr.

The oxide or carbonate is first slightly supersaturated with hydrochloric acid, then taken to dryness and heated at 120°C. in the air bath to expel the excess acid. Chloride is determined on an aliquot portion.

The restriction of the Mohr method to titration of the chloride in neutral or alkaline solution may be overcome by using the method of Fajans. This procedure makes use of the adsorption indicator, dichlorofluorescein, or its sodium salt and may be used in mildly acidic solutions. Dextrin is used to prevent coagulation of the precipitated silver nitrate, and the end point is characterized by a sharp, deep pink coloration of the milk-white silver chloride suspension.

## DETERMINATION OF STRONTIUM WITH ETHYLENEDIAMINE-TETRAACETIC ACID (EDTA, COMPLEXONE, TRILON)

Ethylenediaminetetraacetic acid may be used for the titrimetric determination of strontium after the element has been separated from barium, calcium, and magnesium. Phthaleincomplexone is used as the indicator, and heavy metals are masked with potassium cyanide.

*Procedure.*—The test solution containing strontium is mixed with an equal volume of ethanol. Two or three drops of 0.1% aqueous solution of phthaleincomplexone (containing a little $NH_3$) and 5.0 ml. of concentrated ammonium hydroxide are added to each 100-ml. portion of the mixture and the solution titrated immediately with a 0.1 $M$ solution of standard EDTA (the EDTA solution may be standardized against $CaCO_3$). The end point of the reaction is characterized by an abrupt disappearance of the red color. The presence of carbonate causes a turbidity which redissolves very slowly at the end point and may cause a reappearance of the red color. If this should happen the ethanol is added *after* most of the EDTA has been introduced. The reaction is then carried on to the end point. One ml. EDTA = 8.762 mg. strontium.

Alternatively, the strontium-EDTA end point may be determined electrometrically, as first proposed by Reilley, by utilizing an electrode of the third kind. The electrode is a small mercury pool which is in equilibrium in solution with a small quantity of Hg(II)-EDTA and the metal-EDTA complex, in this case strontium. As the Hg-EDTA complex is more stable than the corresponding strontium ion, the electrode responds to the (Sr″/Sr-EDTA″) ratio according to the following equation:

$$E = E' + 0.0296 \log \frac{[\text{Hg-EDTA}][\text{Sr}^{+2}] \cdot K_{Sr}}{[\text{Sr- EDTA}] \cdot K_{Hg}}$$

The terms, $K_{Sr}$ and $K_{Hg}$, are the complexity constants of the system, and [Hg-EDTA],[Sr-EDTA] refer to the metal complex concentrations. The solution must be free of substances which preferentially react with Hg(I) or Hg(II).

Strontium is best determined by this method at a pH of 10 which is achieved with an ammonium hydroxide, triethanolamine, or ethanolamine buffer. Oxygen may be removed from the solution by bubbling with purified nitrogen.

## ELECTROMETRIC METHODS

Strontium may be determined quantitatively at the dropping mercury electrode in aqueous or 80% ethanol solutions providing tetramethylammonium iodide is used as the supporting electrolyte. The half-wave potential is a linear function of the mole percentage of ethanol, i.e., $E^{1/2} = -2.110 + 0.0010P$. In addition, the diffusion current constant, $i_d/m^{2/3}t^{1/6}C$, passes through a minimum as the ethanol concentration is increased to 80%.

Strontium may be determined in a twenty-fold excess of barium. The waves of calcium and magnesium which occur at more negative potentials allow these elements to be present in even larger excess. Alkali metals, except lithium, interfere.

## DETERMINATIONS IN SPECIFIC SUBSTANCES

### AEC METHOD FOR STRONTIUM-90

In this method [1] fuming nitric acid is used to remove most of the cations, leaving behind essentially all the strontium as nitrate. Subsequent treatments are made with barium chromate to remove the lead and radium, and with yttrium hydroxide to remove traces of other fission products. After standing long enough to reach the $Sr^{90}$-$Y^{90}$ equilibrium, the $Y^{90}$ is precipitated as the hydroxide, converted to the oxalate, and a beta-radiation count is made (see Chapter on Radium).

*Apparatus.*—Stainless Steel Pots, for collecting samples of rainwater.

**Platinum Crucible, 40 ml.**

**Muffle Furnace.**

**Stirring Equipment with Teflon Stirrers.**

**Fluorethene Funnels and Centrifuge Tubes.**

**Centrifuge.**

**Mylar Discs and Covers.**

**Beta-Radiation Counting Equipment.**

*Reagents.* Strontium Carrier Solution.—Dissolve 0.280 g. of strontium nitrate in water and make up volume to 10.0 ml.

**Nitric Acid Solution (1:9).**

**Perchloric Acid (60%).**

**Hydrochloric Acid Solution (1:9).**

**Calcium Carrier Solution.**—Dissolve 3.75 g. of calcium chloride in water, and make up volume to 10.0 ml.

**Sodium Carbonate Solution.**—Dissolve 10 g. of sodium carbonate in 90 ml. of water.

**Fuming Nitric Acid (90%).**

**Yttrium Carrier Solution.**—Dissolve 0.280 g. of yttrium nitrate in water, and make up volume to 10.0 ml.

**Barium Carrier Solution.**—Dissolve 0.250 g. of barium chloride in water and make up to 10 ml.

**Acetic Acid Solution, 6 *M*.**

**Ammonium Acetate Solution.**—Dissolve 23.15 g. of ammonium acetate in water and make up to 50 ml.

**Sodium Chromate Solution.**—Dissolve 2.43 g. of sodium chromate in water and make up to 50 ml.

**Hydrogen Peroxide, 30%.**

**Sodium Carbonate Solution, Saturated.**

**Oxalic Acid Solution, Saturated.**

*Procedure.*—Samples of rainwater are usually collected over 1-month periods. Add 1 ml. concentrated nitric acid and 1 ml. strontium carrier solution to 1 liter of

[1] Atomic Energy Commission, E-38-01, 1957.

sample. Evaporate to 100 ml. Transfer to a 250-ml. beaker, washing collecting pot thoroughly with water and nitric acid (1:9), and adding washings to beaker. Evaporate to 20 ml., transfer to platinum crucible, and evaporate to dryness. Ignite in muffle furnace at 500°C. until all organic matter is destroyed. Return the residue to the platinum crucible, add four times its volume of sodium carbonate, place in a muffle furnace, and fuse at 900°C. to a clear melt.

Cool, add 25 ml. of water and 5 ml. of the perchloric acid. Place the contents of the crucible (the melt will usually not be completely dissolved) in a 400-ml. beaker, and add enough additional perchloric acid to completely dissolve the carbonates in the residue. Wash the crucible with perchloric acid and water, and add the washing to the solution. Add another 25 ml. of perchloric acid and evaporate to dense white fumes. Add enough water to redissolve any perchlorate crystals that may have formed, heat to 80°C., and filter while hot, using a suction filter and Whatman No. 40 paper. Wash any remaining precipitate (silica) in the beaker onto the filter with hot hydrochloric acid (1:9). Wash the precipitate repeatedly with hot hydrochloric acid (1:9), transfer filtrate and washings back to the 400-ml. beaker, and reject the precipitate. Add 1 ml. of the calcium carrier solution to the beaker.

Put stirring equipment in position, start stirring, and add sodium hydroxide pellets to bring pH to 8. Add 2.5 g. of sodium carbonate. Continue stirring for about 15 minutes, then let stand for precipitate to settle, and filter with suction through a glass fiber filter. Wash the precipitate with the sodium carbonate solution, and then dissolve it with hot nitric acid solution (1:9) putting the solution in a 400-ml. beaker. Evaporate until crystallization occurs, and add 60 ml. of water. Connect stirring equipment and start stirring. Then add 210 ml. of fuming 90% nitric acid, slowly until the crystals dissolve, and then more rapidly. Continue stirring for about 0.5 hour. Crystallization of the calcium and strontium nitrates should now occur. Let them settle, and filter with suction, using the fluorethene funnel and glass fiber filter. Make sure that any crystals remaining in beaker are drained of all solution. Disconnect suction and reject filtrate, washing and replacing receiving flask of filter. Transfer precipitate remaining in beaker to filter with water, using enough water to dissolve the precipitate on the filter. Transfer the filtrate so obtained to a 250-ml. beaker.

Evaporate to dryness and redissolve in 23 ml. of water. Connect stirring equipment and start stirring. Add 77 ml. of 90% fuming nitric acid slowly and continue stirring for 0.5 hour. Allow precipitate to settle, and filter, using fluorethene funnel and glass fiber filter with suction. Discard filtrate, and install a 40-ml. centrifuge tube as receiver. Transfer any precipitate remaining in the beaker with water to the filter, using enough water to dissolve all the precipitate on the filter. If volume is not at least 20 ml., dilute with water. Adjust pH to 8; if a precipitate forms, repeat procedure from addition of 77 ml. of 90% fuming nitric acid; if no precipitate appears, adjust pH to 2, and add 1 ml. of the yttrium carrier solution.

Heat to 90°C., and at that temperature readjust pH to 8 with ammonium hydroxide. Cool to 20°C., allow precipitate to settle, centrifuge, and transfer supernatant liquid to another tube. Add to precipitate enough HCl to dissolve it, dilute with water to 10 ml., heat to 90°C., readjust pH to 8 with ammonium hydroxide, cool to 20°C., centrifuge, allow precipitate to settle, and combine supernatant liquid with that obtained previously. Reject precipitate, and add 1 ml. barium carrier solution to combined solutions.

Now add 1 ml. of the 6 $M$ acetic acid and 2 ml. of the ammonium acetate solution. If pH is not close to 5.5, add more of the latter. Heat to 90°C., and while at that temperature, add with stirring and drop by drop 1 ml. of the sodium chromate solution, or enough additional to give solution a yellow color.

Cool, centrifuge for 5 minutes and decant supernatant solution, using a 60 ml. polyethylene bottle. Adjust pH to 2, add 1 ml. of yttrium carrier solution, and let stand for 2 weeks. Transfer to centrifuge tube, heat to 90°C., while at that temperature, add with stirring ammonium hydroxide to a pH of 8. Add 6 drops of 30% hydrogen peroxide. Hold temperature at 90°C. until the residual peroxide has decomposed, cool to 20°C., centrifuge, and decant the supernatant liquid into a 150-ml. beaker, noting the time. Add 25 ml. of water to the precipitate, and then add concentrated HCl drop by drop with stirring until solution is complete. Continue stirring and adjust pH to 8 with ammonium hydroxide, while heating to 90°C. Add 6 drops of the 30% hydrogen peroxide and hold at 90°C. until it has decomposed. Cool to 20°C., centrifuge, and add the supernatant liquid to the 150 ml. beaker containing the previous solution, noting the time. Treat the precipitate as described in the second paragraph following.

Bring to boiling the combined supernatant liquids, and add with stirring 10 ml. of the saturated sodium carbonate solution. Cool, filter through glass fiber filter, transfer precipitate to weighing bottle, and weigh as strontium carbonate. The yield should be about 85%, a figure which for the most accurate work, should be plotted as a function of the amount of natural strontium in the sample.

Dissolve the precipitate by adding 25 ml. if water and HCl (1:1) drop by drop until it just dissolves. Heat to 90°C., add with stirring 20 drops of the saturated oxalic acid solution. Continue 0.5 hour at 90°C., cool to 20°C., filter with suction using fluorethene funnel and glass fiber filter. Dry precipitate at 110°C. Mount it on a Mylar disc with Mylar cover. Make beta-radiation count (see Chapter on Radium). Standardize with known Y-90 sample, noting time of count.

**Calculation.**—The method of calculating strontium activity from the measured counting rate of the Y-90 product is best illustrated by an example.[2]

In this example, the efficiency of Y-90 counting is taken to be 75%, the ingrowth time (i.e., the period from time of removal of rare earths to time of final extraction) is found to be 67 hours, while the decay time (i.e., period from time of final extraction to time of counting Y-90) is 3 hours. The measured counting rate of Y-90 is found to be 5.0 counts per minute (net).

Then the Y-90 activity when counted, $A_2$, is given by

$$A_2 = \frac{R}{\eta/100} = \frac{5.0}{75/100} = 6.67 \text{ disintegrations per minute}$$

where $R$ is the measured counting rate of Y-90 and $\eta$ is the efficiency of counting.

And the Y-90 activity when extracted, $A_2{}^0$, is given by

$$A_2{}^0 = A_2 e^{\lambda t_1} = 6.75 \, e^{(0.693)(3/64)} = 6.67 \, (1.041) = 6.9 \text{ disintegrations per minute}$$

where $e$ is the base of natural logarithmic base, $\lambda$ is the radioactive constant, and $t_1$ is the ratio of decay time to ingrowth time less decay time.

[2] Golden, A. S., Strontium-90 Determination, Sanitary Engineering Center, U. S. Public Health Service, 1957.

And the strontium-90 activity $A_1{}^0$ is given by

$$A_1{}^0 = \frac{A_2{}^0}{1 - e^{\lambda t_2}} = \frac{6.9}{1 - e^{(0.693)(67/64)}} = \frac{6.9}{0.516} = 13.4 \text{ disintegrations per minute}$$

where $t_2$ is the ratio of ingrowth time to ingrowth time less decay time.

Finally, the strontium-90 activity is given in micromicrocuries by the relation $A = A_1{}^0/2.22 = 13.4/2.22 = 6.0$ micromicrocuries, since 1 micromicrocurie is equal to 2.22 disintegrations per minute.

## METHODS FOR STRONTIUM IN ANALYSIS
## IN OTHER CHAPTERS

Strontium in Barite         See Analysis of Barite (Barium Chapter)

# Chapter 44

# SULFUR

*S, at. wt.* 32.064; *sp. gr.* 2.07; *m.p.* 112.8°C.; *b.p.* 444.6°C.; *oxides,* $S_2O_3$, $SO_2$, $SO_3$, $S_2O_7$; *principal acids,* $H_2S_2O_4$, $H_2SO_3$, $H_2SO_4$, $H_2S_2O_3$, *and* $H_2S_2O_8$

Sulfur occurs free in nature, generally mixed with earthy matter. The commercial product is exceedingly pure. The element occurs combined in sulfides—iron pyrites, $FeS_2$, ferroferri sulfide, $Fe_2O_3 \cdot 5FeS$; pyrrhotite, $Fe_7S_8$; copper pyrites, $CuFeS_2$; realgar, $As_2S_2$; orpiment, $As_2S_3$; galena, PbS; cinnabar, HgS; zinc blende, ZnS. Sulfate ores, gypsum, $CaSO_4 \cdot 2H_2O$, very abundant; barites or heavy spar, $BaSO_4$; celestite, $SrSO_4$; kieserite, $MgSO_4 \cdot H_2O$; epsom salts, $MgSO_4 \cdot 7H_2O$; glauber salt, $Na_2SO_4 \cdot 10H_2O$; sulfates of alkalies, etc. In silicate and carbonate rocks it occurs generally as sulfite. It is found in gaseous form in $H_2S$ and $SO_2$.

Sulfur was one of the earliest of chemical elements known to man. Mention is made of this in the records of the alchemists. The name of brimstone (burning stone) is of early origin. It is used in the manufacture of a large number of compounds including sulfuric acid. It finds uses in medicine, insecticides, manufacture of dyes, gunpowder, matches, rubber (vulcanization) and has more recently proven of value in improving highly alkaline soils. Sulfur compounds are extensively used in arts and sciences, in the home, in medicine, in the industries, in chemical manufacture, in agriculture, in the analytical laboratory.

Sulfur is a polymorphous, yellow, brittle, odorless and tasteless solid; existing in the rhombic, monoclinic and triclinic crystalline forms, and also in an amorphous state. At 112°C. it melts to a pale yellow liquid; at 180°C. it thickens to a dark gum-like material, containing a large percentage of amorphous sulfur; at 260°C. it becomes a liquid again, and at 444.6°C. it boils, giving off a brownish-red vapor.

The important commercial forms of elemental sulfur are: Flowers of Sulfur, consisting of rhombic sulfur and not less than 30% of amorphous sulfur with a small amount of occluded free acid; Powdered Sublimed Sulfur (often called flour sulfur, a confusing term that should be abolished), consisting essentially of finely ground sublimed sulfur all in the rhombic form though at times a small percentage of amorphous sulfur is present; Refined Brimstone and Roll Sulfur (in some sections termed Virgin Lump Sulfur), consisting entirely of sublimed sulfur in the rhombic form; Powdered Brimstone (often termed Commercial Flour, Superfine Flour and the like); and Brimstone or Crude Lump Sulfur. In these commercial sulfurs the physical form and the presence of certain small amounts of impurity are the characteristics of most importance as all the varieties named, even the Brimstones, usually contain in excess of 99.5% available sulfur.

## DETECTION

The following tests include the detection of free sulfur and its more importan combined forms.

*Elemental Sulfur.*—Heated in the air sulfur burns with a blue flame, and i oxidized to $SO_2$, a gas with a characteristic pungent odor. This gas passed into $\epsilon$ solution of potassium permanganate will decolorize it, if $SO_2$ is in excess of the amount that will react with the $KMnO_4$ in the solution.

If sulfur is dissolved in a hot alkali solution and a drop of this then placed on a silver coin, a stain of black $Ag_2S$ will be evident, due to the action of the sulfur

*Sulfides.*—Hydrogen sulfide, $H_2S$, is liberated when a sulfide is treated with $\epsilon$ mineral acid. This gas blackens moist lead acetate paper. $H_2S$ has a very dis agreeable odor, which is characteristic.[1]

*Sulfates.*—A white compound, $BaSO_4$, is precipitated in presence of free hydro chloric acid when a solution of barium chloride is added to a solution of a sulfate

Insoluble sulfates are decomposed by boiling or fusion with alkali carbonates forming water-soluble alkali sulfates.

*Sulfites.*—Sulfur dioxide, $SO_2$, is evolved when a sulfite is treated with hydro chloric acid. The odor of the gas is characteristic.

Sulfur dioxide decolorizes a solution of potassium permanganate. (Use very dilute solution.)

Sulfites are distinguished from sulfates by their failure to form a white precipi tate, when barium chloride is added to the solution acidified with hydrochloric acid; also by the fact that $H_2S$ is formed when zinc is added to a solution of $\epsilon$ sulfite, acidified by hydrochloric acid.

*Thiosulfates.*—Sulfur dioxide is evolved and free sulfur precipitated when $\epsilon$ thiosulfate is acidified with dilute mineral acids. In presence of oxidizing agents sulfides will also liberate free sulfur.

Thiosulfates are strong reducing agents.

*Persulfates.*—Potassium iodide is slowly oxidized to iodine, and manganous ion to manganese dioxide, and manganous ion in the presence of silver ion to per manganate ion, but titanic ion does not give a yellow color, nor does dichromate ion give a blue color.

## ESTIMATION

The determination of sulfur may be required in a great variety of substances minerals, rocks, sulfur ores, acids, salts, water, gas, coal, and other organic matter insecticides, fungicides, stock medicants, fertilizer, and other agricultural materials

The gravimetric determination of sulfur, by procedures of technical importance depends upon its precipitation as barium sulfate, $BaSO_4$, after converting it into sulfuric acid, or a soluble sulfate, if not already in this form. Oxidation of free sulfur, sulfides, sulfites, metabisulfites, thiosulfates may be accomplished by either dry or by wet methods, details of which are given under subsequent procedures.

The titrimetric methods of determining sulfur depend upon titration with

[1] Truesdale, E. C. (Ind. Eng. Chem., Anal. Ed. **2**, 299, 1930, found that 1 part of $H_2S$ in about 10 million of air can be detected by passing the gas through a capillary tip against a moist filter containing alkaline lead acetate reagent. A spot appeared corre sponding to $1.5 \times 10^{-9}$ g. $H_2S$.

oxidizing agents, or by acids, or by alkalies, according to the form of the sulfur compound, or by means of a substance forming an insoluble compound with sulfuric acid. For example sulfides are treated with a strong mineral acid (HCl), the evolved $H_2S$ absorbed in a suitable reagent, and the sulfide formed is titrated with standard iodine. Sulfites may be determined either by oxidation with iodine or by titration with an acid in presence of methyl orange. Acid sulfites or metabisulfites may be determined by the iodine titration or by titration with an alkali in presence of phenolphthalein. Thiosulfates are titrated with iodine.

## PREPARATION AND SOLUTION OF THE SAMPLE

In the preparation of the material for analysis, fine grinding is apt to oxidize sulfide sulfur [2] resulting in loss and lower percentage content. On the other hand contamination by sulfur from the flame during fusions must be guarded against. If a flame is used the crucible should be guarded by an asbestos shield as is shown in Fig. 44-8, page 1034. The use of electric ovens avoids this contamination.

In presence of barium, lead, strontium and large amounts of calcium, the sulfur oxidized to sulfate will be found in part or in entirety combined with these in the silica residue after the acid attack and extraction. Fusion of this residue with sodium carbonate transposes the sulfate (and silica) to sodium salt which may now be leached out with water and separated from the water insoluble carbonates.

Loss of sulfide sulfur will occur if the ore is attacked by an acid without previous oxidation to sulfate form. The gravimetric method, which is preferred to volumetric methods, depends upon oxidation of the sulfur to sulfate form and precipitation as $BaSO_4$. Popoff and Neumann have shown that better crystals are formed and results are more accurate if the sulfate solution is added to the hot barium chloride reagent, acidified with HCl.[3] The presence of nitrates is objectionable.

*Sulfide.*—Sulfides of Na, K, Cs, Rb, Ca, Sr, Ba, Mg, Mn, Fe are soluble in dilute mineral acids. The sulfides of Ag, Hg, Pb, Cu, Bi, Cd, Co, Ni require strong acids for decomposition. These are also insoluble in sodium hydroxide and potassium hydroxide solutions. As, Sb and Sn sulfides are insoluble in dilute acids, but soluble in alkalies.

*Sulfate.*—With exception of $BaSO_4$, $CaSO_4$, $SrSO_4$ and $PbSO_4$, sulfates are soluble in water.

*Thiosulfate.*—Nearly all are soluble in water.

*Sulfite.*—With exception of the sulfites of the alkalies, sulfites of the metals are difficultly soluble in water, but readily decomposed by acids.

### DECOMPOSITION OF SULFUR ORES

The wet procedure for oxidation and decomposition of sulfur ores is given in detail under the "Gravimetric Methods." This process is used for the valuation of the ore, and is applicable to a wide range of substances.

*Fusion Procedure.*—One gram of the finely ground ore (80-mesh) is intimately mixed with 6 g. of zinc oxide sodium carbonate mixture (4 parts ZnO + 1 part $Na_2CO_3$), placing 2 g. more of the mixture over the charge. The material is fused and sulfur extracted according to the procedure described for coal—Eschka's method, below.

[2] Allen, E. T., and Johnston, J., Ind. Eng. Chem., 2, 196, 1910.
[3] Popoff, Stephen, and Neumann, E. W., Ind. Eng. Chem., Anal. Ed., 2, 45, 1930.

## SULFUR IN COAL, ESCHKA'S METHOD

*Procedure.*—One gram of coal is intimately mixed with 3 g. of Eschka's mixture, consisting of 2 parts of porous, calcined magnesia and 1 part of anhydrous sodium carbonate. The mixture, placed in a platinum crucible, is covered with about 2 g. more of Eschka's mixture. The charge is placed in an open platinum crucible, which is protected from the flame by a shield, as shown in Fig. 44-8, page 1034. If possible, a sulfur-free flame should be used to avoid contaminating the material. With proper precautions, the shield will prevent this. Heating in a crucible electric furnace completely avoids sulfur contamination. The mixture is heated very gradually, to drive off the volatile matter, the charge being stirred frequently with a platinum wire to allow free access of air. The heat is increased, after half an hour, to a dull redness. When the carbon has burned out, the gray color having changed to a yellow or light brown, the heat is removed and the crucible cooled.

The powdered fusion is digested with 100 ml. of hot water for half an hour, and the clear liquor decanted through a filter into a beaker. The residue is washed twice more with hot water, by decantation, and finally on the filter, until the volume of the total filtrate amounts to about 200 ml. About 5 ml. of bromine and a little hydrochloric acid are added, and the solution boiled. Sulfuric acid is now precipitated as $BaSO_4$ by addition of barium chloride to the hot solution, and sulfur determined by the first of the gravimetric procedures.

## SULFUR IN ROCKS, SILICATES, AND INSOLUBLE SULFATES

*Procedure.*—The material in finely powdered form is fused in a large platinum crucible with about six times its weight of sodium carbonate (sulfur free) mixed with about 0.5 g. of potassium nitrate. The charge is protected from the flame by an asbestos board or silica plate with an opening to accommodate the crucible snugly, as shown in Fig. 44-8, page 1034. The fusion is extracted with water, the filtrate evaporated to dryness and silica dehydrated. The residue is moistened with strong hydrochloric acid, then taken up with a little water, boiled free of $CO_2$, and silica filtered off. The filtrate contains the sulfate, which is now precipitated as barium sulfate according to one of the standard procedures.

*Barium Sulfate.*—This is transposed by fusion with sodium carbonate, as stated above. Barium carbonate remains in the water-insoluble residue. It is advisable to wash the residue in this case with hot sodium carbonate solution, to insure complete removal of the sodium sulfate. The filtrate is acidified with HCl, boiled free of $CO_2$, then precipitated.

*Lead Sulfate.*—This may be transposed by digesting the compound with a strong solution of sodium carbonate saturated with $CO_2$, keeping the solution at boiling temperature for half an hour or more. The sulfate will be in solution and the lead is precipitated as the water-insoluble carbonate.

*Strontium or calcium sulfates* may be transposed by the procedure described for lead.

## SEPARATIONS

*Substances Containing Iron.*—When precipitating barium sulfate, in presence of ferric salts, from hot solutions by the gravimetric procedure commonly followed, considerable iron is carried down by the precipitate. Since $Fe_2(SO_4)_3$ loses $SO_3$

upon ignition, and since $Fe_2O_3$ weighs much less than $BaSO_4$, low results will be obtained. Hence the removal of iron is necessary, or a method should be followed in which iron does not interfere. It is found that barium sulfate precipitated from a large volume of cold solution, in which the iron has been reduced to ferrous condition, is free from iron. Details of this procedure are given in the second of the gravimetric methods.

If sulfur is to be precipitated from hot solution of comparatively small volume (200 to 400 ml.), it is necessary to remove iron. This is accomplished by precipitating it as $Fe(OH)_3$ by addition of ammonium hydroxide in decided excess (5 to 10 ml. excess of strong $NH_4OH$, sp. gr. 0.90). If the solution is barely neutralized with ammonia, the iron hydroxide carries down considerable of the sulfate. Even with the precaution recommended some of the combined sulfuric acid is occluded by the precipitate, so that it is necessary to recover this by dissolving the precipitate with hydrochloric acid and reprecipitating the ferric hydroxide with an excess of ammonia. The combined filtrates are now treated with barium chloride, upon acidification with hydrochloric acid, according to the procedure first given.

**Separation of Sulfur from Metals Forming an Insoluble Sulfate.**—This is accomplished by fusion of the compound with sodium carbonate and extraction of the mass with water. The metal remains with the residue and the sulfate of the alkali passes into solution. For details see subject under "Preparation and Solution of the Sample."

*Nitrates and Chlorates.*—These are carried down with the precipitate as barium salts if they are present in appreciable amount. They may be removed from the solution by evaporation to dryness with hydrochloric acid.

*Silica.*—Silica will be carried down with the barium sulfate precipitate if present in appreciable amounts. It is removed by evaporation of the solution with hydrochloric acid, dehydrating the silicic acid, taking up with HCl and water and filtering.

*Ammonium and Alkali Salts.*—These have a negligible effect on the precipitate of $BaSO_4$ if this is precipitated from a large volume, according to the second gravimetric procedure. Their effect is evident when sulfur is determined in small volume.

## GRAVIMETRIC METHODS

## PRECIPITATION AS BARIUM SULFATE

The general laboratory procedure for precipitation of sulfate sulfur is to add to the solution diluted to 300–400 ml. and containing 4–8 ml. of 3 $N$ HCl an excess of barium chloride reagent, the sulfur solution being previously heated to boiling. Popoff and Neumann have shown that the reverse order is preferable.[4] The procedure worked out in the laboratories of the General Chemical Company is to add the barium chloride reagent to the sulfate solution diluted to a large volume, the solution being at room temperature. The crystals of $BaSO_4$ thus obtained are comparatively large and are less apt to be contaminated. The three optional methods are given.

[4] Popoff, S., and Neumann, E. W., Ind. Eng. Chem., Anal. Ed., **2**, 45–54, 1930.

## PRECIPITATION OF BARIUM SULFATE FROM HOT SOLUTIONS

*Procedure.*—The sulfur should be present in solution either as free sulfuric acid or as a sulfate salt. The solution is made acid by addition of hydrochloric acid (phenolphthalein indicator), and then 4 ml. added in excess (HCl, sp. gr. 1.2). After diluting to a volume of 400 ml. with hot water, the mixture is heated to boiling, and a 10% solution of barium chloride added in a fine stream, through a funnel with a capillary stem, or from a burette, at the rate of 10 ml. in 2 to 10 minutes. The reagent is added in slight excess of that required to react with the sulfuric acid or sulfate. (Ten ml. of 10% $BaCl_2 \cdot 2H_2O$ solution will precipitate about 0.13 g. of sulfur.) The beaker is placed on a steam bath and the precipitate allowed to settle for about an hour. The solution is filtered through a fine grade of filter paper (B. and A. grade A, or S. and S. grade No. 90), or through a tared Gooch crucible. Since the precipitate frequently passes through the filter it is advisable always to pass the solution through the same filter a second time. The precipitate is washed ten times with hot water, then dried, and ignited gently over a Bunsen burner, or in a muffle, for half an hour. (Blasting is not necessary, nor desirable.) The white $BaSO_4$ is cooled in a desiccator, and then weighed. If a filter paper has been used in place of a Gooch crucible, the ignition is best made in a porcelain crucible, with free access of air, the ignited sulfate, upon cooling, is brushed out of the crucible and so weighed.

Factors. $BaSO \times 0.1374 = S$
$\times 0.4202 = H_2SO_4$
$\times 0.3767 = FeS$
$\times 0.2745 = SO_2$
$\times 0.3430 = SO_3$
$\times 0.4116 = SO_4$

NOTE.—If much iron or alumina is present it is advisable to precipitate the sulfate from a large volume, by the second method, rather than attempt to remove these substances. If $BaSO_4$ is present in the original material its weight should be included with that of the precipitate.

### OPTIONAL METHOD

*Procedure.*—Barium chloride solution (0.1 $N$), in sufficient quantity to precipitate the sulfur of the test solution completely with about 5 ml. in excess, is acidified with 4–8 ml. of 3 $N$ HCl and heated to boiling. The sulfate solution is now added, dropwise with constant stirring, and the resulting precipitate digested for 1 hour near the boiling point with occasional stirring. The precipitate is washed by decantation and on the filter with hot water until free of chlorides. (A Gooch crucible may be used.) The precipitate is ignited (800°C.) for an hour and weighed.

NOTE.—A final volume of 350 ml. with 0.8 g. of precipitate under the above conditions has proven to be highly satisfactory. The presence of $KNO_3$ and probably any nitrate is objectionable.[2]

### PRECIPITATION OF BARIUM SULFATE FROM COLD SOLUTIONS— LARGE VOLUME

The method worked out by Allen and Bishop, General Chemical Company,[5] is especially adapted to the determination of sulfur in iron pyrites and materials

[5] Paper before Eighth International Congress of Applied Chemistry: An Exact Method for the Determination of Sulfur in Pyrite Ores, W. S. Allen and H. B. Bishop.

high in sulfur, 30 to 50% sulfur, but by varying the amount of material used the range may be extended from smaller to greater amounts. The finely ground sample is oxidized by means of a mixture of bromine and potassium bromide followed by nitric acid. The nitric acid is expelled by evaporation to dryness, followed by a second evaporation with hydrochloric acid, which dehydrates the silica. Iron is now reduced to the ferrous condition and the silica and residue, undissolved by addition of hot water and HCl, is filtered off. The sulfur is precipitated in a large volume of cold solution, by barium chloride solution, as $BaSO_4$ and so weighed.

**Reagents.** **Bromine-Potassium Bromide Solution.**—320 g. of potassium bromide are dissolved in just sufficient water to cause solution and mixed with 200 ml. of bromine, the bromine being poured into the saturated bromide solution. After mixing well the solution is diluted to 2000 ml.

**Bromine-Carbon Tetrachloride Solution.**—Carbon tetrachloride saturated with bromine.

**Barium Chloride,** anhydrous, 5% solution; or crystals, 6% solution.

**Procedure.** **Preparation of Sample.**—The sample ground to pass an 80-mesh sieve is carefully mixed and quartered down to 10 g. This is dried for one hour at 100°C. and then placed in a weighing tube.

A factor weight, 1.373 g. of the sample, is placed in a deep beaker, 300-ml. capacity, 2½ by 4½ inches.

**Oxidation of Sulfur.**—Ten ml. of the bromine-potassium bromide mixture for pyrrhotite ore, or bromine-carbon tetrachloride reagent for pyrite ores, are added and the beaker covered with a dry watch glass cover. After standing fifteen minutes in the cold bath (a casserole of water will do), with occasional shaking of the beaker, 15 ml. of concentrated nitric acid are added and the mixture allowed to stand fifteen minutes longer, at room temperature, and then warmed on an asbestos board on the steam bath until the reaction has apparently ceased and the bromine has been volatilized. The beaker is now placed within the ring of the steam bath so that the lower portion is exposed to steam heat. The solution is evaporated to dryness, the cover of the beaker being raised above the

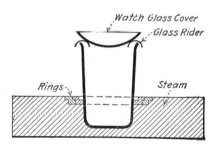

FIG. 44-1. Apparatus for Evaporator.

rim by means of riders (U-shaped glass rods), Fig. 44-1, 10 ml. of concentrated hydrochloric acid are now added and the solution again evaporated to dryness to expel the nitric acid. The silica is dehydrated by heating in the air oven at 100°C. for one hour, or overnight if preferred.

**Reduction of Iron.**—Four ml. of hydrochloric acid (sp. gr. 1.20), followed five minutes later by 100 ml. of hot water, are added, the sides of the beaker and the cover being rinsed into the solution. The riders being removed, the sample is gently boiled for five minutes to insure the solution of the sulfate. After cooling for about five minutes, approximately 0.2 gram powdered aluminum is stirred into the solution, keeping covered during the intervals between stirring. When the iron has been reduced, the solution becoming colorless, the sample is filtered into a 2500-ml. beaker, through a 12.5-cm. filter paper. The beaker should be copped out and the residue on the filter washed nine times with hot water, filling the filter funnel and draining each time.

**Precipitation of the Sulfur.**—The solution in the large beaker is diluted to 1600 ml. with cold water and 6 ml. HCl (sp. gr. 1.20) added, and mixed by stirring. The barium chloride solution is now added by means of a special delivering cup

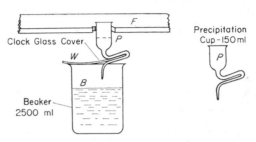

FIG. 44-2. Apparatus for Precipitating Sulfur.

(Fig. 44-2), which should drain at the rate of 5 ml. per minute. 125 ml. of barium chloride solution are added for ores containing 30 to 50% sulfur, the factor weight being taken. The solution is not stirred while the barium chloride is being added, but when the cup has drained, the solution is mixed by stirring. The BaSO$_4$ is allowed to settle, two or three hours being advisable, overnight being preferred.

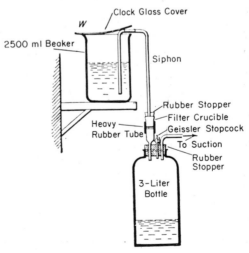

FIG. 44-3. Apparatus for Filtering Barium Sulfate.

**Filtration.**—The clear solution is filtered through a filter crucible (35 ml.), using suction. This is best done by the automatic arrangement shown in Fig. 44-3. The beaker containing the solution is placed on a shelf; a siphon dipping to within half an inch of the precipitate at the bottom of the beaker is connected to the filter crucible by means of a tightly fitting stopper. The crucible and thistle tube are best connected by heavy rubber tubing. The suction flask, or bottle, should have a capacity of about 3 liters. A Geissler stopcock passes through the rubber stopper in the suction flask to relieve the pressure when the filter crucible is to be removed. The precipitate is washed onto the asbestos mat in the crucible and washed with cold water six times, the beaker being copped out as usual.

**Ignition.**—The precipitate is dried by placing the crucible on an asbestos board over a flame for twenty-five minutes and then heated over a direct flame for thirty minutes.

**Calculation.**—$BaSO_4 \times 10 = \%$ S.  (If factor weight is taken.)

Factor.  $BaSO_4 \times 0.1374 =$ gram S.

## TITRIMETRIC METHODS

## TITRIMETRIC METHODS FOR SULFATE

Two general procedures deserve mention: addition of barium chloride in known amount in slight excess of that required by the sulfate, and titrating the excess either with a soluble carbonate or a chromate; or addition of barium chromate and titrating the alkali chromate formed by the reaction. The sulfate is also determined by precipitation with a weak organic base benzidine, added in form of the hydrochloride salt; the benzidine sulfate, filtered off, is titrated with caustic. The typical procedures given below will meet general requirements for the titrimetric determination of sulfates.

### *TITRATION WITH BARIUM CHLORIDE AND POTASSIUM CHROMATE—WIDENSTEIN'S METHOD MODIFIED*

Reaction.—

$$Na_2SO_4 + BaCl_2 \rightarrow BaSO_4 + 2NaCl \text{ and excess } BaCl_2 + K_2CrO_4 \rightarrow BaCrO_4 + 2KCl$$

**Procedure.**—The sample containing the sulfate in solution is diluted to 50 ml. in a small flask, acidified with hydrochloric acid, if necessary, heated to boiling, and precipitated with a slight excess of 0.25 $N$ barium chloride added from a burette (1 ml. $BaCl_2 = 0.01$ g. $SO_3$). The precipitate settles rapidly, so that a large excess of the reagent may readily be avoided. The mixture is cautiously neutralized with ammonia, free from carbonate ($CO_2$ may be precipitated with $CaCl_2$ solution), the solution heated to boiling, and 0.25 $N$ potassium chromate added from a burette in 0.5-ml. portions, each time removing the flask from the heat, allowing the precipitate to settle and examining the clear solution. A faint yellow color will appear as soon as the excess of barium has been precipitated and a few drops of the chromate in excess are present in the solution. The value of the chromate being equivalent to that of the barium chloride, the difference between the two titrations is due to the barium chloride required by the sulfate.

One ml. 0.25 $N$ $BaCl_2 = 0.01001$ g. $SO_3$

Notes.—Salts of the alkalies, alkaline earths (Sr and Ca), and zinc and cadmium do not interfere. Nickel, cobalt, and copper, however, give colored solutions which prevent the yellow chromate being seen. Should the latter be present, the end point may be recognized by using ammoniacal lead acetate as an outside indicator (1 vol. $NH_4OH$ + 4 vols. $PbC_2H_3O_2 \cdot 3H_3O$, 5% sol.), the indicator and titrated solution being mixed drop per drop on a white tile. A yellowish red color indicates the presence of chromate.

H. Roth [6] has shown the use of a test paper containing diaminodiphenylamine ($NH_2C_6H_4NHC_6H_4NH_2$) indicator as a delicate test for chromate. The paper, a pale gray color when treated with the compound, is kept in a closed, opaque container. When a drop of solution containing a trace of chromate is placed on the paper a blue colored spot is obtained. In the titrimetric determination of sulfates, by addition of an excess of $BaCl_2$ solution and determining the excess of Ba by precipitation with a chromate or dichromate, the exact end point may be determined by spot tests with the indicator paper, the slightest excess of chromate being detected.

## PRECIPITATION WITH BARIUM CHROMATE AND TITRATION OF LIBERATED CHROMATE, HINMAN'S METHOD

The sulfate, precipitated by barium chromate, liberates an equivalent amount of chromate, which is determined by treating with potassium iodide and titrating the liberated iodine with thiosulfate.

Reactions.—

$$Na_2SO_4 + BaCrO_4 \rightarrow BaSO_4 + Na_2CrO_4$$

$$2CrO_4^= + 6I^- + 16H^+ \rightarrow 2Cr^{+3} + 8H_2O + 3I_2$$

$$2S_2O_3^= + I_2 \rightarrow 2I^- + S_4O_6^=$$

**Procedure.**[7]—The solution of the sulfate, containing not over 2% of $SO_3$, if acid, is almost neutralized with potassium hydroxide, then heated to boiling, and an excess of barium chromate solution added.[8] After boiling for one to five minutes, the hot solution is neutralized by adding calcium carbonate [9] until no further effervescence occurs. The precipitate is filtered off and washed with hot water. The combined filtrates containing the chromate liberated by the sulfate through double decomposition, is acidified with 5 ml. concentrated hydrochloric acid per each 100 ml. of filtrate and an excess of potassium iodide added. Iodine equivalent to the chromic acid is liberated. This is titrated with 0.1 $N$ sodium thiosulfate.

One ml. of 0.1 $N$ thiosulfate = 0.003269 g. $H_2SO_4$ [10]

## TITRATION WITH STANDARD BARIUM CHLORIDE SOLUTION [11]

**Reagents. Standard Barium Chloride Solutions.**—Prepared in any convenient range from 1 ml. equivalent to from 1–50 mg. of sulfate.

**Indicator.**—Disodium tetrahydroxyquinone, 1 part, ground with 300 parts of dried potassium chloride.

---

[6] Z. angew. Chem., **39**, 1599, 1926.

[7] Treadwell and Hall, Analytical Chemistry, II, 4th Ed., p. 716.

[8] The barium chromate used should be free from soluble chromate, barium carbonate, or soluble barium salt. The compound may be prepared by precipitation with potassium chromate added to a boiling solution of barium chloride. The precipitate is washed with boiling water containing a little acetic acid, and finally with pure water, and then dried. Four grams of the dry salt are dissolved in a liter of $N$ hydrochloric acid.

[9] In presence of iron, zinc, and nickel, the solution is neutralized with ammonium hydroxide and an excess added; after boiling, the solution is filtered. By using calcium carbonate insoluble basic chromates of these elements would be formed, and low results for $SO_3$ would follow. This is avoided by the use of ammonia.

[10] $0.1 \ N \, Na_2S_2O_3 = \dfrac{H_2SO_4}{3 \times 10 \times 1000} = 0.003269$ g.

[11] Schroeder, Ind. Eng. Chem., Anal. Ed., **5**, 403, 1933. This paper includes a bibliography of 120 references on the determination of sulfur. The application of the method to water analysis is described by Sheen and Kahler, *ibid.*, **8**, 127, 1936; the same authors also applied the method to the determination of sulfur in rubber, *ibid.*, **9**, 69, 1937. Details are quoted from the latter papers.

*Procedure A.*—Sulfate range up to 2000 parts per million.  Twenty-five ml. of the solution is made just acid to phenolphthalein with 0.02 $N$ hydrochloric acid. Twenty-five ml. of ethyl alcohol, isopropyl alcohol, or alcohol denatured according to formula No. 30 are added.  The amount of indicator shown in the following table is added, and with the solution at 20 to 25°C. standard barium chloride solution is titrated in slowly with thorough agitation until the yellow color changes to rose.

*Procedure B.*—Sulfate range 2000 to 30,000 parts per million.  Solid sodium chloride is to be added (see table).  The neutralization and titration are as described under A.

*Procedure C (with phosphate up to 60 parts per million).*—Carefully neutralize a 25-ml. filtered sample with 0.02 $N$ HCl until bromcresol green just changes to the acid tint (yellow range, pH about 4).  Follow procedure A or B.

Conditions for Various Concentrations of Sulfate

| Sulfate Parts per Million | Amount of Indicator Mixture | BaCl$_2$ 1 ml. = mg. of SO$_4$ | Sodium Chloride Needed, g. |
|---|---|---|---|
| Up to 100 *......... | 0.1 | 1 | — |
| 100–1000 *.......... | 0.2 | 1 | — |
| 1000–2000........... | 0.2 | 4 | — |
| 2000–4000........... | 0.4 | 10 | 2. |
| 4000–10000.......... | 0.4 | 10 | 4. |
| 10000–20000......... | 0.6 | 50 | 8. |
| 20000–30000......... | 0.8 | 50 | 8. |

* Subtract 0.1 ml. as a blank correction.

Interference is caused by more than 5 parts per million of ferrous or ferric iron, by more than 6 p. p. m. of aluminum, or 60 p. p. m. of phosphate.  Amounts of silicate up to 1500 p. p. m.; Mg up to 1440, Ca to 344 and Cl$^-$ up to 15000 p. p. m. or higher do not interfere.  In examining rubber, after oxidation by one of the standard methods, a measured excess of standard barium chloride is added, and the zinc, iron, etc. are precipitated by potassium hydroxide at pH 8.3 (barely alkaline to phenolphthalein), and the mixed precipitate is filtered off.  The excess of barium in the filtrate is titrated with standard sodium sulfate, after the alkali has been neutralized with 0.02 $N$ HCl.  For percentages of sulfur ranging from 1.7 to 5.8 the maximum deviation from the percentage found gravimetrically was 0.05%.

### BENZIDINE HYDROCHLORIDE METHOD—RASCHIG

Benzidine sulfate, $C_{12}H_8(NH_2)_2 \cdot H_2SO_4$, is scarcely soluble in water containing hydrochloric acid.  The weak base benzidine is neutral to phenolphthalein and the acid in its sulfate may be titrated with an alkali.[12]  The method gives reliable results in the analysis of all sulfates, provided no substances are present which

[12] Method suggested by Raschig, Z. anal. Chem., **42,** 617 and 818, 1903.

attack benzidine, and provided the amount of other acids and salts present is not too great.[13]

Reaction.—

$$Na_2SO_4 + C_{12}H_8(NH_2)_2 \cdot 2HCl \rightarrow 2NaCl + C_{12}H_8(NH_2)_2 \cdot H_2SO_4$$

$$C_{12}H_8(NH_2)_2 \cdot H_2SO_4 + 2NaOH \rightarrow C_{12}H_8(NH_2)_2 \cdot 2H_2O + Na_2SO_4$$

*Reagent.* **Benzidine Hydrochloride.**—Prepared by taking 6.7 g. of the free base, or the corresponding amount of the hydrochloride and mixing into a paste with 20 ml. of water in a mortar. Twenty ml. of hydrochloric acid (sp. gr. 1.12) are added and the mixture diluted to exactly 1000 ml. One ml. of this solution corresponds to 0.00357 g. $H_2SO_4$. The solution has a brown color. Brown flakes are likely to separate out on standing, but these do no harm.

*Procedure.*—The sulfate solution is diluted with water so that there is at least a 50-ml. volume for each 0.1 g. sulfuric acid present. An equal volume of the reagent is vigorously stirred in, and the precipitate allowed to settle for ten minutes. The solution is filtered onto a double filter, placed on a porcelain, perforated plate in a funnel (a Buchner is satisfactory), gentle suction being applied. The last portions of the precipitate are transferred to the filter by means of small portions of the clear filtrate, and the compound then washed with 20 ml. of cold water added in small portions and sucked dry with each addition. The precipitate and filter are placed in an Erlenmeyer flask, 50 ml. of water added, and the mixture shaken until homogeneous. Phenolphthalein indicator is now added, the mixture heated to about 50°C. and titrated with 0.1 $N$ sodium hydroxide. When the end point is nearly reached, the liquid is boiled for five minutes, and the titration then completed.

One ml. 0.1 $N$ NaOH = 0.004904 g. $H_2SO_4$

## SCHÖNIGER COMBUSTION METHOD [*]

By this method sulfur may be determined in a wide variety of materials, ranging from organic substances to finely ground alloys, by burning them in a closed flask filled with oxygen. It has the advantage of speed and ready adaptability to a micro or semimicro scale. The method is useful for the determination of the halogens as well as sulfur. (See Chapter on Chlorine.) The sample is wrapped in filter paper attached to a platinum wire sealed in the stopper of a flask, and the paper is ignited immediately before placing the stopper; the products of combustion being dissolved in a solution placed in the flask.

*Apparatus.* **Conical Flask.**—250–1000 ml., with a ground glass stopper fitted with a platinum wire coming to about the middle of the flask. The sample is attached to the end of the wire by twisting it or clamping it to the wire by platinum gauze.

*Reagents.* **Oxygen Supply.**—Tank oxygen is preferred, although its purification by passage through solid NaOH is desirable.

**Hydrogen Peroxide (30%).**

**Sodium Hydroxide Solution (0.01 $N$).**

**Methyl Red-Methylene Blue Indicator.**

---

[13] Friedheim and Nydegger (Z. anal. Chem., **49**, 464, 1910) have found that there should not be more than 10 mol. HCl, 15 mol. $HNO_3$, 20 mol. $HC_2H_3O_2$, 5 mol. alkali salt, or 2 mol. ferric iron present to 1 mol. $H_2SO_4$.

[*] Schöniger, Microchim. Acta, 1956, 869.

*Procedure.*—Weigh on a small piece of Whatman No. 44 filter paper (3 x 3 cm.) 10–100 micrograms of sample, depending upon its expected sulfur content. Fold and cut the paper so as to leave hanging a short end. Attach the folded paper to the wire. Place in the flask 10 ml. of water to which 5–20 drops of 30% hydrogen peroxide has been added. Pass a rapid current of oxygen into the flask until all air has been displaced. Ignite the short end of the paper and immediately place the stopper in the flask. It is well to tilt the flask so that the solution wets the edge of the stopper to make sure that it is completely sealed. After combustion has ended, shake the flask frequently for 10 minutes. Remove the stopper and rinse it in the flask with water. Titrate the solution in the flask with the sodium hydroxide solution and indicator.

NOTE.—If halogens or nitrate ions are likely to be present, use 80% alcohol instead of water, plus the hydrogen peroxide, as the absorbing solution; wash the platinum wire with alcohol instead of with water and titrate with barium perchlorate solution (0.01 $M$), using an alizarin red S as indicator.

## TITRIMETRIC METHODS FOR PERSULFATES

### FERROUS SULFATE METHOD

Ferrous salts in cold solutions are oxidized to ferric form by persulfates. Advantage is taken of this reaction in the quantitative determination of persulfates.

Reaction.—$2FeSO_4 + H_2S_2O_8 \rightarrow Fe_2(SO_4)_3 + H_2SO_4$.

*Procedure.*[14]—About 2.5 g. of the persulfate, weighed out, are dissolved in water and diluted to 100 ml. Ten ml. of this solution, equivalent to one-tenth of the sample are placed in a flask and a considerable excess of standard ferrous sulfate solution [15] added, say 100 ml. measured out from a burette. The solution is diluted with an equal volume of hot, distilled water (70 to 80°C.), and the excess ferrous sulfate titrated with 0.1 $N$ potassium permanganate. This titration is deducted from the permanganate equivalent of 100 ml. of the ferrous solution taken (if this amount was used). The difference is due to persulfate oxidation.

One ml. 0.1 $N$ $KMnO_4 = 0.009707$ g. $H_2S_2O_8$
$= 0.01141$ g. $(NH_4)_2S_2O_8$
$= 0.01352$ g. $K_2S_2O_8$

### OXALIC ACID METHOD

Oxalic acid, in presence of silver sulfate, reduces persulfates in accordance with reaction,

$$H_2C_2O_4 + H_2S_2O_8 \rightarrow 2H_2SO_4 + 2CO_2$$

*Procedure.*—About 0.5 g. of the persulfate is placed in an Erlenmeyer flask, 50 ml. of 0.1 $N$ oxalic acid added, together with 0.2 g. silver sulfate in 20 ml. of

[14] Method suggested by Le Blanc and Eckardt, Chem. News, **81**, 38, 1900.

[15] About 30 grams of ferrous sulfate or ferrous ammonium sulfate crystals are dissolved in 900 ml. of water and the volume made to 1000 ml. with concentrated sulfuric acid. The reagent is standardized against 0.1 $N$ potassium permanganate and the value per milliliter in terms of the standard permanganate noted, the milliliter permanganate solution required divided by the milliliter of ferrous sulfate solution taken for titration, gives the value of the reagent in terms of the permanganate.

The solutions are best verified upon a persulfate of known purity.

10% sulfuric acid solution. The mixture is heated on the water bath for about half an hour to expel carbon dioxide. When the evolution ceases the liquid is diluted to 100 ml. with warm water and titrated warm (about 40°C.) with 0.1 $N$ potassium permanganate. The excess of oxalic acid is titrated, the difference is due to oxidation by the persulfate.

For calculation see factors in previous method.

### ALKALI TITRATION OF THE BOILED SOLUTION

The aqueous solutions of potassium, sodium, and barium persulfates are decomposed by boiling as follows (M = metal Na, K, or ½Ba):

$$2M_2S_2O_8 + 2H_2O \rightarrow 2M_2SO_4 + O_2 + 2H_2SO_4$$

*Procedure.*—About 0.2 g. of the persulfate salt is dissolved in 200 ml. of water and the solution boiled about 15 minutes, then cooled and titrated with 0.1 $N$ NaOH, using methyl orange indicator.

One ml. 0.1 $N$ NaOH = 0.02008 g. $BaS_2O_8 \cdot 4H_2O$, or 0.01191 g. $Na_2S_2O_8$.

Ammonium persulfate cannot be determined by the above method but may be determined by the ferrous sulfate method, above.

## TITRIMETRIC METHODS FOR SULFITES
## AND SULFUR DIOXIDE

### TITRATION WITH IODINE. SULFUROUS ACID, SULFITES, METABISULFITES, THIOSULFATES

Sulfurous acid, combined or free, may be titrated with iodine solution, the following reaction taking place:

$$SO_2 + I_2 + 2H_2O \rightarrow H_2SO_4 + 2HI$$

The titration is accomplished by adding the solution of sulfurous acid, sulfite, or thiosulfate to the iodine, not in the reverse order, since in the latter order low results are obtained, unless the solution is very dilute (less than 0.04% $SO_2$).[16]

*Procedure.*—Five grams of the sample (sulfurous acid solution may be titrated directly) are dissolved in a little water and transferred to a 500-ml. volumetric flask, then made to volume. Each milliliter of this solution contains 0.01 g. of the sample; 100 ml. of 0.1 $N$ iodine, or their equivalent if the solution is stronger or weaker, are placed in a beaker together with a few drops of hydrochloric acid. A portion of the sample in a 100-ml. burette is now run into the iodine, with constant stirring, until the color of the free iodine has almost faded out; a little starch solution is now added and the titration continued to the complete fading of the blue color.

Since each milliliter of the sample contains 0.01 g. of the material, it follows that the 100-ml. iodine equivalent in terms of the material titrated expressed to the fourth decimal place as a whole number, if divided by the milliliter of the

---

[16] A secondary reaction takes place, the hydriodic acid formed reducing the $SO_2$ to S, e.g., $SO_2 + HI \rightarrow 2H_2O + 2I_2 + S$. (Volhard, J., Ann. d. Chem. u. Pharm., **242**, 94.) The solution, if not too dilute, will show a distinct separation of sulfur. (Treadwell and Hall, Analytical Chemistry, **2**, 3d Ed.) Raschig believes that a loss of $SO_2$ occurs, due to evaporation. (Z. Angew. Chem., 580, 1904.) See Sutton, Volumetric Analysis, 10th Ed., pp. 128, 129. Gooch, Methods in Chemical Analysis, 1st Ed., pp. 364–368.

sample required, will give the per cent of the substance sought, provided other titratable substances are absent.

**Example.**—Suppose sodium sulfite is being titrated, then since 100 ml. of 0.1 $N$ iodine are equivalent to 0.6302 g. $Na_2SO_3$, 6303 divided by the milliliter $Na_2SO_3$ solution required gives per cent $Na_2SO_3$. If 63 ml. were required the salt would be 100% pure.

NOTE.—When the iodine equivalent is over unity, it is necessary to take a larger sample per 500-ml. volume to avoid having a titration of over 100 ml. For example in the *analysis of sodium thiosulfate*, a 20-g. sample is diluted to 500 ml. and a portion of this added to 100 ml. of 0.1 $N$ iodine solution. In this case it must be kept in mind that each milliliter of the sample contains 0.04 g. of thiosulfate and the percentage calculated accordingly upon completing the titration.

If the titration of the iodine is made in a casserole, the end point may readily be recognized without the addition of starch.

**Equivalents.**—One hundred ml. 0.1 $N$ iodine solution will oxidize:

Sodium sulfite (anhydrous), $Na_2SO_3 = 0.6302$ g., or 0.3202 g. $SO_2$.
Sodium sulfite, $Na_2SO_3 \cdot 7H_2O = 1.2607$ g.
Sodium bisulfite (acid sodium sulfite), $NaHSO_3 = 0.5203$ g.
Sodium metabisulfite, $Na_2S_2O_5$ (anhydride of $NaHSO_3$) = 0.4753 g.
Sodium thiosulfate, $Na_2S_2O_3 \cdot 5H_2O = 2.4818$ g.

NOTE.—Hydrogen sulfide or sodium sulfide are also titrated with iodine. Equivalents for 100 ml. 0.1 $N$ iodine = 0.1704 g. $H_2S$, or 0.3902 g. $Na_2S$.

## TITRATION WITH ALKALI. SULFITES, BISULFITES, ACID SULFITES, OR SULFUROUS ACID

The choice of indicator is important for the titration with one may be different from that obtained in presence of another. For example the titration of sulfurous acid by an alkali in presence of phenolphthalein is twice the titration necessary to obtain an alkaline reaction with methyl orange. The reason for this is evident by the fact that $Na_2SO_3$ is neutral to phenolphthalein and alkaline to methyl orange, whereas $NaHSO_3$ is neutral to methyl orange but is acid to phenolphthalein. Advantage is taken of this in the analysis of salts containing a mixture of the normal and acid salts.

Reaction.

With phenolphthalein $\quad H_2SO_3 + 2NaOH \rightarrow Na_2SO_3 + 2H_2O$

With methyl orange $\quad H_2SO_3 + NaOII \rightarrow NaHSO_3 + H_2O$

On the other hand if a salt is being titrated, methyl orange cannot be used for the titration of metabisulfite or acid sulfite, since these salts are neutral to this indicator; here phenolphthalein is required and an alkali titration made.

Reaction.

$NaHSO_3 + NaOH \rightarrow Na_2SO_3.$ $\quad (Na_2S_2O_5 + H_2O \rightarrow 2NaHSO_3)$

Again if sodium sulfite, $Na_2SO_3$, is to be titrated, phenolphthalein would not do as an indicator, since $Na_2SO_3$ is neutral to this indicator. Here an acid titration is required with methyl orange indicator present:

$2Na_2SO_3 + H_2SO_4 \rightarrow 2NaHSO_3 + Na_2SO_4$

### TITRATION WITH ALKALI. SODIUM METABISULFITE

Sodium acid sulfite does not exist in dry form, since the salt loses water and anhydrous $Na_2S_2O_5$ results. This is analogous to sulfurous acid, which exists only in water solution. It has been found that the acid sulfite solution evaporated to crystallization yields a product, which though dried with extreme care, forms the anhydrous salt, $Na_2S_2O_5$. For correct report, therefore, the solid should be reported as metabisulfite, and the solution of the salt as acid sulfite.

Since metabisulfite in solution, or acid sulfite, is neutral to methyl orange, phenolphthalein indicator must be used and an alkali titration made. Carbon dioxide-free water and reagents should be used.

Reaction.

$$Na_2S_2O_5 + H_2O \rightarrow 2NaHSO_3; \quad NaHSO_3 + NaOH \rightarrow Na_2SO_3 + H_2O$$

*Procedure.*—9.506 g. of the finely ground powder are dissolved in about 50 ml. of cold saturated salt solution, to which has been added from a burette 50 ml. of $N$ sodium hydroxide. The salt solution should be made neutral to phenolphthalein. One ml. of 0.1% solution of the indicator is added and the excess acid sodium sulfite titrated with $N$ sodium hydroxide until a permanent faint pink color is obtained.

Since the normal equivalent of the salt has been taken for analysis the ml. alkali titration, including the 50 ml. originally present, will give the percentage directly in terms of $Na_2S_2O_5$.

NOTE.—The NaCl serves to give a sharp and more permanent end point. It may be necessary to add more of the indicator towards the end of the titration.

### TITRATION WITH ALKALI. SODIUM SULFITE

Sodium sulfite, $Na_2SO_3$, is neutral to phenolphthalein and alkaline to methyl orange. The titration of this salt is accomplished by addition of standard acid in presence of methyl orange.

*Procedure.*—The normal factor weight (12.6 g.) of the salt is dissolved in about 250 ml. of distilled water, 1 ml. of methyl orange added, followed by $N$ sulfuric acid, added from a burette until a faint orange end point is obtained. As in the case of the metabisulfite, each ml. of $N$ sulfuric acid equals 1% $Na_2SO_3$. Hence the percentage is obtained directly from the burette reading.

NOTES.—Organic coloring matter may be removed from the solution by filtering through charcoal.

If sodium carbonate is present, it will also be titrated. A correction must be applied for this. In the presence of sodium carbonate the solution will be alkaline to phenolphthalein. An approximate estimation of this may be obtained by titration with normal acid in presence of this indicator, remembering that sodium bicarbonate, $NaHCO_3$, is neutral to phenolphthalein, hence twice this titration must be deducted from the total methyl orange titration, i.e., $Na_2CO_3 + H_2SO_4$ (M.O.) $= Na_2SO_4 + H_2CO_3$ and $2Na_2SO_3 + H_2SO_4$ (P.) $= 2NaHSO_4 + 2NaHCO_3$. (Alkaline hydroxides will also be titrated.) $CO_2$ may also be obtained by the standard procedure under carbon, the $SO_2$ being oxidized by addition of chromic acid. $Na_2CO_3 \times 1.8 =$ equivalent $Na_2SO_3$.

Sodium carbonate may be detected in a sulfite or metabisulfite by adding cold, dilute acetic acid (25%) to the dry powdered salt. An effervescence is due to the presence of carbonate, since a sulfite or metabisulfite does not effervesce under similar conditions.

## TITRIMETRIC METHODS FOR SODIUM HYDROSULFITE

*Reagents.* **Standard Indigo Solution.**—To about 150 ml. concentrated sulfuric acid in a casserole, are added 4.2 g. of indigo, slowly with stirring. The solution is kept at 80°C. for an hour in an oven, stirring once or twice during this time. After cooling the solution it is made up to four liters with distilled water. This reagent is now standardized against 0.02 *N* KMnO₄ solution. To do this 25 ml. of the indigo solution is diluted in a casserole with 300 ml. of water and titrated with 0.02 *N* KMnO₄ reagent.

One ml. 0.02 *N* KMnO₄ is equivalent to 0.0015 g. indigotin.

.505:1 = g. indigotin:*x*, where *x* = gram Na₂S₂O₄ in 25 ml. indigo solution.

$$\frac{2 \times 10,000}{\text{ml. titration}} = \% \text{ Na}_2\text{S}_2\text{O}_4$$

2.5 g. of solid) or grams per liter (25 ml. sample made up to 500 ml.).

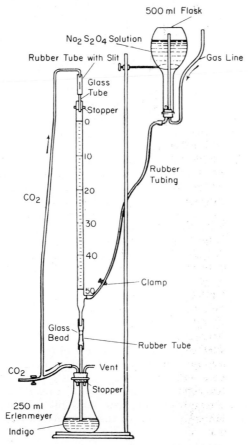

Fɪɢ. 44-4. Apparatus for Determining Hydrosulfite.

**Procedure. Titration of Sodium Hydrosulfite Against Standard Indigo Solution.** —Fifty ml. of standard indigo solution are pipetted into a 300-ml. Erlenmeyer flask. The titrating apparatus as well as the 500-ml. volumetric flask are filled with $CO_2$ gas ($C_2H_2$ may be used in place of $CO_2$). Two and a half grams of the solid are now taken, or 25 ml. of the solution (if the material is already dissolved as a 10% solution) and placed in the 500-ml. flask and made to mark with distilled water. The flask is stoppered and connections made with the burette, etc., as shown in Fig. 44-4. The burette is filled with the sample and the flask containing the indigo solution is placed under the burette as shown in the figure. The air is displaced from the apparatus by $CO_2$, the flow of this gas being continued during the titration. The hydrosulfite solution is now added to the indigo solution until it changes from the blue to a yellow or brown color.

$$\frac{\text{Factor for Indigo}}{\text{ml. titration}} = \%\ Na_2S_2O_4 \text{ in solids, or grams per liter in liquids.}$$

NOTES.—The hydrosulfite solution should be made alkaline with NaOH, then made up rapidly to volume and titrated in an atmosphere of $CO_2$ to prevent oxidation.

The size of the sample may be varied, but the titration should be over 10 ml.

The tip of the burette should dip below the surface of the indigo until near the end point, then withdrawn and the titration completed with the tip above the surface.

## PHOTOMETRIC METHODS

### GENERAL METHOD

This method [17] consists of solution of the sample in water, or if insoluble (as is a metal or alloy) in a mixture of hydrochloric and nitric acids, destruction of the nitric acid, reduction of the sulfate to sulfide by means of hydriodic acid, distillation of the hydrogen sulfide into a strong aqueous ammonia solution, and finally precipitation as colloidal lead sulfide and measurement of its trasmittancy at 370 m$\mu$. This method is suitable for the determination of 0.001 to 0.050 mg. of S in 0.1 to 1.0 g. of most of the common metals and alloys.

*Reagents.* **Standard Potassium Sulfate Solution (1 ml. = 5 micrograms of sulfur).**—Transfer 27.2 mg. of pure dry potassium sulfate to a 1-liter volumetric flask, dissolve, and dilute to the mark with distilled water.

**Redistilled Hydrochloric Acid.**—Transfer 500 ml. of hydrochloric acid (specific gravity 1.19) and 450 ml. of distilled water to a 1500-ml. standard-taper round-bottomed Pyrex flask and add a few grains of 12-mesh silicon carbide. Connect to an all-glass water-cooled distillation apparatus and heat to boiling. When enough of the acid has been distilled over to wash out the condenser system and to ensure that the acid coming over is constant-boiling, e.g., 50 ml., replace the receiver with a clean Pyrex bottle. Continue the distillation until the volume in the flask has been reduced to 100 ml. Stopper and reserve the distilled acid.

**Redistilled Nitric Acid.**—Distill undiluted nitric acid (sp. gr. 1.42) in the manner described above into a clean Pyrex bottle, discarding the first 25-ml. portion of acid that comes over. Stopper and reserve.

**Redistilled Formic Acid.**—Oxidize the sulfite in commercial formic acid by titration with 0.1 $N$ potassium permanganate until the solution acquires a pink tint which persists for a few seconds. Distill as directed above. Stopper and reserve.

[17] Luke, C. L., Anal. Chem., **21**, 1369–70, 1949.

**Hydriodic Acid-Hypophosphorous Acid Mixture.**—Transfer 100 ml. of hydriodic acid (sp. gr. 1.70) and 25 ml. 50% of hypophosphorous acid to a clean 250-ml. Vycor Erlenmeyer flask. Add a few grains of clean 12-mesh silicon carbide, heat to vigorous boiling without a cover on a hot electric plate, and boil for exactly 3 minutes. Cover and cool to room temperature. Ignore any iodine that may appear in the solution on standing.

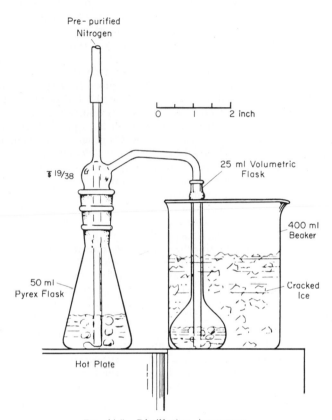

FIG. 44-5. Distillation Apparatus.

**Lead Citrate Solution.**—Dissolve 5 g. of lead nitrate in 50 ml. of distilled water and dilute to 100 ml. Add 20 g. of citric acid and warm to dissolve. If a precipitate appears on standing, use only the supernatant solution or allow to stand overnight and then decant from the precipitate.

*Procedure.* **Preparation of Calibration Curve.**—Add from a burette 0, 2, 4, 6, 8, and 10 ml. of standard potassium sulfate solution (1 ml. = 5 micrograms of sulfur) to clean 50-ml. standard-taper Pyrex Erlenmeyer flasks (Fig. 44-5). (Take care to prevent contamination of the samples with sulfate from unclean glassware or impure chemicals. Whenever an acid or acid mixture is called for, use the redistilled acids described under reagents.) Carry each sample separately through the steps indicated below.

Evaporate nearly to dryness on a hot plate, in an oven or over a flame, providing the flaming is done in a hood and the flask is held in such a position that any sulfur acids from the flame do not enter the flask. Cool to room temperature and add 5 ml. of hydrochloric acid. Add 15 ml. of the hydriodic-hypophosphorous acid mixture, making sure that a drop or two falls on the ground-glass joint, so that the latter will be wet in the subsequent distillation. Stopper at once with the distillation head and immediately dip the arm into 15 ml. of ammonium hydroxide (1:2) in a clean 25-ml. volumetric flask. [It is imperative that the volumetric flask and the side arm of the distillation head be freed of any lead salts (which may be present from a previous analysis) by washing in nitric acid (1:1) and then distilled water.]

Place the Erlenmeyer flask on a definite spot on a hot plate, so that the center of the flask is 5 cm. in from the edge of the plate. Arrange to surround the volumetric flask with a crushed ice bath as indicated in Fig. 44-5. The surface temperature of the hot plate should be adjusted previously with a Variac, so that a thermometer will read $185° \pm 3°C.$ when its bulb is suspended near the bottom of a 30-ml. beaker (containing 15 ml. of Dow Corning 550 silicone oil) placed next to the spot on the plate reserved for the 50-ml. Erlenmeyer flask. (The temperature chosen for the distillation is not critical, providing that it is somewhere in the region of 185°C. and is maintained constant.)

Connect the distillation head immediately to a tank of pure nitrogen (previously adjusted to a definite rate of flow), using a flexible tubing that is not likely to give off any sulfur or sulfur compounds to the nitrogen that passes through it. (To prevent oxidation of the sulfide it is essential that the sample be at room temperature and that the nitrogen line be connected immediately, in order that removal of air from the flask will be completed before distillation of the sulfide begins.) The rate of flow of nitrogen must be rather closely controlled if reproducible results are to be obtained. To do this it is recommended that the flow be regulated by means of the usual pressure gauge until the rate is such that 100 ml. of water are displaced in $30 \pm 1$ seconds from an inverted water-filled 100-ml. graduate when the end of the rubber hose is held under the graduate as the latter is suspended to a depth of 2.5 cm. in a water bath.

Distill for exactly 5 minutes after the first appearance of white fumes escaping from the volumetric flask, keeping the latter in intimate contact with crushed ice by removal of excess water and replacement with ice. (Sulfide will be lost if the ammonium hydroxide solution is not kept cold. Even with this precaution the amount of sulfide that can be held safely is limited.) Finally remove and separate the flasks. Immediately pipette 1 ml. of lead citrate solution into the volumetric flask, swirl, dilute to the mark, mix well, and transfer to a dry absorption cell. Read the percentage transmittancy at 370 m$\mu$ with the instrument set at 100% transmittancy with distilled water. (It is essential that all operations from the finish of the distillation to the reading of the percentage transmittancy be done as quickly as is convenient in order to prevent oxidation of the ammonium sulfide and to obtain the photometric reading before appreciable agglomeration of the colloidal lead sulfide takes place.)

Prepare a standard curve by plotting, on semilog paper, micrograms of sulfur against percentage transmittancy values that have been corrected for the blank. The latter should correspond to not more than about 0.5 microgram of sulfur. The corrected transmittancy values are obtained as follows:

$$\frac{\% \text{ T of sample versus } H_2O}{\% \text{ T of blank versus } H_2O} \times 100 = \text{corrected } \% \text{ T.}$$

**Analysis of Sample.**—Transfer 0.1 to 1 g. of the sample depending on the sulfur content, to a clean 50-ml. standard-taper Pyrex Erlenmeyer flask (Fig. 44-5). (For samples that dissolve with unusual violence—tin, aluminum, and magnesium alloys —the initial solution is best accomplished in a clean, covered 150-ml. beaker.) For a 1-g. sample add 10 ml. of a freshly mixed solution of 80 ml. of hydrochloric acid and 20 ml. of nitric acid. (If a sample smaller than 1 g. was taken in order to keep the amount of sulfur to be determined below 50 micrograms, it will be necessary to reduce proportionately the amount of solvent acids used, or boil off the excess after solution of the sample, in order to avoid using too much formic acid.) Cover and heat gently to start dissolution of the sample. Cool in an ice bath if the initial reaction becomes too violent. Continue to heat gently until solution of the sample is complete. (If hydrolysis occurs at any time up to the point where complete destruction of the nitrates has been accomplished, add 5 ml. of hydrochloric acid.)

Place the flask on a hot plate with surface temperature of about 130°C. and add from a medicine dropper about 0.5 ml. of formic acid. Cool the flask in an ice bath if the reaction becomes too violent. Continue the addition of small portions of formic acid until gas ceases to be evolved from the solution and it is evident that nitrogen acids have been completely destroyed. In general, not more than 1 or 2 ml. of formic acid will be required. Boil down as far as possible—to 1 or 2 ml. volume—on a flame, to expel formic acid. Add 10 ml. of hydrochloric acid and boil down to 5 ml. on a flame. Cool to room temperature.

Add 15 ml. of the hydriodic-hypophosphorous acid mixture, cap with the distillation head, and dip the arm into 15 ml. of ammonium hydroxide solution (1 to 2) in a clean 25-ml. volumetric flask as directed above. (For copper and copper alloys it is best to use 20 ml. of the hydriodic-hypophosphorous acid mixture to ensure complete solution of the cuprous iodide and thus to prevent bumping.) If heat is generated on adding the acid mixture or if iodine is liberated in the solution in the distilling flask, cool to room temperature, allow to stand, and shake occasionally until the iodine has been reduced. Finally place the flask on the hot plate, connect it to the nitrogen, and proceed with the distillation and photometric determination as directed above. Run a blank through the entire procedure, using equivalent quantities of acids and taking precautions not to lose sulfuric acid during the evaporations. The blank should correspond to not more than about 1 microgram of sulfur. (The destruction of the nitric acid with formic acid is more difficult to initiate when running a blank than it is for a sample. This suggests that the reduction reaction is catalyzed by certain metal ions.) Obtain the corrected percentage transmittancy for the sample and read from the standard curve the weight of sulfur present in the sample.

## MODIFICATIONS IN PROCEDURE REQUIRED IN ANALYSIS OF CERTAIN METALS

### ARSENIC, ANTIMONY, TIN, AND GERMANIUM

Arsenic precipitates first as the iodide and then as metal during the sulfide distillation. For this reason it is best to limit the sample size to 0.5 g. to minimize bumping. If a larger sample is to be analyzed it may be best to resort to removal of the arsenic by distillation as bromide, using the method described in a subsequent section below for selenium.

When analyzing antimony it is necessary to add an extra 5 ml. of hydrochloric acid with the 10 ml. of hydrochloric-nitric acid mixture used for solution of the sample. This precaution plus that of keeping the flask covered during solution of the sample will prevent hydrolysis of the antimony. The hydrolysis is harmful only in that it may prevent complete destruction of the nitrates in the solution.

Care must be taken in the solution of tin alloys to prevent loss of the sample due to the violent boiling that occurs as the divalent tin suddenly goes over to the oxidized state.

Germanium precipitates as the oxide on solution in the acid mixture. In order to reduce the bumping and to minimize the amount of germanium that accompanies the sulfide in the subsequent distillation, it is best to remove the bulk of the germanium by distillation as follows:

Dissolve 0.5 g. of the sample in 10 ml. of hydrochloric-nitric acid mixture in the usual manner. Remove the cover and boil down on a flame to about 0.5 ml. Repeat the distillation one or more times by adding 10 ml. of hydrochloric acid and boiling down to 0.5 ml. volume. Care must be taken to avoid loss of sulfuric acid. Finally add 10 ml. of hydrochloric acid, destroy the nitrates, and proceed with the distillation in the usual manner.

Some arsenic, tin, germanium, and probably antimony will accompany the sulfide in the distillation, but this usually causes no trouble. Evidence of the presence of these metals in the distillates comes from the fact that the absorbancy of the lead sulfide solutions increases rather than decreases on standing. It is necessary to have sufficient hypophosphorous acid present to ensure complete reduction of tin to the less volatile stannous state; otherwise marked contamination of the distillate will take place.

## TELLURIUM AND SELENIUM

Tellurium precipitates as the metal during the sulfide distillation. In order to minimize bumping it is best, therefore, to limit the sample size to 0.5 g. Selenium metal cannot be analyzed as directed in the procedure, for although most of it precipitates as metallic selenium during the distillation, appreciable quantities accompany the sulfide and precipitate as lead selenide in the photometric analysis. In order to obtain correct results for sulfur it is necessary, therefore, to resort to removal of the selenium by distillation as bromide.

Dissolve 1 g. of selenium metal plus 0.25 g. of relatively sulfur-free zinc or zinc alloy—e.g., Bureau of Standards zinc base No. 94—in 10 ml. of the hydrochloric-nitric acid mixture in the usual manner. Boil off the excess acid on a flame until a precipitate begins to appear—i.e., reduce the solution to 1 or 2 ml. volume. Cool, add 10 ml. of redistilled hydrobromic acid (prepare the sulfur-free acid by distilling 1 liter of hydrobromic acid, sp. gr. about 1.38, in an all-glass still, discarding the first 50 ml. that comes over), and boil down on a flame to about 0.5 ml. volume. (There is danger of loss of sulfuric acid during the expulsion of the selenium if the sample is flamed to dryness and if zinc or some other metal is not present.) Transfer the flask to the hot plate used in the distillation of the sulfide and allow the rest of the hydrobromic acid to boil off, flaming the sides and top of the flask to expedite the expulsion of the acid. When all or nearly all of the excess hydrobromic acid has been expelled, cool the flask, add 2 ml. of hydrobromic acid, and repeat the distillation process. After the second removal of excess hydrobromic acid on the plate, add 2 ml. of the hydrochloric-nitric acid mixture, boil down on a flame to 0.5 ml. volume, add 5 ml. of hydrochloric acid and 0.5 ml. of formic acid, boil down to 0.5 ml. on a flame, add 5 ml. of hydrochloric acid, cool, add 15 ml. of the hydriodic-hypophosphorous acid mixture, and distill as usual. Run a reagent blank, adding the 0.25-g. portion of zinc or zinc alloy.

## LEAD ALLOYS

Because of the low solubility of lead chloride it is necessary, if solution in the hydrochloric-nitric acid solution is desired, to obtain the sample in as great a state of subdivision as possible before solution of the alloy is attempted. Even so, it is not always possible nor indeed necessary to accomplish complete decomposition of lead alloys, for this will usually take place upon subsequent boiling with the distillation mixture. Decomposition is best accomplished by heating gently on an asbestos pad, keeping the flask covered to prevent loss of too much acid, and adding more hydrochloric acid if necessary. Because little or no oxidizing action occurs during solution of a lead alloy, more formic acid will be required than is the case in alloys of copper or tin.

## LEAD METAL

Metallic lead must be dissolved in nitric acid. Dissolve 0.5 g. of the sample in a mixture of 4 ml. of distilled water and 1 ml. of nitric acid, with gentle heating. When solution is complete, boil on a flame until the volume is reduced to 1 ml. or until salts begin to precipitate. Add 25 ml. of hydrochloric acid and heat to dissolve all the lead chloride. Treat with formic acid to destroy nitrates, and proceed in the recommended manner, adding 15 rather than 10 ml. of hydrochloric acid after the expulsion of the formic acid.

## SILVER AND SILVER ALLOYS

Silver alloys that can be decomposed in the recommended hydrochloric-nitric acid mixture can be analyzed as directed. If severe bumping is encountered it is best to remove the silver chloride before treatment with formic acid.

The following procedure is recommended for silver metal: Dissolve 1 g. in a covered 100-ml. beaker in a mixture of 2 ml. of nitric acid and 6 ml. of water, with gentle heating. Add 10 ml. of hydrochloric acid, stir, and warm gently to coagulate the precipitate. Allow to settle and tamp down the precipitate. Decant the solution into a 50-ml. standard-taper Erlenmeyer distilling flask and wash the precipitate twice by decantation, using 3-ml. portions of hydrochloric acid. Ignore traces of silver chloride that may precipitate on cooling. Boil the solution down to 15 ml. volume, add formic acid to destroy the nitric acid, and proceed with the analysis in the usual manner.

## MERCURY

In the analysis of metallic mercury dissolve a 1-g. portion in 5 ml. of nitric acid with gentle heating. Boil the solution down to 0.5 ml., add 10 ml. of hydrochloric acid followed by formic acid, and proceed in the usual manner.

## MOLYBDENUM

When molybdenum metal is analyzed by the unmodified method very low results are obtained. Thus, when a 1-g. sample is analyzed only about 15% of the sulfur is recovered. By reducing the sample size the percentage recovery can be greatly increased. When a 0.5-g. sample is taken the recovery is about 85% and for a 0.25-g. sample it is about 95%. The low results may be due to depletion of reducing power of hydriodic-hypophosphorous acid solution due to the large valence change that occurs in the reduction of the molybdenum during the distillation. [Almost complete recovery of the sulfur can be obtained in the analysis of 1 g. of chromium (present as chromic chloride) or 1 g. of vanadium (present as ammonium vanadate).]

In view of the low results mentioned it is desirable, when analyzing samples containing over 0.1 g. of molybdenum, to remove most of the latter by an ether extraction before performing the sulfur distillation.

Dissolve 0.5 g. of the sample in 5 ml. of hydrochloric-nitric acid solution in the usual manner. Boil down on a flame until the molybdenum just starts to precipitate. (Oxidizing acids must be present during the ether extraction to keep the molybdenum in the oxidized state; otherwise incomplete extraction will result.) Add 10 ml. of hydrochloric acid and heat to dissolve all material that has precipitated. Cool to room temperature. Pour the solution into a clean 150-ml. separatory funnel and wash the flask with 2 ml. of hydrochloric acid, added from a medicine dropper. Reserve the flask. Add 50 ml. of pure ethyl ether, stopper, and shake vigorously to extract the molybdenum, relieving the pressure by opening the stopcock or removing the top from time to time. After the excess pressure has been eliminated shake for a few seconds and then allow the layers to separate. Drain off the lower acid layer into the reserved flask. Add 5 ml. of hydrochloric acid to the separatory funnel and shake for a few seconds. Drain the acid into the flask. Place the flask on an electric hot plate and boil off the ether. Add about 1 ml. of formic acid and heat gently to destroy nitrates. Boil down on a flame to 5 ml. volume. Cool, add 15 ml. of hydriodic-hypophosphorous acid mixture, and continue as directed in the procedure.

## ALUMINUM AND MAGNESIUM

Because of the large amount of heat generated during solution of aluminum and magnesium alloys, it is best to add small portions of the sample to the acid in the flask while the latter is resting in an ice bath. Even with these precautions enough acid may boil off to permit hydrolysis to take place. In view of this and because of the fact that some of these alloys contain considerable amounts of silicon, it is often more convenient to limit the sample size to 0.5 g.

## NICKEL

To analyze metallic nickel, dissolve 1 g. of the sample in 10 ml. of nitric acid, boil off all the nitric acid, bake on a flame until most of the nitrates have been converted to oxides, cool, add 10 ml. of hydrochloric acid, heat to dissolve all the salts, destroy the nitrates, and proceed in the usual manner.

## CHROMIUM, SILICON, TUNGSTEN, AND ZIRCONIUM

Materials that are not soluble in nitric or hydrochloric-nitric acid mixtures cannot be analyzed by this recommended method. If the materials are alloyed sufficiently to permit solution or disintegration, an analysis can usually be performed. In some instances it may be possible to resort to a preliminary alkaline fusion.

## IRON AND STEEL

In the case of ferrous alloys containing more than 0.01 mg. of S per g. of sample, redistillation of the reagent acids is unnecessary, and the procedure may be shortened materially.[18] The changes in it are as follows:

**Reagents.** **Hydriodic-Hypophosphorous Acid Mixture.**—Transfer 300 ml. of hydriodic acid (sp. gr. 1.70) plus 75 ml. of 50% hypophosphorous acid to an uncovered 500-ml. conical flask and boil moderately for 5 minutes. Avoid excessive boiling or too much hydriodic acid will be lost. Cool, transfer to a stoppered brown glass bottle, and keep in a dark place.

**Ammoniacal Zinc Chloride Solution.**—Dissolve 25 g. of zinc chloride in 500 ml. of ammonium hydroxide (1:1) in a stoppered glass bottle.

**Procedure.**—Dissolve 1.000 g. of the sample in 10 ml. of hydrochloric-nitric acid mixture (4:1) plus 2 drops of hydrofluoric acid and then destroy the nitric acid by reduction with formic acid. When foaming ceases, remove the cover, boil for 1 minute, and cool to room temperature. Add 15 ml. of hydriodic-hypophosphorous acid mixture, stopper with a distillation head, and dip the side arm into 30 ml. of water plus 5 ml. of ammoniacal zinc chloride solution contained in a 50-ml. standard taper conical flask. Swirl the acid solution to mix and let stand for a few minutes until all iodine in and above the solution in the distillation flask is reduced. Distill on a 150°C. hot plate, using a nitrogen flow rate of 40 to 50 ml. per minute for 5 minutes after the first appearance of white fumes in the receiving flask. Titrate with iodate standardized against an iron or steel of known sulfur content, e.g., National Bureau of Standards sample 55-d or 101-c. Correct for a reagent blank carried through all steps of the procedure (about 0.3 ml. of potassium iodate).

High-silicon steels such as NBS Sample 125 or titanium steels such as NBS Sample 170 should be dissolved in 10 ml. of hydrochloric-nitric acid mixture plus 1 ml. of hydrofluoric acid. Following this, solutions containing titanium should be boiled gently for 5 to 10 minutes to decompose refractory titanium-sulfur compounds. When more than a few drops of hydrofluoric acid are used in the dissolution of the sample or when the reagent blank analysis is made, the solution must be evaporated to 2 ml. to expel excess hydrofluoric or nitric acid and then diluted to 10 ml. with hydrochloric acid (1:1) before adding the formic acid. When incomplete dissolution or excessive foaming occurs in the analysis of iron or steel high in carbon, it is best to dissolve the sample in a mixture of 10 ml. of nitric acid plus 1 ml. of hydrofluoric acid and boil gently until most of the carbon compounds are oxidized. If desired, most iron and steel samples can be dissolved in the same nitric-hydrofluoric acid mixture. After dissolution it is necessary to evaporate on a flame or hot plate to 2 ml., add 10 ml. of hydrochloric acid, evaporate to 2 ml., and then add 8 ml. of hydrochloric acid (1:1) before adding the formic acid. When it is necessary to expel nitric or hydrofluoric acid by boiling, 7 rather than 5 ml. of ammoniacal zinc chloride solution should be used in the subsequent distillation to keep the distillate alkaline.

[18] Luke, C. L., Anal. Chem., **31**, 1393–94, 1959.

## ANALYSIS OF MIXTURES OF SULFUR COMPOUNDS

### DETERMINATION OF THIOSULFATE IN PRESENCE OF SULFIDE AND HYDROSULFIDE

The sulfide and hydrosulfide sulfur is removed from the solution by adding an excess of freshly precipitated cadmium carbonate. The solution is filtered and diluted to a definite volume and the thiosulfate determined on an aliquot portion by running it into an excess of 0.1 $N$ iodine solution and titrating the excess of iodine with 0.1 $N$ thiosulfate solution.

One ml. 0.1 $N$ iodine = 0.02482 g. $Na_2S_2O_3 \cdot 5H_2O$

### DETERMINATION OF SULFATES AND SULFIDES IN PRESENCE OF ONE ANOTHER

In one portion of the sample the sulfide is decomposed and the hydrogen sulfide expelled by boiling the solution (in presence of $CO_2$ replacing air in the flask) after acidifying with hydrochloric acid. The sulfate sulfur may now be precipitated as $BaSO_4$ by the usual methods.

In a second portion total sulfur is determined after oxidizing the sulfide with an excess of bromine and boiling out the excess of halogen. Total sulfur minus sulfate sulfur = sulfide sulfur.

The sulfide may be oxidized with fuming nitric acid by boiling the solution in a flask with reflux condenser. The nitric acid is expelled by evaporating the solution down to a moist residue. The sulfate is now precipitated by taking up the residue with water, adding HCl and then sufficient $BaCl_2$ to cause complete precipitation.

### DETERMINING THE SULFUR IN THIOCYANIC (SULFOCYANIC) ACID AND ITS SALTS

Oxidation of the sulfur may be accomplished as described for sulfides in the preceding method either by means of bromine or by fuming nitric acid. The sulfur is then precipitated as $BaSO_4$ as usual.

### DETERMINATION OF A SULFIDE AND A HYDROSULFIDE IN PRESENCE OF EACH OTHER

When a mixture of sulfide and hydrosulfide is treated with iodine the following reactions take place:

$$H_2S + I_2 \rightarrow 2HI + S \text{ and } NaHS + 2I_2 \rightarrow NaI + HI + S$$

It will be noticed that the acidity produced by the first reaction is twice that caused by the iodine action on the hydrosulfide, and that the acidity in the latter titration remains unaffected. The reactions with the alkali salts is effected by addition of a standard iodine solution containing a known amount of hydrochloric acid. The reactions in this case are as follows:

$$Na_2S + 2HCl \rightarrow 2NaCl + H_2S \text{ and } NaSH + HCl \rightarrow NaCl + H_2S$$

The iodine reacts with the $H_2S$ as in first equation above.

From the second set of reactions it is evident that the quantity of hydriodic acid formed by the action of iodine on the sulfide is equivalent to the hydrochloric acid required to decompose the sulfide, so that the acidity remains unchanged. On the other hand with hydrosulfide, NaSH, the hydriodic acid formed by the iodine oxidation, is twice the equivalent of hydrochloric acid required to decompose the acid salt. Hence it is evident that the acidity is a measure of the quantity of hydrosulfide present in the mixture. From the second set of reactions the following procedure is devised.

**Procedure.**—To a measured amount of 0.1 $N$ iodine solution containing a measured amount of 0.1 $N$ hydrochloric acid (the mixture diluted to 400 ml.) is added the solution containing the sulfide and hydrosulfide from a burette, until the stirred solution becomes a pale yellow color. (The milliliters of solution added is noted and its equivalent of the sample calculated.) Starch is now added and the excess of the iodine titrated with 0.1 $N$ sodium thiosulfate. The milliliters of thiosulfate in terms of 0.1 $N$ solution subtracted from the milliliters of 0.1 $N$ iodine solution taken give milliliters of iodine required by the sample added. The acidity of the solution is now determined by titration with 0.1 $N$ sodium hydroxide. The milliliters of NaOH required by the HI give total NaOH minus milliliters of 0.1 $N$ HCl present in the iodine solution.

**Calculation.**—*A.* Ml. 0.1 $N$ iodine required by the sample minus twice the ml. of 0.1 $N$ NaOH required by HI formed by the reaction multiplied by 0.003903 give weight of $Na_2S$.

*B.* Ml. 0.1 $N$ NaOH required by the HI multiplied by 0.005607 gives gram weight of NaHS. Or in brief: ml. NaOH $\times$ 0.005606 = g. NaHS.

## DETERMINATION OF SULFITES, METABISULFITES, THIOSULFATES, SULFATES, CHLORIDES AND CARBONATES IN PRESENCE OF ONE ANOTHER

### SODIUM SULFITE, $Na_2SO_3$

This is determined by titration with standard acid in the presence of methyl orange indicator according to the standard procedure previously described. If a carbonate is present, allowance must be made for this as stated.

One ml. $N$ $H_2SO_4$ = 0.1260 g. $Na_2SO_3$. Calculate to per cent.

$Na_2CO_3 \times 1.8$ = equivalent $Na_2SO_3$

### SODIUM METABISULFITE, $Na_2S_2O_5$

This is determined by titration with a standard alkali in the presence of phenolphthalein indicator according to the procedure previously described.

One ml. $N$ NaOH = 0.09505 g. $Na_2S_2O_5$. Calculate to per cent.

### SODIUM THIOSULFATE, $Na_2S_2O_3$

One gram of the mixed salts is placed in 100 ml. of 0.1 $N$ iodine solution, and the excess of iodine titrated with 0.1 $N$ sodium thiosulfate according to the standard procedure.

**Calculation.**—

$\{$(ml. 0.1 $N$ $I_2$ − ml. 0.1 $N$ $Na_2S_2O_3$) − [(% $Na_2S_2O_5 \times 2.104$)

$+$ (% $Na_2SO_3 \times 1.5868$)]$\} \times 1.5812$ = % $Na_2S_2O_3$

## SODIUM SULFATE

The sample is dissolved in a little water, hydrochloric acid added, and the solution boiled to expel all of the $SO_2$. Barium sulfate is now precipitated and determined according to the standard procedure.

$$BaSO_4 \times 0.6086 = Na_2SO_4$$

NOTE.—The amount of the sample required is governed by the per cent $Na_2SO_4$ present.

## SODIUM CHLORIDE

The sample is dissolved in water, nitric acid added and the solution boiled until all the $SO_2$ has either been volatilized or oxidized. The chlorine of the chloride is now precipitated with silver nitrate from a hot solution by the usual procedure.

$$AgCl \times 0.4078 = NaCl$$

NOTE.—The amount of the sample taken is governed by the per cent of NaCl present.

## SODIUM CARBONATE, $Na_2CO_3$

Carbon dioxide is evolved from the mixture by means of chromic and sulfuric acids, the former being used to oxidize the $SO_2$ of the sample. The evolved gas is bubbled through a mixture of concentrated sulfuric and chromic acids to remove any $SO_2$ that may have escaped oxidation, as shown in Fig. 12-13, p. 298. The $CO_2$ is absorbed either in caustic and weighed or is passed into a standard solution of barium hydroxide and titrated according to the standard procedures given under carbon.

NOTE.—The amount of the sample taken is governed by the per cent of $Na_2CO_3$ present.

# DETERMINATIONS IN SPECIFIC SUBSTANCES

## DETERMINATION OF FREE SULFUR IN A MIXTURE

Free sulfur is an essential component in many types of mixtures and the method of estimation will vary with the nature of the other ingredients.

*Procedure.*—For example, an insecticide dust containing coarse crude or refined sulfur, instead of flowers or superfine, would be valueless even though the chemical analysis showed that the mixture contained the specified percentage of total sulfur. Therefore, the microscope and a little ingenuity will indicate the proper combination of methods to follow.

From 1 to 10 grams of the material, depending upon the amount of sulfur present, is extracted in a Soxhlet extractor (see modified form, Fig. 44-6) with carbon disulfide (freshly distilled) for twelve hours. The extract is evaporated to dryness, adding 10 ml. of bromine-carbon tetrachloride mixture together with 15 ml. of nitric acid. The residue is taken up with 10 ml. of hydrochloric acid, diluted with 150 ml. of distilled water, heated to boiling and the sulfuric acid precipitated with 10% barium chloride solution, washed, dried, ignited and weighed according to the procedure for sulfur.

$$\frac{BaSO_4 \times 100 \times 0.1373}{\text{Weight of sample}} = \% \text{ free rhombic sulfur}$$

After extraction carefully dry the thimble and contents. Examine under a microscope a small portion of the dried material. Remaining sulfur if present will be in the amorphous form and have the charac-
teristic "droplet" structure seen in flowers of sulfur. Presence of much sulfur at this stage indicates that flowers of sulfur were used in the mixture, and the proper procedure to follow will depend on the nature of the other components. If a soluble sulfate such as nicotine sulfate or epsom salts is indicated, then an aliquot of the residue in the extraction thimble can be leached with hot water and the sulfur determined by one of the usual methods after wet oxidization. If an insoluble material such as gypsum is indicated, then the free sulfur may be burned off in the air and the combined sulfur determined in the residue after solution by one of the standard methods; the total sulfur having first been determined in another aliquot after wet oxidation with bromine and nitric acid. Whatever procedure is followed, the content of amorphous sulfur is calculated by difference and thus the percentage of flowers established by adding the amount thus found to the $CS_2$ soluble sulfur.

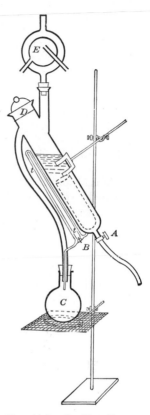

Fig. 44-6. Soxhlet Extractor (Sanders' Modification).

Sanders' modification of the Soxhlet extractor [19] has several advantages that make this apparatus desirable for laboratory use, where a number of daily extrac-
tions are required. As may be seen from Fig. 44-6, by simply removing the glass stopper D the cylinder may be charged without disconnecting the apparatus. The extraction is carried on with the traps A and B closed, the siphon t–t' acting automatically as in case of the Soxhlet. With A closed and B open the apparatus may be used as a reflux condenser. The solvent liquid may be drawn off by opening A. With B closed and A open the apparatus may be used as a condenser and the ether, chloroform, carbon disulfide, etc., distilled from C. The globe-shaped Soxhlet condenser may be replaced by Allihn's or Liebig's condenser, if desired. The ball form, however, is more compact.

## AVAILABLE HYDROGEN SULFIDE IN MATERIALS HIGH IN SULFIDE SULFUR BY EVOLUTION METHOD

Since it is desired to obtain the $H_2S$ that ordinarily would be obtained when the sulfide is treated with a strong acid, the mat of metallic aluminum or zinc and the addition of stannous chloride solution used in the procedure given on page 1034 is omitted here.

*Procedure.*—0.5 to 1 g. of the sulfide is placed in the dry evolution flask. All connections are now made as directed in the general procedure. Three absorption bulbs containing neutral solution of cadmium sulfate are connected to the condenser, and supported by wires attached to the thistle tube and the arm of the

19 Sanders, Proc. Chem. Soc., **26**, 227, 1910; Analyst, **35**, 556, 1910.

condenser. All connections being tight, 100 ml. of dilute sulfuric acid, 1:4 are added through the thistle tube and $H_2S$ evolved.

**Titration.**—When the evolution of the $H_2S$ is complete, the bulbs containing the precipitate are emptied into a beaker and carefully washed out. The precipitate is now filtered and washed five or six times until free of acid. Methyl orange is added to the filtrate and the free acid titrated with 0.1 $N$ NaOH.

The precipitate may be titrated with iodine according to the "Alternate Titration Procedure" on p. 1036, using an excess of iodine, followed by starch and acid and then titrating back with sodium thiosulfate solution. A double check may thus be obtained.

If it is desired to weigh the CdS precipitate, it is best to evolve the $H_2S$ into a neutral solution of cadmium salt. The precipitate formed in a neutral or slightly acid solution is crystalline and easily filtered, whereas that formed in an ammoniacal solution is gelatinous.

When a neutral $CdSO_4$ or $CdCl_2$ solution is used, $H_2S$ should be evolved by sulfuric acid and not by hydrochloric acid, as the latter is volatile, and will pass through the condensing bulb recommended in the general procedure.

$$\text{One ml. 0.1 } N \text{ NaOH} = 0.001704 \text{ g. } H_2S$$
$$\text{``} \qquad \text{``} \qquad = 0.004396 \text{ g. FeS}$$
$$\text{``} \qquad \text{``} \qquad = 0.003902 \text{ g. } Na_2S$$

The above weights multiplied by 100 and divided by the weight of sample used in the iodine titration give percentage of constituents in the sample.

The method is of value in the analysis of alkali sulfides in absence of other compounds, which are decomposed by hydrochloric acid and which react with iodine.

# EVOLUTION METHOD FOR DETERMINING SULFUR IN IRON, STEEL, ORES, CINDERS, SULFIDES, AND METALLURGICAL PRODUCTS

The method depends upon the fact that hydrogen sulfide is evolved when a sulfide is acted upon by a strong acid such as hydrochloric acid. This gas, absorbed by a suitable reagent, may be determined gravimetrically [20] by weighing directly the precipitated sulfide, or by oxidation of either the hydrogen sulfide evolved or the sulfide formed in the absorbing reagent and precipitating sulfur as $BaSO_4$. It may be determined titrimetrically [21] by titrating the precipitated sulfide with iodine or by titrating the acid, formed by the reaction, with standard caustic. The iodine and caustic titrations may be made on the same run, or the sulfide may be weighed and the filtrate containing the free acid titrated, thus double checking

[20] *Gravimetrically.* (a) Evolution of $H_2S$ into solutions of $ZnCl_2$, KOH, $KMnO_4$, $AgNO_3$, $Hg(CN)_2$, $H_2O_2$, Br + HCl and subsequent oxidation to sulfate when necessary, and precipitation as $BaSO_4$. (b) Absorption of $H_2S$ by neutral or alkaline solutions of lead, oxidation of PbS to $PbSO_4$ and weighing as such. (c) Absorption of $H_2S$ in solutions of $AgNO_3$, $CdCl_2$, and weighing the precipitated sulfide.
[21] *Titrimetrically.* (a) Absorption in a solution of KOH, $CdCl_2$ or $CdSO_4$, $ZnCl_2$ or $ZnSO_4$, $Na_2HAsO_3$ and titration with iodine solution. (b) Absorption in iodized KI and titration of the excess of iodine with $Na_2S_2O_3$ solution. (c) Absorption in a neutral solution of a metallic salt and titration of the liberated acid. (d) Absorption in NaOH and addition to an acid solution of a reducible salt, e.g., $Fe_2O_3$ and titration of the lower oxide, FeO.

results. The following reaction takes place when the gas is evolved and absorbed by neutral cadmium sulfate:

$$H_2S + CdSO_4 \rightarrow CdS \text{ precipitate} + H_2SO_4 \text{ free acid}$$

The method is especially adapted to the determination of sulfur in iron and steel or in metallurgical products containing small amounts of sulfide. It may be applied to products containing larger amounts of sulfur as sulfides or sulfates, the latter condition requiring a special preliminary treatment.

The method is not applicable for determining free sulfur or sulfur in iron pyrites.

**Reagents. Iodine Solution.**—Two strengths of this reagent should be at hand for general work:

For iron and steel and low sulfur briquettes, etc. = 0.01 to 0.5% S........0.0333 $N$ I
For sulfur products containing over 0.5% S...........................0.1 $N$ I

**Starch Solution.**—Made from a good grade of soluble starch, 1 gram per 200 ml. of water. Fresh solutions are desirable, as the deteriorated material produces a greenish-brown color in place of the delicate blue desired. Flocks of insoluble starch will cause the same difficulty.

**Cadmium Chloride or Cadmium Sulfate Solutions.** *Ammoniacal Solution.*—Fifty-five g. of $CdCl_2 \cdot 2H_2O$ or 70 g. of the sulfate are dissolved in 500 ml. of distilled water. To this are added 1200 ml. $NH_4OH$ (sp. gr. 0.90) and the solution diluted to 2500 ml. The solution is of such strength that 50 ml. will precipitate approximately 0.175 g. sulfur evolved as $H_2S$. This is equivalent to about 3.5% sulfur on a 5 g. sample.

*Neutral Solution.*—To be used where titration with caustic is desired. Seventy grams of $CdSO_4$ are dissolved in water and made up to 2500 ml. The solution should be neutral to methyl orange, otherwise add the requisite amount of $H_2SO_4$ or NaOH necessary, determined by titration of an aliquot portion.

**Hydrochloric Acid (1:1).**—One part concentrated acid to an equal volume of distilled water.

**Sulfuric Acid (1:4).**—One volume of concentrated acid to four volumes of distilled water.

**Reducing Mixture for Reduction of Sulfates.**—Five parts of $NaHCO_3$, 2 parts of C.P. aluminum powder and 1 part of pure carbon, best made by charring starch. A blank should be determined on this material and allowance made accordingly.

**Stannous Chloride.**—Ten per cent solution.

**Fine Granular Aluminum or Zinc Metal.**—Sulfur free, 20-mesh.

*Apparatus.*—The apparatus shown in the illustration, Fig. 44-7, is a useful apparatus for determining sulfur in iron and steel. This consists of an Erlenmeyer flask $A$ of about 500-ml. capacity with large base. With material in which violent foaming occurs, during the evolution of hydrogen sulfide, it is advisable to use a wash bottle with large base, in preference to an Erlenmeyer flask. Through a rubber stopper is inserted a thistle tube with glass stopcock $D$, by which the acid is introduced into the flask. The hydrogen sulfide passes through a potash connecting bulb with trap as shown. A hole blown in the side of the tube prevents liquid being swept through. Connected to the potash bulb is the absorption bulb $C$, which is suspended by a wire attached to the thistle tube. The apparatus is compact, so that on a large hot plate, 30 by 20 ins., a dozen outfits may readily be accommodated. With the use of this apparatus over 75 determinations of sulfur in steel may be made in an ordinary day's run.

*Preparation and Amount of Sample.*—The amount of material to be taken for the determination depends upon the sulfur content as shown by the following table:

|  | Amount to |
| :---: | :---: |
| *Approximate % of sulfur present* | *take for analysis* |
| 0.01 to 1 . . . . . . . . . . . . . . . . | 5      grams |
| 1.0  to 10 . . . . . . . . . . . . . . . . | 1 |
| 10.00 to 30 . . . . . . . . . . . . . . . . | 0.5 |
| Above 30 . . . . . . . . . . . . . . . . | 0.25 |

The class of material will govern the method of procedure.

**Iron and Steel.**—A 5-g. sample of drillings or finely divided material is treated directly in the evolution flask with hydrochloric acid (1:1) and the hydrogen sulfide absorbed in ammoniacal cadmium chloride. The sulfide formed is titrated with iodine.

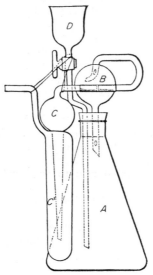

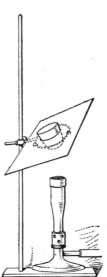

Flame.

FIG. 44-7. Apparatus for Determining Sulfur in Iron and Steel.

FIG. 44-8. Arrangement for Protecting Crucible from the

**Iron Ore Briquettes and Materials Containing Sulfates.  Low Sulfur.**—A 5-g. sample is intimately mixed with an equal weight of reducing mixture ($NaHCO_3$ + Al + C) and wrapped in a 9-cm. ashless filter. The charge is placed in a 50-ml. nickel crucible with cover. The crucible is inserted half way into an asbestos board or perforated silicate plate (see Fig. 44-8) and after covering, placed over a low flame of a Meker blast burner. The flame of the blast is gradually increased during the first five minutes and the charge blasted for about twenty minutes. The crucible will appear a bright red and carbon monoxide gas escaping from under the crucible lid will burn. The loss of sulfur, however, is not appreciable. The crucible is cooled without removing the cover. When cold, the fused mass is quickly pulverized and placed in the dry evolution flask containing a mat of aluminum granules or C.P. zinc dust or granulated tin. Hydrogen sulfide is best evolved with hydrochloric acid to which 4 or 5 ml. of 10% stannous chloride has been added to reduce ferric iron. The gas is absorbed in ammoniacal cadmium chloride and the cadmium sulfide formed titrated with iodine.

**Iron Sulfide for Available H₂S.**—Since this product runs over 20% available hydrogen sulfide not over 0.5-g. sample should be taken. The $H_2S$ is evolved by addition of dilute sulfuric acid (1:4) in place of hydrochloric acid, and is absorbed by neutral cadmium sulfate. The acid formed by the reaction is titrated by standard 0.1 $N$ NaOH.

**Sodium Sulfide or Water-Soluble Sulfides for Available H₂S.**—Ten grams dissolved in water and diluted to 1000 ml.; 50 ml. = (0.5 g.) taken for analysis.

*Procedure.* **Evolution of Hydrogen Sulfide.**—One-half to 1 gram of aluminum or zinc granules, 20-mesh, is placed over the bottom of the evolution flask and the sample placed above this mat of metal. The stopper with the thistle tube and condenser is inserted snugly into the neck of the flask. An absorption bulb containing about 20 ml. of distilled water is attached to the condenser. This bulb serves as a trap for the HCl that is driven out of the flask during the boiling. To this bulb is attached a second bulb containing 50 ml. of ammoniacal cadmium chloride. A third bulb may be attached if the sulfur content of the material examined is high; this, however, is seldom necessary when ammoniacal cadmium chloride is used. The rubber stopper and all rubber connections being air tight, 100 ml. of warm HCl (1:1) is poured into the flask through the thistle tube, the stem of which should now dip well below the acid. The stopcock is closed during the violent action of the acid on the sample and opened when this has subsided. The acid trap prevents loss of H₂S through the thistle tube. The apparatus is now placed on the hot plate and the sample boiled vigorously for about twenty minutes. The flask is taken off the hot plate and the contents allowed to cool. At this stage it may be advisable to draw a current of air through the apparatus to sweep out any residual H₂S that may remain in the flask. Hydrogen gas is preferable to air.

**Titration.**—The contents of the bulbs are poured into a 600-ml. beaker containing about 400 ml. of distilled water. The bulbs are washed out first with water and then with dilute acid. The excess of ammonia is neutralized with concentrated HCl, 5 ml. of starch solution added and the sulfide immediately titrated with standard iodine, additional hydrochloric acid being added from time to time during the titration to insure complete decomposition of the sulfide. The liquid appears yellowish red, orange, purplish red, and finally a deep blue. Since the sulfide, when present in appreciable quantity, decomposes slowly, the solution should be strongly acid at the completion of the titration, and five minutes should be allowed for a permanent end point.

Knowing the amount of iodine necessary, a check run may be made by adding to the neutral solution an excess of iodine followed by 5 ml. of starch solution and a large excess of concentrated hydrochloric acid. The excess of iodine is titrated with 0.1 $N$ thiosulfate, $Na_2S_2O_3$, solution. (Arsenious acid will not do.) This procedure will prevent the loss of H₂S, which is apt to occur in samples high in sulfide.

**Alternate Titration Procedure.**—This is frequently advisable in high sulfurs. The precipitate is separated from the solution containing ammonia by filtration. The cadmium sulfide is now placed in the 600-ml. beaker with water and an excess of iodine run in. Starch is added, followed by hydrochloric acid. The excess of iodine is titrated with sodium thiosulfate, $Na_2S_2O_3$. By this method the heat action during the neutralization of ammonia is avoided and only the precipitate is titrated.

When the iodine titration exceeds 50 ml. of 0.1 $N$ iodine, a smaller amount of the sample should be taken for analysis; the iodine titration for amounts of sulfur exceeding 0.1 g. is not satisfactory, owing to a fading end point. The method for determining available hydrogen sulfide in high sulfide products, dealing with the titration of the free acid formed during the reaction, permits larger samples being taken.

One ml. 0.1 $N$ iodine = 0.001603 gram S.

*Tenth Normal Equivalents*

One ml. of 0.1 $N$ iodine = 0.001704 gram $H_2S$
"                  "              = 0.004396 gram FeS
"                  "              = 0.003902 gram $Na_2S$
"                  "              = 0.003607 gram CaS
"                  "              = 0.008470 gram BaS
"                  "              = 0.005662 gram $Sb_2S_3$
"                  "              = 0.011963 gram PbS
"                  "              = 0.011633 gram HgS
"                  "              = 0.004780 gram CuS
"                  "              = 0.007223 gram CdS
"                  "              = 0.004872 gram ZnS
"                  "              = 0.003269 gram Zn

NOTE.—M. H. Steinmetz [22] makes use of a condenser so that all the hydrochloric acid and water vapors are returned to the flask while the non-condensable hydrogen sulfide passes over freely. In the final operation when the temperature is raised to produce boiling, no extra attention is necessary, thus simplifying the operation.

The condenser is connected to a Johnson sulfur flask by means of a sulfur-free rubber stopper. Connections are made to the condenser for the water circulation and also for the hydrogen sulfide gas, which is absorbed in a beaker containing the ammoniacal cadmium chloride solution. The test is started by adding 75 ml. hydrochloric (1:1) acid through the thistle tube. As soon as the violent action has ceased, heat may be applied rapidly until the sample is dissolved and the solution boils. The hydrogen sulfide gas evolved passes between the condenser walls and the tube delivering the acid into the flask.

## COMBUSTION METHOD FOR EVALUATION OF SULFIDE ORES

When a sulfide ore (pyrrhotite) is heated to redness in presence of oxygen both sulfur dioxide and trioxide are evolved. The first may be absorbed in suitable reagents and estimated titrimetrically or gravimetrically. The trioxide mist is best retained by asbestos and weighed. The combustion furnace with silica tube used for determinations of carbon is adapted for sulfide ores.

*Procedure.*—The finely powdered dry sample, spread in a thin layer in a 3-inch porcelain boat, is placed in the red hot tube and burned in a current of oxygen, which has been purified by passing through sodium hydroxide, concentrated sulfuric acid, and phosphorus pentoxide. The trioxide mist is removed by passing the evolved gases through an asbestos filter ($P_2O_5$ bulb with asbestos in one arm adjacent to the combustion tube and $P_2O_5$ in the other). The $SO_2$ is absorbed in a mixture of bromine and nitric acid, and the sulfuric acid formed is titrated after removing the reagent by evaporation; or it is absorbed in an excess of standard iodine, the excess titrated with sodium arsenite or thiosulfate, and sulfur calculated. The iodine method is preferable to the bromine, as it is more rapid and the reagent less disagreeable to handle. The gravimetric method is the most reliable. The dioxide is absorbed in chromic acid and weighed (caustic will not give correct results owing to its affinity for carbon dioxide, a product of combustion of the free and combined carbon, that are generally present in sulfide ores; pyrrhotite frequently contains as much as 1% carbon). The combustion method cannot be recommended for extreme accuracy. The procedure may be used for the estimation of available sulfur, but does not give the total sulfur of the ore, since 0.2 to 0.5% remains in the cinder. Error may result from the following causes: (1) Incomplete combustion of the sulfur—due to sublimation of the sulfur to cooler zones of the combustion tube, and to a fine mist of sulfur passing unburned into the asbestos, where it is retained with $SO_3$ and weighed as such. (2) Error due to combined water of the ore. The results are apt to be 0.05 to 0.5% lower than those obtained by the barium sulfate procedures, the sulfur of the cinder being included with the available sulfur.

NOTES AND PRECAUTIONS.—Although barium sulfate is only slightly soluble in water, it is appreciably soluble in the salts of the alkalies (Na, K, and $NH_4$), and in a large excess of hydrochloric acid.

Barium sulfate occludes salts, especially nitrates and chlorides. Ferric chloride is carried down with this precipitate, though ferrous chloride is not; hence the reduction of iron is necessary. Occlusion of iron causes low results, as will be seen from the fact that with heating of $Fe_2(SO_4)_3$, $SO_3$ is volatilized, the salt decomposing to $Fe_2O_3 + SO_3$. With the iron reduced the precipitate burns perfectly white, whereas with ferric iron present the precipitate is invariably red or yellow. Aluminum powder used by W. H. Seamon,[23] for reduction of iron in determination of sulfur, suggested its value in the method above given.

Potassium bromide is added to the bromine mix as a diluent to prevent too vigorous a reaction. Cooling the solution is for the same purpose as a loss of sulfur will result if the reaction is violent. This is especially the case in pyrrhotite ore.

Otto Folin[24] shows that precipitation of $BaSO_4$ in a large volume of cold solution produces large crystals.

Mechanical loss and reduction of $BaSO_4$ is avoided by the Gooch crucible.

Allen and Johnston have shown that the solubility of $BaSO_4$ varies directly with the acidity and the amount of wash water used.[25]

There is also a tendency of co-precipitation of $BaCl_2$ with $BaSO_4$. This is greater when the sulfate is poured into the chloride than when the $BaCl_2$ is poured into the sulfate. The co-precipitation varies directly with the acidity, concentration of the $SO_4$ radical and rapidity of precipitation.

Potassium will contaminate the precipitate to a greater extent than will sodium.

## DETERMINATION OF SULFATE IN CHROMIUM PLATING BATHS [26]

The chromic acid must be reduced to a chromic salt. Acetic acid is added to displace sulfate from its combination in the form of complex chromium ions.

23 Chemical Engineer, September, 1908.
24 Journal of Biological Chem., 1, 131–159, 1905.
25 Allen, E. T., and Johnston, J., J. Am. Chem. Soc., 32, 588, 1910.
26 Willard and Schneidewind, Trans. Electro-Chem. Soc., 46, 333–349, 1929.

Either alcohol, hydroxylamine hydrochloride, or concentrated hydrogen peroxide may be used as a reducing agent.

*Procedure.*—To 20 ml. of a 20 to 25% solution of chromic acid or 10 ml. of a 40% solution, diluted and filtered if necessary, add 15 to 20 ml. water, 7 ml. concentrated HCl, 25 ml. glacial acetic acid, 15 ml. alcohol and boil gently for 10 to 15 minutes (methyl alcohol may need a longer time). The solution should have a deep bluish-green color free from brown or yellow tints, unless iron is present.

Dilute to 150 ml., heat to boiling, precipitate by the slow addition of 6 to 8 ml. of 10% $BaCl_2$, let stand hot at least one hour, filter, wash with water containing 1 ml. of concentrated HCl per 100 ml. to remove chromium salts, then with pure water ignite and weigh as $BaSO_4$. It should be white or at most faintly greenish. If yellowish it indicates contamination with $BaCrO_4$, due to incomplete reduction, or perhaps the presence of iron.

## EVALUATION OF SPENT OXIDE FOR AVAILABLE SULFUR

Spent oxide is the by-product of gas works, and refers to the spent $Fe_2O_3$ used in the scrubber for the removal of hydrogen sulfide from the gas. The FeS, as in case of pyrites, is used in the manufacture of sulfuric acid, and is evaluated by its available sulfur content.

### TOTAL SULFUR

The oxide is sampled, brought into solution and the sulfur determined exactly as is given under the standard method for determination of sulfur in pyrites ore.

### RESIDUAL SULFUR

Two grams of the material are ignited to expel volatile sulfur, a porcelain crucible being used. The residue is treated with concentrated hydrochloric acid and after digestion on the steam or water bath is diluted with water and filtered. (If $SiO_2$ is present evaporation to dryness is necessary.) Sulfur is determined in the filtrate as usual.

### AVAILABLE SULFUR

The per cent of residual sulfur is subtracted from the per cent total sulfur, the difference being available sulfur.

### IRON

This may be determined on an ignited sample according to a standard procedure for iron. See Chapter on Iron.

## ANALYSIS OF SULFUR [27]

### SAMPLING

In the sampling of bulk or solid sulfur, the amount of sulfur to be taken depends more upon the size of the individual lumps than upon the size of the shipment or stockpile. Care must be taken to obtain a representative sample with

[27] Based on material from "Analysis of Sulfur," Texas Gulf Sulphur Co. and Freeport Sulphur Handbook, contributed by Mr. James R. West, Texas Gulf Sulphur Co., and Mr. P. T. Comiskey, Freeport Sulphur Co.; method for determination of sulfur is T616 M-59 of Technical Association of Pulp and Paper Industry.

approximately the same proportion of lumps to fines as in the shipment. The sample may be collected in a covered can. Samples from rail, barge, or vessel shipments are best taken during the loading or unloading operations. Often, the samples can be taken from a conveyor belt.

Sample package shipments with a trier, from at least 10% of the packages. Sample bulk shipments preferably at regular intervals from the conveyor while the car is being unloaded. If this is not possible, take approximately equal portions from all parts of the car or other carrier, preferably at different depths to give a fair average of the whole cargo. Crush, mix and quarter the total sample down to a convenient size for the laboratory (about 1 quart). Before the last quartering, if necessary grind the final sample to pass a No. 10 screen so that all particles will pass. Preserve the sample in an airtight container.

In the sampling of liquid sulfur either from transport equipment or from storage, a suitable quantity may, from time to time, be withdrawn from either the discharge or the loading line. A heavy glazed china or heat-resistant glass container with sides tapering outward from bottom to top is preferred for the individual samples comprising the total sample, for the sulfur contracts slightly upon cooling and may then be shaken from the "mold."

If the sample is taken to the laboratory immediately upon collection, no precautions need be observed other than excluding dust and moisture. However, if a delay is anticipated in submitting the sample to the laboratory, it should be placed in a sealed container.

In the laboratory, the gross sample is processed by passing it through a jaw crusher set at ½". The crushed sample is then split on a Jones splitter to yield a sample which will fill a quart mason jar. The jar is securely sealed with a cover and is taken to another laboratory sample room, where it is first processed through a Braun WC 18 chipmunk crusher set at ¼" and then split into two equal parts:

1. The first portion is returned to the jar and the cover screwed in place. This is used for determining moisture.

2. The second portion is ground with a stainless steel muller on a stainless steel buck board to minus 10 mesh. After thorough mixing, this portion is placed in a large sample envelope for use in determining ash, carbon, acid, and, when necessary, arsenic, selenium and tellurium, and water-soluble chloride.

NOTES.— 1. Samples from molten sulfur shipments are brought to the laboratory as small sulfur castings. These samples are first crushed on the Braun WC 18 crusher, then cut on the Jones splitter, and finally ground to minus 10-mesh as above. Moisture tests are not run on molten sulfur shipments as they are free of moisture.

2. Filtered, compressed air is used to clean all sample equipment.

3. Equipment which will rust or otherwise contaminate the sample must be carefully excluded from all sample preparation techniques.

## DETERMINATION OF SULFUR

*Apparatus.*—**Extraction Apparatus,** Underwriters' Laboratory type. An extraction thimble with a fritted glass disk having a fine porosity is preferable.

*Reagents.* **Carbon Disulfide.**—$CS_2$, Reagent Grade.

**Barium Chloride.**—10% $BaCl_2$ solution, Reagent Grade.

**Sulfur Dioxide.**—$SO_2$ gas.

**Starch-Iodide Paper.**

**Nitric Acid, Concentrated.**

**Sodium Chloride, Solid.**

**Hydrochloric Acid, Concentrated.**
**Hydrochloric Acid, 1:1.**
**Sodium Carbonate.**
**Sodium Nitrate.**
**Liquid Bromine.**

For ordinary routine work Procedure 1 is sufficiently accurate. For very accurate determinations use Procedure 2.

*Procedure 1.*—Weigh a 1-g. specimen in the fritted glass extraction thimble and extract in the extraction apparatus for at least 15 minutes with carbon disulfide. Remove the container, dry and weigh. Report the percentage of insoluble residue as foreign matter. (This includes the ash.) Report the percentage of sulfur as the difference between 100 and the percentage of foreign matter to the nearest 0.1%.

NOTE.—Organic impurities may dissolve in the $CS_2$, causing a slight inaccuracy.

*Procedure 2.*—Weigh a 0.5-g. specimen into a 250-ml. porcelain dish, warm to 30°C. and add about 6 ml. of bromine. Keep the mixture at this temperature for about 10 minutes then add 15 ml. of concentrated $HNO_3$ previously brought to 30°C. After the violent reaction has subsided, heat the mixture, cautiously at first, then boil to drive off the $HNO_3$. Add about 0.5 g. of NaCl to avoid loss of $H_2SO_4$ and evaporate the mixture to a small volume. Repeat the evaporation three or four times, adding after each evaporation about 5 ml. of concentrated HCl. Evaporate to dryness on the steam bath and heat the residue gently. Take up this residue with 5 ml. of HCl (1:1) and about 100 ml. of water, filter out the insoluble matter and wash thoroughly on the filter paper with hot water. (This may be ignited and weighed, if the amount of insoluble matter is desired.)

Transfer the filtrate to a 500-ml. volumetric flask, dilute to the mark and thoroughly mix. Pipette a 100-ml. aliquot into a beaker, heat to boiling and add 10 ml. of 10% $BaCl_2$ solution drop by drop to the boiling solution with constant stirring. Stir the solution thoroughly, preferably let it stand overnight and filter through an ignited and weighed Gooch crucible with asbestos mat, wash with boiling water, dry, ignite at 700–750°C. and weigh as $BaSO_4$. Calculate to the percentage of sulfur to the nearest 0.01%, correcting for the aliquoting of the solution.

**Calculation.**—

$$\text{Weight of BaSO}_4 \times 0.1374 = \text{Weight of S in sample}$$

## MOISTURE

*Procedure.*—Weigh 50 g. of the undried prepared laboratory sample into a previously dried, cooled, and weighed 100- by 15-mm. Petri dish. Place in an oven at 105°C. for 1 hour. Then remove, cool in a desiccator, and weigh

**Calculation.**—

$$\% \text{ moisture} = \frac{\text{sample wt.} - \text{dried wt.}}{\text{sample wt.}} \times 100$$

NOTES.—1. This dried sample may be used for the ash, elemental sulfur, combined sulfur, arsenic, and selenium determinations. However, since approximately 100 g. of dried sulfur will be required for all of these determinations, it is suggested that the moisture determination be made in duplicate.

2. Avoid prolonged drying or overheating, since vaporization of the sulfur will cause the moisture estimate to be too high. It is advisable to place the dish in the top portion of the oven on two small pieces of insulating material, such as ¼-in. asbestos board, so that there will be an air space between the bottom of the dish and the shelf of the oven, to avoid localized overheating.

3. The moisture determination may be run at 80°C. overnight (16 hr.) if more convenient.

4. Some sulfurs of high hydrocarbon content may contain an appreciable amount of hydrocarbon which is volatile at the 105°C. temperature used to determine moisture. The determination of carbon in sulfur as described below is made on an undried sample which avoids loss of this volatile carbon. The error introduced by dividing by $\left(1 - \dfrac{\%\ \text{moisture}}{100}\right)$ to convert to the dry basis is negligible since the volatile hydrocarbon is usually only a few tenths of one per cent.

The amount of hydrocarbon volatilized in the moisture determination may be estimated by analyzing the dried, as well as the undried, sample for carbon. The difference obtained in the two carbon contents is the carbon lost by volatilization, and, when multiplied by the factor 1.17, is the hydrocarbon ($CH_2$) volatilized. This loss of $CH_2$ may be subtracted from the value obtained in the moisture determination to obtain a corrected moisture content. It is advisable to make this correction when sulfur of high carbon content is analyzed, if a very accurate determination of moisture content is necessary.

## ASH

**Procedure.**—Weigh 25 g. of the dried sulfur into a previously ignited, cooled, and weighed Coors No. 1 high-form porcelain crucible and place on a hot plate. Control the hot plate so that the sulfur burns slowly but completely. After the sulfur has burned off completely, ignite in a muffle furnace at 800°C., cool in a desiccator, and weigh. Repeat the ignition until the weight is constant. One 30-minute ignition is usually sufficient.

**Calculation.**—

$$\%\ \text{ash} = \frac{\text{residue wt.}}{\text{sample wt.}} \times 100$$

## ACIDITY AND CHLORIDE

**Procedure for Acidity.**—Weigh 20 g. of the undried sample, which has been ground to pass a 60-mesh sieve, into a 250-ml. flask. Add 25 ml. normal propyl alcohol and shake until the sulfur is completely wetted by the alcohol. Then add 50 ml. of distilled water, shake for 1 to 2 minutes more, and allow to stand for 20 minutes with occasional shaking. Titrate with 0.025 N standard sodium hydroxide solution, using phenolphthalein as the indicator, until a slight pink coloration is obtained. Similarly titrate a mixture of 25 ml. of alcohol and 50 ml. of distilled water as a blank.

**Calculation.**—

$$\%\ H_2SO_4 = \frac{\text{ml. solution titration} - \text{ml. blank titration}}{\text{grams sample}} \times \text{normality} \times 4.904$$

NOTES.—1. An alcohol-water mixture wets the sulfur more thoroughly than does water alone. Ethyl, water-white denatured, methyl, or isopropyl alcohol may be substituted for the normal propyl alcohol specified. Commercial wetting agents are generally not sufficiently neutral and unbuffered to be satisfactory.

2. If the sample contains appreciable soluble iron, ferric hydroxide will precipitate before the phenolphthalein end point is reached. In this case repeat, substituting methyl orange as the indicator.

After determining acidity, the same neutralized sample can be used for determining chloride.

*Procedure for Chloride.*—An important point to remember in titrating chloride is that the solution must be neutral or very slightly alkaline. Acidity tends to prevent the formation of $Ag_2CrO_4$ which is the indicator. Also if, as in rare cases, the sulfur should yield $H_2S$ to the solution, it must be removed by making the solution acid to methyl orange and boiling off the $H_2S$. Neutralization can then be performed on the cooled solution.

Water soluble chloride is generally run on the same 50-ml. extraction (representing 50 g. of sample) on which acid was titrated. After the acid titration is made, add 0.5 ml. of $K_2CrO_4$ indicator and titrate with $AgNO_3$ solution (1 ml. = 0.0005 g. Cl) to the red brown end point. A blank must be run on the distilled water used.

**Calculation.**—

$$\% \text{ Cl} = \frac{(\text{ml. titration} - \text{ml. blank})\ 0.0005(100)}{\text{ml. in sample}}$$

$$\% \text{ Cl} = 0.001\ (\text{ml. titration} - \text{ml. blank})$$

$$\% \text{ NaCl} = 0.00165\ (\text{ml. titration} - \text{ml. blank})$$

## SELENIUM, TELLURIUM, AND ARSENIC

*Reagents.* **Standard Selenium.**—Dissolve 1 g. of pure selenium in strong nitric acid. Evaporate to dryness. Add water and repeat evaporation two or three times to assure complete removal of nitric acid. Dilute to 1 liter with water, 1 ml. = 1 mg. of Se. Dilute this solution 10 ml. to 1 liter with water for a solution in which 1 ml. = 0.01 mg. of Se.

**Standard Tellurium.**—Dissolve 1 g. of pure tellurium in nitric acid. Add 50 ml. of sulfuric acid and evaporate to fumes. Dilute in a 1-liter volumetric flask with water. 1 ml. = 1 mg. of Te. Dilute this solution 10 ml. to 1 liter with water for a solution in which 1 ml. = 0.01 mg. of Te.

**Standard Arsenic.**—Dissolve 1.32 g. of $As_2O_3$ in 25 ml. of 20% NaOH in a 1000-ml. volumetric flask keeping the solution cool, neutralize with dilute $H_2SO_4$, and make to the mark with 1% $H_2SO_4$. 1 ml. = 1 mg. of As. Dilute this solution 10 ml. to 1 liter with 10% $H_2SO_4$. 1 ml. = 0.01 mg. of As. A further dilution of 100 ml. of the second solution to 1 liter with 1% $H_2SO_4$ gives a standard in which 1 ml. = 0.001 mg. of As.

**Nitric Acid.**—C.P. analyzed arsenic less than 0.000001%. Sp. gr. 1.42.

**Sulfuric Acid.**—C.P. analyzed arsenic less than 0.000001%. Sp. gr. 1.84.

**Bromine-Carbon Tetrachloride Mixture.**—Into a 500-ml. bottle empty a 1-lb. container of liquid bromine. Fill the bottle with carbon tetrachloride.

**Hydrazine Sulfate.**—Eastman powder. (#575)

**Stannous Chloride Solution.**—80 g. of $SnCl_2 \cdot 2H_2O$ dissolved in 100 ml. of water to which is added 5 ml. of HCl. Solution is slow.

**Lead Acetate Paper.**—Hard surface filter paper cut into 35-mm. wide strips and saturated with 20% lead acetate and dried.

**5% Lead Acetate Solution.**—12.5 g. of lead acetate dissolved in 250 ml. of water. Add a few drops of acetic acid.

**Ferric Ammonium Alum.**—Dissolve 84 g. of ferric ammonium alum in 1% $H_2SO_4$ in a 1-liter volumetric flask. Dilute to the mark with 1% $H_2SO_4$.

**Zinc Shot.**—Analyzed. Arsenic less than 0.0000001%. Shot should be uniform in size with a minimum of fines. May have to be especially prepared.

**3% $HgBr_2$ Solution.**—Dissolve 3 g. of $HgBr_2$ in 100 ml. of 95% ethanol.

*Procedure for Selenium.*—The final solution from the oxidation of 50 g. of sulfur should produce about 150 g. (80 ml.) of $H_2SO_4$. Dilute this cooled solution with 80 ml. of water and bring to a boil on a hot plate. While boiling, add 0.1 to 0.3 g. of hydrazine sulfate. A pink color indicates the presence of selenium.

A quantitative determination of selenium can be made with Nessler tubes filled with standards of dilute sulfuric acid to which known amounts of selenium have been added. For quantitative determinations, the solutions must be cooled to room temperature because the color is much more pronounced in cooled solutions.

*Procedure for Tellurium.*—If the solution which was tested for selenium shows no color, the solution can be used as such for the determination of tellurium. However, if selenium is present, it must be removed. The red selenium is colloidal but it can be converted to black crystalline selenium by digesting overnight on a water bath, and then filtering off through a medium porosity sintered glass filter. (Corning Glass #32960—30 M)

Bring the solution to a boil and add 0.5 ml. of stannous chloride solution. A gray or black color indicates the presence of tellurium. A quantitative determination of tellurium can be made with Nessler tubes filled with dilute sulfuric acid to which known amounts of tellurium have been added.

*Procedure for Arsenic.*—The solution on which the selenium and tellurium have been determined is rinsed into a 500-ml. volumetric flask and made to volume with distilled water. An aliquot of 100 ml. (representing 10 g. of the original sample) is used for determining arsenic by the Gutzeit Method. (See Chapter on Arsenic.)

The Gutzeit apparatus consists of a 250-ml. flask surmounted by a tower consisting of three sections of scrubbers and a tube in which an $HgBr_2$ strip is inserted. All connections are made with ground joints. Numbering the scrubbers in ascending order, they contain:

No. 1—5% lead acetate solution.
No. 2—Lead acetate paper coiled loosely.
No. 3—Absorbent cotton moistened with 5% lead acetate.

The $HgBr_2$ strip is made from paper specially cut for the Gutzeit test. It is sensitized just before the determination by soaking it in a 3% solution of $HgBr_2$ dissolved in ethyl alcohol and allowing it to dry. It is suspended as close to the center of the tube as possible and placed at the top of the tower. This completes the assembly of the tower.

Prepare an ice tray so that the flask may be set in it as soon as hydrogen starts to evolve.

Empty the 100-ml. aliquot of the original sample into the flask. Add 2 ml. of ferric ammonium alum solution and 1 ml. of stannous chloride solution. Add 15 g. of arsenic-free zinc shot and immediately put the tower in place. Gently rotate the flask to assure a uniform evolution of hydrogen and place the flask in ice water.

Arsenic, if present, will stain the $HgBr_2$ paper brown. The intensity and length of the stain can be compared with standards prepared in sulfuric acid solutions of the same strength containing known amounts of arsenic.

## CARBON BY THE COMBUSTION METHOD

The method consists of completely burning the sulfur and carbon compounds, in a current of pure oxygen, to form sulfur dioxide and carbon dioxide. The sulfur dioxide in this gas mixture is then converted to sulfuric acid and absorbed by chromic acid solution. The gas mixture, now free of sulfur compounds, is dried with Anhydrone which does not absorb carbon dioxide. The carbon dioxide is

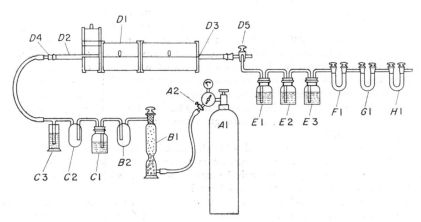

Fig. 44-9. Combustion Train for Determining Carbon in Sulfur.

finally absorbed from the gas mixture by Ascarite. The Ascarite, contained in a glass U-tube, is weighed before and after conducting the combustion, and its gain in weight is a direct measure of the amount of carbon dioxide produced in the combustion, and thus of the amount of carbon burned.

*Apparatus.*—The combustion train (Fig. 44-9), functionally, consists of eight successive systems:

A. The Oxygen Supply and Flow Control System.
B. The Oxygen Purification System.
C. The Oxygen Flow-Indicating and Pressure-Relief System.
D. The Combustion System.
E. The $SO_2$ Absorption System.
F. The Gas Drying System.
G. The $CO_2$ Absorbing and Measuring System.
H. The Gas Discharge System.

A. The oxygen supply and flow control system consists of:
1. A cylinder (*A1*) of oxygen equipped with a pressure-reducing valve.
2. A needle valve (*A2*), at the outlet of the pressure-reducing valve, to control the rate of oxygen flow, followed by a length of rubber tubing that connects it with the oxygen purifying system.

**B. The oxygen purification system consists of:**

1. A glass tower (*B1*) whose lower section is packed with Anhydrone (anhydrous magnesium perchlorate), to dry the oxygen, and whose upper section is packed with Ascarite, to remove any carbon dioxide.

2. A glass trap (*B2*) to insure that sulfuric acid from the following bottle cannot flow back into the Ascarite in tower (*B1*).

**C. The oxygen flow-indicating and pressure-relief system consists successively of:**

1. A 125-ml., low-form Drechsel gas-washing bottle (*C1*) containing concentrated sulfuric acid, to indicate oxygen flow rate by bubble counting.

Longitudinal Section Though Combustion Furnace and Combustion Tube

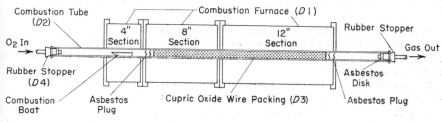

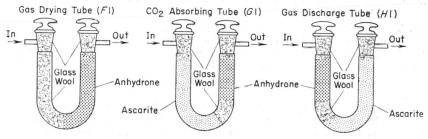

Fig. 44-10.  Combustion System (*D*).

2. A glass trap (*C2*) to insure that no sulfuric acid can be carried further into the system.

3. An excess-pressure-relief valve (*C3*), consisting of a T-tube with its vertical leg immersed about 2 inches into a bottle of mercury.

**D. The combustion system (Fig. 44-10) consists of:**

1. A three-section electric combustion furnace (*D1*), containing, in succession, in the direction of gas flow, a 4-inch, an 8-inch and a 12-inch heating section, each section being equipped with independent means of controlling the power input. Each heating section is divided into a lower and an upper half-section and hinged, to permit it to be opened.  The three sections are placed in contact with one another, with no gaps between.

2. A Corning 172 combustion tube (*D2*), 19 mm. I.D., 25 mm. O.D., 900 mm. long, mounted in the combustion furnace.

3. A 20-in. length of packing (*D3*), consisting of 24-gauge cupric oxide wire, in that portion of the combustion tube that lies within the 8-inch and 12-inch sections of the furnace.  This packing insures oxidation of all carbonaceous matter before it leaves the combustion tube.

4. A rubber stopper (*D4*), in the inlet end of the combustion tube, through which passes a glass tube that is connected, by means of rubber tubing, to the preceding excess-pressure-relief valve. This rubber stopper is removed momentarily from the combustion tube to permit introduction of the sulfur sample.

5. A three-way stopcock (*D5*), one arm of which passes through a rubber stopper which closes the outlet end of the combustion tube. A second arm of the stopcock is connected, by means of rubber tubing to the following unit of the train. The third arm of the stopcock is unconnected. The stopcock permits stopping the flow of gas, directing the flow into the following train, or discharging the gas into the atmosphere.

6. A porcelain combustion boat, size No. 6, in which the sulfur sample is weighed, inserted into the portion of the combustion tube that lies within the 4-in. furnace section, and burned.

**E. The SO$_2$ absorption system consists successively of:**

1. A 125-ml. Drechsel low-form gas-washing bottle (*E1*), containing 50% chromic acid solution, to absorb sulfur dioxide and trioxide in the gas stream by converting them into sulfuric acid.

2. Another 125-ml. Drechsel low-form gas-washing bottle (*E2*), containing 50% chromic acid solution, to supplement the action of bottle (*E1*).

3. A 125-ml. Drechsel low-form gas-washing bottle (*E3*), containing concentrated sulfuric acid, saturated with chromic acid, to absorb any sulfur dioxide and trioxide remaining in the gas stream.

**F. The gas drying system (Fig. 44-10) consists of:**

1. A Schwartz U-tube, 100 mm. long (*F1*), with glass stoppers that, upon rotation, isolate the contents of the tube from the connecting tubes. The inlet half of this tube is packed with glass wool to remove entrained acid. The outlet half is packed with Anhydrone to absorb all moisture from the gas, without absorbing any CO$_2$.

**G. The CO$_2$ absorbing and measuring system (Fig. 44-10) consists of:**

1. A Schwartz U-tube, 100 mm. long (*G1*), with glass stoppers that, upon rotation, isolate the contents of the tube from the connecting tubes. The inlet half and lower bend of this tube is packed with Ascarite to absorb the CO$_2$ contained in the gas. The outlet side of the tube is packed with Anhydrone to absorb and prevent the loss of any moisture that the Ascarite liberates as it absorbs the CO$_2$. A plug of glass wool separates the Ascarite packing from the Anhydrone packing.

**H. The gas discharge system (Fig. 44-10) consists of:**

1. A Schwartz U-tube, 100 mm. long (*H1*), with glass stoppers that, upon rotation, isolate the contents of the tube from the connecting tubes. The inlet half of this tube is packed with Anhydrone to absorb moisture from any air that enters in case of slight backward gas flow in the system. The outlet half of the tube is packed with Ascarite to absorb CO$_2$ from any air that enters in case of backward flow or diffusion. A plug of glass wool separates the Anhydrone packing from the Ascarite packing.

All of the units throughout the train are connected together with the shortest possible pieces of rubber tubing, with the exception of the rubber tubing between the oxygen cylinder (*A1*) and the following tower (*B1*) which is as long as convenient, and the rubber tubing between the excess-pressure-relief valve (*C3*) and the following rubber stopper (*D4*) which is long enough to permit removal and insertion of the stopper in the combustion tube without disturbing the other units.

***Procedure.***—Test for and correct any leaks in the system. Admit oxygen from the cylinder (*A1*) at a rate of about three bubbles per second through the bubble counter (*C1*), by adjustment of the needle valve (*A2*). Turn on the electrical power to the three furnace section (*D1*), and adjust the individual inputs so that the temperature in the portion of the combustion tube within the 4-inch furnace section is 700 to 800°C., and the temperature of the packing, lying within the 8-inch and 12-inch furnace sections is only 500 to 600°C. (just under dull red heat). Allow the oxygen to sweep through the system overnight to drive out all moisture and carbon dioxide. After this flushing, remove the carbon dioxide absorption tube (*G1*), after closing by rotating the stoppers, weigh, and replace in the train. At the end of another hour, again remove the tube (*G1*), weigh and replace. Continue this weighing at hourly intervals until the weight gain during an hour is not over 0.5 mg. Record the final hourly weight gain for later use as a blank correction.

While weighing the sulfur sample in the boat and absorption tube (*G1*), in preparation for an analysis, open the 4-inch furnace section so that that portion of the combustion tube will be relatively cool at the time of introduction of the sample. After weighing the absorption tube (*G1*), weigh a 1-g. sample of the undried prepared laboratory sample into a previously ignited porcelain combustion boat. Place the absorption tube (*G1*) in its proper location in the train. Remove the stopper (*D4*) from the inlet end of the combustion tube, insert the boat with sulfur into the tube (*D2*) to about the middle of the 4-inch furnace section, and replace the stopper (*D4*). Leave the 4-inch furnace section open until the blue flame from the burning of the sulfur expires, to avoid vaporizing unburned sulfur by the application of excessively intense heat. Then close the 4-inch furnace section and allow all of the combustible material in the boat to burn.

During the initial burning of the sulfur, oxygen may be consumed more rapidly than it is being introduced, causing the blue sulfur flame to move upstream in the combustion tube, toward the oxygen inlet. If this occurs, increase the oxygen flow temporarily to keep the flame directly over the combustion boat.

Sometimes, just at the completion of the burning of the sulfur, the solution in the gas washing bottle (*E1*) begins to rise in the inlet tube of the bottle, in imminence of backing into the combustion tube. To correct this condition, close the three-way stopcock (*D5*) completely, and slightly increase the flow of oxygen, with needle valve (*A2*) until the pressure in the combustion system builds up, as evidenced by discharge of a bubble from the excess-pressure-relief valve (*C3*). At this point the three-way stopcock (*D5*) may again be set to permit gas flow into the $SO_2$ absorption system and the rate of oxygen flow may be reduced to normal.

After combustion of the sample is complete, allow the oxygen to pass through the system for another hour to insure complete sweeping of the carbon dioxide into the absorption tube. Then remove the absorption tube (*G1*), after closing by rotating the stoppers, and weigh.

**Calculation.—**

$$\% \text{ Carbon} = \frac{\text{wt. gain from sample} - \text{wt. gain from blank}}{\text{sample wt.} \times \left(1 - \dfrac{\% \text{ moisture}}{100}\right)} \times 27.29$$

NOTES.—1. Reproducible weights of the absorption tube will be obtained if a chamois is used in handling it, avoiding direct contact with the fingers. Occasional cleaning by wiping with the chamois is permissible, but a long period should ensue between wiping and weighing because of the danger of developing an electrical charge that will vitiate the weighing.

2. If the carbon content of the sulfur is under 0.1%, the accuracy of the determination may be improved by using a sulfur sample larger than the 1 g. specified. The analysis of a sample as large as 2.5 g. is feasible.

3. After about twenty combustion determinations, incidental conversion of the cupric oxide packing to cupric sulfate has usually progressed to such a point that sulfur trioxide fumes appear either at the outlet of the combustion tube or in the bottle (EI). The cupric oxide wire packing should be renewed before this condition occurs. If the fumes appear during a determination, discard that determination and repeat after renewing the packing.

4. Replace the solution in bottle (EI) with fresh solution after every four carbon determinations. Replace the solutions in washing bottles (E2) and (E3) and the contents of U-tube (FI), after every twenty carbon determinations.

5. If the sulfur is contaminated with carbonate, the carbon of the carbonate will be included in the organic carbon determination. In such a case, it will be necessary to determine the carbonate separately by a method such as the standard wet evolution method, and to make the appropriate correction in the total carbon determination.

6. The undried sample is used, since drying at 105°C. causes loss of some volatile hydrocarbon if volatile hydrocarbons are present.

## ULTRAMICRODETERMINATION OF SULFIDES IN AIR [28]

Hydrogen sulfide and other sulfides can be determined in the part per billion range in air if the air is bubbled through an absorption mixture of an alkaline suspension of cadmium hydroxide contained in a Greenburg-Smith impinger. Rates as high as 1 cubic foot per minute can be used, or 0.1 cubic foot per minute with a midget impinger. The concentration of the trapped sulfides is then estimated by the methylene blue method, which has the advantage that it can also be used for the determination of traces of sulfide in any material from which they can be evolved as $H_2S$.

*Apparatus.*—**Impinger tube,** 175 ml., as shown in Fig. 44-11.

*Reagents.*—All reagents should be refrigerated for optimum results.

**Amine-Sulfuric Acid Stock Solution.**—Add 50 ml. of concentrated sulfuric acid to 30 ml. of water and cool. Add 12 g. of $N,N$-dimethyl-$p$-phenylenediamine. Stir until solution is complete.

**Amine-Sulfuric Acid Test Solution.**—Dilute 25 ml. of stock solution to 1 liter with 1:1 sulfuric acid.

**Ferric Chloride Solution.**—Dissolve 100 g. of ferric chloride hexahydrate in enough water to make 100 ml. of solution.

Fig. 44-11. Impinger Tube for Absorbing $H_2S$ from Air (Fisher).

**Absorption Mixture.**—Dissolve 4.3 g. of cadmium sulfate, $3CdSO_4 \cdot 8H_2O$, in water. Dissolve 0.3 g. of sodium hydroxide in water. Add to the cadmium solution and dilute to 1 liter. Stir well before using.

*Procedure for low concentrations of hydrogen sulfide* (less than 20 parts per billion), either a colorimetric or spectrophotometric variation may be used.

**Colorimetric.**—Place 50 ml. of absorption mixture in a large impinger and pass air through the apparatus for 30 minutes at the rate of 1 cubic foot per minute. Add 0.6 ml. of amine test solution and 1 drop of ferric chloride solution to the impinger and agitate after each addition. Transfer to a 50-ml. volumetric flask, make up to volume, and allow to stand for 30 minutes. To 45 ml. of absorption mixture in a 50-ml. volumetric flask, add amine test reagent and ferric chloride

[28] Jacobs, Braverman, and Hochheiser, Anal. Chem., **29**, 1349, 1957.

solution, agitate after each addition, make up to volume, let stand for 30 minutes, and use as a reference in setting the apparatus to zero. Read the absorbance of the sample and determine hydrogen sulfide concentration from the working curve.

To calculate hydrogen sulfide, use the following equation.

$$H_2S, \text{ in parts per billion} = \frac{\text{micrograms } H_2S \times 719}{\text{volume in liters}}$$

This calculation is set empirically at 25°C. and 760 mm., using the factor 719. To correct for other conditions of temperature and pressure, the usual gas law equations are used.

**Spectrophotometric.**—A 25-ml. aliquot is taken of both the final sample mixture and the reference blank. The final calculation is multiplied by 2. The readings should be made at 670 m$\mu$.

In both of the above methods, if the concentration of hydrogen sulfide is above the working curve, the solution is diluted to the appropriate range. An analogous dilution must also be performed on the reference reagent blank; the apparatus should be set at zero again with this solution before measuring the absorbance of the diluted sample.

*Procedure for higher concentrations of hydrogen sulfide* (20 parts per billion and above), the midget impinger has been used successfully.

Place 10 ml. of absorption mixture in the midget impinger and aspirate at 0.1 cubic foot per minute through the mixture for about 15 minutes. (The midget impinger apparatus is especially useful in field work.) Add 0.6 ml. of amine test solution and 1 drop of ferric chloride solution, agitate after each addition, and transfer to a 25-ml. volumetric flask for spectrophotometric determination or to a 50-ml. volumetric flask for colorimetric determination. Dilute to the mark and allow to stand for 30 minutes. Repeat the same procedure (without aspiration) for the reference reagent blank, set the apparatus at zero, and read the absorbance of the sample. Refer to the working curves for amount of hydrogen sulfide present and calculate as before.

*Preparation of Standard Curves.*—Because two methods of estimating the amount of methylene blue formed are used, two standard curves must be prepared—one with the Klett-Summerson colorimeter and one with the Coleman spectrophotometer.

**Colorimetric.**—Add 0, 1, 3, 5, 7, and 9 micrograms of hydrogen sulfide separately to 50-ml. volumetric flasks containing 45 ml. of alkaline cadmium hydroxide absorption mixture. Add 0.6 ml. of amine test solution and 1 drop of ferric chloride solution and stir after each addition. Dilute each to 50 ml., allow to stand for 30 minutes, and transfer the first mixture containing no hydrogen sulfide to the colorimeter cell. Insert the red filter, place the cell in position, and adjust the reading to zero. Read the transmittance of the five remaining mixtures. Plot absorbance versus concentration in micrograms.

**Spectrophotometric.**—Add 0, 1, 2, 3, and 4 micrograms of hydrogen sulfide separately to 20 ml. of absorption mixture in 25-ml. volumetric flasks. Add 0.6 ml. of amine test solution and 1 drop of ferric chloride solution. Stir after each addition. Dilute to 25 ml. and allow to stand 30 minutes. Set the instrument at 670 m$\mu$, place the first mixture containing no hydrogen sulfide in a cuvette, test in the reference position, and set the scale at zero. Set the other mixtures in the sample position in increasing order and note the increase in absorbance. Plot absorbance versus concentration of hydrogen sulfide in micrograms.

## METHODS FOR SULFUR IN ANALYSIS IN OTHER CHAPTERS

# Chapter 45

# THALLIUM *

Tl, *at. wt.* 204.37; *sp. gr.* 11.85; *m.p.* 303.5°C.; *b.p.* 1457°C. ± 10°C.; *oxides*, Tl$_2$O, Tl$_2$O$_3$

Thallium occurs in quantity only in a few rare minerals, such as crookesite, (Cu,Tl,Ag)$_2$Se, and lorandite, TlAsS$_2$. It is usually found in small quantities in association with the alkali metals, zinc, iron, and lead, and is obtained from the flue dust formed in the calcination of iron pyrites and lead ores.

The chief use of thallium appears to be in the manufacture of rat and vermin poison, because the metal and its compounds are extremely toxic. It is further used in the preparation of artificial stones and optical glass of very high refracting power.

Thallium forms two series of salts. In thallous salts the metal is monovalent and in thallic trivalent. Thallous sulfate, hydroxide and carbonate are soluble in water, while the cobaltinitrite, chloroplatinate, and perrhenate are only very slightly soluble; all these salts resemble the corresponding potassium compounds. On the other hand, the halides and the chromate have only small solubilities recalling those of the corresponding lead compounds. Thallous sulfide is insoluble in alkaline solution but readily dissolves in acids, even in acetic acid.

Thallic salts are formed by oxidation of thallous salts with chlorine, permanganate, or some other oxidizing agents; they resemble ferric salts in being readily hydrolized, yielding brown basic salts, and giving a brown flocculent precipitate with ammonia; sulfur dioxide reduces them to the thallous state.

## DETECTION

In systematic qualitative analysis, thallium is found in the zinc-nickel group, being precipitated by ammonium sulfide from ammoniacal solution.

The solution to be tested is evaporated with sulfuric acid to eliminate lead, the filtrate saturated with hydrogen sulfide, and the precipitate filtered off. The filtrate is freed from hydrogen sulfide by boiling, and oxidized with nitric acid. Iron, aluminum, the zinc-nickel group, and the alkaline earths are next precipitated by boiling the solution with sodium carbonate, and removed by filtration. The filtrate is treated with ammonium sulfide; if a brown precipitate is formed, it is collected and boiled with a little dilute sulfuric acid, and the cold solution treated with potassium iodide. A yellow crystalline precipitate proves the presence of thallium. The precipitate, tested in the loop of a platinum wire in the

* Chapter by A. R. Powell, Research Manager, Johnson, Matthey & Co., Ltd., Wembley, England.

Bunsen flame, gives a characteristic brilliant green flame which, viewed through the spectroscope, shows a broad green line at 5350.7 A.

## ESTIMATION

### PREPARATION AND SOLUTION OF THE SAMPLE

Practically all the materials containing thallium yield it to treatment with hydrochloric acid, nitric acid, or aqua regia, the solution then being evaporated with sulfuric acid to fumes.  Glasses and artificial stones must, however, be fused with sodium carbonate, the melt extracted with water and acidified with sulfuric acid, and the solution evaporated to fumes.  The cold sulfate mass is dissolved in water and the solution filtered to remove silica and lead sulfate.  The filtrate is boiled with strips of zinc until effervescence ceases and basic salts begin to be precipitated.  Two ml. of 1:1 sulfuric acid are added, and the solution is filtered while a feeble evolution of hydrogen from the zinc is maintained.  The precipitate is collected, washed, digested with hot 20% sulfuric acid, and the solution containing the thallium filtered.

### SEPARATIONS

*General Procedure.*—The sulfate solution, obtained by one of the above methods, is neutralized with sodium carbonate, 5 g. of potassium cyanide and a further 2 g. of sodium carbonate are added, and the mixture is warmed on the water bath. The precipitate is collected and washed with a 1% solution of sodium carbonate. The filtrate contains all the thallium, which is precipitated as thallous sulfide by adding a few milliliters of colorless ammonium sulfide; the precipitate is collected, washed with a very dilute solution of ammonium sulfide and dissolved in a minimum of hot 10% sulfuric acid; the solution is boiled to expel hydrogen sulfide, and the thallium estimated as iodide or chromate (see below).

*Special Procedure.*  **From Ferric Iron, Aluminum, and Chromium.**—The sulfuric acid solution is approximately neutralized with sodium carbonate and stirred with a thin suspension of finely ground zinc oxide until the precipitate flocculates and settles readily.  The precipitate is collected on a Whatman No. 41 paper and washed with hot water.  The filtrate is evaporated to 100 ml. and treated as in the next paragraph to recover the thallium as chromate.

**From Zinc, Cadmium, Nickel, Cobalt.**[1]—The acid solution, warmed to 60°C., is treated with ammonia until the precipitate has redissolved, when a decided excess of ammonia is added.  The thallium is then precipitated as chromate.  (See "Gravimetric Methods.")

### GRAVIMETRIC METHODS

#### DETERMINATION AS CHROMATE

*Procedure.*—This procedure is recommended as the most accurate by Moser and Brukl.[2]  Thallous chromate, $Tl_2CrO_4$, is soluble to the extent of 0.006 g. per liter of solution containing 2% of ammonia, 4% of potassium chromate, and 10% of alcohol.  The acid sulfate solution is made ammoniacal, boiled, and stirred

[1] Moser and Brukl, Monatsh. Chem., **47**, 709, 1926.
[2] Flawky, J. Am. Chem. Soc., **29**, 300, 1907.

during additions of potassium chromate solution, the excess of which should yield an approximately 2% solution. After settling for 12 hours in the cold the yellow precipitate is filtered by decantation on a porous crucible, washed with 1% chromate solution, then with 50% alcohol, dried at 120°C., and weighed. Factor for Tl, 0.77895.

## DETERMINATION AS IODIDE

*Procedure.*—The sulfate solution (less than 100 ml.), if acid, is neutralized with sodium carbonate, and treated at 80°C. with a 10% potassium iodide solution drop by drop until no further precipitate forms; 1 g. of solid iodide is then added in excess. The precipitate is allowed to stand overnight, collected in a porous crucible, washed first with a minimum quantity of cold 1% potassium iodide solution, then with 80% alcohol until the washings cease to react for iodide, dried at 110°C., and weighed. Factor for Tl, 0.6169.

## TITRIMETRIC METHODS

### PERMANGANATE METHOD [2]

Thallous sulfide, obtained as described under "Separations" is dissolved in 4 ml. of hydrochloric acid and a little water. The solution is boiled to expel hydrogen sulfide, cooled, diluted to 60 ml., and titrated with 0.1 $N$ permanganate solution standardized against pure thallous chloride.[3]

### IODIMETRIC METHOD [4]

Small amounts of thallium are estimated by the liberation of iodine from thallic chloride, $TlCl_3$, by the addition of potassium iodide, with the formation of thallous iodide, $TlI$, and free iodine which is subsequently titrated by standard sodium thiosulfate solution. An ether extraction step is added for many materials, including organic substances.

*Procedure.*—Destroy organic matter with concentrated hydrochloric acid and potassium chlorate, or with 4 $N$ hydrochloric acid and potassium chlorate, using 0.1 $N$ potassium permanganate solution as a catalyst, or with nitric and sulfuric acids in the usual manner. In the latter instance it is necessary to add some free chlorine as, for instance, by use of a heated solution of potassium chlorate in 4 $N$ hydrochloric acid.

Transfer the sample containing free chlorine to a Jacobs-Singer separatory flask (see Fig. 26-3, p. 582). Check the reaction with starch-iodide paper. Add an equal volume of ether. Shake vigorously, allow the layers to separate, and draw off the ether layer into a separatory funnel. Add 1 to 2 ml. of sulfur dioxide water to the ether layer and shake vigorously, until the aqueous layer no longer reacts with starch-iodide paper. Adjust the volume of the aqueous layer to about 15 ml. and draw off into an evaporating dish. Shake out the ether layer with 2 ml. of water and add this washing to the evaporating dish. Repeat the extraction of the sample an additional two times with ether. Extract the second and third ether extractions successively with sulfur dioxide water and water. Add each aqueous extract and wash to the evaporating dish, making a total of six additions.

[3] Ceric sulfate may be used in the titration. For 0.1–0.3 g. Tl the solution should contain 10–30 ml. HCl and be titrated at 50°; ICl may be used as catalyst. Willard and Young, J. Am. Chem. Soc., **52**, 36, 1930. See Appendix on Standard Solutions.
[4] Jacobs, Chemical Analysis of Food and Food Products, 3rd Ed., 1958, Van Nostrand.

Evaporate the combined aqueous sulfur dioxide extracts on a steam bath in a hood. Transfer, with the aid of a glass rod and a few drops of nitric acid, to a 50 x 18-mm. Pyrex glass tube, add 0.2 ml. of concentrated sulfuric acid, and digest in the customary manner. Wash the evaporating dish with drops of nitric acid adding the washing to the digestion tube. The digestion may be considered complete when the sulfuric acid remains colorless or a light yellow.

Add 0.8 ml. of water, mix, cool, and filter with suction through a micro filter of sintered glass into precipitation tube 40 x 10 mm. Adjust the volume to 1.8 ml., add 0.1 ml. of a freshly prepared saturated solution of sodium sulfite, $Na_2SO_3 \cdot 7H_2O$, and mix with a glass rod. Add 0.2 ml. of 10% potassium iodide solution and mix. An orange-yellow precipitate indicates thallium. Rinse off the rod and allow the covered tube to stand for 12 to 18 hours in the dark. Centrifuge at 1500 rpm. for 5 minutes, pour off the supernatant liquid with the aid of a glass rod, and wash the precipitate with 2 ml. of 50% alcohol, stirring the precipitate with the rod, which is rinsed off with a few drops of alcohol. Centrifuge and decant. Wash again with 2 ml. of 90% alcohol. At this point the precipitate may be estimated gravimetrically by the usual micro-gravimetric methods, the factor Tl/TlI being 0.6160.

Dry the tube. In the range of 10 to 25 micrograms of thallium add 0.1 ml. of glacial acetic acid and a small drop of bromine. Shake for a moment every 5 minutes until no solid particles are visible and allow to stand an additional 15 minutes. Transfer the contents of the tube to a 25-ml. flask with not more than 2 ml. of water. Heat until the mixture is light yellow, allow to cool, add 2 $M$ sodium formate solution, prepared by dissolving 24.2 g. of sodium formate, $HCOONa \cdot 3H_2O$, in water and diluting to 100 ml., until the solution is colorless, and then add an excess of 0.2 ml. Mix carefully and moisten the walls of the flask. Allow to stand 5 minutes. Add 2 ml. of 30% sodium chloride solution, 1 drop of 10% potassium iodide solution, 0.2 ml. of 4 $N$ sulfuric acid, and 5 drops of 0.2% starch-indicator solution. Titrate with 0.01 $N$ sodium thiosulfate solution.

Comparison solutions of thallium must be standardized because many salts are of dubious purity. Dissolve 131 mg. of thallous carbonate, $Tl_2CO_3$, or an equivalent amount of another salt in water and dilute to 100 ml. This is approximately 1 mg. of thallium per ml. Transfer 1 ml. of this solution to a 100-ml. flask, add 10 ml. of water, 0.3 ml. of glacial acetic acid, and sufficient bromine water to give a yellow color and 2 drops in excess. Allow to stand for 15 minutes, and remove the excess bromine with 2 $M$ sodium formate solution. Allow to stand an additional 5 minutes, add 20 ml. of 30% sodium chloride solution, 0.5 ml. of 10% potassium iodide solution, 1 ml. of 4 $N$ sulfuric acid solution, 2 ml. of 0.2% starch-indicator solution, and titrate with 0.01 $N$ sodium thiosulfate solution. One milliliter of the latter is equivalent to 1.022 mg. of thallium.

Lead, mercury, copper, arsenic, antimony, bismuth, and iron do not interfere in this method.

## COLORIMETRIC/PHOTOMETRIC METHODS

This method [5] has been developed for the determination of thallium in air and in urine, but is generally applicable to solutions free from interfering metals. It

[5] Campbell, Milligan and Lindsay, Amer. Indus. Hygiene J., **20**, 23, 1959.

s based upon the absorptivity of the methyl violet complex at 585 m$\mu$, in a suitable spectrophotometer.

Any thallous ions present are oxidized by bromine to the thallic state, the thallic ions then form tetrabromothallate anions, which combine with the methyl violet (designated by $R_3N$ in the equations below) to form the colored complex:

$$Tl^+ + Br_2 \rightarrow Tl^{+3} + 2Br^-$$

$$Tl^{+3} + 4Br^- \rightarrow TlBr_4^-$$

$$TlBr_4^- + R_3NH^+ \rightarrow R_3NHTlBr_4$$

*Reagents.*—Sulfuric Acid, Concentrated.

**Sulfuric Acid, 0.5 N.**

**Nitric Acid, Concentrated.**

**Hydrobromic Acid, Concentrated (47%).**—The bromine usually present is not removed.

**Hydrobromic Acid, Dilute.**—Dilute 1 part of the concentrated acid with 10 parts of water.

**Bromine Water, Saturated.**

**Perchloric Acid, 72–74%.**

*n*-**Octyl Alcohol.**

*n*-**Amyl Acetate.**

**Methyl Violet Stock Solution.**—Dissolve 0.1 g. of methyl violet (Eastman Kodak Co. #1309 if available) in 100 ml. of water.

**Methyl Violet Working Solution.**—Just prior to use, dilute 5 ml. of the stock solution with 1 ml. of 0.5 N sulfuric acid and 4 ml. of water.

**Thallium Standard Solution.**—Weigh out 1.303 g. of thallium nitrate (TlNO$_3$), place in a 1-liter volumetric flask, and dilute to volume with 0.5 N sulfuric acid. By serial dilution prepare a diluted thallium solution so that 1 ml. = 1 microgram of thallium. (A fresh dilute solution should be prepared every two or three days.)

**Sulfuric-Nitric Acid Digestion Mixture (1:9).**—Add one volume of sulfuric acid to nine volumes of nitric acid.

**Perchloric-Nitric Digestion Mixture (1:8).**—To eight volumes of nitric add one volume of sulfuric acid and one volume of perchloric acid.

**Boiling Chips.**—Carborundum Brand, Silicon Carbide Grain, 20 grit.

*Procedure.* **Digestion of Filter Paper Samples from Air.**—Thallium is sampled in air by passing a sufficient sample of air through 1⅛″ or 2⅛″ filter papers. (For apparatus, see Chapter on Beryllium for "Zenia Method for Beryllium in Air.") The filter papers are folded and placed in 90-ml. round-bottom centrifuge tubes, and 5 ml. of the 1:9 digestion mixture is added. The tube is then heated in a sand bath at 180°C. until fumes of nitric acid are no longer seen or until the charred solution is not boiling. The tube is cooled, 2 ml. of the 1:8 digestion mixture is added, and the tube is heated in a sand bath at 350°C. until the solution is colorless and fumes of sulfuric trioxide are evolved. Copious fumes of sulfur trioxide must be seen prior to removal of the tube from the sand bath. The filter paper samples are now ready for the oxidation procedure.

**Digestion of Urine Samples.**—Transfer 100 ml. of urine to a 500-ml. round-bottom flask, add boiling chips, 10 ml. of 1:9 digestion mixture, and several drops of antifoam (*n*-octyl alcohol). Evaporate the urine to fumes of sulfur trioxide and cool; add nitric acid to aid in destruction of organic matter. Four to six drops of sulfuric acid must be added if the flask becomes dry during the process. When the residue is white and damp with sulfuric acid, the samples are ready for the oxidation procedure.

**Preparation of Standards for Oxidation.**—To five 90-ml. tubes add 0, 1, 4, and 10 ml. of the dilute thallium standard. To each tube add sufficient 0.5 $N$ sulfuric acid so that the total volume is 10 ml.; the tubes then contain 0, 1, 2, 4, and 10 micrograms of thallium, respectively. Add 5 ml. of 1:9 digestion mixture and heat

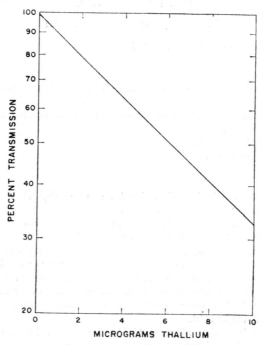

FIG. 45-1. Standard Curve.

at 180°C. until the solution no longer boils. Transfer to a 350°C. sand bath and evaporate to fumes of sulfuric trioxide. Do not heat after fumes begin to evolve from the tube. The standards are now ready for the oxidation procedure.

**Oxidation Procedure.**—Wash down the walls of the urine flasks, of the air sample tube, and of the standard tubes with distilled water to make the volume of each about 20 ml. Add 1 ml. of 47% hydrobromic acid and heat in a 180°C. sand bath until the solution is a light brown. (The standards will form only a fleeting tan which is easily seen.) The tube should be heated only until fumes of sulfur trioxide are just visible in the tube. Allow the flasks and tubes to cool, and again wash down the walls with distilled water to a volume of 20 ml.; warm to dissolve all solids. Add 1 ml. dilute hydrobromic acid and, if no free bromine is seen, add several drops of bromine water; place the solutions in a 180°C. sand bath and boil until the solutions are clear and colorless, indicating removal of bromine. Without undue delay, transfer the solutions to 125-ml. separatory funnels for extraction.

**Extraction and Determination.**—Make the final volume of the solution in the separatory funnel to 50 to 75 ml. with distilled water and allow the solutions to cool to room temperature. Add 10 ml. n-amyl acetate to each funnel and 1 ml. of the working methyl violet solution to one funnel; shake this funnel immediately for 10 to 15 seconds, continue with the addition of methyl violet to other funnels, and shake each as before. Finally shake each funnel for an additional 45 to 50 seconds. When the layers have separated, discard the aqueous lower phase and drain the n-amyl acetate layer into a 15-ml. centrifuge tube. Centrifuge the tubes to free the solution of water. Decant the blue-violet n-amyl acetate layer into matched cuvettes (Coleman 19 x 105 mm.) and measure the percentage of transmission at 585 m$\mu$ using pure n-amyl acetate as a reference. Determine the amount of thallium in the unknowns from a plot of the standard curve on semilog paper (Fig. 45-1).

NOTES.—Control of acid normality is imperative during the extraction. The thallium-methyl violet complex is completely extracted from the aqueous solutions 0.5 to 1 N in mineral acid. At lower acidities, the free base ($R_3N$) is preferentially extracted by the organic solvent; at higher acidities, the complex is not formed. The presence in the aqueous phase of free phosphoric nitric or perchloric acids interferes with the extraction. The thallium-methyl violet complex is very stable in the amyl acetate solution; it should not, however, be allowed to stand for protracted periods in contact with the aqueous acid from which it has been extracted. It is possible to extract the complex from acid solutions of normality as high as 1.5 with greatly lowered efficiency of extraction.

## DETERMINATION IN SPECIFIC SUBSTANCES

### DETERMINATION IN RAT POISON [6]

*Procedure.*—The paste or ground grain (5 g.) is heated with 100 ml. of nitric acid and 10 ml. of sulfuric acid in a Kjeldahl flask till the nitric acid is expelled; sodium nitrate is added in small portions till the solution is colorless or pale yellow. The solution is diluted to 70 ml., and boiled; 2.5 ml. of 6% sulfurous acid is added to reduce any thallic sulfate formed, and the sulfur dioxide boiled off. The liquid is neutralized with ammonia against rosolic acid. The contents of the Kjeldahl flask are transferred to a 200-ml. flask, 5 ml. of glacial acetic acid are added, and the volume adjusted; 100 ml. of the filtered solution are heated to 90°C. and the thallium is precipitated with 25 ml. of 4% potassium iodide solution. After cooling overnight the precipitate is collected, washed, and treated as above under "Gravimetric Methods," 80% acetone being substituted for the alcohol.

[6] Lepper, Z. anal. Chem., **79**, 321, 1930.

# Chapter 46

# THORIUM *

Th, *at. wt.* 232.038; *sp. gr.* 11.3–11.7; *m.p.* 1845°C.; *b.p.* 4500°C.+; *oxides,* $ThO$
($ThO_3$ *and* $Th_2O_7$ *known only in hydrate form*)

The possible use of thorium as a source of fissionable material has renewed th
interest in this element which had begun to lag with the curtailment of the in
candescent gas mantle industry, which was the principal user of thorium oxide
Thorium-bearing minerals are widespread but generally in small amounts. Mona
zite, the principal source, is found in reasonably large deposits in India and Soutf
America. Recently, deposits of monazite have been discovered in Idaho. Metalli
thorium has been made in quantity and is a silvery white metal with a density o
11.7 g./cm³.

## DETECTION

Thorium is found under normal analytical schemes with the ammonium hydrox
ide group. It is generally advisable to separate thorium as oxalate, together witf
scandium and the rare earths, from the common elements and also from zirconium
and titanium. This is accomplished by dissolving the ammonium hydroxide group
in hydrochloric acid and adding an excess oxalic acid to the hot, weakly acid (no‡
over 1 $N$) solution. The solution should be allowed to stand at least six hours.
and preferably overnight, before filtration. The presence of ammonium salts is
not desirable at this point. The precipitate is ignited at a temperature not higher
than 600°C. and the oxide dissolved in 1:1 nitric acid. To part of the acid solution hydrogen peroxide is added in excess. The pH is adjusted to 0.5 to 1.5 using
ammonium hydroxide and the mixture is warmed to 50 or 60°C. and allowed to
stand. A white precipitate indicates the presence of thorium.

A confirmatory test for thorium can be made on the remaining part of the nitric
acid solution from the above solution of the oxide. It consists in the precipitation
of thorium iodate in nitric acid solution. Two reagent solutions are necessary:
(1) 15 g. of potassium iodate, 50 ml. of concentrated nitric acid, and 100 ml. of
water. (2) 4 g. of potassium iodate, 50 ml. of concentrated nitric acid, and 450 ml.
of water. The solution to be tested for thorium, which must contain no hydrochloric acid, is boiled with a little sulfurous acid to reduce any cerium present.
To this solution is added twice its volume of reagent (1), which causes precipitation of thorium iodate, and more or less rare earth iodates according to their
concentration in the solution. By now adding reagent (2) in volume equal to four
times the original volume, and boiling, any rare earth iodate is dissolved, while
thorium iodate (also any zirconium iodate) remains undissolved. If the absence

* Chapter prepared by C. J. Rodden, Director of New Brunswick Laboratory, U. S.
Atomic Energy Commission.

of zirconium is not known with certainty, the iodate precipitate may be boiled with 50 ml. of 10% oxalic acid solution until iodine vapors are no longer given off. Any precipitate remaining is thorium oxalate.

Spectrum analysis for thorium may be of some value but the sensitivity is not great. The most characteristic lines which may be used for the identification of the element are 2870.4 A and 4019.1 A.

The radioactive detection of thorium is generally complicated by the presence of uranium.[1] A measurement with a Geiger-Müller counter may be made but a positive result is not necessarily indicative of thorium.

## ESTIMATION

Quantitative methods for the estimation of thorium are complicated by several factors. The interferences of zirconium and hafnium are in general not so troublesome as is that of scandium, yttrium, and the rare earth elements. Separation from these elements many times is not complete and repetition of operations is often necessary. Thorium has been separated from interfering elements by an ether extraction of the nitrate on a cellulose column. Since thorium has but one valence there are no direct titrimetric methods for this element. Thorium may be readily determined when alone but usually in ores its estimation is difficult and tedious. In the regular procedure, thorium will be counted as aluminum if the latter is taken by difference. Two reviews on the analytical chemistry of thorium contain much valuable information.[2]

## PREPARATION AND SOLUTION OF THE SAMPLE— MONAZITE SAND

The peroxide and fluoride fusions given below for monazite can be used for breaking up most ores containing thorium. Several methods of decomposing monazite have been used in the past. At present the sodium peroxide fusion or the bifluoride fusion is preferred for umpire analysis over the older sulfuric acid digestion method. Perchloric acid can also be used for the decomposition of monazite sand.[3] In general, the sample should be finely pulverized (less than 100-mesh) except with the older routine analysis of monazite sand employing sulfuric acid, where coarser material can be used.

*Sodium Peroxide Fusion.*[4]—One gram of 250-mesh monazite sand is placed in a 30-ml. platinum crucible and mixed with 4.0 g. of sodium peroxide, which should be fresh. The mixture is covered with a small amount of sodium peroxide and placed in a muffle furnace at 480°C. ± 20°C. for seven minutes, after which it is allowed to cool.

The sintered mass is treated with approximately 50 ml. of cold water and allowed to stand until disintegrated. This mass is transferred to a 600-ml. beaker and acidified with hydrochloric acid and 25 ml. of hydrochloric acid in excess is added. After bringing the solution to the boiling point, any small residue is filtered off through a Whatman No. 42 paper, and washed with hot water. The

[1] Rodden, Anal. Chem., **21**, 333, 1949.

[2] Moeller, Schweitzer, and Starr, Chemical News, **42**, 63, 1948; Anal. Chem. of the Manhattan Project, Rodden, page 160, McGraw-Hill Book Co., New York, 1950.

[3] Willard and Gordon, Anal. Chem., **20**, 165, 1948.

[4] Rafter, Decomposition of Monazite Sand by Sintering with Sodium Peroxide, Analyst, **75**, 485, 1950.

paper is placed in a platinum crucible, dried, and ignited at 1000°C. for a few minutes. A few drops of 1:1 sulfuric acid plus 10 ml. hydrofluoric acid is added to the residue which is then evaporated to complete dryness. If a small residue remains after this treatment, it is sintered with a small amount of sodium peroxide as above.

**Fluoride Fusion.**—The fluoride fusion method is satisfactory for the decomposition of ores and minerals, as well as monazite. The procedure is given on page 1066 under "Determination of Thorium in Ores."

**Decomposition with Sulfuric Acid.**—Fifty grams of the sand are weighed and placed in a porcelain casserole of about 500-ml. capacity. Seventy-five ml. of concentrated sulfuric acid are added, and the mixture is heated for about 4 hours with frequent stirring, a gentle evolution of fumes being maintained during the course of the operation. When the mass has become pasty, it is allowed to cool, and the sulfates are extracted by the addition of about 400 ml. of ice-cold water, or enough to cool the solution sufficiently so that the sulfates become soluble. This solution is decanted into a liter volumetric flask, and the remaining sulfates are extracted with small portions of cold water and decanted into the flask. A point is reached toward the end of the extraction when, because of the decreasing acidity, the small wash portions show a slight separation of rare earth phosphates. A few more extractions are made beyond this point, but these portions are not added to the volumetric flask. They are temporarily reserved in a separate beaker. To the remaining sand, which has been dried, 10 ml. of concentrated sulfuric acid are added, and the digestion is carried out as before, except that a somewhat higher temperature is used, enough to maintain copious evolution of white fumes, and the duration of the digestion need not exceed 1.5 hours. After cooling, extraction is started with the last portions of the previous extraction liquor, i.e., those which were reserved in the separate beaker. The sand is now thoroughly washed with cold water, and the washings are all decanted into the liter flask. This flask now contains all the thorium and the rare earths as soluble sulfates. A little suspended silica is usually visible at this point, but this will not be mistaken for undissolved sulfates.

After cooling, the sulfate solution is made up exactly to the liter mark, thoroughly mixed, and filtered through a dry filter, discarding the first 25 or 30 ml., and receiving the remainder in a dry flask or bottle. The whole need not be filtered, and no washing is to be done. Each 100 ml. of this solution represents 5 g. of the sample.

## SEPARATIONS

Thorium is separated from practically all elements excepting the rare earth elements yttrium and scandium by precipitation as the oxalate in somewhat acid solution (pH about 2). Zirconium may be precipitated in part along with thorium and the rare earths, especially in the absence of a sufficient excess of oxalic acid. If considerable quantities of calcium, and, to a lesser extent, strontium and barium, are present, there may be contamination unless the mineral acid concentration be kept dangerously high. In the presence of much calcium, it is better first to separate thorium from it by precipitation with freshly distilled ammonium hydroxide, and then to precipitate the thorium as oxalate.

Thorium oxalate is not entirely insoluble in strong mineral acids, and for accurate work it is generally desirable to remove excess acid by evaporation to dryness.

The presence of ammonium salts is not desirable and it is generally preferred to remove excess acid by evaporation rather than by neutralizing with ammonium hydroxide.

Thorium fluoride is relatively insoluble in dilute mineral acids. The precipitation of the fluoride is utilized generally as a means of separating thorium and the rare earths from other elements. Usually, large amounts of calcium are carried down as is also some iron. The separation should be made by dissolving the ammonium hydroxide precipitate in dilute hydrofluoric acid and allowing it to stand for several hours.

One of the most satisfactory methods for separating the rare earths from thorium is that in which thorium is precipitated with hexamethylenetetramine (hexamine or urotropine [5]). It is necessary to remove phosphate from the solution prior to treatment with hexamine. This may be done by a double oxalate precipitation. The chloride solution is cautiously treated with ammonium hydroxide (1:10) until a faint turbidity is produced, which is cleared by the addition of a few drops of hydrochloric acid (1:1); the solution is diluted to 200 ml., treated with 10 g. of ammonium chloride, and heated to 70 to 80°C.; the thorium is precipitated by the slow addition of a 2% solution of hexamine until no further turbidity is produced. The precipitate is collected on a filter paper, washed with warm 5% ammonium chloride solution, returned to the beaker, and dissolved by the addition of a few drops of hydrochloric acid. The solution is neutralized, diluted, and treated with ammonium chloride and hexamine as before; a third precipitation is advisable if a considerable amount of rare earths is present. The final hexamine precipitate is dissolved in hydrochloric acid and the thorium is precipitated as oxalate. Zirconium and titanium accompany the thorium in the hexamine process but they are eliminated by the oxalate precipitation.[5]

The iodate method of Meyer and Speter [6] is satisfactory for routine thorium determinations provided the thorium content is not small and provided that the samples are not too badly contaminated with phosphate. The results with monazite of low thorium content are sometimes erratic.[7] The procedure is given above under detection.

The separation of thorium from rare earths by the use of hydrogen peroxide in acid solution is satisfactory. Either nitric acid or sulfuric acid solutions can be used. The precipitate formed from sulfuric acid solution tends to be more granular. The thorium solution, containing 10 to 30 mg. of thorium per 50 ml., is adjusted to $1 N$ to $2 N$ in sulfuric acid. Since acid is formed by the reaction, the initial hydrogen-ion concentration should be lower for those samples that are high in thorium. The final acid concentration should not exceed $2 N$. An excess of 30% hydrogen peroxide is added, and the mixture is stirred, heated to 55 to 60°C. and allowed to cool at room temperature. After standing 1 hour or longer, the thorium peroxysulfate is filtered and washed with water.

One of the newer methods for separating thorium from most interfering elements is that employing solvent extraction of thorium nitrate with ether. By using alumina and cellulose adsorbents in a column, thorium and uranium can be simultaneously determined in ores.[8] Phosphate does not interfere when complexed with iron. The procedure is given under Analysis of Ores on page 1066.

[5] Ismail and Harwood, Analyst, **62**, 185, 1937.
[6] Meyer, R. J., and Speter, M., Chem. Zgt., **34**, 306, 1910.
[7] Private communication, H. S. Kremer.
[8] Williams, Analyst, **77**, 297–306, 1952.

Thorium nitrate is readily soluble in mesityl oxide and this property has been used in analysis.[9] This extraction has been used for the analysis of monazite sand.[10] The combined thorium and rare earth fluorides are dissolved in aluminum nitrate and extracted with mesityl oxide. The determination of thorium is finished colorimetrically.

In the fluoride extraction method, the combined fluorides are dissolved in a beaker containing 19 g. of aluminum nitrate enneahydrate ($Al(NO_3)_3 \cdot 9H_2O$) and 2.5 ml. of nitric acid using the minimum amount of water. The solution is warmed to dissolve the salts. The volume is reduced to 20 ml. and cooled. The sample solution is poured from a beaker into a 125-ml. separatory funnel. Twenty ml. of mesityl oxide (boiling point, 128° and 130°C.) are measured into the beaker, swirled and added to the separatory funnel. [Caution: The extraction should be conducted in a hood since excessive inhalation of mesityl oxide may cause serious respiratory difficulties.] It is shaken for 20 seconds, and the aqueous phase is drained into a second separatory funnel. (Frequently a white suspension or emulsion forms at the interface during the extraction. Usually this will not be excessive, but if it is, the effect can usually be minimized by adding an additional 1 ml of nitric acid. Since nitric acid will oxidize the reagent, further addition of the acid is not recommended. Ten ml. of the solvent are added to the second separatory funnel; it is shaken for 20 seconds and the aqueous phase is discarded.

The solvent is combined with the original portion and 20 ml. of the scrub solution are added. It is again shaken for 20 seconds and the aqueous phase is discarded. This operation is repeated twice more. The thorium is stripped from the solvent by agitation for 20 seconds with 20 ml. of water. The water layer is drained into a 200-ml. volumetric flask and the procedure is repeated. The contents of the flask are diluted to volume.

## GRAVIMETRIC METHOD

### BY PRECIPITATION AS OXALATE

Thorium is nearly always precipitated as oxalate and ignited to thorium dioxide in which form it is weighed.

*Procedure.*—The nitrate, chloride, or perchlorate solution of thorium, which is free of sulfate and phosphate, is adjusted so that its thorium content is 100 mg or less per 100 ml., and its pH is about 2. The use of filter pulp is helpful but is not necessary. The solution is heated to boiling, and either oxalic acid crystals (dihydrate) or a saturated solution of the same is added slowly. The suspension is boiled a few minutes, removed from the hot plate, and allowed to stand at least 1 hour, and preferably 10 hours or overnight. After filtering through a medium paper, it is washed with a solution containing 25 g. of oxalic acid dihydrate per liter

Thorium oxalate is ignited with the filter paper in a porcelain or platinum crucible to constant weight at 1000°C. If a platinum crucible is used, the full heat of a Meker burner is sufficient. The thorium oxide finally weighed should be pure white in color. A yellow color shows cerium earths or iron and is an indication of faulty work.

9 Levine and Grimaldi, AECD-3186, 1950. Atomic Energy Commission.
10 Banks and Byrd, Anal. Chem., **25**, 417, 1953.

## TITRIMETRIC METHOD

Because of the constancy of the valence of the thorium ion, titrimetric methods are not well adapted to its determination. As a result the available titrimetric methods are somewhat slow, and not especially accurate, and involve the precipitation of an insoluble thorium compound. The excess of the precipitating agent is determined with an indicator or electrometrically, or, in most cases, the insoluble thorium compound is filtered and washed, and the thorium is determined indirectly by some reaction of the acid radical of the salt (molybdate, iodate, oxalate, oxinate, etc.).

## MOLYBDATE METHOD [11]

*Procedure.*—A sample containing 0.15 to 0.2 g. of thorium is weighed out and placed in a 250-ml. beaker. After the sample has been dissolved any large excess of mineral acid is destroyed by evaporating the solution nearly to dryness. The sample is then diluted to 150 ml. with water and made about 7% in acetic acid by addition of 11 ml. of glacial acid. Fifteen milliliters of thick filter pulp and ml. of a diphenylcarbazide solution (0.5 g. per 200 ml. of 95% ethanol) are added. The ammonium paramolybdate solution (7.6 g. per liter) is added from a burette with stirring until the indicator imparts a deep pink color to the solution. After the precipitate has settled the supernatant liquid may be tested for complete precipitation. The contents of the beaker is heated to boiling and filtered while hot through an 11-cm. Whatman No. 42 filter into a 400-ml. beaker. The precipitate is washed 5 to 6 times with hot 1 to 100 acetic acid. The 250-ml. beakers need not be scrubbed out with a policeman but only carefully rinsed 2 to 3 times with wash solution.

The washed precipitate and filter are transferred to the 250-ml. beaker in which the precipitation was carried out and 25 ml. of concentrated hydrochloric acid are added to the beaker. The contents are stirred until the filter disintegrates. Seventy-five milliliters of water is added and the mixture is heated to boiling (long boiling results in reduction of molybdenum and decomposition of the filter pulp) and filtered while hot through an 11-cm. Whatman No. 42 filter into a 400-ml. beaker. The filter pulp and filter are washed 5 to 6 times with hot 1 to 100 hydrochloric acid. The filtrates, after being cooled to room temperature, are passed through an amalgamated zinc Jones reductor into an excess (5 times the theoretical of 10%) of ferric alum to which 2 to 3 ml. of concentrated phosphoric acid have been added and titrated with 0.1 $N$ ceric sulfate, 2 drops of 0.025 $M$ ferroin (1,10-phenanthroline ferrous sulfate) being used as indicator. The end point is taken as that point when the pink color of the solution changes to colorless or light blue.

## COLORIMETRIC METHOD

Colorimetric methods for the determination of thorium are relatively few. The method which has proved most satisfactory is based on the work of V. I. Kuznetsov [12] in which a strawberry-red precipitate is formed with 2-(2-hydroxy-3,6-disulfo-1-naph-thylazo)-benzenearsonic acid and thorium salts. This serves as the basis of a colorimetric determination. It can be used without separation from the excess re-

[11] Banks and Diehl, Anal. Chem., **19**, 222, 1947.
[12] J. Gen. U.S.S.R., **14**, 914, 1944.

agent, but the absorption bands are such that the amount of reagent must be care
fully measured, and an idea of the approximate thorium range must be known
The method has been used for the determination of microgram quantities o
thorium. The color is stable for at least 24 hours. The best pH range is 0.3 to 1
Errors are about 5% when a carefully standardized technique is used. The proce
dure is given under "Colorimetric Determination of Thorium in Low Grad
Materials."

## DETERMINATION IN SPECIFIC SUBSTANCES

### ANALYSIS OF ORES

The following procedures are in current use and at present are considere
reliable.

#### DETERMINATION OF THORIUM AND RARE EARTH OXIDES IN MONAZITE [13]

**Procedure.**—The sample weight of ground (100-mesh) monazite should be 0.5
1.0 g. depending on the probable thorium oxide content. For example, for Indi
monazite containing more the 5% thorium oxide, a 0.5-g. sample is sufficient; fo
Brazil, Florida, Idaho, etc., monazites containing less than 5% thorium oxide, u
to a 1.0-g. sample should be taken.

Place the sample in a No. 1 tall-form porcelain crucible, add 3 g. sodium per
oxide and 3 to 6 pellets sodium hydroxide, mix well, and cover with a layer o
peroxide by adding 3 g. more. Set the uncovered crucible in place on a triangl
and heat carefully at first to expel moisture. Use a soft free flame, and brus
the bottom and sides of the crucible keeping the flame in motion continuousl
and withdrawing the flame completely at any sign of a tendency to sputter.

After all moisture is expelled, grasp the crucible in the belly of the tongs an
heat the crucible by holding it over the free flame, keeping the crucible in motion
Withdraw it from the flame at any tendency to sputter. Continue until th
material is in quiet fusion. Swirl continuously while heating. Raise the tempera
ture a trifle, but do not in any case heat the crucible to redness even at the poin
of contact of the flame on the crucible. The material is kept in fusion for fiv
minutes and then finally, the contents are swirled upon cooling so as to coat th
walls of the crucible.

It is most important that the temperature of the fusion be kept at the minimun
necessary, otherwise the material becomes very inert to subsequent treatment an
the process must be repeated. The fusion process requires about 10–15 minute
overall.

Allow the crucible to cool (room temperature) and then place it in 150 ml
warm water contained in a 400-ml. beaker. Digest (do not boil) until the mel
is completely disintegrated. (This should proceed rapidly; should it be slow, i
indicates that the fusion temperature was too high.) Remove the crucible an
rinse it with hot water. Any adhering film may be removed with a policema
and/or a little hydrochloric acid. The hydrochloric acid solution is added to th
contents of the beaker.

Neutralize the hot suspension with 1:1 hydrochloric acid. The end point ma
be taken as that point where the material dissolves upon adding the hydrochlori

[13] Kremers, H. E., Lindsay Light, Private Comm.

cid slowly with stirring, keeping the solution hot. Add a few milliliters hydro-
hloric acid in excess. Silicic acid will remain undissolved, but it is easily
ecognized.

Add 2 ml. 30% hydrogen peroxide solution and then make the solution alkaline
vith 50% sodium hydroxide solution. Add 15 ml. in excess. Digest (steam bath)
ntil the precipitate settles readily. Filter through a 12.5-cm. Whatman No. 41
aper and wash well with 0.1% sodium chloride wash solution. Discard the filtrate
nd washings. It is not necessary to scrub the beaker.

NOTE.—The water leach of the melt is acidified and a reprecipitation is made because
ue melt slurry is too difficult to filter. The sodium hydroxide-hydrogen peroxide treat-
ient removes the bulk of the silica, phosphorus and alumina.

Transfer the precipitate and paper back into the original beaker. Add 20 ml.
oncentrated nitric acid and heat on a low hot plate about 30 minutes. Cool,
nd add carefully 20 ml. concentrated perchloric acid. Heat with swirling over a
ree flame to fumes of perchloric acid.

Cool and take up in 100 ml. hot water. Filter through an 11-cm. Whatman
No. 40 paper, and wash the paper 5–7 times with hot 1% perchloric acid and
hen with hot water until free of acid (test with Congo red paper). Catch the
olution and washings in a clean 400-ml. beaker. Reserve the filtrate.

Transfer the filter and residue to a platinum crucible and ignite. Cool, moisten
vith a few drops of concentrated sulfuric acid, and add 10–15 ml. concentrated
ydrofluoric acid. Heat gently to fumes of sulfur trioxide.

Fuse the residue with the smallest possible amount of potassium bisulfate to a
lear melt. Cool and place crucible and contents into a 150-ml. beaker containing
ufficient 5% hydrochloric acid to cover the crucible. Digest on the steam bath
intil the fusion disintegrates (about 30 minutes). Filter off any insolubles through
small Whatman No. 40 paper, washing the paper well with hot 1% hydrochloric
cid. To the hot filtrate, add sufficient freshly filtered 1:1 ammonium hydroxide
o precipitate any rare earths and add 10 ml. in excess. Heat the filtrate from
tep above, where reserved, and precipitate the rare earths with freshly filtered
:1 ammonium hydroxide and add 10–15 ml. in excess. Digest both precipitates
n a steam bath until they settle. Filter both precipitates with paper pulp on a
2.5-cm. Whatman No. 41 paper, washing the precipitate and the beakers with
% ammonium chloride-10% ammonium hydroxide. Discard the filtrate and wash-
ngs. Wash the precipitate off the paper back into the beaker from reserved solu-
ion with a jet of hot water. Heat 25–35 ml. 1:4 hydrochloric acid in the other
eaker and use this solution to dissolve any residue on the filter, catching the
vashings in the beaker containing the precipitate. Then wash the paper thor-
ughly with hot 5% hydrochloric acid and then with hot water. Discard the filter.

Evaporate the solution to dryness. Take up in 20 ml. of water, add 15 ml. of a
aturated oxalic acid solution and bring to boil. Allow to stand at room tempera-
ure overnight.

Filter quantitatively through an 11-cm. Whatman No. 42 paper, washing four
r five times with cold 2% oxalic acid wash solution. Discard the filtrate and
vashings. Transfer the paper and precipitate to the original beaker, add 20 ml.
oncentrated nitric acid and 7.5 ml. concentrated perchloric acid. Heat on a hot
late or with swirling over a free flame until the paper dissolves. Then continue
leating cautiously until carbon dioxide begins to evolve vigorously. Remove
juickly from the heat and continue holding until the action ceases. Then swirl
ver a flame to fumes of perchloric acid. Cool and dilute to 100 ml. with water.

Filter if necessary, washing the paper with hot water until free of acid (test wit Congo red paper). Discard paper and residue.

Bring to 200 ml. volume, heat to boiling, and add slowly and with constar stirring, 60 ml. of a clear 10% solution of oxalic acid. Digest for several minute at the near boiling temperature, then allow to stand on the steam bath for 1 hou and finally allow to stand at room temperature for at least 8 hours, or preferabl overnight.

Filter quantitatively through an 11-cm. Whatman No. 42 paper, washing 6– times with cold 2% oxalic acid wash solution. Discard the filtrate and washing

Place the paper and precipitate in a clean tared platinum crucible and cha over a low (Fisher burner) flame until carbonization is complete. Ignite at 950 1000°C., for 1 hour or to constant weight. Cool in a desiccator and weigh as rar earth and thorium oxides (Total Oxides).

## DETERMINATION OF THORIUM OXIDE

**Procedure.**—Transfer the oxides from the preceding determination to a 250-m beaker (brush); add about 5 ml. concentrated hydrochloric acid to the crucible an warm carefully (radiator recommended). Any oxide adhering to the walls of th platinum crucible will be dissolved. Add the solution to the contents of th beaker, rinsing the crucible out with a jet of hot water. Add 10 ml. more of cor centrated hydrochloric acid to the contents of the beaker, cover, and heat until th oxides dissolve.

Add freshly filtered 1:4 ammonium hydroxide dropwise to the solution until faint turbidity is obtained and then add 3 $N$ hydrochloric acid dropwise carefull until the solution is just cleared. Dilute to about 150 ml. volume, add enoug ammonium chloride to make the solution 5% in the salt, stir well until it dissolve add 1 ml. 10% sodium nitrite, heat to 50–60°C., and then add 2% hexamine solt tion slowly until precipitation is complete. Add 5 ml. in excess. Digest at 50 60°C. for 2–3 minutes. Allow the precipitate to settle.

Filter through a Whatman No. 40 paper and wash 2–3 times with 5% ammoniur chloride solution which contains 2 g. hexamine per liter. It is not necessary t scrub the beaker.

Dissolve the precipitate on the paper with 25 ml. hot 3 $N$ hydrochloric acid an wash the paper thoroughly with hot 5% hydrochloric acid. Catch the filtrate an washings in the original beaker. Wash the paper several times with water unti the last wash is basic to Congo red paper and discard the washings. Reserve th filter.

Neutralize the solution with 1:1 ammonium hydroxide as before and rececip tate as before. Filter quantitatively through the same paper and wash four or fiv times with the ammonium chloride-hexamine wash solution.

Place the paper and precipitate in a clean tared platinum crucible and cha over a low (Fisher) flame until carbonization is complete. Ignite at 950–1,000°C for half an hour or to constant weight. Cool in a desiccator and weigh as thorun oxide.

## DETERMINATION OF THORIUM IN ORES

The sample is decomposed by evaporation with hydrofluoric acid and fusio with potassium bifluoride. The residue insoluble in hydrofluoric acid solutio contains the thorium which is dissolved by fuming with sulfuric acid. Thoriun and the rare earths are precipitated with ammonium hydroxide, the thorium sepa rated from rare earths with hexamine, then precipitated as the oxalate which is ignited to thorium oxide and weighed.

*Procedure.*—Transfer a finely ground, accurately weighed sample (about 1 g.) of the ore to a 30-ml. platinum crucible. Moisten with a little water, add about 20 ml. 48% hydrofluoric acid, and evaporate to dryness on a steam bath. Repeat the treatment if the sample contains much silica. After the hydrofluoric acid treatment add about 10 g. of potassium bifluoride, which has been dried in a desiccator, to the crucible and fuse as follows: Place the covered crucible over a very low flame and carefully drive off the moisture and reaction gases. Gradually increase the flame until the melt is a clear red hot molten mass over the full flame of the Meker burner. Swirl the clear melt to mix the fusion. Care must be used throughout the fusion because the material tends to foam, creep and sputter. Swirl the melt on cooling to form a thin coating on the sides of the crucible. After the crucible is cool, place in a large platinum dish, and add about 200 ml. water and about 25 ml. 48% hydrofluoric acid. Remove the melt from the crucible and break up with a platinum rod. Digest on the steam bath for 1 hour, cool, and filter through a Whatman No. 42 filter paper. Wash with dilute hydrofluoric acid and finally with water. Ignite the residue at 450–500°C. in a 30-ml. platinum crucible. Add 15–20 g. of potassium persulfate and carefully melt the mixture with a Bunsen burner, then fume rather strongly for several minutes. Cool and transfer the fusion cake to a 600-ml. beaker by means of 100 ml. of hot water. Digest and stir on the steam bath to dissolve the residue solids. If some insoluble material remains in the platinum dish dissolve this in warm hydrochloric acid (1:1) and add to the beaker. Usually all the material is soluble at this point but if some insoluble material remains it will dissolve after the addition of ammonium hydroxide and sodium sulfite. Nearly neutralize the solution with ammonium hydroxide and add a few crystals of sodium sulfite to effect reduction of cerium(IV) (yellow) to cerium(III) (colorless). If cerium is present, the solution will probably be yellow and the addition of sodium sulfite will give a colorless liquid unless iron or some other colored ion is present. Make ammoniacal to 10% excess. Allow the solution to cool and the precipitate to settle before filtering through a Whatman No. 40 paper. Wash with a little cold 2% ammonium chloride—10% ammonium hydroxide solution. Dissolve the precipitate on the paper with hot hydrochloric acid (1:2) returning the solution to the original beaker. If the precipitate is large, it may be necessary to remove the paper from the funnel and slurry with 10 to 15 ml. hot hydrochloric acid (1:1) in a small beaker. Filter into the beaker containing the dissolved precipitate and wash well with hot 5% hydrochloric acid. (See Note 1.) To the combined filtrates and washings add ammonium hydroxide (1:1) until a faint permanent turbidity or precipitate is formed and then add a few drops of hydrochloric acid (1:1) to dissolve the precipitate. Dilute to 200 ml. and add enough ammonium chloride to make a 5% solution of the salt. Add 0.5 to 1 ml. of 10% sodium sulfite and stir well and warm the solution to about 60–70°C. Slowly add 2% hexamine solution until a turbidity is just produced—then add 3 to 4 ml. more. Stir well and heat (not over 75°C.) to coagulate the precipitate and then allow the precipitate to settle. Add 1 ml. more of hexamine solution to the clear supernatant liquid. If no more turbidity is produced (the precipitation is complete), stir, and allow to settle. If more turbidity forms (the precipitation is not complete), add more hexamine in 1-ml. portions, allowing the precipitate to settle before each addition until precipitation is complete. After the precipitate has settled, filter through a Whatman No. 40 paper (see Note 2) and wash with 5% ammonium chloride. Test the filtrate for complete precipitation by adding 1 ml. hexamine solution. Dissolve the precipitate on the paper with hot hydrochloric acid (1:2) finally washing the paper with hot 5% hydrochloric acid and repeat the hexamine precipitation twice (or until the filtrate from the hexamine precipitation gives no precipitate when made strongly ammoniacal). Dissolve the final hexamine precipitate as before, collecting the solution in a 100-ml. platinum dish. Evaporate to dryness on the steam bath and pour 20–25 ml. of a 10% oxalic acid solution onto the residue. Stir and then dilute to 100-ml. volume. Cover the beaker, gently boil the solution for a few minutes, adjust the volume to 100 ml., and let stand overnight. Filter through a Whatman No. 42 paper, wash with 1–2% oxalic acid, ignite at 1100°C., cool, and weigh as thorium oxide.

NOTES.—1. If much $R_2O_3$ other than thorium and rare earth is present it is advisable either to remove the iron by an ether extraction or make an oxalate precipitation at this point. To extract the iron, dissolve the ammonia precipitate with hot hydrochloric acid (1:1) and shake with ether. The oxalate precipitation is a longer procedure. Evaporate the hydrochloric acid solution of the dissolved ammonia precipitate to dryness and follow the method for oxalate precipitation given under "Determination of Thorium in Ores by the Column Method," page 1070. Ignite the oxalates at 500°C. for at least 2 hours, dissolve in hot concentrated nitric acid, dilute and precipitate with ammonium hydroxide, dissolve the precipitate with hot hydrochloric acid (1:2) and continue with the hexamine separation. If nitric acid will not dissolve the ignited oxalates, a pyrosulfate fusion is necessary.
2. It is best to place a pad of macerated filter paper in the apex of the filter paper when filtering all precipitates encountered in this method.

## COLORIMETRIC DETERMINATION OF THORIUM IN LOW GRADE MATERIALS [14]

A rapid colorimetric method for the determination of thorium in low-grade materials using lanthanum and mercury as gatherers and measuring the color intensity of the thorium-thoron complex is given. The method is generally applicable to the determination of small amounts of thorium in minerals.

*Procedure.* **Solution of Sample.**—Weigh 50 to 400 mg. of the sample into a platinum dish. Moisten with water and add 10 ml. of 48% hydrofluoric acid and 5 ml. of concentrated sulfuric acid. Heat the sample under a heat lamp until the sulfuric acid fumes. Cool the sample and wash down the sides of the dish with water. Repeat the fuming and wash down again with water. When most of the sulfuric acid has fumed off, cool the sample, and then add 5 ml. of concentrated nitric acid and about 30 ml. of water. Warm over a steam bath and stir occasionally. Filter into a 100-ml. volumetric flask and wash the filter paper with water. If a residue remains, wash it back into the platinum dish. Burn the paper separately and add the residue. Evaporate any water present and then add 1 to 1.5 g. of sodium fluoride. Fuse over a Meker burner and then cool. Add 5 ml. of concentrated sulfuric acid, being careful that the acid wets all the fluoride. Place the sample under the heat lamp. When the acid fumes copiously, cool, wash down the sides of the dish, and fume again. Wash down the sides of the dish again and fume under the heat lamp to remove excess sulfuric acid. Fuse the sample at low red heat until a clear melt is obtained. Cool and add 5 ml. of concentrated nitric acid and 35 ml. of water. Heat on a steam bath and stir

14 Kronstadt, R., and Eberle, A. R., RMO-838, Jan. 1952.

occasionally. Filter into the same volumetric flask. If there is a residue, treat it in the same manner as the first residue.

**Alternate Procedure for Solution of Sample.**—Weigh 50 to 400 mg. of the sample into a 20-ml. nickel crucible. Add 4 to 5 grams of sodium peroxide. Mix the sample and cover the mixture with about 1 gram of the peroxide. Fuse slowly at a temperature between 600 and 700°C. for 5 minutes. Cool and loosen the melt by striking the crucible sharply against some solid object. Transfer the melt to a 400-ml. beaker. Cover the melt with water and neutralize cautiously with concentrated nitric acid and then add 5 ml. excess. Heat the solution to boiling. If manganese dioxide is present, add a 20% sodium nitrite solution until clear. Continue boiling until the volume is less than 75 ml. Filter into a 100-ml. volumetric flask and wash the filter paper thoroughly with water. In the presence of appreciable amounts of silica the melt from the fusion is leached with water and filtered. The precipitate is then dissolved in hot nitric acid (1:1) containing a few drops of 20% sodium nitrite and diluted to 100 ml. in a volumetric flask.

**Analysis of Solution.**—Make up the solution to the mark on the volumetric flask. Mix the solution well and pipette out an aliquot estimated to contain from 20 to 200 micrograms of thorium. Transfer the aliquot, which must be less than 30 ml., to a 50-ml. centrifuge tube. In another centrifuge tube pipette 5 ml. of a standard thorium solution which contains 20 micrograms of thorium oxide per milliliter. Reserve an empty centrifuge tube for a blank. To all three centrifuge tubes add 2 ml. of a lanthanum nitrate solution which contains 15 mg. of lanthanum per ml. Add 1 ml. of concentrated nitric acid to each tube and then adjust the volume of each tube to 35 ml. with water. Add a moderate excess of ammonium hydroxide and stir each tube with a platinum rod. Efficient stirring can be obtained by attaching the platinum rod to an electric stirrer. Centrifuge the mixtures at about 2500 r.p.m. for about 2 minutes. Discard the liquid. Drain the tubes for a minute by standing them inverted on a paper towel. Dissolve the precipitate by adding 1 ml. of concentrated nitric acid. Agitate gently, if solution is slow proceed to the next step in which the oxalic acid will aid in solution. Add water to bring all volumes to 20 ml. Heat on a steam bath for 5 minutes. Add 15 ml. of a hot 13.3% oxalic acid solution to each tube and immediately stir by hand with a glass rod until precipitation seems complete. Rinse the glass rod back into the tube. Stir with the platinum rod attached in the electric stirrer. Centrifuge for 2 minutes. Discard the liquid and drain tubes on a paper towel. Add 1 ml. of concentrated nitric acid. Agitate gently until solution is completed and then add 20 ml. of water. Heat on a steam bath for 5 minutes and then add 15 ml. of the hot 13.3% oxalic acid solution. Immediately stir by hand with a glass rod and rinse the rod back into the tube. Stir with the platinum rod attached in the electric stirrer. Centrifuge for 2 minutes and then discard the liquid and drain on a paper towel. Add 35 ml. of an oxalic acid wash solution which contains 2 grams of oxalic acid and 2 ml. of concentrated nitric acid per 100 ml. Stir with a platinum rod attached to an electric stirrer. Centrifuge, discard the liquid, and drain on a paper towel. Add 20 ml. of 35% nitric acid. Agitate gently until solution is complete. Heat on a steam bath for 5 minutes. Add 1 ml. of a 10% sodium sulfite solution to reduce cerium and then add 1 ml. of a mercuric nitrate solution which contains 15 mg. of mercury per ml. Remove the tubes individually from the steam bath and immediately pour in, in a turbulent manner to mix the tube contents, 15 ml. of a 6.67% potassium iodate solution. Wait until incipient precipitation and then stir with a platinum rod attached to an elecric stirrer.

Centrifuge, discard the liquid, and drain for 1 minute on a paper towel. Add 35 ml. of an iodate wash solution containing 30 grams of potassium iodate dissolved in 20% nitric acid and which is made up to 1 liter. Stir with a platinum rod until the precipitate is well dispersed through the wash. Centrifuge, discard the liquid, and drain thoroughly on a clean paper towel for at least 10 minutes. Wipe off any adhering liquid around the tube lip with a lintless paper. Add exactly 0.8 ml. of concentrated hydrochloric acid. Agitate gently until solution is completed. Pipette in 10 ml. of water and add exactly 2 ml. of 20% sodium nitrite. Stir with a platinum rod. Transfer as completely as possible, without washing, to a 60-ml. separatory funnel. Add exactly 10 ml. of methyl ethyl ketone. Stopper and shake well for 30 seconds. Have 10-ml. volumetric flasks ready prepared at this point by adding just 1 ml. of Thoron solution (0.1% solution of the sodium salt of 2-(2-hydroxy-3,6-disulfo-1-naphthylazo)-benzenearsonic acid) and just 2 ml. of ethyl alcohol to each dry flask. After extracting with the ketone, wait only until the interface clears of bubbles and then drain a sufficient quantity of the lower aqueous phase into the prepared 10-ml. volumetric flasks to just bring to the mark. Mix the solutions thoroughly. Pour into clean 1-cm. cuvettes and measure the optical density with a Beckman spectrophotometer at 545 m$\mu$ with about an 0.02-mm. slit width. The blank solution carried through the analysis is used as the reference solution. The thorium oxide content is directly proportional to the optical density and the thorium oxide content of the sample is calculated from the optical density of the 100-microgram standard.

## DETERMINATION OF THORIUM IN ORES BY THE COLUMN METHOD [15]

*Procedure.* **Solution of Sample.**—Weigh 10 g. (15 g. for a 2-g. sample) of potassium hydroxide pellets into a 100-ml. nickel crucible and heat over a Meker burner until water is driven off and the melt turns red. During this operation keep the crucible covered and place an asbestos shield around it so that only one-third of the outer crucible surface is in the direct flame. Cool the melt and place a 1-g. sample in the crucible. Heat slowly to red heat as before and continue at red heat for 1 hour. Cool. Immerse the crucible in a 400-ml. beaker containing about 200 ml. of nitric acid (1:3) and wash out the crucible with water after the reaction ceases to be violent. Boil for about 20 minutes, then add 3–4 drops of hydrofluoric acid (1:40) and boil until clear.

**Preparation of Sample for Column.**—Carry out an ammonium hydroxide precipitation and filter on 15-cm. Whatman No. 41H paper. Wash the beaker and filter paper twice each with boiling 0.5% ammonium hydroxide, transfer the precipitate to the original beaker and dissolve it in nitric acid. Evaporate to a low volume on the side of the hot plate and evaporate further by means of an infrared lamp until the contents are just moist. Add 20 ml. of 25% by volume nitric acid, cover and heat for 5 minutes under the lamp. After cooling somewhat, add 0.5–1.0 ml. 30% hydrogen peroxide and heat for 10 minutes more. Finally add in the proper order, 8 g. ferric nitrate and then 1.4 g. disodium hydrogen phosphate, following each addition with 5–10 minutes heating under the infrared lamp. (In the case of pure monazite add 4.0 g. ferric nitrate and 0.3 g. disodium hydrogen phosphate.) Cool for 30 minutes.

[15] Guest, R. J., The Determination of Thorium in Ores by the Column Method, Technical Paper No. 1, Department of Mines and Technical Surveys, Canada, 1953.

**Column Extraction.**—Add 50 g. activated alumina (80–200-mesh Fisher) to the thoroughly chilled mix and stir thoroughly until the wad is a dry homogeneous mass. Cool. Prepare the column, Fig. 46-1, with 12.5% ether-nitric acid solvent (redistilled ether containing 12.5% nitric acid by volume) which has been kept cool. Place a porcelain disc covered by a disc of Whatman No. 41H filter paper in the bottom of the column. Add 12.5% ether-nitric acid solvent to the column and add activated cellulose pulp (Whatman ashless), mixing well with a glass plunger until a cellulose layer 5 cm. thick is formed. Add activated alumina (80–200-mesh, Fisher) to the column until a layer of 6 cm. has formed. Mix the activated alumina

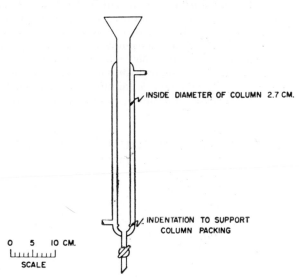

INSIDE DIAMETER OF COLUMN 2.7 CM.

INDENTATION TO SUPPORT COLUMN PACKING

0  5  10 CM.
SCALE

FIG. 46-1.

with the glass plunger to obtain a homogeneous layer. The layers of cellulose and alumina should be distinctly separate. Keep these layers covered by ether nitric acid solvent at all times. Transfer the contents of the beaker to the column. Rinse the beaker several times with the solvent and pass the solvent through the column extract, transfer the residual solution to a 250-ml. beaker and evaporate to period). Add 20 ml. water and then, cautiously, 50 ml. ammonium hydroxide. Remove the ether on the steam bath. If uranium is required or if the thorium is less than 1%, a second column extraction will be necessary as outlined below.

**Oxalate Precipitation.**—Transfer the residual solution to a 250-ml. beaker, boil for 5 minutes and add 10 ml. hydrochloric acid. Warm cautiously until most of the activity has subsided and then take to dryness on the side of the hot plate. Dissolve the residue in a little 1:1 hydrochloric-nitric and evaporate to dryness again. Filter on Whatman No. 42 paper, wash twice with 2% oxalic acid solution containing 0.1% hydrochloric acid, and ignite the precipitate at about 900°C. in a tared porcelain or platinum crucible. Weigh as thorium oxide ($ThO_2$).

**Second Column Extraction.**—After the ether has been removed from the first column extract, transfer the residual solution to a 250-ml. beaker and evaporate to a low volume. Take the solution just to dryness with nitric acid or until most of the ammonium salts are removed. Add a little nitric acid and evaporate the solution by means of an infrared lamp until just moist. Add 5 ml. nitric acid (1:3) and heat for 5 minutes under the infrared lamp. Then add 0.5 ml. hydrogen peroxide (30%) and heat 5 minutes more. Add 0.25 g. ferric nitrate and heat for 5 minutes. Finally add 0.05 g. disodium hydrogen phosphate and heat for 5 minutes more. Cool. Add 12.5 g. activated alumina to the beaker, stir, cool, and transfer to the column which has been prepared as above except that 1% ether-nitric solvent (redistilled ether containing 1% nitric acid by volume) has been used and the column consists of 4 cm. activated cellulose and 5 cm. activated alumina. Elute with 1% ether-nitric acid solvent and collect 250 ml. This fraction can be used for the uranium determination. When the level of the 1% ether-nitric acid solvent has dropped to the top of the wad, add 12.5% ether-nitric acid solvent and beat up the wad with a glass plunger. Pass 12.5% ether-nitric acid solvent through the column and collect 350 ml. for the thorium determination. Add 20 ml. water and 25 ml. ammonium hydroxide. Remove the ether, transfer the residual solution to a beaker, boil 5 minutes, add hydrochloric acid, and cautiously evaporate to dryness. Continue as above, finally precipitating the thorium as the oxalate.

## METHODS FOR THORIUM IN ANALYSES
## IN OTHER CHAPTERS

# Chapter 47

# TIN

Sn, *at. wt.* 118.69; *sp. gr.* 6.56 (rhombic); *m.p.* 232°C.; *b.p.* 2270°C.; *oxides,* SnO$_2$ *and* SnO

Tin occurs native to a very limited extent. It occurs as sulfide and extensively as oxide. It is found combined in silicic rocks such as granite, etc. It occurs in small amounts in feldspars, niobates, ilmenite, tantalate. The mineral cassiterite (stream tin, tin stone) is of commercial importance and is the chief source of tin. The mineral stannite (tin pyrites), Cu$_2$S·FeS·SnS$_2$, is another source of less importance.

In the early periods tin was thought to be identical with lead, but during the period of Pliny (23–79 A.D.) a distinction was recognized between these metals. The metal was brought to Egypt and Greece by the Phoenicians from the British Isles (Cassiterides). Tin is used as a coating for iron in the manufacture of numerous articles for industrial and domestic use. Block tin pipes are used for conveying distilled water. Tin foil for wrapping material. Tin is a constituent of a number of alloys such as Babbitt metal (Sn, Cu, Sb), bronze (Sn, Cu), pewter (Sn, Pb), solder (Sn, Pb), and type metal (Sn, Pb, Sb). Tin compounds are used in the arts and industries.

## DETECTION

*Hydrogen Sulfide* precipitates, from dilute acid solutions, SnS, brown, or SnS$_2$, yellow, according to the valence of the tin ions in solution. The sulfides are soluble in yellow ammonium sulfide (distinction from sulfides of Hg, Pb, Bi, Cu, and Cd). The sulfides will not precipitate in a concentration of 1:4 HCl (sp. gr. 1.19) (distinction from Sb and As sulfides). The sulfides are easily soluble in concentrated HCl (distinction from As sulfides).

*Mercuric Chloride* is reduced to white Hg$_2$Cl$_2$ or gray Hg and Hg$_2$Cl$_2$ by addition of stannous chloride solution. In the usual procedure of detection tin is precipitated from dilute HCl or H$_2$SO$_4$ solutions as sulfide by H$_2$S (2.5 ml. HCl or 1.5 ml. H$_2$SO$_4$ per 40 ml., later diluted to 100 ml. and again saturated with H$_2$S). It is separated from the sulfides of Hg, Pb, Bi, Cu, and Cd by extraction with ammonium polysulfide. It is precipitated from the extract by acidification (filter). It is separated from As sulfide by extraction with concentrated HCl. The extract is filtered from As sulfide, tin reduced by addition of metallic iron wire, or granulated lead [1] or aluminum foil [2] and the reduced solution added to an excess of

---

[1] The tin solution may be passed through a column of granulated lead.

[2] A tin mineral placed on a piece of zinc in dilute HCl will coat the zinc with gray metallic tin. If Al is used a piece of foil $\frac{1}{32}$" x $\frac{1}{4}$" x 1" is recommended. This dissolves completely and makes it possible to detect 1 mg. of Sn in presence of 500 mg. of Sb and As.

$HgCl_2$ solution; a white precipitate of $Hg_2Cl_2$, insoluble in dilute (1:2) HCl proves the presence of tin (SbOCl dissolves).

## ESTIMATION

The estimation of tin is required in connection with the analysis of tin ores, dross, ashes, dust, tin plate, alloys such as solder, canned foods, and general analysis.

Due to the volatility of many tin compounds, loss of this element may occur during the decomposition and solution of the ore. Owing to hydrolysis some of the element will remain as an oxide with silica causing an error in the silica determination. The portion still remaining in solution will precipitate with the $NH_4OH$ precipitate causing an error in the determination of aluminum. Due to its complete reduction to metallic state it does not interfere with the titrimetric determination of iron when zinc is used as a reducing agent.

In the decomposition of the sample special precautions must be observed to prevent the loss of tin due to volatilization. H. B. Knowles found that no loss occurs if dilute hydrochloric acid solutions are boiled in covered beakers or when $H_2SO_4$ is present with the HCl with evaporation to fumes.[3] Chlorides, especially $SnCl_4$, volatilize on evaporation.

Decomposition of the silicate ores may be effected by fusion with NaOH, or $Na_2O_2$ or with a mixture of $Na_2CO_3$, $K_2CO_3$, and S. Minerals are first extracted with dilute $HNO_3$ followed by fusion of the insoluble residue.

As the oxides of tin are not readily soluble in acids, the tin can be most easily removed by assay. Ores, slags, dross, and ashes are first subjected to the assay process. The button obtained is then analyzed either titrimetrically or gravimetrically by one of the methods given below. Having the weight of the button and the per cent of tin in it, the per cent of tin in the sample as received can be calculated.

There are two general processes of assaying, namely, the Cyanide Method and the Sodium Carbonate Method.

## THE CYANIDE METHOD

The theory of this method is that the oxides are reduced to the metal by the action of potassium cyanide, the reaction being represented as follows:

$$SnO_2 + 2KCN \rightarrow Sn + 2KCNO$$

Potassium cyanide reduces other metals also, so that the button obtained is not pure.

*Procedure.*—Take 100 g. of the sample which has been dried and finely powdered. (For complete analysis the moisture should be determined in the usual way.) Mix thoroughly with four times its weight of powdered potassium cyanide. Place about 1″ of potassium cyanide in the bottom of a number H (height $5\frac{7}{8}$″, diameter $3\frac{3}{4}$″) Battersea clay crucible. Place the mixture of sample and cyanide on top of the cyanide in the crucible and cover with enough more cyanide to fill the crucible to within 1″ of the top.

Place the crucible in the assay furnace and heat slowly until it has been thoroughly warmed and the cyanide begins to melt. Then increase the heat gradually to a pure white, taking care that the cyanide does not boil over. Grasp the crucible with the tongs and tap it gently on the hearth to assist in settling the metal. Con-

3 Hillebrand and Lundell, Applied Inorganic Analysis, John Wiley and Sons.

tinue the heating until all of the organic matter has disappeared, adding more cyanide from time to time if necessary. Near the end of the process the molten mass becomes clear and transparent and finally pasty and translucent. When this last condition appears, remove the crucible from the furnace and allow it to cool slowly at room temperature.

When cool, break the crucible and slag away from the button. The appearance of the button and the slag immediately surrounding it indicates whether or not the process has been properly manipulated. The button itself should be firm and compact and the slag around it should be white or greenish in color. If the button is spongy or if the slag has a dirty black color, the assay should be discarded and a new determination made, using a fresh sample.

$$\text{Weight of button in g.} = \%\text{ metal in sample}$$

$$\%\text{ Sn in button} \times \%\text{ metal in sample} = \%\text{ Sn in the sample}$$

NOTE.—This process should be carried on under a *hood* in a segregated room, and every precaution should be taken to avoid breathing the poisonous fumes of potassium cyanide.

## THE SODIUM CARBONATE METHOD

The sample is fused with equal parts of sodium carbonate and sulfur.[4] The fusion is then dissolved in water. The tin goes into solution as a thiostannate of sodium. Iron and copper are then separated by the addition of sodium sulfite, leaving arsenic, antimony, and tin in solution.

## OTHER METHODS OF EXTRACTION

*Fusion with Sodium Hydroxide.*—The sample of ore is fused with ten times its weight of sodium hydroxide. The process is carried out in a 60-ml. iron crucible, first fusing the NaOH and then adding the powdered mineral. A nickel crucible may be used, adding a little powdered charcoal to the NaOH before fusing. The fused mass is dissolved in water and the tin determined in the usual way, after acidification with HCl.

*Reduction by Means of Hydrogen.*—The ore may be reduced by strongly igniting in a porcelain tube in a current of hydrogen. The reduced metal is then dissolved in hydrochloric acid and the tin estimated by a standard method.

*Fusion with Sodium Peroxide.*—J. Darroch and C. Meiklejohn [5] treated ores, slags, etc., by fusing with sodium peroxide in a nickel crucible. They dissolved the fused mass in hot water and acidify with hydrochloric acid. The sample is then ready for the necessary separations.

## SEPARATIONS

Tin is separated from iron, aluminum, chromium, etc., by the insolubility of its sulfide in dilute hydrochloric acid. Tin, together with antimony, arsenic, platinum, and gold, is separated from lead, mercury, copper, cadmium, and bis-

---

[4] Very finely divided carbon is sometimes preferred. Air must not be allowed to enter the crucible, or decomposition will not be complete. If carbon is used instead of sulfur the process becomes one of reduction to the metal and is carried out in the assay furnace. The details of operation are similar to the cyanide process. The metal separates as a button in the bottom of the crucible. The button contains other metals with the tin and must be analyzed further for exact percentages.

[5] Eng. Mining J., **81**, 1177, 1906.

muth, by the solubility of its sulfide in yellow ammonium sulfide. Antimony, arsenic, platinum, and gold are precipitated as metals from a hydrochloric acid solution by the action of metallic iron, leaving tin in solution.

A few special separations are of interest.

*Tin and Lead.*—For the analysis of an alloy of lead and tin, it is usually preferable to make the estimations on different samples. In this case, lead is estimated by Thompson's method and the tin by Baker's modification of the iodine method. Lead can also be separated from tin by $H_2S$ passed into an alkaline solution of $NH_4OH$. Lead may be separated as $PbSO_4$, no occlusion of tin occurs.

*Tin and Copper.*—This alloy can be dissolved in concentrated hydrochloric acid by the addition of potassium chlorate. A large excess of ammonium tartrate is added and the solution made alkaline with ammonia. Copper is then precipitated as sulfide by the addition of hydrogen sulfide water until no more precipitate is formed.

*Tin and Antimony.*—Antimony is separated, in the metallic form, from the hydrochloric acid solution of the alloy, by the action of metallic iron placed in the solution. The tin may be determined by the iodine method without the removal of the antimony. If the antimony is desired, it may be filtered off and determined in the usual way.

As in the case of lead, it is usually quicker and more accurate to make these determinations on separate samples. Precipitation of copper by addition of red phosphorus and filtering has been recommended.[6]

*Tin and Phosphorus.*—One-half gram of the alloy is dissolved in 15 ml. of concentrated hydrochloric acid containing potassium chlorate. This is diluted to 200 ml. with water and warmed. It is then treated for a long time with hydrogen sulfide gas. The tin is all precipitated as sulfide while the phosphorus remains in solution.

*Tin and Iron and Aluminum.*—Tin is separated from iron and aluminum by precipitation, as sulfide, from the hydrochloric acid solution (2.4 ml. HCl per 100 ml.).

Iron may also be separated from tin with copper, and lead by precipitation as sulfide from the alkaline ammonium tartrate solution.

*Tin and Tungstic Acid.*—Donath and Mullner[7] separate tin oxide from tungstic acid by mixing the sample with zinc dust and strongly igniting in a covered crucible for 15 minutes—boiling with dilute hydrochloric acid; oxidizing with potassium chlorate to change the blue tungstic oxide to tungstic acid and diluting with water. It is then allowed to stand overnight and filtered. The tin is in solution.

*Tin and Silicon.*—Dehydrate the silica by addition of $H_2SO_4$ and evaporation. Dissolve the tin sulfate. No loss of tin occurs.

*Tin, Copper, and Nickel.*—Precipitate the tin, in presence of ammonium salts, by addition of $NH_4OH$ according to the gravimetric method described on page 1077.

*Tin from Ag, Pb, Cu, Sb(III), As(III), Hg.*—Copper, lead, silver or mercury may be deposited electrolytically from a solution containing nitric and hydrofluoric acids (5 ml. of each per 100 ml.). The tin may be recovered by evaporating the filtrate in platinum to remove $H_2F_2$, or by adding boric acid to bind the fluoride; the stannic tin may then be precipitated by $H_2S$, by cupferron or electrolytically,

6 Silberstein, J., Chemist-Analyst, **19,** 14, 1930.

7 J. Chem. Soc. Absts., **54,** 531, 1888.

working in glass or polyethylene vessels.[8] In general the other metallic ions of the silver and copper-tin groups may be separated from stannic tin in sulfuric-hydrofluoric acid solution (5 ml. of each acid) per 100 ml. by hydrogen sulfide (sodium acetate may be added after most of the precipitation has occurred in order to reduce the acidity sufficiently to cause antimony and cadmium to precipitate). Arsenic and antimony are precipitated completely only if present in the trivalent state. Attack of materials by sulfuric acid and sulfur causes antimony and arsenic to remain trivalent, whereas tin goes readily to the tetravalent state when the solution is diluted and treated with $H_2F_2$.

*$SnO_2$ from Other Metallic Oxides*.[9]—Stannic oxide which is contaminated with ferric and cupric oxides, such as is obtained when copper-tin alloys are treated with nitric acid may be weighed. After treatment with ammonium iodide, the tin is volatilized in the form of $SnI_4$. The residual iodides may be converted back to the oxides ($Fe_2O_3$ and $CuO$) and weighed.

**Procedure.**—Ignite the separated metastannic acid to constant weight in a porcelain crucible. Then add to the impure tin oxide about fifteen times its weight of powdered ammonium iodide, and mix the two in the crucible intimately by means of a small spatula. Place the charged crucible in an electric crucible or muffle furnace maintained between 425° and 475°C. Allow it to remain there until all fumes have ceased to come from the crucible, about 15 minutes. Then remove the crucible and, after having allowed it to cool sufficiently, add 2 to 3 ml. of concentrated nitric acid. Evaporate to dryness on the hot plate and cautiously decompose the residual nitrates over a low burner flame. Follow this by ignition at low red heat to constant weight. The difference between this weight and the original weight gives the amount of pure stannic oxide present. A suitable correction should be applied if there is a weighable amount of nonvolatile matter in the ammonium iodide. To continue the analysis, dissolve the oxide residue out of the crucible by digestion with a few milliliters of hot concentrated hydrochloric acid. Dilute the resulting solution and filter it to remove small amounts of silica that may come from the filter paper ash. Finally add the solution and washings to the filtrate being evaporated down for the determination of lead as sulfate. The remainder of the analysis is conducted in the usual way.

## GRAVIMETRIC METHODS

## DETERMINATION OF TIN OR THE OXIDES OF TIN BY HYDROLYSIS

This method depends upon the precipitation of metastannic acid in the presence of ammonium nitrate when the stannic chloride is diluted to considerable volume and heated to boiling. It is especially applicable to the determination of tin oxide in tin paste, but may be extended to all chloride solutions of the higher oxides. The reaction involved proceeds as follows:

$$SnCl_4 + 4NH_4NO_3 + 3H_2O \rightarrow H_2SnO_3 + 4NH_4Cl + 4HNO_3 \text{ [10]}$$

8 McCay, J. Am. Chem. Soc., **31**, 373, 1909; **32**, 1241, 1910; **45**, 1187, 1923; McCay and Furman, *ibid.*, **38**, 640, 1915; Furman, *ibid.*, **40**, 895, 1918; Kling and Lassieur, Compt. rend., **170**, 1112, 1920; **173**, 1081, 1921; Furman, J. Ind. Eng. Chem., **15**, 1071, 1923.

9 Caley, E. R., and Burford, M. G., Ind. Eng. Chem., Anal. Ed., **8**, 114, 1936.

10 Sodium sulfate may be used instead of ammonium nitrate. In that case the reaction is $SnCl_4 + 4Na_2SO_4 + 3H_2O \rightarrow H_2SnO_3 + 4NaCl + 4NaHSO_4$.

Stannous tin may be determined by oxidizing the chloride solution to the stannic form. The method gives concordant results and is rapid.

*Procedure.*—For the analysis of tin paste take a catch weight of about 10 g. for a sample. Dissolve this sample by heating it in a beaker with 300 ml. of concentrated hydrochloric acid. Transfer the acid solution to a 500-ml. volumetric flask and make up to the mark with dilute (1:1) hydrochloric acid.

Take 50 ml. (approximately 1 g.) for a working sample. (If the determination is to be made on tin paste, the sample may be obtained directly by one of the methods described under "Estimation.") Dilute to 100 ml. with cold water. Nearly neutralize with concentrated ammonia and finish by adding drop by drop from a burette, dilute ammonia until a slight permanent precipitate is formed. A large amount of ammonia will tend to precipitate iron as $Fe(OH)_3$ if present, and to redissolve the metastannic acid.[11] Add 50 ml. of a saturated solution of ammonium nitrate. Dilute to 400 ml. with boiling water, stirring constantly. Bring the solution to boiling, remove from the flame and allow the beaker to stand on the steam bath until the precipitate has settled.[12] The solution above the precipitate should be clear. Decant the supernatant liquor through an ashless filter paper and wash the precipitate by decantation [13] 6 times, using 200 ml. of boiling water containing 6 g. $NH_4NO_3$ and allowing the precipitate to settle thoroughly at each washing. Transfer the precipitate to the filter, clean out the beaker and wash down with hot water in the usual way. After the precipitate has been allowed to drain, transfer to a porcelain or a silica crucible and dry carefully on an asbestos board over a Bunsen flame. When dry, ignite at a low temperature until the filter paper has been consumed.[14] Increase the heat and finally blast to constant weight.[15]

$$\frac{\text{Weight } SnO_2 \times 100 \times 0.7877}{\text{Weight of sample}} = \% \text{ Sn}$$

Note.—If present in the solution the following would contaminate the $SnO_2$ oxides of Si, Nb, Ta, W, Sb, As, P (Fe, Cu, and Zn).

## PRECIPITATION OF TIN AS SULFIDE

The determination of tin as a sulfide involves many difficulties and should be avoided if possible. Better results can be obtained by the titrimetric methods and in most cases without the necessity of preliminary separations of other elements. If tin must be separated as a sulfide, better results will be obtained if the precipitate is dissolved and the tin content determined by the iodine method.

*Procedure.*—Having the hydrochloric acid solution of tin after the interfering elements have been separated, to precipitate tin sulfide, neutralize with ammonia and then acidify with acetic acid. Pass hydrogen sulfide until the solution is saturated. Allow the precipitate to settle overnight. Pour the supernatant liquor

---

[11] Some practice is required to judge accurately the exact point when the necessary amount of ammonia has been added. The precipitate should appear white.

[12] If the boiling continues more than a few seconds the precipitate will not settle properly. Time will be saved in this case if the sample is discarded and a new determination commenced.

[13] If metastannic acid is washed over onto the filter at this point, clogging will result and a great deal of time will be lost.

[14] Spattering is likely to occur here, causing loss.

[15] If care is not exercised in this ignition some metallic tin due to carbon reduction will be obtained.

off through a Gooch crucible and wash the precipitate six times by decantation, using a solution of ammonium nitrate [16] for wash water. Finally transfer to the crucible and wash free from chlorides. Dry the crucible in an oven at 100°C. Heat slowly in a Bunsen flame until all the sulfur has been expelled. Care should be taken at this point to avoid forming fumes of stannic sulfide by heating too rapidly. Remove the lid of the crucible, which should be kept in place during the first part of the heating, and raise the temperature gradually, finally finishing with the blast. As sulfuric acid is usually present in some quantity, the crucible should be cooled and a small piece of ammonium carbonate should be placed in it. Repeat the ignition to drive out the acid. Cool and weigh as $SnO_2$.[17]

NOTES.—Tin may be separated from a number of elements by reduction with Zn, Al, or Cd in dilute HCl solution and then precipitated as metastannic acid by addition of $NH_4OH$.
Stannic chloride may be volatilized from a sulfuric acid solution by heating to 200°C. and passing HCl gas through the solution.

## PRECIPITATION BY CUPFERRON; WEIGHING AS THE OXIDE [18]

This reagent is chiefly useful for the recovery of tin from the filtrate after separating it from other metals in solution containing 3–5% of concentrated HF.

*Procedure.*—The filtrate is warmed with 4 g. boric acid to convert the fluoride to fluoborate. After cooling, preferably to 5 to 15°C., add an excess of 10% cupferron solution slowly with thorough stirring. The precipitate tends to become brittle after 20–30 minutes, and may then be filtered and washed very speedily with cold water. The precipitate is then dried and ignited very carefully and slowly until it is converted to $SnO_2$, in which form it is weighed after strong ignition.

The reagent separates stannic ion from Al, Cr, Mn, Zn, Ni, Co, and from moderate quantities of As and Sb provided they are in the form of arsenate and antimonate, which can readily be provided for by boiling the nearly neutral solution containing fluoride with ammonium persulfate. The solution should contain 5–10 ml. of free mineral acid per 200–500 ml. during the precipitation with cupferron.

## TITRIMETRIC METHODS

## TIN BY THE IODIMETRIC TITRATION METHOD [19]

When tin is to be reduced to the stannous state and determined by titration with standard iodine or iodate solution, air must be excluded during the reduction and titration to prevent oxidation of the stannous tin. This is usually accomplished by keeping the solution under a blanket of gaseous $CO_2$.

*Apparatus.*—Fig. 47-1 shows one of the many forms of apparatus that may be used when gaseous $CO_2$ is employed. It shall consist of a flask closed with a three-hole rubber stopper containing an inlet tube for $CO_2$, in air condenser, and a hole for the burette (glass plugged). During reduction a very slow stream of $CO_2$ should

[16] Sulfide of tin separates as a slimy mass which tenaciously retains alkaline salts, especially in the absence of ammonium salts.
[17] This method is generally used only when minute traces of tin are present, and then it is considered best to dissolve the sulfide in hydrochloric acid and make the final determination by the iodine method.
[18] Kling and Lassieur, Compt. rend., **170**, 1112, 1920; Furman, J. Ind. Eng. Chem., **15**, 1071, 1923; Pinkus and Claessens, Bull. Soc. Chim. Belg., **31**, 413, 1927.
[19] ASTM Methods, Chemical Analysis of Metals, 1960.

be passed through the flask. When reduction is complete, the flow should be increased to maintain a protecting blanket of $CO_2$ during the cooling and titration.

**Reagents. Ferric Chloride Solution (6 g. $FeCl_3$ per l.).**—Dissolve 10 g. of $FeCl_3 \cdot 6H_2O$ in water and dilute to 1 liter.

**Ammonium Chloride Wash Solution.**—Dissolve 10 g. of $NH_4Cl$ in 1 liter of water made slightly alkaline with a few drops of $NH_4OH$.

**Iron.**—Relatively pure iron (not less than 99.85% Fe).

**Nickel.**—A roll of sheet nickel having an exposed area of at least 10 sq. in.

**Aluminum.**—Sheet or rolled foil of aluminum.

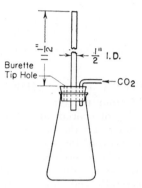

FIG. 47-1.   Apparatus for the Reduction of Tin.

**Antimony Chloride Solution (20 g. $SbCl_3$ per l.).**—Dissolve 2 g. of $SbCl_3$ in 50 ml. of HCl and dilute to 100 ml. with water.

**Potassium Iodide Solution (100 g. KI per l.).**—Prepare fresh as required.

**Starch Solution (10 g. per l.).**—Make a paste of 1 g. of soluble (or arrowroot) starch in about 5 ml. of water and add to 100 ml. of boing water. Cool, add 5 g. of KI, and stir until the KI is dissolved. Prepare fresh as needed.

**Standard Tin Solution (1 ml. = 0.001 g. Sn).**—Dissolve 1.0000 g. of tin in a covered 500 ml. beaker in 300 ml. of HCl (1:1) by warming gently until the metal has dissolved. If solution is difficult, add 0.05 to 0.1 g. of $KClO_3$. Cool, and dilute to 1 liter in a volumetric flask. This is a primary standard.

**Standard Iodine Solution (1 ml. = 0.003 g. Sn, approximately 0.05 N).**—Dissolve 6.35 g. of iodine and 20 g. of KI in 25 ml. of water. When solution is complete, dilute to 1 liter. Store in a cool place in a dark-colored, glass-stoppered bottle. Standardize the iodine solution as follows: Pipette 50 ml. of the standard tin solution into a 300-ml. Erlenmeyer flask, and continue as described under "Procedure" (c), (d), or (e), and (f) and (g).

**Standard Potassium Iodate Solution (0.05 N).**—Twice recrystallize $KIO_3$ from water and dry at 180°C. to constant weight. Dissolve 1.7835 g. of the $KIO_3$ in 200 ml. of water containing 0.5 g. of NaOH and add 5 g. of KI. When solution is complete, dilute to 1 liter in a volumetric flask. Standardize the $KIO_3$ solution as prescribed for the iodine solution.

**Procedure.**—(a) Transfer 1.000 to 2.000 g. of the sample, depending on the tin content, to a 250-ml. beaker, cover, and dissolve in 5 ml. of HCl and 20 ml. of $HNO_3$ (1:1), adding more HCl, if necessary, to keep the tin in solution. When dissolution is complete, boil gently to expel brown fumes. Wash down the cover glass and sides of the beaker, and dilute to 125 ml. with water. Add 5 to 10 ml. of $FeCl_3$ solution.

(b) Add $NH_4OH$ (1:1) until the basic salts are just dissolved and the solution becomes clear. Toward the end the addition should be made drop by drop. Bring the solution to incipient boiling. Filter through a coarse paper, and wash the beaker and precipitate several times with hot $NH_4Cl$ wash solution. Discard the filtrate and washings, place the original beaker beneath the funnel, and dissolve the precipitate through the paper with hot HCl (1:1). Wash the paper several times with hot water and retain it in the funnel for the next filtration. Reprecipitate with $NH_4OH$ (1:1), heat, filter, and wash thoroughly with $NH_4Cl$ wash solution until all nitrates have been removed. Dissolve the precipitate through the paper with hot HCl (1:1) into a 500-ml. Erlenmeyer flask and wash thoroughly with hot water. Transfer the paper to a 300-ml. Erlenmeyer flask and add 20 ml. of $HNO_3$ and 10 ml. of $H_2SO_4$. Heat to destroy organic matter, adding $HNO_3$ as necessary. Evaporate to dense white fumes. Cool, wash the sides of the flask with water, and again evaporate to fumes. Cool, and combine with the solution in the 500-ml. flask. Reduce the solution as described in paragraph (c), (d), or (e), following.

(c) **Reduction with Iron.**—Dilute the solution to 200 ml. Add 60 ml. of HCl, 2 drops of $SbCl_3$ solution, and at least 5 g. of iron. Stopper the flask as described under "Apparatus" and pass in $CO_2$. Heat the solution to boiling, and boil with continuous evolution of gas for at least 30 minutes. Some undissolved iron should remain after the reduction.

(d) **Reduction with Nickel.**—Dilute the solution to 200 ml. Add 75 ml. of HCl and 2 drops of $SbCl_3$ solution and introduce a roll of sheet nickel. Stopper the flask as described under "Apparatus" and pass in $CO_2$. Heat the solution to boiling, and boil with continuous evolution of gas for at least 45 minutes.

(e) **Reduction with Aluminum.**—Dilute the solution to 200 ml. Add 80 ml. of HCl and 2 drops of $SbCl_3$ solution, and introduce about 2 g. of aluminum into the cool solution. When the aluminum is nearly dissolved, stopper the flask as described above and pass in $CO_2$. Heat the solution to boiling, and boil for 10 to 15 minutes (until all the aluminum and metallic tin are in solution).

(f) After reduction is complete, maintain the atmosphere of $CO_2$ gas in the flask and cool to about 10°C. if reduced with iron or nickel, or to 25°C. if reduced with aluminum. Add 5 ml. of KI solution and 5 ml. of starch solution and titrate with either iodine or $KIO_3$ solution [20] to a persistent blue tint.

(g) **Blank.**—Make a blank determination, following the same procedure and using the same amount of all reagents.

**Calculation.**—Calculate the percentage of tin as follows:

$$\text{Tin, \%} = \frac{(A - B)C}{D} \times 100$$

where $A$ = milliliters of iodine or $KIO_3$ solution required to titrate the sample,
  $B$ = milliliters of iodine or $KIO_3$ solution required to titrate the blank,
  $C$ = tin equivalent of the iodine or $KIO_3$ solution, in grams per milliliter, and
  $D$ = grams of sample used.

## FERRIC CHLORIDE METHOD [21]

This method depends upon the reduction of ferric chloride by stannous chloride in hot solution.

$$SnCl_2 + 2FeCl_3 \rightarrow SnCl_4 + 2FeCl_2$$

[20] In the analysis of alloys low in tin, iodine solution (1 ml. = 0.001 g. Sn, approximately 0.02 $N$) or $KIO_3$ solution (1 ml. = 0.001 g. Sn, approximately 0.02 $N$) may be substituted for the solutions above and 1 to 2 g. of KI should be added to the flask at the start of the titration. This applies particularly to blanks.

[21] Mene, C., Dinglers Polytech. J., **117**, 230, 1850; Pallet, K., and Allart, A., Bul. Soc. Chim. (2), **27**, 43, 438, 1877; Rawlins, H. J. B., Chem. News, **107**, 53, 1913; Nelsmann, H., Z. Anal. Chem., **16**, 50, 1877.

Antimony, copper, arsenic, bismuth, mercuric chloride, tungsten, and titanium must be absent.

**Reagent. Standard Solution of Ferric Chloride.**—Made by dissolving pure iron wire in hydrochloric acid. To standardize this solution, dissolve 1 g. of pure tin in 200 ml. of C.P. HCl, preventing air from coming in contact with the solution by means of a trap, or by passing carbon dioxide over it.[22] Titrate this standard sample with the ferric chloride solution. The end point is indicated by the yellow color, due to a slight excess of the iron solution.

**Procedure.**—Tin is first separated from the interfering metals in the usual way. If lead, copper, arsenic, antimony, or bismuth are present, the sample is first reduced, in the hydrochloric solution, with iron wire. The solution is then filtered. Lead and tin remain in the filtrate. Neutralize by adding strips of zinc until the action ceases. Tin and lead are precipitated. The clear liquid should show no trace of tin with hydrogen sulfide. Allow the precipitate to settle and wash by decantation, keeping the precipitated metals in the flask. Add 150 ml. of concentrated hydrochloric acid, keeping the contents of the flask protected from the air, and bring to a boil. When everything is dissolved, titrate to a yellow color with the ferric chloride solution.[23] This part of the analysis should be done very quickly to prevent oxidation by the oxygen of the air.

## COLORIMETRIC/PHOTOMETRIC METHODS

### DITHIOL METHOD [24]

An important feature of this method is the use of the dispersing agent 30% Santomerse S (Monsanto Chemical Co.). This reagent, when used as directed, renders the tin-dithiol complex entirely suitable for absorptiometric measurements, made at 530 m$\mu$. Solutions are stable for at least three hours.

Although satisfactorily stable colors can be prepared, a number of the heavy metals (bismuth, copper, iron, nickel, cobalt, silver, mercury, lead, cadmium, arsenic, antimony, molybdenum, etc.) react with dithiol and direct application of the reagent is not feasible without first isolating the tin. While a number of methods are available for isolating tin from various elements, distillation is very effective, since certain elements such as arsenic, antimony, etc., can first be distilled over as the chloride. Tin can then be distilled with a hydrobromic acid–hydrochloric acid mixture which leaves behind the remaining nonvolatile interfering metals.

Briefly, the method consists of destroying organic matter, if present, first distilling over arsenic, antimony, etc., as chloride and then distilling over the tin. The resulting tin solution which is free from interfering elements is treated with sulfuric acid and hydrogen peroxide to remove bromides, the tin is reduced with thioglycolic acid, and the color is developed with dithiol in the presence of Santomerse S as a dispersing agent. The red color is measured at 530 m$\mu$.

**Reagents. Standard Tin Solution. Strong, 1 ml. = 0.4 mg. of tin.**—Weigh and transfer 0.2000 g. of pure tin to a 500-ml. volumetric flask and add 50 ml. of hydrochloric acid. When solution is complete, dilute with water, cool, make up to volume, and mix well. This solution is stable for at least 1 month.

[22] A Sellars apparatus can be used with advantage for this purpose.
[23] The end point can be easily identified by looking at a blue Bunsen flame through the solution. When a small quantity of ferric chloride is present, the flame appears green.
[24] Farnsworth and Pekola, Anal. Chem., **26**, 735, 1954.

**Standard Tin Solution. Weak, 1 ml. = 0.04 mg. of tin.**—Pipette 25 ml. of the strong standard tin solution into a 250-ml. volumetric flask, dilute to volume, and mix well. This solution is not stable and should be prepared just before use.

**Sulfuric Acid Solution (3 to 7).**—Add 75 ml. of sulfuric acid to 100 ml. of water, cool, transfer to a 250-ml. volumetric flask, dilute to volume, and mix well.

**Thioglycolic Acid.**

**Dithiol Reagent (0.30%).**—Weigh 0.15 g. of dithiol into a 100-ml. beaker, add 8 drops of thioglycolic acid, and then add 50 ml. of sodium hydroxide solution (2%). Stir until the dithiol is completely dissolved. If the solution is not perfectly clear, filter through a dry, very fine-grained filter paper into a clean, dry, glass-stoppered bottle and store in a refrigerator. The solution is stable for 1 week.

**Santomerse S (30%).**—Use as received from the Monsanto Chemical Co.

**Hydrazine Sulfate.**

*Preparation of Calibration Curve.* **Calibration Solutions.**—Into four 50-ml. volumetric flasks pipette 5 ml. of sulfuric acid solution (3 to 7), add 5 ml. of water to each, and cool. Pipette 2, 5, 10, and 20 ml. of the standard tin solution (1 ml. = 0.04 mg. of tin) into the four 50-ml. volumetric flasks and then immediately add 5 drops of thioglycolic acid to each and swirl to mix. Dilute to about 45 ml. with water and swirl to mix. Proceed as described below.

**Blank Solution.**—Pipette 5 ml. of sulfuric acid solution (3 to 7) into a 50-ml. volumetric flask, add 5 ml. of water, cool, add 5 drops of thioglycolic acid, and swirl to mix. Dilute to about 45 ml., swirl to mix, and proceed as described below.

**Color Development.**—To the first flask add 2 drops of 30% Santomerse S and swirl for about 0.5 minute to mix. The flask should be swirled gently to avoid foaming. Proceed in a like manner with the remaining solutions. Pipette 1 ml. of 30% dithiol reagent into the first flask and immediately swirl solution (gently to avoid excess foaming) for 1 minute. Add 8 drops more of Santomerse S and swirl gently for 1 minute. Proceed in a like manner with the remaining solutions. Dilute each solution to volume with water, stopper, invert, and shake for about 5 seconds. Repeat this mixing twice.

The solution may become turbid after the addition of the dithiol reagent or after the addition of the 8 drops of Santomerse S later on. There is no need for concern should this occur, as the solution will become clear after being made up to volume and mixed.

**Photometry.**—Transfer suitable portions of the solutions to absorption cells (1 cm.) and, with the blank solution set at 100% transmittancy, measure the transmittance of the solution at 530 m$\mu$. The color is stable for at least 3 hours.

**Calibration Curve.**—Plot the photometric readings of the calibration solutions against milligrams of tin per 50 ml. of solution.

*Procedure.*—If the material is of a biological or other organic nature, add 25 ml. of sulfuric acid and destroy the organic matter through repeated additions of nitric acid and evaporation to fumes of sulfur trioxide. When the organic matter has been destroyed, cool, wash down sides of beaker with water, and evaporate to fumes of sulfur trioxide. Repeat twice to ensure complete removal of nitric acid and then cool.

If the material does not contain organic matter, dissolve in hydrochloric acid or sulfuric acid. If nitric acid is required to effect solution, this then must be removed as described in the paragraph above. Tin, especially in the oxidized condition, hydrolyzes readily from a sulfuric acid medium. Hydrolysis of tin will also occur, though not so readily, from a hydrochloric acid medium, if the acid concentration becomes too low. In the event that an aliquot of the sample is to be used for analysis, it is recommended that the entire sample be at least 1 to 9 in hydrochloric acid, even if sulfuric acid is present. With both organic and inorganic materials, a blank should be carried through the entire procedure with the sample.

Introduce 2 g. of hydrazine sulfate (powdered solid) with the aid of a minimum amount of water to the distillation apparatus (see Fig. 47-2). Transfer the sulfuric or hydrochloric acid solution of the sample, containing not less than 0.04 mg. and not more than 0.8 mg. of tin, to the distillation apparatus with the aid of not more than 20 ml. of water. Add 10 ml. of phosphoric acid, 20 ml. of hydrochloric acid and increase the sulfuric acid content to a total of 25 ml., if this amount is not already present.

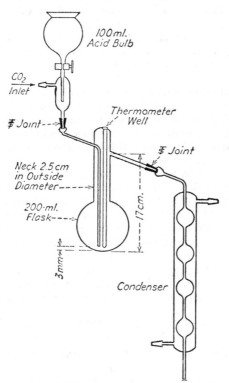

100 ml. Acid Bulb

$CO_2$ Inlet

Thermometer Well

Joint

Joint

Neck 2.5 cm in Outside Diameter

200 ml. Flask

17 cm.

3 mm.

Condenser

FIG. 47-2. Apparatus for the Distillation of Tin.

Add 50 ml. of water to a 400-ml. beaker and place under the condenser so that the tip is submerged at least 0.25 inch. The apparatus should be so arranged that the distillate can be removed at any time. Place 150 ml. of hydrochloric acid in the acid bulb, start a slow stream of carbon dioxide through the solution, bring to a boil, and boil gently. When the temperature has reached 165°C., introduce the hydrochloric acid from the bulb into the flask at such a rate that the temperature remains between 155 to 170°C. (about 40 drops per minute). When about 125 ml. of hydrochloric acid has been introduced into the flask, allow the distillation to continue but remove distillate, wash down stem of condenser, and replace the first beaker with a 100-ml. beaker containing 25 ml. of water. When only approximately 1 to 2 ml. of hydrochloric acid remain in the bulb, close the stopcock to shut off the flow of hydrochloric acid, shut off the heat, lower the distillate until free of the condenser, and wash down the stem of the condenser with water. Discard both distillates.

Place a 200-ml. tall-form beaker containing 40 ml. of water under the condenser so that the tip of the condenser is about 0.25″ from the bottom of the beaker. Place 45 ml. of a mixture of hydrochloric acid (15 ml.) and hydrobromic acid (30 ml.) in the acid bulb; when the temperature has dropped to 130°C., start the heat and begin to introduce the acid from the bulb when the temperature begins to rise. Introduce the acid into the flask at a rate of 30 to 40 drops per minute and maintain the temperature between 137 to 147°C. When only approximately 1 ml. of the acid remains in the bulb, close the stopcock to shut off the flow of acid, shut off the heat, and lower the distillate until free of the condenser. Shut off the flow of carbon dioxide and wash down the stem of the condenser with water.

Pipette 5 ml. of sulfuric acid (3 to 7) into the distillate, stir, place on a hot plate, and bring to a boil. Boil gently for 5 minutes and then cool to room temperature. Add 10 ml. of 30% hydrogen peroxide, stir, cover with a ribbed watch glass, and place on a hot plate. (Some brands of peroxide give a very high blank and should not be used. Merck's Superoxol C.P. is satisfactory.) Boil the solution gently until it becomes almost colorless or until no more red fumes of bromine are given off. Remove from the hot plate, shift the cover slightly, and add 10 ml. of 30% hydrogen peroxide in small portions, stirring and waiting for the reaction to subside before each addition. Replace on the hot plate and boil gently until the solution is colorless. Remove from the hot plate and add at one time, an additional 5 ml. of 30% hydrogen peroxide. Replace on the hot plate and boil down to a volume of 5 to 10 ml. Remove and wash down the cover and sides of the beaker with water. Evaporate uncovered and without boiling to fumes of sulfur trioxide, cover with a flat watch glass, and allow to fume for 3 minutes. If the solution becomes slightly tan or brownish from the presence of some organic matter, add a small pinch of ammonium persulfate to destroy this organic matter and allow the solution to fume an additional minute. Remove, allow to cool, wash down the sides of the beaker with water and evaporate uncovered to fumes of sulfur trioxide. Then cover with a flat watch glass and allow to fume again for 3 minutes. Remove and allow to cool.

Add 10 ml. of water to the first beaker, swirl to mix, immediately add 5 drops of thioglycolic acid, and swirl to mix. Proceed in a like manner with any remaining solutions. Transfer each solution to a 50-ml. volumetric flask, quantitatively, with the aid of water. Swirl to mix and cool. The volume in each flask should be approximately 45 ml. Proceed in accordance with the method described above for the preparation of a calibration curve for tin.

Convert the photometric readings for the sample to milligrams of tin by means of the calibration curve.

## DETERMINATION IN SPECIFIC SUBSTANCES

## RAPID TITRIMETRIC DETERMINATION IN BABBITT METAL [25]

The titrimetric tin determination with iodine is not accurate in presence of copper exceeding 3%. High grade genuine babbitts often contain from 5 to 8% copper and the copper has therefore to be removed previous to the tin determination. This is most rapidly and conveniently accomplished by precipitating the copper with red phosphorus.

Vogel [26] in 1836 observed that yellow phosphorus precipitated copper from a solution of copper sulfate. This reaction takes place even if the solution contains as little as one gram molecule copper sulfate per 1,000,000 liters $H_2O$ which corresponds to a sensitivity of 0.0000065% Cu. [27] Yellow phosphorus is however not as convenient to handle as the red, amorphous modification, which also can be used for precipitation of copper. [28]

[25] Silberstein, Chemist-Analyst, 19, 14, 1930.
[26] J. prakt. Chem., 8, 109, 1836.
[27] Z. anorg. allgem. Chem., 35, 460, 1903.
[28] J. Am. Chem. Soc., 42, 883, 1920.

To save time it is to be recommended to determine both tin and antimony in the same sample.

*Procedure.*—After having dissolved the sample in sulfuric acid and determined the antimony by titration with permanganate the solution is transferred to a 400-ml. beaker, about a half teaspoonful red phosphorus added and the solution boiled for 15 minutes. The solution is then filtered through a Munktells No. 00 filter into a 500-ml. Erlenmeyer flask. Wash a few times with dilute $H_2SO_4$ (1:10) and discard the precipitate which contains the copper as copper phosphide. Add HCl and nickel strip to the solution, reduce and titrate the tin as usual with iodine using starch as indicator.

On precipitating the copper the phosphorus is oxidized to a state lower than orthophosphoric. This has, however, no influence on the subsequent tin determination.

## TITRIMETRIC METHOD FOR TIN IN ALLOYS

The titration of stannous solutions by iodine may be represented by the following reaction:

$$Sn^{++} + I_2 \rightarrow Sn^{++} + 2I^-$$

Here the equivalent weight of tin is half of its atomic weight, hence a normal solution contains one-half the molecular weight of Sn, or 59.35 g. per liter of solution.

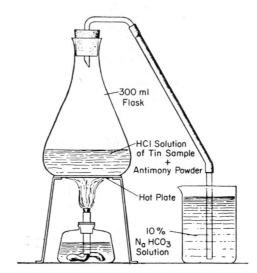

FIG. 47-3. Apparatus for the Determination of Tin.

*Apparatus.*—This consists (see Fig. 47-3) of a 300-ml. Erlenmeyer flask, with a one-hole stopper, through which passes a quarter-inch glass tube, connected with a rubber tube 12 to 15 inches in length, the other end of the rubber tubing is connected with 2–3 inches of glass tubing, which dips in the beaker containing a bicarbonate of sodium solution.

*Reagents.* **0.1 N Iodine Solution.**—Standardize against pure tin, using the procedure below. One ml. 0.1 N I = 0.005935 g. of Sn.

**Starch Solution.**
**Sulfuric Acid.**
**Hydrochloric Acid.**
**Antimony, or Iron, Powder or Test Lead.**

*Procedure.*—Tin alloys generally decompose in hydrochloric acid, but more readily in concentrated, hot sulfuric acid.

A sample containing, preferably, 0.1 g. Sn or less, is placed in a 300-ml. Erlenmeyer flask and 10 ml. of concentrated sulfuric acid added. The mixture is heated, preferably over a free flame, until the alloy completely disintegrates. Nearly all of the excess of free acid is expelled, keeping the flask in motion over the flame to lessen the tendency towards bumping, which is apt to occur during the concentration. The moist residue is allowed to cool.

One hundred ml. of (air-free) water are added followed by 50 ml. of concentrated hydrochloric acid and the mixture gently warmed until the solution begins to clear. The apparatus is now assembled as shown in Fig. 47-3, about 15 ml. of 10% (saturated solution) sodium bicarbonate being placed in the test tube (or 50 ml. in the beaker, if this is preferred to a test tube).

About 1 g. of very finely powdered reducing metal is placed in the flask, followed by 10 ml. of saturated sodium bicarbonate solution, the stopper being removed during the addition and then immediately replaced. The air is displaced by the $CO_2$ generated.[29]

The apparatus is now placed on a hot plate, or on an inverted sand-bath dish over a flame, and the solution is gently boiled for 10 to 15 minutes. The antimony should be of such fineness as to remain suspended during the ebullition of the liquid at this stage.

The beaker is now nearly filled with saturated sodium bicarbonate and the apparatus removed to cool for a few minutes, and then placed in a cold water bath of running water or under tap water, until the solution cools down to near room temperature. During this cooling carbonate will be sucked back into the flask *A* to establish pressure equilibrium, $CO_2$ being generated in the flask. Sufficient solution will remain in the test tube to act as a seal and prevent admission of air, which would spoil results by its oxidation of the tin.

The tubes are disconnected and 5 ml. of starch solution added by means of a pipette passing through the hole in the stopper (which should be loosened in the throat of the flask).

Standard iodine solution is now added, the tip of the burette passing through the hole of the stopper, agitating the solution by a swirling motion of the flask. The end point is a blue color, which does not fade on stirring the solution.

If a factor weight has been taken, each ml. of the iodine of 0.1 N strength is equivalent to 1% of tin.

NOTES.—In the presence of copper a separation must be effected for over 3% copper interferes in this titrimetric method especially when the percentage of the tin is low. High copper alloys do not decompose readily in hydrochloric or sulfuric acids, but easily in dilute nitric acid. The solution obtained is evaporated to dryness, the residue is taken up with concentrated nitric acid, the oxide of tin (and antimony) remains insoluble, hot water is added and the solution filtered (hot) and the oxide washed once or twice with hot water. The tin (and antimony) is now best dissolved [30] by digesting for 3–5 minutes

29 The method is capable of giving very excellent results and compares very favorably with the more elaborate procedure of passing $CO_2$ through the apparatus during the reduction and cooling.
30 Stelling, Ernest, J. Ind. Eng. Chem., **16**, 346, 1924.

with 50 ml. of water saturated with $SO_2$ (at 60–70°C.), then 10 ml. of strong HCl are added to the solution heated to boiling and the $SO_2$ expelled by boiling. The solution is now ready for reduction with antimony by the method outlined above.

Tin may be reduced by iron, nickel, or lead. If much copper is present this should be removed.

NOTE.—If iron is used for the reduction of tin $HNO_3$, W, Mo, and V should be absent from the solution. W is reduced and colors the solution blue, masking the end point. Mo causes a brown coloration and will titrate, causing high results for tin. V produces a purple color and also is titrated. If test lead is used for reduction the above do not interfere. The following do not interfere: $SO_4$, $PO_4$, I, Br, F, Fe, Ni, Co, Zn, Mn, Cl, Al, Cr, Pb, Bi, Sb, Mg, Ca, Ba, Sr, Mg.

## IODIMETRIC METHOD FOR TIN IN WHITE METAL ALLOYS

The National Lead Company uses the following procedure.

*Apparatus.*—A delivery tube made of glass tubing 5 mm. inside diameter is bent into an inverted letter L, the small end of which is fitted in a No. 6 rubber stopper. When the stopper is inserted in the mouth of the flask, the short end of the tube should just pass through the stopper and the other end should reach to a level 1 in. from the bottom of the flask and be 1 in. distant from the flask.

*Reagents.* **Sodium Bicarbonate Solution.**—Place 10 g. of $NaHCO_3$ in a 100-ml. beaker and fill with cold distilled water.

**Starch Solution.**—To 1000 ml. of boiling water add a cold suspension of 6 g. of starch in 100 ml. of distilled water: cool, add a few drops of oil of cassia, mix and reserve for use.

**Standard 0.1 $N$ Iodine Solution.**—Weigh out 12.7 g. of pure sublimed iodine and 18 g. of potassium iodide, transfer to a 500-ml. beaker, add about 35 ml. of cold distilled water and allow to digest in the cold for several days. Dilute to nearly 700 ml. with distilled water and filter through glass wool into a 1000-ml. graduated flask. Do not wash. Make up to the mark and mix thoroughly.

Standardize by weighing out 0.3 g. of pure tin filings and 0.1 g. of powdered metallic antimony into a 300-ml. cone flask. Add 20 ml. $H_2SO_4$ and proceed exactly as described from the addition of the 20 ml. of $H_2SO_4$ early in the method below for samples containing less than 0.03 g. of copper.

### METHOD A: FOR SAMPLES CONTAINING LESS THAN 0.03 GRAM OF COPPER

*Procedure.*—Weigh out from 0.5 to 2 g. of the sawings,[31] brush into a 300-ml. cone flask, add 20 ml. $H_2SO_4$ (sp. gr. 1.84) and heat on a bare hot plate [32] until completely decomposed. Cool, add 100 ml. of cold distilled water and 20 ml. HCl (sp. gr. 1.18), introduce four pieces of iron [33] and heat on an asbestos covered hot plate over a low flame until the iron is almost but not entirely dissolved. A reduction of 40 minutes duration is sufficient to completely reduce the tin.

Filter off the precipitated metals through glass wool into a 500-ml. cone flask in which has been placed four pieces of iron, washing the flask three times and the funnel three times with hot distilled water. The volume at this point should be

---

[31] Pass a hand magnet through the sample before weighing.

[32] Too high a heat will cause the solution to spit.

[33] The iron for reducing the tin is the ordinary strap iron used for strapping shipping cases. Each piece should be 2 in. long and ½ in. wide, weigh about 2 g. and be free from grease, lacquer and rust.

about 250 ml. Fit the delivery tube in the mouth of the flask, set over a low flame and reduce as before.

When the reduction is complete, set the bicarbonate solution so that the free end of the delivery tube is immersed in it. When gas bubbles start to pass through the $NaHCO_3$ solution, remove both flask and beaker from the stove, allow to cool at room temperature for about 10 minutes and then cool [34] the flask in running water. When cold, remove the delivery tube, withdraw any undissolved iron with a magnetic file, washing both removed iron and file with cold distilled water, add 2 ml. of starch solution and titrate with the standard iodine solution to the first permanent tinge of blue.

Run a blank by treating 0.1 g. of powdered metallic antimony exactly as the metal itself was treated.

Make correction for the blank and calculate for tin content.

**Accuracy.**—Duplicate titrations should not disagree more than 0.1 ml.

## METHOD B: FOR SAMPLES CONTAINING MORE THAN 0.03 GRAM OF COPPER

**Procedure.**—Weigh out from 0.5 to 2 g. of the sawings, brush into a 250-ml. beaker, add 15 ml. $HNO_3$ (1:1) and heat until completely decomposed. Evaporate to near dryness, add 5 ml. $HNO_3$ (sp. gr. 1.42), dilute to a volume of 150 ml., bring to boiling, and allow to stand in a warm place one hour. Filter on a 9-cm. paper to which has been added a little pulp [35] and wash two or three times with hot dilute $HNO_3$ (1:50). Transfer the paper and precipitate to a 300-ml. cone flask, add 20 ml. $H_2SO_4$ (sp. gr. 1.84) and 5 g. of $K_2S_2O_7$ and heat over a flame until the paper has been completely decomposed and the clear solution is perfectly colorless. Cool, add 100 ml. of water, 20 ml. of HCl (sp. gr. 1.18), four pieces of iron and proceed as in Method $A$, above.

## FUSION MODIFICATION OF FOREGOING METHOD FOR TIN IN A WHITE METAL ALLOY

This modification [36] is used for alloys which do not decompose completely under the $H_2SO_4$ treatment. Consequently a preliminary fusion is carried out, followed by the above procedure. Furthermore, for accurate work, this requires a corresponding change in the method of standardizing the iodine solution.

**Reagents. Standard 0.1 N Iodine Solution.**—Prepare a solution of iodine as described in the Iodimetric Method above. Standardize by weighing out 0.3 g. of pure tin filings, brush into a 300-ml. cone flask, add 20 ml. $H_2SO_4$ (sp. gr. = 1.84) and heat on a hot place, until dissolved. Cool and dilute with 50 ml. of water. In the meantime, fuse 20 g. of $Na_2O_2$ in an iron crucible, leach out with least amount of water; carefully transfer to the flask containing the tin, add 70 ml. HCl (sp. gr. = 1.18), dilute to a volume of 250 ml., add 4 pieces of iron and heat over a low flame until nearly dissolved.[37] Introduce four more pieces of iron, insert a

[34] Keep the delivery tube in the mouth of the flask and the free end immersed in the $NaHCO_3$ solution during the whole cooling operation.

[35] Paper pulp may be prepared by tearing several 11-cm. Whatman No. 40 filter papers into small pieces, introducing them into a 300-ml. cone flask, adding 100 ml. of hot distilled water, stopper, and shaking vigorously until pulped.

[36] By courtesy of the National Lead Company.

[37] The time required to nearly dissolve the iron should be about 40 minutes and the solution should show no tinge of yellow. If a yellow color persists, add two pieces of iron and continue the reduction.

rubber stopper carrying a delivery tube and reduce as before. Proceed as described in the second paragraph of Method *A* above.

*Procedure.*—Weigh out 0.5–1.0 g. of the finely ground sample, brush into an iron crucible of 60-ml. capacity in which has been placed 10 g. $Na_2O_2$, mix, cover with 10 g. $Na_2O_2$, place lid loosely on crucible and heat over a good sized Bunsen flame. As soon as the melt is in quiet fusion, hold the crucible with a pair of tongs, impart a twirling motion and fuse for two minutes longer. Allow the melt to cool on the sides of the crucible by slow twirling as the mass solidifies. When cold, set the crucible on its side in a 400-ml. beaker, cover with a clock glass, add 100 ml. of water and leach. Remove lid and crucible, washing with least amount of water, add 120 ml. HCl (sp. gr. = 1.18); transfer to a 500-ml. cone flask, add iron wire and reduce over a low flame. When the iron is nearly all dissolved and the solution shows no tinge of yellow, filter through glass wool into another 500-ml. cone flask in which has been placed iron wire. Wash flask 3 times and glass wool 3 times with hot distilled water. The volume of solution should now be about 250 ml. Insert a rubber stopper carrying a bent delivery tube and continue the reduction. Proceed as described in the third paragraph of Method *A* above.

## ESTIMATION OF TIN IN CANNED FOOD PRODUCTS [38]

### *SULFIDE METHOD*

Canned food products sometimes contain tin, due to the action of fruit or organic acids, which exert a solvent action on the tin. It is best to obtain the tin for quantitative determination by the wet ash process, for heat ashing often yields low results. The tin is precipitated as stannous sulfide and separated from the sulfides insoluble in polysulfide by solution in polysulfide and filtration. The metal is then reprecipitated as the sulfide, and estimated as the oxide after roasting.

*Gravimetric Procedure.*—Add 200 ml. of water to the digested sample and transfer to a 600-ml. beaker. Rinse the Kjeldahl flask with 3 portions of boiling water making a total volume of approximately 400 ml. Cool and add ammonium hydroxide until just alkaline, then 5 ml. of hydrochloric acid or 5 ml. of sulfuric acid (1:3) for each 100 ml. of solution. Place the beaker, covered, on a hot plate. Heat to about 95°C. and pass in a slow stream of hydrogen sulfide for 1 hour. Digest at 95°C. for 1 hour and allow to stand 30 minutes longer. Filter, and wash the precipitate of stannous sulfide alternately with 3 portions each of wash solution and hot water. The wash solution consists of 100 ml. of saturated ammonium acetate solution, 50 ml. of glacial acetic acid, and 850 ml. of water.

Transfer the filter and precipitate to a 50-ml. beaker, add 10–20 ml. of ammonium polysulfide, heat to boiling, and filter. Repeat the digestion with ammonium polysulfide and the filtration twice, and then wash the filter with hot water. Acidify the combined filtrate and washings with acetic acid (1:9), digest on a hot plate for 1 hour, allow to stand overnight, and filter through a double 11-cm filter. Wash alternately with two portions each of the wash solution and hot water and dry thoroughly in a weighed porcelain crucible. Ignite over a Bunsen flame very gently at first to burn off filter paper and to convert the sulfide to oxide, then partly cover the crucible and heat strongly over a large Meker burner. Weigh as stannic oxide, $SnO_2$ and calculate to metallic tin, using the factor, 0.7876.

---

[38] Jacobs, M. B., Chemical Analysis of Food and Food Products, 3rd Edition, pp. 234–236, D. Van Nostrand Co., Inc., Princeton, N. J., 1958.

*Colorimetric Procedure.*—Tin may also be determined colorimetrically by dissolving the purified stannous sulfide in 2.5 ml. of hydrochloric acid. Place this solution in a test tube fitted with a cork and delivery tube. Add a small piece of zinc and, when it is dissolved, pass in carbon dioxide to replace the air, add 2 ml. of 0.2% dinitrodiphenylamine-sulfoxide in 0.1 $N$ sodium hydroxide solution. Boil the mixture for a few minutes and dilute to 100 ml. Add a few drops of ferric chloride solution. The violet color so obtained may be matched against standard solutions of tin treated the same way.

## THIOGLYCOLIC ACID METHOD

In this method the tin is separated as stannous sulfide, it is redissolved in sodium hydroxide solution, and after being made acid with hydrochloric acid, the color obtained with a reagent containing thioglycolic acid is compared against standards.

*Procedure.*—Convert the tin to stannous sulfide as described above and filter. Digest the paper and precipitate with 10 ml. of 10% sodium hydroxide solution on the steam bath for at least 10 minutes. Filter and wash well. Make the solution just acid by adding concentrated hydrochloric acid, add 2 drops of thioglycolic acid, and dilute to 100 ml. with water. Take an aliquot of 5 ml. in a boiling tube with 5 ml. of water, 0.5 ml. of concentrated hydrochloric acid and 0.5 ml. of a reagent containing 0.1 g. dithiol and 0.25 ml. of thioglycolic acid dissolved in 50 ml. of 1% sodium hydroxide solution.[39] Immerse in a bath of boiling water for 30 seconds, allow to stand for one minute, and compare with standards treated similarly.

## STANNOUS CHLORIDE

Stannous chloride is of great importance in some of the industries, especially textiles. It is necessary to have exact analytical control of the processes in which this compound is used in order to insure uniform results and to certify the efficiency and economy of the process. Several methods have been developed for this purpose. The ones given below have proven to be satisfactory.

### STANNIC ACID METHOD: HOT-WATER PRECIPITATION

In the textile industry where bichloride of tin is used, the efficiency of the process depends directly on the neutrality of the tin liquor. If there is more than enough chloride present in the stannous chloride solution to oxidize all the tin to the stannic form, this excess is called "free HCl." If there is not enough chloride present to do this, the deficiency is spoken of as "basic HCl." The difficulty of determining the "free" or "basic" HCl is apparent when it is known that $SnCl_4$ readily decomposes in water, liberating free acid. The following method has been developed especially for this purpose and has given good results.

The important point in this analysis is to determine whether the liquor has "free" HCl present or whether it is "basic" in nature. It has been found that hot water hydrolyzes the $SnCl_4$ solution to precipitate $Sn(OH)_4$.

$$SnCl_4 + 4H_2O = Sn(OH)_4 + 4HCl$$

The $Sn(OH)_4$ separates as a colloidal precipitate which may be filtered off and the tin estimated as $SnO_2$. The liberated acid may be determined in the filtrate, and from this data the "free" or "basic" HCl can be calculated.

[39] The reagent is best kept in an atmosphere of hydrogen but should be rejected as soon as a white precipitate of disulfide appears. It seldom keeps longer than two weeks.

*Procedure.*—For accurate work about 20 g. of the liquor should be weighed out in a tared weighing bottle, but for plant control, where time is an important factor, it is sufficiently accurate to get the specific gravity of the liquor by means of a hydrometer and take a measured quantity for a sample, calculating the weight from these data.

Transfer the sample to a 100-ml. volumetric flask. Make up to volume with cold distilled water. Draw out of this solution 10 ml. (approximately 2 g.) and place in a 150-ml. tall beaker. Fill the beaker nearly full with boiling hot water, stirring continuously while the water is being poured in.[40] Place the beaker on top of the steam bath and allow the precipitate to settle. Decant the liquid through an 11-cm. S. & S. No. 590 filter [41] and wash the precipitate six times by decantation, using hot water. Now transfer the precipitate to the filter and continue the washing until 1 drop of the filtrate gives no test for chlorine. After most of the water has drained out of the filter, place the paper and precipitate in a tared silica crucible. If there is plenty of time, dry the contents of the crucible on an asbestos board over a low Bunsen flame. In case the analysis must be made in a hurry, cover the crucible [42] and heat it very carefully over a low flame until all the water has been driven out and the paper has been charred. Then remove the cover and increase the heat to the full Bunsen flame and finally blast to constant weight. Weigh as $SnO_2$. Titrate the filtrate with $N$ NaOH, using methyl orange as the indicator.

**Calculation:**

$$SnO_2 \times 0.7876 = Sn$$

$$Sn \times 2.1950 = SnCl_4$$

$$SnCl_4 - Sn = Cl \text{ equiv. to Sn}$$

$$Cl \times 1.0285 = HCl \text{ equiv. to Sn}$$

$$\frac{\text{Weight HCl} \times 100}{\text{Weight of sample}} = \% \text{ HCl equiv. to Sn}$$

$$\frac{\text{ml. } N \text{ NaOH} \times 0.03646 \times 100}{\text{Weight of sample}} = \% \text{ HCl (actual)}$$

The difference between these last two figures equals "free" or "basic" HCl.

## THE ACKER PROCESS METHOD

The theory of this method is practically the same as that of the hot-water method, except that in this case the liberated acid is neutralized with ammonia before the stannic hydroxide has been filtered off, the advantage being that any solution of the stannic hydroxide, by either acid or alkali, is prevented. The method is not applicable for the determination of "free" or "basic" HCl.

*Procedure.*—Weigh out 25 ml. of the stannous chloride solution. Transfer to a 500-ml. volumetric flask and make up to volume with cold water. With a standardized pipette, transfer 25 ml. of this solution in a beaker. Dilute with hot water

---

[40] If the solution is not stirred at this point, the precipitate will not settle and trouble will be experienced during the filtering process.

[41] Time may be saved by using a platinum cone with the filter and applying a gentle vacuum. This can be done with very little danger of breaking the paper.

[42] This precaution must be taken, else there will be a loss by decrepitation.

to precipitate most of the tin as stannic hydroxide. Add 10 drops of phenolacetolin (1 g. of phenolacetolin dissolved in 200 ml. of water). Titrate very carefully with dilute $NH_4OH$ until the appearance of a rose-red color. Boil a few minutes on the hot plate. Allow the tin precipitate to settle. Decant through an 11-cm. filter paper. Wash rapidly with hot water without allowing the precipitate to cake down in the filter until the washings are free from chlorine. Dry the precipitate in an oven at 100°C. When dry, invert the filter into a tared porcelain crucible, and heat on a gauze until the paper has disappeared. Remove the gauze and heat with the full Bunsen flame for a few minutes. Finally blast to constant weight.[43] Weigh as $SnO_2$.

Take the filtrate and washings and dilute them to a volume of 1000 ml. Warm 500 ml. of this solution and saturate it with hydrogen sulfide. If any tin separates, filter, and ignite in a tared porcelain crucible. Moisten with a little nitric acid and heat very slowly to drive out the acid. Ignite to constant weight. Weigh as $SnO_2$. Add this result to the $SnO_2$ obtained above when calculating the final result.

## METHODS FOR TIN IN ANALYSES IN OTHER CHAPTERS

| Tin in Aluminum Alloys | See Analysis of Aluminum Alloys |
| Tin in Magnesium Alloys | See Magnesium Chapter |

[43] If the oxide of tin is contaminated it may be dissolved by adding water saturated with $SO_2$ and acidifying with dilute HCl. Heat in a covered beaker (to prevent loss of tin). Stelling, E., J. Ind. Eng. Chem., **16**, 346, 1924.

# Chapter 48

# TITANIUM *

Ti, *at. wt.* 47.90; *sp. gr.* 4.5; *m.p.* 1795°C.($\pm$15°); *b.p.* above 3000°C.; *oxides,* TiO, Ti$_2$O$_3$, TiO$_2$, TiO$_3$

Titanium is an abundant element, occurring only in the combined state in nature. It is a characteristic constituent of igneous and metamorphic rocks and of the sediments derived from them. The chief mineralogical occurrences are as oxides, titanates and silicotitanates. Titanium is frequently associated with magnetite and hematite and may constitute a considerable proportion of such deposits. The principal minerals [1] are: ilmenite, FeTiO$_3$, containing 35–60% TiO$_2$; rutile, TiO$_2$, containing 90 to 100% TiO$_2$; titanite, CaTiSiO$_5$, containing 34 to 42% TiO$_2$; perovskite, CaTiO$_3$, containing about 60% TiO$_2$.

Titanium was discovered in the mineral ilmenite by Gregor (1789) and later found in rutile and named titanium by Klaproth (1793).

Titanium dioxide is now extensively used as a white pigment in protective coatings, paper, rubber, rayon, etc. It is commercially produced in the pure form as composite pigments such as titanium-calcium pigments (30% TiO$_2$, 70% CaSO$_4$; 50% TiO$_2$, 50% CaSO$_4$), the white titanium pigments are characterized by their exceptional tinting strength and hiding power, excelling in this respect other commercial white pigments.

Titanium metal and its alloys have developed rapidly during the last few years. Titanium metal and its alloys possess an unusual combination of intrinsic properties which will assure their place as a prominent structural metal. "Commercially pure" titanium is classed as a light metal (0.16 lb./in.³) being 60% heavier than aluminum, but only 56% as heavy as alloy steel. Titanium is extremely strong and has excellent ductility. This is especially important in the strength-weight ratio. The corrosion resistance is excellent in marine environments, chloride containing solutions, and oxidizing solutions.

Another important application of titanium is the use of ferrotitanium in the iron and steel industry. The function of the titanium is to remove oxygen and nitrogen from steel and consequently to yield a product free from blowholes and at the same time prevent segregation to a great extent, especially of carbon, phosphorus, and sulfur. In a steel thus purified the natural strength and resistant properties of the material are developed to the highest degree. Titanium is used in small amounts in the 18-8 stainless steels to prevent intergranular carbide precipitation thereby improving the corrosion resistance.

Titanium has also found application in the textile and leather industries. The use of titanous chloride and titanous sulfate for bleaching or discharging colors is

---

* Dr. Edward R. Scheffer, Titanium Division, National Lead Research Laboratory, South Amboy, N. J.
[1] List by Wm. M. Thornton, Jr., A.C.S. Monograph Series, No. 83, p. 23.

increasing. Such bleaching agents are particularly applicable for silk and wool, which are injured by the action of those bleaching agents in which chlorine is the active element.

Titanium compounds are also used for electric light filaments, arc-light electrodes, ceramics, fine brown glazes, paint for iron and steel, coating of welding rods, etc.

## DETECTION

*Spectral lines* for identification of Ti are as follows: 4981.7 A, 3653.5 A, 3361.2 A, 3349.4 A, and 3341.8 A.

*Hydrogen Peroxide.*—The powdered ore is fused with potassium pyrosulfate until effervescence ceases. The cooled mass is dissolved in 10% sulfuric acid by boiling. Hydrogen peroxide, $H_2O_2$, added to this titanium solution, produces a yellow to orange color, according to the amount of titanium present. Hydrofluoric acid, or fluoride, destroys the color. Vanadium also produces this color with hydrogen peroxide, but the color is not destroyed by HF. The reaction is often assumed to be due to the formation of pertitanic acid, $H_4TiO_5$, but is more apt to be from an ion like $TiO_2(SO_4)_2 =$.[2] Uranium, molybdenum, and chromate also give colors with hydrogen peroxide.

*Morphine* produces a crimson color with solutions of titanium in sulfuric acid. (A thymol color reaction has also been reported.[3])

*Zinc* added to hydrochloric acid solutions of titanium produces a violet color,[4] tin a fine violet solution.[5] A green color results if fluorides are present.

*Sulfur dioxide,* passed into a solution of titanium containing iron, reduces the latter and permits the precipitation of white hydrous titanium oxide by boiling a slightly acid solution.

*Bead Test on Charcoal.*—A small portion of the powdered mineral heated on charcoal with microcosmic salt (sodium ammonium hydrogen phosphate) and tin produces a violet-colored bead if titanium is present. A platinum wire loop may be used in the reducing flame.

*Field Test.*[6]—The mineral sample is ground and 4 mg. of material is fused in a test tube with about 150 mg. of potassium pyrosulfate. To this is added 150 mg. of Tiron powder (disodium 1,2-hydroxybenzene-3,5-sulfonate) and 15 ml. of acetate buffer solution (40 g. of ammonium acetate dissolved in 15 ml. of acetic acid diluted to 1 liter). The addition of 10 mg. of sodium dithionate prevents interference of any iron which may be present. The titanium content is indicated by the resulting yellow color. Another organic agent [7] sodium 1,8-dihydroxynaphthalene-3,6-disulfonate has been applied to detect Ti in minerals.

## ESTIMATION

Both gravimetric and titrimetric methods are used in the determination of titanium. In recent years the gravimetric method has given place to the accurate, rapid, and less involved titrimetric and colorimetric procedures.

2 Schwartz, R., Z. anorg. allgem. Chem., **210,** 303, 1933.
3 Lenher and Crawford, J. Am. Chem. Soc., **35,** 138, 1913.
4 Sainte-Claire Deville, M. H., Chem. News, **4,** 241, 1861.
5 Cahen, E., and Wooton, W. O., The Mineralogy of the Rarer Elements, London, Charles Griffin Co., 1920, p. 127.
6 Shapiro, L., U. S. Geological Survey, 1952.
7 Vanossi, R., Anales Asoc. quim Argentina, **32,** 5–17, 1944.

In the usual analytical procedures a part of the titanium may remain with the silica residue, from which it must be recovered. The remainder precipitates upon addition of $NH_4OH$ with iron, aluminum, etc., and unless accounted for will lead to an error in iron and aluminum determinations. If the reduction of iron is made by use of zinc, the error will fall largely on iron, as titanium is also reduced by zinc; if $SO_2$ or $H_2S$ are used for reducing iron the error will fall largely on aluminum, as titanium is not affected by these reagents.

Titanium ores are readily attacked by hydrofluoric acid; the acid, however, must be removed completely by repeated evaporation with sulfuric acid, otherwise it interferes with the colorimetric determination of titanium by means of peroxide, since it bleaches the color. In titanium solutions a moderate amount (10–20%) of acid must be present to prevent precipitation of titanium by hydrolysis.

In dissolving titanium precipitates from filter paper loss is apt to result by incomplete solution, small amounts remaining on the filter and escaping attention.

## PREPARATION AND SOLUTION OF THE SAMPLE

A knowledge of the solubility of the element and its oxides is of value in dissolving the sample.

*Element.*—Titanium is soluble in cold dilute hydrochloric or sulfuric acids, more readily so when the acids are heated. It is soluble in cold, concentrated hydrochloric acid; readily soluble in hot, concentrated hydrochloric or sulfuric acids. It is scarcely acted upon by nitric acid, but dissolves most readily in hydrofluoric acid. It was considered that dissolving titanium with hydrofluoric acid caused loss of material;[8] however, if care is exercised to prevent too rapid and violent a reaction, this is not the case. In most applications a few milliliters of hydrofluoric acid in combination with hydrochloric or sulfuric acid will greatly speed the solution of the sample. It is soluble by fusion in potassium pyrosulfate.

*Oxides.*—$Ti_2O_3$, which has a black or blue color, is soluble in concentrated hydrochloric or sulfuric acids, forming, in the latter case, a violet-colored solution.[9] The oxide is insoluble in water and in ammonium hydroxide.

$TiO_2$ is difficultly soluble in concentrated sulfuric acid, less soluble if strongly ignited. The hydrous titanium oxide, precipitated at elevated temperatures, requires concentrated hydrochloric or sulfuric acid to effect solution; when precipitated at room temperature (by addition of alkali) it is readily soluble in cold, dilute acids. $TiO_2$ is soluble in acids after fusing with alkalies; it is also soluble in hydrofluoric acid, forming $TiF_4$, which is volatile, unless an excess of sulfuric acid is present (distinction from silica). The ignited oxide is best dissolved by fusion with $K_2S_2O_7$ and heating the fused mass with dilute sulfuric acid solution.

Artificially prepared ignited titanium dioxide dissolves readily in a mixture of concentrated sulfuric acid and ammonium sulfate on boiling.

Titanium dioxide, on being fused with an alkali, gives a titanate. If this be treated with water, an acid titanate is formed, which remains almost entirely undissolved. This residual material, however, may be dissolved with the aid of concentrated mineral acid.

*Salts.*—Many titanium salts are decomposed through the agency of water, hydrous titanium oxide being precipitated; the extent of the hydrolysis depends upon the quantity of water added, the temperature, and other conditions. Titanium sulfate is soluble in water, if care is taken to add water to the salt gradually and in small

[8] Hunter, M. A., J. Am. Chem. Soc., **32**, 335, 1910.
[9] Ebelman, M., Ann. Chem. (3), **20**, 392, 1847.

increments; concentrated solutions are reasonably stable, although titanyl sulfate, $TiOSO_4 \cdot 2H_2O$, may crystallize on standing; dilute solutions gradually hydrolyze. Some of the double salts are readily soluble and their solutions stable, e.g., potassium titanium oxalate.

*Solution of Steel.*—The sample may be dissolved in hydrochloric acid (1:2). If a residue remains, it is treated with a mixture of equal parts of hydrofluoric and sulfuric acids and a few drops of nitric acid, in a platinum dish, and the mixture evaporated to sulfuric anhydride fumes and to complete expulsion of hydrofluoric acid. The colorimetric procedure is now used for estimating titanium.[10]

*Alloys.*—In those alloys in which titanium exists as the base metal methods of solution can be employed as given for the element, usually some combination of acids including hydrofluoric. Those alloys in which titanium is one of the lesser constituents can be dissolved in concentrated nitric acid, aqua regia, or a mixture of the dilute acids. Should nitric acid be used, the excess is expelled by evaporation to dryness with hydrochloric acid. The metals of the hydrogen sulfide group are removed in an acid solution by precipitation with $H_2S$, and titanium determined colorimetrically in the filtrate.

*Ores.*—One gram of the ore is treated with 10 to 50 ml. of a mixture of sulfuric and hydrofluoric acids (1:5), a few drops $HNO_3$ added, and the solution evaporated to fumes to expel HF. If a residue remains upon dissolving with water containing a little sulfuric acid, it is filtered and fused with $K_2S_2O_7$ as directed under the fusion method.

*Fusion Method for Ores.*—The finely powdered sample is fused with four to five times its weight of potassium pyrosulfate, and the cooled fusion dissolved with dilute sulfuric or hydrochloric acid. In the presence of silica potassium fluoride is added to assist in the decomposition of the material.

Fusion with sodium carbonate or sodium pyrosulfate are frequently recommended. Sears and Quill have found [11] that in the decomposition of rutile it is advisable to use 12.5 parts of pyrosulfate to 1 part of the mineral and in case of titanate the proportion must be increased to 35:1. The titanium is leached with water for the pyrosulfate or dilute acid for carbonate. Most of the silica, and if present, the tantalum and niobium, remain in the insoluble residue. Some alkali silicate goes into solution, and must be removed in gravimetric determinations. See Analysis of Titaniferous Ores, page 1113.)

*Titaniferous Slags.*—One-half gram of the finely ground sample is decomposed in a platinum dish by a mixture of 5 ml. water, 5 ml. concentrated sulfuric acid, and 10 ml. of hydrofluoric acid, the reagents being added in the order named. The solution is evaporated rapidly to $SO_3$ fumes to expel fluorides and excess sulfuric acid until the residue is left nearly dry. After cooling it is dissolved with 40 ml. of dilute hydrochloric acid (1:3), which will give a clear solution containing all the constituents of the slag except silica, which has been volatilized as $SiF_4$.

## SEPARATIONS

Less interferences occur in the titrimetric and colorimetric methods, therefore these are generally preferred to the gravimetric procedures. Occasions may demand one or more of the methods of separation given below.

---

[10] See also O. L. Barnebey and R. M. Isham's work (J. Am. Chem. Soc., **32,** 957, 1910) on the colorimetric determination of titanium in hydrochloric acid solution.
[11] Sears, G. W., and Quill, L., J. Am. Chem. Soc., **47,** 929, 1925.

*Separation of Titanium from the Hydrogen Sulfide Group Elements, Hg, Pb, Cu Cd, As, Sb, Sn, Rh, Pd, Os, Ru, Au, Pt, Ir, Mo, Te, and Se.*—The members of the hydrogen sulfide group with a solution acidity of 1.5 ml. $H_2SO_4$ or 2.4 ml. HCl [1] per 40 ml. are precipitated if the solution is saturated with $H_2S$ and diluted to 100 ml. and again saturated with $H_2S$. The addition of 1 g. of citric acid per 0.2 g. of oxides present is recommended, especially if a further separation from certain members of the ammonium sulfide group is to be made. The sulfides are filtered and washed, titanium passing into the filtrate.

*Separation of Titanium from Iron, Cobalt, Nickel, Zinc (and the greater portion of Manganese).*—The filtrate from the above separation is taken and 0.5–1 g ammonium bisulfite added (to assist in complete precipitation of Ni and Co), ammonium hydroxide added in slight excess and the solution again saturated with $H_2S$. Titanium (Be, Nb, Cr, Ta and Zr) remains in solution, while Fe, Co, Ni, Zn (and a large portion of Mn) precipitate as sulfides. The solution is filtered and titanium determined in the filtrate.

NOTES.—It is advisable to dissolve the precipitate and reprecipitate the sulfides to recover minute amounts of occluded Ti.

Citric acid in the solution containing titanium is removed by evaporating to fumes with $H_2SO_4$ and adding $HNO_3$ and again evaporating. (See "Gravimetric Method" following.

*Separation from Copper, Zinc, Aluminum, Iron, etc.*—Titanium is precipitated from a slightly acid solution [13] by boiling, passing sulfur dioxide through the solution to keep the iron reduced and prevent its precipitation.

*Separation from the Bivalent Metals, Manganese, Nickel, Cobalt, Zinc.*—Titanium is precipitated along with aluminum and iron by hydrolysis of its acetate in a hot, dilute solution, whereas manganese, nickel, cobalt, and zinc remain in solution.

A sharp separation of titanium from manganese can be effected with ammonium hydroxide alone. [14]

*Separation of Titanium by Cupferron Method.*—By this procedure large amount of aluminum may be separated from small amounts of titanium (one part of Ti and 28 parts of Al). Cupferron (nitrosophenylhydroxylamine) is added to the decidedly acid solution containing titanium and aluminum, a flocculent titanium salt precipitating and aluminum remaining in solution. A 9% water solution of the reagent is added until a fine precipitate appears (after complete precipitation of the curdy titanium precipitate), which redissolves in an excess of the reagent. [1]

The titanium precipitate is washed by decantation and then on the filter with very dilute hydrochloric acid to remove traces of aluminum. The procedure afford a separation of titanium from chromium, nickel, cobalt, manganese. Copper, iron zirconium, vanadium, tungsten, and uranium ($UO_2$) precipitate with the titanium if present in the solution.

Solvent extraction can be readily applied to the cupferrate precipitate of titanium, and affords a cleaner separation than filtration and washing as given above. The solution is transferred to a 500-ml. separatory funnel and 75 ml. of 9% cupferron solution is added. Shake the funnel to coagulate the precipitate and add

[12] Noyes, A. A., and Bray, W. C., Tech. Quarterly, **19**, 235, 1906.

[13] Acidity exactly 0.5% is best according to L. Levy, Chem. News, **56**, 206, 1887.

[14] Lundell, G. E. F., and Knowles, H. B., J. Am. Chem. Soc., **45**, 676, 1923.

[15] Thornton, Jr., W. M., Am. J. Sci. (4), **37**, 407-14, 1914; Thornton, Jr., W. M. Titanium, A.C.S. Monograph Series, No. 33, Reinhold Publishing Co., 1927; Lundell G. E. F., and Knowles, H. B., J. Ind. Eng. Chem., **12**, 344, 1920.

100 ml. of chloroform. Shake for about one minute and then allow five minutes for the aqueous and chloroform layers to separate. Drain the chloroform layer and add 50 ml. of chloroform, shake and add 5 ml. of the cupferron solution. If a white flash of cupferron appears, enough cupferron has been added. If a colored precipitate appears more cupferron must be added. This test is repeated on subsequent extractions until the white flash appears. The extraction is continued with 25-ml. portions of chloroform until both layers appear almost water white.

NOTE.—Cupferron precipitates titanium (as well as zirconium, thorium, etc.) notwithstanding the presence of tartaric, citric, and other organic acids containing hydroxyl groups. See also under "Separations" in the Chapter on Zirconium.

**Separation of Titanium from the Alkaline Earths, etc.**—The hydroxide is precipitated when a titanium solution containing ammonium chloride is treated with sufficient ammonium sulfide; whereas barium, strontium, calcium, and magnesium remain in solution. Titanium hydroxide may be precipitated by making the solution containing titanium slightly alkaline with $NH_4OH$.

**Separation of Titanium from Iron. Ether Extraction of Iron.**—Details of this procedure are given in the Chapter on Iron under "Separations." Iron must be in ferric form (trivalent) as the divalent iron is not extracted. The chloride solution containing free HCl is repeatedly extracted with ether in a separatory funnel. All but 1–2 mg. of ferric iron passes into the ether layer. Ether also extracts trivalent gallium,[16] quantitatively, pentavalent Sb, hexavalent Mo, trivalent Tl, trivalent Au, considerable trivalent As, while the following remain in solution: Al, Bi, Ca, Cd, Cu, Fe(II), Pb, Mn, Ni, Se, V, Ti, U, Zn, Zr, members of the platinum group, rare earths, W (with $PO_4$).[16,17]

The separation of titanium from iron and aluminum can be effected with fluoride.[18]

Ion exchange has also been used to separate small amounts of titanium from iron.[19]

**Separation of Titanium from Zirconium and Thorium.**[20]—The nitric acid solution is carefully treated with a solution of sodium carbonate to neutralize the greater part of the free acid and to the boiling hot solution is slowly added a 20% solution of ammonium salicylate in sufficient excess to precipitate completely the zirconium (and thorium, if present). The mixture is boiled gently for about half an hour or more, diluted to about 200 ml. and filtered hot. The precipitate is washed with a hot, 20% solution of ammonium salicylate until its color is only faintly yellow or white. Titanium passes into the filtrate.

Separation of titanium, zirconium, etc. from chromium, vanadium, molybdenum, tungsten, phosphorus, and arsenic may be effected by fusing with sodium carbonate and a little sodium nitrate and thereafter extracting with water.[21]

A very satisfactory procedure has been developed using ion exchange with nitrate complexes of the metals.[22]

**Separation of Titanium from Molybdenum, Phosphorus, and Vanadium.**—The separation is necessary when the colorimetric determination of titanium is to be

[16] Swift, E. H., J. Am. Chem. Soc., **46**, 2376, 1924.
[17] Cr(VI), Al, Ga(III) also dissolve.
[18] Talipov, Sh. T., and Sofeibova, Z. T., Zavodskaya Lab., **13**, 316–19, 1947.
[19] Yoshino, Yukichi, and Kojima, Masuo, Bull. Chem. Soc. Japan, **23**, 46–7, 1950.
[20] Dittrich, M., and Freund, S., Z. anorg. allgem. Chem., **56**, 344, 1908.
[21] See W. F. Hillebrand, U. S. Geol. Survey, Bull. 700, 185, 1919.
[22] Brown, W. E., and Reiman, W., J. Am. Chem. Soc., **74**, 1278, 1952.

made, since these elements interfere. The presence of ferric iron is necessary for complete precipitation of titanium. The separation is made by carefully neutralizing the greater part of the free acid present by addition of a solution of NaOH and pouring the mixture into 150 ml. of a hot, normal solution of NaOH, filtering and washing with hot 0.5 $N$ NaOH.[23] It is advisable to repeat the precipitation to remove traces of the interfering elements, the titanium being brought into solution with $HNO_3$ and $H_2SO_4$ or by fusing with $K_2S_2O_7$.

The separation of aluminum from titanium, tantalum, niobium, molybdenum, arsenic, fluorine, and boron with the aid of 8-hydroxyquinoline is of interest.[24]

*Separation from Tantalum and Niobium.*—See Chapter on Niobium and Tantalum.

## GRAVIMETRIC METHOD

### MODIFIED GOOCH METHOD [25]

This method is applicable to minerals and metallurgical products that are comparatively high in titanium. The method provides for the separation of titanium from iron and from aluminum and phosphoric acid with which it commonly occurs. The procedure as proposed by F. A. Gooch and modified for nonaluminous rocks by Wm. M. Thornton, Jr., gives reliable results. The details of the method with a few slight changes found to be advantageous are given below. Iron is separated from titanium by precipitation as a sulfide in presence of tartaric acid, the organic acid is destroyed by oxidation and titanium precipitated from a boiling acetic acid solution. In the presence of alumina and phosphoric acid, Gooch, in his original process,[26] fused the first precipitate of titanium oxide (after ignition) with sodium carbonate, treated the melt with boiling water, filtered, ignited and the residue, fused again with a little sodium carbonate, dissolved the entire mass in sulfuric acid, and then precipitated the titanium again by hydrolysis of the acetate.[27] The removal of zirconium (see Separations) is necessary.

*Procedure.* **Preparation of the Sample.** *Ores High in Silica.*—These may be decomposed by taking to $SO_3$ fumes with a mixture of 10 to 15 ml. of 50% hydrofluoric acid, and 3 to 4 ml. of concentrated sulfuric acid per gram of sample.

*Oxides.*—Decomposed by fusion with sodium or potassium pyrosulfate. The fusion is dissolved in 10% sulfuric acid, keeping the volume as small as possible. The sample should contain not over 0.2 g. titanium.

**Precipitation of Iron.**—To the solution containing titanium, tartaric acid, equal to three times the weight of the oxides to be held in solution, is added. This should not exceed 1 g. of the organic acid, as the subsequent removal of larger amounts would be troublesome. $H_2S$ is passed into the solution to reduce the iron and $NH_4OH$ added to slight alkalinity followed by a further treatment with $H_2S$ to precipitate FeS completely. The solution should be faintly alkaline (lit

[23] Addition of a little $Na_2SO_4$ to the NaOH solution is recommended.

[24] Lundell and Knowles, J. Research Nat. Bur. Standards, **3**, 94, 1929.

[25] Gooch, F. A., Proc. Am. Acad. Arts and Sci., New Series, **12**, 435, 1885; Thornton, Wm. M., Chem. News, **107**, 121, 1913.

[26] Gooch, F. A., Proc. Am. Acad. Arts and Sci., New Series, **12**, 444, 1885.

[27] All things being considered, the cupferron method is far superior to the acetate hydrolysis involving the destruction of the tartaric acid by sulfuric and nitric acids; even though the latter process yields reasonably accurate results; Thornton, Jr., W. M., Am. J. Sci. (4), **34**, 214, 1912.

mus). After filtration and washing of the ferrous sulfide with very dilute and colorless ammonium sulfide, the titanium is entirely in the iron-free filtrate.

**Oxidation of Tartaric Acid.**—The organic acid is oxidized by addition of 15 to 20 ml. of concentrated sulfuric acid to the sample placed in a 500-ml. Kjeldahl flask. The solution is evaporated to incipient charring of the tartaric acid. After cooling slightly, about 10 ml. of fuming nitric acid are added cautiously, a few drops at a time, and when the violent reaction has subsided the flask is heated gradually (hood), a vigorous reaction taking place accompanied by much effervescence and foaming with evolution of copious brown fumes. The organic matter gradually disappears, the effervescence becomes steady and finally ceases and white fumes of $SO_3$ are given off. The solution is cooled and the pale yellow syrup poured into 100 ml. of cold water, the flask washed out, adding the rinsings to the main solution. The solution is filtered, if necessary.

**Precipitation.**—$NH_4OH$ is added until the solution is nearly neutral (a point where the solution is lightly turbid, the precipitate dissolving upon vigorous stirring). If a trace of iron is suspected about 1 ml. of 10% ammonium bisulfite is added. Five ml. of glacial acetic acid followed by 15 grams of ammonium acetate or its equivalent in solution is added and the volume of the solution made up to about 350 ml. The solution is brought rapidly to boiling and maintained in ebullition for about 3 minutes. The titanium will precipitate in a white, flocculent and readily filterable condition. The precipitate is washed first with water containing acetic acid and finally with pure water. The filter and the precipitate are ignited cautiously at first over a low flame and finally over a Meker blast for 20 minutes. The residue is weighed as $TiO_2$.

In the presence of large amounts of alumina and phosphoric acid, the residue above obtained is fused with sodium carbonate in a platinum dish and the fusion leached by boiling with pure water. Alumina and phosphoric acid go into solution as soluble sodium salts and titanium oxide remains insoluble in the residue.

NOTES.—Titanium may be separated from aluminum by fusing the residue with potassium pyrosulfate, and precipitation of titanium in an acid solution by cupferron. $Al_2O_3$ is in solution.

The interfering action of rare earths should be kept in mind, also of members of the hydrogen sulfide group (these can be removed by an extra filtration in the course of separating the iron as ferrous sulfide), vanadium (especially pentavalent), tungsten, and uranium (tetravalent but not hexivalent).[28]

## TITRIMETRIC METHODS

It is impossible to include all the variations of the various titrimetric procedures. This includes those titrated to an end point with an indicator as well as potentiometric titrations. Basically, all rely on the reduction of titanium(IV) to titanium(III) and then titration with standard oxidizing solution to titanium(IV). One potentiometric method [29] applies the principle of a standard reducing solution, chromous ion; however, the relative instability of the chromous solution has limited its widespread use. Three reduction techniques will be described separately. The titrimetric methods which follow can employ any one of the three reduction techniques. All three reduction techniques will give equally satisfactory results.

28 See W. F. Hillebrand and G. E. F. Lundell, Applied Inorganic Analysis, p. 434, John Wiley & Sons, Inc., 1929.
29 Lingane, J. J., Anal. Chem., **20**, 797–80, 1948.

## REDUCTION METHODS

### *JONES REDUCTOR METHOD*

The following reduction technique originally recommended by the National Lead Co., Titanium Division, is essentially that described by P. W. and E. B. Shimer. Proceedings of the Eighth International Congress of Applied Chemistry.

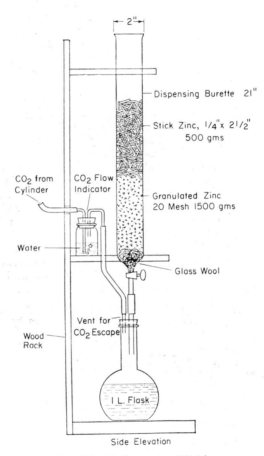

FIG. 48-1. Reductor for Titanium.

*Apparatus.*—A dispensing burette, Fig. 48-1, about 22 inches long, 2 inches in diameter and equipped with a glass stopcock and delivery tube 6 mm. wide × 3.5 inches long. The reductor (Fig. 25-2, in the Chapter on Iron) is charged with an 8-inch column of 20-mesh amalgamated zinc (1500 g.) and on top of this a 6-inch column of broken amalgamated stick zinc (about 750 g.). The delivery tube is connected to a one-liter flask through a two-hole rubber stopper. One hole is used as an inlet and another as an outlet for carbon dioxide gas.

The zinc is amalgamated by immersing it in a solution of mercuric chloride in hydrochloric acid. Eleven grams of $HgCl_2$ is dissolved in 100 ml. of concentrated HCl. Two hundred fifty grams of zinc is covered with distilled water in a one-liter suction flask and the $HgCl_2$ solution is poured in, slowly mixing and shaking for about two minutes. The solution is poured off, the zinc washed thoroughly with hot tap water and finally with distilled water.

*Reduction Procedure.*—The titanium solution should not contain more than 0.25 gram $TiO_2$, with 10–15% $H_2SO_4$, and it should have a volume of 125–150 ml.

Drain the reductor to the top of the fine mesh zinc. Add 200 ml. of a hot, freshly boiled, 5% solution of $H_2SO_4$. Slowly drain the reductor; then wash at least four times with hot freshly boiled water (tap water may be used). Drain the reductor to the top of the fine mesh zinc; wash the hot titanium solution into it and allow to remain from 15 to 20 minutes. During the whole period of reduction a slow stream of carbon dioxide is passed through the receiving flask. Slowly drain the reductor into the receiving flask while continuously passing carbon dioxide through the flask. When the solution has reached the level of the fine mesh zinc, add a hot, freshly boiled, 5% solution of sulfuric acid and bring the level of the solution to the top of the stick zinc. Drain to fine mesh zinc; then wash in the same manner four times with hot freshly boiled water. Tap water may be used but should be boiled sufficiently long (about 20 minutes) to expel dissolved oxygen. Remove the flask.

Determine titanium by "Oxidation Titration" on page 1104.

## LIQUID AMALGAM REDUCTOR METHOD [30]

*Liquid Zinc Amalgam.*—Pour 1600 g. of Hg into a porcelain casserole and add 40 g. of zinc. Add 30 ml. 1:4 $H_2SO_4$ and heat on a hot plate at 70–80°C. for 0.5 hour or until all the zinc has dissolved in the mercury. Cool and transfer to a separatory funnel. Add two short pieces of stick zinc and 5–10 ml. of 10% $H_2SO_4$. Stopper the funnel and keep until needed.

NOTE.—The amalgam becomes fouled with use This is evident by its dirty appearance. The amalgam is washed by shaking in a separatory funnel with 30 ml. of 1:4 $H_2SO_4$ for several minutes. The amalgam is again heated on the hot plate, separated from the dilute acid and is ready for use.

*Reduction Procedure.*—The titanium solution should not contain more than 0.25 g. of $TiO_2$, with 10–15% $H_2SO_4$, and it should have a volume of 125–150 ml.

Pour 20 ml. of zinc amalgam into a 250-ml. cylindrical separatory funnel fitted with a rubber stopper in place of the ground glass stopper. Add the cooled titanium solution to the funnel, and then displace the air with $CO_2$ by passing the gas into the funnel for 5–10 seconds. Replace the stopper and shake for 5 minutes. (The use of a shaking machine is recommended.) Remove the rubber stopper and wash carefully. Wash the side walls of the funnel and add 5 ml. of $CCl_4$. Drain off the amalgam and a minimum quantity of $CCl_4$. (The amalgam is drawn off into the storage funnel for revivification and any necessary cleaning.) Run out part of the $CCl_4$ into a separatory funnel for future use. The titration can now be carried out in the cylindrical separatory funnel.

Determine titanium by titration method on page 1104.

[30] Kano, J. Japan Chem. Soc., **43**, 333, 1922; this modification was developed by the National Lead Company Titanium Division.

## ALUMINUM FOIL REDUCTION [31]

This method of reduction is the simplest and as a result its use is general. The method given is essentially the same as developed by Rahm and is recommended by the National Lead Company, Titanium Division.

*Aluminum Foil.*—Any high purity aluminum foil can be used which contains no more than 0.03% $TiO_2$ or other interfering ions. The apparatus consists of a 250-ml. wide mouth Erlenmeyer flask with 2-hole rubber stopper. In one hole is placed a solid pointed rod nearly touching the bottom of the Erlenmeyer flask to which the aluminum foil is attached. Into the other hole is placed a delivery tube with short end in the Erlenmeyer flask and the long end into a 400-ml. beaker containing saturated sodium bicarbonate solution.

*Reduction Procedure.*—The titanium solution should contain not more than 0.25 g. of $TiO_2$, with 10–15% $H_2SO_4$, and it should have a volume of 125 ml.

The titanium solution is added to the Erlenmeyer flask and 20 ml. of HCl is added.

NOTE.—The reduction with aluminum will not take place unless HCl is present.

Boil the solution, remove from the burner, and attach the aluminum foil (amount necessary indicated for the material to be analyzed) to the end of the glass rod. Immediately insert the rubber stopper. The delivery tube is placed below the level of a saturated sodium bicarbonate solution. When all the aluminum appears to be dissolved, it is necessary to boil the solution gently for 3 to 5 minutes. During this step the delivery tube must remain immersed in the sodium bicarbonate solution.

The solution is cooled to less than 60°C. As the solution cools the sodium bicarbonote solution is drawn into the Erlenmeyer flask and the $CO_2$ formed gives the necessary protective atmosphere. After the solution is cool, the delivery tube is removed and the titration can be carried out in the Erlenmeyer flask.

## OXIDATION TITRATION

### (To follow the three preceding Reduction Methods)

The titration of the titanous ion can be carried out by several methods.

1. To the solution from the reductor an excess of ferric sulfate is added, and the ferrous ion formed by oxidation of the titanous ion, is titrated with standard permanganate.[32]

2. The titanous solution can be titrated directly with standard permanganate.[33]

In each of the above methods the common interfering ion is iron; however, other interference may be caused by organic matter, As, Sn, Nb, Cr, Mo, V, U, and W. If these ions are present separations must be made as given in the previous section.

3. The solution of titanous ion is titrated with a standard ferric solution. This procedure is the one most commonly used because it is equally applicable to ores as well as titanium dioxide pigments (see page 1117). There is interference from the ions listed above other than iron, and the appropriate separations must be made.

*Reagents.* **Standard Ferric Ammonium Sulfate Solution (1 ml. is equivalent to 0.005 grams of $TiO_2$).**—This solution can be standardized by reduction and titration with 0.1 $N$ potassium permanganate which has been standardized against

[31] Rahm, J. A., Anal. Chem., **24**, 1832–3, Nov. 1952.
[32] Newton, H. D., Am. J. Sci. (4), **25**, 130–4, 1908.
[33] Ball, T. R., and Smith, G. McP., J. Am. Chem. Soc., **36**, 1839, 1914.

N.B.S. No. 406 sodium oxalate or against N.B.S. No. 154 $TiO_2$ using the same procedure as given for titanium dioxide pigment.

Dissolve 60 g. of ferric ammonium sulfate in 600 ml. of distilled water acidified with 20 ml. of $H_2SO_4$. Add potassium permanganate solution dropwise until the first pink color appears. Dilute the solution to 2 liters.

To standardize the solution using N.B.S. No. 154 $TiO_2$ the same type of reduction technique should be used for standardization as for analysis of unknown sample.

*Indicator.*—A solution of ammonium thiocyanate is prepared by dissolving 24 grams of $NH_4CNS$ in 100 ml. of water.

*Procedure.*—Add 2 ml. of the ammonium thiocyanate indicator and titrate rapidly with the standard ferric ammonium sulfate solution. In titrating titanium solutions with ferric ammonium sulfate, great accuracy is obtained by adding nearly all of the ferric ammonium sulfate before agitation. Then agitate by shaking with a general rotary motion, and continue to the final end point which is a light straw color. With the Jones reductor, 0.1 ml. is deducted from the titration for a blank if the standardization has been made against potassium permanganate.

## COLORIMETRIC/PHOTOMETRIC METHODS

### DETERMINATION WITH THYMOL [34]

Titanium dioxide dissolved in sulfuric acid is colored red by addition of thymol, the depth of color being directly proportional to the amount of titanium present. The intensity of the color is claimed by Lenher and Crawford to be twenty-five times that produced by hydrogen peroxide with the same amount of titanium.

As in case of hydrogen peroxide, fluorides destroy the color, hence must be absent. Dilution with water has no effect until the concentration of sulfuric acid falls below 79.4 (i.e., sp. gr. 1.725). The color then fades in direct proportion to dilution. Warm solutions are lighter in color than cold solutions with the same amount of titanium, hence the standard and the sample compared must have the same temperature. The color fades on heating but returns on cooling. The temperature should be kept below 100°C. Chlorides, phosphates, and tin seem to have no effect. Tungsten, $WoO_3$, interferes, as it intensifies the color of the solution in direct proportion to the amount present; hence it must be removed or allowance made by adding an equivalent amount to the standard or subtracting the equivalent blank.

*Reagents.* **Thymol Solution, 1%.**—The thymol is dissolved in a little glacial acetic acid containing 10% ethyl alcohol, and this solution added to concentrated sulfuric acid. Addition of the thymol directly to the acid would produce a colored solution. The reagent should be kept protected from strong light, otherwise it will become colored.

*Procedure.*—About 0.3 g. of the material is fused with potassium pyrosulfate, and the melt dissolved in concentrated sulfuric acid. Enough thymol reagent is added so that there is present at least 0.006 g. thymol for every 0.0001 g. $TiO_2$. Concentrated sulfuric acid is added to bring up the volume to 50 or 100 ml. in a Nessler tube exactly as in the case of the colorimetric determination of titanium with $H_2O_2$. The depth of color is compared with a standard solution of titanium dissolved in

[34] Lenher, V., Crawford, W. G., Chem. News, **107**, 152, 1913; Griel, J. V., Robinson, R. J., Anal. Chem., **23**, 1871, 1951.

concentrated sulfuric acid added to 5 ml. of thymol solution made up to a convenient volume with concentrated sulfuric acid. The procedure is the same described in the $H_2O_2$ method, below.

Note.—Vanadium also produces a color with thymol under conditions above.

If a spectrophotometer is used to measure the transmittancy prepare the standard solution as given for the $H_2O_2$ procedure. Use the appropriate volume of standard solution, add thymol and dilute with concentrated sulfuric acid. Transmission is measured at 550 m$\mu$.

## DETERMINATION WITH HYDROGEN PEROXIDE

Hydrogen peroxide added to acid solutions of titanium produces a yellow to orange color, the depth of the color depending upon the amount of titanium present. The method is based upon this fact. It is of special value in determining small amounts of titanium, as it is possible to detect less than one part of the metal per hundred thousand parts of solution. Color comparisons can best be made on samples containing 0.005 to 5 mg. of the element; larger amounts produce a color too deep for accurate comparison.

The following interferences should be noted, e.g., nickel, copper, cobalt, molybdenum, vanadium, and chromium which produce colors that would lead to error.

To eliminate the interference of these ions various procedures have been reported. A. Weissler [35] reports that if a perchlorate solution is used and the proper wavelengths are chosen vanadium, and molybdenum will not interfere. Iron if present in relatively large quantity produces a color that must be allowed for; e.g., 0.1 g. $Fe_2O_3$ in 100 ml. of solution. Fluorides destroy the color, hence must be absent.[36] Phosphoric acid and alkali sulfates have a slight fading action,[37] hence must be allowed for by adding equivalent amounts to the standard if they are present in the sample. The addition of an excess of sulfuric acid partly counteracts the action of phosphates or alkali sulfates.[38] The color intensity is increased by increase of temperature, hence the standard and the sample examined should have the same temperature.[39] Since hydrous titanium oxide produces only slight if any color with hydrogen peroxide, its formation must be prevented; the presence of 5% of free $H_2SO_4$ accomplishes this.[40]

Other methods of separation are given.[41, 42, 43]

The actual measurement of the color can be made in Nessler tubes, Duboscq type of colorimeter, or any filter colorimeter or spectrophotometer.

### HYDROGEN PEROXIDE DETERMINATION OF TITANIUM IN PLAIN CARBON STEELS, ALLOYS, STEELS AND CAST IRONS [44]

**Reagents. Standard Titanium Sulfate Solution.** (See Note.)—Prepared from titanium-potassium oxalate. $K_2TiO(C_2O_4)_2 \cdot 2H_2O$. Transfer 2.214 g. of the oxalate

35 Weissler, A., Ind. Eng. Chem., Anal. Ed., **17**, 695–8, 1945.
36 Hillebrand, W. F., J. Am. Chem. Soc., **17**, 7.–19, 1895; News, **72**, 158, 1895.
37 Faber, P., Z. anal. Chem., **46**, 277, 1907.
38 Merwin, H. E., Am. J. Sci. (4), **28**, 121, 1909.
39 Hillebrand, W. F., U. S. Geol. Survey, Bull. 700, p. 155, 1919.
40 Dunnington, F. P., J. Am. Chem. Soc., **13**, 210, 1891; Chem. News, **64**, 302, 1891.
41 Silverman, L., Ind. Eng. Chem., Anal. Ed., **14**, 791–2, 1942.
42 Jutkovskaya, Z. P., Zavodskaya Lab., **15**, 109–10, 1949.
43 Thomas, A., et al., Proc. Am. Soc. Testing Materials, **44**, 796–78, 1944.
44 By Best. Method of analysis recommended by Titanium Alloy Manufacturing Division of the National Lead Co. References are: Chemical Analysis of Iron and Steel,

(13.55% of Ti) to a 250-ml. beaker. Add about 10 g. of $(NH_4)_2SO_4$, 50 ml. of $H_2SO_4$ (1:1), 10 ml. of $HNO_3$. and digest on the hot plate until copious fumes are given off. Cool, carefully wash the cover glass and sides of the beaker, and again evaporate until copious fumes of sulfuric are evolved. Cool, dilute, and transfer the solution to a 1000-ml. volumetric flask, containing an additional 50 ml. of $H_2SO_4$ (1:1). Adjust the temperature, dilute to volume, and thoroughly mix.

NOTE.—Other materials can be used as sources of titanium for the preparation of the standard titanium solution, titanium tetrachloride (Pleckner, W. W., and Jarmus, J. M., Inc. Eng. Chem., Anal. Ed., **6**, 447, 1934), potassium titanium oxalate (Thornton, W. W., and Roseman, R., Am. J. Sci. (5), **20**, 14, 1930) and $K_2TiF_6$. The preparation with potassium titanium oxalate is given in the following procedure for titanium in plain carbon steels, alloy steels, and cast irons. A most convenient source of titanium for preparation of a standard solution is National Bureau of Standards $TiO_2$ sample No. 154. Dissolve 0.1013 g. of the N.B.S. sample No. 154 (98.7% $TiO_2$) in 10 g. of $(NH_4)_2SO_4$ and 35 ml. of concentrated $H_2SO_4$ as given under the titrimetric procedure for $TiO_2$. After the sample has dissolved, cool and add 90 ml. of water and filter through Whatman No. 42 paper into a 200-ml. volumetric flask, dilute to volume and mix. One ml. of this solution contains 0.0005 gram of $TiO_2$. Transfer 5-, 10-, 15-, 20-, 25-, and 30-ml. portions to 100-ml. volumetric flasks. Add the amount of acids and other ions which will be present in the unknown solutions to each portion. Generally, 20 ml. of 1:1 $H_2SO_4$ is sufficient. Add 15 ml. of 3% $H_2O_2$, dilute to volume, mix, and measure the transmission at 420 m$\mu$ utilizing a 0.5-cm. cell. The solution concentrations can be varied depending upon the method of measuring the color. The above directions are used for filter or spectrophotometers.

*Standardization.*—Pipette 50 ml. portions into 250-ml. beakers, add 20 ml. of $H_2SO_4$ (1:1), and dilute to about 100 ml. Add some ashless paper pulp and cool to 10° to 15°C. Slowly add a cold 6% water solution of cupferron, while stirring constantly, until precipitation is complete. Place the beaker in the cooling bath for 5 to 10 minutes, then filter with gentle suction through a close-texture paper, supported by a platinum cone. Police the beaker with a piece of filter paper and wash the precipitate 12 to 15 times with a cold HCl (1:9) solution. containing 20 ml. of cupferron reagent per liter. Drain the precipitate thoroughly, then transfer the paper and precipitate to a weighed small platinum dish. Cautiously dry, as the precipitate tends to liquefy if heated too rapidly. After the volatile matter is expelled, increase the temperature until the carbon is burned off. Finally ignite at 1050° to 1100°C.

One ml. = 0.0003 g. Ti.

***Procedure for Total Titanium in Steels.***—1. Transfer 0.5 to 5.0 g. of the sample to a 400-ml. beaker, add 100 ml. of $H_2SO_4$ (1:9) or 100 ml. of HCl (1:2), and heat gently until all action has ceased. Cool the solution to 10° to 15°C., and add a cold 2% water solution of cupferron drop by drop, while stirring constantly, until the precipitate just assumes a reddish-brown color. Ten to twenty milliliters of the cupferron reagent are generally sufficient, a large excess only precipitates additional iron, which may vitiate the final results. Add some ashless paper pulp and thoroughly stir the mixture. Filter with gentle suction through a close-texture paper, supported by a platinum filter cone. Wash the precipitate 12 to 15 times with a cold solution of HCl (1:9).

2. Transfer the paper and precipitate to the original beaker, add 3 to 4 g. of

Lundell, Hoffman, and Bright. John Wiley and Sons, Inc.; Sampling and Analysis of Carbon and Alloy Steels, By Chemists of the United States Steel Corporation, Reinhold Publishing Company.

anhydrous sodium sulfate, 25 ml. of $H_2SO_4$ (1:1), 25 ml. of $HNO_3$, and 7 ml. of 70% $HClO_4$. Digest on the hot plate until organic matter is destroyed, if organic matter persists add more $HNO_3$, then evaporate the solution until copious fumes of sulfuric acid are evolved. Cool, carefully add about 125 ml. of cold water, and heat until all the salts are in solution.

*Caution:* The destruction of organic matter with hot perchloric acid is violent and can lead to serious explosions; therefore nitric acid must be present in all evaporations!

As applied for the destruction of cupferron precipitates and filter papers: To the beaker containing the mixed acids, add the paper and precipitate, and allow the reaction which is vigorous to proceed in a good fume hood until it subsides. Place the beaker on the hot plate and evaporate the solution until excessive frothing occurs, then add several drops of $HNO_3$ from a dropping bottle, evaporate, and repeat the treatment with $HNO_3$ until the tar-like matter is destroyed.

3. Transfer the cool solution (paragraph 2) to a 250-ml. volumetric flask. Adjust the temperature, dilute to volume, and thoroughly mix. Pipette a suitable portion (50 ml.) of the solution into a Nessler comparison tube. To a second tube, add an equal volume of blank solutions, prepared by adding 3 to 4 g. of anhydrous sodium sulfate to 25 ml. of $H_2SO_4$ (1:1), and diluting to 250 ml. To the unknown add $H_3PO_4$ drop by drop until any iron color is destroyed and add an equal volume to the blank. Add 5 ml. of 3% peroxide solution to each tube and mix. From a 10-ml. burette, add small amounts of the standard titanium sulfate solution to the blank until the color matches the unknown, when the volumes are equal. Mix the blank solution thoroughly after each addition of standard solution.

$$\% \text{ Titanium} = \frac{\text{Ml. of standard titanium sulfate} \times 0.0003 \times 100}{\text{Weight of sample (aliquot portion)}}.$$

4. The color intensity of the peroxidized solution may also be evaluated by means of a photoelectric colorimeter or a spectrophotometer, after plotting a suitable calibration curve. If photoelectric equipment is used, transfer portions of the unknown solution into two absorption cells. Use one cell for making the initial null adjustment; to the other cell add *four drops of 30% hydrogen peroxide,* and mix. From the scale reading of the peroxidized solution, determine the titanium content of the sample by reference to the calibration curve.

NOTE.—1. If appreciable amounts of copper, molybdenum, or tungsten are present in the steel, add about a 5 ml. excess of $NH_4OH$ to the dilute sulfuric acid solution, obtained from destroying the cupferron precipitate, paragraph 2. Heat to boiling, filter, and wash with a hot 2% $NH_4OH$ solution. Transfer the paper and precipitate to the original beaker and complete the determination as described in paragraphs 1 and 2.

2. If any vanadium is present in the steel, add a cold 50% solution of NaOH to the dilute sulfuric acid solution, obtained from destroying the cupferron precipitate (paragraph 2), until most of the acid is neutralized. Slowly pour the clear-almost neutral solution, while stirring constantly, into 100 ml. of a hot 10% NaOH solution. Boil for a few minutes, let settle, and filter on a close-texture paper. Police the beaker with a piece of filter paper and wash the precipitate with a hot 2% NaOH solution. Transfer the paper and precipitate to the beaker and complete the determination as described in paragraphs 2 and 3.

**Procedure for Total Titanium in Cast Irons.**—Transfer 5 g. of the sample to a 400-ml. beaker, add 100 ml. of $H_2SO_4$ (1:9) or 100 ml. of HCl (1:2), and heat gently. When all action has ceased, add a few drops of HF, and stir thoroughly. Cool and add cupferron as described for Steels, paragraph 1.

Transfer the paper and cupferron precipitate to a platinum crucible, dry, and ignite under good oxidizing conditions until all the carbon is burnt off. Moisten the residue with 8 to 10 drops of $H_2SO_4$ (1:1), add 2 to 3 ml. of HF, and evaporate to dryness on the sand bath.

Fuse the residue with 3 to 4 g. of sodium bisulfate (fused). Cool and dissolve the melt in 25 ml. of $H_2SO_4$ (1:1). Transfer the cool solutions to a 250-ml. volumetric flask and complete the determination as described for Steels, paragraph 3.

The blank solution should contain the same concentration of $NaHSO_4$. and $H_3PO_4$ that are present in the unknown solution.

If the cast iron contains copper, molybdenum, or vanadium, treat the solution from the sodium bisulfate fusion as described in the Notes above and complete the determination as described in paragraphs 2 and 3.

## COLORIMETRIC DETERMINATION OF TITANIUM IN PAPER, FABRIC OR OTHER ORGANIC MATERIALS

The colorimetric procedure using hydrogen peroxide can be applied to paper, fabric, and other organic materials.

*Procedure.*—Transfer a 1-g. sample to a platinum crucible. Carefully ash the sample. Add 8 g. of anhydrous sodium carbonate, cover the crucible and fuse at 900°C. for 1 hour on a Meker burner. Cool and transfer the crucible and contents to a 250-ml. beaker and add 40 ml. of water and 20 ml. of concentrated HCl. When the sample is dissolved, remove the crucible and cover and evaporate to a volume of 75 ml. If insoluble matter is present, filter through Whatman No. 42 paper. Transfer to a 100-ml. volumetric flask and add 15 ml. of 3% $H_2O_2$, dilute to volume and mix. The color develops immediately. Measure the transmission at 420 m$\mu$ in a 0.5-cm. cell and obtain the $TiO_2$ content from calibration curve prepared as previously directed.

## OTHER COLORIMETRIC METHODS

Other procedures have been developed using various organic reagents. Yoe and Armstrong [45] use disodium-2-dihydroxybenzene-3,5-sulfonate which is sensitive to 1 part titanium in 100,000,000 parts of solution. The yellow colored complex obeys Beer's Law over the useful range of concentration; eliminating ferric ion interference by reducing it to the ferrous state with sodium dithionite. Hines and Boltz [46] measured the complex formed with a large excess of ascorbic acid at a pH from 3.5 to 6 at 360 m$\mu$. This yellow complex conforms to Beer's Law from 0.1 to 25 parts per million.

Chromotropic [47,48] acid has been used to determine traces of titanium.

[45] Yoe and Armstrong, Ind. Eng. Chem., Anal. Ed., 19, 100, 1947.
[46] Hines and Boltz, Anal. Chem., 24, 947–8, 1952.
[47] Orensten, Parker, and Hatchard, Anal. Chem. Acta., 6, 7–22, 1952.
[48] Rosatte and Jandon, Anal. Chem. Acta., 6, 149–65, 1952.

## DETERMINATIONS IN SPECIFIC SUBSTANCES

## DETERMINATION OF TITANIUM IN FERROCARBON TITANIUM

### GRAVIMETRIC METHOD [49]

*Procedure.*—Into a 6-in. porcelain evaporating dish, weigh 0.6 gram (factor weight) of alloy.

Dissolve in a mixture of 15 ml. of dilute sulfuric acid (one vol. of acid to one of water), 5 ml. of nitric acid, and 10 ml. of hydrochloric acid. Evaporate to fumes of sulfuric anhydride.

Cool and take up by boiling with 50 to 60 ml. of water and 5 to 10 ml. hydrochloric acid. Filter into a 500-ml. beaker and wash the residue with hot water and dilute hydrochloric acid.

In the filtrate precipitate iron and titanium by ammonia in slight excess. Filter without boiling and wash precipitate twice on filter with hot water.

Reject filtrate. Dissolve the precipitate in a very little dilute hydrochloric acid, washing the filter with hot water and collecting the solution and washings in the original beaker.

Nearly neutralize the solution with ammonia or ammonium carbonate; dilute to 300 ml.; saturate with sulfur dioxide gas, and boil until hydrous titanium oxide is precipitated and the solution smells faintly of sulfur dioxide.

Filter and wash with hot water and dilute sulfurous acid.

Dry, ignite, and weigh as titanium dioxide.

Since the factor weight of sample has been used, 1 mg. of titanium dioxide is equal to 0.1% metallic titanium.

Cupferron may be applied with advantage to the estimation of titanium in either ferrocarbon-titanium or carbon-free ferrotitanium.[50]

Other gravimetric procedures have been developed such as the use of tannin to precipitate titanium from a chloride solution.[51]

## DETERMINATION OF SILICON, ALUMINUM, TITANIUM, AND CARBON IN LOW CARBON 25% FERROTITANIUM AND LOW CARBON 40% FERROTITANIUM [44]

### DETERMINATION OF SILICON

*Procedure.*—Transfer 0.4672 g. of the 80-mesh sample to an extra heavy 25-ml Armco iron crucible, containing approximately 10 g. of sodium peroxide. Thoroughly mix the contents of the crucible and then cover the charge with about 2 g additional $Na_2O_2$. Grasp the crucible around the outside near the top with a pair of heat-resisting tongs and slowly heat over a moderate flame until the contents have melted. Continue the fusion by rotating the melt in the crucible at a

[49] Method of analysis originally used in the laboratories of the Titanium Alloy Manufacturing Division, National Lead Co.

[50] Thornton, Jr., W. M., A.C.S. Monograph Series, No. 33, p. 200, Reinhold Publishing Co., 1927; Cunningham, Ind. Eng. Chem., Anal. Ed., **5**, 305, 1933; Brit. Standards Inst. S.W.I. Brit. Standard 1121, 1951 (pt. 17). P. I. Shportenko. Zavodskaya Lab., **8**, 96, 1939.

[51] Schoeller and Holness, Analyst, **70**, 319–23, 1945; *p*-hydroxybenzenearsenic acid Richter, Z. Anal. Che., **212**, 1–16, 1941; or complexons, Pribil and Schneider, Chem. Listy **45**, 7–10, 1951.

dull red heat for about five minutes. Cool, cover the crucible, and tap the bottom of the crucible to loosen the melt.

Transfer the melt to a dry 800-ml. beaker. Cover the beaker and add at one stroke 60 ml. of $H_2SO_4$ (1:1). Wash the crucible with about 10 ml. of $H_2SO_4$ (1:1), then with water, and add the washings to the beaker. Wash the cover glass and sides of the beaker, add 10 ml. of HCl, and one quarter of a 9-cm. filter paper. Place the beaker and contents on the hot plate and evaporate until strong sulfuric acid fumes are evolved. If excessive frothing occurs from the destruction of the filter paper, add a few drops of $HNO_3$. Finally allow the solution to fume for about five minutes. Remove the beaker from the hot plate and cool. Carefully add about 250 ml. of cold water and 10 ml. of HCl. Stir and digest on the warm plate until all the salts are in solution. Add some ashless paper pulp to the solution and filter through a Whatman No. 40 filter paper, supported by a platinum filter cone. Police the beaker with a piece of filter paper, wash the paper and residue a few times with a hot HCl (5:95) solution, and finally with hot water.

Place the filter and residue in a platinum crucible, carefully char the paper with flaming, then ignite until the carbon is burnt off, and finally heat at about 1100°C. for 25 to 30 minutes. Cool in a desiccator and weigh.

Cautiously moisten the residue with a few drops of water, add 6 to 8 drops of $H_2SO_4$ (1:1), about 10 ml. of HF, and evaporate to dryness on the sand bath. Gradually heat the crucible in the front of the muffle and then heat for about ten minutes at the above temperature. Cool and weigh.

$$\text{Silicon, } \% = \text{Loss in weight} \times 100$$

## ALUMINUM

*Procedure.*—Transfer 0.5 g. of the 80-mesh sample to a 250-ml. platinum dish with cover. Add 30 ml. of $H_2SO_4$ (1:1), 20 to 30 drops of $HNO_3$, about 5 ml. of HF. Gently warm until reaction is complete. Wash and remove the cover, wash the sides of the dish, and then evaporate the solution until dense fumes of sulfuric acid are given off. Cool, add about 75 ml. of water, 5 ml. of HCl, and digest until the salts are in solution.

Transfer the solution to a 400-ml. beaker and cool to about 10°C. Add some ashless paper pulp, then while stirring, slowly add a filtered cold 6% water solution of cupferron until precipitation is complete. Allow the beaker and contents to stand for about five minutes in the cooling bath. Support a 12.5-cm. close-texture filter paper in a funnel with a filter cone, and filter the solution with the aid of gentle suction. Wash the precipitate 15 to 20 times with a cold HCl (10:90) solution containing 20 ml. of cupferron solution per liter. Drain the precipitate thoroughly. Reserve the precipitate.

Transfer the filtrate to an 800-ml. beaker, add 40 ml. of $HNO_3$, 20 ml. of $HClO_4$, and evaporate to perchloric acid fumes. If organic matter persists, add 5 to 10 ml. of $HNO_3$ and again evaporate to perchloric acid fumes. (*Caution:* The destruction of organic matter with hot perchloric acid is violent and can lead to serious explosions; therefore, nitric acid must be present in all evaporations.) Cool, carefully dilute to about 200 ml., add 5 ml. of HCl, and heat to boiling for 5 minutes. Filter and wash with hot water. Add $NH_4OH$ to the filtrate until most of the aluminum is precipitated, then add about ten drops of HCl, a few drops of methyl red indicator solution, and finally $NH_4OH$ until the color just changes to a distinct yellow. Add some ashless paper pulp and boil the solution one minute. Filter through a

Whatman No. 40 filter paper supported by a platinum cone. Police the beaker with a piece of filter paper and wash the precipitate with a hot 2% $NH_4Cl$ solution.

Place the paper and precipitate in a tared platinum crucible with a well-fitting cover. Carefully burn off the paper in the open crucible, cover and finally heat at 1100°C. for 30 minutes. Cool in a desiccator and weigh rapidly. Return the covered crucible and contents to the muffle and heat for 10 to 15 minutes. Cool and weigh to check for constant weight.

Any phosphorus in the sample must be corrected for in the alumina precipitate.

$$\text{Aluminum, } \% = \frac{\text{Weight of Al}_2\text{O}_3 \times 0.5291 \times 100}{\text{Weight of sample}}$$

### TITANIUM

*Procedure.*—Add to the 400-ml. beaker which contained the cupferron precipitate about 5 g. of anhydrone sodium sulfate, 30 ml. of $H_2SO_4$ (1:1), 30 ml. of $HNO_3$, and 10 ml. 70% $HClO_4$. Transfer the reserved cupferron precipitate to this beaker and allow the reaction to proceed in a good fume hood. When the reaction has subsided, place the beaker on the hot plate and evaporate until excessive frothing occurs. Add several drops of $HNO_3$ from a dropping bottle to the solution and again evaporate. Continue the treatment with $HNO_3$ until the tar-like matter is destroyed. Finally evaporate until copious fumes of sulfuric acid are given off. Cool, carefully wash the cover glass and sides of the beaker, and again evaporate to strong fumes. Cool, carefully dilute to about 200 ml. with water and digest until all the salts are in solution.

Reduce the titanium by the zinc reductor technique or with aluminum foil. Add 10 ml. of ammonium thiocyanate indicator solution and titrate the reduced titanium with a standard ferric ammonium sulfate solution, 1 ml. equivalent to 0.003 g. titanium.

$$\text{Titanium, } \% = \frac{\text{Ml. of standard solution} \times 0.003 \times 100}{\text{Weight of sample}}$$

### CARBON

Transfer 2.727 g. of the 80-mesh sample to a combustion boat bedded with 60-mesh alundum, cover the charge with additional alundum, and burn the sample at approximately 1350°C. in the regular carbon combustion apparatus.

$$\text{Carbon, } \% = \text{Weight of CO}_2 \times 10$$

## DETERMINATION OF SILICON, TITANIUM, AND CARBON IN MEDIUM-CARBON FERROTITANIUM AND HIGH-CARBON FERROTITANIUM [44]

### DETERMINATION OF SILICON

*Procedure.*—Transfer 0.5 g. of the 80-mesh sample to a 250-ml. beaker. Add about 5 g. of anhydrous sodium sulfate, 25 ml. of $H_2SO_4$ (1:1), 15 ml. of HCl and 10 ml. of $HNO_3$. Cover the beaker and digest at a moderate temperature until the reaction subsides, then heat on the hot plate until copious fumes of sulfuric acid are given off. Cool the solution, carefully wash the cover glass and the sides of the beaker, and again evaporate to strong fumes. Cool, carefully add about 150 ml. of cold water, 5 ml. of HCl, and digest on the hot plate until the salts are in solution.

Filter the solution, police the beaker with a piece of filter paper, wash the filter and residue a few times with a hot HCl (5:95) solution, and finally with hot water. Reserve the filtrate, $A$.

Transfer the filter and residue to a platinum crucible, carefully char the paper without flaming, then ignite until the carbon is burnt off, and finally heat at about 1100°C. for 25 to 30 minutes. Cool in a desiccator and weigh. Cautiously moisten the residue with a few drops of water, add 6 to 8 drops of $H_2SO_4$ (1:1), about 5 ml. of HF, and evaporate to dryness on the sand bath. Gradually heat the crucible in the front of the muffle and then heat for about ten minutes at the above temperature. Cool and weigh.

$$\text{Silicon, \%} = \frac{\text{Loss in weight} \times 0.4674 \times 100}{\text{Weight of sample}}$$

### TITANIUM

**Procedure.**—Fuse the residue in the platinum crucible from the silicon determination with a few small lumps of sodium bisulfate (fused) and add the cool melt to the reserved filtrate $A$. Warm and stir the solution until the melt has dissolved.

Reduce the titanium by the zinc reductor technique or with aluminum foil. Add 10 ml. of ammonium thiocyanate indicator solution and titrate the reduced titanium with a standard ferric ammonium sulfate solution, one ml. equivalent to 0.003 g. titanium.

$$\text{Titanium, \%} = \frac{\text{Ml. of standard solution} \times 0.003 \times 100}{\text{Weight of sample}}$$

### CARBON

Transfer 0.5454 g. of the 80-mesh sample to a clean porcelain crucible, add 1 g. of red lead, and thoroughly mix with a small glass rod. Transfer the mixture to a combustion boat bedded with 60-mesh alundum. Cover the charge with additional alundum and burn the sample at approximately 1200°C. in the regular carbon combustion apparatus. Correct the weight of $CO_2$ for any blank from the red lead and carbon train.

$$\text{Carbon, \%} = \text{Corrected weight of } CO_2 \times 50$$

## THE ANALYSIS OF TITANIFEROUS ORES [52]

### DETERMINATION OF TITANIUM

**Procedure.**—Decompose the ore by fusion with potassium pyrosulfate, dissolving the fusion in water, hydrochloric and sulfuric acids. This is usually sufficient to insure having all of the titanium in solution. However, if any doubt exists, filter the insoluble residue. Calcine the residue, add a few drops of sulfuric acid and sufficient hydrofluoric acid to dissolve silica, evaporate to fumes of sulfuric anhydride and then heat to redness.

[52] Method of Analysis used in the laboratories of the National Lead Company, Titanium Division.

If a residue now remains, bring it into solution directly in acids or fuse with a little potassium pyrosulfate, then dissolve and finally add the solution to the main solution as before described.

If desired, the sample of ore can first be partially dissolved in hydrochloric and sulfuric acids, and the insoluble residue then fused with potassium pyrosulfate or treated with sulfuric and hydrofluoric acids.

Some ores may be completely decomposed by a mixture of nitric, hydrofluoric and sulfuric acids, evaporating to fumes of sulfuric anhydride in a platinum dish to free the solution from nitric and hydrofluoric acids.

The complete decomposition of the sample having been accomplished, the titanium in the solution is determined by the titrimetric methods.

### IRON IN THE PRESENCE OF TITANIUM

**Procedure for Determination of $Fe_2O_3$.**—The sample is decomposed by fusion with potassium pyrosulfate. This is satisfactory if all the iron-bearing materials are soluble. If insoluble iron silicates are present the sample is dissolved with sulfuric acid and hydrofluoric acid. Usually only a few milliliters of hydrofluoric acid are required. The insoluble residue is filtered and silica removed as recommended under the determination of titanium. The residue is fused with potassium pyrosulfate dissolved and added to the original solution. If a platinum dish is available complete solution can usually be affected by using 1:3 sulfuric acid and hydrofluoric acid in about equal proportions. The resulting solution is heated to fumes of $SO_3$. It is then diluted with 25 ml. of water.

Twenty ml. of hydrochloric acid is added to the solution. The solution is either evaporated or diluted to approximately 50 ml. and the iron is determined by the standard procedure using stannous chloride as the reductant, mercuric chloride, protective solution of phosphoric-sulfuric acid mixture, and titrating to the blue end point of barium diphenylaminesulfonate indicator with standard potassium dichromate solution. The total Fe is thus determined: the $Fe_2O_3$ is calculated from the FeO determination.

NOTE.—Occasionally titanium phosphate will precipitate after the addition of the protective solution. A few milliliters of HF will redissolve this precipitate.

**Procedure for Determination of FeO.**—Weigh 0.5 gram of sample into a 500-ml. Erlenmeyer flask. The sample is moistened with water and swirled to make certain it spreads evenly over the bottom of the flask. $CO_2$ is passed into the flask for 15 minutes. The $CO_2$ delivery tube is placed well into the lower quarter of the flask. This delivery tube passes through a glass funnel with no stem which is placed into the neck of the Erlenmeyer flask.

The solutions are added as follows:

1. Add 30 ml. 1:3 $H_2SO_4$. Simmer for 15 minutes.
2. Add 10 ml. HF. Simmer for 10 minutes and swirl the flask from time to time.
3. Add 10 ml. 1:3 $H_2SO_4$. Simmer for 15 minutes.
4. Add 2–3 ml. HF. Simmer for 5 minutes and swirl from time to time.
5. Add 5 ml. 1:3 $H_2SO_4$. Simmer until as much of the sample that will go into solution is in solution. Do not heat to $SO_3$ fumes.
6. Let the solution cool. Dilute to 200 ml. and add 4–5 grams of boric acid, remove the $CO_2$ delivery tube and funnel, cool rapidly under the tap, and titrate with 0.1 $N$ $KMnO_4$ to faint pink end point.

NOTE.—Sometimes several more HF and $H_2SO_4$ additions will have to be made. The sample usually goes completely into solution.

There have been many combinations for carrying out the iron and titanium analysis. The most common is to determine the titanium and then with a second sample determine iron and titanium by titration of the solution from a Jones reductor with a standard potassium permanganate. Shippy[53] has improved on this method by using methylene blue for the titanium end point and the o-phenanthroline ferrous complex for the iron. The solution reduced in a Jones reductor is titrated with potassium permanganate.

Potentiometric methods have been proposed as indicated previously.

## SILICA

*Procedure.*—This determination is conveniently combined with the determination of titanium, the ore being preferably decomposed by fusion with potassium pyrosulfate. The fusion is dissolved and evaporated with excess sulfuric acid to fumes of sulfuric anhydride and the silica determination finished as usual—weighing, volatilizing with hydrofluoric acid, etc. If the ore contains quartz or a silicate undecomposable by treatment with potassium pyrosulfate and hydrofluoric acid, the residue filtered from the sulfuric acid solution should be fused with sodium carbonate and the silica then determined as usual.

In the determination of silicon, a radiant heating device is useful for volatilizing silicon fluoride.[54]

## ALUMINA

*Procedure.*—Prepare a solution of 0.5 g. of ore as indicated under the determination of titanium. Make up the final filtrate so that a cupferron extraction can be carried out as given under separations. To the final extracted product add 2 drops of methyl red indicator, dilute to about 200 ml., heat to boiling, add 5 g. of $NH_4Cl$ and then $NH_4OH$ (1:3) dropwise until the solution changes to a yellow color. Boil two or three minutes and filter through Whatman No. 41H filter paper. Wash once or twice with hot 2% $NH_4Cl$ solution. Dissolve the precipitate by adding 20 ml. HCl, and heating precipitate with $NH_4OH$, filter through same paper, wash with dilute $NH_4Cl$ police beaker and wash the precipitate 3–4 times with hot 2% $NH_4Cl$. Dissolve the paper and residue in 50 ml. $HNO_3$ + 10 ml. $H_2SO_4$. Evaporate to fumes, add more $HNO_3$ if charring is evident. Repeat until solution is white. Dilute to 200 ml., neutralize with $NH_4OH$ to methyl red. Acidify with HCl, add 3 ml. excess. Heat to 70°–80°C. and add enough 8-hydroxyquinoline to provide a slight excess allowing 1 ml. for each 100 ml. of solution present. Stir and allow to stand for one hour without further heating. The supernatant liquid should be yellow. Filter the precipitate on a tared Gooch crucible, wash well with cold water and dry in an oven at 130°C. for 1 hour. Cool in a desiccator and weigh as aluminum quinolate.

NOTE.—If chromium is present in relatively large amounts it may be separated by adding perchloric acid to the final solution from the cupferron extraction in which the organic material has been destroyed. The solution is fumed until the Cr is oxidized as indicated by the chromate color then the procedure is followed as given.

[53] Shippy, B. A., Anal. Chem., 21, 698–9, 1949.
[54] As recommended by Whitfield (A. A. Blair, The Chemical Analysis of Iron, 1918, p. 17, J. B. Lippincott Company), W. F. Hillebrand (U. S. Geol. Survey, Bull. 700, 33, 1919), or the simple nickel crucible heater, as proposed by Thornton, Titanium, A.C.S. Monograph series No. 33, p. 125, Reinhold Publishing Co., 1927.

A more detailed method for the determination of aluminum as the oxyquinolate is given under "Analysis of Titanium and Titanium-Base Alloys" below.

## PHOSPHORUS

*Procedure.*—The phosphoric acid may be separated from the titanium and iron by fusion of the ore with alkaline carbonate and extraction of the alkali phosphate with water.

The phosphorus is then determined colorimetrically [55] depending on the formation of yellow phosphovanadomolybdate.

If greater concentrations of phosphorus are present various methods are given under the Chapter on Phosphorus.

The analysis of the other elements such as Mg, Ca, Cr, and V are carried out by the methods given under the appropriate chapters. Magnesium can be determined with 8-hydroxyquinoline, calcium by precipitation as the oxalate, and subsequent titration with permanganate, chromium and vanadium potentiometrically with ferrous ammonium sulfate and potassium dichromate solutions.

# DETERMINATION OF IRON, TITANIUM, AND ZIRCONIUM IN BAUXITE

An article by Lundell and Hoffman [56] is important as a contribution to the literature on bauxite giving details of a complete accurate method of analysis including the determination of titanium. The separation of titanium is accomplished by oxidizing titanium in solution to peroxide by addition of hydrogen peroxide and then separating the zirconium as phosphate.

In the course of the general analysis the iron, titanium, and zirconium are precipitated together by addition of a mixture of sodium hydroxide and sodium peroxide in solution, digesting for an hour on steam bath, filtering out and washing, thus separating from chromium, vanadium, and phosphoric acid.

*Procedure.*—The iron, titanium, and zirconium are then determined as follows: "Dissolve the reserved precipitate in 25 ml. of hot dilute HCl (1:2), add 5 g. of tartaric acid, dilute with water to a volume of 200 ml. and neutralize with $NH_4OH$. Add 2 ml. of HCl per 100 ml. of solution, heat to boiling and saturate with $H_2S$. Allow to cool and filter off any platinum sulfide which may have separated and wash with a 1% solution of $H_2SO_4$ saturated with $H_2S$.

"Render the filtrate slightly ammoniacal, pass in a rapid stream of $H_2S$ for five minutes and digest at the side of the steam bath (40°C.) 15 to 30 minutes. Filter and wash with a dilute solution of $(NH_4)_2S$ (5:95) containing 5 g. of $NH_4Cl$ per liter. Reserve the filtrate *A*.

"Dissolve the iron sulfide in hot dilute HCl (1:1) to which has been added a little $KClO_3$, evaporate to dryness, take up in 25 ml. of dilute HCl (5:95), and add $KMnO_4$ until the usual pink color is obtained. Reduce with $SnCl_2$ and titrate slowly with a standard solution of $KMnO_4$, as in the Zimmermann-Reinhardt method.

"The filtrate, *A,* contains the titanium and zirconium. Acidify this solution with $H_2SO_4$ dilute to 200 ml., adjust the acidity so that the solution contains 10 ml. of $H_2SO_4$, sp. gr. 1.84 per 100 ml., and cool in ice water. It is unnecessary to destroy tartaric acid. Precipitate the titanium and zirconium with an excess of a

[55] Murray, W. M., and Ashley, S. E. Q., Ind. Eng. Chem., Anal. Ed., **10,** 1, 1938.
[56] Bureau of Standards Journal of Research, Vol. 1, No. 1, July, 1928, pages 91 to 104.

cold 6% water solution of cupferron. An excess of the precipitant is indicated by the formation of a fine white precipitate which redissolves, instead of a curdy one which persists. Stir in a little macerated paper, allow to settle for five minutes, filter by suction through a paper and cone, and test the filtrate for complete precipitation. Thoroughly wash the precipitate with cold dilute HCl (1:9). Transfer to a weighed platinum crucible, carefully dry, then cautiously char and burn the carbon and finally heat at approximately 1200°C. over a blast lamp or its equivalent. Cool in a desiccator, weigh as $ZrO_2 + TiO_2$, and repeat the ignition until constant weight is obtained. The correction of the weighed oxides for $SiO_2$ by direct treatment with $H_2SO_4$ and HF is a difficult procedure and is well nigh impossible if the residue is large. The amount of $SiO_2$ is usually small and can be determined if desired by evaporating the $H_2SO_4$ solution of the pyrosulfate melt obtained in the next step to fumes of $H_2SO_4$, diluting so that the solution contains 10% of the acid by volume, and recovering the $SiO_2$ by filtering and washing.

"Fuse the precipitate of $TiO_2$ and $ZrO_2$ with a small amount of $K_2S_2O_7$, dissolve the melt in 50 ml. of dilute $H_2SO_4$ (1:9), add sufficient $H_2O_2$ to oxidize all of the titanium (an excess does not harm), add 0.5 g. of $(NH_4)_2HPO_4$, allow to stand at the side of the steam bath (40°C.) overnight, filter, wash with a 5% solution of $NH_4NO_3$, ignite, and weigh as $ZrP_2O_7$. Calculate to $ZrO_2$ and subtract from the total weight of $TiO_2 + ZrO_2$. As a check, titanium can be determined colorimetrically, before the precipitation of zirconium. In very accurate analyses the $ZrP_2O_7$ should be fused with a little $K_2S_2O_7$, the melt dissolved in 10% $H_2SO_4$ as before, and the precipitation repeated. More phosphate must be added in the second precipitation, and an excess of $H_2O_2$ should be present at all times."

## DETERMINATION OF TITANIUM DIOXIDE IN PURE TITANIUM DIOXIDE PIGMENT

*Procedure.*—Weigh 0.2 grams of sample into a 250-ml. beaker (Erlenmeyer flask if the Al reduction is to be used), add 10 grams of ammonium sulfate and 20 ml. of concentrated sulfuric acid; cover with a watch glass. Heat until the sample is dissolved using a Meker burner. Cool and dilute with water to 125–150 ml. The solution is reduced by any of the three procedures on pages 1102–1104. If the aluminum foil procedure is used, take 1 gram of the foil. After reduction, add 2 ml. of the ammonium thiocyanate indicator and titrate rapidly with the standard ferric ammonium sulfate solution.

NOTE.—In titrating titanium solution with ferric ammonium sulfate, greater accuracy is obtained by adding nearly all of the ferric ammonium sulfate before agitating. Then agitate by shaking with a gentle rotary motion and continue until the final end point, which is a light straw color. With the Jones Reductor 0.1 ml. is deducted from the titration for a blank if the standardization has been made against potassium permanganate.

## ANALYSIS OF MIXED PIGMENTS CONTAINING TITANIUM DIOXIDE

*Procedure.*—Weigh a 1-g. sample into a 400-ml. Pyrex glass beaker, add 10 g. ammonium sulfate and 40 ml. concentrated sulfuric acid. Heat on hot plate for one-half hour and then increase the heat, by placing the beaker directly over the coils of an electric hot plate and boiling for about 10 minutes. The solution should acquire a temperature of about 335°C.

Cool, dilute the solution to 300 ml., boil 20 minutes, filter while hot and wash residue and precipitate with 5% sulfuric acid. On the filter will be silica and undecomposed silicates and all the lead and barium as sulfates. The residue and precipitates can be analyzed by well-known methods if desired. The filtrate will contain the titanium, iron, aluminum, zinc, and calcium.

The iron can be determined either colorimetrically by the thiocyanate procedure, or titrimetrically as indicated under the analysis of titaniferous ores. The titanium can be determined directly titrimetrically and the calcium as indicated under the subsequent section on the analysis of "Titanox-C Pigment." The zinc can be determined most easily potentiometrically with potassium ferrocyanide.

For the examination of pure titanium pigments, the foregoing method is very satisfactory, but cannot be used when the titanium pigment is mixed with other pigments containing iron. In such cases the more general methods described in previous sections of this chapter are satisfactory.

## ANALYSIS OF TITANOX-C PIGMENT

### DETERMINATION OF TITANIUM DIOXIDE ($TiO_2$)

**Procedure.**—Weigh 0.5 grams of titanium-calcium pigment into a 250-ml. Pyrex beaker, or 500-ml. Erlenmeyer flask if the aluminum reduction technique is to be used. Carry out the solution of the sample, reduction, and titration as given under the determination of pure titanium dioxide. If this analysis is performed reasonably rapidly the calcium will remain in solution long enough to carry out the determination for Jones Reductor or liquid amalgam techniques where no hydrochloric acid is added.

### TOTAL CALCIUM OXIDE ($CaO$)

**Procedure.**—Weigh 0.5 g. of sample into a 250-ml. Pyrex beaker. Add 10 g. of ammonium sulfate and 20 ml. of concentrated sulfuric acid. Cover the beaker with a watch glass and dissolve the sample, heating with a Meker burner. After cooling transfer to a 600-ml. beaker and dilute to about 150 ml. Add methyl red indicator and neutralize the solution with $NH_4OH$. If the calcium precipitates it can be redissolved by adding HCl. The neutralization is then carried out again. The oxalic acid-ammonium oxalate procedure as given under the Chapter on Calcium is followed. The calcium oxalate is titrated with potassium permanganate as indicated under the titrimetric procedure.

## DETERMINATION OF IRON AND TITANIUM IN TITANIFEROUS SLAGS

### TITANIUM

The method is the same as given for titanium in titaniferous ores.

### DETERMINATION OF REDUCED TITANIUM [57]

Determine the iron content of the sample utilizing the procedure given below.

**Procedure.**—Transfer 0.5 g. of the ground slag to a platinum dish. Pipette precisely 10.0 ml. of $V_2O_5$ solution and add to the sample. Add 30 ml. of 1:3 $H_2SO_4$ and 10 ml. of 48% HF. Slowly bring the sample to a boil over a burner provided with a wire gauze and asbestos pad. When the sample is completely decomposed, transfer it to a 400-ml. beaker containing 100 ml. of water and 10 ml. of $H_3PO_4$. Add 7 drops of barium diphenylaminesulfonate indicator and titrate with 0.1 $N$

[57] MacCardle, L. E., and Scheffer, E. R., Anal. Chem., **23**, 1169, 1951.

ferrous ammonium sulfate to a blue-green end point. For purposes of calculation, the value thus obtained is called *B*.

Transfer precisely 10.0 ml. of the $V_2O_5$ solution to a 400-ml. beaker containing
150 ml. of water and 10 ml. each of $H_2SO_4$ and $H_3PO_4$. Add 7 drops of barium
diphenylaminesulfonate indicator and titrate with 0.1 *N* ferrous ammonium sulfate to a blue-green end point. The value thus obtained is called *A* for purposes
of calculation.

1. The solution should assume the typical dark blue coloration due to the oxidized form of barium diphenylaminesulfonate. If it fails to do this, insufficient
$V_2O_5$ solution was present and the determination must be repeated using double
the quantity of $V_2O_5$ solution. This will require doubling the value of *A* in the
calculation of the result.

2. It is necessary to exercise good titrimetric technique in order to insure the
exact reproduction of the volume of $V_2O_5$ employed throughout the analyses.

The reduced titanium is calculated using both this value, and the iron value determined as given above.

$$\frac{(A - B) \times N(\text{Fe NH}_4\text{SO}_4) \times 0.0479 \times 100}{\text{Weight of sample}} - (\% \text{ Fe in sample} \times 0.8577) = \% \text{ Ti(III)}$$

## TOTAL IRON

*Procedure.*—A 0.5-g. sample of slag can be dissolved in a platinum dish with
sulfuric acid and hydrofluoric acid, or in a manner as indicated under solution of
the sample for iron in titaniferous ores. When solution has taken place it is
necessary to add dropwise 1% $KMnO_4$ solution until an excess is present as indicated by a permanent pink coloration. Then add 15 ml. of concentrated HCl,
and proceed with the titrimetric method as given for iron in titaniferous ores.

## METALLIC IRON [58]

*Procedure.*—Transfer 0.5 g. of the sample to a dry 250-ml. beaker and add 5
grams of $HgCl_2$. Add 100 ml. of boiling water, cover the beaker with a watch
glass, and boil the solution actively for ten minutes. Filter through Whatman
No. 40 paper and wash the paper and precipitate 5 times with hot water. To the
clear filtrate add 5 drops of barium diphenylaminesulfonate indicator and 10 ml.
of 85% $H_3PO_4$. Titrate with 0.1 *N* $K_2Cr_2O_7$ solution to a permanent violet color
employing a semimicroburette. The iron value is equivalent to the metallic iron.

## DETERMINATION OF $TiO_2$ IN FRITS [59]

The analysis of $TiO_2$ can be carried out in high silicate materials by the following procedure.

*Procedure.*—The appropriate amount of ground frit (0.5 g. for $TiO_2$ content 10
to 25%) is weighed into a 100-ml. platinum dish. To this dish is added 30 ml. of
1:3 sulfuric acid and 20–25 ml. of 48% hydrofluoric acid. The platinum dish is
heated gently and the solution evaporated until fumes of $SO_3$ appear. The sample
is cooled, 5–10 ml. of water is added, and the solution is evaporated to fumes of
$SO_3$ again. The sample is cooled, 50 ml. of water added, and the solution is
ready for $TiO_2$ determination. The reduction can be carried out as recommended

[58] Lundell, Hoffman, Bright, Chemical Analysis of Iron & Steel, page 151, John Wiley
& Sons, 1931.

[59] MacCardle, L. E., and Scheffer, E. R., A.C.S. Bulletin, **31**, 145, 1952.

under titrimetric procedure. If Al reduction is used 2 g. of aluminum foil should be used.

## ANALYSIS OF TITANIUM AND TITANIUM-BASE ALLOYS [60]

These methods cover procedures for the chemical analysis of titanium and titanium-base alloys having chemical compositions within the following limits:

| | |
|---|---|
| Aluminum, per cent.......... | 0.05 to 20 |
| Carbon, per cent............ | 0.04 to 0.40 |
| Chloride, per cent........... | 0.02 to 1.0 |
| Chromium, per cent......... | 0.005 to 20 |
| Niobium, per cent........... | 0.25 to 5.0 |
| Iron, per cent.............. | 0.005 to 20 |
| Magnesium, per cent........ | 0.02 to 1.0 |
| Manganese, per cent........ | 0.005 to 20 |
| Molybdenum, per cent...... | 0.05 to 10 |
| Nitrogen, per cent.......... | 0.005 to 0.20 |
| Oxygen, per cent........... | 0.03 to 0.50 |
| Silicon, per cent............ | 0.005 to 5.0 |
| Tantalum, per cent.......... | 0.25 to 5.0 |
| Tin, per cent............... | 0.25 to 10 |
| Tungsten, per cent.......... | 0.005 to 1.0 |
| Vanadium, per cent......... | 0.03 to 10 |

### ALUMINUM BY THE 8-HYDROXYQUINOLINE (GRAVIMETRIC) METHOD

This method covers the determination of aluminum in titanium and titanium-base alloys in the range from 0.05 to 20%.

After dissolution in hydrochloric acid, interfering elements are separated by extraction of the cupferrates with chloroform and electrolysis over a mercury cathode. The aluminum is then precipitated with 8-hydroxyquinoline from an acetic acid–acetate buffered solution, and the compound separated, dried, and weighed.

The recommended aluminum content of the portion used for analysis is 0.5 to 25 mg.

All elements normally found in titanium and titanium-base alloys that interfere are removed prior to the precipitation of the aluminum. When the required separations were made, no interference was found for the following elements in the amounts shown either singly or in combinations: 10% chromium, manganese, molybdenum, or zirconium; 5% iron or vanadium; 1% copper; 0.5% magnesium, tungsten, cobalt, or nickel.

*Apparatus.*—**Separatory Funnel,** 500 ml., pear-shaped.

**Mercury Cathode.**

**Filtering Crucible.**—A fritted-glass crucible of medium porosity.

*Reagents.* **Ammonium Acetate Buffer Solution (pH 5).**—Dissolve 154 g. of ammonium acetate ($NH_4C_2H_3O_2$) in 500 ml. of water. Add 60 ml. of acetic acid and dilute to 1 liter.

---

[60] ASTM Methods for Chemical Analysis for Titanium and Titanium Base Alloys Designation E120-60 and E120-60T. Latest revision accepted by the Administrative Committee on Standards, December 29, 1960.

**Cupferron Solution (60 g. per liter).**—Dissolve 6 g. cupferron in 80 ml. of cold water, dilute to 100 ml. and filter. Prepare fresh as needed.

**Hydrogen Peroxide (10%).**—Dilute 5 ml. of hydrogen peroxide ($H_2O_2$, 30%) to 15 ml. with water. Prepare fresh before use.

**8-Hydroxyquinoline Solution (25 g. per liter).**—Dissolve 25 g. of 8-hydroxyquinoline in 50 ml. of acetic acid and dilute to 1 liter with water. Prepare fresh every 5 days.

**Sodium Hydroxide Solution (100 g. per liter).**—Dissolve 100 g. of sodium hydroxide (NaOH) in water in a polyethylene beaker. Dilute to 1 liter and store in a polyethylene bottle.

**Sodium Hydroxide Wash Solution.**—Dilute 50 ml. of the NaOH solution (100 g. per liter) to 1 liter.

**Procedure.**—(a) Transfer 1 g. of the sample, weighed to the nearest 1 mg. to a 250-ml. Erlenmeyer flask (Note 1). Add 80 ml. of HCl (1:1), cover with a 2-hole rubber stopper fitted with two short pieces of glass tubing to minimize oxidation, and heat until the sample is dissolved. If the expected aluminum content is less than 1%, proceed as directed in paragraph (b), otherwise transfer the solution to a 100-ml. volumetric flask, dilute to the mark with HCl (1:1), and mix. Transfer an aliquot containing not more than 25 mg. of aluminum to a 250-ml. beaker and dilute to 50 ml. with HCl (1:1).

NOTE 1.—A blank determination is especially desirable for low aluminum contents.

(b) Add 10% $H_2O_2$ until the solution has a definite orange color and boil until the color is light yellow to white (Note 2). Cool to 15°C., transfer to a 500-ml. separatory funnel, and wash the beaker a few times with HCl (1:1). If an aliquot of the sample was used, add 20 ml. of HCl. Dilute to 150 ml., add an excess of cupferron solution (1 g. of titanium requires 18 g. of cupferron), and shake to coagulate the precipitate. Add 75 ml. of chloroform per gram of sample in the separatory funnel, but add at least 30 ml. Shake to dissolve the precipitate and allow the solutions to separate for at least 5 minutes. Draw off the chloroform layer, discard it, and add 1 ml. of cupferron solution to the acid layer. Sufficient cupferron solution was added if a white precipitate forms and quickly redissolves. If the precipitate is persistent, add 5 ml. of the cupferron solution, shake, and extract with 25 ml. of chloroform. Check for completeness of extraction by adding 1 ml. of cupferron solution. Remove the excess cupferron by extracting with 10-ml. portions of chloroform until the chloroform layer is water white.

NOTE 2.—In the presence of chromium or other elements that form colored solution, the color will be retained in this step and in the aqueous layer after the chloroform extraction.

(c) Transfer the acid layer to a 400-ml. beaker, rinse the separatory funnel with HCl (1:9), and evaporate to about 50 ml. Add sufficient $H_2SO_4$ to provide a concentration of 3 ml. of $H_2SO_4$ per 100 ml. of solution required for the mercury cathode apparatus. Add 25 ml. of $HNO_3$ and evaporate until dense white fumes appear (Note 3), adding more $HNO_3$ if necessary to destroy all organic matter. Cool, wash down the sides of the beaker, and evaporate again to dense white fumes. Cool, add 50 ml. of water, and heat to dissolve salts. If silica is present, filter and wash with water. If manganese, chromium, cobalt, nickel, and copper are absent, proceed as directed in paragraph (*f*); otherwise adjust the solution to the required volume for electrolysis.

NOTE 3.—Very dense fumes are to be avoided, especially if chromium is present. Excessive fuming will produce insoluble salts and may necessitate repeating the determination.

(*d*) Transfer to the mercury cathode apparatus and electrolyze at 5 to 10 volts and 2 amperes until the reducible metals are in the mercury layer (about 1 to 3 hours) (Notes 4 and 5). Without interrupting the current, transfer the solution to a 400-ml. beaker, preferably of a very high-silica glass such as Vycor. Wash the cell and mercury with water, and evaporate to about 150 ml.

NOTE 4.—With other types of mercury cathode apparatus, higher current densities and shorter deposition times can be used.

NOTE 5.—Test for completeness of deposition by adding to a drop of the solution on a test plate a drop of $NH_4OH$ followed by a drop of dimethylglyoxime solution. A blue color with $NH_4OH$ or a red color with dimethylglyoxime indicates incomplete removal of copper or nickel, respectively. If chromium is present, the solution in the mercury cathode cell should change from green to colorless when deposition is complete. A spot test with diphenylcarbazide solution is recommended to determine complete deposition of chromium.

(*e*) Cool, neutralize with NaOH solution, and add an excess of 5 to 10 ml., depending on the amount of manganese present. Add 1 ml. 10% of $H_2O_2$ and heat to boiling for 2 to 10 minutes to coagulate the manganese precipitate. Filter through an alkali-resistant filter paper into a 600-ml. beaker, washing the precipitate a few times with NaOH wash solution. Wash with hot water, discard the precipitate, and acidify the filtrate with HCl.

(*f*) Heat to 55 to 60°C. and add 1.0 ml. of 8-hydroxyquinoline solution for each milligram of aluminum present, adding at least 10 ml. (Note 6). Maintain the temperature at 55 to 60 C. and add $NH_4OH$ dropwise to produce a slight turbidity which disappears slowly. Add 20 ml. of the buffer solution, stir, and allow the precipitate to settle (Note 7). Filter through a weighed medium-porosity fritted-glass crucible, washing the precipitate with cold water. Dry the crucible at 130 to 140°C. to constant weight (usually 2 hours). Cool in a desiccator and weigh as aluminum oxyquinolate.

NOTE 6.—One milliliter of 8-hydroxyquinoline solution will precipitate about 1.6 mg. of aluminum. A large excess is to be avoided.

NOTE 7.—When the titanium alloy contains iron, molybdenum, vanadium, and possibly zirconium and tungsten, the aluminum oxyquinolate will not have a distinct yellow color. The removal of these elements is not quite complete. The remaining amount, usually less than 0.1 mg., appears to compensate for the slight loss of aluminum in the chloroform layer.

**Calculation.**—Calculate the percentage of aluminum as follows:

$$\text{Aluminum, } \% = \frac{(A - B) \times 0.0587}{C} \times 100$$

where $A$ = grams of aluminum oxyquinolate found in the aliquot used,
  $B$ = grams of aluminum oxyquinolate in the blank, and
  $C$ = grams of sample represented in the aliquot used.

## *ALUMINUM BY THE TITRIMETRIC METHOD*

This method covers the determination of aluminum in titanium-base alloys in the range from 1 to 10%.

The sample is dissolved in a mixture of hydrochloric and sulfuric acids and oxidized by dropwise addition of nitric acid. The solution is made strongly basic to form soluble sodium aluminate. After separation of the hydroxides of titanium and other metals by filtration, potassium fluoride is added to react with the sodium aluminate to form an alkali hydroxide. The hydroxide is titrated with standard acid.

Elements ordinarily present in titanium alloys do not interfere.

**Apparatus.** **pH Meter.**—Hydrogen ion meter, equipped with glass and calomel electrodes and having an accuracy of 0.05 pH unit.

**Magnetic Stirrer and Stirring Bars.**

**Reagents.** **Aluminum, Standard Solution (1 ml. = 2.33 mg. Al).**—Dissolve 4.66 g. of high-purity, reagent grade aluminum (99.7% Al) in 225 ml. of HCl (1:2) in a 600-ml. beaker. Dilute to 2 liters in a volumetric flask.

NOTE 1.—If aluminum powder is used, add the acid slowly so that the reaction may be contained.

**Hydrochloric Acid, Standard Solution (1 ml. = 1.7 mg. Al).**—Add 20 ml. of HCl to 500 ml. of water, mix, and dilute to 1 liter. Standardize with the standard aluminum solution as follows:

Pipette 25 ml. of standard aluminum solution into a 600-ml. beaker containing 300 ml. of water. Using a pH meter, adjust the pH of the solution to 12.0 to 12.5 with NaOH solution. Next, adjust the pH of the solution to 11.0 with HCl (1:1). Rinse the sides of the beaker and the electrodes with water. Add HCl (1 ml. = 1.7 mg. Al) to the solution until pH 10.2 is reached. Add 40 ml. of KF solution and titrate with the HCl (1 ml. = 1.7 mg. Al) to the same pH that was obtained in the preparation of the KF solution as directed below. Record the milliliters of acid used for this titration.

Calculate the aluminum equivalent, to five decimal places, as follows:

$$\text{Equivalent} = \frac{A}{B}$$

where $A$ = grams of aluminum in 25 ml., and
$B$ = milliliters of standard HCl solution used.

**Potassium Fluoride Solution (313 g. per liter).**—Dissolve 313 g. of anhydrous potassium fluoride (KF) or 405 g. of potassium fluoride dihydrate (KF·2H$_2$O) in water and dilute to 1 liter, in a polyethylene bottle. Adjust the pH as follows:

Add 40 ml. of the solution to 300 ml. of water that has been adjusted to pH 10.2 with NaOH solution, and note the resulting pH. If the pH is not within the range of 10.0 to 11.1, adjust the KF solution with NaOH solution or HCl until the addition of 40 ml. to 300 ml. of water at pH 10.2 does produce a pH in the range of 10.0 to 11.1. The specific pH thus obtained is to be used as the end point for the titrations in the standardization of the hydrochloric acid above and in the Procedure (g).

**Potassium Permanganate Solution (30 g. per liter).**—Dissolve 30 g. of potassium permanganate (KMnO$_4$) in water and dilute to 1 liter.

**Sodium Hydroxide Solution (317 g. per liter).**—Dissolve 317 g. of sodium hydroxide (NaOH) in water and dilute to 1 liter. Store in a polyethylene bottle.

*Procedure.*—(*a*) Transfer 2 g. of the sample, weighed to the nearest 1 mg., to a 600-ml. beaker. Add 160 ml. of HCl (1:1) and 20 ml. of $H_2SO_4$ (1:1). Cover and heat on a hot plate until the sample is dissolved.

(*b*) Add $HNO_3$ dropwise until the solution is completely oxidized; then add 5 ml. in excess. Evaporate to dense white fumes and cool.

(*c*) Add 200 ml. of water and heat gently to dissolve the salts and cool. Using a pH meter, adjust the pH of the solution to 12.0 to 12.5 by addition of NaOH solution. Place the beaker on a hot plate and, with constant stirring, boil for 1 minute. Cool in a water bath to room temperature.

(*d*) Transfer to a 500-ml. volumetric flask, dilute to volume, and mix thoroughly. Transfer to a dry 600-ml. beaker and allow the precipitate to settle. Filter through an 18.5-cm., rapid, fluted paper, discarding the first 25 ml. of filtrate and collecting 250 ml. in a volumetric flask.

(*e*) Transfer the solution to a 600-ml. beaker. Rinse the flask with two 25-ml. portions of water, adding the rinsings to the solution. Add $KMnO_4$ solution dropwise until a persistent pink color is obtained.

(*f*) Adjust the solution to pH 11.0 with HCl (1:1). Rinse the sides of the beaker and electrodes with water and adjust the pH to 10.2 with HCl (1 ml. = 1.7 mg. Al).

(*g*) Add 40 ml. of KF solution and titrate the released hydroxide with HCl (1 ml. = 1.7 mg. Al) to the same pH obtained in the potassium fluoride solution, above.

**Calculation.**—Calculate the percentage of aluminum as follows:

$$\text{Aluminum, \%} = \frac{AB}{C} \times 100$$

where $A$ = milliliters of HCl required for titration,

$B$ = aluminum equivalent of the HCl, in grams per milliliter, and

$C$ = grams of sample in aliquot used for titration.

## CHLORIDE BY THE GRAVIMETRIC METHOD

This method covers the determination of chloride in titanium sponge in the range from 0.02 to 1%.

The sample is dissolved in dilute hydrofluoric acid and oxidized with nitric acid. The chloride is precipitated with silver nitrate and weighed as silver chloride.

Elements normally present in titanium sponge do not interfere.

*Apparatus.* **Filtering Crucibles.**—Fritted-glass, fine-porosity, 30 ml.

**Plastic Beakers, 400 or 600 ml.**

**Plastic Graduated Cylinder, 25 ml.**

*Reagents.* **Boric Acid ($H_3BO_3$).**

**Silver Nitrate Solution (5.8 g. per liter).**—Dissolve 5.8 g. of silver nitrate ($AgNO_3$) in water and dilute to 1 liter.

**Silver Nitrate Wash Solution (0.05 g. per liter).**—Dissolve 0.05 g. of silver nitrate ($AgNO_3$) in 1 liter of water.

*Procedure.*—(*a*) Transfer 20 ml. of HF and 50 ml. of water to a plastic beaker and mix. Weigh 5 g. of the sample to the nearest 1 mg. Transfer 1 to 2 g. of the sample, in small portions, to the dilute HF solution. Add 5 ml. of $HNO_3$ and then add the remainder of the sample in small portions. After all of the metal has been added, allow to stand until dissolution is complete.

NOTE 1.—Dissolution of the sample is usually complete in 5 minutes, with a colorless solution being obtained. If the solution is not colorless, add $HNO_3$ dropwise until the color disappears.

(b) Carry a reagent blank through all steps of the procedure.

(c) Add 5 g. of $H_3BO_3$ to the solution, transfer to a 400-ml. glass beaker, and dilute to 200 ml. Stir and heat gently until the $H_3BO_3$ dissolves. With stirring, slowly add 10 ml. of the $AgNO_3$ solution. Heat to approximately 60°C. and maintain at this temperature until the supernatant liquid clears. Test for completeness of precipitation by adding a few drops of the $AgNO_3$ solution. If additional precipitate forms, add an additional 5 ml. of $AgNO_3$ solution and repeat the above operation. Allow to stand in a dark place for 2 hours.

(d) Filter, using a low-ash, fine-texture, paper, and wash thoroughly with the $AgNO_3$ wash solution. Dissolve the precipitate by pouring 50 ml. of $NH_4OH$ (1:1) in 10-ml. increments through the filter, collecting the filtrate in the original beaker. If necessary, pour the $NH_4OH$ through a second time to dissolve the silver chloride (Note 2). Wash the paper thoroughly with water.

NOTE 2.—Residual titanium hydroxide on the paper should not be confused with silver chloride.

(e) Make the filtrate slightly acid with $HNO_3$, using methyl orange indicator. Add 5 ml. of the $AgNO_3$ solution and stir to coagulate the precipitate. Check for complete precipitation as described in paragraph (c). Allow to stand in a dark place for 2 hours. Filter through a weighed fritted-glass crucible. Police the beaker and stirring rod and wash thoroughly with the $AgNO_3$ wash solution. Finally, wash twice with water.

(f) Dry the crucible and contents at 130 to 150°C. to constant weight (approximately 2 hours). Cool in a desiccator and weigh.

**Calculation.**—Calculate the percentage of chloride as follows:

$$\text{Chloride, } \% = \frac{(A - B) \times 0.2474}{C} \times 100$$

where $A$ = grams of AgCl from the sample,
$B$ = grams of AgCl from reagent blank, and
$C$ = grams of sample used.

## CHROMIUM BY THE PERSULFATE OXIDATION METHOD

This method is applicable to titanium alloys containing more than 0.1% chromium. For samples containing less than 0.1% chromium, the photometric method following is recommended.

After dissolution in $H_2SO_4$ and HF and oxidation with $HNO_3$, the chromium is further oxidized with $(NH_4)_2S_2O_8$ in the presence of $AgNO_3$ and $KMnO_4$. After reducing the excess $HMnO_4$ with HCl, the chromium is titrated either potentiometrically with ferrous ammonium sulfate or by adding an excess of ferrous ammonium sulfate and back-titrating with $KMnO_4$.

The recommended chromium content of the sample used for analysis is 1 to 25 mg.

None of the elements found in titanium alloys interfere, with the exception of vanadium. Vanadium does not interfere if the visual end point titration is used, but a correction for vanadium must be applied in the potentiometric titration.

*Apparatus.*  **Apparatus for Potentiometric Titration.**—The essential parts of a potentiometer are shown in Fig. 48-2.  The battery, *B*, produces a potential drop across the resistance wire, *R*, which will be uniform along the length because the wire is of uniform resistance.  To determine the actual magnitude of this potential drop, connect a standard cell between the terminals of the electrodes $E_1$ and $E_2$ in such a way as to furnish a back emf.  Adjust the slide *S* until the galvanometer shows no current flowing.  The potential drop between *a* and *S* produced by *B*

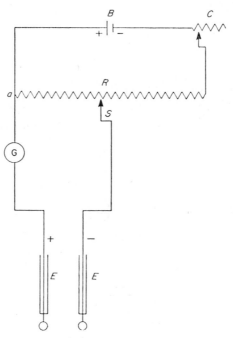

Fig. 48-2.  Diagram of the Essential Parts of a Potentiometer.

*B* = Voltaic source;  *R* = Uniform resistance wire;  *S* = Slide contact;  *G* = Galvanometer; *E* = Electrodes;  *C* = Calibration adjustment.

will then be equal to that of the standard cell.  Measure the length *aS* and the total length of the wire and calculate the total potential drop by proportion.

In actual practice it is convenient to have a permanent calibration of the resistance scale in terms of millivolts.  Changes in potential of the battery *B* that would otherwise alter this calibration are compensated for by variation of the calibration adjustment *C*.  By changing the resistance at *C*, the total potential drop across *R* can be altered, within limits, to the pre-established value.

There are available commercially many fine potentiometric instruments that are accurate and convenient to operate.  Most of these have sensitive vacuum tube amplifying circuits, contain a standardizing cell, and are calibrated to read potentials directly.

The most common indicator electrode for oxidation-reduction measurements is bright platinum.  The reference electrode most commonly used is the saturated calomel electrode. This calomel electrode may be either the commercial, pencil-type unit that is immersed directly in the solution, or may be an external cell contacting the solution by means of an agar-agar salt bridge or a salt solution bridge. An example of the latter is shown in Fig. 48-3. Many other types of electrodes and electrode pairs may be employed, the platinum-tungsten system for example.

To measure the potential of a solution, electrodes $E+$ and $E-$ of suitable nature are immersed in the solution. The slide $S$ is adjusted to the null point as indicated by the galvanometer, and the potential is read or is calculated from the measured length $aS$, the total length of the wire, and the previously determined total potential drop along the wire.

To conduct a potentiometric titration the electrodes are immersed in the solution and the potential measured as described. A measured volume of titrant is added from the burette, the solution is stirred, and the potential measured. Another measured volume of titrant is added, the solution is stirred, and the potential measured. This process is repeated until the reaction has been carried slightly beyond completion. It is characteristic of an oxidation-reduction titration that the greatest rate of change of potential occurs at the equivalence point. This

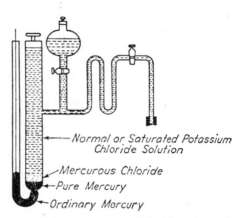

— Normal or Saturated Potassium Chloride Solution

— Mercurous Chloride

— Pure Mercury

— Ordinary Mercury

FIG. 48-3. Mercurous Chloride (Calomel) Half Cell for Potentiometric Titration.

point can be readily identified by examining or plotting the data, and it corresponds to the end point. In many cases it is necessary only to add titrant dropwise as the end point is approached and stop the titration when one drop is observed to produce a large change of potential.

*Reagents.* **Boric Acid Solution (50 g. per liter).**—Dissolve 50 g. of $H_3BO_3$ in water and dilute to 1 liter.

**Silver Nitrate Solution (2.5 g. per liter).**—Dissolve 2.5 g. of $AgNO_3$ in water and dilute to 1 liter.

**Ammonium Persulfate Solution (150 g. per liter).**—Dissolve 15 g. of $(NH_4)_2S_2O_8$ in water and dilute to 100 ml. Prepare fresh before use.

**Potassium Permanganate Solution (25 g. per liter).**—Dissolve 25 g. of $KMnO_4$ in water and dilute to 1 liter.

**Standard Potassium Permanganate Solution (0.05 N).**—Dissolve 1.6 g. of $KMnO_4$ in 1 liter of water. Let stand in the dark for 2 weeks and filter, without washing, through a Gooch crucible or a fritted-glass crucible of fine porosity, avoiding contact with rubber or other organic material. Store in a dark-colored, glass-stoppered bottle.

*Standardization.*—Transfer 0.1500 g. of the National Bureau of Standards standard sample of sodium oxalate dried at 105°C., to a 600-ml. beaker. Add 250 ml. of $H_2SO_4$ (5:95), previously boiled for 10 to 15 minutes and then cooled to $27 \pm 3$°C. Stir until the oxalate has dissolved. Add 39 to 40 ml. of the $KMnO_4$ solution at a rate of 25 to 35 ml. per minute, while stirring slowly. Let stand until the pink color disappears (about 45 seconds). Heat to 55 to 60°C., and complete the titration by adding the $KMnO_4$ solution until a faint pink color persists for 30 seconds. Add the last 0.5 to 1 ml. drop by drop, with particular care to allow each drop to become decolorized before the next is introduced.

Determine the amount of $KMnO_4$ required to impart a faint pink color to the solution by adding the $KMnO_4$ solution to the same volume of the boiled and cooled $H_2SO_4$ (5:95) at 55 to 60°C. This correction usually amounts to 0.03 to 0.05 ml.

**Standard Ferrous Ammonium Sulfate Solution.**—Dissolve 19.6 g. of $Fe(NH_4)_2$-$(SO_4)_2 \cdot 6H_2O$ in 500 ml. of cold $H_2SO_4$ (5:95) and dilute to 1 liter with $H_2SO_4$ (5:95). Standardize against 0.05 $N$ potassium dichromate solution to a visual end point using a sodium diphenylamine sulfonate as an indicator.

**Standard Potassium Dichromate Solution (0.05 $N$).**—Twice recrystallize $K_2Cr_2O_7$ from water. Dry the crystals at 110°C., pulverize, and dry at 180°C. to constant weight. Dissolve 2.4518 g. of the $K_2Cr_2O_7$ in water and dilute to 1 liter in a volumetric flask.

*Procedure.*—(*a*) Select a sample weight in accordance with the following table:

| Chromium, per cent | Sample weight, g. |
|---|---|
| 0.10 to 1.0 | 1.000 |
| 1.0 to 5.0 | 0.500 |
| 5.0 and over | 0.250 |

Transfer the weighed portion to a 600-ml. beaker. Add 50 ml. of $H_2SO_4$ (1:3) and a few drops of HF, and heat gently until the sample is dissolved. Oxidize by the dropwise addition of $HNO_3$ until the purple color of reduced titanium has disappeared, add 5 ml. of $H_3BO_3$ solution, and evaporate to first dense white fumes. Cool, dilute to 100 ml., and heat to dissolve salts.

(*b*) Add 10 ml. of $AgNO_3$ solution and 25 ml. of $(NH_4)_2S_2O_8$ solution and heat to boiling. If manganese is absent, add 1 or 2 drops of $KMnO_4$ solution. Boil for 10 minutes after the $HMnO_4$ color or precipitate of manganese appears. If incomplete oxidation is indicated by the nonappearance or disappearance of the manganese color or precipitate, add an additional 10 ml. of the $(NH_4)_2S_2O_8$ solution and again boil for 10 minutes. Add 5 ml. of HCl (1:3) to the boiling solution. If after 5 minutes of boiling the manganese color or precipitate persists, add an additional 5 ml. of HCl (1:3). Boil for 10 minutes after the solution turns yellow.

(*c*) Remove from the hot plate, cool to room temperature, and dilute to 200 ml. Add a measured volume of 0.05 $N$ ferrous ammonium sulfate solution, sufficient to reduce the chromate, and vanadate if present, and to provide an excess of 2 to 5 ml. Titrate the excess ferrous ammonium sulfate with 0.05 $N$ $KMnO_4$ until an end point is obtained that persists with continued stirring for 1 minute (Notes 1 and 2).

NOTE 1.—The end point may be obtained by potentiometric titration with standard ferrous ammonium sulfate solution. In this case the ferrous ammonium sulfate solution is standardized with 0.05 $N$ $K_2Cr_2O_7$ solution. Vanadium is included in the titration. If present, it must be determined and subtracted from the apparent chromium value (vanadium, % × 0.34 = chromium, %).

NOTE 2.—In the absence of vanadium, the first end point persists; but, if vanadium is present, the end point will fade at first owing to the slow oxidation of vanadium from the V(IV) to the V(V) state in a cold solution.

(*d*) The titration must be corrected for dilution effect and color interference. The correction may be made by one of the three following methods: (*1*) empirically (Note 3), (*2*) by titrating the same volume of ferrous ammonium sulfate in a solution of like volume and acidity containing the same amounts of the coloring elements in their final valences, or (*3*) by a second titration of the final solution after it has been boiled for 10 minutes and again cooled to room temperature. It is then titrated to the color that was originally taken as the end point.

NOTE 3.—In this case the dilution effect is ignored and the volume of $KMnO_4$ solution used to overcome the green color is taken as equivalent to 0.6% of the chromium present. Usually this correction is applied to the chromium equivalent of the solution by using the factor 0.01744 g. instead of 0.01734 g. of chromium per ml. of 1 $N$ ferrous ammonium sulfate solution.

**Calculation.**—Calculate the percentage of chromium as follows:

$$\text{Chromium, } \% = \frac{[AB - (C - D)]E \times 0.01734}{F} \times 100$$

where $A$ = milliliters of 0.05 $N$ ferrous ammonium sulfate solution added,

$B$ = milliliters of 0.05 $N$ $KMnO_4$ solution equivalent to 1 milliliter of 0.05 $N$ ferrous ammonium sulfate solution,

$C$ = milliliters of 0.05 $N$ $KMnO_4$ solution required to titrate the excess ferrous ammonium sulfate,

$D$ = milliliters of 0.05 $N$ $KMnO_4$ required for the end-point correction,

$E$ = normality of the 0.05 $N$ $KMnO_4$ solution, and

$F$ = grams of sample used.

## CHROMIUM BY THE DIPHENYLCARBAZIDE (PHOTOMETRIC) METHOD

This method is recommended for titanium and titanium alloys containing 0.005 to 0.1% chromium, but may be extended up to 4% chromium.

The sample is dissolved in $H_2SO_4$ and oxidized with $HNO_3$. The chromium is further oxidized with $(NH_4)_2S_2O_8$, in the presence of $AgNO_3$ and $KMnO_4$. After reduction of $HMnO_4$, the diphenylcarbazide–chromium complex is formed and photometric measurement made at approximately 580 m$\mu$. The wavelength of 580 m$\mu$ was chosen to minimize absorption due to iron, vanadium, and molybdenum complexes.

The recommended concentration range is from 0.005 to 0.1 mg. of chromium in 50 ml., for a 1-cm. cell (Note 1).

NOTE 1.—This procedure has been written for a cell having a 1.0-cm. light path. Cells having other dimensions may be used, provided suitable adjustments can be made in the amount of sample and reagents used.

The color is stable for at least 40 minutes. Measurement should be made within 10 to 40 minutes after the final addition of reagents and dilution of the solution.

Elements commonly found in commercial titanium alloys, including iron, vanadium, molybdenum, tungsten, aluminum, copper, cobalt, nickel, silicon, calcium, magnesium, manganese, tin, boron, carbon, and nitrogen, do not interfere.

**Reagents. Standard Chromium Solution (1 ml. = 0.010 mg. Cr).**—Recrystallize and dry $K_2Cr_2O_7$ as described in the preparation of the standard potassium dichromate solution in the preceding method. Dissolve 2.83 g. of the $K_2Cr_2O_7$ in water and dilute to 1 liter in a volumetric flask. Pipette 20 ml. of this solution into a 2-liter volumetric flask and dilute to the mark with water.

**Diphenylcarbazide Solution (0.25%).**—Dissolve 0.125 g. of diphenylcarbazide in 50 ml. of ethanol (95%). Alternatively, acetone and water (1:1) may be used as the solvent. Prepare fresh before use.

**Silver Nitrate Solution (10 g. per liter).**—Dissolve 10 g. of $AgNO_3$ in water and dilute to 1 liter.

**Ammonium Persulfate Solution (150 g. per liter).**—Dissolve 15 g. of $(NH_4)_2S_2O_8$ in water and dilute to 100 ml. Prepare fresh before use.

**Potassium Permanganate Solution (25 g. per liter).**—Dissolve 25 g. of $KMnO_4$ in water and dilute to 1 liter.

*Preparation of Calibration Curve.* (a) **Calibration Solutions.**—Transfer 0.5, 1, 2, 3, 5, 8, and 10 ml. of chromium solution (1 ml. = 0.010 mg. Cr) to 50-ml. volumetric flasks. Add 5 ml. of $H_2SO_4$ (1:19), dilute to about 40 ml., and swirl. Add 2.0 ml. of diphenylcarbazide solution, swirl, dilute to the mark, and mix.

(b) **Reference Solution.**—Add 5 ml. of $H_2SO_4$ (1:19) to a 50-ml. volumetric flask, dilute to about 40 ml., add 2.0 ml. of diphenylcarbazide solution, and swirl. Dilute to the mark and mix.

(c) **Photometry.**—After 10 minutes but before 40 minutes have elapsed, transfer a suitable portion of the reference solution to an absorption cell and adjust the photometer to the initial setting, using a light band centered at approximately 580 m$\mu$. While maintaining this photometer adjustment, take the photometric readings of the calibration solutions.

(d) **Calibration Curve.**—Plot the photometric readings of the calibration solutions against milligrams of chromium per 50 ml. of solution.

*Procedure.*—(a) Transfer 1.00 g. of the sample to a 600-ml. beaker, add 160 ml. of water and 25 ml. of $H_2SO_4$, and heat until the sample is dissolved. Oxidize by the dropwise addition of $HNO_3$ until the purple color of reduced titanium has disappeared, and evaporate to dense white fumes. Cool, dilute to about 300 ml., and heat to boiling for 1 or 2 minutes.

(b) Add 10 ml. of $AgNO_3$ solution and 20 ml. of $(NH_4)_2S_2O_8$ solution and heat to boiling. Add $KMnO_4$ solution dropwise until the solution becomes definitely pink and then add a few drops in excess. Boil for 10 minutes, and if the permanganate color disappears add more $KMnO_4$. (Be sure the solution boils vigorously and not merely simmers, as boiling is necessary to insure the decomposition of the $(NH_4)_2S_2O_8$.) Add 3 ml. of HCl (1:3) and boil for 10 minutes. If the permanganate color does not disappear during the first 2 minutes of boiling, add 2 ml. more of HCl (1:3).

(c) Cool, transfer the solution to a 500-ml. volumetric flask, dilute to the mark, and mix. Allow the flask to stand until the AgCl precipitate has settled (approximately 30 minutes). Time may be saved by filtering through a fritted-glass crucible or by centrifuging the solution.

(d) Pipette a 5-ml. aliquot of the clear solution into a 50-ml. volumetric flask. Dilute to about 40 ml., swirl, add 2.0 ml. of diphenylcarbazide solution, and swirl. Dilute to the mark and mix.

(e) Take the photometric reading of the sample as described in "Preparation of the Calibration Curve (c)."

**Calculation.**—Convert the photometric reading of the sample solution to milligrams of chromium by means of the calibration curve. Calculate the percentage of chromium as follows:

$$\text{Chromium, } \% = \frac{A}{B \times 10}$$

where $A$ = milligrams of chromium found in the aliquot used, and
$B$ = grams of sample represented in the aliquot used.

## IRON BY THE SULFIDE SEPARATION–DICHROMATE TITRATION METHOD

Although this method is satisfactory for titanium and titanium alloys containing between 0.2 and 20% iron, the photometric method is recommended for samples containing less than 1% iron.

After dissolution in HCl and HF in the presence of tartaric acid, iron is precipitated as the sulfide from ammoniacal tartrate solution, the sulfide separated, redissolved in $HNO_3$ and $HClO_4$, and reprecipitated with $NH_4OH$ and $(NH_4)_2S_2O_8$. The precipitate is dissolved in HCl, ferric ion reduced to ferrous with $SnCl_2$, and the excess $SnCl_2$ oxidized with $HgCl_2$. The reduced iron is titrated with $K_2Cr_2O_7$.

For the solutions specified, the optimum amount of iron is about 25 mg. If a more concentrated $K_2Cr_2O_7$ solution is used, up to 200 mg. of iron may be determined.

Elements normally occurring in titanium alloys do not interfere.

**Reagents.** **Ammonium Sulfide Wash Solution.**—Add 10 ml. of $NH_4OH$ to 5 g. of tartaric acid and 500 ml. of water. Pass $H_2S$ through the solution for about 10 minutes.

**Stannous Chloride Solution (50 g. per liter).**—Add 5 g. of $SnCl_2 \cdot 2H_2O$ to 10 ml. of HCl and dilute to 100 ml.

**Mercuric Chloride Solution (saturated).**—Add an excess of $HgCl_2$ to water to give a saturated solution.

**Sodium Diphenylaminesulfonate Indicator Solution.**

**Standard Potassium Dichromate Solution (1 ml. = 0.001 g. Fe).**—Recrystallize and dry $K_2Cr_2O_7$ as described in the preparation of the standard potassium dichromate solution on p. 1128. Transfer 0.8780 g. of the $K_2Cr_2O_7$ to a 1-liter volumetric flask. Dissolve in water and dilute to the mark.

**Procedure.** (a) Transfer a sample weight containing approximately 25 mg. of iron (not to exceed 2.5 g.) to a 600 ml. beaker and add 15 to 25 g. of tartaric acid crystals. Add 100 ml. of HCl (1:1) and 5 to 30 drops of HF, as necessary, and allow to dissolve.

(b) Dilute to 300 ml., neutralize with $NH_4OH$, and add 5 to 10 ml. in excess. Pass in a rapid stream of $H_2S$ for 20 to 30 minutes and allow to stand for about 30 minutes at 40 to 50°C. Filter, using gentle suction if desired, through a medium-texture 11-cm. paper containing some paper pulp, and wash 8 to 10 times with the $(NH_4)_2S$ wash solution. Discard the filtrate and return the paper and precipitate to the original beaker. Add 50 ml. of $HNO_3$ and 15 to 30 ml. of $HClO_4$. (A few ml. of HCl may be added to accelerate the action.) Evaporate to white fumes and heat until all organic matter is destroyed. Cool somewhat, add 50 ml. of water, and boil for several minutes. Dilute to 100 to 125 ml., neutralize with $NH_4OH$, and add 25 ml. of $NH_4OH$ in excess. Add 3 to 5 g. of $(NH_4)_2S_2O_8$, boil for 5 minutes and let settle 1 to 2 minutes. Using gentle suction if desired, filter on a hardened paper (Whatman No. 41H, or equivalent, filter paper has been found satisfactory for this purpose) containing some paper pulp and wash thoroughly with hot water. Discard the filtrate. Place the original 600-ml. beaker under the funnel and dissolve the precipitate through the paper with small additions of hot HCl (1:2). Wash with hot HCl (1:19) and discard the paper.

(c) Dilute the filtrate to 200 ml., add 10 ml. of HCl, and heat to boiling for several minutes. While stirring, add SnCl₂ solution dropwise until the color of the ferric iron is discharged and then add 1 or 2 drops. Wash down the sides of the beaker and quickly cool the solution to room temperature. Add at one stroke 10 ml. of HgCl₂ solution. Stir, wash down the sides of the beaker, and allow to stand for 2 to 3 minutes. Add 3 ml. of H₃PO₄, 2 to 3 drops of sodium diphenylaminesulfonate indicator solution, and 100 ml. of water. Titrate immediately and slowly with K₂Cr₂O₇ solution (1 ml. = 0.001 g. Fe). When the end point is approached, the color deepens to a blue-green, which changes to a purple or violet-blue on the addition of 1 drop of the K₂Cr₂O₇ solution.

(d) Make a blank determination, following the same procedure and using the same amount of all reagents (Note 1).

NOTE 1.—Ferric iron must be present in the solution in order to obtain the purple or violet blue end-point color. If the color fails to form, the blank is less than the equivalent of 1 drop of 0.02 N FeSO₄ as this contains sufficient iron to yield an end point.

**Calculation.**—Calculate the percentage of iron as follows:

$$\text{Iron, } \% = \frac{(A - B)C}{D} \times 100$$

where  $A$ = milliliters of K₂Cr₂O₇ solution required to titrate the sample,
        $B$ = milliliters of K₂Cr₂O₇ solution required to titrate the blank,
        $C$ = iron equivalent of the K₂Cr₂O₇ solution, in grams per milliliter, and
        $D$ = grams of sample used.

## IRON BY THE 1-10–PHENANTHROLINE (PHOTOMETRIC) METHOD

This method is recommended for samples containing 0.005 to 1% iron but, with care, may be extended up to 5% iron.

After dissolution in HCl and HF, H₃BO₃ is added, the solution diluted, and the iron in an aliquot reduced with hydroxylamine hydrochloride, converted to the 1-10-phenanthroline complex, and photometric measurement made at approximately 490 mμ, although the maximum absorption is at 508 mμ.

The recommended concentration range is 0.02 to 0.40 mg. of iron in 100 ml. for a 1-cm. cell.

The complex is quite stable. No significant change was noted in 20 hours.

The following elements, up to the percentages indicated, do not interfere: 10% aluminum, chromium, manganese, molybdenum, or zirconium; 5% vanadium; 3% tin; 1% cobalt, nickel, or tungsten; and 0.5% copper or magnesium. The pH of the solution should be maintained near 6 to minimize interference of molybdenum and fluorides.

**Reagents. Low-Iron Titanium.**—Iron less than 0.005%.

**Boric Acid Solution (50 g. per liter).**—Dissolve 50 g. of H₃BO₃ in water and dilute to 1 liter.

**Standard Iron Solution (1 ml. = 0.020 mg. Fe).**—Dissolve 0.702 g. of Fe(NH₄)₂(SO₄)₂·6H₂O in water, add 10 ml. of HCl, and dilute to 1 liter. Transfer 200.0 ml. to a 1-liter volumetric flask, add 10 ml. HCl, dilute to the mark, and mix.

**Hydroxylamine Hydrochloride Solution (20 g. per liter).**—Dissolve 10 g. of hydroxylamine hydrochloride in 500 ml. of water. Prepare fresh as required.

**Ammonium Tartrate Solution (100 g. per liter).**—Dissolve 100 g. of ammonium tartrate in water and dilute to 1 liter.

**Sodium Acetate Solution (100 g. per liter).**—Dissolve 100 g. of sodium acetate in water and dilute to 1 liter.

**Test Paper, pH Range 2 to 10.**

**1-10-Phenanthroline Solution (2 g. per liter).**—Dissolve 0.4 g. of 1-10-phenanthroline monohydrate in 200 ml. of water. Filter if necessary.

*Preparation of Calibration Curve.* (a) **Calibration Solutions.**—(*1*) Transfer 0.5 g. of low-iron titanium to a 400-ml. beaker, add 40 ml. of HCl (1:1) and 6 drops of HF. When dissolution is complete, add 20 ml. of $H_3BO_3$ solution, cool, and transfer to a 200-ml. volumetric flask. Dilute to the mark and mix.

(*2*) Transfer 10-ml. aliquots of the titanium solution to nine 100-ml. volumetric flasks. From a burette, add 2.5, 5.0, 7.5, 10.0, 12.5, 15.0, 17.5, and 20.0 ml. of iron solution (1 ml. = 0.020 mg. of Fe) to eight of the flasks and dilute to about 40 ml. Carry the ninth flask through the procedure for use as a reference solution.

(*3*) Add successively 10 ml. of hydroxylamine hydrochloride solution, 5 ml. of ammonium tartrate solution, and 25 ml. of sodium acetate solution. Check the pH of the solution with pH test paper having a pH range of 2 to 10 and adjust to pH 6 using $NH_4OH$. Add 10 ml. of 1-10-phenanthroline solution, dilute to the mark, and mix. Allow 1 hour for the color to develop. In the case of vanadium alloys, allow to stand overnight at room temperature or place in a water bath at 60 to 70°C. for 30 minutes, remove, and cool to room temperature.

(b) **Reference Solution.**—Use the solution to which no iron was added as the reference solution.

(c) **Photometry.**—Transfer a suitable portion of the reference solution to an absorption cell and adjust the photometer to the initial setting, using a light band centered at 490 m$\mu$. While maintaining this photometer adjustment, take the photometric readings of the calibration solutions.

(d) **Calibration Curve.**—Plot the photometric readings of the calibration solutions against milligrams of iron per 100 ml. of solution.

*Procedure.*—(a) If the expected iron content is 0.2% or more, transfer 0.50 g. of the sample to a 500-ml. Erlenmeyer flask. If the expected iron content is less than 0.2%, use a 1.00-g. portion. Carry through a blank including all reagents. Add 40 ml. of HCl (1:1) and 6 drops of HF and heat gently until solution is complete (Note 1).

NOTE 1.—Additional HCl (1:1) may be added to make up for evaporation losses. If the solution is allowed to go to dryness, titanium precipitates as the insoluble oxide and the analysis must be started again.

(b) Cool, add 20 ml. of $H_3BO_3$ solution, transfer to a 200-ml. volumetric flask, dilute to the mark, and mix. Pipette a 10-ml. aliquot into a 100-ml. volumetric flask, dilute to approximately 40 ml., and proceed as directed in "Preparation of the Calibration Curve (*a*)(*3*)."

(c) **Reference Solution.**—Use the reagent blank as the reference solution. For titanium alloys containing over 10% chromium, correct the reading of the test solution for the color introduced by the chromium by subtracting the reading obtained on another 10-ml. aliquot of the sample solution (paragraph (*b*)) to which all the reagents except *o*-phenanthroline have been added.

(d) **Photometry.**—Take the photometric reading of the sample solution and blank as directed in "Preparation of the Calibration Curve (c)."

**Calculation.**—Convert the photometric reading of the sample solution to milligrams of iron by means of the calibration curve. Calculate the percentage of iron as follows:

$$\text{Iron, } \% = \frac{A}{B \times 10}$$

where $A$ = milligrams of iron in the aliquot used, and

$B$ = grams of sample represented in the aliquot used.

## MAGNESIUM BY THE 8-HYDROXYQUINOLINE (GRAVIMETRIC) METHOD

This method covers the determination of magnesium in titanium sponge and unalloyed titanium in the range from 0.02 to 1.0%.

The sample is dissolved in dilute sulfuric acid and the magnesium separated from the bulk of the titanium by precipitation with sodium hydroxide in the presence of hydrogen peroxide. The magnesium hydroxide is then dissolved in dilute hydrochloric acid and the remaining titanium (and iron) separated as the hydroxide by precipitation with ammonium hydroxide. Magnesium is then determined in the filtrate by precipitation with 8-hydroxyquinoline.

Elements normally present in titanium sponge and unalloyed titanium do not interfere.

**Apparatus.** Flask, Suction, 500 ml.

**Buechner Funnels, Fritted-glass, Medium-porosity, 350 ml.**

**Gooch Crucibles, Fritted-glass, Medium-porosity, 30 ml.**

**Reagents. Ammonium Hydroxide Wash Solution.**—Dilute 10 ml. of ammonium hydroxide ($NH_4OH$) to 1 liter with water.

**Hydrogen Peroxide (30%).**—Concentrated hydrogen peroxide ($H_2O_2$).

**8-Hydroxyquinoline Solution (50 g. per liter).**—Dissolve 5 g. of 8-hydroxyquinoline in 10 ml. of glacial acetic acid and dilute to 100 ml. with water. Filter, and store in an amber bottle. Do not keep the solution longer than a week.

**Sodium Hydroxide Solution (350 g. per liter).**—Dissolve 350 g. of sodium hydroxide (NaOH) in water and dilute to 1 liter.

**Sodium Hydroxide Wash Solution (10 g. per liter).**—Dissolve 10 g. of NaOH in water and dilute to 1 liter.

**Procedure.**—(a) Transfer 10 g. of the sample, weighed to the nearest 1 mg., to a 600-ml. beaker. Add 300 ml. of $H_2SO_4$ (1:5) and boil gently until solution is complete, adding water as needed to maintain the volume of the solution.

(b) Filter through a medium paper and transfer the filtrate to a 500-ml. volumetric flask. Cool the contents of the flask to room temperature, dilute to the mark with water, and mix.

(c) Pipette a 200-ml. aliquot into a 600-ml. beaker. While stirring, add 150 ml. of NaOH solution (350 g. per liter), then heat to boiling and boil for 5 minutes. Cool to approximately 50°C., add 35 ml. of $H_2O_2$ (30%), and stir gently until the titanium hydroxide has dissolved (Note 1).

NOTE 1.—If all of the titanium does not go into solution after approximately 5 minutes, add more $H_2O_2$ and stir until solution of titanium is complete. Hydrogen peroxide must be at full strength when used.

(*d*) Filter through a 350-ml. fritted-glass Buechner funnel (medium porosity) and wash with the hot NaOH wash solution. Discard the filtrate and rinse the filter-flask.

(*e*) Dissolve the precipitate from the filter with 40 ml. of hot HCl (1:3), wash with hot water, and transfer the solution to a 400-ml. beaker. Make ammoniacal, add 5 ml. of $NH_4OH$ in excess, and dilute to 150 ml. with water (Note 2). Boil the solution for 5 minutes, filter through a coarse paper into a 400-ml. beaker, and wash with hot water. Retain the filtrate.

NOTE 2.—If manganese is present, add 10 ml. of bromine water (saturated solution).

(*f*) Dissolve the precipitate with 40 ml. of hot HCl (1:3) and reprecipitate with $NH_4OH$. Filter and wash as before. The final volume of the filtrate should be about 75 ml. Combine this filtrate with that from the paragraph (*e*) (Note 3).

NOTE 3.—Copper, cobalt, and nickel, if present, may be removed at this point by treatment of the combined ammoniacal filtrate with hydrogen sulfide.

(*g*) Adjust the volume of the combined filtrates to approximately 225 ml., add 5 ml. of $NH_4OH$, 5 or 10 ml. of the 8-hydroxyquinoline solution, depending upon the magnesium content, and heat to boiling (Note 4). Remove from the heat and let stand for 20 to 30 minutes to allow the precipitate of magnesium quinolinate to form. Filter on a weighed fritted-glass, medium-porosity crucible and wash with the hot $NH_4OH$ wash solution. Dry in an oven for 2 hours at 160°C., cool in a desiccator, and weigh.

NOTE 4.—Ten milliliters of 8-hydroxyquinoline solution is sufficient for 0.03 g. of magnesium, but more may be needed for higher magnesium contents. A large excess should be avoided, because the reagent salts out and is difficult to remove by washing from the magnesium precipitate.

**Calculation.**—Calculate the percentage of magnesium as follows:

$$\text{Magnesium, } \% = \frac{A \times 0.0778}{B} \times 100$$

where $A$ = grams of magnesium quinolinate, and
$B$ = grams of sample present in the 200-ml. aliquot.

## MANGANESE BY THE PERSULFATE–ARSENITE METHOD

This method is recommended for titanium and titanium alloys containing more than 0.1% manganese.

After dissolution in HCl, $H_2SO_4$, and HF, the HCl is removed by fuming. The manganese is oxidized with $(NH_4)_2S_2O_8$ in the presence of $AgNO_3$ and the $HMnO_4$ titrated with $NaAsO_2$ solution.

The recommended concentration range is from 1 to 10 mg. of manganese in the aliquot titrated.

Elements normally occurring in titanium alloys do not interfere, except for chromium under certain conditions. In these cases the chromium must be separated.

**Reagents. Low-Manganese Titanium.**—Manganese less than 0.005%.

**Standard Manganese Solution.** *Method A: Preparation from manganese metal.* —Transfer 0.1000 g. of manganese metal to a 150-ml. beaker and add 10 ml. of

$HNO_3$ (1:1). Heat gently to dissolve the sample and to expel the brown fumes. Cool, and dilute to 1 liter in a volumetric flask.

*Method B: Preparation from Potassium Permanganate.*—Transfer 90.9 ml. of 0.1000 $N$ $KMnO_4$ solution to a 400-ml. beaker and add 10 ml. of $H_2SO_4$ (1:1). Reduce the $KMnO_4$ by additions of $H_2SO_3$ and boil until free of $SO_2$. Cool, and dilute to 1 liter in a volumetric flask.

**Sodium Hydroxide Solution (200 g. per liter).**—Dissolve 20 g. of NaOH in water and dilute to 100 ml.

**Sodium Carbonate Wash Solution (6 g. per liter).**—Dissolve 3 g. of $Na_2CO_3$ in 500 ml. of water.

**Silver Nitrate Solution (8 g. per liter).**—Dissolve 8 g. of $AgNO_3$ in water and dilute to 1 liter.

**Ammonium Persulfate Solution (250 g. per liter).**—Dissolve 25 g. of $(NH_4)_2S_2O_8$ in water and dilute to 100 ml. Prepare fresh.

**Standard Sodium Arsenite Solution.**—Dissolve 20 g. of $NaAsO_2$ in water, dilute to 1 liter, and allow to age for 3 weeks. Dilute 100 ml. of the aged solution to 1 liter, and filter if not clear. Saturate the solution with $CO_2$. Since the titer of the $NaAsO_2$ solution varies somewhat with the amount of manganese being titrated, the solution should be standardized against a synthetic standard which contains approximately the same amount of manganese as the unknown sample.

Standardize as follows: Dissolve a 1.0-g. portion of low-manganese titanium as directed in section (*a*) below and add enough manganese solution to give the desired manganese content. Continue as directed in section (*e*) below and calculate the manganese equivalent of the $NaAsO_2$ solution.

*Procedure.*—(*a*) Where aliquots of the sample are to be used for the determination of other elements, it may be advantageous to dissolve the sample in 100 ml. of $H_2SO_4$ (1:1), oxidize with $HNO_3$, heat to dispel red fumes, and then proceed as directed in paragraph (*b*), (*c*), or (*d*). If manganese only is desired, transfer 1.00 g. of the sample to a 500-ml. Erlenmeyer flask, add 80 ml. of water, 20 ml. of HCl, and 20 ml. of $H_2SO_4$ (1:1). Heat to boiling, add 10 drops of HF, and heat gently until dissolution is complete. Add $HNO_3$ dropwise to oxidize the solution and finally add 3 drops in excess. Evaporate to dense white fumes, cool, dilute to 125 ml., and heat to dissolve salts.

(*b*) For samples containing less than 1% manganese and less than 1% chromium, proceed as directed in paragraph (*e*).

(*c*) For samples containing over 1% manganese and less chromium than manganese, cool, transfer to a 250-ml. volumetric flask, and dilute to the mark. Transfer an aliquot containing not over 10 mg. of manganese to a 500-ml. Erlenmeyer flask. Add enough $H_2SO_4$ (1:1) to bring the total $H_2SO_4$ to 10 ml. Dilute to 125 ml. with water, heat almost to boiling, and proceed as directed in paragraph (*e*).

(*d*) For samples containing over 1% chromium and more chromium than manganese, transfer to an 800-ml. beaker, make alkaline with NaOH solution, and add 6 g. of $Na_2O_2$. Boil for 10 minutes, filter through double 12.5-cm. medium-texture filter papers, and wash with $Na_2CO_3$ wash solution. Discard the filtrate. Place a 500-ml. flask under the funnel and dissolve the precipitate through the paper with small portions of hot HCl (1:1), and wash with hot HCl (1:19). Add 12 ml. of $H_2SO_4$ and evaporate to dense white fumes. Cool, dilute with water, and heat to dissolve salts. If the manganese content of the sample is less than 1%, proceed as directed in paragraph (*e*). If it is above 1%, proceed as directed in paragraph (*c*).

(e) Add 10 ml. of $HNO_3$ (1:1), 10 ml. of $AgNO_3$ solution, heat almost to boiling, and add 15 ml. of $(NH_4)_2S_2O_8$ solution. Swirl, bring to a boil, and immediately remove from the heat. Allow to stand 2 to 3 minutes until the evolution of oxygen ceases and cool to about 20°C. Add 70 ml. of cold water and titrate with standard $NaAsO_2$ solution to the disappearance of permanganate color.

**Calculation.**—Calculate the percentage of manganese as follows:

$$\text{Manganese, } \% = \frac{A \times B}{C} \times 100$$

where $A$ = milliliters of $NaAsO_2$ solution used for the titration,

$B$ = manganese equivalent of $NaAsO_2$ solution, in grams per milliliter, and

$C$ = grams of sample represented in the aliquot used.

## MANGANESE BY THE PERIODATE (PHOTOMETRIC) METHOD

This method is recommended for titanium metal and titanium alloys containing less than 0.2% manganese but may also be used for higher percentages.

After dissolution in $H_2SO_4$, the solution is oxidized with $H_2O_2$, the manganese further oxidized with $KIO_4$, and photometric measurement made at approximately 545 m$\mu$. A band centered at 545 m$\mu$ is used instead of 525 m$\mu$ to minimize the interference of chromium.

The recommended concentration range is from 0.01 to 1.0 mg. of manganese in 200 ml. for a 1-cm. cell.

The color is stable as long as evaporation is prevented and excess periodate is present.

Effect of interfering elements such as relatively large amounts of copper, nickel, cobalt, chromium, and iron is eliminated by reducing a portion of the test solution and using it as the reference solution. Sufficient $KIO_4$ must be used to oxidize chromium as well as manganese if the sample contains chromium.

**Reagents. Titanium Dioxide.**—Manganese content less than 0.005%.

**Standard Manganese Solution (1 ml. = 0.05 mg. Mn).**

**Potassium Periodate Solution (40 g. per liter).**—Dissolve 40 g. of $KIO_4$ in 200 ml. of hot $HNO_3$ (1:1). Cool and dilute to 1 liter with $HNO_3$ (1:1).

**Sodium Nitrite Solution (20 g. per liter).**—Dissolve 2 g. of $NaNO_2$ in water and dilute to 100 ml. Prepare as needed.

**Sulfuric Acid Solution (233:767).**—Mix 233 ml. of $H_2SO_4$ with about 750 ml. of water, cool and dilute to 1 liter.

**Preparation of Calibration Curve.** (a) **Calibration Solutions.**—Transfer 0.835-g. portions of low-manganese $TiO_2$ to seven 400-ml. beakers. Add 30 ml. of $H_2SO_4$ and 10 g. of $(NH_4)_2SO_4$ to each and dissolve the $TiO_2$ by heating strongly. Cool, dilute with 75 ml. of water, and add to six of the seven beakers 1.0, 3.0, 5.0, 10.0, 15.0, and 20.0 ml., respectively, of the manganese solution (1 ml. = 0.05 mg. Mn). Carry the seventh beaker through as the reagent blank. Dilute to 100 ml., add five or six glass beads, and bring the solution to a boil. Cautiously add 20 ml. of $KIO_4$ solution and boil 10 minutes. Cool, transfer to a 200-ml. volumetric flask, and dilute to the mark.

(b) **Reference Solution.**—Remove a suitable portion of the reagent blank solution and reduce with a few drops of $NaNO_2$ solution. The photometric measurement must be made promptly as the solution will reoxidize on standing.

**(c) Photometry.**—Transfer the reference solution to an absorption cell and adjust the photometer to the initial setting, using a light band centered at approximately 545 m$\mu$. While maintaining this photometer adjustment, take the photometric readings of the calibration solutions.

**(d) Calibration Curve.**—Plot the photometric readings against milligrams of manganese per 200 ml. of solution.

*Procedure.* **(a) Sample Solution.**—Transfer 0.500 g. of the sample to a 400-ml. beaker and add 150 ml. of H$_2$SO$_4$ (233:767). After the reaction has ceased, add 25 ml. of 3% H$_2$O$_2$. Evaporate to dense white fumes, cool, add 100 ml. of water, cool again, and filter, if not clear. Add five or six glass beads and bring the solution to a boil. Cautiously add 20 ml. of KIO$_4$ solution and boil for 10 minutes (Note 1). Cool, transfer to a 200-ml. volumetric flask, and dilute to the mark.

NOTE 1.—If chromium is present, sufficient periodate must be added to oxidize both the chromium and the manganese. Twenty ml. of KIO$_4$ solution are sufficient to completely oxidize 1 mg. of manganese in the presence of 50 mg. of chromium. In the absence of chromium, 10 ml. of KIO$_4$ solution may be used.

**(b) Reference Solution.**—Reduce a portion of the sample solution with a few drops of NaNO$_2$ solution.

**(c) Photometry.**—Take the photometric reading of the sample solution as directed in "Preparation of the Calibration Curve (c)."

**Calculation.**—Convert the photometric reading of the sample to milligrams of manganese by means of the calibration curve. Calculate the percentage of manganese as follows:

$$\text{Manganese, } \% = \frac{A}{B \times 10}$$

where $A$ = milligrams of manganese found in the aliquot used, and
$B$ = grams of sample represented in the aliquot used.

## MOLYBDENUM BY THE SULFIDE–PERMANGANATE TITRATION METHOD

This method is applicable for titanium and titanium alloys containing more than 0.25% molybdenum.

After dissolution in H$_2$SO$_4$ and HF, the solution is oxidized with H$_2$O$_2$, molybdenum is precipitated with H$_2$S, and the precipitate dissolved in HNO$_3$-H$_2$SO$_4$. After removing nitrates, the molybdenum is reduced with zinc, collected under Fe$_2$(SO$_4$)$_3$, and titrated with KMnO$_4$.

The method is satisfactory for molybdenum in the range of 2.5 to 100 mg. in the sample used.

Interference of tungsten is avoided by complexing it with tartaric acid. Copper and tin do not interfere. Titanium will interfere if it is not completely removed in the sulfide separation.

*Apparatus.*—**Platinum Dishes,** 100 ml. or larger.

**Plastic Graduate,** 10 or 25 ml.

**Jones Reductor.**—See Chapter on Iron, Figs. 25-2 and 25-3, pp. 540–541.

*Reagents.* **Tartaric Acid Solution (200 g. per liter).**—Dissolve 200 g. of tartaric acid in water and dilute to 1 liter.

**Sulfuric Acid-Hydrogen Sulfide Wash Solution.**—Saturate H$_2$SO$_4$ (1:65) with H$_2$S.

**Sulfuric Acid-Tartaric Acid-Hydrogen Sulfide Wash Solution.**—To 500 ml. of water, add 15 ml. of $H_2SO_4$, 20 ml. of tartaric acid solution, dilute to 1 liter, and saturate with $H_2S$.

**Potassium Permanganate Solution (50 g. per liter).**—Dissolve 50 g. of $KMnO_4$ in water and dilute to 1 liter. Filter if necessary.

**Ferric Ammonium Sulfate Solution (100 g. per liter).**—Dissolve 100 g. of $FeNH_4(SO_4)_2 \cdot 12H_2O$ in water and dilute to 1 liter.

**Standard Potassium Permanganate Solution (0.1 N).**—Dissolve 3.2 g. of $KMnO_4$ in 1 liter of water. Let stand in the dark for 2 weeks and filter, without washing, through a Gooch crucible or a fritted-glass crucible of fine porosity, avoiding contact with rubber or other organic material. Store in a dark-colored, glass-stoppered bottle.

*Standardization.*—Transfer 0.3000 g. of the National Bureau of Standards standard sample of sodium oxalate [61] dried at 105°C., to a 600-ml. beaker. Add 250 ml. of $H_2SO_4$ (5:95), previously boiled for 10 to 15 minutes and then cooled to 27° ± 3°C. Stir until the oxalate has dissolved. Add 39 to 40 ml.[62] of the $KMnO_4$ solution at a rate of 25 to 35 ml. per minute, while stirring slowly. Let stand until the pink color disappears (about 45 seconds).[63] Heat to 55 to 60°C., and complete the titration by adding the $KMnO_4$ solution until a faint pink color persists for 30 seconds. Add the last 0.5 to 1 ml. drop by drop, with particular care to allow each drop to become decolorized before the next is introduced.

Determine the amount of $KMnO_4$ required to impart a faint pink color to the solution by adding the $KMnO_4$ solution to the same volume of the boiled and cooled $H_2SO_4$ (5:95) at 55 to 60°C. This correction usually amounts to 0.03 to 0.05 ml.

**Standard Potassium Permanganate Solution (0.03 N).**—Prepare as above, except for use 0.96 g. of $KMnO_4$.

*Procedure.*—(*a*) Transfer 1.000 g. of the sample to a platinum dish, add 10 ml. of water and 2 ml. of $H_2SO_4$. Using a plastic graduate, add 5 ml. of HF in small portions. When dissolution is complete and the reaction has ceased, add 1.5 ml. of $H_2O_2$ and dilute to about 60 ml. If the solution is not yellow add more $H_2O_2$. Heat until the yellow titanium peroxide complex is destroyed, while maintaining a volume of at least 50 ml. Cool to room temperature and dilute to approximately 80 ml.

(*b*) If the sample contains 0.2% tungsten or less, transfer the solution to a 250-ml. beaker containing 50 ml. of water. If the tungsten content is more than 0.2%, replace 25 ml. of the water with 25 ml. of tartaric acid solution. Dilute to about 150 ml., pass a rapid stream of $H_2S$ through the solution for 5 minutes, and then a moderately rapid stream for an additional 10 minutes. Allow to stand overnight.

(*c*) Add paper pulp, and filter through a close-texture paper. In the absence of tungsten wash the precipitate with $H_2SO_4$-$H_2S$ wash solution. In the presence of

[61] If the Bureau of Standards standard sample of sodium oxalate is unavailable, pure sodium oxalate may be prepared according to Sörensen by (*a*) two recrystallizations from water of the reagent grade substance, or (*b*) precipitation from an aqueous solution with alcohol. See "Sodium Oxalate as a Standard in Volumetric Analysis," Circular C40, Natl. Bureau Standards, p. 5, 1913.

[62] 0.3 g. of sodium oxalate requires 44.78 ml. of 0.1 N $KMnO_4$.

[63] If the pink color should persist because the $KMnO_4$ is too strong, discard, and begin again, adding a few milliliters less of the $KMnO_4$ solution.

tungsten wash with $H_2SO_4$-tartaric acid-$H_2S$ wash solution. Transfer the paper and precipitate to a 250-ml. beaker, add 10 ml. of $HNO_3$, and swirl until the paper is broken up. Add 10 ml. of $H_2SO_4$ and evaporate to dense white fumes. Cool, add 5 ml. of $HNO_3$, evaporate again, and repeat until the solution shows no yellow color (Note 1).

NOTE 1.—The amount of titanium carried down with the molybdenum sulfide precipitate, reduced in the reductor, and finally titrated as molybdenum is usually considered negligible. If there is reason to believe that appreciable titanium was precipitated with the molybdenum, then the titanium should be separated at this point by precipitation with $NH_4OH$ or $NaOH$ solution, followed by filtration. Before the precipitation, it is desirable to add a solution containing about 0.1 g. of $Fe_2(SO_4)_3$ in order to insure complete precipitation of the titanium. Wash the precipitate and filter paper with hot water, acidify the filtrate with $H_2SO_4$, and add an excess of 10 ml. of $H_2SO_4$. Add 10 ml. of $HNO_3$, evaporate to dense white fumes, and proceed as directed in paragraph (d).

(d) Cool, wash down the cover and sides of the beaker, and cautiously add a few drops of the $KMnO_4$ solution (50 g. per liter) to insure the decomposition of organic nitrogen compounds. Continue adding the $KMnO_4$ dropwise until the solution becomes slightly pink and evaporate to dense white fumes. Cool, wash down the sides of the beaker, dilute to 100 ml. (Note 2), and allow the solution to cool to room temperature.

NOTE 2.—Copper and tin will be removed from the solution by deposition on the zinc in the reductor but, to avoid fouling of the zinc column, it is recommended that they be removed by treating the solution with 2 g. of 20-mesh zinc and boiling until the copper is reduced to the metallic form. Filter through a 9-cm. paper and wash with hot water. Add a slight excess of $KMnO_4$ solution to the filtrate and proceed as directed in paragraph (e).

(e) If the Jones Reductor has been standing idle for a time, reactivate by passing 100 ml. of warm (40° to 50°C.) $H_2SO_4$ (5:95) through it, followed by a little cold water and discard the wash solution. Place 30 ml. of ferric ammonium sulfate solution in the receiving flask of the Jones Reductor, making sure the discharge end of the reductor is immersed in the ferric ammonium sulfate solution. Pass the following solutions through the Jones Reductor in the order given:

(1) 100 ml. of $H_2SO_4$ (1:39),
(2) The solution being analyzed for molybdenum,
(3) 200 ml. of $H_2SO_4$ (1:39), and
(4) 100 ml. of water.

(f) Remove the receiving flask, add 3 to 5 ml. of $H_3PO_4$, and titrate the solution to a pink end point with 0.1 N $KMnO_4$ solution. Use 0.03 N $KMnO_4$ if 1% or less molybdenum is expected.

(g) **Blank.**—Make a blank determination including all reagents and solutions, following the procedure described in paragraphs (a) to (f).

**Calculation.**—Calculate the percentage of molybdenum as follows:

$$\text{Molybdenum, } \% = \frac{(A - B)C \times 0.032}{D} \times 100$$

where $A$ = milliliters of $KMnO_4$ required for titration of the reduced molybdenum solution,

$B$ = milliliters of $KMnO_4$ required for titration of the blank,
$C$ = normality of $KMnO_4$ solution, and
$D$ = grams of sample used.

## MOLYBDENUM BY THE THIOCYANATE (PHOTOMETRIC) METHOD

This method is recommended for titanium and titanium alloys with molybdenum contents from 0.05 to 3% and is applicable up to 9%.

After dissolution of the sample in HF and $HNO_3$, an aliquot is fumed with $HClO_4$ in the presence of ferric ion. A mixture of NaCNS and $SnCl_2$ solutions is added to develop the red-colored molybdenum thiocyanate complex and photometric measurement is made at approximately 460 m$\mu$.

The recommended concentration range is from 0.03 to 0.6 mg. of molybdenum in 100 ml. of solution, for a 1-cm. cell.

The photometric measurement should be made after 5 minutes. The color is reasonably stable for at least 30 minutes, but it does fade slowly.

None of the elements usually present in titanium alloys interferes except tungsten. However, the interference is not significant unless the tungsten content of the sample is above 0.6% and the molybdenum content is below 1%. Platinum will interfere if present.

**Apparatus.** **Plastic Graduates, 10 or 25 ml.**
**Plastic Beakers, 250 or 400 ml.**

**Reagents.** **Low-Molybdenum Titanium.**—Molybdenum content less than 0.005%.

**Standard Molybdenum Solution (1 ml. = 0.1 mg. Mo).** Dissolve 0.372 g. of ammonium molybdate $(NH_4)_6Mo_7O_{24}\cdot4H_2O)$ in 1800 ml. of water. Transfer to a 2-liter volumetric flask, fill to the mark and mix.

*Standardization.*—Pipette 100 ml. of the molybdenum solution into a 250-ml. beaker, add 10 ml. of $H_2SO_4$ (1:1), and reduce in a Jones Reductor (see Chapter on Iron, Figs. 25-2 and 25-3, p. 540), as follows: If the Jones Reductor has been standing idle, pass 100 ml. of $H_2SO_4$ (5:95) through it, then some water, and discard the wash solution. Add 30 ml. of ferric phosphate solution to the receiver, and then enough water so that the tip of the reductor dips beneath the surface of the solution. (To prepare the ferric phosphate solution, dissolve 100 g. of $Fe_2(SO_4)_3$ in 1 liter of water to which 150 ml. of $H_3PO_4$ and 20 ml. of $H_2SO_4$ (1:1) have been added. Add $KMnO_4$ (25 g. per l.) until the solution is just tinted pink.) Draw the molybdenum solution, by gentle suction, through the reductor. Just before the surface of the liquid reaches the zinc, add a 50-ml. portion of water, and finally rinse by adding two more 50-ml. portions each time just before the surface of the solution reaches the zinc. Close the stopcock, disconnect, and raise the reductor as a little water is allowed to run through the stem. Rinse the stem and titrate the solution with 0.1 N $KMnO_4$. Make a blank determination, following the same procedure and using the same amounts of all reagents.

**Standard Molybdenum Solution (1 ml. = 0.01 mg. Mo).**—Pipette 100 ml. of the molybdenum solution (1 ml. = 0.1 mg. Mo) into a 1-liter volumetric flask and dilute to 1 liter with water containing 4.5 ml. of $H_2SO_4$.

**Perchloric Acid (60%).**—If only 70% $HClO_4$ is at hand, prepare 60% $HClO_4$ by mixing 700 ml. of 70% $HClO_4$ with 195 ml. of water. (The 60% $HClO_4$ is commercially available.)

**Iron Perchlorate Solution (1 ml. = 0.005 g. Fe).**—Dissolve 5 g. of iron wire in 100 ml. of 60% $HClO_4$ and evaporate to white fumes. While still hot, add 200 ml. of 60% $HClO_4$, cool, and make up to 1 liter with $HClO_4$ (60 per cent).

**Sodium Thiocyanate Solution (100 g. per liter).**—Dissolve 100 g. of NaCNS in water and dilute to 1 liter.

**Stannous Chloride Solution (250 g. per liter).**—Dissolve 250 g. of $SnCl_2\cdot2H_2O$

in 200 ml. of HCl. Digest on a hot plate until clear. Cool, add 5 g. of tin, and dilute to 1 liter.

**Reagent Mixture.**—Mix 1 part of NaCNS solution with 2 parts of $SnCl_2$ solution. Filter through an open texture fluted paper. Prepare as needed.

*Preparation of Calibration Curve A (Molybdenum 0.05 to 1.0%).* (a) **Calibration Solutions.**—(*1*) Transfer 1.0 g. of the sample of low-molybdenum titanium to a plastic beaker, add 20 ml. of HF (1:4) and allow the sample to dissolve at room temperature. Add 5 to 7 ml. of $HNO_3$ to dissolve any black residue that remains after the HF dissolution. Dilute to 200 ml., transfer to a 500-ml. volumetric flask, fill to the mark, and mix.

(*2*) Transfer 25-ml. aliquots to each of five 250-ml. beakers. Add to these beakers 2.5, 5.0, 10.0, 30.0, and 60.0 ml., respectively, of the molybdenum solution (1 ml. = 0.01 mg. Mo).

(*3*) Add 15 ml. of 60% $HClO_4$ and 10 ml. of iron perchlorate solution to each beaker. Heat the solution *rapidly* to fumes, using a hot plate (not an open flame), and fume strongly for 3 minutes, applying sufficient heat so that heavy fumes issue from the beaker and no fumes condense inside the beaker. Allow the solution to cool, dilute to approximately 30 ml., and transfer to a 100-ml. volumetric flask using a small quantity of water. Mix and cool to room temperature.

(*4*) Add 30 ml. of the reagent mixture and mix at once. Dilute to the mark, mix, and allow to stand for 5 minutes.

(b) **Reference Solution.**—Transfer 25 ml. of the titanium solution (paragraph (a) (*1*)) to a 250-ml. beaker and proceed as directed in paragraph (a) (*3*).

(c) **Photometry.**—Transfer a suitable portion of the reference solution to an absorption cell and adjust the photometer to the initial setting using a light band centered at approximately 460 m$\mu$. While maintaining this photometer adjustment take the photometric readings of the calibration solutions.

(d) **Calibration Curve.**—Plot the photometric readings of the calibration solutions against milligrams of molybdenum per 100 ml. of solution.

*Preparation of Calibration Curve B (Molybdenum 0.6 to 9%).*—(*a*) Repeat the preparation of the calibration curve, as directed above, sections (*a*) (*2*) and (*3*), except to use the molybdenum solution (1 ml. = 0.1 mg. Mo) and to add 25 ml. of 60% $HClO_4$ instead of 15 ml., but at this time omitting the 10 ml. of iron perchlorate solution.

(*b*) Dilute the solution to the mark and mix. Transfer a 10-ml. aliquot to another 100-ml. volumetric flask. Add 10 ml. of water, 10 ml. of 60% $HClO_4$, and 10 ml. of iron perchlorate solution. Mix, cool to room temperature, and proceed as directed in "Preparation of Calibration Curve A."

*Procedure.* **Sample Solution.**—Transfer 0.500 g. of the sample to a plastic beaker, add 20 ml. of HF (1:4), and allow the sample to dissolve at room temperature. Add 5 to 7 ml. of $HNO_3$ to dissolve any black residue remaining after the HF dissolution (Note 1).

NOTE 1.—Occasionally molybdenum alloys are encountered that do not yield a clear solution at this point. For such alloys, start the sample over again in a 150-ml., or larger, platinum dish and treat with 20 ml. of HF (1:4) at room temperature. Add 20 ml. of 60% $HClO_4$ and digest on a hot plate until a clear solution is obtained. Cool, dilute, and proceed as directed in paragraph (*b*). If platinum dishes are available, this general method of decomposing the sample may be found superior to that described above, although fuming in platinum is normally to be avoided.

Dilute to 200 ml., transfer to a 250-ml. volumetric flask, fill to the mark, and mix (Note 2). Transfer a 25-ml. aliquot to a covered 250-ml. beaker. Depending on the molybdenum content expected, proceed as directed in "Preparation of Calibration Curve A (*a*) (*3*) for 0.05 to 1.0% molybdenum or that "Section and Preparation of Calibration Curve B" (*b*) for 0.6 to 9% molybdenum. When proceeding by the former for 0.6 to 9% of molybdenum, use 25 ml. of 60% $HClO_4$ instead of 15 ml. and at this point omit the 10 ml. of iron perchlorate solution.

NOTE 2.—The dilute solution of HF does not produce any marked etching action on the volumetric flask, but prolonged storage in the flask is not recommended.

**Reference Solution.**—Use a freshly prepared reference solution made by adding 25 ml. of $HClO_4$ to 25 ml. of water (cool the solution after the addition of the $HClO_4$), followed by 30 ml. of reagent mixture, prepared as directed under "Reagents," above, and dilute with water to a volume of 100 ml.

**Photometry.**—Take the photometric reading of the sample solution as described in "Preparation of Calibration Curve A" under the heading "Photometry."

**Calculation.**—Convert the photometric reading of the sample solution to milligrams of molybdenum by means of the appropriate calibration curve based on the aliquot used. Calculate the percentage of molybdenum as follows:

$$\text{Molybdenum, } \% = \frac{A}{B \times 10}$$

where $A$ = milligrams of molybdenum in the aliquot used, and
$B$ = grams of sample represented in the aliquot used.

## NIOBIUM AND TANTALUM BY THE ION-EXCHANGE–CUPFERRON (GRAVIMETRIC) METHOD

This method covers the determination of niobium and tantalum in titanium alloys in the range from 0.25 to 5.0%.

The sample is dissolved in a hydrochloric-hydrofluoric acid mixture and transferred to an anion-exchange resin column. Interfering elements are eluted with an ammonium chloride-hydrochloric acid-hydrofluoric acid mixture, while the niobium and tantalum remain in the column. Niobium and tantalum are separated by eluting, first with an ammonium chloride-hydrofluoric acid mixture (niobium), and second with an ammonium chloride-ammonium fluoride solution adjusted to a pH of 5 to 6 (tantalum). The separate eluates are treated with boric acid to decompose the complex fluorides, and the niobium and tantalum precipitated with cupferron, ignited, and weighed as the pentoxides.

The sample size should be adjusted so that the content of niobium or tantalum, or both, is between 12.5 and 250 mg.

Provision has been made for the removal of all interfering elements.

**Apparatus. Ion-Exchange Columns.**—The columns should be constructed of polystyrene and should be approximately 12 in. long and 1 in. in inside diameter. A suitable column can be prepared from a 12-in. length of polystyrene tubing as follows: Insert a waxed No. 5 rubber stopper with a $\frac{3}{16}$-in. hole into the bottom of the polystyrene tube. Insert a 6-in. length of polystyrene tubing ($\frac{3}{16}$-in. outside diameter and $\frac{1}{16}$-in. inside diameter) into the hole flush with the upper surface of the stopper. Connect this tubing to another 6-in. length of the same tubing by means of a 2-in. length of polyvinyl tubing. (Tygon-R tubing has been found satisfactory for this purpose.)    Control the flow by a hosecock on the polyvinyl tubing.

If a number of analyses are to be made, it is convenient to arrange the columns so that several can be operated with a minimum of attention.    Plastic columns equipped with "Dole-type" fittings of polystyrene have been developed for such an assembly.[64]    Inlet and outlet tubes are of polyethylene; flexible connections where necessary are made of polyvinyl tubing.    The flow of solutions from plastic bottles placed above the columns is controlled by hosecocks on these flexible connections.    The assembling should be carefully done and checked in order to avoid any possibility of leakage of the solutions containing HF.

**Plastic Ware** (polyethylene, polypropylene, or tetrafluorethylene).

**Beakers and Covers,** heat-resistant, 250 and 600 ml.

**Bottles,** 1 liter.

**Graduated Cylinders,** 50- and 250-ml.

*Reagents.*    **Ammonium Chloride Solution (240 g. per liter).**—Dissolve 480 g. of ammonium chloride ($NH_4Cl$) in 1600 ml. of water by warming, cool, and dilute to 2 liters with water.    Filter to remove insoluble material.    This solution is used as a stock solution in preparing the solutions described below.

**Ammonium Chloride-Ammonium Fluoride Solution.**—Transfer 600 ml. of the $NH_4Cl$ solution and 40 ml. of HF to a plastic bottle.    Adjust the solution to a pH of 5 to 6 with $NH_4OH$ (approximately 80 to 85 ml. will be required) and dilute to 1 liter with water.    This solution must be prepared with reasonable care, as a solution that is too acid will not completely elute the tantalum in the volume specified in the procedure.    A solution that is too alkaline will precipitate tantalum in the column, spoiling the determination being run and the one that follows.

**Ammonium Chloride-Hydrochloric Acid-Hydrofluoric Acid Solution.**—Transfer 300 ml. of the $NH_4Cl$ solution, 200 ml. of HF, and 125 ml. of HCl to a plastic bottle.    Dilute to 1 liter with water and mix well.

**Ammonium Chloride-Hydrofluoric Acid Solution.**—Transfer 600 ml. of the $NH_4Cl$ solution and 40 ml. of HF to a plastic bottle, dilute to 1 liter with water, and mix well.

**Boric Acid** ($H_3BO_3$).

**Cupferron Solution (60 g. per liter).**—Dissolve 6 g. cupferron in 80 ml. of warm water, dilute to 100 ml., and filter.    Prepare fresh as needed.

**Cupferron Wash Solution.**—Dilute 25 ml. of cupferron solution to 1 liter with cold HCl (1:9).    Prepare as needed.

**Hydrochloric-Hydrofluoric Acid Mixture.**—Add 250 ml. of HCl to 300 ml. of water, add 200 ml. of HF, dilute to 1 liter with water, and mix well.

**Ion-Exchange Resin.**—Strongly basic anion-exchange resin, 200- to 400-mesh, chloride form, capacity of $3.0 \pm 0.3$ milliequivalents per gram of dry resin (*Caution,* see Note 1).    The mesh-size of the resin may vary considerably from lot to lot. In order to avoid this difficulty, air-dry the resin as received and pass it through a No. 270 (53-$\mu$) sieve.    Discard the material retained on the No. 270 sieve.    Prepare a suspension of the material passing the No. 270 sieve in HCl (1:19), allow the coarser fraction to settle 10 to 15 minutes, and remove the fines by decantation. Repeat the process several times until most of the very fine material has been removed and discarded.

NOTE 1: *Caution.* This method as written is based on the use of Dowex 1-X10 anion-exchange resin. Comparable results may not be obtained with other resins.

***Preparation of Ion-Exchange Column.***—Cover the bottom of the ion-exchange column with a ¼- to ⅜-in. layer of acid-resistant (polyvinyl chloride) plastic fiber.[65] Add the resin suspension in small portions to obtain a settled column of the resin 6 to 7 in. high. Wash the loaded column with approximately 100 ml. of $HNO_3$ (1:9), and then run through several elution cycles with alternate additions of HCl (1:9) and HCl (3:1) until the remainder of the fines have been removed. The final wash should be with HCl (1:3). (Note 2.) When not in use the column should be filled with HCl (1:3) to a level above the resin.

NOTE 2.—Resin columns prepared in this way have been used for several years, the only maintenance required being to empty and refill the column with the resin charge if the flow rate becomes excessively slow due to packing.

***Procedure.***—(*a*) As the sample dissolves quite rapidly, the rate of dissolution must be controlled by adding the sample in small portions to the cooled acid mixture. Transfer 100 ml. (Note 3) of the HCl-HF mixture to a covered 250-ml. plastic beaker. Add 5 g. of the sample, weighed to the nearest 1 mg., in small portions to the acid until the sample is completely transferred. When dissolution is complete, warm slightly (40 to 50°C.) on the steam bath, and oxidize the titanium by the dropwise addition of $HNO_3$ (Note 4). Approximately 1 to 2 ml. will be required, but the addition should be kept to a minimum because of the strong replacing power of $HNO_3$ for niobium on the exchange column. Digest on the steam bath for 10 to 15 minutes to remove nitrous oxide fumes. Rinse down the plastic cover and walls of the beaker with the HCl-HF mixture, and dilute the solution to a volume of 150 ml. with the same mixture.

NOTE 3.—If smaller samples are used, approximately 25 ml. of HCl-HF mixture should be used for each gram of sample, and an extra 25-ml. portion added to maintain the high fluoride ion concentration required for a satisfactory separation of niobium.

NOTE 4.—Potassium permanganate ($KMnO_4$) solution (25 g. per liter) can be used as an oxidant if the tantalum content does not exceed the solubility limits of potassium fluo-tantalate. If vanadium is present, oxidation by $HNO_3$ is preferred since the vanadium (IV) produced is more easily eluted from the column than the vanadium (V) form which results from oxidation by $KMnO_4$.

(*b*) Tranfer 50 ml. of the HCl-HF mixture to the column in small increments (5 to 10 ml.), and drain the acid to 1 cm. above the resin bed, catching the eluate in a 600-ml. plastic beaker. Transfer the sample solution in small increments (5 to 10 ml.) to the column, adding the sample solution as it moves down the column until all the solution has been transferred. Wash the beaker four or five times with 5-ml. portions of the HCl-HF mixture, transferring the washings to the column. Finally wash down the column above the resin, using approximately 50 ml. of the same solution in 10-ml. increments.

(*c*) Add 300 ml. of the $NH_4$Cl-HCl-HF mixture at a flow rate of approximately 100 to 125 ml. per hr. Allow the solution to drain to the top of the resin. Discard this first eluate containing the titanium, vanadium, iron, tin, etc., and replace the beaker with another 600-ml. beaker.

[65] Dynel staple fiber, available from Union Carbide Chemicals Co., Textile Fibers Department, 270 Park Ave., New York 17, N. Y., has been found satisfactory for this purpose.

(d) Wash down the column above the resin with four or five portions (a total of about 25 ml.) of the $NH_4Cl$-HF mixture, allowing the solution to drain to the top of the resin each time. Add 300 ml. of the $NH_4Cl$-HF mixture, eluting at a rate of 100 to 125 ml. per hour (Note 5). Remove the beaker containing the second fraction, and reserve for the determination of niobium. Replace the beaker with another 600-ml. plastic beaker.

NOTE 5.—This point in the procedure provides a convenient and satisfactory place to stop overnight if the elution is not carried through as a continuous operation.

(e) Wash down the column above the resin with approximately 25 to 30 ml. of the $NH_4Cl$-$NH_4F$ neutral mixture in 5-ml. portions. Add 350 ml. of the $NH_4Cl$-$NH_4F$ neutral mixture, eluting at a rate of 100 to 125 ml. per hour, and reserve the eluate for the determination of tantalum.

(f) Clean the column by adding, in 10-ml. increments, 50 ml. of HCl (1:3). The column is then ready for the next sample.

(g) To the second fraction, containing the niobium (paragraph (d)), add 70 ml. of HCl, 80 ml. of water, and 15 g. of $H_3BO_3$. Warm on the steam bath (30 to 35°C.) to dissolve the $H_3BO_3$. Cool to 5°C., and add slowly, with good stirring, 30 to 50 ml. of cupferron solution. Add paper pulp, stir well, and allow to stand 10 to 15 minutes. Filter by suction on a Büchner funnel, using a double thickness of 9-cm., low-ash, fine paper precoated with a little filter pulp. Transfer the precipitate to the funnel, and wash well with 400 ml. of ice-cold (5°C.) cupferron wash solution.

(h) Transfer the precipitate and paper to a weighed 25-ml. porcelain crucible, and ignite at a low temperature until the carbon is gone. Finally ignite to constant weight at 1000°C., and weigh as niobium pentoxide ($Nb_2O_5$) (Note 6).

NOTE 6.—Blank determinations have been found to be unnecessary since the blank usually amounts to less than 0.5 mg. when the reagents conform to ACS specifications and is ordinarily counterbalanced by the few tenths of a milligram of earth acids lost in the precipitation.

(i) To the third fraction, containing the tantalum (paragraph (e)), add 75 ml. of HCl, 80 ml. of water, and 8 g. of $H_3BO_3$. Warm to dissolve the $H_3BO_3$; precipitate, filter, wash, and ignite the tantalum as described in paragraphs (g) and (h) for niobium. Weigh as tantalum pentoxide ($Ta_2O_5$) (Note 6).

**Calculations.**—Calculate the percentages of niobium and tantalum as follows:

$$\text{Niobium, } \% = \frac{A \times 0.699}{C} \times 100$$

$$\text{Tantalum, } \% = \frac{B \times 0.819}{C} \times 100$$

where $A$ = grams of $Nb_2O_5$ (paragraph (h)),
$B$ = grams of $Ta_2O_5$ (paragraph (i)), and
$C$ = grams of sample used.

## NITROGEN BY THE DISTILLATION–TITRATION METHOD

This method is suitable for titanium and titanium alloys.

The sample is dissolved in a mixture of $HBF_4$ and HCl, thus converting the nitrides to ammonium salts. The $NH_3$ is distilled from an alkaline solution into $H_3BO_3$ and titrated with standard acid.

The method is satisfactory for nitrogen in the range 0.05 to 1.0 mg. in the sample used.

There are no known interferences.

***Apparatus.*** **Microdistillation Apparatus.**—Parnas-Wagner microkjeldahl, or equivalent (see Fig. 48-4).

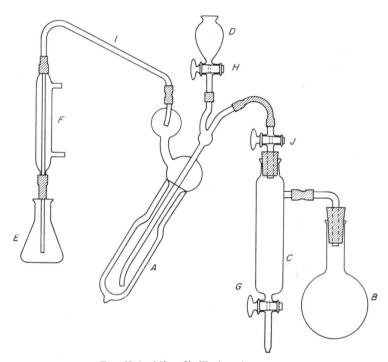

FIG. 48-4. Microdistillation Apparatus.

$A$ = Vacuum-jacketed 175-ml. distillation flask. $B$ = One-liter round-bottom borosilicate flask, about two-thirds full with water containing 4 to 5 ml. of $H_2SO_4$, and containing a few beads or boiling chips to prevent bumping; $C$ = Steam trap, closed at the top with stopcock $J$ and at the bottom with stopcock $G$ or rubber tubing and a pinch clamp. $D$ = Funnel connected to flask $A$ with rubber tubing and stopcock $H$ or a pinch clamp; $E$ = 5-ml. Erlenmeyer flask; $F$ = Condenser jacket with silver condenser tube $I$.

**Microburette, 10 ml.**
***Reagents.*** **Fluoboric Acid (48 to 50%).**
**Sodium Hydroxide Solution (40%).**—Dissolve 400 g. of NaOH in 600 ml. of water.
**Boric Acid Solution (10 g. per liter).**—Dissolve 10 g. of $H_3BO_3$ in water and dilute to 1 liter.
**Methyl Purple Indicator.**
**Standard Ammonium Chloride Solution (1 ml. = 0.0001 g. nitrogen).**—Transfer 0.3820 g. of dry $NH_4Cl$ to a 1-liter volumetric flask and fill to the mark with water.
**Sulfuric Acid (0.007 N).**—Dilute 2 ml. of $H_2SO_4$ to 1 liter and transfer 100 ml. of this to a 1-liter volumetric flask. Dilute to the mark and mix. Obtain the

nitrogen equivalent as follows: Transfer 10.0 ml. of the standard $NH_4Cl$ solution to a 125-ml. Erlenmeyer flask. Add $HBF_4$ and HCl, but no titanium, and continue as directed in the "Procedure," including the determination of blanks.

$$\text{Nitrogen equivalent} = \frac{0.001}{C - D}$$

where $C$ = milliliters of $H_2SO_4$ required to titrate the standard ammonium chloride solution, and

$D$ = milliliters of $H_2SO_4$ required to titrate the blank.

**Procedure.**—(a) If the expected nitrogen content is 0.07 to 0.20%, transfer 0.50 g. of the sample to a 125-ml. Erlenmeyer flask. If the expected nitrogen content is less than 0.07%, use a 1.0-g. portion (Note 1). Add 25 ml. of HCl (1:1) and 2 to 3 ml. of $HBF_4$. Allow to stand at room temperature until vigorous action ceases. Place on a steam bath (90° to 100°C.) and heat until dissolution is complete, or nearly so (Note 2).

NOTE 1.—It is good practice to run the low-nitrogen samples first and the higher ones last, similar to the practice employed in determining carbon by combustion.

NOTE 2.—In the case of alloys of titanium that have insoluble residues due to refractory nitrides or high-carbon content, proceed as follows: Decant, and reserve the solution. Add to the residue a crystal of selenium and 5 ml. of $H_2SO_4$ (1:1), heat to dense white fumes to dissolve the residue, and combine with the main solution. An alternate procedure is to filter the residue on a small paper, digest the paper and precipitate with $HF$-$H_2O_2$-$H_2SO_4$, evaporate to dense white fumes, continue heating to a clear solution, and combine with the main solution.

(b) Cool the solution and, with stopcock $J$ closed, transfer to the microkjeldahl apparatus through funnel $D$ and stopcock $H$ (Fig. 48-4), rinsing with 10 to 15 ml. of water. While this is being done, the water in $B$ should be at the boiling point, with the source of heat, a Bunsen burner, to one side and stopcock $G$ open. Pour 25 ml. of the NaOH solution through funnel $D$ at a slow rate so that two layers form in vacuum-jacketed flask $A$ and then close stopcock $H$. Add 10 ml. of $H_3BO_3$ solution and 2 drops of methyl purple indicator to the 50-ml. Erlenmeyer flask, $E$, and adjust it under the receiving condenser so that the tip of the outlet is just above the solution in the flask. Increase the heat by placing the Bunsen burner under flask $B$ and, when boiling occurs, close stopcock $G$ and open stopcock $J$, forcing the steam into flask $A$ and mixing the two layers. After the initial vigorous action in flask $A$ (no loss of ammonia takes place), raise flask $E$ until the tip of the condenser is below the level of the solution. After the color of the solution in flask $E$ changes to green (about 1 minute), continue the distillation for 3.5 minutes (collecting a distillate of approximately 10 to 20 ml.). Remove the flask $E$, rinse the tip of the condenser with about 1 ml. of water and at the same time remove the source of heat from $B$. (The contents in flask $A$ will transfer to funnel $C$, from which they are discarded by opening stopcock $G$ before the next sample is run.)

(c) Titrate the distillate with 0.007 $N$ $H_2SO_4$, using a 10-ml. microburette, until the color changes from green to light purple.

(d) Determine an average blank by carrying all the reagents through the entire procedure before and after a run of samples and averaging the two results (Note 3).

Note 3.—No provision has been made for removing last traces of nitrogen from the distilled water, since the blank determinations will correct for the presence of nitrogen. However, specially purified water is preferable if blanks exceed 0.25 ml. It is desirable that the analysis be made in a room where no ammonia or ammonium salts are used or stored.

**Calculation.**—Calculate the percentage of nitrogen as follows:

$$\text{Nitrogen, } \% = \frac{(A - B)C}{D} \times 100$$

where $A$ = milliliters of $H_2SO_4$ required to titrate the sample,
$B$ = milliliters of $H_2SO_4$ required to titrate the blank,
$C$ = nitrogen equivalent, and
$D$ = grams of sample used.

## SILICON BY THE MOLYBDENUM BLUE (PHOTOMETRIC) METHOD

This method is recommended for the determination of silicon in titanium and titanium-base alloys in the range from 0.005 to 0.1%, but may be extended to 0.5% silicon by taking an appropriate aliquot of the sample.

The sample is dissolved in dilute hydrofluoric acid and the titanium precipitated by hydrolysis. The silicomolybdenum blue color is developed at a controlled temperature in the presence of the precipitate. After filtration, the intensity of the color is measured at 700 m$\mu$.

The recommended silicon content is 0.025 to 0.5 mg. per 250 ml. of solution, using a cell depth of 1.0 cm. (Note 1).

Note 1.—This method has been written for a cell having a 1.0-cm. light path. Cells having other dimensions may be used, provided appropriate adjustments can be made in the amounts of sample and reagents used.

There is no interference by any of the elements ordinarily present in titanium metal and alloys.

*Apparatus.* **Polyethylene Bottles.**—Hydrofluoric acid bottles are satisfactory.
**Graduated Cylinder,** plastic.

*Reagents* (All solutions should be stored in polyethylene bottles.). **Ammonium Molybdate Solution (50 g. per liter).**—Dissolve 50 g. of ammonium molybdate $((NH_4)_6Mo_7O_{24}\cdot4H_2O)$ in water and dilute to 1 liter.

**Boric Acid Solution (40 g. per liter).**—Dissolve 40 g. of boric acid $(H_3BO_3)$ in 800 ml. of hot water, cool, and dilute to 1 liter.

**Potassium Permanganate Solution (30 g. per liter).**—Dissolve 30 g. of potassium permanganate $(KMnO_4)$ in water and dilute to 1 liter.

**Reducing Solution.**—Dissolve 30 g. of sodium bisulfite $(NaHSO_3)$, 1 g. of anhydrous sodium sulfite $(Na_2SO_3)$, and 0.5 g. of 1-amino-2-naphthol-4-sulfonic acid in 175 ml. of water by gentle heating to about 50°C. Cool, dilute to 200 ml. with water, and filter. Prepare fresh weekly.

**Silicon, Standard Solution (1 ml. = 0.05 mg. Si).**—Fuse 0.1070 g. of anhydrous silicon dioxide $(SiO_2)$ with 1.0 g. of sodium carbonate $(Na_2CO_3)$ in a platinum crucible. Cool the melt, dissolve completely in water, and dilute to 1 liter in a volumetric flask. Store the solution in a plastic or paraffin-lined bottle. If anhydrous $SiO_2$ is not available, the weight should be adjusted according to the actual silicon content of the $SiO_2$ used, as determined by analysis.

**Tartaric Acid Solution (200 g. per liter).**—Dissolve 200 g. of tartaric acid in 500 ml. of water, bring to a boil, cool, and dilute to 1 liter.

**Preparation of Calibration Curve.**—(*a*) Transfer 0.500 g. of low-silicon titanium (less than 0.003% Si) to each of seven polyethylene bottles and add 0, 1.0, 3.0, 5.0, 7.0, 9.0, and 11.0 ml. of silicon solution (1 ml. = 0.05 mg. Si), respectively. Add 40 ml. of water and 5 ml. of HF (3:7) to each bottle, using a plastic graduate. Place the loosely stoppered (rubber stopper) bottle in a 1-liter, borosilicate glass (Pyrex glass has been found satisfactory for this purpose.) beaker containing about 800 ml. of boiling water. The sample will dissolve in about 0.5 hours or less, with no loss of silicon.

(*b*) Remove the bottle from the hot water and add 100 ml. of $H_3BO_3$ solution and 50 ml. of water. Add $KMnO_4$ solution dropwise until a persistent pink color is developed. Add 5 drops in excess. Place the bottle in a beaker of boiling water for 90 minutes, swirling occasionally. The titanium is hydrolyzed in this step.

(*c*) Remove the bottle from the hot water and cool it in running water or an ice bath to the working temperature (any fixed temperature in the range from 22° to 27°C.) All manipulations from this point should be conducted at this temperature, controlled to ±1°C., and the reagents used after this step should be prepared and stored at this temperature. A temperature-controlled room is convenient, though not indispensable, for this purpose. Add 10 ml. of ammonium molybdate solution from a pipette, mix by swirling, and allow to stand for 10 minutes ± 15 seconds. Add 5 ml. of tartaric acid solution from a pipette and *immediately* follow with 3 ml. of reducing solution from a burette. Mix by swirling.

(*d*) Let stand for 25 minutes and then transfer to a 250-ml. volumetric flask, dilute to the mark with water, and mix well. Filter into a 50-ml. beaker through a dry, fine, low-ash paper, discarding the first 20 to 25-ml. portion.

**Photometry.**—Transfer a portion of the reference solution (blank) to an absorption cell and adjust the photometer to the initial setting, using a light band centered at 700 m$\mu$. While maintaining this photometric adjustment, take the photometric readings of the calibration solutions.

**Calibration Curve.**—Plot the photometric readings of the calibration solutions against milligrams of silicon per 250 ml. of solution.

**Procedure.**—Transfer 0.5 g. of the sample, weighed to the nearest 1 mg., to a polyethylene bottle. Proceed as in "Preparation of the Calibration Curve" (*a*) through (*d*). Carry through a blank on all reagents. It is not necessary to add $KMnO_4$ to the blank.

**Photometry.** Transfer a portion of the reference solution (reagent blank) to an absorption cell and adjust the photometer to the initial setting, using a light band centered at 700 m$\mu$. While maintaining this photometric adjustment, take the photometric reading of the sample solutions.

**Calculation.**—Convert the photometric reading of the sample solution to milligrams of silicon by means of the calibration curve. Calculate the percentage of silicon as follows:

$$\text{Silicon, \%} = \frac{A}{B \times 10}$$

where $A$ = milligrams of silicon from calibration curve, and
$B$ = grams of sample used.

## SILICON BY THE GRAVIMETRIC METHOD

This method covers the determination of silicon in titanium metal and alloys in the range from 0.05 to 5.0%.

The sample is fused with sodium bisulfate, the melt dissolved in dilute sulfuric acid, and the silicic acid dehydrated. The residue is ignited to silicon dioxide, weighed, and treated with sulfuric and hydrofluoric acids. The resulting silicon tetrafluoride is volatilized and the silicon calculated from the loss of weight.

None of the elements thus far encountered in commercially available titanium and its alloys interferes.

**Apparatus.**—Beakers, quartz or high-silica glass, 400 ml.

**Reagent.**—Sodium Bisulfate ($NaHSO_4$), fused.

**Procedure.**—(a) Transfer to a 400-ml. quartz or high-silica glass beaker between 0.5 and 2 g. (Note 1) of the sample, weighed to the nearest 1 mg. Add about 25 g. of $NaHSO_4$ per gram of sample (Note 1), and cover the beaker with a borosilicate watch glass.

Note 1.—The following sample weights and corresponding amounts of $NaHSO_4$ are recommended:

| Silicon, % | Weight of Sample, g. | Weight of Fused $NaHSO_4$, g. |
|---|---|---|
| Under 0.2, . . . . . . . . . | 2 | 50 |
| 0.2 to 1.0. . . . . . . . . . . | 1 | 25 |
| 1.0 to 5.0. . . . . . . . . . . | 0.5 | 15 |

Sodium bisulfate, crystal, reagent grade, may be used if the above amounts are increased by 20%. The crystals should be fused in the high-silica beaker to drive out contained water before adding the sample of titanium; otherwise, considerable spitting may occur during fusion of the sample.

(b) Place the beaker on a ring support without a wire gauze and directly over a low flame of a Meker or blast burner. When the sample starts to fuse, the reaction becomes quite vigorous and some of the sample and salts creep up the side of the beaker. Gradually increase the flame to full heat and apply the full flame of another burner against the side of the beaker so that the salts and chips are melted down. When a clear melt is obtained and all the chips are fused, remove the burners and swirl the melt so that most of it solidifies on the wall of the beaker (Note 2).

Note 2.—With the added heat from the second burner, a fusion should be completed in 15 to 20 minutes when the sample is in the form of chips or turnings.

(c) Cool the melt and add $H_2SO_4$ (1:1) in the amount appropriate for the weight of the sample as follows:

| Sample, g. | $H_2SO_4$ (1:1), ml. |
|---|---|
| 2.0. . . . . . . . . . . | 100 |
| 1.0. . . . . . . . . . . | 60 |
| 0.5. . . . . . . . . . . | 40 |

(d) Heat the beaker on a hot plate until the melt is dissolved, evaporate to dense white fumes, and fume for 5 minutes. Cool in a water bath, rinse the cover and beaker with cold water, dilute to 300 ml. with hot water, and filter, using a low-ash, fine paper, being careful to police the beaker thoroughly. Wash the paper and residue twice with hot HCl (5:95) and at least 10 times with hot water to insure complete removal of sodium salts.

(e) Transfer the paper and residue to a platinum crucible, and ignite for 15 to 20 minutes in a muffle furnace at 1100°C. (The ignition may be accomplished over a Meker or blast burner.) Cool in a desiccator and weigh.

(f) Wet the residue with a drop of water, and add a drop of $H_2SO_4$ and 10 ml. of HF. Evaporate slowly to dryness and repeat the ignition described in paragraph (e). Cool in a desiccator and weigh (Note 3).

NOTE 3.—When tungsten is present in the sample, the ignition temperature in this step should be 800°C.

(g) Carry a blank through the entire procedure starting with the same amount of $NaHSO_4$ as was used with the samples.

**Calculation.**—Calculate the percentage of silicon as follows:

$$\text{Silicon, \%} = \frac{(A - B - C) \times 0.4674}{D} \times 100$$

where $A$ = weight of crucible plus impure $SiO_2$ from paragraph (e),
       $B$ = weight of crucible plus impurities, from paragraph (f),
       $C$ = weight of $SiO_2$ determined in blank, obtained by subtracting weight in paragraph (f) from weight in paragraph (e) in the determination of the blank, and
       $D$ = grams of the sample used.

## TIN BY THE IODIMETRIC METHOD

This method is applicable to titanium alloys containing over 0.25% tin.

After dissolution of the sample in $HBF_4$ and $H_2SO_4$, titanium is oxidized with $H_2O_2$, HCl added, and the tin reduced with iron. The reduced tin is titrated with $KIO_3$ or iodine solution.

This method is satisfactory for tin in the range of 2.5 to 100 mg. per gram of sample.

Copper in excess of 0.5% interferes. No interference was found with 10% chromium, 6% molybdenum, 4% vanadium, or 1% tungsten.

**Reduction Apparatus. Type A.**—When tin is to be reduced to the stannous state and determined by titration with standard iodine or iodate solution, air must be excluded during the reduction and titration to prevent oxidation of the stannous tin. This is usually accomplished by keeping the solution under a blanket of gaseous $CO_2$. It may be accomplished in a variety of ways. One of the simplest methods is by means of the apparatus shown in Fig. 48-5 in which the reduction of the tin solution is made in a flask capped with a rubber stopper containing an L-shape siphon tube. When reduction is complete, the end of the siphon shall be dipped into a saturated solution of $NaHCO_3$ and set aside to cool. When cool, the stopper is removed and the solution titrated.

**Type B.**—For work of high accuracy, it is best to keep the tin solution under gaseous $CO_2$. Fig. 48-6 shows one of the many forms of apparatus that may be used when gaseous $CO_2$ is employed. It consists of a flask closed with a three-hole rubber stopper containing an inlet tube for $CO_2$, an air condenser, and a hole for the burette (glass plugged). During reduction a very slow stream of $CO_2$ is passed through the flask. When reduction is complete, the flow is increased to maintain a protecting blanket of $CO_2$ during the cooling and titration.

**Reagents.—Fluoboric Acid (48 to 50%).**

**Iron Powder.—**Iron powder, reduced by hydrogen, of such purity that it will dissolve in HCl leaving a negligible residue.

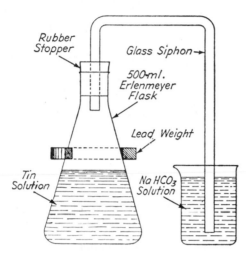

FIG. 48-5. Apparatus for Reduction of Tin, Type *A*.

**Antimony Trichloride (10 g. per liter).—**Dissolve 1 g. of $SbCl_3$ in 20 ml. of HCl and dilute to 100 ml.

**Sodium Bicarbonate Solution (100 g. per liter).—**Dissolve 100 g. of $NaHCO_3$ in water and dilute to 1 liter.

**Marble Chips.**

**Starch Solution (10 g. per liter).**

**Titanium, Low-Tin.—**Tin content less than 0.005%.

**Standard Tin Solution (1 ml. = 0.001 g. Sn).—**Dissolve 1.0000 g. of tin [66] in a covered 400-ml. beaker in 300 ml. of HCl (1:1) by warming gently until the metal has dissolved. If solution is difficult, add 0.05 to 0.1 g. of $KClO_3$. Cool, and dilute to 1 liter in a volumetric flask.

**Standard Potassium Iodate Solution (0.02 N).—**Standardize against synthetic standards containing approximately the same amount of tin as the samples to be tested. Prepare the standards by adding standard tin solution to 1-g. portions of low-tin titanium and carrying them through the procedure described below.

**Standard Iodine Solution (0.02 N).—**Standardize as for the $KIO_3$ solution.

**Procedure.—**(*a*) Transfer 1.00 g. of the sample to a 500-ml. Erlenmeyer flask and

---

[66] National Bureau of Standards standard sample No. 42*e* of standard melting point tin is satisfactory for this purpose.

add 60 ml. of water, 10 ml. of $H_2SO_4$ (1:1), and 10 ml. of $HBF_4$. Warm gently until dissolution is complete. Oxidize by dropwise addition of $H_2O_2$ to the appearance of a light straw color. Add 150 ml. of water, 5 g. of iron powder (Note 1), 60 ml. of HCl, and 2 drops of $SbCl_3$ solution. Stopper with the special stopper of Apparatus Type $A$ or $B$, heat gently until all of the iron powder has dissolved, and boil briefly. Place the flask in a cooling bath with the outlet of the siphon tube immersed in the $NaHCO_3$ solution. When the solution is cold, rapidly remove the stopper and add a few marble chips and a few ml. of starch solution (Note 2).

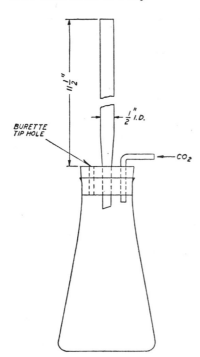

BURETTE
TIP HOLE

$1\frac{1}{2}$″

$\frac{1}{2}$″ I.D.

CO$_2$

FIG. 48-6.   Apparatus for Reduction of Tin, Type $B$.

NOTE 1.—Nickel strip may be used instead of iron powder to effect the reduction of the tin.

NOTE 2.—Instead of marble chips, sodium bicarbonate tablets (5-grain) have been found satisfactory. Start with two tablets and when dissolved add one or two more. Keep adding one or two tablets to maintain a blanket of CO$_2$ over the solution during the titration.

(b) Titrate rapidly with the 0.02 $N$ $KIO_3$ or 0.02 $N$ iodine solution to the first faint blue color. Determine a blank by carrying a 1.0-g. portion of low-tin titanium through the entire procedure.

**Calculation.**—Calculate the percentage of tin as follows:

$$\text{Tin, }\% = \frac{(A - B)C}{D} \times 100$$

where $A$ = milliliters of 0.02 $N$ $KIO_3$ or 0.02 $N$ iodine solution required to titrate the sample,

$B$ = milliliters of $KIO_3$ or iodine solution required to titrate the blank,

$C$ = tin equivalent of the $KIO_3$ or iodine solution, in grams per milliliter, and

$D$ = grams of sample used.

## TUNGSTEN BY THE DITHIOL (PHOTOMETRIC) METHOD

This method covers the determination of tungsten in titanium and titanium-base alloys in the range from 0.005 to 1.0%.

The sample is obtained in a sulfuric-citric acid solution, and molybdenum is removed by extraction with dithiol and chloroform. Tungsten is reduced by heating with hydrochloric acid and stannous chloride, and a blue compound is formed by the addition of dithiol. The blue compound is extracted with butyl acetate and measured photometrically at 635 m$\mu$.

The recommended concentration range is from 0.001 to 0.05 mg. of tungsten in 20 ml. of butyl acetate, using a cell depth of 2.0 cm. (Note 1).

NOTE 1.—This procedure has been written for a cell having a 2.0-cm. light path. Cells having other dimensions may be used provided suitable adjustments can be made in the amount of sample and reagents used.

The color is stable for several hours if protected from direct sunlight and if evaporation of the solvent is prevented. The color has a slight temperature sensitivity between 20° and 40°C., amounting to about 0.2% per degree Centigrade.

Provision has been made for the removal of all commonly encountered interfering elements. A filtration will be required if combinations of molybdenum and copper in excess of 0.25% each are present.

**Apparatus.—Steam Bath,** capable of holding separatory funnels.

**Reagents.—Butyl Acetate.**

**Chloroform ($CHCl_3$).**

**Dithiol Solution (2 g. per liter).—**Dissolve 5 g. of sodium hydroxide (NaOH) in 50 ml. of water and dilute to 500 ml. with water. Add 1 g. of 3,4-dimercaptotoluene (dithiol) (Note 2).

NOTE 2.—Storage for longer than one week, even under refrigeration, is not recommended. It is better to prepare a fresh batch of solution for each group of samples.

**Ferric Sulfate Solution (50 g. per liter).—**Transfer 5 g. of ferric sulfate ($Fe_2(SO_4)_3 \cdot xH_2O$) to a 250-ml. beaker and dissolve by heating with 90 ml. of $H_2SO_4$ (1:9). Dilute to 100 ml. with $H_2SO_4$ (1:9).

**Stannous Chloride Solution (200 g. per liter).—**Dissolve 100 g. of stannous chloride ($SnCl_2 \cdot 2H_2O$) and 5 mg. of cupric chloride ($CuCl_2 \cdot 2H_2O$) in 400 ml. of HCl (1:1) by heating on a steam bath. Cool and dilute to 500 ml. with HCl (1:1).

**Sulfuric-Citric Acid Solution.—**Dissolve 20 g. of citric acid monohydrate in 500 ml. of $H_2SO_4$ (1:3), and dilute to 1 liter with $H_2SO_4$ (1:3).

**Sulfuric-Sulfurous Acid Solution.—**Saturate $H_2SO_4$ (1:3) with sulfur dioxide ($SO_2$) gas.

**Tungsten, Standard Solution (1 ml. = 0.100 mg. W).—**Transfer 0.1794 g. of sodium tungstate ($Na_2WO_4 \cdot 2H_2O$) to a 100-ml. volumetric flask, dilute to the mark with water, and mix well. Pipette 10 ml. into a 100-ml. volumetric flask, dilute to the mark with water, and mix well. The final dilute solution should be prepared as needed.

**Preparation of Calibration Curve.—**(a) Prepare a standard tungsten solution containing titanium as follows: Transfer 0.2 g. of titanium metal low in tungsten and molybdenum to a 125-ml. Erlenmeyer flask, add 20 ml. of $H_2SO_4$ (1:3) and 2 or 3 drops of HF; heat gently until the sample is dissolved, and add 10 ml. of tungsten solution (1 ml. = 0.100 mg. W).

(b) Add 30% $H_2O_2$ dropwise until the purple color of reduced titanium is discharged and a permanent yellow color of peroxidized titanium is formed. Evaporate the solution to fumes and cool.

(c) Add 50 ml. of sulfuric-citric acid solution and digest a few minutes to obtain a clear solution. Cool, transfer the solution to a 100-ml. volumetric flask, and dilute to the mark with $H_2SO_4$ (1:3).

(d) To each of five 250-ml. separatory funnels add 25 ml. of $H_2SO_4$ (1:3). Transfer 1.0, 2.0, 3.0, and 5.0 ml. of the standard tungsten-titanium solution prepared in paragraphs (a) through (c) to four of the funnels and use the fifth as a blank. Add 0.2 ml. of $Fe_2(SO_4)_3$ solution.

(e) Add 50 ml. of HCl and 5 ml. of $SnCl_2$ solution to the funnel, and place in the steam bath. Heat for 3 minutes, add 15 ml. of dithiol solution, mix well, and heat for 10 minutes. Cool the solution in a cold water bath and add exactly 20 ml. of butyl acetate from a pipette. Shake for 20 seconds, allow the layers to separate, drain the acid layer, and discard it.

(*f*) Transfer the butyl acetate layer to a dry test tube and stopper the tube.

**Photometry.**—Transfer a portion of reference (blank) solution to an absorption cell and adjust the photometer to the initial setting, using a light band centered at approximately 635 m$\mu$. While maintaining this photometric adjustment, take the photometric reading of the sample solution.

**Calibration Curve.**—Plot the photometric readings of the calibration solutions against milligrams of tungsten per 20 ml. of solution.

**Procedure.**—(*a*) Transfer 0.2 g. of the sample, weighed to the nearest 0.5 mg. (Note 3), to a 125-ml. Erlenmeyer flask and add 20 ml. of H$_2$SO$_4$ (1:3) and 2 or 3 drops of HF. Heat gently until the sample is dissolved. Carry through a blank on all reagents.

NOTE 3.—For material containing 0.5 to 1.0% tungsten, use 0.1 g. of the sample.

(*b*) Proceed as described in "Preparation of the Calibration Curve" (*b*) and (*c*).

(*c*) Add 7.5 ml. of H$_2$SO$_4$ (1:1), 5 ml. of H$_2$SO$_4$-H$_2$SO$_3$ solution, and 0.2 ml. of Fe$_2$(SO$_4$)$_3$ solution to a 250-ml. separatory funnel. Transfer a suitable aliquot (Note 4) of the prepared sample to the funnel, and place the funnel in a water bath maintained at 30° to 40°C.

NOTE 4.—A suitable aliquot will contain less than 0.050 mg. of tungsten, and not more than 0.5 mg. of molybdenum or 20 mg. of iron.

(*d*) Add 5 ml. of dithiol solution, shake for 5 to 10 seconds, and allow to stand for 5 minutes in the water bath. Cool, add 10 ml. of chloroform, shake for 40 seconds, allow the layers to separate, and drain and discard the chloroform layer. Repeat the extraction with 5 ml. of chloroform (Note 5).

NOTE 5.—Filtration of the acid layer through glass wool into a 250-ml. separatory funnel is necessary at this point if insoluble dithiol complexes (primarily copper) are present. The filtration is conveniently accomplished by connecting the stem of the funnel to a glass tube containing glass wool and inserting the tube through a 2-hole stopper into a second funnel; suction is applied through the other hole.

(*e*) Place the separatory funnel in a steam bath for 10 minutes, cool in a 30 to 40°C. water bath, add 2.5 ml. of dithiol solution, and shake for 5 to 10 seconds. Return the funnel to the water bath and allow to stand for 5 minutes.

(*f*) Cool, add 5 ml. of chloroform, shake for 40 seconds, allow the layers to separate, and drain and discard the chloroform layer. Repeat the extraction with another 5 ml. of chloroform, finally discarding the chloroform layer (Note 6).

NOTE 6.—These treatments should suffice to remove about 0.5 mg. of molybdenum. More molybdenum will require additional treatments.

(*g*) Place the funnel in a steam bath and heat for 15 minutes (Note 7).

NOTE 7.—The 15-minute heating period is required to remove sulfur dioxide (SO$_2$), which inhibits the tungsten color development, and to remove the chloroform, which would increase the volume of solvent used to extract the tungsten dithiol complex.

(*h*) Proceed as described in "Preparation of the Calibration Curve" (*e*) and (*f*).

**Photometry.**—Transfer a portion of the reference solution (reagent blank) to an absorption cell and adjust the photometer to the initial setting, using a light band centered at approximately 635 m$\mu$. While maintaining this photometric adjustment, take the photometric reading of the sample solution.

**Calculation.**—Convert the photometric reading of the sample solution to milligrams of tungsten by means of the calibration curve. Calculate the percentage of tungsten as follows:

$$\text{Tungsten, } \% = \frac{A}{B \times 10}$$

where $A$ = milligrams of tungsten from calibration curve, and
$B$ = grams of sample represented in the sample or aliquot used.

## METHODS FOR TITANIUM IN ANALYSES
## IN OTHER CHAPTERS

| | |
|---|---|
| Titanium in Aluminum Alloys | See Analysis of Aluminum Alloys |
| Titanium in Bauxite | See Analysis of Bauxite (Aluminum Chapter) |
| Titanium in Hydrated Alumina | See Analysis of Hydrated Alumina |
| Titanium in Calcined Alumina | See Analysis of Calcined Alumina |
| Titanium in Alloys by Ion Exchange | See Method in Chromium Chapter |
| Titanium in Phosphorus Ores | See Analysis of Phosphorus Ores |

# Chapter 49

# TUNGSTEN*

W, *at. wt.* 183.85; *sp. gr.* 19.3; *m.p.* 3410°C.; *b.p.* 5900°C.; *oxides,* $WO_2$ (brown); $WO_3$ (yellow); *acids,* $H_2WO_4$, orthotungstic; $H_2W_4O_{13}$, metatungstic

The element occurs in rocks high in silica. It is found commonly associated in form of tungstate with calcium, copper, iron and manganese. It occurs as sulfide, $WS_2$. The more important minerals are ferberite, $FeWO_4$; hübnerite, $MnWO_4$; wolframite, $(FeMn)WO_4$; scheelite, $CaWO_4$; cuproscheelite, $(CaCu)WO_4$; tungstenite, $WS_2$; stolzeit, $PbWO_4$. In addition to the evaluation of the tungsten ores the chemist is called upon to determine tungsten in concentrates, in alloys—steels, ferrotungsten, silico-tungsten, tungstic oxide, tungsten powder, alkali tungstates, and high purity metals such as niobium, tantalum, titanium, zirconium, and their alloys.

Tungsten was discovered by Scheele (1781) in the mineral calcium tungstate named scheelite after the discoverer. The metal stands at the top of the list in melting point (3370°C.), a property that led to its use in filaments of the incandescent lamp. High speed cutting tools contain 18–20% of tungsten. Tungsten steel is used in springs, valves, axles, magnetos, phonograph needles, contact points, spark plugs, steel rails and numerous products where strength, hardness, durability, resistance to corrosion, high melting point are essential. The hardest cutting tool, Carbaloy, is the carbide of tungsten ($W_2C$). Sodium tungstate is used as a mordant and to fireproof fabrics.

## DETECTION

*Minerals.*—The finely powdered material is decomposed by treating with mixed acids according to the procedure given for ores. Tungsten is precipitated with cinchonine, the precipitate filtered off and dissolved in ammonium hydroxide, then acidified with hydrochloric acid and reprecipitated with cinchonine as described.

Tungsten oxide may be confirmed as follows:

1. The residue is suspended in dilute hydrochloric acid and a piece of zinc, aluminum, or tin placed in the solution. In the presence of tungsten a blue-colored solution or precipitate is seen, the color disappearing upon dilution with water.

2. A portion of the precipitate is warmed with ammonium hydroxide and the extracts absorbed with strips of filter paper.

(*a*) A strip of this treated paper is moistened with dilute hydrochloric acid and warmed. In the presence of tungstic acid a yellow coloration is produced.

* Based on a chapter in the Fifth Edition, revised and rewritten by Arnold R. Gahler, Research and Development Analytical Laboratory, Union Carbide Metals Co., Niagara Falls, N. Y.

(*b*) A second strip of paper is moistened with a solution of stannous chloride. A blue color is produced in the presence of tungsten.

(*c*) A third strip dipped into cold ammonium sulfide remains unchanged until warmed, when the paper turns green or blue if tungsten is present.

*Iron, Steel and Alloys.*—These decomposed with concentrated hydrochloric acid followed by nitric acid as directed under "Preparation and Solution of the Sample" leave a yellow residue in the presence of tungsten. If this residue is digested with warm ammonium hydroxide and the extract evaporated to dryness a yellow compound, $WO_3$, will remain if tungsten is present. This oxide may be reduced in the reducing flame to the blue-colored oxide.

*Detection with Dithiol.*[1]—Dissolve 10 mg. of steel by heating in a test tube with 0.15 ml. $H_3PO_4$ (sp. gr. 1.75) and 0.07 ml. of $HClO_4$ (sp. gr. 1.68). Add further 0.1 ml. of $HClO_4$ and 0.2 ml. of 80% $H_2SO_4$ and expel, first, the excess water, and then the $HClO_4$. Raise the temperature until the sulfuric acid fumes cool, and add 1 ml. of concentrated HCl, 100 mg. of stannous chloride, and heat for 5 minutes at 70°C. Add 0.25 of isoamyl acetate and about 5 mg. of dithiol. Heat in water bath at 70°C. for 5 to 10 minutes, shaking tube vigorously at intervals. Add a little more dithiol and heat for an additional 5 minutes. The color in the organic layer ranges from pale blue to deep emerald-green for 0.5 to 25 micrograms of tungsten.

## ESTIMATION

The material should be finely ground for analysis. The minerals hübnerite and scheelite decompose easily, ferberite not so readily and wolframite with difficulty. The alloys require special treatment according to the composition.

In analytical procedures some tungsten as $WO_3$ may be found with the $SiO_2$ residue. The oxide is readily volatile at 900°C. The residue of $WO_3$ (and $SiO_2$) should be ignited to not over 750°C. The tungsten remaining in solution from the silica and tungsten residue will not precipitate completely with iron and alumina when $NH_4OH$ is added to the solution; unless provision has been made for its previous removal, some may pass into solution of the alkaline earth group causing error there. Separation of tungsten must be made in the initial steps of analysis.

Details of preparation and solution of the materials containing tungsten follow later.

## PREPARATION AND SOLUTION OF THE SAMPLE

For solution of the sample the following facts should be kept in mind regarding solubilities:

The metal is practically insoluble in HCl and $H_2SO_4$. It is slowly attacked by $HNO_3$, aqua regia and by alkalies. It is readily soluble in a mixture of $HNO_3$ and HF to form $WF_6$ or $WOF_4$.

*Oxides.*—$WO_2$ is soluble in hot HCl and in hot $H_2SO_4$ (red soln.) also in KOH (red soln.). The oxide $WO_3$ is scarcely soluble in acids, but is readily soluble in KOH, $K_2CO_3$, and in $NH_4OH$, $(NH_4)_2CO_3$, $(NH_4)_2S_x$ unless strongly ignited, when it is insoluble. Both the acid and the alkali solutions deposit the blue oxide on standing.

[1] Miller, C. A., Analyst, **69**, 109, 1944.

*Acids.*—Ortho tungstates. A few are soluble in water and in acids. The alkali salts only slightly soluble. The metatungstates are easily soluble in water. Tungstates are precipitated from alkali salts by dilute $H_2SO_4$, HCl, $HNO_3$, as yellow $WO_3 \cdot H_2O$ or white $WO_3 \cdot 2H_2O$. Metatungstates are not precipitated by cold acids, but are precipitated by boiling and by long standing.

*Solution of Minerals.*—The material may be decomposed by acid treatment as described on page 1162. Use of a fusion as a means of decomposition of tungsten ores preliminary to either the qualitative detection or the quantitative determination of tungsten may also be employed. The precipitation of tungsten by boiling with acids in presence of considerable amounts of alkali salts (such as result from acidification of a fusion) is feasible if the solution is diluted sufficiently. When the amount of tungsten present is small, and especially if the ore contains much phosphorus, there is small likelihood that any of the tungsten will be precipitated. The use of cinchonine is necessary in order completely to precipitate tungsten under these conditions; ferric iron has a retarding effect on the cinchonine precipitation.

## SEPARATIONS

*Separation of Tungsten from Silica.*—The oxide of tungsten, as ordinarily obtained, is frequently contaminated with silica. The removal of silica is accomplished by heating the mixture in a platinum dish with sulfuric and hydrofluoric acids and volatilizing the silica. After taking to dryness and igniting gently, the last traces of sulfuric acid are expelled by adding ammonium carbonate and again igniting.

The dehydration of silica by slow evaporation with $HClO_4$, heating to fumes of $HClO_4$ and a temperature of 205°C. is an effective procedure.

In presence of small amounts of silica (0.1 to 0.2%) and large amounts of tungsten (75 to 85%) J. A. Holladay recommends evaporation with sulfuric and phosphoric acids, filtration to remove the bulk of the tungsten, and subsequent ignition and volatilization with sulfuric and hydrofluoric acids.

*Separation from Tin.*—The weighed residue is mixed with six to eight times its weight of ammonium chloride (free from non-volatile residue) in a platinum crucible, placed in a larger crucible, both vessels being covered. Heat is applied until no more vapors of ammonium chloride are evolved. Additional ammonium chloride is added and the treatment is repeated three times. The fourth treatment is followed by weighing of the residue and the treatment repeated once more. If no further loss of weight takes place it is assumed that all the stannic oxide has been driven off. The inner crucible is now placed directly over the flame and heated to dull redness for a few minutes and the oxide, $WO_3$, weighed.

*Separation of Tungsten from Arsenic and Phosphorus.*—Both arsenic and phosphorus may be precipitated by cold magnesia mixture in an ammoniacal solution, tungsten remaining in solution. The separation of arsenic is difficult, as it is tenaciously retained by tungsten as a complex salt. The following process is outlined by Kehrmann.[2]

One to 2 g. of the sample are fused with twice as much sodium hydroxide as is required to combine with the arsenic oxide, the resulting cake is dissolved in a little water and boiled in an Erlenmeyer flask for 0.5 hour. After cooling, three

[2] Kehrmann, F., Ber., **20,** 1813, 1887.

times as much ammonium chloride as is needed to form chlorides with the alkalies present is added, and then ammonium hydroxide equal to one-fourth the volume of the solution under investigation, followed by sufficient magnesia mixture, added cold, drop by drop with constant stirring. After settling several hours, the solution is filtered and the residue washed with a weak solution of ammonia and ammonium nitrate. It is advisable to dissolve the residue in dilute acid and repeat the precipitation several times. The filtrates containing the tungsten are combined and concentrated by evaporation if necessary.

NOTE.—Low values for phosphorus are apt to be obtained when the material to be tested contains $WO_3$ and is fused with NaOH, $Na_2O_2$, etc.

*Volatilization of Molybdenum with Dry Hydrochloric Acid Gas. Pechard's Process.*[3]—The procedure depends upon the fact that molybdenum oxide heated in a current of dry hydrochloric acid gas at 250 to 270°C. is sublimed, whereas tungsten is not affected.

The oxides of the two elements, or their sodium salts, are placed in a porcelain boat and heated in a hard glass tube, one end of which is bent vertically downward and connected with a Peligot tube containing a little water. A current of dry hydrochloric acid gas is conducted over the material, heated to 250 to 270°C. From time to time the sublimate of molybdenum ($MoO_3 \cdot 2HCl$) is driven towards the Peligot tube by careful heating with a free flame. This enables the analyst to observe whether any more sublimate is driven out of the sample and to ascertain when the tungsten is freed of molybdenum. From one and a half to two hours are generally sufficient to accomplish the separation. If sodium salt is present it is leached out of the residue, and is then ignited to $WO_3$. Molybdenum may be determined in the sublimate.

*Separation from Molybdenum.*—Trace amounts of molybdenum in a cold (below 10°C.) 4 N HCl solution with chlorostannous acid as reductant are extracted as the dithiol complex into amyl acetate. Increasing the acidity to 9 to 11 N HCl, the tungsten dithiol complex is extracted into amyl acetate and the concentration measured spectrophotometrically. (Refer to "Colorimetric Dithiol Method for the Determination of Tungsten in Tantalum and Niobium.")

In a cold (12 to 20°C.) sulfuric acid-phosphoric acid medium the molybdenum dithiol complex can be extracted into petroleum ether in the absence of chlorostannous acid. The concentration of the sulfuric acid should be between 6 and 14 N. Subsequent extraction of tungsten from the aqueous solution may be achieved by reducing the acidity to a pH range between 0.5 to 2.0.[4]

*Separation from Vanadium.*[5]—Tungstic and vanadic acids are precipitated with $HgNO_3$ and HgO, the moist precipitate dissolved in HCl and the solution largely diluted; $WO_3$ is precipitated free from vanadium.

*Separation from Titanium.*—Powell, Schoeller and Jahn found that the following method gives quantitative results.[6]

The mixed oxides (about 0.25 g.) are fused with 3 g. of $Na_2CO_3$ in platinum for 20 minutes. The crucible and contents, when cold, are placed in a nickel dish containing 10 g. NaOH in 50 ml. of water. The covered dish is placed on a boiling water bath for 2–3 hours, and the water lost by evaporation is replaced. The

3 Pechard, E., Comp. rend., **114**, 173, 1891.
4 Allen, S. H., and Hamilton, M. B., Anal. Chim. Acta, **7**, 483, 1952.
5 Friedheim, Chem. News, **61**, 220, 1890.
6 Analyst, **60**, 506, 1935.

crucible is cleaned and rinsed with 50 ml. of hot water. The solution is allowed to cool or to stand overnight. The residue (A) is washed with half-saturated NaCl solution.

The filtrate is treated with diluted HCl until phenolphthalein is decolorized, then heated on the water bath, and the red color is discharged from time to time with a few drops of the acid. The precipitate (B) is washed in the same way as (A).

Precipitates A and B are treated with a little normal HCl, and after dilution to 100 ml., the titania is recovered by heating, making the solution ammoniacal, filtering, washing with $NH_4NO_3$ solution, and ignition. Unless the precipitate is small, it is leached with dilute acid, reprecipitated, etc.

The tungsten in the combined filtrates from the titania precipitate is recovered in the usual manner.

**Separation of Tungsten from Iron.**—The procedure is given under "Preparation and Solution of the Sample," Iron, Steel and Alloys. The impure oxide $WO_3$ is fused with $Na_2CO_3$ and the melt extracted with water. $Fe(OH)_3$ remains on the filter. The filtrate is evaporated to dryness with $HNO_3$ and the residue extracted with water. The insoluble $WO_3$ is washed with 2% HCl solution, then dissolved in $NH_4OH$ and tungsten determined in the solution.

**Separation of Tungsten from Uranium.**[7]—The sample is evaporated with nitric acid nearly to dryness, 5 ml. of $HNO_3$ is added and the uranium is dissolved out by extraction with ether.

**Separation of Tungsten from Lead.**—In the acid attack if sulfates are present lead sulfate will remain with tungsten. Tungsten is separated by dissolving with $NH_4OH$. Lead remains in the residue. Any entrained lead in the tungsten filtrate may be separated by precipitation as sulfide by addition of ammonium sulfide, tungsten remaining in solution.

**Separation of Tungsten from Nickel, Chromium, Cobalt, Iron, Titanium, Molybdenum, Niobium, and Tantalum by Anion Exchange.**—By use of an anion-exchange separation techniques involving elutions with various eluents as described under the separation and determination of nickel, chromium, cobalt, iron, titanium, tungsten, molybdenum, niobium, and tantalum in a high temperature alloy by anion exchange, tungsten can be performed.[8, 9]

## GRAVIMETRIC METHODS

Since there is no highly commendable titrimetric method for determining tungsten, the gravimetric methods are preferred.

The element is determined as tungstic oxide, $WO_3$. It may be isolated preferably by precipitation with cinchonine, or in the form of tungstic acid, ammonium tungstate, or as mercurous tungstate, in the usual course of analysis, all of which forms may be readily changed by ignition to the oxide, $WO_3$.

The oxide, $WO_3$, may be contaminated with Ag, Fe, Mo, P, Cr, Si, Sn, Sb, Nb or Ta compounds. The pure oxide upon fusion with $Na_2CO_3$ and extraction with water leaves no residue. Na, K and $NH_4$ salts, P, As, and Mo retard precipitation. A temperature of 750°C. is necessary for dehydration of tungstic acid. The ignition temperature should not exceed 850°C. due to the volatility of $WO_3$.

See "Determinations in Specific Substances."

[7] Pierle, C. A., Jour. Ind. Eng. Chem., **12**, 61–63, 1920.
[8] Hague, J. L., Brown, E. D., and Bright, H. A., J. of Res. NBS, **53**, 261, 1954.
[9] Wilkins, D. H., Talanta, **2**, 355, 1959.

## COLORIMETRIC/PHOTOMETRIC METHODS

Several reagents are commonly used for the colorimetric determination of tungsten. The systems of most importance include tungsten with dithiol (toluene-3,4-dithiol), and thiocyanate. The dithiol system is sensitive and more specific than the other systems. It is especially useful for the determination of traces of tungsten in high-purity titanium, niobium, tantalum, and zirconium metals. The dithiol and thiocyanate complexes with tungsten are extractable into organic solvents, thus removing interferences from colored ions such as chromium and nickel.

## DITHIOL METHOD

Dithiol (toluene-3,4-dithiol) forms a highly colored complex with tungsten in the presence of a reductant in 9 to 11 $N$ HCl which can be extracted with immiscible organic solvents such as amyl acetate and butyl acetate. The absorbance of the blue-green system, which follows Beer's Law, is measured near 640 m$\mu$. Molybdenum, if present, must first be removed in some manner preferably by extraction with dithiol into the organic solvent from a cold solution 4 $N$ or less in HCl. After increasing the acidity to 9 to 11 $N$, the tungsten is extracted. The method is not applicable in the presence of large concentrations of molybdenum because of the difficulty in removal of the molybdenum. Tungsten is extracted from aqueous solutions containing hydrofluoric, hydrochloric, and sulfuric acids. Traces of nitric acid must be removed. Another procedure involves extraction of tungsten from a sulfuric-phosphoric acid mixture without the presence of stannous chloride.[14] The dithiol procedure with various modifications has been applied to the determination of tungsten in titanium,[10,11,12] tantalum,[10] niobium, zirconium,[10] steels,[11,13] and biological materials.[14] Several salts of dithiol are now commercially available of greater solubility than dithiol. The solutions of the dithiol salts, however, are relatively instable and should be prepared fresh before use.

For application of this method see "Determinations in Specific Substances."

## THIOCYANATE METHOD

Tungsten(VI) in a sulfuric-hydrochloric acid solution with thiocyanate and a reducing agent such as stannous chloride forms a yellow complex with tungsten(V) which follows Beer's Law with maximum absorption near 400 m$\mu$.[15,16,17,18,19] The colored complex may be developed and measured in either an aqueous or 60% acetone solution, or it can be extracted into isopropyl or ethyl ether.

Color development for the aqueous system is best in a solution at least 8 $M$ in chloride, 0.2 $M$ in thiocyanate, and 10 $M$ in total acid concentration. Careful

[10] Greenberg, P., Anal. Chem., **29**, 896, 1957.
[11] Machlan, L. A., and Hague, J. L., J. of Research of the National Bureau of Standards, **0**, 415, 1947.
[12] Short, H. G., Analyst, **76**, 710, 1951.
[13] Standard Methods of Analysis of Iron, Steel and Ferro-Alloys, p. 127, United Steel Companies, Ltd., Lund, Humphries & Co., Ltd., Publisher, 1951.
[14] Allen, S. H., and Hamilton, M. B., Anal. Chim. Acta, **7**, 483, 1952.
[15] Sandell, E. B., Colorimetric Determination of Traces of Metals, 3rd Ed., pp. 886–889, Interscience Publishers, Inc., 1959.
[16] Clark, S. G., Analyst, **52**, 466, 1927.
[17] Crouthamel, C. E., and Johnson, C. E., Anal. Chem., **26**, 1228, 1954.
[18] Freund, H., Wright, M. L., and Brookshier, R. K., Anal. Chem., **23**, 781, 1951.
[19] Geld, I., and Carroll, J., Anal. Chem., **21**, 1098, 1949.

control of temperature to within 5°C. insures better color development and color stability.

The most serious interference in the aqueous colored system is vanadium which can be removed by a cupferron separation in the presence of fluoride.[16] It is advantageous to determine tungsten in aqueous solution if large amounts of niobium and titanium are present because of their interference in the organic system. The fact that tungsten and niobium both form complexes, the color of which can be measured in 20 volume per cent acetone medium, is the basis of a method for the simultaneous spectrophotometric method for these elements in complex alloys and stainless steels.[20] In this method the total absorbance from both elements is measured, oxalate is added to bleach the niobium color and the absorbance due to tungsten alone is then measured. The niobium concentration is then related to the differences in the two absorbance readings. Tantalum, titanium, and molybdenum do not interfere under the conditions of the method. Since the molybdenum complex fades rapidly in a 10 normal acid solution, from 75 to 100 times more molybdenum than tungsten may be present without interference.

The thiocyanate method with variations has application for the determination of tungsten in complex alloy and stainless steels,[20] high temperature alloys,[19] silicate rocks,[15] ores, and biological materials.[15]

For applications of this method, see "Determinations in Specific Substances."

## DETERMINATIONS IN SPECIFIC SUBSTANCES

### DETERMINATION OF WO₃ IN LOW-GRADE TUNGSTEN ORES

This procedure is designed for the determination of $WO_3$ in low-grade Scheelite and similar ores containing from 0.25 to 2.5% $WO_3$. Fluorides may be present, but this method is not suitable when niobium, tantalum, or major amounts of phosphorus or tin are present. After decomposing the ore with HCl and HF, HClO₄ is added and the solution evaporated to fumes. $WO_3$ and $MoO_3$ are separated with cinchonine-α-benzoinoxime, ignited, weighed, the crude $WO_3$ purified, and corrected for $MoO_3$.

*Reagents.* **Cinchonine Solution.**—Dissolve 125 g. of the reagent in 1 liter of HCl (1:1), and filter.

**Alpha-benzoinoxime.**—Dissolve 5 g. of the reagent in 95 ml. of acetone and 5 ml. of cold water, and filter if not clear. Store in a cool place, and do not use if more than 5 days old.

**Ferric Sulfate Solution.**—Dissolve 80 g. of $Fe_2(SO_4)_3$ in 1 liter of $H_2SO_4$ (1 + 9).

**Sodium Thiocyanate Solution.**—Dissolve 50 g. of NaCNS in 1 liter of water.

**Stannous Chloride Solution.**—Dissolve 20 g. of $SnCl_2$ in 200 ml. of HCl (1 + 4).

**Sodium Molybdate Solution (1 ml. = Approx. 0.0005 g. of Mo).**—Dissolve 1.25 g. of $Na_2MoO_4 \cdot 2H_2O$ in 1 liter of $H_2SO_4$ (1 + 9).

*Procedure.*—Grind the ore in an agate mortar to pass a 200-mesh sieve, then dry for 1 to 2 hours at 105 to 110°C. Transfer 2.000 g. of the dried sample to a 600-ml. beaker. Add 5 ml. of water and stir to moisten all the ore. Add 100 ml. of HCl while stirring the residue to prevent caking. Cover and digest at approximately 65°C. with occasional stirring for 1 to 2 hours until there appears to be no further attack. Evaporate to about 40 ml., add 5 ml. of $HNO_3$, 20 ml. of HClO₄

[20] McDuffie, B., Bandi, W. R., and Melnick, L. M., Anal. Chem., **31**, 1311, 1959.

and 1.0 ml. of HF. Evaporate to dense fumes of $HClO_4$ and continue the fuming for about 5 minutes. Do not fume off all the $HClO_4$.

Cool, add 100 ml. of hot water and 1 g. of boric acid. Boil for a few minutes to expel free chlorine. Dilute to 200 ml. with hot water and add 5 ml. of cinchonine solution. Stir well, heat to boiling, then cool to $<20°C$. (Note 1). Add 10 ml. of molybdenum solution, some paper pulp, then 5 ml. of $\alpha$-benzoinoxime solution. Stir vigorously for several minutes, allow the precipitate to settle, then filter through an 11-cm. Whatman No. 40 filter paper or equivalent containing a little paper pulp. Reserve the precipitation beaker.

Wash the residue about 20 times with a wash solution containing 5 ml. of cinchonine solution and 5 ml. of $\alpha$-benzoinoxime solution per liter. Ignite in a 20-ml. platinum dish at a low temperature until the carbon is oxidized (Note 2). Cool, and moisten the residue with 5 ml. of water. Add 5 ml. of $HNO_3$ and 5 ml. of HF and evaporate just to dryness. Repeat the treatment with $HNO_3$ and HF and evaporate to about 2 ml. Add 10 ml. of $HClO_4$ and evaporate to dense fumes of $HClO_4$.

Cool and transfer to the reserved beaker. Wash the dish successively with hot water, a little hot NaOH solution (1:9), and finally with hot water. Dilute to 50 ml., add 5 ml. of cinchonine solution, heat to boiling, and boil for 3 to 5 minutes. Cool to $<20°C.$, then add 5 ml. of $\alpha$-benzoinoxime solution. Stir thoroughly, filter, and wash about 20 times with the cinchonine-$\alpha$-benzoinoxime wash solution.

Ignite in a 50-ml. platinum dish at a temperature of 500 to 600°C. to burn off the paper, then cool, add 2 ml. of HF, 10 drops of $HClO_4$, and evaporate to dryness. Again ignite, finally to constant weight at 750 to 800°C., cool, and weigh.

Add 2 g. of NaOH pellets and 20 ml. of water to the dish, stir, and warm until the $WO_3$ is dissolved. Transfer to a 150-ml. beaker with about 50 ml. of hot water. Heat to boiling and boil for a few minutes. Rinse the dish with a few drops of $H_2SO_4$ (1:1) and add to the beaker. Add 30 ml. of $NH_4OH$. Boil for a few minutes, cool, and filter through a 9-cm. Whatman No. 42 filter paper, catching the filtrate in a 250-ml. beaker. Wash about 15 times with $(NH_4)_2SO_4$ solution (20 g. per l.). Reserve the filtrate for the molybdenum determination.

Return the paper and precipitate to the beaker, add 25 ml. of HCl (1:9), heat to boiling, and repeat the precipitation with $NH_4OH$. Filter as before and wash about 20 times with the $(NH_4)_2SO_4$ wash solution. Add the filtrate and washings to the reserved filtrate.

Ignite the paper and residue in the platinum dish until the carbon is gone, then to constant weight at 750 to 800°C., cool, and weigh. The difference in the two weights represents "crude $WO_3$."

**Molybdenum Correction.**—(For high molybdenum, see Note 3 below.)

Add 20 ml. of tartaric acid solution (500 g. per l.) to the reserved filtrates, make just acid with $H_2SO_4$ (1:1), and add 10 ml. of ferric sulfate solution (80 g. per l.), cool to 25°C., add 5 ml. of NaCNS solution (100 g. per l.), 10 ml. of $SnCl_2$ solution, and sufficient $H_2SO_4$ (1:1) to give a solution containing $10\%$ $H_2SO_4$ by volume. Stir well, cool to 25°C., and transfer to a 250-ml. separatory funnel, using approximately 50 to 75 ml. of isopropyl ether (ethyl ether or butyl acetate may also be used). Stopper the funnel, shake vigorously for from 3 to 5 minutes, and let stand until the liquids have separated into two distinct layers. Draw off the lower or acid layer into the original beaker, and then the ethereal layer containing the molybdenum into a 100-ml. volumetric flask. Rinse the funnel with a few ml. of ether that has been prepared by shaking with 100 ml. of $H_2SO_4$ (1:9) containing 0.8 g. of $Fe_2(SO_4)_3$, 5 ml. of NaCNS, and 10 ml. of $SnCl_2$ as described in the method draw off the lower layer and discard. Return the solution from the original 250-ml. beaker to the funnel, shake with an additional 10 to 25 ml. of ether, and again draw off the lower layer. Add the ethereal layer to the main molybdenum solution in the 100-ml. volumetric flask, dilute to the mark with ether that has just been shaken with 100 ml. of $H_2SO_4$ (1:9) containing 0.8 g. of $Fe_2(SO_4)_3$, 5 ml. of NaCNS and 10 ml. of $SnCl_2$.

The ethereal solution should not contain more than 0.03 mg. of molybdenum per ml., and the solution should be allowed to stand for several minutes before measuring the absorbance of the solution at 470 m$\mu$ in a photometer.

Prepare a calibration curve with known amounts of molybdenum by adding from 0.1 to 3 mg. of molybdenum to 100 ml. of $H_2SO_4$ (1:9) containing 0.8 g. of $Fe_2(SO_4)_3$, and putting through all steps of the method. Calculate any molybdenum found to $MoO_3$.

**Calculation.**—Calculate the percentage of $WO_3$ as follows:

$$\frac{A - B}{C} \times 100 = \% \ WO_3$$

where $A$ = weight of "crude $WO_3$" in grams,
$\quad\quad B$ = grams of $MoO_3$ in "crude $WO_3$," and
$\quad\quad C$ = weight of sample taken in grams.

NOTES.—1. If the precipitate does not settle readily, add 2 ml. of HF, boil for 10 minutes, then add 2 g. of boric acid and again boil for 10 minutes.

2. For low-grade ores containing lead, treat a 1-g. sample as described in the preceding paragraph up to and including the first precipitation with alpha-benzoinoxime, filtration and washing; then ignite in porcelain at a temperature of 350 to 400°C. to burn off the paper, cool, and transfer to a 50-ml. platinum crucible. (If the ore contains an appreciable amount of $SiO_2$, add from 3 to 5 ml. of HF and 0.5 ml. of $H_2SO_4$ and evaporate to dryness.) Add 5 g. of $Na_2CO_3$, mix well, and fuse first at 800°C., then at about 1050 to 1100°C. for at least 10 minutes; allow to cool. Leach the fusion with 100 ml. of hot water, and filter through a 9-cm. paper containing a little ashless paper pulp into a 600-ml. beaker; wash the insoluble residue containing the lead about 20 times with $Na_2CO_3$ solution (10 g. per l.), and discard. Add an excess of 20 ml. of HCl to the filtrate and evaporate to a volume of approximately 50 ml.; then add 5 ml. of $HNO_3$ and 50 ml. of $HClO_4$, and continue the evaporation to dense fumes of $HClO_4$. Complete the determination of the tungsten as described in paragraph 3.

3. When the amount of molybdenum exceeds 0.01 g., it is determined in the NaOH filtrate as follows: Pass in a brisk stream of $H_2S$ for about 30 minutes; add a little paper pulp, and then, carefully, small amounts of tartaric acid solution, with stirring, until the solution is acid, finally adding an excess of from 3 to 5 ml. Heat just to boiling, allow to digest for 15 minutes at approximately 75°C., filter through an 11-cm. paper containing a little paper pulp, and wash the paper and precipitate about 15 times with hot water. Return the paper and precipitate to the beaker, add 50 ml. of water, from 2 to 3 g. of $Na_2O_2$, and stir until the molybdenum sulfide has dissolved; then again pass in $H_2S$ for at least 15 minutes. Acidify with tartaric acid, heat to boiling, and filter and wash as before.

Return the paper and precipitate to the beaker, add 25 ml. of $HNO_3$, 6 ml. of $H_2SO_4$ and 1 ml. of $HClO_4$, and heat until dense fumes of sulfur trioxide are freely evolved. Cool, add 10 ml. of water and several drops of $KMnO_4$ solution (25 g. per l.) and repeat the evaporation to fumes of sulfur trioxide. Add 100 ml. of cold water, cool to room temperature, and pass through a 9-in. Jones Reductor (that has just been cleaned with $H_2SO_4$ (2:98) into 25 ml. of ferric phosphate solution and 25 ml. of water in the reductor flask. The lower end of the reductor tube should dip beneath the surface of the solution in the flask. Wash first with 50 ml. of cold $H_2SO_4$ (5:95), finally with 100 ml. of water

Add a few drops of a 0.01 $M$ solution of $o$-phenanthroline, and titrate with 0.05 $N$ KMnO$_4$ (1 ml. = 0.0016 g. Mo) until clear or slightly green in color. Run a "blank" on the same amount of H$_2$SO$_4$ and water, and deduct. Calculate the molybdenum found to MoO$_3$ by multiplying by 1.5.

## DETERMINATION OF TUNGSTEN IN FERROTUNGSTEN AND TUNGSTEN METAL

This procedure is suitable for ferrotungsten, tungsten metal, and high-tungsten alloys that can be decomposed by the solution procedures described.

After decomposing the sample with Na$_2$O$_2$, the fusion is acidified with HCl, WO$_3$ precipitated with cinchonine-$\alpha$-benzoinoxime, reprecipitated, ignited, weighed, and corrected for Mo and other impurities.

**Reagents.** **Cinchonine Solution.**—Dissolve 125 g. of the reagent in 1 liter of HCl (1:1) and filter.

**Alpha-benzoinoxime Solution.**—Dissolve 5 g. of the reagent in 95 ml. of acetone and 5 ml. of water, and filter if not clear. Store in a cool place, and do not use if more than five days old. One ml. of this solution will precipitate 5 mg. of molybdenum.

**Ferric Sulfate Solution.**—Dissolve 80 g. of Fe$_2$(SO$_4$)$_3$ in 1 liter of H$_2$SO$_4$ (1:9).

**Sodium Thiocyanate Solution.**—Dissolve 50 g. of NaCNS in 1 liter of water.

**Stannous Chloride Solution.**—Dissolve 20 g. of SnCl$_2$ in 200 ml. of HCl (1:4).

**Sodium Molybdate Solution (1 ml. = approx. 0.0005 gram Mo).**—Dissolve 1.27 g. of Na$_2$MoO$_4$·2H$_2$O in 1 liter of H$_2$SO$_4$ (1:9).

**Procedure.**—Transfer 1.0000 g. of the sample crushed to pass an 80- or 100-mesh sieve to a nickel crucible containing 10 g. of dry Na$_2$O$_2$ (for alternate solution procedures see Note 1) and mix thoroughly with a small platinum or glass rod. Clean the rod by scraping with a small spatula, then cover the mixture with 1 or 2 g. of Na$_2$O$_2$. Put on goggles and rotate the crucible *around the outer edge of a gas flame* until the mass has blackened. As the mixture begins to fuse, rotate the crucible vigorously to stir up any particles adhering to its bottom or sides, and increase the temperature to about 900°C. for 3 to 5 minutes. Allow the crucible to cool almost to room temperature, cover with a nickel lid, and tap on a solid object to loosen the melt.

Transfer the cold cake to a *dry* 600-ml. beaker, cover, and add 65 ml. of HCl all at once. Rinse the crucible first with 10 ml. of HCl (1:1) and then thoroughly with warm water. Add the rinsings to the beaker. The melt does not dissolve rapidly in the strong acid, but the reaction is accelerated when the rinsings from the crucible are added. After the reaction has largely subsided, dilute to 150 ml. with hot water, and boil for about 3 minutes.

Dilute to 400 ml. with boiling water, add 10 ml. of cinchonine solution and some ashless paper pulp, and boil for about 5 minutes longer. Cool to room temperature, add with a pipette 5.0 ml. of sodium molybdate solution, then 5 ml. (or a sufficient amount) of alpha-benzoinoxime solution to precipitate any molybdenum that might be present. Stir vigorously for a few minutes, cool to 10 to 5°C. and allow to stand for at least 2 hours or preferably overnight. Filter through an 11-cm. Whatman No. 40 paper, or equivalent, containing a little paper pulp, and wash the paper and precipitate from 12 to 15 times with cold HCl (1:99) containing 5 ml. of cinchonine solution and 5 ml. of alpha-benzoinoxime solution per liter. Take care not to stir up the precipitate once it has been transferred to the filter paper.

Return the paper and precipitate to the original 600-ml. beaker, add 40 ml. o HCl (1:1), macerate the paper with a glass rod, and heat just short of boiling fo several minutes; then add 3 ml. of $HNO_3$, stir well, and continue the heating fo a few minutes longer. Dilute to 400 ml. with boiling water, add 5 ml. of cincho nine solution, boil for from 3 to 5 minutes, and cool to room temperature a before. Add 5 ml. of alpha-benzoinoxime solution, stir vigorously for several min utes, allow to settle, filter, and wash as previously described. Make sure that al the $WO_3$ is removed from the beaker.

Ignite in a 50-ml. platinum dish at a temperature of 500 to 600°C. until the carbon of the filter paper has been destroyed; then cool, add 1 ml. of $HNO_3$ and 1 to 2 ml. of HF, and carefully evaporate to dryness. Again ignite cautiously for a few minutes at 500 to 600°C. and then for 30 minutes (to constant weight) at 75( to 800°C.; cool and weigh.

Add 2 g. of NaOH pellets and 20 ml. of water to the dish, stir, and heat cau tiously until the $WO_3$ has dissolved completely. Transfer the solution to a 150-ml beaker using about 50 ml. of hot water, and rinse the dish with a few drops of ho HCl (1:1) and then with hot water, and add to the beaker. Add 30 ml. of $NH_4OH$ boil for a few minutes, filter through a 9-cm Whatman No. 40 paper containing a little paper pulp into a 200-ml. volumetric flask. Wash the paper and residue about 20 times with hot $NH_4Cl$ (50 g. per l.). Reserve the filtrate for molybdenum

Return the paper to the beaker, add 25 ml. of HCl (1:9), macerate the pape and heat just to boiling. Repeat the precipitation with $NH_4OH$. Filter and wasl as previously described. Discard the filtrate. Ignite the paper and residue in the 50-ml. platinum dish first at about 600°C. to burn off the paper, then at 750 t 800°C. for at least 15 minutes (to constant weight), cool, weigh. The differenc between the two weights represents "crude $WO_3$."

**Molybdenum Correction.**—Cool the solution in the 200-ml. volumetric flask t room temperature, dilute to the mark, and mix thoroughly. Withdraw a 20- t 50-ml. aliquot portion (not to contain more than 3 mg. of molybdenum), transfe to a 250-ml. beaker, and add 10 ml. of tartaric acid solution (500 g. per l.). Ad 10 ml. of $Fe_2(SO_4)_3$ solution and sufficient $H_2SO_4$ (1:1) to give a solution contair ing 10% of $H_2SO_4$ by volume, and cool to 25°C. Add 5 ml. of NaCNS solution 10 ml. of $SnCl_2$ solution, stir well, and transfer to a 300-ml. separatory funnel, usin approximately 75 ml. of isopropyl ether (ethyl or butyl acetate may also be used (Note 2). Stopper the funnel, and shake vigorously for several minutes. Releas the pressure by loosening the stopper, allow the two layers to separate, and dra off the lower or acid layer into the 250-ml. beaker and the ethereal layer into 100-ml. volumetric flask. Return the lower layer to the separatory funnel, add 1 to 25 ml. of isopropyl ether, stopper, and again shake well for several minute Again draw off the lower layer, combine the ethereal layer with that in the 100-ml flask, and dilute to the mark with ether that has just been shaken with 100 ml. o $H_2SO_4$ (1:9) containing 0.8 g. of $Fe_2(SO_4)_3$, 5 ml. of NaCNS, and 10 ml. of $SnCl_2$

Mix the molybdenum solution well, and measure the absorbance versus wate in a spectrophotometer. Refer to a curve set up on known amounts of molybdenur to obtain the amount of molybdenum in the aliquot portion taken.

Prepare a calibration curve with known amounts of molybdenum by addin from 0.1 to 3 mg. of molybdenum to 100 ml. of $H_2SO_4$ (1:9) containing 0.8 g. o $Fe_2(SO_4)_3$ and putting through all steps of the method. Calculate the amount o molybdenum found to a 1-gram basis, and multiply by 1.5 to obtain the corre sponding amount of $MoO_3$.

**Calculation.**—Calculate the percentage of tungsten as follows:

$$\frac{A - B \times 0.79298}{C} \times 100 = \% \ W$$

where $A$ = weight of "crude $WO_3$" in grams,
$B$ = grams of $MoO_3$ found in "crude $WO_3$," and
$C$ = weight of sample taken in grams.

Notes.—If precautions are used to prevent loss by spattering, the following solution procedure may be used.

Transfer 1.0000 g. of the 80- to 100-mesh sample to a 100-ml. platinum dish provided with a platinum cover, add 10 ml. of HF and then $HNO_3$ slowly and carefully from a dropping bottle until a complete solution is obtained. Remove and rinse the cover with water, and also rinse down the sides of the dish. Evaporate the solution on a steam bath until its volume has been reduced to about 5 ml., or just before tungsten salts begin to separate. Transfer the solution to a 100-ml. beaker containing 100 ml. of boric acid solution (40 g. per l.) and rinse the dish successively with hot water, 1 ml. of hot $NH_4OH$ (1:2), then hot water, 2 ml. of HCl, and finally hot water. Add 20 ml. of HCl, and boil for from 3 to 5 minutes. Dilute to 400 ml. with boiling water, add cinchonine, and proceed as described for the fusion method.

If butyl acetate is used, wash the ester layer once with 25 ml. of $H_2SO_4$ (1:9) saturated with butyl acetate and discard the washings.

## DETERMINATION OF TUNGSTEN AND MOLYBDENUM (NIOBIUM AND TANTALUM) IN ALLOYS

This method is designed for highly alloyed steels and complex alloys containing major amounts of niobium, tantalum, tungsten, and molybdenum.

After decomposing the sample with HCl, $HNO_3$, and $HClO_4$, tantalum and niobium are hydrolyzed and precipitated by boiling with $H_2SO_3$. Any soluble tungsten is precipitated with cinchonine and the combined precipitate (I) of niobium, tantalum, tungsten, and some molybdenum removed and treated with NaOH. Most of the niobium and tantalum is separated as the sodium salts and from the filtrate, the co-precipitated molybdenum is precipitated with $H_2S$ in tartaric acid solution. This sulfide precipitate is combined with the main molybdenum precipitate (II) which is separated from the filtrate from (I) by alpha-benzoinoxime, purified and weighed as $MoO_3$. The fraction of the niobium and tantalum soluble in NaOH is recovered by precipitation with cupferron in tartaric-formic solution and tungsten is precipitated in the filtrate after destroying the organic acids, ignited, and weighed as $WO_3$. $Nb_2O_5$ and $Ta_2O_5$ are recovered by hydrolysis and $Nb_2O_5$ determined by the $H_2O_2$ colorimetric procedure.

**Reagents. Cinchonine Solution.**—Dissolve 125 g. of cinchonine in 1 liter of HCl (1:1) and filter off any insoluble material.

**Cinchonine Wash Solution.**—Dilute 80 ml. of cinchonine solution to 1 liter with HCl (1:49).

**$H_2SO_4$-$H_3PO_4$ for Niobium Determination.**—Mix 500 ml. of $H_2SO_4$ with 500 ml. of $H_3PO_4$. Heat to 215 to 220°C. and hold at this temperature for 20 minutes. Cool and store in a glass-stoppered bottle.

### SOLUTION OF SAMPLE

**Procedure.**—1. Transfer 2 to 5 g. of the sample to a 400-ml. beaker, add 20 to 40 ml. of HCl and 10 to 20 ml. of $HNO_3$, cover the beaker, and heat gently until all action ceases. Then add from 30 to 50 ml. of $HClO_4$ and evaporate to light fumes. Cool somewhat, rinse the cover with 3 to 5 ml. of $HNO_3$ from a dropping bottle, add one ml. of HF, and swirl the beaker to mix the contents. Then with the aid of a glass rod and several more milliliters of $HNO_3$, wash down the sides until free of adhering $SiO_2$ and undissolved carbides.

2. With the cover still off, evaporate until the solution shows an orange-red color due to oxidized chromium. Cool and wash down the sides of the beaker with 5 ml. of a saturated solution of boric acid. Replace the cover on the beaker and again evaporate to strong fumes of $HClO_4$ (Note 1).

3. Cool, add 175 ml. of water, stir to dissolve salts, and add $H_2SO_3$ until the chromium is reduced, then 20 ml. in excess. Boil for 15 to 20 minutes. Add 15 ml. of cinchonine solution and some paper pulp and heat at 70 to 80°C. for 2 to 3 hours or until the supernatant liquid is perfectly clear.

4. Filter through an 11-cm. paper containing some paper pulp and wash about 20 times with cinchonine wash solution. Catch the filtrate in a 600-ml. beaker and reserve for the determination of molybdenum.

5. Transfer the paper and precipitate, which contain all the niobium, tantalum and tungsten, and small amounts of the molybdenum and titanium, back to the original beaker. Add 10 ml. of $HClO_4$ and 10 ml. of $HNO_3$ and heat, adding more $HNO_3$ if necessary, until all organic matter is destroyed. Cool somewhat, wash down the cover glass with 2 to 3 ml. of $HNO_3$ from a dropping bottle, then with the cover removed, evaporate to dryness, and heat for 10 minutes at a temperature of approximately 200°C.

6. Cool to room temperature, add 10.0 ml. of water and 0.5 g. of NaOH, boil for 5 minutes, then with the aid of a glass rod and a small piece of filter paper scrub all the adhering precipitate from the sides of the beaker. Again wash down the sides of the beaker with water and boil for 5 minutes. The sides and bottom of the beaker should now be perfectly clean, and all the tungsten and molybdenum along with varying amounts of niobium-tantalum, should be dissolved.

7. Dilute with 50 ml. of water and filter through a 9-cm. tight paper containing paper pulp. Wash about 20 times with NaOH (10 g./liter) catching the filtrate and washings in a 250-ml. beaker. Return the paper containing the insoluble niobium and tantalum salts, along with any titanium, to the 400-ml. beaker and reserve for the determination of niobium, tantalum, and titanium (paragraph 19).

8. Saturate the alkaline filtrate, which should have a volume of approximately 100 ml., with $H_2S$. This is assured by the formation of the dark straw-to-red color depending on the amount of molybdenum present. Add slowly tartaric acid solution (200 g./liter) until just acid-to-litmus, then an excess of 10 ml. When foaming has subsided, add some paper pulp, warm the solution to approximately 75°C., and let stand at this temperature until the precipitate settles. A 1–2 hour standing at this temperature, with occasional stirring, usually gives a perfectly clear supernatant liquid. Filter the precipitate on a 9-cm. paper containing some paper pulp catching the filtrate in a 400-ml. beaker. Wash the precipitate and paper about 20 times with tartaric acid (10 g./liter) saturated with $H_2S$. Reserve the filtrate for the determination of tungsten.

9. Return the precipitate and paper to the original beaker and treat with 10 ml of $H_2SO_4$ and sufficient $HNO_3$ to destroy all organic matter. Combine this solution with molybdenum filtrate reserved in paragraph 4 and treat as described under "Determination of Molybdenum."

10. To the filtrate containing all the tungsten and a small amount of niobium and tantalum, having a volume of approximately 150 ml., add 20 ml. of formic

acid and cool to 15°C. Add slowly, with stirring, 20 ml. of cupferron solution
(60 g./liter) and some paper pulp, then stir until the precipitate is coagulated.
A slightly turbid solution at this point is not unusual due to the presence of small
amounts of free sulfur.

11. Filter through a tight 9-cm. paper containing paper pulp, catching the
filtrate in an 800-ml. beaker. Wash about 20 times with cupferron solution (25
ml. of formic acid and 2 g. of cupferron per liter). Transfer the precipitate to the
beaker containing the bulk of niobium and tantalum reserved in paragraph 7, and
treat by the procedure given under "Determination of Niobium and Tantalum."

## DETERMINATION OF TUNGSTEN

*Procedure.*—12. Evaporate the filtrate from the cupferron precipitation down to
a pasty, gelatinous mixture. Cool slightly and add rapidly 100 ml. of $HNO_3$.
Allow to stand. If no frothing occurs, warm gently on a hot plate until frothing
starts. Remove from the hot plate and allow to stand until the frothing ceases.
Add 30 ml. of $HClO_4$ and 10 mg. of sodium chromate, and evaporate to fumes
of $HClO_4$, adding $HNO_3$ dropwise as the sample comes to fumes of $HClO_4$ and
frothing occurs. Repeat $HNO_3$ additions and fuming until no frothing occurs on
coming to fumes of $HClO_4$ and the chromium is oxidized.

13. Cool the solution, add 20 ml. of water and a few drops of $H_2SO_3$ to reduce
the chromium. Boil for a few minutes to remove excess $SO_2$ and dissolve soluble
salts. Cool, transfer to a 250 ml. beaker, and rinse the beaker with water. Add
0.1 g. of NaOH to the 800-ml. beaker. Dilute with 10 ml. of water and scrub off
the adhering $WO_3$ with a glass rod and paper. When all the $WO_3$ is dissolved,
add this solution and washings to the 250-ml. beaker. Add 10 ml. of cinchonine
solution, dilute to 200 ml., and let stand at a temperature of 70 to 80°C. until the
supernatant liquid is clear. Filter the tungsten on a 9-cm. tight paper containing
paper pulp. Wash about 20 times with cinchonine wash solution, and transfer the
precipitate and paper to a 50-ml. platinum dish.

14. Ignite at 650°C. until the paper is gone, then cool. Moisten the precipitate
with a few drops of water, 10 drops of HF, and 2 drops of $HClO_4$. Evaporate
to dryness and heat at 700°C. for 10 minutes. Cool and weigh. Treat the $WO_3$
in the dish with 5 ml. of water and 0.5 g. of NaOH, and heat on a sand bath for
10 minutes, allowing the solution to evaporate to a pasty consistency or even just
to dryness. Cool, dilute with 40 ml. of water, digest for 5 minutes, filter through
a 9 cm. tight paper containing paper pulp, wash about 15 times with NaOH (10 g./
liter), and discard the filtrate.

15. Transfer the paper to a 150-ml. beaker containing 10 ml. of HCl (1:3) and
wash the dish free of NaOH with dilute HCl (5:95) and water, transferring the
washings to the beaker containing the paper. Macerate the paper, make the solution just alkaline with $NH_4OH$, bring to a boil, filter, and wash with ammonium
chloride solution (20 g./liter). Return the paper to the platinum dish, burn off
the paper at 700°C., cool, and weigh.

16. The difference between this weight and the original weight of the dish plus
$WO_3$ is the weight of the purified $WO_3$. Divide by the weight of the sample and
multiply by 79.31 to obtain the percentage of tungsten in the alloy (Note 2).

## DETERMINATION OF MOLYBDENUM

*Procedure.*—17. To the combined molybdenum solution recovered as described in
paragraphs 4 and 9, which has been cooled to 20°C., add 10 ml. of alpha-benzoin-

oxime (50 g./liter of acetone). Stir two minutes and add 15 ml. of saturated bromine water, followed by 5 ml. more of alpha-benzoinoxime solution. Add some paper pulp, stir for 2 to 3 minutes, and filter using suction. Wash about 20 times with a wash solution containing 10 ml. of 5% alpha-benzoinoxime and 10 ml. of $H_2SO_4$ per liter (Note 3).

18. Transfer the paper and precipitate to a 50-ml. platinum dish, char the paper well at 350 to 400°C. gradually increasing the temperature to 500°C., then heat at this temperature until the carbon is oxidized. Cool and weigh. Dissolve the precipitate in hot $NH_4OH$, filter any insoluble residue through a 9-cm. paper, and wash about 15 times with $NH_4Cl$ wash solution (50 g./liter). Ignite at a temperature of 525°C., cool, and weigh. Multiply the difference between the two weights by 66.67 and divide by the weight of sample taken to obtain the percentage of molybdenum in the alloy.

## DETERMINATION OF NIOBIUM + TANTALUM

**Procedure.**—19. To the combined niobium + tantalum fractions recovered as described in paragraphs 7 and 11, add 12 to 15 ml. of $HNO_3$ and 10 ml. of $HClO_4$. Bring slowly to fumes with further addition of $HNO_3$ if necessary to destroy completely the paper and oxidize the organic precipitate. Cool and wash down the cover glass with 2 to 3 ml. of $HNO_3$ from a dropping bottle. Add 3 to 5 drops of HF which on heating will drive off all $SiO_2$, and dissolve a greater part, if not all, of the niobium and tantalum. With the aid of a glass rod and more $HNO_3$, clean the sides of the beaker of all adhering $SiO_2$. With the cover still off, evaporate to fairly strong fumes of $HClO_4$, cool, and wash down the sides of the beaker with 5 ml. of saturated boric acid solution. Bring to strong fumes again with the cover off, cool, dilute with 50 ml. of water, and add 20 ml. of $H_2SO_3$ and some paper pulp. Cover the beaker and boil for 15 minutes. Let stand until the supernatant liquid is clear. Filter on a 9-cm. tight paper containing paper pulp. Wash about 15 times with dilute HCl (2:98) and then 5 times with $H_2SO_4$ (5:95).

20. Transfer the precipitate and paper to a weighed platinum dish, ignite slowly to destroy the paper, and finally heat to 900 to 1000°C. to constant weight. Weigh as $Nb_2O_5 + Ta_2O_5 + TiO_2$.

## DETERMINATION OF NIOBIUM (COLORIMETRICALLY)

**Procedure.**—21. If the relative amounts of the three elements are desired, fuse the weighed combined oxides of niobium, tantalum, and titanium (paragraph 20) in 5.0 g. of potassium pyrosulfate. Cool, add 10 ml. of $H_2SO_4$, and heat until a clear solution is obtained. Cool, pour into a 150-ml. beaker containing 5 ml. of $H_2SO_4$ (1:1) and 10 drops of 30% $H_2O_2$. Rinse the dish 4 to 5 times with dilute $H_2SO_4$ (5:95) containing 10 ml. of $H_2O_2$ per liter. Transfer to a 100-ml. volumetric flask and dilute to the mark with water. Determine the titanium content colorimetrically (Note 3). Calculate the weight of $TiO_2$ and record. This is to be deducted from the weight of total oxides. Reserve the solution for the determination of niobium (paragraph 22).

22. Transfer to a 150-ml. beaker an aliquot containing between 8 and 12 mg. of $Nb_2O_5$. Evaporate to fumes of $H_2SO_4$, cool, add enough concentrated $H_2SO_4$ to bring the volume to approximately 30 ml., and fume strongly for 5 minutes to remove water. Cool to room temperature and transfer to a 100-ml. volumetric flask, rinsing the beaker with five 10-ml. portions of the $H_2SO_4 \cdot H_3PO_4$ solution. Cool, dilute to the mark with the acid mixture, and mix thoroughly. Fill a one-

cm. cell of the spectrophotometer with a portion of the solution and hold this to be used for the null setting. Next add three drops of 30% $H_2O_2$ (0.1 ml.) to the solution in the flask, and mix thoroughly. Let stand for 5 minutes. Fill another 1-cm cell and read the absorption at 400 m$\mu$ after nulling the spectrophotometer on the unperoxidized solution.

23. Calculate the weight of $Nb_2O_5$ from a previously prepared graph set up using an oxide of known niobium content. Multiply the weight of $Nb_2O_5$ by 69.91 and divide by the weight of sample taken to obtain the percentage of niobium in the alloy. Subtract the weights of $Nb_2O_5$ and $TiO_2$ from the total oxides, multiply the remainder by 81.89, and divide by the weight of sample taken to obtain the percentage of tantalum in the alloy.

NOTES.—1. It is very important that all carbides are decomposed at this point and no black residue remains. If a residue remains, retreat with HCl, $HNO_3$, and $HClO_4$.

2. If the amount of NaOH insoluble recovered from the tungsten determination is over 1.5 mg., dissolve in HF, fume with $HClO_4$, and add to the beaker containing the niobium and tantalum fractions, paragraph 19.

3. Measure the absorbance of the solution at 410 m$\mu$ in a 1-cm. cell versus a reference solution. Prepare the reference solution by dissolving 5.0 g. of potassium pyrosulfate in 70 ml. of $H_2SO_4$ (1:4) and diluting to 100 ml. The calibration graph is prepared by developing the colored system in solutions containing from 0.05 to 7.0 mg. of titanium in 100 ml. of solution, measuring the absorbance of these solutions, and plotting absorbance against titanium concentration.

## COLORIMETRIC DITHIOL METHOD FOR DETERMINATION OF TUNGSTEN IN TANTALUM AND NIOBIUM

The method is applicable for the determination of tungsten in niobium or tantalum within the range of 0.005 to 0.10%.

The sample is dissolved in HF and $HNO_3$, and then fumed gently in $H_2SO_4$ to remove the $HNO_3$. Molybdenum is separated by extraction from a dilute HCl (1:4) solution with dithiol in amyl acetate. Tungsten is reduced in 9 to 11 $N$ HCl with Ti(III), extracted with dithiol, and determined spectrophotometrically.

The range extends from 0.01 to 0.20 mg. of tungsten in 25 ml. of amyl acetate using 1-cm. cells if the absorbance is measured at 640 m$\mu$.

Molybdenum is the sole interfering element under the conditions for the extraction of tungsten; it is removed during the procedure. However, if appreciable molybdenum is present, this method is not applicable (Note 1).

**Reagents.** **Dithiol (toluene-3,4-dithiol).**—The reagent should be kept refrigerated until needed, and, if possible, under an inert atmosphere (Note 2).

**Dithiol Solution.**—Dissolve 1.0 g. of dithiol in 100 ml. of NaOH (10 g./liter) solution and store in a refrigerator. *Prepare just before use.*

**Amyl Acetate.**—Purified grade. The liquid should be colorless.

**Tin(II) Chloride Solution.**—Dissolve 200 g. of $SnCl_2 \cdot 2H_2O$ in 500 ml. of HCl and dilute to one liter with water. Place a few pieces of metallic tin in the solution.

**Titanium(III) Chloride Solution.**—Dissolve 10 g. of tungsten-free titanium metal with 200 ml. of HCl (1:1) in an Erlenmeyer flask. As soon as the metal has dissolved, cool the solution, dilute to 500 ml. with HCl (1:1), and store in a stoppered bottle.

**Standard Tungsten Stock Solution (100 micrograms per ml.).**—Dissolve 0.1794 g. of $Na_2WO_4 \cdot 2H_2O$ in water. Add 100 ml. of sodium hydroxide solution (100 g./liter) and dilute to one liter. Store in a caustic-resistant bottle.

**Dilute Standard Tungsten Solution (10 micrograms per ml.).**—Dilute 50 ml. of the standard tungsten stock solution (100 micrograms per ml.) to 500 ml. with water.

*Preparation of Calibration Graph.*—Transfer 0-(blank), 1-, 2-, 5-, 10-, 15-, and 20-ml. aliquots of the dilute standard tungsten solution (10 micrograms/ml.) to a 125-ml. flask. Add 3 ml. of sulfuric acid and evaporate to light fumes of sulfuric acid. Cool. Cautiously add 40 ml. of HCl, 5 ml. of tin(II) chloride solution, and 10 ml. of titanium(III) chloride solution. Heat to about 80 to 90°C. in a hot water bath for 25 minutes. Transfer the solution while hot to a separatory funnel, rinse with two 5-ml. portions of HCl (5:1), add 10 ml. of dithiol solution, and shake vigorously for one minute. Cool under cold water, add 25.0 ml. of amyl acetate with a pipette, and shake vigorously for one minute. Allow the layers to separate, draw off the aqueous phase, and discard. Wash the organic layer with 3-ml. portions of HCl (4:1). Discard the acid washings.

Transfer a portion of the colored organic solution to 1-cm. cells. Measure the absorbance of the solution at 640 mμ versus the blank which is placed in the reference cell of the spectrophotometer. Prepare a calibration graph by plotting concentration versus absorbance of the solution. The colored system follows Beer's Law and is stable for 24 hours.

*Procedure.*—Transfer a sample containing not more than 0.2 mg. of tungsten to a 50-ml. platinum dish. Add 5 ml. of HF and $HNO_3$ dropwise until the sample is in solution (Note 3). Add 3 ml. of $H_2SO_4$ and evaporate to light fumes. Cool and add 0.5 ml. of HF.

Add 15 ml. of HCl (1:4). Transfer to a 125-ml. Erlenmeyer flask and use 5 ml. of HCl (1:4) to rinse the platinum dish. Cool to below 10°C. and add 5 ml. of tin(II) chloride. Add 10 ml. of dithiol amyl acetate solution (0.5 g. of dithiol (not zinc dithiol) per ml. of amyl acetate), cork with a rubber stopper, and shake 5 minutes on a mechanical shaker. Transfer to a separatory funnel and rinse the flask with two 5-ml. portions of amyl acetate. Allow the layers to separate. Transfer the acid layer containing the tungsten quantitatively back to the Erlenmeyer flask. (Discard the amyl acetate layer which contains the molybdenum.) Evaporate to fumes of sulfuric acid. If charring occurs, add several drops of $HNO_3$, and again evaporate to fumes of sulfuric acid (Note 4).

Cool, add 0.5 ml. of HF, and cautiously add 40 ml. of HCl. Continue as in the "Preparation of Calibration Graph."

NOTES.—1. About 0.4 of a milligram of molybdenum may be removed by extraction in the procedure; therefore, the method is not applicable if more than this concentration of molybdenum is present in the sample or aliquot.

2. Zinc dithiol is now commercially available. This salt is a more stable reagent than dithiol. The solution is prepared in the same manner as described for the dithiol solution. The zinc dithiol solution has the same stability as the dithiol solution.

3. If the sample is greater than 65-mesh, transfer a riffled 10-g. sample to a 300-ml. platinum dish. Add 100 ml. of HF and cover with a platinum cover. Add $HNO_3$ dropwise until solution is complete. Transfer to a 500-ml. volumetric flask and dilute to the mark with water. Immediately transfer to a clean, dry polyethylene bottle. Using a plastic pipette, transfer 10 ml. of the solution to a 50-ml. platinum dish. Continue with the procedure by addition of 3 ml. of $H_2SO_4$ and evaporating to light fumes as described in the procedure.

4. The molybdenum separation may be eliminated because the molybdenum content is usually extremely low.

## SPECTROPHOTOMETRIC DITHIOL METHOD
## FOR DETERMINATION OF TUNGSTEN
## IN LOW-GRADE ORES AND SLAGS

This method is applicable for materials containing 0.01 to 1% tungsten which dissolve in a mixture of hydrochloric, hydrofluoric, and phosphoric acids. Molybdenum is pre-extracted with dithiol before extraction and determination of the tungsten.

*Procedure.*—Transfer a sample containing not more than 5 mg. of tungsten to a platinum dish. Carry a blank through all the steps of the procedure if molybdenum is to be determined. Add 15 ml. of HCl, 10 ml. of HF, 5 ml. of $H_3PO_4$, and heat gently until all action ceases. Dilute to 50 ml. and filter into a 100-ml. volumetric flask. Wash the paper and residue 10 times with HCl (1:20). Cool, dilute to volume, and transfer an aliquot containing not more than 0.20 mg. of tungsten to a 125-ml. glass-stoppered Erlenmeyer flask. Add sufficient hydrochloric acid so that the solution is about 4 $N$ in HCl and extract molybdenum first and then tungsten as described under the method for the "Determination of Tungsten in Tantalum and Niobium Metal."

## COLORIMETRIC THIOCYANATE METHOD OF
## DETERMINATION OF TUNGSTEN IN ORES

This method is designed for the rapid control determination of tungsten in ores, concentrates, and digester solutions from 0.02% to major concentrations of tungsten.

The sample is fused with a sodium peroxide-sodium carbonate mixture, water leached, and diluted to volume. A suitable aliquot of the clear solution is acidified (about 9 $N$) with sulfuric acid and hydrochloric acid. The tungstate ion is reduced with stannous chloride, potassium thiocyanate added, and the color measured spectrophotometrically.

Since many of the ions sensitive to thiocyanate are separated by the sample decomposition technique, there are no serious interferences except vanadate. Up to 5 mg. of molybdate may be present in the aliquot (Note 1).

*Reagents.* **Stannous Chloride, 2 $M$.**—Dissolve 452 g. of $SnCl_2 \cdot 2H_2O$ in 500 ml. of concentrated HCl by warming in a covered 800-ml. beaker. Transfer to a liter flask and dilute to the mark with HCl. The solution is stable for one month if stoppered tightly.

**Potassium Thiocyanate, 2 $M$.**—Dissolve 194 g. of KCNS in 500 ml. of water by warming. Cool and dilute to one liter. The solution is stable for one month if stored in a cool, dark place.

**Standard Tungsten Solution.**—Dissolve 1.7940 g. of reagent-grade $Na_2WO_4 \cdot 2H_2O$ in water. Add one pellet of NaOH, dissolve, and dilute to one liter. 1 ml. = 1.00 mg. of tungsten. With a pipette, transfer 10.00 ml. of this stock solution to a 100-ml. volumetric flask and dilute to the mark. 1 ml. = 0.100 mg. of tungsten.

*Preparation of Absorbance-Concentration Curve.*—With pipettes, transfer 1-, 2-, 5-, 7-, 10-, and 15-ml. aliquots of the diluted tungsten stock solution to 100-ml. Pyrex volumetric flasks. The aliquots represent 0.10, 0.20, 0.50, 0.70, 1.0, and 1.5 mg., respectively, of tungsten. Dilute to 25 ml. and continue according to the procedure below, starting with "Add 10 ml. of concentrated $H_2SO_4$ . . ." Measure the absorbance in a spectrophotometer in 1-cm. cells at 400 m$\mu$ using water as a null. Plot the absorbance versus mg. of tungsten on co-ordinate paper (Note 2). The system follows Beer's Law.

**Procedure. Decomposition.** *A. Ores and Residues.*—Transfer a weighed sample (0.2 to 2 g.) containing not more than 150 mg. of tungsten to a 30-ml. iron crucible containing 3 g. of $Na_2O_2$ and 2 g. of $Na_2CO_3$. Mix well and fuse over a burner (Note 3). Cool until solid, then with tongs place the crucible on its side in a 250-ml. beaker. Cover and carefully add 50 ml. of water. When disintegration is complete, remove and rinse the crucible. Police it with a rubber finger cot. Add 10 ml. of ethanol (95%), boil 3 or 4 minutes, cool, and transfer to a 200-ml. volumetric flask (Note 4). Cool and dilute to volume, mix well, and settle 10 minutes. Decant the supernatant liquor through a dry filter and collect about 50 ml. of the filtrate.

*B. Digester Solutions and Leach Liquors.*—Transfer a sample of the acid solutions containing not more than 150 mg. of tungsten to a 250-ml. beaker. Remove any organic solvent by evaporation. Add 10 ml. of $HNO_3$ and 10 ml. of $HClO_4$, and evaporate to dense fumes. Cool, dilute to 25 ml., and add NaOH solution (20%) until the pH is about 2. Pour slowly with stirring into a beaker containing 25 ml. of hot NaOH solution (20%). Wash the contents back into the original beaker, add 10 ml. of ethanol (95%), and boil 3 or 4 minutes. Transfer to a 200-ml. volumetric flask, cool, and dilute to volume. Mix well and settle 10 minutes. Decant the supernatant liquor through a dry filter and collect about 50 ml. of the filtrate.

*C. Ammoniacal or Neutral Aqueous Solutions.*—Transfer a sample containing not more than 150 mg. of tungsten to a 250-ml. beaker. Add 10 ml. of NaOH (20%) and boil to remove the ammonia. Transfer to a 200-ml. volumetric flask, cool, and dilute to volume. Collect about 50 ml. of the filtered solution as described in *A* and *B*.

**Color Development.**—With a pipette, transfer an aliquot, containing 0.1 to 1.0 mg. of tungsten, of the filtered sample solution to a 100-ml. Pyrex volumetric flask. Dilute, if necessary, to 25 ml., and add 10 ml. of concentrated $H_2SO_4$ and 20 ml. of concentrated HCl. Add 10 ml. of $SnCl_2$ solution (2 $M$), mix, and digest on a steam bath for 5 minutes. Remove from heat and immediately stopper tightly with a rubber stopper. Chill in an ice water bath to 10°C. or less (Note 5). Remove the stopper and quickly add 10 ml. of KCNS solution (2 $M$), dilute to the mark, and mix well. Return to the ice water bath for 2 or 3 minutes. Remove, and after 5 minutes measure the absorbance in 1-cm. cells in a spectrophotometer at 400 m$\mu$ using water for a null. From the calibration curve, read milligrams of tungsten present in the aliquot sample.

NOTES.—1. Vanadium reacts almost identically to tungsten under the conditions of $SnCl_2$ reduction. Separations can be made by the usual chloroform-cupferron extraction if tungsten is complexed with NaF. Fortunately, vanadium is a rarity in tungsten ores. Molybdenum thiocyanate fades very rapidly in 9 $N$ acid medium. The absorbance of 5 mg. of molybdenum is equivalent to about 0.05 mg. of tungsten.

2. A reagent blank has an absorbance of about 0.007, which is equivalent to 0.01 mg. of tungsten. Therefore, better accuracy is obtained by aliquoting at least 0.2 mg. of tungsten for the sample.

3. Sodium carbonate precipitates calcium (usually present in large amounts) which would cause a turbidity in color development. To avoid spattering loss, do not fuse at temperatures above 800°C.

4. Alcohol is added to destroy excess peroxide, permanganate, etc., which consumes $SnCl_2$. The error in volume due to precipitate is less than 1%.

5. Glass stoppers frequently are not air-tight and jam badly under partial vacuum. The reduced tungsten is unstable and easily oxidized by air. However, after the addition of KCNS, the color is stable for at least 1 hour.

## METHODS FOR TUNGSTEN IN ANALYSES
## IN OTHER CHAPTERS

Tungsten in Alloys by Ion Exchange      See Method in Chromium Chapter

Tungsten in Cobalt Alloys      See Analysis of Stellite etc., (Cobalt Chapter)

# Chapter 50

# URANIUM*

U, *at. wt.*, 238.03; *sp. gr.* 18.58–19.05; [1] *m.p.* 1150°C.; *oxides,*[2] UO, $(U_4O_7)$ $UO_2$, $U_2O_5$, $U_3O_8$; $(U_6O_{17})$ $UO_3$

Uranium is not an excessively rare element. Its minerals occur most frequently in highly siliceous rocks, granites, and sedimentary sandstones. It is estimated that about 4 parts per million represents the average distribution in the earth's crust. The element occurs combined in association with silicates, phosphates, and zirconates of the rare earths and with niobium, tantalum, and thorium. Pitchblende is an amorphous oxide approximating the composition $U_3O_8$, often occurring in association with sulfide minerals in the deposits of Joachimsthal, Bohemia, in the Belgian Congo, and in the Canadian deposits. Uraninite, a crystalline material approximates the composition $UO_2$, but it is usually partially oxidized; its association is with pegmatites; frequently Ca, Th, Fe, Bi, Cu, and Zn compounds are present. Carnotite, $K_2O \cdot 2UO_3 \cdot V_2O_5$, and related secondary minerals are the major components of the uranium ores of western Colorado and eastern Utah.

Since 1940 the exploration of nuclear energy has caused an intensive investigation of all phases of uranium chemistry and the establishment of the properties of the transuranic elements. Prior to this period uranium was chiefly derived as a by-product of the production of radium and of vanadium. Its early uses were in the ceramic industry for producing various tints—greens, yellows, browns, and gray or black tints. Uranium glass is yellow and fluorescent. It has been used as a mordant in silk and wool dyeing; also in photography, and in the production of pyrophoric alloys. Uranyl acetate is an important reagent in the detection and estimation of sodium.

## DETECTION

*Radioactivity.*—Under suitable conditions uranium is detected by the radioactivity of the accompanying radium. In given geological occurrences where the uranium-radium ratio is unaltered, or altered to a constant amount, it is possible to assay ores by counting techniques after representative samples have been analyzed to set up the calibration.

*Fluorescence* under ultraviolet illumination may sometimes be used directly. After separation of uranium, the fluorescence of a fluoride or a fluoride-carbonate

---

* By N. H. Furman.

[1] The measured density varies with the carbon content. The following equation expresses the variation: Density = $19.05 - (2.14 \times \%$ carbon) (by weight).

[2] Katz, J. J., and Rabinowitch, E., The Chemistry of Uranium, VII-5, National Nuclear Energy Series, McGraw-Hill, 1951. The oxides UO and $U_2O_5$ are not commonly encountered in analytical practice. $UO_4 \cdot 2H_2O$ is precipitated by hydrogen peroxide in acidic medium. One oxygen atom of the compound is peroxide oxygen.

fusion of the uranium residue can be used for detection or estimation of uranium down to $10^{-11}$ g.

The emission spectrum of uranium is very complex and the sensitivity is not high for individual lines.

*Chemical Detection.*—Many minerals and ores yield their uranium completely upon treatment with 1:1 nitric acid. Others yield to hydrofluoric acid plus nitric or other acid. Fusion is necessary if estimation of silica is important. The solution, plus excess sodium carbonate, is boiled and the filtrate and washings are acidified with nitric acid and the $CO_2$ is expelled. Sodium hydroxide is added and uranium is indicated by the formation of a yellow precipitate that is insoluble in excess sodium carbonate, but soluble in ammonium carbonate.

If one of the traditional separation methods is used, e.g., ether extraction from nitric acid-nitrate solution, double cupferron separation once with uranium as U(VI) and again after reduction of U(VI) to U(IV), the detection is then more certain if the amount of uranium is very small.

Uranium metal, when freshly cut is silvery, but soon tarnishes on exposure to the atmosphere with formation of a golden film that darkens and becomes black. The massive metal slowly burns in air at 500–550°C. to give $U_3O_8$. The metal dissolves slowly in nitric acid or phosphoric acid. Hydrochloric acid attacks it vigorously with immediate appearance of a purplish red color due to $U^{+3}$; the solution rapidly turns green to give $U^{+4}$ even when air is excluded. Apparently the reaction: $2U^{+3} + 2H^+ \rightarrow 2U^{+4} + H_2$, is rapid and quantitative. Two moles of hydrogen are evolved per gram-atom of U if air is excluded. Finely divided uranium metal is pyrophoric and in quantity has caused disastrous fires. Larger pieces of metal, e.g., 0.05 to 1 g., burn slowly in air due to the accumulation of oxides; they may be burned in air or in air enriched with oxygen to measure the content of C, H, etc., in a combustion train.

The metal and the oxides $UO_2$, $U_3O_8$, and $UO_3$ are frequently encountered.

The solutions of the tripositive salts, e.g. $UCl_3$, $UF_3$, etc. are oxidized by hydrogen ion and other oxidants.

The oxide $UO_2$ is brown and its solutions are greenish due to the $U^{+4}$ ions. Many of the solid salts are green, e.g. $UF_4$, $M^IUF_5$, etc. $UO_2$ is oxidized to $U_3O_8$ upon heating in air.

$U_3O_8$ is black. When dissolved with exclusion of air it yields $U(SO_4)_2$ and $2UO_2SO_4$. The best solvent for the oxide is nitric acid. The composition of the oxide is very close to $U_3O_8$ over a range of temperatures at atmospheric pressure. Its composition may be modified by reducing or increasing the pressure of oxygen in contact with it.

Uranium in state +5 is encountered during the polarographic reduction of $U^{+6}$, or by other methods of reduction at about pH 2. $UCl_5$ upon heating disproportionates to $UCl_4$ and $UCl_6$.

$UO_3$ is orange in color. It is best prepared by heating the nitrate, $UO_2(NO_3)_2 \cdot 6H_2O$. (Final temperature about 300°C.) Uranyl salts, $UO_2X_2$ are in general yellow, and their solutions are also yellow. The only uranium(VI) compounds that do not contain the uranyl radicle are $UF_6$ and $UCl_6$.

$UO_4 \cdot 2H_2O$ is precipitated by hydrogen peroxide in the pH range 0.5 to 3.5. Th, Zr, and Hf are precipitated also. Iron is co-precipitated and also catalyzes the decomposition of hydrogen peroxide unless it is complexed.

$U^{+4}$ is precipitated by ammonia but the dark brown hydrous oxide is soluble in ammonium carbonate solution.

$UO_2^{++}$ is precipitated by ammonia to give yellow ammonium diuranate, $(NH_4)_2U_2O_7$, insoluble in slight excess of ammonia. If carbonate is present in the ammonia or if ammonium carbonate is added, some or all the precipitate dissolves.

Potassium ferrocyanide gives a brownish color or a brown precipitate when added to $U^{+4}$ or $UO_2^{++}$ solutions. The precipitate is soluble in excess hydrochloric acid. Sodium hydroxide converts the ferrocyanide precipitate to yellow diuranate which distinguishes uranyl ferrocyanide from cupric ferrocyanide.

Barium carbonate precipitates uranyl ion completely in contrast to its action on ions of Ni, Co, Mn, and Zn.

Disodium hydrogen phosphate added to uranyl solutions in presence of alkali acetates or free acetic acid gives a yellowish white precipitate, $UO_2HPO_4 \cdot xH_2O$ that is soluble in mineral acids.

Tartaric acid and certain other organic complexing agents, also hydroxylamine hydrochloride and ammonium carbonate prevent the precipitation of uranium by alkalies and ammonia.

## ESTIMATION

Due to the critical demands of nuclear processes, frequent assays of raw materials are required. A chain reacting pile or other reactor requires stringent purification, with special emphasis upon removal of substances of high neutron capture cross sections. In the course of nuclear energy developments most of the older methods of separating other substances from uranium, and of the detection and determination of small or large relative amounts of uranium in old and new alloys, and in compounds have been studied very critically. A bewildering array of methods and techniques has evolved.

Most minerals yield uranium to nitric acid attack, if finely divided. Some require hydrofluoric-nitric or other special acid attack. Pyrosulfate fusion is required in other cases. The attack must be varied to suit the nature of the material.

### PREPARATION AND SOLUTION OF THE SAMPLE

The element and many of its alloys with the more familiar metals are decomposed rapidly by 12 N hydrochloric acid. The finely divided metal reacts very vigorously with nitric acid, whereas pieces, even small ones, react slowly. Hot concentrated phosphoric acid reacts rather rapidly to form a solution of U(IV) phosphate; addition of an oxidant accelerates the reaction. Dilute sulfuric or perchloric acid dissolves uranium slowly. The metal reacts violently with hot concentrated perchloric acid. Alloys or mixtures containing Sb, Sn, W, Mo, Zr, and other elements that form fluo-complexes, such as Nb and Ta, may generally be dissolved in dilute nitric-hydrofluoric acid mixtures.

Uranium and many of its compounds are dissolved by alkaline solutions containing peroxide to form peruranates. The light absorbance of uranium compounds in such solutions forms the basis of an important photometric method.

The oxides of uranium dissolve readily in nitric acid. $UO_4 \cdot 2H_2O$ is dissolved by acids plus a reductant. The hydrous oxides, the diuranates, and salts such as the phosphate dissolve in dilute acids.

$UF_3$ and $UF_4$ are converted to $U_3O_8$ and HF by heating with steam [3] for pur-

[3] Warf and Cline, Chicago Report CC-2723, June 30, 1945; Warf, Cline and Tevebaugh, Anal. Chem., **26**, 342, 1954.

poses of determining fluoride or for dissolution of the oxide that is formed. The tetrafluoride may also be removed simply by roasting in air,[4] by heating with ammonium carbonate [5] or with ammonium oxalate.[6] Fusion with boric acid [7] or $K_2S_2O_7$ [8] also serves to remove the fluoride.

Ammonium oxalate in heated solution dissolves $UF_4$ but not $UO_2$ or $U_3O_8$.[9] This simple test was made routinely to check the efficiency of the conversion of $UO_2$ to $UF_4$.

Both $UF_4$ and $(UO_2)HPO_4 \cdot 4H_2O$ are practically insoluble in water but dissolve in concentrated mineral acids.

*Dissolution of Ores.*—The majority of ores and concentrates in the range of 3–70% $U_3O_8$ yield the uranium to solution when treated as follows:

From 1.000 g. to 5.000 g. of the ore, previously ground, sampled, and dried is treated in a 250-ml. beaker with 30 ml. of 1:1 nitric acid after wetting the sample and heated on a low temperature hot plate 1–2 hours. After cooling 6 ml. of concentrated sulfuric acid added to 10 ml. of water is added and after continued heating at "low" the temperature is raised until the heavy fumes of $SO_3$-$H_2O$ are strongly evolved. After cooling, water to a total volume of 100 ml. is added, and the silica and insolubles are filtered and washed with 1–2:98 sulfuric acid.

The foregoing treatment is altered to cover special cases. If it is desired to expel As, Sb, and Sn, several evaporations and fumings follow the initial one, each time adding 20 ml. of a solution containing 5 ml. each of concentrated HCl and HBr. Highly siliceous low-grade materials are treated repeatedly in a platinum dish with hydrofluoric acid, then taken up in nitric acid and heated finally with 10 ml. of 18 $N$ (1:1) sulfuric acid to expel nitric acid.

*Low-Grade Carnotites.*—A 10.00 g. sample is heated in a 600-ml. beaker after moistening with water, adding 10–15 ml. of concentrated nitric acid, 30 ml. of 18 $N$ sulfuric acid, 3 ml. of HF and 3 ml. of 70% perchloric acid. After final fuming with sulfuric acid, cooling and diluting to 100 ml., the insoluble material is filtered off.

Highly refractory substances may require a pyrosulfate fusion, as for example with titanoniobates (columbates).

## SEPARATIONS

It is axiomatic that the more complete the prior separation from other elements, the more effective and simple are the final procedures for estimation. Testing of precipitates that are to be discarded is made by spectrographic methods in developing effective procedures.

*Hydrogen Sulfide Separation.*—In order to effect the separation of uranium from copper, lead, bismuth, arsenic, antimony, and other members of the hydrogen sulfide group, the solution, prepared by the conventional treatment with nitric acid followed by sulfuric acid, is treated with hydrogen sulfide for 0.5 hour and then allowed to stand for several hours, or overnight. The precipitate is filtered

[4] Rodden *et al.*, A.C.M.P. Collected Paper No. 43, Natl. Bur. Standards.
[5] Furman and Stanley, Chicago Report CC-258, Sept. 15, 1942.
[6] Tevebaugh, Report CC-682, May 15, 1942.
[7] Bricker and Furman, Report MSA A-1078, Apr. 3, 1945.
[8] Cunningham, Report A-1016, Oct. 31, 1943.
[9] Furman, Met. Lab. Chicago, CC-238, sec. IV-5, p. 21, Aug. 15, 1942. Also Collected Papers, Princeton Univ., The Development of the Oxalate Test for the amount of $UO_2$ and other Insoluble Impurities.

and washed with sulfuric acid (2 ml. per 100 ml.) that has been saturated with hydrogen sulfide. The filtrate containing the uranium is boiled to remove the remaining hydrogen sulfide.

It has been demonstrated that "homogeneous precipitation" using thioacetamide will separate major quantities of bismuth, e.g. 0.2 g. effectively from minor amounts of uranium. The $U_{233}$ tracer and counting technique proved that the separation was essentially quantitative.[10] The efficiency of this technique has not been tested in more general separations.

*Peroxide-Carbonate Separation.*—The filtrate, from which the hydrogen sulfide group elements have been removed, is treated with 15 ml. of 3% hydrogen peroxide per 150 ml. of solution, followed by neutralization with sodium carbonate. The addition of 3 g. in excess to cause the precipitation of iron and those elements having insoluble carbonates. The precipitate is filtered, redissolved in nitric acid, and again precipitated by the peroxide-carbonate method. The combined filtrates are used for the determination of uranium.

*Cupferron Separations.*—Cupferron separates many elements from uranyl solutions either by precipitation or by extraction of the cupferrates by chloroform, ether, or other solvents.[11] After destruction of cupferron and reduction of $UO_2^{++}$ to $U^{+4}$, the tetravalent uranium may either be precipitated as the cupferrate, or extracted by chloroform or other solvent. Thus the reagent is capable of isolating uranium in a two-stage procedure from nearly all of the elements. Grimaldi[12] reversed the foregoing procedure, after removal of iron from hydrochloric acid solution by extraction by ethyl acetate, by passage through a Jones Reductor into cold 6% cupferron solution. The ignited cupferron precipitate is fused with potassium pyrosulfate and sodium nitrate. With uranium now in the uranyl state, $UO_2^{++}$, other elements are extracted as cupferrates. The alkaline peroxide photometric method is suitable for the final determination.

*Solvent Extraction Separations.*—The solubility of uranyl nitrate in diethyl ether has long been known[13] and Soxhlet type extraction of the dried nitrate salts, moistened with concentrated nitric acid, has long been used.[14] Hixson and Miller[15] patented a countercurrent process for recovering U, Re, W, etc. from ores. The first appreciation of the use of a salting agent added to saturation appears to have been work of Hecht and Grünwald[16] on the use of ammonium nitrate added to saturation.

As a result of the work of various groups during World War II it became recognized that at least a minimum of nitric acid was essential and that certain nitrates added to the same gross nitrate molarity greatly enhanced the distribution of uranyl nitrate to the solvent layer. It was soon recognized that many ethers other than diethyl ether still further enhanced the distribution. Also ketones and tributyl phosphate were found to be excellent extractants. The great bulk of

10 Stoner, G. A., and Finston, H. L., Anal. Chem., 29, 570, 1957.
11 Baudisch, O., Chem. Ztg., 33, 1298, 1909; Baudisch and King, V. L., J. Ind. Eng. Chem., 3, 629, 1911. A comprehensive review, The Extraction of Cupferrates, is given by Furman, N. H., Mason, W. B., and Pekola, J. S., Anal. Chem., 21, 1325, 1949.
12 Grimaldi, F. S., Geol. Survey Bull. 1006 (1954), pp. 17–27.
13 Peligot, E., Ann. chim. phys., 5, 5, 1842.
14 Pierle, C. A., Ind. Eng. Chem., 12, 60, 1920.
15 Hixson, A. W., and Miller, R., U. S. Patent No. 2,227,833, Jan. 7, 1941.
16 Hecht, F., and Grünwald, A., Mikrochemie ver Mikrochim. Acta, 30, 279, 1943.

the work has been done with diethyl ether, Cellosolve, ethyl acetate, methyl iso-butyl ketone and tributyl phosphate.[17]

The elements that extract are uranium, Am(VI), Np(VI), Pu(VI), and Ce(IV), Au(III), Sc(III) to a considerable extent. Vanadium(V) is the chief element that interferes in many methods for estimating uranium and although it is not too soluble in concentrated nitric acid, its behavior detracts from the general utility of ether extraction as an isolation method for uranium. Uranyl nitrate solutions in diethyl ether and other solvents may be contacted with water, or with various reagents, e.g. ammonium carbonate, ammonium sulfate, added in order to transfer the uranium back to an aqueous medium.

A particular merit of the ether extraction process is that rare earth elements are well separated from the uranium.[18] Fluoride and phosphate interfere with the transfer of uranium to the ether layer. Addition of aluminum nitrate as a salting agent is then desirable.

**Other Extraction Methods.**—Many compounds of uranyl ion with chelating agents are extractable by solvents. For example, in a solution complexed with EDTA at pH 8.8 the uranyl complex of 8-hydroxyquinoline is extractable to chloroform. 1-Nitroso-2-naphthol or diethyldithiocarbamate complexes are similarly extractable.[19]

Long chain aliphatic amines dissolved in kerosine (Varsol) or in xylene are acid extractants and will remove uranium and thorium as anionic species from solutions of diluted mineral and organic acids.[20] Their action resembles strongly the behavior of ion-exchange resins.

J. C. White[21] has shown that tri-$n$-octylphosphine oxide (TOPO) in 0.001 to 0.1 $M$ solution in cyclohexane extracts various metallic complexes from acidic solutions. Species extracted appear to be $H_2Cr_2O_7 \cdot 2TOPO$; $HFeCl_4$ and $FeCl_3$; $ZrCl_4 \cdot 2TOPO$; $MoO_2Cl_2 \cdot 2TOPO$; $UO_2Cl_2 \cdot 2TOPO$; $UO_2(NO_3)_2 \cdot 2TOPO$; $ThCl_4 \cdot 3TOPO$; $TiOSO_4 \cdot 2TOPO$; also $Bi^{+3}$, $Nb(V)$; and $Ta(V)$ are appreciably extracted. Stannic, auric, hafnium, antimonous, indium, arsenic(V), mercuric and platinum(II) compounds are extracted under certain conditions.

Tris-2-ethylhexylphosphine oxide is much more selective and discriminates

[17] Analytical extractions of the nitrate are well reviewed in Solvent Extraction in Analytical Chemistry, G. H. Morrison and H. Freiser, J. Wiley & Sons, Inc., New York, 1957, pp. 137–142. R. J. Mundy, N. H. Furman, and G. H. Morrison discovered in 1943 the superiority of nitrates of Al, Cu, Fe, Li, Zn, etc., in aiding in the effective recovery of uranyl nitrate. A series of upwards of a score of analytical studies is summarized in The Distribution of Uranyl Nitrate from Aqueous Solutions to Diethyl Ether, N. H. Furman, R. J. Mundy and G. H. Morrison, AECD 2938, Nuclear Sci. Abs. 4244, p. 983 (1950) and The Use of Ether Extraction for the Analytical Separation of Uranium, N. H. Furman, R. J. Mundy and G. H. Morrison, AECD 2861, Decl. June 21 (1950). Numerous parallel studies on this and other solvents exist. N. H. Furman and R. J. Mundy, U. S. Patent No. 2,816,005, Dec. 10, 1957, assigned to the U.S.A. rep. by U. S. Atomic Energy Commission.

[18] Hoffman, J. I., J. Wash. Acad. Sci., **38**, 233, 1948.

[19] See Table II, review by G. H. Morrison and H. Freiser, Anal. Chem., **30**, 632–640, 1958.

[20] Moore, F. L., Anal. Chem., **29**, 1660, 1957; Brown, K. B., et al., ORNL-2173 (unclassified report); White, J. C., TID-7555; First Conference on Analytical Chemistry in Nuclear Technology, Nov. 4–6, 1957, Gatlinburg, Tenn., pp. 240–255.

[21] White, J. C., loc. cit. in TID-7555; also A.S.T.M. Special Technical Publication No. 238, Solvent Extraction in the Analysis of Metals. Also ORNL-2161, The Use of Trialkyl Phosphine Oxides as Extractants, issued Nov. 1, 1956.

between uranium and thorium. From molar nitric acid only uranium is completely extracted and the following are partially extracted: chromium, zirconium, molybdenum, tin, antimony, hafnium, gold, mercury, and thorium. From molar hydrochloric or perchloric acid uranium, gold, and tin are completely extracted and the following elements are partially extracted: Cr, Fe, Zn, Zr, Mo, In, Sb, Hg. From molar sulfuric acid U, Zn, Sn, and Au are completely extracted whereas Cr, Mo, Sb, Hg, and Bi are partially extracted.[22]

*Electro-Separations.*—Uranium is deposited at the cathode in the form of mixed hydrous oxides from acetate buffer or carbonate media at pH 5 to 7. This method separates uranium from the alkali and alkaline earth metals or zinc. Depositions may also be made from sodium fluoride medium the deposit then consisting of $UF_4$.[23]

Electrolysis to a mercury cathode is an excellent method for removing impurities,[24] or for collecting impurities in uranium [25] prior to their separation from the mercury and estimation by polarographic, photometric, or other techniques. The completeness of deposition varies with the concentration of acid, either sulfuric or less commonly perchloric acid, the concentration of the uranium, and other conditions such as current density, efficiency of stirring, and temperature. At a concentration of 10 g. of uranium in 125 ml., Cu, Pb, Ni, Co, Zn, Cd, Hg, appear to be completely removed, while Mo, Cr, Mn, and Fe are incompletely separated. It has been shown by McDuffie and Hazelgrove [26] that in sulfuric acid medium at pH 3.75 with sulfite added, Mn can be completely electrolyzed into the mercury. At lower acidities and with concentrations of uranium of about 1 g. per 125 ml., manganese is almost completely electrolyzed into the mercury and other elements are more effectively separated. The mercury cathode separation sometimes makes it possible to remove impurities so completely that one may then oxidize the U(III) which is formed to U(IV) and titrate the latter. If an electrolysis proceeds properly, the uranium will be largely in the U(IV) state, but some U(III) will be formed and its red color will be noticeable.

*Precipitations.*—U(IV) is precipitated quantitatively as $UF_4$ in acidic media. This effects a separation from many elements that form soluble complex fluorides. The cupferrate of U(IV) is precipitated from 1–2 $N$ sulfuric or hydrochloric acid. The precipitate is converted to $U_3O_8$ after filtering, washing, and igniting. In the absence of fluorides, phosphates, and organic complex-formers, the reduced solution is added to 2–5 g. of oxalic acid in 3 $N$ hydrochloric acid solution to precipitate $U(C_2O_4)_2$. Reducing conditions are maintained by adding stannous chloride. The precipitate is finally transformed into $U_3O_8$ before weighing. The hydrous oxide of U(IV) is even less soluble than the corresponding U(VI) precipitate.

Uranyl ion is precipitated quantitatively by ammonia that is free of carbon dioxide or carbonates. Other complexers and fluoride should be absent. This method serves only as a separation from the alkalies, the alkaline earths, and complex ammonia ions such as those of copper, nickel, zinc, etc. A repeated dissolution and precipitation is necessary in the latter cases. The weighing form

[22] White, *loc. cit.*

[23] Rodden, Editor, Analytical Chemistry of the Manhattan Project, National Nuclear Energy series, VIII, pp. 523–535, McGraw-Hill, New York, 1950.

[24] Casto, Analytical Chemistry of the Manhattan Project, pp. 511–522.

[25] Bricker and Furman, Reports CC-73 (1942) and CC-1706, 1943; Furman, Bricker, and McDuffie, J. Wash. Acad. Sci., **38**, 159, 1948.

[26] McDuffie, B., and Hazelgrove, L. S., Anal. Chemistry, **24**, 826, 1952.

is $U_3O_8$. Uranyl ion forms $UO_2HPO_4$ when treated with phosphate at pH 1.3–2.3 whereas the reagent ammonium phosphate yields $UO_2NH_4PO_4$. The method is useful in the separation of uranium from vanadium. 8-Quinolinol is one of the few organic reagents that yields a weighable chelate with uranium. The precipitation is complete from a little above pH 4 to about pH 12–13. After drying at 105°C. the precipitate is weighed as $UO_2(C_7H_6NO)_2 \cdot C_9H_7NO$. The solution should have uranium in the hexavalent state since U(IV) is also precipitated by the reagent.

*Ion-Exchange Separations.*—Anion-exchange resins in the sulfate form are very effective in the separation of uranium from a number of elements. A typical application is to the determination of uranium in ores.[27] A modified Amberlite IRA-400, 40–60-mesh or Dowex-2 is treated with 10 volume per cent sulfuric acid, then washed with water. The column is 5 cm. long and 1 cm. in diameter. The sample prepared by nitric acid attack and by fuming with sulfuric acid contains 0.5 to 40 mg. of U and the equivalent of 1 to 2 ml. of concentrated sulfuric acid per 50 ml. Enough 6% sulfurous acid is added to prevent interference by iron, chromium, or vanadium. The uranium is held in the column as the solution passes through at a rate of one drop per second. The washings and rinsings amount to 50 ml. of hot water. The uranium is then eluted into a 100-ml. volumetric flask with boiling 1 $M$ perchloric acid. After cooling 25 ml. of 6 $N$ sodium hydroxide is added to each flask and after diluting to about 95 ml. and cooling, 1 ml. of 30% hydrogen peroxide is added and the solution made homogeneous. The absorbance is read versus a blank at 380 or 420 m$\mu$. Cationic substances including cerium and thorium do not interfere.

A procedure similar to the foregoing one was effective in separating uranium from bismuth.[28] The separation of uranium prior to determination of the rare earths follows a similar pattern.[29]

## SOLVENT EXTRACTION METHODS

### CONTINUOUS EXTRACTION TO DIETHYL ETHER

A nitrate solution of the uranium containing 5% by volume of concentrated nitric acid is prepared. An extractor devised by J. B. Heberling[30] is used. (Fig. 50-1.)

*Procedure.*—A suitable weight of sample ranging from 1–5 g. or more is placed in a 250-ml. beaker, moistened with distilled water, and digested 30 minutes with 15–20 ml. of concentrated nitric acid. (Organic matter should be absent, or previously destroyed by heating strongly in air.) The solution is diluted, filtered, and the residue is washed with dilute nitric acid (1 ml. per 100 ml.).[31]

The filtrate is concentrated to about 10 ml., treated with enough 0.2% $KMnO_4$ to oxidize reductants, cleared of $MnO_2$ by adding a little sodium nitrate solution, and transferred to the extraction vessel with 5% nitric acid saturated with ammo-

[27] Seim, Morris, and Frew, Anal. Chem., **29**, 443, 1957.

[28] Banergee, G., and Heyn, A. H. A., Anal. Chem., **30**, 1795, 1958.

[29] Banks, C. V., Thompson, J. A., and O'Laughlin, J. W., Anal. Chem., **30, 1792**, 1958.

[30] Heberling and Furman, Mad. Sq. Area Report A-1068, Jan. 16, 1945.

[31] In other dissolution methods involving hydrofluoric, perchloric, or other acids, these acids must be displaced either by repeated evaporations or by taking to dryness and heating followed by dissolution in nitric acid. Another procedure is to precipitate the hydrous oxides with ammonia, wash thoroughly and take up in nitric acid, repeating this step, if necessary.

nium nitrate. About 50 ml. each of water and diethyl ether is placed in the boiling flask of the apparatus. With the apparatus assembled, the boiling flask is surrounded by water which is heated by a low-temperature hot plate. In general, 5 ml. more of the nitric acid-ammonium nitrate solution is added after about 30 minutes, either by removing the heat and disconnecting the flask or through a side tube (not shown in Fig. 50-1). The aqueous solution is stirred either manually, using the tube with dispersion disk, as illustrated, or magnetically with a small glass-enclosed magnet and a magnetic stirrer. After 1 hour the uranyl nitrate is completely removed to the boiling flask along with a minimum of impurities. This flask and solution is then placed in a beaker of water which is warmed in a hood to remove the ether, after which any convenient gravimetric, titrimetric, photometric, polarographic or other suitable procedure may be used to estimate the uranium.

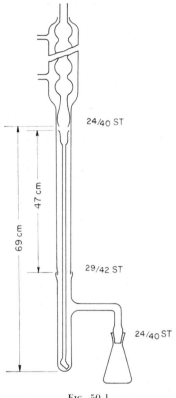

24/40 ST

47 cm

69 cm

29/42 ST

24/40 ST

Fig. 50-1.

If small amounts of fluoride or phosphate are present in the nitric acid solution of the material, their inhibiting effect upon the extraction may be countered by adding a small volume of saturated aluminum nitrate or ferric nitrate in 5% nitric acid. The continuous extraction process has yielded results that are accurate and precise in the range from a few hundredths of 1% up to 95% $U_3O_8$, and in general for the high range the results differ less than 1 part per thousand from the standard titrimetric procedure for ores.

Although fires or peroxide explosions are possible, they have not been encountered in numerous applications of the method. The nitric acid content must not be allowed to exceed 10% in the boiling flask. Receivers may be changed during the extraction, with 50 ml. of water added to dilute the nitric acid that is extracted along with the uranium. This method is not practical at high altitudes, and hence batch extractions with higher-boiling solvents are practiced.

### BATCH EXTRACTIONS TO DIETHYL ETHER
### (WITH ADDED NITRATES)

Other salting agents than ammonium nitrate are used. Calcium or aluminum nitrate added to saturation to a 5% nitric acid solution of the sample makes possible the transfer of essentially all the uranium in a single step to an equal volume of the solvent.

*Procedure.*—Prepare a nitric acid solution of the sample and evaporate the filtered solution, with oxidant ($KMnO_4$) added to destroy reductants, until crystallization begins. Transfer the solution to a separatory funnel with 5% nitric acid saturated with calcium nitrate. After cooling, a single extraction is made to an equal volume of diethyl ether, previously shaken with some of the saturated calcium nitrate-nitric acid solution. Since the distribution of impurities is promoted by the drastic salting condition, the first aqueous layer is drawn off, and the ether extract is "back washed" by one or more portions of the saturated calcium nitrate-5% nitric acid solution. The loss of uranium is negligible for most purposes. In attempting to recover minute traces of uranium a single extraction of the original saturated solution is not adequate and repeated extractions with ether are made. In most cases 99.5% or more of the uranium present is recovered.

## TRIBUTYL PHOSPHATE EXTRACTIONS

Warf [32] studied the extraction of ceric nitrate to tributyl phosphate and noted also that uranyl and thorium nitrate were extracted. Subsequently numerous investigators have worked with this extractant.[33]

*Procedure for Phosphate Rock, Carnotite, and Low-Grade Pitchblende.*—Treat 5 g. of the finely powdered material with 50 ml. of 1:1 nitric acid in a 250-ml. beaker. After 5–10 minutes boiling, filter, and transfer the insoluble matter to an 11-cm. Whatman No. 42 paper. The paper is ignited in platinum. After cooling, a few drops of sulfuric acid and 10 ml. of hydrofluoric acid are added and after taking to dryness the residue is fused with 5 g. of potassium pyrosulfate. The cold melt is taken up in 4.7 $N$ nitric acid and added to the filtrate from the initial dissolution step. Ten grams of crystallized aluminum nitrate, $Al(NO_3)_2 \cdot 9H_2O$, are dissolved in the solution [34] which is then diluted to 250 ml. with 4.7 $N$ nitric acid. An aliquot expected to contain 50 to 500 micrograms is shaken in a 250-ml. separatory funnel with 25 ml. of tributyl phosphate and 25 ml. of diethyl ether. The lower aqueous phase is rejected, and the solvent phase is washed 5 times with 50-ml. portions of 4.7 $N$ nitric acid. The uranium is then removed from the solvent layer by shaking it with 20-, 15-, and 15-ml. portions of 25% ammonium acetate solution prior to a photometric estimation. See under "Photometric Methods," 8-quinolinol procedure. A procedure similar to this one applies to uranium in bismuth.

*Procedure for Materials Containing Thorium or Zirconium.*—The foregoing procedure is not applicable to materials containing thorium and zirconium.

**Monazite Ores.**—A 0.5-g. sample of the finely powdered ore is heated with 10 ml. of concentrated sulfuric acid, and after evaporating nearly to dryness and cooling, 100 ml. of ice water is added and the salts are dissolved. After addition of 25 ml. of concentrated nitric acid the solution is made uniform at 250 ml. Some ores may need a fusion treatment with sodium peroxide, followed by appropriate acid treatment.

An aliquot judged to contain 50–100 micrograms of uranium is diluted to 200 ml., ammonia is added after adding filter pulp and the hydrous oxides are filtered on a large filter funnel with medium porosity sintered glass bed. Then the hydrous oxides are dissolved in 7 $N$ hydrochloric acid, followed by extraction with 25 ml. of tributyl phosphate plus 25 ml. of methyl isobutyl ketone.

The solvent layer is washed with four 50-ml. portions of 4.7 $N$ nitric acid and

[32] Warf, J. Am. Chem. Soc., **71**, 3257, 1949.
[33] Procedures are based here on a paper by Eberle and Lerner, Anal. Chem., **29**, 1134, 1957. These authors give detailed references to work of Moore, Wright, Bartlett and others in the development of the use of this technique.
[34] This addition applies to phosphate rock, but not to carnotite or pitchblende.

the uranium is extracted to aqueous ammonium acetate as in the procedure for ores not containing thorium or zirconium.

**Thorium** metal is dissolved by a mixture of concentrated nitric acid and 5 ml. of dilute hydrofluoric acid (10 ml. of 48% HF per 200 ml.). After evaporation and heating at 400°C. for 30 minutes, the residue is dissolved in 50 ml. of concentrated HCl and 5 ml. of the dilute hydrofluoric acid. The solution while still warm is transferred to a funnel and extracted with 25 ml. of tributyl phosphate plus 25 ml. of methyl isobutyl ketone, and the extract is treated as for monazite ores.

## EXTRACTION TO METHYL ISOBUTYL KETONE

Small amounts of uranium in the milligram or microgram range are quite specifically extracted by methyl isobutyl ketone if tetrapropylammonium nitrate is added to an acid-deficient salting solution, i.e., aluminum nitrate containing ammonia and tetrapropylammonium hydroxide.[35] The absorbance of the tetrapropylammonium uranium trinitrate can be read at 452 m$\mu$ in the solvent when the amount of uranium in a 2-ml. extract is from 0.5 to 12 mg. However, for samples containing 2 mg. or less, a portion of the extract is treated with dibenzoylmethane which gives a greater molar absorbance that can be read at 415 m$\mu$.

*Reagents.* **A. 0.005 *M* Tetrapropylammonium Nitrate in 1 *N* Acid-Deficient Salting Solution.**—Prepared from 1050 g. Al(NO$_3$)$_3$·9H$_2$O warmed with 850 ml. water, then 67.5 ml. concentrated ammonia added and the mixture stirred until clear, cooled below 50°C. and 10 ml. of 10% tetrapropylammonium hydroxide added and the volume finally made up to 1 liter. The salting solutions are given a preliminary extraction with methyl isobutyl ketone.

**B. 0.025 *M* Tetrapropylammonium Nitrate.**—Prepared as in A except that 50 ml. of 10% tetrapropylammonium hydroxide is used.

**C. 0.25 *M* Tetrapropylammonium Nitrate, 1 *N* Acid-Deficient Solution.**—100 ml. of 10% tetrapropylammonium hydroxide is neutralized to pH 7 with 5 *N* nitric acid. The solution is allowed to stand in a large evaporating dish until a slurry of crystals forms (about 4 days). The slurry is transferred to a beaker containing 210 g. of crystalline aluminum nitrate using 20 ml. of water. Water is added to 180 ml. and 13.5 ml. of concentrated ammonia is added. After stirring until the solution is clear it is diluted to 200 ml.

**D. Scrub Solution for Dibenzoylmethane Method.**—940 g. of Al(NO$_3$)$_3$·9H$_2$O, 33 g. of tartaric acid, 31 g. of oxalic acid, and 64 g. of ethylenedinitrilotetraacetic acid are added to 100 ml. of water and 150 ml. of concentrated ammonia and the mixture is warmed and stirred until clear. The solution is diluted to 1 liter and extracted with methyl isobutyl ketone to remove uranium contamination.

**E. Special solutions** when the dibenzoyl methane method is applied to samples containing cerium(IV).

E-1. An aluminum nitrate solution is prepared as in *A* except that no tetrapropylammonium hydroxide is added.

E-2. A scrub solution is prepared by dissolving 154 g. of ammonium acetate and 20 g. of the sodium salt of diethyldithiocarbamate in 900 ml. of water. Adjust to pH 7, filter, and make up to 1 liter.

E-3. Dissolve 0.063 g. of mercuric nitrate in 90 ml. of 1 *N* nitric acid and make up to 100 ml. with *N* nitric acid.

[35] Maeck, Booman, Elliott and Rein, Anal. Chem., **30**, 1902, 1958; Anal. Chem., **31**, 1130, 1959.

**F. Dibenzoylmethane-Pyridine Reagent.**—0.1140 g. of dibenzoylmethane in 500 ml. of 5% by volume solution of ethanol in pyridine.

*Procedure for Milligram Amounts of U.*—Samples containing more than 2 milli-equivalents of acid per 0.5 ml. are first neutralized. The salting solution *B* will handle 0.5 ml. samples that do not contain more than 0.05 millimole of U(VI), Th, and Ce(IV) in all. If the aggregate of these three elements is greater than 0.05 millimole, solution *C* is used.

Pipette a sample of solution containing 0.5 to 12 mg. of U into a 125 x 25 mm. test tube with a polyethylene stopper. The aliquot should be 0.5 ml. or less. 4 ml. of salting solution (*B* or *C*) is used and 2 ml. of methyl isobutyl ketone. Agitate mechanically for 3 minutes, then centrifuge to separate the phases. Pipette the solvent into a 1-cm. cell and measure the absorbance versus a blank of 1 *N* nitric acid. A calibration curve is prepared by the same technique.

*Procedure for Microgram Amounts of U.*—Samples containing up to 2 mg. of U and as much as 8 *N* in acid can be quantitatively extracted using salting solution *A*.

**Cerium and Thorium Absent.**—Pipette a sample of 0.500 ml. or less containing 0.8 to 75 micrograms of U into a test tube containing 5.0 ml. of salting solution *A*. Add 2 ml. of methyl isobutyl ketone, stopper and agitate 3 minutes. Centrifuge. Transfer as much as possible of the solvent phase to tube containing 5 ml. of scrub solution *D*. Stopper, agitate 3 minutes, centrifuge, then remove a 1.00-ml. aliquot of the organic phase to a 25-ml. calibrated flask. Add 15 ml. of dibenzoylmethane-pyridine reagent and mix.

After 15 minutes measure the absorbance in a 5-cm. Corex cell at 415 m$\mu$ versus a blank of 1 *N* nitric acid.

**Samples Containing Ce(IV) or Th.**—An aliquot of 0.500 ml. or less, containing 0.8 to 75 micrograms of U, is transferred to a tube containing 5.0 ml. of salting solution *E-1* and 4.00 ml. of methyl isobutyl ketone are added. After three minutes of agitation and centrifuging, as much of the organic phase as possible is transferred to a tube containing 5.0 ml. of *E-2*. After 20 minutes mixing and centrifuging as before, at least 3.00 ml. of the extract are transferred to a test tube containing 5.0 ml. of solution *E-1*. Add 0.5 ml. of scrub solution *E-3*. Stopper and mix for 10 minutes, then centrifuge. Transfer a 2.00-ml. aliquot of the solvent to a 25-ml. flask, add 15 ml. of the dibenzoylmethane-pyridine reagent and mix thoroughly. After 15 minutes read the absorbance in a 5-cm. Corex cell at 415 m$\mu$ versus a 1 *N* nitric acid blank.

## GRAVIMETRIC METHODS

### AMMONIA METHOD

*Procedure.*—The solution obtained after any adequate separation procedure is usually either a sulfuric acid or a nitric acid one. It is warmed or boiled until carbon dioxide is expelled, then treated with freshly prepared ammonia solution that is free from carbonate until the solution is distinctly ammoniacal. The change of methyl red to the yellow color will serve as an indication. Filter pulp added prior to the ammonia will facilitate washing and ignition. A 2% ammonium nitrate solution is used. The precipitate is filtered off. The precipitate and paper are dried carefully in a weighed platinum crucible, if available, and the temperature is kept as low as possible during the destruction of the paper. The final heating is at about 1000°C. The precipitate is brought to constant weight as $U_3O_8$.

The gravimetric method is accurate provided sufficient prior separations have been made.

$$U_3O_8 \times 0.8480 = U.$$

## OTHER METHODS

The other precipitation processes that have been mentioned under separations lead to the weighing form $U_3O_8$ except for the precipitate formed by 8-quinolinol. In all cases a gravimetric estimation can only be quantitative if all interfering ions have been separated. Organic complexing agents must, in general, be destroyed during early stages of the procedure. However, Carter and Weber [36] have found that ammonium phosphate precipitates uranium as uranium ammonium phosphate, $UO_2NH_4PO_4$, from a solution complexed with "Versenol" (trisodium salt of $N$-hydroxyethylethylenediaminetriacetic acid). The precipitate is dissolved and then the uranium is precipitated as the 8-quinolinol salt and ignited to yield pure $U_3O_8$.

## TITRIMETRIC METHODS: OXIDATION-REDUCTION

The most frequently used processes involve the prior reduction of a uranyl solution, previously separated from impurities that undergo reduction or oxidation changes in the range of reduction potentials in question. The uranium is converted to the U(IV) state and then titrated with a standardized oxidant.

### REDUCTION PROCEDURES

The most frequently used reductants are a zinc amalgam, and lead. The former always produces some $U^{+3}$, whereas the latter produces $U^{+4}$ only.

#### ZINC REDUCTION

Zinc amalgam in the form of a Jones Reductor consists of a column of 20-mesh zinc amalgamated to the extent of 2% Hg.

It was found that ore samples that had been freed of Fe, V, Ti, Mo, and $H_2S$ group metals (acid group) were not quantitatively reduced after a number of samples had been passed through the reductor.[37] The cause was the deposition of finely divided nickel on the amalgam. It then became easier for the reductor to produce hydrogen than to reduce the uranium properly.

Grimaldi [38] found that zinc amalgamated with 10% of mercury could be used repeatedly without "poisoning" by nickel.

The use of fresh portions of fluid zinc amalgam for each reduction eliminates the difficulty caused by nickel.[39] The amalgam is prepared by warming 1000 parts of mercury with 25 parts of 20-mesh zinc under $N$ sulfuric acid. The liquid portion of the mixture is drained off in a separatory funnel after several hours and kept under $N$ sulfuric acid until used. The reduction is to the $U^{+4}$ state.

[36] Carter, J. A., and Weber, C. M., U. S. Atomic Energy Comm. Report TID-7516, 1956, pp. 186–207.

[37] Observations of Pekola. Further studied by Heberling and Furman, Report M-4248.

[38] Grimaldi, Bulletin 1006, U. S. Geological Survey, p. 37.

[39] Work of Mason and Pekola, Studies on the Quantitative Reduction of Uranium by Saturated Liquid Zinc Amalgam. MSA Information Report A-1061 Special. Manual of Analytical Methods, MSA A-2912, **1**, p. 67.

When sulfuric acid solutions of uranium are reduced by passage through a Jones Reductor the uranium is mainly in the $U^{+4}$ state with sometimes a third present as $U^{+3}$. One may titrate potentiometrically with any one of a number of standard oxidants, realizing one break at the end of the oxidation of $U^{+3}$ to $U^{+4}$ and a second when the $U^{+4}$ has been converted quantitatively to $UO_2^{++}$. Alternatively the $U^{+3}$ may be oxidized by a brisk stream of air for an arbitrary time, e.g. 15 minutes or longer, followed by titration of the $U^{+4}$. The further "aeration" of $U^{+4}$ is known to be catalyzed by traces of Cu or Mo ions.

**Reduction to $U^{+3}$.**—It has been shown by Kennedy [40] that 0.01 uranyl solution as chloride or as perchlorate in the corresponding 1 $M$ acid is reduced quantitatively to $U^{+3}$ by a Jones Reductor (5% Hg; 95% Zn) provided the effluent from the reductor flows into 0.5 $M$ ferric sulfate in 1 $M$ sulfuric acid, previously deaerated by a stream of oxygen-free inert gas, such as nitrogen. The $Fe^{++}$ that is formed is equivalent to the $U^{+3}$. Reaction: $3Fe^{+3} + U^{+3} + 2H_2O = 3Fe^{++} + UO_2^{++} + 4H^+$. The ferrous ion is then titrated by a standard procedure. Sulfate must be absent from the original $UO_2^{++}$ solution because reduction to the trivalent stage is far from complete (maximum about 68% reduction to $U^{+3}$).

## LEAD REDUCTION

Cooke et al.[41] proved that granulated lead reduces uranyl ion only to the $U^{+4}$ state either in hydrochloric acid solution or in presence of sulfuric acid provided the solution is also 3 $N$ in hydrochloric acid. If perchloric acid is used in place of sulfuric acid in preparing samples containing much calcium, barium, etc., the perchloric-hydrochloric acid solution may be reduced conveniently in the lead reductor.

**Procedure.**—The reductor consists of a column 2 cm. in diameter and 25 cm. long in a conventional Jones Reductor tube. The granulated lead must be of reagent grade. The column is stored overnight or between intermittent use with the lead covered with 10% hydrochloric acid containing about 0.1% ferric ion. Before use it is washed with six 25-ml. portions of hydrochloric acid (1:15). The sample solution of about 50 ml. volume containing up to 0.2 g. of uranium, and 3 $N$ in hydrochloric acid and 0 to 9 $N$ in sulfuric acid is passed through the lead column at a rate less than 175 ml. per minute. The reduced solution is passed into 10 ml. of 5% ferric sulfate solution and the reductor is washed with five to six 25-ml. portions of the 1:15 hydrochloric acid. The titration is made either with potassium dichromate or with ceric sulfate solution standardized in the usual manner.

This reduction technique has met with much favor for the reduction of large or small amounts of uranium.

## THE REDUCTION OF URANYL ION BY OTHER METALS AND AMALGAMS

Silver reduces uranyl ion only to the tetravalent state in hydrochloric acid medium. Antimony, cadmium, aluminum reduce uranyl ion completely, but mercury in hydrochloric acid medium does not give complete reduction to the $U^{+4}$

---

[40] Kennedy, Anal. Chem., **32**, 150, 1960.
[41] Cooke, Hazel, and McNabb, Anal. Chem., **22**, 654, 1950.

state.  Cadmium, bismuth, lead, or zinc liquid amalgams reduce uranium to the $U^{+4}$ state.[42]

The zinc amalgam reductor generates hydrogen peroxide when the moist amalgam is exposed to air.  One may add hydrogen peroxide to dilute sulfuric acid and pass the solution through a Jones Reductor without adding to the amount of an oxidant needed for the titration of the resulting solution.  On the contrary, if one shakes a very dilute solution of ferric ion, uranyl ion, etc. vigorously, in a flask containing air, with a liquid zinc or cadmium amalgam there comes a point where none of the iron or uranium is reduced, but on the contrary a steady state concentration of hydrogen peroxide is built up.  Mercury, dilute hydrochloric acid and air when shaken together can produce a steady state concentration of 3% or more of hydrogen peroxide.[43]

There have been conclusions reached that the consumption of standard oxidant per unit weight of uranium varies with the amount of uranium titrated.  It should be emphasized that a careful blank on reagents should be established for any reductor by experiment.  The quality of obtainable reagent-grade lead appears to be such that the blank is usually very small.

### SOLUBLE REDUCTANTS

Titanous or chromous ions added in small excess reduce $UO_2^{++}$ ion to $U^{+4}$. The uranium may be estimated by titrating with a standard oxidant and location of a succession of potentiometric end points.

## OXIDATION PROCEDURES (TITRATION OF REDUCED URANIUM SOLUTIONS WITH VARIOUS STANDARD OXIDANTS)

$U^{+4}$ and $U^{+3}$ are oxidized "completely" enough for quantitative estimation by any one of a number of standard solutions of oxidants.  In precise assay work preference is often given to potassium dichromate because it can be obtained so pure that determinate solutions may be prepared directly.  Almost equal use has been made of ceric sulfate solutions in 0.5–1.0 N sulfuric acid.  Standard ferric sulfate in sulfuric acid solution (about 1 N) is often used when it is not desirable to separate iron from uranium.  If standard ferric sulfate is added to a solution containing $U^{+4}$ and $Fe^{++}$, obviously only the $U^{+4}$ will be titrated by the reagent.  The titration of $U^{+4}$ with standard potassium permanganate may be made at room temperature or at 80°C.; chlorides should not be present.  The titration of $U^{+4}$ in concentrated sulfuric acid medium, after precipitation with phosphate and dissolution of the precipitate, may be made with a standard solution of ammonium metavanadate, $NH_4VO_3$ using N-phenylanthranilic acid as indicator.  Zr, Ti, and Th are coprecipitated with the uranium phosphate, but do not interfere in the titration.[44]  Potassium bromate oxidizes $U^{+4}$ quantitatively through the intermediary of added ferric chloride and copper chloride as catalyst in 20% HCl solution (vol. % of concentrated HCl).

[42] The general topic of reduction prior to titrations with oxidants is well reviewed in Volumetric Analysis, **III**, by Kolthoff, Belcher, Stenger, and Matsuyama, pp. 7–23, Interscience Publishers, Inc., 1957.
[43] Furman and Murray, Jr., J. Am. Chem. Soc., **58**, 429, 1936.
[44] Pinto, C. M., Moyses, E., and Ribeiro, E., Photon, **1**, 13–20, 1959 through Anal. Abstracts, **7**, 3226, 1960.

## DICHROMATE TITRATION OF U+4

*Procedure.*—The reduced uranium solution should be of 100–300 ml. volume containing about 5% by volume of concentrated sulfuric acid. If a lead reductor has been used the solution will contain about the same percentage by volume of combined concentrated sulfuric and hydrochloric acids. Then 20 ml. of 4% crystallized ferric chloride, $FeCl_3 \cdot 6H_2O$, solution, 10–15 ml. of 85% phosphoric acid, and, if needed, sulfuric acid. The ferric ion oxidizes $U^{+4}$ and the phosphoric acid lowers the pH to make possible the complete reoxidation of the ferrous ion before the indicator changes. The indicator is 8 drops of sodium diphenylamine-sulfonate, 0.01 $M$. An indicator correction must be deducted from the gross volume of the titrant. It is usually 0.1 ml. The titration is made with 0.1 $N$ potassium dichromate solution, or with other concentrations, 0.05 or 0.01 $N$ depending on the range of concentration of the uranium. Smaller volumes of indicator and appropriate corrections are then applied.

In the foregoing procedure a determinate solution of $K_2Cr_2O_7$ may be prepared by direct weighing. It has been found that $U_3O_8$ of approximately 99.95% purity may be prepared from uranyl nitrate purified by ether extraction.[45] This material is weighed, dissolved with nitric acid followed by sulfuric, freed from nitric by dilution and taking down to fumes again. The sulfuric acid solution is then reduced by any valid method.

## CERIC SULFATE TITRATION OF U+4

The standard solutions of ceric sulfate are made up from sulfatoceric acid or from pure ceric oxide or other preparations, in sulfuric acid of such concentration that the final solution is 1 $N$ in sulfuric acid. It has been shown by Kirk[46] that 0.01 $N$ and more dilute ceric solutions may be prepared from pure ceric sulfate, redistilled water and redistilled sulfuric acid by diluting portions of 0.1 $N$ stock solutions with 2 $N$ sulfuric acid and heating the diluted solution for 10–12 hours at steam-bath temperature.

According to much experience, ceric sulfate solutions in the 0.1 or 0.05 $N$ ranges may be standardized against arsenious oxide or sodium oxalate from the National Bureau of Standards or against $U_3O_8$ of tested purity with equally satisfactory results.

The $U^{+4}$ solutions containing about 5% by volume of concentrated sulfuric, or 5% for the sum of sulfuric and hydrochloric acids if the lead reductor method has been used, are treated with 5 ml. of syrupy phosphoric acid (85%) and 30 ml. of cold 1:1 sulfuric acid and titrated with the standard ceric solution using 2 drops of 0.025 1,10-phenanthroline-ferrous sulfate indicator (Ferroin). A blank is run through the whole process from first treatment of the sample through reduction and titration.

## FERRIC SULFATE TITRATION OF U+4

The most effective prereduction method is to add chromous sulfate to the uranyl solution. The reduced solution is then titrated potentiometrically with ferric sulfate solution. The uranium solution should contain about 5% by volume of concentrated sulfuric acid. During the titration of the $U^{+4}$ the temperature should be

[45] Analytical Chemistry of the Manhattan Project, Natl. Nuclear Energy Series, Vol. VIII-1, pp. 53–55, Rodden, Ed. McGraw-Hill Co., New York, N. Y., 1950.
[46] Kirk, Quantitative Ultramicro Analysis, J. Wiley & Sons, Inc., N. Y., 1950, pp. 130–131.

90–95°C. and air should have been expelled with a stream of nitrogen or carbon dioxide. The potentiometric indication of the two end points is more suitable than in a corresponding procedure using titanous solution, or in successive end points for the changes $U^{+3}$ to $U^{+4}$ and $U^{+4}$ to $UO_2^{++}$, respectively. Chlorides should be absent. The chief merit of the procedure is that iron, chromium, nickel, manganese, aluminum, and lead in the amounts apt to be present due to the reductors or to mild corrosion of stainless steel, or moderate amounts of zinc do not interfere. Elements that interfere seriously are Cu, W, Mo, and V.[47]

### PERMANGANATE TITRATION OF $U^{+4}$

The sulfuric acid solution containing $U^{+3}$ and $U^{+4}$ is usually aerated to oxidize $U^{+3}$ to $U^{+4}$, then after removing dissolved air by a stream of carbon dioxide or nitrogen, the $U^{+4}$ is titrated at 80°C. with exclusion of air until the self indication or a potentiometric indication is reached.

## TITRATION OF URANYL SOLUTIONS WITH STANDARD SOLUTIONS OF REDUCTANTS

The preparation and storage of powerful reductants and the necessity of shielding the solutions that are being titrated from air, have made these methods rather unpopular. Chromous, $Cr^{++}$, and titanous, $Ti^{+3}$, are the most practical reagents. Chromous sulfate has met with favor in prereduction of uranyl solutions, and to some extent in direct determinations. It is possible to dispense 0.1 $N$ chromous solutions of definite concentration by storing them in large bulbs containing mossy zinc amalgamated to the extent of about 2%.[48] Zinc for Jones Reductors and other purposes should be amalgamated by shaking it with an appropriate amount of mercuric chloride solutions. (Mercuric nitrate appears to produce reduced nitrogen compounds that do not separate from the mercury during a reasonable amount of washing.) The chromium is obtained in the trivalent state by heating potassium dichromate in sufficient sulfuric acid to give a final normality of about 1, with pure hydrogen peroxide to reduce the chromium to the $Cr^{+3}$ state. The $Cr^{+3}$ is then reduced by amalgamated zinc placed in the storage bulb. The solution is transferred to the burette by a stream of inert gas, previously bubbled through a vanadous or chromous solution.

The titration of uranyl solutions as well as those containing vanadium, copper, and dichromate by chromous acetate in nonaqueous media has been reported.[49] For example, uranyl nitrate dissolved in 30 ml. of ethanol with 0.5 ml. of sulfuric acid is titrated with 0.02 to 0.1 $N$ chromous acetate dissolved in dioxan. It is stated that tributyl phosphate or ethyl acetate may be used as a solvent for the uranium. Potentiometric indication is used.

[47] Analytical Chemistry of the Manhattan Project, *op. cit.*, pp. 70–71.
[48] Lingane and Pecsok, Anal. Chem., **20**, 425, 1948.
[49] Mincewski *et al.*, Nukleonika (Warsaw), **3**, spec. number, p. 62–66, 1958 through Anal. Abs., **7**, 16, 1960 and Chem. Anal., Warsaw, **3**, 467, 1958 through Anal. Abs., **7**, 116, 1960.

## TITRIMETRIC METHOD: PRECIPITATION

## TITRATION OF URANYL ION WITH STANDARD PHOSPHATE SOLUTION

It was shown by Caley [50] that an indirect method for determining sodium may be based on the titration of the uranyl portion of the precipitate $NaMg(UO_2)_3$-$(C_2H_3O_2)_9 \cdot 6\frac{1}{2}H_2O$ after dissolving the pure precipitate in 2.0–2.4 ml. of acetic acid plus 40–50 ml. of water and heating to 90°C. The standard solution is one of disodium hydrogen phosphate, 35 g. per liter, standardized against a known solution of uranium. The end point is indicated by the disappearance of the uranyl reaction on an indicator paper treated with potassium ferrocyanide or by spot tests on solid $K_4Fe(CN)_6$ crystals on a spot plate. The method has been used chiefly for rough estimations only of uranium.

Uranyl ion in solutions containing no interfering ions may be titrated with a standardized ammonia solution, using an empirical standardization factor. Fluoride may be present. Potentiometric indication is normally used.

## THE TITRIMETRIC ESTIMATION OF URANIUM IN ORES OR IN SYNTHETIC MIXTURES

### GENERALLY APPLICABLE METHOD

This procedure evolved due to the efforts of scientists at the National Bureau of Standards. [51] In simple outline a properly prepared, dried, and weighed sample is decomposed by nitric acid and sulfuric acid, and converted to sulfates by fuming. The hydrogen sulfide group of metals is removed and then a cupferron group by extraction after removing hydrogen sulfide and oxidation. The determination is completed by the dichromate titration procedure. The samples and the titrant normality are adapted to the expected range of uranium in the sample. The following procedure is essentially for ores or other materials containing several per cent of uranium. [52]

*Reagents.* **Potassium Dichromate, 0.1 N.**—4.903 g. is dissolved in water and made up to 1 liter.

**Phosphoric-Sulfuric Acid Mixture.**—150 ml. concentrated sulfuric acid is mixed with 350 ml. of phosphoric acid, 85%.

**Sodium Diphenylaminesulfonate.**—Add 0.32 g. of the barium salt plus 80–90 ml. water and 0.5 g. sodium sulfate in a little water. Stir thoroughly and let stand several hours. Filter through a tight paper, e.g., Whatman No. 42, and dilute to 100 ml.

**Ferric Chloride.**—4% crystalline ferric chloride, $FeCl_3 \cdot 6H_2O$, in water.

**Hydrochloric-Hydrobromic Acid.**—5 ml. each of concentrated hydrochloric and hydrobromic acids in 20 ml.

[50] Caley, J. Am. Chem. Soc., **52**, 1349, 1930.
[51] Rodden, Tregoning and others, in the years 1940–42.
[52] For low grade siliceous materials a 20.00-g. sample is taken down with hydrofluoric acid in platinum, starting with 50 ml. of the acid and repeating until silica is removed. The fluorides are then displaced by fuming with sulfuric acid and a cupferron separation is then generally adequate, followed by titration of the uranium after reduction and aeration with 0.027 N potassium dichromate solution with sodium diphenylaminesulfonate as the indicator and ferric chloride and phosphoric acid added.

*Procedure.*[53]—A weighed 2.000-g. sample of the finely ground and dried ore, or other material, is placed in a 250-ml. beaker, moistened with water and treated with 25–30 ml. of 1:1 nitric acid, covered with a watch glass and heated 2 hours at a low temperature on a hot plate. Add 12 ml. of 1:1 sulfuric acid and heat 1 hour at low temperature. Support the watch glass to permit evaporation, heat to the fuming temperature of sulfuric acid and allow strong fuming to continue 3 minutes. Cool, add 90 ml. of water, and heat on a hot plate to dissolve as much material as possible.

The solution is transferred completely to a 500-ml. suction flask, washing the beaker thoroughly. With a stopper loosely put on, hydrogen sulfide is passed in through the side arm for 30 minutes. With stopper firmly placed and side arm stopped the flask is allowed to stand overnight. The solution is filtered through a Whatman No. 40 filter and washed completely with 2% by volume of sulfuric acid saturated with hydrogen sulfide. The filtrate, probably of volume over 200 ml. is evaporated to 90 ml.

**Cupferron Extraction.**—The solution is treated with permanganate until its color persists, chilled to 6°C. or below and transferred to a 250-ml. separatory funnel, with shortened stem and perfectly fitting stopper. After adding 25 ml. of cold (6°C.) 6% cupferron solution, and allowing to stand a few minutes after shaking or mixing, shake vigorously with 25 ml. of chloroform, let layers separate, draw off practically all of the chloroform. Repeat the extractions until the chloroform layer is colorless. Add 5 ml. more of cupferron, and mix; if the color of the precipitated cupferron acid is pure white iron, vanadium, etc. have been removed.[54] If not, continue the process.

The aqueous layer is transferred to the beaker in which the dissolution step was made, and after adding 15 ml. of concentrated nitric acid, the covered beaker[55] is heated until strong fumes of sulfuric acid appear and fumed 3 minutes longer. After cooling, the cover and sides of beaker are washed down, and 1 ml. of perchloric acid is added, followed by evaporating and fuming. This process is repeated twice more to expel organic matter and nitric acid. After the last fuming, and cooling, the material is dissolved by adding 60–75 ml. of water and heating. There should be the equivalent of 5 ml. of concentrated sulfuric acid present. More is added if too much was lost by the fuming operations.

If it is desired to titrate with 0.027 N potassium dichromate, high grade materials must be made up to volume in a calibrated flask and suitable aliquots taken.

The solution, or suitable aliquot is treated with a little permanganate, then reduced in a Jones Reductor, and after washing the reduced solution is aerated for 15 minutes, treated with 20 ml. of 4% ferric chloride solution, 15 ml. of sulfuric-phosphoric acid mixture and 8 drops of diphenylaminesulfonate indicator. Titration is then made with 0.027 N potassium dichromate standard solution.

The dichromate solution is standardized by running samples of $U_3O_8$, of known purity, through the entire procedure. As a check, pure samples of the oxide are dissolved in nitric acid, then fumed with sulfuric acid and reduced and titrated.

For some materials it may be desirable to remove arsenic and probably antimony and tin as well. In these cases after the preliminary dissolution step and fuming

---

[53] Based on AEC Report A-2912, Vol. **I,** p. 65.

[54] The addition of a little alpha-benzoinoxime during the latter part of the extraction process is advisable if the material contains molybdenum. Cupferron removes all but about 10 parts per million of this element.

[55] A glass with ribs or other rapid evaporation device is used.

with sulfuric acid, the residue is cooled, diluted with 25 ml. of water, placed on a steam bath and 20 ml. of hydrochloric-hydrobromic acid mixture is added. Evaporation to a low volume and repetitions of this treatment are followed by final fuming of sulfuric acid. The rest of the procedure is as outlined above.

## METHOD APPLICABLE TO MANY TYPES OF ORES, CONCENTRATES AND OTHER MATERIALS [56]

The material must be capable of dissolution with final conversion to sulfate medium. Normally dissolution is by nitric and sulfuric acids. After removal of insoluble matter, the cupferron extraction separation is made. After decomposing reagent and conversion to sulfate medium, the uranium is reduced by fresh liquid zinc amalgam which produces $U^{+4}$. Titration is then made with ceric sulfate of suitable normality using Ferroin indicator.

**Reagents.** Ceric sulfate solutions 0.1, 0.05, and 0.02 $N$ made up in 0.5 $M$ sulfuric acid are prepared as needed and standardized against $U_3O_8$ or arsenious oxide from the National Bureau of Standards.

**"Ferroin" indicator,** 1,10-phenanthroline-ferrous sulfate, 0.025 $M$ is obtained from the G. F. Smith Chemical Co.

**Liquid Zinc Amalgam.** Prepared as described under "Reduction Procedures," p. 1190.

**Apparatus. Separatory Funnels.**—250-ml. Pyrex funnels, each provided with a rubber stopper to fit a 125-ml. filter flask.

**Filter Flask.**—Capacity 125 ml. fitted with tube and rubber bulb and valve to aid in washing the amalgam during separation from the $U^{+4}$ solutions, Fig. 50-2.

**Procedure.**—Powdered and dried samples of 1.000 to 4.000 g. are weighed and transferred to 250-ml. beakers, moistened, and treated with 15 ml. of concentrated nitric acid and 10 ml. of concentrated sulfuric acid. The size of sample is based on an expected titration of 30 to 40 ml. of an appropriate standard solution. After taking down to fumes of sulfur trioxide and fuming strongly for 5 minutes, the mixture is cooled, diluted to 50 ml. with water, digested slightly below boiling for a few minutes, and filtered into a 400-ml. beaker. After thorough washing with hot 0.5% sulfuric acid by volume, the residue is discarded.

FIG. 50-2.
Filter Flask.

The filtrate and washings are concentrated to 50 ml. and treated while hot with 0.2% potassium permanganate solution until a permanent pink color results. The solution is cooled in an ice bath and transferred to a 250-ml. separatory funnel, using cold water in the transfer to a volume of approximately 100 ml. Cold 5% cupferron is added (15 ml.). Extractions are made with 25-ml. portions of chloroform until the last extraction is colorless. The extracts are discarded. Upon adding 5 ml. more of cupferron solution a fine, perfectly white precipitate of hydrogen cupferrate should form. If it is at all discolored, add a second 5-ml. portion and repeat the chloroform extractions. Finally, remove excess cupferron by chloroform extractions. Transfer the aqueous solution to the 400-ml. beaker that it previously occupied before the cupferron treatment.

[56] Details of this procedure were evolved by J. S. Pekola and W. B. Mason in the Frick Chemical Laboratory, 1943–44.

Carefully drive out entrained chloroform by warming at a low temperature on a hot plate, then increase the temperature of the plate and evaporate to fumes of sulfur trioxide, allowing fuming to continue for 10 minutes. Cool the solution, dilute with 30 ml. of water and heat gently until all salts have dissolved. Add to the hot solution 5 ml. of 0.2% permanganate and warm for ten minutes at about 75°C. If no brown manganese oxide separates, or if the permanganate color vanishes, add 5 ml. more of the permanganate and repeat the heating. Finally destroy manganese dioxide or permanganate by addition of small portions of sodium sulfite to the hot solution and continue the heating until sulfur dioxide is no longer evolved.[57]

When the solution has cooled to room temperature, add 5 ml. of concentrated sulfuric acid and aqueous permanganate dropwise until a permanent pink tint is formed. Transfer to a 250-ml. funnel by washing with enough ice-cold water to bring the volume to 100–110 ml. Add 5 ml. of liquid zinc amalgam, and shake the mixture vigorously for 5 minutes. Invert the funnel and carefully release pressure. Wash the stopper catching the washings in a 500-ml. Erlenmeyer flask.

Insert the stem and stopper of the separatory funnel into the 125-ml. filter flask containing 75 ml. of 1% sulfuric acid. Build up pressure with the atomizer bulb, until when the stopcock of the funnel is opened, the wash acid flows up cleaning the amalgam as it flows down. Pressure is applied until the wash solution has been completely pumped up into the funnel. If amalgam remains in the funnel, addition of a few drops of mercury, followed by the washing technique will enable it to be brought down.

The solution in the funnel is transferred to the flask containing the washings from the stopper, and the process is completed by washing. After the addition of 30 ml. of cold 1:1 sulfuric acid, 2 drops of Ferroin indicator and 5 ml. of 85% phosphoric acid, titrate with standard ceric sulfate to the change from red to pale yellow due to uranyl solution.

A reagent blank is run through the complete procedure.

The foregoing method has been applied to a great many materials that were also analyzed by the more complete "N.B.S." procedure. Cupferron extraction alone seemed to remove interferences as well as the combined hydrogen sulfide-cupferron procedure for the great majority of materials. Trivalent arsenic, if any reaches the final titration stage, is not oxidized unless a catalyst is added.

## PHOTOMETRIC METHODS

There are a great diversity and variety of procedures that will give accurate results with a pure uranium solution. Very few methods will tolerate as many impurities as the peroxide process. The color of the uranyl solutions may sometimes be used. Uranium(IV) in phosphoric acid medium has a strong absorption at 630 m$\mu$ where the absorbance due to U(VI) is negligible. Uranyl nitrate has a maximum absorbance at 410 m$\mu$.[58]

[57] The success of this procedure depends upon the thorough extraction of organic matter by chloroform prior to the evaporation and permanganate treatment.

[58] Analytical Chemistry of the Manhattan Project, *op. cit.*, pp. 77 and following, gives an extensive review of methods.

## PEROXIDE METHODS

In an alkaline medium uranyl salts and peroxides give a yellow color with maximum absorbance at 340 m$\mu$. Of the elements soluble in such media, chromium causes serious interference and its prior removal is necessary. The interference due to vanadium is removed by boiling the solution which destroys the vanadium-peroxide complex but not that of uranium. The molybdenum-peroxide complex color fades out on standing 2 hours. When applied to material containing 0.015 down to 0.002% of uranium complete decomposition of the sample is necessary and a considerable amount of prior separation.[59]

*Procedure.*—In the 0.015% range a 5.000-g. sample is used. Organic matter is destroyed by ignition, if present. An initial attack with nitric acid (40 ml. of 1:1 acid) and 15 ml. of HF is made in platinum. After evaporating twice to dryness with nitric acid, the residue is transferred to a glass vessel with final use of 1:1 HCl to remove adhering matter. After adding 10 ml. of concentrated hydrochloric acid the solution is evaporated to dryness. After filtering and washing with hot 1:1 hydrochloric acid, the residue is treated with HF and taken down, with sulfuric acid added, in platinum. The remaining residue is sintered with sodium carbonate, converted to chlorides, and added to the main solution.

If silica appears in later evaporations it is broken down with HF and finally obtained in hydrochloric acid solution.

Two extractions with ethyl acetate serve to remove iron from the 1:1 HCl solution. The ethyl acetate extracts are back-washed with 1:1 HCl twice (5 ml. each) and the acid is added to the original aqueous solution. The solution is concentrated to 25 ml.

After dilution to about 300 ml., sodium hydroxide is added to a slight persistent cloudiness and then dry sodium carbonate until effervescence ceases then 2 more grams. In about 1 hour the solution is filtered through a 12.5-cm. Whatman No. 40 paper. The precipitate is washed from the paper, dissolved, and retreated with sodium hydroxide-sodium carbonate.

The combined filtrates are acidified with hydrochloric acid, adding 2 ml. in excess and noting the bulk of any aluminum precipitate near neutrality. After concentrating to 150 ml., add aluminum chloride equivalent to 35–50 mg. of $Al_2O_3$ unless presence of aluminum is observed, when about half as much aluminum chloride should suffice. If a turbidity appears it is cleared with dilute HCl. Add to the boiling solution 1 g. of diammonium hydrogen phosphate, then ammonia to the hot solution until barely alkaline to methyl red. A buffer solution (308 g. ammonium acetate and 460 ml. acetic acid per liter) is added to make the solution decidedly acid. The solution is heated to boiling and digested on a steam bath for 30 minutes, filtered, and washed with portions of a solution containing 20 ml. of the ammonium acetate-acetic acid buffer per 100 ml. (Whatman No. 42 paper is used.) The precipitate is transferred to a flask by less than 50 ml. of water, followed by the addition of hydrochloric acid dropwise, then 2 ml. in excess. If very little vanadium is present as indicated after adding 3 drops of "Superoxol" (50% hydrogen peroxide), sodium hydroxide is added past the neutral point to 5 ml. in excess. Filter through a paper moistened with sodium hydroxide-"Superoxol" and after adjusting to 50 ml. is read at 370 m$\mu$ versus a uranium standard in the same concentration of "Superoxol" and sodium hydroxide.

[59] Foster and Grimaldi, Bull. 1006, U. S. Geol. Survey, 1954.

If too much vanadium is found with the uranium solution, the phosphate precipitation is repeated.

An alternate procedure for isolating the uranium is the double cupferron method applied after first extracting ferric chloride to ethyl acetate.

## ETHER EXTRACTION-PEROXIDE METHOD

After any appropriate attack on low-grade material, provided a nitrate solution can be made with only minor amounts of fluoride or phosphate, the use of ferric or aluminum nitrate as a salting agent permits the extraction of the uranium to ether. The ether is then vaporized off and the aqueous residue is treated with 2 ml. of sulfuric, 3 ml. of nitric, and 3 ml. of perchloric acids and taken to fumes of $SO_3$. The addition of the acids and the fuming is repeated. After cooling and diluting to 100 ml., the solution is neutralized with 1:1 sodium hydroxide and 10 ml. in excess is added. After boiling, cooling, and making up to 140 ml., about 2 g. of sodium peroxide is added by spatula and the solution is filtered through Whatman No. 50 paper. The absorbance is read relative to water at 425 m$\mu$. A calibration curve is made by similar color development procedure.[60]

## 8-HYDROXYQUINOLINE PHOTOMETRIC METHOD

As explained under "Solvent Extraction Methods," uranium that has been extracted to tributyl phosphate may be transferred back to an aqueous buffer containing ammonium acetate. The solution should be in the pH range 7–9, and will be close to pH 7 when obtained by the tributyl phosphate method as above indicated. To the acetate solution is added 5 ml. of a 1% solution of 8-hydroxyquinoline in 70% ethanol. The uranium complex is extracted with two 5-ml. portions of chloroform and the combined extracts are filtered through a small dry paper and the absorbance is read at 425 m$\mu$ vs. a blank.

## FERROCYANIDE METHOD

In a solution free of substances that are precipitated by or that form colored complexes (Fe, Cu, Ni) with ferrocyanide, and preferably in nitric acid medium, uranyl ion forms a reddish-brown complex. The nitric acidity should be closely the same in calibration solutions and in analytical samples, 0.01 to 0.1 $N$. The best uranium range is 0.2 to 1 mg.

*Procedure.*—The uranium solution in a 25-ml. volumetric flask is neutralized to phenolphthalein, then 3 drops of concentrated nitric acid are added. One ml. of 3% potassium ferrocyanide is added and the solution is diluted, mixed, and allowed to stand. The absorbance is then read in a 1-cm. cell versus a blank. The calibration is good only from 0.2 mg. to 1 mg. of U per 25.00 ml.[61]

If the calibrations and analyses are made in a solution made by nitric acid treatment followed by sulfuric acid fuming, then upon adding to the solution of the sulfate 10 ml. of a formate-formic acid buffer (68 g. sodium formate and 2 ml. concentrated nitric acid in 500 ml. adjusted to pH 5), diluting to 100 ml., and filtering into a 100-ml. flask, the color is developed by adding 25 ml. of 10% ferrocyanide and adding water to the mark and mixing. This procedure eliminates fluoride, acetate, citrate, tartrate, and carbonate interferences and stabilizes the amount of sulfate in samples and calibration solutions.

60 Rodden, AEC Report A-2912, Vol. **I,** p. 6.
61 Analytical Chemistry of the Manhattan Project, p. 102.

## DIBENZOYLMETHANE METHOD

As has been pointed out, the methyl isobutyl ketone solvent extraction procedure generally results in a solution suitable for the development of a photometric completion of the estimation with the aid of dibenzoylmethane, p. 1188.

This photometric method was developed by Yoe et al.[62] Two moles of the reagent unite with one of uranyl in an optimum range of pH 6.5 to 8.5. The lower limit is 1 microgram of U per ml. of solution. The reagent is 1 g. of dibenzoylmethane per 100 ml. of 95% ethanol. The authors used the ether extraction procedure from molar nitric acid saturated with ammonium nitrate. After evaporating off the ether from four combined ether extracts, the aqueous layer was neutralized with sodium hydroxide. The precipitate was dissolved in nitric acid and then sodium carbonate was added to give a 1–5% concentration. After boiling the small amount of ferric hydroxide was filtered on Whatman No. 42 paper, and the filtrate and washings were collected in a 100-ml. volumetric flask, cooled, diluted to 100 ml., and made homogeneous. An aliquot was pipetted to a beaker containing 28 ml. of 95% alcohol and water was added to 45 ml. The pH was adjusted to 5.0 to 5.5. One ml. of the reagent was added and the solution mixed, adjusted to pH 7, and made up to 50 ml. in a volumetric flask. The absorbance is read at 395 m$\mu$ vs. an appropriate blank.

The method is useful only after fairly complete separation of uranium from other metallic ions.

## FLUORESCENCE METHODS

Fluorescence is the most sensitive means for determining minute amounts of uranium for analytical purposes. The uranium is obtained in a fused wafer of sodium fluoride or of sodium-potassium carbonate or in a mixed fluoride carbonate melt after appropriate prior treatment. Certain substances quench the fluorescence, notably iron, manganese, chromium, copper, etc. while others enhance the fluorescence and still others fluoresce under like conditions. One school of thought has advocated the use of an effective separation procedure prior to the preparation of the fused disc. Another school of thought has favored ultrasensitive detectors and amplifiers, and to dilute the sample so far that all quenching effects are "diluted" out.[63]

One of the earliest fluorimeters for solid work was improvised by Neuman [64] using a simple ultraviolet lamp, a filter to screen out visible light, another filter to screen out the reflected ultraviolet light from the visible fluorescent light, and a photographic search unit as a detector. Determination down to 0.005 microgram per gram of soft tissue could be made. Many of the fluorimeters for solids now in use employ the reflection principle, while others employ the transmission assembly, with appropriate filters as a more sensitive technique.

Exhaustive studies of the method have been made by Grimaldi and associates.[65] In general, uranium is separated from a small sample (0.15 g.) of low-grade rock after fusion with a sodium hydroxide-nitrate mixture in an iron crucible (1.5 g. NaOH and 0.1 g. $NaNO_3$), and is transferred to a 100-ml. beaker with water. After neutralizing with nitric acid and adding 7.5 ml. in excess, boiling, cooling,

[62] Yoe, J. H., Will, III, F., and Black, R. A., Anal. Chem., 25, 1200, 1953.
[63] Price, Ferretti and Schwartz, AECD 2282, 1945.
[64] Neuman, Fleming, Carlson and Glover, J. Biol. Chem., 173, 41–52, 1948.
[65] Geological Survey Bulletin 1006.

and making up to 50 ml., a 5.00-ml. aliquot is transferred to a glass-stoppered test tube and 9.5 g. of $Al(NO_3)_3 \cdot 9H_2O$ is added and dissolved by heating. After cooling, 10 ml. of ethyl acetate is added and the tube is shaken vigorously for at least 1 minute. Most of the ethyl acetate layer is withdrawn and filtered through a dry Whatman No. 42 filter paper into a dry tube. 5.00 ml. of the filtrate is transferred to a platinum crucible and burned carefully. The residue is dried at 100°C. and fused with 3 g. of sodium fluoride at a temperature below 700°C. After the melt cools it can be compared visually with melts containing 0.000 to 0.010% in increments of 0.002% based on an aliquot containing 7.5 mg. of the sample. The standards thus have for 3.0 g. of melt 0.00, 0.15, etc., to 0.75 microgram of uranium.

More sophisticated techniques can employ any valid separation method, and the one just described involving ethyl acetate and aluminum nitrate as salting agent has met with considerable usage. The extraction is followed by taking a small aliquot of the extract, e.g., 0.1 ml. and adding it to a small pellet (0.4 g.) of 2% lithium fluoride and 98% sodium fluoride in a platinum dish 0.015″ thick and 0.75″ in diameter made on a die from foil. Pellets are dried and heated in a definite time and temperature sequence with a propane-air flame.[66] A sensitive fluorimetric instrument is used in reading the intensities of analytical samples versus calibration samples. Several instrument makers, e.g., Jarrell-Ash, etc., now produce fluorimeters for measurements on solid samples. Much further detail is given by DeSesa.[67]

The direct determination of micro amounts of uranium in solid or solution samples has been intensively studied.[68] The transmission type of fluorimeter is found to be inherently more sensitive and simpler in construction than the reflection type because of the short path of the exciting ultraviolet radiation and the short path beyond the filter on the other side to the sensing photocell.

The fusion mixture that was adopted consisted of 9 g. NaF, 45.5 g. $Na_2CO_3$, and 45.5 g. of $K_2CO_3$. After 20 minutes heating in a platinum dish at 650°C., fusion is completed over a Meker burner, swirling the melt to make it homogenous. After cooling and breaking up the fused mass in a mortar to 5-mesh size, the mixture is ground for 3 hours in a ball mill and stored with protection from atmospheric moisture until used.

Solid samples are fused by taking 3.00 mg. of sample to 3 g. of fusion mixture. Aliquots of solution samples of 0.100 ml. are put into the crucible lid or platinum shallow dish made of foil, and evaporated, then fused with the 3.00 g. fusion mixture. The time and temperature of the fusion are most important. For this process a temperature of 650°C. for 25 minutes is adequate. With standard-sized dishes the possible variation in thickness of the fused cake introduces very little error. The method is stated to be so sensitive that a few thousandths of 1% of uranium can be determined in an 0.02 mg. sample.[69]

## POLAROGRAPHIC METHOD

Uranyl ion shows markedly different behavior polarographically depending upon the pH and presence of complex-formers. In 0.01 $M$ HCl plus 0.1 $M$ KCl there

[66] Centanni, Ross, and DeSesa, Anal. Chem., **28**, 1651, 1956.
[67] DeSesa, First Gattlinburg Conference on Analytical Chemistry in Nuclear Reactor Technology, U. S. A.E.C. document TID-7555, p. 57 ff.
[68] Fletcher, p. 51; Grimaldi, Ward and Fuyat, p. 69 in U. S. Geol. Survey Bulletin 1006; the design of fluorimeters is also given in this bulletin.
[69] *Loc. cit.*, Bulletin 1006, p. 64.

is a U(VI) to U(V) wave at about $-0.2$ volt versus S.C.E. followed by a coalesced U(V) to U(III) wave approximately twice as large at $-0.94$ volt. A $U^{+4}$ solution in the same medium shows only the wave at $-0.94$ volt. Its height clearly indicates a one-electron change, $U^{+4}$ to $U^{+3}$. In an acetate medium (0.2 $M$ acetic acid) three waves appear at about $-0.2$, $-0.7$, and $-1.2$ versus S.C.E., respectively; the waves are of unequal height. In 2 $N$ HCl or $M$ sulfuric acid the U(VI) to U(V) and U(V) to U(IV) waves are coalesced with $E_{1/2}$ at about $-0.2$ volt. The reason is that disproportionation of U(V) into U(VI) and U(IV) occurs very rapidly near the mercury droplets and the process appears to be a 2-electron process. Similar behavior is shown in 2 $M$ hydroxylamine hydrochloride solution; a buffer 0.1 $M$ each in potassium citrate and citric acid shows a similar effect, the 2 electron wave having an $E_{1/2}$ of $-0.38$. In most alkaline mixtures the U(VI) to U(V) is found at various half-wave potentials: 0.1 $M$ $NH_3$, $-1.0$ volt; 0.5 $M$ ammonium carbonate, $-0.83$; 0.1 $M$ sodium carbonate, $-1.13$; 0.1 $M$ sodium hydroxide, $-0.71$ volt $M$ all versus S.C.E. In those cases where further reduction occurs the $E_{1/2}$ for the U(V) to U(IV) reduction is from $-1.34$ to $-1.45$ volts.

Complexing solutions have been studied with a view to determining uranium in complex mixtures. The hydroxylamine hydrochloride background prevents ferric iron interference by reduction whereas the use of citrate or EDTA complexes iron. In general uranium waves coalesce with or are interfered by Cu, Mo, and V in hydroxylamine hydrochloride media, by lead in this medium if tartrate is added, and by lead in ammonium citrate medium if phosphate is present.

Nitrate and vanadate enhance uranium waves and in case of the former the process is limited by uranium content under special conditions with no foreign metallic ions present.

The foregoing material presents a brief abstract of much of the classical material on the polarography of uranium.[70]

The method is well adapted to the final estimation of small amounts of uranium that have been separated from the majority of impurities. It has been much used to determine smaller or larger amounts of U(VI) in the presence of U(IV). For example, $UO_2F_2$ if present in $UF_4$ has been stated to be extracted by alcohol. According to Burd and Goward[71] $U^{+6}$ in oxide samples can be determined by dissolving the uranium oxide sample in hot concentrated phosphoric acid and making the polarogram with a sulfuric-phosphoric medium. The method is stated to handle 0.2 to 20% content of $U^{+6}$ in uranium oxides and fuel elements to $+4\%$ at the 95% confidence level.

## OTHER METHODS

Uranium hexafluoride has been a key compound in the preparation of materials enriched in $U^{235}$ for power or weapons applications. It is prepared by the fluorination of $UF_4$. Analytical use has sometimes been made of the treatment of materials with anhydrous HF then with $F_2$ for the separation of uranium from many other elements. The first treatment is at 300–400°C. starting with a paste

[70] Watters and Furman, Analytical Chemistry of the Manhattan Project, pp. 586–610, Analytical Chemistry of the Manhattan Project, Rodden, Ed., McGraw-Hill Co., New York, 1950.
[71] Burd and Goward, U. S. A.E.C. Report WAPD-205, 1959.

of material.  The treatment with anhydrous HF is at 700°C. in a nickel boat. After this treatment, elemental fluorine is introduced at 400°C.  One of the chief contaminants of the $UF_6$ is molybdenum.[72]

The analysis of $UF_6$ for enrichment is done mass-spectrographically.  The testing of purified $UF_6$ is in part done by freezing a sample and determining the melting point.  This gives a measure of total impurities, e.g., HF.  For impurity identification and estimation a sample of the $UF_6$ is hydrolyzed and conventional impurity determinations are made after conversion to the sulfate or the nitrate. Uranium is determined in order to establish the weight of sample.

Increasing use is being made of x-ray fluorescence for determination of uranium in various situations.  The procedure calls for standard samples that must usually be established in the first instance by chemical analysis.

## METHODS FOR URANIUM IN ANALYSES
## IN OTHER CHAPTERS

Uranium in Vanadium Ores          See Analysis of Vanadium Ores

[72] Analytical Chemistry of the Manhattan Project, *op. cit.*, p. 39.

# Chapter 51

# VANADIUM

V, *at. wt.* 50.942; *sp. gr.* 6.025; *m.p.* 1710°C.; *b.p.* 3000°C.; *oxides,* $V_2O$, $V_2O_2$, $V_2O_3$, $V_2O_4$, $V_2O_5$; *vanadates—meta* $NaVO_3$, *ortho* $Na_3VO_4$, *pyro* $Na_4V_2O_7$, *tetra* $Na_3HV_6O_{17}$, *hexa* $Na_2H_2V_6O_{17}$

Vanadium is widely distributed in nature in ores, clays, hard coal, igneous rocks, limestones, sandstones; but not in appreciable amounts in high silicious rocks. It occurs in ores of copper and lead, in basalts, in soda ash, phosphate soda, blast furnace slags. The following are the more important vanadium minerals: vanadinite, $(PbCl)Pb_4(VO_4)_3$, (8–21% $V_2O_5$), associated with lead ores, a deep red, yellow or brown mineral, with white to pale yellow streak; patronite, the principal source of vanadium, a sulfide of vanadium (28–34% $V_2O_5$), associated with pyrites and carbonaceous matter, greenish-black, resembling slaty coal; roscoelite, a vanadium mica with variable composition, dark green to brown; carnotite, $K_2O \cdot 2UO_3 \cdot V_2O_5 \cdot 3H_2O$ (19–20% $V_2O_5$); other minerals in which vanadium is associated with lead, zinc, copper, aluminum, manganese, bismuth, calcium, and barium.

Vanadium was discovered by Manuel del Rio in 1801 in the lead ores of Mexico. Thirty years later Sefstrom found the element in iron produced from the ores of Taberg in Sweden. Berzelius contributed much to the knowledge of the element.

Vanadium is used in production of many special steels. Tool steels also very frequently contain vanadium either alone or in combination with other elements, the amounts ranging from 0.20 to 1.00%. All American high speed tool steels contain vanadium associated with tungsten and chromium and sometimes other elements; in these products the proportions are generally from 0.75 to 2.50%.

In the chemical industries vanadium compounds have been used in indelible inks, in the mordanting of aniline black on silk, in calico printing, in photography, and similar minor applications. Vanadium pentoxide is also used in glass to absorb ultraviolet light and both this compound and the metallic vanadates have been employed for coloring glass and ceramic glazes. The principal chemical use, however, is in the preparation of catalytic bodies for various oxidation reactions, chiefly in the oxidation of sulfur dioxide in the production of sulfuric acid and in the manufacture of phthalic anhydride from naphthalene; these uses now consume large quantities. Other catalytic uses are in the control of motor vehicle exhaust gas and in petroleum refining.

Other products used in the manufacture of vanadium and uranium alloys or in other lines of industry are vanadium oxide (as high as 99% $V_2O_5$), sodium vanadate (as high as 66% $V_2O_5$), iron vanadate, uranium concentrates (as high as 67% $U_3O_8$), uranium oxide (99% $U_3O_8$), etc.

## DETECTION

*Ammonium sulfide or hydrogen sulfide* passed into an ammoniacal solution of vanadium precipitates brown $V_2S_5$, soluble in an excess of alkali sulfide and in alkalies, forming the brownish-red thio-solution, from which the sulfide may be reprecipitated by acids.

*Reducing Agents.*—Metallic zinc, sulfites ($SO_2$), oxalic acid, tartaric acid, sugar, alcohol, hydrogen sulfide, hydrochloric acid, hydrobromic and hydriodic acids (KI) reduce the acid solutions of vanadates with formation of a blue-colored liquid. (See Titrimetric Methods.) Reduction is hastened by heating.

*Hydrogen peroxide* added to a cold acid solution of vanadium produces a brown color, changing to blue upon application of heat. See Detection of Vanadium in Steel.

The oxide, $V_2O_5$, is distinguished from $Fe_2O_3$ by the fact that it fuses very readily with the heat of Bunsen burner, whereas the oxide of iron, $Fe_2O_3$, is infusible in the heat of a blast lamp.   M.p. $V_2O_5 = 658°C.$; m.p. $Fe_2O_3 = 1548°C.$

*Comparison of Vanadium and Chromium Salts.*—Vanadium, like chromium, forms a soluble salt upon fusion with sodium carbonate and potassium nitrate or with sodium peroxide. The solution of vanadates and of chromates are yellow or orange; the color of the chromate becomes more intense when strongly acidified, whereas that of the vanadate is reduced. The yellow color of the vanadate solution is destroyed by boiling with an excess of alkali, but may be restored by neutralizing the alkali with acid. The chromate color is not destroyed. (Yellow with alkalies, orange in acid solution.) Silver nitrate produces a dark-maroon precipitate with a soluble chromate and an orange-colored precipitate with a vanadate; mercurous nitrate produces a red-colored precipitate with chromates and a yellow with vanadates. Vanadates are also distinguished from chromates by the reduction test; [1] reducing agents such as a soluble sulfite, or sulfurous acid added to acid solutions, form a blue-colored liquid with vanadates and a green color with chromates. Ammonium hydroxide added in excess to the cold reduced solutions gives a brown color, or a brown to dirty green precipitate with vanadium, and violet or lavender color or a light green-colored precipitate with chromium, depending upon the concentration of the solutions. Hydrogen peroxide added to the reduced cold acid solutions changes the vanadium blue to reddish brown; the chromium green remains unchanged.

*Detection of Vanadium in Steel.*—One gram of the sample is dissolved in dilute nitric acid, the nitrous fumes boiled off, the solution cooled, and an excess of sodium bismuthate added. After filtering through an asbestos filter an excess of concentrated ferrous sulfate solution is added, and the solution divided into two equal parts in test tubes. To one portion 10 ml. of hydrogen peroxide are added and to the other 10 ml. of water. If vanadium is present the peroxide solution will show a deeper color than the untreated solution. A deep red color is produced with high vanadium steels and a brownish-red with low. Since titanium also causes this color, it would interfere, if it were not for the fact that the color produced with titanium is destroyed by hydrofluoric acid and fluorides, whereas that of

---

[1] Reduction with zinc is rapid with vanadates, much less vigorous with chromates. $V_2O_5$ reduced to $V_2O_2$, color changes to blue, green, lavender and finally violet. $SO_2$ or $H_2S$ reduces $V_2O_5$ to $V_2O_4$. $V_2O_2$ forms vanadyl salts.

vanadium is not. In presence of titanium, 5 ml. of hydrofluoric acid are added to the treated sample.

The brown color produced by hydrogen peroxide, with vanadium solutions, will remain in the water portion when shaken with ether. The ether layer is colored a transient blue in presence of chromium.

Hydrogen peroxide is the most satisfactory test for general work. Iron, an element usually associated with vanadium, offers little interference. Titanium and large amounts of molybdenum will give trouble, but the first mentioned can be taken care of with hydrofluoric acid. Hydrogen sulfide gas passed through a vanadate made alkaline with ammonia gives a red color to the solution. This is the most sensitive test known for vanadium. Unfortunately, many of the common elements precipitate or render the test useless unless previously removed. With some experience, the analyst can detect 0.01% V providing the steel contains not more than small amounts of chromium and no titanium. The chromium reduces the sensitivity of the test due to the pronounced green color of its reduced [2] salts.

## ESTIMATION

The materials in which the estimation of vanadium is desired are essentially ores, metallurgical products, and chemical products.

In the process of analysis in presence of considerable ferric iron vanadium is quantitatively precipitated by $NH_4OH$ leading to an error in the iron and aluminum determination unless accounted for. If aluminum alone is present the precipitation of vanadium is not complete. $NH_4OH$ alone does not precipitate vanadium.

## PREPARATION AND SOLUTION OF THE SAMPLE

While many vanadium and uranium ores can be completely, or almost completely, decomposed by treatment with mineral acids, the only universally applicable method of decomposition consists in fusion with sodium peroxide. Because of the presence of carbonaceous matter and free sulfur in patronite, this ore is best decomposed by the last-mentioned method. Vanadinite, descloizite, mottramite, etc., can in general be decomposed with acids. Roscoelite is not readily soluble in acids. Carnotite is easily soluble even in cold dilute mineral acids, but some of the vanadium minerals that accompany it are not (Hillebrand).

*Element.*—The metal is not attacked by aqueous alkalies, but is soluble by fusion with potassium or sodium hydroxide, and sodium carbonate containing potassium nitrate. It is insoluble in dilute hydrochloric and sulfuric acids. It dissolves in concentrated sulfuric acid and in dilute and concentrated nitric acid forming blue solutions.

*Oxides.*—$V_2O_2$ is easily soluble in dilute acids, giving a lavender-colored solution.

$V_2O_3$ is insoluble in hydrochloric and sulfuric acids, and in alkali solutions. It dissolves in hydrofluoric acid and in nitric acid.

$V_2O_4$ is easily soluble in acids, forming blue-colored solutions. It dissolves in alkali solutions.

$V_2O_5$ is soluble in acids, alkali hydroxide, and carbonate solutions; insoluble in alcohol and acetic acid.

[2] L. E. Harper.

*Salts.*—Ammonium metavanadate, $NH_4VO_3$, is slightly soluble in cold water, readily soluble in hot water. The presence of ammonium chloride renders the salt less soluble. The vanadates of lead, mercury, and silver are difficultly soluble in water. These are dissolved, or are transposed by mineral acids, the vanadium going into solution; i.e., lead vanadate treated with sulfuric acid precipitates lead sulfate and vanadic acid passes into solution.

*General Procedure for Decomposition of Ores.*—One gram (or more) of the finely divided material is placed in a large platinum crucible together with five times its weight of a mixture of sodium carbonate and potassium nitrate ($Na_2CO_3$ = 10, $KNO_3$ = 1). The product is heated to fusion over a blast lamp and, when molten, about 0.5 to 1 g. more of the nitrate added in small portions. (*Caution*— platinum is attacked by $KNO_3$. A large excess of $Na_2CO_3$ tends to prevent this.) The material should be kept in quiet fusion for ten to fifteen minutes, when most of the ores will be completely decomposed. The cooled fusion is extracted with boiling water, whereby the vanadium goes into solution. Arsenic, antimony, phosphorus, molybdenum, tungsten, and chromium pass into solution with the vanadium. These must be removed in the gravimetric determination of this element. (Iron remains insoluble in the water extract.)

Should there be any undecomposed ore, the residue from the water extract will be gritty. If this is the case, a second fusion with the above fusion mixture should be made.

Small amounts of occluded vanadium may be recovered from the water-insoluble residue by dissolving this in nitric acid and pouring the solution into a boiling solution of sodium hydroxide. Vanadium remains in solution.

Vanadium may be determined titrimetrically after removal of the hydrogen sulfide group, by titration with potassium permanganate according to the procedure given later. The isolation and determination of vanadium by the gravimetric procedures are given in detail later.

**Ores and Material High in Silica.**—The sample is treated in a platinum dish with about ten times its weight of hydrofluoric acid (10 to 50 ml.) and 2 to 5 ml. of concentrated sulfuric acid. The silica is expelled as $SiF_4$ and the hydrofluoric acid driven off by taking the solution to $SO_3$ fumes. The residue is extracted with hot water containing a little sulfuric acid. Any undissolved residue may be brought into solution by fusion with potassium acid sulfate, $KHSO_4$, and extraction with hot water containing a little sulfuric acid. By this treatment the iron passes into solution with vanadium.

**Products Low in Silica.**—Decomposition may be effected by fusion in a nickel crucible with sodium peroxide and extraction with water. The water should be added cautiously, as the reaction is vigorous. One gram of the finely divided ore is intimately mixed with 3 to 4 g. of $Na_2O_2$ and 1 g. of the peroxide placed on the charge. The material is then fused as stated.[3]

*Iron and Steel.*—The solution of the sample, isolation of vanadium and its volumetric determination are given at the close of the chapter.

*Alloys.*—These may be decomposed with nitric acid, or aqua regia. The isolation of vanadium with mercurous nitrate or lead acetate are given under the gravimetric methods.

---

[3] Direct reduction and titration of vanadium in presence of a large accumulation of salts leads to erroneous results. The vanadium should be separated by precipitation with lead acetate.

## SEPARATIONS

Fusion with sodium carbonate and potassium nitrate and extraction of the melt with water effect a separation of vanadium from most of the metals, which remain insoluble as carbonates or oxides. Arsenic, molybdenum, tungsten, chromium, and phosphorus, however, pass into the filtrate with vanadium.

*Removal of Arsenic.*—This element generally occurs in vanadium ores. It may be removed when desired, by acidifying the water extract of the fusion with sulfuric acid, and after reducing arsenic with $SO_2$, precipitating the sulfide, $As_2S_3$ with $H_2S$ gas. Vanadium passes into the filtrate.

*Removal of Molybdenum.*—The procedure is similar to that used for arsenic. The solution is treated with $H_2S$. It is advisable to resaturate the solution with $H_2S$ before filtering off the sulfide. Some vanadium invariably accompanies the molybdenum on the first precipitation of molybdenum when separating from large amounts of vanadium.

*Separation from Phosphoric Acid.*—In the gravimetric procedure phosphorus and vanadium are precipitated together as mercurous vanadate and phosphate. The mercury is expelled by heat and the oxides $V_2O_5$ and $P_2O_5$ weighed. ($V_2O_5$ in presence of $P_2O_5$ does not melt as it does in pure form, but only sinters.) The oxides are fused with an equal weight of sodium carbonate, the melt dissolved in water, then acidified with sulfuric acid and vanadium reduced to the vanadyl condition by $SO_2$ gas. The excess of $SO_2$ is expelled by boiling and passing in $CO_2$, then cooled to room temperature and phosphoric acid now precipitated with ammonium molybdate (50 ml. of a solution containing 75 grams ammonium molybdate dissolved in 500 ml. of water and poured into 500 ml. nitric acid—sp. gr. 1.2) in presence of a large amount of ammonium nitrate and a little free nitric acid. It is advisable to dissolve the precipitate in ammonia and reprecipitate in presence of additional ammonium molybdate and nitrate by acidifying with nitric acid. The equivalent $P_2O_5$ is deducted from the weight of the combined oxides, the difference being due to $V_2O_5$.

NOTE.—Vanadium must be completely reduced to the vanadyl form, as vanadic acid will precipitate with phosphoric acid.

*Separation of Vanadium and Chromium.*—A titrimetric procedure for determining vanadium and chromium in the presence of one another is given later. If a separation is desired the following procedures may be used:

*A.* The solution is acidified with nitric acid. If hydrochloric acid is present it is expelled by taking to near dryness twice with nitric acid, the residue is taken up with water and $SO_2$ gas passed in to reduce the vanadium completely. This solution is poured into a boiling solution of 10% sodium hydroxide. After boiling a few minutes, the solution is filtered and the residue washed. The filtrate contains vanadium, the residue chromium. It is advisable to pour the filtrate into additional caustic to remove the small amount of chromium that passes into solution.

*B.* One hundred ml. of the neutral solution is made acid with about 15 ml. of glacial acetic acid and hydrogen peroxide added. The solution is boiled for a few minutes. Chromium is thereby reduced to $Cr_2O_3$, whereas vanadium appears as $V_2O_5$. Lead acetate will now precipitate lead vanadate, the reduced chromium remaining in solution. The lead vanadate now treated with concentrated sulfuric acid is decomposed upon heating. Addition of water precipitates $PbSO_4$, the vanadium remaining in solution.

*Separation of Vanadium by Precipitation with Cupferron.*—This method is more efficient, consumes less time, and is the basis of separating numerous other elements. The chromium having been reduced to the trivalent condition by hydrogen peroxide, alcohol, or sulfur dioxide, and the excess expelled, cupferron (6% water solution) is then added to a 4% $H_2SO_4$ solution of the two metals. Complete precipitation of V is indicated by the appearance of a milky white precipitation. This separation should be conducted in cold solutions, i.e., 0° to 20°C.

## GRAVIMETRIC METHODS

The following procedures presuppose that vanadium is present in the solution as an alkali vanadate, the form in which it occurs in the water extract from a fusion with sodium carbonate and potassium nitrate, as is described in the method of solution of ores containing vanadium. Chromium, arsenic, phosphorus, molybdenum, and tungsten, if present in the ore will be found in this solution.

Vanadium is best determined by titrimetric methods but the following procedures may have occasional use.

### PRECIPITATION WITH MERCUROUS NITRATE [4]

A nearly neutral solution of mercurous nitrate precipitates vanadium completely from its solution. The dried precipitate when ignited forms the oxide, $V_2O_5$, mercury being volatilized.

*Procedure.*—To the alkaline solution or an aliquot portion of the water extract from the sodium carbonate potassium nitrate fusion nearly neutralized with nitric acid [5] (the solution should remain slightly alkaline) is added drop by drop, a nearly neutral solution of mercurous nitrate in slight excess of that necessary to precipitate completely the vanadium present, as may be determined by allowing the precipitate to settle and adding a few drops more of the reagent. The mixture is heated to boiling and then placed on the water bath or steam plate and the gray-colored precipitate allowed to settle. The precipitate is filtered off, and washed several times with water containing a few drops of mercurous nitrate, then washed once or twice by decantation and finally on the filter paper. The precipitate is dried, then ignited in a porcelain crucible in a hood over a Bunsen burner to a red heat. The fused red residue is $V_2O_5$.

$$V_2O_5 \times 0.5602 = V$$

### PRECIPITATION WITH LEAD ACETATE [6]

From a weakly acetic acid solution, vanadium is quantitatively precipitated by lead acetate. The precipitate is dissolved in nitric acid, lead removed as a sulfate,

---

[4] Method of Rose. J. W. Mellor, "A Treatise on Quantitative Inorganic Analysis."

[5] Should the alkaline solution of the vanadate be made acid, nitrous acid, from the nitrate fusion, will be liberated and cause reduction of the vanadate to the vanadyl salt, in which form it is not precipitated by mercurous nitrate; hence great care should be used in neutralizing the alkaline solution to avoid making it acid. It is a good practice to measure the acid added, having determined on an aliquot portion the amount necessary to add to neutralize the solution. This is readily accomplished when a comparatively large sample has been prepared for analysis and an aliquot portion taken for analysis, several determinations being made on the same fusion.

[6] Method by Roscoe, Ann. Chem. Pharm., Supplement 8, 102, 1872.

and vanadium determined in the filtrate by taking to dryness and igniting to the oxide, $V_2O_5$.

*Procedure.*—To the alkaline solution or an aliquot portion obtained by extraction of the carbonate fusion of the ore with water, just sufficient amount of nitric acid is added to nearly neutralize the alkali present, as in the case of the method described for precipitation of vanadium by mercurous nitrate, and then a 10% solution of lead acetate is added in slight excess with continuous stirring. The precipitate is allowed to settle on the steam bath. The vanadate, first appearing orange colored, will fade to white upon standing. The lead vanadate is filtered and washed free of the excess of lead acetate with water containing acetic acid. The precipitate is washed into a porcelain dish with a little dilute nitric acid, and brought into solution by warming the lead salt with nitric acid. To this, the ash of the incinerated filter is added. Sufficient sulfuric acid is added to precipitate the lead completely, and the solution taken to small volume on the water bath and then to $SO_3$ fumes, but not to dryness. About 100 ml. of water are added and the mixture filtered; lead sulfate will remain upon the filter and the vanadium will be in solution. The lead sulfate is washed free of vanadium (i.e., until the washings no longer give a brown color with hydrogen peroxide).

The filtrate containing all the vanadium is evaporated to small volume in the porcelain dish, then transferred to a weighed platinum crucible and evaporated to dryness on the water bath and finally the residue ($V_2O_5$) heated to a dull redness over a Bunsen flame.

$$V_2O_5 \times 0.5602 = V$$

NOTES.—Lead may be separated from the vanadium by passing $H_2S$ through the nitric acid solution, the excess of $H_2S$ volatilized by boiling and the liberated sulfur filtered off. The filtrate is evaporated to dryness and the vanadium ignited with a few drops of nitric acid to the oxide $V_2O_5$.

Lead may also be separated as lead chloride in the presence of alcohol, the solution taken to dryness and vanadium oxidized by addition of nitric acid and ignited to $V_2O_5$.

## TITRIMETRIC METHODS

### POTASSIUM PERMANGANATE METHOD

Vanadium in solution as a vanadate is reduced to the vanadyl salt by $H_2S$ or $SO_2$, the excess of the reducing agent expelled and the solution titrated with standard $KMnO_4$, vanadium being oxidized to its highest form, $V_2O_5$.

Reactions.

$a.$ $2VO_3^- + SO_2 + 4H^+ \rightarrow 2VO^{++} + SO_4^= + 2H_2O$

$b.$ $MnO_4^- + 5VO^{++} + 6H_2O \rightarrow 5VO_3^- + 2Mn^{++} + 12H^+$

*Procedure.*—An aliquot portion of the solution containing vanadium, as obtained by one of the procedures given for the solution of the sample, is taken for analysis; dilute sulfuric acid (1:1) is added to acid reaction and 5 ml. of acid per 100 ml. of solution added in excess. The vanadium content should be not over 0.5 g. V when a tenth normal permanganate is used for the titration. If arsenic or molybdenum is present these may be removed from the solution by passing in $H_2S$, although molybdenum does not interfere. The insoluble sulfides are filtered off and washed with $H_2S$ water. The filtrate is boiled down to two-thirds of its volume and the sulfur filtered off. In the absence of members of the $H_2S$ group, this portion of the procedure is omitted. Before reduction of vanadium, should $H_2S$ have been used, it is necessary to first oxidize the polythionic compounds by addition of $KMnO_4$ to a faint pink color. See below.

**Oxidation with $KMnO_4$.**—The solution containing the vanadium is oxidized by adding, from a burette, 0.1 $N$ potassium permanganate to a faint permanent pink. If the solution has been treated with $H_2S$, the vanadium is in the vanadyl condition, and the amount of permanganate required to oxidize the solution completely will give a close approximate value for the vanadium present, each ml. of 0.1 $N$ $KMnO_4$ being equivalent to 0.005094 g. vanadium.

**Reduction.**—The vanadate is now reduced to vanadyl salt by passing through the acid solution, containing approximately 5% free sulfuric acid, a steady stream of $SO_2$ gas. Reduction may also be accomplished by adding sodium metabisulfite, or sodium sulfite, to the acid solution. The excess $SO_2$ is now removed by boiling (a current of $CO_2$ passed into the hot solution will assist in the complete expulsion of the $SO_2$).

NOTE.—$KMnO_4$ is reduced by $SO_2$.

**Test for Iron.**—A drop test with potassium ferricyanide, $K_3Fe(CN)_6$, on a white tile will give a blue color in the presence of ferrous iron. Since ferrous iron will titrate with potassium permanganate, its oxidation is necessary. This is accomplished by adding 0.1 $N$ potassium dichromate solution cautiously to the cold liquid until no blue color is produced by the spot test with $K_3Fe(CN)_6$ outside indicator. If the sample is sufficiently dilute, the blue color of the vanadyl solution will not interfere in getting the point where the iron is completely oxidized. Care must be taken not to pass this end point, otherwise $V_2O_4$ will also be oxidized and the results will be low.

NOTE.—The action of the dichromate is selective to the extent that iron is first oxidized and then $V_2O_4$. If the amount of iron present is large a separation must be made. In case a sodium carbonate potassium nitrate fusion has been made and vanadium has been extracted by water, iron will not be present. A special procedure for determination of vanadium in steel is given, page 1225.

**Potassium Permanganate Titration.**—0.1 $N$ $KMnO_4$ is now cautiously added until a pink color, persisting for 1 minute, is obtained. During the titration the solution changes from a blue color to a green, then a yellow and finally a faint pink. The reaction towards the end is apt to be slow if made in a cold solution.

NOTES.—In absence of chromium, it is better to make the titration in a hot solution, 60 to 80°C., the end point being improved by heat. In case an excess of permanganate has been added, the excess may be determined by a back titration with 0.1 $N$ thiosulfate. The solution may be rerun, if desired, by repeating the reduction with $SO_2$ and the titration with $K_2Cr_2O_7$ and $KMnO_4$.

One milliliter 0.1 $N$ $KMnO_4$ = 0.005094 g. V, or = 0.009094 g. $V_2O_5$

For solutions containing less than 0.5% vanadium a weaker permanganate reagent should be used. A 0.02 $N$ permanganate solution will be found to be useful for materials low in vanadium.

One can obtain excellent results by the above procedure on materials containing small amounts of iron and chromium; with amounts equal to that of vanadium present in the solution no interference was experienced. The titration with potassium permanganate is made in cold solutions if chromium is present, as the permanganate will oxidize chromium in hot solutions. Potassium permanganate added to samples containing chromic salts, and the mixture boiled, will oxidize these quantitatively to chromates. This reaction does not take place in cold solutions to any appreciable extent during a titration and only slowly in warm solutions.

## ZINC REDUCTION METHOD

The procedure proposed by Gooch and Edgar is to reduce vanadic acid to the V(II) state in presence of sulfuric acid, by zinc; oxidation of the unstable V++ by the air is anticipated by means of ferric chloride or sulfate, in the receiver of the Jones Reductor, the highest degree of reduction being registered by the ferrous salt formed by the reaction of the reduced vanadate on the ferric salt, i.e., $V(II) + 3Fe(III) \rightarrow 3Fe(II) + V(V)$. Compounds reduced by zinc and oxidized by $KMnO_4$ must be absent or allowed for.

*Procedure.*—The Jones Reductor is set up as directed under "Titrimetric Methods," Chapter on Iron. The receiver attached to the tube containing the column of zinc is charged with a solution of ferric alum in considerable excess of that required for the oxidation of the reduced vanadium. (The amalgamated zinc is cleaned by passing through the column, a dilute solution of warm sulfuric acid. The final acid washings should show no further reducing action on permanganate when the reductor is clean.)[7] Gentle suction is applied, and through the column of clean amalgamated zinc are passed in succession—100 ml. of hot water, 100 ml. of 2.5% sulfuric acid, and then the solution of vanadic acid diluted to 25 ml. in a 2.5% sulfuric acid solution, and finally 100 ml. of hot water. To the receiver is added a volume of 4 ml. of syrupy phosphoric acid to decolorize the solution. The reduced iron salt is now titrated with 0.1 $N$ $KMnO_4$.

One ml. 0.1 $N$ $KMnO_4$ = 0.001698 g. V, or = 0.003031 g. $V_2O_5$

## TITRIMETRIC DETERMINATION OF MOLYBDENUM AND VANADIUM

Sulfur dioxide reduces V(V) to V(IV), but does not reduce molybdic acid provided the sample contains 1 ml. of free sulfuric acid per 50 ml. of solution and not more than 0.2 g. of molybdic acid. By means of amalgamated zinc $V_2O_5$ is reduced to $V_2O_2$ and $MoO_3$ to $Mo_2O_3$. Upon these two reactions the determination is based according to the procedure worked out by Edgar.[8] Details of the method are given in the Chapter on Molybdenum.

## TITRIMETRIC DETERMINATION OF VANADIUM, ARSENIC OR ANTIMONY (EDGAR'S METHOD [9])

Tartaric or oxalic acid reduces $V_2O_5$ to $V_2O_4$, but does not act upon arsenic or antimony. On the other hand $SO_2$ causes the reduction of all three. Therefore if aliquot portions of the solution are taken, one portion being treated with tartaric acid and vanadium determined by titration with iodine, and another portion reduced with $SO_2$ and again titrated with iodine, the difference between the two titrations is due to the volume of reagent required for the oxidation of the reduced arsenic or antimony.[10]

---

[7] Corrections should be made for the action of zinc upon the reagents without the vanadic acids, as it is almost impossible to get a condition where no blank is obtained with permanganate. The reductor is cleaned first by passing about 500 ml. of dilute 2.5% sulfuric acid through the column of zinc. A blank is now obtained with the same quantity of reagents as is used in the regular determination, only omitting the vanadium, and this is deducted from the titration obtained for each sample reduced.

[8] Graham, Edgar, Am. Jour. Sci. (4), **25**, 332.

[9] Edgar, G., Am. Jour. Sci. (4), **27**, 299.

[10] See Am. J. Sci. (4), **27**, 174, also Gooch, Methods in Chemical Analysis, p. 510, for procedure determining iron, chromium and vanadium, in presence of one another.

Reactions.

$$2V(IV) + I_2 \rightarrow 2V(V) + 2I^-$$

$$As(III) + 2V(IV) + 2I_2 \rightarrow As(V) + 2V(V) + 4I^-$$

$$Sb(III) + 2V(IV) + 2I_2 \rightarrow Sb(V) + 2V(V) + 4I^-$$

**Procedure for Vanadium.**—One portion is boiled with about 2 g. of tartaric or oxalic acid, until the solution turns the characteristic blue of vanadium tetroxide. After cooling, the solution is nearly neutralized with potassium bicarbonate, and an excess of standard iodine solution added. Neutralization is now completed, an excess of bicarbonate added, and after 15 to 30 minutes the excess iodine titrated with standard arsenious acid, starch being used as an indicator. This titration measures the vanadium present.

**Procedure for Arsenic or Antimony.**—A second portion of the solution is placed in a pressure flask and acidified with sulfuric acid. A strong solution of sulfurous acid is added, the flask closed and heated for 1 hour on the steam bath. After cooling, the flask is opened and the solution transferred to an Erlenmeyer flask and the excess of $SO_2$ removed by boiling, a current of $CO_2$ being passed through the liquid. The cooled solution is treated with bicarbonate, iodine added and the titration conducted exactly as described for determination of vanadium in the first portion. The difference between the first titration and the second is a measure of the volume of $I_2$ solution required for oxidation of arsenic or antimony.

## DETERMINATION OF VANADIUM AND IRON

The solution slightly acidified with sulfuric acid is treated with sulfurous acid, the excess expelled and the reduced vanadium and iron titrated with standard potassium permanganate.[11]

$$5Fe^{++} + 5VO^{++} + 2MnO_4^- + 2H_2O \rightarrow 5Fe^{+3} + 5VO_3^- + 2Mn^{++} + 4H^+$$

The solution is now reduced with zinc in the Jones Reductor and again titrated with permanganate.[10] V(V) is reduced by zinc to V(IV), the sample being caught in ferric alum solution (details for determination of vanadium by reduction with zinc are given under the titrimetric methods for this element).

$$5Fe^{++} + 5V^{++} + 4MnO_4^- + 2H^+ \rightarrow 5Fe^{+3} + 5VO_3^- + 4Mn^{++} + H_2O$$

The difference between the two titrations multiplied by 0.00455 = vanadic oxide $(V_2O_5)$ originally present.

[11] When the color has changed from a bluish-green to greenish-yellow the solution is heated to 70 to 80°C., and the permanganate titration completed in a hot solution.

## COLORIMETRIC/PHOTOMETRIC METHODS

### VANADIUM AS PHOSPHOTUNGSTATE

This method [12] is relatively select and sensitive. The molecular ratio of sodium tungstate to orthophosphoric acid may vary from 3 to 20 without causing visible change. However, the concentration range of sodium tungstate should not be outside 4–34 g. per liter. Interference is caused by the ions of tin, titanium, zirconium, and ammonium; by molybdenum in excess of 0.5 mg. per ml.; by chromate above 0.01 mg. per ml., cobalt or copper above 0.1 mg. per ml., nickel over 0.35 mg. per ml., manganese over 0.4 mg. per ml., and uranium or iron over 1.0 mg. per ml.

The basis of the method is the formation and colorimetric determination of yellow phosphotungstovanadic acid.

*Reagents.* **Standard Vanadium Solution (1.0 mg. per ml.).**—Ignite 1.7852 g. of pure vanadium(V) oxide, $V_2O_5$, at 500°C. After cooling, dissolve in 45 ml. of 6 $N$ NaOH solution, neutralize with 1 $N$ $H_2SO_4$ solution, adding 1 ml. in excess, and dilute to 1 liter. Use aliquots of this standard vanadium solution to prepare for comparison in the range 0.002–0.1 mg. vanadium per ml.

**Standard Sodium Tungstate Solution (0.5 $M$).**—Dissolve in water 16.5 g. of $Na_2WO_4 \cdot 2H_2O$ and dilute to 100 ml.

*Procedure.* **Visual.**—Place a sample containing 0.02–0.2 mg. of vanadium to a Nessler tube, and add slightly less water to a similar tube. To each add 1 ml. of 1:8 sulfuric acid, 0.3 ml. of 85% orthophosphoric acid, and 0.1 ml. of 0.5 $M$ sodium tungstate solution. Add a suitable vanadium standard to the duplicate until the tubes match in color, adjusting to equal volume.

**Instrumental.**—Add 1:8 sulfuric acid (or 1:4 nitric or hydrochloric acid) to the solution of the sample until it is about 0.5 $N$ in the acid. Add 1 ml. of 1:2 orthophosphoric acid and 0.5 ml. of the sodium tungstate solution for each 10 ml. of the solution of the sample. Dilute to volume and determine the absorbance at 400 m$\mu$. (If iron is present or if the vanadium exceeds 0.01 mg. per ml., heat sample solution to boiling and cool before diluting.) Read against a blank solution in the reference cell, or deduct the absorbance of the blank from that of the sample.

### VANADIUM BY REACTION WITH HYDROGEN PEROXIDE

This method is based upon the reddish brown color produced by reaction of pentavalent vanadium and hydrogen peroxide in (mineral) acid solution. Interference by nickel, cobalt, and small amounts of chromium may be resolved with moderate accuracy by adding similar concentrations of the interfering substances to the standard. Tungsten, chromium, and molybdenum, however, must be removed.

*Procedure.*—Measure an aliquot of sample containing about 1.5 mg. of vanadium and dilute to 80 ml. Add enough 1:1 sulfuric acid to make this solution 1 to 2 $N$. If titanium is present, add 1 ml. of 48% hydrofluoric acid to prevent color interference. (The hydrofluoric acid also decolorizes ferric iron, however, if iron but not titanium is present, use 2 ml. 85% orthophosphoric acid instead of hydro-

[12] Vinogradov, A. P., Compt. rend. akad. sci. (U.S.S.R.), **1931A**, 249–52; Sandell, E. B., Ind. Eng. Chem., Anal. Ed., **8**, 236–41, 1936; Wright, E. R., and Mellon, M. G., *ibid.*, **9**, 251–4, 1937.

fluoric to avoid the necessity of using visual methods. If HF is not present, a photometer may be used.) Add 3 ml. of 3% hydrogen peroxide and dilute to volume. Read the absorbance at 450 m$\mu$; against a similarly prepared standard to which 3 ml. of water was added instead of the $H_2O_2$; however, if phosphoric acid was used to decolorize the iron, the maximum absorbance is lower, and better results may be obtained closer to 400 m$\mu$.

## VANADIUM BY 8-QUINOLINOL (OXINE) METHOD

This method is sensitive, being capable of detecting as little as 0.001 mg. (photometrically) of vanadium. In the determination of larger quantities of vanadium (e.g., 0.03 mg.), good results are obtainable in the presence of 0.5 mg. quantities of aluminum, bismuth, cobalt, chromium, copper, manganese, molybdenum, nickel, tin, titanium, uranium, and zinc.[13]

Aluminum, bismuth, and titanium give turbid solutions which do not interfere. Iron, however, must be removed since the black ferric derivative also is extracted at pH 4.0 and absorbs strongly at 550 m$\mu$. Separation of iron is accomplished by shaking the chloroform extract with an ammoniacal buffer solution having a pH of 9.4. The iron remains quantitatively in the chloroform layer while the vanadium transfers to the aqueous phase from which it may again be extracted after adjustment of the pH to 4.0.

The basis of the method is the intensity of magenta-black color of the compound of vanadium and 8-quinolinol (8-hydroxyquinoline or oxine) in chloroform solution.

*Reagents.* **Methyl Orange Indicator, 0.1%.**—Dissolve 0.1 g. of C.P. methyl orange in 100 ml. distilled water.

**Sulfuric Acid, 4 N.**

**Nitric Acid, 4 N.**—Bubble filtered air through concentrated nitric acid until the acid is water-white, standardize by any convenient means, and dilute the appropriate volume to 1 liter.

**Ammonium Hydroxide, 4 N.**—Standardize ammonium hydroxide by titrating with the 4 N nitric acid using methyl orange indicator. Dilute the appropriate volume to 1 liter.

**Ammoniacal Buffer Solution, pH 9.4.**—Dilute a mixture of 200 ml. of 4 N ammonium hydroxide and 100 ml. of 4 N nitric acid to 2 liters with distilled water. It is not necessary to check the pH of this solution if the ammonium hydroxide and nitric acid used are exactly equivalent in strength.

**Phthalate Buffer Solution, pH 4.0.**—Dissolve 12.77 g. of C.P. potassium biphthalate in water and dilute to 250 ml.

**Alcohol-Free Chloroform.**—Extract the alcohol from 2 liters of reagent-grade chloroform by shaking vigorously with six separate portions of distilled water, each portion being one-fourth the volume of the chloroform. Cover with a layer of water and store in a refrigerator if possible.

**8-Quinolinol Solution, 0.5%.**—Dissolve 5 g. of reagent grade 8-quinolinol in 1 liter of alcohol-free chloroform.

**8-Quinolinol Solution, 0.1%.**—Dilute 100 ml. of 0.5% 8-quinolinol solution to 500 ml. with alcohol-free chloroform.

**Standard Vanadium Solution.**—One milliliter should contain 100 micrograms of vanadium. Dissolve 0.2296 g. of C.P. ammonium metavanadate in 25 ml. of 4 N

[13] Talvitie, N. A., Anal. Chem., **25**, 604–607, 1953.

sulfuric acid and dilute to 1 liter with distilled water. Make tenfold dilutions of the stock solution as needed.

*Procedure.*—In the case of samples prepared by wet ashing, transfer 25 ml. of the sample solution to a 125-ml. separatory funnel, using enough rinse water to make a total volume of about 50 ml. Add a drop of methyl orange indicator and neutralize to the intermediate color of the indicator with 4 N ammonium hydroxide or 4 N nitric acid and 1 to 50 dilutions of these reagents.

In the case of samples fused with sodium carbonate, transfer 50 ml. of the clear extract from the fusion to a 125-ml. separatory funnel, neutralize with 4 N sulfuric acid to the intermediate color of methyl orange, and remove carbon dioxide by alternately shaking and releasing the gas through the stopcock. Clean the stem of the funnel with a cotton swab.

Extract the vanadium by shaking for 2.5 minutes with each of three successive 5 ml. portions of 0.5% 8-quinolinol in chloroform, drawing off the chloroform layers into a second separatory funnel containing 50 ml. of the ammoniacal buffer solution. Shake the combined chloroform extracts with the ammoniacal buffer solution for 5 minutes, then draw off and discard the chloroform layer. Wash the aqueous phase by shaking for a minute with 5 ml. of chloroform. If the chloroform layer has a distinct color, repeat washing with a second 5-ml. portion of chloroform.

Add a drop of methyl orange indicator to the aqueous phase and neutralize to the intermediate color of the indicator with 4 N nitric acid. Before final adjustment of the pH with the diluted reagents, stopper, and invert the funnel, and open the stopcock to allow any chloroform or ammoniacal buffer in the bore to drain back into the funnel. Clean the stem of the funnel with a cotton swab, add 2 ml. of phthalate buffer and then re-extract the vanadium by shaking for 2.5 minutes with each of two successive 5.0-ml. portions of 0.1% 8-quinolinol in chloroform. Draw off these extracts into a glass-stoppered, graduated cylinder, note the total volume, and invert gently to mix. The cylinder will retain water droplets when the chloroform extract is transferred to a photometer cell.

Measure the absorbancy at 550 m$\mu$ using 0.1% 8-quinolinol solution in the reference cell. Determine the vanadium content from a calibration curve obtained by treating a series of known solutions of vanadium in the same manner as the prepared samples. Each of the known solutions may be prepared by adding 4 ml. of 4 N nitric acid and the appropriate volume of standard vanadium solution to 50 ml. of water contained in a 125-ml. separatory funnel.

## DETERMINATIONS IN SPECIFIC SUBSTANCES

### ANALYSIS OF VANADIUM ORES

#### *VANADIUM AND URANIUM BY HYDROCHLORIC ACID REDUCTION METHOD (METHOD 1)*

**Reagents.** **Ferrous Ammonium Sulfate, Approximately 0.1 N.**—Prepared by dissolving 49 g. of C.P. $FeSO_4 \cdot (NH_4)_2SO_4 \cdot 6H_2O$ in water, adding 10 ml. of sulfuric acid (sp. gr. 1.84) and making up with water to one liter at room temperature. (The exact titer of this solution need not be known.)

**Potassium Permanganate, Approximately 0.1 N.**—Prepared by dissolving 3.18 g. of pure $KMnO_4$ in boiling distilled water, cooling to room temperature, filtering on asbestos, making up to one liter and mixing thoroughly. The solution is standardized against pure sodium oxalate obtained from the National Bureau of Standards according to their procedure.

**Procedure for Separation.**—From one to 5 g. of the 100-mesh sample, the amount used being determined by the uranium and vanadium contents of the ore, are treated with from 20 to 60 ml. of hydrochloric acid (sp. gr. 1.19) in a 600-ml. beaker provided with a clock-glass cover. The solution is heated at a temperature of about 60°C. until the reaction appears to be complete. Approximately 2 g. of potassium chlorate are added and the solution is boiled for a few minutes. Twelve ml. of sulfuric acid (sp. gr. 1.84) are then introduced and the liquid is evaporated until fumes of sulfur trioxide are given off. When the beaker and its contents have cooled, approximately 50 ml. of water are added and the solution is boiled until all soluble salts have dissolved, then it is filtered on an 11-cm paper into a 250-ml. beaker. The residue of silica, lead sulfate (if the ore contains lead), etc., is washed thoroughly with 1% sulfuric acid and treated as described in the next paragraph.

Inasmuch as carnotite is easily soluble in acids there is little likelihood of uranium being held back in the siliceous residue. However, some of the carnotite ores contain vanadium in combinations which are not so readily broken up by acids, consequently unless experiments on the type of ore being analyzed have shown that the acid treatment extracts all uranium and vanadium it is necessary to treat the insoluble residue as further described. If the ore contains lead, the lead sulfate is dissolved out of the siliceous residue with ammonium acetate. This is accomplished by returning the paper and precipitate to the original beaker, adding an excess of a 25% solution of ammonium acetate and a few milliliters of ammonia, and heating the liquid to boiling. After having beaten the paper to a pulp with a glass rod, the contents of the beaker are transferred to an 11-cm. paper and the filter and residue are washed thoroughly with a hot, slightly ammoniacal 10% solution of ammonium acetate. The filter and its contents are ignited in a porcelain crucible at a low red heat until the carbon of the filter paper has been oxidized, when the residue is transferred to a large platinum crucible. Approximately 2 ml. of nitric acid (sp. gr. 1.42) and 5–10 ml. of 48% hydrofluoric acid are added and the solution is evaporated slowly to dryness. If much quartz is present the treatment with nitric and hydrofluoric acids is repeated. One ml. of sulfuric acid (1:1) is then added and the crucible is heated until sulfur trioxide is freely expelled. The residue is dissolved in water and added to the main solution. Fusion of the residue with potassium pyrosulfate should be used only as a last resort, as the presence of potassium sulfate is objectionable in the subsequent operations.

The procedure described in the preceding paragraphs insures the solution of all uranium and vanadium and the removal of silica and lead. The solution, which should have a volume of approximately 200 ml. and an acidity of 5%, is heated nearly to boiling and saturated with hydrogen sulfide, which will result in the vanadium being reduced to the tetravalent form and copper and other metals of the copper group being precipitated as sulfides. If arsenic is present the hot liquid should be given a prolonged treatment with the hydrogen sulfide. Some ashless paper pulp is added and the solution is filtered on an 11-cm. paper into a 400-ml. beaker. The precipitate of copper sulfide, etc., is washed with 1% sulfuric acid containing hydrogen sulfide and either used for the determination of copper or discarded.

The filtrate from the copper sulfide, etc., which will contain all of the uranium, vanadium, iron, aluminum, magnesium, phosphorus, etc., is boiled to expel most of the hydrogen sulfide and to reduce the volume to about 100 ml. The divanadyl sulfate, ferrous sulfate, free sulfur, any remaining hydrogen sulfide, etc., are then oxidized by adding to the hot liquid a slight excess of a strong solution (25 g. per liter) of potassium permanganate. The volume of the solution is then determined by comparison with a measured amount of water in another 400-ml. beaker; the essential thing is that the acidity of the solution be adjusted so that approximately 10 ml. of sulfuric acid (sp. gr. 1.84) are present in each 100 ml. of solution, which end can be accomplished by either evaporation or dilution. If the acidity is not properly regulated uranium will be held back with the vanadium or the vanadium will not be completely precipitated. The beaker and its contents are then cooled to approximately 10°C.

To the solution obtained as described in the preceding paragraph there is added a slight excess of a cold, freshly prepared, 6% solution of cupferron (ammonium nitrosophenylhydroxylamine, $C_6H_5N(NO)ONH_4$). This will cause the complete precipitation of the vanadium and iron, while uranium, zinc, aluminum, calcium, magnesium, phosphorus, etc., will remain quantitatively in solution. As soon as a drop of the reagent causes the formation of a transient snow-white crystalline precipitate, the reaction is complete. Some ashless paper pulp is added and the precipitate is filtered on an 11-cm. paper and washed fifteen or eighteen times with cold 10% $H_2SO_4$. It is necessary that a record be kept of the volume of $H_2SO_4$ introduced into the filtrate in the wash solutions. Both the precipitate and the filtrate are reserved.

*Procedures for Determination of Vanadium.*—The vanadium precipitate is treated for the determination of the vanadium by one of the following procedures:

(a) The precipitate is ignited carefully in a platinum crucible and fused with 4 or 5 g. of potassium pyrosulfate. The fusion is dissolved in the least necessary amount of water and the solution is transferred to a 300-ml. Erlenmeyer flask. An excess of strong $KMnO_4$ solution (25 g. per liter) and 15 ml. of sulfuric acid (sp. gr. 1.84) are added and the solution is evaporated until fumes of sulfur trioxide are given off. The vanadium is then reduced by evaporation with hydrochloric acid and determined by titration with 0.05 $N$ potassium permanganate as described in the "Procedure for Determination of Vanadium" of Method 2.

(b) The precipitate is ignited in an iron crucible, fused with 4 or 5 g. of sodium peroxide and determined by the "Procedure for the Determination of Vanadium" of Method 3.

*Procedure for Determination of Uranium.*—The filtrate and washings from the vanadium and iron precipitate are boiled down to a volume of about 50 ml., 30 ml. of nitric acid (sp. gr. 1.42) are added, and the evaporation is continued until fumes of sulfur trioxide are freely given off. Several small additions of ammonium persulfate, made after the solution has been evaporated to a low volume but before sulfur trioxide has begun to come off, will aid materially in the destruction of the organic compounds present. The solution is then evaporated until strong fumes of sulfur trioxide are evolved. When the beaker and its contents have cooled 120 ml. of water are added and the solution is heated until all salts have dissolved. The next step in the process consists in the reduction of the uranium to the uranium(IV) ($UO_2$) condition preliminary to its precipitation with cupferron as described in the next paragraph.

If the weight of uranium in the sample exceeds 0.3 g., 2 g. of zinc (containing

0.002% or less iron) are added and the solution is warmed until most of the zinc has dissolved, which will result in the partial reduction of the uranium. When working with ordinary carnotite ores this step is unnecessary. The solution is cooled to room temperature (20 to 25°C.) and passed through a Jones Reductor having a zinc column about 10″ long. All uranium is washed out of the zinc column by passing 130 ml. of water through the reductor. Approximately six minutes are as a rule consumed in passing the uranium solution and the wash water through the reductor.

The reduced solution, which should have a volume of 250 ml. and consequently an acidity of approximately 6%, is transferred to a 400-ml. beaker cooled to 5° to 10°C., and treated with an excess of a cold, freshly prepared, 6% solution of cupferron. If the solution contains less than 4 ml. of sulfuric acid (sp. gr. 1.84) per 100 ml. the uranium precipitate will drag down aluminum and phosphorus, while if the amount of acid exceeds 8 ml. per 100 ml. of solution, the precipitation of the uranium will not be quantitative. For this reason it is important that the amount of acid present in the solution be known and that the acidity be adjusted to approximately 5% by appropriate dilution. The precipitate does not begin to form until from 5 to 10 ml. of the reagent have been added. If uranium is present it will be completely thrown down as a brown crystalline precipitate having the composition $U(C_6H_5N_2O_2)_4$. Some ashless paper pulp is added and the precipitate is filtered on a 9-cm. paper and washed 18 or 20 times with cold 4% sulfuric acid. Aluminum, chromium, manganese, calcium, magnesium, phosphorus, and zinc (from the reductor) pass quantitatively into the filtrate.

The precipitate is ignited in a large weighed platinum crucible at a very low red heat until the carbon has been destroyed. The presence of the paper pulp is essential since it causes the precipitate to form a porous, friable mass, easily penetrated by air or oxygen, thus rendering it much easier to burn off the carbon and oxidize the uranium to $U_3O_8$. The temperature is then increased to 1050° to 1100°C. for approximately 15 minutes. The crucible and its contents are cooled in a desiccator and weighed. Multiplication of the weight of the uranosouranic oxide, $U_3O_8$, by 0.8481 and divided by the weight of sample taken, gives the percentage of uranium in the sample.

If desired, the result obtained by weighing the $U_3O_8$ can be checked by fusing the precipitate with a small amount of potassium pyrosulfate and dissolving the fusion in 100 ml. of 6% sulfuric acid. If the amount of uranium exceeds 0.3 g., the solution is given a preliminary reduction by adding 2 g. of zinc (0.002% or less iron). The solution is cooled to room temperature passed through a Jones Reductor, stirred vigorously for from three to five minutes, and titrated with 0.05 N or 0.1 N potassium permanganate (each ml. equals 0.005955 or 0.01191 g. uranium) which has been standardized against sodium oxalate obtained from the Bureau of Standards. The time required for passing the solution and 100 ml. of wash water through the reductor is approximately 5 minutes.

In titrating a uranium solution with permanganate it is necessary to determine a blank on the reductor and reagents and, in addition, a blank is run to determine the volume of permanganate required to produce a pink color to the yellow solution of the uranyl sulfate. The blank (usually about 0.1 ml.) on the reductor and reagents is conducted in exactly the same way the determination was made except that 100 ml. of 6% sulfuric acid is substituted for the uranium solution. The blank (varies with the amount of uranium involved; however, not more than 0.1 ml. of 0.1 N $KMnO_4$ is required to produce a pink tint to a solution containing

0.3000 g. uranium) is run in the following manner: In a regular analysis after reducing and titrating the uranium, the solution is treated with several drops (sufficient amount to discharge the pink color of the permanganate) of approximately 0.1 $N$ solution of ferrous ammonium sulfate, and the excess of ferrous iron over that required to destroy the excess of permanganate is oxidized by adding 8 ml. of 15% ammonium persulfate solution and stirring the solution vigorously for one minute. The reaction that occurs is shown by the following equation:

$$2Fe^{++} + S_2O_8^= \rightarrow 2Fe^{+3} + 2SO_4^=$$

A 0.1 $N$ solution of potassium permanganate is then carefully run into the liquid with constant stirring until the first permanent pink tinge appears. The volume of 0.1 $N$ $KMnO_4$ required to produce the pink color constitutes the blank due to the yellow color of the uranyl sulfate.

Therefore, in a regular analysis, the volume of 0.1 $N$ $KMnO_4$ remaining after deducting the blank on the reductor, reagents and that due to the influence of yellow color of the uranyl sulfate, multiplied by 0.01190, gives the weight of uranium in the sample.

### HYDROCHLORIC ACID-FERRIC IRON REDUCTION METHOD FOR VANADIUM (METHOD 2)

*Procedure for Separation.*—This method is recommended as being excellent for the determination of vanadium (no provision is made for the determination of uranium) in vanadinite, mottramite, or other ores or concentrates which can be completely or almost completely decomposed with acids. The process was originally proposed by Campagne and modified and perfected by A. M. Smoot of Ledoux & Company, who discovered that the reduction of the vanadium to the tetravalent form is complete even in the presence of a large amount of sulfuric acid provided sufficient ferric iron is present. None of the elements ordinarily found in vanadium ores, including copper, zinc, or arsenic, even when present in large amounts, interfere.

From 2 to 5 grams of the 100-mesh sample of the ore or concentrate, the amount used being determined by the vanadium content, are heated in a 600-ml. covered beaker with from 40 to 60 ml. of hydrochloric acid (sp. gr. 1.19) at a temperature of 50 to 60°C. until the decomposition appears to be complete. To oxidize any carbonaceous matter, potassium chlorate is next added, a little at a time, until a total weight of about 2 g. has been introduced. Twenty ml. of sulfuric acid (1:1) are added and the solution is evaporated until fumes of sulfur trioxide are freely evolved. Approximately 100 ml. of water are then introduced cautiously and the solution is boiled and filtered into a 500-ml. Erlenmeyer flask. The precipitate of lead sulfate, silica, etc., is treated to recover any vanadium as given in the second paragraph of Method 1, the solution of any material remaining after the lead sulfate has been extracted and the silica volatilized being added to the Erlenmeyer flask containing the main solution.

*Procedure for Determination of Vanadium.*—Five ml. of nitric acid (sp. gr. 1.42) are added to the sulfuric acid solution containing all of the vanadium and the liquid is evaporated to a volume of approximately 40 ml. A sufficient volume of a solution of potassium permanganate (25 g. per liter) to give a strong pink color is next introduced from a dropping bottle, and the evaporation is continued until fumes of sulfur trioxide appear. After having allowed the flask and its contents to cool somewhat, 20 ml. of sulfuric acid (1:1) and 50 ml. of hydrochloric acid (sp. gr. 1.19) are added in the order mentioned. A weight of ferric sulfate or chloride containing a weight of iron approximately equal to that of the vanadium present in the solution of the ore is next introduced and the solution is then boiled down to a volume of about 30 ml. Twenty-five milliliters of hydrochloric acid (sp. gr. 1.19) are added and the liquid is boiled down as rapidly as possible without causing bumping until the hydrochloric acid has been expelled and sulfur trioxide begins to come off. The flask is kept on the hot plate for a period of 10 minutes at a sufficiently high temperature to cause the rapid expulsion of sulfur trioxide, when it is removed and allowed to cool. Long continued fuming (more than 20 minutes) will cause the re-oxidation of some of the tetravalent vanadium to the pentavalent state. Approximately 50 ml. of cold water and five ml. of phosphoric acid (syrup. sp. gr. 1.72) are then added and the solution is diluted with hot water to 350 ml., heated until all soluble matter has dissolved, cooled, and titrated at 20°–25°C. with 0.05 $N$ or 0.1 $N$ potassium permanganate (the former for low vanadium and the latter for high vanadium products) which has been standardized against pure sodium oxalate obtained from the Bureau of Standards. The completion of the reaction is marked by the development of a pink color which remains permanent for 30 seconds.

The blank (usually about 0.1 ml.) is run in the manner described on page 1220.

## THE FUSION METHOD FOR ORES CONTAINING SMALL AMOUNTS OF COPPER OR ZINC (METHOD 3) [14]

**Procedure for Separation.**—This method, which can be used for the determination of vanadium in any of its ores except those containing significant amounts of copper or zinc, includes no provision for the determination of uranium. It is especially applicable to roscoelite, vanadiferous sandstones, or ores that contain large amounts of carbonaceous matter.

From 1 g. of the 100-mesh sample, the amount used being regulated by the vanadium content of the ore, is fused with 15 g. of sodium peroxide in a 40-ml. pure iron crucible. The contents of the crucible are fused carefully over the flame of a laboratory burner or in an electric furnace. The fusion is best accomplished by holding the crucible with a pair of tongs and slowly revolving it around the outer edge of the flame until the contents have melted down quietly, care being taken not to raise the temperature so rapidly as to cause spattering. When the fusion is molten, a slight rotary motion is imparted to the crucible to stir up any unattacked particles of ore on the bottom and sides, the crucible and contents being maintained at a very low red heat. Five minutes' heating is usually sufficient. Where a large (3 or 4 g.) sample is used and difficulty is experienced in obtaining a fluid fusion, complete decomposition can often be secured by heating at a temperature just short of that necessary to melt the mixture.

When cool, the crucible is placed in a 600-ml. beaker and treated with 150–200 ml. of warm water. The reaction between the water and the excess of sodium peroxide is quite violent, consequently care should be taken to avoid loss by spattering. The crucible is removed with a pair of tongs and rinsed with a jet of hot water.

High grade vanadium oxide (about 80% $V_2O_5$) can often be conveniently decomposed in the following manner: Six-tenths gram of the 100-mesh sample is transferred to a 600-ml. beaker and treated with 15 ml. of water. Sodium peroxide

[14] Method of the Electro Metallurgical Company.

is then added, a pinch at a time, with stirring, until decomposition appears to have been effected. The solution is then warmed slightly to complete the reaction, which required only a few minutes all told.

The advantages of the sodium peroxide fusion are that it insures complete decomposition of the ore and thorough oxidation of carbonaceous matter, free sulfur, sulfides, etc., in a single, rapid clean-cut operation.

The solution obtained as described in the preceding paragraphs is acidified with 50 ml. of sulfuric acid (1:1) and 15 ml. of nitric acid (sp. gr. 1.42). If the ore contains much lead, a precipitate of lead sulfate will be noticeable. Some scales of relatively inert magnetic iron oxide from the crucible will remain undissolved. The solution is then cooled to room temperature preliminary to the titration of the vanadium. The vanadium is determined by the following procedure.

*Procedure for the Determination of Vanadium* (**Ammonium Persulfate Procedure**).—One to 4 g. of the ore are fused with from 8 to 15 g. of sodium peroxide and the fusion is dissolved in water, acidified with 70 ml. of sulfuric acid (1:1) and transferred to an 800-ml. beaker jar and diluted to 400 ml. as previously described. Ores containing high percentages of lead should be treated as described under Method 2, paragraph 2.

To the acid solution of the ore obtained as described by either of the above methods there is added, with constant stirring, an approximately 0.1 $N$ solution of $KMnO_4$ (the titer of the solution need not be known) until a strong pink color has developed which remains permanent for 30 seconds. The solution is cooled to 15°C., then an approximately 0.1 $N$ solution of ferrous ammonium sulfate (it is unnecessary to determine the exact strength of this solution) is run in with constant stirring until a drop of the solution when added on a spot plate to a drop of a 0.1% solution of potassium ferricyanide results in the immediate formation of a blue color, showing that an excess of ferrous iron is present. A sufficient number of spot tests must be made so that only a comparatively small excess of the reducing agent is added. Five milliliters excess of the ferrous ammonium sulfate are then introduced and after having stirred the solution for one minute, the excess of ferrous salt over that required to reduce the vanadium is oxidized by adding 8 ml. of 15% ammonium persulfate solution and vigorously stirring the liquid for one minute longer. The temperature of the solution should not exceed 18°C. when the persulfate is added and the titration with standard $KMnO_4$ should be made at a temperature of 18 to 20°C. The reactions which occur are shown by the following equations:

$$VO_3^- + Fe^{++} + 4H^+ \rightarrow VO^{++} + Fe^{+3} + 2H_2O$$

$$2Fe^{++} + S_2O_8^= \rightarrow 2Fe^{+3} + 2SO_4^=$$

A 0.05 $N$ or 0.1 $N$ solution of potassium permanganate is then run into the solution with constant stirring until a faint pink color, which remains permanent for 30 seconds, has developed.

$$5VO^{++} + MnO_4^- + 6H_2O \rightarrow 5VO_3^- + Mn^{++} + 12H^+$$

The blank (usually about 0.1 ml.) is run in the following manner: In the regular analysis after completing the determination, the solution is immediately treated with one drop (just sufficient amount to discharge the pink color of the permanganate) of approximately 0.1 $N$ ferrous ammonium sulfate, and the excess of ferrous iron over that required to destroy the excess of permanganate is oxidized by adding 8 ml. of 15% ammonium persulfate solution and stirring the solution vigorously for one minute. A 0.1 $N$ solution of potassium permanganate is then carefully run into the liquid with constant stirring until the first permanent pink tinge appears. The volume of 0.1 $KMnO_4$ required to produce the pink color constitutes the blank due to the yellow color of the vanadic acid.

Therefore, the volume of 0.1 $N$ $KMnO_4$ required in the analysis, less the blank, multiplied by 0.005095, gives the weight of vanadium in the sample.

## ANALYSIS OF FERROVANADIUM

### DETERMINATION OF VANADIUM

**Reagents. Ammonium Persulfate.**—Ten grams of the salt dissolved in 100 ml. of water.

**Potassium Ferricyanide.**—Ten grams of salt dissolved in 100 ml. of water.

**Ferrous Ammonium Sulfate Approximately 0.1 $N$.**—Forty-nine grams of salt dissolved in water, 30 ml. of (1:3) sulfuric acid added, and dilute to a liter.

**Potassium Permanganate 0.1 $N$.**—Dissolve 3.2 g. of $KMnO_4$ in 1000 ml. distilled water, allow to age for at least 10 days and filter through purified asbestos. Standardize the permanganate solution against Bureau of Standards sodium oxalate. One ml. of 0.1 $N$ $KMnO_4$ is equivalent to 0.005094 g. of vanadium in the following method.

**Procedure.**—Treat 0.5094 g. of the alloy, dried to 105°C., in a 250-ml. covered beaker with 60 ml. of sulfuric acid (1:2) and 25 ml. of nitric acid (1:1). If the alloy does not decompose readily, add 2 or 3 ml. of hydrofluoric acid. When the reaction has abated, evaporate to copious fumes. Cool, add 100 ml. of water, and boil until salts are in solution. Transfer the contents to a 600-ml. beaker and dilute to 300 ml. with water. Cool the solution to 15 or 20°C. Add 0.1 $N$ potassium permanganate until very strong pink color remains for a minute, and excess does no harm. Next reduce the vanadium by the use of approximately 0.1 $N$ ferrous ammonium sulfate added until a drop withdrawn from the beaker and placed on a drop of potassium ferricyanide shows ferrous iron present; normally this reduction will take from 35 ml. to 40 ml. of solution. Add 3 ml. to 5 ml. in excess and stir for 1 minute, oxidize the excess ferrous ammonium sulfate with 15 ml. of 10% ammonium persulfate freshly made and stir vigorously for one minute. The temperature of the solution should not exceed 18°C. when the persulfate is added and the titration with standard $KMnO_4$ should be made at a temperature of 18 to 20°C.

Titrate the solution with an 0.1 $N$ potassium permanganate solution, added with constant stirring until a faint pink appears which will remain for 1 minute. A blank test is made by dissolving 0.5094 g. of ingot iron using the same concentration of acid as the test and putting the blank through all the operations of the analysis. This blank found is subtracted from the number of milliliters used in the test. Having used a factor weight (0.5094 g.) the number of milliliters used is the % vanadium in the alloy.

## CARBON

**Procedure.**—1.3646 g. of 100-mesh alloy are mixed with 2 g. of red lead. This charge is placed on an alundum cushion in the combustion boat. The boat is then placed in the electric furnace and burned at 1100°C. for 10 minutes. The

$CO_2$ is absorbed in Ascarite using Midvale type bulb. A blank must be determined and a correction made for carbon found in the red lead.

## SILICON

**Procedure.**—Dissolve 0.9348 g. (2 factor weights) using 20 ml. hydrochloric acid, 10 ml. nitric acid, and 30 ml. sulfuric acid (1:2) in a 600-ml. beaker; evaporate to copious fumes. Some samples of ferrovanadium containing silicon are not soluble in acid and must be fused. 0.4674 g. (1 factor weight) of the alloy are mixed with 6 to 8 g. of sodium peroxide in an iron crucible and thoroughly mixed. The crucible is heated over a Meker burner near the top of the mixture while rotating the crucible.

As the fusion progresses the crucible can be lowered into the hotter zone of the flame. With the proper rotation of crucible a melt can be obtained in which all the alloy is fused in about 3 minutes. The melt is allowed to cool and leached out in a platinum dish with water. The solution is acidified with hydrochloric acid and 30 ml. concentrated sulfuric acid added and evaporated to fumes. Cool the sulfuric acid solution obtained by either procedure and add 200 ml. to 300 ml. of water and boil until all the salts are in solution. Filter on a 9-cm. paper, wash with hot hydrochloric acid (10:100) and hot water until iron and vanadium salts are removed and then wash free from acid with water. Transfer precipitate to a platinum crucible, ignite at 1100 to 1150°C. for 40 minutes. Weigh and purify precipitate by adding 4 drops concentrated sulfuric acid and 10 ml. of hydrofluoric acid. Evaporate to dryness, ignite and weigh. Difference in weights divided by 2 or 1 (depending on amount taken) multiplied by 100 gives the silicon in the alloy.

## DETERMINATION OF VANADIUM IN CUPROVANADIUM, BRASSES AND BRONZES

**Procedure.**—Dissolve 1.019 g. of cuprovanadium in aqua regia. Evaporate to small bulk and add excess of peroxide of hydrogen. Dilute to 600 ml. and add ammonia until all copper goes into solution. Heat to boiling and add sufficient barium chloride solution to precipitate all the vanadium. Boil and filter. Wash all copper out of filter with hot ammonia water. Transfer the filter to a beaker, add 100 ml. 1:2 sulfuric acid, boil and filter on close filter paper. Titrate the filtrate with 0.1 $N$ ferrous ammonium sulfate and 0.1 $N$ potassium dichromate the same as for ferrovanadium (above), except that since 2 factor weights of sample were taken, the % of vanadium in the alloy is the titration in ml. divided by 2.

Vanadium copper, brasses and bronzes are treated in the same manner except that a ten-factor weight is used and the titration carried out with 0.02 $N$ solution instead of 0.1 $N$.

## DETERMINATION OF VANADIUM IN STEEL

### TITRIMETRIC PHOSPHOMOLYBDATE METHOD

**Reagents. Ammonium Molybdate.**—Solution No. 1. Place in a beaker 100 g. of 85% molybdic acid, mix it thoroughly with 240 ml. of distilled water, add 140 ml. of $NH_4OH$, sp. gr. 0.90, filter and add to 60 ml. of $HNO_3$, sp. gr. 1.42.

Solution No. 2. Mix 400 ml. of $HNO_3$, sp. gr. 1.42, and 960 ml. of distilled water.

When the solutions are cold, add solution No. 1 to solution No. 2, stirring constantly, then add 0.1 g. of ammonium phosphate dissolved in 10 ml. of distilled water, and let stand at least 24 hours before using.

**Ammonium Dihydrogen Phosphate.**—Fifty grams salt per liter of water.

**Acid Ammonium Sulfate.**—Fifty milliliters concentrated $H_2SO_4$, 950 ml. water and 15 ml. strong ammonium hydroxide. Use hot, 80°C.

**Nitric Acid.**—One hundred milliliters concentrated $HNO_3$ and 1200 ml. water.

**Nitric Acid for Washing.**—Twenty milliliters concentrated $HNO_3$ per liter.

**Potassium Permanganate Standard.**—0.35 g. salt per liter of solution. Standardized against sodium oxalate. Adjust so that 1 ml. will equal 0.0005 g. vanadium, or 0.02% on a 2.5-g. sample. One gram $Na_2C_2O_4 = 0.7603$ g. V.

**Potassium Permanganate,** for oxidation. Twenty-five grams salt per liter of solution.

**Sodium Bisulfite,** for reduction. Thirty grams salt per liter of solution.

*Procedure.*—A sample of 2.5 g. of steel in a 300-ml. beaker or Erlenmeyer flask is dissolved in 50 ml. of the nitric acid, and to the boiling solution are added 6 ml. of the permanganate oxidation solution, the boiling being continued until $MnO_2$ precipitates. The precipitate is now dissolved by cautious additions of sodium bisulfite solution and the boiling continued until no brown fumes are evident. Now 5 ml. of ammonium phosphate solution are added and 10 g. ammonium nitrate. The solution is removed from the heat and 50 ml. of ammonium molybdate reagent immediately added. After standing for 1 minute, the solution is agitated for 3 minutes. then allowed to settle and the clear solution decanted through an asbestos filter, the residue is washed three times with hot acid ammonium sulfate reagent, decanting each time through the filter. The flask containing the bulk of the residue is placed under the filter. (The washings are best conducted with suction, using a bell jar filter.) The precipitate on the filter is dissolved by successive portions of hot concentrated $H_2SO_4$, catching the solution in the vessel containing the bulk of the precipitate. The precipitate is now dissolved by heating and to the solution a few drops of the nitric acid are added and the heating continued to strong fumes.

The solution is cooled and hydrogen peroxide added in small quantities with vigorous shaking after each addition, until the solution takes on a deep brown color. The solution is again heated for 4 or 5 minutes, then cooled and 100 ml. of water added, the solution again heated to about 80°C. and titrated to a permanent pink color with standard potassium permanganate.

NOTE.—If the peroxide treatment followed by heating does not result in a clear green or blue color, the solution should be evaporated to strong sulfuric acid fumes and the peroxide treatment repeated. The presence of nitric acid interferes with the reduction of vanadium.

## ETHER EXTRACTION—HYDROCHLORIC ACID REDUCTION METHOD

*Reagents.* **Hydrochloric Acid.**—600 ml. concentrated HCl and 400 ml. water.

**Sulfuric Acid.**—Equal volumes of concentrated $H_2SO_4$ and water.

**Other Reagents.**—See Phosphomolybdate Method, above.

*Procedure.*—A sample of 2.5 g. of steel in a 250-ml. beaker is dissolved in 50 ml. of the HCl, and then small portions of $HNO_3$ added to oxidize the iron. After expelling the brown fumes by heating, the solution is cooled and transferred to an 8-oz. separatory funnel, together with the rinsings (small portions of HCl) of the beaker. Now 50 ml. of ether are added and the mixture shaken for 5 minutes. After settling for 1 minute the clear lower layer is drawn into another separatory funnel. The first funnel is treated with 10 ml. of concentrated HCl, again shaken vigorously and the settling repeated, the lower layer being added to the solution in the second separatory funnel. The combined solutions in the second separatory funnel are treated with 50 ml. of ether and shaken for 5 minutes, allowed to settle 1 minute and the clear lower layer drawn into a 150-ml. beaker. This aqueous solution is warmed gently to expel the ether, 25 ml. of the $H_2SO_4$ (1:1) added and the mixture concentrated to strong fumes. After cooling, 25 ml. of water are added followed by a slight excess of potassium permanganate solution and the sample heated to boiling. Fifteen ml. of concentrated HCl are added and heat applied until the solution again fumes. The heating is continued for 10 minutes. After cooling, 100 ml. of water are added, the solution heated to 80°C. and titrated with standard potassium permanganate reagent to a permanent pink color.

NOTES.—In heating the solution to expel the brown fumes of oxides of nitrogen, the solution should not be boiled.

In presence of chromium, the pink color will fade on standing owing to the oxidation of chromium. The oxidation of chromium is reduced by titrating the solution cold, but only ten seconds are allowed for the pink color to remain. A blank must be run with the same amount of chromium and allowance made for its oxidation. The blank is conveniently made by putting a suitable amount of chrome steel or chrome-nickel steel through the recommended procedure. By varying the amounts of steel and hence the amount of chromium in solution, data for a charted curve may be obtained that will be convenient for a blank deduction.

## METHODS FOR VANADIUM IN ANALYSES
## IN OTHER CHAPTERS

# Chapter 52

# ZINC*

**Zn, *at. wt.* 65.37; *sp. gr.* 7.14; *m.p.* 419.5°C.; *b.p.* 907°C.; *oxide,* ZnO**

Although the alloys used by the Romans undoubtedly contained zinc and the name zinc was used by Paracelsus in the sixteenth century, a clear knowledge of zinc as a distinct metal was not gained until the latter part of the seventeenth century, and an additional hundred years elapsed before the metal began to assume industrial importance. Zinc is now one of the most useful of the metals. It is an important constituent of a number of alloys as brass (Zn, Cu) and German silver (Zn, Cu, Ni) and die casting alloys (Zn, Cu, Al). Granulated zinc is a necessary substance in the chemical laboratory. Its resistance to rusting makes zinc valuable as a protective coating on iron surfaces (galvanized iron). Considerable quantities of zinc are used as anodes in electrical batteries. The oxide, ZnO, is used as a pigment and chemical in rubber goods, including automobile tires, and extensively as a paint pigment. It is used in glazes, in enamels, as an ointment, as dusting powder, etc. The chloride is used as a preservative of wood. The sulfide is a valuable white pigment; with barium sulfate it forms lithopone. Recently zinc and boron have been shown to be necessary to the growth of plants.

Zinc is found in nature only in combined form. Its ores in order of commercial importance are the sulfide, zinc blend, or sphalerite; the carbonate, zinc spar or smithsonite; the silicate, willemite. The following minerals are of less importance —calamine, a hydrated silicate, franklinite, a complex oxide containing iron, manganese, and zinc.

## DETECTION

*General Procedure.*—Zinc is brought into solution by extraction of the ore with HCl and $HNO_3$. The solution is evaporated to strong fumes with an excess of $H_2SO_4$ and the $H_2S$ group is separated from an acid solution containing 5 ml. of 1:1 $H_2SO_4$ in 100 ml. of solution. ZnS is precipitated by $H_2S$ from a faintly acid solution, so it is necessary to remove the $H_2S$ by boiling, neutralize the solution and acidify to 0.01 $N$ ZnS is white.

Potassium ferrocyanide precipitates a white zinc ferrocyanide of complex composition. ("See Titrimetric Methods.")

*In Presence of Iron.*[1]—Transfer 10 ml. of a solution of the sample to a small beaker; add 2 ml. of 85% $H_3PO_4$ (sp. gr. 1.7) to eliminate interference of Fe. Add 1 drop of copper-acid solution (0.5 g. $CuSO_4 \cdot 5H_2O$, 0.5 g. concentrated $H_2SO_4$,

---

* Revised for the Sixth Edition by C. Manning Davis of the International Nickel Company.
[1] Method of W. H. Hammond, Chemist-Analyst, **17**, 14, 1928.

100 ml. $H_2O$) and stir. Add mercuric thiocyanate mixture (8 g. $HgCl_2$, 9 g. $NH_4CNS$, 100 ml. $H_2O$), stir and allow to stand for 1 minute. Zn is indicated by a violet-colored precipitate.

*Blowpipe Test.*—Heat the finely powdered mineral on charcoal in the reducing flame of the blowpipe; zinc if present in amount exceeding 5% will leave an incrustation which is yellow when hot and white when cold.

*Cobalt Nitrate Test.*—In the ZnS test free S may make the test doubtful. To identify ZnS, dissolve the $H_2S$ precipitate in 5 ml. of 2 N $HNO_3$. Prepare a ball of ignited asbestos, half the size of a pea, held by means of a platinum wire and dip into a solution of 0.05 N $Co(NO_3)_2$ and ignite. Then dip the asbestos in the $HNO_3$ solution and again ignite. In presence of Zn the asbestos fiber is colored green (blue from Al).

*Instrumental Detection.*—Zinc can be detected easily by spectrographic or polarigraphic methods.

## ESTIMATION

The determination of zinc is called for in the buying and selling of ores for smelters, refuse material, e.g., from galvanizing plants, foundries, brass mills, and blast furnaces, in manufacture of brass, white metals, and alloys in general, paints and pigments, zinc chloride for preservation purposes, and in the control work of smelting of zinc and lead ores.

*Preliminary.*—The method to be followed in the estimation of zinc will depend largely on the nature of the material in which it occurs, the quantity present, and the experience of the analyst. Each of the methods outlined will give correct results only on the materials for which they are indicated, there being but one method recommended which is applicable to all zinciferous materials. It cannot be emphasized too strongly that each step has a definite purpose (which may not be at once apparent to the analyst making only an occasional zinc determination), and no part of the procedure should be varied or omitted, excepting after abundant experience.

Zinc compounds are readily extracted from ores by attack with acids, HCl and $HNO_3$, the acid insoluble residue seldom containing zinc.

During the analysis, if proper provision is not made for zinc, a portion will be occluded in the aluminum precipitate, while a portion will appear with the magnesium ammonium precipitate. Unless the ammonium hydroxide precipitate is small, zinc should be separated as sulfide from acid solution, according to the procedure described later, the hydrogen sulfide group first being removed. It should be kept in mind that copper and cadmium precipitated from 0.4 N acid solutions are apt to occlude zinc. Zinc is precipitated quantitatively from 0.01 N solution of acid.

## PREPARATION AND SOLUTION OF SAMPLE

The representative sample should be ground to pass a 100-mesh screen or finer. If the material contains shot metal, it should be screened out and the percentage present calculated. It is then treated as given under "General Procedure for Material Containing Other Metals," page 1239.

*Moisture Determination in the Pulp.*—One of the commonest causes of differences in zinc ore analysis is the failure to take moisture determinations on the pulp sample.

In order that analyses made on the same pulp at different times and in different laboratories may be compared it is absolutely necessary that all determinations be corrected to a dry basis. It is not sufficient that the sample be dried before or after having been pulped, but a sample for moisture must be weighed out at the same time as the sample for analysis, and the analytical result corrected for the percentage of moisture found at the time of weighing. This is especially true on roasted zinc ores which contain sulfates of zinc, iron, and lime and which take up moisture quite rapidly under ordinary atmospheric conditions.

The usual temperature for drying should be 110°C., but on special ores, e.g., those containing sulfates, it is necessary to dry at 250°C., unless it is first shown that there is no loss of water above 110°C.

The determination is best made by weighing approximately two grams in a small glass-stoppered weighing bottle and drying to constant weight, the weighing bottle being closed with the glass stopper as soon as the tube is taken from the drying oven.

*Ores.*—Decomposition is best effected by attack with HCl, $HNO_3$ followed by the customary evaporation and separation of $SiO_2$. Details are given under the methods of analysis.

*Alloys.*—Decomposition is effected by treatment of HCl, $HNO_3$ or $H_2SO_4$. Details are given under the methods for determining zinc in alloys.

## SEPARATIONS

*Silica.*—Evaporate with hydrochloric acid or take to fumes of sulfuric acid. The dehydration with sulfuric acid is complete and gives silica that is easily filtered and washed.

*Cadmium, Lead, Arsenic, Antimony, Bismuth, and Copper.*—Aluminum may be used to separate all the metals, except cadmium, the latter being only partially separated.

The separation may also be made as follows: Evaporate the solution of the zinciferous material to fumes with 7 ml. of 1:2 sulfuric acid. Cool, take up in about 50 ml. of water and warm, add 10 ml. of 10% sodium thiosulfate, boil until evolution of sulfur dioxide ceases, then filter. Cadmium if present is not completely precipitated and should be removed as CdS by precipitation with $H_2S$. The procedure is given under Titration in Acid Solution separating Zinc as Sulfide. If the cadmium is removed with $H_2S$ it is not necessary to also use sodium thiosulfate since lead, arsenic, antimony, bismuth, and copper are also removed.

*Iron, Aluminum and Manganese.*—This separation may be effected by precipitation with ammonia and bromine, providing the quantities present are small. When large amounts are present the separation might best be made by precipitating the zinc as a sulfide in acetic acid solution buffered with ammonium acetate. The precipitate is redissolved and reprecipitated.

*Separation of Zinc from Aluminum, Iron, Cobalt, Nickel, Manganese and Chromium by Precipitaton as Sulfide.*—Zinc may be precipitated as sulfide by $H_2S$ from a solution with a hydrogen-ion concentration ranging between pH 2 to pH 3. This may be accomplished in a dilute sulfuric acid solution (0.01 $N$) according to the procedure recommended by G. Weiss and F. G. Breyer as outlined in the titrimetric method given on page 1233, or from a formic acid solution as recommended by H. A. Fales and G. M. Ware.[2] Ammonium formate and

2 J. Am. Chem. Soc., **41**, 487, 1919.

citrate are used as buffers to hold the hydrogen ion concentration during the reaction with $H_2S$.

$$ZnSO_4 + H_2S \rightarrow ZnS + H_2SO_4.$$

The precipitate that forms in presence of dilute sulfuric acid is more readily filterable than that obtained in formic acid, according to the experience of W. W. Scott. Washing by decantation is advisable in any case.

If the removal of the hydrogen sulfide group has been made with $H_2S$ as described under "Separations," the $H_2S$ is first expelled and the acid cautiously neutralized with $NH_4OH$ until a slight precipitate forms. The acidity with $H_2SO_4$ is now carefully adjusted by addition of 0.1 $N$ acid. The normality should be less than 0.01 $N$ since the action of $H_2S$ will increase the acidity, so that allowance should be made for this.

## GRAVIMETRIC METHODS

In the analysis of ores, separation of zinc from other elements, that interfere in its determination, has been considered in previous paragraphs. Zinc is best isolated as zinc sulfide, first removing the hydrogen sulfide group in an acid concentration exceeding 0.4 $N$. A double precipitation is recommended, especially if copper and cadmium are present. The filtrate, boiled free of $H_2S$ is neutralized, preferably with $NH_4OH$ (methyl red indicator) and then acidified, dropwise, with very dilute $H_2SO_4$, so that the normality is less than 0.01 $N$ in respect to this acid (0.2 ml. concentrated $H_2SO_4$ per liter). Zinc is now separated as ZnS by precipitation with $H_2S$, the solution being at room temperature. The precipitate is washed free of contamination by cold water. This treatment also applies to alloys.

This precipitate may now be converted to the oxide by ignition to a temperature of 800–900°C. It may be converted to sulfate by dissolving in HCl and evaporating with $H_2SO_4$. It may be weighed as ZnS after a special treatment. It may be converted to zinc ammonium phosphate and so weighed, or ignited to pyrophosphate. It may be determined electrolytically. Further details follow.

## DETERMINATION AS ZINC OXIDE

Zinc is separated from interfering elements as outlined above. The zinc sulfide is filtered into a weighed Gooch crucible and washed. It is now ignited, preferably in a muffle furnace at a temperature of 900°C. for an hour and weighed as ZnO. Since the oxide is hygroscopic, cooling must be effected in a desiccator and the weighing done rapidly.

$$ZnO \times 0.8034 = Zn$$

## DETERMINATION AS SULFATE

The zinc sulfide obtained as outlined above, after washing free of impurities, is dissolved in hydrochloric acid and the chloride treated in a weighed crucible with a slight excess of sulfuric acid. The solution is very cautiously evaporated to fumes of $H_2SO_4$, then cooled and a few drops of water added and the evaporation repeated, heating finally to 500°C.

$$ZnSO_4 \times 0.4049 = Zn$$

NOTE.—At 650°C. the sulfate starts to decompose to ZnO and $SO_3$. It may be completely converted to the oxide by heating to 900–950°C.

## DETERMINATION AS THE PHOSPHATE

The phosphate method is generally considered to be the most accurate of the gravimetric methods. The determination is applicable for determining zinc in ores and in alloys. In the analysis of a copper alloy such as brass the filtrate from the copper determination is taken for the estimation of zinc. Zinc is precipitated as phosphate from a neutral solution containing ammonium salts. From a cold solution a product of doubtful composition, probably the normal phosphate $Zn_3(PO_4)_2$, an amorphous compound, precipitates on addition of the phosphate reagent. On heating to 60°–90°C. the precipitate becomes crystalline and a compound having the formula $Zn(NH_4)PO_4 \cdot H_2O$ is formed. The precipitation of zinc phosphate occurs *only in a neutral solution*, since the compounds are soluble in small concentrations of either acids or ammonium hydroxide. The crystalline product loses its water of crystallization at 105°C. On strong ignition the pyrophosphate, $Zn_2P_2O_7$ is formed.

*Procedure.*—The solution containing the zinc, free from elements of the previous groups and from elements precipitating as phosphates (see Notes), is carefully neutralized by adding $NH_4OH$ or HCl drop by drop using litmus paper or methyl orange as indicator. The volume of the solution should be 50–100 ml. per 0.1 g. of Zn present. Heat the solution nearly to boiling and add slowly a large excess of filtered diammonium hydrogen phosphate, $(NH_4)_2HPO_4$, reagent (15 ml. of 10% solution per 0.1 g. Zn present). Heat gently until the precipitate becomes crystalline (more reagent may be necessary since about 12 times the theoretical amount is advisable). Allow the solution to cool.

Filter off the precipitate in a weighed Gooch crucible (filter paper will do; see Notes). Wash with a 1% $(NH_4)_2HPO_4$ solution and finally with 50 ml. of cold water or 50% solution of alcohol.

Dry the precipitate at 105°C. for an hour and weigh as $Zn(NH_4)PO_4$. Multiply by 0.3665 = Zn. If preferred ignite at low heat at first and then at a cherry red and weigh as $Zn_2P_2O_7$.

$$Zn_2P_2O_7 \times 0.4291 = Zn$$

NOTES.—Preparation of diammonium hydrogen phosphate reagent. Dissolve 15 grams of the salt in a little water. This is sufficient for over 1 gram of zinc. Carefully neutralize with $NH_4OH$, added drop by drop, using phenolphthalein indicator. Dilute to 140 ml.

If precipitation is conducted in a cold solution the amorphous $Zn_3(PO_4)_2$ is formed. In presence of ammonium salts on heating the crystalline $Zn(NH_4)PO_4 \cdot H_2O$ forms.

The solubility of the compound is about 5 mg. per liter of water (20°C.). The solubility is very much less in 50% alcohol.

Free ammonia must not be present as the soluble complex cation $Zn(NH_3)_4^{++}$ would form.

In the analysis of brass the tin, lead and copper have been removed as $SnO_2$, $PbSO_4$ and Cu. If iron is present it is precipitated as $Fe(OH)_3$ and filtered off. Zinc is determined in the filtrate. In the analysis of an ore on removal of previous group elements Zn is isolated as ZnS from a formic or a 0.01 $N$ sulfuric acid solution to separate it from elements of the following groups. The sulfide is dissolved in HCl and zinc now determined in a neutral solution. If there has been an exceptionally large accumulation of ammonium salts in operations prior to the zinc determination these should be destroyed by the standard method of evaporation with nitric and hydrochloric acids before precipitating the zinc ammonium phosphate.

## ELECTROLYTIC METHOD

The determination is best made from an alkaline solution or one slightly acid with acetic acid and containing a considerable amount of sodium acetate. The alkaline solution tends to give high results, due to the presence of zinc oxide or hydroxide in the deposit. The best results are obtained with a solution weakly acid with one of the weaker organic acids. The procedure for the use of acetate is as follows:

*Procedure.*—The zinc is separated from other elements by precipitating with hydrogen sulfide in dilute sulfuric acid solution, as given under the standard method. The precipitate is filtered and washed, dissolved in hot hydrochloric acid—5 ml. 1:1 sulfuric acid added and the whole evaporated to fumes to expel hydrochloric acid. Cool and dilute, neutralize with sodium hydrate solution, make slightly alkaline, then acidify with acetic acid, and add about 5 g. of sodium acetate. The volume of solution should now be about 100 to 125 ml. Electrolyze with a platinum gauze electrode with 0.5 ampere per 100 sq. cm.

The electrolytic methods, on account of the special apparatus needed, the experience and care necessary to get reliable results, and the unavoidable errors involved in their use, are less desirable than the gravimetric oxide method and still less desirable than the ferrocyanide method.

## TITRIMETRIC METHODS

### STANDARD METHOD: TITRATION IN ACID SOLUTION AFTER SEPARATING ZINC AS SULFIDE

The method of separating zinc as sulfide in a solution slightly acid with sulfuric acid is of almost universal application and can be used on any class of zinciferous material that has come under the author's observation. The steps fit together, so that copper and cadmium are easily separated and any zinc in the insoluble state, e.g., spinels, etc., can readily be looked for. The method of decomposing (taking to fumes of sulfuric acid) tends to take into solution material that would be overlooked in the rapid decompositions effected in other methods. Moreover, the use of the internal indicator gives a very sharp end point, so that this method is fully as accurate as any gravimetric method. The method is more time consuming than other methods given, but it is not designed for rapid routine work, but rather as a standard procedure that will give absolutely reliable results on all classes of material. This method is also recommended for routine work in case the analyst is called on to make only occasional zinc analyses.

*Reagents.* **Sulfuric Acid 1:1.**—Mix equal volumes of $H_2SO_4$ (sp. gr. 1.84) and water.

**Sodium Hydroxide.**—Dissolve 20 g. of C.P. NaOH in 100 ml. of water.

**Sulfuric Acid 1:4.**—Mix 200 ml. of 1:1 $H_2SO_4$ with 300 ml. of water.

**Sulfuric Acid 5%.**—Mix 10 g. of $H_2SO_4$ (sp. gr. 1.84) with 200 ml. of water.

**Hydrochloric Acid 1:4.**—Mix 250 ml. of HCl (sp. gr. 1.19) with 1000 ml. water.

**Potassium Ferrocyanide.**—Dissolve 31.4 g. of $K_4Fe(CN)_6$ (C.P.) or dissolve 34.8 g. of $K_4Fe(CN)_6 \cdot 3H_2O$ in 1000 ml. of water. Add 0.3 g. of $K_3Fe(CN)_6$ before using. The factor of the ferrocyanide solution will decrease with aging; more rapidly at first because of oxidation by dissolved air. Hence it is advisable to allow the solution to age for a week or two before using. For accurate work it is necessary to standardize the solution daily.

**Ferrous Sulfate.**—Dissolve 1.25 g. of $FeSO_4 \cdot 7H_2O$ in water, add 3 ml. of HCl (sp. gr. 1.19) and dilute to 250 ml. Add about 1 g. of powdered aluminum.

*Procedure.*—The amount of sample taken should be such that 0.25 g. to 0.35 g. of Zn are titrated. When the desired amount is not present it is necessary to add additional $K_3Fe(CN)_6$ to produce the proper end-point colors. The addition of three drops of a 1% solution of $K_3Fe(CN)_6$ before titrating is recommended. Weigh the sample into a tall 150-ml. Pyrex beaker, add 15 ml. of HCl (sp. gr. 1.19) and 5 ml. of $HNO_3$ (sp. gr. 1.42) and boil moderately in a covered beaker for 0.5 hour. Wash off cover glass and sides of beaker, add 15 ml. of 1:1 sulfuric acid and evaporate to strong fumes of sulfuric acid. Cool, wash down sides of beaker, rub insoluble from bottom of beaker, dilute to 50 ml. and add 1.0 g. of zinc-free 20-mesh aluminum.[3] Boil for 15 minutes, or until water white, cool and transfer to a 200-ml. graduated flask. Wash out beaker thoroughly, and make up to mark in flask. Mix well and filter through a dry filter paper. Pipette 100 ml.,[4] into a tall 400-ml. beaker. Add NaOH solution until just alkaline, add 1:4 sulfuric acid until neutral to methyl orange and then 3 ml. of 5% $H_2SO_4$. Dilute to 200 ml. and pass a steady stream of hydrogen sulfide gas through for 40 minutes and let settle for 10 minutes. Filter through a 11-cm. filter paper and wash precipitate and paper twice with cold water. Then place original 400-ml. beaker under funnel, punch hole in filter paper, and wash precipitate back into beaker with hot water. Put the $H_2S$ gas tube into a small beaker with 10 ml. of HCl (sp. gr. 1.19) and hot water, to dissolve the coating of ZnS. Wash down filter paper with this HCl solution, then wash filter paper and funnel stem three times with hot 1:4 HCl and hot water. Boil off hydrogen sulfide, add 13 ml. of $NH_4OH$ (sp. gr. 0.90), neutralize with HCl (sp. gr. 1.19) and add 3 ml. excess. Dilute to 200 ml., heat to boiling and titrate as under standardization.

*Procedure for Standardization of Potassium Ferrocyanide.*—(The second paragraph of this procedure also is used for the titration portion of the analytical procedure.) Weigh into tall 400-ml. beakers several portions of C.P. zinc[5] ranging from 0.30 to 0.35 g. Cover with water and dissolve on warm plate with 10 ml. of HCl (sp. gr. 1.19). Cool, add 13 ml. of $NH_4OH$ (sp. gr. 0.90), neutralize to litmus with HCl (sp. gr. 1.19) and add 3 ml. in excess. Dilute to 200 ml. and heat to boiling.

Add 0.3 ml. of ferrous sulfate solution. Pour about one-quarter of the solution into a 200-ml. beaker and run the standard potassium ferrocyanide solution, while stirring, into the remaining portion to a considerable excess. Add all excepting 1 to 2 ml. of the solution in the 200-ml. beaker and continue the addition of standard solution until the end point is passed by a few drops. Stir vigorously to complete reactions. Add the remainder of the solution in the 200-ml. beaker and wash out with water. Continue the titration one to two drops at a time until the end point is reached. (The change of color from blue to pea green is very sharp.

[3] Granulated aluminum should be tested for zinc. In case ore carries copper, it is well to add a few drops of a saturated solution of sodium thiosulfate. Cadmium is partially precipitated but goes back in solution.

[4] The 100-ml. pipette should be graduated to deliver one-half the contents of the 200-ml. flask. Evaporation of the filtrate can cause a serious error if the beakers receiving the filtrate are not kept covered during filtration and the 100-ml. portion is not measured out promptly.

[5] Zinc sticks (C.P.) are rolled down to about .010″ thickness and the surface cleaned by wiping with gasoline.

It should be observed by looking down through the solution and not from the side. The change in color may be explained as follows: the few tenths of a milligram of ferrous iron added acts with the ferricyanide giving the ferrous ferricyanide blue as long as the ferrocyanide is not in excess. When it is in excess the blue is decomposed and gives the colorless ferrous ferrocyanide.)

**Procedure to Separate Cadmium as Sulfide.**—After measuring 100 ml. of the filtrate add 5 ml. of 1:1 sulfuric acid and pass a rapid stream of hydrogen sulfide through the solution for fifteen minutes. Add dilute ammonia, a drop at a time until yellow cadmium sulfide precipitates. Then heat the solution to 70° to 90°C. and continue to pass hydrogen sulfide for a few minutes. Filter at once through a close paper previously packed by washing with a polysulfide, an acid and water.[6] The precipitate is washed with cold 8 to 10% sulfuric acid and finally with hot water. The filtrate is boiled to remove hydrogen sulfide, cooled, neutralized and the zinc sulfide precipitated as in the procedure above.

**Procedure for Materials Containing High Iron and Manganese.**—The ZnS precipitate prepared as above will be contaminated with iron and manganese when the sample contains excessive amounts of these elements. As iron interferes with the end point and manganese will titrate in similar manner to zinc neither may be present in the solution to be titrated. The quantity of iron and manganese contamination may be reduced to a negligible amount by slightly increasing the acid concentration of the solution before precipitation. For materials high in iron and manganese add 5 ml. excess of 5% $H_2SO_4$ in place of 3 ml. excess given above. A second precipitation of the ZnS precipitate will serve the same purpose.

**Procedure with Material Containing Insoluble Zinc.**—Proceed as usual up to point where the solution is to be reduced. Filter off the silica and insoluble material, wash with hot water and reserve the filtrate. Burn the insoluble residue in a platinum crucible, taking the usual precautions in case lead is present. Fume off the silica with hydrofluoric and sulfuric acids and fuse with sodium carbonate. Dissolve in water and sulfuric acid and add to the filtrate above and proceed as in the regular method.

## TITRATION IN ACID SOLUTION WITH AN OUTSIDE INDICATOR

### PROCEDURE WITH URANIUM NITRATE INDICATOR

This method is adapted to most zinc-bearing materials. If copper or cadmium are present in large quantities these elements should be separated by an $H_2S$ separation as outlined under the Standard Method. Interference due to moderate amounts of cadmium may be eliminated by the addition of sodium thiosulfate just before titration.

**Reagents. Ammonia Wash Solution.**—Dissolve 100 g. of $NH_4Cl$ (C.P.) in 1000 ml. of distilled water and add 100 ml. of $NH_4OH$ (sp. gr. 0.90).

**Sulfuric Acid (1:1).**—Mix cautiously 500 ml. of $H_2SO_4$ (sp. gr. 1.84) with 500 ml. of distilled water.

**Uranium Nitrate.**—Dissolve 5 g. in 100 ml. of distilled water.

**Potassium Ferrocyanide.**—Dissolve 31.4 g. in 1000 ml. of distilled water and allow to stand for three months before using.

---

[6] All the cadmium is separated, except about 0.05%, which does not interfere with the titration at the given acidity.

*Procedure for Standardization of Potassium Ferrocyanide.*—Weigh 0.3 to 0.4 g. of zinc (C.P.) (Note 1) into a 600-ml. beaker and dissolve in 50 ml. of distilled water and 15 ml. HCl (sp. gr. 1.19). Add 25 g. $NH_4Cl$, dilute to 300 ml. neutralize (Note 2) with $NH_4OH$. Acidify with HCl, add 1.0 g. of granulated test lead and boil for 30 minutes. Add 10 ml. HCl (sp. gr. 1.19) and heat to boiling.

Pour about 100 ml. into a small beaker, and add $K_4Fe(CN)_6$ solution to remaining portion until a drop added to uranium nitrate test solution on a spot plate gives a brown color. Add most of zinc solution in the small beaker to the main portion and continue addition of $K_4Fe(CN)_6$ solution until the end point is just passed. Now wash all remaining solution from the small beaker into the 600-ml. beaker and finish the titration 2 drops at a time.

*Procedure.*—Weigh the sample (Note 1) into a 400-ml. beaker, moisten with water and add 30 ml. of HCl (sp. gr. 1.19). Boil gently for 10 minutes with the beaker covered, add 20 ml. of $HNO_3$ (sp. gr. 1.42) and continue the boiling for 10 minutes more. Wash the cover and the sides of the beaker, add 15 ml. of $H_2SO_4$ (1:1) and evaporate to dryness (Note 2). Cool, add 5 ml. of HCl (sp. gr. 1.19), 10 g. of $NH_4Cl$ and dilute to 50 ml. with water. Warm until all salts are in solution. Cool, add 1 ml. of liquid bromine (Note 3), neutralize with $NH_4OH$ (sp. gr. 0.90) and add 20 ml. in excess. Heat to boiling and boil for 1 minute.

Filter (Note 4) the solution into a 600-ml. beaker and wash the precipitate three times with ammonia wash solution (Note 5). Wash the precipitate from the paper into the original beaker, add 5 ml. of HCl (sp. gr. 1.19) and 5 ml. 3% $H_2O_2$ to dissolve the manganese. Cool, add 1 ml. of liquid bromine (Note 3), neutralize with $NH_4OH$ (sp. gr. 0.90) and add 20 ml. in excess. Heat to boiling and boil for 1 minute. Filter and wash as before, catching the filtrate and washings in the beaker containing the first filtrate and washings.

Add 1 g. of test lead to the combined filtrates and boil for 20 minutes, acidify (Note 6) with HCl (sp. gr. 1.19) and boil for 10 minutes more. Add 10 ml. of HCl (sp. gr. 1.19), dilute to 450 ml. with water, heat to boiling and titrate with standard $K_4Fe(CN)_6$ as described under standardization.

Calculate the percentage of zinc as follows:

$$\frac{(A - B) \times F \times 100}{W} = \% \text{ Zn}$$

where $A$ = ml. of $K_4Fe(CN)_6$ solution required for the sample.

$B$ = ml. of $K_4Fe(CN)_6$ solution required for the blank.

$F$ = g. of Zn per ml. of $K_4Fe(CN)_6$ solution.

$W$ = Weight of the sample in grams.

NOTES.—1. The size of the sample depends on the zinc content. Weigh 0.5 g. of zinc concentrates to 5.0 g. of tails. Larger samples should be taken of high grade materials that contain metallic shot and after solution aliquots equivalent to 0.4 to 0.5 g. should be used.

2. Evaporation should be carried out on a warm plate until the solution is ready to emit $SO_3$ and then continued on a hot plate. Samples high in lead should be diluted at this point with 100 ml. of water, boiled, cooled and after standing for about 1 hour the $PbSO_4$ should be filtered off and, after adding 10 g. of $NH_4Cl$ to the filtrate the method should be carried out as written.

3. Sufficient bromine should be added to precipitate all the manganese. If no manganese is present the bromine may be omitted. If the manganese is high the filtrate should be tested with additional bromine to be sure all the manganese has been removed.

4. Use a 15-cm. Whatman No. 2 filter or similar paper. With large precipitates a larger paper may be used.

5. A precipitate of $Fe(OH)_3$ holds zinc by occlusion. It is desirable to remove as much zinc as possible, especially in samples where the zinc is high, so that the amount of zinc retained in the second precipitate will be reduced to a negligible quantity.

6. Use litmus paper as an indicator. If necessary add more test lead to remove large amounts of copper. Most of the $NH_4OH$ should be removed during the boiling.

**Blank Determination.**—Dissolve 25 g. $NH_4Cl$ in 300 ml. of distilled water in a 600-ml. beaker and acidify (Note 2) with HCl (sp. gr. 1.19). Add 1 g. of granulated test lead and boil for 30 minutes. Add 10 ml. HCl (sp. gr. 1.19), titrate to the end point (Note 3).

Calculate the factor as follows:

$$F = \frac{W}{A - B}$$

where $A$ = ml. of $K_4Fe(CN)_6$ solution required for the standard zinc solution.

$B$ = ml. of $K_4Fe(CN)_6$ solution required for the blank.

$W$ = Weight of zinc in the standard solution.

$F$ = Grams of zinc per ml. of $K_4Fe(CN)_6$ solution.

NOTES.—1. This is satisfactory for standardizing a $K_4Fe(CN)_6$ solution for concentrates. In case of tails the standardization should follow the method of analysis adding an equivalent amount of iron and lime present in the tails, and making the same number of separations in the prescribed manner. Another suitable method is to standardize the $K_4Fe(CN)_6$ solution by means of similar tails of known zinc content. The point of all this is that the retention of zinc by the ferric hydroxide precipitate will give low results if the factor obtained with pure zinc is used. The higher factor obtained for tails must, of course, only be used for titrations of solutions from that type of material.

2. Use litmus paper as the indicator.

3. Titrate all samples and standards to the same coloration as the blank. A white porcelain plate covered with a smooth layer of clean paraffin makes a better spot plate than the usual plates provided with hollows.

## METHOD WITH DIPHENYLAMINE INDICATOR

In the standard method the zinc may be determined by titration with potassium ferrocyanide using diphenylamine for an internal indicator. The amount of ammonium chloride present in titrating the sample must be the same as present when standardizing. The following method may be used for determining zinc in zinc oxide or zinc sulfide where there are no interfering elements present.

*Reagents.* **Potassium Ferrocyanide.**—Dissolve 31.4 g. of $K_4Fe(CN)_6 \cdot 3H_2O$ in 1 liter of water. Add 0.3 g. of $K_3Fe(CN)_6$ before using. Standardize the solution by titrating against C.P. zinc (0.32–0.34 g.) in accordance with the "Procedure" below. Calculate the weight of ZnO equivalent to 1.00 ml. of solution.

**Diphenylamine Indicator.**—Dissolve 1 g. of diphenylamine in 100 ml. of sulfuric acid (sp. gr. 1.84).

**Sulfuric Acid (30%).**—Mix 300 ml. of $H_2SO_4$ (sp. gr. 1.84) with 500 ml. of distilled water and dilute to 1 liter.

*Procedure for Total Zinc as ZnO.*—Transfer 0.4000 g. of sample into a tall 400-ml. beaker, moisten with distilled water (about 20 ml.) and dissolve in 15 ml. HCl (sp. gr. 1.19). Neutralize with $NH_4OH$ (sp. gr. 0.90), using litmus as the indicator. Add an excess of 15 ml. of 30% $H_2SO_4$. Dilute to 200 ml., heat to approximately 60°C., add 2 drops of the diphenylamine indicator and titrate with standard $K_4Fe(CN)_6$ with vigorous stirring. The true end point is a sharp permanent change from a purple to a yellowish green. At the beginning of the titration a deep blue color is developed after addition of a few milliliters of ferrocyanide solution. About 0.5 to 1.0 ml. before the true end point is reached the solution changes from the blue to a purple. After the purple color is developed the titration should be continued dropwise to the permanent end point.

$$\frac{A \times B \times 100}{\text{Weight of sample}} = \% \text{ ZnO}$$

where $A$ = ml. of $K_2Fe(CN)_6$ solution used in test.
     $B$ = grams of ZnO equivalent to 1 ml. $K_4Fe(CN)_6$

## METHOD FOR TITRATION IN ALKALINE SOLUTION

This method is designed for rapid routine work on roasted or oxidized ores, especially those high in silica, alumina, iron, and manganese. It should only be used on unroasted sulfides, copper, or high cadmium-bearing ores, when the operator has had long experience. It is designed to give the zinc content of materials soluble in hydrochloric or nitric acid. For materials containing insoluble zinc, the titration in acid solution, in which zinc is separated as sulfide, is preferred.

*Reagents.* **Potassium Ferrocyanide.**—34.8 g. of pure salt in 1000 ml. of water. One ml. = approximately 0.010 g. Zn.

**Ferric Nitrate.**—One part of salt in 6 parts of water. It is well to add a little nitric acid to prevent hydrolysis.

**Citric Acid.**—One part of acid in 3 parts of water. 20 ml. of nitric acid should be added to each liter to prevent mould growth.

*Procedure.*—For ores or materials containing above 50% Zn, weigh 1.0 g. of sample into a tall 400-ml. beaker. (For lower grade materials larger samples can be taken provided the iron content in the solution to be titrated does not exceed 400 mg.) Moisten the sample with water and add 25 ml. hydrochloric acid (sp. gr. 1.20). Rotate the beaker to prevent caking. Place on a hot plate or steam bath and evaporate to dryness.[7] Add 40 ml. of nitric acid (sp. gr. 1.42), cover with a watch crystal and boil off all nitrous fumes. Then add 3 to 4 g. of $KClO_3$ and boil to a volume of about 20 ml. Cool, wash off the watch crystal and sides of the beaker and dilute to about 100 ml. Wash into a 500-ml. graduated flask, make up to the mark and shake well. Filter through a close, dry, 24-cm. qualitative paper. Return the first portions of the filtrate until the filtrate comes through clear and colorless.

Measure out 250 ml.[8] of the filtrate into a 600-ml. beaker, add ferric nitrate solution to bring the iron content up to approximately 350 mg. and proceed exactly as under "Standardization."

*Standardization.*—Weigh into 600-ml. beakers several portions of C.P. zinc ranging from 0.4 to 0.5 g. Cover with water and dissolve with 10 ml. of $HNO_3$ (sp. gr. 1.42). Boil gently for five minutes to remove the nitrous fumes and dilute to 250 ml. with water.

Add 10 ml. of ferric nitrate solution and 20 ml. of citric acid solution. Neutralize with $NH_4OH$ (sp. gr. 0.90) using a piece of litmus paper as the indicator, and add 25 ml. in excess.[9] Heat just to boiling and titrate with the ferrocyanide

---

[7] The temperature of the hot plate should not be over 120°C. as $ZnCl_2$ is appreciably volatile at higher temperatures.

[8] The graduated flasks should be standardized against one another so that exactly half the sample is taken.

[9] The excess $NH_4OH$ depends on the amount of zinc present and should be varied between 25 ml. for samples containing 0.4 to 0.5 g. of zinc to a few drops excess for samples containing less than 0.05 g. of zinc.

solution, using 50% acetic acid as an external indicator placed in the depressions of a test plate.

The end point is a change in color from yellow to green produced by the formation of ferric ferrocyanide as soon as the ferrocyanide is in excess of the zinc and the solution is acidified by the acetic acid.[10] The end point may be approached by reserving a portion of the solution in a small beaker as given under titration in an acid solution with uranium nitrate as the outside indicator.

A blank determination must be made and the value of this blank subtracted from the titrations of standardizations and samples. The blank titration is approximately 0.2 ml. Add only a few drops excess $NH_4OH$ to the blank determination.

*General Procedure for Material Containing Other Metals.*—On account of the lack of uniformity in the case of metallic zinciferous material containing lead and iron, it is well to work on large samples. Five or 10 g. of the metallics reduced to as fine a size as possible are weighed out and dissolved in nitric acid. The nitrous fumes are boiled off and the whole made up to 500 ml. or 1000 ml. Fifty or 100 ml. are now pipetted off into a 600-ml. beaker and the zinc titrated as usual. In case the metallic portion contains manganese, which is unusual, it can be separated by the regular procedure. Copper is separated as directed below. Material containing cadmium should be analyzed by other methods, as given under "Standard Method," page 1233.

*Separation of Copper by Aluminum.*—The sample is treated as usual up to the point where manganese has been separated and 250 ml. of the clear filtrate measured out. Add 25 ml. of 1:1 sulfuric acid and evaporate to strong fumes, cool, dilute to 100 ml., add a gram or two of 20-mesh zinc-free aluminum. Heat until all the copper separates, filter, wash and proceed with the filtrate as in the regular method, after oxidizing iron with a few drops of nitric acid.

*Separation of Copper by Hydrogen Sulfide.*—After separation of the manganese with chlorate, sulfuric acid is added and the solution taken to fumes, as in above. Cool, dilute to 100 ml., and add sulfuric acid so that 12% is present. Warm slightly and pass hydrogen sulfide through the solution. Filter off the copper sulfide, wash, boil $H_2S$ out of the filtrate, and proceed as in the regular method, after oxidizing iron with a few drops of nitric acid.

*Material Containing Cadmium.*—If the material contains cadmium in quantities sufficient to warrant separation (0.15% or more), it is best to use the titration in acid solution, separating zinc as sulfide.

*Material Containing Carbonaceous Matter.*—If the material under examination contains carbonaceous matter, coal, etc., it must be separated by taking to dryness with hydrochloric acid. Take up in acid and water, filter and wash, and evaporate the filtrate to dryness. Take up in nitric acid and proceed as in the regular method.

If the carbonaceous material is not removed, the manganese does not separate cleanly, due to the reducing action of carbonaceous compounds.

[10] It is necessary that the acetic acid be zinc free so that it is advisable to redistill it to remove traces of zinc it may contain or have taken up by standing in glass bottles containing zinc.

## TURBIDIMETRIC DETERMINATION

This method is especially useful for determining small amounts of zinc.

*Reagent.* **Standard Zinc Solution.**—Dissolve 0.1 g. of zinc (C.P.) in 10 ml. of HCl (sp. gr. 1.20) and dilute to 1000 ml. 1 ml. = 0.0001 g. Zn.

*Procedure.*—Take an amount of sample such that it will contain between 0.1 and 2.0 mg. of zinc. Dissolve the sample and take to fumes of sulfuric acid as directed in the procedure of the "Standard Method." Dissolve the residue in water and adjust the acidity to contain about 5% free $H_2SO_4$ and precipitate the heavy metals with $H_2S$.

Filter off the heavy metals and boil the filtrate to remove the $H_2S$, cool, neutralize with $NH_4OH$ and add 10 ml. of 50% citric acid solution. Heat the solution to boiling and, if no calcium citrate separates, add small quantities of calcium carbonate at a time until a precipitate of about 1.0 g. of calcium citrate is formed. Remove from heat and pass a stream of $H_2S$ through the solution until it has cooled. Filter the solution through a small filter paper and wash with a 2% solution of $NH_4CNS$. Dissolve the precipitate in 3 ml. of HCl (sp. gr. 1.20) diluted to 10 ml. with water, and wash the paper with water.

Wash the solution into a 100-ml. Nessler tube and hold until a series of the standards covering the range in which the samples fall has been prepared by measuring portions of the standard zinc solution into 100-ml. Nessler tubes. Dilute the standard and sample solutions to about 90 ml. and add 3 ml. of HCl (sp. gr. 1.20) to the standard solutions, and 2 ml. of ferrocyanide solution to all solutions. Dilute each Nessler tube to the mark and mix thoroughly. After standing for at least five minutes compare the turbidity of the standards and the sample. Calculate the percentage of zinc from the quantity of sample taken and the standard solution similar in turbidity to that of the sample.

## POLAROGRAPHIC DETERMINATION

This method may be used for practically any sample of zinc ore, slag, or metal and normally no separations need be made, except where appreciable manganese is present. In this case, the manganese is simply precipitated by adding a small amount of bromine before the addition of $NH_4OH$.

In determining small amounts of zinc, as in soils, slags, residues, etc., it may be necessary sometimes to remove copper where that element is present in much larger concentration than the zinc.

Any polarograph may be used though this is written specifically for manual operation using an instrument similar to the Sargent Model-III. In using the two-point system, it must be remembered that the form of the wave may be affected by changes in concentration of other elements present or changes in concentration of the element being determined. The blank may also be affected by changes in concentration of various elements present. In the case of zinc, for example, the blank will decrease (becoming negative) as the concentration of copper increases, due to the fact that the diffusion current plateau of copper gradually decreases with increasing applied potential. It is possible, however, to plot the zinc blank, determined on solutions with varying amounts of copper, against the concentration of copper and use the appropriate blank for the sample in question. If copper is not to be determined on the sample it may be removed by adding a small amount of test lead, after dissolving the sulfated sample, and boiling a few minutes.

If the method is followed as written there will be no appreciable loss of zinc by occlusion even on samples high in iron and zinc.

In the concentration range up to 5% zinc the method is more accurate than the titrimetric methods; in the range of 5 to 20% zinc the method is equal to the titrimetric methods.

The method may be used in routine control work on concentrations up to 60–70% or higher depending on the accuracy needed. The accuracy of a particular determination will of course depend upon the instrument and manner in which the determination is carried out. It might be noted that a large number of determinations have been made on a standard sample containing 37.4% zinc with a standard deviation of 0.3%.

In determining small concentrations of zinc it is necessary to avoid any contamination and to destroy completely any organic matter present.

**Reagents.** **Standard Copper Solution (1 ml. = 0.001 g. Cu).**—Dissolve 1.000 g. of pure copper in 15 ml. of $HNO_3$ (1:3), add 20 ml. of $H_2SO_4$ (1:1) and evaporate to dense white fumes. Cool, dilute to 1 liter in a volumetric flask, and mix.

**Standard Cadmium Solution (1 ml. = 0.001 g. Cd).**—Dissolve 2.0315 g. C.P. $CdCl_2 \cdot 2\frac{1}{2}H_2O$ in 100 ml. of hot water. Cool, dilute to 1 liter in a volumetric flask, and mix.

**Standard Zinc Solution (1 ml. = 0.002 g. Zn).**—Dissolve 2.4894 g. of freshly ignited pure zinc oxide in 50 ml. of hot HCl (1:10). Cool, dilute to 1 liter in a volumetric flask, and mix.

**Gelatin (0.2%).**—Dissolve 2 g. of gelatin in boiling water. Cool, dilute to clear solution to 1 liter, and mix. Add a few drops of chloroform as a preservative.

**Diammonium Phosphate (10%).**—Dissolve 100 g. of $(NH_4)_2HPO_4$ in 1 liter of water. Neutralize with HCl.

**Ammonia and Acids.**—Where strengths of ammonia or acid are not indicated, the concentrated reagent is used.

**Procedure for Determination of Copper, Cadmium, and Zinc Factors.**—Transfer to three low 400-ml. beakers 5-ml., 10-ml., and 20-ml. portions of the standard copper solution, respectively. Transfer like amounts of the standard cadmium solution to a second set of three beakers. To a third set of three beakers transfer 5 ml., 25 ml., and 50 ml. of the standard zinc solution, respectively. Carry another beaker along as a blank. Add to each of the beakers 16.6 g. (Note 1) of $NH_4Cl$, 5 ml. of HCl, and dilute to approximately 150 ml. with distilled water. Add 15 ml. of $NH_4OH$ and 10 ml. of 0.2% gelatin. Cool to room temperature, dilute to 200 ml. in a volumetric flask and mix.

Transfer a suitable portion of the resulting solutions to electrolysis cells. Add a small amount of mercury to serve as the anode (1 cm.$^2$ surface area). Place the cells in the constant temperature bath and remove the dissolved oxygen by bubbling nitrogen through the solutions for 10 minutes.

Introduce the dropping electrode assembly, making sure the contact electrode dips into the mercury pool, into each cell one at a time (Note 2) and record the increase in galvanometer deflection and the current multiplier setting (Note 3) when changing the applied potential from 0.26 to 0.56 volt on the copper standards, 0.56 to 0.80 volt on the cadmium standards, and 1.06 to 1.40 volts on the zinc standards (Note 4). Determine the three increases on the blank.

Multiply the increases in galvanometer deflection by the current multiplier setting used and plot against the corresponding grams of copper, cadmium, and zinc, respectively. Since these points should fall on a straight line, it is only necessary to use the highest concentration in calculating the factors.

Calculate the copper, cadmium, and zinc factors as follows:

$$F = \frac{C}{(R \times S) - (B \times S')}$$

where $C$ = grams of copper, cadmium, or zinc,

$R$ = increase in galvanometer deflection due to copper, cadmium, or zinc, respectively,

$B$ = the increase in galvanometer deflection for the blank corresponding to copper, cadmium, or zinc, respectively,

$S$ = current multiplier setting used to obtain $R$,

$S'$ = current multiplier setting used to obtain $B$, and,

$F$ = the grams of copper, cadmium, or zinc, respectively, per millimeter increase in galvanometer deflection on full sensitivity.

*Procedure.*—Transfer 1.000 g. of the sample (Note 5) to a low 400-ml. beaker. Moisten with a small amount of water, add 10 ml. of HCl, 5 ml. of $HNO_3$, and 10 ml. of $H_2SO_4$ (1:1). Boil gently for 15–20 minutes then evaporate to strong white fumes. Break up any organic matter by cautiously adding $HNO_3$ dropwise. Evaporate to dryness. Cool and add 16.6 g. of $NH_4Cl$, 5 ml. of HCl, and about 50 ml. of water. Heat to boiling and boil gently until solution is complete. Cool and dilute to 150 ml. with distilled water. Add 3–4 drops of $(NH_4)_2HPO_4$ (Note 6), 15 ml. of $NH_4OH$ (Note 7), and 10 ml. of gelatin. Dilute to 200 ml. and mix (Note 8).

Allow to settle for a few minutes, transfer a suitable portion to a cell and continue as under Procedure for Determination of Factors.

Calculate the percentages of copper, cadmium, or zinc as follows:

$$\% \text{ Cu, Cd, or Zn} = \frac{[(R \times S) - B] \times F \times 100}{W}$$

where $R$ = increase in galvanometer deflection for copper, cadmium, or zinc, respectively,

$S$ = current multiplier setting used in obtaining $R$,

$B$ = blank obtained under Determination of Factors—except for samples containing more than 0.5% copper in which case the cadmium and zinc blanks should be determined on a solution containing a similar amount of copper.

$F$ = the grams of copper, cadmium, or zinc, respectively, per millimeter increase in galvanometer deflection on full sensivity and,

$W$ = weight of the sample in grams.

Notes.—1. A small marked beaker may be used to measure the $NH_4Cl$.

2. The samples should be polarographed as quickly as possible to avoid solution of oxygen.

3. The current multiplier should be set so as to obtain optimum increases in galvanometer deflection.

4. A current voltage curve should be plotted to determine that the voltage settings used actually fall on the residual and diffusion current plateaus, respectively.

5. A smaller sample may be necessary when the concentration of the element to be determined is high.

If the sample is a metal, a large enough portion should be used to insure a representative sample and an aliquot used.

6. More $(NH_4)_2HPO_4$ is necessary for samples high in lead.

7. If the sample contains enough manganese to interfere with the diffusion current plateau of the zinc, add 1–2 ml. of bromine followed by 20 ml. of NH₄OH. Heat just to boiling, cool and continue with the addition of gelatin.

8. A carefully marked tall-form 200-ml. beaker may be used.

## DETERMINATION IN SPECIFIC SUBSTANCES

## DETERMINATION OF METALLIC ZINC IN ZINC DUST

There have been various methods proposed for determining the metallic zinc content of zinc dust. Most of these are based upon its reducing power. The latter may be determined by any one of many ways, although the results from different methods will not be concordant, due to the inaccuracies inherent with most of the methods. Potassium dichromate, iodate, ferric sulfate, and iodine have been used for measuring the reducing power of zinc dust. Fresenius also proposed dissolving the zinc dust in dilute sulfuric acid and after drying passing the hydrogen over heated copper oxide in a combustion tube, absorbing the water formed in a calcium chloride tube and weighing.

There have also been methods devised based on the volume of hydrogen evolved when a sample of zinc dust is dissolved in dilute acid. Several investigators have concluded from comparative investigations that the gasometric (i.e., titrimetric) determination of the hydrogen evolved gives the most consistently accurate results. The best arrangement of apparatus for carrying out this hydrogen evolution method is shown in Fig. 52-1. The time required for a determination is about 1.5 hours.

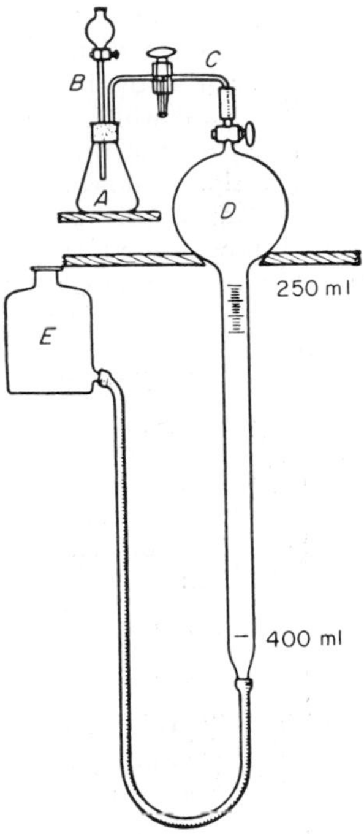

Fig. 52-1. Apparatus for Determining Metallic Zinc.

*Procedure.*—One gram of zinc dust is weighed and transferred as rapidly as possible to a small Erlenmeyer flask $A$, of 100 or 200-ml. capacity, in which is placed a piece of sheet platinum about 1.5 cm. square. About 5 g. of clean unoxidized ferrous sulfate crystals are added on top of the zinc dust and the flask nearly filled with distilled water saturated at room temperature with hydrogen gas.

The object of adding the sheet platinum and ferrous sulfate is to increase the rate of hydrogen evolution by catalytic action. A further reason for adding the ferrous sulfate on top of the zinc dust sample is to coagulate the latter as much as possible when it becomes wetted, and thus prevent the floating of more than an unappreciable amount of the sample.

The rubber stopper containing separatory funnel $B$ and connecting tube $C$ is tightly inserted into the neck of the flask. A little distilled water is poured into $B$ and the three-way stopcock in $C$ turned to connect the flask with the downward outlet. Enough water is now run in from the separatory funnel to displace all the air in the flask and the connecting tube through the bore in its stopcock. The stopcock in $C$ is now turned so that the downward outlet is in connection with the measuring tube $D$. By raising the leveling bottle $E$, containing 10% sulfuric acid also saturated with hydrogen at room temperature, all the gas in $D$ is displaced. The stopcock in $C$ is now turned through 90 degrees so as to connect the decomposing flask $A$ with the measuring tube $D$. The system is hence completely filled with liquid and ready for the generation of hydrogen. The measuring tube $D$ has a total capacity of 400 ml. and is graduated from 250 to 400 ml. by 0.25 ml.

Thirty milliliters of 1:1 sulfuric acid are now poured into the separatory funnel. A small portion of this acid is allowed to run into the decomposing flask until a brisk but not too rapid evolution of hydrogen takes place. The acid, being much heavier than water, settles to the bottom of the flask and the action commences immediately. The gas evolved, together with some solution and a very small amount of zinc dust passes over into the measuring tube, displacing the acid there. The rubber tubing connecting $C$ and $D$ should be long enough so the flask $A$ can be held in a horizontal position when the first acid is run in. The gas will be collected first at the bottom of flask $A$, and when $A$ is returned to a vertical position the liquid will no longer be against the stopper. In this way very little zinc dust will pass into the measuring tube $D$. When the action in the decomposing flask has slowed down, more concentrated acid is introduced until all has been added. During this time the acid in the measuring tube and flask is shaken so as to wash down the particles of zinc dust from the upper parts of the flask and tube now filled with gas. The particles in the measuring tube on coming in contact with the 10% sulfuric acid are readily dissolved and generate their portion of hydrogen.

When all the zinc dust has been dissolved, water is run in from the separatory funnel to force the hydrogen over into the measuring tube and to fill the flask and connecting tube with water through the stopcock which is then closed. After leveling with the leveling bottle the volume of hydrogen generated from the 1-g. sample at the prevailing atmospheric conditions is read from the measuring tube. The percentage of metallic zinc in the sample is then calculated from the following expression:

$$\% \text{ Metallic Zn} = \frac{V \times (P - b - a) \times 0.29183}{(1 + 0.00367t)760}$$

in which $V$ = volume of gas in measuring tube at atmospheric conditions, $P$ = barometric pressure, $p$ = vapor tension of water above 10% sulfuric acid at room temperature, $a$ = temp. correction for expansion of Hg in the barometer (this is approximately $0.13t$), and $t$ = room temperature in °C.

*Necessary Precautions.*—To obtain results of the highest accuracy, it is necessary when weighing out samples of zinc dust which are very finely divided, to keep the time of exposure as small as possible in order to minimize the oxidation that takes place with the oxygen of the air. It is also highly important when samples are to be held, that they be kept in ground-glass stoppered bottles, completely filled, and sealed with paraffin or wax.

The two variables most likely to affect the results are temperature and barometric pressure. A change in the barometric pressure is practically always extended over a reasonable length of time. A careful reading of the barometer when the volume of gas in the measuring tube is read will eliminate any error from this source. A temperature change, on the other hand, affects not only the volume of gas, according to Charles' law, but also affects the vapor tension of water and hence the actual pressure of the hydrogen when measured.

The rubber connection between the connecting and measuring tubes must be of heavy rubber and should be shellacked.

The vapor tension of water is slightly lower above 10% sulfuric acid than above pure water, and for accurate work should be used in place of the ordinary vapor tension tables.

The result obtained should be corrected for any metallic impurities, as Fe, Al, etc., which evolve hydrogen when dissolved in sulfuric acid.

## ANALYSIS OF SLAB ZINC (SPELTER) [11]

In these methods, the grades of slab zinc are classified according to the following table:

| Grade | Pb Not Over | Fe Not Over | Cd Not Over | Sum Pb + Fe + Cd Not Over | Al |
|---|---|---|---|---|---|
| No. 1a Special High Grade. | 0.006% | 0.005% | 0.004% | 0.010% | None |
| No. 1  High Grade....... | 0.07 | 0.02 | 0.07 | 0.10 | " |
| No. 2  Intermediate...... | 0.20 | 0.03 | 0.50 | 0.50 | " |
| No. 3  Brass Special...... | 0.60 | 0.03 | 0.50 | 1.0 | " |
| No. 4  Selected.......... | 0.80 | 0.04 | 0.75 | 1.25 | " |
| No. 5  Prime Western..... | 1.60 | 0.08 | | | |

### LEAD BY THE ELECTROLYTIC METHOD

*Apparatus.*—Platinum electrodes of the stationary or rotating type. The cathodes are open or closed cylinders, 30 mm. in diameter and 50 mm. in height. The overall height of the cathode is 130 mm. They are formed either from sheet platinum, which may be perforated or made from wire gauze, which is suitably reinforced by doubling or by use of a platinum band or ring at top and bottom. The stem consists of a Pt-Ir, Pt-Rh or Pt-Ru wire, flattened, and welded the entire length of the gauze. The anodes are of wire gauze, and are similar in construction to the cathodes. The anode cylinder is 20 mm. in diameter, 50 mm. in height, and the overall height of the anode is about 130 mm. Platinum electrodes are sandblasted before use.

*Reagents.*—**Copper Nitrate, lead-free.**

**Urea.**

**Hydrogen Peroxide, 3%.**

**Sodium Bismuthate.**—The sodium bismuthate shall contain enough active oxygen to correspond to at least 75% $NaBiO_3$. Manganese and chlorides should not exceed 0.0005 and 0.001%, respectively.

*Procedure for Grade 1a.*—Transfer 86.6 ± 0.4 g. of the sample to a 1500 ml. beaker, cover, and add $HNO_3$ (1:1) in small portions until solution is complete; about 530 ml. will be required. Boil the solution until about 150 ml. have evaporated. Add $NH_4OH$ (1:5), while stirring vigorously, and continue boiling the solution until the locally precipitated hydroxides dissolve but slowly. Transfer the solution to a 600-ml. beaker with hot water. Add 2 g. of $Cu(NO_3)_2$ and about 0.2 g. of urea.

Electrolyze the solution for 2 hours at 60 to 70°C. and at a current density of 1

11 ASTM Methods E40-58, Adopted 1945; Revised 1958.

to 1.5 amp. per sq. dm. If the blue color of the solution begins to disappear before the lead is all plated out, add more $Cu(NO_3)_2$.

When deposition of the lead is complete, as indicated by failure to plate on a new surface exposed when the level of the solution is raised, wash the deposit by removing the beaker containing the electrolyte and immediately replacing it with a beaker of water. Repeat the washing with still another beaker of water. Turn off the current, remove the anode, and dry at 110 to 120°C. for 30 minutes. The deposit is fragile and must be handled carefully. Cool the anode and weigh the deposit as $PbO_2$.

**Calculation.**—Calculate the percentage of lead as follows:

$$\text{Lead, } \% = \frac{A \times 0.866}{B} \times 100$$

where $A$ = grams of $PbO_2$, and
$B$ = grams of sample used.

*Procedure for Grades 1 and 2.* **Grade 1.**—Transfer 17.3 ± 0.1 g. of the sample to a 400-ml. beaker and dissolve in 75 ml. of water and 60 ml. of $HNO_3$.

**Grade 2.**—Transfer 8.66 ± 0.05 g. of the sample to a 400-ml. beaker and dissolve in 50 ml. of water and 40 ml. of $HNO_3$.

When solution of the sample is complete, cover, and boil until approximately one-third of the solution has evaporated. Transfer the solution to a 200-ml. tall-form beaker, dilute to 190 ml., and complete the determination in accordance with "Procedure for Grade 1a" except that the addition of $Cu(NO_3)_2$ is not necessary.

*Procedure for Grades 3, 4, and 5.*—Transfer 21.65 ± 0.03 g. of the sample to a 400-ml. beaker and dissolve in 90 ml. of water and 75 ml. of $HNO_3$. When solution of the sample is complete, boil until the volume is reduced to about 75 ml. Cool the solution and dilute to 500 ml. in a volumetric flask. Mix thoroughly and transfer a 100-ml. aliquot with a pipette to a 300-ml. tall-form beaker. Add 10 ml. of $HNO_3$, and boil for 10 minutes. Dilute to 190 ml., heat to 80°C., and complete the determination as in "Procedure for Grade 1a."

If the sample contains manganese, it may be deposited in part as $MnO_2$ along with $PbO_2$. To determine the presence of manganese, strip the electrode of its deposit by treating it with $HNO_3$ to which some 3% $H_2O_2$ has been added. Boil the resultant solution to remove excess $H_2O_2$, nearly neutralize with $NH_4OH$, and precipitate the lead with $H_2S$. Filter the solution on a close-texture paper and evaporate the filtrate almost to dryness. Test for manganese by the addition of a little $NaBiO_3$. If appreciable quantities of manganese are found, dissolve the precipitate of PbS by pouring 25 ml. of hot $HNO_3$ (1:1) through the paper. Wash with hot water, and dilute to 100 ml.

Electrolyze the solution for 2 hours at 60 to 70°C. and at a current density of 1 to 1.5 amperes per sq. dm., and complete the determination as in "Procedure for Grade 1a."

## LEAD BY THE DITHIZONE (PHOTOMETRIC) METHOD

This method covers the determination of lead in amounts of 0.0005 to 0.1%. Higher concentrations are best determined by the electrolytic method preceding.

Lead dithizonate is extracted from a buffered cyanide solution at pH 8.5 to 9.5 with a chloroform solution of dithizone. The excess dithizone in the chloroform is removed by extraction with an ammoniacal sodium sulfite solution of a higher pH. Photometric measurement of the lead dithizonate is made at approximately 515 m$\mu$.

The recommended concentration range is from 0.0025 to 0.04 mg. of lead in 25 ml. of chloroform, using a cell depth of 2 cm. (This procedure has been written for a cell having a 2-cm. light path. Cells having other dimensions may be used, provided suitable adjustments can be made in the amounts of sample and reagents used.)

The color is quite stable, but due to the volatile nature of the solvent it is advisable to make the reading promptly.

Under the conditions specified in the method, bismuth, thallium, and indium will cause high results, but ordinarily these elements are not present. Tin will cause loss of lead by occlusion in metastannic acid and should be removed by volatilization with HBr. Sulfide will cause low lead results (in most instances KCN is sufficiently low in sulfide so that no interference is encountered in lead extractions). Phosphates may interfere and oxidizing agents should be absent.

*Reagents.* **Standard Lead Solution (1 ml. = 0.1 mg. Pb).**—Dissolve 0.100 g. of lead in 20 ml. of $HNO_3$ (1:1) and heat moderately to expel brown fumes. Cool, dilute to 1 liter in a volumetric flask, and mix.

**Standard Lead Solution (1 ml. = 0.005 mg. Pb).**—Dilute 5.0 ml. of lead solution (1 ml. = 0.1 mg. Pb) to 100 ml. in a volumetric flask and mix. Prepare this solution immediately before using.

**Citrate-Acetate Buffer Solution.**—Dissolve 100 g. of sodium citrate and 100 g. of ammonium acetate in water and dilute to 500 ml.

**Potassium Cyanide Solution (200 g. per liter).**—Dissolve 200 g. of KCN (low in lead and sulfide) in water and dilute to 1 liter. (*Caution:* cyanide is extremely poisonous and care should be taken in its use and in its disposal.) Allow to stand overnight, filter through a hardened paper, and store in a polyethylene bottle.

**Dithizone Solution, Stock.**—Dissolve 0.025 g. of diphenylthiocarbazone in chloroform, dilute to 250 ml. with chloroform, and mix. Store in a cool, dark place.

**Dithizone Solution, Dilute.**—Dilute 25 ml. of the stock dithizone solution to 250 ml. with chloroform and mix. Prepare this solution immediately before using.

**Extraction Solution, High pH.**—Dissolve 1 g. of $Na_2SO_3$ in about 300 ml. of water in a 1-liter volumetric flask. Add 475 ml. of $NH_4OH$ (1:1), prepared from a freshly opened bottle. Add 20 ml. of KCN solution. Dilute to the mark and mix.

*Preparation of Calibration Curve.* **Calibration Solution.**—Transfer 1.0, 2.0, 3.0, 5.0, 4.0, 6.0, 7.0, and 8.0 ml. of lead solution (1 ml. = 0.005 mg. Pb) to 125-ml. conical flasks. Add 20 ml. of $HNO_3$ (15:85) to each flask, heat to boiling, and cool.

Add 5.0 ml. of citrate-acetate buffer solution, about 10 mg. of hydroxylamine hydrochloride, and a small piece of indicator (Hydrion) paper. Adjust to about pH 8 by carefully adding $NH_4OH$ (1:1), prepared from a freshly opened bottle of $NH_4OH$. Add 10 ml. of acetic acid (1:4) and cool. Pour 20 ml. of the KCN solution into a 250-ml. separatory funnel and transfer the lead solution to the funnel, using a minimum amount of wash water. Add 25.0 ml. of dilute dithizone solution, stopper, and shake vigorously for 1 minute. Release the stopper and let stand for 3 minutes to allow the layers to separate. Transfer the chloroform layer only to a second separatory funnel containing 50 ml. of the high pH extraction solution. The bore of the stem of the second funnel must be dry. Stopper, and shake vigorously for 1 minute. Remove the stopper and let stand 3 minutes to allow the layers to separate. Draw off a few ml. of the chloroform layer through the funnel stem and discard. Filter 15 or 20 ml. of the chloroform solution through a dry, hardened, rapid filter paper into a dry flask.

Transfer 20 ml. of $HNO_3$ (15:85) to a 125-ml. conical flask, heat to boiling, and cool. Continue as directed above.

Transfer a suitable portion of the reference solution to a dry absorption cell and adjust the photometer to the initial setting, using a light band centered at approximately 515 m$\mu$. While maintaining this photometer adjustment, take the photometric readings of the calibration solutions.

Plot the photometric readings of the calibration solutions against milligrams of lead per 25 ml. of solution.

*Procedure.*—Transfer 0.5 g. of the sample (if the sample contains tin, add 1 ml. of HBr containing 5 drops of bromine to the flask. After dissolution of the sample, add 10 ml. of $HClO_4$ and heat to copious white fumes. Cool, add more $HBr-Br_2$ mixture if the solution is cloudy, and heat to fumes again. Evaporate the solution just to dryness to expel $HClO_4$, add 20 ml. of $HNO_3$ (15:85), boil, and proceed as directed above) to a 125-ml. conical flask and add 20 ml. of $HNO_3$ (15:85). Heat to dissolve the sample and boil to expel oxides of nitrogen. Cool and treat the sample solution or, if the lead is higher than 0.008%, treat a suitable aliquot portion of it containing from 0.0025 to 0.04 mg. of lead plus a total of 20 ml. of $HNO_3$ (15:85), as directed above.

Carry through a reagent blank, following the same procedure and using the same amounts of all reagents, for use as a reference solution.

Take the photometric reading of the sample solution as described above.

**Calculation.**—Convert the photometric readings of the sample solution to milligrams of lead by means of the calibration curve. Calculate the percentage of lead as follows:

$$\text{Lead, } \% = \frac{A}{B \times 10}$$

where $A$ = milligrams of lead found, and
$B$ = grams of sample used.

## CADMIUM BY THE SULFIDE METHOD

*Apparatus.* **Crucible of Fritted-Glass and of Medium Porosity.**

**Platinum Electrodes.**—Similar to those used in "Lead by the Electrolytic Method."

*Reagents.* **Sodium Hydrosulfide Solution.**—Dissolve 50 g. of NaOH in 500 ml. of water, saturated with $H_2S$, and dilute to 1 liter.

**Potassium Ferrocyanide Solution (50 g. per l.).**

**Alcoholic Phenolphthalein Solution (10 g. per l.).**

**Potassium Cyanide or Sodium Cyanide Solution (100 g. per l.).**

*Procedure for Grade 1a.*—Transfer 200 ± 1 g. of the sample to a 3-liter beaker, add 650 ml. of HCl, and after a few minutes, add carefully 100 ml. of $HNO_3$. Boil until solution is complete, dilute to 1 liter with water, and cool in running water. Add 1 liter of $NH_4OH$ and stir until all zinc salts are in solution. Heat to 80°C. and add slowly from a pipette 50 ml. of NaSH solution, while stirring constantly. Stir the solution for 5 minutes, allow to settle in a warm place for 30 minutes, and filter on a 15-cm. close-texture paper, using a Buchner funnel with suction. Wash the beaker once with water. Transfer the paper with precipitate to the 3-liter beaker, add 150 ml. of $H_2SO_4$ (1:5), and boil gently for several minutes, using a stirring rod to disintegrate the paper and effect solution of the ZnS and CdS.

Filter on a close-texture paper into a 600-ml. beaker and wash well with hot water. Discard the precipitate.

Cool the filtrate and dilute to 400 ml. with water. Add slowly, while stirring constantly, 25 ml. of NaSH solution and continue stirring for about 1 minute. Allow to settle for 10 minutes; enough ZnS should be precipitated with the CdS to give a settled layer about ¼ inch in depth. If this is not the case, add more NaSH solution. Filter on a close-texture paper and wash with cold water.

Transfer the paper and precipitate to the 600-ml. beaker, add 50 ml. of $H_2SO_4$ (1:9), and heat gently until the sulfides have dissolved and no stain of yellow CdS is visible. Filter and wash well with hot water. Adjust the volume to 200 ml., heat to 60°C., and pass $H_2S$ into the solution. Add $NH_4OH$ drop by drop until precipitation starts, and continue to pass $H_2S$ into the solution for 20 minutes, allowing the solution to cool in the meantime. Filter through a close-texture paper. Wash four times with warm water and again add 50 ml. of $H_2SO_4$ (1:9) to dissolve the sulfides.

Filter and wash with hot water. Dilute to 200 ml. and again precipitate at 60°C. with $H_2S$. Test the filtrate for zinc by the addition of 5 ml. of $K_4Fe(CN)_6$ (50 g. per l.). If other than a faint turbidity develops, repeat the $H_2S$ separation. When the zinc has been completely removed, complete the determination of cadmium gravimetrically or electrolytically, as below.

**Gravimetric Procedure.**—To complete the determination by weighing, filter the CdS precipitate through a weighed Gooch crucible or fritted-glass crucible. Wash thoroughly with warm water, dry for 2 hours at 110°C., cool, and weigh as CdS. Calculate the percentage of cadmium as follows:

$$\text{Cadmium, } \% = \frac{A \times 0.778}{B} \times 100$$

where $A$ = grams of CdS, and
$B$ = grams of sample used.

**Electrolytic Procedure.**—To determine the cadmium electrolytically, filter the CdS precipitate on paper. Dissolve with hot $H_2SO_4$ (1:9), filter into a 200-ml tall-form beaker, and wash with hot water. Add a drop of alcoholic phenolphthalein (10 g. per l.) to the filtrate and add KOH (100 g. per l.) until the solution is pink. Add KCN or NaCN (100 g. per l.) drop by drop, while stirring constantly, until the $Cd(OH)_2$ just dissolves, avoiding an excess. Electrolyze for 5 hours at a current density of 0.5 to 0.7 amperes per sq. dm. Increase the current density to 1.0 to 1.2 amperes per sq. dm. and continue the electrolysis for 1 hour. Remove the cathode, and quickly rinse with water and then with ethanol. Dry the electrode at 110°C. for 3 to 5 minutes, cool, and weigh the deposit as metallic cadmium. Calculate the percentage of cadmium as follows:

$$\text{Cadmium, } \% = \frac{A}{B} \times 100$$

where $A$ = grams of cadmium and
$B$ = grams of sample used.

***Procedure for Grade 1.***—Transfer 25 ± 0.1 g. of the sample to a 400-ml. tall-form beaker, cover with 50 ml. of water, and add carefully 100 ml. of $HNO_3$. When solution of the sample is complete, add 50 ml. of $H_2SO_4$ (1:1) and evaporate to white fumes. Cool, and add 150 ml. of water. Heat and stir until all soluble salts are in solution. Again cool, and allow the solution to stand until the $PbSO_4$ precipitate has settled. Filter and wash the precipitate six times with cold water.

Dilute the lead-free solution of sample obtained as described in "Procedure for Grade 1a," to a 500-ml. beaker, heat to 60°C., and pass $H_2S$ into the solution. Add $NH_4OH$ drop by drop until considerable ZnS forms, and continue the passage of $H_2S$ for 10 minutes. Filter the solution and wash once with water. Transfer the paper and precipitate to the original beaker, add 50 ml. of cold HCl (1:2) [12] and allow to stand until solution of the ZnS and CdS is complete. Filter the solution, wash well with water, and discard the precipitate.

Add 10 ml. of $H_2SO_4$ to the filtrate and evaporate to dense white fumes. Cool the residue, dilute to 200 ml., heat to 60°C., and pass $H_2S$ into the solution. Add $NH_4OH$ drop by drop until the precipitate has formed, and continue the passage of $H_2S$ for 10 minutes. Filter the solution and wash with water. Dissolve in 100 ml. of $H_2SO_4$ (1:9), dilute to 200 ml., heat to 60°C., and pass $H_2S$ into the solution. Add $NH_4OH$ drop by drop until the precipitate has formed, and continue the passage of $H_2S$ for 10 minutes. Complete the determination by the gravimetric method given above in the "Procedure for Grade 1a."

**Procedure for Grades 2, 3, 4, and 5.**—Transfer $10 \pm 0.1$ g. of the sample to a 400-ml. tall-form beaker, cover with 50 ml. of water, and add carefully 50 ml. of $HNO_3$. When solution of the sample is complete, add 25 ml. of $H_2SO_4$ (1:1) and evaporate to white fumes. Cool, and add 150 ml. of water. Heat and stir until all soluble salts are in solution. Again cool, and allow the solution to stand until the $PbSO_4$ precipitate has settled. Filter and wash the precipitate six times with cold water.

Complete the determination as described in "Procedure for Grade 1a." If the cadmium is to be determined gravimetrically, it may be necessary to use only 5 g. of samples of grades 4 and 5. Quantities of cadmium over 60 mg. are best determined electrolytically.

### IRON BY THE PERMANGANATE METHOD

*Apparatus.* **Filtering Crucible.**—A fritted-glass crucible of medium porosity.
*Reagents.*—**Metallic Zinc (20-mesh).**
**Standard Potassium Permanganate Solution (0.05 N).**
*Procedure for Grade 1a.*—Transfer 100 g. of the sample, from which adventitious iron has been removed, to a 1500-ml. beaker, cover, and add 400 ml. of HCl. When the action almost ceases, add 25 ml. of $HNO_3$ and allow to stand until solution is complete. Boil for 5 minutes, dilute with 100 ml. of water, and then add $NH_4OH$ until the precipitated zinc salts dissolve; about 600 ml. of $NH_4OH$ will be needed. Allow the solution to stand on a steam bath for 30 minutes. Filter on a rapid paper and wash the precipitate twice with $NH_4OH$ (2:98) and then with hot water.

---

[12] In material that may carry appreciable quantities of metals of the $H_2S$ group other than cadmium, it is important that the sulfides first obtained be treated with HCl instead of $H_2SO_4$, as the separation of arsenic, antimony, or bismuth sulfides from cadmium sulfide by boiling with diluted $H_2SO_4$ is imperfect. The separation is complete only in the case of copper; if this is known to be the only contaminating metal present, the original sulfide precipitate can be treated directly with $H_2SO_4$ (1:9), thus obviating the necessity of evaporating the solution for removal of the HCl. On the other hand, if a black precipitate separates on diluting the solution of the sulfides in HCl (1:2) some bismuth sulfide has been dissolved by the strong acid, and has later precipitated. It must be removed by a second filtration.

Dissolve the precipitate on the filter in hot $H_2SO_4$ (1:4). Wash the filter well with hot water, catching the solution in a small beaker. Reprecipitate the iron in a hot solution with $NH_4OH$. Filter and wash the precipitate six times with $(NH_4)_2SO_4$ (20 g. per l.).

Heat 50 ml. of $H_2SO_4$ (1:25) to boiling, and pour it onto the filter in small portions to dissolve the precipitate, receiving the liquid in a 300-ml. flask.

Add 1 g. of metallic zinc to the solution and close the flask with a one-hole rubber stopper containing a Bunsen valve. Heat gently on a hot plate for 30 minutes or until most of the zinc is dissolved. Cool quickly and filter at once through a fritted-glass crucible. Wash twice with cold water. Titrate immediately with 0.05 $N$ $KMnO_4$, using a 10-ml. burette (graduated in 0.05 ml. divisions).

Make a blank determination, following the same procedure and using the same amounts of acid and reagent zinc as used in the determination.

**Calculation.**—Calculate the percentage of iron as follows:

$$\text{Iron, } \% = \frac{(A - B)C \times 0.0558}{D} \times 100$$

where $A$ = milliliters of $KMnO_4$ solution required to titrate the sample,
$\quad B$ = milliliters of $KMnO_4$ solution required to titrate the blank,
$\quad C$ = normality of the $KMnO_4$ solution, and
$\quad D$ = grams of sample used.

***Procedure for Grades 1, 2, 3, and 4.***—Transfer 25 g. of the sample to a 1500-ml. beaker and complete the determination in accordance with the procedure described in "Procedure for Grade 1a," reducing the amounts of reagents used in proportion to the size of the sample.

***Procedure for Grade 5.***—Transfer 10 g. of the sample to a 1500-ml. beaker and complete the determination in accordance with the procedure described in "Procedure for Grade 1a," reducing the amounts of reagents used in proportion to the size of the sample.

## IRON BY THE THIOCYANATE (PHOTOMETRIC) METHOD

Ferric iron forms a red-brown soluble complex with thiocyanate in acid solution. Photometric measurement is made at approximately 480 m$\mu$.

The recommended concentration range is from 0.04 to 0.8 mg. of iron in 100 ml. of solution, using a cell depth of 1 cm. (This procedure has been written for a cell having a 1-cm. light path. Cells having other dimensions may be used, provided suitable adjustments can be made in the amounts of sample and reagents used.)

The color develops immediately and is reasonably stable for 30 minutes in the presence of hydrogen peroxide if the solution is protected from direct sunlight.

The elements ordinarily present in slab zinc (spelter) do not interfere if their contents are under the maximum limits shown on page 1245.

**Reagents.** **Zinc (low-iron).**—Zinc containing under 0.001% of iron.[13]

**Standard Iron Solution (1 ml. = 0.05 mg. Fe).**—Dissolve 0.050 g. of iron[14] in

---

[13] National Bureau of Standards standard Sample No. 109 of zinc spelter is satisfactory for this purpose.

[14] National Bureau of Standards standard Sample No. 55d of ingot iron is satisfactory for this purpose.

50 ml. of $HNO_3$ (1:3). Boil to expel brown fumes, cool, dilute to 1 liter in a volumetric flask, and mix.

**Hydrogen Peroxide (3%).**—Dilute 10 ml. of 30% $H_2O_2$ to 100 ml. Store in a dark bottle in a cool place.

**Ammonium Thiocyanate Solution (100 g. per liter).**—Dissolve 100 g. of $NH_4CNS$ in 300 ml. of water. Filter and dilute to 1 liter. Store in a dark bottle.

*Preparation of Calibration Curve.*—Transfer to each of eight 150-ml. beakers, 1-g. portions of low-iron zinc (it is necessary to have zinc present in the standard since zinc forms a colorless complex that reduces the intensity of the ferric thiocyanate color).

Add 20 ml. of $HNO_3$ (1:3) to each beaker. After dissolution is practically complete, transfer to a hot plate and boil to expel brown fumes. Cool and transfer to 100-ml. volumetric flasks.

Transfer 1.0-, 2.0-, 3.0-, 4.0-, 5.0-, 6.0-, and 7.0-ml. aliquots of the standard iron solution to seven of the flasks, and carry the eighth through as a blank.

Dilute each solution to about 50 ml.; add 1.0 ml. of 3% $H_2O_2$, mix, and add 20 ml. of $NH_4CNS$ solution. Dilute to 100 ml. and mix.

Transfer a suitable portion of the solution to an absorption cell, and measure the transmittancy or absorbancy at approximately 480 m$\mu$. Compensate or correct for blank.

Plot the values obtained against milligrams of iron per 100 ml. of solution.

*Procedure.*—Transfer 1.00 g. (in case a 1-g. portion of the sample is not representative, 25 g. should be dissolved and an aliquot equivalent to 1 g. of the sample used for the determination) of the sample, from which adventitious iron has been removed, and 1 g. of low-iron zinc, for the blank, to 150-ml. beakers. Continue in accordance with "Preparation of Calibration Curve."

Using the value obtained, read from the calibration curve the number of milligrams of iron present in the sample.

**Calculation.**—Calculate the percentage of iron as follows:

$$Iron, \% = \frac{A}{B \times 10}$$

where $A$ = milligrams of iron, and
$B$ = grams of sample used.

## POLAROGRAPHIC DETERMINATION OF LEAD, CADMIUM AND COPPER IN SLAB ZINC, GRADES 1, 2, 3, 4, AND 5

*Reagents.* **Standard Copper Solution.**—Dissolve 0.100 g. of pure copper in 15 ml. of $HNO_3$ (1:3), add 10 ml. of $H_2SO_4$ (1:1) and evaporate to dense white fumes. Cool, dilute to 1 liter in a volumetric flask and mix (1 ml. = 0.0001 g. Cu).

**Standard Lead Solution.**—Dissolve 2.684 g. of $PbCl_2$ (C.P.) in 500 ml. of hot water. Cool, dilute to 1 liter in a volumetric flask and mix (1 ml. = 0.002 g. Pb).

**Standard Cadmium Solution.**—Dissolve 3.262 g. of $CdCl_2$ (C.P.) in 100 ml. of hot water. Cool, dilute to 1 liter in a volumetric flask and mix (1 ml. = 0.002 g. Cd).

**Ammonia and Acid.**—Where strengths of acid or ammonia are not indicated, the concentrated reagent is used.

*Determination of Copper, Lead, and Cadmium Factors.*—Transfer to each of four 400-ml. beakers, 5.00-g. portions of zinc of low copper, lead, and cadmium content (under 0.001%). Add 30 ml. of water and 30 ml. of HCl. After vigorous action has subsided, heat on a warm plate until solution is complete. Cool, and transfer 10-, 20-, 30-, and 40-ml. aliquots of the standard copper solution, like amounts of the standard lead solution and 5-, 10-, 15-, and 20-ml. aliquots of the standard cadmium solution to the four beakers, respectively. Dilute to 200 ml. in a volumetric flask and mix.

Transfer a suitable portion of the resulting solutions to electrolysis cells. Add a small amount of mercury to serve as the anode (1 cm.² surface area). Place the cells in the constant temperature bath and remove the dissolved oxygen by bubbling nitrogen through the solutions for 10 minutes.

Introduce the dropping electrode assembly, making sure the contact electrode dips into the mercury pool, into each cell one at a time and record the increase in galvanometer deflection and the current multiplier setting (Note 1) when changing the applied potential from 0.15 to 0.35 volts (due to copper), from 0.35 to 0.60 volts (due to lead) and from 0.60 to 0.80 volts (due to cadmium) (Note 2).

Multiply the increases in galvanometer deflection by the current multiplier setting used and plot against the corresponding grams of copper, lead and cadmium, respectively. Since these points should fall on a straight line, it is only necessary to use the highest concentration in calculating the factors.

Calculate the copper, lead, and cadmium factors as follows:

$$F = \frac{C}{R \times S}$$

where $C$ = grams of copper, lead, or cadimum,

$R$ = increase in galvanometer deflection due to copper, lead, or cadmium, respectively,

$S$ = current multiplier setting used in obtaining $R$ and,

$F$ = the grams of copper, lead, or cadmium, respectively, per mm. increase in galvanometer deflection on full sensitivity.

*Procedure.*—Transfer 5.00 g. of the sample to a 400-ml. beaker. Add 30 ml. of water and 30 ml. of HCl. After vigorous action has subsided, heat on a warm plate until solution is complete (Note 3). Cool, dilute to 200 ml. in a volumetric flask and mix (Note 4). Transfer a suitable portion of the resulting solution to electrolysis cells and continue as under "Determination of Copper, Lead, and Cadmium Factors."

Calculate the percentages of copper, lead, and cadmium as follows:

$$\% \text{ Cu, Pb, or Cd} = \frac{(R \times S) \times F \times 100}{5}$$

where $R$ = increase in galvanometer deflection for copper, lead, or cadmium, respectively,

$S$ = current multiplier setting used in obtaining $R$, and

$F$ = the grams of copper, lead, or cadmium, respectively, per mm. increase in galvanometer deflection on full sensitivity.

NOTES.—1. The current multiplier should be set so as to obtain optimum increases in galvanometer deflection.

2. A current voltage curve should be plotted to determine that the voltage settings used actually fall on the residual and diffusion current plateaus, respectively.

3. If necessary a few milliliters of $H_2O_2$ may be added. The excess must be removed by boiling.

4. If the sample contains appreciable tin or indium dilute to approximately 180 ml. and add 5 drops of methyl red. Add $NH_4OH$ until the pink color has just disappeared and add one drop excess. Cool the solution and adjust the pH to 5.6, using a pH meter with a glass electrode, by adding dilute $NH_4OH$ (1:10) drop-wise with stirring. Dilute to 200 ml. in a volumetric flask, mix, and continue with the method.

## POLAROGRAPHIC DETERMINATION OF LEAD AND CADMIUM IN GRADE 1A AND HORSE HEAD SPECIAL SLAB ZINC

This method is similar to the Polarographic Determination above for grades 1, 2, 3, 4, and 5, except for the following:

1. Use a 20.00-g. sample.
2. Use 70 ml. HCl and a few drops of 3% cobaltous chloride.
3. Dilute to 100 ml. final volume.

In standardizing the polarograph, use solutions in which, 1 ml. = 0.0001 g. Pb and 1 ml. = 0.0001 g. Cd and use C.P. zinc which contains no more than 0.0002% lead and cadmium. The percentage of each should be determined by special chemical analysis. A blank obtained from a plot of the lead and cadmium concentration (including the lead and cadmium in the zinc metal used), against the galvanometer deflection must be subtracted from readings obtained when running a sample.

## COPPER IN METALLIC ZINC

**Reagents.** $H_2SO_4$ (1:1).—Mix cautiously 500 ml. of $H_2SO_4$ (sp. gr. 1.84) with 500 ml. of cold distilled water.

**Sodium Thiosulfate (25%).**—Dissolve 25 g. of $Na_2S_2O_3 \cdot 5H_2O$ (C.P.) in distilled water and dilute to 100 ml.

**Nitric Acid (1:4).**—Mix 30 ml. of $HNO_3$ (sp. gr. 1.42) with 120 ml. of distilled water.

**Nickel Sulfate Solution.**—Dissolve 80 g. of $NiSO_4 \cdot 6H_2O$ in water and dilute to 1000 ml.

**Standard Copper Sulfate.**—Dissolve 0.3929 g. of $CuSO_4 \cdot 5H_2O$ (C.P.) in distilled water, add 5 ml. of $H_2SO_4$ (1:1) and dilute to exactly 1000 ml.

*Procedure.*—Weigh 100 g. of sample into a 2000-ml. beaker. Add 1000 ml. of $H_2O$, 25 ml. of nickel sulfate solution and then add slowly 225 ml. of $H_2SO_4$ (1:1). After all the zinc has been dissolved, heat the solution to boiling and add 10 ml. of 25% sodium thiosulfate solution. Boil until precipitate coagulates, let settle a few minutes. Filter through a No. 2 Whatman 15-cm. paper, and wash thoroughly with cold water.

Transfer the paper and precipitate to the original beaker, add 50 ml. of $HNO_3$ (1:4), and boil gently for several minutes using a stirring rod to disintegrate the paper and effect solution of the copper sulfide. Filter through a No. 1 Whatman 12.5-cm. paper into a 250-ml. beaker and wash well with hot water. Discard the paper.

Add 10 ml. of $H_2SO_4$ (1:1), evaporate to strong fumes, destroy the organic matter by adding $HNO_3$ (sp. gr. 1.42) dropwise to the hot acid solution and take to complete dryness over a Meker burner.

Take up in a few drops of $H_2SO_4$ (1:1) and 10 ml. water. Heat to boiling, cool, filter through a No. 2 Whatman 15-cm. paper into a 50-ml. beaker, and wash filter well with cold water. Discard the paper.

Reduce the volume of the filtrate to 2 to 3 ml. by boiling, neutralize to litmus with $NH_4OH$ (sp. gr. 0.90) and add 2 ml. excess. Heat to boiling and filter, catching the filtrate in a small flat bottom color comparison tube, and wash with five 1-ml. increments of cold water. (Volume in comparison tube should not exceed 10 ml.)

Make a standard copper solution for comparison in a similar comparison tube as follows:

Add 2 drops $H_2SO_4$ (1:1) to 3 ml. water, neutralize with $NH_4OH$ (sp. gr. 0.90) and add 2 ml. in excess. Then add standard copper solution from a burette in 1-ml. increments until the blue color matches the color in the tube containing the copper from the sample when diluted to the same volume. If the sample contains more than 0.001% Cu a smaller sample should be used or an aliquot of the final solution may be taken. Samples containing over 0.01% Cu should be completed electrolytically as described under "Procedure for Standardization of the Copper Sulfate Solution."

Calculate the percentage of copper as follows:

$$\frac{(A - B) \times 0.0001 \times 100}{100} = \% \text{ Cu}$$

where $A$ is the number of ml. of the standard copper solution required to equal the color of the sample, $B$ is the number of ml. of the standard copper solution required to equal the color, if any, obtained by a blank determination, i.e., carrying all quantities of reagents and water through the procedure. 0.0001 is the weight in grams of copper per ml. of standard copper solution.

*Procedure for Standardization of the Copper Sulfate Solution.*—Measure 100 ml. of the copper sulfate solution into a tall form 200-ml. beaker and add 2 ml. of $HNO_3$ (sp. gr. 1.42) and 10 ml. of $H_2SO_4$ (1:1). Dilute to 150 ml. with water and electrolyze for 3 hours with a current density of one ampere per 100 sq. cm. Wash the cathode with water by lowering the beaker of electrolyte out from under the electrodes and immediately replacing it with a beaker of distilled water. Washing is accomplished by moving the beaker of water up and down several times. This operation is repeated twice with fresh water and once with alcohol. The current must be left on until the last washing is finished. The first washing of the electrodes must be carried out as soon as possible after the beaker of electrolyte has been removed, since the film of the solution which remains on the electrode tends to redissolve the deposit. Wash with alcohol (95%) and dry at 110°C. in an oven. Cool and weigh.[15]

Calculate the grams of copper per ml. as follows:

$$\frac{A - B}{100} = \text{g. Cu per ml.}$$

where $A$ is the weight of platinum electrode with deposit of copper, $B$ is the weight of platinum electrode initially.

## ZINC IN METALLIC CADMIUM

### *TURBIDIMETRIC METHOD*

**Reagents. Sulfuric Acid (1:1).**—Mix cautiously 200 ml. of $H_2SO_4$ (sp. gr. 1.84) with 200 ml. of cold distilled water.

---

[15] The weight of copper sulfate taken should make a solution which will contain 0.0001 g. copper per 1 ml. If this strength is not obtained, adjust the solution and restandardize as above.

**Hydrochloric Acid (1:2).**—Mix 300 ml. of HCl (sp. gr. 1.20) with 600 ml. of distilled water.

*Procedure.*—Weigh 10 g. of sample into an 800-ml. beaker, add 200 ml. of water, cover beaker and add 25 ml. of $HNO_3$ (sp. gr. 1.42). When action has ceased, add 15 ml. of $H_2SO_4$ (1:1), remove cover and evaporate to complete dryness. Cool, add 200 ml. of water and 40 ml. of $H_2SO_4$ (1:1), cover, bring to a boil slowly [16] and boil until all soluble salts are dissolved. Cool, make the volume 400 ml., and pass a rapid stream of $H_2S$ gas through the solution for 15 minutes.[17] Allow to settle, and filter,[18] catching the filtrate in an 800-ml. beaker. Wash the precipitate once by decantation with water and transfer the precipitate to the paper. Permit to drain, then remove the beaker containing filtrate and place it on warm plate to evaporate.

Place beaker, in which the precipitation was made, under funnel and dissolve the precipitate into the beaker by washing with HCl (1:2) washing finally with cold water. Add 15 ml. of $H_2SO_4$ (1:1) to the solution and evaporate to complete dryness. Cool, add 200 ml. of water and 40 ml. of $H_2SO_4$ (1:1), cover, bring to a boil slowly and boil until all soluble salts are dissolved. Cool, make the volume 400 ml. and pass a rapid stream of $H_2S$ gas through the solution for 15 minutes.[17] Filter,[18] washing the precipitate once on the paper. Discard the paper and precipitate. Add this filtrate to that previously obtained.

Evaporate the combined filtrates to complete dryness. Cool, add 100 ml. of water and 25 ml. of $H_2SO_4$ (1:1), heat to boiling, and boil until the soluble salts are dissolved. Cool, make the volume 400 ml. and pass a rapid stream of $H_2S$ gas through the solution for 15 minutes. Filter,[19] catching the filtrate in a 600-ml. beaker and washing with cold water. Evaporate to complete dryness. Add 3 ml. of HCl (sp. gr. 1.20) and 20 ml. of water and heat until solution is complete. Cool and wash into a 100-ml. Nessler tube and estimate the zinc by the "Turbidimetric Determination," page 1240.

## POLAROGRAPHIC DETERMINATION

*Procedure.*—Dissolve 1.00 g. of the sample in 30 ml. of $H_2SO_4$ (1:1), dilute to 400 ml. and pass a rapid stream of $H_2S$ through the sample for 20 minutes. Filter, wash precipitate, adding washings to filtrate and add 10 ml. of $H_2SO_4$ to filtrate and evaporate to dryness. Continue with the determination according to the procedure under "Polarographic Determination," page 1240.

Special care must be taken in this determination to avoid contamination of the sample. A blank must be run using the same amount of all reagents.

## ZINC IN BRASS

*Procedure.*—The sample is dissolved in $HNO_3$ and HCl and evaporated to dryness. It is now treated with 2.5 ml. of HCl or 1.5 ml. of $H_2SO_4$ and 50 ml. of water and saturated with $H_2S$, then diluted to 100 ml. and again saturated with $H_2S$. Copper sulfide, etc., are filtered off and washed to recover occluded zinc. The filtrate containing the zinc is neutralized with ammonia added dropwise after

---

[16] The residue cake might crack the beaker if heated too strongly at first. It is well to break up the residue with a glass stirring rod before heating.

[17] To precipitate the bulk of the cadmium as CdS.

[18] Use a 15-cm. qualitative paper. This is a rough separation. Any CdS which goes through the paper will be removed later.

[19] Use a close 11-cm. paper. This is the final removal of the last traces of cadmium.

expelling the $H_2S$ by boiling. The zinc is now determined gravimetrically as $Zn_2P_2O_7$ by precipitation from the neutral solution with $(NH_4)_2HPO_4$ as described under "Gravimetric Methods," or precipitated as ZnS in a slightly acid solution and determined volumetrically by titrating with standard potassium ferrocyanide solution as described under "Standard Method."

## DETERMINATION OF ZINC IN RUBBER GOODS

### FERROCYANIDE METHOD

*Procedure.*—Carefully ash a 2-g. sample of the rubber keeping the temperature low (under 550°C.) to prevent reduction and volatilization of zinc. Dissolve the ash in 15 ml. of hydrochloric acid (sp. gr. 1.19) in a 250-ml. beaker. Remove the crucible, wash thoroughly with a minimum amount of hot water, and boil down to 5 ml. volume. Cool, and wash down sides of beaker. Add 10 ml. of saturated bromine water, 5 g. of ammonium chloride, 15 ml. of $NH_4OH$ (sp. gr. 0.90), and boil vigorously for 3 minutes.

Filter off the precipitated hydroxides and insoluble material, and wash four times with 100 ml. of hot water, in 25-ml. portions, containing 50 g. of $NH_4Cl$ and 25 ml. of $NH_4OH$ (sp. gr. 0.90) per liter. Dilute the solution to 200 ml., heat to boiling, and add 4 drops of a concentrated ammonium sulfide solution to destroy oxidizing agents. Carefully neutralize with hydrochloric acid (sp. gr. 1.19) using litmus paper as an indicator and add 3 ml. excess. Titrate with standard potassium ferrocyanide solution as directed under "Titration in Acid Solution with Outside Indicator."

Interfering elements such as manganese, copper, cadmium, etc., are rarely used in rubber compounds.

## DETERMINATION OF ZINC IN SOLDER [20]

*Reagent.* **Mixed Acid.**—Dissolve 20 g. of $NH_4Cl$ in 500 ml. of distilled water, add 400 ml. of HCl (sp. gr. 1.19), mix and add 100 ml. of $HNO_3$ (sp. gr. 1.42).

**Dilute Hydrochloric Acid for Dilution.**—To 500 ml. of cold distilled water, add 10 ml. of HCl (sp. gr. 1.19) and pass in $H_2S$ for 15 minutes.

**Citric Acid Solution.**—Dissolve 250 g. of $H_3C_6H_5O_7 \cdot H_2O$ in 500 ml. of distilled water.

**Ammonium Thiocyanate Wash Solution.**—Dissolve 20 g. of $NH_4CNS$ in 1000 ml. of distilled water and filter through a dry paper.

**Standard Zinc Solution.**—Dissolve exactly 0.1 g. of U. S. Bureau of Standards pure zinc in 10 ml. of HCl (sp. gr. 1.19) and dilute to exactly 1000 ml. with distilled water.

**Potassium Ferrocyanide Solution.**—Dissolve 21.54 g. of $K_4Fe(CN)_6 \cdot 3H_2O$ in about 800 ml. of distilled water. When dissolved dilute to 1000 ml. with distilled water and mix.

*Procedure.*[21]—Weigh 6.25 g. of the sawings, free from metallic iron, into a 250-ml. beaker, add 150 ml. of the mixed acid and heat over a low flame or hot plate. When $PbCl_2$ begins to form, decant the clear solution into a 400-ml. beaker, again add 150 ml. of the mixed acid to the undissolved alloy and continue heating until solution is complete. Two 150-ml. additions of the mixed acid should suffice to completely dissolve the alloy without the formation of appreciable $PbCl_2$ in the

[20] Standard Method by the National Lead Company through kindness of W. J. Brown.
[21] See Determination of Small Quantities of Zinc, by M. Bodansky. J. Ind. Eng. Chem., **13**, 696, 1921.

hot solution. When completely dissolved, combine the two solutions and evaporate down to a volume of about 75 ml. Allow to stand in the cold overnight. Separate the $PbCl_2$ by decantation, washing 3 times with cold HCl (1:2) into a 600-ml. beaker. Discard the residue. Evaporate the solution nearly to dryness, add 10 ml. of HCl (sp. gr. 1.19), dilute with 100 ml. of water, bring to boiling and pass $H_2S$ through the solution. As the sulfides precipitate gradually dilute with hot distilled water until a volume of 300 ml. is attained and continue passing $H_2S$ for 30 minutes. Transfer to a 500-ml. graduated flask, cool to room temperature, make up to the mark with dilute hydrochloric acid for dilution, and mix. Filter off 400 ml. through a dry filter, discarding the first 20 ml. of the solution. Transfer the filtered solution to a 600-ml. beaker,[22] add 5 ml. of $H_2SO_4$ (sp. gr. 1.84) evaporate to fumes, cool, add 50 ml. of distilled water, bring to boiling, allow to stand in the cold for an hour or so, filter and wash with dilute $H_2SO_4$ (1:9). Discard the residue. Bring the filtrate to boiling, add 3 or 4 ml. of $HNO_3$ (sp. gr. 1.42) to oxidize iron, make strongly alkaline with $NH_4OH$, again bring to boiling and allow to stand in a warm place an hour or so for the iron to completely precipitate. Filter and wash into a 600-ml. beaker.

Boil the filtrate to expel $NH_4OH$, add 10 ml. of the citric acid solution, dilute to a volume of 350 ml., again bring to boiling, and add, a little at a time, solid $CaCO_3$[23] until about 1 g. of calcium citrate separates. Pass $H_2S$ through the solution until cold and allow to stand several hours, part of the time on a water bath. Filter and wash with the $NH_4CNS$ wash solution.

Wash the precipitate back into the beaker with as little water as possible and set under the funnel. Now pour through the filtrate 10–15 ml. of hot HCl (1:1) and replace the beaker with a 100-ml. graduated flask. Bring the solution in the beaker to boiling and filter through the same filter. Wash several times with hot distilled water. Cool the solution in the flask to room temperature, make up to the mark with distilled water at room temperature and mix. Reserve as solution No. 1. At the same time the sample is being run a "blank" should be carried along. The solution on the blank in another 100 ml.-graduated flask should be reserved as solution No. 2.

Pipette off 25 ml. of solution No. 1 into a 100-ml. Nessler tube, add 2 ml. of the $K_4Fe(CN)_6$ solution, make up to the mark with distilled water and shake well. Into another 100-ml. Nessler tube, pipette 25 ml. of solution No. 2, add 2 ml. of $K_4Fe(CN)_6$ solution, make up to the mark with distilled water, mix and add the standard zinc solution a few drops at a time until the turbidities match. Shake well between each addition of the standard. Before the final comparison is made both solutions No. 1 and No. 2 should stand about 5 minutes to allow the maximum turbidity to develop.

Comparison is best made by setting the tubes over a sheet of fine print and looking down the tubes.

[22] It might be expedient at this stage to pass $H_2S$ through the solution to ascertain if all the tin has been precipitated. If a precipitate forms, filter and wash with "dilute HCl for dilution."

[23] When $CaCO_3$ is added to the hot solution violent frothing takes place. Unless extreme care is taken in adding the $CaCO_3$, the determination may be spoiled.

## DETERMINATION OF ZINC IN PIG LEAD [24]

*Apparatus.* **Nessler Tubes.**

*Reagents.* **Standard Zinc Solution.**—Dissolve 4.0000 g. of zinc (National Bureau of Standards standard sample No. 43f of standard melting point zinc is satisfactory for this purpose) (1 ml. = 0.01 mg. Zn).

**Potassium Ferrocyanide Solution (6 g. $K_4Fe(CN)_6$ per l.).**—Dissolve 6.8 g. of $K_4Fe(CN)_6 \cdot 3H_2O$ in water and dilute to 1 liter.

**Hydrogen Sulfide Wash Solution.**—Saturate $H_2SO_4$ (2:98) with $H_2S$.

**Bromine Water (saturated).**

**Citric Acid Solution (200 g. per l.).**

**Formic Acid Mixture.**—Dilute 200 ml. of formic acid (sp. gr. 1.20) to 970 ml. with water and add 30 ml. of $NH_4OH$.

**Formic Acid Mixture Wash Solution.**—Dilute 25 ml. of the formic acid mixture to 1 liter with water and saturate with $H_2S$.

**Talc Suspension.**—Prepare a suspension of 50 g. of talc in 1 liter of water.

*Preparation of Turbidity Standards.*—Transfer portions of zinc solution (1 ml. = 0.01 mg. Zn), corresponding to 0.01 to 0.1 mg. of zinc in increments of 0.01 mg., to ten 50-ml. Nessler tubes. Add 15 ml. of HCl (1:9) and dilute to 45 ml. with water. Add 5 ml. of $K_4Fe(CN)_6$ solution and mix. The $K_4Fe(CN)_6$ solution should be added to the standards and to the sample at the same time.

*Procedure.*—Transfer 50 g. of the sample to a 600-ml. beaker. To this and to a second beaker to be carried through the entire procedure as a blank, add 200 ml. of water and 50 ml. of $HNO_3$. Heat gently to dissolve the sample, and boil to expel brown fumes. Remove from the hot plate and add, while stirring, 35 ml. of $H_2SO_4$ (1:1). Filter through a fine paper on a Buechner funnel with the aid of gentle suction, and wash the beaker and precipitate with water. Discard the precipitate.

Transfer the filtrate to a 600-ml. beaker and evaporate to dense white fumes. Continue heating until the volume of $H_2SO_4$ is reduced to about 2 ml. Cool, add 100 ml. of water, and boil for several minutes. Cool, pass $H_2S$ into the solution for about 15 minutes, and allow the precipitated sulfides to settle. Filter through a fine paper and wash with $H_2S$ wash solution. Discard the precipitate.

Boil the filtrate to expel $H_2S$, add a few drops of bromine water to oxidize the iron, and boil to expel the excess bromine. Neutralize the solution to litmus with $NH_4OH$ and add 2 ml. in excess. Add citric acid solution until just acid to litmus and add 25 ml. of formic acid mixture. Dilute to about 200 ml. and add 1 ml. of talc suspension. Heat to 90 to 100°C., and pass in a rapid stream of $H_2S$ for 30 minutes, while the solution is cooling. Allow to stand for 1 hour, filter on a 9-cm. fine paper, and wash well with the formic acid mixture wash solution.

Dissolve the ZnS through the filter paper with 30 ml. of HCl (1:9), collecting the filtrate in a 100-ml. volumetric flask. Wash the paper thoroughly with hot water, collecting the washings in the flask. Cool the solution to 20°C., dilute to 100 ml. and mix.

Transfer a suitable aliquot, containing not more than 0.1 mg. of zinc, to a 50-ml. Nessler tube. Add HCl (1:9) to make a total volume of 15 ml. of HCl (1:9). Dilute to 45 ml. with water, and add 5 ml. of $K_4Fe(CN)_6$ solution. Mix, allow to stand 10 minutes, and compare the turbidity with that of the zinc standards.

[24] ASTM Method E-37-56.

**Calculation.**—Calculate the percentage of zinc as follows:

$$\text{Zinc, \%} = \frac{A - B}{C \times 10}$$

where $A$ = milligrams of zinc found in aliquot used,
    $B$ = milligrams of zinc found in blank aliquot used, and
    $C$ = grams of sample represented by aliquot used.

## DETERMINATION OF ZINC IN POLLUTED WATER, SEWAGE, AND INDUSTRIAL WASTES [25]

Samples of polluted water or sewage are evaporated and digested with acid to destroy organic matter. The procedure to be followed depends on the organic content. Digestion with a mixture of nitric and sulfuric acids serves for most samples; but when the organic matter is difficult to oxidize, perchloric acid is substituted for sulfuric acid. Perchloric acid digestion is also recommended when lead is to be determined.

The amount of sample to be evaporated depends on the concentration of the zinc to be determined. A 1-liter sample should be taken if analyses are to be made if the zinc is present in less than 1 p. p. m. concentration.

Zinc is separated from other metals by extraction with dithizone and determined by measuring the color of the zinc-dithizone complex in carbon tetrachloride. Specificity in the separation is achieved by extracting from a nearly neutral solution containing bis(2-hydroxyethyl) dithiocarbamyl ion and cyanide ion, which prevent moderate concentrations of cadmium, copper, lead, and nickel from reacting with dithizone.

The color reaction is extremely sensitive, and precautions must be taken to avoid introducing extraneous zinc during the analysis. Contamination may arise from water, reagents, and from glassware (such as beakers and separatory funnels on which zinc has been adsorbed during previous use). Appreciable blanks are generally found, and the analyst must satisfy himself that these blanks are representative and reproducible.

**Apparatus.**—Photoelectric filter photometer, with green filter (about 535 m$\mu$) or photoelectric spectrophotometer.

**Separatory funnels,** 125 ml. Squibb form with ground-glass stoppers.

*Reagents.* **Acetic Acid, Glacial.**

**Ammonium Hydroxide, Zinc-Free, 5 $M$.**—Commercial $NH_4OH$ reagent usually contains zinc and is unacceptable. Prepare a concentrated solution by passing $NH_3$ gas from a cylinder into redistilled water and store the product in a plastic or a paraffin-lined bottle. If a cylinder of $NH_3$ gas is unavailable, C.P. ammonium hydroxide may be distilled using Pyrex apparatus.

**Bis(2-hydroxyethyl) Dithiocarbamate Solution.**—Dissolve 4.0 g. of diethanolamine and 1 ml. of $CS_2$ in 40 ml. of methanol. Prepare fresh every three or four days.

**Carbon Tetrachloride, Zinc-Free.**

**Dithizone Solution, 0.01% in $CCl_4$.**—Dissolve 50 mg. of diphenylthiocarbazone in 500 ml. of $CCl_4$. Keep in the dark in a cool place.

**Dithizone Solution, 0.005% in $CCl_4$.**—Prepare a purified solution as follows: Measure 125 ml. of 0.01% dithizone into a 500-ml. separatory funnel and add 100 ml. of water followed by 3 ml. of $NH_4OH$. Shake well and discard the $CCl_4$

[25] Butts, Gahler, and Mellon, Sewage and Industrial Wastes, **22**, 1543, 1950.

layer. Add 125 ml. of pure $CCl_4$, make just acidic with HCl, and shake. Draw off the $CCl_4$ layer and wash it twice by shaking with 50-ml. portions of redistilled water, then dilute to 250 ml. with pure $CCl_4$. Keep in a cool, dark place and do not use if more than one week old.

**Potassium Cyanide Solution.**—Dissolve 5 g. KCN in 95 ml. of redistilled water.

**Sodium Citrate Solution.**—Dissolve 10 g. of $Na_3C_6H_5O_7 \cdot 2H_2O$ in 90 ml. of water. Shake with 10 ml. of 0.01% dithizone in chloroform to remove zinc, then filter.

**Sodium Sulfide, 1% Solution.**—Dissolve 3.0 g. of $Na_2S \cdot 9H_2O$ in 100 ml. of water.

**Sodium Sulfide, 0.04% Solution.**—Prepare just before use by diluting 4 ml. of 1% $Na_2S$ to 100 ml.

**Zinc-Free Distilled Water.**—For preparation of reagents and dilution water. Ordinary distilled water usually contains traces of zinc, and should be redistilled using an all-Pyrex apparatus.

**Zinc Standard Solution, 1.000 mg. Zinc per ml.**—Dissolve 1.000 g. of C. P. zinc metal in 10 ml. of 1:1 $HNO_3$. Dilute and boil to expel oxides of nitrogen. Transfer to a 1000-ml. volumetric flask, dilute to volume, and mix.

*Preparation of Calibration Curve.*—Prepare just before use a zinc solution containing 0.00200 mg. of zinc per ml. by diluting 5 ml. of the standard zinc solution to 250 ml., then diluting 10 ml. of the latter solution to 100 ml. with redistilled water. Pipette 5.00-, 10.00-, 15.00-, and 20.00-ml. portions of the resulting solution into separate 125-ml. separatory funnels and adjust the volumes to about 20 ml. Another funnel containing 20 ml. of water is carried through as a blank. Add two drops of methyl red indicator and 2.0 ml. of sodium citrate to each; if the indicator is not yellow at this point, add $NH_4OH$ a drop at a time until the indicator just turns yellow. Next add 1.0 ml. of KCN and then sufficient acetic acid a drop at a time just to turn the indicator to a neutral peach color.

Extract the methyl red by shaking with 5 ml. of $CCl_4$ and discard the yellow $CCl_4$ layer. Then add 1 ml. of methanolic bis(2-hydroxyethyl) dithiocarbamate. Extract with 10 ml. of purified dithizone, shaking for 1 minute. Draw off the $CCl_4$ layer into another separatory funnel and repeat the extraction with successive 5-ml. portions of dithizone until the last one shows no change from the green dithizone color when viewed by transmitted light. Discard the aqueous layer.

Shake the combined dithizone extracts with 10 ml. of 0.04% $Na_2S$, then separate the layers and repeat the washing with further 10-ml. portions of $Na_2S$ until the unreacted dithizone has been completely removed, as shown by the aqueous layer remaining colorless or very pale yellow; usually three such washings are sufficient. Finally, remove any water adhering to the stem of the funnel with a cotton swab and drain the pink $CCl_4$ solution into a dry 50-ml. volumetric flask, using a few milliliters of fresh $CCl_4$ to rinse the last droplets from the funnel. Dilute to the mark with fresh $CCl_4$.

Determine the absorbancy of the zinc dithizonate solutions at 535 m$\mu$ and plot an absorbancy-concentration curve after subtracting the absorbancy of the blank. The calibration curve is linear if monochromatic light is used.

If large or erratic blanks are obtained despite the exercise of care in purifying water and reagents, it is probably caused by zinc adsorbed on the glass surface of the separatory funnels. These should be rinsed with 4 $M$ $HNO_3$, then with distilled water, and finally shaken for several minutes with 5 ml. of sodium citrate and 5 ml. of dithizone. If possible, separatory funnels used for zinc analyses should be reserved for this purpose and not used for other determinations.

*Procedure.*—Take an aliquot of the sample containing between 10 and 40 micrograms of zinc, transfer to a clean 125-ml. separatory funnel, and adjust the volume to about 20 ml. Determine the zinc in this solution exactly as described for preparing the calibration curve.

Generally not more than 30 ml. of 0.005% dithizone should be needed to extract the zinc completely; if more is required, the aliquot taken contains too much zinc or the quantity of other metals which react with dithizone exceeds the amount which can be withheld by the complexing agent. In the latter case, the following procedure should be followed. Place the aliquot in a 100-ml. beaker, adjust the volume to about 20 ml. and the acidity to 0.4 to 0.5 $N$, by adding dilute $HNO_3$ or $NH_4OH$ as necessary. Pass $H_2S$ into the cold solution for 5 minutes. Filter off the precipitated sulfides using a sintered glass filter, washing the precipitate with two small portions of hot water. Boil the filtrate 3 or 4 minutes to remove $H_2S$, then cool, transfer to a separatory funnel, and determine the zinc as described above.

## ANALYSIS OF ZINC CHLORIDE SOLUTION [26]

The methods to be used for the analysis of zinc chloride solution or fused zinc chloride are essentially those given under the various chapters for the various elements. It seems advisable, however, to include a set of methods of analysis suitable for the commercial evaluation of zinc chloride.

### DETERMINATION OF SPECIFIC GRAVITY AT 15°C.

*Procedure.*—The specific gravity is determined by means of a pycnometer. The volume is brought to the graduation after the solution in the pycnometer has been brought to 15°C., using a water bath. The weight of this volume of boiled distilled water is determined at 15°C., and the specific gravity of the zinc chloride solution calculated, compared to water at 15°C.

### ZINC (MANGANESE AND COPPER ABSENT)

*Procedure.*—About 25 g. of the well shaken solution is weighed out in a weighing bottle and transferred to a 500-ml. graduated flask. Sufficient nitric acid is added to clarify the solution upon dilution. The flask is filled to the mark with distilled water and thoroughly mixed.

A portion, approximately equivalent to 1 g. of $ZnCl_2$ is accurately measured from a pipette or a burette and the zinc determined by titration with a standard potassium ferrocyanide solution as given under procedure for zinc in ores.

### ZINC (MANGANESE OR COPPER PRESENT)

*Procedure.*—If manganese or copper is present an aliquot portion is measured out and the manganese or copper separated according to the methods given under procedures for ores, before titration with potassium ferrocyanide.

### CHLORINE

*Procedure.*—Another portion of this solution, approximately equivalent to 0.5 g. of $ZnCl_2$ is measured off into a 500-ml. Erlenmeyer flask; 15 ml. of distilled water, 100 ml. of standard 0.1 $N$ silver nitrate solution and 40 ml. of nitric acid are added to the flask and boiled until all nitrous fumes are driven off. After cooling, the

[26] Contributed by L. S. Holstein and L. A. Wilson.

excess silver nitrate is titrated with standard 0.1 $N$ ammonium thiocyanate solution using 5 ml. of (1:6) ferric nitrate solution as an indicator. A blank is run at the same time and the amount of chlorine determined from the difference in volumes of ammonium thiocyanate required. The factor for the standard ammonium thiocyanate solution is best determined with C.P. sodium chloride.

## SULFURIC ANHYDRIDE ($SO_3$)

**Procedure.**—Twenty-five ml. of the original well-shaken solution of zinc chloride are measured off with a pipette into a 400-ml. beaker, diluted to 300 ml. with hot water and a few drops of hydrochloric acid added. Any insoluble matter is filtered off, 5 ml. of bromine water are added to the filtrate and the solution boiled until excess bromine is all driven off. The $SO_3$ in the filtrate is precipitated with 25 ml. of hot 10% barium chloride solution. After standing on the steam plate for 3 hours, the barium sulfate is filtered off, ignited and weighed. The weight of the sample is determined from the specific gravity.

## IRON (Fe)

**Procedure.**—A portion of the well-shaken solution, equivalent to 10 g. of zinc is evaporated to a syrupy consistency and the iron determined by the colorimetric method as under spelter.

In case the iron is too high to estimate colorimetrically it is separated with ammonia, filtered off, washed with hot water and dissolved in hot dilute sulfuric acid. This solution is cooled, run through a Jones Reductor and titrated with standard potassium permanganate solution, or the iron may be determined by the hydrogen sulfide method as given under analysis of slab zinc.

## IRON AND ALUMINUM ($Fe_2O_3 + Al_2O_3$)

**Procedure.**—Either 10 or 20 ml. of the original well-shaken solution are transferred to a 200-ml. beaker, diluted with 150 ml. of water and hydrochloric acid added to a very faint excess (2 drops concentrated acid). A rapid stream of hydrogen sulfide is passed through the solution for 30 to 40 minutes. The precipitate of zinc sulfide is filtered off and washed thoroughly. The filtrate is boiled for about 15 minutes to remove hydrogen sulfide, cooled, sufficient bromine water added to more than oxidize all the iron, and then boiled to remove the excess bromine. Ammonium hydroxide is now added in slight excess, the precipitate of iron and alumina filtered off and washed with hot water. The precipitate is dissolved from the paper with hot hydrochloric acid (1:4) reprecipitated, filtered off, washed free from chlorides, ignited and weighed.

## MANGANESE

**Procedure.**—Either 10 or 20 ml. of the original well-shaken solution are transferred to a 400 ml. beaker, 25 ml. of sulfuric acid (1:1) added and evaporated to practically complete expulsion of all excess sulfuric acid. Nitric acid (1:3) is now added and the manganese determined according to the bismuthate method.

## LIME

**Procedure.**—Twenty-five ml. of the well-shaken solution are measured off with a pipette, a few drops of hydrochloric acid added, and the solution diluted to 150 ml. Twenty grams of ammonium chloride and a few drops of bromine water are added. The iron and manganese are precipitated by ammonia and filtered off after bringing to boiling. The filtrate is evaporated to 150 ml., the lime precipitated with 25 ml. of ammonium oxalate solution (saturated solution) and allowed to stand for 3 hours. The calcium oxalate is filtered off and washed four times with hot water. A hole is then punched in the filter paper, the precipitate washed into a 400-ml. beaker with boiling water, 10 ml. of sulfuric acid (1:1) poured over the paper and the paper washed with boiling water. The solution is diluted to 150 ml. with hot water and titrated with standard potassium permanganate solution.

## MAGNESIA

*Procedure.*—The filtrate and washings from the lime determination is made slightly acid with hydrochloric acid and 15 ml. of a saturated solution of microcosmic salts added. The solution is cooled and the magnesia precipitated by the slow addition of ammonia. Sufficient ammonia must be added to hold all zinc in solution, an excess of about 50 ml. being required. The precipitate after standing 12 hours is filtered off, and redissolved in hot 1:4 hydrochloric acid. Twenty grams of ammonium chloride are added to this solution, then a few drops of microcosmic solution, and precipitation effected with ammonia as before, the excess of ammonia being only 10 ml. in this case. After standing 12 hours, the precipitate is filtered off, washed six times with 1:10 ammonia water, or until free from chlorides, ignited and weighed as $Mg_2P_2O_7$.

## ALKALI SALTS (NaCl + KCl)

*Procedure.*—A sample of about 10 g. is taken and made up to a volume of 500 ml. From this a portion equivalent to approximately 2 g. is measured off, slightly acidified with hydrochloric acid and the zinc precipitated with hydrogen sulfide. After filtering, the filtrate is made slightly alkaline with ammonia and tested with a small amount of ammonium sulfide, and any zinc, iron and manganese precipitated is filtered off. The filtrate is acidified with HCl and boiled for about 30 minutes to drive off the hydrogen sulfide. A small amount of bromine water is added and the boiling continued until the excess of bromine has been removed. The solution is diluted to about 200 ml. with hot water, and 10 ml. of hot 10% $BaCl_2$ solution added, to precipitate $SO_3$. Without filtering off the barium sulfate, the solution is made ammoniacal, 1 g. of ammonium carbonate and 5 ml. of ammonium oxalate solution added and the precipitates allowed to settle in a warm place. The precipitate is filtered off, washed with hot water, and the combined filtrate and washings evaporated to dryness in a porcelain dish. The ammonium salts are completely driven off by ignition over a low flame. The residue remaining is dissolved in a small amount of water with two drops of hydrochloric acid, transferred to a weighed platinum dish, the porcelain dish being washed with a minimum amount of water, evaporated to dryness on a hot plate, and after cooling weighed.

Any magnesia which may be present with the alkali chlorides is determined, calculated to $MgCl_2$ and deducted from the weight of the salts in the dish. This difference is expressed as combined alkali chlorides KCl + NaCl.

## COPPER

*Procedure.*—Twenty ml. of solution are taken, 5 g. of ammonium chloride, and 20 ml. of ammonium hydroxide added, diluted to 100 ml. in a color comparison tube and compared with a zinc chloride solution of equal strength, to which a measured amount of standard copper solution is added to give the same depth of color. If iron interferes with the color comparison, it should be filtered off before diluting to volume. When the color of copper present is over 0.05%, the determination should be carried out by some other method. See Chapter on Copper.

## BARIUM

*Procedure.*—If sulfuric anhydride ($SO_3$) is found to be present, it is not worth while to make a determination for barium. If no sulfuric anhydride is present, barium should be looked for and determined by diluting 10–20 ml. to 300 ml. with water, adding slight excess of hydrochloric acid, heating to boiling, and precipitating the barium with ammonium sulfate solution 10%.

## ANALYSIS OF FUSED ZINC CHLORIDE

The analysis of fused zinc chloride for zinc, etc., is carried out by the same methods as given under "Analysis of Zinc Chloride Solution," working on a solution of the fused salt in water. This solution is made up by rapidly transferring approximately 20 g. of fused salt to a weighing bottle, weighing, dissolving in water in a 2000-ml. volumetric flask to which a few drops of nitric acid has been added to prevent precipitation of basic zinc chloride, and filling to the mark. Aliquot portions are taken from this solution for the various determinations.

Special determinations are sometimes called for with fused zinc chloride which is to be used for some special purpose. It is very essential that such analyses be carried out carefully according to the method prescribed in order that the results, which are largely empirical, may be comparable. One analysis of this sort which is commonly called for is "basicity" expressed in some empirical way to give a measure of the relative quantities of the basic zinc chloride, which will settle out upon dissolving fused zinc chloride in water. It may be expressed as the volume of standard hydrochloric acid (usually 0.5 N) required to neutralize 10 ml. of a 40° Baume solution of the fused zinc chloride, diluted with 300 ml. of water, when using methyl orange as indicator, or the weight of basic chloride obtained by treating 10 g. of the sample, weighed in a weighing bottle, with 400 ml. of water, agitating to complete all possible solution, filtering off insoluble on a Gooch crucible and washing with water until combined filtrate and washings total just 1000 ml.

## AMMONIA (NH₃)

*Procedure.*—It is often of value to know if ammonium chloride is present. A sample of 5 10 g. is weighed and transferred to a 500-ml. distilling flask, 100 ml. of water, 50 ml. of sodium hydroxide (20%) and a small quantity of granulated zinc added. The ammonia and water are distilled over into an absorption bottle containing a measured quantity of standard acid. The excess of acid is titrated with standard alkali solution, using methyl orange.

## METHODS FOR ZINC IN ANALYSES IN OTHER CHAPTERS

# Chapter 53

# ZIRCONIUM AND HAFNIUM

Zr, *at. wt.* 91.22; *sp. gr.* 6.5 g./cm.³; *m.p.* 1857°C.
Hf, *at. wt.* 178.6

Zirconium is used for refractories, enamels, and metallurgical products.

Until recently zirconium and hafnium were classed together since there was no satisfactory method for separating these elements. Lately, in connection with the use of zirconium in nuclear reactors, zirconium and hafnium have been separated. For most analytical work, however, they are not separated even though hafnium occurs in all minerals. The hafnium content of minerals varies, in some instances as much at 5% $HfO_2$ having been found.[1]

The main ores of zirconium are baddeleyite, essentially zirconium dioxide; and zircon, essentially zirconium orthosilicate. While zircon is the most widely distributed ore, the most important commercially is the Brazilian baddeleyite, which, mixed with a little zircon, comes under the trade name of zirkite, and contains about 75% $ZrO_2$.

## DETECTION

*Spectrographic Method.*—The spectrographic detection of zirconium in ores and minerals is not always easy. Zirconium itself is not one of the more sensitive elements. In addition, the ores in which it appears are usually complex containing many elements that would interfere with the detection of very low amounts of the element. Using a 15-amp. D.C. arc it is possible to detect 0.01% zirconium using the spectral line 3391.98 A. The sensitivity of detection can be improved by making concentrates that would contain the zirconium. The presence of zirconium should be verified by checking the spectral lines at 3438.23, 3387.87, and 3326.80 A.

*Chemical Methods.*—The material to be tested is brought into solution by one of the methods given in the section on the "Preparation and Solution of the Sample." In the regular course of qualitative analysis the zirconium will be found in the main precipitate formed either by ammonium hydroxide alone or by the combined action of ammonium hydroxide and ammonium sulfide. This precipitate can be dissolved in sulfuric acid (see "Estimation"), the acidity then adjusted so that 10% of the solution by volume is concentrated sulfuric acid, 10 ml. of 3% hydrogen peroxide and 1 ml. more of concentrated sulfuric acid added, and then a large excess of $Na_2HPO_4$ or $(NH_4)_2HPO_4$ solution, to which has also been added ¹⁄₁₀ of its volume of concentrated sulfuric acid. A white precipitate proves the

[1] Hevesy, G. de, Kgl. Danske Vid. Selskab. Math.-Fysiske Medd., **VI**, 7, 1925.

presence of zirconium since no other elements (titanium having been peroxidized) have phosphates which are insoluble in such an acid concentration.[2]

As a confirmatory test the solution of zirconium is precipitated with ammonium hydroxide, the precipitate is dissolved in 10% hydrochloric acid and heated with 15% mandelic acid. A white precipitate indicates zirconium.

## ESTIMATION

Owing to the insolubility of zirconium phosphate great care must be taken in the analysis of ores which may contain phosphate. The zirconium in this case will appear with the $SiO_2$ and must be dissolved and returned to the solution.

Up to the present time the gravimetric method is the most widely used for the determination of zirconium. For small amounts colorimetric and fluorescent methods are more applicable. Titrimetric methods are seldom used. For accurate work the zirconium-hafnium ratio should be determined and the results corrected accordingly.

### PREPARATION AND SOLUTION OF THE SAMPLE

An acid treatment will not decompose ordinary zirconium ores. The following fluxes are most commonly used.

*Sodium peroxide* is used in a nickel crucible which has been lined by fusing some sodium carbonate,[3] and causing it to cool in an even layer on the sides and bottom. This, in large measure, prevents the attack of the crucible by the peroxide and avoids the subsequent introduction of large amounts of nickel into the solution. Several grams of sodium peroxide are melted in the crucible after lining with sodium carbonate and allowed to solidify on the bottom. This prevents particles of the ore from being caught in the carbonate lining and remain unfused. The sample of finely ground ore (0.5 g.) is mixed with 8–10 g. of sodium peroxide in the crucible thus prepared, and fused at low red heat over a small flame, by gently swirling the crucible which is held by means of tongs. Five to ten minutes fusion should suffice. When cool, the crucible is placed in a large platinum dish, or porcelain casserole, and covered with warm water, the vessel is covered with a watch glass and the solution is boiled until the carbonate lining has dissolved. The crucible is then removed. The solution is next made decidedly acid with hydrochloric acid and boiled until carbon dioxide is expelled. This should give a clear solution containing the zirconium and all the other constituents of the ore. If a very small amount of undecomposed ore is found here, it should be filtered off, ignited, fused with a little potassium pyrosulfate, dissolved in 5% sulfuric acid, filtered if necessary, and added to the main solution.

The use of sodium peroxide in a platinum crucible at a temperature of 480°C. for the decomposition of refractory ores has been recommended.[4,5]

*Sodium carbonate* has also been used for the decomposition of zircon concentrates. The procedure is given on pages 1274–1275.

[2] Biltz and Mechlenburg, Z. angew. Chem., **25**, 2110, 1912; Lundell and Knowles, J. Am. Chem. Soc., **41**, 1801, 1919.

[3] Method of J. A. Holladay, Electro Metallurgical Co., Niagara Falls, N. Y.

[4] Rafter, T. A., Analyst, **75**, 485, 1950.

[5] J. P. Highfill of New Brunswick Laboratory found that 65% of a zircon was decomposed under the conditions recommended.

*Potassium hydrogen fluoride* was used by Smith and James [6] in the following manner: The finely ground ore is fused with 12 to 15 times its weight of potassium hydrogen fluoride. The mixture of ore and fluoride, in a platinum dish, is carefully heated over a small flame. When the mixture has softened, it is stirred with a platinum rod, the size of the flame is gradually increased, and finally heated over a Meker burner until the mass just fuses to a clear liquid.[7] The cooled melt is treated with 50 ml. of 1:1 sulfuric acid, gently heated until nearly all water is expelled, and then more strongly until abundant fumes are evolved. The cold residue is boiled with water. This solution contains all the zirconium.

*Lithium fluoride* has been used in a similar manner and is also recommended.[8]

*Borax* is recommended by Lundell and Knowles [9] for the decomposition of all ores of zirconium. This flux is particularly suited to the decomposition of samples in which zirconium only is to be determined, and by precipitation with cupferron, since boric acid does not interfere with this reagent. If other elements of the sample are to be determined, the boric acid must be removed by volatilization as methyl borate. In such cases it is generally better to employ the sodium peroxide fusion method. In using the borax method, Lundell and Knowles recommended the following procedure: 4 g. of the flux are melted in a platinum crucible and allowed to cool. About 0.3 g. of the finely ground ore is placed on top of the fused borax, the crucible is covered, and heated over a Meker burner until thorough fusion has taken place, which does not ordinarily require more than 0.5 hour. During the operation it is well to stir the melt occasionally with a short platinum rod or stiff wire, which is allowed to remain in the crucible, and which may be conveniently handled with the crucible tongs. When the decomposition of the ore is complete, the platinum rod is removed, and it is put into the beaker to be used for the solution of the melt. As the melt cools, the crucible is gently twirled in order to run the fusion up on the sides in a thin layer. The cooled melt is dissolved in 150 ml. of 1:5 hydrochloric acid in a 250-ml. beaker by filling the crucible with acid, inverting in such a manner that one edge of the crucible rests on the crucible cover, which has been placed on the bottom of the beaker—thus allowing free circulation of the solvent—and then gently warming on the steam bath. The solution is transferred to a platinum dish or porcelain casserole, 20 ml. of 1:1 sulfuric acid are added, and the mixture is evaporated until heavy fumes escape.[10] The cooled solution is next diluted to about 100 ml., the impure silica filtered off, and washed with hot water. This solution is allowed to stand warm overnight. If the ore contained interfering amounts of phosphorus, it will be precipitated as zirconium phosphate by this digestion. If a precipitate appears, it is filtered and washed with 5% ammonium nitrate solution. This precipitate will contain zirconium and there is still apt to be a little zirconium in the impure silica first

[6] Smith and James, J. Am. Chem. Soc., **42,** 1764, 1920.

[7] Experiments by Tohru Kameda indicate that there is no loss of zirconium by volatilization if the process is carried out as here described. Continuing the heating for 5 minutes after clear fusion has been attained may cause a loss of as much as 2 mg. of $ZrO_2$.

[8] Private communication, R. M. Fowler, Union Carbide and Carbon Research Labs., Inc., Niagara Falls, N. Y.

[9] Lundell and Knowles, J. Am. Chem. Soc., **42,** 1439, 1920.

[10] During the evaporation boric acid will separate and form a crystal skin over the surface, thus retarding evaporation. Occasional stirring during this period will hasten the evaporation. As the sulfuric acid becomes more concentrated by evaporation, the boric acid eventually dissolves again.

filtered off. Also there may be some phosphoric acid in the filtrate. To this filtrate 5 g. of ammonium chloride are added and then ammonium hydroxide in slight excess. After boiling for several minutes the precipitated hydroxides are filtered and washed with 2% ammonium nitrate solution. This filtrate is discarded. The precipitate and paper are digested in 100 ml. of hot 5% sulfuric acid solution, and the filter shreds and any insoluble residue are filtered and washed well with hot water. This solution, containing most of the zirconium of the sample, is temporarily set aside. The last residue filtered, the impure silica, and any zirconium phosphate obtained by the overnight digestion are all ignited in the original platinum crucible. The ignited residue is moistened with water, 1 ml. of 1:1 sulfuric acid, and 5 ml. of hydrofluoric acid are added, and the mixture is heated until all sulfuric acid has been expelled. The residue in the crucible is fused with a little sodium carbonate, digested in water, and filtered, washing with hot water. The filtrate is discarded. The insoluble residue is again ignited in the platinum crucible, fused with potassium pyrosulfate; and, after cooling, the melt is dissolved in hot 5% sulfuric acid. This solution is added to the main solution, thus giving one solution in which is contained all the zirconium originally present in the sample.

## SEPARATIONS

As a general method for separating zirconium, the use of mandelic acid or phosphate as described below under gravimetric methods are satisfactory.

*From Members of the Copper and Tin Groups.*—The members of these groups are precipitated free from zirconium by hydrogen sulfide in slightly acid solution.

*From Titanium.*—Zirconium may be separated from titanium by precipitating the zirconium with $Na_2HPO_4$ or $(NH_4)_2HPO_4$ in 10% (by volume) sulfuric acid solution, in the presence of hydrogen peroxide. See "Phosphate Precipitation" under "Gravimetric Methods."

Powell and Schoeller [11] recommend the separation of zirconium from titanium by precipitation of the latter by tannin from a neutralized oxalate solution which is half saturated with ammonium chloride.

*From Thorium and Rare Earth Elements.*—These elements may be precipitated with an excess of oxalic acid, leaving the zirconium in the filtrate (see "Detection" in Chapter on Thorium). For complete separation the rare earth oxalates should be boiled with concentrated sulfuric acid until decomposed, diluted, nearly neutralized with ammonia, and again precipitated with an excess of oxalic acid. The combined filtrates contain all the zirconium.

*From Aluminum, Chromium, and Uranium.*—Zirconium is quantitatively separated from these three elements by precipitation with cupferron in 10% (by volume) sulfuric acid solution. The uranium must be in the hexavalent condition or it will contaminate the zirconium precipitate. (Nitric acid should not be used to oxidize uranium, as it decomposes cupferron. Uranium will practically always be in the hexavalent condition without special oxidation. If in doubt, the 10% sulfuric acid solution may be boiled with a little hydrogen peroxide.)

*From Molybdenum.*—By precipitation of molybdenum sulfide in acid solution. (See Chapter on Molybdenum.)

[11] Powell, A. R., and Schoeller, W. R., Analyst, **55**, 605, 1930; *ibid.*, **57**, 550, 1932. The procedure is given in detail in Chemical Abstracts, **25**, 51, 1931.

*From Tungsten.*—By precipitation of tungsten in acid solution by cinchonine hydrochloride. (See Chapter on Tungsten.)

*From Vanadium.*—By fusion of the mixed oxides with sodium peroxide or sodium carbonate, and leaching out the soluble sodium vanadate with water.

## GRAVIMETRIC METHODS

### PHOSPHATE PRECIPITATION

The precipitation of zirconium as phosphate in 10% sulfuric acid solution has been used for many years. Care should be taken during washing since the precipitated phosphate tends to hydrolyze and less phosphate is consequently in the final ignited precipitate than should be. When titanium is present, an excess of hydrogen peroxide must be kept in the solution at all times. Niobium and tantalum should be separated prior to the phosphate precipitation.

*Procedure.*[12]—The sulfate solution prepared as above and containing about 0.05 g. zirconium in 100 ml. is treated with a few drops of hydrogen peroxide. If a yellow color is produced, an excess of hydrogen peroxide is added and an excess kept throughout the precipitation. The solution is adjusted so that it contains about 10% sulfuric acid by volume. A freshly prepared 10% solution of $(NH_4)_2HPO_4$ is added so as to have about 50-fold excess. The acidity is readjusted to 10% acid content and the precipitate digested at 40 to 50°C. For large amounts of zirconium a digestion time of 2 hours is sufficient while for smaller amounts the solution is allowed to stand for 24 hours.

The solution is filtered through a Whatman No. 42 paper, or equivalent, and washed with cold 5% $NH_4NO_3$ solution until excess phosphate is removed. About 250 ml. is usually sufficient for large amounts of precipitate.

The wet paper is placed in a platinum crucible and the paper dried and very carefully ignited. Care must be taken to avoid damage to the platinum crucible. Finally the precipitate is heated at 1000°C. and weighed as $ZrP_2O_7$. For the most accurate work it is preferable to decompose the phosphate precipitate by fusing with sodium carbonate, dissolving in water and washing with water. The precipitate is ignited and fused with $KHSO_4$, dissolved in $H_2SO_4$ and precipitated with ammonium hydroxide. After washing with hot 2% $NH_4NO_3$ solution the precipitate is ignited at 1000°C. and weighed as $ZrO_2$. The fusion with carbonate may have to be repeated.

### CUPFERRON PRECIPITATION

Precipitation of zirconium, etc., with cupferron in a cold 10% $H_2SO_4$ solution containing alkali salts (sodium and potassium), filtering and washing and igniting to $ZrO_2$, causes high results. It is essential that the alkali salts be first removed by precipitation with ammonia and filtration and the precipitate dissolved in 10% sulfuric acid. For detailed procedure see pages 1274–1275.

*Procedure.*—The solution, which has a volume of 300–400 ml. and contains 10% of concentrated sulfuric acid by volume (any tartaric acid present does not interfere) is cooled to about 10°C., and then an excess of cupferron solution (6 g. dissolved in 100 ml. of cold water and filtered) is added. The formation of a fine white precipitate (nitrosophenylhydroxylamine) which redissolves shows that an

[12] Lundell and Knowles, J. Am. Chem. Soc., **41**, 1806, 1919; Hillebrand, *op. cit.*, p. 173; Nicolardot and Reglade, Compt. rend., **168**, 349, 1919.

excess of the reagent has been added. The zirconium precipitate is white and curdy, but any titanium present is also quantitatively precipitated, and it will impart a yellow color to the precipitate. A brownish color indicates that the previous separation from iron has been faulty. The precipitate is filtered and washed with cold 1:10 hydrochloric acid solution. The precipitate and paper are carefully and slowly ignited in a weighed platinum crucible until the rush of gases from decomposition of the organic matter has ceased. It is then heated to 1000°C. The weight thus found represents all the zirconium and titanium dioxides and possibly some rare earth oxides, if these elements have not previously been completely removed.

To correct for titanium and rare earths, the ignited oxides are fused with potassium pyrosulfate, dissolved in 1:10 sulfuric acid, and diluted to exactly 100 ml. in a volumetric flask. By means of a dry 50-ml. pipette exactly one-half of the solution is taken for the determination of titanium, and the pipette and the contents of the 100-ml. flask are completely rinsed into another vessel, thus giving the other half for the determination of rare earths.

**Titanium.**—Small amounts of titanium are determined by the colorimetric method; while for larger amounts the zinc reductor—permanganate titration method—is used. For details of these see Chapter on Titanium.

**Rare Earths.**—Rare earths may be determined according to Hillebrand's method [13] as follows: Precipitate the hydroxides with an excess of potassium hydroxide, decant the liquid, wash by decantation with water once or twice and then slightly on the filter. Wash the precipitate from the paper into a small platinum dish, treat with hydrofluoric acid, and evaporate nearly to dryness. Take up in 5 ml. of 5% by volume of hydrofluoric acid. If no precipitate is visible, rare earths are absent. If a precipitate is present, collect it on a small filter held by a perforated platinum or rubber cone and wash it with from 5 to 10 ml. of the same acid. Wash the crude rare earth fluorides into a small platinum dish, burn the paper in platinum, add the ash to the fluorides and evaporate to dryness with a little sulfuric acid. Dissolve the sulfates in dilute hydrochloric acid, precipitate the rare earths by ammonia, filter, redissolve in hydrochloric acid, evaporate the solution to dryness, and treat the residue with 5 ml. of boiling hot 5% oxalic acid. Filter after 15 minutes, collect the oxalates on a small filter, wash with not more than 20 ml. of cold 5% oxalic acid, ignite, and weigh as rare earth oxides which are to be deducted from the weight of the cupferron precipitate.

While the recovery of the rare earths by this method is not absolutely complete, the error is negligible for the amounts ordinarily found.

**Calculation.**—The sum of the weights of rare earth oxides and titanium dioxide found are subtracted from the weight of the ignited cupferron precipitate to obtain the true weight of $ZrO_2$.

## SELENIOUS ACID PRECIPITATION [14]

The selenious acid method does not require separation from iron and titanium and in this respect has certain advantages over the cupferron method.

**Procedure.**—To the nearly neutral solution, which should be free from phosphate, sulfate, niobium and tantalum, and which should have a volume not much

[13] Hillebrand, W. F., The Analysis of Silicate and Carbonate Rocks, U. S. Geol. Survey Bulletin 700, p. 176; Lundell and Knowles, *loc. cit.*, p. 1446.
[14] Smith, M. M., and James, C., J. Am. Chem. Soc., **42**, 1764, 1920.

greater than 100 ml., 20 ml. of 12 N hydrochloric acid and 20 ml. of ethanol are added. The solution is heated nearly to boiling, diluted to 500 ml., again heated to boiling, and 20 ml. of 10% selenious acid solution are added. After standing hot until the supernatant liquid is sufficiently clear for filtration (preferably not over 2 hours), the precipitate is filtered and washed a few times with hot water. The paper is punctured and the precipitate is washed into the original beaker with as little hot water as possible. The paper is set aside for further treatment. Fifteen ml. of 12 N hydrochloric acid are added to the contents of the beaker and the mixture is heated until the precipitate is dissolved. (A slight turbidity may be neglected.) Twenty ml. of 3% hydrogen peroxide are added, the solution is warmed, diluted to 500 ml., heated to boiling, and again precipitated with 20 ml. of 10% selenious acid solution. After filtration, and washing with hot water, the paper is again punctured, and the precipitate is rinsed into the original beaker.

(A) In a small beaker the two papers are digested with 40 ml. of hot 10% oxalic acid solution. The pulp is filtered and washed, and the filtrate and washings are added to the zirconium precipitate. The mixture is diluted to 200 ml., heated to boiling, and 10 ml. of 1 N hydrochloric acid are added. After allowing to stand at room temperature for at least 10 hours, the precipitate is filtered and washed with a solution containing 25 g. of oxalic acid per liter. To the filtrate 30 ml. of 18 N sulfuric acid are added, and evaporation on the water bath is started.

(B) If the oxalate precipitate is large it is flushed off into a 400-ml. beaker, 5 ml. of 18 N sulfuric acid are added, and the mixture is evaporated on the water bath until oxalate has been destroyed, as shown by the cessation of gas bubbles. The solution is diluted with water, made ammoniacal and the precipitate is filtered, and dissolved in 12 ml. of 6 N hydrochloric acid. After diluting to 160 ml. and heating to boiling, 40 ml. of 10% oxalic acid solution are added. After standing for at least 10 hours, the solution is filtered into the main solution. The solution is now evaporated on the water bath until oxalate is destroyed, the sides of the beaker and the watch glass are rinsed down, and any precipitated selenium is filtered off. If a small amount of red selenium runs through the paper it may be neglected. The solution is made ammoniacal, and the precipitate is filtered and washed a few times with hot water. The paper is punctured and the precipitate is flushed off with as little hot water as possible. Fifteen ml. of hot 12 N hydrochloric acid are poured over the paper into the zirconium hydroxide suspension and the mixture is heated until the precipitate is entirely dissolved.

(C) Twenty ml. of 3% hydrogen peroxide are added, and the solution is warmed, diluted to 500 ml., and heated to boiling. Twenty ml. of 10% selenious acid solution are added, and the precipitate is filtered after the supernatant liquid is clear. After ignition over the Bunsen flame, and finally for 5 minutes over the Meker burner, the $ZrO_2$ is weighed.

In the known absence of thorium the above method may be shortened by omitting the oxalate precipitation involved in the above directions A and B. In this case, the zirconium selenite precipitate obtained at A is dissolved by adding 20 ml. of 12 N hydrochloric acid, and heating to boiling. The method is continued from the point C. The two filter papers from which the first two precipitates were washed are ignited, and the weight of their ignition products are added to the final weight of $ZrO_2$.

## MANDELIC ACID PRECIPITATION

Kumins [15] indicated that mandelic acid was a specific reagent for the precipitation of zirconium. This procedure has been used to a considerable extent in the past few years. For small amounts of zirconium it is a much faster method than the phosphate one described above in a preceding section.[16]

The procedure as applied to ores is given on page 1277.

## COLORIMETRIC/PHOTOMETRIC METHODS

Zirconium forms a lake with alizarin the color of which is stable in strong acids. Liebhafsky and Winslow [17] using this property, developed a colorimetric method which was applied to clays by Green.[18]

The procedure used is given on page 1279.

## FLUORESCENT METHODS

For small amounts of zirconium the fluorescent method has some advantages.[19] The method is based on the blue fluorescence given by zirconium and flavanol (3-hydroxyflavone) in strong sulfuric acid under ultraviolet light. Hafnium interferes as is to be expected. The procedure for clays and refractories is given on page 1278.

## DETERMINATION OF HAFNIUM-ZIRCONIUM RATIO

Several methods have been employed for the determination of the zirconium to hafnium ratio. Amongst these are the use of the x-ray spectrograph,[20] x-ray fluorescence,[21] spectrographic methods,[22,23] and a chemical method employing p-bromomandelic acid.[24] The simplest of these is the spectrographic method. The procedure of Fassel and Anderson is given below.[25]

*Procedure.*—The ignited oxides are mixed in the ratio of one part of the oxide to four parts of special spectrographic powder (grade SP-1, National Carbon Co.) and pressed into ¼-inch diameter pellets with an Applied Research Laboratory briquetting press at a total load of 8000 lbs.

The pellet is placed in a metal holder and used as the lower electrode of an over-damped condenser, 60-cycle discharge, with arc-like characteristics. The upper electrode is a ⅛-inch pointed graphite rod placed 4 mm. above the pellet. The spectrum from an exposure of 40 seconds duration is photographed in the region 2300–3500 A on an Eastman spectrum analysis, No. 1 emulsion, plate.

This procedure is usable for the determination of the hafnium to zirconium ratio from 1 to 100% by slightly modifying the exposure conditions, and the method can be extended down to hafnium to zirconium ratio of 0.1%. The line

15 Kumins, C. A., Anal. Chem., **19,** 376, 1947.
16 Hahn, R. B., Anal. Chem., **21,** 1579, 1949.
17 Liebhafsky, H. A., and Winslow, E. H., J. Am. Chem. Soc., **60,** 1782, 1938.
18 Green, D. E., Anal. Chem., **20,** 371, 1948.
19 Alford, W. C., Shapiro, L., and White, C. E., Anal. Chem., **23,** 1149, 1951.
20 Hevesy, G. de, Kgl. Danske Vid. Selskab. Math.-Fysiske Medd., **VI,** 7, 1925.
21 Birks, L. S., and Brooks, E. J., Anal. Chem., **22,** 1017, 1950.
22 Feldman, C., Anal. Chem., **21,** 1211, 1949.
23 Fassel, V. A., and Anderson, C. H., J. Opt. Soc., **40,** 742, 1950.
24 Hahn, R. B., Anal. Chem., **23,** 1259, 1951.
25 Fassel, V. A., and Anderson, C. H., J. Opt. Soc., **40,** 742, 1950.

pairs and the concentration range for which they are useful are shown in the following tables.

Line Pairs Employed in the Analysis of Hafnium-Zirconium Mixtures

| | Wavelength A | Concentration range (per cent hafnium) |
|---|---|---|
| 1) | Hf II 2861.696 | 0.1– 6.4 |
| | Zr II 2856.055 | |
| 2) | Hf II 2861.696 | 6.4 –20 |
| | Zr II 2839.339 | |
| 3) | Hf II 2975.882 | 20 –44 |
| | Zr II 3003.736 | |
| 4) | Hf II 3109.117 | 31 –58 |
| | Zr II 3164.310 | |
| 5) | Hf II 3000.096 | 54 –78 |
| | Zr II 3003.736 | |
| 6) | Hf II 3000.096 | 72 –89 |
| | Zr II 3028.040 | |
| 7) | Hf II 2857.650 | 89 –99.5 |
| | Zr II 2844.579 | |

## DETERMINATION IN SPECIFIC SUBSTANCES

## CUPFERRON METHOD FOR THE ANALYSIS OF ZIRCON CONCENTRATES [26]

### DETERMINATION OF SILICA

**Procedure.**—Reduce the laboratory sample with a Jones sampler or by quartering to 25 to 30 g. and grind in an agate mortar until any segregation is eliminated (about 20 minutes if mechanically operated). Reduce this fraction by quartering to about 5 g. and grind to approximately 325-mesh (about 30 minutes).

Thoroughly mix 0.5 g. of the 325-mesh sample with 0.5 g. of powdered anhydrous $Na_2CO_3$ in a 30-ml. platinum crucible, and cover the mixture with an additional 0.2 g. of $Na_2CO_3$. Gradually heat the covered crucible and its contents to about 950°C. with a Fisher blast burner, and maintain this temperature for 20 to 25 minutes. Remove the crucible from the source of heat, add 6 to 7 g. of $Na_2CO_3$ to the sintered mass, and thoroughly fuse at 1000°C. to 1100°C. for 30 to 40 minutes. After the fusion has progressed for about 20 minutes, grasp the hot crucible with a pair of tongs, and with a rotatory motion thoroughly mix the melt. Repeat this mixing procedure 4 to 5 times. When the fusion is considered complete, remove the crucible from the heat, and rotate it, so that the turbid melt will solidify on the sides of the crucible.

Transfer the cool crucible and its contents to a 250-ml. beaker containing 30 ml. of $H_2SO_4$ (1:1) and about 50 ml. of hot water. After the melt has disintegrated, forming a milky solution, remove and thoroughly rinse the crucible. Carefully dry the crucible, fuse any residue with a few lumps of sodium bisulfate (fused),

[26] Private communication, C. A. Best, Titanium Alloy Mfg. Division, National Lead Co., Niagara Falls, N. Y.

and add the cool melt to the main solution. Add 2 to 3 ml. of 30% $H_2O_2$ to the solution, then evaporate on the hot plate until sulfuric fumes are evolved, and continue the fuming until most of the opaque material has dissolved. Remove the beaker from the source of heat and allow it to cool for a few minutes. Loosen the residue on the sides of the beaker with the stirring rod, and then wash the sides clean with $H_2SO_4$ (1:1). Stir the solution, and again evaporate until sulfuric acid fumes are given off and the opaque material is in solution. Cool until fuming has ceased, then carefully add cold water from a wash bottle until the reaction subsides. Dilute to about 125 ml. and stir occasionally while heating to boiling. Support a close-texture paper with a platinum cone, add some ashless paper pulp to the filter, and filter the solution. After the bulk of the residue has been transferred to the filter, policeman the beaker twice with pieces of filter paper, and wash the paper and residue with hot water. Reserve the filtrate ($A$).

Transfer the paper and residue to a platinum crucible, carefully ignite until the carbon is burned off, and then heat at 1050°C. to 1100°C. for 30 to 40 minutes. Cool in a desiccator and weigh. Cautiously moisten the residue with a few drops of water, add 8 to 10 drops of $H_2SO_4$ (1:1), about 10 ml. of HF, and evaporate to dryness on the sand bath. Heat the crucible for a few minutes at the above temperature, cool, and weigh. The difference in weight is $SiO_2$ from the first dehydration.

The nonvolatile residue from the $SiO_2$ must be carefully examined for undecomposed zircon. Therefore, fuse the residue with a few lumps of sodium bisulfate and dissolve the cool melt in 5 ml. of $H_2SO_4$ (1:1) in a small beaker. If no insoluble residue is detected, decomposition is complete, and the solution is added to the reserved filtrate ($A$). If an insoluble residue is observed, filter the solution through a small paper into the reserved filtrate ($A$) and wash the paper and residue with hot water. Ignite the paper and residue in the fusion crucible until the carbon is destroyed. Add 2 to 3 g. of $Na_2CO_3$ to the crucible, mix, and then fuse with the Fisher blast burner. Transfer the cool melt to the reserved solution ($A$).

Evaporate the above solution on the hot plate until copious fumes of sulfuric acid are given off. Cool, dilute, filter, and wash the paper and residue with hot water. Reserve the filtrate ($B$).

Ignite the paper and residue in a platinum crucible until the carbon is burned off, then heat at 1050°C. to 1100°C. for about 15 minutes. Cool in a desiccator and weigh. Carefully treat the residue with 4 to 5 drops of $H_2SO_4$ (1:1), 3 to 5 ml. of HF, evaporate to dryness on the sand bath. Heat the crucible for a few minutes, cool, and weigh. The difference in weight is $SiO_2$ from the second dehydration. The sum of the $SiO_2$ values can generally be considered as total $SiO_2$.

## DETERMINATION OF ZIRCONIA

**Procedure.**—Fuse the nonvolatile residue left after the volatilization of the $SiO_2$ from the second dehydration with a few lumps of sodium bisulfate and add the cool melt to the reserved filtrate ($B$). Thoroughly stir the solution and allow it to stand overnight. (This is a precautionary measure if much phosphorus is present and is seldom necessary with high grade zircon concentrates.) If a precipitate appears (zirconium phosphate), filter the solution through a small paper and wash with 5% $NH_4NO_3$ solution. Reserve the filtrate ($C$).

Ignite the paper and precipitate in the 30-ml. platinum fusion crucible until the carbon is destroyed. Add 2 to 3 g. of $Na_2CO_3$, mix, and fuse with the Fisher blast burner. When the fusion is complete, solidify the melt on the sides of the crucibles and cool. Transfer the crucible and its contents to a platinum dish and thoroughly digest the melt in about 50 ml. of hot water. Filter the solution through a small paper and wash moderately with hot water. Discard the filtrate. Ignite the paper and residue in a platinum crucible until the carbon is oxidized, fuse the residue with a few lumps of sodium bisulfate, and add the cool melt to the reserved filtrate $(C)$.

Add about 5 g. of $NH_4Cl$ to the solution, a few drops of methyl red indicator solution, then $NH_4OH$ until the color just changes to a distinct yellow. Heat the solution to boiling for 1 minute, filter through a Whatman No. 40 paper supported by a platinum cone, and wash with a hot 2% $NH_4Cl$ solution. Sluice the precipitate into the beaker in which the precipitation was made, place the beaker under the funnel, and dissolve any remaining precipitate on the paper with 50 ml. of hot $H_2SO_4$ (1:5). Wash the paper with hot water. Reserve the paper in the funnel.

Warm the solution while stirring until the precipitate is dissolved, then filter the solution through the reserved paper, and wash the filter with hot water. Ignite the paper in a platinum crucible until the carbon is burnt off, fuse any residue with a few lumps of sodium bisulfate, and add the cool melt to the main solution.

Add 1.5 g. of either citric or tartaric acid to the filtrate, 4 to 5 drops of methyl red indicator solution, then $NH_4OH$ until the color changes to yellow. Add 2 ml. of $H_2SO_4$ for each 100 ml. of solution, heat to 70 to 80°C., and then pass in a rapid stream of $H_2S$ for about 25 minutes. Allow the solution to stand 4 to 5 hours, preferably overnight. Filter through a close-texture paper and thoroughly wash with a 1% by volume $H_2SO_4$ solution saturated with $H_2S$. Discard the residue.

Add 45 ml. of $H_2SO_4$ (1:1) to the filtrate, boil to expel $H_2S$ and also to reduce the volume of approximately 125 ml. If any sulfur or sulfides appear, filter and wash with hot water. Cool the solution to about 10°C. and add a few drops of permanganate solution to oxidize any reduced iron. If a permanganate color develops, destroy it by adding a few drops of HCl. Add some ashless paper pulp to the cold solution, then while stirring, slowly add a filtered cold 6% water solution of cupferron (40 to 50 ml.) until precipitation appears complete. Add 15 to 20 ml. of boiling hot water to coagulate the fluffy organic precipitate and thoroughly stir the solution. Add to the supernatant liquor a few drops of the cupferron reagent. The formation of a fine white precipitate which redissolves instead of a white curdy precipitate which persists, indicates that precipitation has been complete. Place the beaker in the cooling bath for about 5 minutes and then filter by the aid of gentle suction through a close-texture paper, supported by a platinum cone. Policeman the beaker twice with pieces of filter paper and wash the precipitate 15 to 20 times with a cold 10% by volume HCl solution containing 20 ml. of cupferron reagent per liter. Drain the precipitate thoroughly.

Transfer the paper and precipitate to a tared 75-ml. platinum dish and cautiously dry, as the organic precipitate tends to liquefy and to effervesce if heat is applied too rapidly. Slowly ignite the dried precipitate until the volatile matter is expelled, then increase the temperature to burn off the carbon, and finally heat at 1050°C. to 1100°C. to constant weight. Cool in a desiccator and weigh. The difference in weight represents the oxides of zirconium, titanium, and iron. Therefore to obtain the weight of $ZrO_2$, the precipitate must be corrected for the weights of $TiO_2$ and $Fe_2O_3$.

Carefully transfer the precipitate to a 60-ml. Vycor crucible. Crush the precipitate with a glass rod, add 10 to 12 g. of sodium bisulfate (fused) and fuse over a low flame. When the fusion is complete, rotate the crucible to solidify the clear melt on the sides of the crucible. Dissolve the cool melt in 30 ml. of $H_2SO_4$ (1:1) in a 250-ml. beaker. Transfer the cool solution (*D*) to a 250-ml. volumetric flask, dilute to volume, and thoroughly mix.

## DETERMINATION OF $TiO_2$

*Procedure.*—Pipette an aliquot portion (50 ml.) of the above solution into a 100-ml. Nessler comparison tube. To a second tube, add an equal volume of blank solution prepared by dissolving 10 to 12 g. of sodium bisulfate in 30 ml. of $H_2SO_4$ (1:1) and diluting the cool solution to 250 ml. If the unknown shows an iron color, add $H_3PO_4$ drop by drop until the color is destroyed, then add an equal volume to the blank. Add 5 ml. of the peroxide solution (4 g. of $Na_2O_2$ dissolved in 125 ml. of cold $H_2SO_4$ (1:3) and diluted to 500 ml.) to each tube and mix. From a 10-ml. burette add 0.2 to 0.3 ml. of a standard titanium sulfate solution (0.4 g. $TiO_2$ per 1000 ml. of dilute $H_2SO_4$) (5:95) to the blank and an equal volume of dilute $H_2SO_4$ (5:95) to the unknown, thoroughly mix the solution in each tube, and then compare the color intensities against a white background. Repeat the above addition and mixing until the color of the blank matches the unknown. From the volume of standard titanium sulfate added to the blank, calculate the weight of $TiO_2$ in the mixed oxides. If photoelectric equipment is used for this determination, transfer portions of the unknown solution into two absorption cells. Use one cell with a blue filter (425 m$\mu$) and adjust the instrument for 100% transmittancy. Add four drops of 30% hydrogen peroxide to the other cell, thoroughly mix, and then measure the transmittancy of the peroxidized solution at 425 m$\mu$. Refer the observed scale reading to the calibration curve to determine the $TiO_2$ concentration.

## DETERMINATION OF $Fe_2O_3$

*Procedure.*—Pipette (25 to 50 ml.) of solution (*D*) into a Nessler comparison tube and to a second tube add an equal volume of the blank solution. Add 5 ml. of a 1% ammonium persulfate solution to each tube, then 5 ml. of ammonium thiocyanate solution (100 g. per 500 ml.), and thoroughly mix the solutions. From a 10-ml. burette add small increments of a standard ferric ammonium sulfate solution to the blank and finish the determination as described above for titanium. The weight of $Fe_2O_3$ in the mixed oxides is then calculated from the titer of the standard iron solution.

## MANDELIC ACID METHOD FOR ZIRCONIUM ORES [27]

*Procedure.*—A sodium peroxide fusion using a nickel crucible is made on a 0.5-g. sample as described in the method above. The melt is dissolved in hydrochloric acid, precipitated with ammonium hydroxide, and filtered on a 15-cm. Whatman No. 40 filter paper. The precipitate is transferred to a 400-ml. beaker and any remaining precipitate on the filter is dissolved with hot 5% sulfuric acid, the filtrate being caught in the beaker containing the bulk of the precipitate.

[27] Private communication, Stephen M. Shelton, Bureau of Mines, Albany, Oregon.

After adding 15 ml. of $H_2SO_4$ the solution is taken to fumes, covered with a watch glass, and allowed to reflux for 30 minutes. After cooling, 250 ml. of water are added. The solution is filtered through the original filter paper and washed five times with water. The filtrate is retained. The precipitate of silica on the filter paper is ignited in a platinum crucible, two drops of sulfuric acid are added, plus 1 to 2 ml. of HF, and the solution is evaporated to dryness on the hot plate. After igniting to 1000°C., a bisulfate fusion is made on the residue and the cake is added to the filtrate retained above. The solution is precipitated with ammonium hydroxide and filtered on a 12.5-cm. Whatman No. 40 filter paper. The precipitate is transferred with a minimum of water (50 ml.) into a 250-ml. beaker. The filter paper is washed with hot 1:2 hydrochloric acid and the washings are caught in the beaker containing the precipitate. Fifty milliliters of a 16% mandelic acid solution are added and the temperature is slowly raised to 85°C. and maintained at this temperature for 20 minutes. The precipitate is filtered using a 12.5-cm. Whatman No. 40 paper and washed five times with a hot solution containing 5% mandelic acid and 2% hydrochloric acid. The precipitate is placed in a platinum crucible in a cool furnace. The temperature is raised to 1000°C. and is kept at this temperature for 1 hour. After cooling the residue is weighed as $ZrO_2$.

## FLUORIMETRIC METHOD FOR CLAYS, SANDS, AND REFRACTORIES [28]

*Procedure.*—Weigh out a sample of powdered mineral estimated to contain from 0.050 to 0.250 mg. of zirconium dioxide. Place a quantity of the fusion mixture (3 parts $Na_2CO_3$ and 1 part borax glass) about 10 to 15 times the weight of the sample in a medium-sized platinum crucible and fuse over a Meker burner. Cool and place the sample on top of the melt. Cover and carefully fuse again for 15 to 20 minutes over a Meker burner or in a muffle furnace at 900°C. to 1000°C. Gently swirl the contents of the crucible two or three times during the course of the fusion. Cool slightly and then immerse the crucible to one-half its depth in 100 ml. of distilled water in a 400-ml. beaker. This helps to crack the melt as it cools and speeds up solution later. Drop the crucible into the water, cover with a watch glass, boil for a few minutes, and then digest on the steam bath until the melt is thoroughly disintegrated (an overnight period is convenient). Break up any lumps with the aid of a flat-end stirring rod. Remove the crucible and wash any adhering particles into the beaker.

Bring to boil again, stir vigorously to break up the precipitate, cool slightly, and filter through a 9-cm. Whatman No. 40 paper. Wash the beaker and precipitate two or three times with 2% sodium carbonate solution and twice with water. Discard the filtrate and place the original beaker under the filter. Dissolve the precipitate by the dropwise addition of 5 $N$ sulfuric acid.

When all precipitate is dissolved, wash thoroughly with water. Make the filtrate alkaline to phenolphthalein with 5 $N$ sodium hydroxide, then add a 5 ml. excess of the alkali. Stir, let stand for a few minutes, and filter, using the same paper employed in the first filtration. Wash five or six times with water, discard the filtrate, and place a 100-ml. volumetric flask under the filter. Dissolve the precipitate with exactly 20 ml. of 1.00 $N$ sulfuric acid, added dropwise in two proportions from a 10-ml. pipette. Wash the paper thoroughly with water and dilute the filtrate to 100 ml. with distilled water. Pipette a 10-ml. aliquot into a Melaven cell

[28] Alford, W. C., Shapiro, L., and White, C. E., Anal. Chem., **23**, 1149, 1951.

and electrolyze for 45 minutes at a current of about 0.5 ampere to remove iron and any other heavy metals. Drain into a 25-ml. glass-stoppered cylinder and wash the cell with about 10 to 12 ml. of 0.2 $N$ sulfuric acid. Add 1 ml. of 0.01% flavianic acid (50 mg. in 500 ml. of 95% ethanol), make up to 25 ml. with 0.2 $N$ sulfuric acid, mix and let stand for 20 minutes out of direct sunlight. At the same time, prepare the reagent blank and a series of standard zirconium dioxide solutions (made from a solution containing 1 mg. $ZrO_2$ per ml. of 5 $N$ $H_2SO_4$; before use 5 ml. of stock solution is diluted with 120 ml. of $H_2O$ and 375 ml. 0.2 $N$ $H_2SO_4$ to give a solution having 0.010 mg. $ZrO_2$ per ml.), each containing 1 ml. of 0.01% flavianic acid and 0.2 $N$ sulfuric acid to make a volume of 25 ml.

The amount of zirconium dioxide in the standards may be from 0.010 to 0.050 mg., depending on the quantity in the sample. The blank and standard readings are plotted on straight graph paper and the amount of zirconium dioxide in the unknown is obtained by reference to the calibration curve thus obtained. It is necessary to establish the linearity of the instrument used under the above experimental conditions.

Calculate the percentage zirconium dioxide as follows:

$$\frac{\text{Mg. of } ZrO_2 \text{ in standard } (U - B) \text{ Aliquot factor} \times 100}{(S - B) \text{ Sample weight in mg.}} = \% ZrO_2 \text{ in mineral}$$

where $S$, $U$, and $B$ = scale reading of standard, unknown, and blank, respectively.

## COLORIMETRIC METHOD FOR CLAYS [29]

*Procedure.*—A 0.5-g. sample of clay is weighed into a 20-g. nickel crucible, approximately 4 g. of sodium hydroxide pellets are added, and the fusion is made. The completed fusion is then digested on a hot plate with distilled water. The insoluble portion of the digestion is filtered out with a 9 cm. Whatman No. 40 filter paper and thoroughly washed with distilled water. Since the insoluble matter will contain the sodium zirconate, the filtrate is rejected. The insoluble portion is digested with about 12 ml. of hot, concentrated hydrochloric acid and washed with hot distilled water into a 100-ml. beaker. The total amount of solution should not exceed 75 ml. The filter paper with residue is retained for further analysis.

The solution is cooled to room temperature, 2 drops of phenolphthalein indicator are added, and the solution is neutralized cautiously, not permitting the temperature to rise, with a 50% sodium hydroxide solution. Five milliliters of 1 $N$ hydrochloric acid are added and the mixture is passed through a silver reductor of 12-ml. capacity. The reductor is rinsed out with 5 ml. of 1 $N$ hydrochloric acid and 5 ml. of distilled water. The reduced solution is received in a 100-ml. volumetric flask. 2 ml. of 0.05% sodium alizarinsulfonate are added, and the solution is brought up to 100 ml. volume with distilled water. The final solution is mixed well by shaking. The pH should be 1:1. It is allowed to stand 20 hours or overnight for color development. The optical density of the solution is read at 5200 A.

The filter paper from the hot hydrochloric acid digestion of the sodium zirconate is burned at 925°C., and the residue is fused with a few pellets of sodium hydroxide. The second fusion is digested and filtered in the same manner as the initial fusion. The insoluble residue is similarly leached with hydrochloric acid and washed. The resulting solution is analyzed for zirconium as above. The small amount of

[29] Green, D. E., Anal. Chem., **20,** 371, 1948.

iron present permits the omission of the reduction step. The number of milligrams of zirconium oxide contained in the two solutions are taken from the previously plotted standardization curve of density versus milligrams of zirconium oxide and added for the final zirconium content of the sample. The method is accurate to 0.0006% zirconium oxide with the 0.5-g. sample used.

## METHODS FOR ZIRCONIUM IN ANALYSES IN OTHER CHAPTERS

Zirconium in Bauxite      See Analysis of Bauxite (Aluminum Chapter)

Zirconium in Magnesium Alloys      See Magnesium Chapter

# QUALITATIVE TESTS OF SUBSTANCES

# QUALITATIVE TESTS OF SUBSTANCES

## BLOWPIPE AND FLAME TESTS OF SOLIDS

### BLOWPIPE TESTS ON CHARCOAL

Heat a small portion of the material on charcoal in the oxidizing flame, using a blowpipe. Scoop out a round hole in the charcoal, place a little of the substance in the cavity, and direct the inner flame of the blowpipe against it at an angle of thirty degrees.

| Result of Test | Inference |
|---|---|
| Melts and runs into the charcoal | Alkalies, K, Na, etc. |
| An alkaline residue on charcoal | Ca, Sr, Ba, Mg |
| A residue which, when moistened with a drop of $Co(NO_3)_3$ and heated in O. F., produces a color which is blue | Aluminum, silicon |
|     Produces a color which is green | Zinc, tin, antimony |
|     Produces a color which is red | Barium |
|     Produces a color which is pink or rose-red | Manganese |
| Deflagrates | Nitrates, chlorates |
| Leaves an incrustation which is white near the flame | Antimony |
|     White, garlic odor | Arsenic |
|     Dark red | Silver |
|     Red to orange | Cadmium |
|     Lemon yellow (hot), light yellow (cold) | Lead |
|     Orange yellow (hot), light yellow (cold) | Bismuth |
|     Yellow (hot), white (cold) | Zinc or tin, latter nonvolatile |

*Blowpipe Tests.—Substance fused with $Na_2CO_3$ on charcoal.* Place a small amount of the substance on charcoal with a little sodium carbonate, and fuse, using reducing flame.

| Result of Test | Inference |
|---|---|
| Metallic globules, without incrustation | |
|     Yellow flakes | Gold |
|     Red flakes | Copper |
|     White globule, moderately soft | Silver |
| Metallic globules, with incrustation | |
|     White, moderately soft beads | Lead or tin (volatilized lead leaves yellow coat) |
|     White, brittle beads | Bismuth or antimony (yellowish) |
| Yellow in O. F. | Chromium |
| Green in O. F. | Manganese |
| A substance (in R. F.) which, when moistened and placed on a silver coin, leaves a brown or black stain | Sulfur compounds |

| Test | Inference |
|---|---|
| Dark gray magnetic powder which, when moistened on a filter paper with a drop of dilute HCl and NHO$_3$, and gently dried over a flame, leaves a stain which is faint pink, turning blue | Cobalt |
| Green stain, turning yellow | Nickel |
| A stain turned blue by K$_4$Fe(CN)$_6$ | Iron |

In place of using charcoal the above tests may be made with a splinter of wood covered with a coating of fused Na$_2$CO$_3$. The test is made by dipping the heated splinter into a mixture of the powdered substance with fused sodium carbonate and plunging for a moment in the reducing flame. Examine the material on the splinter, scrape off on a piece of glazed paper and examine.

**Blowpipe Test with Cobalt Nitrate.**—Substance moistened with cobalt nitrate solution and ignited.

| Color of Residue or Incrustation | Inference |
|---|---|
| Brick red | BaO |
| Pink | MgO |
| Gray | SrO, CaO |
| Yellowish green | ZnO |
| Dark muddy green | Sb$_2$O$_5$ |
| Bluish green | SnO |
| Blue | Al$_2$O$_3$, SiO$_2$ |

## FLAME TEST

Moisten a platinum wire in concentrated HCl, dip into the powdered substance and insert into a Bunsen flame. If sodium is prominent, examine through a blue glass. (Test the cobalt glass to see if it is effective in cutting out the yellow sodium light by examining a sodium flame through it.)

| Flame Color | Color through Blue Glass | Element |
|---|---|---|
| Carmine red | Purple | Lithium |
| Dull red | Olive green | Calcium |
| Crimson | Purple | Strontium |
| Golden yellow | Absorbed | Sodium |
| Greenish yellow | Bluish green | Barium, molybdenum |
| Green | | Cu, −PO$_4$, −B$_2$O$_3$, |
| Blue | | Cu, Bi, Pb, Cd, Zn, Sb, As |
| Violet | Violet red | Potassium |

The platinum wire should be cleaned before making the test. This can be accomplished by dipping it into concentrated HCl and holding it in the Bunsen, or, better, a flame of a blast lamp, until the flame is no longer colored. Repeated dipping into the HCl may be necessary.

Examine the flame through a spectroscope, if available, and compare the spectra with a spectra chart. Mere traces of the alkali and alkaline earth metals can be detected in this way by their characteristic spectral lines.

# BEHAVIOR OF SUBSTANCES FUSED WITH MICROCOSMIC SALT AND BORAX BEADS

*A clear bead is formed by fusing the flux on a loop of platinum wire. Dip the bead in the finely powdered substance to be examined, and heat again—first in the oxidizing flame; second in the reducing or inner flame. Metallic salts are mostly changed to oxides.* **In the Table** *—h. signifies hot; c., cold; sups., supersaturated with oxide; s. s., strongly saturated; h. c., hot and cold.*

| Color of the Bead | With Microcosmic Salt, Sodium Ammonium Hydrogen Phosphate | | With Sodium Tetraborate (Borax) | |
|---|---|---|---|---|
| | *In outer or oxidizing flame* | *In inner or reducing flame* | *In outer or oxidizing flame* | *In inner or reducing flame* |
| Colorless | **Si** (swims undissolved). **Al, Mg, Ca, Sr, Ba, Sn** (*s. s., opaque*). **Ti, Zn, Cd, Pb, Bi, Sb** (*not sat.*). | **Si** (swims undissolved). **Al, Mg, Ca, Sr, Ba** (*sups. not clear*). **Ce, Mn, Sn.** | h. c.: **Si, Al, Sn** (*sups. opaque*). **Al, Mg, Sr, Ca, Ba, Ag** (*not sat.*). **Zn, Cd, Pb, Bi, Sb, Ti, Mo.** | **Si, Al, Sn** (*s. s. opaque*). Alkaline earths and earths. h. c.: **Mn, Ce.** h.: **Cu.** |
| Yellow or Brownish | h. (*s. s.*): **Fe, U, Ce.** c.: **Ni.** | h.: **Fe, Ti.** c.: **Ni.** | h. *not sat.*: **Fe, U.** h., sups.: **Pn, Bi, Sb.** | h.: **Ti, Mo.** |
| Red | h. (*s. s.*): **Fe, Ni, Cr, Ce.** | c.: **Cu** h.: **Ni, Ti** with **Fe.** | h.: **Fe, Ce.** c.: **Ni.** | c.: **Cu** (*sups. opaque*). |
| Violet or Amethyst | h. c.: **Mn.** | c.: **Ti.** | h. c.: **Mn.** h.: **Ni** with **Co.** | c.: **Ti.** |
| Blue | h. c.: **Co.** c.: **Cu.** | h. c.: **Co.** c.: **W.** | h. c.: **Co.** c.: **Cu.** | h. c.: **Co.** |
| Green | h.: **Cu, Mo; Fe** with **Co** or **Cu.** c.: **Cr.** | h. c.: **Cr.** h.: **U, Mo.** | c.: **Cr.** h.: **Cu, Fe** with **Co.** | **Cr.** sups.: **Fe.** |
| Gray and Opaque | | **Ag, Pb, Sb, Cd, Bi, Zn, Ni.** | | The same as with microcosmic salt. |

## GENERAL SUMMARY OF TESTS FOR ACIDS

| Acids | Detecting Reagents | Reactions Resulting from Test |
|---|---|---|
| Acetates | $H_2SO_4$ (conc.) | Odor of vinegar |
| Arsenates | (a) $(NH_4)_2MoO_4 + HNO_3$ | Yellow precipitate |
| | (b) Magnesia mixture | White granular precipitate |
| | (c) Reduced on C + $Na_2CO_3$ | Garlic odor, arsenic mirror |
| Arsenites | (a) Magnesia mixture | No reaction |
| | (b) $H_2S + HCl$ | Yellow precipitate |
| Bromides | (a) $H_2SO_4$ (conc.) | Red Br vapor |
| | (b) Chlorine water + $CS_2$ | Reddish color, due to Br |
| Borates | $H_2SO_4$ (conc.) + alcohol | Green flame |
| Carbonates | Dilute acids | $CO_2$ evolved.  Limewater test |
| Chlorates | (a) $H_2SO_4$ (conc.) | Explosive liberation of Cl + $ClO_2$ |
| | (b) Heated alone | O given off |
| Chlorides | $AgNO_3 + HNO_3$ | White precipitate, sol. in $NH_4OH$ |
| Chromates | (a) $H_2SO_4$ (conc.) | O liberated (sol. yellow to green) |
| | (b) HCl | Chlorine of HCl liberated |
| | (a) Alcohol + NaOH | Reduced and $Cr(OH)_3$ precipitated |
| Cyanides | $H_2SO_4$ (conc.) | HCN (POISON).   Odor, bitter almonds |
| Ferricyanides | $FeSO_4 + HCl$ | Turnbull's blue precipitate |
| Ferrocyanides | $FeCl_3 + HCl$ | Prussian blue precipitate |
| Fluorides | $H_2SO_4$ (conc.) | HF gas liberates silicic acid from glass rod with drop of $H_2O$ |
| Hypochlorites | Dilute acids | Cl liberated, yellow gas |
| Iodides | (a) $H_2SO_4$ (conc.) | Violet vapor of iodine |
| | (b) Chlorine water + $CS_2$ | Violet color to $CS_2$ |
| Nitrates | $FeSO_4 + H_2SO_4$ (conc.) | Brown ring |
| Nitrites * | Dilute acids | $N_2O_3$ brown evolved |
| Oxalates | $H_2SO_4$ (conc.) | CO + $CO_2$ evolved |
| Permanganates | Reducing agents | Decolorized |
| Phosphates | $HNO_3 + (NH_4)_2MoO_4$ at 40° | Yellow precipitate |
| Silicates | (a) Fused with $Na_2CO_3$ and HCl added | Silicic acid precipitated |
| | (b) HF | $SiF_4$ gas liberated |
| Sulfates | $HCl + BaCl_2$ | White precipitate of $BaSO_4$ |
| Sulfides | Dilute acids | $H_2S$ gas blackens $Pb(C_2H_3O_2)_2$ |
| Sulfites | Dilute acids | $SO_2$ gas |
| Sulfocyanides | $FeCl_3$ | Deep red color |
| Thiosulfates | Dilute acids | $SO_2$ gas + free S |
| Tartrates | Ignited | Char.  Odor of burnt sugar |
| Organic acids | Heated | Generally char |

* Nitrites + KI + $CS_2$ = violet color in $CS_2$ due to free I.

# TABLES OF REACTIONS

## BASES AND ACIDS

# TABLES OF REACTIONS OF THE BASES

## HYDROGEN CHLORIDE GROUP

| Reagent | Lead, $Pb(NO_3)_2$ | Mercury, $HgNO_3$ | Silver, $AgNO_3$ |
|---|---|---|---|
| Hydrochloric acid, HCl | Lead chloride, $PbCl_2$, white ppt. Slightly sol. in cold water. Solubility in 100 ml. $H_2O$, $0° = 673$ mg. $100° = 3340$ mg. Converted into the insol. basic salt by $NH_4OH$ | Mercurous chloride, HgCl, white ppt. Sol. in hot $HNO_3$ and in aqua regia. $NH_4OH$ converts it to $HgCl \cdot NH_2 + Hg$, black. 100 ml. $H_2O$ dissolves 0.31 mg. (cold), 10 mg. (hot) | Silver chloride, AgCl, white ppt. Insol. in acids. Sol. in $NH_4OH$, KCN, and $Na_2S_2O_3$. $AgC_3$ darkens in the light. Solubility in 100 ml. $H_2O$, $0.152^{20°}$ mg., $2.2^{100°}$ mg. |
| Ammonium hydroxide, $NH_4OH$ | $(PbO)_2Pb(NO_3)_2$. Basic salt, white ppt. Insol. in excess. Only slightly sol. in water | Mercuric ammonium salt and mercury; $HgNH_2NO_3 + Hg$, black ppt. Insol. in excess | Silver oxide, AgO, brown ppt. Sol. in excess. Sol. in KCN. $4.3^{20°}$ mg. in 100 ml. $H_2O$ |
| Hydrogen sulfide, $H_2S$ | Lead sulfide, PbS, black ppt. Insol. in $(NH_4)_2S_x$. Sol. in $HNO_3$. Cold water dissolves 0.1 mg. Hot water, insol. | Mercuric sulfide, HgS + Hg, black ppt. Slightly sol. in $HNO_3$. Sol. in aqua regia. Insol. in water | Silver sulfide, $Ag_2S$, black ppt. Insol. in $(NH_4)_2S_x$. Sol. in hot $HNO_3$, 0.02 mg. in cold water. Sol. in conc. $H_2SO_4$ |
| Potassium chromate, $K_2CrO_4$ | Lead chromate, $PbCrO_4$, yellow ppt. Slightly sol. in $HNO_3$. Sol. in $NH_4OH$. Solubility $0.02^{18°}$. Insol. in hot water and in acetic acid | Mercurous chromate, $Hg_2CrO_4$, brick red. Slightly sol. in $HNO_3$. Sol. in aqua regia. Sol. in hot water and in KCN | Silver chromate, $Ag_2CrO_4$, dark red ppt. Sol. in $HNO_3$ and in $NH_4OH$. $2.8^{18°}$ mgs. in 100 ml. $H_2O$. Sol. in KCN |

| | Lead salts | Mercurous/Mercury salts | Silver salts |
|---|---|---|---|
| Potassium ferrocyanide, $K_4Fe(CN)_6$ | Lead ferrocyanide, $Pb_2Fe(CN)_6$, white ppt. Insol. in cold water | Mercurous ferrocyanide, × $Hg_4Fe(CN)_6$, white ppt. | Silver ferrocyanide, $Ag_4Fe(CN)_6$, yellowish white ppt. Insol. in acids and in $NH_4OH$. Sol. in KCN |
| Sodium carbonate, $Na_2CO_3$ | Basic lead carbonate, $2\ PbCO_3 \cdot Pb(OH)_2$, white ppt., "white lead." Insol. in hot and cold water | Basic salt, yellow ppt., becoming black | Silver carbonate, $Ag_2CO_3$, white ppt. Sol. in $NH_4OH$, $3.1^{15°}$, 50 mg. at 100° in $H_2O$. Sol. in $Na_2S_2O_3$ |
| Sodium hydroxide, NaOH | Lead hydroxide, $Pb(OH)_2$, white ppt. Sol. in excess. Scl. in $HNO_3$. Insol. in $NH_4OH$. Sol. in KOH. Slightly sol. in water | Mercurous oxide, $Hg_2O$, black ppt. Sol. in $HNO_3$. Insol. in $NH_4OH$ and alkalies. Sol. in glacial acetic acid | Silver oxide, $Ag_2O$, brown ppt. Sol. in $NH_4OH$ and in $HNO_3$. 4.3 mg. at 20° in $H_2O$. Sol. in KCN |
| Stannous chloride, $SnCl_2$ | Lead chloride, $PbCl_2$. Sol. in hot water (See above) | Mercury, Hg, dark gray ppt. Sol. in $HNO_3$, conc. $H_2SO_4$. Insol. in HCl | Silver chloride, AgCl, white ppt. (See above) |
| Sulfuric acid $H_2SO_4$ | Lead sulfate, $PbSO_4$, white ppt. Insol. in excess. Slightly sol. in $HNO_3$. Sol. in $NaOH$, $NH_4C_2H_3O_2$. 4.2 at 20° | Mercurous sulfate, $Hg_2SO_4$, white ppt. Slightly sol. in water, 200 mg. Sol. in $H_2SO_4$, $HNO_3$ | Silver sulfate, $Ag_2SO_4$, white ppt. Formed only in conc. solutions. Insol. in alkalies. Sol. in $H_2SO_4$ and in $HNO_3$. 580 mg. in $H_2O$ |
| Miscellaneous | Zn ppts. Pb in crystalline form. Pb sol. in $HNO_3$. Hot conc. $H_2SO_4$ | Pptd. in acid solutions by Cu, Zn, from its salts as metallic Hg. $SO_2$ reduces mercurous salts to Hg, which collects as globules on boiling solution. Hg sol. in $HNO_3$. Insol. ir HCl | Insoluble salts, AgBr, AgI. Ag is displaced from its salts in crystalline form by Zn, Cu, Hg, and in gray form by $SO_2$, $SnCl_2$, $FeSO_4$, etc. Ag sol. in $HNO_3$. Insol. in alkalies |

The numerals indicate milligrams of the substance that will dissolve in 100 ml. of water at stated temperature.

# THE HYDROGEN SULFIDE GROUP

## INSOLUBLE SUBGROUP

Sol. = Soluble.  Insol. = Insoluble.

| Reagent | Bismuth, $BiCl_3$ | Cadmium, $CdSO_4$ | Copper, $CuSO_4$ | Mercury (= ic), $HgCl_2$ |
|---|---|---|---|---|
| Hydrogen sulfide, $H_2S$ | Bismuth sulfide, $Bi_2S_3$, brown ppt. Sol. in $HNO_3$. Insol. in $(NH_4)_2S_x$ and in KCN. Cold water 100 ml. dissolves 0.018 mg. | Cadmium sulfide, CdS, yellow ppt. Sol. in $HNO_3$, $H_2SO_4$ (hot dil.). Insol. in $(NH_4)_2S_x$, KCN. Cold $H_2O$, 0.13 mg. Hot $H_2O$ forms colloidal solution | Copper sulfide, CuS, black ppt. Sol. in $HNO_3$, KCN. Slightly sol. in $(NH_4)_2S_x$. Insol. in $H_2SO_4$ (hot dil.). Cold $H_2O$, 0.033 mg. | Mercuric sulfide, HgS, white → yellow → red → brown → black. Insol. in $HNO_3$, $(NH_4)_2S_x$. Sol. in $Br + KClO_3$ or aqua regia, $Na_2S$. Cold $H_2O$, 2.5 mg. |
| Ammonium hydroxide, $NH_4OH$ | Bismuth hydroxide, $Bi(OH)_3$, white ppt. Insol. in excess. Changed by boiling to $Bi_2O_3$. Insol. in $H_2O$ Insol. in alkalies | Cadmium hydroxide, $Cd(OH)_2$ white ppt. Sol. in excess. Insol. in water, e.g. $0.26^{25°}$ mg. Sol. in $NH_4$ salts | Basic copper ammonium sulfate. Sol. in excess = a deep blue. $Cu(NH_3)_4 \cdot SO_4'' \cdot H_2O$, characteristic test | Amido mercuric chloride, $HgNH_2Cl$, white ppt. |
| Potassium chromate, $K_2CrO_4$ | Bismuth chromate, $(BiO)_2CrO_4$, yellow ppt. Sol. in $HNO_3$. Insol. in KOH (See Pb) | Basic chromate, $Cd_2(OH)_2CrO_4$, yellow. Insol. in NaOH | Copper chromate, $CuCrO_4$, reddish brown ppt. Sol. in $NH_4OH$, forming a green solution | Mercuric chromate, $HgCrO_4$, reddish yellow ppt. Sol. in $HNO_3$. Slightly sol. in water |
| Potassium cyanide, KCN | | Cadmium cyanide, $Cd(CN)_2$, white ppt. Sol. in excess = $Cd(CN)_2(KCN)_2$. From this $H_2S$ ppts. CdS, yellow | Copper cyanide, $Cu(CN)_2$, greenish yellow ppt. Sol. in excess = $Cu(CN)_2(KCN)_2$. No pptn. by $H_2S$ | $Hg(CN)_2$. Sol. in water. 12,500 mg. |

| Reagent | Bismuth | Cadmium | Copper | Mercury |
|---|---|---|---|---|
| Potassium ferrocyanide, K₄Fe(CN)₆ | Bismuth ferrocyanide, Bi₄(Fe(CN)₆)₃, white ppt. Insol. in HCl | Cadmium ferrocyanide, Cd₂Fe(CN)₆, yellowish white ppt. Sol. in HCl. Insol. in H₂O | Copper ferrocyanide, Cu₂Fe(CN)₆, reddish brown ppt. Slightly sol. in NH₄OH. Insol. in acids | |
| Sodium carbonate, Na₂CO₃ | Basic bismuth carbonate, (BiO)₂CO₃, white ppt. Insol. in water. Sol. in acids. Insol. in Na₂CO₃ | Cadmium carbonate, CdCO₃, white ppt. Insol. in excess. Sol. in NH₄OH. Sol. in acids | Basic copper carbonate, Cu₂(OH)₂CO₃, blue. Changed to black CuO on boiling | Mercuric basic carbonate, HgCO₃(HgO)₃, reddish brown ppt. Changed to yellow HgO on boiling. Insol. in H₂O |
| Sodium hydroxide, NaOH | Bismuth hydroxide, Bi(OH)₃, white ppt. See above | Cadmium hydroxide, Cd(OH)₂, white ppt. Insol. in excess (See above) | Copper hydroxide, Cu(OH)₂, light blue. Insol. in excess. Changed to black CuO on boiling | Mercuric hydroxide, Hg(OH)₂. Easily changed to HgO, yellow. Insol. in excess. In presence of NH₄Cl = HgNH₂Cl, white ppt. |
| Sulfuric acid, H₂SO₄ | No precipitate | No precipitate | No precipitate | No precipitate |
| Stannous chloride, SnCl₂ | Darkens. Precipitate of BiOOH changes to Bi₂O₃ | | Cuprous chloride, CuCl, white ppt. Sol. in HCl, NH₃ aq., NH₄Cl. Insol. in H₂O | Mercurous chloride, HgCl, white ppt. In excess = gray, Hg |
| Miscellaneous | In water Bi salt precipitates as BiOCl, white. Reduced by Na₂SnO₂ to metallic Bi, black. Bi sol. in HNO₃, conc. H₂SO₄ | Na₂HPO₄ ppts. Cd₃(PO₄)₂, white. Sol. in NH₄OH and in dilute acids. Cd sol. in acids. Sol. in NH₄NO₃ | Na₂HPO₄ precipitates Cu₃(PO₄)₂, greenish blue. Sol. in NH₄OH. KI ppts. Cu₂I₂, white + I = brown. Cu sol. in HNO₃, hot conc. H₂SO₄ | Precipitated by Cu. KI ppts. HgI₂, red. Sol. in excess. Hg sol. in HNO₃, conc. H₂SO₄. Insol. in HCl |

1293

| | Arsenic | | Antimony | |
|---|---|---|---|---|
| | (ous) $K_3AsO_3$ | (ic) $KH_2AsO_4$ | (ous) $SbCl_3$ | (ic) $KSbO_3$ |
| Hydrogen sulfide $H_2S$ | Arsenic trisulfide, $As_2S_3$, yellow ppt. Sol. in alkalies, $(NH_4)_2S_x$, $(NH_4)_2S$. Insol. in conc. HCl | Arsenic trisulfide + S, and $As_2S_5$, yellow. The ppt. forms slowly by heat | Antimony trisulfide, $Sb_2S_3$, orange ppt. Sol. in alkalies, $(NH_4)_2S_x$, $(NH_4)_2S$, HCl (conc.). 0.17 mg. | Antimony pentasulfide, $Sb_2S_5$, orange ppt. Sol. in alkalies, $(NH_4)_2S_x$, $(NH_4)_2S$, HCl (conc.) |
| Ammonium hydroxide, $NH_4OH$ | | | Antimonious hydroxide, $Sb(OH)_3$, white ppt. Sol. in excess | Ammonium metantimonate, $NH_4SbO_3$. Very slightly sol. in excess |
| Copper sulfate, $CuSO_4$ | Copper arsenite, $CuHAsO_3$, yellowish green ppt. Sol. in $NH_4OH$, NaOH, $HNO_3$ | Copper arsenate, $Cu_3(AsO_4)_2$, greenish blue ppt. Sol. in $NH_4OH$ and in $HNO_3$ | Antimony oxychloride, white, SbOCl, caused by dilution. Insol. alk. Sol. HCl, $CS_2$ | Copper antimonate, brown ppt. |
| Mercuric chloride, $HgCl_2$ | Mercuric arsenite, $Hg_3(AsO_3)_2$, white ppt. Sol. in acids | | Antimony oxychloride, caused by dilution. Sol. in conc. HCl | |
| Silver nitrate, $AgNO_3$ | Silver arsenite, $Ag_3AsO_3$, yellow ppt. Sol. in $HNO_3$, $NH_4OH$, $HC_2H_3O_2$ | Silver arsenate, $Ag_3AsO_4$, reddish brown ppt. Sol. in $HNO_3$ and $NH_4OH$ | Silver chloride and antimony trioxide, AgCl + $Sb_2O_3$, white ppts. | Silver antimonate, $AgSbO_3$, white ppt. Sol. in $NH_4OH$ |
| Miscellaneous | Magnesia mixture. No ppt. Arsenic sol. in $HNO_3$, $Cl_2$, $H_2O$, aq. reg., hot alkalies<br><br>Marsh test (Zn + HCl, etc.) | Magnesia mixture ppts. $MgNH_4AsO_4$, white crys. ppt. Sol. in acetic acid. $AsH_3$ flame deposits arsenic. Sol. in NaOCl. Sol. in $(NH_4)_2S$. Residue insol. in HCl (conc.). | KOH ppts. $Sb(OH)_3$. $Na_2CO_3$ ppts. $Sb(OH)_3$<br><br>Marsh test (Zn + HCl) | Sb sol. in hot conc. $H_2SO_4$ and in aq. reg.<br><br>$SbH_3$ in flame deposits antimony. Insol in NaOCl |

SUBGROUP

| Tin | | Platinum | Gold |
|---|---|---|---|
| (ous) SnCl$_2$ | (ic) SnCl$_4$ | PtCl$_4$ | AuCl$_3$ |
| Stannous sulfide, SnS, dark brown. Sol. in alkalies. Difficultly sol. in (NH$_4$)$_2$S$_x$. Sol. in HCl (conc.). 100 ml. H$_2$O diss. 0.002 mg. | Stannic sulfide, SnS$_2$, yellow ppt. Sol. in alkalies, (NH$_4$)$_2$S$_x$, (NH$_4$)$_2$S and alkali carbonates. HCl (conc.). H$_2$O = 0.02 mg. | Platinic sulfide, PtS$_2$, dark brown ppt. Difficultly sol. in alkali sulfides. Sol. in aqua regia. Insol. in HCl (conc.) | Gold sulfide, Au$_2$S$_3$, black ppt. Sol. in alkali sulfides, aqua regia. Insol. in HCl (conc.) |
| Stannous hydroxide, Sn(OH)$_2$. Insol. in excess. Darkens on standing. Insol. in H$_2$O. Sol. in dilute acids, alk. | Stannic hydroxide, Sn(OH)$_4$. Slightly sol. in excess | Ammonium chloro-platinate, (NH$_4$)PtCl$_6$, yellow ppt. Sol. in large excess. 679$^{20°}$ mg. | Fulminating gold, Au$_2$O$_3$·2 NH$_3$, yellow ppt., insol. in excess |
| Cuprous chloride, 2 CuCl, white ppt. Sol. in acids. Reduction by SnCl$_2$ | | | |
| Mercurous chloride, HgCl, white ppt. Insol. in cold HCl (conc.). Reduction by SnCl$_2$ | | | |
| Silver chloride and silver, AgCl + Ag. Reduction by SnCl$_2$ | Silver chloride, AgCl | Silver chloride and platinum oxide, AgCl + PtO, brown ppt. | Silver chloride and gold oxide, AgCl + Au$_2$O$_3$, brown ppt. |
| KOH ppts. Sn(OH)$_2$, Na$_2$CO$_3$ ppts. Sn(OH)$_2$. Insol. in excess | KOH ppts. Sn(OH)$_2$. NaCO$_3$ ppts. Sn(OH)$_2$. Insol. in excess | KOH ppts. K$_2$PtCl$_6$. Na$_2$CO$_3$ gives no ppt. Pt sol. in aq. r., fused alk. | SnCl$_2$ solution ppts. "Purple of Cassius," red ppt. Au sol. in KCN, aq. reg. |
| Metallic Sn deposited by Zn in Marsh test | Stannic salts reduced by H, generated by Sn | Zn ppts. Pt, black, from its salts | Zn ppts. Au from its salts |

## THE AMMONIUM SULFIDE GROUP

Numbers refer to mgs. soluble in 100 ml. cold water

| Reagent | Aluminum $Al_2K_2(SO_4)_4$ | Chromium $Cr_2K_2(SO_4)_4$ | Iron — Ferrous, $FeSO_4$ | Iron — Ferric, $FeCl_3$ |
|---|---|---|---|---|
| Ammonium sulfide, $(NH_4)_2S$ | Aluminum hydroxide, $Al(OH)_3$, white flocculent ppt. Sol. in acids. $H_2S$ gas liberated | Chromium hydroxide, $Cr(OH)_3$ grayish green, ppt. $H_2S$ liberated. Sol. in acids and alkalies | Iron sulfide, FeS, black ppt. sol. in acids. Oxidizes in the air to $FeSO_4$ and finally to a brown basic ferric sulfate. 0.89 mg. | Iron sulfide, FeS($+$S), black ppt. Sol. in acids. S remains undissolved |
| Ammonium hydroxide, $NH_4OH$ | Aluminum hydroxide, $Al(OH)_3$, white. Very slightly sol. in excess of reagent | Chromium hydroxide, $Cr(OH)_3$, grayish green. Slightly sol. in excess, forming a reddish solution when cold and concentrated | Ferrous hydroxide, white ppt. becoming green, then reddish brown, in the air and in presence of $NH_4Cl$. $Fe(OH)_3$ slowly forms. Sol. in $NH_4Cl$. 6.7 mgs. | Ferric hydroxide, $Fe(OH)_3$, reddish brown ppt. Insol. in excess of reagent |
| Ammonium carbonate, $(NH_4)_2CO_3$ | Aluminum hydroxide, $Al(OH)_3$, white ppt. $CO_2$ gas | Chromium hydroxide, $Cr(OH)_3$, grayish green. Sol. in excess of reagent $CO_2$ liberated | Ferrous carbonate, $FeCO_3$, white ppt. sol. in excess. Slowly changed to hydroxide | Basic salt changing to $Fe(OH)_3$, reddish brown ppt. |
| Barium carbonate, $BaCO_3$ | Aluminum hydroxide, $Al(OH)_3$, white | Basic salt, $CO_2$, liberated, and $Cr(OH)_3$ formed | Iron not pptd. in ferrous form by $BaCO_3$ | Same as above |
| Borax bead $NaB_4O_7 \cdot 10\ H_2O$ | | OF, yellowish green when hot, changing to emerald-green, cold | OF, yellow. RF, green | OF, yellow. RF, green |

| Reagent | | | (in presence of sodium acetate, FeS pptd.) | ($Fe^{+3}$ reduced to $Fe^{+2}$ ...) |
|---|---|---|---|---|
| Hydrogen sulfide, $H_2S$ | | | in presence of sodium acetate, FeS pptd. | $Fe^{+3}$ reduced to $Fe^{+2}$ with liberation of free S. (Also reduced by $SnCl_2$) |
| Potassium ferricyanide, $K_3Fe(CN)_6$ | | (All Cr compounds oxidized to compounds of chromic acid; e.g. $2\,Na_2CO_3 + 3\,KNO_3 + 2\,Cr(OH)_3 \rightarrow 2\,Na_2CrO_4$ + etc.) | Ferrous ferricyanide (Turnbull's blue), $Fe_3(FeC_6N_6)_2$, dark blue ppt. Insol. in HCl. Decomposed by NaOH to $Fe(OH)_2$ | Reddish brown color produced |
| Potassium ferrocyanide, $K_4Fe(CN)_6$ | White ppt. forms slowly | | Potassium ferrous ferrocyanide, $K_2Fe_3(FeC_6N_6)_2$, bluish white, oxidized in air to blue | Ferric ferrocyanide, $Fe_4(FeC_6N_6)_3$, (Prussian blue), dark blue. Insol. in mineral acid. NaOH forms $Fe(OH)_3$ |
| Sodium hydroxide, NaOH | ‡ Aluminum hydroxide, $Al(OH)_3$, white. Sol. in excess, forming $Na_3 \rightarrow AlO_3'''$·($NaAlO_2$). Repptd. by $NH_4Cl$ | ‡ Chromium hydroxide, $Cr(OH)_3$, greenish ppt. Sol. in excess, forming green solution $NaCrO_2$. Repptd. by boiling or by addition of $NH_4Cl$ | ‡ Ferrous hydroxide, $Fe(OH)_2$, white becoming $Fe(OH)_3$. Insol. in excess. Non-volatile organic substance prevents ppt.ion. | ‡ Ferric hydroxide, $Fe(OH)_3$, reddish brown ppt. Insol. in excess. Sol. in mineral acids |
| Sodium phosphate, $Na_2HPO_4$ | $AlPO_4$, white. Sol. in NaOH. Insol. in $HC_2H_3O_2$ | $CrPO_4$ green ppt. Sol. in mineral acids and in NaOH | $Fe_3(PO_4)_2$, white ppt. becoming blue in the air | $FePO_4$, yellowish white, sol. in excess. Insol. in $HC_2H_3O_2$ |
| Miscellany | Sodium acetate in excess boiled with Al salt ppts. basic $Al(OH)_2(C_2H_3O_2)$ in neutral solutions | $NaC_2H_3O_2$ forms no ppt. unless Fe and Al are present, in which case Cr partially pptd. by boiling | KCNS, no color. KCN ppts. $Fe(CN)_2$, brown. Sol. in excess | KCNS = red $Fe(SCN)_3$. Boiling with $NaC_2H_3O_2$ in neutral solutions a red brown ppt. formed of $(FeOH)_2(C_2H_3O_2)$ |

‡ Presence of nonvolatile organic substances, tartrates, citrates, and sugar prevents precipitation.

# THE AMMONIUM SULFIDE GROUP—*Continued*

| Reagent | Cobalt, $CoCl_2$ | Nickel, $NiCl_2$ | Manganese, $MnSO_4$ | Zinc, $ZnSO_4$ |
|---|---|---|---|---|
| $(NH_4)_2S$ | Cobalt sulfide, CoS, black ppt. Insol. in $HC_2H_3O_2$. Very slightly sol. in HCl. Sol. in aqua regia and warm $HNO_3$. 0.38 mg. | Nickel sulfide, NiS, black ppt. Slightly sol. in excess, forming a brown solution. Very slightly sol. in HCl. Sol. in aqua regia. 0.36 mg. | Manganese sulfide, MnS, buff-colored ppt. Sol. in HCl, $HC_2H_3O_2$. Oxidizes in the air. 0.6 mg. | Zinc sulfide, ZnS, white ppt. Insol. in $HC_2H_3O_2$. Sol. in HCl. Presence of $NH_4Cl$ aids pptn. |
| $NH_4OH$ | Blue basic salt, sol. in excess, forming red solution. No ppt. formed in presence of $NH_4Cl$. Solution becomes red | Nickel hydroxide, $Ni(OH)_2$, green ppt. Sol. in excess, forming a blue solution. No ppt. formed in presence of $NH_4Cl$ | Manganese hydroxide, $Mn(OH)_2$, white ppt. turning brown. In presence of $NH_4Cl$ a dark brown ppt. slowly forms by oxidation, $Mn(OH)_3$ | Zinc hydroxide, $Zn(OH)_2$, white ppt. Sol. in excess, $ZnSO_4(NH_3)_4$ formed. In presence of $NH_4Cl$ no ppt. forms |
| $(NH_4)_2CO_3$ | Basic carbonate, red, lilac, or pink ppt. Sol. in excess, forming red solution, becoming brown by air oxidation | Basic carbonate of variable compositions, green ppt. Sol. in excess | Manganese carbonate, $MnCO_3$, white ppt. Sol. in excess. Boiling aids pptn. | Basic zinc carbonate, usually $Zn_2(OH)_2CO_3$, white ppt. Sol. in excess (Acid carbonate ppts. $ZnCO_3$ white) |
| $BaCO_3$ | No ppt. in cold | No ppt. in cold | No ppt. in cold | No pption. in cold. ($Na_2CO_3$ ppts. above aided by boiling) |
| Borax bead | Blue | Violet, hot. Yellowish brown, cold | OF, violet-red, hot. Amethyst-red, cold. RF, colorless | |
| $H_2S$ | From neutral or alkaline solutions, CoS, black. No ppt. in acid solutions | From neutral or alkaline solutions, NiS. No ppt. in acid solutions | MnS forms slowly from alkaline solutions. No ppt. in acid solutions | From neutral or alkaline solutions, or in solutions acidified with $HC_2H_3O_2$. |

| | Cobalt | Nickel | Manganese | Zinc |
|---|---|---|---|---|
| $K_3Fe(CN)_6$ | Cobalt ferricyanide, $Co_3(FeC_6N_6)_2$, dark brown ppt. Insol. in HCl | Nickel ferricyanide $Ni_3(FeC_6N_6)_2$, yellowish green ppt. Insol. in HCl | Manganese ferricyanide, $Mn_3(FeC_6N_6)_2$, brown ppt. Insol. in HCl | Zinc ferricyanide, $Zn_3(FeC_6N_6)_2$, yellowish brown ppt. Sol. in HCl and in $NH_4OH$ |
| $K_4Fe(CN)_6$ | Cobalt ferrocyanide, $Co_2Fe(CN)_6$, green ppt. becoming greenish blue. Insol. in HCl. Sol. in KCN | Nickel ferrocyanide, $Ni_2Fe(CN)_6$, light green ppt. Insol. in HCl | Manganese ferrocyanide, $Mn_2Fe(CN)_6$, faint red ppt. Diff. sol. in HCl. Easily sol. in $H_2SO_4$, $HNO_3$ | Zinc ferrocyanide, $Zn_2Fe(CN)_6$, white ppt. Insol. in dilute acids and in $NH_4OH$ |
| NaOH | Basic salt, blue. Boiled with excess = red. Insol. in excess. Sol. in $HC_2H_3O_2$, HCl, $NH_4OH$ | Nickel hydroxide, $Ni(OH)_2$, apple green ppt. Insol. in excess. Sol. in $HC_2H_3O_2$, HCl, $NH_4OH$. Oxidized by Br to $Ni(OH)_3$ | Manganese hydroxide, $Mn(OH)_2$, white ppt. turning brown. Insol. in excess. Sol. in $NH_4Cl$ | Zinc hydroxide, $Zn(OH)_2$, white ppt. Sol. in excess, forming $Na_2ZnO_2$. Repptd. by boiling |
| $Na_2HPO_4$ | $Co_3(PO_4)_2$, blue ppt. Sol. in $NH_4OH$. Col. in dil. acids. Sol. in $H_3PO_4$ | $Ni_3(PO_4)_2$, green ppt. Sol. in $NH_4OH$. Sol. in dil. acids | $Mn_3(PO_4)_2$, white ppt. Sol. in $NH_4OH$, mineral acids, and $HC_2H_3O_2$. Boiled with $NH_4OH$ + $NH_4Cl$ = $MnNH_4PO_4$, rose colored | $Zn_3(PO_4)_2$, white ppt. Sol. in excess and in dil. acids and in $NH_4OH$ |
| Miscellaneous | HCN ppts. reddish brown, $Co(CN)_2$. Sol. in excess. Addition of Br + NaOH → $K_3Co(CN)_6$. (Ni is pptd.) | HCN ppts. greenish yellow, $Ni(CN)_2$. Sol. in excess. Reppt. by HCl. Pptd. by Br + NaOH as $Ni(OH)_3$, black + CNBr (poison gas) | $PbO_2$ + $HNO_3$ + Mn salt warmed = red $HMnO_4$. $Na_2CO_3$ + $KNO_3$ fused on Pt = green, $Na_2MnO_4$ | KCN ppts. $Zn(CN)_2$, white. Sol. in excess. From this solution $(NH_4)_2S$ ppts. ZnS, white |

## THE AMMONIUM CARBONATE GROUP

Solubility in milligrams per 100 ml. of water cold, "c," and hot, "h"

| Reagent | Barium, $BaCl_2$ | Calcium, $CaCl_2$ | Strontium, $SrCl_2$ | Soluble in Presence of $NH_4$ Salts. Magnesium, $MgSO_4$ |
|---|---|---|---|---|
| Ammonium carbonate, $(NH_4)_2CO_3$ | Barium carbonate, $BaCO_3$, white ppt. Sol. in acids. Slightly sol. in $NH_4Cl$. Precipitation aided by excess of $NH_4OH$ and by boiling. "c" 2.2 mg.; "h" 6.5 mg. | Calcium carbonate, $CaCO_3$, white ppt. Sol. in acids. Slightly sol. in $NH_4Cl$. Rendered less sol. by boiling with $NH_4OH$. "c" 1.3 mg.; "h" 88 mg. | Strontium carbonate, $SrCO_3$, white ppt. Sol. in acids. Slightly sol. in $NH_4Cl$. Rendered less sol. by boiling with excess of $NH_4OH$. "c" 1.1 mg. | Basic magnesium carbonate $MgCO_3 + Mg(OH)_2$, white ppt. on warming. No ppt. formed if $NH_4$ salts are present. But if absent, solubility only 10.6 mgs. |
| Ammonium hydroxide, $NH_4OH$ | | | | Magnesium hydroxide, $Mg(OH)_2$. Sol. in $NH_4Cl$ |
| Ammonium oxalate, $(NH_4)_2C_2O_4$ | Barium oxalate, $BaC_2O_4$, white ppt. Sol. in HCl. Slightly sol. in $HC_2H_3O_2$ and water. "c" 9.3; "h" 22.8 | Calcium oxalate, $CaC_2O_4$, white ppt. Sol. in HCl. Almost insol. in $HC_2H_3O_2$ or in $H_2C_2O_4$. "c" 0.68 mg.; "h" 1.4 mg. | Strontium oxalate, $SrC_2O_4$, white ppt. Sol. in HCl. Slightly sol. in $HC_2H_3O_2$ and water. "c" 5.1 mg. Sol. in hot solutions | |
| Ammonium sulfate, $(NH_4)_2SO_4$, or sulfuric acid, $H_2SO_4$ | Barium sulfate, $BaSO_4$, white ppt. Insol. in $H_2O$ and in acids. "c" 0.17 mg.; "h" 0.3 mg. | Calcium sulfate, white ppt. Somewhat sol. in $H_2O$. Sol. in $(NH_4)_2SO_4$. Insol. in alcohol. "c" 179 mg.; "h" 178 mg. | Strontium sulfate, $SrSO_4$, white ppt. Slightly sol. in $H_2O$ and in $(NH_4)_2SO_4$. "c" 11.4 mg.; "h" 10.4 mg. | |

| | Barium | Calcium | Strontium | Magnesium |
|---|---|---|---|---|
| Potassium chromate, $K_2CrO_4$ | Barium chromate, $BaCrO_4$, yellow ppt. Insol. in $HC_2H_3O_2$ in presence of $K_2CrO_4$. Sol. in HCl. $HNO_3$. "c" 0.38 mg.; "h" 4.3 mg. | | | |
| Sodium hydroxide, NaOH | Barium hydroxide, $Ba(OH)_2$, white ppt. formed only in conc. solutions. "c" 5560 mg.; "h" very soluble | Calcium hydroxide, $Ca(OH)_2$, white ppt. Difficultly sol. in water. Sol. in $NH_4Cl$. "c" 170 mg.; "h" 80 mg. | Strontium hydroxide, $Sr(OH)_2$, white ppt. Slightly sol. in water; "c" 410 mg.; "h" very soluble. | Magnesium hydroxide, $Mg(OH)_2$, white ppt. Sol. in $NH_4Cl$ |
| Sodium phosphate, $Na_2HPO_4$ | Barium hydrogen phosphate, $BaHPO_4$, white ppt. "c" 10–20 mg. Sol. in acids. If $NH_4OH$ present, $BaNH_4PO_4$ formed | Calcium hydrogen phosphate, $CaHPO_4$, white ppt. "c" = 28 mg. Sol. in acids. In presence of $NH_4OH$, $Ca_3(PO_4)_2$ pptd. "c" 3 mg. to 8 mg. | Strontium hydrogen phosphate, $SrHPO_4$, white ppt. Sol. in acids. See $BaHPO_4$. Insol in $H_2O$. | Magnesium hydrogen phosphate, $MgHPO_4$, white ppt. Boiled = $Mg_3(PO_4)$. In presence of $NH_4Cl$ and $NH_4OH$ a white crystalline ppt. of $MgNH_4PO_4$ slowly forms. Sol. in acetic acid |
| Flame | Yellowish green | Yellowish red | Crimson | White |
| Spectra | Green $\alpha$ and $\beta$ bands. Fainter yellow and red bands | Sharp orange line $\alpha$ and bluish line $\beta$ | Several orange and red lines. Brilliant blue line | |
| Miscellaneous | $H_2SiF_6$ ppts. $BaSiF_6$. Insol. in alcohol and dilute acids. "c" 26 mg.; "h" 90 mg. | No ppt. by $H_2SiF_6$ | No ppt. by $H_2SiF_6$ | No ppt. by $H_2SiF_6$. Boiled with $Na_2CO_3$ = white $Mg_3(OH)_2(CO_2)_2$. No ppt. if $NH_4Cl$ present |

# THE SOLUBLE METAL GROUP

| Reagent | Ammonium, $NH_4Cl$ | Lithium, LiCl | Potassium, KCl | Sodium, NaCl |
|---|---|---|---|---|
| Hydrofluosilicic acid, $H_2SiF_6$ | | | Potassium fluosilicate, $K_2SiF_6$. Transparent ppt. Slightly sol. in water. "c" = 120 mg.; "h" 955 mg. | Sodium fluosilicate, $Na_2SiF_6$, white ppt. Somewhat sol. in water. "c" = 650 mg.; "h" 2460 mg. |
| Nessler's reagents, $HgI_2(KI)_2 \cdot KOH$ | Reddish brown or yellow, according to amount of ammonia. Test very delicate | | | |
| Platinic chloride, $PtCl_4$. $H_2PtCl_6$ | Ammonium chloroplatinate, $(NH_4)_2PtCl_6$, yellow ppt. Slightly sol. in water. Insol. in alcohol. "c" 670.0 mg. Very sol. in hot water | | Potassium-chloroplatinate, $K_2PtCl_6$, yellow ppt. Slightly sol. in water. Insol. in alcohol or ether. "c" 480 mg.; "h" 5180 mg. | |
| Potassium pyroantimonate, $H_2K_2Sb_2O_7$ | | | | Sodium pyroantimonate, $Na_2H_2Sb_2O_7$, white cryst. ppt. Best formed in slightly alkaline solutions. $NaSbO_3$ + aqua. "c" = 31 mg. |

| Reagent | | | | |
|---|---|---|---|---|
| Sodium carbonate, $Na_2CO_3$ | Ammonia gas evolved on boiling | Lithium carbonate, $Li_2CO_3$, white ppt. Slightly sol. in water. Less sol. in hot than in cold. "c" = 1539 mg.; "h" 728 mg. | | No ppt. in acetic acid solutions of sodium salts |
| Sodium cobaltinitrite $Co(NO_2)_3 \cdot 3 NaNO_2$ | In acetic acid solutions (see Na), $Co(NO_2)_3 \cdot 3 NH_4NO_2$, yellow ppt. Sol. in inorganic acids | | Potassium cobaltinitrite, $K_3Co(NO_2)_6$, yellow, or $K_2NaCo(NO_2)_6$ in presence of an excess of sodium. Insol. in acetic acid. Sol. in inorganic acids. Hastened by warming. Solution should have acetic acid present. 70 mg. 25° | |
| Sodium or potassium hydroxide, NaOH or KOH | Ammonia gas evolved when salt is warmed with NaOH or KOH | | | |
| Sodium phosphate, $Na_2HPO_4$ | | Lithium phosphate, $Li_3PO_4$, white ppt. Slightly sol. in water. Sol. in HCl. "c" = 40 mg. | | |
| Tartaric acid, $H_2C_4H_4O_6$ | Monoammonium tartrate, $NH_4HC_4H_4O_6$, white cryst. ppt. Hastened by shaking. Slightly sol. in $H_2O$ | | Monopotassium tartrate, $KHC_4H_4O_6$, white cryst. ppt. Hastened by stirring. Somewhat sol. in $H_2O$. "c" 370 mg. | |
| Flame and spectrum | | Red flame. Bright crimson line with feeble orange line | Violet flame. A red and blue line | Yellow flame. Single yellow line |

# REACTIONS OF THE ACIDS

## INORGANIC ACIDS

Reagents

| Acids | Silver Nitrate, $AgNO_3$ | Barium Chloride, $BaCl_2$ | Calcium Chloride, $CaCl_2$ | Lead Acetate, $Pb(C_2H_3O_2)_2$ | Characteristic Reactions |
|---|---|---|---|---|---|
| Arsenic $H_3AsO_4$, arsenates | Reddish brown ppt., $Ag_3AsO_4$. Sol. in $NH_4OH$, $HNO_3$ | White ppt., $Ba_3(AsO_4)_2$. Sol. in acids | White ppt. $Ca_3(AsO_4)_2$. Sol. in acetic acid | Lead acetate ppts. white salt. Insol. in acetic acid. Sol. in $HNO_3$ | $(NH_4)_2MoO_4$ produces a yellow ppt. $MgSO_4 + NH_4Cl + NH_4OH$ = white ppt. |
| Arsenious, $H_3AsO_3$, arsenites | Yellow ppt., $Ag_3AsO_3$. Sol. in $NH_4OH$, $HNO_3$ | White ppt., $Ba_3(AsO_3)_2$. Sol. in acids | White ppt. Sol. in $C_2H_4O_2$ | Lead acetate ppts. white arsenious salt. Sol. in acetic acid, $HNO_3$ | Marsh's test with both forms—-ous and -ic—gives arsenic mirror. Sol. in NaOCl. $H_2S$ produces yellow $As_2S_3$ and $As_2S_5$. Gutzeit test |
| Boric, $H_3BO_3$, ($H_2B_4O_7$), borates | White ppt. Sol. in $NH_4OH$, $HNO_3$ | White ppt. Not readily sol. in water. Sol. in acids | White ppt. Sol. in acids | White ppt. Caused by lead acetate. Sol. in excess | $H_2SO_4 + C_2H_5OH$ colors flame green. Turmeric paper dipped in boric acid salt acidified with HCl, dried, turns red |
| Carbonic, $H_2CO_3$, carbonates | Grayish white ppt., $Ag_2CO_3$. Sol. in $HNO_3$. $3.1^{15°}$ mg. | White ppt., $BaCO_3$. Sol. in acids. 22 mg. | White ppt., $CaCO_3$. Sol. in acids. 2.2 mg. | Lead acetate ppts. white lead. Sol. in $HNO_3$ | Effervesces with dilute inorganic acids, HCl, $H_2SO_4$, $HNO_3$, etc., $CO_2$ gas being evolved. Limewater clouded by $CO_2$, $CaCO_3$ being formed |

| | AgNO₃ | BaCl₂ | Pb(C₂H₃O₂)₂ / lead | |
|---|---|---|---|---|
| Chloric, HClO₃, chlorates | | | H₂SO₄, conc., warmed with salt causes explosion | Heated on charcoal deflagrates. H₂SO₄ evolves yellow gas, ClO₂ |
| Chromic, H₂CrO₄, chromates | Dark red ppt., Ag₂CrO₄. Sol. in HNO₃. $2.8^{18°}$ mg. | Yellow ppt., BaCrO₄. Sol. in HCl, HNO₃. Insol. in acetic acid. 0.38 mg. | Pb(C₂H₃O₂)₂ ppts. yellow PbCrO₄. Sol. in NaOH $0.028^{c}$ mg. | Reduced to green CrCl₃ by warming with alcohol and HCl |
| Hydriodic, HI, iodides | Yellow ppt., AgI₂. Very difficultly sol. in NH₄OH. $0.035^{21°}$ mg. | | Soluble, lead salt ppts. PbI₂, yellow. Sol. in hot water. 39,000 mg. | I₂ liberated from its salts by HNO₂, or Cl water. Imparts in free form violet color to CS₂, blue to starch |
| Hydrobromic, HBr, bromides | Light yellow ppt., AgBr. Difficultly sol. in NH₄OH | | Pb(C₂H₃O₂)₂ ppts. PbBr₂, white. Sol. in hot water. 455 mg. | Br₂ liberated from its salts by Cl, colors CS₂ reddish yellow |

1305

| Acids | $AgNO_3$ | $BaCl_2$ | $CaCl_2$ | $Pb(C_2H_3O_2)_2$ | Characteristic Reactions |
|---|---|---|---|---|---|
| Hydrochloric, HCl, chlorides | White ppt., AgCl. Insol. in $HNO_3$. Sol. in $NH_4OH$, KCN. 0.152 mg. | | | $PbCl_2$, white, is pptd. Sol. in hot water. Insol. in alcohol. 673 mg. | $K_2Cr_2O_7 + H_2SO_4$ (conc.), gives $CrO_2Cl_2$. $MnO_2 + H_2SO_4$ gives Cl gas. $KMnO_4 + HCl$ evolves Cl |
| Hydrocyanic, HCN, cyanides | White ppt., AgCN. Sol. in $NH_4OH$, KCN. 0.021 mg. | | | White ppt. with sol. Pb salt, $Pb(CN)_2$. Sol. in $HNO_3$. | Warmed with $NaOH + FeSO_4 + FeCl_3$ and acidified with HCl, "Prussian Blue" formed. Warmed with $(NH_4)_2S_x = NH_4CNS$, which produces a blood-red color with $FeCl_3$ |
| Hydroferricyanic, $H_3Fe(CN)_6$, ferricyanides | Orange ppt., $Ag_3Fe(CN)_6$. Sol. in $NH_4OH$, KCN. Insol. in $NHO_3$ | | | On warming, $PbO_2$ is pptd. | Dark blue, Turnbull's blue, ppt. with $FeSO_4(Fe^{..})$ |
| Hydroferrocyanic, $H_4Fe(CN)_6$, ferrocyanides | White ppt. Sol. in KCN. Insol. in $NHO_3$ | | | White ppt. Sol. in $NHO_3$ | Prussian Blue with $FeCl_3$ $(Fe^{+3})$. Red ppt. with copper salts $(Cu^{+2})$ |
| Hydrofluoric, HF, fluorides | | White ppt., $BaF_2$. Sol. in HCl. $163^{18}$ mg. | White ppt., $CaF_2$. Sol. in HCl. Insol. in acetic acid. 1.6 mg. | $Pb(C_2H_3O_2)$ ppts. white salt. Sol. in $HNO_3$ | $H_2SO_4$ evolves HF, which etches glass |

| Substance | | | | | |
|---|---|---|---|---|---|
| Hydrofluo-silicic, $H_2SiF_6$, fluosilicates | | White ppt. $BaSiF_6$. Insol. in HCl. $26^{17°}$ mg. | | | Decomposed by $H_2SO_4$ into HF and $SiF_4$. Ppts. K in concentrated solution, as $K_2SiF_6$, white |
| Hydrosul-furic, $H_2S$, sulfides | Black ppt., $Ag_2S$. Sol. in hot $HNO_3$. 0.02 mg. | | | Black ppt., PbS. Sol. in hot $HNO_3$. 0.1 mg. | Most sulfides decomposed by strong inorganic acids, with odor of rotten eggs (see $AgNO_3$ and $Pb(NO_3)_2$ tests). Colors sodium nitro prussiate, violet |
| Hypochlorous, HClO, hypochlorites | White ppt., AgClO. Sol. in $HNO_3$ | | | White ppt., becomes brown on boiling | Cl evolved when salt is treated with HCl and many other acids. Ppts. $MnO_2$ black from solution of $MnSO_4$ |
| Iodic, $HIO_3$, iodides | White ppt., $AgIO_3$. Sol. in $NH_4OH$. Reduced by $SO_2$ to AgI. 4.4 mg. | White ppt., $Ba(IO_3)_2$. Sol. in HCl. 8 mgs. | | White ppt. Sol. in $HNO_3$ | With acetic acid and KI, free iodine formed. $CS_2$ colored violet. Starch colored blue |
| Metaphos-phoric, $HPO_3$, metaphos-phates | White ppt. Sol. in $NH_4OH$, $HNO_3$ | White ppt. Sol. in excess of meta-phosphate | White ppt. Sol. in dil. acids | White ppt. Sol. in $HNO_3$ | Coagulates albumen. Boiled with $HNO_3 = H_3PO_4$ |

## INORGANIC ACIDS

| Acids | AgNO$_3$ | BaCl$_2$ | CaCl$_2$ | Pb(C$_2$H$_3$O$_2$)$_2$ | Characteristic Reactions |
|---|---|---|---|---|---|
| Nitric, HNO$_3$, nitrates | | | | | H$_2$SO$_4$ (conc.) poured into a mixture of a nitrate salt with FeSO$_4$ produces a brown ring at upper surface of heavier H$_2$SO$_4$ |
| Nitrous, HNO$_2$, nitrites | White ppt., AgNO$_2$. Sol. in hot water. 330 mg. | | | | With an iodide, when acidified with HCl, liberates iodine, which will color CS$_2$ violet |
| Phosphoric, H$_3$PO$_4$, phosphates | Yellow ppt., Ag$_3$PO$_4$. Sol. in NH$_4$OH and HNO$_3$. 1.93 mg. | White ppt., Ba$_3$(PO$_4$)$_2$. Sol. in acids | White ppt. Sol. in inorganic and in acetic acids | White ppt. with Pb salt. Sol. in NaOH. Insol. in NH$_4$OH. Insol. in HC$_2$H$_3$O$_2$. 0.014 mg. | (NH$_4$)$_2$MoO$_4$ + HNO$_3$ ppts. at 40°, yellow ammonium phosphomolybdate. Magnesia mixture produces a white ppt., MgNH$_4$PO$_4$ |
| Phosphorus, H$_3$PO$_3$, phosphites | White ppt. On warming, causes reduction of silver salt to Ag | White ppt. Sol. in acids, acetic acid | White ppt. Sol. in NH$_4$Cl | White ppt. Insol. in HC$_2$H$_3$O$_2$. Sol. in HNO$_3$ | Reducing action. Very concentrated solutions heated evolve PH$_3$ |
| Pyrophosphoric, H$_4$P$_2$O$_7$, pyrophosphates | White ppt. Sol. in NH$_4$OH, HNO$_3$ | White ppt. Sol. in HCl. 10 mg. | White ppt. Sol. in excess of the pyrophosphate | Pb salt same as Ca salt | Does not coagulate albumen as does the metaphosphoric acid. Boiled with HNO$_3$ changes to H$_3$PO$_4$ |

| | | | | | |
|---|---|---|---|---|---|
| Silicic, H₂SiO₃, silicates | Yellow ppt. Sol. in HNO₃ | White ppt. | White ppt. | White ppt. Insol. in HNO₃ | Heated with Na₂CO₃, evolves CO₂. SiO₂ skeleton with NaPO₃ bead. Decomposes when evaporated to dryness, SiO₂ separating |
| Thiocyanic, HCNS, thiocyanates or sulfocyanates | White ppt., AgCNS. Difficultly sol. in NH₄OH. 0.021 mg. | | | White ppt. | FeCl₃ produces a blood-red color, which is destroyed by HgCl₂ |
| Sulfuric, H₂SO₄ sulfates | Conc. AgNO₃ produces white ppt., Ag₂SO₄. Sol. in water. 580 mg. | White ppt., BaSO₄. Insol. in acids. 0.172 mg. | White ppt. Sol. in water and acids | White ppt. Sol. in NaOH, NH₄C₂H₃O₂, (NH₄)₂C₄H₄O₆ | Sulfates heated with Na₂CO₃ on charcoal in reducing flame form Na₂S, which blackens a silver coin when it is moistened |
| Sulfurous, H₂SO₃ sulfites | White ppt., Ag₂SO₃. Decomposed by boiling into Ag + Ag₂SO₄ + SO₂ | White ppt. Sol. in HCl. 19.7 mg. | White ppt. Sol. in HCl | White ppt. | Reducing agent. Reduces KI (starch sol. test). Decolorizes KMnO₄. SO₂ evolved when salt is acidified with HCl |
| Thiosulfuric, H₂S₂O₃, thiosulfates | Ag₂S₂O₃, white ppt. Sol. in Na₂S₂O₃. Decomposed by boiling, forming H₂SO₄ + Ag₂S | Conc. solution produces white ppt. | | White ppt. On boiling becomes gray. PbSO₄ + PbS | Decomposed by HCl to SO₂ + S. Na₂S₂O₃ dissolves AgCl |

## ORGANIC ACIDS

| Acids | AgNO$_3$ | CaCl$_2$ | FeCl$_3$ | H$_2$SO$_4$ Conc. | Special Tests |
|---|---|---|---|---|---|
| Acetic, H·C$_2$H$_3$O$_2$ | White ppt. Sol. in hot water | | Reddish brown solution. Ppts. on boiling of ferric acetate = Fe$_2$(OH)$_2$A$_4$. Sol. in HCl | Heated, gives odor of vinegar | H$_2$SO$_4$ + alcohol = ethyl acetate, recognized by characteristic odor |
| Benzoic, C$_6$H$_5$COOH | White ppt. C$_6$H$_5$COOAg. Sol. in hot water | | Buff-colored ppt. (CH$_5$COO)FeOH. Sol. in HCl | Dissolves without charring or evolution of gas | Pb(C$_2$H$_3$O$_2$)$_2$. ppts white compound. m.p. 121° sublimes when heated. H$_2$SO$_4$ + C$_2$H$_5$OH heated = ethyl benzoate. |
| Carbolic, C$_6$H$_5$OH | | | Deep violet. Color destroyed by acetic acid (not destroyed in case of salicylic acid) | | Bromine water, even in very dilute solutions, gives a white ppt. sol. in NaOH, KOH. C$_6$H$_5$OH + 1 ml. H$_2$SO$_4$ + NaNO$_2$ warmed = deep green or blue color |
| Citric, C$_3$H$_4$OH-(COOH)$_3$ | White ppt. Sol. in NH$_4$OH. No reduction on heating | White ppt. Less sol. in hot than cold water. Sol. in NH$_4$Cl. Insol. in NaOH. Crystalline form insol. in NH$_4$Cl | | | White ppt. with lead acetate. Sol. in ammonium citrate. Prevents pption. of Fe(OH)$_3$ by alkalies. CdCl$_2$ ppts. Cd(C$_6$H$_5$O$_7$)$_2$. Insol. in hot water. Sol. in acetic acid (Cd salts, no ppt. with tartrates) |
| Formic, HCOOH | White ppt. in conc. solutions. Becomes dark from reduced | | Red ppt. Color destroyed by HCl | With reducing agent heated, gives CO which burns with blue | H$_2$SO$_4$ (conc.) + ethyl alcohol = ethyl formate, pleasant characteristic odor |

| | Metallic Ag from reduction | | | |
|---|---|---|---|---|
| Gallic, $C_6H_2(OH)_3$-COOH | Metallic Ag from reduction | Blue-black ppt. Sol. in excess = green | | Melts at 200°. The alkaline solution absorbs O. Limewater or $Ba(OH)_2$ produces a blue ppt. |
| Lactic, $C_2H_4OH$-COOH | Reduction results. Ag formed (no action on Fehling's sol.) | | Charring on heating with evolution of CO | Decolorizes $KMnO_4$ and effervescence takes place, with odor of acetaldehyde |
| Malic, $C_2H_3OH$-$(COOH)_2$ | White ppt. | White ppt. only in presence of strong alcohol (distinction frcm citric) | | Lead acetate ppts. white salt. Sol. in hot water. Prevents pptn of $Fe(OH)_3$ by alkalies |
| Oxalic, $H_2 \cdot C_2O_4$ | White ppt. Sol. in $HNO_3$, $NH_4OH$ | White ppt. Insol. in acetic acid. Sol. in HCl, $HNO_3$ | Heated, $CO_2$ and CO evolved | $H_2SO_4$ (dilute) + $MnO_2$ gives $CO_2$. Destroys color of $KMnO_4$ when heated with that reagent in presence of dilute $H_2SO_4$ |
| Salicylic, $C_6H_4$-COOH | White ppt. Sol. in hot water, $C_6H_4OHCOOAg$ | Deep violet color. Destroyed by mineral acids | Dissolves. Prolonged heating darkens solution and gas is evolved | Lead acetate ppts. a white salt. Acid m.p. 156°. $HNO_3$ heated with salt produces yellow picric acid. Color is intensified by caustic soda |
| Tannic, $C_{14}H_{10}O_9$ | White ppt. | Blue-black color (ink) | | Lead acetate gives a yellow ppt., with astringent taste. The acid ppts. a solution of glue. Limewater produces a gray ppt. |
| Tartaric, $H_2 \cdot C_4H_4O_6$ | White ppt. Sol. in excess of tartrate, HCl, $NH_4OH$. Reduction on heating | White crystalline ppt. Action similar to magnesium precipitation | | Chars when heated. Odor of burnt sugar. Prevents pption. of $Fe(OH)_3$ by alkalies. |

# TABLES AND USEFUL DATA

## COMPARISON OF CENTIGRADE AND FAHRENHEIT SCALE

| °C. | −100 | −0 | +0 | +100 | +200 | +300 | +400 | +500 | +600 | +700 | +800 | +900 | °C. |
|---|---|---|---|---|---|---|---|---|---|---|---|---|---|
|  | °F. | F. | F. | F. | F. | F. | F. | F. | F. | F. | F. | F. |  |
| 0 | −148 | + 32 | 32 | +212 | 392 | 572 | 752 | 932 | 1112 | 1292 | 1472 | 1652 | 0 |
| 5 | −157 | + 23 | 41 | 221 | 401 | 581 | 761 | 941 | 1121 | 1301 | 1481 | 1661 | 5 |
| 10 | −166 | + 14 | 50 | 230 | 410 | 590 | 770 | 950 | 1130 | 1310 | 1490 | 1670 | 10 |
| 15 | −175 | + 5 | 59 | 239 | 419 | 599 | 779 | 959 | 1139 | 1319 | 1499 | 1679 | 15 |
| 20 | −184 | − 4 | 68 | 248 | 428 | 608 | 788 | 968 | 1148 | 1328 | 1508 | 1688 | 20 |
| 25 | −193 | − 13 | 77 | 257 | 437 | 617 | 797 | 977 | 1157 | 1337 | 1517 | 1697 | 25 |
| 30 | −202 | − 22 | 86 | 266 | 446 | 626 | 806 | 986 | 1166 | 1346 | 1526 | 1706 | 30 |
| 35 | −211 | − 31 | 95 | 275 | 455 | 635 | 815 | 995 | 1175 | 1355 | 1535 | 1715 | 35 |
| 40 | −220 | − 40 | 104 | 284 | 464 | 644 | 824 | 1004 | 1184 | 1364 | 1544 | 1724 | 40 |
| 45 | −229 | − 49 | 113 | 293 | 473 | 653 | 833 | 1013 | 1193 | 1373 | 1553 | 1733 | 45 |
| 50 | −238 | − 58 | 122 | 302 | 482 | 662 | 842 | 1022 | 1202 | 1382 | 1562 | 1742 | 50 |
| 55 | −247 | − 67 | 131 | 311 | 491 | 671 | 851 | 1031 | 1211 | 1391 | 1571 | 1751 | 55 |
| 60 | −256 | − 76 | 140 | 320 | 500 | 680 | 860 | 1040 | 1220 | 1400 | 1580 | 1760 | 60 |
| 65 | −265 | − 85 | 149 | 329 | 509 | 689 | 869 | 1049 | 1229 | 1409 | 1589 | 1769 | 65 |
| 70 | −274 | − 94 | 158 | 338 | 518 | 698 | 878 | 1058 | 1238 | 1418 | 1598 | 1778 | 70 |
| 75 | −283 | −103 | 167 | 347 | 527 | 707 | 887 | 1067 | 1247 | 1427 | 1607 | 1787 | 75 |
| 80 | −292 | −112 | 176 | 356 | 536 | 716 | 896 | 1076 | 1256 | 1436 | 1616 | 1796 | 80 |
| 85 | −301 | −121 | 185 | 365 | 545 | 725 | 905 | 1085 | 1265 | 1445 | 1625 | 1805 | 85 |
| 90 | −310 | −130 | 194 | 374 | 554 | 734 | 914 | 1094 | 1274 | 1454 | 1634 | 1814 | 90 |
| 95 | −319 | −139 | 203 | 383 | 563 | 743 | 923 | 1103 | 1283 | 1463 | 1643 | 1823 | 95 |
| 100 | −328 | −148 | +212 | 392 | 572 | 752 | 932 | 1112 | 1292 | 1472 | 1652 | 1832 | 100 |

| °C. | −200 | −100 | +100 | +200 | +300 | +400 | +500 | +600 | +700 | +800 | +900 | +1000 | °C. |
|---|---|---|---|---|---|---|---|---|---|---|---|---|---|

| C° | 1100 | 1200 | 1300 | 1400 | 1500 | 1600 | 1700 | 1800 | 1900 | 2000 |
|---|---|---|---|---|---|---|---|---|---|---|
| F° | 2012 | 2192 | 2372 | 2552 | 2732 | 2912 | 3092 | 3272 | 3452 | 3632 |

Degrees C. × 1.8 + 32 = Degrees F.        Degrees F. − 32 ÷ 1.8 = Degrees C.

Absolute zero, −273 °C. = −459 °F.

## COMPARISON OF CENTIGRADE AND FAHRENHEIT SCALE FOR EVERY 1°C. FROM 0° TO 100° C.

| C. | 0 | 10 | 20 | 30 | 40 | 50 | 60 | 70 | 80 | 90 | C. |
|----|----|----|----|----|----|----|----|----|----|----|----|
|   | F. | F. | F. | F. | F. | F. | F. | F. | F. | F. |   |
| 0 | 32 | 50 | 68 | 86 | 104 | 122 | 140 | 158 | 176 | 194 | 0 |
| 1 | 33.8 | 51.8 | 69.8 | 87.8 | 105.8 | 123.8 | 141.8 | 159.8 | 177.8 | 195.8 | 1 |
| 2 | 35.6 | 53.6 | 71.6 | 89.6 | 107.6 | 125.6 | 143.6 | 161.6 | 179.6 | 197.6 | 2 |
| 3 | 37.4 | 55.4 | 73.4 | 91.4 | 109.4 | 127.4 | 145.4 | 163.4 | 181.4 | 199.4 | 3 |
| 4 | 39.2 | 57.2 | 75.2 | 93.2 | 111.2 | 129.2 | 147.2 | 165.2 | 183.2 | 201.2 | 4 |
| 5 | 41.0 | 59 | 77 | 95 | 113 | 131 | 149 | 167 | 185 | 203 | 5 |
| 6 | 42.8 | 60.8 | 78.8 | 96.8 | 114.8 | 132.8 | 150.8 | 168.8 | 186.8 | 204.8 | 6 |
| 7 | 44.6 | 62.6 | 80.6 | 98.6 | 116.6 | 134.6 | 152.6 | 170.6 | 188.6 | 206.6 | 7 |
| 8 | 46.4 | 64.4 | 82.4 | 100.4 | 118.4 | 136.4 | 154.4 | 172.4 | 190.4 | 208.4 | 8 |
| 9 | 48.2 | 66.2 | 84.2 | 102.2 | 120.2 | 138.2 | 156.2 | 174.2 | 192.2 | 210.2 | 9 |
| C. | 9 | 19 | 29 | 39 | 49 | 59 | 69 | 79 | 89 | 99 | C. |

100 °C. = 212 °F.

# COMPARISON OF METRIC AND CUSTOMARY UNITS (U. S.)

## LENGTH

| | |
|---|---|
| 1 millimeter, mm. = 0.03937 inch. | 1 inch = 25.4001 millimeters. |
| 1 centimeter, cm. = 0.39371 inch. | 1 inch = 2.54001 centimeters. |
| 1 meter, m.  = 3.28083 feet. | 1 foot = 0.304801 meter. |
| 1 meter  = 1.09361 yards. | 1 yard = 0.914402 meter. |
| 1 kilometer  = 0.62137 (U. S.) mile. | 1 mile = 1.60935 kilometers. |

## AREAS

| | |
|---|---|
| 1 square millimeter, sq. mm. = 0.00155 sq. in. | 1 sq. in. = 645.16 sq. mm. |
| 1 square centimeter, sq. cm. = 0.1550 sq. in. | 1 sq. in. = 6.452 sq. cm. |
| 1 square meter, sq. m.  = 10.764 sq. ft. | 1 sq. ft. = 0.0929 sq. m. |
| 1 square meter  = 1.196 sq. yd. | 1 sq. yd. = 0.8361 sq. m. |
| 1 square kilometer  = 0.3861 sq. mi. | 1 sq. mi. = 2.5900 sq. km. |
| 1 hectare  = 2.471 acres. | 1 acre = 0.4047 hectare. |

## VOLUMES

| | |
|---|---|
| 1 cubic millimeter, cu. mm. = 0.000061 in. | 1 cu. in. = 16,387.2 cu. mm. |
| 1 milliliter, ml.  = 0.06103 cu. in. | 1 cu. in. = 16.3872 ml. |
| 1 cubic meter  = 35.314 cu. ft. | 1 cu. ft. = 0.02832 cu. m. |
| 1 cubic meter  = 61,028 cu. in. | 1 cu. ft. = 28.32 liters |
| 1 cubic meter  = 1.3079 cu. yd. | 1 cu. yd. = 0.7645 cu. m. |

## CAPACITIES

| | |
|---|---|
| 1 milliliter, ml. = 0.03381 (U. S.) liquid ounce. | 1 ounce = 29.574 ml. |
| 1 milliliter = 0.2705 (U. S.) apothecaries' dram. | 1 dram = 3.6967 ml. |
| | 1 scruple = 1.2322 ml. |
| 1 milliliter = 0.8115 (U. S.) apothecaries' scruple. | 1 quart = 0.94636 liter. |
| | 1 gallon = 3.78543 liters. |
| 1 liter = 1.05668 (U. S.) liquid quarts. | 1 peck = 8.80982 liters. |
| 1 liter = 0.26417 (U. S.) gallon. | 1 bushel = 0.35239 hectoliter. |
| 1 liter = 0.11351 (U. S.) peck. | |
| 1 hectoliter = 2.83774 (U. S.) bushels. | |

## MASSES

| | |
|---|---|
| 1 gram = 15.4324 grains. | 1 grain = 0.06480 gram. |
| 1 gram = 0.03527 avoirdupois ounce. | 1 ounce (av.) = 28.3495 grams. |
| 1 gram = 0.03215 troy ounce. | 1 ounce (troy) = 31.10348 grams. |
| 1 kilogram = 2.20462 pounds (av.). | 1 pound (av.) = 0.45359 kilogram. |
| 1 kilogram = 2.67923 pounds (troy). | 1 pound (troy) = 0.37324 kilogram. |

## AVOIRDUPOIS WEIGHT

The system of weights in ordinary use by which common or heavy articles are weighed.

| | | |
|---|---|---|
| 16 drams | = 1 ounce | = 28.35 grams. |
| 16 ounces | = 1 pound | = 453.59 grams. |
| 25 pounds | = 1 quarter | = 11.34 kilograms. |
| 4 quarters | = 1 hundredweight | = 45.359 kilograms. |

1 avoirdupois pound contains 7000 grains.
1 avoirdupois ounce contains 437.5 grains.

### APOTHECARIES' WEIGHT

The system of weights employed in weighing medicines.

| | | | |
|---|---|---|---|
| 1 grain | | = | 0.0648 gram. |
| 20 grains | = 1 scruple | = | 1.296 grams. |
| 3 scruples | = 1 drachm | = | 3.888 grams. |
| 8 drachms | = 1 ounce | = | 31.103 grams. |
| 12 ounces | = 1 pound | = | 373.236 grams. |

1 apothecaries' (or troy) pound contains 5760 grains.
1 apothecaries' (or troy) ounce contains 480 grains

### FLUID MEASURE

| | | | |
|---|---|---|---|
| 1 minim | | = | 0.06161 milliliter. |
| 60 minims | = 1 fluid drachm | = | 3.696 milliliters. |
| 8 fluid drachms | = 1 fluid ounce | = | 29.573 milliliters. |
| 16 fluid ounces | = 1 pint | = | 473.179 milliliters. |
| 8 pints | = 1 gallon | = | 3.785 liters. |

1 gallon contains 231 cubic inches.

# REAGENTS, STANDARD SOLUTIONS
# AND INDICATOR SOLUTIONS *†

**Acid No. 1 (Aluminum Chapter).**—Mix with 350 ml. of water, in order, 250 ml. of (1:1) $H_2SO_4$, 200 ml. of concentrated $HNO_3$, and 200 ml. of concentrated HCl.

**Acid No. 2 (Aluminum Chapter).**—Add 400 ml. of concentrated $HNO_3$ to 600 ml. of (2:1) $H_2SO_4$.

**Acid No. 3 (Aluminum Chapter).**—Mix with 425 ml. of $H_2O$, in order, 200 ml. of (1:1) $H_2SO_4$, 125 ml. of concentrated $H_3PO_4$, and 250 ml. of concentrated $HNO_3$.

**Alizarin-S Solution.**—Dissolve 0.020 g. of sodium alizarinmonosulfonate (alizarin-S) in water, add 100 ml. of the dilute acidified thorium nitrate solution, and 14.3 ml. of $N$ hydrochloric acid and make up to 200 ml. Two ml. of this solution added to 50 ml. of fluorine-free water and 10 ml. of 2 $N$ sodium chloride solution in a Nessler tube should give the correct end-point color; if not impurities in the salt or other chemicals may be responsible and the proportion of the dilute standard thorium nitrate solution used should be modified accordingly. The color should be judged when making this solution for it is likely to alter on standing.

**Alkaline Tartrate Solution.**—See Tartrate Solution.

**Aluminon Solution.**—Ammonium salt of aurin tricarboxylic acid $C_{22}H_{23}O_9N_3$, mol. wt. 473.44. A 0.1% solution of the substance in water is used as reagent. The lake is formed in faintly acid solution (acetic acid acetate buffer) then ammonia and ammonium carbonate are added. Iron and phosphate should be absent. Beryllium gives a lake similar to the red one formed by aluminum. See the Chapter on Aluminum.

**Aluminum Chloride Standard Solution (1 ml. = 0.01 mg. Al).**—Dissolve 0.100 g. of pure aluminum metal in 20 ml. of HCl (1:1). Transfer to a 500-ml. volumetric flask, add 100 ml. of HCl and make to volume. Pipette 25 ml. into a 500-ml. volumetric flask and make to volume.

**Amine-Sulfuric Acid Stock Solution.**—Add 50 ml. of concentrated sulfuric acid to 30 ml. of water and cool. Add 12 g. of $N,N$-dimethyl-$p$-phenylenediamine. Stir until solution is complete.

**1-Amino-2-Naphthol-4-Sulfonic Acid Solution (ANSA Solution).**—In 100 ml. of water, dissolve 15 g. of sodium bisulfite and 0.5 g. of sodium sulfite. Then add 0.25 g. of 1-amino-2-naphthol-4-sulfonic acid and let stand, shaking periodically. If not clear after several hours, filter. Store in dark-glass bottle.

**Ammonia-Cyanide Solution.**—Each liter of mixture contains 20 g. of potassium cyanide (200 ml. purified 10% potassium cyanide) and 150 ml. lead-free ammonium hydroxide, or its equivalent; it is brought to volume with double-distilled water. This solution should be kept in a cool place.

---

* This table gives the more generally used reagents and standard solutions. Special variants for more limited use are described under the particular method.

† For pH indicators, see Chapter on Hydrogen.

**Ammonia-Sodium Nitrate Solution.**—Dissolve 200 ml. of 28% ammonia water and 100 g. of sodium nitrate in water and dilute with water to 1 liter.

**Ammonium Acetate Solution (70%).**—Use the salt, or add cautiously 1000 ml. of ammonium hydroxide to 1200 ml. of glacial acetic acid.

**Ammonium Benzoate Solution.**—Dissolve 100 g. of pure ammonium benzoate $(NH_4C_7H_5O_2)$ in 1 liter of warm water and add 1 mg. of thymol as preservative.

**Ammonium Carbonate Solution.**—250 g. of powdered salt per liter of solution, containing 100 ml. of concentrated ammonia. The solution contains approximately 22% of $(NH_4)_2CO_3 \cdot NH_4CO_2NH_2$.

**Ammonia Chloride Solution.**—Dissolve 3.82 g. of ammonium chloride in 1 liter of distilled water. Dilute 10 ml. of this solution to 1 liter with ammonia-free water. 1 ml. = 0.00001 g. of nitrogen.

**Ammonium Citrate Solution for Colorimetric Lead Determination.**—Dissolve 400 g. of citric acid in water, and add sufficient reagent ammonium hydroxide to make the solution alkaline to phenol red. Dilute the solution to 1 liter with water and purify by shaking it with repeated portions of a solution of dithizone in chloroform until the dithizone retains its original green color. Remove excess dithizone by repeated extractions with chloroform.

Sodium citrate may be used in place of citric acid, thus eliminating the necessity of neutralizing with ammonium hydroxide. The solution is purified with dithizone as described in the preparation of ammonium citrate.

**Ammonium Mercuric Thiocyanate Solution.**—Dissolve 68 g. of ammonium thiocyanate and 54 g. of mercuric chloride in 500 ml. of water, add 5 ml. of (1:1) hydrochloric acid, and allow to stand overnight. Filter and dilute to 1 liter.

**Ammonium Molybdate Solution.**—(1) 100 g. of pure molybdic acid are thoroughly mixed with 400 ml. of cold distilled water and 80 ml. of concentrated ammonia are added. When solution is complete, pour the ammonium molybdate slowly and with constant stirring into a mixture of 400 ml. of concentrated nitric acid and 500 ml. of distilled water. This order of procedure should be followed, since a difficultly soluble oxide of molybdenum is formed if the nitric acid is poured into the ammonium molybdate, and filtration will be necessary. Fifty mg. (0.05 g.) of microcosmic salt dissolved in a little water, are added to clarify the reagent; the precipitate is agitated, then allowed to settle for 24 hours and the clear solution is decanted through a filter into a large reagent bottle.

(2) 4.75 g. of the salt are dissolved and made up to 1 liter. One ml. is equivalent to approximately 1% of Pb if a half gram sample is weighed for analysis. Used in lead determinations.

**Ammonium Persulfate Solution.**—Dissolve 300 g. of ammonium persulfate in 100 ml. of water.

**Ammonium Polysulfide Solution (Yellow).**—To an Ammonium Sulfide Solution made according to the direction given for that reagent, add 75 g. of flowers of sulfur and shake thoroughly.

**Ammonium Sebacate Solution (50 mg. per liter).**—Dissolve 50 g. of sebacic acid $[COOH(CH_2)_8COOH]$ in 400 ml. of $NH_4OH$ and 300 ml. of water. Filter, dilute to 1 liter with water, and mix. Store in a polyethylene bottle.

**Ammonium Sulfate, Alcoholic Solution.**—Dissolve 1 g. of ammonium sulfate in 20 ml. of distilled water and add slowly, with stirring, 100 ml. of 95% ethanol. Remove, by filtering, the excess ammonium sulfate that precipitates and to the clear filtrate add a few crystals to keep the solution saturated.

**Ammonium Sulfate Solution.**—Dissolve 5 g. of reagent grade ammonium sulfate in 100 ml. of distilled water.

**Ammonium Sulfide Solution (Colorless).**—Saturate 750 ml. of concentrated ammonia with hydrogen sulfide gas and add 500 ml. of concentrated ammonia and 1000 ml. of water.

**Ammonium Tartrate Solution.**—Dissolve 30 g. of ammonium tartrate $(NH_4)_2(C_4H_4O_6)$ in 500 ml. of water, add 120 ml. of $NH_4OH$ and dilute to one liter.

**Ammonium Thiocyanate Solution.**—See entry entitled "Potassium or Ammonium Thiocyanate Solution."

**Antimony Chloride Solution.**—Six grams of reagent-grade pulverized antimony are dissolved in 500 ml. of concentrated hydrochloric acid together with 100 ml. of saturated bromine solution. After expelling excess bromine by boiling, about 200 ml. of concentrated hydrochloric acid are added and the solution is made homogeneous at 1 liter. Fifty ml. equals 0.3 g. of antimony.

**Antimony Potassium Tartrate Solution.**—A stock solution is made up by weighing out 0.553 g. of $KSbOC_4H_4O_6$ which is dissolved in distilled water and diluted to 2000 ml. which represents 0.0001 g. Sb per ml.

From the above stock solution take 100 ml. and make up to 1000 ml.; this solution now contains 0.00001 g. Sb per ml., and it is used for making standard stains and for color comparison purposes.

**Arsenious Oxide Standard.**—Obtainable from the National Bureau of Standards. The reagent grade article may be further purified, if qualitative tests prove this to be necessary, by dissolving the oxide in hot HCl, filtering the hot saturated solution, cooling, decanting, washing the oxide free of acid, drying and finally subliming. Used in preparing Arsenic Standard Solution and Sodium Arsenite Standard Solution.

**Arsenic Standard Solution.**—One gram of resublimed arsenious oxide, $As_2O_3$, is dissolved in 25 ml. of 20% sodium hydroxide solution (arsenic free) and neutralized with dilute sulfuric acid. Dilute with fresh distilled water to which 10 ml. of concentrated $H_2SO_4$ have been added, to a volume of 1000 ml. Ten ml. of this solution is again diluted to 1 liter with the distilled water plus 1% sulfuric acid. One ml. of the final solution contains 0.001 mg. of $As_2O_3$. Used in arsenic determinations by Gutzeit and Marsh methods.

**Barium Carrier Solution.**—Dissolve 0.250 g. of barium chloride in water and make up to 10.0 ml.

**Barium Chloride Solution.**—For sulfate determinations; 5% solution of the anhydrous salt or a 6% solution of the crystals.

**Barium Diphenylaminesulfonate Indicator.**—Dissolve 0.5 g. of reagent in 100 ml. of water and filter.

**α-Benzoin Oxime Solution.**—Dissolve 2 g. of the reagent in 100 ml. of alcohol. In ammoniacal tartrate solution the reagent separates copper from Co, Ni, Fe, Al, Pb; the precipitate $Cu(C_{14}H_{11}O_2N)$ contains 22.01% Cu if dried at 110°C. In acid solution the reagent precipitates only Mo(VI), W, Pd, Cr(VI), V(V) and Ta. Chromium and vanadium do not interfere if reduced to the tri- and tetravalent states, respectively. A solution containing 5% of sulfuric acid by volume is preferable. The molybdenum precipitate is carefully charred while moist in a platinum crucible, and the oxide, $MoO_3$, is brought to constant weight after heating at 500–525°C. in a muffle.

Copper is precipitated from hot ammoniacal solution. A maximum of about

0.05 g. of copper should be present and 10 ml. of reagent (0.2 g.) should be required. The voluminous green precipitate is collected on a weighed filtering crucible, washed thoroughly with hot 1% ammonia and finally with 2 or 3 small portions of hot alcohol to remove any excess of reagent. The precipitate is dried to constant weight at 110°C.

**Beryllium Standard Solution for Be in Atmosphere.**—Dissolve sufficient beryllium powder of known assay in a small quantity of (1:1) $H_2SO_4$ so that when made up to 1 liter, the strength will be such that 1 ml. equals 100 micrograms. After the initial reaction between beryllium and the acid, it is usually necessary to boil the liquid to get all beryllium into solution.

**Beryllium Sulfate Solution for Standardizing 1 N Sulfuric Acid.**—Using beryllium metal of known assay (99% Be or better, with low Al content) make up an ample quantity of stock solution such that each 50 ml. will contain 0.2 g. of Be. Use 20 ml. of (1:1) $H_2SO_4$ for each gram of metal to be dissolved, boiling thoroughly, filtering, cooling, and making up to volume (at 20°C.) with boiled and cooled distilled water. The temperature of the solution in the flask should be adjusted to 20°C. prior to removal (by standardized 50-ml. pipette) of aliquot portions for titration. Using a 25-ml. aliquot portion, the Be content and the Al content of the standard $BeSO_4$ solution are predetermined, preferably in triplicate, by the gravimetric BeO and quinolate methods. The corrected Be content plus ½ the Al content of the solution gives the standard beryllium equivalent value to the 25-ml. aliquot portion taken. This sum doubled gives the beryllium equivalent per 50 ml. of standard $BeSO_4$ solution.

**Bis-(2-hydroxyethyl) dithiocarbamate Solution.**—Dissolve 4.0 g. of diethanolamine and 1 ml. of $CS_2$ in 40 ml. of methanol. Prepare fresh every three or four days.

**Bismuth Nitrate Standard Solution.**—One gram of metallic bismuth is dissolved in the least amount of (1:1) nitric acid that is necessary to keep it in solution and diluted to 1000 ml. in a calibrated flask. One hundred ml. of this solution is diluted to 1000 ml. One ml. of this diluted solution contains 0.0001 g. of bismuth.

**Bismuth Sulfate Standard Solution (Equivalent to 0.1 mg. Bismuth per ml.)**—Dissolve 0.100 g. of bismuth metal in nitric acid. Add 50 ml. of (1:1) sulfuric acid and evaporate to sulfur trioxide fumes. Cool and dilute to exactly 1 liter.

**Boron Standard Stock Solution (1 ml. = 0.05 mg. B).**—Dissolve 0.1430 g. of boric acid ($H_3BO_3$) in water and dilute to 500.0 ml. Store in a polyethylene bottle.

**Boron Standard Dilute Solution (1 ml. = 1 microgram B).**—Dilute 10 ml. of the Boron Stock Solution to 500 ml. Store in a polyethylene bottle.

**Bromine $CCl_4$ Solution.**—An approximate N/3 solution of bromine is made by dissolving 26.6 g. of bromine in 1 liter of carbon tetrachloride.

**Bromine-Hydrochloric Acid Solution, Saturated.**—500 ml. of concentrated hydrochloric acid saturated with 70 ml. of bromine.

**Bromine-Potassium Bromide Solution.**—320 g. of potassium bromide are dissolved in water barely sufficient to cause solution and mixed with 200 ml. of bromine, the latter being poured into the saturated bromide solution. After mixing well the solution is diluted to 2000 ml. Used for sulfur determinations.

**Brucine Sulfate Solution.**—Dissolve 2 g. of brucine sulfate in 100 ml. of a 5% solution of acetic acid. Warm to 60° to 70°C. if necessary, to dissolve the crystals.

**n-Butyl Alcohol.**—Reagent grade, having a boiling range of 116° to 117.7°C., prepared by fractional distillation of the reagent (sp. gr. 0.8065 at 25°/4°C.) preferably dried by refluxing over metallic calcium.

*n*-Butyl Alcohol Containing 20% HCl.—Prepared by passing dry HCl gas into the *n*-butyl alcohol. Prepare a dilute solution containing 6–7% HCl by diluting 40 ml. of the 20% solution with 100 ml. of *n*-butyl alcohol.

Cadmium Chloride Standard Solution.—Prepare a stock solution so that the cadmium concentration is approximately 1000 p. p. m. Pipette 25.00 ml. of the stock solution into an electrolytic beaker and make alkaline to phenolphthalein indicator with NaOH. Add 10% sodium or potassium cyanide dropwise until the precipitate of $Cd(OH)_2$ just dissolves. Dilute the solution to 100 ml. with water, and electrolyze for 30 minutes at a current density of 0.6 amp. per sq. dm., then for 30 minutes more at 1.2 amp. per sq. dm. Test for complete deposition by passing $H_2S$ through a small sample of the electrolyte. If a yellow precipitate or color forms, continue the electrolysis until no cadmium remains in solution. Wash the plated platinum cathode in ethanol, dry at 110°C. for 3–5 minutes, cool, and weigh. Dissolve the cadmium in $H_2SO_4$ (1:1), wash the electrode, dry, and weigh as before. The difference in weight is the amount of cadmium present in the aliquot taken. If $Cd(NO_3)_2$ is used instead of $CdCl_2$, the sample taken for electrolysis must be fumed with $H_2SO_4$ to remove the nitrate.

Calcium Carrier Solution.—Dissolve 3.75 g. of calcium chloride in water, and make up volume to 10.0 ml.

Calcium Chloride Acid Solution.—Saturate a mixture of 90 parts of water and 10 parts concentrated HCl with calcium chloride.

Calcium Hydroxide Solution (Lime Water).—A saturated solution of $Ca(OH)_2$. Keep tightly stoppered; decant or filter before use.

Calcium Hydroxide Suspension.—Calcine low-boron calcium carbonate ($CaCO_3$) in a platinum crucible at 1100°C. to the oxide, and cool in a desiccator. Transfer 3 g. of the oxide to a polyethylene bottle, add 500 ml. of water, and mix. Shake frequently when using to insure that the suspension withdrawn is uniform.

Calcium Standard Solution, 0.05 *M*.—Weigh 5.0050 g. of primary standard calcium carbonate and transfer it to a 400-ml. beaker. Add 50 ml. of water and dissolve in 10.6 ml. of HCl, added in small increments. When the dissolution is complete, boil the solution to remove carbon dioxide. Cool the solution to room temperature, transfer to a 1-liter volumetric flask, and dilute to volume with water.

Ceric Perchlorate Standard Solution (1 ml. = 1.00 mg. Ce).—Transfer 0.614 g. of freshly ignited, 99.9% ceric oxide ($CeO_2$) to a 250-ml. beaker and add 50 ml. of water. Add 10 ml. of $HClO_4$, 1 ml. of 30% hydrogen peroxide, and cover with a ribbed watch glass. Heat on a hot plate to effect dissolution, add more hydrogen peroxide if necessary. Evaporate the solution to incipient dryness on the hot plate, then cool. Rinse the walls of the beaker first with ten ml. of $HClO_4$ and then with water, and re-evaporate to incipient dryness to remove the last traces of hydrogen peroxide. Cool, rinse the walls of the beaker with 15 ml. of $HClO_4$ and boil 3 minutes to dissolve cerium perchlorate. Cool, wash the watch glass and beaker walls with water, transfer the solution to a 500-ml. volumetric flask and dilute to volume with water.

Ceric Sulfate Standard Solution.—The solution must contain enough sulfuric acid to prevent hydrolysis. For 0.1 N solutions prepared from the sulfate, the double sulfates, the oxide or from hexanitrato ammonium cerate the concentration of the acid should be 0.51–1 N. The following procedures give 1 liter of 0.1 N solution: (*a*) Dissolve 0.1 mole = 33.22 g. anhydrous ceric sulfate in 0.5–1 N sulfuric acid and make up to 1 liter with the acid. (*b*) Dissolve 63.24 g. of $Ce(SO_4)_2 \cdot 2(NH_4)_2SO_4 \cdot 2H_2O$ in 0.5–1 N sulfuric acid and dilute to 1 liter with the acid.

(*c*) Dissolve 17.21 g. of pure $CeO_2$ or an equivalent amount of impure oxide in enough sulfuric acid to make the final acid concentration 1 $N$ or slightly under. Pure ceric oxide must be heated with hot concentrated sulfuric acid in excess to convert it into the sulfate; the latter dissolves upon dilution of the solution. Crude oxide is transposed to the sulfate by heating at 120°C. with 1:1 sulfuric acid. (*d*) Dissolve 54.82 g. of $(NH_4)_2Ce(NO_3)_6$ in 0.5–1 $N$ $H_2SO_4$ and make up to 1 liter with the acid. If applications are anticipated in which nitrate would interfere, the nitrate may be expelled by evaporating and heating to fumes of sulfur trioxide before diluting to the final volume.

If the solution prepared in any of the foregoing ways deposits insoluble matter, the latter should be removed by filtration. Hexanitrate ammonium cerate gives promise of being obtainable 99.9% pure or better; the other substances are not readily obtainable in a state of purity at present.

*Standardization Against Arsenious Oxide. Gleu's Procedure.*—To the solution of the arsenious oxide in sodium hydroxide is added enough sulfuric acid to make 20 ml. of 5 $N$ after neutralizing the alkali. Add 0.15 ml. of 0.01 $M$ osmium tetroxide (0.2542 g. $OsO_4$ in 100 ml. of 0.1 $N$ sulfuric acid) and 3 drops of 0.01 $M$ 1,10-phenanthroline ferrous sulfate indicator, and dilute to 100 ml. Titrate with ceric sulfate to a sharp change from red to pale blue. Free HCl is not harmful up to 0.1 $N$ concentration. The end point is sharper in sulfuric acid solution.

If osmium tetroxide is not available use 5 ml. of 0.005 $M$ iodine monochloride catalyst, and have 20 ml. of concentrated HCl present per 100 ml. of the arsenic solution. Use chloroform or carbon tetrachloride as indicating layer (5 ml.) and titrate to the disappearance of the iodine color from the layer of solvent. Alternatively, the solution may be titrated using *o*-phenanthroline ferrous sulfate indicator and ICl catalyst, heating to 50°C. toward the end of the titration. The color should not return within 1 minute at this temperature if the end point has been reached.

Sodium oxalate may be used as a primary standard, and the conditions of titration are as described at the end of the last paragraph (ICl catalyst; temperature 50°C.).

Other good standard substances are pure electrolytic iron, the reduced solution of a sample of standard iron ore, the solution of pure dried potassium ferrocyanide, etc. In these latter instances diphenylamine, *o*-phenanthroline ferrous sulfate, erio green, etc., may be used as indicators.

The applications of standard ceric sulfate are very numerous and include the direct or indirect determination of the following: Sb, As, Pb, Ca, Cr, Fe, $Fe(CN)_6{}^{-4}$, K, Cu, Mo, Na, $NO_2{}^-$, Hg$^-$, $H_2TeO_3$, Tl, $S_2O_3{}^{-2}$, Ti, U, V, Sn, I$^-$, and many organic acids hydroquinones, and other substances. One of the best applications of the reagent is in the titration of ferrous iron in the presence of HCl, $SnCl_4$ and $Hg_2Cl_2$ after reduction by stannous chloride. The indicators erio green, erio glaucine and *o*-phenanthroline ferrous sulfate are especially suitable for this titration.

**Chromic Sulfate Standard Solution (Equivalent to 0.01 mg. Chromium per ml.).**— Weigh 74.7 mg. of potassium chromate into a 2-liter volumetric flask, dissolve in water, add 10 ml. of (1:1) sulfuric acid, and 0.5% hydrogen peroxide drop by drop. Destroy the excess peroxide by adding potassium permanganate (10 g. per liter) to a faint pink color. Dilute to 2 liters. This procedure gives a chromic sulfate solution comparable to filtrate obtained after titrating iron.

**Cinchonine Solution.**—Dissolve 125 g. of the alkaloid in dilute HCl (1 part of acid to 1 of water) and diluting to 1 liter with HCl of the same strength.

**Cinchonine Potassium Iodide Solution.**—10 g. of cinchonine are dissolved by treating with the least amount of nitric acid that is necessary to form a viscous mass and taking up with about 100 ml. of water. The acid is added a drop at a time and an excess must be avoided. Twenty grams of potassium iodide are dissolved separately and the cinchonine solution is added. The resulting mixture is diluted with water to 1000 ml. After allowing the reagent to stand 48 hrs., any precipitate that forms is filtered off and the clear product is ready for use. The reagent preserved in a glass-stoppered bottle keeps indefinitly. It should be filtered free of suspended matter before use.

**Citric Acid Solution.**—One part of acid in 3 parts of water. One hundred ml. of nitric acid should be added to each liter to prevent growth of molds.

**Cobalt Nitrate Solution.**—Weigh 5.00 g. cobalt nitrate, dissolve in water, and make up to 1 liter. Standardize the solution by determining the cobalt electrolytically. One ml. of this solution should contain approximately 1 mg. Co.

**Cobalt Sulfate Solution.**—Dissolve 0.2385 g. $CoSO_4 \cdot 7H_2O$ in water and make up to 1 liter. (1 ml. = 0.05 mg. Co).

**Copper Nitrate Standard Solution.**—(1) (1 ml. = 1.00 mg. Cu). Dissolve 1.0000 mg. of pure copper in 30 ml. of water and 6 ml. of $HNO_3$. When dissolution is complete, boil out all nitrogen oxide fumes, and dilute to 1 liter with water. (2) (1 ml. = 0.01 mg. Cu). Proceed as above with 0.2000 mg. of pure copper, 15 ml. of water and 3 ml. of $HNO_3$. After boiling and diluting to 1 liter, pipette 50 ml. of this solution into a 1-liter flask and dilute with water to 1 liter.

**o-Cresolphthalein Complexone Indicator.**—0.1 g. per 100 ml. of a mixture of 28 ml. of dilute $NH_4OH$ and 72 ml. of water. Prepared fresh each day.

**Cupferron Solution.**—Ammonium $\beta$-nitrosophenylhydroxylamine. $C_6H_5N(NO)\text{-}ONH_4$. The aqueous solution of the reagent is not very stable; it is best to use a fresh cold 5 or 6% solution. (The solution rapidly darkens, but may be used for precipitations for a few days after its preparation.) The reagent is not a specific one, for it gives quantitative or substantial precipitations of the following in acid solutions: Cu, Ag, Pb, Hg, Sn, Fe(III), Ti, Zr, V(V), Nb, Ta, U(VI), Th, Ce, W. Arsenic and antimony are partially precipitated if trivalent, but not if pentavalent. In general the reagent is useful for certain separations, or for determinations after preliminary separations. The precipitates can not be weighed directly, but must be transferred to the corresponding oxides by cautious ignition at the proper temperature.

The chief uses of cupferron are: The separation of iron and other precipitable ions from Al, Cr, Mn, Ni, Zn and phosphoric acid; separation of V(V) from U(VI); separation of Nb and Ta from other substances; the determination of any precipitable element after the preliminary separations have been made.

**Cuprous Chloride, Acid, for Carbon Monoxide.**—Cover the bottom of a two-liter bottle with a layer of copper oxide or "scale" ⅜" deep; place in the bottle a number of pieces of rather stout copper wire reaching from the top to the bottom, and sufficient to make a bundle an inch in diameter; fill the bottle with HCl (1:1). The bottle is shaken occasionally, and when the solution is colorless, or nearly so, it is poured into half-liter reagent bottles, containing copper wire, ready for use. The space left in the stock bottle should be filled immediately with hydrochloric acid (1:1).

By adding copper wire, oxide or acid when necessary, a constant supply of this reagent may be kept on hand.

The absorption capacity of the reagent per ml. is 15 ml. of CO according to Winkler; and 4 ml. according to Hempel.

Care should be taken that the copper wire does not become entirely dissolved and that it extend from the top to the bottom of the bottle; further, the stopper should be greased thoroughly in order to exclude air more completely and thus avoid oxidation of the cuprous salt (indicated by brown color) and weakening of the absorbing power.

**Cuprous Chloride, Ammoniacal, for Carbon Monoxide.**—The preceding acid cuprous chloride is treated with ammonia until a faint odor of the latter is perceptible; copper wire should be kept in the solution just as with the acid reagent. The alkaline solution has the advantage that it can be used when traces of hydrogen chloride might be harmful to subsequent determinations after that of CO, as, for example, in the determination of hydrogen by absorption with palladium. It has the further advantage of not soiling mercury as does the acid reagent.

**Devarda's Alloy.**—Forty-five parts of aluminum, 50 parts of copper and 5 parts of zinc. The aluminum is placed in a Hessian crucible in a furnace until the aluminum begins to melt, copper is now added in small portions until liquified and zinc is then plunged into the molten mixture. The liquid is heated for a few moments, covered and then stirred with an iron rod, allowed to cool slowly with the cover on and the crystallized mass is pulverized.

**Dianthrimide Reagent Solution.**—Dissolve 0.4 g. of 1,1'-dianthrimide in 100 ml. of concentrated sulfuric acid. Store this solution in a lightly stoppered bottle in a desiccator. For use, transfer 5 ml. of the solution to a dry 100-ml. volumetric flask and dilute to the mark with concentrated sulfuric acid.

**Dichlorofluorescein Indicator.**—A 0.1% solution of the sodium salt in water or of the acid in 60–70% alcohol is used. This indicator is well adapted for the determination of chloride.

**Dimercaptothiodiazole Solution.**—The reagent is prepared by the interaction of carbon disulfide and hydrazine hydrate. It is non-specific, but very sensitive for bismuth, copper and lead. Dissolve 0.7 g. in 35 ml. of 0.1 $N$ KOH for use as a reagent.

**$p$-Dimethylaminobenzylidenerhodanine Solution.**—The best solvent for the reagent is acetone. Silver, copper, mercury, gold, platinum and palladium solutions give precipitates with the reagent. A 0.03 g. per 100-ml. solution is used. The reagent is useful for the colorimetric determination of traces of silver. Soft glass should not be used for extremely dilute silver solutions (about 1 p. p. m.) because of adsorption of Ag+ by the vessel.

**Dimethylglyoxime Solution.**—Nickel is the only element that gives a definite weighable compound with the reagent, $Ni(C_4H_7N_2O_2)_2$; palladium may be precipitated quantitatively by the reagent, but the precipitate must be ignited to give the metal. Bismuth, cobalt and certain other ions give delicate color reactions with the reagent. A 1 or 2% solution of the compound in hot alcohol is used as reagent. For details see Chapter on Nickel.

**2,5-Dinitrophenol Indicator Solution.**—Dilute an aliquot of a standard fluoride solution made from sodium fluoride prepared from the purest sodium carbonate and hydrofluoric acid, containing 100 micrograms of fluorine, to 50 ml. with water. Add 10 ml. of 2 $N$ sodium chloride solution, 2 ml. of the acid indicator solution,

20 ml. of the dilute standard thorium nitrate solution, and mix. This color is stable for several hours.

**Diphenylamine Indicator Solution.**—Melt 1 g. of diphenylamine (m.p. 52.9°C.), add 100 ml. of concentrated $H_2SO_4$ and shake the mixture for 15–30 seconds. One to 3 drops (0.05 ml.) of this solution serve for the titration of ferrous solution with potassium dichromate (0.1 $N$) or the reverse. The solution titrated should contain 5 ml. of concentrated $H_2SO_4$ or 10 ml. concentrated HCl per 150–200 ml., and 15 ml. of a mixture of 150 ml. concentrated $H_2SO_4$ and 150 ml. concentrated $H_3PO_4$, sp. gr. 1.7 per liter. Knop gave 0.05 ml. as the correction to be subtracted from the volume of the 0.1 $N$ dichromate. This was not confirmed by Brennecke who found no correction.

The correction depends upon the conditions of reaction; the amounts of correction for very dilute solutions have been determined and tabulated. The uncertainty of the correction may be avoided by using oxidized indicator solution. A 0.1% solution of the indicator is prepared by dissolving 0.1 g. in 10 ml. of concentrated $H_2SO_4$ and adding 90 ml. of glacial acetic acid. The equivalent of 100 ml. of 0.01 $M$ indicator is oxidized with 25 ml. of 0.1 $N$ $K_2Cr_2O_7$ after dilution to 300 ml. After the oxidizing agent has been slowly added, 8 ml. of 0.1 $N$ ferrous sulfate are added. The resulting green solution is allowed to stand 3–4 days and the solution is siphoned away from the green precipitate which is the oxidized indicator. Centrifuging is effective for recovery of the product. The green precipitate is shaken with 100 ml. of water. Then 0.5 ml. of this suspension is equivalent in coloring power to 0.3 ml. of 0.01 $M$ indicator. Such indicator solution gives a reliable blank or correction in titrations of chromium and vanadium with 0.025 $N$ $FeSO_4$, 0.03 ml. of reagent per 0.1 ml. of indicator.

**Diphenylaminesulfonic Acid Solution.**—Mix 0.512 g. of the barium salt in 125 ml. water with 0.117 g. of anhydrous $Na_2SO_4$ in a little water. Filter off the barium sulfate and dilute the filtrate to 250 ml. The solution is 0.006 $M$. Unknown and standard nitrate solutions should contain from 0.1–5 mg. nitrate and 10 g. KCl per liter. To 10 ml. of nitrate-KCl solution is added 10 ml. concentrated $H_2SO_4$ and after cooling, 0.1 ml. of 0.006 $M$ sodium diphenylamine sulfonate. The colors are compared. The procedure is empirical and is a test for oxidizing power. A pretreatment of the solution to be tested with ammonium chloride is necessary if nitrite is present. A 100-ml. sample of solution plus 0.5 g. $NH_4Cl$ is boiled down to 25 ml. and made up to the original volume after adding 0.5 g. KCl.

**Diphenylcarbazide Solution.**—Dissolve 0.2 g. of the compound in 10 ml. of glacial acetic acid and dilute to 100 ml. with 95% alcohol. The reagent is unstable and should be prepared daily or every few days (latter for Cr test). For chromate, 25 ml. of the solution to be tested is treated with 2 ml. of the reagent. If the chromate solution contains a slight amount of acetic acid, as little as 1 part of chromate in $71 \times 10^6$ parts of solution can be detected. The color is violet for small amounts and reddish for large. Cadmium, copper and mercury give similar colors in neutral solution.

**Dithizone Solution.**—Diphenylthiocarbazone. Stock solution: 0.1 g. dithizone in 100 ml. of chloroform. The reagent may be used for the sensitive detection of Pb, Zn, Hg, Ag, Sn, Cd, Cu, Co, Ni, Mn, Tl, Bi. Only Pb, Tl and Bi are extracted from an ammoniacal cyanide solution by the reagent. In the absence of interfering ions the reagent is very sensitive for zinc.

**Dithizone (Extraction) Standard Solution.**—One liter of chloroform is shaken with 100 ml. of water containing about 0.5 g. hydroxylamine hydrochloride, which has been made alkaline to phenol red with ammonium hydroxide. The chloroform is drained off and 40 mg. of dithizone are dissolved in it. Approximately 5 ml. of alcohol are added to the solution if part of it is to be kept for several days. Filtration is not necessary. The quantity of dithizone solution to be used for one day is shaken with 100 ml. of dilute hydrochloric acid (1 ml. per 100 ml. solution) just before use.

**Dipicrylamine Solution.**—Hexanitrodiphenylamine. The reagent forms slightly soluble salts with K, Rb and Cs, but not with Li, Na, Mg and Ca. The ammonium salt is more soluble than the potassium salt. The magnesium or the sodium salt of dipicrylamine is used as reagent. In the presence of very large quantities of sodium, the potassium salt must be dissolved and reprecipitated.

The commercial ammonium salt is dissolved in hot water, filtered, and the free acid is precipitated with sulfuric acid filtered and washed. The yellow free acid is heated with an aqueous suspension of magnesium carbonate, and the dark red solution is filtered and converted into the sodium salt with concentrated salt solution. Fifty grams of the sodium salt are dissolved in 10 liters of water, impurities allowed to settle, and the free acid is again precipitated by diluted sulfuric acid. The acid is converted into the sodium or magnesium salt of 0.2 to 0.5 $N$ concentration. (Mol. wts. $NaC_{12}H_4O_{12}N_7 = 461.2$; $Mg(C_{12}H_4O_{12}N_7)_2 = 900.72$). Determination: The potassium solution should be neutral; a $25\%$ excess of reagent should be added. The precipitate is collected on a Jena G 4 filtering crucible, transferring the last traces of precipitate to the crucible with ice-cold distilled water, and the precipitate is washed once with the latter, then with a solution of the potassium salt (0.5 g. of $KC_{12}H_4O_{12}N_7$ per liter). Finally it is washed once more with a little ice water, then dried at $100°C.$ for 1 hour. The weight of the precipitate $\times$ 0.08191 gives weight of potassium found.

NOTES.—If the potassium solution contains phosphate the sodium reagent rather than the magnesium one must be used.

Sulfates do not interfere.

The reagent is recovered as follows: The potassium salt is dissolved in acetone, and the free acid is precipitated by adding sulfuric acid (dilute). The precipitate is washed, and transposed into the sodium or the magnesium reagent of proper concentration (0.2 to 0.5 $N$).

**E.D.T.A. Solutions.**—Solutions of the disodium salt of ethylenedinitrilo tetraacetic acid, $Na_2H_2C_{10}H_{12}O_8N_2 \cdot 2H_2O$.

*0.01 M Solution (approx.).*—Dissolve 4.00 g. of the sodium salt and 0.10 g. of magnesium chloride hexahydrate and make up to one liter after adding a few pellets of sodium hydroxide to prevent the eventual separation of the magnesium salt which is very slightly soluble at pH 4. Standardize the solution against aliquots of an accurately prepared solution of calcium made by dissolving 1.000 g. of pure calcium carbonate in a very slight excess of HCl and dilution to a liter. The 0.01 $M$ E.D.T.A. solution is used for the determination of the hardness of water.

*0.05 M E.D.T.A. Solution.*—Dissolve 18.61 g. of the disodium salt and make it homogeneous at a volume of one liter. Standardize against aliquots of a calcium solution prepared by dissolving 5.0050 g. of calcium carbonate, of standardization grade, dissolved in 50 ml. of water plus 10.6 ml. of HCl added in small increments. The solution is boiled to remove carbon dioxide and made up to 1 liter after cooling. The E.D.T.A. is standardized against the calcium solution using cal-red indicator solution.

**Eosin Indicator Solution.**—Dissolve 0.5 g. of the sodium salt, $C_{20}H_4Br_4O_5Na_2$, in 100 ml. of water. Suitable indicator for the titration of bromide, iodide or thiocyanate with silver nitrate.

**Eriochrome Black T Solution.**—Dissolve 1.0 g. of Eriochrome Black T and 1.0 ml. of 1 $N$ sodium carbonate solution in 30 ml. of distilled water, and dilute to 100 ml. with isopropyl alcohol.

**Eriochrome Cyanine R Solution.**—Dissolve 1.80 g. Eriochrome Cyanine R in water and dilute to 200 ml. The National Aniline product labeled "Alizarol Cyanone RC" has been used successfully. With other products, a precipitate sometimes forms when the indicator solution is prepared.

**Ferric Indicator Solution.**—Saturated solution of ferric ammonium alum. If the alum is not available, $FeSO_4$ may be oxidized with nitric acid and evaporated with sulfuric acid to expel nitrous fumes. A 10% solution is desired. Five ml. of either reagent is used per titration. Used in titrating silver by the Volhard method.

**Ferric Nitrate Standard Solution.**—Dissolve 0.1000 g. of electrolytic iron in 50 ml. of (1:3) $HNO_3$, expel oxides of nitrogen by boiling, then dilute to one liter with iron-free distilled water. This solution may be further diluted with 0.2 $M$ $HNO_3$.

**Ferric Phosphate Solution.**—Dissolve 100 g. of $Fe_2(SO_4)_3$ in 1 liter of water to which 150 ml. of $H_3PO_4$ (85%) and 20 ml. of $H_2SO_4$ (1:1) have been added. Add $KMnO_4$ solution (25 g. per l.) until the solution is just tinted pink, due to the excess of $KMnO_4$.

**Ferric Sulfate Solution (Equivalent to 0.1 mg. Fe per ml.).**—Dissolve 0.0250 g. pure iron wire in 25 ml. $H_2SO_4$ (1:1) oxidize with $KMnO_4$ and dilute to exactly 250 ml.

**Ferrous Ammonium Sulfate Standard Solution, 0.1 $N$.**—This solution contains 39.214 g. of $(NH_4)_2SO_4 \cdot FeSO_4 \cdot 6H_2O$ per liter. Dissolve 39.5 g. of the salt in water and add enough sulfuric acid to prevent hydrolysis (as much as 10 ml. per liter may be present). Relatively permanent solutions may be prepared by storing them under hydrogen, nitrogen, or carbon dioxide. Standardize by titration with standard dichromate, permanganate or ceric sulfate solution.

**Ferrous Sulfate, Standard Solution.**

*A. Reagent to Be Used in Titration of Nitric Acid in Sulfuric Acid, Oleum, etc.*—176.5 g. of $FeSO_4 \cdot 7H_2O$ are dissolved in 400 ml. of water and 500 ml. of 60% $H_2SO_4$ (1 vol. of 66° Bé acid per 1 vol. of $H_2O$) are added with constant stirring and the solution, cooled if necessary, is made up to 1000 ml. One ml. is equivalent to approximately 0.02 g. $HNO_3$, the exact value being determined by standardization.

*B. Reagent for Titration of Nitric in Phosphoric or Arsenic Acid.*—This ferrous sulfate solution is made by dissolving 264.7 g. $FeSO_4 \cdot 7H_2O$ in 500 ml. of water; 50 ml. of concentrated $H_2SO_4$ are added and the solution is made up to 1000 ml. The exact concentration is determined by titrating a known amount of nitric acid in phosphoric or arsenic acid, warming to 40 or 50°C.

**Fluorescein Indicator Solution.**—A 0.2% solution of sodium fluoresceinate (Uranine) in water, or 0.2% solution of fluorescein in alcohol is used. Used in the titration of chloride, bromide or iodide with silver.

**Hydrogen Peroxide Solution, 30%.**—If this is not available sodium peroxide added to sulfuric acid will serve for many of its applications.

**8-Hydroxyquinoline (Orthohydroxyquinoline).**—Triturate 2.5 g. of the reagent with 5 ml. of glacial acetic acid and made up to 100 ml. with hot water. After cooling and filtering the reagent is 0.15–0.2 $M$; 1 ml. of it should precipitate about 1.5 mg. of Al; 2.25 mg. of Mg, etc.

The reagent is used at present primarily for separation and determination of Al, Be, Mg, Zn, Cd and Bi, but it is nonspecific and precipitates many other ions under various conditions. In mineral acid solutions no ions are precipitated by the reagent. In acetic acid-acetate buffer the reagent precipitates: Bi, Cd, Cu, Al and Zn. (Also precipitated in acetic acid solution: Ag, Pb, Hg(ic), Sb(III or V), Fe(ous or -ic), Ti, Zr, Mn, Co, Ni, U, V, Ta, Nb). In ammoniacal and in sodium hydroxide solution nearly all of the elements that are precipitated in acid solution are also insoluble, and in addition Mg, Be, Ca, Sr, Ba, etc. are precipitated. The reagent is very useful in the separation of Al from Be or Mg. In ammoniacal solution or in ammoniacal peroxide solution Al may be separated from phosphate, pervanadate, permolybdate, pertitanate, pertantalate, perniobate, arsenate, fluoride and borate.

**Indium Chloride Solution (1 ml. = 2.0 mg. In).**—Dissolve 2.00 g. of pure indium metal in 25 ml. of water and a minimum of HCl. Mild heating and a few drops of $HNO_3$ will aid in dissolving the metal. Dilute to 1 liter with water and store in a polyethylene bottle.

**Iodine Standard Solution, 0.1 N.**—Dissolve 20–25 g. KI in the minimum volume of water and add 12.7 g. of iodine (resublimed; theoretical amount 12.692 g.) and dilute to 1000 ml. after all of the iodine has been dissolved in the small volume of KI solution. Preserve in a dark bottle or covered bottle, to shield the solution from the action of light.

*Standardization.*—Aliquot portions are titrated with standard thiosulfate or with standard arsenite. Alternatively, separate weighed portions of primary standard arsenious oxide may be dissolved and titrated.

For the determination of tin in tin plate an iodine solution is adjusted so that 1 ml. equals 0.0579 g. of tin. Then if a sample with a total surface of 8 sq. in. is taken, 1 ml. of the iodine solution is equivalent to 0.1 pound of tin per base box. Starch is used as the indicator.

**Iron Standard Solutions.**—(1) A ferric solution, the iron content of which has been determined, is diluted and divided so as to obtain 0.0004 g. of Fe. This is made up to 2 liters with water containing 200 ml. of iron-free $H_2SO_4$. One hundred ml. of this solution, together with 10 ml. of $N$ ammonium thiocyanate solution, is used as a standard. One hundred ml. contain 0.00002 g. of Fe.

Normal ammonium thiocyanate contains 76.1 g. $NH_4CNS$ per liter.

(2) 8.6341 g. of ferric ammonium alum are dissolved in dilute hydrochloric acid and made up to 1 liter. The iron is determined in 100 ml. portions by the dichromate method. One ml. will contain about 0.001 g. of iron.

**Lanthanum Standard Solution (1 ml. = 0.100 mg. La).**—Transfer 0.586 g. of freshly ignited, 99.9% lanthanum oxide ($La_2O_3$) to a 250-ml. beaker and add 50 ml. of water and 10 ml. of $HClO_4$. Heat on a hot plate to effect dissolution, cool, and transfer the solution to a 500-ml. volumetric flask. Dilute to volume with water.

**Lead Acetate Test Paper ($H_2S$ Removal).**—Large sheets of qualitative filter paper are soaked in a 10% solution of lead acetate and dried. The paper is cut into strips 7 x 5 cm.

**Lead Acetate, Cotton Preparation.**—A roll of absorbent cotton is opened and saturated with a 10% solution of lead acetate, and the surplus drained off. The material is dried on a line in a warm place away from hydrogen sulfide, rather than in an oven. The dry material is stored in a stoppered bottle until needed.

**Lead Citrate Solution.**—Dissolve 5 g. of lead nitrate in 50 ml. of distilled water and dilute to 100 ml. Add 20 g. of citric acid and warm to dissolve. If a precipitate appears on standing, use only the supernatant solution or allow to stand overnight and then decant from the precipitate.

**Lead Nitrate Standard Solution for Colorimetric Determinations.**—A stock solution is prepared by dissolving 1.5985 g. recrystallized lead nitrate in 1 liter of 1% nitric acid (1 ml. = 1.0 mg. Pb). From the stock prepare by dilution with 1% nitric acid, standards containing 0.01 mg. lead per ml. and 0.001 mg. lead per ml. All solutions will keep indefinitely in glass-stoppered Pyrex containers.

**Lead Standard Solution.**—Dissolve 0.1831 g. of lead acetate, $Pb(C_2H_3O_2)_2 \cdot 3H_2O$, in 100 ml. of water and add a few drops of acetic acid if necessary to clear up the cloudiness (basic salt) and dilute to 1000 ml. When 10 ml. of this solution are diluted to 1000 ml. each ml. of the resulting solution contains 0.000001 g. Pb.

**Lithium Chloride Solution (1 ml. = 10.0 mg. Li).**—Dissolve 53.24 g. of reagent grade, dried lithium carbonate ($Li_2CO_3$) in 300 ml. of water and a minimum of HCl. Heat to boiling on a hot plate to evolve carbon dioxide. Dilute to 1 liter with water and store in a polyethylene bottle.

**Magnesia Mixture.**—For precipitation of ammonium magnesium phosphate, 110 g. of magnesium chloride ($MgCl_2 \cdot 6H_2O$) are dissolved in a small amount of water. To this are added 280 g. of ammonium chloride and 700 ml. of ammonia (sp. gr. 0.90); the solution is now diluted to 2000 ml. with distilled water. The solution is allowed to stand for several hours and then filtered into a large bottle with glass stopper. Ten ml. of this solution should be used for every 0.1 g. of $P_2O_5$ present in the sample analyzed. For quantitative use the reagent should be prepared frequently in small lots, or if prepared in large lots should be stored in a resistant vessel. For qualitative use the solution must be filtered if any sediment of silica appears.

**Magnesium Chloride Solution (1 ml. = 50.0 mg. Mg).**—Dissolve 50.0 g. of pure magnesium metal in 300 ml. of water and a minimum of HCl added in small increments and dilute to 1 liter with water. Store in a polyethylene bottle.

**Magnesium Uranyl Acetate.**—(*A*) Dissolve 90 g. of uranyl acetate ($UO_2(C_2H_3O_2)_2 \cdot 2H_2O$) in 60 ml. of glacial acetic acid and distilled water to make 1 liter by warming the solution to 70°C. and stirring. Dissolve 600 g. of magnesium acetate ($Mg(C_2H_3O_2)_2 \cdot 4H_2O$) in 60 ml. of glacial acetic acid and distilled water to make 1 liter by warming to 70°C. and stirring. Mix the two solutions, when completely dissolved, at 70°C., allow the solution to cool and stand at 20°C., preferably overnight. Filter through a dry paper at 20°C. and store in an amber glass-stoppered bottle. Do not allow the reagent to cool below 20°C.

(*B*) Dissolve 160 g. of uranyl acetate ($UO_2(C_2H_3O)_2 \cdot 2H_2O$), 180 g. of magnesium acetate ($Mg(C_2H_3O_2)_2 \cdot 4H_2O$), and 45 ml. of glacial acetic acid in 750 ml. of distilled water at 70°C. with stirring. Cool to 25°C., dilute to 1 liter and let stand for several hours at 25°C. Filter and store in an amber bottle at 25°C.

**Mandelic Acid Solution.**—Dissolve 8.0 g. of reagent grade DL-mandelic acid in water and dilute to 100 ml. with water. Prepare fresh as needed.

**Manganese Standard Solution (1 ml. = 0.10 mg. Mn).**—Dissolve 0.100 g. of high purity manganese in 5 ml. of water and 5 ml. of $HNO_3$. Boil to expel brown fumes. Cool, dilute to 1 liter in a volumetric flask.

**Manganous Sulfate Solution.**—Dissolve 48 g. of manganous sulfate in 100 ml. of water.

**Mercuric Chloride or Bromide Paper, Sensitized.**—20″ x 20″ Munktells No. 0 Filter Paper is cut into four equal squares. For use in the large Gutzeit apparatus the paper is dipped into a 3.25% solution of mercuric chloride (mercuric bromide may be used in place of the chloride) or if it is to be used in the small Gutzeit apparatus, it is dipped into a 0.35% mercuric solution. (The weaker the solution the longer and less intense will be the stain.) The paper should be of uniform thickness, otherwise there will be an irregularity in length of stain for the same amount of arsenic. See Chapter on Arsenic.

**Mercuric Chloride Solution.**—Saturated solution of $HgCl_2$ (60–80 g. per liter). The solubility rises rapidly with temperature rise.

**Mercuric Chloride Standard Solution.**—Weigh out exactly 0.1354 g. of mercuric chloride and dissolve in 0.25 $N$ sulfuric acid. Transfer to a 100-ml. volumetric flask and dilute to the mark with 0.25 $N$ sulfuric acid. This solution contains 1 mg. of mercury per milliliter.

**Mercuric Nitrate Solution, 0.025 $N$.**—Dissolve 4.17 g. $Hg(NO_3)_2 \cdot \frac{1}{2}H_2O$ in water and dilute to 1 liter. Standardize this solution against 5.00-ml. aliquots of an accurately prepared 0.1 $N$ sodium chloride solution.

**Methanol Acid Solution.**—1 ml. concentrated hydrochloric acid added to 450 ml. of methanol.

**Methanol Alkaline Solution.**—Dissolve 0.4 g. NaOH in 1 liter of absolute $CH_3OH$. Store in a boron-free container.

**Methyl Orange-Xylene-Cyanol Indicator Solution.**—Dissolve 3.00 g. of Xylene Cyanol FF (Eastman Kodak Co.) and 1.33 g. of methyl orange in water and dilute to 1 liter.

**Methyl Violet Stock Solution.**—Dissolve 0.1 g. of methyl violet (Eastman Kodak Co. No. 1309 is available) in 100 ml. of water.

**Molybdenum Standard Solution (1 ml. = 0.0005 g. Mo).**—Dissolve 0.2522 g. of pure $Na_2MoO_4 \cdot 2H_2O$ in 1 liter of water containing 5 ml. of $H_2SO_4$. To standardize this solution pipette 100 ml. of it into a 250-ml. beaker, and 10 ml. of $H_2SO_4$ (1:1), and reduce it in the Jones Reductor as follows: If the reductor has been standing idle, pass 100 ml. of $H_2SO_4$ (5:95) through it, then some water, and discard the wash solution. Add 30 ml. of ferric phosphate solution to the receiver, and then enough water so that the tip of the reductor dips beneath the surface of the solution. (To prepare the ferric phosphate solution, dissolve 100 g. of $Fe_2(SO_4)_3$ in 1 liter of water to which 150 ml. of $H_3PO_4$ and 20 ml. of $H_2SO_4$ (1:1) have been added. Add $KMnO_4$ (25 g. per l.) until the solution is just tinted pink.) Draw the molybdenum solution, by gentle suction, through the reductor. Just before the surface of the liquid reaches the zinc, add a 50-ml. portion of water, and finally rinse by adding two more 50-ml. portions each time just before the surface of the solution reaches the zinc. Close the stopcock, disconnect, and raise the reductor as a little water is allowed to run through the stem. Rinse the stem and titrate the solution with 0.1 $N$ $KMnO_4$. Make a blank determination, following the same procedure and using the same amounts of all reagents.

**Murexide Indicator.**—Mix 0.20 g. of Murexide and 100 g. of sodium chloride, and grind intimately to a fine powder.

**Neodymium Standard Solution (1 ml. = 3.00 mg. Nd).**—Transfer 1.750 g. of freshly ignited, 99.9% neodymium oxide ($Nd_2O_3$) to a 250-ml. beaker and add 50 ml. of water. Add 10 ml. of $HClO_4$, cover and heat on a hot plate. When dissolution is complete, cool, transfer the solution to a 500-ml. volumetric flask and dilute to volume with water.

**Nessler's Solution.**—Dissolve 50 g. of potassium iodide in the smallest possible quantity of cold water. Add a saturated solution of mercuric chloride until a faint show of excess is indicated. Add 400 ml. of 50% KOH solution. After the solution has clarified by settling, make up to 1 liter with water, allow to settle and decant; solution used for determining $NH_3$ in water.

**Nickel Nitrate Standard Solution (1 ml. = 0.005 mg. Ni).**—Dissolve 0.1000 g. of pure nickel metal in 10 ml. of water and 5 ml. of $HNO_3$ in a 150-ml. beaker. When the dissolution is complete, boil the solution to remove the lower oxides of nitrogen. Cool the solution to room temperature, transfer to a 1-liter volumetric flask, dilute to volume with water. Pipette 25.0 ml. of this solution into a 500-ml. volumetric flask, dilute to volume with water. Other dilutions may be made as necessary. Optionally, the original solution may be prepared from a nickel salt and standardized gravimetrically.

**Nitrogen Standard Solution (1 ml. = 0.0001 g. N).**—Dissolve 0.3819 g. of dried $NH_4Cl$ (reagent grade, fine crystals, dried at 110°C.) in water and make up to 1 liter in a volumetric flask.

**Nitron Solution.**—(Diphenylendoanilodihydrotriazole) $C_{20}H_{16}N_4$. Forms nitron nitrate, $C_{20}H_{16}N_4 \cdot HNO_3$, containing 16.52% $NO_3$. A 10% solution of nitron in 0.1 N acetic acid is used. 10–12 ml. of the reagent will precipitate 0.1 g. of nitrate.

**p-Nitrophenylazoorcinol (Zenia) Solution.**—Dissolve 0.25 g. of the reagent in 1 liter of 0.1 N NaOH. Stir in darkness for at least five hours, using a magnetic stirrer, or equivalent, then filter under vacuum. Allowing this solution to stand for 8 hours in darkness and refiltering tends to stabilize the resultant standardization curve. This reagent is not uniform; a new standardization curve must be plotted for each lot of dye made up. Colorimetric reagent for beryllium.

**α-Nitroso-β-Naphthol Solution.**—A saturated solution of the reagent in 50% acetic acid is used. For 100 ml. of solution 2 g. of reagent are added to 100 ml. of hot 50% acid, and the undissolved excess is filtered off after cooling the solution. This quantity of reagent is required per 0.1 g. of cobalt. Palladium, iron and copper also react with the reagent.

**Nitroso-R-Salt Solution.**—Dissolve 1 g. $C_{10}H_4OH \cdot NO(SO_3 \cdot Na)_2$ in water and make up to 500 ml.

**Oxalic Acid-HCl Solution.**—Add 5 ml. of HCl to 20 ml. of warm oxalic acid stock solution. Prepare fresh as needed and keep warm to avoid crystallization.

**Oxalic Acid, Stock Solution.**—Dissolve 20 g. of $H_2C_2O_4 \cdot 2H_2O$ in water and dilute to 100 ml. Store in a low-boron glass container. Crystals formed on standing will dissolve when the solution is warmed.

**Palladous Chloride Solution.**—Five grams of palladium wire are dissolved in a mixture of 30 ml. of HCl and 2 ml. of $HNO_3$; the solution is evaporated just to dryness on a water bath, treated with 5 ml. of HCl and 25 ml. of water, and warmed until solution is complete. Upon dilution to 750 ml. the solution contains about 1% of palladous chloride and will absorb about two-thirds of its volume of hydrogen.

**Perchloric Acid Extraction Solution.**—Absolute ethyl alcohol containing 0.2% of 70% perchloric acid.

**1,10-Phenanthroline-Ferrous Sulfate Indicator Solution.**—A 0.025 molar ferrous sulfate solution is treated with enough 1-10-phenanthroline monohydrate to make the solution 0.075 $M$ in $o$-phenanthroline (mol. wt. $C_{12}H_8N_2 \cdot H_2O = 198.2$). With 0.1 $N$ solutions the indicator correction is negligible. The indicator is especially suited for titrations with ceric sulfate; it may also be used in permanganate titrations, or for titration of dichromate with ferrous sulfate; in the reverse titration the change is sluggish at the end point.

**2,9-Dimethyl-1,10-phenanthroline Solution (Neo-Cuproine).**—Dissolve 0.250 g. of 2,9-Dimethyl-1,10-phenanthroline in 10 ml. of ethanol and dilute to 100 ml. with water.

**Phenylarsonic Acid, Propylarsonic Acid Solutions.**—These substances are almost specific reagents for zirconium under certain conditions. Propyl arsonic acid is suitable for the determination of zirconium in the presence of tin, thorium and titanium. The solution should contain 10% of concentrated HCl by volume or 4.5% of concentrated $H_2SO_4$. Antimony and bismuth interfere. The zirconium is weighed as $ZrO_2$. A 5% aqueous solution of the reagent is used.

**Phenylthiohydantoic Acid Solution.**—The reagent is soluble to the extent of about 1% in water or alcohol at 20°C. About 10 g. dissolve in 100 ml. of water at 100°C. The reagent is much more soluble in acetone than in alcohol or water. From a hot slightly ammoniacal solution the reagent separates cobalt quantitatively in one operation from As, U, V, Ti, W, Mo, Zn, Mn, Cr, Al, Mg and Ca. Citrate may be present to hold iron, etc. in solution. From 1–5 mg. of iron and part of any nickel present will be found with the cobalt precipitate. In solutions slightly acidified with acetic acid the reagent precipitates Cu, Pb, Hg, Cd, Bi, Sb quantitatively while Sn, As, and metals not in the $H_2S$ group are not precipitated. The compositions of the precipitates are variable so that each metal must be determined by some standard titrimetric or gravimetric process after destroying the organic matter.

**Phenyltrimethylammonium Iodide Solution.**—Cadmium, in neutral or slightly acid solution gives a white crystalline with potassium iodide and the reagent of composition $[C_6H_5(CH)_3N]_2CdI_4$. A 2.5% aqueous reagent is used. Other hydrogen sulfide group metals should be removed by reduction with metallic iron. Before precipitation the solution is treated with a few drops of sulfurous acid and an excess (5 g.) of Rochelle salt, and potassium iodide (2–3 g.). After standing at least 6 hrs. the precipitate is collected on a filtering crucible, washed with small portions of a solution containing both KI (0.5%) and phenyltrimethylammonium iodide (0.5%). The precipitate is dissolved in 2 $N$ ammonia, neutralized and made 1 $N$ in HCl and titrated with potassium iodate after adding 5 ml. of 10% KCN solution and starch indicator. When the iodide of the precipitate has been converted into iodine cyanide the starch end point (blue to colorless) appears. One ml. of M/40 $KIO_3 = 0.001405$ g. Cd since $2KIO_3 = 4I^- = Cd$.

**Phosphate Standard Solution.**—Dissolve in water exactly 0.4394 g. of pure $KH_2PO_4$ and make up to 1 liter with distilled water in a volumetric flask. This solution contains 0.1 mg. (100 micrograms) of phosphorus in 1 ml. Use this solution for preparing more dilute solutions containing 10 and 1 micrograms, respectively, in 1 ml., by dilution in the exact proportions.

**9-Phosphomolybdic Acid (Luteo Acid) Solution.**—Heat dodecaphosphomolybdic acid, carefully with continual stirring, until the temperature reaches 300° to 350°C. and the color of the dry acid turns from orange to green. Continue heating until no orange particles remain. Cool and extract with distilled water. Filter if not clear and oxidize the green solution with a little bromine water. Evaporate the solution slowly to obtain short, stout yellow prisms of the luteo acid ($P_2O_5 \cdot 18MoO_3 \cdot 24$–$30H_2O$). Filter off the crystals and prepare a 20% solution of the crystals by dissolving in distilled water.

**Phosphomolybdic Acid Solution.**—Dissolve 20.6 g. of anhydrous sodium molybdate in 80 ml. of water. Add 3 g. of dibasic sodium phosphate dodecahydrate. Dissolve in 25 ml. of water by heating. Add nitric acid (1:1) dropwise until the solution turns to a golden yellow color and is approximately at pH 3.0. Make volume up to 100 ml. with water. This reagent must be prepared as required.

**Picrolonic Acid Solution** (3-methyl-4-nitro-1-(p-nitrophenyl)-5-pyrazolone). The reagent is soluble in water or alcohol. A 2.5–2.64 g./l. aqueous solution is used as reagent. The elements determinable are Cu, Pb, Ca, Mg and Th. Precipitates of the composition $M(II)(C_{10}H_7O_5N_4)_2 \cdot nH_2O$, are formed. Gravimetric, colorimetric and titration methods are used in the final measurement.

**Potassium Bromate Solution, 0.1 N.**—This substance is readily obtained pure by recrystallization and drying at 150°C. For an 0.1 N solution the theoretical weight, 2.7835 g. (1/60th mol. wt.) is dissolved and made up to 1 liter. The solution is stable if prepared from a pure specimen; its wide uses are in the determination of arsenic, antimony and organic substances, the latter by bromination. See Chapters on Antimony and Arsenic.

**Potassium Chloride Standard.**—Primary standard for silver solutions. The reagent salt may be further purified, if necessary, by precipitating the potassium chloride from a nearly saturated solution by leading hydrogen chloride gas into the solution through an inverted funnel. The precipitated potassium chloride is collected on a sintered glass or other suitable filter medium, washed sparingly with cold saturated KCl solution (from purified material), dried and heated to fusion in a platinum vessel. The material is powdered and bottled while still hot.

**Potassium Chloride Solution (1 ml. = 1.00 mg. K).**—Dissolve 1.91 g. of pure, dried potassium chloride (KCl) in water and dilute to 1 liter with water. Store in a polyethylene bottle.

**Potassium Dichromate Standard Solution.**—Many manufacturers supply reagent grade potassium dichromate of sufficient purity to be used as a primary standard. The material is fused at the lowest possible temperature, then broken up and dried finally at 100–110°C. For a tenth normal solution 1/60th of the gram-molecular weight, or 4.903 g., is dissolved in water and made up to one liter. The solution is very stable if care is taken to exclude reducing substances.

If it is necessary to standardize the potassium dichromate solution the following methods may be recommended:

(1) *Against Pure Iron.*—About 0.25 g. of pure iron (electrolytic or prepared from iron carbonyl) is dissolved in an Erlenmeyer flask provided with a Bunsen valve. The air is displaced from the flask before adding the iron by treating 2 g. of sodium bicarbonate with 20 ml. of 5 N sulfuric acid. The metal is dropped in and a rubber stopper with the valve is inserted. When the reaction has ceased, the ferrous solution is titrated with potassium dichromate, after the addition of 0.3 ml. of 0.01 M diphenylamine sodium sulfate as indicator, and 10 ml. of phosphoric acid (one volume of concentrated phosphoric acid + one volume of water). The titration must be slow near the end point which is a change to purplish or blue-violet.

Other indicators may be used as, for example, one drop of 1% diphenylamine solution, etc. Alternatively, the external or spot-plate method may be used in which case no phosphoric acid is added to the iron solution, and the indicator is 1% potassium ferricyanide placed in drops on a white tile (spot-plate) provided with depressions. The end point is, of course, found when a small drop taken from the solution fails to produce a blue color with a drop of the ferricyanide.

Since it is difficult to exclude air perfectly from the iron solution, one may reduce the iron after it has been dissolved by adding stannous chloride in slight excess to the hot solution, followed by 10 ml. of saturated mercuric chloride solution after the iron solution has been cooled and diluted to 150 ml. If the solution contains mercuric salt, sodium diphenylaminesulfonate indicator or the spot-plate method should be used.

(2) *Against Standard Iron Ore.*—A standard iron ore secured from the U. S. Bureau of Standards, Washington, D. C., may be used as a primary standard. The advantage of such procedure is that the standard contains the same substances in approximately the same percentages as many typical ores. For accurate work a chamber burette should be used; the graduations from 75 to 90 ml. are in tenths and from 90 to 100 ml. in twentieths of a ml. A titration of 90 to 100 ml. of 0.2 $N$ solution would require 0.9 to 1.1 g. of iron or half of this amount for 0.1 $N$ solution. If the ore contains 69% of iron a sample of $1 \times 100/69 = 1.45$ (approx.) g. would be suitable for 0.2 $N$ solution. The solution, reduction and titration of the sample are performed as described in the Chapter on Iron.

**Potassium Ferricyanide Solution.**—The salt should be free of ferrocyanide, since the latter produces a blue color with ferrous salts. A crystal the size of a pinhead is dissolved in 50 ml. of water. The solution is made up fresh for each set of spot tests.

**Potassium Ferrocyanide, Standard Solutions for Zinc Determination.**—(*A*) 21.12 g. of the crystallized salt (trihydrate) per liter. One ml. of the solution is equivalent to about 1% of Zn in a 0.5 g. sample.

*Standardization. Low's Method.*—Weigh carefully 0.2 g. of pure zinc, place in an 8-oz. flask and add 10 ml. of concentrated HCl. When the zinc has dissolved, dilute with 25 ml. of water, add a few drops of litmus solution and make slightly alkaline with ammonia. Again acidify with HCl adding 3 ml. in excess. Dilute to about 250 ml. with hot water and titrate with the ferrocyanide solution using a 15% uranium nitrate solution as an outside indicator, making the tests by the usual spot-plate technique. A brown tinge obtained by adding a drop of the solution titrated to a drop of uranium nitrate on a white tile is the end point desired. It is advisable to divide the solution and to reserve a portion which is added near the end point, in order to avoid overstepping the end point. (See Chapter on Zinc for use of internal indicators.)

(*B*) 42.24 g. of the pure crystallized reagent are dissolved and made up to 1 liter. One ml. = approximately 0.010 g. Zn. The solution should be allowed to stand about 4 weeks before using.

*Standardization. New Jersey Zinc Co. Method.*—Weigh into tall 400-ml. beakers several portions of pure zinc of about 0.35 g. each. Cover with water and add 10 ml. of concentrated HCl, to dissolve. Now add 13 ml. of concentrated ammonia, then make acid with HCl and add 3 ml. in excess. Add 0.03 or 0.04 mg. of ferrous iron in the form of ferrous sulfate solution and dilute to about 200 ml. with distilled water. Heat to boiling and titrate as follows: About ¼ of the solution is reserved in a small beaker and the ferrocyanide is added to the main solution with vigorous stirring. The solution takes on a blue color which changes to a creamy white when an excess of ferrocyanide is added. Now add a few ml. more and pour in the reserved portion of the zinc solution, excepting about 5–10 ml. Add ferrocyanide until the end point is reached and add about 0.5 ml. more. The last of the reserved zinc solution is then poured into the beaker, washing out the small beaker with a portion of the main solution, and the ferrocyanide is added drop by drop until the blue color fades sharply to a pea-green with one drop of ferrocyanide. This is the end point. Repeat until concordant values are obtained for the normality.

**Potassium Fluoride Solution.**—Dissolve 100 g. of potassium fluoride in about 1200 ml. of hot $CO_2$-free water; neutralize with hydrofluoric acid or potassium hydroxide as the reagent may require, using 5 ml. of phenolphthalein as indicator. Dilute sulfuric acid may be used in place of hydrofluoric acid in the final acid adjustment to get a neutral product. One ml. of the solution in 10 ml. of $CO_2$-free water should appear a faint pink. The concentrated mixture is filtered if necessary and then diluted to 2000 ml. with $CO_2$-free water. The sp. gr. will now be approximately 1.32 or about 35° Baumé. One ml. contains 0.5 g. of potassium fluoride.

**Potassium Hydroxide Solution.**—For carbon dioxide determinations, 500 g. of the commercial hydroxide are dissolved in 1 liter of water. Absorption capacity: 1 ml. absorbs 40 ml. of $CO_2$.

**Potassium Iodate.**—The analytical reagent grade material may often be relied on to be 99.8 pure or better. The substance is readily purified by recrystallization from water and drying at 180°C. It is one of the most useful standard substances since thiosulfate may be standardized against it; also it will serve in the field of acidimetry. In the latter case weighed samples or aliquot portions of a standard solution of the iodate are treated with excess of KI solution and neutral sodium thiosulfate and methyl red indicator is added and the solution is titrated with the acid to be standardized. One ml. of $N$ acid = 0.035667 g. $KIO_3$. Each ml. of 0.1 $N$ ($M/60$) potassium iodate solution is equivalent to 1 ml. of 0.1 $N$ acid. The standardization of thiosulfate is described under sodium thiosulfate.

A standard solution of potassium iodate may be used to determine a very great variety of inorganic or organic substances. It is especially useful for sulfur in steel, arsenic, antimony, copper (indirect through cuprous thiocyanate), hydrazine, etc. The titrations are made under iodine monochloride conditions in 4–6 $M$ HCl solution. Ten ml. of 0.005 $M$ ICl is used as a catalyst, and a layer of $CHCl_3$ (10 ml. as indicator). Disappearance of the iodine color from the chloroform layer marks the end point; the titrations are made in a glass-stoppered bottle.

The iodine monochloride is prepared by dissolving 0.279 g. KI and 0.178 g. $KIO_3$ in 250 ml. of water and adding 250 ml. of concentrated HCl. The solution is adjusted by adding dilute KI or $KIO_3$ to equivalence as indicated by chloroform or potentiometrically. The solution is 0.005 $M$ in ICl.

**Potassium Iodide Solution.**—Dissolve 250 g. of potassium iodide, free from iodate, in distilled water and dilute to 1000 ml.

**Potassium Nitrate Standard.**—Recrystallize the purest obtainable material and dry first at 100° and then at 210°C. to constant weight. Chlorides, sulfates, carbonates, Ca, Mg, and Na are tested for and if present are determined and corrections applied.

Use as a standard in the Devarda method for determining nitrate.

**Potassium or Ammonium Thiocyanate, Standard Solution, 0.1 $N$.**—About 8 g. of ammonium or 10 g. of potassium thiocyanate are dissolved in water and diluted to 1 liter. The normality of the solution is determined by titrating aliquot portions of standard silver nitrate, or by titrating the solutions of separate weighed portions of pure silver.

**Potassium Periodate Solution, Alkaline.**—Dissolve 24 g. of potassium hydroxide in 100 ml. of distilled water. When cool add 10 g. of potassium metaperiodate and dissolve. Store in a polyethylene bottle in the dark and discard after 1 month.

**Potassium Permanganate Solution.**—For oxidation purposes. A 2% solution filtered free of the dioxide is required.

**Potassium Permanganate Standard Solution.**—Convenient strengths to use for standard solutions are 0.2 $N$, 0.1 $N$ or 0.05 $N$.

Since commercial potassium permanganate is seldom or never pure and since the substance reacts with organic matter or other reducing agents that may be present in distilled water, it is necessary to prepare the solution empirically and to standardize it.

*Preparation.*—One mole of potassium permanganate is equivalent to 5H. Therefore ⅕th of the molecular weight or 31.61 g. is needed for 1 liter of normal solution, or 3.160 g. would be needed for one liter of 0.1 $N$ solution. It is advisable to use more than the theoretical amount, namely 3.25 g.

This quantity of the salt is dissolved in one liter of hot water. After standing twelve hours or longer, the solution is either siphoned through glass, or filtered through asbestos in order to free it from manganese dioxide which catalyzes the decomposition of the reagent. The solution should be shielded from the action of light by using a dark bottle or a suitable covering for the bottle.

(*a*) *Standardization Against Sodium Oxalate.*—This process has been investigated at the National Bureau of Standards, and it is recommended that the McBride procedure be replaced by the following procedure.

Transfer 0.3 g. of sodium oxalate (dried at 105°C.) to a 600-ml. beaker. Add 250 ml. of dilute sulfuric acid (5:95) previously boiled for 10 to 15 minutes and then cooled to 27 ± 3°C. Stir until the oxalate has dissolved. Add 39 to 40 ml. of 0.1 $N$ potassium permanganate at a rate of 25 to 35 ml. per minute while stirring slowly. Let stand until the pink color disappears (about 45 seconds). Heat to 55 to 60°C. and complete the titration by adding permanganate until a faint pink color persists for 30 seconds. Add the last 0.5 to 1 ml. dropwise with particular care to allow each drop to become decolorized before the next is introduced.

Determine the excess of permanganate required to impart a pink color to the solution. This can be done by matching the color by adding permanganate to the same volume of the boiled and cooled diluted sulfuric acid at 55° to 60°C. This correction usually amounts to 0.03 to 0.05 ml.

In potentiometric titrations the correction is negligible if the end point is approached slowly.

The equivalent weight of sodium oxalate is one-half of its molecular weight or 134/2 = 67. The weight of sodium oxalate used divided by ml. of permanganate required, equals weight of sodium oxalate equivalent to 1 ml. of the permanganate, and this quantity divided by 0.067 gives the normality of the solution. Illustration: 0.2060 g. of sodium oxalate require 30.69 ml. permanganate. 0.2060/30.69 = 0.006712; then 0.006712/0.067 = 0.1002 normal.

(*b*) *Standardization Against Iron or Iron Compounds.*—If pure iron or pure ferric oxide or a standard iron ore of suitable composition is available, a solution containing a suitable quantity of iron (about 0.2 g.) is prepared, iron is reduced to the ferrous state and titrated with potassium permanganate. If the solution contains hydrochloric acid, a suitable quantity of Zimmermann-Reinhardt mixture must be added before the titration.

(c) *Standardization Against Arsenious Oxide.*—Portions of a standard arsenite solution measured from the burette or a pipette (see section on sodium arsenite solution) may be titrated with permanganate, or weighed samples of 0.2 g. each of arsenious oxide may be dissolved in alkali and acidified.

(1) Lang's Procedure.—Add enough acid to make the solution 0.5–2 $N$ in hydrochloric acid or at least 0.5 $N$ in sulfuric acid. Add 1 g. of sodium chloride and 1 drop of about $\frac{1}{400}$ $N$ iodide or iodate solution and titrate with potassium permanganate. If the solution contains no chloride it should be warmed to 40–50° and titrated after adding one drop of the catalyst.

(2) Glen's Procedure.—The solution prepared as described under (1) should be acidified with 20–30 ml. of 5 $N$ sulfuric acid and two drops of 0.01 $M$ osmium tetroxide solution added as a catalyst. The titration with potassium permanganate is then made.

**Potassium Pyrogallate Solution.**—This solution should be prepared only when wanted. The most convenient method is to weigh out 5 g. of the solid acid on paper, pour it into a funnel inserted in the reagent bottle, and pour upon it 100 ml. of potassium hydroxide containing 120 g. of KOH. The acid dissolves at once, and the solution is ready for use. Attention is called to the fact that the use of potassium hydroxide purified by alcohol has given erroneous results.

**Potassium Sulfate Standard Solution (1 ml. = 5 micrograms S).**—Transfer 27.2 mg. of pure dry potassium sulfate to a 1-liter volumetric flask, dissolve, and dilute to the mark with water.

**Praseodymium Standard Solution (1 ml. = 3.00 mg. Pr).**—Transfer 1.812 g. of freshly ignited, 99.9% praseodymium oxide ($Pr_6O_{11}$) to a 250-ml. beaker and add 50 ml. of water. Add 10 ml. of $HClO_4$, cover and heat on a hot plate to effect dissolution. Cool, transfer the solution to a 500-ml. volumetric flask and dilute to volume with water.

**Quinaldinic Acid Solution ($C_{10}H_7NO_2$).**—Chief use: Separation of zinc from Fe, Al, Ti, Cr, Be, $UO_2$ in alkaline tartrate solution; separation of copper from Cd, Mn, Ni, Co, etc. The zinc is weighed in the form of $Zn(C_{10}H_6O_2N)_2 \cdot H_2O$ after drying at 105°C.

**Quinalizarin Solution** (1,2,5,8-Tetrahydroxyanthraquinone).—For color tests or colorimetric determination of Be, Al, etc., a 0.05% solution of the dye in 0.25 $N$ NaOH or an alcoholic solution is used. Beryllium may be detected in the presence of magnesium since the complex of the latter with the reagent is readily oxidized by bromine. Zr, Ce, Th, La, etc. (rare earths) give a reaction analogous to that of beryllium—blue in alkaline solution.

**Rubeanic Acid** ($NH_2$-CS-CS-$NH_2$).—This reagent appears to react in the imide form. A saturated solution of the compound in alcohol is used as the reagent. The compounds of the substance and the ions of copper, lead, cobalt, nickel and the platinum metals (Ru, Pd, Pt) may be detected and estimated colorimetrically under proper conditions. Silver and mercurous ions also give reactions (black precipitates; sulfides).

**Salicylaldoxime Solution** ($C_6H_4(OH)CHNOH$).—A 1% solution in 5% alcohol is used, the substance first being dissolved in the alcohol and diluted. Copper is precipitated by the reagent in a solution containing 10% of glacial acetic acid; Ni and Co are precipitated from neutral solution and lead from neutral or alkaline solution. The compounds $Cu(C_7H_6O_2N)_2$, $Ni(C_7H_6O_2N)_2$ and $Pb(C_7H_6O_2N)_2$ may be dried at 100°C. and weighed. Alternatively the precipitates may be dissolved in sulfuric acid, decomposed by heating in the presence of excess ferric sulfate and the ferrous sulfate that is formed may be titrated.

**Selenium Standard Solution.**—Dissolve 1 g. of pure selenium in strong nitric acid. Evaporate to dryness. Add water and repeat evaporation two or three times to assure complete removal of nitric acid. Dilute to 1 liter with water, 1 ml. = 1 mg. of Se.

**Silicon Standard Solution (1 ml. = 0.05 mg. Si).**—Fuse 0.1070 g. of $SiO_2$ with 1.0 g. of $Na_2CO_3$ in a platinum crucible. Cool the melt, dissolve completely in water and dilute to 1 liter in a volumetric flask. The solution should be stored in a polyethylene bottle, or prepared fresh as needed.

**Silver Nitrate Standard Solution, 0.1 N.**—This solution contains 10.789 g. of Ag or 16.987 g. of $AgNO_3$ per liter. The silver nitrate dried at 120°C. or pure silver may be used; the required weight of the latter may be dissolved in nitric acid and made to 1 liter. If pure materials are not available a solution may be prepared of approximately 0.1 N concentration and standardized against pure NaCl.

**Silver, Preparation of Pure Metal.**—The titrimetric methods used for the determination of silver in materials rich in silver require silver of high purity. The electrolytic method described below is preferred by many laboratories which are suitably equipped.

By Knorr's method, a solution of silver nitrate from which excess of nitric acid has been removed by evaporation is freed of metallic impurities by precipitating about ⅒th of the silver with sodium carbonate, boiling and filtering. The silver in the filtrate is precipitated by adding sodium carbonate, and the precipitate is decomposed without addition of reducing agent by melting in a crucible. Excess sodium carbonate carried down by the precipitate serves to cover the melt; the sodium carbonate that adheres to the metal is removed by hydrochloric acid. The metal is smelted under charcoal. Weighed portions are used for the standardization.

**Sodium Arsenite Reagent.**—Dissolve 5 g. of sodium arsenite in distilled water and dilute to 1 liter.

**Sodium Arsenite Standard Solution, 0.1 N.** (a) *Solution for Titrating Iodine.*—Dissolve 4.946 g. of pure arsenious oxide in a warm solution of 10 g. of pure NaOH in 30–40 ml. of water. Dilute the solution to about 250 ml. and saturate it with carbon dioxide. Remove the tube, washing it thoroughly and letting the washings flow into the flask. Make the solution uniform after diluting to 1 liter. A solution prepared carefully in this manner is stable and does not need to be standardized.

**Alternate Procedure.**—The weighed quantity of arsenious oxide is dissolved by adding 2–3 g. of sodium hydroxide in a little water; the excess of alkali is neutralized with dilute sulfuric acid until a few drops of phenolphthalein indicator are just decolorized. Then 500 ml. of a solution of sodium bicarbonate (about 25 g.) are added; if the color returns add a few drops of sulfuric acid to destroy it. The solution is made up to the final volume.

If necessary, the reagent is standardized against an iodine solution or against weighed quantities of pure iodine.

(b) A convenient solution for standardizing various oxidizing agents (potassium permanganate, ceric sulfate, potassium bromate, potassium iodate, iodine) is made by dissolving 4.946 g. of the pure arsenious oxide in a solution of 2–3 g. of sodium hydroxide in 30–40 ml. of water. The solution is then made slightly acid with dilute sulfuric or hydrochloric acid and diluted to 1 liter.

**Sodium Biphenyl Solution.**—Disperse 58 g. sodium in 300 ml. dry toluene under an atmosphere of nitrogen, with vigorous stirring, in a flask provided with a reflux condenser, and means for warming to melt the sodium. When the dispersion is complete, cool to 10°C. Remove the reflux condenser and add 1250 ml. anhydrous ethylene glycol dimethyl ether. Continue passing the stream of nitrogen slowly through the apparatus. Add, with moderate stirring, 390 g. biphenyl. During this operation, the reaction vessel must be immersed in a cooling bath, composed of a medium that is not reactive with sodium, e.g., an oil bath. The reaction should be complete in 1 hour. The reagent will keep for one or two months if protected from moisture and air. It should be stored in small bottles, filled to the top, and tightly closed by foil-lined caps, the bottles being stored in a refrigerator at 5°C. Under these conditions the reagent will keep for as long as a year.

**Sodium Bismuthate.**—Prepare as follows: Heat 20 parts of sodium hydroxide to redness in an iron or nickel crucible, and add in small quantities at a time, 10 parts of basic bismuth nitrate, previously dried in an oven. Then add 2 parts of sodium peroxide and pour the brownish yellow fused mass on an iron plate to cool; when cold, break it up in a mortar, extract with water, and collect on an asbestos filter. The residue after being washed four or five times by decantation is dried in a water oven, then broken up and sieved to give a finely powdered product.

**Sodium Bismuth Nitrite Solution.**—Dissolve 50 g. of reagent grade sodium nitrite ($NaNO_2$) in 100 ml. of distilled water, neutralize with a few drops of nitric acid if necessary, add 15 g. of reagent grade bismuth nitrate, $Bi(NO_3)_3 \cdot 5H_2O$, and stir until solution is complete. Filter the solution and store in a well-stoppered bottle to prevent absorption of oxygen from the air. Use a fresh solution for analyses.

**Sodium Borate Solution.**—Dissolve 10 g. sodium borate decahydrate in 500 ml. of water.

**Sodium Chloride Hanging Drop Solution.**—Dissolve 1.0 g. of pure sodium chloride and 3.0 g. of pure glycerol in water, add 2 drops of 40% formaldehyde to preserve the reagent, dilute to 100 ml., and filter through paper into a glass reagent bottle.

**Sodium Chloride Solution (1 ml. = 1.00 mg. Na).**—Dissolve 2.54 g. of pure, dried sodium chloride (NaCl) in water and dilute to 1 liter with water. Store in a polyethylene bottle.

**Sodium Chloride, Standard.**—Analytical reagent grade material may be purified, if qualitative tests indicate this to be necessary, in the same manner as described for potassium chloride. The pure material is dried and 5.845 g. are made up to 1 liter for 0.1 $N$ solution.

**Sodium Chromate Solution.**—Dissolve 2.43 g. of sodium chromate in water and make up to 50 ml.

**Sodium Citrate Solution.**—Dissolve 10 g. of $Na_3C_6H_5O_7 \cdot 2H_2O$ in 90 ml. of water.

**Sodium Diethyldithiocarbamate Solution.**—1 g. of the salt per liter of water. Filter into an amber bottle and protect from strong light.

**Sodium Dimethylglyoximate Solution.**—Dissolve 2.6 g. of the octahydrate in 100 ml. of water and filter.

**Sodium Fluoride Standard Solution.**—Dissolve 0.2210 g. of pure sodium fluoride in water and dilute to 250 ml. Each milliliter of solution contains 50.0 micrograms of fluorine.

**Sodium Fluosilicate Standard Solution.**—Dissolve 0.1650 g. of pure sodium fluosilicate in water and dilute to 200 ml. Each milliliter of solution contains 50 micrograms of fluorine.

**Sodium Formate Solution.**—Dissolve 80 g. of sodium hydroxide in 500 ml. of water, and neutralize it to litmus with a solution of 100 g. formic acid in 500 ml. water. Make up to 1 liter.

**Sodium Hydrosulfide Solution.**—Dissolve 50 g. of NaOH in 500 ml. of water, saturated with $H_2S$, and dilute to 1 liter.

**Sodium Hydroxide-Butanol Solution.**—0.1 $N$ sodium hydroxide solution with 2 ml. of butanol per liter.

**Sodium Hydroxide Solution, Alcoholic.**—Dissolve pure sodium hydroxide in 95% alcohol in proportion 22 g. NaOH per liter. Let stand in a stoppered bottle. Decant the clear liquid into another bottle and keep well stoppered. This solution should be colorless or only slightly yellow when used; it will remain colorless longer if the alcohol is previously treated with NaOH (about 80 g. to 1000 ml., kept at about 50°C. for 15 days and then distilled).

**Sodium Hydroxide Solution (for Si Determination in Aluminum Chapter).**—Prepare in a nickel vessel by dissolving 450 g. of sodium hydroxide in 1 liter water. This solution must not be prepared or stored in glass.

**Sodium Hydroxide, Standard Solutions.**—Standard normal sodium hydroxide is made by dissolving approximately 50 g. of NaOH sticks with 1 to 2 g. of $Ba(OH)_2$ in 200 to 300 ml. of water and diluting to 1000 ml. The caustic is standardized against normal or tenth normal hydrochloric or sulfuric acid, using phenolphthalein indicator. Other standard acids may be employed, such as oxalic, benzoic, and phthalic acids. The solution is adjusted to the exact strength desired by addition of distilled water. The solution should be protected from $CO_2$ of the air.

NOTE.—The addition of $Ba(OH)_2$ is made to precipitate the carbonate in the caustic, as this would interfere with titrations in presence of phenolphthalein. As the presence of barium would produce a cloudiness with $H_2SO_4$, it is advisable to add only an amount sufficient to precipitate the carbonate. Milk of lime may be added in place of $Ba(OH)_2$.

**Sodium Hypochlorite Standard Solution.**—Transfer 8.0 ml. of a commercial preparation of sodium hypochlorite solution containing 5% of available chlorine to a glass-stoppered brown-glass bottle, and dilute with water to about 2 liters. If necessary, add sufficient sodium hydroxide (1 g.) to raise the pH to about 12.5, the optimum pH for stability. To ascertain if the proper pH has been reached, the customary colorimetric methods for the determination of pH in the range 12 to 14 may be used. Since adjustment of normality with water is usually needed, obtain the titer of the solution by titration against a primary standard of sodium arsenite made as follows:

Weigh 0.2473 g. of arsenious oxide (National Bureau of Standards) and dissolve in 25 ml. of 10% sodium hydroxide solution. Transfer to a 1-liter volumetric flask, make slightly acid with sulfuric acid (1:6), and dilute with water to 1 liter. This solution is 0.005 $N$.

**Sodium Monofluoroacetate Standard Solution.**—Dissolve 0.05 g. of sodium monofluoroacetate in water and dilute to 250 ml. Each milliliter of solution contains 0.2 mg. of the salt; 0.05 ml. of solution contains 1.9 micrograms of fluorine.

**Sodium Nitrite Solution.**—Prepare by dissolving 150 mg. of sodium nitrite in 1 liter of water and diluting 10 ml. of this solution to 100 ml. (1 ml. = about 10 micrograms $NO_2$).

**Sodium Silicate Standard Solution (equivalent to about 0.04 mg. Silicon per ml.).** —To prepare a stock solution, dissolve 0.6 g. of silicic acid in water and a few pellets of sodium hydroxide, warm, dilute to 500 ml., and filter into a plastic bottle. To standardize, dehydrate a suitable aliquot with sulfuric acid, ignite, and weigh the residue. Volatilize with hydrofluoric and sulfuric acids, ignite, and reweigh.

**Sodium Sulfide Solution, 10%.**—Sodium sulfide may be made by saturating a concentrated solution of sodium hydroxide with hydrogen sulfide, then adding an equal volume of the sodium hydroxide. The solution is diluted to the required volume, allowed to stand several days, and filtered.

**Sodium Tetraphenylboron, 1% Solution.**—Dissolve 2.5 g. of sodium tetraphenylboron in 250 ml. of distilled water, add 0.5–1.0 g. of reagent grade aluminum hydroxide, stir for 5 minutes, and filter. Reject or refilter the first 20–30 ml. of filtrate.

**Sodium Thiosulfate Standard Solutions for Copper Determination (equivalent to about 1 mg. and 4 mg. Copper per ml.).**—Dissolve, respectively, 4 g. and 16 g. sodium thiosulfate pentahydrate in water containing 1 g. of sodium bicarbonate. Dilute each solution to 1 liter. Store in dark bottles. To standardize, transfer a measured quantity of standard copper sulfate solution into a 250-ml. Erlenmeyer flask, add 3 ml. of acetic acid and 5 ml. of potassium iodide solution. After mixing and allowing the solution to stand a few minutes, titrate with the sodium thiosulfate, adding a few drops of starch solution near the end of the titration. Calculate the equivalency in grams of copper per ml. of thiosulfate solution.

**Sodium Thiosulfate, Standard 0.1 N Solution for General Analysis.**—For 1 liter of 0.1 N sodium thiosulfate 0.1 mole, or 24.818 g. of $Na_2S_2O_3 \cdot 5H_2O$ is required; generally an excess—25 g. of the reagent salt—is used. The material is dissolved in hot distilled water that has just been boiled to remove $CO_2$. For each liter, 0.1 g. of $Na_2CO_3$ should be added to the water. When prepared in this way the solution requires little or no aging (to allow $CO_2$ to be used up and sulfur to settle); otherwise the solution has to stand a week or 10 days.

*Standardization.*—Iodine sublimed from a mixture of lime and KI and then resublimed may be used for standardization. Pure potassium iodate or pure potassium dichromate may be weighed and allowed to liberate an equivalent amount of iodine from KI. If the resublimed iodine is used, the procedure is as follows: Dissolve 2–3 g. of pure KI in ½ ml. of water in a weighing bottle, stopper, let come to room temperature and weigh. Add 0.5 g. of the iodine, allow temperature to come to that of the room and reweigh, the increase due to iodine dissolved being noted. Open the bottle under 200 ml. of water containing 1 g. of KI and titrate. Divide wt. of iodine by ml. of thiosulfate to get wt. of iodine per ml. and divide the latter by the milliequivalent of iodine, 0.12692 to find the normality of the thiosulfate solution.

**Sodium Tungstate Solution.**—Dissolve 10 g. of reagent grade sodium tungstate ($Na_2WO_4 \cdot H_2O$) in water and dilute to 100 ml. with water. Prepare fresh as needed.

**Sodium Tungstate Solution, 0.5 N.**—Dissolve in water 16.5 g. of $Na_2WO_4 \cdot 2H_2O$ and dilute to 100 ml.

**Spekker Acid.**—Mix 150 ml. $H_3PO_4$ and 150 ml. $H_2SO_4$, and make up to 1 liter.

**Stannous Chloride Standard Solution.**—(1) Dissolve 2 g. of stannous chloride crystals in hot concentrated HCl and make up to 1 liter. The solution should be kept in a dark bottle provided with burette and attachments for excluding air. The solution is protected from the oxygen of the air by passing the latter through alkaline pyrogallol when solution is transferred to the burette. It is advisable to restandardize every ten or fifteen days. One ml. of the solution is equivalent to about 0.001 g. of iron.

(2) Dissolve 50 mg. of National Bureau of Standards Sample No. 42 (melting point standard for tin) by warming gently with a small amount of hydrochloric acid. Add 100 ml. of water and 50 ml. of hydrochloric acid. Reduce the tin and titrate according to the procedure for tin in aluminum in Chapter on Aluminum.

**Starch Solution.**—One gram of potato or arrowroot starch or soluble starch are rubbed up to a paste with cold water, and the paste is poured into 1 liter of boiling distilled water.

*Preservatives.*—Various substances may be used: (*a*) 2 mg. of mercuric iodide added to the hot solution; (*b*) A few ml. of 5% NaOH added to the hot solution; (*c*) 10 ml. of 1% solution of salicylic acid per liter of starch solution; (*d*) A few drops of chloroform per liter of the starch solution; (*e*) A few ml. of 10% $ZnCl_2$ solution per liter of starch. (*f*) Sodium chloride and acetic acid.—The starch solution is prepared by adding 500 ml. of a saturated solution of sodium chloride (filtered), 100 ml. of 80% acetic acid and 3 g. of starch, mixing the substances in the cold, then boiling about 2 minutes. A solution thus prepared keeps indefinitely.

**Strontium Carrier Solution.**—Dissolve 0.280 g. of strontium nitrate in water and make up volume to 10.0 ml.

**Sulfanilamide Solution.**—Prepare a saturated solution of *p*-aminobenzenesulfonamide in water. This solution contains about 0.4 g. per 100 ml.

**Sulfuric Acid Standard Solution.**—Normal sulfuric acid contains 49.039 g. of $H_2SO_4$ per liter of solution. To make a liter of the normal acid the amount of the standard acid required is calculated by the formula:

$$\frac{100 \times 49.039}{\text{per cent } H_2SO_4 \text{ in standard}} = \text{grams standard acid necessary}$$

The acid is weighed out in a small beaker, a slight excess being taken (0.1 g.). The acid is washed into a liter flask and made to volume. An aliquot portion is standardized against the standard sodium carbonate. The solution may now be adjusted to the exact strength required.

**Sulfurous Acid, Dilute.**—Saturate water with sulfur dioxide and dilute to 1:50.

**Superchrome Garnet Y Standard Solution.**—Mix 50 ml. each of 2 *M* acetic acid and 2 *M* sodium acetate, 40 ml. of aluminum chloride solution (50 micrograms of aluminum per ml.), 48 ml. of 0.1% aqueous solution of the National Aniline dye or 33.2 ml. of the 0.1% aqueous solution of the Du Pont dye, and water to make 1 liter.

**Tartrate Solution, Alkaline.**—25 g. of sodium potassium tartrate, $NaKC_4H_4O_6 \cdot 4H_2O$, is dissolved in 50 ml. of water. A little ammonia is added and then sodium sulfide solution. After settling for some time the reagent is filtered. The filtrate is acidified with hydrochloric acid, boiled free of $H_2S$, again made ammoniacal and diluted to 100 ml.

**Tellurium Standard Solution.** Dissolve 1 g. of pure tellurium in nitric acid. Add 50 ml. of sulfuric acid and evaporate to fumes. Dilute in a 1-liter volumetric flask with water, 1 ml. = 1 mg. of Te.

**Thallium Standard Solution.**—Weigh out 1.303 g. of thallium nitrate ($TlNO_3$), place in a 1-liter volumetric flask, and dilute to volume with 0.5 $N$ sulfuric acid. By serial dilution prepare a diluted thallium solution so that 1 ml. = 1 microgram of thallium. (A fresh dilute solution should be prepared every two or three days.)

**2-Thenoyltrifluoroacetone (TTA) Solution.**—Dissolve 5.5 g. of technical grade 2-thenoyltrifluoroacetone in methyl isobutyl ketone and dilute to 250 ml. with additional solvent. Store in a cool, dark place.

**Thionalide Solution** (Thioglycolic-β-Aminonaphthalide, $C_{10}H_7NHCOCH_2SH$).— The compound is only slightly soluble in water (0.08 g. per 100 ml. at 95°C. and 0.01 at 20°C.). It is readily soluble in $C_2H_5OH$, glacial acetic acid or concentrated $H_2SO_4$; on warming the last solution decomposes. In 0.2 $N$ nitric or sulfuric acid Cu, Ag, Au, Hg, Sn, As, Sb, Bi, Pt and Pd give precipitates. The following precipitate in alkaline tartrate solution: Cu, Ag, Au, Hg, Cd, Tl, Mn, Fe(ous); in tartrate-cyanide solution: Au, Tl, Sn, Pb, Sb, Bi; and in NaOH-KCN solution: Tl, Hg, Pb, Bi. The precipitates may be weighed after drying at 105°C. The reagent may be titrated by iodine (2 moles dye are equivalent to 1 of $I_2$).

**Thorium Nitrate Acidified Stock Solution.**—Dissolve 1.27 g. of thorium nitrate, $Th(NO_3)_4 \cdot 4H_2O$, and 72 ml. of $N$ hydrochloric acid in water and make up to 100 ml.

*Dilute Solution.*—Dilute 5 ml. of the stock solution to 500 ml. with fluorine-free water. One ml. of the dilute solution is equivalent to 5 micrograms of fluoride.

**Thorium Standard Solution (1 ml. = 1.00 mg. Th).**—Dissolve 2.38 g. of reagent grade thorium nitrate tetrahydrate ($Th(NO_3)_4 \cdot 4H_2O$) in 50 ml. of water and 50 ml. of HCl. Dilute to 1 liter with water. Standardize this solution by precipitating the thorium in aliquot portions with oxalic acid and by igniting the thorium oxalate to the oxide.

**Thoron Dye Solution.**—Dissolve 3.0 g. of the disodium salt of o-(2-hydroxy-3,6-disulfo-1-naphthylazo)-benzenearsonic acid (Eastman Kodak Company) in 1 liter of water. Filter if necessary.

**Thymol Solution 1%.**—The thymol is dissolved in a little glacial acetic acid containing 10% ethyl alcohol, and this solution is added to concentrated sulfuric acid. Addition of the thymol directly to the acid would produce a colored solution. The reagent should be kept protected from strong light, otherwise it will become colored.

**Titanium Chloride Solution.**—Dissolve 10 g. of tungsten-free titanium metal with 200 ml. of HCl (1:1) in a flask. As soon as the metal has dissolved, cool the solution, dilute to 500 ml. with HCl (1:1), and store in a stoppered bottle.

**Titanium Sulfate Standard Solution (equivalent to about 0.6 mg. Titanium or 1 mg. Titanium Dioxide per ml.).**—Weigh 4.44 g. of reagent grade titanium potassium oxalate, $K_2TiO(C_2O_4)_2 \cdot 2H_2O$, into a 500-ml. Kjeldahl flask. Add 4 g. of ammonium sulfate and 50 ml. of sulfuric acid. Heat carefully until foaming subsides and then boil 10 minutes to decompose the oxalate. Cool and pour carefully into 500 ml. of water. To insure absence of oxalate add potassium permanganate solution until a permanent pink color is obtained. Dilute to 1 liter.

**o-Tolidine Reagent.**—Dissolve 1.35 g. o-tolidine dihydrochloride in 500 ml. of distilled water, and add it to a mixture of 150 ml. concentrated HCl and 350 ml. of distilled water. Store in the dark.

**Triacid (Aluminum Chapter).**—Prepare a mixture of 715 ml. of (1:2) $H_2SO_4$, 215 ml. concentrated HCl, and 70 ml. concentrated $HNO_3$.

**Triphenyltin Chloride Solution.**—Saturate 95% alcohol with $(C_6H_5)_3SnF$ at room temperature; it will contain about 0.02 g. per ml.

**Tungsten Standard Solution (1 ml. = 100 micrograms W).**—Dissolve 0.1707 g. of $Na_2WO_4 \cdot 2H_2O$ in water. Add 100 ml. of sodium hydroxide solution (100 g./liter) and dilute to 1 liter. Store in a caustic-resistant bottle.

**Turmeric Extract.**—Stir 1 g. of powdered tumeric with 100 ml. of isopropyl alcohol (or 95% ethyl alcohol) for 2 hours, and filter.

**Uranium Nitrate Solution.**—Dissolve 5 g. in 100 ml. of water.

**Vanadium Solution Standard (1 ml. = 1 mg. V).**—Ignite 1.7852 g. of pure vanadium(V) oxide, $V_2O_5$, at 500°C. After cooling, dissolve in 45 ml. of 6 $N$ NaOH solution, neutralize with 1 $N$ $H_2SO_4$ solution, adding 1 ml. in excess, and dilute to 1 liter.

**Volhard's Indicator.**—Dissolve 106.4 g. of ferric alum $(FeNH_4(SO_4)_2)$ in 13.3 ml. $HNO_3$ and water. Dilute the solution to 1 liter.

**Wagner's Solution.**—Twenty-five grams of citric acid and 1 g. of salicylic acid are dissolved in water and made to 1000 ml. This reagent is used in preventing precipitation of iron and alumina.

**Yttrium Carrier Solution.**—Dissolve 0.280 g. of yttrium nitrate in water, and make up volume to 10.0 ml.

**Zinc, Amalgamated.**—Mercuric chloride in sufficient quantity to make 1–2% of mercury in the amalgam is dissolved in a suitable volume of water, and the zinc (shot, or feathered 20-mesh) is poured into the mercury solution. In a few minutes the amalgam is washed well by decantation with distilled water. If the amalgam is to be used immediately it should be kept under distilled water; otherwise the powder should be dried and bottled. (Per 1 kg. of zinc use 13.5–27 g. mercuric chloride dissolved in 1 liter of water.)

**Zinc Chloride Ammoniacal Solution.**—Dissolve 25 g. of zinc chloride in 500 ml. of ammonium hydroxide (1:1) in a stoppered glass bottle.

**Zinc Standard Solution (1 ml. = 1.00 mg. Zn).**—Dissolve 1.000 g. of pure zinc in 50 ml. of water and 22.6 ml. of HCl. Dilute to volume in a 1-liter volumetric flask.

**Zinc Uranyl Acetate.**—Weigh 100 g. of crystallized uranyl acetate $(UO_2(C_2H_3O_2)_2 \cdot 2H_2O)$ in a 600-ml. beaker, add 15 ml. of glacial acetic acid, 500 ml. of distilled water, warm to about 70°C. and stir until dissolved. Weigh 27.8 g. of crystallized zinc acetate $(Zn(C_2H_3O_2)_2 \cdot 2H_2O)$ in a 600-ml. beaker, add 12 ml. of glacial acetic acid, 400 ml. of distilled water, warm to about 70°C. and stir until dissolved. Mix the solutions at about 70°C., add a few milligrams of sodium chloride and let stand for 24 hours. Filter at 20°C. and store in a glass-stoppered bottle. The reagent should be used at 20°C. At lower temperatures, high results will obtain; at higher temperatures, low results will be experienced.

**Zirconium Chloride Solution (1 ml. = 0.2 mg. Zr).**—Dissolve 0.353 g. of zirconyl chloride $(ZrOCl_2 \cdot 8H_2O)$ in about 100 ml. of water, add 100 ml. of HCl and dilute to 500 ml.

**Zirconium Nitrate Solution.**—1 g. $Zr(NO_3)_4 \cdot 5H_2O$ in 250 ml. water.

**Zirconyl Nitrate Solution.**—Dissolve 0.40 g. $ZrO(NO_3)_2 \cdot 2H_2O$ in 100 ml. (1:1) HCl.

# STANDARD LABORATORY CONSTANTS

## BUOYANCY CONSTANTS (MG./ML.)

Difference in milligrams between the mass and the apparent weight of one milliliter of water weighed with brass weights ($d = 8.4$) in air at various temperatures and barometer readings (unreduced). A humidity of 50% saturation is assumed. To find the weight of one milliliter of air under the conditions assumed in this table, multiply the buoyancy constant by 1.135 (42/37).

| Pressure | Temperature in Degrees Centigrade | | | |
|---|---|---|---|---|
| | 15 | 20 | 25 | 30 |
| 640 | 0.904 | 0.886 | 0.869 | 0.852 |
| 650 | 0.918 | 0.900 | 0.883 | 0.866 |
| 660 | 0.932 | 0.914 | 0.897 | 0.879 |
| 670 | 0.946 | 0.928 | 0.911 | 0.893 |
| 680 | 0.960 | 0.942 | 0.924 | 0.906 |
| 690 | 0.975 | 0.956 | 0.938 | 0.920 |
| 700 | 0.989 | 0.970 | 0.952 | 0.933 |
| 705 | 0.996 | 0.977 | 0.958 | 0.940 |
| 710 | 1.003 | 0.984 | 0.965 | 0.947 |
| 715 | 1.010 | 0.991 | 0.972 | 0.953 |
| 720 | 1.017 | 0.998 | 0.979 | 0.960 |
| 725 | 1.024 | 1.004 | 0.985 | 0.967 |
| 730 | 1.031 | 1.011 | 0.992 | 0.973 |
| 735 | 1.038 | 1.018 | 0.999 | 0.980 |
| 740 | 1.045 | 1.025 | 1.006 | 0.987 |
| 745 | 1.052 | 1.032 | 1.013 | 0.994 |
| 750 | 1.059 | 1.039 | 1.020 | 1.000 |
| 755 | 1.067 | 1.046 | 1.027 | 1.007 |
| 760 | 1.074 | 1.053 | 1.034 | 1.014 |
| 765 | 1.081 | 1.060 | 1.040 | 1.020 |
| 770 | 1.088 | 1.067 | 1.047 | 1.027 |
| 775 | 1.095 | 1.074 | 1.054 | 1.034 |
| 780 | 1.102 | 1.081 | 1.061 | 1.041 |

## DENSITY (IN G. PER ML.) OF WATER AT TEMPERATURES FROM 0° TO 102° C.

| Temp. °C. | Density | Temp. °C. | Density | Temp. °C. | Density |
|---|---|---|---|---|---|
| 0 | 0.99987 | 35 | 0.99406 | 70 | 0.97781 |
| 1 | 0.99993 | 36 | 0.99371 | 71 | 0.97723 |
| 2 | 0.99997 | 37 | 0.99336 | 72 | 0.97666 |
| 3 | 0.99999 | 38 | 0.99299 | 73 | 0.97607 |
| 4 | 1.00000 | 39 | 0.99262 | 74 | 0.97548 |
| 5 | 0.99999 | 40 | 0.99224 | 75 | 0.97489 |
| 6 | 0.99997 | 41 | 0.99186 | 76 | 0.97428 |
| 7 | 0.99993 | 42 | 0.99147 | 77 | 0.97368 |
| 8 | 0.99988 | 43 | 0.99107 | 78 | 0.97307 |
| 9 | 0.99981 | 44 | 0.99066 | 79 | 0.97245 |
| 10 | 0.99973 | 45 | 0.99024 | 80 | 0.97183 |
| 11 | 0.99963 | 46 | 0.98982 | 81 | 0.97120 |
| 12 | 0.99952 | 47 | 0.98940 | 82 | 0.97057 |
| 13 | 0.99940 | 48 | 0.98896 | 83 | 0.96994 |
| 14 | 0.99927 | 49 | 0.98852 | 84 | 0.96930 |
| 15 | 0.99913 | 50 | 0.98807 | 85 | 0.96865 |
| 16 | 0.99897 | 51 | 0.98762 | 86 | 0.96800 |
| 17 | 0.99880 | 52 | 0.98715 | 87 | 0.96734 |
| 18 | 0.99862 | 53 | 0.98669 | 88 | 0.96668 |
| 19 | 0.99843 | 54 | 0.98621 | 89 | 0.96601 |
| 20 | 0.99823 | 55 | 0.98573 | 90 | 0.96534 |
| 21 | 0.99802 | 56 | 0.98524 | 91 | 0.96467 |
| 22 | 0.99780 | 57 | 0.98478 | 92 | 0.96399 |
| 23 | 0.99756 | 58 | 0.98425 | 93 | 0.96330 |
| 24 | 0.99732 | 59 | 0.98375 | 94 | 0.96261 |
| 25 | 0.99707 | 60 | 0.98324 | 95 | 0.96192 |
| 26 | 0.99681 | 61 | 0.98272 | 96 | 0.96122 |
| 27 | 0.99654 | 62 | 0.98220 | 97 | 0.96051 |
| 28 | 0.99626 | 63 | 0.98167 | 98 | 0.95981 |
| 29 | 0.99597 | 64 | 0.98113 | 99 | 0.95909 |
| 30 | 0.99567 | 65 | 0.98059 | 100 | 0.95838 |
| 31 | 0.99537 | 66 | 0.98005 | 101 | 0.95765 |
| 32 | 0.99505 | 67 | 0.97950 | 102 | 0.95693 |
| 33 | 0.99473 | 68 | 0.97894 | | |
| 34 | 0.99440 | 69 | 0.97838 | | |
| 35 | 0.99406 | 70 | 0.97781 | | |

## APPARENT WEIGHT (IN G.) OF WATER IN AIR

(This table gives the apparent weight, for temperatures between 15° and 30°C., humidity 50%, unreduced barometer reading 76 cm., of certain volumes of water weighed with brass weights. This table is based on the data given in Tables 1 and 2, and may be conveniently employed to determine definite volumes of water for calibrating instruments. The table assumes the air to be at the same temperature as the water.)

| Temp. °C. | 2000 ml. | 1000 ml. | 500 ml. | 400 ml. | 300 ml. | 250 ml. | 150 ml. |
|---|---|---|---|---|---|---|---|
| 15 | 1996.11 | 998.05 | 499.03 | 399.22 | 299.42 | 249.51 | 149.71 |
| 16 | 1995.80 | 997.90 | 498.95 | 399.16 | 299.37 | 249.48 | 149.68 |
| 17 | 1995.48 | 997.74 | 498.87 | 399.10 | 299.32 | 249.43 | 149.66 |
| 18 | 1995.13 | 997.56 | 498.78 | 399.03 | 299.27 | 249.39 | 149.63 |
| 19 | 1994.76 | 997.38 | 498.69 | 398.95 | 299.21 | 249.34 | 149.61 |
| 20 | 1994.36 | 997.18 | 498.59 | 398.87 | 299.15 | 249.30 | 149.58 |
| 21 | 1993.95 | 996.97 | 498.49 | 398.79 | 299.09 | 249.24 | 149.55 |
| 22 | 1993.51 | 996.76 | 498.38 | 398.70 | 299.03 | 249.19 | 149.51 |
| 23 | 1993.06 | 996.53 | 498.26 | 398.61 | 298.96 | 249.13 | 149.48 |
| 24 | 1992.58 | 996.29 | 498.15 | 398.52 | 298.89 | 249.07 | 149.44 |
| 25 | 1992.09 | 996.04 | 498.02 | 398.42 | 298.81 | 249.01 | 149.41 |
| 26 | 1991.57 | 995.79 | 497.89 | 398.31 | 298.74 | 248.95 | 149.37 |
| 27 | 1991.04 | 995.52 | 497.76 | 398.21 | 298.66 | 248.88 | 149.33 |
| 28 | 1990.49 | 995.24 | 497.62 | 398.10 | 298.57 | 248.81 | 149.29 |
| 29 | 1989.92 | 994.96 | 497.48 | 397.98 | 298.49 | 248.74 | 149.24 |
| 30 | 1989.33 | 994.66 | 497.33 | 397.87 | 298.40 | 248.67 | 149.20 |

NOTE.—The term milliliter, ml., 1/1000 liter, based on the volume occupied by a kilogram of water at its greatest density, has been adopted by the Bureau of Standards and is frequently found on calibrated apparatus. This form has been used in the section on volumetric apparatus in place of the term cc., generally used throughout this book. Owing to the expansion of water, 1000 grams would occupy a greater volume at room temperature than at 4° C. so that 1 cc. would be less than 1/1000 of this expanded volume. The difference of 1 ml. and 1 cc., under convenient workable temperatures, could not be measured by the ordinary burette, so that for practical purposes the volumes represented by ml. and cc. may be considered the same. This expansion has been taken into consideration in calibration of apparatus, the cc. and the liter being volumes in ratio of 1:1000, a relativity demanded in volumetric analysis, so that the terminology is of little importance, provided the apparatus used is thus calibrated.

# STANDARDIZATION OF WEIGHTS

Precision measurement of mass is the first requisite in accurate analysis. The chemist has at his command instruments for the measurement of mass which by far surpass in accuracy the major operations of his work. This is probably largely responsible for the negligence in the care of the balance and weights too frequently observed in the technical laboratory. It is often the case that the average technical laboratory uses analyses calculated to one decimal place more than warranted by the accuracy of the weights used. Assuming all other operations without error, an analysis made on a 1-g. sample and reported as 98.53% requires a weight accuracy of 0.0001 g. if the last figure is intended to have any significance.

Laboratories doing accurate analytical or research work should always be in possession of a set of standard weights and these weights should be used only in standardizing those in constant use. Where a large number of balances are used, it is advisable to have two sets of standard weights, a Primary and a Secondary set, each ranging from 100 g. to 1 mg. The Primary set is used exclusively for checking the Secondary set and is checked annually by the Bureau of Standards at Washington, D. C. The Secondary set is used for standardizing the weights assigned to the various balances. Where balances are used constantly, it is advisable to have the weights checked at least monthly against the Secondary set, and the Secondary likewise checked monthly against the Primary set. While this frequent checking may appear excessive, it is inexpensive insurance against errors which cannot easily be detected in any other way.

It is advisable to use one-piece gold-plated weights for the Primary Standard. The type designated Class M by the Bureau of Standards is very satisfactory. Lacquered brass weights are very satisfactory for general use.

The practice frequently observed in chemical laboratories of setting out the weights on the balance plate is very bad. While it expedites weighing, the chance of contaminating and changing the accuracy of the weights more than counterbalances the advantage of speed.

Students are frequently taught that it is not necessary for weights to bear true values so long as they are comparable to one another; that is, to bear true relation to each other. This contention holds good so long as all work done by the chemist is related to his balance. This condition does not exist in the majority of technical laboratories. The chemist frequently uses standard solutions made by use of other balances and for this reason his weighings must be comparable to others in the laboratory. This condition necessitates the standardization of all weights to true values.

Although there are several methods for weighing in use in the various technical laboratories, that of the double swing or vibration is probably the best for standardization of weights.

## STANDARDIZATION

There are three methods for standardizing weights:
1. Standardizing the weights to true or absolute values.
2. Standardizing the weights to weigh true or absolute weights.
3. Standardizing the weights to bear true relation to each other.

The procedure followed in the first method is dependent upon the comparative arm lengths of the balance. If the arm lengths are equal, the weights are standardized by direct weighing or balancing on the opposite pans. If unequal, by substitution weighing or having both weights, when placed alternately on the left pan, balance a given mass on the right pan.

The standardization of the weights by the second method is independent of arm length. The weights are standardized by adjusting them so that when they are placed on the right pan they balance the standard weights of a similar denomination placed on the left pan.

In small laboratories where there is but one balance used for fine work, or for students' use, the third method is very satisfactory.

In the first two methods of standardization, each weight is standardized independently.

In all cases of two or more weights of one denomination, the second and third should be marked with one and two dots respectively.

It is, of course, assumed that high-grade balances are used and are thoroughly understood by the chemist, and that in weighing, objects to be weighed are placed on the left pan.

*First Method.* (Assuming the arm lengths unequal).—It is both convenient and time saving in this work to have an extra set of weights to use as counterpoises.

Place a standard 5- or 10-mgm. weight on the left pan and the 5- or 10-mgm. rider on the right beam. Adjust the weight of the rider until it balances the weight on the left pan when it is located at a point indicating that denomination. Remove both weights. Place the standard 100-g. weight on the left pan and balance it with the counterpoise set. Replace the standard with the 100-g. weight to be standardized and adjust the weight until it balances the counterpoise. Continue in this manner throughout the entire set.

In case the balance arms are equal, the counterpoise set may be dispensed with and the set being standardized placed on the right pan. Of course when weights of absolute value are used on a balance having unequal arm lengths, corrections must be made on all weighings.

*Second Method.*—This method is the more practical since it is independent of arm length. However weights standardized in this way can only be used on the balance on which they have been standardized.

Place the standard 5- or 10-mgm. weight on the left pan and the 5- or 10-mgm. rider on the right beam, adjust the rider until it balances the weight on the left pan when it is on the point indicating the denomination of that weight. Remove both weights. Place the standard 100-g. weight on the left pan and the 100-g. weight to be standardized on the right pan. Adjust the weight until it balances the standard. Continue with all other weights in the same manner one at a time.

**Adjustment of Weights.**—Since it is not practical in commercial work to use corrections on weights, they should be adjusted when standardized. In the case of brass weights, by removing the top and either adding or removing granulated aluminum or lead (20–40-mesh) as required, and in the case of platinum fractional weights, fusing on gold shavings cut from foil or wire, if light, or removing platinum with a small file if heavy. When aluminum is used for fractional weights and one is found light, it is advisable to destroy it and replace with another.

When making the adjustment of the brass weight, the weight should be gripped with pieces of heavy linen cloth or chamois skin, never with the fingers. The metal should be added or removed with a pair of tweezers and the weight allowed to stand 15 minutes before final checking. While it is standing other weights may be adjusted. In this way little time is lost.

*Third Method.*—If the arms of the balance are equal, the weights may be compared with each other. If, however, they are unequal, the method of substitution must be used and another set of weights will be required. In the latter case the counterbalance weights are placed in the left pan and the set being standardized on the right.

The following method assumes the arm lengths equal or practically so:

Place the 5- or 10-mgm. weight on the left pan and the 5- or 10-mgm. rider on the right beam. Adjust the rider with fine emery cloth until it balances the weight when on the point indicating its denomination. Take a 10-mgm. weight from another box for use as a tare and call it $T$. Place $T$ on the left pan and one of the 10-mgm. weights on the right and balance with the rider if necessary. Record the weight, e.g.,

$$0.01 = T + 0.0001$$

Replace the weight on the right with the other 10-mgm. weight and again balance.

Record the weight, e.g.,

$$0.01_2 = T + 0.0001$$

Replace the tare with the 20-mgm. weight and put both 10-mgm. weights on the right pan and balance. Record weights as follows:

$$0.02 = 0.01 + 0.01_2 + 0.0001$$

or

$$0.02 = 2T + 0.0003$$

Replace the 20-mgm. weight with the 50-mgm. weight and place the 20-mgm. weight and tare on the right pan with the two 10-mgm. weights. Balance and record the weights, e.g.,

$$0.05 = 0.02 + 0.01 + 0.01_2 + T + 0.0000$$

or

$$0.05 = 5T + 0.0005$$

Place the 50-mgm. weight on the right pan and the 100-mgm. weight on the left pan. Balance and record the weight, e.g.,

$$0.10 = 0.05 + 0.02 + 0.01 + 0.01_2 + T - 0.0003$$

or

$$0.10 = 10T + 0.0007$$

The remaining decigram and gram weights are tested in this manner and the results compiled as follows:

| Nominal Value | Value Found on Test | Values Using $T = 0.01$ | Corrected Using 1.0005 as Std. | Corrections |
|---|---|---|---|---|
| 0.01 | $T + 0.0001$ | 0.0101 | 0.0100 | +0.0001 |
| $0.01_2$ | $T + 0.0001$ | 0.0101 | 0.0100 | +0.0001 |
| 0.02 | $2T + 0.0003$ | 0.0203 | 0.0200 | +0.0003 |
| 0.05 | $5T + 0.0005$ | 0.0505 | 0.0500 | +0.0005 |
| 0.10 | $10T + 0.0007$ | 0.1007 | 0.1001 | +0.0006 |
| $0.10_2$ | $10T + 0.0006$ | 0.1006 | 0.1001 | +0.0005 |
| 0.20 | $20T + 0.0007$ | 0.2007 | 0.2001 | +0.0006 |
| 0.50 | $50T + 0.0004$ | 0.5004 | 0.5003 | +0.0001 |
| 1.00 | $100T + 0.0005$ | 1.0005 | 1.0005 | +0.0000 |
| 2.00 | $200T + 0.0006$ | 2.0006 | 2.0010 | −0.0004 |
| $2.00_2$ | $200T + 0.0009$ | 2.0009 | 2.0010 | −0.0001 |
| etc. | | | | |

*Effect of Buoyancy.*—In making accurate weighings the buoyant effect of air on the weight and mass being weighed must be considered. When the mass being weighed has a specific gravity differing with that of the weights, the buoyancy of the air on the two masses will affect the accuracy of the weighing. Thus the weighing of a 1-g. sample of potassium chloride with brass weights without correction for buoyancy results in an error of 0.00046 g. or approximately 0.05%.

The following formula may be used in making this correction for general work carried on under normal conditions:

$$\text{Correct weight} = W + 0.0012\, \frac{W}{S} - \frac{W}{S_1}$$

where $W$ = the apparent weight of the object, $S$ and $S_1$ the specific gravities of the object and weights respectively.

0.0012 is the weight of 1 ml. of air at normal laboratory conditions.

The specific gravities of metal generally used in weights are Platinum 21.5, Brass 8.4 and Aluminum 2.7.

*Precision and Tolerances of Weights.*—The following is a table of the Precision of Corrections and Tolerances of Class S analytical weights issued by the U. S. Bureau of Standards, Washington, D. C. While it is quite evident that the Precision of Correction is beyond the accuracy of a $\frac{1}{10}$ mgm. or even a $\frac{1}{20}$ mgm. balance, it is however advisable to standardize the weights to the limit of sensitiveness of the balance.

| Denomination | Tolerance | Precision of Correction |
|---|---|---|
| 100 grams | 0.5 mgm. | 0.1 mgm. |
| 50 | 0.3 | 0.1 |
| 20 | 0.2 | 0.1 |
| 10 | 0.15 | 0.05 |
| 5 | 0.15 | 0.05 |
| 2 | 0.1 | 0.05 |
| 1 | 0.1 | 0.05 |
| 500 mgms. | 0.05 | 0.01 |
| 200 | 0.05 | 0.01 |
| 100 | 0.05 | 0.01 |
| 50 | 0.03 | 0.01 |
| 20 | 0.03 | 0.01 |
| 10 | 0.02 | 0.01 |
| 5 | 0.02 | 0.01 |
| 2 | 0.01 | 0.01 |
| 1 | 0.01 | 0.01 |

## COMMON LOGARITHMS OF NUMBERS
### To Five Decimal Places

| N | 0 | 1 | 2 | 3 | 4 | 5 | 6 | 7 | 8 | 9 |
|---|---|---|---|---|---|---|---|---|---|---|
| 100 | 00 000 | 043 | 087 | 130 | 173 | 217 | 260 | 303 | 346 | 389 |
| 01 | 432 | 475 | 518 | 561 | 604 | 647 | 689 | 732 | 775 | 817 |
| 02 | 860 | 903 | 945 | 988 | *030 | *072 | *115 | *157 | *199 | *242 |
| 03 | 01 284 | 326 | 368 | 410 | 452 | 494 | 536 | 578 | 620 | 662 |
| 04 | 703 | 745 | 787 | 828 | 870 | 912 | 953 | 995 | *036 | *078 |
| 05 | 02 119 | 160 | 202 | 243 | 284 | 325 | 366 | 407 | 449 | 490 |
| 06 | 531 | 572 | 612 | 653 | 694 | 735 | 776 | 816 | 857 | 898 |
| 07 | 938 | 979 | *019 | *060 | *100 | *141 | *181 | *222 | *262 | *302 |
| 08 | 03 342 | 383 | 423 | 463 | 503 | 543 | 583 | 623 | 663 | 703 |
| 09 | 743 | 782 | 822 | 862 | 902 | 941 | 981 | *021 | *060 | *100 |
| 110 | 04 139 | 179 | 218 | 258 | 297 | 336 | 376 | 415 | 454 | 493 |
| 11 | 532 | 571 | 610 | 650 | 689 | 727 | 766 | 805 | 844 | 883 |
| 12 | 922 | 961 | 999 | *038 | *077 | *115 | *154 | *192 | *231 | *269 |
| 13 | 05 308 | 346 | 385 | 423 | 461 | 500 | 538 | 576 | 614 | 652 |
| 14 | 690 | 729 | 767 | 805 | 843 | 881 | 918 | 956 | 994 | *032 |
| 15 | 06 070 | 108 | 145 | 183 | 221 | 258 | 296 | 333 | 371 | 408 |
| 16 | 446 | 483 | 521 | 558 | 595 | 633 | 670 | 707 | 744 | 781 |
| 17 | 819 | 856 | 893 | 930 | 967 | *004 | *041 | *078 | *115 | *151 |
| 18 | 07 188 | 225 | 262 | 298 | 335 | 372 | 408 | 445 | 482 | 518 |
| 19 | 555 | 591 | 628 | 664 | 700 | 737 | 773 | 809 | 846 | 882 |
| 120 | 918 | 954 | 990 | *027 | *063 | *099 | *135 | *171 | *207 | *243 |
| 21 | 08 279 | 314 | 350 | 386 | 422 | 458 | 493 | 529 | 565 | 600 |
| 22 | 636 | 672 | 707 | 743 | 778 | 814 | 849 | 884 | 920 | 955 |
| 23 | 991 | *026 | *061 | *096 | *132 | *167 | *202 | *237 | *272 | *307 |
| 24 | 09 342 | 377 | 412 | 447 | 482 | 517 | 552 | 587 | 621 | 656 |
| 25 | 691 | 726 | 760 | 795 | 830 | 864 | 899 | 934 | 968 | *003 |
| 26 | 10 037 | 072 | 106 | 140 | 175 | 209 | 243 | 278 | 312 | 346 |
| 27 | 380 | 415 | 449 | 483 | 517 | 551 | 585 | 619 | 653 | 687 |
| 28 | 721 | 755 | 789 | 823 | 857 | 890 | 924 | 958 | 992 | *025 |
| 29 | 11 059 | 093 | 126 | 160 | 193 | 227 | 261 | 294 | 327 | 361 |
| 130 | 394 | 428 | 461 | 494 | 528 | 561 | 594 | 628 | 661 | 694 |
| 31 | 727 | 760 | 793 | 826 | 860 | 893 | 926 | 959 | 992 | *024 |
| 32 | 12 057 | 090 | 123 | 156 | 189 | 222 | 254 | 287 | 320 | 352 |
| 33 | 385 | 418 | 450 | 483 | 516 | 548 | 581 | 613 | 646 | 678 |
| 34 | 710 | 743 | 775 | 808 | 840 | 872 | 905 | 937 | 969 | *001 |
| 35 | 13 033 | 066 | 098 | 130 | 162 | 194 | 226 | 258 | 290 | 322 |
| 36 | 354 | 386 | 418 | 450 | 481 | 513 | 545 | 577 | 609 | 640 |
| 37 | 672 | 704 | 735 | 767 | 799 | 830 | 862 | 893 | 925 | 956 |
| 38 | 988 | *019 | *051 | *082 | *114 | *145 | *176 | *208 | *239 | *270 |
| 39 | 14 301 | 333 | 364 | 395 | 426 | 457 | 489 | 520 | 551 | 582 |
| 140 | 613 | 644 | 675 | 706 | 737 | 768 | 799 | 829 | 860 | 891 |
| 41 | 922 | 953 | 983 | *014 | *045 | *076 | *106 | *137 | *168 | *198 |
| 42 | 15 229 | 259 | 290 | 320 | 351 | 381 | 412 | 442 | 473 | 503 |
| 43 | 534 | 564 | 594 | 625 | 655 | 685 | 715 | 746 | 776 | 806 |
| 44 | 836 | 866 | 897 | 927 | 957 | 987 | *017 | *047 | *077 | *107 |
| 45 | 16 137 | 167 | 197 | 227 | 256 | 286 | 316 | 346 | 376 | 406 |
| 46 | 435 | 465 | 495 | 524 | 554 | 584 | 613 | 643 | 673 | 702 |
| 47 | 732 | 761 | 791 | 820 | 850 | 879 | 909 | 938 | 967 | 997 |
| 48 | 17 026 | 056 | 085 | 114 | 143 | 173 | 202 | 231 | 260 | 289 |
| 49 | 319 | 348 | 377 | 406 | 435 | 464 | 493 | 522 | 551 | 580 |
| 150 | 609 | 638 | 667 | 696 | 725 | 754 | 782 | 811 | 840 | 869 |
| N | 0 | 1 | 2 | 3 | 4 | 5 | 6 | 7 | 8 | 9 |

### P P

| | 44 | 43 | 42 |
|---|---|---|---|
| 1 | 4.4 | 4.3 | 4.2 |
| 2 | 8.8 | 8.6 | 8.4 |
| 3 | 13.2 | 12.9 | 12.6 |
| 4 | 17.6 | 17.2 | 16.8 |
| 5 | 22.0 | 21.5 | 21.0 |
| 6 | 26.4 | 25.8 | 25.2 |
| 7 | 30.8 | 30.1 | 29.4 |
| 8 | 35.2 | 34.4 | 33.6 |
| 9 | 39.6 | 38.7 | 37.8 |

| | 41 | 40 | 39 |
|---|---|---|---|
| 1 | 4.1 | 4.0 | 3.9 |
| 2 | 8.2 | 8.0 | 7.8 |
| 3 | 12.3 | 12.0 | 11.7 |
| 4 | 16.4 | 16.0 | 15.6 |
| 5 | 20.5 | 20.0 | 19.5 |
| 6 | 24.6 | 24.0 | 23.4 |
| 7 | 28.7 | 28.0 | 27.3 |
| 8 | 32.8 | 32.0 | 31.2 |
| 9 | 36.9 | 36.0 | 35.1 |

| | 38 | 37 | 36 |
|---|---|---|---|
| 1 | 3.8 | 3.7 | 3.6 |
| 2 | 7.6 | 7.4 | 7.2 |
| 3 | 11.4 | 11.1 | 10.8 |
| 4 | 15.2 | 14.8 | 14.4 |
| 5 | 19.0 | 18.5 | 18.0 |
| 6 | 22.8 | 22.2 | 21.6 |
| 7 | 26.6 | 25.9 | 25.2 |
| 8 | 30.4 | 29.6 | 28.8 |
| 9 | 34.2 | 33.3 | 32.4 |

| | 35 | 34 | 33 |
|---|---|---|---|
| 1 | 3.5 | 3.4 | 3.3 |
| 2 | 7.0 | 6.8 | 6.6 |
| 3 | 10.5 | 10.2 | 9.9 |
| 4 | 14.0 | 13.6 | 13.2 |
| 5 | 17.5 | 17.0 | 16.5 |
| 6 | 21.0 | 20.4 | 19.8 |
| 7 | 24.5 | 23.8 | 23.1 |
| 8 | 28.0 | 27.2 | 26.4 |
| 9 | 31.5 | 30.6 | 29.7 |

| | 32 | 31 | 30 |
|---|---|---|---|
| 1 | 3.2 | 3.1 | 3.0 |
| 2 | 6.4 | 6.2 | 6.0 |
| 3 | 9.6 | 9.3 | 9.0 |
| 4 | 12.8 | 12.4 | 12.0 |
| 5 | 16.0 | 15.5 | 15.0 |
| 6 | 19.2 | 18.6 | 18.0 |
| 7 | 22.4 | 21.7 | 21.0 |
| 8 | 25.6 | 24.8 | 24.0 |
| 9 | 28.8 | 27.9 | 27.0 |

P P

## COMMON LOGARITHMS OF NUMBERS (Continued)

| N | 0 | 1 | 2 | 3 | 4 | 5 | 6 | 7 | 8 | 9 |
|---|---|---|---|---|---|---|---|---|---|---|
| **150** | 17 609 | 638 | 667 | 696 | 725 | 754 | 782 | 811 | 840 | 869 |
| 51 | 898 | 926 | 955 | 984 | *013 | *041 | *070 | *099 | *127 | *156 |
| 52 | 18 184 | 213 | 241 | 270 | 298 | 327 | 355 | 384 | 412 | 441 |
| 53 | 469 | 498 | 526 | 554 | 583 | 611 | 639 | 667 | 696 | 724 |
| 54 | 752 | 780 | 808 | 837 | 865 | 893 | 921 | 949 | 977 | *005 |
| 55 | 19 033 | 061 | 089 | 117 | 145 | 173 | 201 | 229 | 257 | 285 |
| 56 | 312 | 340 | 368 | 396 | 424 | 451 | 479 | 507 | 535 | 562 |
| 57 | 590 | 618 | 645 | 673 | 700 | 728 | 756 | 783 | 811 | 838 |
| 58 | 866 | 893 | 921 | 948 | 976 | *003 | *030 | *058 | *085 | *112 |
| 59 | 20 140 | 167 | 194 | 222 | 249 | 276 | 303 | 330 | 358 | 385 |
| **160** | 412 | 439 | 466 | 493 | 520 | 548 | 575 | 602 | 629 | 656 |
| 61 | 683 | 710 | 737 | 763 | 790 | 817 | 844 | 871 | 898 | 925 |
| 62 | 952 | 978 | *005 | *032 | *059 | *085 | *112 | *139 | *165 | *192 |
| 63 | 21 219 | 245 | 272 | 299 | 325 | 352 | 378 | 405 | 431 | 458 |
| 64 | 484 | 511 | 537 | 564 | 590 | 617 | 643 | 669 | 696 | 722 |
| 65 | 748 | 775 | 801 | 827 | 854 | 880 | 906 | 932 | 958 | 985 |
| 66 | 22 011 | 037 | 063 | 089 | 115 | 141 | 167 | 194 | 220 | 246 |
| 67 | 272 | 298 | 324 | 350 | 376 | 401 | 427 | 453 | 479 | 505 |
| 68 | 531 | 557 | 583 | 608 | 634 | 660 | 686 | 712 | 737 | 763 |
| 69 | 789 | 814 | 840 | 866 | 891 | 917 | 943 | 968 | 994 | *019 |
| **170** | 23 045 | 070 | 096 | 121 | 147 | 172 | 198 | 223 | 249 | 274 |
| 71 | 300 | 325 | 350 | 376 | 401 | 426 | 452 | 477 | 502 | 528 |
| 72 | 553 | 578 | 603 | 629 | 654 | 679 | 704 | 729 | 754 | 779 |
| 73 | 805 | 830 | 855 | 880 | 905 | 930 | 955 | 980 | *005 | *030 |
| 74 | 24 055 | 080 | 105 | 130 | 155 | 180 | 204 | 229 | 254 | 279 |
| 75 | 304 | 329 | 353 | 378 | 403 | 428 | 452 | 477 | 502 | 527 |
| 76 | 551 | 576 | 601 | 625 | 650 | 674 | 699 | 724 | 748 | 773 |
| 77 | 797 | 822 | 846 | 871 | 895 | 920 | 944 | 969 | 993 | *018 |
| 78 | 25 042 | 066 | 091 | 115 | 139 | 164 | 188 | 212 | 237 | 261 |
| 79 | 285 | 310 | 334 | 358 | 382 | 406 | 431 | 455 | 479 | 503 |
| **180** | 527 | 551 | 575 | 600 | 624 | 648 | 672 | 696 | 720 | 744 |
| 81 | 768 | 792 | 816 | 840 | 864 | 888 | 912 | 935 | 959 | 983 |
| 82 | 26 007 | 031 | 055 | 079 | 102 | 126 | 150 | 174 | 198 | 221 |
| 83 | 245 | 269 | 293 | 316 | 340 | 364 | 387 | 411 | 435 | 458 |
| 84 | 482 | 505 | 529 | 553 | 576 | 600 | 623 | 647 | 670 | 694 |
| 85 | 717 | 741 | 764 | 788 | 811 | 834 | 858 | 881 | 905 | 928 |
| 86 | 951 | 975 | 998 | *021 | *045 | *068 | *091 | *114 | *138 | *161 |
| 87 | 27 184 | 207 | 231 | 254 | 277 | 300 | 323 | 346 | 370 | 393 |
| 88 | 416 | 439 | 462 | 485 | 508 | 531 | 554 | 577 | 600 | 623 |
| 89 | 646 | 669 | 692 | 715 | 738 | 761 | 784 | 807 | 830 | 852 |
| **190** | 875 | 898 | 921 | 944 | 967 | 989 | *012 | *035 | *058 | *081 |
| 91 | 28 103 | 126 | 149 | 171 | 194 | 217 | 240 | 262 | 285 | 307 |
| 92 | 330 | 353 | 375 | 398 | 421 | 443 | 466 | 488 | 511 | 533 |
| 93 | 556 | 578 | 601 | 623 | 646 | 668 | 691 | 713 | 735 | 758 |
| 94 | 780 | 803 | 825 | 847 | 870 | 892 | 914 | 937 | 959 | 981 |
| 95 | 29 003 | 026 | 048 | 070 | 092 | 115 | 137 | 159 | 181 | 203 |
| 96 | 226 | 248 | 270 | 292 | 314 | 336 | 358 | 380 | 403 | 425 |
| 97 | 447 | 469 | 491 | 513 | 535 | 557 | 579 | 601 | 623 | 645 |
| 98 | 667 | 688 | 710 | 732 | 754 | 776 | 798 | 820 | 842 | 863 |
| 99 | 885 | 907 | 929 | 951 | 973 | 994 | *016 | *038 | *060 | *081 |
| **200** | 30 103 | 125 | 146 | 168 | 190 | 211 | 233 | 255 | 276 | 298 |
| N | 0 | 1 | 2 | 3 | 4 | 5 | 6 | 7 | 8 | 9 |

**P P**

| | 29 | 28 |
|---|---|---|
| 1 | 2.9 | 2.8 |
| 2 | 5.8 | 5.6 |
| 3 | 8.7 | 8.4 |
| 4 | 11.6 | 11.2 |
| 5 | 14.5 | 14.0 |
| 6 | 17.4 | 16.8 |
| 7 | 20.3 | 19.6 |
| 8 | 23.2 | 22.4 |
| 9 | 26.1 | 25.2 |

| | 27 | 26 |
|---|---|---|
| 1 | 2.7 | 2.6 |
| 2 | 5.4 | 5.2 |
| 3 | 8.1 | 7.8 |
| 4 | 10.8 | 10.4 |
| 5 | 13.5 | 13.0 |
| 6 | 16.2 | 15.6 |
| 7 | 18.9 | 18.2 |
| 8 | 21.6 | 20.8 |
| 9 | 24.3 | 23.4 |

| | 25 |
|---|---|
| 1 | 2.5 |
| 2 | 5.0 |
| 3 | 7.5 |
| 4 | 10.0 |
| 5 | 12.5 |
| 6 | 15.0 |
| 7 | 17.5 |
| 8 | 20.0 |
| 9 | 22.5 |

| | 24 | 23 |
|---|---|---|
| 1 | 2.4 | 2.3 |
| 2 | 4.8 | 4.6 |
| 3 | 7.2 | 6.9 |
| 4 | 9.6 | 9.2 |
| 5 | 12.0 | 11.5 |
| 6 | 14.4 | 13.8 |
| 7 | 16.8 | 16.1 |
| 8 | 19.2 | 18.4 |
| 9 | 21.6 | 20.7 |

| | 22 | 21 |
|---|---|---|
| 1 | 2.2 | 2.1 |
| 2 | 4.4 | 4.2 |
| 3 | 6.6 | 6.3 |
| 4 | 8.8 | 8.4 |
| 5 | 11.0 | 10.5 |
| 6 | 13.2 | 12.6 |
| 7 | 15.4 | 14.7 |
| 8 | 17.6 | 16.8 |
| 9 | 19.8 | 18.9 |

## COMMON LOGARITHMS OF NUMBERS (Continued)

| N | 0 | 1 | 2 | 3 | 4 | 5 | 6 | 7 | 8 | 9 |
|---|---|---|---|---|---|---|---|---|---|---|
| **200** | 30 103 | 125 | 146 | 168 | 190 | 211 | 233 | 255 | 276 | 298 |
| 01 | 320 | 341 | 363 | 384 | 406 | 428 | 449 | 471 | 492 | 514 |
| 02 | 535 | 557 | 578 | 600 | 621 | 643 | 664 | 685 | 707 | 728 |
| 03 | 750 | 771 | 792 | 814 | 835 | 856 | 878 | 899 | 920 | 942 |
| 04 | 963 | 984 | *006 | *027 | *048 | *069 | *091 | *112 | *133 | *154 |
| 05 | 31 175 | 197 | 218 | 239 | 260 | 281 | 302 | 323 | 345 | 366 |
| 06 | 387 | 408 | 429 | 450 | 471 | 492 | 513 | 534 | 555 | 576 |
| 07 | 597 | 618 | 639 | 660 | 681 | 702 | 723 | 744 | 765 | 785 |
| 08 | 806 | 827 | 848 | 869 | 890 | 911 | 931 | 952 | 973 | 994 |
| 09 | 32 015 | 035 | 056 | 077 | 098 | 118 | 139 | 160 | 181 | 201 |
| **210** | 222 | 243 | 263 | 284 | 305 | 325 | 346 | 366 | 387 | 408 |
| 11 | 428 | 449 | 469 | 490 | 510 | 531 | 552 | 572 | 593 | 613 |
| 12 | 634 | 654 | 675 | 695 | 715 | 736 | 756 | 777 | 797 | 818 |
| 13 | 838 | 858 | 879 | 899 | 919 | 940 | 960 | 980 | *001 | *021 |
| 14 | 33 041 | 062 | 082 | 102 | 122 | 143 | 163 | 183 | 203 | 224 |
| 15 | 244 | 264 | 284 | 304 | 325 | 345 | 365 | 385 | 405 | 425 |
| 16 | 445 | 465 | 486 | 506 | 526 | 546 | 566 | 586 | 606 | 626 |
| 17 | 646 | 666 | 686 | 706 | 726 | 746 | 766 | 786 | 806 | 826 |
| 18 | 846 | 866 | 885 | 905 | 925 | 945 | 965 | 985 | *005 | *025 |
| 19 | 34 044 | 064 | 084 | 104 | 124 | 143 | 163 | 183 | 203 | 223 |
| **220** | 242 | 262 | 282 | 301 | 321 | 341 | 361 | 380 | 400 | 420 |
| 21 | 439 | 459 | 479` | 498 | 518 | 537 | 557 | 577 | 596 | 616 |
| 22 | 635 | 655 | 674 | 694 | 713 | 733 | 753 | 772 | 792 | 811 |
| 23 | 830 | 850 | 869 | 889 | 908 | 928 | 947 | 967 | 986 | *005 |
| 24 | 35 025 | 044 | 064 | 083 | 102 | 122 | 141 | 160 | 180 | 199 |
| 25 | 218 | 238 | 257 | 276 | 295 | 315 | 334 | 353 | 372 | 392 |
| 26 | 411 | 430 | 449 | 468 | 488 | 507 | 526 | 545 | 564 | 583 |
| 27 | 603 | 622 | 641 | 660 | 679 | 698 | 717 | 736 | 755 | 774 |
| 28 | 793 | 813 | 832 | 851 | 870 | 889 | 908 | 927 | 946 | 965 |
| 29 | 984 | *003 | *021 | *040 | *059 | *078 | *097 | *116 | *135 | *154 |
| **230** | 36 173 | 192 | 211 | 229 | 248 | 267 | 286 | 305 | 324 | 342 |
| 31 | 361 | 380 | 399 | 418 | 436 | 455 | 474 | 493 | 511 | 530 |
| 32 | 549 | 568 | 586 | 605 | 624 | 642 | 661 | 680 | 698 | 717 |
| 33 | 736 | 754 | 773 | 791 | 810 | 829 | 847 | 866 | 884 | 903 |
| 34 | 922 | 940 | 959 | 977 | 996 | *014 | *033 | *051 | *070 | *088 |
| 35 | 37 107 | 125 | 144 | 162 | 181 | 199 | 218 | 236 | 254 | 273 |
| 36 | 291 | 310 | 328 | 346 | 365 | 383 | 401 | 420 | 438 | 457 |
| 37 | 475 | 493 | 511 | 530 | 548 | 566 | 585 | 603 | 621 | 639 |
| 38 | 658 | 676 | 694 | 712 | 731 | 749 | 767 | 785 | 803 | 822 |
| 39 | 840 | 858 | 876 | 894 | 912 | 931 | 949 | 967 | 985 | *003 |
| **240** | 38 021 | 039 | 057 | 075 | 093 | 112 | 130 | 148 | 166 | 184 |
| 41 | 202 | 220 | 238 | 256 | 274 | 292 | 310 | 328 | 346 | 364 |
| 42 | 382 | 399 | 417 | 435 | 453 | 471 | 489 | 507 | 525 | 543 |
| 43 | 561 | 578 | 596 | 614 | 632 | 650 | 668 | 686 | 703 | 721 |
| 44 | 739 | 757 | 775 | 792 | 810 | 828 | 846 | 863 | 881 | 899 |
| 45 | 917 | 934 | 952 | 970 | 987 | *005 | *023 | *041 | *058 | *076 |
| 46 | 39 094 | 111 | 129 | 146 | 164 | 182 | 199 | 217 | 235 | 252 |
| 47 | 270 | 287 | 305 | 322 | 340 | 358 | 375 | 393 | 410 | 428 |
| 48 | 445 | 463 | 480 | 498 | 515 | 533 | 550 | 568 | 585 | 602 |
| 49 | 620 | 637 | 655 | 672 | 690 | 707 | 724 | 742 | 759 | 777 |
| **250** | 794 | 811 | 829 | 846 | 863 | 881 | 898 | 915 | 933 | 950 |
| N | 0 | 1 | 2 | 3 | 4 | 5 | 6 | 7 | 8 | 9 |

**P P**

| | 22 | 21 |
|---|---|---|
| 1 | 2.2 | 2.1 |
| 2 | 4.4 | 4.2 |
| 3 | 6.6 | 6.3 |
| 4 | 8.8 | 8.4 |
| 5 | 11.0 | 10.5 |
| 6 | 13.2 | 12.6 |
| 7 | 15.4 | 14.7 |
| 8 | 17.6 | 16.8 |
| 9 | 19.8 | 18.9 |

| | 20 |
|---|---|
| 1 | 2.0 |
| 2 | 4.0 |
| 3 | 6.0 |
| 4 | 8.0 |
| 5 | 10.0 |
| 6 | 12.0 |
| 7 | 14.0 |
| 8 | 16.0 |
| 9 | 18.0 |

| | 19 |
|---|---|
| 1 | 1.9 |
| 2 | 3.8 |
| 3 | 5.7 |
| 4 | 7.6 |
| 5 | 9.5 |
| 6 | 11.4 |
| 7 | 13.3 |
| 8 | 15.2 |
| 9 | 17.1 |

| | 18 |
|---|---|
| 1 | 1.8 |
| 2 | 3.6 |
| 3 | 5.4 |
| 4 | 7.2 |
| 5 | 9.0 |
| 6 | 10.8 |
| 7 | 12.6 |
| 8 | 14.4 |
| 9 | 16.2 |

| | 17 |
|---|---|
| 1 | 1.7 |
| 2 | 3.4 |
| 3 | 5.1 |
| 4 | 6.8 |
| 5 | 8.5 |
| 6 | 10.2 |
| 7 | 11.9 |
| 8 | 13.6 |
| 9 | 15.3 |

## COMMON LOGARITHMS OF NUMBERS (Continued)

| N | 0 | 1 | 2 | 3 | 4 | 5 | 6 | 7 | 8 | 9 |
|---|---|---|---|---|---|---|---|---|---|---|
| **250** | 39 794 | 811 | 829 | 846 | 863 | 881 | 898 | 915 | 933 | 950 |
| 51 | 967 | 985 | *002 | *019 | *037 | *054 | *071 | *088 | *106 | *123 |
| 52 | 40 140 | 157 | 175 | 192 | 209 | 226 | 243 | 261 | 278 | 295 |
| 53 | 312 | 329 | 346 | 364 | 381 | 398 | 415 | 432 | 449 | 466 |
| 54 | 483 | 500 | 518 | 535 | 552 | 569 | 586 | 603 | 620 | 637 |
| 55 | 654 | 671 | 688 | 705 | 722 | 739 | 756 | 773 | 790 | 807 |
| 56 | 824 | 841 | 858 | 875 | 892 | 909 | 926 | 943 | 960 | 976 |
| 57 | 993 | *010 | *027 | *044 | *061 | *078 | *095 | *111 | *128 | *145 |
| 58 | 41 162 | 179 | 196 | 212 | 229 | 246 | 263 | 280 | 296 | 313 |
| 59 | 330 | 347 | 363 | 380 | 397 | 414 | 430 | 447 | 464 | 481 |
| **260** | 497 | 514 | 531 | 547 | 564 | 581 | 597 | 614 | 631 | 647 |
| 61 | 664 | 681 | 697 | 714 | 731 | 747 | 764 | 780 | 797 | 814 |
| 62 | 830 | 817 | 863 | 880 | 896 | 913 | .929 | 946 | 963 | 979 |
| 63 | 996 | *012 | *029 | *045 | *062 | *078 | *095 | *111 | *127 | *144 |
| 64 | 42 160 | 177 | 193 | 210 | 226 | 243 | 259 | 275 | 292 | 308 |
| 65 | 325 | 341 | 357 | 374 | 390 | 406 | 423 | 439 | 455 | 472 |
| 66 | 488 | 504 | 521. | 537 | 553 | 570 | 586 | 602 | 619 | 635 |
| 67 | 651 | 667 | 684 | 700 | 716 | 732 | 749 | 765 | 781 | 797 |
| 68 | 813 | 830 | 846 | 862 | 878 | 894 | 911 | 927 | 943 | 959 |
| 69 | 975 | 991 | *008 | *024 | *040 | *056 | *072 | *088 | *104 | *120 |
| **270** | 43 136 | 152 | 169 | 185 | 201 | 217 | 233 | 249 | 265 | 281 |
| 71 | 297 | 313 | 329 | 345 | 361 | 377 | 393 | 409 | 425 | 441 |
| 72 | 457 | 473 | 489 | 505 | 521 | 537 | 553 | 569 | 584 | 600 |
| 73 | 616 | 632 | 648 | 664 | 680 | 696 | 712 | 727 | 743 | 759 |
| 74 | 775 | 791 | 807 | 823 | 838 | 854 | 870 | 886 | 902 | 917 |
| 75 | 933 | 949 | 965 | 981 | 996 | *012 | *028 | *044 | *059 | *075 |
| 76 | 44 091 | 107 | 122 | 138 | 154 | 170 | 185 | 201 | 217 | 232 |
| 77 | 248 | 264 | 279 | 295 | 311 | 326 | 342 | 358 | 373 | 389 |
| 78 | 404 | 420 | 436 | 451 | 467 | 483 | 498 | 514 | 529 | 545 |
| 79 | 560 | 576 | 592 | 607 | 623 | 638 | 654 | 669 | 685 | 700 |
| **280** | 716 | 731 | 747 | 762 | 778 | 793 | 809 | 824 | 840 | 855 |
| 81 | 871 | 886 | 902 | 917 | 932 | 948 | 963 | 979 | 994 | *010 |
| 82 | 45 025 | 040 | 056 | 071 | 086 | 102 | 117 | 133 | 148 | 163 |
| 83 | 179 | 194 | 209 | 225 | 240 | 255 | 271 | 286 | 301 | 317 |
| 84 | 332 | 347 | 362 | 378 | 393 | 408 | 423 | 439 | 454 | 469 |
| 85 | 484 | 500 | 515 | 530 | 545 | 561 | 576 | 591 | 606 | 621 |
| 86 | 637 | 652 | 667 | 682 | 697 | 712 | 728 | 743 | 758 | 773 |
| 87 | 788 | 803 | 818 | 834 | 849 | 864 | 879 | 894 | 909 | 924 |
| 88 | 939 | 954 | 969 | 984 | *000 | *015 | *030 | *045 | *060 | *075 |
| 89 | 46 090 | 105 | 120 | 135 | 150 | 165 | 180 | 195 | 210 | 225 |
| **290** | 240 | 255 | 270 | 285 | 300 | 315 | 330 | 345 | 359 | 374 |
| 91 | 389 | 404 | 419 | 434 | 449 | 464 | 479 | 494 | 509 | 523 |
| 92 | 538 | 553 | 568 | 583 | 598 | 613 | 627 | 642 | 657 | 672 |
| 93 | 687 | 702 | 716 | 731 | 746 | 761 | 776 | 790 | 805 | 820 |
| 94 | 835 | 850 | 864 | 879 | 894 | 909 | 923 | 938 | 953 | 967 |
| 95 | 982 | 997 | *012 | *026 | *041 | *056 | *070 | *085 | *100 | *114 |
| 96 | 47 129 | 144 | 159 | 173 | 188 | 202 | 217 | 232 | 246 | 261 |
| 97 | 276 | 290 | 305 | 319 | 334 | 349 | 363 | 378 | 392 | 407 |
| 98 | 422 | 436 | 451 | 465 | 480 | 494 | 509 | 524 | 538 | 553 |
| 99 | 567 | 582 | 596 | 611 | 625 | 640 | 654 | 669 | 683 | 698 |
| **300** | 712 | 727 | 741 | 756 | 770 | 784 | 799 | 813 | 828 | 842 |
| N | 0 | 1 | 2 | 3 | 4 | 5 | 6 | 7 | 8 | 9 |

**P P**

| | 18 | 17 | 16 | 15 | 14 |
|---|---|---|---|---|---|
| 1 | 1.8 | 1.7 | 1.6 | 1.5 | 1.4 |
| 2 | 3.6 | 3.4 | 3.2 | 3.0 | 2.8 |
| 3 | 5.4 | 5.1 | 4.8 | 4.5 | 4.2 |
| 4 | 7.2 | 6.8 | 6.4 | 6.0 | 5.6 |
| 5 | 9.0 | 8.5 | 8.0 | 7.5 | 7.0 |
| 6 | 10.8 | 10.2 | 9.6 | 9.0 | 8.4 |
| 7 | 12.6 | 11.9 | 11.2 | 10.5 | 9.8 |
| 8 | 14.4 | 13.6 | 12.8 | 12.0 | 11.2 |
| 9 | 16.2 | 15.3 | 14.4 | 13.5 | 12.6 |

## COMMON LOGARITHMS OF NUMBERS (Continued)

| N | 0 | 1 | 2 | 3 | 4 | 5 | 6 | 7 | 8 | 9 |
|---|---|---|---|---|---|---|---|---|---|---|
| **300** | 47 712 | 727 | 741 | 756 | 770 | 784 | 799 | 813 | 828 | 842 |
| 01 | 857 | 871 | 885 | 900 | 914 | 929 | 943 | 958 | 972 | 986 |
| 02 | 48 001 | 015 | 029 | 044 | 058 | 073 | 087 | 101 | 116 | 130 |
| 03 | 144 | 159 | 173 | 187 | 202 | 216 | 230 | 244 | 259 | 273 |
| 04 | 287 | 302 | 316 | 330 | 344 | 359 | 373 | 387 | 401 | 416 |
| 05 | 430 | 444 | 458 | 473 | 487 | 501 | 515 | 530 | 544 | 558 |
| 06 | 572 | 586 | 601 | 615 | 629 | 643 | 657 | 671 | 686 | 700 |
| 07 | 714 | 728 | 742 | 756 | 770 | 785 | 799 | 813 | 827 | 841 |
| 08 | 855 | 869 | 883 | 897 | 911 | 926 | 940 | 954 | 968 | 982 |
| 09 | 996 | *010 | *024 | *038 | *052 | *066 | *080 | *094 | *108 | *122 |
| **310** | 49 136 | 150 | 164 | 178 | 192 | 206 | 220 | 234 | 248 | 262 |
| 11 | 276 | 290 | 304 | 318 | 332 | 346 | 360 | 374 | 388 | 402 |
| 12 | 415 | 429 | 443 | 457 | 471 | 485 | 499 | 513 | 527 | 541 |
| 13 | 554 | 568 | 582 | 596 | 610 | 624 | 638 | 651 | 665 | 679 |
| 14 | 693 | 707 | 721 | 734 | 748 | 762 | 776 | 790 | 803 | 817 |
| 15 | 831 | 845 | 859 | 872 | 886 | 900 | 914 | 927 | 941 | 955 |
| 16 | 969 | 982 | 996 | *010 | *024 | *037 | *051 | *065 | *079 | *092 |
| 17 | 50 106 | 120 | 133 | 147 | 161 | 174 | 188 | 202 | 215 | 229 |
| 18 | 243 | 256 | 270 | 284 | 297 | 311 | 325 | 338 | 352 | 365 |
| 19 | 379 | 393 | 406 | 420 | 433 | 447 | 461 | 474 | 488 | 501 |
| **320** | 515 | 529 | 542 | 556 | 569 | 583 | 596 | 610 | 623 | 637 |
| 21 | 651 | 664 | 678 | 691 | 705 | 718 | 732 | 745 | 759 | 772 |
| 22 | 786 | 799 | 813 | 826 | 840 | 853 | 866 | 880 | 893 | 907 |
| 23 | 920 | 934 | 947 | 961 | 974 | 987 | *001 | *014 | *028 | *041 |
| 24 | 51 055 | 068 | 081 | 095 | 108 | 121 | 135 | 148 | 162 | 175 |
| 25 | 188 | 202 | 215 | 228 | 242 | 255 | 268 | 282 | 295 | 308 |
| 26 | 322 | 335 | 348 | 362 | 375 | 388 | 402 | 415 | 428 | 441 |
| 27 | 455 | 468 | 481 | 495 | 508 | 521 | 534 | 548 | 561 | 574 |
| 28 | 587 | 601 | 614 | 627 | 640 | 654 | 667 | 680 | 693 | 706 |
| 29 | 720 | 733 | 746 | 759 | 772 | 786 | 799 | 812 | 825 | 838 |
| **330** | 851 | 865 | 878 | 891 | 904 | 917 | 930 | 943 | 957 | 970 |
| 31 | 983 | 996 | *009 | *022 | *035 | *048 | *061 | *075 | *088 | *101 |
| 32 | 52 114 | 127 | 140 | 153 | 166 | 179 | 192 | 205 | 218 | 231 |
| 33 | 244 | 257 | 270 | 284 | 297 | 310 | 323 | 336 | 349 | 362 |
| 34 | 375 | 388 | 401 | 414 | 427 | 440 | 453 | 466 | 479 | 492 |
| 35 | 504 | 517 | 530 | 543 | 556 | 569 | 582 | 595 | 608 | 621 |
| 36 | 634 | 647 | 660 | 673 | 686 | 699 | 711 | 724 | 737 | 750 |
| 37 | 763 | 776 | 789 | 802 | 815 | 827 | 840 | 853 | 866 | 879 |
| 38 | 892 | 905 | 917 | 930 | 943 | 956 | 969 | 982 | 994 | *007 |
| 39 | 53 020 | 033 | 046 | 058 | 071 | 084 | 097 | 110 | 122 | 135 |
| **340** | 148 | 161 | 173 | 186 | 199 | 212 | 224 | 237 | 250 | 263 |
| 41 | 275 | 288 | 301 | 314 | 326 | 339 | 352 | 364 | 377 | 390 |
| 42 | 403 | 415 | 428 | 441 | 453 | 466 | 479 | 491 | 504 | 517 |
| 43 | 529 | 542 | 555 | 567 | 580 | 593 | 605 | 618 | 631 | 643 |
| 44 | 656 | 668 | 681 | 694 | 706 | 719 | 732 | 744 | 757 | 769 |
| 45 | 782 | 794 | 807 | 820 | 832 | 845 | 857 | 870 | 882 | 895 |
| 46 | 908 | 920 | 933 | 945 | 958 | 970 | 983 | 995 | *008 | *020 |
| 47 | 54 033 | 045 | 058 | 070 | 083 | 095 | 108 | 120 | 133 | 145 |
| 48 | 158 | 170 | 183 | 195 | 208 | 220 | 233 | 245 | 258 | 270 |
| 49 | 283 | 295 | 307 | 320 | 332 | 345 | 357 | 370 | 382 | 394 |
| **350** | 407 | 419 | 432 | 444 | 456 | 469 | 481 | 494 | 506 | 518 |
| N | 0 | 1 | 2 | 3 | 4 | 5 | 6 | 7 | 8 | 9 |

**P P**

| | 15 | | 14 | | 13 | | 12 |
|---|---|---|---|---|---|---|---|
| 1 | 1.5 | 1 | 1.4 | 1 | 1.3 | 1 | 1.2 |
| 2 | 3.0 | 2 | 2.8 | 2 | 2.6 | 2 | 2.4 |
| 3 | 4.5 | 3 | 4.2 | 3 | 3.9 | 3 | 3.6 |
| 4 | 6.0 | 4 | 5.6 | 4 | 5.2 | 4 | 4.8 |
| 5 | 7.5 | 5 | 7.0 | 5 | 6.5 | 5 | 6.0 |
| 6 | 9.0 | 6 | 8.4 | 6 | 7.8 | 6 | 7.2 |
| 7 | 10.5 | 7 | 9.8 | 7 | 9.1 | 7 | 8.4 |
| 8 | 12.0 | 8 | 11.2 | 8 | 10.4 | 8 | 9.6 |
| 9 | 13.5 | 9 | 12.6 | 9 | 11.7 | 9 | 10.8 |

## COMMON LOGARITHMS OF NUMBERS (Continued)

| N | 0 | 1 | 2 | 3 | 4 | 5 | 6 | 7 | 8 | 9 |
|---|---|---|---|---|---|---|---|---|---|---|
| 350 | 54 407 | 419 | 432 | 444 | 456 | 469 | 481 | 494 | 506 | 518 |
| 51 | 531 | 543 | 555 | 568 | 580 | 593 | 605 | 617 | 630 | 642 |
| 52 | 654 | 667 | 679 | 691 | 704 | 716 | 728 | 741 | 753 | 765 |
| 53 | 777 | 790 | 802 | 814 | 827 | 839 | 851 | 864 | 876 | 888 |
| 54 | 900 | 913 | 925 | 937 | 949 | 962 | 974 | 986 | 998 | *011 |
| 55 | 55 023 | 035 | 047 | 060 | 072 | 084 | 096 | 108 | 121 | 133 |
| 56 | 145 | 157 | 169 | 182 | 194 | 206 | 218 | 230 | 242 | 255 |
| 57 | 267 | 279 | 291 | 303 | 315 | 328 | 340 | 352 | 364 | 376 |
| 58 | 388 | 400 | 413 | 425 | 437 | 449 | 461 | 473 | 485 | 497 |
| 59 | 509 | 522 | 534 | 546 | 558 | 570 | 582 | 594 | 606 | 618 |
| 360 | 630 | 642 | 654 | 666 | 678 | 691 | 703 | 715 | 727 | 739 |
| 61 | 751 | 763 | 775 | 787 | 799 | 811 | 823 | 835 | 847 | 859 |
| 62 | 871 | 883 | 895 | 907 | 919 | 931 | 943 | 955 | 967 | 979 |
| 63 | 991 | *003 | *015 | *027 | *038 | *050 | *062 | *074 | *086 | *098 |
| 64 | 56 110 | 122 | 134 | 146 | 158 | 170 | 182 | 194 | 205 | 217 |
| 65 | 229 | 241 | 253 | 265 | 277 | 289 | 301 | 312 | 324 | 336 |
| 66 | 348 | 360 | 372 | 384 | 396 | 407 | 419 | 431 | 443 | 455 |
| 67 | 467 | 478 | 490 | 502 | 514 | 526 | 538 | 549 | 561 | 573 |
| 68 | 585 | 597 | 608 | 620 | 632 | 644 | 656 | 667 | 679 | 691 |
| 69 | 703 | 714 | 726 | 738 | 750 | 761 | 773 | 785 | 797 | 803 |
| 370 | 820 | 832 | 844 | 855 | 867 | 879 | 891 | 902 | 914 | 926 |
| 71 | 937 | 949 | 961 | 972 | 984 | 996 | *008 | *019 | *031 | *043 |
| 72 | 57 054 | 066 | 078 | 089 | 101 | 113 | 124 | 136 | 148 | 159 |
| 73 | 171 | 183 | 194 | 206 | 217 | 229 | 241 | 252 | 264 | 276 |
| 74 | 287 | 299 | 310 | 322 | 334 | 345 | 357 | 368 | 380 | 392 |
| 75 | 403 | 415 | 426 | 438 | 449 | 461 | 473 | 484 | 496 | 507 |
| 76 | 519 | 530 | 542 | 553 | 565 | 576 | 588 | 600 | 611 | 623 |
| 77 | 634 | 646 | 657 | 669 | 680 | 692 | 703 | 715 | 726 | 738 |
| 78 | 749 | 761 | 772 | 784 | 795 | 807 | 818 | 830 | 841 | 852 |
| 79 | 864 | 875 | 887 | 898 | 910 | 921 | 933 | 944 | 955 | 967 |
| 380 | 978 | 990 | *001 | *013 | *024 | *035 | *047 | *058 | *070 | *081 |
| 81 | 58 092 | 104 | 115 | 127 | 138 | 149 | 161 | 172 | 184 | 195 |
| 82 | 206 | 218 | 229 | 240 | 252 | 263 | 274 | 286 | 297 | 309 |
| 83 | 320 | 331 | 343 | 354 | 365 | 377 | 388 | 399 | 410 | 422 |
| 84 | 433 | 444 | 456 | 467 | 478 | 490 | 501 | 512 | 524 | 535 |
| 85 | 546 | 557 | 569 | 580 | 591 | 602 | 614 | 625 | 636 | 647 |
| 86 | 659 | 670 | 681 | 692 | 704 | 715 | 726 | 737 | 749 | 760 |
| 87 | 771 | 782 | 794 | 805 | 816 | 827 | 838 | 850 | 861 | 872 |
| 88 | 883 | 894 | 906 | 917 | 928 | 939 | 950 | 961 | 973 | 984 |
| 89 | 995 | *006 | *017 | *028 | *040 | *051 | *062 | *073 | *084 | *095 |
| 390 | 59 106 | 118 | 129 | 140 | 151 | 162 | 173 | 184 | 195 | 207 |
| 91 | 218 | 229 | 240 | 251 | 262 | 273 | 284 | 295 | 306 | 318 |
| 92 | 329 | 340 | 351 | 362 | 373 | 384 | 395 | 406 | 417 | 428 |
| 93 | 439 | 450 | 461 | 472 | 483 | 494 | 506 | 517 | 528 | 539 |
| 94 | 550 | 561 | 572 | 583 | 594 | 605 | 616 | 627 | 638 | 649 |
| 95 | 660 | 671 | 682 | 693 | 704 | 715 | 726 | 737 | 748 | 759 |
| 96 | 770 | 780 | 791 | 802 | 813 | 824 | 835 | 846 | 857 | 868 |
| 97 | 879 | 890 | 901 | 912 | 923 | 934 | 945 | 956 | 966 | 977 |
| 98 | 988 | 999 | *010 | *021 | *032 | *043 | *054 | *065 | *076 | *086 |
| 99 | 60 097 | 108 | 119 | 130 | 141 | 152 | 163 | 173 | 184 | 195 |
| 400 | 206 | 217 | 228 | 239 | 249 | 260 | 271 | 282 | 293 | 304 |
| N | 0 | 1 | 2 | 3 | 4 | 5 | 6 | 7 | 8 | 9 |

**P P**

**13**
| 1 | 1.3 |
| 2 | 2.6 |
| 3 | 3.9 |
| 4 | 5.2 |
| 5 | 6.5 |
| 6 | 7.8 |
| 7 | 9.1 |
| 8 | 10.4 |
| 9 | 11.7 |

**12**
| 1 | 1.2 |
| 2 | 2.4 |
| 3 | 3.6 |
| 4 | 4.8 |
| 5 | 6.0 |
| 6 | 7.2 |
| 7 | 8.4 |
| 8 | 9.6 |
| 9 | 10.8 |

**11**
| 1 | 1.1 |
| 2 | 2.2 |
| 3 | 3.3 |
| 4 | 4.4 |
| 5 | 5.5 |
| 6 | 6.6 |
| 7 | 7.7 |
| 8 | 8.8 |
| 9 | 9.9 |

**10**
| 1 | 1.0 |
| 2 | 2.0 |
| 3 | 3.0 |
| 4 | 4.0 |
| 5 | 5.0 |
| 6 | 6.0 |
| 7 | 7.0 |
| 8 | 8.0 |
| 9 | 9.0 |

## COMMON LOGARITHMS OF NUMBERS (Continued)

| N | 0 | 1 | 2 | 3 | 4 | 5 | 6 | 7 | 8 | 9 |
|---|---|---|---|---|---|---|---|---|---|---|
| **400** | 60 206 | 217 | 228 | 239 | 249 | 260 | 271 | 282 | 293 | 304 |
| 01 | 314 | 325 | 336 | 347 | 358 | 369 | 379 | 390 | 401 | 412 |
| 02 | 423 | 433 | 444 | 455 | 466 | 477 | 487 | 498 | 509 | 520 |
| 03 | 531 | 541 | 552 | 563 | 574 | 584 | 595 | 606 | 617 | 627 |
| 04 | 638 | 649 | 660 | 670 | 681 | 692 | 703 | 713 | 724 | 735 |
| 05 | 746 | 756 | 767 | 778 | 788 | 799 | 810 | 821 | 831 | 842 |
| 06 | 853 | 863 | 874 | 885 | 895 | 906 | 917 | 927 | 938 | 949 |
| 07 | 959 | 970 | 981 | 991 | *002 | *013 | *023 | *034 | *045 | *055 |
| 08 | 61 066 | 077 | 087 | 098 | 109 | 119 | 130 | 140 | 151 | 162 |
| 09 | 172 | 183 | 194 | 204 | 215 | 225 | 236 | 247 | 257 | 268 |
| **410** | 278 | 289 | 300 | 310 | 321 | 331 | 342 | 352 | 363 | 374 |
| 11 | 384 | 395 | 405 | 416 | 426 | 437 | 448 | 458 | 469 | 479 |
| 12 | 490 | 500 | 511 | 521 | 532 | 542 | 553 | 563 | 574 | 584 |
| 13 | 595 | 606 | 616 | 627 | 637 | 648 | 658 | 669 | 679 | 690 |
| 14 | 700 | 711 | 721 | 731 | 742 | 752 | 763 | 773 | 784 | 794 |
| 15 | 805 | 815 | 826 | 836 | 847 | 857 | 868 | 878 | 888 | 899 |
| 16 | 909 | 920 | 930 | 941 | 951 | 962 | 972 | 982 | 993 | *003 |
| 17 | 62 014 | 024 | 034 | 045 | 055 | 066 | 076 | 086 | 097 | 107 |
| 18 | 118 | 128 | 138 | 149 | 159 | 170 | 180 | 190 | 201 | 211 |
| 19 | 221 | 232 | 242 | 252 | 263 | 273 | 284 | 294 | 304 | 315 |
| **420** | 325 | 335 | 346 | 356 | 366 | 377 | 387 | 397 | 408 | 418 |
| 21 | 428 | 439 | 449 | 459 | 469 | 480 | 490 | 500 | 511 | 521 |
| 22 | 531 | 542 | 552 | 562 | 572 | 583 | 593 | 603 | 613 | 624 |
| 23 | 634 | 644 | 655 | 665 | 675 | 685 | 696 | 706 | 716 | 726 |
| 24 | 737 | 747 | 757 | 767 | 778 | 788 | 798 | 808 | 818 | 829 |
| 25 | 839 | 849 | 859 | 870 | 880 | 890 | 900 | 910 | 921 | 931 |
| 26 | 941 | 951 | 961 | 972 | 982 | 992 | *002 | *C12 | *022 | *033 |
| 27 | 63 043 | 053 | 063 | 073 | 083 | 094 | 104 | 114 | 124 | 134 |
| 28 | 144 | 155 | 165 | 175 | 185 | 195 | 205 | 215 | 225 | 236 |
| 29 | 246 | 256 | 266 | 276 | 286 | 296 | 306 | 317 | 327 | 337 |
| **430** | 347 | 357 | 367 | 377 | 387 | 397 | 407 | 417 | 428 | 438 |
| 31 | 448 | 458 | 468 | 478 | 488 | 498 | 508 | 518 | 528 | 538 |
| 32 | 548 | 558 | 568 | 579 | 589 | 599 | 609 | 619 | 629 | 639 |
| 33 | 649 | 659 | 669 | 679 | 689 | 699 | 709 | 719 | 729 | 739 |
| 34 | 749 | 759 | 769 | 779 | 789 | 799 | 809 | 819 | 829 | 839 |
| 35 | 849 | 859 | 869 | 879 | 889 | 899 | 909 | 919 | 929 | 939 |
| 36 | 949 | 959 | 969 | 979 | 988 | 998 | *008 | *018 | *028 | *038 |
| 37 | 64 048 | 058 | 068 | 078 | 088 | 098 | 108 | 118 | 128 | 137 |
| 38 | 147 | 157 | 167 | 177 | 187 | 197 | 207 | 217 | 227 | 237 |
| 39 | 246 | 256 | 266 | 276 | 286 | 296 | 306 | 316 | 326 | 335 |
| **440** | 345 | 355 | 365 | 375 | 385 | 395 | 404 | 414 | 424 | 434 |
| 41 | 444 | 454 | 464 | 473 | 483 | 493 | 503 | 513 | 523 | 532 |
| 42 | 542 | 552 | 562 | 572 | 582 | 591 | 601 | 611 | 621 | 631 |
| 43 | 640 | 650 | 660 | 670 | 680 | 689 | 699 | 709 | 719 | 729 |
| 44 | 738 | 748 | 758 | 768 | 777 | 787 | 797 | 807 | 816 | 826 |
| 45 | 836 | 846 | 856 | 865 | 875 | 885 | 895 | 904 | 914 | 924 |
| 46 | 933 | 943 | 953 | 963 | 972 | 982 | 992 | *002 | *011 | *021 |
| 47 | 65 031 | 040 | 050 | 060 | 070 | 079 | 089 | 099 | 108 | 118 |
| 48 | 128 | 137 | 147 | 157 | 167 | 176 | 186 | 196 | 205 | 215 |
| 49 | 225 | 234 | 244 | 254 | 263 | 273 | 283 | 292 | 302 | 312 |
| **450** | 321 | 331 | 341 | 350 | 360 | 369 | 379 | 389 | 398 | 408 |
| N | 0 | 1 | 2 | 3 | 4 | 5 | 6 | 7 | 8 | 9 |

**P P**

| | 11 |
|---|---|
| 1 | 1.1 |
| 2 | 2.2 |
| 3 | 3.3 |
| 4 | 4.4 |
| 5 | 5.5 |
| 6 | 6.6 |
| 7 | 7.7 |
| 8 | 8.8 |
| 9 | 9.9 |

| | 10 |
|---|---|
| 1 | 1.0 |
| 2 | 2.0 |
| 3 | 3.0 |
| 4 | 4.0 |
| 5 | 5.0 |
| 6 | 6.0 |
| 7 | 7.0 |
| 8 | 8.0 |
| 9 | 9.0 |

| | 9 |
|---|---|
| 1 | 0.9 |
| 2 | 1.8 |
| 3 | 2.7 |
| 4 | 3.6 |
| 5 | 4.5 |
| 6 | 5.4 |
| 7 | 6.3 |
| 8 | 7.2 |
| 9 | 8.1 |

## COMMON LOGARITHMS OF NUMBERS (Continued)

| N | 0 | 1 | 2 | 3 | 4 | 5 | 6 | 7 | 8 | 9 |
|---|---|---|---|---|---|---|---|---|---|---|
| **450** | 65 321 | 331 | 341 | 350 | 360 | 369 | 379 | 389 | 398 | 408 |
| 51 | 418 | 427 | 437 | 447 | 456 | 466 | 475 | 485 | 495 | 504 |
| 52 | 514 | 523 | 533 | 543 | 552 | 562 | 571 | 581 | 591 | 600 |
| 53 | 610 | 619 | 629 | 639 | 648 | 658 | 667 | 677 | 686 | 696 |
| 54 | 706 | 715 | 725 | 734 | 744 | 753 | 763 | 772 | 782 | 792 |
| 55 | 801 | 811 | 820 | 830 | 839 | 849 | 858 | 868 | 877 | 887 |
| 56 | 896 | 906 | 916 | 925 | 935 | 944 | 954 | 963 | 973 | 982 |
| 57 | 992 | *001 | *011 | *020 | *030 | *039 | *049 | *058 | *068 | *077 |
| 58 | 66 087 | 096 | 106 | 115 | 124 | 134 | 143 | 153 | 162 | 172 |
| 59 | 181 | 191 | 200 | 210 | 219 | 229 | 238 | 247 | 257 | 266 |
| **460** | 276 | 285 | 295 | 304 | 314 | 323 | 332 | 342 | 351 | 361 |
| 61 | 370 | 380 | 389 | 398 | 408 | 417 | 427 | 436 | 445 | 455 |
| 62 | 464 | 474 | 483 | 492 | 502 | 511 | 521 | 530 | 539 | 549 |
| 63 | 558 | 567 | 577 | 586 | 596 | 605 | 614 | 624 | 633 | 642 |
| 64 | 652 | 661 | 671 | 680 | 689 | 699 | 708 | 717 | 727 | 736 |
| 65 | 745 | 755 | 764 | 773 | 783 | 792 | 801 | 811 | 820 | 829 |
| 66 | 839 | 848 | 857 | 867 | 876 | 885 | 894 | 904 | 913 | 922 |
| 67 | 932 | 941 | 950 | 960 | 969 | 978 | 987 | 997 | *006 | *015 |
| 68 | 67 025 | 034 | 043 | 052 | 062 | 071 | 080 | 089 | 099 | 108 |
| 69 | 117 | 127 | 136 | 145 | 154 | 164 | 173 | 182 | 191 | 201 |
| **470** | 210 | 219 | 228 | 237 | 247 | 256 | 265 | 274 | 284 | 293 |
| 71 | 302 | 311 | 321 | 330 | 339 | 348 | 357 | 367 | 376 | 385 |
| 72 | 394 | 403 | 413 | 422 | 431 | 440 | 449 | 459 | 468 | 477 |
| 73 | 486 | 495 | 504 | 514 | 523 | 532 | 541 | 550 | 560 | 569 |
| 74 | 578 | 587 | 596 | 605 | 614 | 624 | 633 | 642 | 651 | 660 |
| 75 | 669 | 679 | 688 | 697 | 706 | 715 | 724 | 733 | 742 | 752 |
| 76 | 761 | 770 | 779 | 788 | 797 | 806 | 815 | 825 | 834 | 843 |
| 77 | 852 | 861 | 870 | 879 | 888 | 897 | 906 | 916 | 925 | 934 |
| 78 | 943 | 952 | 961 | 970 | 979 | 988 | 997 | *006 | *015 | *024 |
| 79 | 68 034 | 043 | 052 | 061 | 070 | 079 | 088 | 097 | 106 | 115 |
| **480** | 124 | 133 | 142 | 151 | 160 | 169 | 178 | 187 | 196 | 205 |
| 81 | 215 | 224 | 233 | 242 | 251 | 260 | 269 | 278 | 287 | 296 |
| 82 | 305 | 314 | 323 | 332 | 341 | 350 | 359 | 368 | 377 | 386 |
| 83 | 395 | 404 | 413 | 422 | 431 | 440 | 449 | 458 | 467 | 476 |
| 84 | 485 | 494 | 502 | 511 | 520 | 529 | 538 | 547 | 556 | 565 |
| 85 | 574 | 583 | 592 | 601 | 610 | 619 | 628 | 637 | 646 | 655 |
| 86 | 664 | 673 | 681 | 690 | 699 | 708 | 717 | 726 | 735 | 744 |
| 87 | 753 | 762 | 771 | 780 | 789 | 797 | 806 | 815 | 824 | 833 |
| 88 | 842 | 851 | 860 | 869 | 878 | 886 | 895 | 904 | 913 | 922 |
| 89 | 931 | 940 | 949 | 958 | 966 | 975 | 984 | 993 | *002 | *011 |
| **490** | 69 020 | 028 | 037 | 046 | 055 | 064 | 073 | 082 | 090 | 099 |
| 91 | 108 | 117 | 126 | 135 | 144 | 152 | 161 | 170 | 179 | 188 |
| 92 | 197 | 205 | 214 | 223 | 232 | 241 | 249 | 258 | 267 | 276 |
| 93 | 285 | 294 | 302 | 311 | 320 | 329 | 338 | 346 | 355 | 364 |
| 94 | 373 | 381 | 390 | 399 | 408 | 417 | 425 | 434 | 443 | 452 |
| 95 | 461 | 469 | 478 | 487 | 496 | 504 | 513 | 522 | 531 | 539 |
| 96 | 548 | 557 | 566 | 574 | 583 | 592 | 601 | 609 | 618 | 627 |
| 97 | 636 | 644 | 653 | 662 | 671 | 679 | 688 | 697 | 705 | 714 |
| 98 | 723 | 732 | 740 | 749 | 758 | 767 | 775 | 784 | 793 | 801 |
| 99 | 810 | 819 | 827 | 836 | 845 | 854 | 862 | 871 | 880 | 888 |
| **500** | 897 | 906 | 914 | 923 | 932 | 940 | 949 | 958 | 966 | 975 |

| N | 0 | 1 | 2 | 3 | 4 | 5 | 6 | 7 | 8 | 9 |
|---|---|---|---|---|---|---|---|---|---|---|

**P P**

| | **10** |
|---|---|
| 1 | 1.0 |
| 2 | 2.0 |
| 3 | 3.0 |
| 4 | 4.0 |
| 5 | 5.0 |
| 6 | 6.0 |
| 7 | 7.0 |
| 8 | 8.0 |
| 9 | 9.0 |

| | **9** |
|---|---|
| 1 | 0.9 |
| 2 | 1.8 |
| 3 | 2.7 |
| 4 | 3.6 |
| 5 | 4.5 |
| 6 | 5.4 |
| 7 | 6.3 |
| 8 | 7.2 |
| 9 | 8.1 |

| | **8** |
|---|---|
| 1 | 0.8 |
| 2 | 1.6 |
| 3 | 2.4 |
| 4 | 3.2 |
| 5 | 4.0 |
| 6 | 4.8 |
| 7 | 5.6 |
| 8 | 6.4 |
| 9 | 7.2 |

# APPENDIX

## COMMON LOGARITHMS OF NUMBERS (Continued)

| N | 0 | 1 | 2 | 3 | 4 | 5 | 6 | 7 | 8 | 9 | PP |
|---|---|---|---|---|---|---|---|---|---|---|---|
| **500** | 69 897 | 906 | 914 | 923 | 932 | 940 | 949 | 958 | 966 | 975 | |
| 01 | 984 | 992 | *001 | *010 | *018 | *027 | *036 | *044 | *053 | *062 | |
| 02 | 70 070 | 079 | 088 | 096 | 105 | 114 | 122 | 131 | 140 | 148 | |
| 03 | 157 | 165 | 174 | 183 | 191 | 200 | 209 | 217 | 226 | 234 | |
| .04 | 243 | 252 | 260 | 269 | 278 | 286 | 295 | 303 | 312 | 321 | |
| 05 | 329 | 338 | 346 | 355 | 364 | 372 | 381 | 389 | 398 | 406 | |
| 06 | 415 | 424 | 432 | 441 | 449 | 458 | 467 | 475 | 484 | 492 | |
| 07 | 501 | 509 | 518 | 526 | 535 | 544 | 552 | 561 | 569 | 578 | |
| 08 | 586 | 595 | 603 | 612 | 621 | 629 | 638 | 646 | 655 | 663 | **9** |
| 09 | 672 | 680 | 689 | 697 | 706 | 714 | 723 | 731 | 740 | 749 | 1  0.9 |
| **510** | 757 | 766 | 774 | 783 | 791 | 800 | 808 | 817 | 825 | 834 | 2  1.8 / 3  2.7 |
| 11 | 842 | 851 | 859 | 868 | 876 | 885 | 893 | 902 | 910 | 919 | 4  3.6 / 5  4.5 |
| 12 | 927 | 935 | 944 | 952 | 961 | 969 | 978 | 986 | 995 | *003 | 6  5.4 / 7  6.3 |
| 13 | 71 012 | 020 | 029 | 037 | 046 | 054 | 063 | 071 | 079 | 088 | 8  7.2 / 9  8.1 |
| 14 | 096 | 105 | 113 | 122 | 130 | 139 | 147 | 155 | 164 | 172 | |
| 15 | 181 | 189 | 198 | 206 | 214 | 223 | 231 | 240 | 248 | 257 | |
| 16 | 265 | 273 | 282 | 290 | 299 | 307 | 315 | 324 | 332 | 341 | |
| 17 | 349 | 357 | 366 | 374 | 383 | 391 | 399 | 408 | 416 | 425 | |
| 18 | 433 | 441 | 450 | 458 | 466 | 475 | 483 | 492 | 500 | 508 | |
| 19 | 517 | 525 | 533 | 542 | 550 | 559 | 567 | 575 | 584 | 592 | |
| **520** | 600 | 609 | 617 | 625 | 634 | 642 | 650 | 659 | 667 | 675 | |
| 21 | 684 | 692 | 700 | 709 | 717 | 725 | 734 | 742 | 750 | 759 | |
| 22 | 767 | 775 | 784 | 792 | 800 | 809 | 817 | 825 | 834 | 842 | **8** |
| 23 | 850 | 858 | 867 | 875 | 883 | 892 | 900 | 908 | 917 | 925 | 1  0.8 |
| 24 | 933 | 941 | 950 | 958 | 966 | 975 | 983 | 991 | 999 | *008 | 2  1.6 / 3  2.4 |
| 25 | 72 016 | 024 | 032 | 041 | 049 | 057 | 066 | 074 | 082 | 090 | 4  3.2 / 5  4.0 |
| 26 | 099 | 107 | 115 | 123 | 132 | 140 | 148 | 156 | 165 | 173 | 6  4.8 / 7  5.6 |
| 27 | 181 | 189 | 198 | 206 | 214 | 222 | 230 | 239 | 247 | 255 | 8  6.4 / 9  7.2 |
| 28 | 263 | 272 | 280 | 288 | 296 | 304 | 313 | 321 | 329 | 337 | |
| 29 | 346 | 354 | 362 | 370 | 378 | 387 | 395 | 403 | 411 | 419 | |
| **530** | 428 | 436 | 444 | 452 | 460 | 469 | 477 | 485 | 493 | 501 | |
| 31 | 509 | 518 | 526 | 534 | 542 | 550 | 558 | 567 | 575 | 583 | |
| 32 | 591 | 599 | 607 | 616 | 624 | 632 | 640 | 648 | 656 | 665 | |
| 33 | 673 | 681 | 689 | 697 | 705 | 713 | 722 | 730 | 738 | 746 | |
| 34 | 754 | 762 | 770 | 779 | 787 | 795 | 803 | 811 | 819 | 827 | |
| 35 | 835 | 843 | 852 | 860 | 868 | 876 | 884 | 892 | 900 | 908 | |
| 36 | 916 | 925 | 933 | 941 | 949 | 957 | 965 | 973 | 981 | 989 | |
| 37 | 997 | *006 | *014 | *022 | *030 | *038 | *046 | *054 | *062 | *070 | **7** |
| 38 | 73 078 | 086 | 094 | 102 | 111 | 119 | 127 | 135 | 143 | 151 | 1  0.7 |
| 39 | 159 | 167 | 175 | 183 | 191 | 199 | 207 | 215 | 223 | 231 | 2  1.4 / 3  2.1 |
| **540** | 239 | 247 | 255 | 263 | 272 | 280 | 288 | 296 | 304 | 312 | 4  2.8 / 5  3.5 |
| 41 | 320 | 328 | 336 | 344 | 352 | 360 | 368 | 376 | 384 | 392 | 6  4.2 / 7  4.9 |
| 42 | 400 | 408 | 416 | 424 | 432 | 440 | 448 | 456 | 464 | 472 | 8  5.6 / 9  6.3 |
| 43 | 480 | 488 | 496 | 504 | 512 | 520 | 528 | 536 | 544 | 552 | |
| 44 | 560 | 568 | 576 | 584 | 592 | 600 | 608 | 616 | 624 | 632 | |
| 45 | 640 | 648 | 656 | 664 | 672 | 679 | 687 | 695 | 703 | 711 | |
| 46 | 719 | 727 | 735 | 743 | 751 | 759 | 767 | 775 | 783 | 791 | |
| 47 | 799 | 807 | 815 | 823 | 830 | 838 | 846 | 854 | 862 | 870 | |
| 48 | 878 | 886 | 894 | 902 | 910 | 918 | 926 | 933 | 941 | 949 | |
| 49 | 957 | 965 | 973 | 981 | 989 | 997 | *005 | *013 | *020 | *028 | |
| **550** | 74 036 | 044 | 052 | 060 | 068 | 076 | 084 | 092 | 099 | 107 | |
| N | 0 | 1 | 2 | 3 | 4 | 5 | 6 | 7 | 8 | 9 | PP |

## COMMON LOGARITHMS OF NUMBERS (Continued)

| N | 0 | 1 | 2 | 3 | 4 | 5 | 6 | 7 | 8 | 9 |
|---|---|---|---|---|---|---|---|---|---|---|
| **550** | 74 036 | 044 | 052 | 060 | 068 | 076 | 084 | 092 | 099 | 107 |
| 51 | 115 | 123 | 131 | 139 | 147 | 155 | 162 | 170 | 178 | 186 |
| 52 | 194 | 202 | 210 | 218 | 225 | 233 | 241 | 249 | 257 | 265 |
| 53 | 273 | 280 | 288 | 296 | 304 | 312 | 320 | 327 | 335 | 343 |
| 54 | 351 | 359 | 367 | 374 | 382 | 390 | 398 | 406 | 414 | 421 |
| 55 | 429 | 437 | 445 | 453 | 461 | 468 | 476 | 484 | 492 | 500 |
| 56 | 507 | 515 | 523 | 531 | 539 | 547 | 554 | 562 | 570 | 578 |
| 57 | 586 | 593 | 601 | 609 | 617 | 624 | 632 | 640 | 648 | 656 |
| 58 | 663 | 671 | 679 | ·687 | 695 | 702 | 710 | 718 | 726 | 733 |
| 59 | 741 | 749 | 757 | 764 | 772 | 780 | 788 | 796 | 803 | 811 |
| **560** | 819 | 827 | 834 | 842 | 850 | 858 | 865 | 873 | 881 | 889 |
| 61 | 896 | 904 | 912 | 920 | 927 | 935 | 943 | 950 | 958 | 966 |
| 62 | 974 | 981 | 989 | 997 | *005 | *012 | *020 | *028 | *035 | *043 |
| 63 | 75 051 | 059 | 066 | 074 | 082 | 089 | 097 | 105 | 113 | 120 |
| 64 | 128 | 136 | 143 | 151 | 159 | 166 | 174 | 182 | 189 | 197 |
| 65 | 205 | 213 | 220 | 228 | 236 | 243 | 251 | 259 | 266 | 274 |
| 66 | 282 | 289 | 297 | 305 | 312 | 320 | 328 | 335 | 343 | 351 |
| 67 | 358 | 366 | 374 | 381 | 389 | 397 | 404 | 412 | 420 | 427 |
| 68 | 435 | 442 | 450 | 458 | 465 | 473 | 481 | 488 | 496 | 504 |
| 69 | 511 | 519 | 526 | 534 | 542 | 549 | 557 | 565 | 572 | 580 |
| **570** | 587 | 595 | 603 | 610 | 618 | 626 | 633 | 641 | 648 | 656 |
| 71 | 664 | 671 | 679 | 686 | 694 | 702 | 709 | 717 | 724 | 732 |
| 72 | 740 | 747 | 755 | 762 | 770 | 778 | 785 | 793 | 800 | 808 |
| 73 | 815 | 823 | 831 | 838 | 846 | 853 | 861 | 868 | 876 | 884 |
| 74 | 891 | 899 | 906 | 914 | 921 | 929 | 937 | 944 | 952 | 959 |
| 75 | 967 | 974 | 982 | 989 | 997 | *005 | *012 | *020 | *027 | *035 |
| 76 | 76 012 | 050 | 057 | 065 | 072 | 080 | 087 | 095 | 103 | 110 |
| 77 | 118 | 125 | 133 | 140 | 148 | 155 | 163 | 170 | 178 | 185 |
| 78 | 193 | 200 | 208 | 215 | 223 | 230 | 238 | 245 | 253 | 260 |
| 79 | 268 | 275 | 283 | 290 | 298 | 305 | 313 | 320 | 328 | 335 |
| **580** | 343 | 350 | 358 | 365 | 373 | 380 | 388 | 395 | 403 | 410 |
| 81 | 418 | 425 | 433 | 440 | 448 | 455 | 462 | 470 | 477 | 485 |
| 82 | 492 | 500 | 507 | 515 | 522 | 530 | 537 | 545 | 552 | 559 |
| 83 | 567 | 574 | 582 | 589 | 597 | 604 | 612 | 610 | 626 | 034 |
| 84 | 641 | 649 | 656 | 664 | 671 | 678 | 686 | 693 | 701 | 708 |
| 85 | 716 | 723 | 730 | 738 | 745 | 753 | 760 | 768 | 775 | 782 |
| 86 | 790 | 797 | 805 | 812 | 819 | 827 | 834 | 842 | 849 | 856 |
| 87 | 864 | 871 | 879 | 886 | 893 | 901 | 908 | 916 | 923 | 930 |
| 88 | 938 | 945 | 953 | 960 | 967 | 975 | 982 | 989 | 997 | *004 |
| 89 | 77 012 | 019 | 026 | 034 | 041 | 048 | 056 | 063 | 070 | 078 |
| **590** | 085 | 093 | 100 | 107 | 115 | 122 | 129 | 137 | 144 | 151 |
| 91 | 159 | 166 | 173 | 181 | 188 | 195 | 203 | 210 | 217 | 225 |
| 92 | 232 | 240 | 247 | 254 | 262 | 269 | 276 | 283 | 291 | 298 |
| 93 | 305 | 313 | 320 | 327 | 335 | 342 | 349 | 357 | 364 | 371 |
| 94 | 379 | 386 | 393 | 401 | 408 | 415 | 422 | 430 | 437 | 444 |
| 95 | 452 | 459 | 466 | 474 | 481 | 488 | 495 | 503 | 510 | 517 |
| 96 | 525 | 532 | 539 | 546 | 554 | 561 | 568 | 576 | 583 | 590 |
| 97 | 597 | 605 | 612 | 619 | 627 | 634 | 641 | 648 | 656 | 663 |
| 98 | 670 | 677 | 685 | 692 | 699 | 706 | 714 | 721 | 728 | 735 |
| 99 | 743 | 750 | 757 | 764 | 772 | 779 | 786 | 793 | 801 | 808 |
| **600** | 815 | 822 | 830 | 837 | 844 | 851 | 859 | 866 | 873 | 880 |
| N | 0 | 1 | 2 | 3 | 4 | 5 | 6 | 7 | 8 | 9 |

P P

| **8** | |
|---|---|
| 1 | 0.8 |
| 2 | 1.6 |
| 3 | 2.4 |
| 4 | 3.2 |
| 5 | 4.0 |
| 6 | 4.8 |
| 7 | 5.6 |
| 8 | 6.4 |
| 9 | 7.2 |

| **7** | |
|---|---|
| 1 | 0.7 |
| 2 | 1.4 |
| 3 | 2.1 |
| 4 | 2.8 |
| 5 | 3.5 |
| 6 | 4.2 |
| 7 | 4.9 |
| 8 | 5.6 |
| 9 | 6.3 |

## COMMON LOGARITHMS OF NUMBERS (Continued)

| N | 0 | 1 | 2 | 3 | 4 | 5 | 6 | 7 | 8 | 9 |
|---|---|---|---|---|---|---|---|---|---|---|
| **600** | 77 815 | 822 | 830 | 837 | 844 | 851 | 859 | 866 | 873 | 880 |
| 01 | 887 | 895 | 902 | 909 | 916 | 924 | 931 | 938 | 945 | 952 |
| 02 | 960 | 967 | 974 | 981 | 988 | 996 | *003 | *010 | *017 | *025 |
| 03 | 78 032 | 039 | 046 | 053 | 061 | 068 | 075 | 082 | 089 | 097 |
| 04 | 104 | 111 | 118 | 125 | 132 | 140 | 147 | 154 | 161 | 168 |
| 05 | 176 | 183 | 190 | 197 | 204 | 211 | 219 | 226 | 233 | 240 |
| 06 | 247 | 254 | 262 | 269 | 276 | 283 | 290 | 297 | 305 | 312 |
| 07 | 319 | 326 | 333 | 340 | 347 | 355 | 362 | 369 | 376 | 383 |
| 08 | 390 | 398 | 405 | 412 | 419 | 426 | 433 | 440 | 447 | 455 |
| 09 | 462 | 469 | 476 | 483 | 490 | 497 | 504 | 512 | 519 | 526 |
| **610** | 533 | 540 | 547 | 554 | 561 | 569 | 576 | 583 | 590 | 597 |
| 11 | 604 | 611 | 618 | 625 | 633 | 640 | 647 | 654 | 661 | 668 |
| 12 | 675 | 682 | 689 | 696 | 704 | 711 | 718 | 725 | 732 | 739 |
| 13 | 746 | 753 | 760 | 767 | 774 | 781 | 789 | 796 | 803 | 810 |
| 14 | 817 | 824 | 831 | 838 | 845 | 852 | 859 | 866 | 873 | 880 |
| 15 | 888 | 895 | 902 | 909 | 916 | 923 | 930 | 937 | 944 | 951 |
| 16 | 958 | 965 | 972 | 979 | 986 | 993 | *000 | *007 | *014 | *021 |
| 17 | 79 029 | 036 | 043 | 050 | 057 | 064 | 071 | 078 | 085 | 092 |
| 18 | 099 | 106 | 113 | 120 | 127 | 134 | 141 | 148 | 155 | 162 |
| 19 | 169 | 176 | 183 | 190 | 197 | 204 | 211 | 218 | 225 | 232 |
| **620** | 239 | 246 | 253 | 260 | 267 | 274 | 281 | 288 | 295 | 302 |
| 21 | 309 | 316 | 323 | 330 | 337 | 344 | 351 | 358 | 365 | 372 |
| 22 | 379 | 386 | 393 | 400 | 407 | 414 | 421 | 428 | 435 | 442 |
| 23 | 449 | 456 | 463 | 470 | 477 | 484 | 491 | 498 | 505 | 511 |
| 24 | 518 | 525 | 532 | 539 | 546 | 553 | 560 | 567 | 574 | 581 |
| 25 | 588 | 595 | 602 | 609 | 616 | 623 | 630 | 637 | 644 | 650 |
| 26 | 657 | 664 | 671 | 678 | 685 | 692 | 699 | 706 | 713 | 720 |
| 27 | 727 | 734 | 741 | 748 | 754 | 761 | 768 | 775 | 782 | 789 |
| 28 | 796 | 803 | 810 | 817 | 824 | 831 | 837 | 844 | 851 | 858 |
| 29 | 865 | 872 | 879 | 886 | 893 | 900 | 906 | 913 | 920 | 927 |
| **630** | 934 | 941 | 948 | 955 | 962 | 969 | 975 | 982 | 989 | 996 |
| 31 | 80 003 | 010 | 017 | 024 | 030 | 037 | 044 | 051 | 058 | 065 |
| 32 | 072 | 079 | 085 | 092 | 099 | 106 | 113 | 120 | 127 | 134 |
| 33 | 140 | 147 | 154 | 161 | 168 | 175 | 182 | 188 | 195 | 202 |
| 34 | 209 | 216 | 223 | 229 | 236 | 243 | 250 | 257 | 264 | 271 |
| 35 | 277 | 284 | 291 | 298 | 305 | 312 | 318 | 325 | 332 | 339 |
| 36 | 346 | 353 | 359 | 366 | 373 | 380 | 387 | 393 | 400 | 407 |
| 37 | 414 | 421 | 428 | 434 | 441 | 448 | 455 | 462 | 468 | 475 |
| 38 | 482 | 489 | 496 | 502 | 509 | 516 | 523 | 530 | 536 | 543 |
| 39 | 550 | 557 | 564 | 570 | 577 | 584 | 591 | 598 | 604 | 611 |
| **640** | 618 | 625 | 632 | 638 | 645 | 652 | 659 | 665 | 672 | 679 |
| 41 | 686 | 693 | 699 | 706 | 713 | 720 | 726 | 733 | 740 | 747 |
| 42 | 754 | 760 | 767 | 774 | 781 | 787 | 794 | 801 | 808 | 814 |
| 43 | 821 | 828 | 835 | 841 | 848 | 855 | 862 | 868 | 875 | 882 |
| 44 | 889 | 895 | 902 | 909 | 916 | 922 | 929 | 936 | 943 | 949 |
| 45 | 956 | 963 | 969 | 976 | 983 | 990 | 996 | *003 | *010 | *017 |
| 46 | 81 023 | 030 | 037 | 043 | 050 | 057 | 064 | 070 | 077 | 084 |
| 47 | 090 | 097 | 104 | 111 | 117 | 124 | 131 | 137 | 144 | 151 |
| 48 | 158 | 164 | 171 | 178 | 184 | 191 | 198 | 204 | 211 | 218 |
| 49 | 224 | 231 | 238 | 245 | 251 | 258 | 265 | 271 | 278 | 285 |
| **650** | 291 | 298 | 305 | 311 | 318 | 325 | 331 | 338 | 345 | 351 |
| N | 0 | 1 | 2 | 3 | 4 | 5 | 6 | 7 | 8 | 9 |

P P

**8**
| | |
|---|---|
| 1 | 0 8 |
| 2 | 1 6 |
| 3 | 2 4 |
| 4 | 3 2 |
| 5 | 4 0 |
| 6 | 4 8 |
| 7 | 5 6 |
| 8 | 6 4 |
| 9 | 7.2 |

**7**
| | |
|---|---|
| 1 | 0 7 |
| 2 | 1 4 |
| 3 | 2 1 |
| 4 | 2 8 |
| 5 | 3 5 |
| 6 | 4 2 |
| 7 | 4 9 |
| 8 | 5 6 |
| 9 | 6 3 |

**6**
| | |
|---|---|
| 1 | 0 6 |
| 2 | 1 2 |
| 3 | 1 8 |
| 4 | 2 4 |
| 5 | 3 0 |
| 6 | 3 6 |
| 7 | 4 2 |
| 8 | 4 8 |
| 9 | 5 4 |

## COMMON LOGARITHMS OF NUMBERS (Continued)

| N | 0 | 1 | 2 | 3 | 4 | 5 | 6 | 7 | 8 | 9 |
|---|---|---|---|---|---|---|---|---|---|---|
| **650** | 81 291 | 298 | 305 | 311 | 318 | 325 | 331 | 338 | 345 | 351 |
| 51 | 358 | 365 | 371 | 378 | 385 | 391 | 398 | 405 | 411 | 418 |
| 52 | 425 | 431 | 438 | 445 | 451 | 458 | 465 | 471 | 478 | 485 |
| 53 | 491 | 498 | 505 | 511 | 518 | 525 | 531 | 538 | 544 | 551 |
| 54 | 558 | 564 | 571 | 578 | 584 | 591 | 598 | 604 | 611 | 617 |
| 55 | 624 | 631 | 637 | 644 | 651 | 657 | 664 | 671 | 677 | 684 |
| 56 | 690 | 697 | 704 | 710 | 717 | 723 | 730 | 737 | 743 | 750 |
| 57 | 757 | 763 | 770 | 776 | 783 | 790 | 796 | 803 | 809 | 816 |
| 58 | 823 | 829 | 836 | 842 | 849 | 856 | 862 | 869 | 875 | 882 |
| 59 | 889 | 895 | 902 | 908 | 915 | 921 | 928 | 935 | 941 | 948 |
| **660** | 954 | 961 | 968 | 974 | 981 | 987 | 994 | *000 | *007 | *014 |
| 61 | 82 020 | 027 | 033 | 040 | 046 | 053 | 060 | 066 | 073 | 079 |
| 62 | 086 | 092 | 099 | 105 | 112 | 119 | 125 | 132 | 138 | 145 |
| 63 | 151 | 158 | 164 | 171 | 178 | 184 | 191 | 197 | 204 | 210 |
| 64 | 217 | 223 | 230 | 236 | 243 | 249 | 256 | 263 | 269 | 276 |
| 65 | 282 | 289 | 295 | 302 | 308 | 315 | 321 | 328 | 334 | 341 |
| 66 | 347 | 354 | 360 | 367 | 373 | 380 | 387 | 393 | 400 | 406 |
| 67 | 413 | 419 | 426 | 432 | 439 | 445 | 452 | 458 | 465 | 471 |
| 68 | 478 | 484 | 491 | 497 | 504 | 510 | 517 | 523 | 530 | 536 |
| 69 | 543 | 549 | 556 | 562 | 569 | 575 | 582 | 588 | 595 | 601 |
| **670** | 607 | 614 | 620 | 627 | 633 | 640 | 646 | 653 | 659 | 666 |
| 71 | 672 | 679 | 685 | 692 | 698 | 705 | 711 | 718 | 724 | 730 |
| 72 | 737 | 743 | 750 | 756 | 763 | 769 | 776 | 782 | 789 | 795 |
| 73 | 802 | 808 | 814 | 821 | 827 | 834 | 840 | 847 | 853 | 860 |
| 74 | 866 | 872 | 879 | 885 | 892 | 898 | 905 | 911 | 918 | 924 |
| 75 | 930 | 937 | 943 | 950 | 956 | 963 | 969 | 975 | 982 | 988 |
| 76 | 995 | *001 | *008 | *014 | *020 | *027 | *033 | *040 | *046 | *052 |
| 77 | 83 059 | 065 | 072 | 078 | 085 | 091 | 097 | 104 | 110 | 117 |
| 78 | 123 | 129 | 136 | 142 | 149 | 155 | 161 | 168 | 174 | 181 |
| 79 | 187 | 193 | 200 | 206 | 213 | 219 | 225 | 232 | 238 | 245 |
| **680** | 251 | 257 | 264 | 270 | 276 | 283 | 289 | 296 | 302 | 308 |
| 81 | 315 | 321 | 327 | 334 | 340 | 347 | 353 | 359 | 366 | 372 |
| 82 | 378 | 385 | 391 | 398 | 404 | 410 | 417 | 423 | 429 | 436 |
| 83 | 442 | 448 | 455 | 461 | 467 | 474 | 480 | 487 | 493 | 499 |
| 84 | 506 | 512 | 518 | 525 | 531 | 537 | 544 | 550 | 556 | 563 |
| 85 | 569 | 575 | 582 | 588 | 594 | 601 | 607 | 613 | 620 | 626 |
| 86 | 632 | 639 | 645 | 651 | 658 | 664 | 670 | 677 | 683 | 689 |
| 87 | 696 | 702 | 708 | 715 | 721 | 727 | 734 | 740 | 746 | 753 |
| 88 | 759 | 765 | 771 | 778 | 784 | 790 | 797 | 803 | 809 | 816 |
| 89 | 822 | 828 | 835 | 841 | 847 | 853 | 860 | 866 | 872 | 879 |
| **690** | 885 | 891 | 897 | 904 | 910 | 916 | 923 | 929 | 935 | 942 |
| 91 | 948 | 954 | 960 | 967 | 973 | 979 | 985 | 992 | 998 | *004 |
| 92 | 84 011 | 017 | 023 | 029 | 036 | 042 | 048 | 055 | 061 | 067 |
| 93 | 073 | 080 | 086 | 092 | 098 | 105 | 111 | 117 | 123 | 130 |
| 94 | 136 | 142 | 148 | 155 | 161 | 167 | 173 | 180 | 186 | 192 |
| 95 | 198 | 205 | 211 | 217 | 223 | 230 | 236 | 242 | 248 | 255 |
| 96 | 261 | 267 | 273 | 280 | 286 | 292 | 298 | 305 | 311 | 317 |
| 97 | 323 | 330 | 336 | 342 | 348 | 354 | 361 | 367 | 373 | 379 |
| 98 | 386 | 392 | 398 | 404 | 410 | 417 | 423 | 429 | 435 | 442 |
| 99 | 448 | 454 | 460 | 466 | 473 | 479 | 485 | 491 | 497 | 504 |
| **700** | 510 | 516 | 522 | 528 | 535 | 541 | 547 | 553 | 559 | 566 |

**P P**

| | 7 |
|---|---|
| 1 | 0.7 |
| 2 | 1.4 |
| 3 | 2.1 |
| 4 | 2.8 |
| 5 | 3.5 |
| 6 | 4.2 |
| 7 | 4.9 |
| 8 | 5.6 |
| 9 | 6.3 |

| | 6 |
|---|---|
| 1 | 0.6 |
| 2 | 1.2 |
| 3 | 1.8 |
| 4 | 2.4 |
| 5 | 3.0 |
| 6 | 3.6 |
| 7 | 4.2 |
| 8 | 4.8 |
| 9 | 5.4 |

## COMMON LOGARITHMS OF NUMBERS (Continued)

| N | 0 | 1 | 2 | 3 | 4 | 5 | 6 | 7 | 8 | 9 |
|---|---|---|---|---|---|---|---|---|---|---|
| **700** | 84 510 | 516 | 522 | 528 | 535 | 541 | 547 | 553 | 559 | 566 |
| 01 | 572 | 578 | 584 | 590 | 597 | 603 | 609 | 615 | 621 | 628 |
| 02 | 634 | 040 | 646 | 652 | 658 | 665 | 671 | 677 | 683 | 689 |
| 03 | 696 | 702 | 708 | 714 | 720 | 726 | 733 | 739 | 745 | 751 |
| 04 | 757 | 763 | 770 | 776 | 782 | 788 | 794 | 800 | 807 | 813 |
| 05 | 819 | 825 | 831 | 837 | 844 | 850 | 856 | 862 | 868 | 874 |
| 06 | 880 | 887 | 893 | 899 | 905 | 911 | 917 | 924 | 930 | 936 |
| 07 | 942 | 948 | 954 | 960 | 967 | 973 | 979 | 985 | 991 | 997 |
| 08 | 85 003 | 009 | 016 | 022 | 028 | 034 | 040 | 046 | 052 | 058 |
| 09 | 065 | 071 | 077 | 083 | 089 | 095 | 101 | 107 | 114 | 120 |
| **710** | 126 | 132 | 138 | 144 | 150 | 156 | 163 | 169 | 175 | 181 |
| 11 | 187 | 193 | 199 | 205 | 211 | 217 | 224 | 230 | 236 | 242 |
| 12 | 248 | 254 | 260 | 266 | 272 | 278 | 285 | 291 | 297 | 303 |
| 13 | 309 | 315 | 321 | 327 | 333 | 339 | 345 | 352 | 358 | 364 |
| 14 | 370 | 376 | 382 | 388 | 394 | 400 | 406. | 412 | 418 | 425 |
| 15 | 431 | 437 | 443 | 449 | 455 | 461 | 467 | 473 | 479 | 485 |
| 16 | 491 | 497 | 503 | 509 | 516 | 522 | 528 | 534 | 540 | 546 |
| 17 | 552 | 558 | 564 | 570 | 576 | 582 | 588 | 594 | 600 | 606 |
| 18 | 612 | 618 | 625 | 631 | 637 | 643 | 649 | 655 | 661 | 667 |
| 19 | 673 | 679 | 685 | 691 | 697 | 703 | 709 | 715 | 721 | 727 |
| **720** | 733 | 739 | 745 | 751 | 757 | 763 | 769 | 775 | 781 | 788 |
| 21 | 794 | 800 | 806 | 812 | 818 | 824 | 830 | 836 | 842 | 848 |
| 22 | 854 | 860 | 866 | 872 | 878 | 884 | 890 | 896 | 902 | 908 |
| 23 | 914 | 920 | 926 | 932 | 938 | 944 | 950 | 956 | 962 | 968 |
| 24 | 974 | 980 | 986 | 992 | 998 | *004 | *010 | *016 | *022 | *028 |
| 25 | 86 034 | 040 | 046 | 052 | 058 | 064 | 070 | 076 | 082 | 088 |
| 26 | 094 | 100 | 106 | 112 | 118 | 124 | 130 | 136 | 141 | 147 |
| 27 | 153 | 159 | 165 | 171 | 177 | 183 | 189 | 195 | 201 | 207 |
| 28 | 213 | 219 | 225 | 231 | 237 | 243 | 249 | 255 | 261 | 267 |
| 29 | 273 | 279 | 285 | 291 | 297 | 303 | 308 | 314 | 320 | 326 |
| **730** | 332 | 338 | 344 | 350 | 356 | 362 | 368 | 374 | 380 | 386 |
| 31 | 392 | 398 | 404 | 410 | 415 | 421 | 427 | 433 | 439 | 445 |
| 32 | 451 | 457 | 463 | 469 | 475 | 481 | 487 | 493 | 499 | 504 |
| 33 | 510 | 516 | 522 | 528 | 534 | 540 | 546 | 552 | 558 | 564 |
| 34 | 570 | 576 | 581 | 587 | 593 | 599 | 605 | 611 | 617 | 623 |
| 35 | 629 | 635 | 641 | 646 | 652 | 658 | 664 | 670 | 676 | 682 |
| 36 | 688 | 694 | 700 | 705 | 711 | 717 | 723 | 729 | 735 | 741 |
| 37 | 747 | 753 | 759 | 764 | 770 | 776 | 782 | 788 | 794 | 800 |
| 38 | 806 | 812 | 817 | 823 | 829 | 835 | 841 | 847 | 853 | 859 |
| 39 | 864 | 870 | 876 | 882 | 888 | 894 | 900 | 906 | 911 | 917 |
| **740** | 923 | 929 | 935 | 941 | 947 | 953 | 958 | 964 | 970 | 976 |
| 41 | 982 | 988 | 994 | 999 | *005 | *011 | *017 | *023 | *029 | *035 |
| 42 | 87 040 | 046 | 052 | 058 | 064 | 070 | 075 | 081 | 087 | 093 |
| 43 | 099 | 105 | 111 | 116 | 122 | 128 | 134 | 140 | 146 | 151 |
| 44 | 157 | 163 | 169 | 175 | 181 | 186 | 192 | 198 | 204 | 210 |
| 45 | 216 | 221 | 227 | 233 | 239 | 245 | 251 | 256 | 262 | 268 |
| 46 | 274 | 280 | 286 | 291 | 297 | 303 | 309 | 315 | 320 | 326 |
| 47 | 332 | 338 | 344 | 349 | 355 | 361 | 367 | 373 | 379 | 384 |
| 48 | 390 | 396 | 402 | 408 | 413 | 419 | 425 | 431 | 437 | 442 |
| 49 | 448 | 454 | 460 | 466 | 471 | 477 | 483 | 489 | 495 | 500 |
| **750** | 506 | 512 | 518 | 523 | 529 | 535 | 541 | 547 | 552 | 558 |
| N | 0 | 1 | 2 | 3 | 4 | 5 | 6 | 7 | 8 | 9 |

P P

| | 7 |
|---|---|
| 1 | 0.7 |
| 2 | 1.4 |
| 3 | 2.1 |
| 4 | 2.8 |
| 5 | 3.5 |
| 6 | 4.2 |
| 7 | 4.9 |
| 8 | 5.6 |
| 9 | 6.3 |

| | 6 |
|---|---|
| 1 | 0.6 |
| 2 | 1.2 |
| 3 | 1.8 |
| 4 | 2.4 |
| 5 | 3.0 |
| 6 | 3.6 |
| 7 | 4.2 |
| 8 | 4.8 |
| 9 | 5.4 |

| | 5 |
|---|---|
| 1 | 0.5 |
| 2 | 1.0 |
| 3 | 1.5 |
| 4 | 2.0 |
| 5 | 2.5 |
| 6 | 3.0 |
| 7 | 3.5 |
| 8 | 4.0 |
| 9 | 4.5 |

## COMMON LOGARITHMS OF NUMBERS (Continued)

| N | 0 | 1 | 2 | 3 | 4 | 5 | 6 | 7 | 8 | 9 | P P |
|---|---|---|---|---|---|---|---|---|---|---|---|
| 750 | 87 506 | 512 | 518 | 523 | 529 | 535 | 541 | 547 | 552 | 558 | |
| 51 | 564 | 570 | 576 | 581 | 587 | 593 | 599 | 604 | 610 | 616 | |
| 52 | 622 | 628 | 633 | 639 | 645 | 651 | 656 | 662 | 668 | 674 | |
| 53 | 679 | 685 | 691 | 697 | 703 | 708 | 714 | 720 | 726 | 731 | |
| 54 | 737 | 743 | 749 | 754 | 760 | 766 | 772 | 777 | 783 | 789 | |
| 55 | 795 | 800 | 806 | 812 | 818 | 823 | 829 | 835 | 841 | 846 | |
| 56 | 852 | 858 | 864 | 869 | 875 | 881 | 887 | 892 | 898 | 904 | |
| 57 | 910 | 915 | 921 | 927 | 933 | 938 | 944 | 950 | 955 | 961 | |
| 58 | 967 | 973 | 978 | 984 | 990 | 996 | *001 | *007 | *013 | *018 | |
| 59 | 88 024 | 030 | 036 | 041 | 047 | 053 | 058 | 064 | 070 | 076 | |
| 760 | 081 | 087 | 093 | 098 | 104 | 110 | 116 | 121 | 127 | 133 | |
| 61 | 138 | 144 | 150 | 156 | 161 | 167 | 173 | 178 | 184 | 190 | |
| 62 | 195 | 201 | 207 | 213 | 218 | 224 | 230 | 235 | 241 | 247 | |
| 63 | 252 | 258 | 264 | 270 | 275 | 281 | 287 | 292 | 298 | 304 | |
| 64 | 309 | 315 | 321 | 326 | 332 | 338 | 343 | 349 | 355 | 360 | |
| 65 | 366 | 372 | 377 | 383 | 389 | 395 | 400 | 406 | 412 | 417 | |
| 66 | 423 | 429 | 434 | 440 | 446 | 451 | 457 | 463 | 468 | 474 | |
| 67 | 480 | 485 | 491 | 497 | 502 | 508 | 513 | 519 | 525 | 530 | |
| 68 | 536 | 542 | 547 | 553 | 559 | 564 | 570 | 576 | 581 | 587 | |
| 69 | 593 | 598 | 604 | 610 | 615 | 621 | 627 | 632 | 638 | 643 | |
| 770 | 649 | 655 | 660 | 666 | 672 | 677 | 683 | 689 | 694 | 700 | |
| 71 | 705 | 711 | 717 | 722 | 728 | 734 | 739 | 745 | 750 | 756 | |
| 72 | 762 | 767 | 773 | 779 | 784 | 790 | 795 | 801 | 807 | 812 | |
| 73 | 818 | 824 | 829 | 835 | 840 | 846 | 852 | 857 | 863 | 868 | |
| 74 | 874 | 880 | 885 | 891 | 897 | 902 | 908 | 913 | 919 | 925 | |
| 75 | 930 | 936 | 941 | 947 | 953 | 958 | 964 | 969 | 975 | 981 | |
| 76 | 986 | 992 | 997 | *003 | *009 | *014 | *020 | *025 | *031 | *037 | |
| 77 | 89 042 | 048 | 053 | 059 | 064 | 070 | 076 | 081 | 087 | 092 | |
| 78 | 098 | 104 | 109 | 115 | 120 | 126 | 131 | 137 | 143 | 148 | |
| 79 | 154 | 159 | 165 | 170 | 176 | 182 | 187 | 193 | 198 | 204 | |
| 780 | 209 | 215 | 221 | 226 | 232 | 237 | 243 | 248 | 254 | 260 | |
| 81 | 265 | 271 | 276 | 282 | 287 | 293 | 298 | 304 | 310 | 315 | |
| 82 | 321 | 326 | 332 | 337 | 343 | 348 | 354 | 360 | 365 | 371 | |
| 83 | 376 | 382 | 387 | 393 | 398 | 404 | 409 | 415 | 421 | 426 | |
| 84 | 432 | 437 | 443 | 448 | 454 | 459 | 465 | 470 | 476 | 481 | |
| 85 | 487 | 492 | 498 | 504 | 509 | 515 | 520 | 526 | 531 | 537 | |
| 86 | 542 | 548 | 553 | 559 | 564 | 570 | 575 | 581 | 586 | 592 | |
| 87 | 597 | 603 | 609 | 614 | 620 | 625 | 631 | 636 | 642 | 647 | |
| 88 | 653 | 658 | 664 | 669 | 675 | 680 | 686 | 691 | 697 | 702 | |
| 89 | 708 | 713 | 719 | 724 | 730 | 735 | 741 | 746 | 752 | 757 | |
| 790 | 763 | 768 | 774 | 779 | 785 | 790 | 796 | 801 | 807 | 812 | |
| 91 | 818 | 823 | 829 | 834 | 840 | 845 | 851 | 856 | 862 | 867 | |
| 92 | 873 | 878 | 883 | 889 | 894 | 900 | 905 | 911 | 916 | 922 | |
| 93 | 927 | 933 | 938 | 944 | 949 | 955 | 960 | 966 | 971 | 977 | |
| 94 | 982 | 988 | 993 | 998 | *004 | *009 | *015 | *020 | *026 | *031 | |
| 95 | 90 037 | 042 | 048 | 053 | 059 | 064 | 069 | 075 | 080 | 086 | |
| 96 | 091 | 097 | 102 | 108 | 113 | 119 | 124 | 129 | 135 | 140 | |
| 97 | 146 | 151 | 157 | 162 | 168 | 173 | 179 | 184 | 189 | 195 | |
| 98 | 200 | 206 | 211 | 217 | 222 | 227 | 233 | 238 | 244 | 249 | |
| 99 | 255 | 260 | 266 | 271 | 276 | 282 | 287 | 293 | 298 | 304 | |
| 800 | 309 | 314 | 320 | 325 | 331 | 336 | 342 | 347 | 352 | 358 | |
| N | 0 | 1 | 2 | 3 | 4 | 5 | 6 | 7 | 8 | 9 | P P |

PP tables:

| | 6 |
|---|---|
| 1 | 0.6 |
| 2 | 1.2 |
| 3 | 1.8 |
| 4 | 2.4 |
| 5 | 3.0 |
| 6 | 3.6 |
| 7 | 4.2 |
| 8 | 4.8 |
| 9 | 5.4 |

| | 5 |
|---|---|
| 1 | 0.5 |
| 2 | 1.0 |
| 3 | 1.5 |
| 4 | 2.0 |
| 5 | 2.5 |
| 6 | 3.0 |
| 7 | 3.5 |
| 8 | 4.0 |
| 9 | 4.5 |

## COMMON LOGARITHMS OF NUMBERS (Continued)

| N | 0 | 1 | 2 | 3 | 4 | 5 | 6 | 7 | 8 | 9 | P P | | |
|---|---|---|---|---|---|---|---|---|---|---|---|---|---|
| **800** | 90 309 | 314 | 320 | 325 | 331 | 336 | 342 | 347 | 352 | 358 | | | |
| 01 | 363 | 369 | 374 | 380 | 385 | 390 | 396 | 401 | 407 | 412 | | | |
| 02 | 417 | 423 | 428 | 434 | 439 | 445 | 450 | 455 | 461 | 466 | | | |
| 03 | 472 | 477 | 482 | 488 | 493 | 499 | 504 | 509 | 515 | 520 | | | |
| 04 | 526 | 531 | 536 | 542 | 547 | 553 | 558 | 563 | 569 | 574 | | | |
| 05 | 580 | 585 | 590 | 596 | 601 | 607 | 612 | 617 | 623 | 628 | | | |
| 06 | 634 | 639 | 644 | 650 | 655 | 660 | 666 | 671 | 677 | 682 | | | |
| 07 | 687 | 693 | 698 | 703 | 709 | 714 | 720 | 725 | 730 | 736 | | | |
| 08 | 741 | 747 | 752 | 757 | 763 | 768 | 773 | 779 | 784 | 789 | | | |
| 09 | 795 | 800 | 806 | 811 | 816 | 822 | 827 | 832 | 838 | 843 | | | |
| **810** | 849 | 854 | 859 | 865 | 870 | 875 | 881 | 886 | 891 | 897 | | | |
| 11 | 902 | 907 | 913 | 918 | 924 | 929 | 934 | 940 | 945 | 950 | | | |
| 12 | 956 | 961 | 966 | 972 | 977 | 982 | 988 | 993 | 998 | *004 | | | |
| 13 | 91 009 | 014 | 020 | 025 | 030 | 036 | 041 | 046 | 052 | 057 | | | **6** |
| 14 | 062 | 068 | 073 | 078 | 084 | 089 | 094 | 100 | 105 | 110 | 1 | | 0.6 |
| 15 | 116 | 121 | 126 | 132 | 137 | 142 | 148 | 153 | 158 | 164 | 2 | | 1.2 |
| 16 | 169 | 174 | 180 | 185 | 190 | 196 | 201 | 206 | 212 | 217 | 3 | | 1.8 |
| 17 | 222 | 228 | 233 | 238 | 243 | 249 | 254 | 259 | 265 | 270 | 4 | | 2.4 |
| 18 | 275 | 281 | 286 | 291 | 297 | 302 | 307 | 312 | 318 | 323 | 5 | | 3.0 |
| 19 | 328 | 334 | 339 | 344 | 350 | 355 | 360 | 365 | 371 | 376 | 6 | | 3.6 |
| **820** | 381 | 387 | 392 | 397 | 403 | 408 | 413 | 418 | 424 | 429 | 7 | | 4.2 |
| 21 | 434 | 440 | 445 | 450 | 455 | 461 | 466 | 471 | 477 | 482 | 8 | | 4.8 |
| 22 | 487 | 492 | 498 | 503 | 508 | 514 | 519 | 524 | 529 | 535 | 9 | | 5.4 |
| 23 | 540 | 545 | 551 | 556 | 561 | 566 | 572 | 577 | 582 | 587 | | | |
| 24 | 593 | 598 | 603 | 609 | 614 | 619 | 624 | 630 | 635 | 640 | | | |
| 25 | 645 | 651 | 656 | 661 | 666 | 672 | 677 | 682 | 687 | 693 | | | |
| 26 | 698 | 703 | 709 | 714 | 719 | 724 | 730 | 735 | 740 | 745 | | | |
| 27 | 751 | 756 | 761 | 766 | 772 | 777 | 782 | 787 | 793 | 798 | | | |
| 28 | 803 | 808 | 814 | 819 | 824 | 829 | 834 | 840 | 845 | 850 | | | |
| 29 | 855 | 861 | 866 | 871 | 876 | 882 | 887 | 892 | 897 | 903 | | | |
| **830** | 908 | 913 | 918 | 924 | 929 | 934 | 939 | 944 | 950 | 955 | | | |
| 31 | 960 | 965 | 971 | 976 | 981 | 986 | 991 | 997 | *002 | *007 | | | |
| 32 | 92 012 | 018 | 023 | 028 | 033 | 038 | 044 | 049 | 054 | 059 | | | **5** |
| 33 | 065 | 070 | 075 | 080 | 085 | 091 | 096 | 101 | 106 | 111 | 1 | | 0.5 |
| 34 | 117 | 122 | 127 | 132 | 137 | 143 | 148 | 153 | 158 | 163 | 2 | | 1.0 |
| 35 | 169 | 174 | 179 | 184 | 189 | 195 | 200 | 205 | 210 | 215 | 3 | | 1.5 |
| 36 | 221 | 226 | 231 | 236 | 241 | 247 | 252 | 257 | 262 | 267 | 4 | | 2.0 |
| 37 | 273 | 278 | 283 | 288 | 293 | 298 | 304 | 309 | 314 | 319 | 5 | | 2.5 |
| 38 | 324 | 330 | 335 | 340 | 345 | 350 | 355 | 361 | 366 | 371 | 6 | | 3.0 |
| 39 | 376 | 381 | 387 | 392 | 397 | 402 | 407 | 412 | 418 | 423 | 7 | | 3.5 |
| **840** | 428 | 433 | 438 | 443 | 449 | 454 | 459 | 464 | 469 | 474 | 8 | | 4.0 |
| 41 | 480 | 485 | 490 | 495 | 500 | 505 | 511 | 516 | 521 | 526 | 9 | | 4.5 |
| 42 | 531 | 536 | 542 | 547 | 552 | 557 | 562 | 567 | 572 | 578 | | | |
| 43 | 583 | 588 | 593 | 598 | 603 | 609 | 614 | 619 | 624 | 629 | | | |
| 44 | 634 | 639 | 645 | 650 | 655 | 660 | 665 | 670 | 675 | 681 | | | |
| 45 | 686 | 691 | 696 | 701 | 706 | 711 | 716 | 722 | 727 | 732 | | | |
| 46 | 737 | 742 | 747 | 752 | 758 | 763 | 768 | 773 | 778 | 783 | | | |
| 47 | 788 | 793 | 799 | 804 | 809 | 814 | 819 | 824 | 829 | 834 | | | |
| 48 | 840 | 845 | 850 | 855 | 860 | 865 | 870 | 875 | 881 | 886 | | | |
| 49 | 891 | 896 | 901 | 906 | 911 | 916 | 921 | 927 | 932 | 937 | | | |
| **850** | 942 | 947 | 952 | 957 | 962 | 967 | 973 | 978 | 983 | 988 | | | |
| N | 0 | 1 | 2 | 3 | 4 | 5 | 6 | 7 | 8 | 9 | P P | | |

## COMMON LOGARITHMS OF NUMBERS (Continued)

| N | 0 | 1 | 2 | 3 | 4 | 5 | 6 | 7 | 8 | 9 |
|---|---|---|---|---|---|---|---|---|---|---|
| **850** | 92 942 | 947 | 952 | 957 | 962 | 967 | 973 | 978 | 983 | 988 |
| 51 | 993 | 998 | *003 | *008 | *013 | *018 | *024 | *029 | *034 | *039 |
| 52 | 93 044 | 049 | 054 | 059 | 064 | 069 | 075 | 080 | 085 | 090 |
| 53 | 095 | 100 | 105 | 110 | 115 | 120 | 125 | 131 | 136 | 141 |
| 54 | 146 | 151 | 156 | 161 | 166 | 171 | 176 | 181 | 186 | 192 |
| 55 | 197 | 202 | 207 | 212 | 217 | 222 | 227 | 232 | 237 | 242 |
| 56 | 247 | 252 | 258 | 263 | 268 | 273 | 278 | 283 | 288 | 293 |
| 57 | 298 | 303 | 308 | 313 | 318 | 323 | 328 | 334 | 339 | 344 |
| 58 | 349 | 354 | 359 | 364 | 369 | 374 | 379 | 384 | 389 | 394 |
| 59 | 399 | 404 | 409 | 414 | 420 | 425 | 430 | 435 | 440 | 445 |
| **860** | 450 | 455 | 460 | 465 | 470 | 475 | 480 | 485 | 490 | 495 |
| 61 | 500 | 505 | 510 | 515 | 520 | 526 | 531 | 536 | 541 | 546 |
| 62 | 551 | 556 | 561 | 566 | 571 | 576 | 581 | 586 | 591 | 596 |
| 63 | 601 | 606 | 611 | 616 | 621 | 626 | 631 | 636 | 641 | 646 |
| 64 | 651 | 656 | 661 | 666 | 671 | 676 | 682 | 687 | 692 | 697 |
| 65 | 702 | 707 | 712 | 717 | 722 | 727 | 732 | 737 | 742 | 747 |
| 66 | 752 | 757 | 762 | 767 | 772 | 777 | 782 | 787 | 792 | 797 |
| 67 | 802 | 807 | 812 | 817 | 822 | 827 | 832 | 837 | 842 | 847 |
| 68 | 852 | 857 | 862 | 867 | 872 | 877 | 882 | 887 | 892 | 897 |
| 69 | 902 | 907 | 912 | 917 | 922 | 927 | 932 | 937 | 942 | 947 |
| **870** | 952 | 957 | 962 | 967 | 972 | 977 | 982 | 987 | 992 | 997 |
| 71 | 94 002 | 007 | 012 | 017 | 022 | 027 | 032 | 037 | 042 | 047 |
| 72 | 052 | 057 | 062 | 067 | 072 | 077 | 082 | 086 | 091 | 096 |
| 73 | 101 | 106 | 111 | 116 | 121 | 126 | 131 | 136 | 141 | 146 |
| 74 | 151 | 156 | 161 | 166 | 171 | 176 | 181 | 186 | 191 | 196 |
| 75 | 201 | 206 | 211 | 216 | 221 | 226 | 231 | 236 | 240 | 245 |
| 76 | 250 | 255 | 260 | 265 | 270 | 275 | 280 | 285 | 290 | 295 |
| 77 | 300 | 305 | 310 | 315 | 320 | 325 | 330 | 335 | 340 | 345 |
| 78 | 349 | 354 | 359 | 364 | 369 | 374 | 379 | 384 | 389 | 394 |
| 79 | 399 | 404 | 409 | 414 | 419 | 424 | 429 | 433 | 438 | 443 |
| **880** | 448 | 453 | 458 | 463 | 468 | 473 | 478 | 483 | 488 | 493 |
| 81 | 498 | 503 | 507 | 512 | 517 | 522 | 527 | 532 | 537 | 542 |
| 82 | 547 | 552 | 557 | 562 | 567 | 571 | 576 | 581 | 586 | 591 |
| 83 | 596 | 601 | 606 | 611 | 616 | 621 | 626 | 630 | 635 | 640 |
| 84 | 645 | 650 | 655 | 660 | 665 | 670 | 675 | 680 | 685 | 689 |
| 85 | 694 | 699 | 704 | 709 | 714 | 719 | 724 | 729 | 734 | 738 |
| 86 | 743 | 748 | 753 | 758 | 763 | 768 | 773 | 778 | 783 | 787 |
| 87 | 792 | 797 | 802 | 807 | 812 | 817 | 822 | 827 | 832 | 836 |
| 88 | 841 | 846 | 851 | 856 | 861 | 866 | 871 | 876 | 880 | 885 |
| 89 | 890 | 895 | 900 | 905 | 910 | 915 | 919 | 924 | 929 | 934 |
| **890** | 939 | 944 | 949 | 954 | 959 | 963 | 968 | 973 | 978 | 983 |
| 91 | 988 | 993 | 998 | *002 | *007 | *012 | *017 | *022 | *027 | *032 |
| 92 | 95 036 | 041 | 046 | 051 | 056 | 061 | 066 | 071 | 075 | 080 |
| 93 | 085 | 090 | 095 | 100 | 105 | 109 | 114 | 119 | 124 | 129 |
| 94 | 134 | 139 | 143 | 148 | 153 | 158 | 163 | 168 | 173 | 177 |
| 95 | 182 | 187 | 192 | 197 | 202 | 207 | 211 | 216 | 221 | 226 |
| 96 | 231 | 236 | 240 | 245 | 250 | 255 | 260 | 265 | 270 | 274 |
| 97 | 279 | 284 | 289 | 294 | 299 | 303 | 308 | 313 | 318 | 323 |
| 98 | 328 | 332 | 337 | 342 | 347 | 352 | 357 | 361 | 366 | 371 |
| 99 | 376 | 381 | 386 | 390 | 395 | 400 | 405 | 410 | 415 | 419 |
| **900** | 424 | 429 | 434 | 439 | 444 | 448 | 453 | 458 | 463 | 468 |
| N | 0 | 1 | 2 | 3 | 4 | 5 | 6 | 7 | 8 | 9 |

**PP**

**6**
| 1 | 0.6 |
|---|---|
| 2 | 1.2 |
| 3 | 1.8 |
| 4 | 2.4 |
| 5 | 3.0 |
| 6 | 3.6 |
| 7 | 4.2 |
| 8 | 4.8 |
| 9 | 5.4 |

**5**
| 1 | 0.5 |
|---|---|
| 2 | 1.0 |
| 3 | 1.5 |
| 4 | 2.0 |
| 5 | 2.5 |
| 6 | 3.0 |
| 7 | 3.5 |
| 8 | 4.0 |
| 9 | 4.5 |

**4**
| 1 | 0.4 |
|---|---|
| 2 | 0.8 |
| 3 | 1.2 |
| 4 | 1.6 |
| 5 | 2.0 |
| 6 | 2.4 |
| 7 | 2.8 |
| 8 | 3.2 |
| 9 | 3.6 |

## COMMON LOGARITHMS OF NUMBERS (Continued)

| N | 0 | 1 | 2 | 3 | 4 | 5 | 6 | 7 | 8 | 9 |
|---|---|---|---|---|---|---|---|---|---|---|
| **900** | 95 424 | 429 | 434 | 439 | 444 | 448 | 453 | 458 | 463 | 468 |
| 01 | 472 | 477 | 482 | 487 | 492 | 497 | 501 | 506 | 511 | 516 |
| 02 | 521 | 525 | 530 | 535 | 540 | 545 | 550 | 554 | 559 | 564 |
| 03 | 569 | 574 | 578 | 583 | 588 | 593 | 598 | 602 | 607 | 612 |
| 04 | 617 | 622 | 626 | 631 | 636 | 641 | 646 | 650 | 655 | 660 |
| 05 | 665 | 670 | 674 | 679 | 684 | 689 | 694 | 698 | 703 | 708 |
| 06 | 713 | 718 | 722 | 727 | 732 | 737 | 742 | 746 | 751 | 756 |
| 07 | 761 | 766 | 770 | 775 | 780 | 785 | 789 | 794 | 799 | 804 |
| 08 | 809 | 813 | 818 | 823 | 828 | 832 | 837 | 842 | 847 | 852 |
| 09 | 856 | 861 | 866 | 871 | 875 | 880 | 885 | 890 | 895 | 899 |
| **910** | 904 | 909 | 914 | 918 | 923 | 928 | 933 | 938 | 942 | 947 |
| 11 | 952 | 957 | 961 | 966 | 971 | 976 | 980 | 985 | 990 | 995 |
| 12 | 999 | *004 | *009 | *014 | *019 | *023 | *028 | *033 | *038 | *042 |
| 13 | 96 047 | 052 | 057 | 061 | 066 | 071 | 076 | 080 | 085 | 090 |
| 14 | 095 | 099 | 104 | 109 | 114 | 118 | 123 | 128 | 133 | 137 |
| 15 | 142 | 147 | 152 | 156 | 161 | 166 | 171 | 175 | 180 | 185 |
| 16 | 190 | 194 | 199 | 204 | 209 | 213 | 218 | 223 | 227 | 232 |
| 17 | 237 | 242 | 246 | 251 | 256 | 261 | 265 | 270 | 275 | 280 |
| 18 | 284 | 289 | 294 | 298 | 303 | 308 | 313 | 317 | 322 | 327 |
| 19 | 332 | 336 | 341 | 346 | 350 | 355 | 360 | 365 | 369 | 374 |
| **920** | 379 | 384 | 388 | 393 | 398 | 402 | 407 | 412 | 417 | 421 |
| 21 | 426 | 431 | 435 | 440 | 445 | 450 | 454 | 459 | 464 | 468 |
| 22 | 473 | 478 | 483 | 487 | 492 | 497 | 501 | 506 | 511 | 515 |
| 23 | 520 | 525 | 530 | 534 | 539 | 544 | 548 | 553 | 558 | 562 |
| 24 | 567 | 572 | 577 | 581 | 586 | 591 | 595 | 600 | 605 | 609 |
| 25 | 614 | 619 | 624 | 628 | 633 | 638 | 642 | 647 | 652 | 656 |
| 26 | 661 | 666 | 670 | 675 | 680 | 685 | 689 | 694 | 699 | 703 |
| 27 | 708 | 713 | 717 | 722 | 727 | 731 | 736 | 741 | 745 | 750 |
| 28 | 755 | 759 | 764 | 769 | 774 | 778 | 783 | 788 | 792 | 797 |
| 29 | 802 | 806 | 811 | 816 | 820 | 825 | 830 | 834 | 839 | 844 |
| **930** | 848 | 453 | 858 | 862 | 867 | 872 | 876 | 881 | 886 | 890 |
| 31 | 895 | 900 | 904 | 909 | 914 | 918 | 923 | 928 | 932 | 937 |
| 32 | 942 | 946 | 951 | 956 | 960 | 965 | 970 | 974 | 979 | 984 |
| 33 | 988 | 993 | 997 | *002 | *007 | *011 | *016 | *021 | *025 | *030 |
| 34 | 97 035 | 039 | 044 | 049 | 053 | 058 | 063 | 067 | 072 | 077 |
| 35 | 081 | 086 | 090 | 095 | 100 | 104 | 109 | 114 | 118 | 123 |
| 36 | 128 | 132 | 137 | 142 | 146 | 151 | 155 | 160 | 165 | 169 |
| 37 | 174 | 179 | 183 | 188 | 192 | 197 | 202 | 206 | 211 | 216 |
| 38 | 220 | 225 | 230 | 234 | 239 | 243 | 248 | 253 | 257 | 262 |
| 39 | 267 | 271 | 276 | 280 | 285 | 290 | 294 | 299 | 304 | 308 |
| **940** | 313 | 317 | 322 | 327 | 331 | 336 | 340 | 345 | 350 | 354 |
| 41 | 359 | 364 | 368 | 373 | 377 | 382 | 387 | 391 | 396 | 400 |
| 42 | 405 | 410 | 414 | 419 | 424 | 428 | 433 | 437 | 442 | 447 |
| 43 | 451 | 456 | 460 | 465 | 470 | 474 | 479 | 483 | 488 | 493 |
| 44 | 497 | 502 | 506 | 511 | 516 | 520 | 525 | 529 | 534 | 539 |
| 45 | 543 | 548 | 552 | 557 | 562 | 566 | 571 | 575 | 580 | 585 |
| 46 | 589 | 594 | 598 | 603 | 607 | 612 | 617 | 621 | 626 | 630 |
| 47 | 635 | 640 | 644 | 649 | 653 | 658 | 663 | 667 | 672 | 676 |
| 48 | 681 | 685 | 690 | 695 | 699 | 704 | 708 | 713 | 717 | 722 |
| 49 | 727 | 731 | 736 | 740 | 745 | 749 | 754 | 759 | 763 | 768 |
| **950** | 772 | 777 | 782 | 786 | 791 | 795 | 800 | 804 | 809 | 813 |
| N | 0 | 1 | 2 | 3 | 4 | 5 | 6 | 7 | 8 | 9 |

**P P**

**5**

| | |
|---|---|
| 1 | 0.5 |
| 2 | 1.0 |
| 3 | 1.5 |
| 4 | 2.0 |
| 5 | 2.5 |
| 6 | 3.0 |
| 7 | 3.5 |
| 8 | 4.0 |
| 9 | 4.5 |

**4**

| | |
|---|---|
| 1 | 0.4 |
| 2 | 0.8 |
| 3 | 1.2 |
| 4 | 1.6 |
| 5 | 2.0 |
| 6 | 2.4 |
| 7 | 2.8 |
| 8 | 3.2 |
| 9 | 3.6 |

## COMMON LOGARITHMS OF NUMBERS (Continued)

| N | 0 | 1 | 2 | 3 | 4 | 5 | 6 | 7 | 8 | 9 |
|---|---|---|---|---|---|---|---|---|---|---|
| **950** | 97 772 | 777 | 782 | 786 | 791 | 795 | 800 | 804 | 809 | 813 |
| 51 | 818 | 823 | 827 | 832 | 836 | 841 | 845 | 850 | 855 | 859 |
| 52 | 864 | 868 | 873 | 877 | 882 | 886 | 891 | 896 | 900 | 905 |
| 53 | 909 | 914 | 918 | 923 | 928 | 932 | 937 | 941 | 946 | 950 |
| 54 | 955 | 959 | 964 | 968 | 973 | 978 | 982 | 987 | 991 | 996 |
| 55 | 98 000 | 005 | 009 | 014 | 019 | 023 | 028 | 032 | 037 | 041 |
| 56 | 046 | 050 | 055 | 059 | 064 | 068 | 073 | 078 | 082 | 087 |
| 57 | 091 | 096 | 100 | 105 | 109 | 114 | 118 | 123 | 127 | 132 |
| 58 | 137 | 141 | 146 | 150 | 155 | 159 | 164 | 168 | 173 | 177 |
| 59 | 182 | 186 | 191 | 195 | 200 | 204 | 209 | 214 | 218 | 223 |
| **960** | 227 | 232 | 236 | 241 | 245 | 250 | 254 | 259 | 263 | 268 |
| 61 | 272 | 277 | 281 | 286 | 290 | 295 | 299 | 304 | 308 | 313 |
| 62 | 318 | 322 | 327 | 331 | 336 | 340 | 345 | 349 | 354 | 358 |
| 63 | 363 | 367 | 372 | 376 | 381 | 385 | 390 | 394 | 399 | 403 |
| 64 | 408 | 412 | 417 | 421 | 426 | 430 | 435 | 439 | 444 | 448 |
| 65 | 453 | 457 | 462 | 466 | 471 | 475 | 480 | 484 | 489 | 493 |
| 66 | 498 | 502 | 507 | 511 | 516 | 520 | 525 | 529 | 534 | 538 |
| 67 | 543 | 547 | 552 | 556 | 561 | 565 | 570 | 574 | 579 | 583 |
| 68 | 588 | 592 | 597 | 601 | 605 | 610 | 614 | 619 | 623 | 628 |
| 69 | 632 | 637 | 641 | 646 | 650 | 655 | 659 | 664 | 668 | 673 |
| **970** | 677 | 682 | 686 | 691 | 695 | 700 | 704 | 709 | 713 | 717 |
| 71 | 722 | 726 | 731 | 735 | 740 | 744 | 749 | 753 | 758 | 762 |
| 72 | 767 | 771 | 776 | 780 | 784 | 789 | 793 | 798 | 802 | 807 |
| 73 | 811 | 816 | 820 | 825 | 829 | 834 | 838 | 843 | 847 | 851 |
| 74 | 856 | 860 | 865 | 869 | 874 | 878 | 883 | 887 | 892 | 896 |
| 75 | 900 | 905 | 909 | 914 | 918 | 923 | 927 | 932 | 936 | 941 |
| 76 | 945 | 949 | 954 | 958 | 963 | 967 | 972 | 976 | 981 | 985 |
| 77 | 989 | 994 | 998 | *003 | *007 | *012 | *016 | *021 | *025 | *029 |
| 78 | 99 034 | 038 | 043 | 047 | 052 | 056 | 061 | 065 | 069 | 074 |
| 79 | 078 | 083 | 087 | 092 | 096 | 100 | 105 | 109 | 114 | 118 |
| **980** | 123 | 127 | 131 | 136 | 140 | 145 | 149 | 154 | 158 | 162 |
| 81 | 167 | 171 | 176 | 180 | 185 | 189 | 193 | 198 | 202 | 207 |
| 82 | 211 | 216 | 220 | 224 | 229 | 233 | 238 | 242 | 247 | 251 |
| 83 | 255 | 260 | 264 | 269 | 273 | 277 | 282 | 286 | 291 | 295 |
| 84 | 300 | 304 | 308 | 313 | 317 | 322 | 326 | 330 | 335 | 339 |
| 85 | 344 | 348 | 352 | 357 | 361 | 366 | 370 | 374 | 379 | 383 |
| 86 | 388 | 392 | 396 | 401 | 405 | 410 | 414 | 419 | 423 | 427 |
| 87 | 432 | 436 | 441 | 445 | 449 | 454 | 458 | 463 | 467 | 471 |
| 88 | 476 | 480 | 484 | 489 | 493 | 498 | 502 | 506 | 511 | 515 |
| 89 | 520 | 524 | 528 | 533 | 537 | 542 | 546 | 550 | 555 | 559 |
| **990** | 564 | 568 | 572 | 577 | 581 | 585 | 590 | 594 | 599 | 603 |
| 91 | 607 | 612 | 616 | 621 | 625 | 629 | 634 | 638 | 642 | 647 |
| 92 | 651 | 656 | 660 | 664 | 669 | 673 | 677 | 682 | 686 | 691 |
| 93 | 695 | 699 | 704 | 708 | 712 | 717 | 721 | 726 | 730 | 734 |
| 94 | 739 | 743 | 747 | 752 | 756 | 760 | 765 | 769 | 774 | 778 |
| 95 | 782 | 787 | 791 | 795 | 800 | 804 | 808 | 813 | 817 | 822 |
| 96 | 826 | 830 | 835 | 839 | 843 | 848 | 852 | 856 | 861 | 865 |
| 97 | 870 | 874 | 878 | 883 | 887 | 891 | 896 | 900 | 904 | 909 |
| 98 | 913 | 917 | 922 | 926 | 930 | 935 | 939 | 944 | 948 | 952 |
| 99 | 957 | 961 | 965 | 970 | 974 | 978 | 983 | 987 | 991 | 996 |
| **1000** | 00 000 | 004 | 009 | 013 | 017 | 022 | 026 | 030 | 035 | 039 |
| N | 0 | 1 | 2 | 3 | 4 | 5 | 6 | 7 | 8 | 9 |

**P P**

**5**

| | |
|---|---|
| 1 | 0.5 |
| 2 | 1.0 |
| 3 | 1.5 |
| 4 | 2.0 |
| 5 | 2.5 |
| 6 | 3.0 |
| 7 | 3.5 |
| 8 | 4.0 |
| 9 | 4.5 |

**4**

| | |
|---|---|
| 1 | 0.4 |
| 2 | 0.8 |
| 3 | 1.2 |
| 4 | 1.6 |
| 5 | 2.0 |
| 6 | 2.4 |
| 7 | 2.8 |
| 8 | 3.2 |
| 9 | 3.6 |

# INDEX